PENGUIN BOOKS
SACRED GAMES

Vikram Chandra was born in New Delhi. His first novel, *Red Earth and Pouring Rain* (1995), won the Commonwealth Writers Prize for Best First Book and the David Higham Prize. His first collection of short stories, *Love and Longing in Bombay* (1997), won the Commonwealth Writers Prize for Best Book (Eurasia region) and was shortlisted for the *Guardian* Fiction Prize. Vikram currently divides his time between Mumbai and Berkeley, where he lives with his wife, Melanie, and teaches at the University of California. His work has been translated into eleven languages.

See www.vikramchandra.com

Critical Acclaim for *Sacred Games*

'Vikram Chandra's *Sacred Games* wins the Hutch Crossword prize for English Fiction because in a crowded field filled with really first rate writing, the jury unanimously felt it was the outstanding novel of this year.'—Anita Roy, Mukul Kesavan, Shoma Chaudhury (judges, 2006 Crossword Book Award for Fiction)

'This is a ravishing, over-exuberant stab at the Great Indian Novel, an extraordinary work of fiction that will reward you in full for your investment of time…There's a superabundance of tumultuous narrative, acres of magnificent prose, and maybe a dozen too many characters. Yet these unruly parts ultimately fit together into a chaotic and luminous whole, one that mirrors Chandra's capacious vision of his homeland.'—Jennifer Reese, *Entertainment Weekly* (USA)

'This is a moment worth marking. It's a landmark in the history of Indian English literature. Decades from now, we'll be looking back at the roster of great contemporary novels, and the title *Sacred Games* will trip off our tongues blithely and reverentially…Then there's the setting. Bombay. It's more than a setting. It's the book itself. Chandra brings it brilliantly, deeply alive—in all her foulness, filth and stained beauty…This is a great novel, perhaps the greatest book on Bombay ever written.'—Ashok Banker, *Hindustan Times*

'"All human life is here" was the old newspaper boast, and so it is in *Sacred Games*, delineated with a master's grandeur and scope and a miniaturist's precision and tenderness. Seven years it took Chandra to write, and such is the haunting precision of its observation and the resonant authority of its narrative voice that one could read it seven times over and still be finding new treasures; missed flourishes of virtuosity. One uses the terms "epic" and "classic" with caution. But if eloquence, confidence, humanity, grace and fine observation are their raw materials, perhaps *Sacred Games* deserves those epithets.'—Jane Shilling, *The Daily Telegraph* (UK)

'It may have taken him three books, but *Sacred Games* is where Chandra really finds humour through his mastery of irony. This is a brutal and passionate tale, always, but Chandra throughout tempts you to seek meaning above and below the narrative, to smile with pleased recognition...Best of all, he effortlessly draws the reader into a tale that actually isn't particularly straightforward at all. The story line is determinedly non-linear, the structure episodically jump-cut, very evocative of Donald Barthelme. That master of spare prose might have taken 380 pages to write a comparable tale, but that's not the point. Don de Lillo might have needed 1,500, and in neither case would these two literary giants have written this gargantuan tale of Bombay/Mumbai and all its little Indias in quite the same heartbreaking, sardonic, funny and violent way...Buy this Rabelaisian masterpiece of mordant homage to Bombay today. Vikram Chandra has set the benchmark for the Bombay novel very high indeed.'—Hari Menon, *Tehelka*

'Like a sculptor making small, delicate chips in stone, Chandra moves things along at a measured pace, building his characters, finding glorious little details in the minutiae of everyday Bombay life, yet remaining sharply focused on the main thrust of his detective story...*Sacred Games* quakes with seismic historical shocks, as if Chandra were intent on blasting open India's historically amnesiac present, a time when India (or at least its media and its political class) is intoxicated by its glorious future. Chandra telescopes the past through the present with a series of historical insets into the narrative, reminding readers, as if he were an adept in palmistry, that "the shape of the future" lies "in the lines of the past..." What we get here is an occult history worthy of Borges. The last hours of Gaitonde's life—his final dialogue with the murdered woman before their deaths, the last of a series of fabulous exchanges between them—are electrifying, a baroque distillation of all that has gone on before. *Sacred Games*'s legacy might prove similar to that of Chandra's brother-in-law's film *Parinda*: By extending the territory of Indian literary fiction, it will allow others to tell crime stories of their own. Chandra's ultimate achievement is both as a genre novelist and as a novelist who uses genre elements. Solving the crime is important, but he also hands us the keys to the city and reveals its sordid mysteries.'—Carl Bromley, *The Nation* (USA)

'Vikram Chandra's masterly new novel—exactly 900 pages long—starts with a white Pomeranian, Fluffy, flying out of the window in upper-middle-class Mumbai...The spare, Hitchcockian funniness of the writing—the sense that it creates of schoolgoing ordinariness and urban kitsch erupting into bizarre and brutal catastrophe, and yet the ordinariness somehow managing to hold it all in eventually, in feats of epic-cinematic, divinely comic inclusiveness—is just one of the many ways in which Chandra's virtuosity unfolds in the novel...Yet, what holds the novel most profoundly and vitally together, and enables its mastery of the actual as well as the fabulous, the real and the surreal, is the cinema of Mumbai. Bollywood is to *Sacred Games* what chivalric romance is to Don Quixote—a living, self-perpetuating mythology, a shimmering universe of images and meanings by which people live and die, make, re-make and know (or resist knowing) themselves and the worlds and stories they inhabit.'—Aveek Sen, *The Telegraph*

'[Chandra] immerses the reader in a rich and utterly convincing world...A monumental portrait of interwoven lives that lingers with a reader long after the case is closed.'—Thomas Wharton, *The Globe and Mail* (Canada)

'For my money, this is the great Bombay book of the last decade. It gets the city's corrosive heat, the absolute knockdown democratic fever of it; and it goes some way to explaining why Bombay engenders loyalty among all those who live or have lived there...And one of the delights, for this reader at least, is the Bambaiyya Hindi, presented without italics, explanation, or apology: the apradhis, khabaris and pocket-maars, the bhais and boys, the gullels and ghodas...These are words that occur so often in Bombay they can be plucked out of the city's dirty air. But Chandra has done more. He uses them with such unerring gusto that they become celebratory, incantatory, not a code for insiders but something shared, like a song on the radio.'—Jeet Thayil, *Outlook*

'*Sacred Games*, though often suspenseful, is never filmi. Although the meat of this novel clings to the bones of a crime story, and there's certainly plenty of crime in it, the book is really a passionate tribute to contemporary India in all its vigor and vulgarity. Because it's not a family saga, it blessedly avoids what have become the clichés of the Indian literary novel.'—Laura Miller, Salon.com (USA)

'Chandra casts an enchanting and enthralling spell that documents two tales of two worlds—the Mumbai police and the Mumbai underworld. And garnishes it with many other tales…In doing so, he takes the enigma of Bombay to a new unparalleled high…This is a novelist at the height of his prowess almost sneering at all the academics who would no doubt try to construct and deconstruct this great Indian fable…Reportedly, Chandra took seven years to pen this epic masterpiece. The effort has well been worth it. For *Sacred Games* does the impossible. It makes an unwieldy hardcover unputdownable without missing a single literary beat.'—Vijay Nair, *Deccan Herald*

'Vikram Chandra's narrative is greater than a gangster story or a cinematic rendering of Indian life, or even an epic battle of good against evil…This is a work that can not only suck a reader in, but also turn an outlaw who should be thoroughly despicable into a heroic figure…The resulting web, intricate and large, comes together in the novel's startling, unexpected climax…[This is] a grand story that is carefully and passionately told. The final chapters, leading to the reason for Gaitonde's death, are breathtaking, as is Chandra's attention to the detail of character and circumstance. The work is so lovely, and so subtle, that it's well worth the cover price.'—Robin Vidimos, *The Denver Post* (USA)

'*Sacred Games* is storytelling at its very peak. Characters leap off the page to punch one in the gut, the narrative keeps the reader panting to know what happens next for every one of its 900 pages…If you've been underwhelmed by recent writing from India that, with a few exceptions, seems all too predictable in image and language, writing that wears its post-colonial heart on its sleeve and its reliance on the plot devices of arranged marriage and East-meets-West on its dust jacket—then run, don't walk towards *Sacred Games*. This thrilling, epic work is nothing less than a kick to the seat of the pants of recent Indian literature.'—Niranjana Iyer, *Asian Review of Books*

'An astonishingly engaging tome…[*Sacred Games*] can be easily acknowledged as a literary masterpiece.'—*Indulge Magazine* (USA)

'There's a vicarious excitement that you feel through the blood and gore of *Sacred Games*. A bewildering feeling that violence, poetry, hope, destruction and love all come together in this epic-of-sorts, to create a throbbing portrait of a city caught in the swirl of history…You grow into the story, and the stories coiled within it, into the restlessness of the characters, trapped as they are by some ghost, some vulnerability. The language is remarkably elastic, bringing a grainy, coarse texture to the narrative, as well as a moving poetry. In the end, *Sacred Games* is a "hard-boiled" thriller with razor-sharp edges, asking questions that unsettle and then don't let you go. In the same way that fears grip both Sartaj and Ganesh, control them, don't let them sleep.'—*First City* magazine

'Bold, fresh and big...Best of all, not only does *Sacred Games* deserve praise for its ambitions but also for its terrific achievement...When, as a reader, you reach the last page of *Sacred Games*, you feel as though you've been expelled from a world that, over weeks of reading, has come to feel like a second home.'—Maureen Corrigan, 'Fresh Air', NPR (USA)

'Vikram Chandra never fails to astonish. Almost like a magician conjuring up his latest trick, Chandra, the writer, has once again shown his ability to move ahead. Not afraid to experiment, he has drawn a variety of characters to build and share his story...Chandra has pulled off a coup of sorts with a masterpiece that dazzles as it races along the Mumbai skyline.'—*The Hindu*

'The novel oscillates splendidly between its two central characters...Chandra makes an enormous meal of Mumbai, the metropolis once called Bombay, each ingredient sharp and memorable...The imagery can be stunning...Submerging in [*Sacred Games*], like the Ganges itself, can restore your wonder.'—Karen Long, *The Plain Dealer* (USA)

'In a colossal romp, Chandra offers a view of Mumbai that many suspect, perhaps have even spoken of, but never confronted...Chandra's virtuosity of language that alternately thrills and repels, gets down to the basics of life in Mumbai. His skills as a storyteller are intact as are those of his minute and painstaking research into the hearts and minds of his characters. *Sacred Games* will tempt even the most reluctant reader with the incredible enthusiasm of its huge cast, the energy of its characters and the plots and subplots that make this many-layered story so memorable. Written with a rare combination of humour and anger, it is easy to see why this will become a popular book bordering on the classic.'—Suchitra Behal, *The Hindu*

'*Sacred Games* becomes much more than the sum of its spiraling parts...Then there's the structure, spider-webbed like a crack in a window across time and space..."If you want to live in the city you have to think ahead three turns, and look behind a lie to see the truth and then behind that truth to see a lie," says Gaitonde, recalling one of the lessons of his youth. One could say as much about the ample splendor of *Sacred Games*. Much more than a simple exercise in crime fiction, Chandra's tour de force is ambitious in all its facets. With its striking prose, ruthless capacity for violence and Gordian composition, *Sacred Games* offers up a world worthy of the effort required to take it all in.'—Clayton Moore, *Rocky Mountain News* (USA)

'One of *Sacred Games*' strengths is that Chandra goes well beyond the headlines, or for that matter, even the body copy of what has appeared in newspapers. His research is phenomenal, his insights, for the most part, extremely perspicacious...On balance *Sacred Games* is a ripping good read. At 900 pages, isn't it too long and bulky? It seems bulky only so long as the hard cover edition is held unopened in a single palm—the wrist may start to ache after a while. Once the book is put down, and the reading begins, it doesn't seem bulky at all...Yeh dil mange still more.'—Debashish Mukerji, *The Week*

'Epic it is, though, in scale and scope and in the quality of the writing, which is superb...*Sacred Games* is a stunning novel and one of the best crime novels of the year.'—Mike Ripley, *Birmingham Post* (UK)

'Meticulously structured and tautly told, it is the kind of novel that one reads hungrily, turning the pages but lingering over every paragraph and sentence, wanting to get to the end but not wanting the book to end at all...The narrative is not only about moves and countermoves. It is sustained by its moments of intense feeling—the suddenness of loss, the pain of having to betray a friend—but the melancholy wisdom that it offers is that the losses and betrayals are also part of the game. Meanwhile, other disparate characters wash up on the shores of the story like migrants to this island city by the sea, and the novel manages to hold them all together. Teeming with people and their individual histories, the book races back and forth between past and present, darkness and daylight, like the trains that whip across the cityscape...With notable effortlessness, the novel traverses the history of the Subcontinent, recalling not only the many griefs but also the steady struggle forward...[A] splendid novel.'—Uma Mahadevan-Dasgupta, *Himal Southasian* (Nepal)

'The ultimate subcontinental noir...Even as Chandra digresses to depict the horrors of partition, he stays in the skin of his characters, never resorting to DeLillo-ish atmospherics...Any book that makes palpable a very foreign city, explores deep moral questions, and teaches you lots of dirty Hindi is well worth lugging around.'—*New York Magazine* (USA)

'Vikram Chandra has achieved the near-impossible. He has constructed a superbly realized world of alien languages, customs and styles, presented on the page without apologies or explanations, and has somehow created a wholly believable universe. Now, in a fiction cunningly disguised as a straightforward crime drama, Chandra comes into his own...Chandra might have been content to simply concentrate on the crime elements, resulting in a lean, bloody entertainment of blackmail, double-crosses and bullets, but there is a heft and passion at work that elevates the plot from its pulpy origins. The expansive breadth of *Sacred Games* reveals a truly Dickensian world view of events and people.'—Corey Redecop, *Winnipeg Free Press* (Canada)

'*Sacred Games* is also a cocky experiment with the conventions of a thriller, breaking every rule a film director tells Gaitonde is necessary for a successful formula film...*Sacred Games* is sweaty, bloody, and unapologetically melodramatic. It's raucous...It's comic...In the end, the book is about this city, the dream factory of India, which remakes everyone and no one is what he seems...In those few inches that separate the myth from the reality, Chandra gives a startling, blood-pumping fallible humanity to his characters.'—Sandip Roy, *San Francisco Chronicle* (USA)

'We read compulsively, unable to put the book down...Once you open it, it owns you...Dismissing this book as a crime novel is like calling *Crime and Punishment* a thriller...*Sacred Games* is huge—as big as ambition, as consuming as love, as deep as compassion and as grand as India itself.'—Erica Eisdorfer, *The Carrboro Citizen* (Canada)

'One of the remarkable achievements in Vikram Chandra's stunning new novel, *Sacred Games*, is its portrayal of the all-encompassing, ingrained nature of the corruption in Mumbai...[*Sacred Games*] is a landmark work, a novel so ambitious and fully achieved it makes most American crime novelists—the Lehanes, the Pelecanos, even the Ellroys—seem naive and timid by comparison...As much as it is a multi-lingual dazzler of ambitious fiction, it's a rich, riveting thriller...Here, there is family, faith, a romantic affair, a sexual obsession, blackmail, betrayal, a city on the brink of chaos, and all of it is lyrically, lovingly conveyed. *Sacred Games* is one of the very few 900-page novels of recent vintage that as I read it, I was always eager for more.'—Jerome Weeks, ArtsJournal.com (USA)

'*Sacred Games* is one of those books you immerse yourself in, a passport to an alien world and, like life, you imagine it could go on forever. It envisions a world—an underworld, actually—that is complete, persuasive and startlingly original.'—Tom Beer, *Newsday* (USA)

'A genre-bending, multilayered saga...Chandra's expertly paced and nuanced unfolding of Gaitonde's life is interwoven with narratives that delve into the lives of various satellite characters...While *Sacred Games* takes an all-encompassing look at crucial issues facing modern-day India...thanks to its muscular prose and Chandra's obvious fondness for even his most deeply flawed characters, the book also succeeds as an entertainment extravaganza: a detective novel in full, and then a good deal more.'—Jenny Feldman, *Elle Magazine* (USA)

'Like Chandra's book, Singh's investigation adds up to much more than appears on the surface, and we read eagerly.'—Francine Prose, 'Critics Choice', *People Magazine* (USA)

'Go ahead. Close the book, turn out the lights. Even then, Ganesh Gaitonde, Sartaj Singh, and their many friends and enemies will whisper in your ear, beckoning from Mumbai and its jarring, joyous madness. Talk about an offer you can't refuse.'—Erik Spanberg, *The Christian Science Monitor* (USA)

'It's hard to do justice to the richness and vitality of this story—it's a full-immersion experience, as if Dickens had written *The Godfather* and placed it in India...Those stories, those glimpses at the myriad subgroups that comprise the city and those uniquely individual people who are drawn into the investigation, give the story its great resonance and depth.'—Rick Sullivan, *The Grand Rapids Press* (USA)

'*Sacred Games*, despite its length, is compulsively readable...This is a novel of voices, each of which is unmistakable. For while stories link the characters, from the poor in their hovels to the rich in their high-rises, the smutty aura of Mumbai arises from the prose itself. To re-create a city Mr. Chandra has fashioned a language equal to it, a promiscuous English open to all comers, as greedy and as vivid as Mumbai itself.'—Eric Ormsby, *The New York Sun* (USA)

'Great books create their necessity, though, and if you can lift this tremendous story into your shopping cart, bring it home and read it, you'll probably wonder how you got by so long without it...It is a terrific, brilliant, earthmover of a book.'—John Freeman, *Newcity Chicago* (USA)

'Chandra pulls strings with a puppeteer's mastery, connecting each disclosure of a concealed affiliation or conspiracy with what has gone before, whetting our appetites for ever more mayhem, depravity, and intrigue. The combination of an elephantine plot with a clockmaker's precise deployment of its sinister particulars is certainly attention-getting...Yet it's the characters who haunt us. Sartaj's tarnished integrity and Ganesh's perverted organizational genius hover over the novel like imperiled twin peaks, and there's something almost Homeric in the fateful intensity of their opposition...Few readers will be un-enthralled...It's a rare pleasure to be arrested by this novel's thunderous momentum, and caught up in its web.'—Bruce Allen, *The Boston Globe* (USA)

'Chandra is a prodigiously talented wordsmith with passion and boundless aspiration, and his intent here is obvious: *Sacred Games* is his ambitious, ostentatious shot at the Great Indian Novel. It is an extraordinary work of fiction and a literary accomplishment of the highest order—artful, educational, and one-of-a-kind.'—Tim Robinson, *The Hamilton Spectator* (USA)

'What keeps the reader interested is Chandra's total mastery of character and atmosphere. Great sheets of characterization wash over the reader like monsoon rains, but all the characters, and there are dozens, ring absolutely true. They become real people, who the reader invests heavily in, even when they're unpleasant...If you're looking for a novel that you can get lost in for weeks at a time over these winter nights, this is the one.'—Barry Hammond, *Edmonton Journal* (Canada)

'In *Sacred Games*, Chandra has surpassed his previous works, both in beauty and in bulk...The splendor of Chandra's prose is quite enough to enrapture a reader for 900 pages.'—Skye K. Moody, *The Seattle Times* (USA)

'Mr. Chandra brilliantly evokes a diverse slice of the population of Mumbai, a city that comes alive in *Sacred Games* in all its vibrant chaos...Perhaps Mr. Chandra's greatest strength is the compassion and understanding he has for all his flawed and needy characters.'—Henny Sender, *The Wall Street Journal* (USA)

'When I'd finished all 900 pages, I felt bereft. From the first, savagely funny paragraph (it requires a health warning for dog lovers) it's a crackerjack, even if you're not familiar with Indian obscenities.'—Chris Patten, *New Statesman* (UK)

'Once in a while you find a book that sucks you so thoroughly into the world it creates that each time you slip your bookmark between the pages and close the cover, you come up blinking, surprised to find yourself in your own skin again. Vikram Chandra's intricate *Sacred Games* is just such a novel.'—Miriam Wolf, *The Sunday Oregonian* (USA)

'Vikram Chandra's Mumbai mammoth of a literary thriller about cops and thugs, film-stars and financiers, unspools with Dickensian brio and at Dickensian length, but seldom loses its touch for street-smart observation and suspense.'—Boyd Tonkin, 'Books of the Year', *Independent* (UK)

'Chandra takes you inside the world of a Bombay cop. After reading the book, you'll swear you know precisely how to collect a bribe from a nightclub owner, how to count the money in a glance, and where to find the smart fellow who will shift the loot to a Swiss bank account. Rarely entirely honest or entirely rotten, Chandra's Bombay exists in a penumbra of moral ambiguity—which is why *Sacred Games* is one of the best novels about India in a long time.'—Aravind Adiga, '10 Best Asian Books of 2006', *Time* (Asia edition)

'Epic, sprawling depiction of Bombay's seedy underworld by one of India's master storytellers. Its protagonist, inspector Sartaj Singh, has earned a place among the world's outstanding fictional detectives. One of the most exhilarating reads of 2006.'—'Books of the Year', *Financial Times* (UK)

'Chandra has captured that gritty, sickeningly sweet, perspiration-soaked, electrifying, addictive quality of India...Chandra has managed to weave the best and worst parts of Mumbai into an utterly spellbinding novel. Though the mafia angle always sells well, it's more than just "The Godfather in India"—Chandra's prose elevates it to a literary masterpiece.'—Julie Welter, *Publishers Weekly* (USA)

'This is an immense, brilliant and bewildering novel. The hardback edition has exactly 900 pages and not one of them is wasted. It took Vikram Chandra seven years to write. I can only hope he has already started on his next book.'—Esme Choonara, *The Socialist Review* (UK)

'Vikram Chandra's novel *Sacred Games* is a gutsy, well-crafted attempt at giving the city the kind of novel it deserves...[It] is a big, bustling...constantly engaging novel that, like the city it explores, inexplicably manages to work.'—Nirpal Dhaliwal, *The Evening Standard* (UK)

'This is no simple Holmes-Moriarty adventure or merely an entertaining read. It works on numerous levels, the most vibrant of which paints a realistic landscape of India and the intrinsic machinery that allows it to move forward, when the laws of sociology suggest the country should have collapsed long ago. It addresses crime, politics, religion, the caste system, history, business, the psychology of power, the juxtaposition of good and evil, and the effects of merging cultures on a nation—to name a few of its topics. It is against this setting that Chandra's stories-within-a-story spin, and what glorious diversions they are.'—Allen Pierleoni, *Sacramento Bee* (USA)

'Between them the two narratives add up to a kaleidoscopic vision of an immense city—glittering and squalid, pullulating with energy, grossly overpopulated, driven by the volatile forces of ambition, despair and religious ardour. That city is the real protagonist of Chandra's book, as well as the stage on which his Comedie Humaine is played out. Appropriately, the disaster, which both master criminal and policeman are struggling to avert, is one that threatens, not any particular person or group, but the whole reeking, noisy, beautiful place...Each of these characters and dozens of others add something—a piece of a glitter or a dark accent—to the immense mosaic Chandra is constructing...[A] hugely ambitious and dazzlingly energetic book.'—Lucy Hughes-Hallett, *Sunday Times* (UK)

'By telling his tale in popular form, Chandra has found a vehicle particularly suited to the New India—to its passions and poverty, its outsize dreams and insecurities. Gaitonde may be larger than life in his appetites but not in his ambitions. The reader can recognize the same desperate striving in him as in a lowly Bihari slum dweller, a cop on the make.'—Nisid Hajari, *Newsweek International*

'One thing Chandra does superbly well is give a sense of the changes and the continuities of modern India...*Sacred Games* conjures up a Mumbai that is far more convincing than others we've been offered, one that accurately portrays the recent changes in Indian society...I was grateful for my full-blooded lesson in Hindi curses. All are brilliantly embedded so that every meaning is clear, a remarkable achievement. Anthony Burgess once did a similar job for Russian in the teenage argot of *A Clockwork Orange*, but his publisher insisted on a glossary, against Burgess's better judgement. Chandra manages without.'—Kevin Rushby, *Guardian Unlimited* (UK)

'Chandra manages to forge an intimacy between the reader and the two often morally unattractive men who rage across these 900 pages...*Sacred Games* is both riveting and brilliantly vile.'—Ruby Lancaster, *Time Out* (UK)

Sacred Games

VIKRAM CHANDRA

PENGUIN BOOKS

PENGUIN BOOKS

USA | Canada | UK | Ireland | Australia
New Zealand | India | South Africa | China

Penguin Books is part of the Penguin Random House group of companies
whose addresses can be found at global.penguinrandomhouse.com

Published by Penguin Random House India Pvt. Ltd
7th Floor, Infinity Tower C, DLF Cyber City,
Gurgaon 122 002, Haryana, India

Penguin
Random House
India

First published in India in Viking by Penguin Books India 2006
Published in Penguin Books 2007

Copyright © Vikram Chandra 2006

All rights reserved

12 11 10 9 8 7 6 5 4

ISBN 9780143063605

For sale in the Indian Subcontinent only
Printed at Repro Knowledgecast Limited, India

www.penguin.co.in

Contents

Acknowledgements

Some of the travel for this book was funded by a University Facilitating Fund grant from George Washington University.

I'm grateful to my erstwhile colleagues at George Washington University for their support and forbearance, especially my friends in the Creative Writing Program: Faye Moskowitz; David McAleavey; Jody Bolz; Jane Shore; Maxine Claire.

S. Hussain Zaidi has been extraordinarily generous with his vast knowledge, warm friendship and unstinting support. I am indebted to him.

Many others offered me aid, information and hospitality during the writing of this book:

Anuradha Tandon; Arup Patnaik, DIG, CBI; API Rajan Gule, CID; Fazal Irani; Akbar Irani; API Sanjay Rangnekar; Violet Monis; Iqbal Khan; Imtiaz Khan; Nisha Jamwal; Rajeev Samant; Rakesh Maria, DIG; Viral Mazumdar; Bandana Tewari; Shernaz Dinshaw; Nonita Kalra; A.D. Singh; Sabina Singh; Rajiv Somani; Aftab Khan; Rasna Behl; Ashutosh Sohni; Shruti Pandit; Kalpana Mhatre; Deepak Jog, DCP; Srila Chatterjee; Sherry Zutshi; Namita Waikar; Shashi Tharoor; Julia Eckert; Jaideep and Seema Mehrotra; Dr Ashok Gupta; Namrata Sharma Zakaria; Dr Amiq Gazdhar; Farzand Ahmed; Menaka Rao; Gyan Prakash.

In Delhi, Punjab and Jammu and Kashmir: Harinder Baweja; A.K. Sehgal; Amit Sehgal; Manohar Singh; Agha Shahid Ali; Shafi; Sumit (Surd) Nurpuri; Praveen Swami.

In Bihar: Sanjay Jha; Vinod Mishra; Ravinder Jadav; Ashok Kumar Singh, SP, Gaya; N.C. Dhoundial, DIG, Gaya; R.K. Prasad, Dy SP, Gaya; Sunit Kumar, IGP, Patna; Subnath Jha; Bibhuti Nath Jha 'Mastan'; Gopal Dubey; Surendra Trivedi; Sh. Shaiwal.

There are others I cannot name. They know who they are.

As always, I'm grateful to my parents, Navin and Kamna, and my sisters, Tanuja and Anupama; my friend and support, Margo True; Eric Simonoff; Julian Loose; David Davidar; Terry Karten; and Vidhu Vinod Chopra.

And to Melanie, who changed everything.

The hymns in the chapter 'Ganesh Gaitonde Explores the Self' are from the *Rig Vega*. I adapted Raimundo Pannikar's translations (*The Vedic Experience*, Motilal Banarsidass, 2001).

Dramatis Personae

Sartaj Singh: a Sikh police inspector in Mumbai

Katekar: a police constable who works with Sartaj Singh

    Shalini, Katekar's wife

    Mohit and **Rohit,** their sons

Mrs Kamala Pandey: a married woman and airline hostess with a lover, an airline pilot named Umesh

Kamble: an ambitious police sub-inspector who works with Sartaj Singh

Parulkar: a deputy commissioner of police in Mumbai

Ganesh Gaitonde: a notorious Hindu gangster and don, leader of the G-Company in Mumbai

Suleiman Isa: a much-feared Muslim gangster and don, leader of a rival gang in Mumbai

Paritosh Shah: a supremely gifted money handler for gangsters, including Ganesh Gaitonde

Kanta Bai: a businesswoman who deals with Paritosh Shah and Ganesh Gaitonde

Badriya: Paritosh Shah's bodyguard

Anjali Mathur: a government intelligence agent investigating Ganesh Gaitonde's death

Chotta Badriya: Ganesh Gaitonde's bodyguard, and the younger brother of Badriya

Juliet (Jojo) Mascarenas: a television producer/agent for aspiring actors and models . . . and a high class Madam

Mary Mascarenas: Jojo's sister who works as a hairdresser

Wasim Zafar Ali Ahmad: a social worker in a poor neighbourhood in Mumbai who has political aspirations

Prabhjot Kaur, 'Nikki': Sartaj Singh's mother, originally from the Punjab

Navneet, her beloved oldest sister

Ram Pari: the maidservant of Nikki's mother in the Punjab

Bunty: Ganesh Gaitonde's right hand man and organizer

Bipin Bhonsle: a Hindu fundamentalist politician whom Ganesh Gaitonde helps get elected to public office

Sharma (aka Trivedi): Bipin Bhonsle's ally who also works, through intermediaries, for Swami Shridhar Shukla

Swami Shridhar Shukla, 'Guru-ji': a Hindu guru and nationalist, a spiritual adviser of international renown, who becomes Ganesh Gaitonde's spiritual mentor

Subhadra Devalekar: Ganesh Gaitonde's wife and mother of his young son

K. D. Yadav (aka Mr Kumar): a pioneering Indian intelligence officer who 'ran' Ganesh Gaitonde and became a mentor to Anjali Mathur

Mr Kulkarni: the intelligence agent who runs Ganesh Gaitonde after K. D. Yadav

Major Shahid Khan: a Pakistani intelligence agent who masterminds a counterfeit money operation against India

Shambhu Shetty: proprietor of the Delite Dance Bar

Iffat-bibi: Suleiman Isa's maternal aunt who is one of his main controllers in Mumbai

Majid Khan: a police inspector in Mumbai, a colleague of Sartaj Singh

Zoya Mirza: an actress and a rising star in the Indian film industry

Aadil Ansari: an educated but poor man from a small rural town who flees to Mumbai to escape the violent conflicts of his native Bihar

Sharmeen Khan: the high-school-age daughter of Major Shahid Khan, who moves to the USA to work in Washington, DC, and brings his family – wife, daughter, and mother – with him

Daddi: Shahid Khan's mother, originally from the Punjab; to her family, she is a Muslim, but she hides a secret

SACRED GAMES

Policeman's Day

꧁꧂

A white Pomeranian named Fluffy flew out of a fifth-floor window in Panna, which was a brand-new building with the painter's scaffolding still around it. Fluffy screamed in her little lap-dog voice all the way down, like a little white kettle losing steam, bounced off the bonnet of a Cielo, and skidded to a halt near the rank of schoolgirls waiting for the St Mary's Convent bus. There was remarkably little blood, but the sight of Fluffy's brains did send the conventeers into hysterics, and meanwhile, above, the man who had swung Fluffy around his head by one leg, who had slung Fluffy into the void, one Mr Mahesh Pandey of Mirage Textiles, that man was leaning on his windowsill and laughing. Mrs Kamala Pandey, who in talking to Fluffy always spoke of herself as 'Mummy', now staggered and ran to her kitchen and plucked from the magnetic holder a knife nine inches long and two wide. When Sartaj and Katekar broke open the door to apartment 502, Mrs Pandey was standing in front of the bedroom door, looking intensely at a dense circle of two-inch-long wounds in the wood, about chest-high. As Sartaj watched, she sighed, raised her hand and stabbed the door again. She had to struggle with both hands on the handle to get the knife out.

'Mrs Pandey,' Sartaj said.

She turned to them, the knife still in a double-handed grip, held high. She had a pale, tear-stained face and tiny bare feet under her white nightie.

'Mrs Pandey, I am Inspector Sartaj Singh,' Sartaj said. 'I'd like you to put down that knife, please.' He took a step, hands held up and palms forward. 'Please,' he said. But Mrs Pandey's eyes were wide and blank, and except for the quivering of her forearms she was quite still. The hallway they were in was narrow, and Sartaj could feel Katekar behind him, wanting to pass. Sartaj stopped moving. Another step and he would be comfortably within a swing of the knife.

'Police?' a voice said from behind the bedroom door. 'Police?'

Mrs Pandey started, as if remembering something, and then she said, 'Bastard, bastard,' and slashed at the door again. She was tired now, and the point bounced off the wood and raked across it, and Sartaj bent her wrist back and took the knife quite easily from her. But she smashed at the door with her hands, breaking her bangles, and her last wiry burst of anger was hard to hold and contain. Finally they sat her down on the green sofa in the drawing room.

'Shoot him,' she said. '*Shoot* him.' Then she put her head in her hands. There were green and blue bruises on her shoulder. Katekar was back at the bedroom door, murmuring.

'What did you fight about?' Sartaj said.

'He wants me not to fly any more.'

'What?'

'I'm an air hostess. He thinks . . .'

'Yes?'

She had startling light-brown eyes, and she was angry at Sartaj for asking. 'He thinks since I'm an air hostess, I keep hostessing the pilots on stopovers,' she said, and turned her face to the window.

Katekar was walking the husband over now, with a hand on his neck. Mr Pandey hitched up his silky red-and-black striped pyjamas, and smiled confidentially at Sartaj. 'Thank you,' he said. 'Thanks for coming.'

'So you like to hit your wife, Mr Pandey?' Sartaj barked, leaning forward. Katekar sat the man down, hard, while he still had his mouth open. It was nicely done. Katekar was a senior constable, an old subordinate, a colleague really – they had worked together for almost seven years now, off and on. 'You like to hit her, and then you throw a poor puppy out of a window? And then you call us to save you?'

'She said I hit her?'

'I have eyes. I can see.'

'Then look at this,' Mr Pandey said, his jaw twisting. 'Look, look, look at this.' And he pulled up his left pyjama jacket sleeve, revealing a shiny silver watch and four evenly spaced scratches, livid and deep, running from the inside of the wrist around to the elbow. 'More, I've got more,' Mr Pandey said, and bowed low at the waist and lowered his head and twisted to raise his collar away from the skin. Sartaj got up and walked around the coffee table. There was a corrugated red welt on Mr Pandey's shoulder blade, and Sartaj couldn't see how far down it went.

'What's that from?' Sartaj said.

'She broke a Kashmiri walking stick on my back. This thick, it was,' Mr Pandey said, holding up his thumb and forefinger circled.

Sartaj walked to the window. There was a group of uniformed boys clustering around the small white body below, pushing each other closer to it. The St Mary's girls were squealing, holding their hands to their mouths, and begging the boys to stop. In the drawing room, Mrs Pandey was gazing brightly at her husband, her chin tucked into her chest. 'Love,' Sartaj said softly. 'Love is a murdering gaandu. Poor Fluffy.'

'Namaskar, Sartaj Saab,' PSI Kamble called across the station house. 'Parulkar Saab was asking after you.' The room was some twenty-five feet across, with four desks lined up across the breadth of it. There was a six-foot poster of Sai Baba on the wall, and a Ganesha under the glass on Kamble's desk, and Sartaj had felt impelled to add a picture of Guru Gobind Singh on the other wall, in a somewhat twisted assertion of secularism. Five constables came jerkily to attention, and then subsided into their usual sprawl on white plastic chairs.

'Where is Parulkar Saab?'

'With a pack of reporters. He's giving them tea and telling them about our new initiative against crime.'

Parulkar was the deputy commissioner for Zone 13, and his office was next door, in a separate building that was the zonal headquarters. He loved reporters, and had a genius for being jovial with them, and a recent knack for declaiming couplets during interviews. Sartaj wondered sometimes if he sat up late with books of poetry, practising in front of a mirror. 'Good,' Sartaj said. 'Somebody has to tell them about all our hard work.'

Kamble let out a snort of laughter.

Sartaj sat at the desk next to Kamble and flipped open a copy of the *Indian Express*. Two members of the Gaitonde gang had been shot to death in an encounter with the Flying Squad in Bhayander. The police had acted on received intelligence and intercepted the two as they proceeded to a factory office in that locality; the two extortionists had been hailed and told to surrender, but they had instantly fired at the squad, who then retaliated, et cetera, et cetera. There was a colour photograph of plain-clothes men bending over two oblong red stains on the ground. In other news, there had been two break-ins in Andheri East, one in Worli, and this last one had ended in the fatal stabbing of a young couple. As Sartaj read, he could hear the elderly man sitting across from Kamble talking about slow death. His eighty-year-old mausi had fallen down a flight of stairs and broken her hip. They had checked her into the Shivsagar Polyclinic, where she had borne with her usual stoicism the unrelenting pain in her old bones. After all, she had marched with Gandhi-ji in forty-two and had suffered her first fracture then – of the collarbone from a mounted policeman's lathi – and also the bare floors of jail cells afterwards. She had an old-fashioned strength, which saw sacrifice of the self as one's duty in the world. But when the pressure ulcers flowered their deep red wounds on her arms and shoulders and back, even she had said, perhaps it is time for me to die. The elderly man had never heard her say anything of the like, but now she groaned, I want to die. And it took her twenty-two days to find relief, twenty-two days before blessed darkness. If you had seen her, the elderly man said, you too would have cried.

Kamble was flipping pages in a register. Sartaj completely believed the elderly man's story, and understood his problem: the Shivsagar Polyclinic wouldn't let him take the body without a No Objection Certificate endorsed by the police. The handwritten note on Brihanmumbai Municipal Corporation stationery would say that the police were satisfied that the death in question was natural, that there was no foul play involved, that the body could be released to relatives for disposal. This was supposed to prevent murders – dowry killings and suchlike – from being passed off as accidents, and Police Sub Inspector Kamble was supposed to sign it on behalf of the ever watchful, khaki-clad guardians of Mumbai, but he had it sitting next to his elbow and he was studiously scribbling in his register. The elderly man had his hands folded together, and his white hair fell over his forehead, and he was looking at the indifferent Kamble with moist eyes. 'Please, sir,' he said.

Sartaj thought it was on the whole a finely considered performance, and that the grief was genuine, but the bit about Gandhi-ji and broken collarbones quite excessively and melodramatically reproving. Both the elderly man and Kamble knew well that a payment would have to be made before the certificate was signed. Kamble

6

would probably hold out for eight hundred rupees; the old man wanted to give only five hundred or so, but the sacrifices of the elders had been done to death in the movies, and Kamble was quite indifferent to the degeneration-of-India gambit. He now closed his red register and reached for a green one. He studied it closely. The old man began the whole story again, from the fall down the stairs. Sartaj got up, stretched, and walked out into the courtyard of the station. In the shade of the gallery that ran along the front of the building, and under the tin portico, there was the usual crowd of touts, hangers-on, relatives of those chained in the detection room inside, messengers and representatives from local businessmen, favour-seekers, and, here and there, those marked by misfortune and sudden misery, now looking up at him in mingled hope and bitterness.

Sartaj walked past them all. There was an eight-foot wall around the whole complex, of the same reddish-brown brick as the station house and the zonal headquarters. Both buildings were two storeys high, with identical red-tiled roofs and oval-topped windows. There was a promise in the grim arches, in the thickness of the walls and the uncompromising weight of the façades, there was the reassurance of bulky power, and so law and order. A sentry snapped to attention as Sartaj went up the stairs. Sartaj heard the laughter from Parulkar's cabin well before he could see it, while he was still twisting through the warren of cubicles piled high with paper. Sartaj knocked sharply on the lustrous wood of Parulkar's door, then pushed it open. There was a quick upturning of laughing faces, and Sartaj saw that even the national newspapers had come out for the story of Parulkar's initiative, or at least for his poetry. He was good copy.

'Gentlemen, gentlemen,' Parulkar said, raising one proud, pointing hand. 'My most daring officer, Sartaj Singh.' The correspondents lowered their teacups with a long clatter and looked at Sartaj sceptically. Parulkar walked around the desk, tugging at his belt. 'One minute, please. I'll talk to him outside for a moment, then he will tell you about our initiative.'

Parulkar shut the door, and led Sartaj around the back of the cabin, to a very small kitchen which now boasted a gleaming new Brittex water filter on its wall. Parulkar pressed buttons and a bright stream of water fell into the glass he held below.

'It tastes very pure, sir,' Sartaj said. 'Very good indeed.'

Parulkar was drinking deep draughts from a steel tumbler. 'I asked them for their best model,' he said. 'Because clean water is absolutely necessary.'

'Yes, sir.' Sartaj took a sip. 'Sir – "daring"?'

'They like daring. And you had better be daring if you want to stay in this job.'

Parulkar had sloping shoulders and a pear-shaped body that defeated the best tailors, and his uniform was crumpled already, but that was only usual. There was a sag in his voice, a resignation in his sideways glance that Sartaj had never known. 'Is something wrong, sir? Is there some complication with the initiative, sir?'

'No, no, no complication with the initiative. No, nothing to do with that at all. It is something else.'

'Yes, sir?'

'They are after me.'

'Who, sir?'

'Who else?' Parulkar said with unusual asperity. 'The government. They want me out. They think I've gone high enough.'

Parulkar was now a deputy commissioner of police, and he had once been a lowly sub-inspector. He had risen through the Maharashtra State Police, and he had made that near-impossible leap into the august Indian Police Service, and he had done it alone, with good police work, a sense of humour, and very long hours. It had been an astonishing and unparalleled career, and he had risen to become Sartaj's mentor. He emptied his glass, and poured more water from his new Brittex filter.

'Why, sir?' Sartaj said. 'Why?'

'I was too close to the previous government. They think I'm a Congress man.'

'So they may want you out. That doesn't mean anything. You have lots of years left before retirement.'

'You remember Dharmesh Mathija?'

'Yes, that's the fellow who built our wall.' Mathija was a builder, one of the more conspicuously successful ones in the northern suburbs, a man whose ambition showed like a sweaty fever on his forehead. He had built, in record time, the extension of the compound wall at the rear of the station, around the recently filled lowland. There was now a Hanuman temple and a small lawn and young trees that you could see from the offices to the rear of the building. Parulkar's passion was improvement. He said it often: we must improve. Mathija and Sons had improved the station, and of course they had done it for free. 'So what about Mathija, sir?'

Parulkar was taking little sips of water, swirling it about in his mouth. 'I was called to the DG's office yesterday, early.'

'Yes, sir.'

'The DG had a call from the home minister. Mathija has threatened to file a case. He said he was forced to do some work for me. Construction.'

'That's absurd, sir. He came himself. How many times he visited you here. We all saw that. He was happy to do it.'

'Not our wall here. At my home.'

'At your home?'

'The roof needed work urgently. As you know, it's a very old house. My ancestral abode really. Also, it needed a new bathroom. Mamta and my granddaughters have moved back home. As you know. So.'

'And?'

'Mathija did it. He did good work. But now he says he has me on tape threatening him.'

'Sir?'

'I remember phoning him to tell him to hurry up. Finish the work before the last monsoons. I may have used some strong language.'

'But so what, sir? Let him go to court. Let him do what he wants. Let him see what we do to his life here, sir. At his sites, all his offices . . .'

'Sartaj, that's just their excuse. It's a way to put pressure on me, and let me know I am not wanted. They're not satisfied with just transferring me, they want to get rid of me.'

'You will fight back, sir.'

'Yes.' Parulkar was the best player of the political game Sartaj had ever known: he was a grandmaster of the subtle art of contact and double-contact and back-channel, of ministers and corporators cultivated and kept happy, business interests allowed room for profits, backslapping and exchanges with commissioners of police, favours finely weighed and dispensed and remembered, deals made and forgotten – he was an aficionado of the subtle sport, he was simply the best. It was incredible that he was so tired. His collar sagged, and the swell of his belly was no longer jaunty, only weighted by regret. He drank another glass of water, fast. 'You had better get in there, Sartaj. They're waiting for you.'

'I'm sorry, sir.'

'I know you are.'

'Sir.' Sartaj thought he should say something else, something full of gratitude and somehow conclusive about what Parulkar had meant to him – the years together, the cases solved and the ones left and abandoned, the manoeuvres learnt, how to live and work and survive as a policeman in the city – and yet Sartaj was able only to come to rigid attention. Parulkar nodded. Sartaj was certain he understood.

Outside the cabin, Sartaj checked the tuck of his shirt, ran a hand over his turban. Then he stepped in, and told the reporters about more policemen on more streets, about community interaction, about strict supervision and transparency, about how things were going to get better.

For lunch Sartaj had an uttapam sent to the station from the next-door Udipi Restaurant. The keen kick of the chillies was invigorating, but when he was finished, Sartaj was unable to get up from his chair. It had been a very light meal but he was crushed, pulped by lassitude. He was barely able to get up and pull the bench from the wall, to slip off his shoes and lie flat and very straight on the wood. His arms were crossed on his chest. A deep breath, then another, and the edge cutting into the back of his thigh receded, and in the swimming drowsiness he was able to forget details, and the world became a receding white blur. Yet a sharp undertow flung him into anger, and after a moment he was able to remember what he was restless about. All of Parulkar's triumphs were going to be wiped away, made meaningless by an engineered disgrace. And once Parulkar was gone, what of Sartaj? What would become of him? Sartaj had begun recently to feel that he himself had accomplished nothing in his life. He was past forty, a divorced police inspector with middling professional prospects. Others from his batch had climbed past him, he was just pedalling along, doing his job. He looked into his future and saw that he would not achieve as much as his own father, and much less than the redoubtable Parulkar. I am quite useless, Sartaj thought, and felt very bleak. He sat up, rubbed his face, shook his head violently, and pulled on his shoes. He stalked into the front room, where PSI Kamble was rubbing his stomach lightly in circles. He looked quite satisfied.

'Good lunch?' Sartaj said.

'Absolute top first-class biryani from that new Laziz Restaurant on S.T. Road,' Kamble said. 'In a fancy clay pot, you know. We're getting very pish-posh in Kailashpada.' Kamble straightened up and leaned closer. 'Listen. You know those two gaandus who were encountered yesterday by the Flying Squad in Bhayander?'

'Gaitonde gang, yes?'

'Right. You know the Gaitonde gang and the Suleiman Isa gang have been stepping up their war again, right? So, I heard the two hits yesterday were a supari given by the S-Company. I heard that the Flying Squad boys made twenty lakhs.'

'You'd better get in the squad then.'

'Boss, what do you think I'm saving up for? I hear the going rate to get in is twenty-five lakhs.'

'Very expensive.'

'Very,' Kamble said. His face was aglow, every pore open and alight. 'But money makes it all happen, my friend, and to make money you have to spend money.'

Sartaj nodded, and Kamble sank into a register again. Sartaj had once heard it from a slumlord convicted of murder, the bitter secret of life in the metropolis: *paisa phek, tamasha dekh*. They had literally bumped into each other, walking round a corner in a basti in Andheri. They had recognized each other instantly, despite Sartaj's plain clothes and the slumlord's new paunch. Sartaj said, arre, Bahzad Hussain, aren't you supposed to be serving fifteen years for offing Anwar Yeda? And Bahzad Hussain laughed nervously, and said, Inspector saab, you know how it is, I got parole and now it says in my file that I'm absconding in Bahrain, *paisa phek, tamasha dekh*. Which was absolutely true: if you had money to throw, you could watch the spectacle – the judges and magistrates trapezing blithely, the hoop-jumping politicians, the happy, red-nosed cops. Bahzad Hussain had the grace and good sense to come quietly to the station, and he was very confident, and wanted only a cup of tea and a chance to make a few phone calls. He made jokes and laughed a lot. Yes, he had thrown his money and watched the spectacle. All of this police jhanjhat was only a slight waste of time, nothing more. *Paisa phek, tamasha dekh*.

Kamble now had a family standing in front of him, a mother and a father and a son in blue-uniform short pants. The father was a tailor who had come back home from the shop early in the afternoon, to get some suiting material he had forgotten. On the way he had taken a short-cut and seen his son, who was supposed to be in school, playing marbles against the factory wall with some faltu street kids. The mother was doing the talking now. 'Saab, I beat him, his father shouts at him, nothing helps. The teachers have given up. He shouts back at us, my son. He thinks he's too smart. He thinks he doesn't need school. I'm tired of it, saab. You take him. You put him in jail.' She made the motion of emptying her hands, and dabbed at her eyes with the end of her blue pallu. Looking at her hands and finely muscled forearms, Sartaj was certain that she worked as a bai, that she washed dishes and clothes for the wives of executives in the Shiva Housing Colony. The son had his head down, and was scraping the side of one shoe against the other.

Sartaj crooked a finger. 'Come here.' The boy shuffled sideways. 'What's your name?'

'Sailesh.' He was about thirteen, quite wise, with a stylish floppy hair-do and flashing black eyes.

'Hello, Sailesh.'

'Hello.'

Sartaj smashed a hand down on to the table. It was very loud, and Sailesh started and backed away. Sartaj grabbed him by the collar and twisted him around the end of the desk. 'You think you're tough, Sailesh? You're so tough you're not scared of anyone, Sailesh? Let me show you what we do with tough taporis like you, Sailesh.' Sartaj walked him around the room and through a door and into the detection room, lifting him off the floor with every stride. Katekar was sitting with another constable at the end of the room, near the squatting line of chained prisoners.

'Katekar,' Sartaj called.

'Sir.'

'Which is the toughest of this lot?'

'This one, sir, thinks he's hard. Narain Swami, pickpocket.'

Sartaj shook Sailesh so that his head wobbled and snapped. 'This big man here thinks he's harder than all of us. Let him see. Give Narain Swami some dum and let the big man see.'

Katekar lifted the cringing Narain Swami and bent him over, and Swami struggled and jingled his chains, but when the first open-palmed blow landed on his back with an awful popping noise he got the idea. With the second one he howled quite creditably. After the third and fourth he was sobbing. 'Please, please, saab. No more.'

After the sixth, Sailesh was weeping fat tears. He turned his face away and Sartaj forced his chin around.

'Want to see more, Sailesh? You know what we do next?' Sartaj pointed at the thick white bar that ran from one wall to the other, close to the ceiling. 'We put Swami on the ghodi. We string him up on the bar, hands and feet, and give it to him with the patta. Show him the patta, Katekar.'

But Sailesh, looking at the thick length of the strap, whispered, 'No, don't.'

'What?'

'Please don't.'

'You want to end up here, Sailesh? Like Narain Swami?'

'No.'

'What's that?'

'No, saab. Please.'

'You will, you know. If you keep going like you are.'

'I won't, saab. I won't.'

Sartaj turned him around, both hands on his shoulders, and walked him towards the door. Narain Swami was still bent over, and flashing an upside-down grin. Outside, sitting on a metal chair with a Coke bottle clutched between his knees, Sailesh listened quietly to Sartaj. He sipped his Coke and Sartaj told him how people like Narain Swami ended up, beaten up, used up, addicted, in jail and out of it, wasted and tired and finally dead. All of it from not going to school and disobeying his mother.

'I'll go,' Sailesh said.

'Promise?'

'Promise,' Sailesh said and touched his throat.

'Better keep it,' Sartaj said. 'I hate people who break promises. I'll come after you.'

Sailesh nodded, and Sartaj led him out. At the station gate, the mother hung back. She came close to Sartaj and held up her fisted hands and opened them. In the right there was the twisted end of her pallu, and in the left a neatly folded hundred rupee note. 'Saab,' she said.

'No,' Sartaj said. 'No.'

She had oiled hair and reddened eyes. She smiled, barely, and held up her hands higher, and opened them further.

'No,' Sartaj said. He turned and walked away.

Katekar drove with an easy grace that found the gaps in the traffic with balletic timing. Sartaj pushed his seat back and drowsily watched him change gears and snake the Gypsy between trucks and autos with less than inches to spare. Sartaj had long ago learned to relax. He still anticipated a crash every few minutes, but he had learned from Katekar not to care. It was all confidence. You went forward, and someone always backed off at the last moment, and it was always the other gaandu. Katekar scratched at his crotch, growled 'Eh, bhenchod,' and stared down a double-decker driver, forced him to an absolute stop. They took a left, and Sartaj grinned at the wide swagger of the turn. 'Tell me, Katekar,' Sartaj said, 'who is your favourite hero?'

'Film hero?'

'What else?'

Katekar was embarrassed. 'When I do watch movies –' He jiggled the gear stick, and wiped a spot of dust from the windscreen. 'When there is some film on television,' – which was only all the time – 'I like to watch Dev Anand.'

'Dev Anand? Really?'

'Yes, sir.'

'But he's my favourite also.' Sartaj liked the old black-and-white ones where Dev Anand listed across the screen at an impossible angle, unbelievably dashing and sublimely suave. In his limp perfection there was an odd comfort, a nostalgia for a simplicity that Sartaj had never known. But he had expected Katekar to be an Amitabh Bachchan extremist, or an enthusiast of the muscle boys, Sunil Shetty or Akshay Kumar, who stood huge on the posters like some new gigantic and bulging species. 'Which Dev Anand film do you like best, Katekar?'

Katekar smiled, and tipped his head to the side. It was a perfect Dev Anand waggle. 'Why, sir, *Guide*, sir. Of course.'

Sartaj nodded. 'Of course.' *Guide* was in bright sixties colour, all the better to savour the intense and ecstatic love that Dev found for Waheeda, and the bitterness of his final tragedy. Sartaj had always found the long-drawn-out death of the guide almost unbearable to watch, all his loneliness and his withered love. But here was Katekar with his unexpected Dev-sympathies. Sartaj laughed, and sang, '*Gata rahe mera dil . . .*' Katekar bobbed his head, and when Sartaj forgot the lyrics after '*Tu hi meri manzil,*' he sang the next couplet, all the way until the antra. Now they were grinning at each other.

14

'They don't make movies like that any more,' Sartaj said.

'No, they don't, sir,' Katekar said. They had a clear stretch of road now, all the way up to the intersection at Karanth Chowk. They sped past clusters of apartment buildings to the right, ensconced behind a long grey wall, and on the left the untidy shacks of a basti opened doors directly on to the road. Katekar stopped at the light smoothly, coming from headlong velocity to an even halt.

'There are rumours about Parulkar Saab,' he said, wiping the inside of the steering wheel with his forefinger.

'What kind of rumours?'

'That he's ill, and is thinking of leaving the force.'

'What's his illness?'

'Heart.'

This was a good rumour, Sartaj thought, as rumours went. It might have been Parulkar himself who'd started this one, working from the basic operational principle that a secret was impossible to keep, that everybody would know something soon, and that it was better you should shape the wild theorizing that would take place, steer it and find advantage in it. 'I don't know about him leaving,' Sartaj said, 'but he is considering his options.'

'For his heart?'

'Something like that.'

Katekar nodded. He didn't seem too concerned. Sartaj knew that Katekar wasn't a great fan of Parulkar Saab, although he would never speak badly of him in front of Sartaj. He had said once, though, that he didn't trust Parulkar. He had offered no reasons, and Sartaj had put his suspicions down to enduring anti-Brahminism. Katekar didn't trust Brahmins, and he disliked Marathas for their middle-caste grabbiness and greed and kshatriya pretensions. Sartaj could see that from Katekar's OBC point of view, there was justification enough for his prejudices. Look at history, he had said more than once. And Sartaj had always accepted, without question, that the backward castes had been treated horribly for interminable centuries. But he argued the caste politics of the past and present with Katekar, and challenged his conclusions. They had always left those dangerous topics amiably enough. Finally, Sartaj was just glad that Katekar's history hadn't included uppity Jatt Sikhs in any immediate way. They had known each other for a long time, and Sartaj had come to depend on him.

They pulled into a narrow parking space in front of the Sindoor Restaurant, Fine Indian and Continental Dining. Sartaj reached back behind his seat for a white Air India bag. He squeezed out past a Peugeot, past a paan-wallah at the gate, and then waited for a line of white-shirted executives to pass. From where he was standing, he could see, at a diagonal across the road, a large white sign with red lettering: 'Delite Dance Bar and Restaurant'. Sartaj's shirt was drenched, plastered to his back from the shoulders to the belt. Inside Sindoor, the decor was altogether wedding-shamiana, down to the band instruments behind the cashier's booth and the mehndi-frills around the edges of the menu. Katekar sat across from Sartaj in a four-customer booth, and they both lowered their heads gratefully under the heavy wash of cold air from a vent just above. A waiter brought two Pepsis, and they both gulped fast, but before they were half-way through, Shambhu Shetty was with them. He slid smoothly in next to Sartaj, neat and trim as always in blue jeans and a blue denim shirt.

'Hello, saab.'

'All good, Shambhu?'

'Yes, saab.' Shambhu shook hands with both of them. Sartaj had his usual moment of envy for the iron of Shambhu's grip, for his taut shoulders and his smooth, twenty-four-year-old face. Once, the year before, he had leaned back in the booth and raised his shirt and shown them his biscuited belly, the little triangles of muscle rising up to his chest. A waiter brought Shambhu a fresh pineapple juice. He never drank aerated drinks, or anything with sugar in it.

'Been trekking, Shambhu?' Katekar said.

'Going early next week, my friend. To Pindari glacier.'

On the red rexine of the seat, between Sartaj and Shambhu, there was a heavy brown envelope. Sartaj slid it into his lap, and raised the flap. Inside, there were the usual ten stacks of hundred-rupee notes, stapled and rubber-banded by the bank into little ten-thousand-rupee bricks.

'Pindari?' Katekar said.

Shambhu was amazed. 'Boss, do you ever leave Bombay? Pindari is in the Himalayas. Above Nainital.'

'Ah,' Katekar said. 'Gone for how long?'

'Ten days. Don't worry, I'll be back by next time.'

Sartaj pulled the Air India bag from between his feet, unzipped it, and slid the envelope in. The station and the Delite Dance Bar had a monthly arrangement. Shambhu and he were merely representatives of the two organizations, dispensing and collecting. The money was not personal, and they had been seeing each other for a year and some months now, ever since Shambhu had taken over as manager of Delite, and they had grown to like each other. He was a good fellow, Shambhu, efficient, low-profile, and very fit. He was trying to persuade Katekar to climb mountains.

'It'll clear out your head,' Shambhu said. 'Why do you think the great yogis always did tapasya way up there? It's the air. It improves meditation, brings peace. It's good for you.'

Katekar raised his empty Pepsi glass. 'My tapasya is here, brother. Here only I find enlightenment every night.'

Shambhu laughed, and clinked glasses with Katekar. 'Don't burn us with your fierce austerities, O master. I'll have to send apsaras to distract you.'

They giggled together, and Sartaj had to smile at the thought of Katekar seated cross-legged on a deerskin, effulgent with pent-up energy. He tugged at the zipper on the bag, and nudged Shambhu with his elbow. 'Listen, Shambhu-rishi,' Sartaj said. 'We have to do a raid.'

'What, again? We just had one not five weeks ago.'

'About seven, I think. Almost two months. But, Shambhu, the government's changed. Things have changed.' Things had indeed changed. The Rakshaks were the new government in the state. What had once been a muscular right-wing organization, proud of its disciplined and looming cadres, was now trying to become a party of statesmen. As state ministers and cabinet secretaries, they had toned down their ranting nationalism, but they would not give up their battle against cultural degeneration and western corruption. 'They promised to reform the city.'

'Yes,' Shambhu said. 'That bastard Bipin Bhonsle. All those speeches about cleaning up corruption since he became minister. And what's all that noise about protecting Indian culture he's been throwing around lately? What are we but Indian? And aren't we protecting our culture also? Aren't the girls doing Indian dances?'

They were doing that exactly, spinning under disco lights to filmi music, quite respectably covered up in cholis and saris, while men held up fans of twenty and fifty-rupee notes for them to pick from, but the Delite Dance Bar as a temple of culture was an audacity that silenced Sartaj and Katekar completely. Then they both said 'Shambhu' together, and he held up his hands. 'Okay, okay. When?'

'Next week,' Sartaj said.

'Do it before I leave. Monday.'

'Fine. Midnight, then.' Under the new edict, the bars were supposed to close at eleven-thirty.

'Oh, come, come, saab. You're taking the rotis from the mouths of poor girls. That's too-too early.'

'Twelve-thirty.'

'At least one, please. Have some mercy. As it is, that's half the night's earning gone.'

'One, then. But you better still have some girls there when we come in. We'll have to arrest some.'

'That bastard Bhonsle. Close down the bars, but what is this new shosha of arresting girls? Why? What for? All they're trying to do is make a living.'

'The new shosha is ruthless discipline and honesty, Shambhu. Five girls in the van. Ask for volunteers. They can give whatever names they like. And it'll be short. Home by three, three-thirty. We'll drop them.'

Shambhu nodded. He did really seem to like his girls, and they him, and from what Sartaj heard, he never tried to push his take of the dancers' tips beyond the standard sixty per cent. From the really popular ones he took only forty. A happy girl is a better earner, he had once said to Sartaj. He was a good businessman. Sartaj had great hopes for him.

'Okay, boss,' Shambhu said. 'Will be organized. No problem.' Outside, he walked in front of the Gypsy as they backed out into the thickening traffic, grinning and grinning.

'What?' Sartaj said.

'Saab, you know, if I can tell the girls you are coming on the raid, you your very own self, I bet I'll get ten volunteers.'

'Listen, chutiya,' Sartaj said.

'Twelve even, if you escorted them in the van,' Shambhu said. 'That Manika asks about you all the time. So brave he is, she says. So handsome.'

Katekar was very serious. 'I know her. Nice home-loving girl.'

'Fair-complexioned,' Shambhu said. 'Good at cooking, embroidery.'

'Bastards,' Sartaj said. 'Bhenchods. Come on, Katekar, drive. We're late.'

Katekar drove, making no attempt to hide a smile as big as Shambhu's. A swarm of sparrows dipped crazily out of the sky, grazing the bonnet of the Gypsy. It was almost evening.

There was a murder waiting at the station for them. Majid Khan, who was the senior inspector on duty, said it had been half an hour since the call had come in from Navnagar, from the Bengali Bura. 'There's nobody else here to take it,' he said. 'Falls to you, Sartaj.'

Sartaj nodded. A murder case three hours before the end of the shift was something that the other officers would be happy to have missed, unless it was especially interesting. The Bengali Bura in Navnagar was very poor, and dead bodies there were just dead, devoid of any enlivening possibilities of professional praise, or press, or money.

'Have a cup of tea, Sartaj,' Majid said. He flipped through the stacks of Delite money, and then put them in the drawer on the right-hand side of the desk. Later he would move the money to the locker of the Godrej cupboard behind his desk, where the larger part of the operating budget of the station was kept. It was all cash, and none of it came from state funds, which weren't enough to pay for the paper the investigating officers wrote the panchanamas on, or the vehicles that they drove, or the petrol they used, or even for the cups of tea that they and a thousand visitors drank. Some of the Delite money Majid would keep, as part of his perquisites as senior inspector, and some of it would be passed on, upwards.

'No, I'd better not,' Sartaj said. 'Better get out there. Sooner there, sooner to sleep.'

Majid was stroking his moustache, which was a flamboyant handlebar like his army father's. He maintained it with faithful indulgence, with foreign unguents and delicate pruning, in the face of all mockery. 'Your bhabhi was remembering you,' he said. 'When are you coming to dinner?'

Sartaj stood up. 'Tell her I said thanks, Majid. And next week, yes? Wednesday? Khima, yes?' Majid's wife was actually not a very good cook, but her khima was not offensive, and so Sartaj professed a great passion for it. Since his divorce the officers' wives had been feeding him regularly, and he suspected that there was other scheming afoot. 'I'm off.'

'Right,' Majid said. 'Wednesday. I'll clear it with the general and let you know.'

In the jeep, Sartaj considered Majid and Rehana, happy couple. At their table, eating their food, he saw the economy of gesture between them, how each simple sentence contained whole histories of years together, and he watched Farah of sixteen and her exasperated teasing of Imtiaz, thirteen and impatient and sure of himself, and Sartaj was part of the easeful sprawl on the carpet afterwards, as they watched some favourite game show. They wanted him there, and most often he couldn't stop wanting to leave. He went each time eagerly, glad to be in a home, with a family, with family. But their happiness made his chest ache. He felt that he was getting used to being alone, he must be, but he also knew he would never be completely reconciled to it. I'm monstrous, he thought, not this and not that, and then he glanced around guiltily to the back of the Gypsy, where four constables sat in identical poses, their two rifles and two lathis hugged close to the chest. They were looking, all of them, at the dirty metal flooring, swaying gently one way and then the other. The sky behind was yellow and drifting rivulets of blue.

The dead man's father was waiting for them at the edge of Navnagar, below the gentle slope covered from nullah to road with hovels. He was small and nondescript, a man who had spent a lifetime effacing himself. Sartaj stepped after him through the uneven lanes. Although they were going up the slope, Sartaj had a feeling of descent. Everything was smaller, closer, the pathways narrow between the uneven walls of cardboard and cloth and wood, the tumbling roofs covered with plastic. They were well into the Bengali Bura, which was the very poorest part of Navnagar. Most of the shacks were less than a man's standing height, and the citizens of the Bengali Bura sat in their doorways, tattered and ragged, and the barefooted children ran before the police party. On Katekar's face there was furious contempt for jhopadpatti-dwellers who let dirt and filth and garbage pile up not two feet from their own doors, who let their little daughters squat to make a mess exactly where their sons played. These are the people who ruin Mumbai, he had said often to Sartaj, these ganwars who come from Bihar or Andhra or maderchod Bangladesh and live like animals here. These were indeed from maderchod Bangladesh, Sartaj thought, although they all no doubt had papers that said they were from Bengal, that each was a bona fide Indian citizen. Anyway, there was nowhere in their watery delta to send them back to, not half a bigha of land that was theirs, that would hold them all. They came in their thousands, to work as servants and on the roads and on the construction sites. And one of them was dead here.

He had fallen across a doorway, chest inside, feet splayed out. He was young, not yet out of his teens. He wore expensive keds, good jeans and a blue collarless shirt. The forearms were slashed deep, to the bone, which was common in assaults with choppers, when the victim typically tried to ward off the blows. The cuts were clean, and deeper at one end than the other. The left hand had only a small oozing stump where the little finger had been, and Sartaj knew there was no use looking for it. There were rats about. Inside the shack it was hard to see, hard to make out anything through the buzzing darkness. Katekar clicked on an Eveready torch, and in the circle of light Sartaj flapped the flies away. There were cuts on the chest and forehead, and a good strong one had gone nearly through the neck. He might have already been walking dead from the other wounds, but that one had killed him, dropped him down with a thud. The floor was dark, wet mud.

'Name?' Sartaj said.

'His, saab?' the father said. He was facing away from the door, trying not to look at his son.

'Yes.'

'Shamsul Shah.'

'Yours?'

'Nurul, saab.'

'They used choppers?'

'Yes, saab.'

'How many of them?'

'Two, saab.'

'You know them?'

'Bazil Chaudhary and Faraj Ali, saab. They live close by. They are friends of my son.'

Katekar was scribbling in a notebook, his lips moving tightly with the unfamiliar names.

'Where are you from?' Sartaj said.

'Village Duipara, Chapra block, district Nadia, West Bengal, saab.' It came out all in a little rush, and Sartaj knew he had rehearsed it many times at night, had studied it on the papers he had bought as soon as he had reached Bombay. A murder case involving Bangladeshis was unusual because they usually kept their heads low, worked, tried to make a living, and tried very hard to avoid attracting attention.

'And the others? Also from there?'

'Their parents are from Chapra.'

'Same village?'

'Yes, saab.' He had that Urdu-sprinkled Bangladeshi diction that Sartaj had learnt to recognize. He was lying about the country the village was in, that was all. The rest was all true. The fathers of the victim and the murderers had probably grown up together, splashing in the same rivulets.

'Are they related to you, those two?'

'No, saab.'

'You saw this?'

'No, saab. Some people shouted for me to come.'

'Which people?'

'I don't know, saab.' From down the lane there was a muttering, a rise and fall of voices, but there was nobody to be seen. None of the neighbours wanted to be caught up in police business.

'Whose house is this?'

'Ahsan Naeem, saab. But he wasn't here. Only his mother was in the house, she is with the neighbours now.'

'She saw this?'

Nurul Shah shrugged. Nobody wanted to be a witness, but the old woman would not be able to avoid it. Perhaps she would plead shortness of vision.

'Your son was running?'

'Yes, saab, from over there. They were sitting in Faraj's house.'

So the dead boy had been trying to get home. He must have tired, and tried to get into a house. The door was a piece of tin hung off the bamboo vertical with three pieces of wire. Sartaj stepped away from the body, away from the heavy smell of blood and wet clay. 'Why did they do this? What happened?'

'They all had been drinking together, saab. They had a fight.'

'What about?'

'I don't know. Saab, will you catch them?'

'We'll write it down,' Sartaj said.

At eleven Sartaj stood under a pounding stream of cold water, his face held up to it. The pressure in the pipes was very good, so he lingered under the shower, moving the sting from one shoulder to the other. He was thinking, despite himself and the rush of water in his ears, about

Kamble and money. When Sartaj had been married, he had taken a certain pride in never accepting cash, but after the divorce he had realized how much Megha's money had protected him from the world, from the necessities of the streets he lived in. A nine-hundred-rupee monthly transportation allowance hardly paid for three days of fuel for his Bullet, and of the many notes he dropped into the hands of informants every day, maybe one or two came from his minuscule khabari allowance, and there was nothing left for the investigation of a young man's death in Navnagar. So Sartaj took cash now, and was grateful for it. Saala Sardar is no longer the saala of rich bastards, so he's woken up: he knew the officers and men said this with satisfaction, and they were right. He had woken up. He took a breath and moved his head so that the solid thrust at the centre of the flow pummelled him between the eyes. The lashing noise of it filled his head.

Outside, in his drawing room, it was very quiet. That there was no sleep yet, however tired he was and despite his yearning for it, he knew. He lay on his sofa, with a bottle of Royal Challenge whisky and one of water on the table next to him. He drank in accurate little sips, timed regularly. He allowed himself two tall glasses at the end of working days, and had been resisting the urge recently to go to three. He lay with his head away from the window, so he could watch the sky, lit still by the city. To the left was a long grey sliver, the building next door, turned by the window frame into a crenellated abstraction, and to the right what was called darkness, what disintegrated softly under the eye into an amorphous and relentless yellow illumination. Sartaj knew where it came from, what made it, but as always he was awed by it. He remembered playing cricket on a Dadar street, the fast *pok* of the tennis ball and the faces of friends, and the feeling that he could hold the whole city in his heart, from Colaba to Bandra. Now it was too vast, escaped from him, each family adding to the next and the next until there was that cool and endless glow, impossible to know, or escape. Had it really existed, that small empty street, clean for the children's cricket games and dabba-ispies and tikkar-billa, or had he stolen it from some grainy black-and-white footage? Given it to himself in gift, the memory of a happier place?

Sartaj stood up. Leaning against the side of the window, he finished the whisky, tipping the glass far over to get the last drop. He leaned out, trying to find a breeze. The horizon was hazy and far, with lights burning hard underneath. He looked down, and saw a glint in the car park far below, a piece of glass, mica. He thought suddenly how easy it would be to keep leaning over, tipping until the weight carried him. He saw himself falling, the white kurta flapping frantically, the bare chest and stomach underneath, the nada trailing, a blue-and-white bathroom rubber chappal tumbling, the feet rotating, and before a whole circle was complete the crack of the skull, a quick crack and then silence.

Sartaj stepped back from the window. He put the glass down on the coffee table, very carefully. Where did that come from? He said it aloud, 'Where did that come from?' Then he sat on the floor, and found that it was painful to bend his knees. His thighs were aching. He put both his hands on the table, palms down, and looked at the white wall opposite. He was quiet.

Katekar was eating left-over Sunday mutton. There was a muscle in his back, to the right and low, that was fluttering, but there was the thick, hot consolation of the mutton with its simple richness of potato and rice, and the stinging pleasure of the green-chilli pickle – with his lips burning he could forget the spasms, or at least ignore them.

'More?' Shalini said.

He shook his head. He settled back in his chair and burped. 'You have some,' he said.

Shalini shook her head. 'I ate,' she said. She was able to resist mutton very late at night, but it was not this alone that kept her arms as thin as the day they had married, nineteen years ago almost to the day. Katekar watched her as she turned the knob on the stove to the left with a single clean movement, high burn to off. There was a pleasing accuracy in her movements as she scoured and stacked the utensils for the wash tomorrow, a clean efficiency that lived very functionally in the very small space that was her. She was a spare woman, inside and out, and she fed his appetites.

'Come, Shalu,' he said, wiping his mouth decisively. 'It's late. Let's sleep.'

He watched as she wiped the tabletop, hard, with her glass bangles clinking. The kholi was small but very clean on the inside. When she had finished, he unlatched the folding legs to the table and swung it up against the wall. The two chairs went in the corners. While she organized the kitchen, he unrolled two chatais where the table had been. Then one mattress on her chatai, and a pillow, and a pillow for

24

himself, but his back would tolerate only the hard ground, and so then the beds were ready. He took a glass of water from the matka, and a box of Monkey tooth powder, and went outside and down the lane, stepping carefully. There was the crowded huddle of kholis, mostly pucca, with electrical wire strung over the roofs and through doorways. The municipal tap was dry at this hour, of course, but there was a puddle of water under the brick wall behind it. Katekar leaned on the wall, dabbed some tooth powder on his forefinger and cleaned his teeth, conserving the water precisely, so that the last mouthful he spat out left his mouth clean.

Shalini was lying on her side when he came into the kholi. 'Did you go?' she said, still facing away. He put the glass down on a shelf in the kitchen. 'Go,' Shalini said. 'Or you'll wake up in an hour.'

At the other end of the lane there was a turn, then another, and then a sudden opening out into an open slope falling to the highway. There was a dense smell rising from the ground, and Katekar squatted into it, and surprised himself with the furious stream that he sent down the tilt, and he sighed and watched the lights approach and vanish below. He came back to the kholi, clicked off the light bulb, took off his banian and pants and lowered himself to his chatai. He lay flat on his back, right leg spread wide, left arm and thigh against Shalini's mattress. After a moment she shifted her weight and settled slowly against him. He felt her shoulder blade on his chest, her hip against the rise of his stomach. She sank into him and he was still. Now, with the quiet and his own silence he could hear, on the other side of the black sheet that divided the kholi into two, the twinned breathing of his sons. They were nine and fifteen, Mohit and Rohit. Katekar listened to his family, and after a while, even in the darkness, he could see the shape of his home. On his side of the sheet there was a small colour television on a shelf, and next to it pictures of his parents and Shalini's parents, all garlanded, and also a large gold-framed photograph of the boys at the zoo. There was a Lux soap calendar turned to June and Madhubala. Under it, a green phone with a lock on the dial. At the foot of the chatais, a whirring table-fan. Behind his head, he knew, there was a two-in-one and his collection of tapes, songs from old Marathi films. Two black trunks stacked on top of each other. Clothes hanging on hooks, his shirt and pants on a hanger. Shalini's shelf with its brass figures of Ambabai and Bhavani, and a garlanded picture of Sai Baba. And the kitchen, with racks all the way to the roof and rows

25

and rows of gleaming steel utensils. And then on the other side of the black sheet, the shelves with schoolbooks, two posters of Sachin Tendulkar at bat, one small desk piled high with pens and notebooks and old magazines. A metal cupboard with two exactly equal compartments.

Katekar smiled. At night he liked to survey his possessions, to feel them solid and real under his heavy-lidded gaze. He lay poised on some twilight border, still far from sleep, the twitch moving up and down his back but not able to travel across the mass of his body to Shalini, and the things he had earned from life encircled him, and he knew how fragile this fortification was, but it was comfortable. In it he was calm. He felt the bulk of his arms and legs lighten, and he was floating in the streaming air, his eyes closed. He slept.

With the sleek little television remote in his hand, Sartaj flicked fast from a car race in Detroit to a dubbed American show about women detectives to a slug, slick and brown, in some huge winding river and then to a filmi countdown show. Two heroines in red miniskirts, smiling and curvy and neither more than eighteen, danced on top of the arches of the vine-wrapped ruin of a palace. Sartaj clicked again. Against a trembling background of news-file clips cut fast, a blonde VJ chattered fast about a bhangra singer from London and his new album. The VJ was Indian, but her name was Kit and her glittering blonde hair hung to her bare shoulders. She thrust a hand at the camera and now suddenly she was in a huge mirrored room filled from end to end with dancers moving together and happy. Kit laughed and the camera moved close to her face and Sartaj saw the lovely angular planes of her face and felt the delicious contentment of her slim legs. He snapped off the television and stood up.

Sartaj walked stiffly to the window. Beyond the fizzing yellow lamps in the compound of the neighbouring building, there was the darkness of the sea, and far ahead, a sprinkling of bright blue and orange that was Bandra. With a good pair of binoculars you could even see Nariman Point, not so far across the sea but at least an hour away on empty night-time roads, and very far from Zone 13. Sartaj felt a sudden ache in his chest. It was as if two blunt stones were grinding against each other, creating not fire but a dull, steady glow, a persistent and unquiet desire. It rose into his throat and his decision was made.

Twelve minutes of fast driving took him through the underpass and on to the highway. The open stretches of road and the wheel slipping easily through his fingers were exhilarating, and he laughed at the speed. But in Tardeo the traffic was backed up between the brightly-lit shops, and Sartaj was suddenly angry at himself, and wanted to turn around and go back. The question came to him with the drumming of his fingers on the dashboard: What are you doing? What are you doing? Where are you going in your ex-wife's car which she left you out of kindness, which might fall to pieces under your gaand on this pitted horror of a road? But it was too late, the journey half-done even though the first glad momentum was gone, and he drove on. By the time he pulled up, parked and walked to the Cave, it was almost one and now he was very tired. But here he was and he could see the crowd around the back door, which was the one open after closing time at eleven-thirty.

They parted for him and let him through. He was older, yes, maybe even much older, but there was no reason for the curious stares and the silence as he stepped through. They were dressed in loose shiny shirts, shorter dresses than he had ever seen, and they made him very nervous. He fumbled at the door, and finally a girl with a silver ring through her lower lip reached out and held it open for him. By the time it occurred to him that he should thank her, he was already inside and the door was closing. He squared his shoulders and found a corner at the bar. With a draught beer in his hand, he had something to do, and so he turned to face the room. He was hedged in close, and it was hard to see more than a few feet, and everywhere they were talking animatedly, leaning close to each other and shouting against the music. He drank his beer quickly, as if he were interested in it. Then his mug was empty and he ordered another one. There were women on all sides, and he looked at each in turn, trying to imagine himself with each one. No, that was too far ahead, so he tried to think of what he would say to any one of them. Hello. No, Hi. Hi, I'm Sartaj. Try to speak English only. And with a smile. Then what? He tried to listen to the conversation on his left. They were talking about music, an American band that he had never heard of, but that was only to be expected, and a girl with her back to Sartaj said, 'The last cut was too slow,' and Sartaj lost the response from the ponytailed boy facing her, but the other girl with the small upturned nose said, 'It was cool, bitch.' Sartaj upended his mug and wiped his mouth. The desire that had brought him across the city had vanished suddenly, leaving a dark residue of bitterness. It was very late and he was finished.

He paid quickly and left. There was a different lot near the door now, but again with the same silence, the same stares, the same beaded necklaces and piercings and practised dishevelment, and he understood that his elegant blue trousers marked him fatally as an outsider. By the time he reached the end of the lane he had no confidence in his white shirt with the button-down collar either. He navigated the right turn on to the main road carefully, stepping over two boys sleeping on the pavement, and walked towards the Crossroads Mall, where he had parked. His feet fell soundlessly on the littered pavement and the shuttered shop doors loomed above. I can't be this drunk on two beers, he thought, but the lampposts seemed very far away and he wanted very much to shut his eyes.

Sartaj went home. He fell into his bed. Now he was able to sleep, it slid heavily on to his shoulders like a choking black landslide. And then instantly it was morning and the shrill grinding of the telephone was in his ear. He groped his way to it.

'Sartaj Singh?' The voice was a man's, peremptory and commanding.

'Yes?'

'Do you want Ganesh Gaitonde?'

Siege in Kailashpada

'You're never going to get in here,' the voice of Gaitonde said over the speaker after they had been working on the door for three hours. They had tried a cold chisel on the lock first, but what had looked like brown wood from a few feet away was in fact some kind of painted metal, and although it turned white under the blade and rang like a sharp temple bell, the door didn't give. Then they had moved to the lintels with tools borrowed from a road crew, but even when the road men took over, wielding the sledgehammers with long, expert swings and huffing breaths, the concrete bounced their blows off blithely, and the Sony speaker next to the door laughed at them. 'You're behind the times,' Gaitonde crackled.

'If I'm not getting in, you're not getting out,' Sartaj said.

'What? I can't hear you.'

Sartaj stepped up to the door. The building was a precise cube, white with green windows, on a large plot of land in Kailashpada, which was on the still-developing northern edge of Zone 13. Here, among the heavy machinery groping at swamp, edging Bombay out farther and wider, Sartaj had come to arrest the great Ganesh Gaitonde, gangster, boss of the G-Company and wily and eternal survivor.

'How long are you going to stay in there, Gaitonde?' Sartaj said, craning his neck up. The deep, round video eye of the camera above the door swivelled from side to side and then settled on him.

'You're looking tired, Sardar-ji,' Gaitonde said.

'I am tired,' Sartaj said.

'It's very hot today,' Gaitonde said sympathetically. 'I don't know how you sardars manage under those turbans.'

There were two Sikh commissioners on the force, but Sartaj was the only Sikh inspector in the whole city, and so was used to being identified by his turban and beard. He was known also for the cut of his pants, which he had tailored at a very film-starry boutique in Bandra, and also for his profile, which had once been featured by *Modern Woman* magazine in 'The City's Best-Looking Bachelors'. Katekar, on the other hand, had a large paunch that sat on top of his belt like a suitcase, and a perfectly square face and very thick hands, and now he came around the corner of the building and stood wide-legged, with his hands in his pockets. He shook his head.

'Where are you going, Sardar-ji?' Gaitonde said.

'Just some matters I have to take care of,' Sartaj said. He and Katekar walked to the corner together, and now Sartaj could see the ladder they had going up to the ventilator.

'That's not a ventilator,' Katekar said. 'It only looks like one. There's just concrete behind it. All the windows are like that. What is this place, sir?'

'I don't know,' Sartaj said. It was somehow deeply satisfying that even Katekar, Mumbai native and practitioner of a very superior Bhuleshwar-bred cynicism, was startled by an impregnable white cube suddenly grown in Kailashpada, with a black, swivel-mounted Sony video camera above the door. 'I don't know. And he sounds very strange, you know. Sad almost.'

'What I have heard about him, he enjoys life. Good food, lots of women.'

'Today he's sad.'

'But what's he doing here in Kailashpada?'

Sartaj shrugged. The Gaitonde they had read about in police reports and in the newspapers dallied with bejewelled starlets, bankrolled politicians and bought them and sold them – his daily skim from Bombay's various criminal dhandas was said to be greater than annual corporate incomes, and his name was used to frighten the recalcitrant. Gaitonde Bhai said so, you said, and the stubborn saw reason, and all roads were smoothed, and there was peace. But he had been in exile for many years – on the Indonesian coast in a gilded yacht, it was rumoured – far but only a phone call away. Which meant that he might as well have been next door, or as it turned out, amazingly enough, in dusty Kailashpada. The early-morning man with the tip-off had hung up abruptly, and Sartaj had jumped out of bed and called the station while pulling on his pants, and the police party had come roaring to Kailashpada in a hasty caravan bristling with rifles. 'I don't know,' Sartaj said. 'But now that he's here, he's ours.'

'He's a prize, yes, sir,' Katekar said. He had that densely snobbish look he always assumed when he thought Sartaj was being naïve. 'But you're sure you want to make him yours? Why not wait for someone senior to arrive?'

'They'll be a long time getting here. They have other business going on.' Sartaj was hoping ardently that no commissioner would arrive to seize his prize. 'And anyway, Gaitonde's already mine, only he doesn't know it.' He turned to walk back towards the door. 'All right. Cut off his power.'

'Sardar-ji,' Gaitonde said, 'are you married?'

'No.'

'I was married once –'

And his voice stopped short, as if cut by a knife.

Sartaj turned from the door. Now it was a matter of waiting, and an hour or two under a hot June sun would turn the unventilated, unpowered building into a furnace that even Gaitonde, who was a graduate of many jails and footpaths and slums, would find as hard to bear as the corridors of hell. And Gaitonde had been lately very successful and thus a little softened, so perhaps it would be closer to an hour. But Sartaj had taken only two steps when he felt a deep hum rising through his toes and into his knees, and Gaitonde was back.

'What, you thought it would be so easy?' Gaitonde said. 'Just a power cut? What, you think I'm a fool?'

So there was a generator somewhere in the cube. Gaitonde had been the first man in any of the city's jails, perhaps the first man in all of Mumbai, to own a cellular phone. With it, safe in his cell, he had run the essential trades of drugs, matka, smuggling and construction. 'No, I don't think you're a fool,' Sartaj said. 'This, this building is very impressive. Who designed it for you?'

'Never mind who designed it, Sardar-ji. The question is, how are you going to get in?'

'Why don't you just come out? It'll save us all a lot of time. It's really hot out here, and I'm getting a headache.'

There was a silence, filled with the murmuring of the spectators who were gathering at the end of the lane.

'I can't come out.'

'Why not?'

'I'm alone. I'm only me by myself.'

31

'I thought you had friends everywhere, Gaitonde. Everyone everywhere is a friend of Gaitonde Bhai's, isn't it? In the government, in the press, even in the police force? How is it then that you are alone?'

'Do you know I get applications, Sardar-ji? I probably get more applications than you police chutiyas. Don't believe me? Here, I'll read you one. Hold on. Here's one. This one's from Wardha. Here it is.'

'Gaitonde!'

'"Respected Shri Gaitonde." Hear that, Sardar-ji? "Respected." So then . . . "I am a twenty-two-year-old young man living in Wardha, Maharashtra. Currently I am doing my MCom, having passed my BCom exam with seventy-one per cent marks. I am also known in my college as the best athlete. I am captain of the cricket team." Then there's a lot of nonsense about how bold and strong he is, how everyone in town's scared of him. OK, then he goes on: "I am sure that I can be of use to you. I have for long followed your daring exploits in our newspapers, which print very often these stories of your great power and powerful politics. You are the biggest man in Mumbai. Many times when my friends get together, we talk about your famous adventures. Please, Shri Gaitonde, I respectfully submit to you my vita, and some small clippings about me. I will do whatever work you ask. I am very poor, Shri Gaitonde. I fully believe that you will give me a chance to make a life. Yours faithfully, Amit Shivraj Patil." Hear that, Sardar-ji?'

'Yes, Gaitonde,' Sartaj said, 'I do. He sounds like a fine recruit.'

'He sounds like a lodu, Sardar-ji,' Gaitonde said. 'I wouldn't hire him to wash my cars. But he would do well as a policeman.'

'I'm getting tired of this, Gaitonde,' Sartaj said. Katekar had his shoulders tensed, he was glowering at Sartaj, wanting him to curse Gaitonde, to shut him up by telling him exactly what kind of bhenchod he was, that they were going to string him up and shove a lathi up his filthy gaand. But, it seemed to Sartaj, to shout abuse at an unhinged man inside an impregnable cube would be spectacularly useless, if momentarily satisfying.

Gaitonde laughed bitterly. 'Are your feelings hurt, saab? Should I be more respectful? Should I tell you about the wonderful and astonishing feats of the police, our defenders who give their lives in service without a thought for their own profit?'

'Gaitonde?'

'What?'

'I'll be back. I need a cold drink.'

Gaitonde became avuncular, affectionate. 'Yes, yes, of course you do. Hot out there.'

'For you also? A Thums Up?'

'I've a fridge in here, chikniya. Just because you're so fair and so hero-like good looking doesn't mean you're extra smart. You get your drink.'

'I will. I'll be back.'

'What else would you do, Sardar-ji? Go, go.'

Sartaj walked down the street, and Katekar fell in beside him. The cracked black tarmac swam and shimmered in the heat. The street had emptied, the spectators bored by the lack of explosions and bullets and hungry for lunch. Between Bhagwan Tailors and Trimurti Music, they found the straightforwardly named Best Cafe, which had tables scattered under a neem tree and rattling black floor fans. Sartaj pulled desperately at a Coke, and Katekar sipped at fresh lime and soda, only slightly sweet. He was trying to lose weight. From where they sat they could see Gaitonde's white bunker. What was Gaitonde doing back in the city? Who was the informant who had given him to Sartaj? All these were questions for later. First catch the man, Sartaj thought, then worry about why and when and how, and he took another sip.

'Let's blow it up,' Katekar said.

'With what?' Sartaj said. 'And that'll kill him for sure.'

Katekar grinned. 'Yes, sir. So what, sir?'

'And what would the intelligence boys say?'

'Sahib, excuse me, but the intelligence boys are mainly useless bhadwas. Why didn't they know he was building this thing?'

'Now, that would have been very-very intelligent, wouldn't it?' Sartaj said. He leaned back in his chair and stretched. 'You think we can find a bulldozer?'

Sartaj had a metal chair brought to the front of the bunker, and he sat on it, patting his face with a cold, wet towel. He was sleepy. The video camera was unmoving and silent.

'Ay, Gaitonde!' Sartaj said. 'You there?'

The camera made its very small buzzing machine noise, nosed about blindly and found Sartaj. 'I'm here,' Gaitonde said. 'Did you get a drink? Shall I phone and order something for you to eat?'

Sartaj thought suddenly that Gaitonde had learned that big voice from the movies, from Prithviraj Kapoor in a smoking jacket being magnanimous to the lowly. 'I'm fine. Why don't you order something for yourself?'

'I don't want food.'

'You'll stay hungry?' Sartaj was trying to calculate the chances of starving Gaitonde out. But he remembered that Gandhi-ji had lasted for weeks on water and juice. The bulldozer would arrive in an hour, an hour and a half, at most.

'There's plenty of food in here, enough for months. And I've been hungry before,' Gaitonde said. 'More hungry than you could imagine.'

'Listen, it's too hot out here,' Sartaj said. 'Come out and back at the station you can tell me all about how hungry you were.'

'I can't come out.'

'I'll take care of you, Gaitonde. There are all sorts of people trying to kill you, I know. But no danger, I promise. This is not going to turn into an encounter. You come out now and we'll be back at the station in six minutes. You'll be absolutely safe. From there you can call your friends. Safe, ekdum safe. You have my promise.'

But Gaitonde wasn't interested in promises. 'Back when I was very young, I left the country for the first time. It was on a boat, you know. Those days, that was the business: get on a boat, go to Dubai, go to Bahrain, come back with gold biscuits. I was excited, because I had never left the country before. Not even to Nepal, you understand. Okay, Sardar-ji, establishing shot: there was the small boat, five of us on it, sea, sun, all that kind of chutmaari atmosphere. Salim Kaka was the leader, a six-foot Pathan with a long beard, good man with a sword. Then there was Mathu, narrow and thin everywhere, always picking his nose, supposed to be a tough boy. Me, nineteen and didn't know a thing. And there was Gaston, the owner of the boat, and Pascal, his assistant, two small dark men from somewhere in the south. It was Salim Kaka's deal, his contacts there, and his money that hired the boat, and his experience, when to go out, when to come back, everything was his. Mathu and I were his boys, behind him all the time. Got it?'

Katekar rolled his eyes. Sartaj said, 'Yes, Salim Kaka was the leader, you and Mathu were the guns and Gaston and Pascal sailed the boat. Got it.'

Katekar propped himself against the wall next to the door and spilled paan masala into his palm. The speaker gleamed a hard, metallic silver. Sartaj shut his eyes.

Gaitonde went on. 'I had never seen such a huge sky before. Purple and gold and purple. Mathu was combing his hair again and again into a Dev Anand puff. Salim Kaka sat on the deck with us. He had huge feet, square and blunt, each cracked like a piece of wood, and a beard that was smooth and red like a flame. That night he told us about his first job, robbing an angadia couriering cash from Surat to Mumbai. They caught the angadia as he got off the bus, tossed him in the back of an Ambassador and went roaring away to an empty chemical godown in the industrial estates at Vikhroli. In the godown they stripped him of his shirt, his banian, his pants, everything, and found sewn inside the pants, over the thighs, four lakhs in five-hundred-rupee notes. Also a money belt with sixteen thousand in it. He was standing there baby-naked, his big paunch shaking, holding his hands over his shrunken lauda, as they left. Clear?'

Sartaj opened his eyes. 'A courier, they got him, they made some money. So what?'

'So the story's not over yet, smart Sardar-ji. Salim Kaka was closing the door, but then he turned around and came back. He caught the guy by the throat, lifted him up and around and put a knee between his legs. "Come on, Salim Pathan," someone yelled to him. "This is no time to take a boy's gaand." And Salim Kaka, who was groping the angadia's bum, said, "Sometimes if you squeeze a beautiful ass, as you would a peach, it reveals all the secrets of the world," and he held up a little brown silk packet which the angadia had taped behind his balls. In it were a good dozen of the highest-quality diamonds, agleam and aglitter, which they fenced the next week at fifty per cent, and Salim Kaka's cut alone was one lakh, and this was in the days when a lakh meant something. "But," Salim Kaka said, "the lakh was the least of it, money is only money." But after that he was known as a lustrous talent, a sharp lad. "I'll squeeze you like a peach," he'd say, cocking a craggy eyebrow, and the poor unfortunate at the receiving end would spill cash, cocaine, secrets, anything.

'"How did you know with the angadia, Salim Kaka?" I asked, and Salim Kaka said, "It is very simple. I looked at him from the door and he was still afraid. When I had my knife at his throat he had said to me in a child's little trembling voice, 'Please don't kill me, my baap.' I hadn't killed him, he was still alive and holding his lauda, the money was gone, but it wasn't his, we were leaving, so why was he still afraid? A man who is afraid is a man who still has something to lose."'

'Very impressive,' Sartaj said. He shifted in his chair, and regretted it immediately as his shoulder blade found a curve of heated metal. He adjusted his turban and tried to breathe slowly, evenly. Katekar was fanning himself with a folded afternoon newspaper, his eyes abstracted and his forehead slack, while into the slow stirring of the air came Gaitonde's voice with its cool electronic hiss.

'I resolved to be sharply watchful for ever after, for I was ambitious. That night I laid my body down along the bow, as close as I could get to the onrushing water, and I dreamed. Did I tell you I was nineteen? I was nineteen and I made myself stories about cars and a high house and myself entering a party and flashbulbs popping.

'Mathu came and sat beside me. He lit a cigarette for himself and gave me one. I drew hard on it like him. In the dark I could see the puff of his hair, his haggard shoulders, and I tried to remember his features, which were too bony to be anywhere close to Dev Anand's, but still every day he stroked talcum powder on to that pointy rat's face and tried. I felt suddenly kindly towards him. "Isn't this beautiful?" I said. He laughed. "Beautiful? We could drown," he said, "and nobody would know what happened to us. We would disappear, *phat*, gone." His cigarette made spirals in the dark. "What do you mean?" I asked. "Oh, you pitiful dehati idiot," he said. "Don't you know? Nobody knows we are out here." "But," I said, "Salim Kaka's people know, his boss knows." I could feel him laughing at me, his knee jogging against my shoulder. "No, they don't." He was leaning closer to me, whispering, and I could smell his banian and see the pale phosphorescence of his eyes. "Nobody knows, he didn't tell his boss. Don't you get it? This is his own deal. Why do you think we're on this little khatara of a boat, not a trawler? Why do you think we are with him, one dehati smelling of farm dirt and a very-very junior member of the company? Eh? Why? This is Salim Kaka's own little operation. He wants to go independent, and to go independent, what do you need? Capital. That's what. That's why we're out here slopping away in this chodu, wheezing tin trap, one pitch away from the big fishes. He thinks he's going to make enough to start himself all new and fresh and shiny. Capital, capital, you understand?"

'I sat up then. He put a hand on my shoulder and swung himself up. "Gaandu," he said, "if you want to live in the city you have to think ahead three turns, and look behind a lie to see the truth and then behind that truth to see the lie. And then, and then, if you want to live well, you need a bankroll. Think about it." Mathu patted my shoulder and drew back. I saw his face for a second in dim light as he lowered himself into the cabin. And I did think about it.'

Under the speaker Katekar turned his head, right and left, and Sartaj heard the small clicking noise of the bones in his neck. 'I remember this Salim Kaka,' Katekar said softly. 'I remember seeing him in Andheri, walking around in a red lungi and a silk kurta. The kurtas were of different colours, but the lungi was always red. He worked with Haji Salman's gang, and he had a woman in Andheri, I remember hearing.'

Sartaj nodded. Katekar's face was puffy, as if he had just woken from sleep. 'Love?' Sartaj said.

Katekar grinned. 'Judging by the silk, it must have been,' he said. 'Or maybe it was just that she was seventeen and had a rear like a prancing deer's. She was an auto mechanic's daughter, I think.'

'Don't believe in love, Katekar?'

'Saab, I believe in silk, and in everything that is soft, and everything else that is hard, but . . .'

Above their heads the speaker rumbled. 'What are you mumbling about, Sardar-ji?'

'Go on, go on,' Sartaj said. 'Just minor instructions.'

'So listen. The next afternoon, we started to see tree branches in the water, pieces of old crates, bottles bobbing down and up, tyres, once the whole wooden roof of a house floating upside down. Gaston stayed on deck the whole time now, one arm around the mast, looking this way and that with binoculars, never stopping. I asked Mathu, "Are we close?" He shrugged. Salim Kaka came up in a new kurta. He stood by the bow, looking to the north, and I saw his fingers dabbing at the silver taveez at his chest. I wanted to ask him where we were, but there was a seriousness on his face that kept me from speaking.'

Sartaj remembered the pictures of Gaitonde, the medium-sized body and the medium face, neither ugly nor handsome, all of it instantly forgettable despite the bright blue and red cashmere sweaters, everything quite commonplace. But now there was this voice, quiet and urgent, and Sartaj tipped his head towards the speaker.

37

'As night came, in the last failing light, there was a pinpoint of red winking steadily to the north. We dropped anchor, then headed towards it in a dinghy. Mathu rowed and Salim Kaka sat opposite, watching our beacon, and I between them. I was expecting a wall, like I had seen near the Gateway of India, but instead there were high rushes that towered above our heads. Salim Kaka took a pole and pushed us through the feathered banks that creaked and whispered, and although I wasn't told to, I had my ghoda in my hand, loaded and ready. Then the wood scraped under my feet, hard on ground. Flashlight in hand, Salim Kaka led us up the island – that's what it was, a soft wet rising in the swamp. We walked for a long time, half an hour maybe, Salim Kaka in front, under a rising moon. He had a brown canvas bag over his shoulder, big as a wheat sack. Then I saw the beacon again, over the top of the stalks. It was a torch tied to a pole. I could smell the tallow; the flames jumped two feet high. Under it there were three men. They were dressed like city people, and in the leaping light I could see their fair skin, their bushy black eyebrows, their big noses. Turks? Iranis? Arabs? I don't know still, but two of them had rifles, muzzles pointed just a little away from us. My trigger was cool and sweaty on my finger. I cramped and thought, You'll fire and finish us all. I took a breath, turned my wrist, feeling the butt against my thumb, and watched them. Salim Kaka and one of them spoke, their heads close together. Now the bag was offered, and a suit-case in return. I saw a gleam of yellow, and heard the clicks of locks shutting. My arm ached.

'Salim Kaka stepped backward, and we edged away from the for-eigners. I felt the smooth, wet rim of a stalk against my neck, and I couldn't find a way out, only the yielding pressure of vegetation, and panic. Then Salim Kaka turned abruptly and slipped between the bushes, the faint beam of his flashlight marking his way, and then Mathu. I came last, sideways, my revolver hand held low, my neck taut. I can still see them watching, the three men. I see the gleam of the metal bands around the rifle muzzles, and their shaded eyes. We were walking fast. I felt as if we were flying, and the tall grass that had pulled and clawed at me at first now brushed softly along my sides. Salim Kaka turned his head, and I saw his frantic smile. We were happy, running.

'Salim Kaka paused at the edge of a little stream where water had cut a drop of three feet, maybe four, and he reached down with his right foot and found a place for his heel. Mathu looked at me, his face cut into angles by the gaunt moonlight, and I looked at him. Before Salim Kaka had completed his step, I knew where we were going. The report of the revolver bounced off the water into my belly. I knew the butt had bruised the base of my thumb. Only when the flare left my eyes could I see again, and my stomach was twisting and loosening and twisting, and at the bottom of the ditch Salim Kaka's feet were treading steadily, as if he were still finding his way to the boat. The water thrashed and boiled. "Fire, Mathu," I said. "Fire, maderchod." Those were the first words I had spoken since we'd come ashore. My voice was firm and strange, the sound of it alien. Mathu tilted his head and pointed his barrel. Again, a flash brought the weeds out from the shadows, but still those feet clambered away, going steadily somewhere. I aimed my revolver into the round, frothy turbulence, and at the first discharge all movement stopped, but I put another one in just to make sure. "Come on," I said, "let's go home." Mathu nodded, as if I were in charge, and he jumped into the ditch and scrabbled for the suitcase. The flashlight was glowing under the water, a luminous yellow bubble that embraced exactly half of Salim Kaka's head. I snapped it up as I went through, though all the way back to the dinghy the fat moon was low overhead and lit us to safety.'

Sartaj and Katekar heard Gaitonde drink now. They heard, clearly, every long gulp and the glass emptying. 'Whisky?' Sartaj whispered. 'Beer?'

Katekar shook his head. 'No, he doesn't drink. Doesn't smoke either. Very health-conscious don he is. Exercises every day. He's drinking water. Bisleri with a twist of lime in it.'

Gaitonde went on, hurrying now. 'When the sun came up on the boat the next day, Mathu and I were still awake. We had spent the night sitting in the cabin, across from each other, with the suitcase tucked under Mathu's bunk but still visible. I had my revolver in my lap, and I could see Mathu's under his thigh. The roof above my head creaked out a stealthy step. We had told Gaston and Pascal that we had been ambushed by the police, the police of whatever country we had been in. Pascal had wept, and they were both moving very gently now, in respect for our mourning. Behind Mathu's head there was the dark brown of the wood, and the white of his banian floating and dipping with the swell of the waves. There was the hazy distance between us, and I knew what he was thinking. So I decided. I put my revolver on the pillow, put my feet up on the bunk. "I'm going to sleep," I said. "Wake me up in three hours and then you can rest." I turned to the wood, with my back towards Mathu, and shut my eyes. Very low down on my back there was a single circle on my skin which twitched and crawled. It expected a bullet. I could not calm it. But I kept my breathing steady, my knuckles against my lips. There are some things you can control.

'When I woke it was evening. There was a thick orange light pushing into the cabin from the hatch, colouring the wood like fire. My tongue filled my throat and mouth, and my hand when I tried to move it had become a loathsome bloated weight. I thought the bullet had found me, or I had found the bullet, but then I jerked once and my heart was thudding painfully and I sat up. My stomach was covered with sweat. Mathu was asleep, his face down on the pillow. I tucked my revolver into my waistband and went up. Pascal smiled at me out of his black little face. The clouds were piled above us, enormous and bulging, higher and higher into the red heaven. And this boat a twig on the water. My legs shook and I sat down and shook. I trembled and stopped and then trembled again. When it was dark, I asked Pascal for two strong bags. He gave me two white sacks made of canvas, with drawstrings.

'"Wake up," I said to Mathu when I went downstairs, and kicked his bunk. He came awake groping for his revolver, which he couldn't find until I pointed to it, between the mattress and the wall. "Calm down, you jumpy chut. Just calm down. We have to share." He said, "Don't ever do that again." He was growling, stretching his shoulders up like a rooster heaving its feathers. I smiled at him. "Listen," I said, "you bhenchod sleepy son of maderchod Kumbhkaran, do you want your half or what?" He calculated for a moment, still all swollen and angry, but then he subsided with a laugh. "Yes, yes," he said. "Half-half. Half-half."

'Gold is good. It moves and slips on your fingers with a satisfying smoothness. When it is near to pure it has that healthy reddish glow that reminds you of apple cheeks. But that afternoon, as we moved the bars from the suitcase into the sacks, one by one, one for one and then one for the other, what I liked best was the weight. The bars were small, a little longer than the breadth of my palm, much smaller than I had expected, but they felt so dense and plump I could hardly bear to put each in my sack. My face was warm and my heart congested and I knew I had done right. When we got to the last bar, which was mine, I put it in my left pants pocket, where I could feel it always, slapping against me. Then the revolver on the other side, at the back of my waistband. Mathu nodded. "Almost home," he said. "How much do you think it's worth?" His smile was slow and faltering. He picked at his nose, as he always did when he was nervous, which was most of the time. I looked down at him and felt only contempt. I knew absolutely and for certain and in one instant that he would always be a tapori, nothing more, maybe even with ten or twelve people working for him, but always nothing more than a nerve-racked small-time local buffoon, jacked up into tottery brutishness with a gun and a chopper under his shirt, that's all. If you think in rupees, you're a sweep-carrying bhangi, nothing more. Because lakhs are dirt, and crores are shit. I thought, what is golden is the future in your pocket, the endless possibility of it. So I shoved the sack under my bunk, nudging the last of it under with my foot as Mathu watched with wide eyes. I turned my back on him and climbed up to the deck, laughing to myself. I was no longer afraid. I knew him now. That night I slept like a baby.'

Katekar snorted, and shook his head. 'And for years he slept a restful sleep every night, while the bodies fell right and left.' Sartaj held up a warning hand, and Katekar wiped the sweat from his face and muttered quietly, 'They're all of them the swinish same, maderchod greedy bastards. The trouble is, when one gets killed, five come up to take his place.'

'Quiet,' Sartaj said. 'I want to hear this.'

The speaker growled again. 'The day after the next, I saw, over the water, a faraway hillock. "What is that?" I asked Gaston. "Home," he said. From the bow Pascal called to another boat leaning out towards the horizon. "Aaa-hoooooooo," he called, and the long cry and its echoing reply wrapped about my shoulders. I was home.

'We helped to beach the boat, and then took leave of Pascal and Gaston. Mathu was whispering threats at them, but I shouldered him aside, not too gently, and said, "Listen, boys, keep this quiet, very quiet, and we'll do business again." I gave them a gold bar each from my share, and shook hands with them, and they grinned and were my fellows for life. Mathu and I walked a little way down the road, to the bus stop, with our white sacks dragging over our shoulders. I waved down an auto-rickshaw and nodded at Mathu. I left him standing there, his finger at his nose, buffeted by exhaust. I knew he wanted to come with me, but he thought more of himself than he was, and he would've forced me to kill him, sooner or later. I had no time for him. I was going to Bombay.'

The speaker was silent. Sartaj stood up, turned and looked up and down the street. 'Eh, Gaitonde?' he said.

A moment passed, and then the answer came: 'Yes, Sartaj?'

'The bulldozer's here.'

Indeed it was there, a black leviathan that now appeared at the very end of the street with a throaty clanking that caused a crowd to appear instantly. The machine had a certain dignity, and the driver had a cap on his head, worn with the flair of a specialist.

'Get those people out of the road,' Sartaj said to Katekar. 'And that thing up here. Pointed this way.'

'I can hear it now,' Gaitonde said. The video lens moved in its housing restlessly.

'You'll see it soon,' Sartaj said. The policemen near the vans were checking their weapons. 'Listen, Gaitonde, this is all a farce that I don't like one bit. We've never met, but still we've spent the afternoon talking. Let's be gentlemen. There's no need for this. Just come out and we can go back to the station.'

'I can't do that,' Gaitonde said.

'Stop it,' Sartaj said. 'Stop acting the filmi villain, you're better than that. This isn't some schoolboy game.'

'It is a game, my friend,' Gaitonde said. 'It is only a game, it is leela.'

Sartaj turned away from the door. He wanted, with an excruciating desire, a cup of tea. 'All right. What's your name?' he said to the driver of the bulldozer, who was leaning against a gargantuan track.

'Bashir Ali.'

'You know what to do?'

Bashir Ali twisted his blue cap in his hands.

'It's my responsibility, Bashir Ali. I'm giving you an order as a police inspector, so you don't have to worry about it. Let's get that door down.'

Bashir Ali cleared his throat. 'But that's Gaitonde in there, Inspector sahib,' he said tentatively.

Sartaj took Bashir Ali by the elbow and walked him to the door.

'Gaitonde?'

42

'Yes, Sardar-ji?'

'This is Bashir Ali, the driver of the bulldozer. He's afraid of help-ing us. He's frightened of you.'

'Bashir Ali,' Gaitonde said. The voice was commanding, like an emperor's, sure of its consonants and its generosity.

Bashir Ali was looking at the middle of the door. Sartaj pointed up at the video camera, and Ali blinked up at it. 'Yes, Gaitonde Bhai?' he said.

'Don't worry. I won't forgive you –' Bashir Ali blanched '– because there's nothing to forgive. We are both trapped, you on that side of the door and me on this. Do what they tell you to do, get it over with and go home to your children. Nothing will happen to you. Not now and not later. I give you my word.' There was a pause. 'The word of Ganesh Gaitonde.'

By the time Bashir Ali had climbed up to his seat on top of the bull-dozer he had understood, it seemed, his starring role in the situation. He put his cap on his head with a twirl and pointed it backward. The engine grunted and then settled into a steady roar. Sartaj leaned close to the speaker. The left side of his head, from the nape of the neck to the temples, was caught in a sweeping pulse of heat and pain.

'Gaitonde?'

'Speak, Sardar-ji, I'm listening.'

'Just open this door.'

'You want me to just open this door? I know, Sardar-ji, I know.'

'Know what?'

'I know what you want. You want me to just open this door. Then you want to arrest me and take me to the station. You want to be a hero in the newspapers. You want a promotion. Two promotions. Deep down you want even more. You want to be rich. You want to be an all-India hero. You want the President to give you a medal on Republic Day. You want the medal in full colour on television. You want to be seen with film stars.'

'Gaitonde . . .'

'But you know, I've had all that. And I'll beat you. Even in this last game I'll beat you.'

'How? You have some of your boys in there with you?'

'No. Not one. I told you, I'm alone.'

'A tunnel? A helicopter hidden inside?'

Gaitonde chuckled. 'No, no.'

'What then? You have a battery of Bofors guns?'

'No. But I'll beat you.'

The bulldozer was shimmering on the black road, flanked by grim-eyed policemen. Their choices were narrowing rapidly, leading them inevitably to this metal door, and they were determined, and helpless, and afraid.

'Gaitonde,' Sartaj said, rubbing his eyes. 'Last chance. Come on, yaar. This is stupid.'

'I can't do it. Sorry.'

'All right. Just stay back from the door when we come in. And have your hands up.'

'Don't worry,' Gaitonde said. 'I'm no danger.'

Sartaj stood up straight, his back to the door, and checked his revolver. He rotated the cylinder, and the yellow bullets sat fat and round in the metal. The heat came through the soles of his shoes, into his feet.

Suddenly the speaker came to life again against his shoulder blade. 'Sartaj, you called me yaar. So I'll tell you something. Build it big or small, there is no house that is safe. To win is to lose everything, and the game always wins.'

Sartaj could feel the tinny trembling in his chest from the speaker. The machine in front of him produced a blare that pressed him back against the door, and it was enough. He palmed the cylinder back into the revolver, and stepped off the porch. 'All right,' he shouted. 'Let's go, let's go, let's go.' He waved towards the door with the weapon. The speaker was buzzing again, but Sartaj wasn't listening. As he walked away, he thought that under the engine's roar he heard a last fragment, a question: 'Sartaj Singh, do you believe in God?'

Sartaj called, 'Come on, Bashir Ali, move.' Bashir Ali raised a hand, and Sartaj pointed a rigid finger at him. 'Get that thing moving.'

Bashir Ali crouched in his high seat, and the behemoth lurched forward, past Sartaj, and smashed against the building with a dull crunch, raising a soaring cloud of plaster. But after a moment, when the bulldozer pulled back, the building still stood complete and sacrosanct, the door not even dented. Only the video camera had been injured: it lay next to the door, flattened neatly half-way along its length. A long jeer rose from the crowd down the street. It grew louder when Bashir Ali switched off his engine.

'What was that?' Sartaj said when Bashir Ali stepped down into the bulldozer's shadow.

'What do you expect when you won't let me do it the way it should be done?'

They were both wiping plaster from their noses. On the sunlit side of the bulldozer the crowd was chanting, 'Jai Gaitonde.'

'Do you know the way to do it?'

Bashir Ali shrugged. 'I have an idea.'

'All right,' Sartaj said. 'Fine. Do it how you want.'

'Get out of my way then. And get your men back from the building.'

As Bashir Ali spun his steed on the gravel, Sartaj saw that he was an artist. He operated with flicks and thumps of his hands on the driving sticks, leaning into the direction of his turns, in sympathy with the groaning gears underneath. He raised and then lowered his blade, positioning it precisely, with its lower extended edge level with the door. He reversed ten feet, twenty, thirty, his arm jauntily on the back of his seat. He came at the building at a diagonal, and as he went past Sartaj he gleamed a white grin. This time there was a scream of metal, and when the violent juddering of the bulldozer had ceased, Sartaj saw that the door had been peeled back, inward. A crack ran three feet up into the masonry.

'Back!' Sartaj shouted. He was running forward, revolver held in front of him. 'Get back, get back.' Then Bashir Ali was gone, and Sartaj was leaning against one side of the doorway, and Katekar on the other. An icy wind came out and Sartaj felt it drying the sweat on his face and his forearms. Suddenly, for a moment, he envied Gaitonde all his air-conditioners, the frigid climate control won by his audacity. And for a moment, rising from somewhere deep in his hips, unbidden and nauseating, like a buoyant dribble of bile, was a tiny bubble of admiration. He took a deep breath. 'Do you think the building will hold?' he said.

Katekar nodded. He was looking in, through the door, and his face was dark with rage. Sartaj touched the tip of his tongue to his upper lip, felt the dryness, and then they went in. Sartaj went ahead, and at the first door inside Katekar went by him. Behind them followed the rustling of the others. Sartaj was trying to hear above the thunderous unclenching of his heart. He had done entries like this before, and it never got better. It was very cold inside the building, and the light was low and luxurious. There was carpet under their feet. There were four square rooms, all white, all empty. And at the exact centre of the building was a very steep, almost vertical, metal staircase going downward through the floor. Sartaj nodded at Katekar, and then followed him down. The metal door at the bottom opened easily, but it was very heavy, and when Katekar finally had it back Sartaj saw that it was as thick as a hatch to a bank vault. Inside it was dark. Sartaj was shivering uncontrollably. He moved past Katekar, and now he saw a bluish light on the left. Katekar slid past his shoulders and went out wide, and then they shuffled forward, weapons held rigidly before them. Another step and now in the new angle Sartaj saw a figure, shoulders, in front of a bank of haze-filled TV monitors, a brown hand near the controls on a black panel.

'Gaitonde!' Sartaj hadn't meant to shout – a gentle admonitory assertion was the preferred tone – and now he squeezed his voice down. 'Gaitonde, put your hands up very slowly.' There was no movement from the figure in the darkness. Sartaj tightened his finger painfully on his trigger, and fought the urge to fire, and fire again. 'Gaitonde. Gaitonde?'

From Sartaj's right, where Katekar was, came a very small click, and even as Sartaj turned his head the room was flooded with white neon radiance, generous and encompassing and clean. And in the universal illumination Gaitonde sat revealed, a black pistol in his left hand, and half his head gone.

Gaitonde's right eye bulged with a bloodshot and manic intensity. Sartaj could see the fragile tracery of pink lines, the hard black of the pupil, the shining seep of fluid from the inside corner, which despite himself he thought of as a tear. But it was only the body reacting to the gigantic blow which had sheared off everything from the chin up on the other side, slicing from the left nostril up into the forehead and spraying a creamy mess on to the white ceiling. A tooth winked pearl-like, whole and undamaged, from the raw red where Gaitonde's tight-lipped grimace stopped abruptly.

'Sir,' Katekar said. Sartaj jerked, and followed the rigidly pointing barrel of Katekar's revolver to a doorway in the white wall. Just where the boundary lay between sharp brightness and darkness, in that shadow, were two small bare feet, toes pointing up at the ceiling. Sartaj stepped up, and he couldn't see the body clearly, just the cuffs of white pants, but he knew somehow, from the indistinct spread of the hips, that it was a woman. Again Katekar found a switch, and there she was, yes, a woman, wearing tight white pants, slung low – Sartaj knew they were called hipsters. She wore a tight pink top, it was elegant. It showed her belly, she must have been proud of the narrowness of her waist and the perfect navel. And there was a hole in her chest, just under the downy spot on her thorax where the top clipped shut.

'He shot her,' Sartaj said.

'Yes,' Katekar said. 'She must have been standing in the doorway.'

Her face was turned to the left, with long hair falling over her cheek.

'Check the rest,' Sartaj said. In the square room where the girl lay, there were three bare beds, in a row, with white night-stands next to each. It looked rather like a dormitory. Against the wall, an exercise cycle and a row of graduated weights on a rack. DVDs of old black-and-white movies. A steel cabinet with a row of AK-56 rifles, and pistols underneath. And there were showers and western-style toilets in a bathroom, and three cupboards full of men's clothing and shoes and boots. In the central room Katekar had finished his survey, and they stood together over Gaitonde.

There was a press of armed policemen behind Sartaj, jostling shoulders and clanking rifle butts as they craned forward to see what the great Gaitonde had come to, and his murdered girlfriend. 'Enough,' Sartaj said. 'What is this, a free tamasha? A film show? I want everyone up and out of here.' But he knew his voice was full of relief and released tension, and they grinned at him as they turned away. He propped himself on the edge of the long desk and waited for the strange liquid elasticity behind his kneecaps to subside. From the back of Gaitonde's chair there was a steady drip on to the floor.

Katekar was opening and shutting the white cabinets that lined the central room, with a blue handkerchief draped over his fingers. He was always methodical in the wake of gunshots, and Sartaj found comfort in the breadth and solidity of his shoulders and the serious set of his jaw.

'Nothing in here, sir,' Katekar said. 'Not one thing.'

Next to Sartaj's leg, there was a drawer in the desk. Sartaj found his own handkerchief and pulled at the handle. A small black book sat in the exact centre of the drawer, the edges lined up with the sides of the drawer.

47

'Diary?' Katekar said.

It was an album, black pages covered with sticky film, behind which photographs had been inserted. Sartaj flipped the pages by the very corners. Women, some very young, in posed studio shots, looking over shoulders and holding their faces and cocking their hips, decently dressed but all glamorous.

'All his women,' Sartaj said.

'All his randis,' Katekar said. He flipped his blue handkerchief over his index finger and edged open the waist-high filing cabinet that stood at the other end of the desk. Sartaj heard the intake of his breath even over the low hum of the generators. 'Sir.'

The filing cabinet was full of money. The money was new money, five-hundred-rupee notes in clean little bundles still in the Central Bank of India wrappers and rubber bands, and the bundles were held together in bricks of five by crisp shrink-wrapped plastic. Katekar pushed at the top layer, into the crack between the stacks. There was more underneath. And then more.

'How much?' Sartaj said.

Katekar thumped the side of the cabinet gently, thoughtfully. 'It's full all the way down. That's a lot of money. Fifty lakhs? More.'

It was more money than either had ever seen in one place before. There was a decision to be made, and they looked at each other frankly, and Sartaj decided. He nudged the cabinet shut with his knee. 'Too much money,' he said.

Katekar exhaled. He was unmistakably wistful for a second, that was all. But it had been him who had taught Sartaj this important lesson of survival, that to lunge for big prizes without enough information was to invite disaster. He shook himself loose now of the enchantment of big money with a huffing noise and a big grin. 'The big people will take care of Gaitonde's money,' he said. 'Now we wait?'

'We wait.'

The bunker was full. There were lab technicians and photographers, and senior officers from three zones and the Crime Branch. Gaitonde sat in the middle, well-lit and somehow shrunken. Sartaj watched as Parulkar leaned over Gaitonde, pointing something out to another zonal commissioner. Parulkar was in his element, discussing a successful operation with those who mattered, and Sartaj was grateful to him. He was sure that Parulkar would polish and improve the story, and give him more credit than he was due. This was a talent Parulkar had. Sartaj depended on him for it.

Three men came down the staircase, moving fast. Sartaj had never seen them before. The one in the lead had his hair cut so close to the skull that Sartaj could see the scalp under the neat grey. This one spoke to Parulkar, and flashed an ID card. Parulkar listened, and although he didn't give anything away, Sartaj saw him become very still. He nodded, and then led Flat-head and the other two over to Sartaj.

'This is the officer,' Parulkar said to Flat-head. 'Inspector Sartaj Singh.'

'I am SP Makand, CBI.' Flat-head was very curt. 'Did you find anything?'

'The money,' Sartaj said. 'An album. We didn't go through his pockets yet, we were waiting until . . .'

'Good,' Makand said. 'We will take over now.'

'Can we do anything?'

'No. We will be in touch. Have your men clear the location.' Makand's two flankers were already moving around the room, telling the technicians to pack up.

Sartaj nodded. That Gaitonde would be taken from him he had expected. That Gaitonde had appeared in Zone 13 was inexplicable, that his career had come to a sudden stop in Kailashpada was a professional gift altogether too perfect to be left to Sartaj alone. Life did not allow such undiluted felicities. But Makand's dismissal – even coming from a man from an elite central agency – was altogether too abrupt. And yet here was Parulkar being as bland as desi butter, with not a protest or small objection. So Sartaj followed his lead, summoned Katekar and got out.

It was evening. Sartaj stood in the lee of the metal door, in the shadows, and he could see the reporters waiting on the other side of the row of police jeeps. Parulkar was next to him, smartening himself up for the press. 'Sir,' Sartaj said, 'why did they kick us out? The CBI doesn't need local help any more?'

Parulkar tucked his shirt in, and tugged at his belt. 'They seemed very tense. My feeling was that they were afraid something in there would get exposed.'

'They're trying to cover something up?'

49

Parulkar tilted his head and allowed himself to look canny. 'Beta,' he said, 'when someone is willing to be that rude to us, it usually means they are trying to hide something. Come on. Let's go and tell our friends from the press how you brought down the great don Ganesh Gaitonde.'

So Sartaj stepped out into the flare of flashbulbs and told the journalists of his coup. He told them that he had talked to Gaitonde before they had knocked down the door, that Gaitonde had seemed unafraid and rational. He did not tell them Gaitonde's story about gold. And he did not tell them, or Katekar or Parulkar, about the question he thought Gaitonde had asked, at the last. He wasn't sure he had heard it, anyway. So he told the reporters about the anonymous tip that morning, and what had followed, and he said no, he had no idea why a mafia don would want to kill himself.

But later, at home that night, he remembered Gaitonde's grandiloquent voice, his rapid speech, his sadness. He had never met Ganesh Gaitonde, and now their lives had crossed and the man was dead. On the edge of sleep, Sartaj remembered all that he had heard and read about Gaitonde, the rumours and legends, the intelligence reports and the news-magazine interviews. He tried to connect the public image to the voice he had heard, and couldn't. There had been the famous gangster, and there was the man this afternoon. But what did it matter, any of it? Gaitonde was dead. Sartaj turned over, thumped his pillows determinedly, arranged them, and lay down his head and slept.

Ganesh Gaitonde Sells His Gold

So, Sardar-ji, are you listening still? Are you somewhere in this world with me? I can feel you. What happened next, and what happened next, you want to know. I was walking under the whirling sky riven by clouds, with the unceasing tug of gold on my back and the city ahead. I was nineteen and I had gold on my back. Here I was, Ganesh Gaitonde, wearing a dirty blue shirt, brown pants, torn rubber-bottomed shoes and no socks, with forty-seven rupees in my pocket and a revolver in my belt and gold on my back. I had nowhere to go, because I couldn't go back to the building in Dadar where I had space to sleep outside the spice-smelling storage room of a restaurant. If Salim Kaka's people were going to look for me, or if anyone else was going to look for me, I would be gone, not found like a simpleton and given a dog's death. Since I had found the gold I had lost trust. I had the problems of a rich man. I thought: in all the world I have only forty-seven rupees and a revolver and this gigantic weight of metal. Gold is no good on my back, I must sell it. Gold is of no consequence until I sell it. How to sell gold, so much of it? Where to sell it? Until I sell it I am a poor man. A poor man with a rich man's problems.

I grinned, and then I laughed. There was a need to find a stash, now, quickly, but the situation was also funny. I sang: '*Mere desh ki dharti sona ugle, ugle heere moti.*' But ten-thirty in the morning was no time to be walking around the outer edges of Borivali with a loaded ghoda and gold, bent by the weight and very tired. There were far fields and thickets of trees and buildings only here and there, small cottages clustered together very village-like, but sooner or later somebody was going to notice, to ask, to want. I had only three bullets left. Thirty or three hundred bullets wouldn't make a difference if someone found out what I was carrying.

There was a barbed-wire fence to the right, guarding a stand of trees. I looked behind, ahead, and my decision was made. I slipped under the lowest strand, pulled the sack after and walked fast, no running, a fast walk to the trees. In the shade I squatted and settled into a wait. I flexed my hands, trying to work off the cramp that came from clutching my sack, from carrying its heavy burden. If anything happened it would happen now. I was enveloped all at once by tiny flying insects, and was willing to take the bites, but they moved in a shivering cloud around my shoulders, a tremble in the air. In the shimmering circle I was remembering the slope of a mountain seen through a window, a schoolbook fluttering in the breeze, my mother's endless weeping in the next room. Endless. Enough – I waved a hand in front of my face and came out of it. I moved forward in a crouch, through the dark under the branches, towards a sheet of water I could see now. A small pond, held in a saucer-like depression, edged around with yellowing weeds. I sat again, squatting with the sack in front. There were no footprints in the soft mud around the pond, no paths through the coarse grass, no man or woman all the way to the barbed wire on the far side of the water, or even beyond, on the road. But I wanted to give it another half an hour. I held firmly on to the smooth rectangle of the bar in my pocket and breathed in, out. I followed the quick iridescent dip of dragonflies on the water. I was determined not to slip again, never to fall gently into the slow whirlpool of the past. There had been a life, I had left it. For Ganesh Gaitonde there was only this day, this day's night and every day ahead.

When it was time, I backed away into the trees, into the darkest shade. I chose a tree and began to dig. The earth was loose, but dry, and it was slow going, and soon my fingers were raw. I should have first found something to dig with, a piece of tin, something. Bad planning. But it was started now, and I went on, moving the dirt in fistfuls. When I reached the harder layer under the topsoil I sat back and scraped at it with my heels until I had loosened it. The work was hard, and I was sweating, and when I stopped it wasn't really a hole, just a shallow depression really, under the dark trunk. I was tired, and hungry, and it would have to be enough. My chest was heaving. I tugged at the drawstring on the sack, and took out two biscuits of gold, and lost a minute or two in the soft bronze burn of them, under the dappled shadows. Then the sack went into the cranny, and I scraped earth back over it. It looked like a small mound, and I scurried about under the trees, finding tufts of grass to pat down over it, leaves and twigs. I stood back and looked down at the arrangement. It looked like an incidental rise under a tree, any tree, and in the dimness it would pass, unless somebody sat down on it maybe. But why would anyone come here, why wander, why sit? It was safe. I felt sure of it. But from the fence I had to come back once, just to make sure I could find my way back. But only once. After that I made myself roll under the fence, walk down the road, take the corner firmly, despite the plunging fall of loss in my stomach, a plummet that hurt so hard I had to hold my belly with both hands. Risk is risk and so comes profit. If it's gone it's gone. You have to make a deal. Make the deal.

All I had was a name: Paritosh Shah. I had heard it twice, once from a man named Azam Sheikh, who had just returned from a four-year sentence for burglary. He came out of prison and executed another clean job within two days, a daytime break-and-enter-and-grab on a newly-wed couple's apartment in Santa Cruz East. 'The good little wife went to the market to buy vegetables for her husband's dinner,' Azam said, 'and we got her gold necklace, and her bangles, and her earrings, and her nose-ring, everything except the mangalsutra, and Paritosh Shah cut us a good price for the lot.' I had been standing behind the kitchen door in the restaurant where I worked as a waiter, taking a break and listening to the boasting, and when Azam saw my feet under the door he cursed me and shut up. I moved away. Afterwards, his waiter told me Azam Sheikh had left a tip of three rupees, after an hour and a half of tangdis and shammi kebabs and beer, but within a month I had the satisfaction of hearing that Azam Sheikh was back in jail, caught in another Santa Cruz East job when a sleeping maidservant woke up and screamed. He was caught by neighbours and beaten bloody. Azam Sheikh walked funny now, there was that satisfaction – that and the name of Paritosh Shah.

Which I had heard again, after I had become close to Salim Kaka, after I had gained Kaka's trust. We had gone out, Mathu and Salim Kaka and me, to Borivali, for shooting practice. In a clearing in the jungle, Mathu and I had fired six shots each, and Salim Kaka had shown us the stance, the grip, and we had loaded and reloaded until it was fast and easy and I could do it without looking. That had pleased Salim Kaka, and he had thumped me on the shoulder. He let us fire two shots more each. The eruptions rolled along my forearms, louder than I had ever imagined, and down my spine, and I exulted, and the birds billowed above. 'Don't clutch your samaan,' Salim Kaka said. 'Hold it smooth, hold it firm, hold it with love.' There was a chalked target on a tree trunk, and I exploded the chips from its very centre. 'With love,' I said, and Salim Kaka laughed with me. On the long walk out of the jungle, under the bare brown branches, through the enveloping thorn bushes, Salim Kaka scared us with tales of leopards. A girl gathering wood had been killed in this very jungle not ten days ago. 'The leopard comes so fast you can't see him, all you feel is his teeth in your neck,' he said. 'I'll blow his eyes out,' I said, and twirled my revolver. Mathu said, 'Of course, maderchod, you're a gold-medal shooter after all.' I spat, and said, 'There'd be money from the leopard skin. I'd skin the bhenchod and sell it.' 'To whom, chutiya?' Mathu wanted to know. I pointed to Salim Kaka: 'To Kaka's receiver.' 'No,' Salim Kaka said. 'He's only interested in jewellery, diamonds, gold, high-price electronics.' 'Not your mangy leopard skin,' Mathu said, and laughed. Afterwards Mathu stood by the highway and waited for an auto-rickshaw, his arm up, and Salim Kaka squatted next to me, we hunkered side-by-side next to a wall, pissing. I stared at the wall, holding myself, impatient suddenly with the long train ride ahead, then the bus and walk to home and sleep. 'What's the matter, yaara?' Salim Kaka said. 'Still thinking about your leopard skin?' Salim Kaka's teeth were stained brown from tobacco, and they were strong and solid. 'Don't worry, you can take the skin to that Paritosh Shah, he'll take anything, I hear.' 'Who?' I said. 'Some new receiver in Goregaon. He's ambitious,' Salim Kaka said. Then Mathu had an auto-rickshaw stopped, and Salim Kaka shook himself and stood up, and I stood and zipped up, and Salim Kaka grinned at me and we walked over, rubbing shoulders. In the bouncing and jerking auto we were all squeezed together and Salim Kaka in the centre held the black bag containing the revolvers. They were his, belonged to him. He held the bag close.

So now I went to Goregaon, which was easy enough, but Paritosh Shah was one man in this locality of lakhs, and he was not advertised among the billboards for sex doctors and real-estate agents and cement dealers at the station. I bought a newspaper, found a vadapau-wallah outside the station and ate and considered the problem. With a glass of tea from the chai-wallah one booth down I began to see a possible solution. 'Bhidu,' I said to the chai-wallah, 'where's the police station here?'

I walked to the station, through narrow roads lined with shops and thelas on either side. I slipped through fast, bending and sliding shoulder-first through the crowds, revived by the tea and eager for the next turn. I found the station, and leaned against the bonnet of a car, facing the long, low, brown façade. I could actually see, even from this distance, through the front door into the receiving room with its long desks, and I knew what lay beyond, the crowded offices, the prisoners squatting in rows, the bare cells at the very back. The small crowd in front shifted and wandered and re-formed but was always there, and I flipped through the newspaper and watched. I could pick out the cops, even the plain-clothes ones, from the coil of their necks and a backward leaning, something like a cobra sprung straight in the middle of fresh furrows, hood fanned, quivering with power and arrogance. They had that glittery belligerence in their eyes. I was looking for something else.

It took until two-thirty and two false starts before I found my informant. There was one narrow-hipped man who sidled out of the side of the gate and angled down the road with the oily reticence of a born pickpocket, and I followed him for half a mile, and finally came to mistrust his long hands, which flexed and relaxed in hungry, doglike greediness. Back at the station, I watched again, and fixed on an older man, perhaps of fifty or so, who came out of the front doors, stood just outside the gate and opened a cigarette pack with a flick of his thumb. He tapped a cigarette on the pack three times, precise and deliberate, and then lit it and pulled at it, all with the same unhurried confidence. I walked behind him and liked the neat curve of the white hair across the back of his neck, and the inconspicuous grey bush-shirt. But at the street crossing, when I came around him and asked for a cigarette, please, the man looked at me with such open friendliness, with such lack of suspicion that I knew he was completely respectable. He was some office-goer who had come to the station to report a stolen bicycle, or loud neighbours, he would have no idea who Paritosh Shah was. I took a cigarette and thanked him and came back to my post.

I was crushing the cigarette butt with my heel when I heard her. It was a deep voice, unmistakably a woman's but bass and resonant, she was arguing with the auto-rickshaw driver, telling him she did the same trip every week and his meter was off and he could expect twelve-sixty from some chutiya fresh from UP, not her. I couldn't see much of her past the auto-rickshaw and the driver, only plump arms

55

and a tight yellow blouse, and when the driver screeched off with nine rupees, I had a glimpse of a deep red sari, a fleshy back and plump waist, a quick and rolling stride, all of it somehow wholly disreputable. Now I was impatient. I no longer bothered to examine the others who went in and out, I was waiting for her. When she emerged forty-five minutes later I was rehearsed and ready.

She crossed the road and stood waiting for an auto-rickshaw, one large hand on her hip and the other waving imperiously at every blaring one that passed. I took a breath and stepped closer, and saw under the sweep of hennaed hair her pouchy cheeks, strong eyebrows, large lotus-shaped gold earrings. She was old, older, marked by time, forty years or fifty, far from youth. I liked her tubby, forward-leaning stance, her feet wide apart and strong. Her pallu hung carelessly from her shoulder, not very modest at all.

'The rickshaws are all full at this time,' I said.

'Go away, boy. I'm not a randi,' she growled. 'Although you don't look like you could afford one.'

I hadn't thought she had looked at me yet. 'I'm not looking for a randi.'

'So you say.' Now she turned her face to me, and her eyes bulged slightly out, not ugly but unusual, it made her face precarious, ready to fall on the world with some jolting surprise. 'What do you want, then?'

'I have a question to ask you.'

'Why would I answer?'

'I need help.'

'You look as if you do. You can't get your pants open and you want me to pull it out for you. Why should I get my hands dirty? Do I look like your mother to you?'

I laughed, and knew my teeth had bared. 'No, you don't. Not even a little bit. But still you might help.'

An auto-rickshaw going the other way slowed and came curvetting across the road towards us. The woman took hold of the iron bar above its meter before it stopped, and swung herself into the seat. 'Go,' she said to the driver.

'Paritosh Shah,' I said, hunching my shoulders and leaning forward into the rickshaw. Now I had her attention.

'What about him?'

'I need to find him.'

'You need to?'

'Yes.'

She slipped forward on the seat, and gave me fully the blank threat of her gaze. 'You look too dirty to be a khabari. They try to look clean and trustworthy.'

'I'm not,' I said. 'I wouldn't know who to inform to.'

'Get in,' she said. She made room on the cracked red rexine, gave instructions to the auto-rickshaw driver and we went put-putting away through unfamiliar lanes. The buildings came closer to each other now, jammed together wall against wall, and the streets were close with people who stepped aside for the auto to pass. I peered out on the left, and then through the oval window in the canvas at the rear.

'Calm down,' the woman said. 'You're safe. If I wanted to harm you, that big ghoda in your pants wouldn't save you.'

I looked down. I had been holding the revolver through stained blue cloth. I let go of it and massaged my right hand with the other. 'I've never been here before,' I said.

'I know,' she said. She leaned over to me. 'What's your name?'

'My name is Ganesh. And yours?'

'I am Kanta Bai. What do you have for Paritosh Shah?'

I said, close to her ear, 'I have gold.' I came closer. 'Biscuits.'

'Be quiet, Ganesh, until we get out of the auto.'

The auto stopped on a busy bazaar square full of wholesale clothing shops, and she led me through rapid turns in narrowing lanes. She was known well here, and people passing greeted her by name, but she hurried by without a pause. At the end of a lane there was a wall with a break in it, a jagged hole lined with shattered bricks, and on the other side there was a basti. I watched my feet and followed her rapid walk. The shacks were closer now, and in some places the pucca buildings were so close to each other across the lane that it was like walking through a tunnel. Men and women and children stood aside to let Kanta Bai pass. There were boys, young men, sitting on ledges and in doorways and I felt their eyes on my neck, and I kept my back straight and kept close to Kanta Bai.

I smelt the overpowering round richness of gur first, and then the vomit. We turned right and passed by a low doorway, and I saw metal tables, and men sitting around them drinking. A boy put a plate with two boiled eggs down on the table nearest the entrance, and his customer shook out the last milky drops from a glass into his mouth. Kanta Bai angled around the side of the building, and the whine of an electric turbine deepened its pitch. She left me in a dark room filled to the ceiling with sacks of gur. 'Wait here,' she said, and so I waited. The warm smell settled on my shoulders, brown as river-bottom earth. Through the unceasing grind of the motor I could hear the highest notes from a radio in the front room, the bar, just the tinny tops of the song, coming to me like froth, and I wondered about the quality of Kanta Bai's product. There had been customers enough, maybe twenty on a work-day afternoon, sipping steadily at the eight and ten-rupee glasses of saadi and satrangi they distilled in the back. It was a good business, raw materials cheap and legally available, overheads low. And the demand for good desi liquor was steady and constant, as continuous and vast as the tramp of feet in the lanes outside. I leaned forward and through the curtained doorway I could see just the bare feet of Kanta Bai's workers and the dragging bottoms of sacks, and occasionally the round gleam of bottles. I recognized her sari, and so was able to turn away and be standing at the furthest end of the room when she turned aside the curtain. When I saw her eyes, burning white despite the sloughy darkness of the gur sacks, I was afraid.

'I spoke to Paritosh Shah on the phone,' she said.

I was unable to speak, buried by the abrupt terror of being alone, inexperienced, alone with gold. I nodded, and in the same motion leaned my shoulder against the doorway, very casual. I put a hand on my hip and nodded again.

Kanta Bai was faintly amused. A very small ripple of pleasure passed through her jaw, and she said, 'Let's see your gold.'

I nodded. I was still very unsafe, queasy inside, but this was necessary. I groped in my right pocket, moved the bars to my left hand, and held them out, two of them weighty in my palm.

Kanta Bai took the bars, tested their heft and weight, and gave them back to me. Her eyes were steady on my face. 'He'll see you now. I'll have one of my boys take you.'

'Good,' I said, now able to find my voice and confidence. The biscuits went back to my pocket, and I fumbled out a thin roll of notes, and fanned them out.

'You can't pay me.'

'What?'

'How much do you have?'

58

I turned my hand to the side, to the light. 'Thirty-nine rupees.'

At this she gurgled out a laugh, and her cheeks bunched and her eyes squeezed almost shut. 'Bachcha, go and meet Paritosh Shah. He'll owe me a favour if things go well. Thirty-nine rupees doesn't make you Raja Bhoj of Bumbai.'

'I'll owe a favour, too,' I said. 'If things go well.'

'Very smart,' she said. 'Maybe you're a good boy after all.'

Paritosh Shah was a family man. I waited for him on a second-floor hallway, near a staircase that exhaled occasional blasts of sharp urine-stink. The building was six storeys tall and ancient, with a bamboo framework roped and nailed to its tottering façade, and worrisome gaps in the ornate scrollwork on the balconies. The second floor was full of male Shahs, who passed by where Kanta Bai's boy had left me on the landing, and they called each other Chachu and Mamu and Bhai, and ignored me entirely. They walked by my dirty shirt and ragged trousers with the barest of glances. They were a flashy, gold-ringed lot who wore mostly white safari suits. I could see their white shoes and white chappals lined up in untidy rows near the uniformed guard at the door. Somewhere inside was the sanctum of Paritosh Shah, guarded by a hoary old muchchad perched on a stool with an absurdly long-barrelled shotgun. He wore a blue uniform with yellow braid, and his moustache was enormous and curved at the ends. After twenty minutes of passing Shahs and piss-stench, I was starting to feel quite insulted, and somehow my resentment focused itself on the ammunition belt the old man wore around his chest, on its cracked leather and three cylindrical red cartridges. I imagined pulling my revolver and putting a hole in the centre of the ammunition belt, just above the saggy stomach. It was an absurd thought, but there was satisfaction in it.

Ten minutes more went by, and that was enough. It was either now or the bullet to his chest. I had a pulsing headache. 'Listen, mamu,' I said to the guard, who was now investigating his left ear with a pencil stub. 'Tell Paritosh Shah I came to do business, not to stand out here and smell his latrine.'

'What?' The pencil came out. 'What?'

'Tell Paritosh Shah I'm gone. Gone elsewhere. His loss.'

'Wait, wait.' The old man leaned back and pointed his moustachios through the doorway. 'Badriya, come and see what this fellow is saying.'

Badriya came, and he was younger by much, and very tall, a quiet-moving muscle-builder, with a deliberate padding way about him in his bare feet. He stood in the doorway with his arms hanging away from his chest, and I was sure he had a weapon tucked away in the small of his back, under the black bush-shirt. 'Is there a problem?'

It was a challenge, no question about it, and the man was blank-faced and hard, but I was riding now on the thin-drawn craziness of the moment, on the exhaustion from the long day and the bracing leap of anger. 'Yes, problem,' I said. 'I'm tired of waiting for your mader-chod Paritosh Shah.'

The old man bristled and started to climb down from his stool, but Badriya spoke quietly. 'He's a busy man.'

'So am I.'

'Are you?'

'I am.'

And that was all it took. The guard had panic in his shoulders. His grip on the shotgun was clumsy, far up the stock, and with one leg on the ground and the other on a cross-bar of the stool he was tilted wrong and unbalanced. I watched him and I watched Badriya. It was absurd to be near death in a sudden moment in a grimy corridor with nostrils full, unreasonable to be almost moneyed and not yet, ludicrous to be Ganesh Gaitonde, poor in the city and standing to the side always, there was no sense in any of it and so there was an exulting eagerness in me, a glad and crazy courage. Here. Now. Here I am. What of it?

Badriya raised his left hand slowly. 'All right,' he said. 'I'll go and see if he's free now.'

I shrugged. 'Okay,' I said, liking the English word, one of the very few I knew then. 'Okay. I'll wait.' I grinned at the muchchad for the next few minutes, frightening the old man more and more, setting his hands trembling on the shotgun. By the time Badriya appeared again, I was sure I could stare the ancient soldier and his martial whiskers straight into a heart attack. But there was business to be done.

'Come,' Badriya said, and I pulled off my shoes and followed. The annexe led into a warren of hallways lined with identical black doors. 'Raise your arms,' Badriya said. I nodded, and raised the front of my shirt, and sucked in my stomach as Badriya gently took up my revolver. Badriya gave it a professional flip back-and-forth of the

60

wrist, looking along its barrel. He raised it to his nose, intent. He was barrel-chested, heavy-necked. 'Been fired not too long ago,' he said.

'Yes,' I said.

Badriya reversed the revolver in his hand, and although I couldn't tell quite how it was done, it was a very stylish move. 'Turn around,' Badriya said. He patted me down quickly, with a series of fluttering taps under my arms and up my thighs, and no more than a very slight pause on the bars in the pockets. It was professionally done, no animosity, and I thought better of Paritosh Shah for having Badriya on his team. 'Last door on the left,' Badriya said with the last pat.

Paritosh Shah was lying on his side on a white gadda, propped up on a round pillow. The room was quite bare, panelled brown walls, smooth and shiny, with frosted white glass high up near the ceiling, all of it air-conditioned to a chill that I found instantly painful. There was a tidy row of three black phones next to the gadda. Paritosh Shah was very relaxed, and he raised a languid hand at a low stool. 'Sit,' he said. I sat, aware of Badriya behind and to the left, and the small click of the black door as it shut. 'You're the boy,' Paritosh Shah said. He wasn't very old himself, maybe six, seven, at most ten years older than I was, but he had an air of tremendous and weary confidence. 'Name?' he said, and somehow his limp drape on the soft gadda, his one leg bent under, his stillness, all of it warned, don't try and fool me, boy.

'Ganesh.'

'You're a rash lad, Ganesh. Ganesh what?'

'Ganesh Gaitonde.'

'You're not a Bombay original. Ganesh Gaitonde from where?'

'Doesn't matter.' I leaned back and brought out two bars. I laid them side by side on the edge of Paritosh Shah's gadda.

'You could've tried selling those to any Marwari jeweller. Why come to me?'

'I want a fair price. And I can get you more.'

'How much more?'

'Many more. If I get fair price for these.'

Paritosh Shah tilted, toppling upright like a child's doll with a weight in the bottom. I saw then that he had thin arms and shoulders, but a round ball of a stomach that he folded his hands over. 'Fifty-gram biscuits. If they check out, seven thousand rupees each.'

'Market price is fifteen thousand for fifty grams.'

'That's the market price. This is why gold gets smuggled.'

'Below half is too much below. Thirteen thousand.'

'Ten. That's as much as I can do.'

'Twelve.'

'Eleven.'

I nodded. 'Done.'

Paritosh Shah whispered into one of the black phones, and with his free hand he held out a silver box filled with silver-flecked paan and supari and elaichi. I shook my head. Money is what I wanted, money to hold and grasp, money in my pocket, I wanted thick wads of notes, the thickness enough for silver boxes, for soft gaddas and red bed-spreads and record players and clean bathrooms and love, enough crisp paper for confidence and safety and life. My mouth was dry. I gripped my hands together tightly, and held them hard against each other through the discreet knock on the door, and then as it shut and Badriya put down a small scale and two stacks of currency, one fat and one thin.

'Just to check,' Paritosh Shah said. And he picked up the bars one by one, by the fingertips, and laid them on the scale against precise little weights. 'Fine.' He smiled. 'Very fine.' He was looking at me expectantly. The money lay on the gadda, and I moved my will like a vibrating steel spring and stilled myself and showed no sign of noticing it until Paritosh Shah stretched out slim fingers to slide the stack forward two inches. So I took it, with a hand that shook only slightly.

I stood up. The room swayed, the frosty oblongs of white light dipped into my eyes and there was a blinking flash of white sky, no horizon.

Then Paritosh Shah said, 'You don't talk very much.'

'I'll talk more next time.' Badriya had the door open, and the corridor was long, and I emerged from it with my cash in my pocket and dizziness tamped firmly down. I bent over easily to pull on my shoes, and when I came up I had the thin curl of thirty-nine rupees in my left hand. I tucked it behind the old guard's ammunition belt, put it in firmly with an extra little polishing motion on the leather. 'Here, mamu,' I said. 'And next time I come, don't keep me standing outside.'

The man stuttered, and Badriya laughed out loud. He held out the revolver, and raised an eyebrow. 'You kept one gold bar back.'

I checked my chambers with a quick motion of my wrist, crisp as I could make it. 'That one's not for sale,' I said.

62

'Why?'

I laid away the revolver, and raised a hand in farewell. 'Not everything is.' On the street outside, I was still very alert. I stood in front of a Bata store and watched the glass on the shoe display, looking for lurkers. The chances were high that I was being followed, that Paritosh Shah had made his swift calculations and sent out someone, perhaps Badriya, to shadow and discover, to uncover much gold. It was only logical. But no reflected pursuers appeared, and I left the window and wandered, ambling slowly and pausing often behind blind corners to watch the faces that passed. I was ready but relaxed, at home in these city streets like I had never been. I felt a lordly compassion for the pretty little bungalows I was walking by now, lit up in the soft evening twilight, for the happy, rich children I could see running in and out. None of it was alien now. And I tried hard to resist comfort, to keep alive the sharp edge of distrust against the euphoria of a profitable deal, the ecstasy of flinging out into the world one throw of dice that rolled fluently to the inevitable condition of victory. Don't be careless. Watch, watch. The numbers fell right but the board moves. What is white will be black. Climb high and fast and the long snakes lie waiting. Play the game.

I stood in front of a temple. I looked left and right and had no idea of how I had got there. There were apartment buildings on one side of the road, lower constructions on the other, the sloping tiled roofs of mill workers, shipping clerks, postmen. The temple stood at a corner, and it must have been the reverberating pealing of the bell that had drawn me to the courtyard, under the high saffron peak of its roof. I leant on a pillar and checked again for followers, for lethal shadows amidst the auto-rickshaws and Ambassadors. If they were out there, smelling of malice and greed, the temple was as good a place as any to wait them out. I had no use for temples, I despised incense and comfortable lies and piety, I did not believe in gods or goddesses, but here was a haven. I took off my shoes and went in. The worshippers sat cross-legged on the smooth floor, crowded together through the length of the long hall. The walls were an austere white, lit up by tubelights, but the dark heads swayed in a field of bright saris, purple and shining green and blue and deep red, all the way to the orange statue of Hanuman flying, suavely holding the mountain above his head. I found a place against the back wall and sat, instantly comfortable with my feet tucked in under. A man in saffron robes sat on a dais in front of Hanuman, and his discourse came easily and strongly to me, that old story about Bali and Sugreev, the conflict, the challenge, the duel, with the ambushing god waiting in the woods. I knew the turns and tricks well, and I nodded along with the old action and the rhythms of the lesson. When the priest recited couplets, holding out both his arms, the congregation chanted behind him and the women's voices rose high in the hall. The arrow flew and Bali lay writhing on the ground, pierced, his heels scraping the forest floor, and I raised my knees and rested my head on them, and I was comfortable.

I awoke to the shaking of the saffron-robed priest. 'Beta,' he said, 'time to go home.' He had white hair and an impish face. 'Time for lock-up here. Hanuman-ji has to go to sleep.'

I rubbed the crick from my neck, hard. 'Yes. I'll go.' I was the last one in the hall.

'Hanuman-ji understands. You were tired. Worked long. He sees everything.'

'Sure,' I said. What fantastic stories the old and the weak tell to each other, I thought. I stretched out my legs, stood and stumbled to the locked donation box in front of Hanuman. Peeling off a five-hundred-rupee note from the thinner wad, I remembered that I hadn't counted the notes when Paritosh Shah had given them. Amateur-like and not to be done again. I slipped the money into the slit, and found the priest ready to my right with a thali full of prasad. I held out my cupped right hand, and ate the small sugary peda on the way out. My mouth flooded painfully with saliva, and I was rested, and life was very sweet.

Now there was no multitude for assassins to hide in, and walking fast down the road, with the crunch of my shoes loud, I felt I was safe. The streetlights left no darkness on this long stretch, and I was completely alone. I waved down an auto-rickshaw, and was at the station three turns and five minutes later. I paid, and was almost at the ticket window when a man leaning against the iron fence raised his chin in inquiry: what do you want? I looked a moment too long, but kept moving, and now the man was walking beside me, with that cheery, insinuating tout's whisper: 'What you looking for, boss? You want some fun, haan? Charas, Calmpose, everything I got. You want a woman? Look at that auto there. All ready for you.' There was an auto parked across the road, pulled in deep at an angle in front of a shuttered shop. The driver was leaning on it, and I saw the glow of his bidi, and knew that the man was looking straight at me. The bidi moved, and the driver motioned against the back window of the auto, knocking, and a figure moved inside it, and a woman's head leaned out on the left side, into the lamplight. All I could see of her was the black shine of her hair, and the strong yellow of her sari, but I didn't need to see any more to know what sort of raddled randi sold her chut at stations in the back of an auto. I laughed, and paid for my ticket.

But the pimp stayed with me. 'Okay, boss,' he whispered chummily on the way to the platform gate. 'I misjudged you, saab. You want something better. You're a man of fine tastes, my mistake. You just look a little, you know . . . But I have the girl for you, boss.' He kissed his fingers. 'Her husband used to work in a bank, was a big saab, poor fellow, then he had an accident. Complete cripple he became. Can't work. So she has to make a living for both of them, what to do? Very exclusive. Only for some gentlemen, you see, in her own apartment. I can take you straight there. You'll see what a high-class cheez she is, boss. Completely convent-educated.'

I stopped. 'Is she fair?'

'Like Hema Malini, bhidu. You touch her skin and you'll get a current. Like fresh malai.'

'How much?'

'Five thousand.'

'I'm not a tourist. One thousand.'

'Two thousand. Don't say anything. You see the girl, and if you think she's not worth the money, you give me whatever you want and I'll leave quietly and not a word more. Believe me, if you saw her outside her husband's bank you wouldn't believe she has to do this, poor woman. Like one phataak memsaab she looks.'

'What's your name?'

'Raja.'

I put the train ticket in my back pocket. 'All right, Raja,' I said. 'Just don't make me angry.'

Raja giggled. 'No, saab, no. Please come.'

She was fair, no question. She opened the door and even in the bleary light from the lift I saw that she was fair, not quite Hema Malini-pale but light like afternoon wheat. She sat on a brown sofa while Raja counted his two thousand and bowed himself out. She wore a dull green sari with gold borders, and round gold earrings, and sat very respectable and contained with her shoulders high and hands in lap.

'What's your name?' I said.

'Seema,' she said, not meeting my stare.

'Seema.' I shifted from one foot to the other by the door, not sure of what to do next. I was experienced all right, but in a different kind of establishment, and the shiny glass table with its vase of flowers and the painting on the wall with just colours dashed together and the short brown carpet, all of these stopped me altogether. But she stood and went further into the apartment, and I stepped up manfully, taking it all in, the stretch of her blouse across the sunken river of her spine and the white phone in its alcove in the wall of the passageway. She clicked on a lamp in the bedroom, and when she flipped back the bedcover I tensed: it was altogether too professional. I had seen the same folding down of the sheets before, the same towel.

'Hold on,' I said, and went back out into the hallway. The bathroom was clean, and I pissed into the western-style commode with some satisfaction, at length. But then I saw that there was no soap near the tap, no bucket. I zipped. The cupboards in the kitchen were empty, not a plate, not a pot, not even a gas or a stove, only two glasses drying upside down next to the basin. Now I was sure that I had been fooled. The apartment was nobody's home, not a bank saab's, not a good wife's, there was no cripple and no memsaab, only a whore got up and powdered. She lay on the bed, naked but for the earrings, her arms crossed over her small breasts and her belly rising and falling under the thin shadow of her hipbone, and one ankle over another. I stood over her, breathing through my mouth.

'Speak English,' I said.

'What?'

In her eyes there was real surprise, and I grew more angry. 'I told you. Speak English.'

She had a sharp little nose and a small retreating chin, and she was puzzled for another moment, and then she laughed, just a very little bit and bitterly amused. 'Shall I speak?' she said. Then she spoke in English, and the words rattled around my head, and I knew that they were really English, I felt it in the crack of the consonants. 'Bas?' she said.

'No,' I said. I was hard, vibrating deep at the root. 'Don't stop.' She spoke English while I took off my clothes. I turned around to take off my pants and hide the revolver from her. When I turned back she was staring at the ceiling and speaking English. I nudged her ankles apart. 'Don't stop,' I said. I ground and bucked on top of her and she turned her face to the side and spoke. I reared up and the skin on her neck was sandy under the lamplight and I could hear her words. I understood none of it but the sound of it was an angry excitement inside my head. Then I felt a distant overflow, far below, and I was still.

I was very tired, Sardar-ji. I leaned forward into my walk. I was going back to my gold. The momentum of nearly falling over at every step kept me moving, but at every exhausted buckling of my knees I grew more afraid. I was very close to the gold now, I recognized every intersection and the shapes of particular buildings and shadowed trees. There was no moon but it was a light night, and out in this unbuilt open ground I saw clearly the black direction of the road and the white of a milestone. The gold was gone, taken, I felt a hole in my chest. It was gone, vanished out of my life. I should give up now. It would be easy for me to find a patch of grass by the road, tip over into it, sleep. Stop it. Ganesh Gaitonde, keep going. You have won every game today. Win again. You know exactly where you are.

The calculation of the precise section of barbed-wire fence was not a problem. I counted off the posts, looked up and down the way, and rolled under. Under the trees I passed into disastrous black, and was lost. With one hand extended I went gliding, rustling through space, not sure of the distances now, but I felt and reached and at the right moment I stopped and turned to the right. A step, and there was the tree. I passed a hand down the trunk and the ground below was flat. All around the trunk I went, feeling with both hands. After two circles, maybe three, I leaned a shoulder against it and made a long bleating sound. Ganesh Gaitonde, Ganesh Gaitonde. I scrabbled to the next tree, stopped when I grazed my head on it. Around it, around it. And then the next one. My cry was high now, a constant shriek under the canopy and darkness. It went without rise or fall in a half-circle. Stopped abruptly, because I had both hands on a fatness. The swelling rose out of the earth and filled both my palms. I traced it softly, up to the tree and down to the bottom of the mound, making out its shape. I moaned and dug both hands into it. I went rooting furiously into it, and welcomed the pain in my fingers. The cloth came first, and then the heavenly, familiar shape of a rectangle. My shoulders shook and I moved my hand and it was all there. All and undisturbed and mine. Up to my forearms in earth, I let my head drop and gulped in the smell of grass and my armpits and my body and knew that the world was mine. As dawn came I wrapped myself around the mound and slept with my revolver under my breast.

Going Towards Home

❧

Sartaj was woken by a reporter who wanted to know what he thought of Ganesh Gaitonde's use of politicians, the corruption of the legal system and recent scandals in the police department. Sartaj cut off the stream of questions with a curt 'No comment' and slammed the phone down. He turned over, pushed his face into the pillow, but the light was seeping over his eyelids and his mind was turning. With a sigh he pushed himself up. Being a minor three-day celebrity was not going to be easy, he could see. He walked around the bed, his eyes half-shut, remembering how Gaitonde loved to give interviews. That bastard liked to talk, Sartaj thought, and pushed open the door to the bathroom.

For breakfast Sartaj had three pieces of toast with butter, a soggy orange and chai left too long on the burner. In the *Indian Express*, Gaitonde was front-page news, posing confidently on a mountain-top, and the story was three columns across and very deep, and Sartaj read it all, the sudden rise, the vast power, the intricate feuds and the executions and the ambushes, the whole game. Sartaj Singh was mentioned, of course, as the intrepid leader of the police party, but there was nothing about the dead woman, not a word. As far as the world knew, Gaitonde had died alone.

The phone rang. Sartaj let it go on, suffering its harsh rattle along the back of his neck. He was sure it was a journalist, but finally he gave in and picked up the receiver.

'Inspector Singh?'

It was Parulkar's PA, Sardesai, speaking in his very peculiar and very nasal half-whisper.

'Sardesai Saab,' Sartaj said. 'Everything all right?' Usually, calls from Parulkar's office were put through by the operator outside his cabin. Sardesai only called when there was urgent, confidential work to be done, or there was some departmental skulduggery afoot.

69

'Yes, there is no problem. But Parulkar Saab would like you to come into his office as soon as possible.'

'Now?'

'Now.'

There would be no more information forthcoming from Sardesai over the phone. Even in person, he was famously secretive, which was as a personal assistant should be. Sartaj hung up, hurried to the shower. He had known Parulkar for a long time, and had never known him to call a subordinate from home without good reason. There were other officers who did that, who treated their juniors as servants. But Parulkar had no arrogance, only proper pride in the work that his men did. That was why he had prospered. So when Parulkar called, Sartaj went, fast.

Katekar's sons were standing by him. He opened his eyes and they knelt, giggling, just off the chatai and tugging on his toes. They were both wearing pressed grey shorts, white shirts and striped blue-and-red ties. They both had the same razor-sharp parting in the hair, on the left and absolutely straight.

'Where's your mother?' Katekar mumbled. His mouth was full of onion gone caustic and unlovely.

'Off to the vegetable market,' Rohit said.

'Fall in outside in exactly five minutes.'

They fled from his growling rise and mock lunge, and in the kitchen he threw water on his face and shoulders. They were waiting for him outside, backs to the wall, feet apart and hands held behind. They came to attention and Katekar inspected their shoes, their shirts and the organization of the books in their blue school-bags. The ritual was complete when he gave them each ten rupees. Katekar dismissed the parade, and the two boys walked down the lane with Katekar following. Mohit was happy with his ten rupees, but Katekar knew that Rohit had started to think of it as only ten rupees, and to long for all the things in the world that ten rupees would not buy. A man edged a scooter slowly around the corner and the two brothers stood sideways to let him pass. Katekar saw the golden down on Mohit's cheek in the early sun, and looked away quickly, afraid of the future that pressed on his heart and made it full.

'Papa?'

'Fast, fast,' he said. 'Or we'll miss the bus.'

After he had waved them on to No 180, watched it nose into the traffic, Katekar bought a copy of *Loksatta* and folded it under his arm. He read it while queuing for the municipal lavatory, with a Dalda can full of water resting between his feet. Bomb blast in Israel, four dead. Exchange of fire across Line of Control, situation in Srinagar tense. Conwoman fools housewives out of jewellery in Ghatkopar. Congress party supremos deny rumours of infighting. There was a front-page story about Gaitonde, about his long career of close shaves and escapes. Why had Gaitonde killed himself, the reporter asked, and could construct no theory. Around Katekar neighbours gossiped and laughed, but everyone knew that he must be left to his paper. When the line jerked forward he moved the water can without looking up from his news.

After his turn in the lavatory, he strode past the line of men, relaxed and easy. He greeted each one expansively, but didn't stop to gossip. He went purposefully home, and was exactly in time. Shalini was sliding open the big steel padlock as he came around the corner. Katekar shut the door behind himself, pushed up the latch. He pulled off his kurta, put it on the last hook to the left, which was its accustomed place. 'There's enough water for your bath,' Shalini said from the kitchen. She handed him a green towel, but as she turned towards the kitchen he touched her neck, just where it curved into the shoulder. She shivered, and giggled. 'Don't,' she said, but when he lay on his chatai she curled over him tightly. He moved her hand – with a jangle of bangles – to his crotch. She had her head tightly pressed into his chest. Even after all these years, she wouldn't look at him, he knew she wouldn't let him turn her face to his, not yet, but he exhaled slowly as the glassy tinkling sounds between them speeded and became a small pealing. Shalini moved and with a quick motion she had her sari up, and they both stirred against each other, reaching, and then she found him. He settled his hands on her hips and shut his eyes. Then he felt her lips, small and warm and agile, against the line of his chin.

Shalini sent him away with a handful of prasad from the Devi Padmavati temple. Katekar ate the tender bits of coconut with particular pleasure. Religion was women's business and also the curse of the nation, but the milky flesh of the coconut was a voluptuous gift anyhow, and his shoulders tingled as he walked.

71

The lane was narrow, narrow enough in some sections that Katekar could have touched the walls on both sides of it with outstretched hands. Most of the doors of the homes were open, for the air. A grandmother sat on her front step, holding her darkly oiled, naked grandson in her lap, laughing into the toothless pink rosebud of his smile. Katekar came around a corner, past a tiny shop selling cigarettes, packets of shampoo, paan, batteries, and then he stood aside to let a row of young women go by, and the girls stepped tidily over the curve of the gutter, powdered and properly salwar-kameezed for shops and offices. Katekar watched the swish of red and yellow fabric. He had one foot propped up on a two-inch pipe that ran along the bottom of the wall. The mohalla committee had collected money for the laying of this secondary water pipe last year, but it worked only when the pressure in the main municipal pipe down near the main road was good. Now they were collecting money for a pump.

On Maganchand Road the thela-wallahs already had their fruit piled high, and the fishsellers were laying out bangda and bombil and paaplet on their slabs. The rush hour had packed the cars close. At the bus stop Katekar stood at the outskirts of a loose cluster of people. He opened his paper and read the editorial, which was about the failure of the civil state in Pakistan. When the double-decker came, Katekar let the crowd rush ahead of him. The conductor finally cut off the shoving influx and rang the bell. The bus lurched forward, and Katekar raised a hand, and the conductor made room for him on the step with a quick, respectful nod. Katekar had ridden on this bus for eight years, ever since he had bought the kholi, and all the conductors on the route knew that he was a policeman. This conductor, whose name was Pawle, moved past Katekar towards the rear of the bus, clicking his ticket-punch at the passengers, and then worked his way towards the front. Katekar listened to the fall of the small coins. Citizens loved to complain about the horror of the morning traffic, which surpassed itself every year, but Katekar loved the enormous bustle of millions on the move, the hurtling local trains with thick clusters of bodies hanging precariously from the doors, the sonorous tramp and hum of the crowd inside the tall hall of Churchgate Station. It made him feel alive. The impatient blare of the horns shivered up his forearms. He leaned out of the bus, stretching his weight against the metal bar he was holding on to. A group of college girls hurried and skipped through the cars, calling out to each other and laughing.

Katekar tapped his fingers on the side of the bus, and sang under his breath: '*Lat pat lat pat tujha chalana mothia nakhriyacha . . .*'

There was a woman in Parulkar's cabin. Makand, the CBI man who had taken over Gaitonde's bunker, was also sitting in front of Parulkar's desk, his head as smooth as grey steel. Sartaj stood very quietly at attention until Parulkar asked him to sit down.

'They need your help, Sartaj,' Parulkar said, 'in an aspect of the Gaitonde matter.'

'Sir,' Sartaj said, and kept his back straight.

'They will tell you what they need.'

Sartaj nodded. 'Yes, sir.' He shifted in his chair towards Makand, leaned forward with what he hoped was exactly the right degree of alert eagerness. But it was the woman who spoke.

'We wanted to talk to you about Gaitonde's death.' Her voice was dry, firm. She hadn't missed a thing, had seen his automatic assumption.

'Yes,' Sartaj said. 'Yes, um, madam.'

'This is DCP Mathur,' Parulkar said. 'DCP Anjali Mathur. She is in charge of the investigation.' Sartaj could see that Parulkar was amused by her and him, by them and the ironies of the new world they were living in.

Anjali Mathur nodded, and spoke without looking at Parulkar. 'You received a call yesterday calling you to the location where you found Gaitonde?'

'Yes, madam.'

'Why you, inspector?'

'Madam?'

'Why do you think you received the call?'

'I don't know, madam.'

'Do you know Gaitonde from before?'

'No, madam.'

'Never met him?'

'No, madam.'

'Did you recognize the voice on the phone?'

'No, madam.'

'You were talking to him a long time before you got into the house.'

'We were waiting for the bulldozer, madam.'

'What did you talk about?'

'He talked, madam. He told one long story about how he started his career.'

'Yes, his career. I read your report. Did he say why he was in Mumbai?'

'No, madam.'

'Are you sure?'

'Yes, madam.'

'Did he say anything else about his purpose, about that house? Anything else at all?'

'No, madam. I'm sure.'

DCP Anjali Mathur had an interest in Gaitonde, and she was looking for details, but Sartaj had none to give her. He looked blandly at her and waited.

Finally she spoke. 'What about the dead woman? Do you know her?'

'No, madam. I don't know who she is. I wrote that in the report. Unknown female.'

'Do you have any ideas?'

There was Katekar's ready theory about filmi randis, but it was based on nothing more substantial than the dead woman's clothes. Sartaj had seen the same clothes at some very expensive clubs in the city. There was no reason to assume that the woman was a whore. 'No, madam.'

'Are you sure?'

'Yes, madam.' She was sceptical, steady in her evaluation of him, and he bore her examination evenly. He felt her come to a decision.

'Inspector, I need you to do some work for us. But first, you need to know that we are not CBI. We are with RAW. But this information is only for you. Nobody else needs to know it. Clear?'

It was not at all clear why RAW, the famed Research and Analysis Wing – with its covert mystique and its exotic reputation – should be sitting here in Parulkar's office. Ganesh Gaitonde was a big criminal, so yes, the Central Bureau of Investigation should investigate him, that made sense. But RAW was supposed to fight foreign enemies of the state outside India's borders. Why were they here, interested in Kailashpada? And this Anjali Mathur was an unlikely international secret agent. But perhaps that was the point. She had a round face, smooth, fair skin. There was no sindoor in her hair, but women no longer signalled their happily married state, Sartaj's ex-wife never had. Sartaj had the uneasy feeling of wading into swiftly pulling waters, of being spun by completely unknown currents, and so he practised Parulkar's principle of polite sarkari obsequiousness. 'Yes, madam,' he said. 'Very clear.'

'Good,' she said. 'Find out. Find out who this woman was.'

'Yes, madam.'

'You would have the local knowledge, so find out. But our interest in this is to be kept in the strictest confidence. We want you to work on this for us, you and that constable, Katekar. Only you two. And only the two of you are aware of this assignment. Nobody else in the station is to know anything. Security concerns at the highest level are involved. Is that clear?'

'Yes, madam.'

'Keep the investigation as quiet as you can. First priority, you are to find out who this woman was, what her relationship with Gaitonde was, what she was doing in that house. Second, we need to know what Gaitonde was doing in Mumbai – why he was here, how long he had been here, what he has done while he was here.'

'Yes, madam.'

'Find anyone you can who worked with him. But proceed with discretion. We can't afford a big noise about this. Keep it quiet, whatever you do. It's natural for you to have an interest in Gaitonde after you found him. So if someone asks, just say you are clearing up a few loose ends. Clear?'

'Yes, madam.'

She slid a thick envelope across the desk. It was plain white, with a phone number in black ink centred on it. 'You report to me, and only me. This envelope contains copies of the photographs from the album we found in Gaitonde's desk. And photographs of the dead woman. Also, these are keys that were in the dead woman's pocket. One looks like a door key, the other is a car key, Maruti. The third key, I don't know what it's for.' The keys were on a steel hoop.

'Yes, madam.'

'Any doubts? Any questions?'

'No, madam.'

'Call me at the number on the envelope if you have any queries, or information to report. Parulkar Saab has told me that you are one of his most dependable officers. I am sure you will produce good results.'

'Parulkar Saab is kind. I will do my best.'

'Shabash,' Parulkar said, looking quite expressionless and unreadable. 'You may leave.'

Sartaj stood up, saluted him, took the envelope and walked smartly out. Outside, in the brilliant light of the morning, he blinked and stood near the railing for a moment, hefting the envelope in his hand. So the Gaitonde incident was not yet closed. Perhaps there were coups to be counted yet, and laurels to be won. Perhaps the great Ganesh Gaitonde still had some gifts to give to Sartaj. This was all very good, being chosen to conduct this secret investigation in the interests of national security, but Sartaj was uneasy. Anjali Mathur's urgency had somehow smelt of fear. Gaitonde was dead, but his terror lived on.

Sartaj stretched, swung his shoulders from side to side and swatted away a fly that buzzed close to his face. He hurried down the staircase and went to work.

*

Majid Khan's office was crowded with representatives of a local traders' association. They were protesting about the shocking police inaction in the face of the flood of extortion calls their members had received in the last few months. Sartaj took a chair at the back of the room and listened to Majid soothe and calm them and ask for their help in return. 'We can't do anything if you don't call us in, if you give in and pay them,' he said. 'But tell us in a timely fashion, and we will do our best.' Fifteen minutes of this and the traders finally all rose together, shifted their paunches about and left, but not before their president, a particularly lardy paan-chewing type, managed to mention that in addition to the burden of constant fear, he had to carry so many weighty expenses for his daughter's wedding next month. Even in these hard times, the wedding was going to have to be respectably expensive, these days people expected so much, and after all, MLA Saab was coming, Ranade Saab was coming. The trader-president bowed low over Majid's hand as he shook it, but nevertheless left behind the fact of his closeness to MLA Saab, and therefore the strong possibility of his being able to cause policemen's transfers to distant and dry postings.

'Bastards,' Majid said dispassionately when the office was emptied of traders.

'Bastards,' Sartaj said, getting up to sit in a chair in front of the desk. The wood was still warm from a trader, and he shifted uncomfortably in it.

'So I hear you had a very important early meeting with important CBI people.'

'Yes, yes.' That Majid knew about the meeting was not surprising, but Sartaj was still sometimes surprised by the speed at which news got around the station. 'That is what I wanted to consult you about, boss. Here.' Sartaj spread the photographs from Gaitonde's album across Majid's desk. 'Do you know any of these women?'

Majid stroked his moustache with both hands, testing it for flair and neatness. 'Actresses? Models?'

'Yes. Or something like that.'

Majid leafed through the photographs. 'To do with Gaitonde?'

'Yes. I'm just curious.'

'You are trying to be discreet, my friend. But don't tell me. I don't want to know.' Majid shook his head. 'One or two look familiar, but I couldn't tell you names. Bombay is full of girls like this. One looks like the next one. They come and they go.'

'And this one?' This one was the dead one, caught in close-up. She looked unmistakably dead, with her blue lips and inert bare shoulders and complete indifference to the camera watching from up close.

'This is the woman inside Gaitonde's house?' Majid said softly. 'Who they are hiding from the papers?'

'Yes.'

Majid gathered up the photographs and slid them back to Sartaj. He leaned back, and folded his arms across his chest. 'No, baba, I don't know. I don't know anything. And you be careful, Sardar-ji. Don't be brave. Parulkar Saab will try to protect you, but he's in trouble himself. Poor fellow, he's not a good enough Hindu for the Rakshaks.'

'Where does that leave you and me?' Sartaj said. 'I'm not a very good Hindu.'

Majid smiled, a big, toothy widening of his face which made him look like a boy, in spite of the moustache's awful grandeur. 'Sartaj,' he said, 'you're not even a good Sikh.'

Sartaj stood up. 'I must be good at something. But I don't know what that is yet.'

Majid gurgled out his long, slow laughter. 'Arre, Sartaj, you used to be good with women. So if you want to know about these women, ask other women.'

Sartaj waved a dismissive hand and left. But he couldn't deny that Majid – lumbering big-footed Pathan that he was – had the right idea

77

about asking women about women. It was early in the day, though, and women and national security would have to wait till later. There was a murder to investigate first.

'This whole area stinks,' Katekar said as he pulled the Gypsy into a narrow parking space between two trucks.

There certainly was a heavy smell that he and Sartaj had to endure as they walked down the road, but Sartaj thought it was a bit unfair of Katekar to single out this locality as especially stinky. The whole city stank at some time or the other. And after all, the citizens of Navnagar had to pile their rubbish somewhere. It was not their fault that the municipality's collection trucks came by only once a fortnight, to make a dent in this undulating ridge of garbage to their left. 'Patience, Maharaj,' Sartaj said. 'We'll be out of the stench soon.'

Katekar refused to let go of his sourness. Sartaj understood that he was being sullen not about the smell, but about being here in Navnagar at all. So a Bangladeshi boy had been murdered by his yaars, but so what? It was a minor case with minor possibilities, and it could easily be investigated on paper, just like the municipality lorries which on paper ran punctually every morning. Nobody would mind too much if this case was left undetected, and so it was silly to be out here, suffering odours and the odiousness of these foreigners. But Sartaj wanted to investigate. He told himself that it was proper officerly ambition to solve cases and get ahead, if only a little, but he knew that it was also just stubbornness. He didn't like people getting killed on his beat, and he hated the thought that murderers could just walk away. He knew that Katekar knew this, that it wasn't even idealism that drove Sartaj through certain cases. It was just a keeda that he had. They had been through this several times, with Sartaj doggedly following a lead and Katekar disapproving but staying close behind. Sartaj sometimes wondered why Katekar didn't just ask to work with someone else, or even for a transfer to some wetter posting. He needed the money, surely. And yet Katekar always went through the ritual of displeasure, and came along anyway. Now Sartaj stepped off the road and started up the slope, and he was sure that Katekar was to his left, a little behind and flanking.

Navnagar in the morning was marginally less crowded, but Sartaj still felt the kholis pressing in on him as he manoeuvred his way through the lanes. People stood aside and pressed up against the walls when they saw his uniform, and still he had to turn his torso to avoid brushing into them. In this city, the rich had some room, and the middle class had less, and the poor had none. This is why Papa-ji had retired to Pune, he said he wanted to be able to wake up and look out long, to feel as if there was still some empty space in the world. Papa-ji had found his little piece of lawn, and a vegetable garden behind the house, but Sartaj suspected that he had sometimes missed these tunnel-like streets of Mumbai's slums, these shacks that crept forward every year, each added-on room seizing ground and holding on. He certainly never stopped reminiscing about them.

Papa-ji had never told a story specifically about Navnagar, perhaps because nothing spectacular or particularly grotesque had ever taken place here. But he had told Sartaj often enough that the way to an apradhi was through the family. Find the mother and father, he had said, and you will find the thief, the murderer, the forger. So Sartaj and Katekar were in Navnagar, looking for the relatives of Bazil Chaudhary and Faraj Ali, who had killed their friend Shamsul Shah. As expected, the immediate families of the killers had fled. They had packed up as many of their belongings as they could take, and had locked their kholis, and had decamped on the day of the murder. Sartaj and Katekar broke the locks, and inside the kholis they found old mattresses, empty gunny sacks and an old colour photograph of Bazil Chaudhary's family. In the picture, Bazil Chaudhary was only a ten-year-old boy in a bright red shirt, but now Sartaj knew what the parents looked like. He had no doubt he would find them, sooner or later. They were poor, they would have to sell the kholi, they would depend on their connections in Navnagar to survive. It was much harder to disappear than people ordinarily thought. The task, for the policeman, was to pick up the strands of their lives, and follow along.

The interviews in Navnagar that morning yielded some information, none of it case-breaking but all of it quite relevant. The Bangladeshi neighbours of the victim and the apradhis were sullen and secretive, and declared they knew nothing. After Katekar loomed over them, and Sartaj threatened a trip to the police station and quick deportation, they allowed that they maybe knew a little, a very insignificant little. Shamsul – the dead one – and Bazil both worked as couriers, and Faraj took temporary jobs here and there. Yet for the last few months they all three had a lot of money, and nobody knew why or how.

In the empty kholis Sartaj and Katekar had searched, there was scant evidence of money. The families of the apradhis had taken their luxuries with them. But in the dead boy's house, there was a brand-new colour television, and a large gas stove in the kitchen area, and shiny steel pots, and his father now confessed that the departed son had bought a new kholi a few days previously.

'He was a good boy,' Nurul Shah said.

This kholi was very small, only one room divided by a faded red sheet. Behind the curtain, Sartaj could hear women rustling and whispering. They needed more space, and the good boy had obtained it for them. The family had been about to move into the new kholi when their son had been cruelly taken from them. 'But,' Sartaj said, 'a big new place, that must have cost a lot of money.'

Nurul Shah lowered his head and watched the floor. He had thinning white hair and taut shoulders toughened by a lifetime of hard work.

'Your neighbours say your family is suddenly rich,' Sartaj said. 'They said your son treated his sisters well. They said he bought new spectacles for his mother.'

Nurul Shah's hands were clamped around each other, and the tips of the fingers now whitened from the pressure. He began to weep, making no sound at all.

'I think,' Sartaj said, 'if I look behind the curtain, I will find other expensive things. Where did your son get all this money from?'

'Eh,' Katekar rumbled, 'Inspector Saab asked you a question. Answer him.'

Sartaj put a hand on Nurul Shah's shoulder, and held on past the man's sudden panic at the touch. 'Listen,' he said very softly. 'Nothing is going to happen to you or your family. I am not interested in bothering you. But your son is dead. If you don't tell me everything, I can't help you. I can't find the bastards who did it.'

The man was scared of the policemen in his home, of what had happened and what could happen, but he was trying to find the courage to speak up.

'Your son was doing some business, some hera-pheri. If you tell me everything, I will find them. Otherwise they will escape.' Sartaj shrugged, and straightened up.

'I don't know, saab,' Nurul Shah said. 'I don't know.' He was shivering and bent over. 'I asked Shamsul what he was doing, but he never told me anything.'

'He and those two, Bazil and Faraj, were doing something together?'

'Yes, saab.'

'Was there anyone else?'

'There was Reyaz Bhai.'

'Another friend of theirs?'

'He was older.'

'Full name?'

'I only know that much: Reyaz Bhai.'

'What does he look like?'

'I never met him.'

'Where does he live?'

'Four lanes down, saab. On the main-road side.'

'He lives here in Navnagar, in the Bengali Bura, and you never met him?'

'No, saab. He didn't come out of his house much.'

'Why?'

'He is a Bihari, saab,' Nurul Shah said, as if that were an explanation.

But the Bihari was gone from his kholi as well, and there was already a new family living there. Sartaj and Katekar found the landlord, a portly Tamil who lived on the other side of Navnagar. He had found the room unoccupied on the day of the murder, and had promptly cleaned it out the next day and rented it again. No, he didn't know anything about this Reyaz except that he had paid in advance, and was no trouble. What did Reyaz look like? Tall, thin, young face but with full white hair. Yes, completely white hair. The man could be forty, fifty, anything. Spoke smoothly, was definitely educated. He had left nothing in the kholi except some books, which the landlord had sold that very afternoon to a paper and raddi shop on the main road. No, he didn't know what the books were.

So Sartaj and Katekar stood at the edge of Navnagar, below the small world it contained. 'All right,' Sartaj said, looking at the terraced, untidy descent of the rusted tin roofs. 'So this Bihari is the boss.'

'He plans everything. These three, these are his boys.' Katekar wiped his face with an enormous blue handkerchief, and then the back of his neck and his forearms. 'They make money.'

'Doing what? Fraud? Robbery? Or are they shooters for some gang?'

81

'Maybe. But I've never heard of that, Bangladeshis in a company.'

'These boys grew up here, maybe they're more Indian than any-thing else. But this Bihari is the key. He's older, he's professional. He lives quietly, doesn't show off his money, he clears out fast and first when there's trouble. Wherever he is, those boys are going to be.'

'Yes, saab,' Katekar said. He put away his handkerchief. 'So we find the Bihari.'

'We find the Bihari.'

Pursuing the Bihari had to wait while Sartaj fulfilled certain obliga-tions. Policing was often a scattered business that required setting aside one job to attend to another. What Sartaj had to do now was strictly unofficial and had nothing to do with any case, and he had to do it alone. He dropped Katekar at the station and drove south to Santa Cruz. He was to meet Parulkar in a sparkling new building just off Linking Road, near Swaraj Ice-cream. Sartaj parked behind the building and marvelled at the green marble in the lobby, and the sleek steel lift. The apartment Parulkar was waiting in was supposed to belong to Parulkar's niece. This niece worked at a bank, and her hus-band was in import-export, but they were barely out of their twenties, and the apartment was very large and very expensive. The gold letters on the nameplate spelled out 'Namjoshi', but Sartaj was certain that the three-bedroom apartment actually belonged to Parulkar. Certainly, the ease with which he sat cross-legged on a huge sofa in the drawing room, like a rotund, khaki-clad sage, suggested a man in charge of his own prime real estate and his own destiny.

'Come, come, Sartaj,' Parulkar said. 'We must hurry.'

'Sorry, sir. The traffic is bad.'

'The traffic is bad all the time.' But Parulkar was not reprimanding Sartaj, he was fatherly and patient, and only mindful of his own hec-tic schedule. He pointed at a frosty glass of water on the table. Sartaj took off the silver cover and drank, and followed Parulkar across the shadowed breadth of the drawing room, to a bedroom.

Parulkar shut the door behind them and padded around the high white bed to the other side of the room. He opened a cupboard, and hefted out a black duffle-bag. 'It's forty today.'

'Yes, sir,' Sartaj said. Parulkar meant forty lakhs. These were Parulkar's recent unofficial earnings, which Sartaj would move over to Worli, and hand over to Parulkar's consultant, Homi Mehta, who would funnel it to a Swiss account and charge only a very reasonable commission. Sartaj ferried Parulkar's money every few weeks, and he had long ago stopped being surprised by the amounts. Parulkar was, after all, the commissioner for a very rich zone. It was a very wet posting, and Parulkar drank deep from its burbling fount of money. He was an avid earner, but not greedy, and he was very careful about the disposal of the money. His personal assistant, Sardesai, handled the collection of the money, but Sardesai knew nothing of what happened to the money once he had given it to Parulkar. Parulkar passed it over to Sartaj, who moved it to Mehta, the consultant. Sartaj only knew that then, somehow, the money disappeared from India and reappeared abroad, where it sat safe and accumulated interest in hard currency.

Parulkar emptied the cash on to the bedspread and handed the bag to Sartaj. 'Eighty bundles of five-hundred-rupee notes,' he said. They trusted each other completely, but this was their ritual each time money went to the consultant. Sartaj gathered up a hefty brick of money and put it into the bag. He would do this eighty times while Parulkar watched, and then they would have an agreed-upon count.

'What are you going to do about this Gaitonde business?' Parulkar said, watching Sartaj's hands.

'I was going to ask you about that, sir.'

Parulkar pulled his legs up on to the bed and took up his meditative posture again. 'I don't know that much about the Gaitonde company. There was a fellow called Bunty who ran their business in Mumbai. Smart fellow, Suleiman Isa's boys shot him, put him in a wheelchair, but he was Gaitonde's trusted man, he stayed in charge from his wheelchair. There was a time when you could just go to Gopalmath and meet Bunty, but after he got shot he went into hiding. Ask Mehta for this Bunty's number, he will have it.' Mehta, as a money manager, was neutral in the gang wars. All sides used his services impartially, and valued him equally.

'Yes, sir.'

'But of course your best intelligence on Gaitonde may come from his enemies. Let me make a couple of calls, and I will get you in touch with someone. Someone who is very, let us say, knowledgeable.'

'Thank you, sir.' What Parulkar meant was that he would use his links inside the Suleiman Isa company to get someone to talk to Sartaj. Since Parulkar's connections with that company went back years, even decades, the source he would provide for Sartaj would no doubt be a highly placed one. So this was a big favour, one more in a long string of kindnesses that Parulkar had bestowed on Sartaj. 'Forty, sir,' Sartaj said, putting the last stack into the bag. 'Sir, what is this all about? Gaitonde is dead, why do they want to know about him now?'

'I don't know, Sartaj. But be careful. What I understand from my sources is that the IB is also involved in this Gaitonde business.'

'IB, sir? Why?'

'Who knows? But it seems this whole investigation is actually a joint operation. IB is letting RAW handle the details, so RAW is talking to you and me. When these big agencies get involved in a case, mere policemen have to watch their backs. Do your work, but don't try to be a hero for them.'

Sartaj zipped the bag. So it was not only international agents who were interested in Gaitonde's demise. The Intelligence Bureau, with its domestic counter-intelligence purview, was also curious. It all made Sartaj feel quite small. 'Of course not, sir. I am never a hero. I don't have the height.'

Parulkar rocked back and forth, gurgling with laughter. 'Nowadays even very short people are becoming heroes, Sartaj. The world has changed, my dear fellow.'

Sartaj thought for a moment that Parulkar would recite a couplet, but Parulkar was in a hurry, and he left it at 'my dear fellow' and sent his cash and Sartaj on their way. He only said, 'My regards to Bhabhi-ji,' and raised a hand, and that was all.

As he drove to Worli, Sartaj thought about Papa-ji. Most people remembered Sartaj's father as a tall man, but he had been only five feet seven and a half. His ramrod posture, his muscular arms and glorious moustache and, above all, his always-perfect turban, all these gave him a stature that magnified him in memory. Sartaj, his son, was a full inch taller, but he knew that he was not nearly as impressive, in his person or reputation, as Papa-ji. Papa-ji had been honest. He had insisted always on the crispest turban, on the finest suit, but he had managed to maintain his style on his wages, and had worn the same blue double-breasted blazer for a decade's worth of weddings and official functions. After his death, Sartaj had found the blazer in a trunk, carefully mothballed and wrapped in crisp paper. And now, long after Papa-ji's death, strangers still said to Sartaj, 'Oh, you are

Sardar Saab's son? He was a good man.' A year ago, in Crawford Market, a diamond merchant had patted Sartaj sadly on his shoulder, and said, 'Beta, your father was the only honest policeman I have ever known.' Sartaj had nodded, and muttered, 'Yes, he was a good man,' and walked away, his shoulders stiff.

Now Sartaj wheeled right towards the sea-front, then pulled a fast U-turn in front of a bus and came coasting back to the pavement. The general provision store to his right was crowded with uniformed children buying ice-creams. They looked as if they were in the third or fourth, but their school-bags were huge and very heavy. They were too young to know yet that medical school positions were bought and sold, that entrance papers for management schools were leaked to those who could afford it. Sartaj pulled Parulkar's duffle-bag from behind the front seat and walked slowly through the kids. When he had been their age, he had known Parulkar already for a year and more. Parulkar had then been a young, slim sub-inspector, a favourite chela of Papa-ji's. Papa-ji had liked Parulkar, had thought him intelligent and hard-working and dedicated. He had often brought Parulkar home for dinner, he said, 'The boy is unmarried and needs to eat good home food once in a while.' But Ma had never really taken to Parulkar. She was civil enough, but she didn't trust him from the start. 'Just because he listens to your stories endlessly you think he's your devoted bhakt,' she said to Papa-ji. 'But mark my words, these Marathas are too clever.' It was no use telling her that Parulkar was not a Maratha, but in fact a Brahmin. She said, 'Whatever he is, he's a sharp one.' Her dislike for Parulkar had intensified with his steady ascent through the ranks, and when he had passed Papa-ji's rank and gone beyond, she had stopped talking about Parulkar altogether. She called him only 'that man', and didn't even argue when Papa-ji spoke about men's destinies, and how each one of us should be grateful with what Vaheguru had given.

Sartaj angled up the narrow stairs next to the general provision store, which led up to Mehta's tiny office. Mehta had worked in these four little cubicles all his life, and he lived close by, in a spacious but simple apartment overlooking the sea. He was a neat, discreet Parsi gent, dressed now, as always, in complete white. 'Arre, Sartaj, come, come,' he said, reaching across the table with a fragile hand for a quick, limp shake. He was thin, but elegant, and Sartaj always admired the cut of his fine grey hair. Homi Mehta reminded him somehow of the black-and-white movies that ran on television on Sunday afternoons, it was easy to imagine him sweeping down the seafront in a black Victoria.

'This is from Saab,' Sartaj said, and put the duffle-bag on the desk.

'Yes, yes,' Mehta said. 'But when are you going to bring me some of your own cash, young man? You need to save for the future.'

'I am a poor man, Uncle,' Sartaj said. 'What to save, when there is hardly enough to survive?'

This was a conversation that Sartaj and Mehta had every time Sartaj visited, but today Mehta wasn't willing to let it go so soon. 'Arre, what are you telling me? The man who got Ganesh Gaitonde has not got even a little money?'

'There was no reward.'

'Some people are saying that you got a good amount from Dubai to put a bullet in Gaitonde's head.'

'Uncle, I didn't kill Gaitonde. He shot himself. And nobody paid me.'

'All right, baba. I didn't say anything. People, you know, people are saying it.'

Mehta was counting Parulkar's money, laying the bricks in orderly stacks on the right-hand side of the desk. He was a meticulous man, and scrupulous in his accounting. A long time ago, during one of their first meetings, he had told Sartaj, 'In a world of dishonesty, I am an entirely honest man.' He had said it without pride, as just a statement of fact. He had explained to Sartaj that finally all the movement of money in and out of the country depended on the consultants. They were also called 'managers', in Delhi they were 'headmasters', but whatever name they were given, everything depended on their honesty. The money came from secret deals and graft, bribery and embezzlement, extortion and murder, and the managers took care of it with discretion and integrity. They made it vanish and they made it reappear. They were the secret magicians who were crucial to all business, and therefore they knew everyone.

'Uncle, I need some help,' Sartaj said.

'Tell me.'

'Parulkar Saab said you may know how I can get in touch with one of Gaitonde's men.'

'Which one?'

'Bunty.'

The old man gave nothing away. He wiped his fingers on a tissue, and started another stack. 'I will have to ask him,' he said. 'What should I tell him?'

'I just want to talk to him. I want to ask him some questions about Gaitonde.'

'You want to ask him some questions about Gaitonde.' Mehta nodded, and squared away the last stack of money. 'Okay. You have a new mobile, write down the number.'

Sartaj grinned, and wrote on a pad. Old man Mehta didn't miss a thing, even the small bulge in his breast pocket. Sartaj had finally succumbed and bought a mobile phone, after years of insisting they were too expensive and the rates were too high. He had paid too much, eventually, for a tiny Motorola because it was so silvery and stylish. The phone was still shiny and unused, and he hadn't given the number to anyone yet, but Homi Mehta was ancient and wise and keen-eyed.

'Here, Uncle,' Sartaj said. 'Thank you.'

'Okay. Forty total,' Mehta said, patting the money.

Sartaj stood up. 'Right. I will see you next time.'

'Next time, bring me something to save for you. Think of your old age.'

Sartaj raised a hand, and left Mehta and the money. There had been a time, when Sartaj had still been married to Megha, when Mehta always told him to save for his future children. After the divorce, Mehta had stopped doing that, and had started with these reminders of age and passing time. I must really be starting to look old, Sartaj thought.

There was a different group of children at the store now, older ones in their early teens, more sophisticated and self-conscious than the lot before. They drank Pepsis and Cokes and whispered to each other. Sartaj walked half-way to the jeep, then came back to the store and bought a Chocobar. There were other, fancier ice-creams available nowadays, but Sartaj liked that old Kwality taste of slightly oily chocolate with the vanilla underneath, it was the flavour of his childhood. The teenagers nudged each other: don't miss the funny sardar policeman chomping at a Chocobar. Sartaj smiled and walked on, and by the time he reached the jeep he was licking at the bare wooden stick. He crunched it between his teeth, as he had always done as a boy, flipped it away and drove.

The rush-hour traffic was coiling around the streets now, stiffening into a congealed mass. Sartaj settled himself in for the long ride. There was a violent shimmer in the air above the metal of the car roofs, and now a sudden quiet as the drivers switched off their engines to wait out the crush. Sartaj peeled his sweaty back away from the seat, and with his forearms on his knees and head hanging he stared at the dusty black of his shoes. The sun gathered its hard heat against his shoulder and neck, but there was nowhere to escape from it. Through the window a bus-driver watched him dispassionately, and when Sartaj met his glance he looked away, shifting in his high seat. Beyond him, a mannequin thrust her hip forward behind glass. Sartaj followed the shop windows, and they receded into the glare of the sky, and he imagined the immense length of the island, all of it stuck and still in this multitudinous evening rush, clogged and moving in jerks and ricocheting little jumps. He sighed, then took the phone out of his pocket and dialled.

'Ma?' he said.

'Sartaj.'

'Peri pauna, Ma.'

'Jite raho, beta. I read about you in the paper.'

'Yes, Ma.' The rumble of engines being switched on swept up the road, and Sartaj turned his ignition over.

'Such a big criminal you caught, why was there no picture of you?'

'Ma, the work is important,' Sartaj said, amused at her and at his own pomposity. 'Not photos in the paper.' He waited expectantly for her sharp retort, but she had already moved on.

'Where are you calling from?'

'Where? Mumbai, Ma.'

'No, I mean where in Bumbai?'

She didn't miss anything, this policeman's wife. Sartaj said, 'I'm driving back from Worli.'

'Oho, so you got a mobile at last.'

'Yes, Ma.' She herself was indifferent to technological advances, and said she didn't want a VCR because she wouldn't know how to work it, but she had long wanted Sartaj to have a mobile.

'What is the number?' she said.

Sartaj gave it to her, and added, 'Remember, no calls during duty hours.'

She laughed. 'I was doing duty before you were born. And always, you are the one who always calls me from work. Like now.'

'Yes, yes.' She would be sitting on the sofa in the small living room, her legs curled up under her, holding the large black handset up to her ear with a small hand. He could hear her smile. She had lost weight this last year, and despite the fine wrinkles and white hair, she sometimes looked like the slim young girl Sartaj had seen in photographs. 'But I'm not working now. I'm just caught in traffic.'

'That Bumbai is impossible to live in now. So expensive. And too many people.'

This was true, but where else was there to go? Maybe many years later, there would be a small house for Sartaj somewhere else. But right now he found it hard to imagine being away permanently from this messy, impossible city. A small holiday, now and then, was all Sartaj needed. 'This Saturday, Ma, I'll come to Pune.'

'Good. I haven't seen you for months.'

Sartaj had gone to Pune exactly four weeks ago, but he knew better than to argue. 'Do you need anything from here?'

She didn't want anything for herself, but she had a list of items for mausis and taus and nephews and nieces. It was no use telling Ma that these things were now surely available in a good-sized city like Pune, because she had specific Mumbai shops that were to be patronized, and instructions to be given to certain shopkeepers she had known for decades. Sartaj always arrived in Pune with a bag for his clothes and a suitcase full of child-sized clothes and mithai and salty snacks and shampoos for Ma to give away to her numerous near and dear. She lived close to family in Pune, and Sartaj trusted her to keep him updated on the network of relatives that stretched all the way up to Punjab and beyond. He thought of her as inextricably embedded in that family, while he himself was distanced from it, not quite separated but gone away somehow, like a planet that had spun out too far from its sun. He liked to listen to her stories of family feuds and ancient tragedies, as long as he could avoid being drawn into their fatal gravity and made a participant. Reminded by a book of nursery rhymes she wanted Sartaj to bring, she started a tale now, about her chacha who used to insist that he could speak English. Sartaj had heard it many times before, but he liked listening to it now, and laughed in all the proper places.

At Siddhi Vinayak he said goodbye to Ma, and settled back into the seat, smiling. It was good to look forward to the trip to Pune. A crowd swirled around the entrance to the Siddhi Vinayak lane, a host of worshippers bringing their entreaties and supplications and gratitude. The temple rose to its golden spire, carrying its huge symmetries easily to the sky. Sartaj wondered if Ganesh Gaitonde had some other place where he went to from the city, some town or village he called his native place. He would ask Katekar.

Ganesh Gaitonde had said something about God and belief at the end. By now Gaitonde would know for sure whether there was a God to believe in, or not. Sartaj didn't particularly care about Gaitonde's soul, but he knew it was time to go and look at his body, his and the dead woman's. He had been avoiding it, but he would have to go. Sartaj cursed Ganesh Gaitonde, and drove on.

The next morning, Katekar protested about the visit to Gaitonde, as Sartaj had expected. The man was dead, Katekar said, and he and the woman would remain dead, so there was no need to go near them now, none at all.

'You can stay outside,' Sartaj told him. 'But you should be used to dead bodies by now.'

The morgue was an ancient sandstone building, pitted and stained but still handsome with its tall arches and flowery stonework. It stood, green-shaded, under a huge banyan tree at the rear of KD Hospital. Sartaj dropped Katekar off at the gate of the hospital, drove around the building and parked near a paan-stained wall. For all his rationalism, Katekar had a horror of the morgue, its doctor and attendants, the emerald light under the banyan tree. He said the whole place smelt, that he could smell it from across the hospital compound, that there was a yellow miasma that slid into your clothes and sank into your pockets and stayed. Sartaj rather enjoyed this unexpected upsurge of superstition deep within the stolid frame of Ganpatrao Popat Katekar, man of science. It gave Sartaj something to point to when Katekar affected a superior sneer at Sartaj's various romanticisms.

Sartaj went past the enquiry window, with its small cluster of anxious men who had come looking for missing relatives and friends. He went down a dark corridor and through the double glass doors marked 'No Entrance'. An attendant in brown shorts and shirt sat behind a scratched metal desk, under muzzy tube-lights. He salaamed Sartaj, who took a deep breath, blinked once and went through another pair of swinging doors, of green-painted wood this time. The room on the other side was quite large, big as a good-sized wedding hall, well-lit from two square skylights and two rows of tube-lights. The floor was smooth brown stone, sloping inwards to a square drain. There were two brown bodies, both male, naked on the stone tables to the left. The top of the far one's skull had been removed, with a precise round cut that made him a cartoon character whose head had come unscrewed. His brain sat in a tidy grey mound on a tray next to his elbow. And here, on the right, was Dr Chopra, analyst at the abyss, working efficiently. He was scooping out intestines into a large tray. Sartaj turned his head away.

'Dr Chopra?'

'Ah, Sartaj. Wait, wait.'

Sartaj watched the wall, followed the cracks in the grey plaster up to the ceiling and then back down again. And then the rusted bars on the closed window, he counted them and examined their thickness. Meanwhile there were small sucking sounds to his right, and a little wet grinding. The first of the many times Sartaj had come in here, into Dr Chopra's dissection house, he had made himself look, on the principle that a policeman must gaze steadfastly at everything, anything, what the world is truly made of, you must know it all unflinchingly, without repugnance or perverse fascination. And he had seen what Dr Chopra had exposed, had been able to look at it, and it wasn't that horrifying after all, just the complicated inner clockwork of the body, a fluid machinery possessed of an intricate, severe harmony. But the surfaces of the corpses followed him and stayed with him into his sleep, the light ring of skin on the third finger of a fisted hand, the tribal tattoo on a woman's chin, the crimson flecks of lipstick on a lower lip, faint but unmistakable. He accumulated fragments of the dead, tiny memories of their lives that cost something to carry, and finally he decided he no longer had a young man's pride, that he would save his will for work, for his own cases. So he no longer looked.

'Done,' Dr Chopra said.

Sartaj heard the snap of rubber gloves, and he turned, keeping his head tilted up. He saw the dead man's face, and stared for a moment. Then he saw the thick thatch of Dr Chopra's hair. The doctor was the hairiest man Sartaj had ever met. It was just past twelve, and Dr Chopra's cheeks and jaw were already shaded dark, and there was a thick black mat of hair that came up from his chest, half-way up his neck. He was washing his hands in a basin.

'Doctor saab,' Sartaj said, 'I need to see Gaitonde and his female friend.'

'Fine,' said Dr Chopra. 'They're in the cold room.'

'Post-mortem done already?'

'Arre, Gaitonde was a big bhai, yes? He and his friend got jumped ahead in the queue.' Dr Chopra laughed, and it was quite genuine, full of pleasure. 'You want me to get the boys to haul them out of the cold room? Quicker if we go there.'

There was a challenge in his stance, in the raising of his bushy, overhanging eyebrow: if you can take it, Mr Policeman. The cold room was what Katekar absolutely hated. He had been inside only once, when he and Sartaj had been looking for the body of a khabari. Katekar had stepped into the cold room, put a hand to his mouth and turned and walked out, walked out to the banyan tree. Sartaj had stayed inside and found the body they were looking for. Sartaj had done it before, he could do it now. He shrugged. 'Cold room is fine.'

A shaded walkway led to the cold room, through the obliterating afternoon glare. Sartaj squinted, and walked, and now there was no avoiding the smell. They passed through a door, into a long dark passageway, and it pressed up against his cheeks. The windows were closed against the heat, against the throbbing of the sun, and the air inside the entryway was engorged with the ripe, round exhalations from the two rows of bodies stacked against the walls, in sheets on double racks. The sheets were damp and the ground below the racks was slimy, slick.

Sartaj nodded at the attendants sitting at the desk at the end of the corridor. He could feel a hiccup curling itself at the back of his throat, and he didn't want to open his mouth.

'Inspector saab,' one attendant said, rising. 'After a long time.' He had been reading a Hindi novel, and his friend was writing a letter. They both stood up.

Sartaj spoke carefully, enunciating. 'It smells worse than last time,' he said as he went past the desk.

'Arre, saab,' the attendant with the novel said, 'wait until the air-conditioners break again. Then you'll really smell something.'

'Wait until it rains and the leaks start coming through the walls,' the other one said with large satisfaction. 'Then you'll really have fun.'

There is a certain pleasure we take in thinking about how bad it gets, Sartaj thought, and then in imagining how it will inevitably get worse. And still we survive, the city stumbles on. Maybe one day it'll all just fall apart, and there was a certain gratification in that thought too. Let the maderchod blow.

Dr Chopra nodded at his attendants. The door to the cold room was shiny steel, very sleek and new and promising high technology and sterility. The fiction-reading attendant touched the heavy door-handle, touched his throat and mouthed a mantra. He grabbed the handle and leaned back, and the door swung open. 'Come,' Dr Chopra said.

And inside there were the jumbled rows of bodies that Sartaj remembered. They lay naked on the tiled floor, jammed up against each other, shoulder to shoulder, shoulder over shoulder, from one side of the long room to the other. Each was stitched up the front, in broad looping knots in thick black thread, where the long incision had been made for the post-mortem. Rusty, dark skin, gone as densely opaque as mud, spiky, petrified pubic hair. Sartaj was thinking, it's not really cold in here. They call it a cold room but there are restaurants that are colder, the upstairs room of the Delite Dance Bar is colder. He could hear the dull, halting rush of the air-conditioner.

'Ladies are over here,' Dr Chopra said.

In this charnel, past all carnality, the decencies were preserved. The ladies were piled on top of each other in a kind of small cabin to the left, with its own metal door. The attendants reached in and shifted the bodies around, tugged and pulled, and something knocked on the door and made a happy bonging. Sartaj found himself concerned with the attendants' hands, they're handling all that without gloves, he hoped they washed their hands afterwards.

'Saab,' the letter-writer said. They had found her.

Sartaj stepped back. His shoes were sticking to the floor.

There was the usual long incision up her front. Her lips had turned the cracked pale blue of old candles, and had drawn back from her upper teeth. The autopsy photo in the file had flattened out her cheekbones, and had made invisible the sharp nose. But the nose had been broken once, there was a small dent in it. In death she was plain, but there was muscle on her shoulders and along her flanks, and Sartaj saw her in a dancer's jaunty stance, glowing and proud of her figure.

'Unknown female deceased,' Dr Chopra read from a long sheet. 'Five foot three and a half inches, 110 pounds, black hair to shoulder length, eyes black, four-inch scar on right knee, had last eaten about eight hours prior to death, cause of death single gunshot trauma to sternum, bullet passed upwards at an angle and exited at T4, causing extensive damage to lungs, spinal cord. Death was instantaneous.'

Instantaneous death. Sartaj wondered if she had seen it coming, the raised barrel and Gaitonde's reddened eye above. 'No distinguishing marks besides the scar?'

'None.'

'All right,' Sartaj said. Sometimes the body of the deceased taught you things that you didn't know before, but this had been a short history. She was unmarked by life, mainly.

'And Gaitonde?' Dr Chopra said, turning.

'Gaitonde. Yes.'

Sartaj followed Dr Chopra down the room, in the small lane between the bodies. There were flows of liquids across the floor, light albumen runs and thick blackish discharges. Sartaj carefully placed one foot, then the other. Gaitonde lay in the middle of a row, indistinguishable from the others but for the ruin of his head. The exposed inner flesh had turned black. 'Five foot six, 151 pounds, he's survived two bullet wounds.' Dr Chopra pointed. 'Interestingly enough, one was in his buttocks. The great Gaitonde must have been running when he got that one. The other wound was in his left shoulder, here.'

Sartaj bent over Gaitonde, and saw that he had a fine profile, with a noble brow. He was born to be a king, Sartaj thought, or maybe a sage. He must have looked in the mirror and wondered what he would become.

Dr Chopra was stroking the hair on the back of his right hand. An air-conditioner kicked itself on with a low rumble, and the fetid smell surged up from Gaitonde and the rest of them. 'Thanks, doctor saab,' Sartaj said, and he had had enough. He straightened and went, going fast. He turned sideways to go past the attendants, who were lifting the female deceased back through the cabin door. He went by them. Light seeped through the angles of the main doorway, and in the brightness Sartaj saw on the floor a tattered rind of black flesh, a small piece of jaw attached to three teeth. He stepped over it and fled into the sunlight.

'Are you all right?' Dr Chopra said.

Sartaj was standing by the banyan tree, one hand on its grainy bark, breathing. 'Why can't you keep that gaandu place cold? Why?'

'The air-conditioners break down, the wiring is old and the fuses blow, and the population is too large. The morgue is too small.'

Yes, it was unfair to blame the good Dr Chopra. It was in no way his fault, that there wasn't enough money, too little electricity, too small a space and far too many dead. 'Sorry, Doc,' Sartaj said. He made a large gesture in the air, an awkward movement that took in everything. Dr Chopra nodded and smiled. 'Thanks,' Sartaj said.

'I hope seeing them was useful.'

'Yes, yes. Very useful.' Sartaj said this, but as he was walking to the jeep he wasn't sure. Now the desire to see the bodies, which only a little while ago had seemed so coherent, seemed bizarre. What had he learnt? Sartaj had no idea. It had all been a waste of time. He was eager to be away, back at the station, but at the jeep he found himself unable to get in. He stepped over a border made of painted half-bricks into what was left of a garden, found a patch of dead brown grass and wiped the bottom of his shoes, rubbed them back and forth on the grass until the stalks broke with small clicking sounds and his grinding heart settled and calmed.

Shalini was cooking by the time Katekar got home. She cleaned at a doctor's house in Saat Bungla, but at only one house, unlike some others who had three jhadoo-katka jobs, or four. It was good to have the money from the doctor, but they had decided that she needed to be home when the boys came in, at home in the afternoons and early evenings so they could feel her presence and she could keep an eye out. But the money was very welcome. And it was good to know a doctor with a clinic, for times of special need. Katekar put down his mat and pillow. Shalini was cooking, and he liked the stir of her motions, they lulled him, the tinkle of the spoons, the flurrying back-and-forth rush of the knife, the fast bubbling of the flames on the stove, the leaping sizzle when she flung in a fistful of goda masala. He was comfortable, with the quiet stirring of air from the table-fan set on 'Low'. He napped easily in the day, stored sleep like a camel hoarded water. In the life of a constable, this was necessary. He took a long breath.

When he awoke it was dark inside the kholi, and there was the bustle of evening in the lane outside. He turned his wrist, and it was six-thirty. 'Where are the boys?' he said. He didn't need to turn his head to know Shalini was sitting in the doorway.

'Playing,' she said.

He sat up, rubbed his eyes. The stove rattled as she pumped it, and then he saw her face, suddenly bronzed out of the shade. 'They're fighting,' he said, and he didn't need to say that he didn't mean the boys.

'Yes.' Amritrao Pawar and his wife Arpana lived two kholis down, and they had been fighting continuously, as nearly as their neighbours could tell, for eleven years. Four years after their marriage, Pawar had acquired another woman. Arpana had left, gone back to her parents, and had been reassured that it was merely a passing thing, that Pawar had quit the other woman, and that it was all over. She had come back, but then the other woman had had a child, and now Pawar maintained two establishments. He and Arpana refused to part, refused to come closer or divide, they fought and fought. For Arpana's neighbours, the other woman was still the other woman, Arpana had not called her by name in eleven years, and Pawar never spoke about her.

Katekar and Shalini drank their tea seated across from each other. She had the kaande pohe he liked on a plate between them. 'I spoke to Bharti yesterday.'

Bharti was her younger sister, who was married to a scrap-metal dealer in Kurla. There was apparently much money in scrap metal, because Bharti always came to visit in a new sari. Last year, she had come the day before Gudi-Padwa, wearing new gold bangles of a conspicuous thickness and glow, and bearing not only batasha garlands but also large, fragrant boxes of puranpoli and chirote for the boys. Katekar had watched his sons lick their glistening, sweet fingers, and he had watched his wife's face as she had put away the boxes and the new sari for herself, and he had marvelled at how generosity can be the subtlest of all weapons, and especially between sisters. So now he took a long sip of his tea. 'Yes?' he said.

'They're buying the next kholi also,' Shalini said.

'In the chawl?'

'Where else?'

The retort had come quick and sharp, and she was not backing down from his quizzical look. So now her sister and brother-in-law would tear down walls, combine rooms, have a home that was expansive enough to contain their sense of themselves. 'They have three children,' Katekar said. 'They need the space.'

Shalini snorted and picked up the plate of biscuits. 'What, those little taporis need a palace to live in?' She got up and began to gather spoons, rattle the bowl about. 'Bharti has been a wastrel since she was this high. Those two never think about the future. Their children will turn out bad, you wait and see.'

She loved her nieces and nephew, smothered them with hugs and unbent more with them than with her own sons, and Katekar knew this well. So he put on his shirt, drew on his pants. She had the pot scoured and hung up already. Katekar grinned at her. 'I heard a joke yesterday,' he said.

'What?'

'Once Laloo Prasad Yadav met some Japanese businessmen who had come to Bihar. The Japanese businessmen said to him, "Chief-minister-ji, your state has great resources. Give us a free hand for three years and we'll turn Bihar into the next Japan." Laloo looked very surprised. He said, "And you Japanese are supposed to be efficient! Three years? Give me a free hand for three days and I'll turn Japan into the next Bihar."'

'Not very funny.' But she was smiling.

'Arre,' Katekar said, 'your family just never had a sense of humour.'

This was a theme they had explored for years: his family was extravagant but fun-loving, hers was thrifty but boring. Variations on this theory took in the boys, Rohit had gone on Katekar, Mohit on his mother. Now Shalini was thinking of her sons. 'Will you be done early enough to stop at Patil's?'

Patil was the tailor who had a shop two lanes down, tucked into a long narrow building that stood on what had once been a broken wall and an unused gutter. Patil had filled in the gutter, closed off the rear, put on a roof, and now he sat two full-time tailors at sewing machines. He made uniforms for the boys, good ones, strong enough that Mohit could wear what Rohit grew out of. 'Not today,' Katekar said. 'I'll pick it up tomorrow. One half-pant, one shirt, yes?'

'Yes,' Shalini said. Her irritation had melted away. She liked that he remembered, he could see that.

Outside, the clouds sat in luxurious orange tiers. It was too early for rain, but Katekar could feel it coming. The sky was histrionically spectacular, but nobody was stopping to look at it. Katekar walked briskly, cutting an efficient loop to go to the bus-stop by way of the play-ground. He was thinking about sex. He had been quite unfaithful in the years immediately after he and Shalini had been married, before Rohit had been born. Looking back now, it seemed like a feverish mad-ness, the visits he had made to dance bars and the money he had spent on girls, on grimy rooms, on taxis late at night. Shalini had been hardly more than a girl herself then, and he had lowered his head into the arc of her neck nightly, and found in the clutch of her hands on his shoul-ders an answering hunger, more carefully quiet than his own but as insistent, as fierce. And still he had gone to other women, randis. There was no reason for it but an urgency he felt at the offering of unknown, anonymous bellies under cheap, diaphanous nylon. It was a kind of common madness, accepted by the men of the world, and at least he had had the sense and the knowledge – even in those long-ago days when the girls themselves were surprised by this carefulness – to always wear a condom. After Rohit had been born, after he had held the tiny body of his son against his chest and felt the enormous, inescapable weight of his own love, it had become almost impossible to spend his hard-earned money elsewhere. There were these new urgencies, first among all desires: school uniforms, books, shoes, hair-oil, cricket bats, evenings at Chowpatty. Yet, it had happened even after he had come to know what amount of childish happiness was contained in a twenty-rupee note, in two kulfis as the sun set over a calm sea, he had still gone to women, despite his two sons and the two futures he was building. But it had happened rarely, the women countable on one hand in twice as many years. Men, Shalini said sometimes, there is madness in men. He always kept quiet, but he always wanted to say, the madness is in their bones, not in their hearts, not in their heads. Logic doesn't fail, it just gets worn down sometimes, a little tired, and it wants to lie down. But I struggle for you.

The maidan held what looked like a dozen games of cricket, with pitches angled to each other and very close. Fielders from various games ran past and behind each other. There must have been a couple of hundred boys racing past each other, on this narrow strip of packed yellow earth backed up between a sludgy nullah and the back wall of a municipal shamshan ghat. Katekar walked along the wall, his right shoulder brushing against its intricate whorls of graffiti and torn posters. He worried sometimes about children playing one wall away from burning bodies, about the billowing smoke depositing unclean ash on to the pitches. But you needed a place to cremate the dead, and the only alternative was to play at the edge of the basti, on the open road next to passing traffic. In any case, today there were no fires, no smoke. There were no more dead on this day. Mohit was sitting on a little rising mound, next to a cluster of chappals. He was looking seawards, dreamy and happy, and Katekar felt something squeeze inside his chest and give way. Rohit was the son just like his father, he was confident and practical, often funny, but it was Mohit, with his thoughtful inwardness, who made Katekar helpless with worry. Rohit's ambition and his anger might get him into trouble, but what would become of sensitive little Mohit? What would happen to such gentleness? Katekar squatted beside him.

'Not playing?' Katekar said.

'Papa.' Mohit shrugged. He looked away, and started biting his lower lip, which he did when he was embarrassed.

'It's all right,' Katekar said, with a pat on Mohit's shoulder. He had told them often, his sons, that sports developed character. 'You didn't feel like it?'

Mohit shook his head, fast. Katekar wanted to ask, what were you thinking about just now? What were you seeing in the little sliver of watery horizon between buildings? But he smiled and rubbed Mohit's head. 'Where's your brother?'

'There.'

Rohit was bowling. It was a fast ball, a little wild but with good speed. The batsman missed it altogether, hardly saw it, and the wicket-keeper took it smoothly and gave it back to Rohit in the same motion. Rohit jogged back to the wicket, easy and thinking about the next delivery. He was a good player, Katekar could tell that just from his effortless poise, from his confidence and his scientific precision as he waved his fielders in, you to the left, a little more, yes, there. Rohit saw his father then, stopped short. And there was just a small moment when Katekar saw him flinch, tighten into a resentful frown at being interrupted, invaded by his heavy-stepping father. Then he smiled and started forward. Katekar waved him back with an overhand motion: bowl. Rohit went back to his crease, stepped out his run-up and now his action was good but the ball was wide. The next one was short.

Katekar got up. 'Mohit,' he said. 'Don't be late going home. Study well. I'll see you tomorrow.'

'Yes, Papa,' Mohit said.

Katekar squeezed Mohit's shoulder, then walked away, fast. He was tempted, but he didn't turn his head to see Rohit playing.

PSI Kamble came along for the raid on the Delite Dance Bar. 'I'll be your undercover man,' he said, and laughed loudly at his own wit, because they knew him at the Delite better than they knew some of their own dancers. He sat always in a prime centre booth facing the dance floor, and there were always special dispensations in his bill. In the van, on the way to Delite, he was in a glorious mood, and he told them jokes. 'How do you fit thirty Marwaris in a Maruti 800? You throw a hundred-rupee note inside.' The constables in the back of the van, including two women, laughed.

Sartaj asked, 'Why so happy, Kamble? What was the score today?'

Kamble shook his head, and was silent and smug, and then jovial again. On they drove, to the sound of his laughter. At the Delite, after they had parked the van, and were waiting for the appointed time, Kamble came out of the building carrying a whisky and water. He drew Sartaj to the side, away from the constables, and walked him a little way down the road. He smelt powerfully of some musky after-shave, and was wearing a white Benetton T-shirt with striped green sleeves, tucked into blue jeans. He leaned back and raised one foot at a time, showing off an impressively complicated and colourful pair of running shoes. 'Very musst shoes, no?' he said.

'Very. Foreign?'

'Yes, boss. Nike.'

'Very expensive.'

'Expense is all relative. When there is money in your pocket, expenses get small. No money, expenses get big.'

'Money got in your pocket?'

Kamble considered Sartaj for a moment, head lowered over his glass. 'Suppose –' he said. 'Suppose a bright young police officer had a khabari, a very useful one who came up with information only once in a while, but ekdum solid information when he did.'

'What khabari is this? Who?'

'Never mind the khabari. Not important. What is important that the intelligent young officer got a tip this morning: that one local small-time thief called Ajay Mota had a stash of stolen mobile phones in his kholi. These are brand-new phones, you understand, taken during a break-in robbery three days ago, at a shop in Kurla.'

'Very good. So this officer goes and arrests Ajay Mota?'

'No, no, no. That is too simple, boss. No, the khabari knows where this Ajay Mota lives. But the officer doesn't reel the bastard in yet. No, he invests some time, he dresses in plain clothes, he takes the khabari, waits outside Ajay Mota's basti and gets the khabari to point out the bastard when he emerges with a bag on his shoulder. This is a risk, of course – what if Ajay Mota had gone another way? But he doesn't. The officer leaves the khabari behind, and follows Ajay Mota. Another risk, this following in busy traffic. It's not easy, but the officer has a motorbike, and Ajay Mota is in an auto. So the apradhi's auto goes along for ten minutes, then the apradhi gets off, goes into a shop. Comes out twenty minutes later, his bag over his shoulder. So now the officer takes him, khata-khat, grabs him by the collar, shows him a revolver, two slaps, you are under arrest, bhenchod, you want to co-operate? Then, without pause, the officer takes him inside the shop, shoves him through to the back, and there's the receiver, with the stolen phones in front of him. So, the officer has two arrests, the stolen goods are recovered and in Ajay Mota's bag is forty thousand rupees.'

'Only forty thousand? How many phones were there?'

Kamble laughed, and emptied his glass, and caught the last few drops on his extended tongue. He was very pleased. 'Never mind how many phones there were, Sartaj Saab. The important thing is, the bad men were caught,' he said, standing up very straight, wagging a finger. 'I need to refill my glass, boss. Again and again.' And he went, humming to himself.

Sartaj thought of Kamble's triumph as they executed the raid. Kamble was right, the bad men had been caught. Kamble himself had taken a good chunk of cash, probably about half of what was in the bag, and maybe one or two phones. The money was a reward for his excellent policing, for his alertness and his risk-taking. He had done well today, and he was celebrating. He deserved it.

The Delite raid itself was very orderly. Shambhu had the five girls waiting for arrest in an orderly row in his office. They were eating paya and making jokes about policemen and their sticks, while the rest of them went outside to their usual appointed cabbies for the ride home. They were a glittery, flashy bunch, mostly young, some of them quite lovely in their thick, big-screen make-up and their pride in the sleek curves of their waists.

Shambhu came walking towards Sartaj now, followed at a few yards by Kamble. They were friends, of a similar age, both body-builders, but where Shambhu was lean and chiselled, Kamble had bulk, rounded masses and bulges.

'All right, saab,' Shambhu said. 'Arrest away.'

One of the women constables stood by the van, and the other opened the Delite door and called. The arrestees trooped out on to the road and climbed into the back of the van, swaying up into it, their elegant heels glinting in the red light from the neon Delite sign.

'Going on that – that walk still?' Katekar said to Shambhu.

'An expedition,' Shambhu said. 'A walk is what you do when you go to the corner paan shop.'

'Expedition, yes, you're going?'

'Tomorrow.'

'Don't fall off a mountain.'

'Safer there than here, boss.'

Sartaj was watching Kamble, who was humming. He had his feet very wide apart and his shoulders thrown back and his elbows out. Sartaj walked around him. 'Tell the young officer I said, good job.'

Kamble grinned. 'I will, boss,' he said. He hummed again, and this time Sartaj could make out the song: '*Kya se kya ho gaya, dekhte dekhte*'. Kamble raised his arms, ducked his head and danced a couple of steps. '*Tum pe dil aa gaya, dekhte dekhte.*'

'We're going,' Sartaj said. 'Are you coming?'

'No,' Kamble said. He shrugged his head over a shoulder, back towards the Delite. 'I have an appointment.'

Not all the girls at the Delite had been arrested, or had gone home. 'Have fun,' Sartaj said.

'Boss,' Kamble said, 'I always do.'

Sartaj thumped on the side of the van, and they pulled away. 'Sartaj Saab,' he heard Shambhu calling after him, 'you could have fun too, sir. You should have fun, once in a while. Fun is good.' Kamble was laughing, Sartaj could hear him.

It was only after they were back at the station that they discovered they had arrested six dancers, not five. The girls sat in a row on a bench in the Detection Room and Sartaj realized they were six, and that the extra sixth was Manika. She lowered her head and looked at him demurely with her chunni over her head, all enormous dark eyes and shyness, and the other girls burst out laughing. Sartaj took a deep breath and walked out of the room.

'This must be Kamble and Shambhu's idea of fun,' he said to Katekar.

'I didn't have anything to do with it, sir,' Katekar said.

Katekar had on a very serious face, and Sartaj believed him. He said, 'Send them in one by one. I'll sit there.'

'Yes, sir, one by one.'

Katekar stood by the door, and the women constables brought the girls in one by one, and also retreated to the door. Sartaj wrote down the names: Sunita Singh, Anita Pawar, Rekha Kumar, Neena Sanu, Shilpa Chawla. They had the names all ready for him, and were relaxed and not perturbed by him at all, and only became hesitant when he pulled the photographs from Gaitonde's album and flipped them over one by one. Then each of them shook their heads, determined and expressionless. 'No, no, no,' Shilpa Chawla said as he showed her the photographs of the young women, the smiling come-hither poses under soft lights.

'Look at the photo before you say no,' Sartaj said. He tapped his forefinger on a young woman in a blue hat. 'Look at her.'

'I don't know her,' Shilpa Chawla said, her jaw tight. When he showed her the dead woman, who he had kept till last, Shilpa Chawla sat back in her chair and crossed her arms across her chest. 'Why are you asking me? Why are you showing me all this? I don't know who this is.' Shilpa Chawla, with her doubly starry pseudonym, was disgusted and angry and frightened, and Sartaj had no evidence that she was lying.

'All right,' he said to Katekar. 'Send in Manika.'

She was older than the others, maybe in her early thirties, although you had to pay very close attention to see that, and even then the age was mainly in her slightly weary confidence, in the forthright straightness of her back and the blunt interest she directed at him. By the door, Katekar and the women constables were grinning at each other, and Sartaj was glad that they were too far away to hear Manika.

'How are you?' she said in English.

'I have some questions to ask you, madam,' Sartaj said, and his Hindi was clipped.

'Ask,' she said. She was dark, slim, very tall, maybe five eight, and not pretty exactly, but she had dimples and she thrust out her chin and her eyes were completely alive, and she made Sartaj uneasy.

'Do you know these women?'

She flipped over the photographs, paying close attention to each one. 'Oh,' she said at the third one, 'how *ugly* that blouse is! Look at those frills on the sleeves, she looks like a joker. Nice-looking girl at that. Someone needs to teach her how to dress.'

'Do you know her?'

'No,' Manika said, and she took the remaining photographs from his hand and leaned back in her chair. She was wearing a black ghagra-choli with silver on it everywhere, and the front of the choli was thick with it, like armour on the thin fabric. She was the only one who had come in her dance-floor clothes. 'Who are these women, inspector saab?' Now she was demure again. 'Girls you want to make friends with?'

'Do you know any of them?'

She was quiet, and her hands had stopped moving. Sartaj knew that she was looking at the dead woman. 'Do you know her?' She shook her head. 'It's very important that you tell me if you know.'

'No, I don't know. What happened to her?'

'She was murdered.'

'Murdered?'

'Shot.'

'By a man?'

'Yes, by a man.'

She put the photographs face-down on the desk. 'Of course by a man. Sometimes I don't know why we care about you. Really I don't know.'

Sartaj could hear the buzzing of the tube-light in the corridor outside, and distant footsteps at the front of the station. 'You are right,' he said. 'Most of the time I don't know either.'

There was an appraising scepticism in her raised eyebrow, not hostility, just a certain weary disbelief. 'Can I go now?' she said softly.

'Yes. What name shall I write down?'

'Whatever you want.'

He started to write, but stopped when she got up. The chunni slipped from her shoulder as she turned, and he saw that the choli was held together at the back by black strings, exposing the fine turns of her shoulder-blades and the long brown column of her back. On the dance floor she must pirouette, he thought, and blaze those eyes over a shoulder at the men in the booths, at the staring men in the darkness.

'I'll tell you,' she said from the door. In the four steps from the chair she had recovered her grin, her jaunty irony.

'Tell me what?'

She came back to the desk, turned the photographs face-up and went past the dead woman, flicked others aside with a long red finger-nail, while she held her chunni close with the other hand. 'This one,' she said.

'What about her?'

'You'll have to be very nice to me,' she said. 'Her name is Kavita, or at least that's what she called herself when she danced at Pritam. She got parts in some videos and stopped dancing. Then I heard she was on some serial. After she got the serial she lived in Andheri East, in a PG. She was very lucky always, that Kavita. Not many girls like us get that far. Not one in a thousand. Ten thousand.'

'Kavita. Are you sure it's her? Is it her real name?'

'Of course I'm sure. And you'll have to ask her if it's her real name. Are you going to be nice?'

'Yes, of course I am.'

'You're lying, but you're a man, so I'll forgive you. Do you know why I told you?'

'No.'

'The man who did this is a rakshasa. And don't feel too good, you're a rakshasa also. But maybe you'll catch that rakshasa. And punish him.'

'Maybe,' Sartaj said. The man who did it had been caught, and yet had escaped, and Sartaj had never been sure about punishment, because it always seemed too much or too little. I catch them because that's what I do, and they run because that's what they do, and the world keeps turning. But there was no explaining this to Manika, and so he said, 'Thanks.'

After she had gone, after they had put the lot of them into a van and sent them home, Sartaj dropped Katekar at the corner of Sriram Road, which was within comfortable walking distance of Katekar's place. Katekar raised his hand to his chest, and turned, and then Sartaj said, 'What does a rakshasa look like?'

Katekar leaned down to the window. 'I don't know, sir. On television they have long black hair, horns. And pointy teeth sometimes.'

'And they go around eating people?'

'I think that's their main job, sir.'

They both laughed. They had spent the day working, and they had made small progress in their investigations, and so they were happy. 'That would be nice to have during some interrogations,' Sartaj said. 'Horns, and teeth like wolves.'

But on the way home it occurred to Sartaj that most people he interrogated were so frightened that he might already have oversized canines. It was the uniform that terrified them, that brought back all those tales of police brutality collected over many generations. Even the ones who wanted help spoke warily around policemen, and the ones who didn't need help tried to be overly friendly in case they ever did. Policemen were monsters, set aside from everyone else. But Parulkar had once told Sartaj, 'We are good men who must be bad to keep the worst men in control. Without us, there would be nothing left, there would only be a jungle.'

A low, yellow haze flitted behind the buildings as Sartaj drove. The streets were quiet. Sartaj imagined the citizens sleeping in their millions, safe for one more night. The image gave him some satisfaction, but not nearly as much as it used to. He couldn't tell if this was because he had become more of a rakshasa, or less so. Still, he had a job to do, and he did it. Now he needed to sleep. He went home.

Ganesh Gaitonde Acquires Land

I took the land between N.C. Road and the hill which overlooks it.
You know Gopalmath basti, from N.C. Road all the way up the hill
and four miles wide, from Sindh Chowk to G.T. Junction? All that
was empty land then, nothing but a wasteland of weeds and bushes –
it was municipal land. The government owned it, and so nobody
owned it. I took it.

You know how it's done, Sartaj. It's easy. You pay off three chutiyas
in the municipality, oil them up properly and then you kill the local
dada who thinks he deserves a percentage on your action, like it's his
bhenchod birthright. That's it. Then the land is yours. I took it, and it
was mine.

I had sold my gold, and I had money. Paritosh Shah, fat Gujarati
that he was, told me I should put all my cash into business: buy this,
sell that. 'I can double it for you within a year,' he said. 'Triple it.' He
knew exactly how much I had, since he had bought all my gold from
me.

I listened to him, as he sprawled elegantly on his gadda, one cushion under his shoulder and another under his knees. I thought about
it, but I knew it in my bones, if you don't own land you are nothing.
You can die for love, you can die for friendship, you can die for
money, but finally the only real thing in the world is land. You can
depend on land. I said, 'Paritosh Bhai, I trust you, but let me follow
my own road.' He thought I was a fool, but I had already seen the
land, and had walked up and down it, and knew it was the right place,
near the road and not so far from the railway station. So we gave
money to the municipality, to one clerk and to two officers, and the
land was mine to build on.

But then there was the problem of Anil Kurup. We had the scrub
cleared, and my contractor had his men digging out the foundations

for the kholis, and we were expecting a truckload of cement, and Anil Kurup's boys stopped the truck on the way down from the main road, and took it to Gopalmath village, which was about a mile up the road. We never saw any cement, and instead they sent a piece of paper with a phone number on it. 'You're a bachcha from nowhere,' Anil Kurup shouted at me when I called. 'And you think you're going to come into my village and spit into my face. Maderchod, one hen doesn't get sold here without me knowing about it. I'll put a truckload of cement up your gaand and send you back to whatever gutter you came out of.' I kept calm and quietly asked for a day to think about it. He cursed me some more and finally told me to call him the next day. He was right, of course. He had grown up in Gopalmath, and this area was his, no question about it, he ruled it like a king. There wasn't much in his raj, just some small shops, a garage or two, but it was all his.

Four days later I went to see him in Gopalmath. I went with Chotta Badriya. You remember that big muscleman Badriya who was Paritosh Shah's bodyguard? This Chotta Badriya was his little brother. He was actually Badrul-Ahmed, and his elder brother's name was Badruddin, their father had been told by some Sufi pir that he should give all his sons names beginning with 'Ba –' for their success and well-being. So they had their fancy long names, but to us they were just Badriya and Chotta Badriya. Badriya and I saw each other every time I went to see Paritosh Shah, and we liked each other, and when I started my project he asked me to take his younger brother with me, to make his life. This Chotta was bigger actually, bigger than his big brother, as big as a mountain. He was a good boy, well-mannered and obedient, so I was glad to have him along with me. I said to his brother, 'If you ask, I give.'

That afternoon, though, with Anil Kurup, I was trying to keep what was mine. Chotta Badriya and I went walking into Gopalmath, and a sad little rubbish dump it was then, one kuchcha road and clustering hovels surrounded by palm trees and fields, and a few shops on the main road. Anil Kurup was waiting for us in the back of a dhaba just off the main road, which in those days was the only place in Gopalmath which had a phone.

His boys searched us, took our ghodas from us, and they were very impressed, I don't think they'd expected us to be carrying pistols. There were five of them. They led us through a door into the back room, past the huge karhais filled with frying puris and bhajiyas. Anil

Kurup was sitting at a table, drinking beer. At two in the afternoon, the ugly bastard was red-eyed and burping. He had thick lips, hair falling over his forehead, white chappals. I put on the table in front of him a newspaper wrapped around twenty thousand in cash.

'Not enough,' he said.

'Bhai,' I said, 'I'll have the rest soon, next week, I promise. And I would have brought this earlier, only I didn't know.'

'What kind of brainless bhenchod are you?' he said. 'You don't find out about an area before you go into it and start digging it up?'

'Sorry,' I said. And I shrugged, small and helpless.

He laughed then, spitting beer on to the table. 'Sit,' he said. 'Both of you. Have some beer.'

I said, 'Just some chai, Anil Bhai.'

'If I offer, you have beer.'

'Yes, Anil Bhai.' And he laughed again, and his three boys who were in the room laughed. They got us beer, a bottle each and glasses, and we drank.

'Where are you from, bachcha?' he said.

'Nashik.'

'You have to grow up in this Mumbai to know how it works,' he said. 'You can't just come in and act like a chutiya, you'll end up with your brains out on the road.'

'Yes, Anil Bhai,' I said. 'He's absolutely right, Badriya,' I said. 'We have to listen to Anil Bhai.'

Anil Kurup was puffed up like an avuncular toad now. 'Arre, go and get us some bhajiyas to eat,' he said. 'And bring some eggs also.'

Two of the boys jumped to attention and hurried out. That left one leaning against the wall to my right.

'Bhai, I have to ask some advice from you,' I said.

'Ask, ask.'

'It's about the municipality and water,' I said. And I scratched my nose.

And right then Chotta Badriya nudged his beer bottle off the table. 'Maderchod,' he said, and bent down to the floor. He came up quick, stood up and leaned forward in one flash, and his arm went suddenly across the table too fast to see, and then Anil Kurup was rocking back in his chair with a wooden handle growing from his right eye.

I had a bottle in my hand, and I smashed it across the face of the boy on my right. He squealed and clutched at himself, and I went past him and slammed the door shut, I threw the bolt and put my shoulder against the wood. I knew none of Anil Kurup's boys had guns, and our own ghodas were unloaded, so there was no danger of a bullet coming through the door, just Anil Kurup's fools shouting and slamming against it.

'Stop,' I shouted. 'Stop! Prashant. Vinod. Amar. He's dead. Anil Kurup is dead. And my boys are outside, and you may kill us, but they'll kill every one of you. I know your names. I know all your names and my boys know who you are. You can get us, but they'll kill every one of you. Amar, just take a step back and think about it. He's dead.'

Anil Kurup was dead, with blood seeping over his cheek. When they found our pistols, they hadn't searched further, and what Chotta Badriya had under his trouser leg was one of those straight picks that you use to break ice, with the handle set crosswise, he had it on the inside of his left leg, held there with three pieces of white medical tape. He was too strong, that Chotta Badriya, and he had put it right into Anil Kurup's eyeball, smashed it in with all his weight and muscle behind it. Very fast he was, and there was nothing they could have done about it. Only afterwards, when he was dead, they could have tried to kill us. But I talked them down. I told them I'd make them rich, that Anil Kurup was a stupid bastard, that he had robbed them for years, and cheated them, and now that he was dead it was mad of them to die for him. Because if they tried to do anything to us, they would die for sure, my boys were sworn to avenge me. I told them to look outside, and sure enough, there were six of my boys, standing in a line across the road.

We walked out of there alive, Chotta Badriya and me, and with our pistols back under our shirts. 'What a speech you gave, Ganesh Bhai,' Chotta Badriya said when we were out and had left Gopalmath behind us. And then he laughed, and he had to stop in the middle of the path and lower his head and put his hands on his knees and laugh. I thumped him on the back, and smiled. We had done it. And we really did it, Sardar-ji. Ask anyone the story of Ganesh Gaitonde and they will begin it there, in that dhaba in Gopalmath. I know that how I killed Anil Kurup has been told so many times that it doesn't seem true any more. In five different movies they put it, and in the last one they had me doing it – the character based on me, that is – with a small pistol that he had strapped to his ankle. But this is really how it happened. And it happened, actually and truly like this, in spite of how untrue all the telling and retelling of it has made it.

News of my victory against Anil Kurup spread through the neighbouring localities, and people started to come to me to settle matters, to give them jobs and protection, to help them deal with the police and the local government. My war with him had been short and decisive, and I realized only after it was over that I had needed to fight it not only for territory, but for legitimacy. I was now recognized as Ganesh Gaitonde of Gopalmath, and nobody could dispute my right to stay in the city. I had succeeded in more ways than one.

But why had I succeeded? I had won because before I went walking into Anil Kurup's home, I knew everything about him. I knew his history, I knew his strength, I knew his weapons, I knew the names of his followers and how long they had been with him. I took the time to investigate him, to learn him, and he – the arrogant gaandu – knew nothing about me. So I had won. But why had Chotta Badriya followed me into the mouth of death itself? He hardly knew me, and he knew the insane risk of my plan, and yet he came with me. I tell you that he came with me because I commanded him to. Most men want to be led, and there are only a very few who can lead. I had a problem, I had a choice and I made a decision. I decided, and so Chotta Badriya and the others followed me. Those who cannot decide are pliable mud in the hands of those who can. I took my boys and made them into my diamond-hard weapon, and I built the basti of Gopalmath. I didn't skimp on the materials or the building itself, we made sturdy, spacious and very pucca kholis, laid them out according to plan. You could tell by looking at them, by feeling the solid brick and plaster that these were homes that would last, that these lanes would remain unflooded even during the heaviest of monsoons. The word spread: Ganesh Gaitonde doesn't dilute his cement with sand, he gives value for money.

Gopalmath filled up fast, there were citizens queuing up for the kholis even before we finished them, before we had the land cleared, before we even imagined the rows of houses. Up and down the road the basti spread, and it went climbing up the hill, it seemed to grow every day. Right from that beginning, we had Dalits and OBCs, Marathas and Tamils, Brahmins and Muslims. The communities tended to cluster together, lane by lane. People like to stay with those they know, like seeks like, and even in the thick crores of the city, in this jungle where a man can lose his name and become something else, the lowest of the low will seek his own kind, and live with them in proud public squalor. I saw this, and thought it strange, that not one man in thousands has the courage to be alone. But it was good, they crowded together, and from them I gathered the boys who made up my company. Gaitonde Company it was called, or G-Company, and we were quickly famous. Not yet in the papers, but in the north and east of Mumbai the basti-dwellers knew us, and the police, and the other companies.

Mothers came to me then. 'A job in the Post Office for my boy, Ganesh Bhai,' one said. 'Settle him somewhere, Ganesh Bhai,' another said. 'You know best.' They wanted jobs, and justice, and blessings. I gave them all that, and water, and electricity over wires pulled from the lines near the main road. I lived in a pucca house at the foot of Gopalmath hill, we had built it with two bedrooms and a big central hall, and on the steps outside every morning a crowd gathered, seekers, supplicants, applicants and yes, devotees. They came to ask for things and to lower their heads. 'We just wanted your darshan, Ganesh Bhai,' some said, and so I gave it to them, and they gazed and folded their hands and retreated, storing goodwill against the certain disasters of the future. And their blessings came to me, and money, cash from the shopkeepers and traders and garage-owners and dhaba-owners of the area, and we kept them and their establishments safe. Businessmen caught up in quarrels and wran-glings came to me, and I listened to all sides of the case and gave a decision, a fair and fast ruling that would be enforced by my boys, with force if necessary, and for this mandvali and for being able to avoid the endless and useless law courts, all the disputants paid me a percentage of the contested value as fee. Money came in and went out. In eight months I had a payroll of thirty-seven people, brawlers to break heads, yes, but not only that, also boys to run errands and others to take care of the police-wallahs and municipality-wallahs and the electricity-wallahs. In my bones I understood something that Paritosh Shah never had to teach me, that you have to spend money to make money. I had good relations with the inspector who had the charge of our area from G.T. station, Samant his name was, week by week we met his sub-inspectors and slipped them envelopes. We gave them many thousands, but it was only money. With a big heart I spent it and more came.

That year we celebrated Diwali with strings of electric lights along all the main lanes, a big dais at the central chowk with bhajan-singing and mithai, and finally, after dark, I stood at the gate of my house and gave basketfuls of atom bombs and rockets and phuljadis to the children of the basti. The sky over Gopalmath showered sparking streams of gold and silver, and the rising detonations sounded the return of good and the victory of virtue over death. My house was outlined in flickering points of light, in the darkness I couldn't see the walls but the flames from the hundreds of diyas told me that I had a place of my own, my earth, and I was home. Paritosh Shah came along then, with Kanta Bai and Bada Badriya, and he found me standing outside, and he drew me into the house. 'Let us welcome Lakshmi,' he said.

We sat on two gaddas pulled together, and we played cards. I said, 'I'm not very good at this.'

Kanta Bai laughed, and said, 'Ganesh Gaitonde, you are the wildest gambler I have ever met. And you're not good at teen-patti? How can that be? But I'll teach you.' She was sitting cross-legged with a pillow in her lap and her elbows resting on the pillow while she shuffled the cards, fast, fast. They made a whirring noise under her fingers. 'But, Paritosh Bhai, pull out some of the good stuff,' she said. Then we had to send out for ice, and three of the boys to Vyas Bazaar, where they took the owner of Parthiv Household Goods from his dinner and down to open his shop, because Paritosh Shah wouldn't drink Johnny Walker out of steel tumblers, which were all I had. He held up the sparkling new glasses my boys brought back, and said they weren't so bad. And when I held my glass in my hand, and ran my finger over the sharp edges patterned into its sides, and felt its solid weight, I had to admit that there was a rightness about it. I knew now that drinking the good stuff meant that you drank it out of good glasses. Paritosh Shah held up his glass and shook it gently, next to his grinning face. 'Listen to it, boss,' he said. 'Listen, listen.' I brought up my glass to my ear and shook it, and heard the small, perfect music the ice made against the glass. 'Cheers,' Paritosh Shah said. I hesitated, it was an English word I had heard before but had never said. 'Chee-yers,' Paritosh Shah said.

'Cheers,' I said. Kanta Bai laughed and dealt a hand. I sipped at Johnny Walker, and liked all of it, the taste of it, the ice against my teeth, the cold, smooth surface under my lower lip. 'Cheers,' I said again, and understood that for Johnny Walker you needed a whole different home, a brand-new setting.

We played cards. I lost and lost all night. The notes went from my side to theirs, but I was happy. I knew it would come back, let Lakshmi go with happiness, don't be afraid, and she comes back to lavish blessings on you, she takes you into her lap and holds you close, like a son. In this going and coming is Lakshmi's happiness. So we slapped the cards down, and the money went, but I was content, it would come back multiplied and grown, from Paritosh Shah and his businesses and his knowledge of all the businessmen in the area who made fortunes, who ate and drank in my kingdom and owed me tribute, from Kanta Bai and her satrangi hooch and the hundreds who drank it and the thousands more who would drink it if I helped her, and that Diwali night was golden. Somebody had put on a cassette recorder and the songs flowed – 'Jab tak hai jaan jaan-e-jahaan' – and outside there was the slam of bombs and the long, hysterical rattles of entire ladhis of crackers, and we played, and the circle of players got wider, and Paritosh Shah told jokes, and Inspector Samant arrived and joined the circle and showed us how to play paplu, and Kanta Bai's palloo slipped from her shoulder and she roared in amusement at Chotta Badriya, who shyly turned his face away from her bountiful brimming-over, her over-run over her blouse, and the cards flew, and I lost, and lost.

I awoke under a sheet pulled from the gadda. I must have dragged it over myself during the night, to protect against the hissing table-fan set on 'High'. The room was empty, filthy with cigarette butts and smeared plates and empty glasses. I stood up and pain pressed up through my neck and into my head. I looked around for my chappals, then gave up and walked outside in my bare feet. Chotta Badriya was asleep just outside the door, his shirt smeared with vomit, the reek of it made me choke, and I rushed to the gate and bent over and heaved endlessly, and brought up only a mouthful, and yet it was hot and bitter as poison. It was still before the first grey, and the road in both directions was completely empty, and anyone could have come into Gopalmath, walked into my house and killed me as I slept. It would've been easy. I turned and went back in, up the stairs to the roof. I sat on top of the water tank and waited for day. I was thirsty but wouldn't drink. I wanted to remember the pain and the disgust.

The shape of what I had built came slowly out of the darkness, in a series of slow leaps. The cement we had used was stained and brownish already, and the people who had moved into the kholis had added colour, the blue and green of their clothes strung up in doorways, the winking pearl of plastic on roofs; there were red slogans on the walls, and brightly coloured women in posters, and all the kholis close to each other, a dense patchwork of rectangles and squares strung over with electric wires, connections taken from here to there and knitting it all close. This was mine.

Chotta Badriya's head came through the roof. 'Bhai?' he said.

'Here.'

He came up, and I saw that his hair was slicked back, wet. He had washed himself, and put on a new shirt. He was a good boy.

'We will sell liquor,' I said, 'but we will never have another drop of it in this house.'

'Bhai?'

'Not satrangi, not narangi, not Johnny Walker, nothing.'

'Yes, bhai.'

'Now go and make some tea. And see if you can find something for us to eat.'

Business grows. I had the boys collecting hafta from the shopkeepers and businessmen around Gopalmath, all the way to Gaikwad Road, which was the border between my territory and the area belonging to the Cobra Gang. I'm not making this up, they were really called the Cobra Gang, like some outfit led by Pran and Ranjit in a movie from thirty years ago. They had the eastern area all the way to the fishing villages at Malad Creek, and so they had smuggling going also, and all in all they were strong, very strong, bigger than us and with a gushing cash-flow. I had never seen their top man, one Rajesh Parab, an old artiste, he had come up with Haji Mastan and must have been fifty, sixty by now. But I had seen his boys on the streets, and now and then in the bars. I went not for the drinking, you understand, after that first Johnny Walker night I never drank again, but for the women, the waitresses and the dancers. My boys followed me in this, none of them touched liquor, not so much as one beer. I never asked them for this, never made a rule, but when I stopped, Chotta Badriya stopped, and then it became a tradition in our ranks. I was glad of this: to give something up together brought the boys close, it made them a team. I

115

hadn't thought of this when I stopped drinking, but I saw clearly how it worked, and I encouraged it. A man of the G-Company never loses his head, I told them, he keeps cold. He stays awake even when he sleeps. Have women, I said, that's a man's pleasure, a diversion worthy of a shooter, have five, have ten. But to pour poison down your own throat, to make yourself stupid and slow, that's a maderchod idiot's game. Let the Cobra Gang do that.

I knew a war was coming. It was inevitable. There had been some minor collisions between my boys and theirs, hard looks in passing on the streets, shoulders jostling in the lobby of a cinema, shoving, a whispered gali. But we were at peace. I sat on the roof at night, turning the future in my head, testing it. Whichever path I chose, and whichever one after that, the events led to conflict, and slaughter. They were big, we were small. The only peace we could keep was one in which they remained big and we small, and we took their leftovers, and stepped aside and bowed when they passed, and ate their shit, today and tomorrow and the day after. This was possible, this unequal calm, but then there was me. I was not made to be small. The G-Company was me, and I looked into myself, without deceit and without mercy, and I knew I could never be small. I was bigger than when I had been born, bigger than when I had come to this city, and I would grow bigger. So war would come. So, I thought, let us accept that fighting will come, and let us prepare for it. And when the day comes, we will fight without hate, without anger. We will prevail.

'Find me names, faces,' I told Chotta Badriya. 'I want to know who they are.' So we spent money, and in small ways helped small people, and before long we had our own network of khabaris, some deep in Cobra Gang territory. There was one paan-wallah who had his shop at the mouth of Nabbargali, where Rajesh Parab lived in the very highest apartment of a three-storey house, and this paan-wallah watched them going and coming all day long, and when in the evenings he walked home, one of our boys joined him for ten minutes, and so we had their daily roster. We paid the paan-wallah, but money alone was not why he did it. Six years before, very late one winter night, Rajesh Parab had driven up drunk in a brand-new Toyota, asked for paan and then told the paan-wallah that his maghai paan sat like a brick on the tongue, that he should go back to UP and relearn his trade. The next afternoon Rajesh Parab had stopped by again, sober and smiling, and had taken his paan as usual, and although he had forgotten what he had said when he was high on his new Japanese horse, an insult can live inside a man for a long time, burrowing like a tiny pin-headed worm and getting thicker and longer until it is wrapped through his gut and squeezing and squeezing. So the paan-wallah remembered, and he helped us, and others did as well.

Under Rajesh Parab there were four Number Twos, each handling different aspects of his business, and I knew their names and where they lived. In a black diary I had pages covered with the names of their controllers and their boys, who they were, their histories, and also list-ings of Rajesh Parab's business associates, his financiers, the builders aligned with him. I studied this black diary until my boys began to smile a little. 'Bhai is reading his Gita,' they whispered among them-selves. I didn't mind. I was looking for an entrance, a chink where I could hurl an attack and break the Cobra Gang into fragments and eat it piecemeal. There was one name in my diary I didn't understand, one name I couldn't fit into the formation I saw arrayed against me. A man called Vilas Ranade had been with Rajesh Parab for a long time, nobody could tell how long, and yet this Vilas Ranade didn't do any-thing for Rajesh Parab. He didn't manage anything, not the smuggling, not the hafta, not the dealings with builders, and some-times he wasn't even seen close to Rajesh Parab's house for weeks, months. Nobody knew where he lived. Nobody could tell me if he was married, if he had children, if he had a taste for gambling, nothing. And yet when he came to the house he walked straight up to Rajesh Parab's apartment, no queuing for him, and even if there was an MLA in deep mid-discussion, Rajesh Parab came out to meet Vilas Ranade. Vilas Ranade had never been in jail, and had been only twice men-tioned in the newspapers. Finally I said to Chotta Badriya, 'I want to know what this bastard looks like. Get me a photograph.'

Meanwhile, there was the matter of weapons. I wouldn't trust my life to country-made guns, and those days a Chinese Star pistol cost ten, twelve thousand. I couldn't afford Glocks, of course, but we hid 9 mm ammunition and Stars in my house, in a dozen kholis in Gopalmath, and in Gopalmath temple, which at that time was just one small shrine and a room for the pujari. It took weeks, months, this slow build-up, and it took much thought, how much money to spend on arms, how much to pay the boys, how much for improve-ments in the basti so that the people were happy. So we prepared for war.

One evening Chotta Badriya came to tell me that we had successfully negotiated for and taken delivery of a load of ammunition. I was sitting in a bar called Mahal, down by the Link Road in Jogeshwari, with four of my boys, I remember clearly it was Mohan Surve, Pradeep Pednekar, Krishna Gaikwad and Qariz Shaikh. Chotta Badriya came into the bar, came straight to us, we were sitting at our usual table. He was grinning as he squeezed in at the end of the booth. 'Good deal, bhai,' he said. 'Three hundred kanchas. All good and guaranteed.' Now this was our own language, kanchas and gullels for bullets and pistols. The Cobra Gang and all the other companies might say daane for bullets, and samaan for pistols, but we said kanche and gullels. This too I encouraged, it set us apart from the rest, made us belong to each other more because we spoke a private tongue, and to become one of us you had to learn it, and in learning it you were changed. I saw this in the new boys as they worked hard, trying to pass from being mere neighbourhood taporis to respected bhais. They learned the language, and then the walk, and they pretended to be something, and then they became it. And so for American dollars, we said choklete, not Dalda like the rest of our world; for British pounds, lalten, not peetal; for heroin and brown sugar, gulal, not atta; for police, Iftekar, not nau-number; a job gone wrong was ghanta, not fachchad; and a girl so impossibly ripe and round and tight that it hurt to look at her was not a chabbis, but a churi.

So we got Chotta Badriya a mango lassi, and Qariz Shaikh talked on. We were discussing the long-ago feud between Haji Mastan and Yusuf Patel, how they had been partners once, but how when betrayal and business rivalry had brought them to war, Haji Mastan had resolved to eliminate his friend. Qariz Shaikh had heard these tales from his father. 'Haji Mastan gave the supari on Yusuf Patel to Karim Lala,' he said. 'But Yusuf Patel survived the hit.'

'I saw that Karim Lala once,' Mohan Surve said. 'Near Grant Road Station. Two years ago.'

'Yes?' I said. 'What did he look like?'

'Big Pathan bastard,' Mohan Surve said. 'Real tall, and big. He has huge hands. He's retired now. Lives around there. But even now at this age he walks like a badshah. What a terror he must have been, in his days.'

I tried to imagine Karim Lala and his frontier swagger, that accent I remembered from the Pathan that Pran had played in *Zanjeer*. I had heard these old stories of bloodshed before, but now I listened to them with desperate attention. I was looking now for lessons, for principles about loss and victory, for the tactics that had been used by the ones who were still alive, those who had survived since those days when Haji Mastan and Yusuf Patel hunted each other through Mohammed Ali Road and Dongri. I listened to Qariz Shaikh, but I was restless. To be sitting and talking and thinking was not enough. I wanted to be back in Gopalmath, back in the lanes. I stood up.

'Chalo,' I said.

'Already, bhai?' Mohan Surve said. 'It's only eleven.'

Chotta Badriya upended his lassi glass and drank steadily and his throat bobbed up and down.

'I'm sick of this place,' I said. 'Let's go.'

I walked fast towards the door. Outside, the road sloped down to the darting lights of the highway. On the left, three rickshaws stood in a row. We were parked to the right, on the other side of the lamppost. It was a decrepit, ancient Ambassador taxi that Qariz Shaikh's father drove during the days. I wanted a better car, but we had money only for guns. Soon, some day, I thought. I started across the road, through the oval of light. I could hear the others behind me. I turned my head over my shoulder, and there was Chotta Badriya, stuffing a handkerchief in his pocket, and close behind him the others. They moved, walking, and their shoulders shifted as they walked, and through a chance gap in the figures I saw Mohan Surve under the neon sign, still near the door, his back against the wall and not moving. It was too far to see his eyes, but he was not walking, not moving. And then, in that instant, I hurled myself to the side, clawing towards the dark, lunging out of the light, and I felt a blow on my shoulder that took me along with it, nearly to the ground, but I found my feet and was running along the side of the building, and I knew I had been hit but I never heard the gunshots. At the corner I stopped myself with a hand on the wall, turned and saw movement in the passage, and twisted around the corner and ran again, and I had my pistol out. Now I heard the shots. I risked a look back, and it was Chotta Badriya, at the corner and firing at something on the other side of the corner.

'Badriya,' I called. 'Come.'

We went over a wall, through a building compound and out of its gate, and down a road. Two more turns and I had to stop. I leaned against a truck, and then bent over and spurted vomit on to the road.

My left arm was shuddering, squeezing in regular spasms of pain. 'Are you hit?' I said to Chotta Badriya.

'Not one touch,' he said. 'Not one. I'm fine.' He laughed, a thin crackling sound.

'Good,' I said, turning my head to look at him. 'I know it's not you.'

'What's not me?'

'The one who sold us to them. Because if you were, you wouldn't be here now. And if you were, you could kill me now.' The barrel of his pistol was six inches from my head, one quick movement from my death.

'Bhai,' he said. 'Really, bhai.' He was shocked. I loved him in that moment, loved him like a brother.

'Wipe your face,' I said. 'You still have mango lassi on it. And get me to a doctor.'

I made phone calls from the doctor's table, as he stitched and worried at my shoulder. I called Paritosh Shah and Kanta Bai and some others of my boys and told them to be ready. Paritosh Shah said that the police were already on the scene at the bar, and that three of my boys were dead. Pradeep Pednekar, Krishna Gaikwad and Qariz Shaikh had died. Pradeep Pednekar had been shot once through the hips, and then again at close range in the head. There was no news of Mohan Surve. And I had survived.

Being shot is a peculiar experience, quite unlike any other. When it first happened I didn't really recognize it, I was so eager to get away that it didn't occur to me that the thing I felt in my skin and muscle was a bullet ploughing in. I didn't feel the pain until later, until I had the possibility of life in my mouth, as succulent as a mango. Now my shoulder and chest were cold, like somebody had frozen my bones from the inside out and was stabbing me with a sliver of ice. I said to Chotta Badriya, 'Get me to Gopalmath.'

Three of our boys had brought a car to the doctors. They and Chotta Badriya took me to the car, surrounding me and shielding me with their own bodies. They followed me. We had once been strangers, but now we were bound together. We had been attacked, we had survived, so now they loved me a little. They asked me, Are you all right, bhai? Are you comfortable? We sped down the empty night road towards Gopalmath. I had made this velocity, and in its wake they came behind me. I was one lone man who had almost died that night, and they clung to me.

'What do we do now?' Chotta Badriya said.

'Find me Mohan Surve,' I said.

In Gopalmath my house had already been cleared, checked twice by my boys. I got in safely, and was back in my own room, sitting on the gadda. I put boys on the peripheries of Gopalmath, to watch for an attack, but I knew I was safe, at least for now. The crowded lanes were my guard, these children who wandered in the streets, the women who sat in the doorways. They all knew each other, up and down the alleys. There was no getting past them for the enemy, not without loss.

'You should sleep,' Chotta Badriya said. It was already morning.

'Yes,' I said. I knew I needed to rest, there was no use in exhausting myself. 'You also. But see to it that there is no gap in the guard.'

I lay in my bed, shaking under my sheet. Vibrations, little tremblings started in my stomach and spread into my chest and then my throat. The left side of my body was aching steadily. But it wasn't the pain that kept me awake. It was rage at myself, at my stupidity. Now, in looking back, it was obvious: you cannot watch someone without changing the world they live in, and if they are alert they will feel these shifts, sense the faint echo of your questions as they roll along the ground, and they will watch you in return. They had watched, and reached the same conclusions as I had, they had read me, they had predicted me and then they took my gaand. They had picked the place, and the time, and the method, and declared war. If not for a chance glance, a trick of time and my body, a bullet finding its way through space along one angle and not another, if not, if not, if not, I would have been dead on the road in front of Mahal, reduced to nothing again, a small man become smaller. The war would have started and been instantly over. This was what I couldn't bear, my foolishness, my blindness.

Finally, I laid aside the past, which cannot be changed but only left. I cut it from me as if with a scalpel. The future is what exists for you, I said. You are a man of the future. I planned. And I slept.

The next day I carried the war to them. They knew we had been watching, but they couldn't hide everything from us. We knew at least something, what business they did, where they went. On that next day we killed five of them. There were two separate attacks, and I led one of them. It was difficult for me to move, I couldn't raise my arm without a struggle, but the boys were watching me, and this was a crucial time. So I sat in the front seat of the car, next to Chotta Badriya, who was driving. There were three other boys in the back seat. We waited for the enemy outside Kamath's Hotel, where we knew they were meeting a builder for cash collection. It was six o'clock, and the road was full of workers coming home, trailing long evening shadows. When I closed my eyes I could still see the burning of the sun, it blazed inside my head.

'That's them,' Chotta Badriya said.

There were three, all young, wearing white shirts and good pressed trousers, like good businessmen making a living in the world. The middle one was carrying a plastic shopping bag in his left hand.

'Pass behind them,' I said.

We came up through the car park, turned right as they reached the bottom of the stairs in front of the hotel, and hummed slowly along, letting them pass directly in front of us. I let them take two more steps, then opened my door with my left hand, pushed it wide, took the pistol from my lap. We all came out at once. Chotta Badriya fired the first shot, and then it was one continual roar. They never even turned around. My hand was unsteady, and I don't think any of my shots hit. But I remember a gout of blood exploding like a momentary flower on the other side of a man's head, he must have seen it hanging in front of his eyes before he dropped down dead. It was all quick and easy. Chotta Badriya got back into the car.

'Get the money,' I said.

Two minutes later we were safely on S.V. Road. Inside the shopping bag there were three lakhs, and a new bottle of Halo anti-dandruff shampoo.

'Bhai, that's for me,' Chotta Badriya said. He was full of glee.

'Here,' I said, and tossed the bottle into his lap. 'You have dandruff?'

'No,' he said. 'And now I won't. I'll prevent it. You see?'

I had to laugh at that. 'You're one mad chutiya,' I said.

'I think I should grow my hair,' he said. 'I think long hair will look good on me.'

'Yes, yes, you'll look like bhenchod Tarzan himself,' I said. I managed a nap on the way back to Gopalmath, and when we got home I was given the news that the other mission – to ambush some of their boys who frequented a carrom club near Andheri station – had netted us two more wickets. So we were ahead of them for now, but the match wasn't over, it had barely begun yet. In the series that followed, we stayed ahead of them, but only just. By the end of the month, they had lost twelve players, and we eleven. Twelve to them was minor losses, they had many many more batsmen waiting to substitute, but we were almost half gone, vanished from Gopalmath. Samant the inspector laughed at me on the phone more than once. 'Gaitonde,' he said, 'they are bajaoing your baja, you better run away and hide, you'll get finished.'

After our thirteenth death, three of my boys just didn't appear for morning attendance the next day. I knew they hadn't been killed, but that they had just walked away from a losing game. I saw the logic of it. We were indeed brothers, and the battles we had suffered together had made us more so, but when defeat is certain, when you are hiding, exhausted and stripped of hope, and the strong enemy is coming to break your thighs, some men will just quit you. This was just another defeat among defeats, and I swallowed it, and looked to those who were still with me. We went on, kept our businesses going, the daily round of living, all the time moving in twos and threes, comforted by the hard metal we carried under our shirts, our weapons that we obsessively cleaned and oiled and caressed. I saw Sunny, one of my boys, raise his pistol to his head, touch it to his forehead in whispered prayer before he went out of the door, and I laughed and asked him if he lit diyas and did puja in front of it every morning, and he ducked his head and smiled, abashed. But we were desperately in need of blessings, and if I thought it would have helped, I would have prostrated myself in front of my garlanded Tokarev without a second's hesitation.

It was a woman who finally showed me the way. I went with Kanta Bai and the boys to Siddhi Vinayak, and we stood in the long queue that wound up the temple steps. It was all nonsense to me, all this praying and whining, but the boys believed and wanted to go, and it was good for morale, so I went along. Despite all her monstrous vulgarity and cynicism, Kanta Bai was a great devotee also. She held a thali in her hands, and had her pallu draped very respectably over her head. Ahead of us and behind us, in line, were my boys, shoulder to shoulder. There was that full, sweet temple smell of rose-water and agarbatties in my head, and I felt safe. Kanta Bai said, 'I know what you are going to ask for.'

'It's obvious,' I said. 'Even *he* already knows, if he exists and knows anything,' I said, with a jerk of my head up the stairs, where Ganesha sat, supposedly knowing everything.

She shook her head. 'He can't give you what you won't take with your own hands.'

'What do you mean?'

She had her head down to the thali, very low, as she neatened up the little piles of rice and sindoor and flower petals. Her neck was puffed up in round folds of flesh. 'They're going to kill you,' she said. 'You're going to die.'

We moved ahead three jerky steps now, up the stairs. On the other side of the passageway came a steady stream of worshippers, hurrying down the stairs, full of hope now, renewed now that they had confronted the god, seen him and shown themselves, shamelessly exposed their need and their pain. 'Why?' I said.

'Because you fight like a fool. All this hero-giri, shooting here and shooting there, you can't win like that. They will win. They've already won. You think war is about showing them you have a big lauda.'

My pistol was in my waistband, heavy against my belly, and as I looked at her, saying this and not even looking at me, I wanted to pull it out and shoot her. I could have done it easily, I saw it clearly, myself doing it, and the anger came up my throat into my head, like a hoarse humming, until it shadowed my eyes. I wiped at my tears with the back of my hand, and said, 'How then?'

'Fight the war to win it. It doesn't matter who kills more men. It doesn't matter if all of Mumbai thinks you are losing. The only thing that matters is victory.'

'But how to win?'

'Cut off their head.'

'Kill Rajesh Parab?'

'Yes. But really he's an old fool. He's the boss, but he's set in his ways.'

'It's Vilas Ranade then. He's the one.'

'Yes,' she said. 'If you get Vilas Ranade, you will leave them deaf and blind.'

Vilas Ranade was the one. He was Rajesh Parab's general, he had decimated us, tricked us, gone in front of us when we had expected him behind, and he had killed us. I knew now that he led them in war. But I still knew nothing about him, whether he had a wife, sons, what he looked like, where he went. He had no pattern, no habitation, no desires that I could see. I didn't know how to track a man who lived only for war. 'I don't even have a photo of him,' I said.

'They keep him out of town,' she said. 'Pune, Nashik, somewhere there. They bring him in only when there is trouble.'

'He sleeps until it's time to wake him up?'

'You don't waste a good shooter on trips to the municipality office. It's too risky. And he's the best of shooters. He's been around for a long time, ten, twelve years.'

'You've seen him?'

'Never.'

I was quiet for the rest of our time up the steps and into the temple, and when we finally got up to Ganesha, I didn't ask him for anything. I just watched him, examined his noose and his goad and laddoos and broken tusk, and wondered how he would scheme his army of ganas out of defeat, how the remover of obstacles would remove an obstacle he couldn't find and pin down. We had to move on then, the pressure of oncoming worshippers was huge and unrelenting, but I carried his image with me all the way home. We were stuck in a monstrous traffic jam in Juhu, and Kanta Bai fell asleep next to me, clutching her prasad from the temple on her lap, and I listened to her snoring, and thought and thought. My shoulder was burning, quiet little eddies of stinging fire, but the endless circling in my head was more painful: I could see the players of the game, the lanes and the buildings they moved from and to, Gopalmath, Nabargali, all of it laid out before me when I shut my eyes, and I went endlessly round and around, looking for an opening, a way to tear it all apart and put it together again. And the traffic growled and choked outside, and here we were, still alive, still breathing.

'Let me out,' I said. I leaned over and opened the door, and got out of the car. Chotta Badriya slid out from behind the wheel. 'No, no, get back in.'

'But, bhai . . .'

'Listen to me, just get back in. I want to walk for a bit.'

He was afraid of a coincidence, of somebody from the other side out for a stroll among the evening walkers and bhelpuri-eaters. It was possible, but I wanted suddenly to be alone. I raised a hand at him, and I think I must have frightened him with the look on my face, because he got right back in.

I walked down the curving road to the beach, past the chat-stalls and on to the sand. There were families walking with me, children excited into laughter by the horses trotting at the edge of the water, by the toy-wallahs and their hovering, silvery clouds of balloons, by the tantalizing kulfi-wallahs and their cool boxes all filmed over with tiny pearls of moisture. Here there was no war. Here was peace. I walked lightly amongst the old couples out for their evening walks, and the ranks of restless young men. The sea rushed steadily up the land, and finally I sat on a half-built brick platform, facing the waves. I was tired, empty-minded, and it was good to have my hair stirred gently by the water's slow breathing. There was a movement to my left. I looked, and under a pile of refuse, palm fronds and soggy paper packets and coconut husks, there was a jerky squirming, quick little dashings and then alert stillness. In the shadows there were more shadows, moving fast, and I saw a white cardboard box shift in a zigzag line, trembling with the urgency of hunger. I got up and walked over, and stood over the box, and I could now smell the strong rot, all the last leftover food, everything that had been thrown away. But there was no movement now. I laughed. 'Rats, I know you're here,' I said. 'I know you are.' But they were too clever for me. They lay still, and if I wanted I could probably kill some of them, but finally they would survive my attack and me.

'Bhai!' The shout came from down the beach. I raised my arm.

'Here,' I called. They came running up, Chotta Badriya and two others.

'Are you all right?' he said.

'I'm fine,' I said. I was, really. There was something moving inside me, a faint scurrying I could hardly see. I knew I had to wait for it to emerge. 'Let's go home,' I said.

I set up a meeting with Inspector Samant the next day. We met at a hotel in Sakinaka. 'This Vilas Ranade,' I said. 'I want his wicket. I have ten petis.'

He laughed in my face. He had a thick moustache, not very much hair on his head and big white teeth. He was sweating through his shirt, big wet dark patches. 'Ten lakhs!' he said. 'For Vilas Ranade. You're too hopeful.'

'Fifteen then.'

'Do you know who you're talking about? He was here when you were still drinking milk.'

I said, 'True. But can you do it?'

'It can be done.'

'You know something. What do you know?'

His eyes were steady, opaque. He was right, it had been a very stupid question. He had no reason to tell me what he knew. I was nervous, over-eager. Then he said, 'Why should I do it?'

'I will be here long after he's gone, Samant Saab. You know that. You've seen my progress. If we can work together, think of what lies in the future. Those Cobra Gang chutiyas have no future, no vision. What they do, they do, but they won't do anything new. The future is worth more than cash.'

He was listening. He wiped his shining takli with a handkerchief. 'Thirty,' he said.

'I can do twenty, saab. And once this is all over, there will be much much more.'

'Twenty-five. And I want it all in advance.'

Which was unprecedented, and insane. But – 'Yes, saab,' I said, 'I'll bring it to you in three days.'

He nodded, and took some saunf from the dish in the middle of the table. The bill he was leaving to me.

'Also, then, in three days,' I said, 'you had better arrest me.'

I didn't have any twenty-five lakhs in cash. I had five lakhs, maybe six and a half if I called in little loans I had made to citizens in Gopalmath, for medicine, for wedding saris. I couldn't do that, and I knew better than to ask Paritosh Shah for so bulky a loan. He was a businessman, and I was not currently a good risk, but he would find it very hard to say no to me, and it might have broken us apart. So I didn't ask that of him, but I did ask him for a big score. 'A target?' he said. 'Worth twenty-five lakhs? In three days?' I knew I was asking much, but he understood the urgency.

'Never mind the risk,' I told him. 'Just think about the prize.' He didn't have to think about it very long. Mahajan Jewellers, on Advani Road. It pleased me that it was right in the middle of Cobra Gang territory, a mile and a half from Rajesh Parab's house. We watched Mahajan Jewellers for one day and one night, and then I decided that we would do it during the day. Night might have been safer, but it would have meant getting in through the heavy sliding grille at the front, through the three locks, then through the shutter door they dropped down and locked also, and then through the glass doors. No, we went in at four in the afternoon, straight through the open door. There was one watchman out front, with the usual single-shot shotgun, and when he saw us coming with our seven pistols and choppers he dropped it without hesitation. On our way out, he held the door open for us. We had two stolen cars waiting outside, and getting away was smooth. No problems.

So now we had the money. The property itself wasn't enough, Paritosh Shah gave us fifteen lakhs for everything we had taken, and he loaned us the rest. I let him give me the money. I had confidence again, I could see my path, and I knew he felt it. It wasn't a favour he was doling out now, but an investment in future earnings. I was now full, and he was adding to my fullness. I was good for his cash, and for more. So I had the money, and straightaway, a day early, I called in Samant and gave it to him. And he arrested me.

Into the lock-up we went, myself and three of my boys. We were arrested for suspected complicity in the Mahajan Jewellers robbery and remanded to custody, that's what it said in the newspapers. On the outside, my boys disappeared from the streets, from Gopalmath, and the Cobra Gang celebrated. G-Company was finished, over and done with, all very quickly and no trouble at all, that was what they said. I sat in my cell and watched the wall. I had my back to one wall and I watched the other. My boys sat on all sides of me. I could stand the narrow space easily, the heat, I forced down the brittle rotis and the watery dal, but the repose of it, not moving and working, the rest and stillness of it crawled just under my skin and made me want to tear myself open. There were busy, buzzing insects in my veins. But I taught myself patience. I watched the wall. I felt it watching me, strong in its blankness. It wanted to outlast me. It knew it could. I stared it down. And I waited.

It took nine days. When the constables came to get us, my boys stood guard and I pissed on the wall. I wrote circles into its indifference while they watched, and then I let them lead me out. There was an advocate who had done the paperwork waiting in the senior inspector's room, and he led us out of the station. Our bail had been posted. It was dark outside, a moonless night and cloudy. Chotta Badriya was waiting outside with a car. He looked very tired, and he had his hair tied back, held back with one of those bands that girls wear.

'What's that in your hair, chutiya?' I said.

'Just like that, bhai,' he said, blushing like a girl and twisting his head down and to the side. And he smiled. When he smiled I knew it was all right.

He drove us fast into the thick of the city, up the spine and on to the highway, past Goregaon, and I felt revived by the crowds, by the weaving rows of trucks and cars, and the children running after a ball on the side of the road, and the ceaseless noise of it. I was quiet but completely awake, alert like a snake. Chotta Badriya wasn't talking, and I didn't want to ask him any questions, not yet. The promise sweltered in the air and it was delicious to hold in my mouth, the anticipation, the not knowing. We turned off the highway on to the slip road, and then off it, past a jhopadpatti, into darkness. Our beams conjured up a dusty road, trees sliding into existence and out again, it was like falling into a tunnel. I went eagerly into it. Then we took a sharp left, and the road changed, we crunched over dirt. There was a car parked at the end of the lane, and the hard black of a building through the overhanging branches, and we got out and walked towards it, around a corner, and now there was a single bulb above a door. And sitting on a crate next to the door, Samant, with his cigarette signalling red.

'Took too long,' he said. 'You're late.'

'It was the lawyers and everything,' Chotta Badriya said.

Samant tugged on the door, which opened with a long metallic squeak. Just inside, there was a man face-down on the floor. A blue shirt and black pants, and his hips cocked up and stiff.

'Vilas Ranade,' Samant said, with a little motion of his hand, palm up as if he was making introductions.

'You did it alone?' I said.

'He was a brown-sugar sniffer,' Samant said. 'The stupid bhenchod. He thought nobody knew. Used to go by himself to get it. I know the dealer who sold to him.'

'The dealer told you when Vilas Ranade would come to buy?'

'He had to, if he wanted to keep dealing.'

'You're sure this is Vilas Ranade?'

'I've seen him twice at the Mulund station when I was posted there. He had friends there.'

'I want to see his face.'

Chotta Badriya stepped over the body, tugged at the shoulder. Vilas Ranade's shirt was black at the front, soggy. Chotta Badriya got behind him, and then Vilas Ranade sat up into the light. He looked sleepy, eyelids half down. I know him, I thought. He looked just like me. I squatted in front of him, leaned closer. Yes, he was my duplicate. I waited for one of the others to remark on it, but nobody spoke.

'What's the matter, bhai?' Chotta Badriya said finally. 'Don't like his face?'

'No, I think the bastard's got an ugly face.' I tapped Vilas Ranade on the cheek lightly, and I stood up. 'What a game you played, Samant Saab,' I said. I took Samant by the hand and shook it violently. I thumped him on the shoulder, and I laughed, and all of them, every one of them, laughed with me. But in me it was all acting. I was making big motions and roaring and celebrating, but inside, inside I was bewildered: what did it mean that Vilas Ranade and I looked alike, and why did none of the others see it? What did it mean that he and I had hunted each other, like ghosts seen in mirrors, and then killed? Where did this coincidence point me, where was it taking me?

I was still dazzled when we got into the cars. Again we drifted through the long, unlit night, and by the time we were near the highway I had solved the conundrum. I had decided it had been a trick of the light. If he had looked so like me, Chotta Badriya would have seen it. Samant would have said something. I was tired from the days in the lock-up. I needed sleep, rest, good food. There was nothing to worry about.

Shooter Vilas Ranade Killed in Encounter, some of the afternoon papers reported the next day. Parab Gang Warlord Dies in Encounter. And then we destroyed the Cobra Gang. We ambushed their boys, we took their money, we intimidated their businessmen, we strolled down their streets. We lost four more of our boys, and one of them was my Sunny, who by now was so fervent in his worship of pistols that he carried two of them. A bullet fired from behind broke something in his back and left him pissing out his life into the road. But we shattered the Cobra Gang, and took their territories. We were still smaller, but now that seemed an advantage. We hit and ran, and then circled back and hit again. They were confused and old, like their Rajesh

Parab, who at the last tried to seek help from the bigger companies, he went here and there, to Dubai even, and everyone gave him assurances, and promises, and nothing else. We were the winning team, and we had a bright, burnished shine about us, and those watching the battle saw this, and placed their bets. They knew the practical lesson, had learnt it already: a small band of fighters, knit by hardship into brotherly love, will easily beat a large, unwieldy organization with its courage failing and its belief vanished.

Rajesh Parab died of a heart attack six weeks later, in his bed, in his sleep at night. Paritosh Shah said, 'He must have dreamed you coming through his door.' But I was glad I didn't have to kill him. I would have felt like a dog-catcher putting down a tired, yelping cur, and there was no pleasure even in the thought of it.

I caught a fever that winter. A dry, jittery whistling in my head and a jerky restlessness tossed me about my sweaty bed. Movies did not calm me, nor music, nor the girl Chotta Badriya brought in. I spat and spat, trying to rid myself of a rush of bitter saliva. I swallowed the pills, drank the salty water, ate the plain white rice. The fever stayed with me.

So I was wide awake at two in the morning when Chotta Badriya tapped at my door. 'We found Mohan Surve,' he said.

'You have him here?'

'Outside in the car.'

'Get him in.'

I got up and dressed. Since he had betrayed us, Mohan Surve had vanished from Bombay. After that night when I had seen his face outside the Mahal Bar, lit red by the neon, he had just gone, phut, away. Once the bullets had started flying, nobody had seen him, ever, not in Bombay and not in Wadgaon, where his sister stayed with her husband and children.

Chotta Badriya came in and helped me with my shoes. 'We watched the sister,' he said. 'The postman was showing us her letters.'

'Good. And then?'

'And then nothing much. Surve thought he was being very smart. Money orders every month from a Manmohan Pansare in Pune. Finding out which post office the money orders came from was simple enough. Then we just watched the post office. He had grown a beard.'

The beard was soft and very thin on Mohan Surve's face and didn't much disguise him. He still had fat cheeks, beady squirrel eyes. I would've known him from fifty feet. He began babbling as soon as he saw me.

'Bhai, I just got scared because of the shots and ran and hid,' he said. 'I didn't want to be part of all this any more, I can't take it, I'm a coward, forgive me, bhai, but that's how I am, forgive me. Sorry, bhai, sorry.'

He kept using that English word 'sorry', and that irritated me, angered me even more sharply than what he had already done.

'How much were his money orders?' I asked Chotta Badriya.

'Five thousand, six thousand, like that. The first one was ten thousand.'

And I looked at Mohan Surve. 'Don't try it, Mohan. Just don't try it.' My voice was a calm whisper, a surprise even to myself.

Then he broke, and threw himself on the ground, and clutched at my ankles, and fell loose. I smelt the piss spilling from him. Chotta Badriya had tied his wrists together with green electrical wire, and now as he twisted and turned, his skin chafed and blood seeped over the wire. On and on Mohan Surve went: the Cobra Gang had come to him first, he had said no to them, but they had threatened to kill his sister and her husband and the children, Vilas Ranade had threatened him personally with a sword. So he had told them I would be at Mahal that night, and they had prepared their ambush.

I had Chotta Badriya peel him away from my legs, and then I went back into my room. I sat on my bed. I thought of my boys who had died first, Krishna Gaikwad, Pradeep Pednekar and Qariz Shaikh with his stories, and I remembered how it felt to run down the side of the building, run from death with the shadows flailing towards me, and the pump of blood down my chest. Mohan Surve was making a wail in the next room now, it had all the force of a scream but not the loudness, and yet it penetrated the wall, this querulous long moan. I called Chotta Badriya in. 'Shut him up,' I said. 'I don't want him making noises. Make him calm. Give him something, whisky, something. And get the boys together. Anyone who is around or is available, tell them to be here in half an hour.'

So Chotta Badriya untied Mohan Surve's hands, gave him nimbu pani with three Calmpose crushed in. By the time the boys were together, Mohan Surve was lying curled on the ground, one arm over his head. The boys picked him up, hauled him up at the wrists and ankles and his head fell back and his eyes rolled, all glassy, dark and moving. I walked out of the house, and they followed. They carried Mohan Surve at four points, four of them, and brought him behind me. He was quiet now. We took him through the empty lanes and left the houses behind, and went up the hill above Gopalmath. I had a large Eveready torch, and I lit the way. I turned around only when we were at the top, at the small upturned bowl. While they all came up, the trailing line of my company, I was looking out at the haze of lights. My fever softened the diamond points into circling halos, and the horizon swam under this swarming, gleamy flux, the breathing of this undulating city.

'We're all here,' Chotta Badriya said.

I turned to them. 'Stretch him out,' I said. And they did. The four who had carried him sat above and below him and pulled him into a wide cross. Mohan Surve lay still, illuminated by the round beams from electric torches. 'You know what he did,' I said to the company. 'Many of us died.' I held out a hand to Chotta Badriya, who snuggled into it the cold handle of a sword. I walked around Mohan Surve until I stood directly over his head, facing the floating fire of the city, and hefted the blade in my hand. It was curiously heavy for such a slim, long thing. Good dense steel. There was a scar high on my shoulder, which I felt as a slight stiff tug sometimes, near my heart, but the strength was back in my arms. I widened my stance, raised the sword above my head, took a breath and dashed it down, into Mohan Surve's right arm, just below the shoulder. At this he raised his head and looked around, turning his eyes from side to side. I had the sword up again, and with the second stroke I separated his arm away from his body. The boy holding his right wrist fell backwards, and there was an immediate thick jet of black blood into the jiggling light. And a sound like a groan came from the company, and Mohan Surve began to talk. A confused jumble of syllables that sounded no sense, that's what it was. Mohan Surve babytalked even as Chotta Badriya took off his left arm with a single sweep of the sword, and I heard the clang of metal on the rock and saw a jumping shower of white sparks, and Mohan Surve's voice rose higher and his head was still up when somebody stepped up from the ranks and took the sword and attacked his left thigh. Then he screamed. But when it came to his right leg he was quiet, and his head was turned to the side. I think he was already dead.

'Take the pieces,' I said, 'and throw them somewhere. And I never want to hear his name again.'

Then I walked down my hill, to my basti, to my home. In the mirror in the alcove immediately to the right of the door, I saw that my shirt was ruined, splashed all over with blood. I took it off, and also my trousers, soggy to the front, and my damp shoes. I took a bath, with hot water. I ate a little sabudane ki khichdi, and drank a glass of milk with almonds in it. Then I slept.

Investigating Women

The next day, Sartaj joined Parulkar on his morning constitutional. They walked in circles around Bradford Park, which was a small circle at the intersection of seven roads near Parulkar's house. It was five-thirty, and the grass underfoot was a little damp. Parulkar was wearing red keds under his flappy white pyjamas and speeding around the circumference, overtaking the other walkers and then lapping them. Sartaj was putting in serious effort to keep up.

'I don't understand the teaching at these new schools,' Parulkar said. 'How can Ajay be five and a half and not be able to read? They call themselves the best school in Mumbai. We had to use a dozen contacts to get the boy in, you know.'

Ajay was Parulkar's grandson, who was in upper KG at the very new and very modern Dalmia school. 'It's a new system of teaching, sir. They don't want to put pressure on the children.'

'Yes, yes, but at least teach them to read "cat" and "bat" by now. And you and I had pressure, and we didn't come out so badly.'

They went past Parulkar's bodyguards now, and then into another lap. 'I didn't do so well under all that pressure, sir. I was terrified by those exams.'

'Arre, you were not so bad. Only you had other things on your mind always, cricket and movies and then later, my God, girls.' Parulkar grinned. 'You remember that time I had to stand guard while you were studying?'

That was when Sartaj was fifteen. He had taken to jumping out of the window during mugging hours at home, and finally Parulkar had volunteered to keep a watch over him the night before his maths exam. They had a fine time actually, with regular dosages of whipped-up Nescafé, and oranges and small bananas, and Parulkar had shown a talent for reducing complex problems to simple questions. Sartaj had passed the exam with a fifty-eight per cent score, which was the highest he ever achieved in maths. 'Yes, sir. And we saw the chowkidar sleeping.'

They had thrown orange peels at the slumbering chowkidar, and now they laughed as they had then.

'Business now, Sartaj.'

'Yes, sir.' This meant they were coming to the end of the walk, which was meant to be mostly free of work distractions.

'I have a contact for you from the S-Company. Her name is Iffatbibi. She is Suleiman Isa's maternal aunt. For a long time, she has been one of his main controllers here in Mumbai. She's old, but don't be fooled by that. She's very intelligent, very ruthless, she has been one of his main assets.'

'Yes, sir.'

'This is the number you can reach her at.' Parulkar slipped a folded note to Sartaj. 'She's always there in the afternoons. She will expect your call.'

'Thank you, sir. This is a big connection, sir.'

Parulkar shrugged, flapped a dismissive hand. 'And be careful. Whatever information she gives you, it's not for free. Sooner or later she'll ask something of you. So don't promise her anything you can't deliver.'

'Right, sir.'

'Interesting woman. There was a time, I was told, that men were killed over her. But when I first met her she was already old. And you know, I thought then that she may have been beautiful once, but she was never any man's trophy. If a man was killed over her, she made it happen. No doubt about that. No doubt at all.'

'I'll be careful, sir.'

Parulkar's walk was over, but he went to his car at the same speed. Sartaj watched him go, and thought that he had never truly repaid Parulkar for everything he had been given. 'Nothing in life is free' had been one of Parulkar's first lessons, but Sartaj had never felt that he had returned equal value. Maybe some day it would all become due.

That morning, Sartaj and Katekar followed Manika's lead to the glossy-pictured Kavita, who had once danced at a bar called Pritam but had made that very rare leap into the lower rungs of show business. Her name was actually Naina Aggarwal, and she was from Rae Bareli. The manager at Pritam Dance Bar looked at the photograph and told them the name of the serial she was acting in: *47 Breach Candy*. He watched it every Thursday, he was very proud of her, even though she had never contacted him once she had started appearing on television. The owner of Jazz Films, which produced *47 Breach Candy*, gave Sartaj her phone number and address and told him to watch the show, which was doing very well, very high TRPs, very good reviews, it was very entertaining, based on an American show but completely Indianized, completely of our culture. Naina Aggarwal lived not in Andheri East any more, but in an apartment in Lokhandwalla with three other girls, who all worked in television. She was small, prettier than her picture, and she started weeping even as Sartaj asked her where she was from, what her father did, if she had any brothers or sisters. Her mascara had blackened her face all the way to her chin by the time he said, 'We know you've been involved in some very bad activity. But we are not about to harass you. If you help us.'

She nodded fast, holding her hands clasped in front of her mouth. She sat on her bed, curled small, and she was very afraid of them, in that room she had managed to earn for herself. There was a shelf above the bed, bolted to the wall, and it was crowded with photographs of Rae Bareilly people in bright shirts, and Sartaj recognized her school-principal father. She came from a very respectable family, and she had danced at the bar only for two months, when she had first come to the city, when her money had rushed from her hands faster than she had imagined possible. She nodded eagerly. She was desperate to get the police away from her room before her flatmates and neighbours knew that she was involved in such nasty police business, that she had once danced in a sleazy bar.

'Here,' Sartaj said. He put the photograph of the dead woman on the bed next to Naina. 'You know this person?' She was terrified now, but couldn't look away from the photograph. 'It's all right. Just tell us her name.'

It took several swallows, three tries, before she could get it out. 'Jojo.'

'Jojo? J-o-j-o?'

'Yes. What has happened to her?'

'She is dead.'

Naina curled her legs up on the bed and looked very young. The serial she acted in was full of intrigue and adultery and murder, but Sartaj could see that she couldn't bring herself to ask how Jojo had died.

'Don't worry,' Sartaj said. 'We are not going to involve you in any of this, if you are honest with us. What was her surname?'

'Mascarenas.'

'Jojo Mascarenas. And you worked for her?'

'Yes.'

'How?'

Without raising her head from her knees, Naina tried a small shrug. 'She is a model co-ordinator and producer. She recommended me to agencies, she put me in videos.'

Sartaj was very soft and gentle now. 'But that wasn't everything, was it?'

Katekar was leaning against the door, letting Sartaj handle the interrogation. He and Sartaj had worked out, over the years, that in certain situations with women Sartaj's solicitousness and care worked better than the blunter tools of intimidation and loud voices. They used each skill impartially, depending on the context and the case. So now Katekar was shrinking himself into the corner and being very still.

'Naina-ji,' Sartaj said, 'this is very serious business. Murder. But I can't protect you if you are not completely honest with me. Don't worry. I promise I will not involve you in this at all, your name will never come up. I am just trying to find out about this Jojo. I am not interested in you at all, you are in no danger. So please, tell me.'

'She, she found clients for me.'

'Clients.'

She wept hard now, doubled over, shaking. They left ten minutes later, with Jojo Mascarenas's phone number and office address, and certain facts: Jojo was a model co-ordinator, and she also owned a TV production company, she produced programmes, and if there wasn't a production under way, roles and campaigns to go around, she could connect supply and demand, send the young, beautiful and needy to the rich and demanding, it was all a matter of a couple of glossies and a few phone calls, it was simple, it was efficient and everyone got what they wanted.

Sartaj and Katekar waited for the lift in a shadowed hallway. 'So crying Naina got the serial,' Katekar said. 'After all that dancing.'

'Yes,' Sartaj said. 'But what happens if the serial flops?'

'Back to Rae Bareilly.'

The unlit lift came and they stepped in, and after Katekar had rattled the folding metal gate shut three times, hard, they dropped, through fleeting bands of light. 'Nobody ever goes back to Rae Bareilly,' Sartaj said. And even if she went, Sartaj thought, would Rae Bareilly take her back? She had come all the way to Lokhandwalla, and to 47 *Breach Candy*, and to Jojo, and Jojo had sent her to other places.

'Time to call the Dilli-wali, sir?' Katekar said. Long bars of black were sliding up his face.

'Not quite yet,' Sartaj said. 'I want to know who this Jojo was.'

Jojo Mascarenas was neat. She had been dead for five days, but her apartment was clean, still shiny and scrubbed and polished. There was a row of gleaming steel ladles on the kitchen wall, hung on steel hooks in graduated order of size. The two phones and the answering machine on the counter next to the dining table were aligned precisely, and the tiled surfaces in the bathroom off the hallway shimmered a deep blue.

'This woman made money,' Katekar said.

But she was careful with it. The office address they had been given turned out to be her apartment, on the third floor of 'Nazara', on Yari Road. She made money but practised economies: the first small bedroom to the right of the hallway was her production office, crammed full with files and three desks and a computer and two phones and a fax machine, all in elegant order, all necessary to the work she did. Even her bedroom was not extravagant, just a simple double mattress on a low frame, no headboard. There was a tall mirror on the wall, and a table in front of it, lined with rows of cosmetics, and a black stool. There were no leather sofas, no chandeliers, no gold statues, none of the extravagances that Sartaj had come to expect from people who traded in images and bodies. When he had slid the key he had been carrying in his pocket into the lock, when it had turned smoothly, he had expected to see a red-satined filmi bordello, or a slattern's mess, but not this sober haven, this quiet home and workplace. It mystified him.

'All right,' Sartaj said. 'Let's search it.'

'What are we looking for?' Katekar said.

'Who this woman was.'

Katekar set to work, but he was impatient, quick, disapproving. Sartaj knew that he liked better the thin, pointed narrative of your ordinary murder case, where there was a corpse, an unknown killer or killers, and you were looking for a motive. Here there were two dead, one had obviously killed the other, and what did it matter what their relationship was? How would you know? Why would you care? Who cared about a gangster and a pimp? Katekar was quiet, but Sartaj knew he was cursing. Aaiyejhavnaya case it was according to Katekar, Sartaj was sure, and aaiyejhavnayi Delhi woman, this was all jhav-ed. 'Jhav-jhav-jhav,' Sartaj hummed as he worked. He did the bedroom first, because it was easy. Anything useful would be in the office, but the bedroom had to be done, and so he went at it. There was a cupboard built deep into the wall, along the entire length of the room, and it had two densely packed rows of hanging saris, blouses, ghagras, trousers, jeans, T-shirts, shirts. There was an order to it, a womanly and very personal logic that Sartaj couldn't quite understand, but it reminded him powerfully of the gradations of shirts in his cupboard by colour, from red to blue. Jojo's cupboard made him like her. He liked her love for shoes, her care for leather, her understanding of the different functions of footwear, why it was necessary to have three pairs of sneakers, from spare to super-technological, and he liked that she had them on the rightmost end of the lowest of three stepped rows of sandals and boots and chappals and stiletto heels. The apartment was simple, almost bare, but the clothes were flamboyant. Sartaj approved.

But, as expected, there was nothing in the bedroom of particular interest. A pink bathroom held a multiplicity of shampoos and soaps, and two pairs of panties and a bra hung on the curtain rod. There were more clothes and some dishes and old lamps in the high-up storage slots above the clothes cupboard, and make-up and various kinds of thread and sewing needles in the drawers of the dressing table, and a stack of *Femina* and *Cosmopolitan* and *Stardust* and *Elle* next to the bed, but that was all. Katekar was finishing up the drawing room when Sartaj came out into the hallway.

'Her big purse was behind the kitchen counter,' he said. 'On the floor. Just sitting there.'

'Anything in it?'

'Lipstick-shipstick, that's all. No driver's licence, but there is a voting card and a PAN card.'

He held the cards out. Juliet Mascarenas, they both said. But this was the first time Sartaj had seen her smile. She was very alive in both pictures, sparkling lazily at the camera, confident that she knew something about you.

'Anything else?' Sartaj said.

'Nothing. But there are no photos.'

'Photos?'

'Photos. There's not one in the entire house. I've never known a woman who didn't stick photos all over the place.'

Katekar was right. When Megha had left him, she had taken many photographs with her, and still Sartaj had spent a Sunday afternoon putting pictures in a shoe box, pulling them from the walls. And Ma had entire walls of them, histories of the family and the branches of it, all laid out, all its connections and losses. 'Maybe this Jojo keeps them in her files,' Sartaj said. And they went into her office. The files were in a black filing cabinet, four chambers high. They were neatly labelled: 'D'Souza Shoe Ad'; 'Sharmila Restaurant Campaign'. The bottom shelf was packed, heavy, it came outwards slowly.

'Actors?' Katekar said.

'Yes, and actresses.' The men were to the right, women to the left, in alphabetized rows of glossies, with résumés stapled to the back. Anupama, Anuradha, Aparna. Not quite actresses yet, but young and hopeful. Full of hope. And there was a fullness of them, there were just too many of them. Most would not be successful, but more kept coming to this city of gold. From this surplus and hunger, from this simple equation, came Jojo's business. They searched on, opening drawers and lifting files off shelves. There was a half-height metal cabinet, which the third key on Jojo's hoop opened, and inside they found her bank books, her cheque books, her bank statements, and jewellery in a metal box: two gold necklaces, three pairs of gold bracelets in different designs, a string of pearls, diamond earrings and a tangled pile of silver.

'Where's her cash?' Katekar said. 'Where does she keep her cash?'

Cash was how clients for a certain commodity paid their debts. There was some black money in Jojo's legitimate television business, but much of it was conducted with honest, above-board cheques. Her little side-business of prostitution generated only cash, this was certain, reams of it. But it wasn't in the metal cabinet. You couldn't keep it in a bank. Where was it? Sartaj went into the hallway, circled the kitchen and the drawing room. He lifted a framed print off the wall. It was a forest scene, but under the verdant glade there was only the wall. He stood on the edge of the tub in the bathroom and tapped the tiles on the ceiling. It was all solid, no hidden hollows, no secret compartments behind the water tank suspended above the door. Back into the hallway, and Sartaj saw that Katekar had moved the cabinets and tables in the office away from the walls and was on his knees testing the edges of the floor. In the past, they had found money in subtle hideaways, in precisely engineered hollows, there was an expertise in this city in hiding money, the builders had perfected the art of crafting shelves and headboards that slid away at the touch of a secret button to reveal money packed away. Once they had discovered gold bars in the pouchy bottoms of rich red brocade curtains. It was called black money, but Sartaj always thought of it as grey: it was illegal and a blight, but taxes were legal and a blight, and so he searched for it but never felt contempt for those who hoarded it. But Jojo made her cash from selling youngsters to the sticky appetites of men, and so her money was blacker than most, despite the cleanliness she practised in her life. Where was it, this reeking money, this pile of paper smelling of crusty hotel sheets and dried sweat? Where? Not in the pink bathroom, and not inside her mattress. Sartaj took her clothes from the cupboard and threw them on to the bed, making a luxurious pile of silky crimson and white and deep greens. He probed the walls of the cupboard, tapping and then pressing with his hands, and he took in her smell, the breath of her body and her perfumes. He stood for a moment with his palms on the roof of the cupboard, flat, and then he went and sat on the bed. Resting on a cascade of blouses and skirts, he asked, where have you hidden it? Where? The most likely place was the bathroom, because tiles were easy to build behind, but it was such an ancient cliché: Hema Malini and Meena Kumari and half a dozen other heroines had been caught with cash in their loos, and Jojo was more complicated than that. Sartaj was sure of it.

Leaning back, he started to see the sense of her shoes. There were three tiers of steps built at the bottom of the cupboard, in the same wood, stretching nearly across the entire width. Bottom step, extreme right, was the most informal, sneakers and bright Bata rubber chappals and then Kolhapuri chappals, a great variety of them. Second step was comfortable shoes, practical ones, professional but hardy, and easy to wear for an entire day of work. But the leftward end of the second step edged over into boots, chunky ones with long thick laces and lashings of attitude, and then the top shelf started on the right with a pair of black boots with needle-sharp heels and soft tops that must have risen half-way up Jojo's thighs. From there the heels were ever more delicate and dangerous, and the uppers and straps thin and thinner, and Sartaj saw how the leftmost and last pair on the top shelf, a diaphanous, burning amber nothing of a shoe, all tapering knife-heel and single diagonal thong, would make Jojo's foot naked even as it clothed it. 'Well done, Jojo,' he said. 'Those are shoes, Jojo.'

He got up, moved the shoes off the middle shelf, and took hold of the plank and tugged at it. It was solid. He bent his head and peered, and he could see the floor and the rear of the cupboard under the shelves. The top row swept down from the boots to the stilettos, and Sartaj said, 'You go from right to left, Jojo.' He leaned low, spread his arms wide, and grasped the sides of the top shelf, and pulled. Still solid, and then his fingers slipped and he felt a groove, two grooves, one on each side. They ran along the sides of the shelves, just under the overhanging lip of the top shelf, a finger-thickness high, a few inches long: handles. Sartaj's nose was an inch from one of Jojo's black stilettos, and his pulse was humming. Got you. Got you. He grasped the handles and pulled backwards. Nothing, no give. Still solid. But there was a little movement at the top of the right handle, a contraction under his fingers. He braced the heel of his hand against the top of the shelf and squeezed, as if he were pressing a very stiff brake on a motorcycle, and yes, yes, a definite movement, a catch gave way. He did it on both sides and pulled backwards and the whole thing, all of it, the three shelves with the shoes on top, the entire construction came away from the back of the cupboard. He went backwards, grinning, scattering chappals and boots and strappy sandals. 'Ay, Katekar,' he yelled. 'Katekar.'

Together, they peered happily into the two-foot-deep compartment that Jojo had hidden her secrets in. There was, of course, the cash: neat stacks of hundred-rupee and five-hundred-rupee bundles, pushed all the way back, to the left. Katekar was measuring it professionally between the outstretched thumb and forefinger of his left hand. 'Not much,' he said. 'Five or six lakhs. Some of it looks the same as Gaitonde's stash.' These five-hundred-rupee bundles were all new, in Central Bank of India wrappers, again stacked inside the same efficient shrink-wrapped plastic.

'Gaitonde must have paid her,' Sartaj said.

'For her randi services.'

On the right, also against the back of the niche, lay three black photo albums on top of each other. But Sartaj felt no urgency, no desire to take them, to flip them open and delve into Jojo's hidden life. He was concentrated on the money, and he knew Katekar was also. He could hear it in the slow drag of Katekar's breath, compressed by the awkward forward squat. The cash was very problematic: six lakhs in black money discovered in a dead woman's apartment was ordinarily a free gift for the good policemen. Not all of it – maybe five lakhs was the surprise present, and one lakh would have to go into the panchnama and therefore into the government's maw, and that was enough. Nobody would ask awkward questions about a dead madam's black money. The amount was small enough for nobody to notice its absence, and so Katekar's rules of prudence would not be violated. Nobody would notice, unless Jojo kept records, or had told somebody about her stash. Unlikely, but possible. In a high-pressure, Delhi-orientated case involving RAW this was too much risk, there was a single glance between them and it was decided.

'Albums,' Sartaj said briskly, and drew them out. The first photograph in the first album was a younger Jojo, younger by many years and much experience. She was wearing a red dress, a child's frock really, with a square neck and a high waist, and looked to be about sixteen. She was sitting on a black couch, her arms intertwined with an older girl's, a young woman with the same broad, toothy smile. The following few pages had the same pair, laughing on a bed, on the seashore, on a balcony against a rising Mumbai skyline.

'Sisters,' Katekar said.

'Right,' Sartaj said. 'But who is taking all the pictures?' He flipped on through the pages of happiness and love. Then there was a blank page, all white. But there had once been a photograph there, he could still see the impression it had made under the sheer plastic. The next page again had the two sisters, this time in the Hanging Gardens. But there had been a photograph removed every two pages or so, and about half-way through the album, the sisters were having a birthday. It wasn't a party really, just them, gifts on the dining table and a pink cake with lots of white icing.

'Seventeenth,' Katekar said. He had, with his quick head for numbers, assessed the bright candle flames.

Sartaj turned the page, and there was a blank, this time with no impression left by an image. The rest of the album was empty. The photography had stopped abruptly. Sartaj put the album aside, and turned to the next one. This one went backwards into childhood. The sisters were in white school shirts and dark skirts. And then they stood barefoot, their identical pigtails sticking straight out like wings, happy in front of a house with a heavy stone lintel and thick wooden doors and a sunlit courtyard inside. 'Village,' said Sartaj. 'But where?'

'South,' Katekar said. 'Somewhere south. Konkan.'

Now they were in a studio, the sisters, in identical blue frocks with puffy sleeves and enormous bursts of lace at the throat, and their mother was with them. She wore sober black, a dress with sleeves down to the wrists, and her head shone with streams of grey, and the lights picked out the crucifix she wore at her neck and made it blaze. She was smiling, but carefully. 'No father,' Sartaj said.

'No father at all,' Katekar said. 'What is it, a farm?'

The sisters played under trees, in groves brimming over with green light, they ran between long rows of plants with broad leaves curling at the edges. 'I don't know,' Sartaj said. He knew nothing about trees, or plants, or farms. This was another world.

The last album was of the old-fashioned type which nobody made any more, with thick black pages, and the first photograph was held on to the page by small black corners, elegant little tabs, Sartaj couldn't remember what they were called. But both he and Katekar said together, 'Father.' The father sat with that particular stiffness which men and women from a long-ago generation assumed in front of cameras, it was the formality owed to a rare event, and he wore a white uniform. His shoulders were thrown back, and his right hand was curled in a fist against his hip.

'Navy,' Katekar said.

'Merchant Navy.'

The father had his daughters' eyes, large and direct. Actually, for the next couple of pages he had only one daughter, who stood between him and his wife, holding both their hands. And then suddenly, on a fresh page, here was the new arrival. She reached out with both her hands and her feet towards the camera, grinning toothlessly, fine-haired and round-faced. She reached towards the name above the photo, the name hand-inked on to the black page in white writing edged with flourishes and decorative marks: Juliet.

'Ju-li-et?' Katekar said.

'Yes,' Sartaj said. 'Like with Romeo.'

Katekar's laugh was long and full. 'So Juliet became Jojo? And Gaitonde was her Romeo?' He pronounced it 'Rom-yo', and Sartaj found his pleasure unfair and ugly, and his guffaws scraped across the base of Sartaj's skull. He thought Katekar very coarse and ganwar and low-class in that moment, and didn't care to correct him. Sartaj was feeling protective of the Juliet-that-was, before Jojo ever existed. She grew up in the pages that followed, under the care of her sister and mother. Soon after Juliet began walking, the mother began to dress the two sisters alike, in identical frocks and the same hair and the same hair-band. This first photograph with the two of them in matching outfits was a studio portrait, in front of a backdrop of the Eiffel Tower. They stood holding hands under the graceful arc towards a red sky, and now there were two names in white ink under the picture: 'Mary' and 'Juliet' separated by a fancy curlicue.

'Mary Mascarenas,' Sartaj said. That was the sister.

This paired dressing ended when Juliet was ten, or maybe eleven, in the last pictures in the album. In that birthday photograph, she had her hair cut short in a smart little bob, much shorter than Mary's, and she had a necklace, bright, light-coloured beads. The frock was the same as her sister's, but it was somehow different. She carried it better. Juliet had started to assert herself, she knew who she was and she was resisting her mother. Sartaj liked the tip-toed exuberance of her stance, her impudence. And then there was the serious Mary.

In Jojo's fat address book, under 'M', Sartaj found 'Mary' and work and home phone numbers, and an address in Colaba. But the number was old, outdated, Sartaj knew that the Colaba exchange had been converted to digital at least seven, eight years ago. Had Jojo not talked to Mary for eight years? Sartaj pondered, and they put the apartment in order, things back to their original positions, everything but the bedroom cupboard. Then Sartaj made the call to the Delhi-walli.

They sat in Jojo's office and waited. Sartaj swivelled slowly on Jojo's office chair and thought about sisters and their quarrels. Ma spoke often about her own older sister, Mani-mausi, and of her stubbornness, her silly communistic refusal to get live-in help despite long illness and weakness, what if she has one of those fainting spells and falls down the stairs or something, how many times I've told her to come here and stay with me, but she's so stubborn. Sartaj could never bring himself to point out that she, Ma, the younger sister, was no less self-willed, no less protective of her own prickly independence, no less devoted to the house she had built, to its high walls, its lambent floors and familiar lights, its corridors of quiet.

Jojo had built herself a home also, and it had been hard-won. Next to the kitchen sink, in a small floor-level cupboard, they had found a box of tools, and two rows of cans of paint in various colours. She had painted the rooms herself. Inside the fridge, there were plastic containers full of left-over food. Jojo threw nothing away. Despite the extravagance of her shoes, she was frugal. She was energetic too, Sartaj thought. You could see that in the photos. She must have been good at what she did.

The Delhi-walli came quickly. She was there in twenty minutes, maybe even less, in a black Ambassador. From Jojo's drawing-room window, Sartaj and Katekar watched the car pull into the building's compound, fast. There was a fast rat-tat-tat of car doors slamming shut, and barely two minutes later there was a knock on the door.

Anjali Mathur led her people in, breathing hard. Today her salwar-kameez was dark brown. The man immediately behind her was Makand, who had thrown Sartaj out of Gaitonde's bunker. 'Bedroom?' Anjali Mathur said.

Sartaj pointed. On the phone, he had already told her Jojo's name, her profession, her professions, and about the secret niche in the cupboard, about the sister named Mary. The number he had called was a land line, but the call must have been forwarded to the mobile phone she carried in her left hand.

'Could you wait outside?' she threw over her shoulder as she marched across the room. One of her short-haired flunkies was already holding the door-knob, and Katekar was barely through the door when it shut firmly. He and Sartaj stood in the corridor, too baffled to be angry.

There was nothing to do but wait, and so they did. 'Those chutiyas with her were the same ones,' Katekar said, 'from that day with Gaitonde.'

Sartaj nodded. The three men with Anjali Mathur had been at Gaitonde's bunker, and they all had the same haircut and the same shoes. What shoes did she have on, with her brown salwaar-kameez?

He hadn't noticed, it had all been too quick. Something eminently sensible, he was sure, flat-heeled and sturdy. She was that sort, with her hair tied tightly back and her dupatta efficiently slung and the square brown leather bag with the strong straps, big enough to hold whatever an international agent carried on her missions. The air in front of the lift was stale and very hot, and Sartaj felt the sweat gather on his forearms. He began to breathe deeply, in a rhythm he had developed in a thousand stake-outs. If he could get it just right, heat and sweat would recede, and time would turn inward on itself until it whirlpooled into stillness, and he was relieved of the world while he was still in it. But he had to get it just right. He breathed, and he could hear Katekar on the other side of the door, trying also to find a repose in the pressing stillness. They perspired together, and after a while they were breathing together. Sartaj was floating, veering up and vanishing into rooms of his childhood where with anxious concentration he whitened his keds for PT in the morning, and showed them to Papa-ji, who was a stickler for perfect white, much more than any monitor at school, and who had impressed upon his son the urgent lesson that the best outfit could be ruined in its effect by a sloppy pair of shoes, and an ordinary one made glorious by soft, mirror-shined, deep brown tasselled loafers. What had Ma done with Papa-ji's shoes, those orderly columns of black and brown in the special narrow cupboard which always stood to the left of the clothes cupboard? And what had become of his suits, of that mothball-tinged wool smell of rain-laden mountainsides? Given away, packed away. Lost now, even a white Filipino shirt that a friend had brought back from Manila, that had set off Papa-ji's white upturned moustaches and the forward sweep of his beard, that he had worn with an entrancing flamboyance on his sixty-seventh birthday with grey twill trousers and a jet-black turban. Sartaj had burst out laughing in admiration when he had first seen him walking down the gravel path at the front of the house. But later that evening, on the way back from the restaurant, they had climbed up three flights of stairs in a new shopping mall, and Papa-ji had had to stop on the second landing to catch his breath, and Sartaj had faced away, looking steadfastly out of a window at neon signs and had listened to the small alternating, fluttering sound, life still finding itself, working on, and he had been afraid.

'Inspector Singh?' It was Makand, poking his grey bullet-head into the corridor. 'Come in, please.' The invitation was for Sartaj only.

Inside, Anjali Mathur was seated at the dining table. She pointed at the bottle of cold water and glasses on the table. 'Sorry about keeping you outside. The case is such that we have to be very careful.'

The rest of her little army was absent from the drawing room. Searching the bedroom, perhaps. Sartaj poured himself a glassful, drank, and waited. The water was deliciously cold. He was content to drink and be quiet because he had no idea what kind of case it was. Anjali Mathur had very direct eyes, very bright, and now she was waiting for him to say something. He poured himself another glass, and drank it slowly this time, sipping. If the case was such, whatever kind of such that was, he had nothing to gain by speaking. He sipped, and looked right back at her, not contesting her stare, but casual and drinking and yet not giving way.

She shifted slightly, and settled into the faintest of smiles. 'Do you want to know what the case is?'

'You'll tell me what I need to know,' Sartaj said.

'I can't tell you very much. But I can tell you that it's very big.'

'Yes.'

'What do you feel about that?'

'It scares me.'

'You don't feel excited that you've been picked to work on a big case?'

Sartaj threw his head back and laughed. 'Excitement is one thing. But big cases can eat up small inspectors.'

She was smiling broadly now. 'But you'll work on it?'

'I do what I'm told.'

'Yes. I'm sorry I can't tell you much more about it. But let us say that it involves national security, great danger to national security.' Again, she was waiting for him to say something. 'You understand what I'm saying?'

Sartaj shrugged. 'That kind of thing seems always filmi to me. Usually the most exciting thing I do is arrest local taporis for extortion. A murder here and there.'

'This is real.'

'Okay.'

'And very big.'

'I understand.' Sartaj didn't understand much at all, but if it was the right kind of big case, perhaps it wasn't bad to be attached to it.

Perhaps there was credit and commendations to be had from doing small things for a big case.

'We need more on what this Jojo and Gaitonde were doing together. What their business was together.'

'Yes.'

'You found this Jojo very fast. Shabash. But we need to know more. Press the investigation from the Gaitonde side. Follow up with his partners, his employees, anyone you can find. See what they say.'

'I'll do that.'

'I'll have this phone number for this sister checked out by someone in the Colaba station, and when we get a fix on her, you go and talk to her, see what you can get about Jojo from her.'

'I should talk to the sister?'

'Yes.'

It was impossible to investigate without changing what you were investigating, without the subjects becoming wary. And Anjali Mathur, for reasons she wasn't about to reveal, wanted very much to have her suspects think that this was a local investigation. Sartaj thought that she had a good investigator's face, curious but neutral, not giving away anything. 'Okay, madam,' he said. 'I can tell her where the sister died?'

'Yes. See if she knows anything about the sister's dealings with Gaitonde. And as before, report to me directly. Only to me. On that phone number.'

And that was it, as far as instructions and clarifications from Anjali Mathur went. Sartaj took the bottle and a glass from the table, and took it into the corridor for Katekar, who was by now quite drenched with sweat from the shoulders down the back. He was much less bothered by summer heat than Sartaj, he thought nothing of walking a couple of miles through a May afternoon, but he sweated much more. Sartaj put this heat-resistant stamina down to a lifetime of conditioning: Katekar had grown up without even fans, and so he survived heatwaves blithely. It was all a question of what you were used to. Katekar drank a glass of water. 'Are we finished with this now?' he said with a little tilt of his head over his left shoulder, towards the apartment, Jojo and Anjali Mathur.

'Not yet,' Sartaj said.

Katekar said nothing.

'Drink up,' Sartaj said, grinning. 'We have lots to do. National security depends on us.'

There was somebody else who wanted to talk about national security waiting for Sartaj at the station. His name was Wasim Zafar Ali Ahmad, and it was printed in Hindi, Urdu and English on the card that he handed to Sartaj. Under the name there was a title, 'Social Worker', and two phone numbers.

'I was surprised, inspector saab,' he said, 'when I heard that you had been twice to Navnagar and had not contacted me. I thought that maybe it was difficult to find me. I am usually not at my home. I move around a lot, for work.'

Sartaj turned the card over with his fingertips and laid it down. 'I went to Bengali Bura.' They were sitting at his desk, across from each other.

'Which is very much in Navnagar. I do a lot of work there.' He was about thirty, this long-named Ahmad, a little plump and a little tall and very confident. He had been waiting for Sartaj at the front of the station and had followed him inside, his card ready. He was wearing a black shirt with small white embroidery at the cuffs, spotless white pants and a determined expression.

'Do you know the boy who was killed?' Sartaj said.

'Yes, I had seen him sometimes.'

Sartaj had seen Ahmad too, he was sure of it. He looked familiar, and no doubt he came and went from the station, social workers often did. 'You live in Navnagar?'

'Yes. On the highway side. My family was one of the first ones there. That time, it was mostly people from UP, from Tamil Nadu. These Bangladeshis, they came later. Too many of them, but what can you do? So I work with them.'

'And you knew the apradhis? And this Bihari fellow who was their boss?'

'Only by face, inspector saab. Not enough to say hi-hello. But I know people who know them. And now this murder they have done. It is very bad. They come from outside and do bad things in our country. And they spoil the name of good people who are from here.'

He meant Indian Muslims, who suffered broad-brushed slander and hatred put abroad by Hindu fundamentalists. Sartaj sat back, rubbed at his beard. Wasim Zafar Ali Ahmad was definitely interesting.

Like most so-called social workers, he wanted to move ahead, to become a big man in the area, a man with connections who would attract a clientele, a man who would be noticed by the political parties as a local organizer and volunteer and finally a potential candidate. Social workers had become MLAs and even MPs, it took a long time but it had been done many times. Ahmad had the politician's gift of mouthing clichés without sounding ridiculous. He looked intelligent enough, and maybe he had the drive and the ruthlessness. 'So,' Sartaj said, 'for the sake of the country and good citizens, you want to help me with this case?'

'Of course, inspector saab, of course.' Ahmad's happiness at being understood came from his belly, his whole body. He put his elbows on the desk and leaned forward towards Sartaj. 'I know everyone in Navnagar, and even in Bengali Bura I have lots of connections, I work with those people, I know them. So I can quietly ask, you know. Try to find out what people are saying, what people know.'

'And what do you know now? Do you know anything?'

Ahmad chortled, 'Arre, no, no, inspector saab. But I have no doubt I can find out something here and there, some little thing.' And he sat back, chubby and self-contained.

Sartaj gave in. Ahmad wasn't stupid enough to give away good tips for nothing, or his sources. 'Good,' Sartaj said. 'I will be grateful if you can render any assistance. And is there anything I can do for you?'

They understood each other now. 'Yes, saab, actually there is.' Ahmad put away his charm and stated his terms quietly, plainly. 'In Navnagar there are two brothers, young boys, one is nineteen, another is twenty. Every day they bother the girls when they are leaving for work, they say this and that. I have asked them to stop, but then they threatened me. They have openly said that they will break my arms and legs. I could take action against them myself, but I have restrained myself. But when the water starts to rise above one's head, inspector saab . . .'

'Names? Age? Where do I find them?'

Ahmad already had the particulars neatly written out in his diary, and he tore the page out for Sartaj with fastidious care. He supplied descriptions and details of the family, and then excused himself. 'I have taken up enough of your time, saab,' he said. 'But please call me any time, day or night, if you need anything.'

'I'll call you after I see to these two,' Sartaj said.

'The citizens of Navnagar will be very happy, saab, if you can rescue their sisters and daughters from this daily trouble.'

With that, Wasim Zafar Ali Ahmad placed a hand on his chest and made his exit. He had invoked the people of Navnagar, but both he and Sartaj knew that the two brothers had to be disciplined because Ahmad wanted it so. This was the first offering in their deal, this test of trust and goodwill. Sartaj would pick up the roadside Romeos, whose main offence was undoubtedly not their harassment of passing women but their disrespect towards Ahmad. Sartaj would see to them, and Ahmad would give him some information. Ahmad would then be seen in the basti as a man who had police connections, and his name would be heard and more people would arrive at his door, seeking his patronage and help, and in turn inflate his influence. If all went well for him, maybe in a few years, Sartaj would be the one calling him 'Saab'. But all that was a long while away, and first there was this little task of the chastisement of the Eve-teasing brothers. All great careers began with these little exchanges and were sustained by them. Mutual interest was the lubricating oil that ran the great and small machinery of the world, and Sartaj would use it to send criminals skidding into captivity. He felt excitement prickle up his neck and through his forearms, that old thrill which came to him when he felt a case opening up. Good, good, this was good. It was foolish to expect success, but Sartaj couldn't help savouring the anticipation. He would find the killers, he would catch them, he would win: the thought of victory sparked in his chest like a tiny burn, and he took energy from it all day.

That evening, over a glass of Scotch, Sartaj told Majid Khan about his new long-named source. Majid wasn't a drinker, but he had a bottle of Johnny Walker Black for Sartaj. Sartaj drank from it every time he came for dinner, and this evening he was depending on it a little too much, gulping it down greedily. He was telling Majid about Wasim Zafar Ali Ahmad while Majid's kids put plates on the table and their mother rattled spoons in the kitchen.

'Yes, I know him, this Ahmad,' Majid said. 'Actually, I know his father.'

'How?'

'I found him during the riots, just next to the highway in Bandra. I was going to Mahim with four constables. From far away, I saw these three bastards standing over something. The streets were completely empty, you know, and there was just this empty road and these three. So I told the driver, go, go. And we sped up, and as soon as they saw the jeep, the three chutiyas ran off. Now I saw this man lying on the ground. You know, grey beard, clean white kurta, white topi, just an old Muslim gentleman. He had tried to run, they had caught up with him, pushed him down. He was very scared, but he wasn't hurt.'

'He would have been. If you hadn't saved him. Dead.'

'Arre, I didn't save him. We happened to come along.' Majid wasn't being falsely modest, he was stating flat facts. He scratched at his chest, and drank from his glass of nimbu pani. 'Anyway, we put him in the back of the jeep, took him along. He couldn't speak for an hour. But ever since then, he comes every Bakr'id to my office, he brings some gosht, I touch it and send him back with it. But he comes without fail. Nice old fellow.'

They were standing on the balcony of Majid's eighth-floor apartment, leaning on the parapet. There was a perfectly round moon hanging low over the staggered oblongs of the rooftops, over the dark rim of watery lowlands and the row of tin-roofed kholis and the sea beyond. Sartaj couldn't think of the last time he had seen this round moon. Maybe, he thought, you needed to be up this high to see it, high above the streets. 'His son never came with the old man? To thank you and ask you for help?'

'No.'

'Smart fellow.' Ahmad was demonstrating his intelligence by not presuming on the thread of gratitude that bound his father and Majid, tugging on it. He was proceeding in the proper manner, going through Sartaj, the local inspector. If Ahmad could make Sartaj and the constables happy, they would recommend him to Majid, who perhaps would make it possible for Ahmad to gain influence and conduct activities of questionable legality, bringing prosperity and further advancement.

'Yes,' Majid said. 'He's not an innocent like his father.'

'Innocents have very good luck sometimes, no?'

'Sometimes. The father said they had some relative who was killed in the riots. Cousin brother.'

'Close cousin?'

'No, far, it sounded like. The old man was making a big fuss about it the first time he came to see me. I told him he was lucky it was only one far cousin. In this country, if you look at any family long enough, you'll find some far cousin whose luck turned bad. If not in this riot, then in some other one.'

This was true. Sartaj had heard stories in his own family, about people fleeing homes in the middle of the night.

'Come on, you two,' Rehana called from inside. She had the familiar plastic bowl with its close-fitting top and red rose pattern in her hand. She had been making rotis in the kitchen. The khima would have been made earlier in the evening in collaboration with her all-purpose maidservant, and between the two of them they could produce delight or devastation. It was always a lottery, and Sartaj pulled up his chair glad of the whisky he had drunk. Imtiaz and Farah were elbowing each other as they settled in. He had known them since they had been toddlers, and now that they were almost grown up the small apartment seemed smaller.

Imtiaz passed him a bowl. 'Uncle, have you seen the CIA website?' he said.

'The CIA, like Americans?' Sartaj said.

'Yes, they have a site, and they let you look at their secret documents.'

Farah was serving raita into a bowl for Sartaj. 'If they let you read it, it's not secret, idiot. Uncle, he spends hours finding weird articles and talking to girls on the internet.'

'You shut up,' Imtiaz said. 'Nobody's talking to you.'

Majid was smiling. 'For this I spent thousands and thousands of rupees, so my son can talk to girls in America?'

'Europe,' Farah said. 'He has a girlfriend in Belgium, and another one in France.'

'You have girlfriends?' Sartaj said. 'How old are you?'

'Fifteen.'

'Fourteen,' Farah said. She was smiling. 'I bet he's told them he was eighteen.'

'At least I sound like I'm eighteen. Not like some people who behave as if they're eleven still.'

Farah reached under the table, and Imtiaz winced. He held up his arm. 'The fingernails of the female,' he said, looking very pleased with himself, 'are deadlier than the male.'

'Stop it, you two,' their mother said. 'Let Uncle eat.'

Sartaj ate and was relieved to find that this evening had somehow been saved from culinary havoc. 'New haircut?' he said to Farah.

'Yes! You are the only man in the world who would notice. My dear Papa didn't figure out for three days why I was looking different.'

'Very nice,' Sartaj said. She looked quite plumply pretty, and Sartaj wondered if she had boyfriends in Belgium, or even in Bandra. But he kept the question to himself, knowing that Majid was very liberal, but that his tolerance of light-hearted romance didn't extend to his daughter. He might spend hard-won cash on a computer for his children, for his son, but that fierce cavalry moustache wasn't just an affectation. Boys under the spell of Farah's new look would have to be madly brave to climb up her castle wall eight floors tall. She was beaming now, and Sartaj was sure that there were lads whose fear had been banished by that glow. He himself had done some wall-climbing in long-ago days, and had braved fierce fathers for a lovely face.

After dinner, Rehana brought Sartaj a cup of tea and sat next to him on the sofa. She had the same broad cheekbones as her children, and a comfortable heaviness. In the gold-framed photograph on the wall she was a slim, hennaed bride, but even then, even with the formally lowered head, she had had the same bright eyes. 'So, Sartaj. Got a girlfriend?'

'Yes,' Sartaj said. 'Yes.'

'Who? Tell me.'

'A girl.'

'So what would a girlfriend be, a pineapple? Sartaj, for a policeman, you're a very-very bad liar.'

'It's a boring topic, Bhabhi.'

'My son doesn't think so.' Her son had walked down to the corner shop with her husband and daughter for ice-cream. 'Sartaj, you're not that old yet. How are you going to get through life like this? You need a family.'

'You sound just like my mother.'

'Because we're both right. We both want you to be happy.'

'I am.'

'What?'

'Happy.'

'Sartaj, anybody looking at you knows exactly how happy you are.'

And looking at her in the haven of her contentment, Sartaj thought he could have said the same thing about her. He felt acutely now the sodden, sweaty weariness of his own body, the whisky misery of it. He was annoyed now, at having the professional momentum of the day dragged down into this useless discussion about happiness with happy Rehana. He was saved from further investigation of the nature of happiness by a knock on the door. 'Ice-cream,' he said. 'Ice-cream.'

He ate a bowl of the ice-cream, and fled.

A violent buzzing woke Sartaj out of a dream about flying across oceans to meet foreign women. There was a very intricate plot involving watchful mothers and speeding jeeps, but it was gone as soon as his eyes opened. He propped himself up, baffled, and couldn't think where the noise came from. For a moment he thought it was the door-bell gone wrong, but then he remembered the mobile phone. He groped for it on the bedside table, dropped it off the side and had to pull it back up by the charging wire. Finally he got it open.

'Sartaj Saab?'

'Who is this?' Sartaj barked.

'Bunty, saab. Somebody told me you wanted to talk to me.'

'Bunty, yes, yes. Good that you called.' Sartaj swung his feet to the ground and tried to collect himself, to recollect a strategy for talking to Gaitonde's man. But he couldn't remember if he had thought one through, and finally he just said, 'I want to meet you.'

'The rumour is that you shot Bhai.'

'I didn't shoot Gaitonde. Forget rumours. What do you think, Bunty?'

'My information is that he was dead when you got in.'

'You have good information, Bunty. It all was very strange. Why should a man like that kill himself?'

'That's what you want to talk about?'

'That and other things. I'll tell you when I see you.'

'What do I know about why he killed himself?'

'Listen, Bunty. I just want to talk to you. If you help me, I may be able to help you. Gaitonde is dead, Suleiman Isa's boys will be looking for you. I've heard that some of your own people have split away already.'

'That is a game I have played for years.'

'True, but now? Alone? How far will you run?'

'You mean in my wheelchair, saab?' Bunty's voice was gravelly, with a little hiss of effort at the end of each breath. Maybe it was how he had to sit, some constriction of the lungs. But he was not sad, only amused. 'I can go faster in this thing than most men can run.'

Sartaj sat up, glad of the chance to be curious and friendly. 'Really? I've never seen a wheelchair like that.'

'This is foreign, saab. It goes up and down stairs also. It can do all sorts of things.'

'That is amazing. It must have been very expensive.'

'Bhai gave it to me. He liked things like that, up to date.'

'So he was a modern man?'

'Yes, very modern. But it is very hard to keep this chair running, you know. Nobody knows how to repair it here, and spare parts and everything you have to bring from vilayat. It breaks down too much.'

'Not built for Indian conditions.'

'Yes. Like one of those new cars. They look good, but finally only an Ambassador can get you to any village you want to go.'

'Meet me, Bunty. Maybe I can get you to your village safely.'

'I was born here in Mumbai, in GTB Nagar only, saab. And you are too eager to meet me. Maybe Suleiman Isa has asked you to send me home.'

'Bunty, you ask anyone. I have no connections to Suleiman Isa or any of his men.'

'You are close to Parulkar Saab.'

'That may be. But I don't do such work for him, Bunty. You know that. I am just a simple man.' Sartaj stood up, walked around the bottom of the bed. He was pushing too hard, at a man who was trying to outmanoeuvre death on his speedy wheelchair. 'Listen, you don't want to meet, no problem. Just think about it, okay?'

'Yes, saab. I have to be careful, especially now.'

'Yes.'

'Saab, but I can help you over the phone. What did you want to know?'

So Bunty was keeping his options open with Sartaj, in case he himself needed help later. He had problems of his own, after all, and he wanted to stay alive. Sartaj relaxed, shook his shoulders loose and stretched his neck. Now they had the possibility of a relationship. 'Tell me, you really know nothing about why Gaitonde took his own wicket?'

'No, saab. I don't know. Really I don't know.'

'You knew he was back in Bombay?'

'I knew. But I hadn't seen him for weeks. We spoke only on the phone. He was hiding out in that thing.'

'That house?'

'Yes. He wouldn't come out.'

'Why?'

'I don't know. He was always careful.'

'What did he sound like on the phone?'

'Sound like? Like Bhai.'

'Yes, but was he sad? Happy?'

'He was a bit khiskela. But he was always like that.'

'Khiskela how?'

'Like his brain was full of things. Sometimes he would talk to me for an hour about something that had nothing to do with business, just talk and talk.'

'Like what?'

'I don't know. One day it was about computers in the old times. He said that there were computers and super-weapons in the *Mahabharata*, he went on and on about Ashwathamma. I didn't listen. Even before, when he was on his boat, he liked to talk long on the phone. It was a big waste of money. But he was Bhai, so you just kept saying, haan, haan, and he went on.'

'Who was that woman with him?'

'Jojo. She sent him items.'

'Sent him?'

'Yes. First-class items for Bhai. He used to have them flown out to Thailand or wherever he was. Virgins. Jojo was the supplier.'

'Virgins all the way from here?'

'Yes, he liked Indian virgins.'

'How many?'

'I don't know. Once a month maybe.'

'And Jojo was his woman also?'

'She was a bhadwi. He must have taken hers also. That was one of his hobbies.'

'Why did he come back to Mumbai, Bunty?'

'I don't know.'

'You were his main boss in Mumbai, Bunty. Of course you know.'

'I was just one of his Number Twos.'

'I was told you were the closest to him.'

'I stayed with him.'

159

'And the others left him? Why?'

There was a thin crackling on the line, of cellophane and card-board, and Sartaj waited as Bunty lit his cigarette and took in a drag.

'Some left. Business was down,' Bunty said.

'Why?'

'It doesn't matter now.'

This was the heart of the matter. Sartaj knew this from Bunty's reluctance to give it away, from his studied casualness. Carefully, very slowly, Sartaj said, 'You're right, Bunty. It doesn't matter now, so tell me.'

Bunty drew on his cigarette. He let the smoke out, wheezed a little. Sartaj waited.

'Saab, business is down for everyone.'

'But more for the Gaitonde company than all others. Bunty, don't be a chutiya. If you are honest with me, I can be straight with you. Tell me.'

'Bhai wasn't concentrating on business. He had us all running here, running there.'

'After what?'

Bunty laughed suddenly. 'He had us chasing a sadhu. He said we had to find a wise man.'

'What sadhu? Chasing where?'

'Three sadhus altogether, and one was the leader. Really, saab, I can't tell you more.'

'Why not?'

'I don't know much more.'

'Tell me what you know.'

'Not like this, saab.'

'So let us meet.'

'Saab, you talk to Parulkar Saab.'

'About what?'

'I want to surrender. But they will do an encounter on me, saab.'

It made sense, that Bunty wanted to come in. He would be safer in custody, and jail would shield him from his many enemies. But he was afraid of being executed before his name ever showed up on an arrest roster. 'If you have something good to give us,' Sartaj said, 'I am sure Parulkar Saab will look after you.'

'I have everything, saab. I was with Bhai for a long time.'

'Okay. I'll speak to Parulkar saab. Then I want to know who this sadhu was, this leader fellow.'

'Once I am safe, saab, I will tell everything I know. I will give you his name. I am the only one who knows.'

'All right. I will talk to Parulkar Saab, and tell you what he says. Give me a phone number.'

'I am calling from a PCO, saab. And I am not in Mumbai. I will call you.'

'Fine.' Bunty must be very afraid, to be this careful even as he searched for a way to secure shelter. 'When will you be back?'

'Monday, saab.'

'Call me on Monday evening, and I will tell you what Parulkar saab says.'

'Yes, saab. I will put down now.'

Bunty hung up, and Sartaj made chai and considered the vagaries of the gangster's life. That death could come suddenly was a given, but what struck Sartaj as poignant was that Bunty was trying to trust Parulkar, his most feared predator. Parulkar had over the years been responsible for the hunting down of many G-Company men. He had used his many sources to obtain intelligence and fix the whereabouts of Gaitonde's functionaries, and had sent out his teams to trap them and kill them. Unless the dead men were prime shooters or eminent Number Twos, the newspapers reported their deaths in one-paragraph stories at the bottom of back pages. Bunty might rate a front-page mention in the city sections, perhaps. For his special wheelchair, maybe, if not his death.

Sartaj finished his chai, and then called the Delhi-walli, to tell her about Gaitonde's search.

'A sadhu was the leader of this group?' Anjali Mathur said.

'Yes, madam.'

'What sadhu? Was there a name?'

'No, madam. The source refused to release any other information at this time. I might know more in a few days.'

'All right. This is very strange. We knew that Gaitonde was very religious, that he conducted pujas quite often. But we don't know of any sadhus in connection with him. And why would he be looking for this man?'

'I don't know, madam.'

'Yes.'

She paused. Sartaj waited. He was getting used to Anjali Mathur's slow deliberation. .

'I have an address for you,' she said. 'Write it down.'

'The sister?'

'Yes, the sister. She's moved. She's in Bandra now.'

Before going to see the sister in Bandra, Sartaj made a stop at the station. He had to make a phone call. The piece of paper that Parulkar had given him with the S-Company contact on it had only a phone number, no name. Sartaj had to make an effort to remember. Iffat-bibi. Yes, that was it. Iffat-bibi, who was Suleiman Isa's maternal aunt and criminal accomplice. Sartaj couldn't conjure up a face for her as he dialled, but when she answered her phone and he heard her voice, he instantly thought of Begum Akhtar. There was the same roughened sweetness about the voice, that old-world heartbreak that floated off worn vinyl albums, full of pain but strong as the edge of a curving Avadhi dagger. 'So you are Parulkar's man?' she said.

'Yes, madam.'

'Arre, don't call me that, you can't be so formal with me. After all, you are Sardar Saab's son.'

'You knew him?'

'Since when?' Iffat-bibi said. 'I knew him when he was a young rangroot, almost. He was so handsome, baap re.'

Papa-ji had never told Sartaj about Iffat-bibi, but maybe she was the sort of woman fathers didn't tell children about. 'Yes, he was very keen about his clothes.'

'Your father,' Iffat-bibi said, 'loved the reshmi kabab from a place we owned called Ashiana. But that restaurant no longer exists.'

Sartaj remembered the kababs, but he didn't know that Iffat-bibi had had anything to do with them. Iffat-bibi wanted to tell stories about Sardar Saab. She said he had once found a destitute twelve-year-old boy wandering around VT, and Sardar Saab had used his own money to buy him food and a reserved train ticket back to Punjab. 'Sardar Saab was a good man,' she sighed. 'Very straight and simple.'

Sartaj looked at his hand, at the steel kara on the wrist and the mark it had left over a lifetime, and nodded. 'Yes.' He waited.

'You should come and visit us some time. I will give you better reshmi kababs than the ones from Ashiana.'

'Yes, Iffat-bibi. I will come some time.'

Iffat-bibi had observed the proprieties, and now she was willing to get down to business. 'What can I do for you?'

'I need information about Gaitonde.'

'That maderchod?' It was a shock to hear the word in that voice which promised song, and now Sartaj understood how she could be counsellor and helpmeet to a bhai, and not just an indulgent grandmother offering food. 'For years he bothered us. Very good that you took care of him at last.'

'I didn't, Bibi,' Sartaj said. 'But tell me about him. What sort of man was he?'

He was a conniving, cowardly cur, she said. He ran from a fight, and he betrayed his own men. He was a sinful lecher who used and destroyed young girls.

'But he ran a big company, Bibi.'

She allowed that he was a good manager, and he had made some money in his day. No, she didn't know what he was doing back in the city. The last she had heard he was skulking off in Thailand or Indonesia, the bastard. She told stories about Gaitonde, about his perfidies. He had killed innocent people, saying they were Suleiman Isa's friends. He was an insect.

'Bibi, do you know of any sadhu in connection with him?'

'Sadhu? No. All that praying and piety, everything was a sham. He never did a bit of good for anyone in his life, may he burn.'

Sartaj thanked her, and said, 'Now I must go, Bibi.'

'You're talking to anyone on Gaitonde's side?'

'Here and there, Bibi.'

She laughed. 'Fine, don't tell me if you don't want to, beta. But if you have a problem, come to me. After all, you are Sardar Saab's son.'

'Yes, Bibi.'

'Phone me some time. I am an old woman, but keep in touch. I may be of use. This is my personal number, write it down.'

Sartaj put the number and name into his diary, but he thought she wouldn't be of much use, this garrulous old woman. She had nothing useful to give him, or perhaps he didn't have anything she thought worth trading good information for. He put the phone down, and went out into the station, looking for Katekar. Now they had to visit another woman.

Mary Mascarenas sat on her bed and shuddered. She held herself around the belly, arms tightly wrapped, and lowered her head and shook. Sartaj waited. Maybe she had quarrelled with Jojo, perhaps she had even wished her sister dead, but now it had happened, a part of her life had fallen away, and she was trembling from the amputation. There was no use trying to talk to her until the agitation was over, and so Sartaj and Katekar were waiting, looking around her very small apartment, one room with an attached kitchen really, and a cupboard of a bathroom. She had a green and black bedspread on the single bed, some small plants on the window-ledge, an ancient black rotary phone, two framed paintings on the wall, a grey-patterned dhurrie on the floor. Sitting on the single wooden chair at the foot of the bed, Sartaj saw how she had built a haven for herself. The walls were a pale green, and he was sure that she had painted them herself, to complement the darker green of the plants and the jungle emeralds of the paintings, where cottages sat amongst exuberant foliage and parrots fluttered through the treetops. Now the bright Mumbai sun slipped through the white blinds and ignited the hues that Mary Mascarenas had arranged for herself, and the shimmering, jerking fall of her hair hid her face.

Katekar rolled his eyes. He padded into the kitchen, and Sartaj could see his head craning, turning. He was taking inventory. He would go into the bathroom next, and take careful note of buckets, toothbrush, face creams. This was something they had in common, this faith in details, in particulars. Sartaj had noticed it the first time Katekar had reported to him, many years ago, about a pickpocket who worked the line from Churchgate to Andheri Station. Katekar had droned on about name, age, height, and then added that the bastard had married three times, and that he had a weakness for papri-chaat and falooda, in the basti where he had grown up this was well known. They'd caught him three weeks later, at the Mathura Dairy Farm near Santa Cruz station, with his head lowered over a plate of bhel-puri after a profitable evening rush-hour, sitting across from a cross-eyed girlfriend who was well on her way to becoming wife number four. Close observation didn't always bring arrests, and success, but what Sartaj appreciated was Katekar's essential understanding of the fact that there were many ways to describe a man, but to say that he was a Hindu, a poor man, a criminal, all of this gave no grip, no hold. Only when you knew which shampoo he favoured, what songs he listened to, who and how he liked to chodo, what paan he ate, only then you caught him, had him, even if you never arrested him. So Katekar was in Mary's bathroom now. Sartaj was sure he was sniffing at her soap.

'Why?' she said suddenly. She pushed the hair back from her face, tugged it back angrily. 'Why?'

She had her sister's cheekbones, and a plumper, round jawline, all blurred now by her loss. She wasn't weeping, but was still quivering, squeezing it down until Sartaj could see it only in the tips of her fingers, and in her chin.

'Miss Mascarenas was involved in nefarious activities with the mafia don Ganesh Gaitonde,' he said. 'This resulted in . . .'

'I heard you before,' she said. 'But why?'

Why everything? she wanted to know. Why a bullet hole in the chest, why a concrete floor, why Ganesh Gaitonde? Sartaj shrugged. 'I don't know,' he said. Why do men kill women? Why do they kill each other? These were questions that bit at him sometimes, but he drowned them in whisky. Otherwise why not ask, why life? That way lay hurtling chasms, the temptations of long heights. Better to do the job. Better to put one apradhi in jail, and then, when you could, another. Katekar was at the bathroom door, his eyes alive with sunlight. 'I don't know, miss,' Sartaj said.

'You don't know,' she said. She nodded heavily, as if this confirmed some great suspicion. 'I want her,' she said.

'Miss?'

'I want her,' she said slowly, with hard-strained patience, 'for burial.'

'Yes, of course. Handing over of body is sometimes difficult when the investigation is still ongoing, you understand. But we will arrange for the body to be released. But I need to ask you some questions.'

'I don't want to answer any questions just now.'

'But these are questions about your sister. You just said that you want to know what happened to her.'

She wiped her face and sat forward a little and suddenly he was the subject of study. Her eyes were a lighter brown than they first appeared, and in a moment he was able to see the flecks dusted through them. He was now very uncomfortable, her scrutiny was shameless, direct and long, and at least his position should have shielded him from the unexpected intimacy of that unending look. But he wouldn't drop his gaze. At last she said, 'What did you say your name was?'

'Inspector Sartaj Singh.'

'Sartaj Singh, have you ever lost a sister?' Her voice rose. 'Have you ever had a sister *murdered*?'

Her utter lack of fear was irritating. Citizens, and especially women, were always subdued with policemen, careful, scared, formal. Mary Mascarenas was dismissively casual. But she had just lost her sister, and so he took a breath and held down his annoyance. 'Miss, I'm sorry to ask you this kind of thing at a time like this . . .'

'Then don't.'

'This is a very important matter. This is a case that involves national security,' Sartaj said. And then he couldn't think of anything to say. He felt quite in the wrong, somehow, and therefore angry. Mary Mascarenas didn't look frightened, but she wasn't brave either. She was saddened, weary, and truly expecting nothing from him except more suffering. She was just going to be very stubborn, and shouting at her wasn't going to help. He took a breath. 'National security. Do you understand?'

'Are you going to hit me?'

'What?'

'Are you going to break my bones? Isn't that what you do?'

'No, we don't,' Sartaj snapped. He caught himself, steadied and held up a hand. 'Miss, we will arrange for the release of the body. Also, there were some possessions, and they are impounded currently, for the investigation. But those will be released to you eventually. I will phone when arrangements are complete. Here is the number at the station where you can get in touch with me.' He carefully put his card at the foot of the bed, at the very edge, and turned away.

On the stairway Katekar turned his head back up to Sartaj. 'She will talk, sir.'

'Why are you whispering?' Usually Katekar was the bulky threat, he was the looming promise of slaps and thumps and kicks, and Sartaj played the understanding friend, the unexpectedly benign and bearded face of authority. With women he was always kind. But Mary Mascarenas had been hostile, and Sartaj was irritated. From the bottom of the yard he looked up at her door, which was shutting as he watched. She had a good little PG at the back of an old house on a quiet residential street, shaded by the interlocked branches of two old trees. The house was one of those unexpected treasures that still survived in Bandra, an old grey cottage with slatted shutters and ironwork on the balconies and white trim on the doors and windows.

The yard was covered with leaves which crackled underfoot. All very pretty, and vexing.

But Katekar was right, she would talk. Sartaj walked down the street. She would feed her anger, tell herself what a beast that sardar inspector was, what a bastard, but finally she would be left with only her guilt, and she would need to tell him what had happened, what had become of Mary and Juliet Mascarenas. She would confess to him because she had to make him understand. Forgiveness was not what they really needed, the survivors, it was always too late for that. What they wanted was only that someone in a uniform, a robe, somebody with three lions on their shoulder should say, yes, I see how it came about, first this happened, and then that, and so you did this and then this. So she would talk. But now it was time to leave her alone. Now it was time to save the body from disposal by incineration, so that Mary Mascarenas could bury her sister. People set great store by small dignities, small illusions. Mary Mascarenas would never see the cold room, he would save her from seeing what really happened to dead sisters. Let her bury Jojo. Then she would talk.

Sartaj shaded his eyes and peered out at the sea, at the shifting sash of quicksilver visible through the trees and the two buildings below. It was late, time for him to go home, to his own family.

Prabhjot Kaur sat in an armchair in her bedroom and listened to her home. The house was black. At night it seemed bigger, the familiar contours pushed back by a moving dark, an absence of light that was somehow alive with ghostly slivers of colour. Prabhjot Kaur could hear Sartaj sleeping. It was a long way, across and down the hall, but at this time she could hear many things: the slow settling of the ancient dining table, the steady plit-tap, plit-tap of drops from the tap behind her neighbour's house, the shivery movement of small animals under the hedge at the front of the house, the hum of the night itself, that low and living vibration that made all other sounds larger. She heard all this, and loud in it, her son's breathing. She knew how he lay, straight on his back with his head turned to one side, and a pillow held against his chest. He had come late, carrying two overstuffed bags as usual, weary from the train ride but also from much else, she could see that. After a quick bath he had eaten the rajma-chawal she had waiting for him, he ate it silently, with relief. She sat across the table from him, warmed by the familiar way he had of eating the rice from left to right, systematic, and patting the food with his fork often, making it neat. He had done that as a small boy, with the fork held crosswise in his fist. Rajma-chawal was his favourite food, his Sunday treat, and he liked the rice with plenty of fried onion.

She asked him questions every now and then, whether the slow leak in the Bombay bathroom wall had been fixed, whether he had written a letter to his Delhi Chacha-ji. It was not Sartaj's answers she wanted as much as the sound of his voice. When he was done, he sat back, stilled, both arms hanging limp at the sides of the chair, blinking slowly. She took his plate. 'Go to sleep, beta,' she said.

The armchair she sat in now was old, the oldest piece of furniture in the house. It had been patched, restrung, re-upholstered, QuickFixed, operated on, saved for her. Sartaj's father had brought it home one evening, tipped it slowly from the back of a tempo, smiling a glory of flashing teeth over her What-is-this? How-much-money-did-you-spend? It had taken him an hour to persuade her to sit in it, to admit it was not too uncomfortable. It was the first big thing they had bought together, the first piece of their small household that had not come in dowry. Now the night was a vast unknown territory she was exploring alone, a drifting plain that rolled its horizons back eternally, and she preferred to suffer it sitting back in her armchair, because it was lazy to be in bed when she was awake. But no, it wasn't true, suffering undiluted and pure it wasn't, even though sometimes loneliness spoke its iron hum of locusts behind her eyes, filled her stomach with blowing sand, gritty and grinding and cruel. There was something else that kept her from living with her son, or from moving into the capacious sprawl of her brother's house just down the street and to the right, into the tumbling warmth of nieces and nephews and shouted quarrels and kulfi-smeared faces. It was something so monstrous she kept it from herself. But she felt it, late at night, hidden under the contours of her face, which she touched and felt as if it were a mask, as she savoured, slowly, the unspeakable pleasure of being alone.

She shook her head angrily against this delight now, pushed it away. It took her a full minute to get up from the armchair, four separate movements of arm and hip and legs. There was no need to switch on the light for the walk into the hallway and down it. The bureau was to the left, good dishes in the first drawer and second, the expensive dishes with the lily pattern that she liked for its neat

168

spiralling circles in a bright blue, and to her right shoulder, the glisten of the photographs she could recite and remember, a wedding picture laminated in hard plastic, the red of her sari darkened into a rich black, she could remember the photographer's two-toned shoes and his head hidden under a black cloth, and her younger devar with his red tie and cheeky smile, 'Come now, Pabi-ji, where's that lovely lovely laugh?' Then there had been an ecstatic glow of light, and she had managed a smile that lingered now, past all decay. And there was Sartaj at ten, in a blue turban too large for his head and a blue blazer with shiny new brass buttons, what you couldn't see in the photograph was his left knee under the flannel trousers, which he had sliced open that morning on a strand of barbed wire, climbing through a fence to short-cut through an empty plot on the way to the school bus, she had told him a hundred times not to. Then there had been the tetanus injections, and the ice-cream his father had bought him, a whole brick of Kwality vanilla, Sartaj's favourite. They had the same tastes, father and son, the same urgent need for a mirror glitter on shoe leather, for a new jacket every other year. At the end of the corridor, he, the father, stood against a grey studio backdrop in his last-but-one jacket, a tweed with a green and black weave, worn with a white shirt and a silky green scarf, his beard now a soft white that he finally no longer fought against with stains and dyes. A white beard looks fully distinguished, she had told him twice a day for months on end, until he had believed her, and now she left him behind and stood in a doorway, and Sartaj slept, breathing quickly.

He spoke now, muttering something into the sheet clumped at the side of his head. At the foot of the bed, she bent slowly and found, on the floor, his pants, shirt, underwear. Sartaj was saying something, she clearly heard the word 'boat' in it. She shut the door quietly because he would want to sleep late, and the servants came early. On the way to the bathroom she turned out his pockets and found a handkerchief, and it all went into the washing bucket for the bai.

In her armchair she listened for the tapping of the watchman's lathi at the very last turn of the road, it was time. He made a large circle around the clustered homes every hour. And listening, she heard the tiniest creak of resentment rising from her bones, a very small rub of resistance, barely heard amidst the larger music of happiness, of a life not without pain but lived well: home, husband, son, and her the wife. It was unseemly, after all these years and years, this unvanquished and sullen spark rising from clothes on the floor, this small spurt of anger at having to always do things for men, always. Yes, unseemly, especially with Sartaj so tired, seeking comfort, he had come to her. She knew this. He had told her he slept deeply in this house, slept better. He had slept bravely in his own bedroom that first night long ago, he must have been six, maybe a little older when they finally had an apartment with a room for him, with a little veranda that looked out into a small garden where she had grown roses and hung wet saris and uniforms on a line. How many clothes had she washed in those early days, how many blue days of Rin and torn blue short pants and matching socks, and had she on some mornings pressed down that same grating itch of annoyance, buried it firmly and deep under tumbling avalanches of love? Prabhjot Kaur pushed the thoughts back, put her hands on the old wood of the armrests and held them hard and rocked her head back and forward, and tried to think of a holiday time in the hills, she and Karamjeet and their son walking on a winding hilly ridge, but she was seeing instead a house in a city very far away, immeasurably further now that it lay on the other side of a new border and a long wire fence that flashed with murderous electricity, and this house had shutters painted green and a big baithak at the front with all new furniture in it and after you went through the dark passage leading from outside to in, there was a bricked courtyard surrounded by arches and rooms. In this courtyard were Prabhjot Kaur's father and mother, her two elder brothers and her two sisters. And one of these sisters was Navneet, beloved and best of all, and now lost for ever. Gone, Navneet-bhenji was gone. With both hands, Prabhjot Kaur wiped her forehead, her face. It was useless to remember. The histories had already been written, and what had happened, had happened. Being alive, having a family, came with its inevitable portion of pain. There was no running away from life, and trying to wish away suffering only made it more present. She took a deep breath: bear it. Carry it all, the small dissatisfactions of every day and the huge murderous tragedies of long ago, carry it all with the help and grace of Vaheguru. Carry it for those you love. Prabhjot Kaur took a deep breath and tried to think of the tasks for tomorrow.

Her breathing was even, slow. From across the garden outside came that steady tapping, the small explosive spatter of water on stones.

❧ INSET: *A House in a Distant City*

The courtyard was washed every morning, and in it sat Prabhjot Kaur, scrubbing a karhai with ash under the hand-pump. She was the best and youngest daughter of three: Navneet, Maninder and Prabhjot. Or actually Navneet-bhenji, Mani and then Prabhjot, or Nikki, for her smallness. Prabhjot Kaur liked to help their Mata-ji, who always said, 'Look at her, this Nikki of a girl, this Prabhjot Kaur, only ten and helping more than the rest of you all put together,' which usually meant that Nikki had to watch out for a pinch from Mani, who loved to catch up the flesh on the inner side of her upper arm with fingers as unrelenting and iron as a chimta and twist and twist, whispering, 'Little rat, I'll show you, rattie.' Nikki wore her bruises with forbearance, and even compassion for Mani, who had big ears and looked like an awestruck dehati scarecrow, after three sudden inches gained in her fourteenth year. Mani wandered around, shrieky and awkward and full of rage, not too good at studies, stuck inextricably in the middle of three sisters, which meant that she was not special even by virtue of position or age, always not here and not quite there. Nikki, on the other hand, was coddled by her two brothers, Iqbal-veerji and Alok-veerji, who at eighteen and seventeen were younger than Navneet-bhenji but more remote than her because of their hulking maleness and their passion for cricket. Her father liked to look at Nikki's notebooks, which she covered with plain brown paper folded into sharp, precise corners and edges, which she adorned with her full, proper name in green ink, with the initial letters of 'Prabhjot' and 'Kaur' especially elaborated and curled. Her Punjabi and Urdu teachers admired her writing in either script and had hopes for her in the annual composition contest sponsored by Sir Syed Atallulah Khan. 'My house is new,' she wrote in flowing green letters, with not a mistake or a blotting because she would discard an entire page for one straggly aleph. She had the universal reputation of being a good girl, serious and obedient, and in her new house she liked to help in the kitchen.

'Are you finished, Nikki?' Mata-ji sang from inside the kitchen.

'Coming, Mata-ji,' Prabhjot Kaur called, and jumped up to pump water, leaning on the handle with all her weight. The water fell in happy gushes, sparking and bouncing in the sunlight. In the kitchen, Mata-ji slapped the paraunthas back and forth between her hands with a sprightliness that made a quick music, tossed them down on the hot tava, each with a final wristy flick. Prabhjot Kaur laid the karhai down carefully. Mata-ji patted at the beaded moisture on her cheeks with the corner of her dupatta, and Prabhjot Kaur watched intently her round red face, with the upturned nose they all teased her about.

'Take these in,' Mata-ji said, putting a perfect, glistening parauntha on a pile of four. 'Then you also sit down.' Prabhjot Kaur always ate second to last. Her two brothers ate mightily, putting away whole dozens of paraunthas, canisters of ghee. Mani was sitting next to them, one knee up under her chin, picking at a pile of bhindi, arranging it in a circle. She paid Prabhjot Kaur no attention, not even a beady stare, she was listening intently to Iqbal-veerji and Alok-veerji, who were talking cricket. Prabhjot Kaur squatted and served herself from the plates scattered on the chatai, and ate, quiet and intent on her food. It was a holiday morning, Sunday, and her father was away, gone to buy a last cartload of bricks. They had been living in the new house for almost a year, but the back was still unfinished. There was to be a store-room and a little separate house of one room and patio, for servants. It seemed like the house had been building for ever. For as long as Prabhjot Kaur could remember, it had been always the Adampur house, for which her father had disappeared on evenings after work, for which her brothers had spent weekends supervising construction, it was a home that had seemed always eternally distant. It had taken them three days to move in, and when they had finally spent their first night, all together in the courtyard on new charpais, none of them had slept until it was almost light. The next morning, through a warm white sheet and puffy, delicious dreams, Prabhjot Kaur had heard the laughter of her mother from the roof. There was a comfortable freedom in the sound, a lack of care so unusual that Prabhjot Kaur still remembered it. This laughter had lingered in their new house, brightened the corridors and mingled with the smell of fresh plaster. Mata-ji now sat down next to Prabhjot Kaur, with the little grunt she always made when she bent her knees, and she was tired from the morning's work, but still there was something different about her, a rotund contentment that had never been there when they had lived for years in the two rooms at the back of Narinder Dhanoa's house. She ate with concentration, bending low over the food, smacking her lips with every bite, and Mani stood up abruptly to her full towering length and went stalking away to the kitchen.

'So, Sethani-ji,' Alok-veerji said, with a hand on his mother's shoulder. 'When is your maid starting work?'

'I was thinking I can manage alone,' Mata-ji said. 'What will I do with my time?'

Alok-veerji collapsed on to Mata-ji's shoulder, laughing.

'We'll just tell her to start coming from tomorrow,' Iqbal-veerji said. 'Otherwise you'll keep doing this for another ten years.' As the oldest son he practised an indulgent authority with her, a smiling patience.

'Right, right,' Alok-veerji said. 'Otherwise our biggest-kanjoos-in-the-world won't let the maid near the house.'

'When you start earning,' Mata-ji said, shrugging his chin off her shoulder, 'then you'll know the price of your paraunthas.'

'When I start earning,' Alok-veerji said, 'I'll get you a motor car, with two flags on front.'

'A laat-saab you'll be straight away,' Mata-ji said. 'It took *him* twenty-one years to build this house.'

Twenty-one years and some bricks which are still coming, Prabhjot Kaur thought, but she could see that despite the toss of her head, Mata-ji was pleased by Alok-veerji as laat-saab in motor car. It made her smile that downward-looking quick quiver of a smile. That afternoon, when Prabhjot Kaur was settled on a corner of the chatai, her arm under her favourite gadda and head on it, falling densely into sleep, she heard the two veerjis still talking as they lay next to each other, going on about the mysterious maid, who must be found and made to come, who must work, who must sweep the house inside all its many many rooms and outside also, who must push the pocha until the tiled floors are glistering gleaming, who must thrash the laundry and hang it dewy and flapping on the lines in the back, who must winnow wheat, light lamps, clean shoes, gather books, get milk, buy vegetables, who must, who must, who must. Prabhjot Kaur thought that it would be a very strong woman who could do all that.

But three days later, when the maid came, she was a tiny woman named Ram Pari who wore a funny red salwar-kameez with a ragged dupatta and spoke a rough, blaring dialect that Prabhjot Kaur understood but found hilarious. Ram Pari called Mata-ji 'Bibi-ji' and squatted in the courtyard to haggle over wages. When she stood up, after agreeing to five rupees a week, Prabhjot Kaur went and stretched herself up next to her, and it was true, Ram Pari was barely a head taller than her, but standing that close, Prabhjot Kaur discovered a smell. She backed away quickly. It wasn't exactly a bad smell, but strong, it was like damp earth, or the back of a halwai's shop, where you got a little dizzy from all the old milky odours. Prabhjot Kaur reeled away from the richness and went and sat next to Navneet-bhenji in the baithak, where as usual Navneet-bhenji had her nose in a big book. Prabhjot Kaur leaned her head on the cottony comfort of Navneet-bhenji's shoulder, and spelt out the title on top of the page: 'Wordsworth'. Under the washed briskness of the soft salwar there was the sweet tinge of soap and warm skin. It was a flavour that Prabhjot Kaur had known all her life, and now she breathed it in, scrunching her nose into the cloth and making little snorting noises. 'What're you doing, jhalli?' Navneet-bhenji asked, and reached around with her other hand to pinch the burrowing nose. Prabhjot Kaur didn't feel crazy, not even close, but it was too difficult to explain why she needed it so, just then. She settled her face into the crook of Navneet-bhenji's arm and was still. Ram Pari was gone from the courtyard, and Mata-ji came across it, with a plate full of peas. She sat near and began to split the pods and rattle the peas into the plate with her thumb, shuck-shuck-shuck, so quickly that the sound was one long hum. Mata-ji was intent on the peas, and Navneet-bhenji kept the book high on her knees. They were quietly cordial with each other nowadays, but Prabhjot Kaur remembered a year ago when they had quarrelled mightily, after Navneet-bhenji had finished her FA and wanted to go to college for a BA. Mata-ji had told her to think of her brothers and sisters, who were being kept back from marriage and happiness by her selfishness, and when Navneet-bhenji had pointed out reasonably that her brothers and sisters were years and years away from any marriage, Mata-ji had screamed at her, something entirely strange about disgracing the family, and then had refused to eat for two days. Finally Papa-ji had put his large fatherly foot down. If Navneet wants to do her BA, he said, she will, and that is that. But Mata-ji had powers that moved in mysterious ways. She had retreated to her room, and Papa-ji had rolled his eyes and followed her in, and when he emerged the next morning, it had been settled that marriage could be delayed but not put off altogether. So now Navneet-bhenji was engaged, to Pritam Singh Hansra, who was a junior engineer in the PWD and stationed at Gujranwalla. After the engagement Papa-ji had gently stroked his beard, which had just some white in it, under his lower lip, and said, happiness follows from reasonable thinking. Mata-ji had kept quiet. And Prabhjot Kaur, awed by Papa-ji's way of commanding things out of the air – a boy for Navneet-bhenji, a house for them all – had nevertheless understood that that was never quite that.

Ram Pari came every day to the house, and Mata-ji engaged in epic struggles with her. Teaching her to wash dishes properly, to a sufficient degree of cleanliness, was a lesson that lasted three days, with many practical demonstrations and stinging criticisms. Ram Pari didn't talk back, shrugged off Mata-ji's homilies, performed at high standards for two bowls and maybe a plate, and then went back to her usual cheerful sloppiness. Her quick sweeping technique, which was efficient and fast but which left snaggles of dust in corners and ignored the spaces underneath almirahs, altogether drove Mata-ji into crescendos of outrage. Meanwhile the two brothers of Prabhjot Kaur fell over laughing and sniggered, not too quietly, about 'Badboo Pari'. Prabhjot Kaur laughed along with them, to show solidarity, but privately she thought the smell wasn't a badboo at all, more like a fierce-boo. Ram Pari was small, with a wiry threadwork of muscles across her stomach, which Prabhjot Kaur saw when Ram Pari lifted her kameez to wipe her mouth, her old woman's wrinkled face. She did that sometimes, in the late afternoon, instead of using the dupatta from over her head, and Prabhjot Kaur thought it was mainly to get cool, get a little bit of breeze on her skin, but it released a huffing breath of smell, round there in the air, as real and inescapable as a cloud of heated sparks from the fire in the chaunka. Prabhjot Kaur flinched from it, but tried also to keep herself still, to experience the sting of it against her skin. She looked forward to it, and was shamed by this, and kept it a secret. It was her most secret secret, more hidden than the one-rupee coin she had found under the cushion of the sofa in the front room, which she had known to be Papa-ji's, but which had gone to school the next day in her pencil box, which had been good for a week's worth of kesar kulfis, not only for herself but also her two best friends, Manjeet and Asha. She told nobody of her hesitating hunger for Ram Pari's smell, the thick tang and savour of it, not even the others of the Terrific Trio, who wore their double plaits in exactly the same neat style, who had sat together in the second row since Class I.

That day in April the Trio were swaying in the back of Daraq Ali's tanga, with Manjeet in the middle as usual. She was the unquestioned leader, in spite of the other two's better marks and fathers with better jobs. Manjeet's father was only a hotel manager, but she had a tall, lean body and a muscular force of personality and a directness that Prabhjot Kaur and Asha admired but couldn't imagine emulating. They were content to shelter under its somewhat risky shade.

'Chacha, go faster,' Manjeet said now to Daraq Ali, with her arm over the back of the seat. 'Go faster, please, or we'll become blackened cinders here on Larkin Road itself. We'll get seared and disappear in a flash of smelly smoke. Go faster, faster.'

It was after three-thirty and hotter than Prabhjot Kaur could ever remember, and the sun caught them all directly in the back of the tanga, and the road was endless ahead, and Daraq Ali was the oldest and slowest tanga driver in the entire city. He picked them up individually in the morning and trotted, no, ambled them over to school, and then waited for them at three in the afternoon for the endless, draggy, creaking trek back. He thrust his bushy hennaed beard over his sweaty shoulder and said what he always said, 'Bibi, she's been working hard all day in this sun. See how tired she is. I'll ask her to go faster and she'll try, but it'll break her heart.' And then, to the bony brown haunches that rose and dipped under the reins, 'Oh, Shagufta, faster, faster. Faster, Shagufta, for the great Mems who wilt in the hot hot sun.'

'That nag of yours is older than you, Chacha,' Manjeet said. 'Sell her to the knackers and get a strong new mare.'

'But see how hard she's trying,' Daraq Ali said. 'See how she goes. How can you say such things, bibi? You'll break her heart.'

Manjeet snorted and held her basta in front of her face to keep off the sun. 'Oh, yes, we're speeding along now. Just risking our lives in a fantastic chase. I'm really really scared.'

Prabhjot Kaur giggled and then instantly wanted a long glass of water from the surahi which Mata-ji kept wet through the whole day.

176

She thought of it, of tilting the surahi, its clay neck round in her palm, and the water in a smooth stream dropping into the glass with a deepening circular gurgle, and the black road slipped away between the dusty tips of her shoes, and the dreary plonk-plunk plonk-plunk of Shagufta's hooves beat slowly at her temples. She shut her eyes, but she knew they were passing Kalra Shoe Emporium on the right, with its sharp-tipped tree of Lady's Pumps, then Manohar Lal Madan Lal Halwai, where at the back there were Family Booths and a huge mirror etched with a turbaned man and a woman sitting by a stream, and then Kiani Fine Furniture, which had a long red sofa in the front window and had been At Your Service for Fifty Years, not the sofa but old Mr Kiani and his three sons. Prabhjot Kaur made a bet with herself and opened her eyes and yes indeed they were directly opposite the Tarapore Bakery, which was a heaven of cakes and fizzy drinks, visited by Prabhjot Kaur only once in her entire life, on her ninth birthday, and she remembered the loud pop of the glass ball-stopper falling into the strawberry-soda bottle under the weight of Papa-ji's palm. The sides of Prabhjot Kaur's mouth ached, actually hurt her as the memory came fully back, the flood of pink eruptions into her mouth, the tingling on the inside of her lips, and Shagufta pulled ahead, drew them beyond the Tarapore Bakery, and right then Prabhjot Kaur saw Ram Pari. She was walking along the side of the road, with her dupatta flapping behind her and her arms straight by her sides. Prabhjot Kaur squiggled back into the seat, unaccountably ashamed. Something about seeing Ram Pari on this wide road, next to the two white ladies with their hats like lacy gardens and gleaming white strappy shoes and astonishing gauzy dresses from deep in the mysterious foreign regions of Perreira's Ladies Wear, something about Ram Pari's wide-legged walk made Prabhjot Kaur not want to know her right now. And so she turned her head, as if she was looking at something on the far side of the street, but the side of her neck burned, not from the sun but from what she thought was Ram Pari's gaze, and she was unable to resist a quick glance backwards. Shagufta was slowly drawing away from Ram Pari, whose face was taut as a sheet billowing under a hot summer wind, whose eyes were hard and unseeing, even though she was looking straight at Prabhjot Kaur. The angry hunch of her shoulders receded slowly into the glare on Larkin Road, and finally Prabhjot Kaur lost sight of her altogether, just before they took the left turn on to Fulbag Gali and into Chaube Mohalla, where

Manjeet jumped off and ran ahead to her house, her two thick plaits jiggling and jogging behind her.

When Prabhjot Kaur got home, her father was sitting in his baithak with his friend Khudabaksh Shafi, who was drinking tea out of a cup that was kept especially for him. Prabhjot Kaur always thought of it as the Muslim teacup, and there was always trouble with Mata-ji when Papa-ji carried it inside and washed it himself under the hand-pump. Mata-ji always made a face and Navneet-bhenji and Mani always rolled their eyes and said she was being horribly silly. Prabhjot Kaur liked Khudabaksh Shafi, who had a great straight moustache across his face and who never came without gifts. Today he had brought a basket of leechies. 'Especially for you, beta,' he said, and laughed. 'Eat them after dinner. And don't let those two mustandas inside cheat you.' Her two brothers were sprawled on charpais in the courtyard, in cricket whites, drinking enormous brass tumblers of khari lassi. Iqbal-veerji jumped up and picked up his bat – which he seasoned every other day with special oil – and showed her how he had hit three sixes in a single over, off that Shahidul Almansoor, who thought he was the best bowler in the entire province. Prabhjot Kaur rocked forward and back on her toes, trying to be interested, but as soon as she could she shifted sideways away to her mother's room, leaned against the door until a triangle of light opened on the floor. She slid herself through and sat on the end of the bed, on Papa-ji's side. The bed was high enough that she had to use both her hands to climb up, and then the shape of her mother's side was a ridge in the close darkness. A table-fan swept the air to and fro.

'What is it?' Mata-ji said finally, still facing away.

'Is there some trouble with Ram Pari?'

Mata-ji took a long breath. 'These people.'

'Did she do something, Mata-ji?'

'No, no. Her husband.'

'She has a husband?'

'Beta, nine children she has. He's not been home in a year and a half. She was sure he had another wife somewhere. Then yesterday he came back. Like a laat-saab he spread his legs and shouted for his dinner. It's my house, he said.'

'Is it his house?'

'He hasn't earned ten rupees in his life.'

That was very conclusive, somehow. Mata-ji's shoulder shifted and settled and her breathing changed, and Prabhjot Kaur let herself down slowly to the floor, her cheeks stinging. Ram Pari was still trudging away somewhere, in a line as straight as fate, but all Prabhjot Kaur could think about was that she herself had never earned a rupee in her life, only stolen one. She stood in the shadow of the fluted pillars at the edge of the courtyard, watching her brothers and the red stains on their pants from the cricket ball, their pleasant exhaustion, and wondered if this house was hers. It slid away from her all evening, the feeling of home that she'd had from the first day she had seen the rising beams and the hole in the ground half-lined with bricks. Even as the sun walked up the pillars and she sprinkled water in the courtyard and the smell rose of fresh evening, she was not able to plant herself in the place. She slept fluttering and light, wafting and skipping and windblown in her dreams over the white rooftops of Sabhwal city, where she had been born.

She awoke to quarrelling. Mani was arguing that Ram Pari must be allowed to stay. 'She has nowhere to go,' she said, and Prabhjot Kaur could hear the effort it cost her to keep her voice low and reasonable, how it thickened her throat.

'That's all very sad,' Mata-ji said. 'But since when has she become my mausi that I should take care of her? Let her go to her relatives.'

'Mata-ji, I *told* you already, she *has* nobody here. Her husband brought her here from her village. Do you want her to sleep on the streets, with all of those children?'

'When did I say I want her to do anything?' Mata-ji was sitting cross-legged near the kitchen, with a big thal in her lap piled high on one side with wheat. The grains skittered across the metal to the other side under her rapid fingers, without cease, and on the floor next to her there was a small pile of black pebbles and husks and stubble. 'I don't want her to do anything at all.'

Prabhjot Kaur ran through the courtyard, out to the front gate. Ram Pari was squatting just inside the gate, her wrists resting on a rolled-up blue mattress. She was surrounded by children, an incredible sprawl of them. A toddler naked but for a black thread tied around its waist clambered over ankles and shins, its fat legs pedalling rapidly. When he had almost escaped the circle of bodies, a girl of Prabhjot Kaur's age bent and reached for his arm and dragged him back.

'Ram Pari,' Prabhjot Kaur said. 'What happened?'

'What to say, Nikki?' Ram Pari said. 'What to say? My man, he came back.' She spread her hands wide, taking in not only the children and Prabhjot Kaur but the world itself.

'But he can't just drive you out. That's not right.' Now Ram Pari was quiet, and Prabhjot Kaur had the uncomfortable feeling that they were all looking at her, even the baby, all these hot black eyes, quite expressionless but still making her shift about and look for some-where else to go. She made herself back away, and then turned and ran into the house. In her chest there was a panic, a biting dread that was coloured black and crimson, that tasted like a rotten apple she had bit into once, all spongy and brown under the crisp skin. She flung herself at Mata-ji's shoulder. With her face in Mata-ji's hair, she panted, 'Oh Mata-ji, let her stay.'

'You also?' Mata-ji rolled her eyes. 'Saints and social workers my daughters have become.'

Navneet-bhenji laughed. She was sitting at the hall table, a little cup of oil in front of her, and she was combing it through her hair with long, slow strokes that lifted up the black lengths and let them fall like undulating waves. In the new light the heart-shape of her face was glowing, and her lips curled red, and Prabhjot Kaur had never seen her so beautiful.

'Navneet-bhenji,' Prabhjot Kaur cried, close to tears. 'Tell Mata-ji to let her stay.'

'Mixing up in these people's quarrels will only lead to trouble,' Mata-ji said. 'Do you want that man walking about in the lane out-side, and in and out of this house? And that dirty brood of hers . . .'

'Mata-ji,' Navneet-bhenji said, 'you can wash them all, three times.'

'Don't you start, Navneet,' Mata-ji said. 'And you two, get dressed for school.'

When she got that swollen look about her face, Mata-ji was as unmovable as a full canister of desi ghee. Prabhjot Kaur buttoned her uniform with trembling fingers, and all day at school was completely distracted by visions of Ram Pari walking through an endless thorny wasteland, her children whimpering from thirst and dropping one by one. Manjeet and Asha watched Prabhjot Kaur quizzically as she struggled to take notes. At recess she told them about Ram Pari's plight, but they were unmoved, or at least only half as, or quarter as, moved as she was. If that. 'These people keep fighting like that only,' Asha said. Prabhjot Kaur heard the words, and saw the prim little twist to Asha's mouth, and fought down a surge of tears. Manjeet just shrugged. Then they both turned to more urgent matters, to the question of whether it would be possible to persuade Manjeet's father to sponsor an outing over the next weekend. Their heads were close together, and Prabhjot Kaur saw their bright plaits and the clean white of their dupattas, and she wanted to speak, but her feeling for Ram Pari belonged in some dim interior fold, in a turn in a cave, and it was impossible to drag it out squirming and scared into the hard summery light. So Prabhjot Kaur took a deep breath, and was quiet. She was quiet all day, and quiet on Daraq Ali's tanga, all the way home.

The children were still outside, still scrambling in the patch of shade, which had moved across the courtyard and narrowed. Ram Pari was inside the house, scrubbing the last of the pots. Navneet-bhenji was dozing with a book spread over her belly, flapping a fan lazily. Without opening her eyes, she told Prabhjot Kaur the tale of the day's struggle: Ram Pari had come in, without asking, and had started sweeping the courtyard, just as usual; she had gone about her tasks, and Mata-ji watched her, and the two women passed each other in silence. They had not said a word to each other the whole day. Even now, as Prabhjot Kaur watched, Mata-ji came diagonally across the baking bricks, holding a wet knot of clothes in her hand, and she passed within a foot of Ram Pari as she went to the staircase leading to the roof, but both of them swept their eyes away from each other, as if clothes and pots left no attention available for anything else.

'She didn't look at her, yes?' Navneet-bhenji said, still with her eyes closed.

'Who?'

'Mata-ji. She didn't even look at Ram Pari?'

'No, she didn't.'

'That's what she's been doing all day. Oof, Nikki, she drives me crazy. All these silences full of meaning, and everyone else is supposed to understand them and do what she wants. And she's very good at it. Everyone does do what she wants.'

Prabhjot Kaur was silent herself now. She had felt, herself, little stabs of resentment at her mother, when she wasn't allowed to go on a school picnic, when she was served last from the bowl of kheer and less than her brothers, but all of these small angers vanished daily under the vast presence of her mother's warm influence, under the damp, all-enfolding embrace of her motherly arms, which you could feel as soon as you entered the main gate, in the half-bricks painted white with which she had lined the walkway, in the lacy trimmings on the table cloths on the tables in the baithak. But to hear this strange, tinny edge of contempt in Navneet-bhenji's voice was to suddenly know a separation between mother and daughter, between Mata-ji and herself, that Prabhjot Kaur had never imagined before. It made her feel queasy and very alone.

Navneet-bhenji opened her eyes. She looked full into Prabhjot Kaur's face, her eyes still hazy and abstracted. Then she blinked twice. 'Arre, why're you looking like that, bachcha?' she said. 'Don't worry. She can be infuriating, but you'll go away from this house also.'

Prabhjot Kaur had to swallow twice before she could speak. 'Away?'

'Yes,' Navneet-bhenji said, and drew her close. She nestled her in the bend of an elbow and whispered into her hair. 'Haven't you heard? A girl is born into a house, but her home is somewhere else. This house doesn't belong to you. Your home is elsewhere.'

Saying this, Navneet-bhenji stretched and sighed luxuriously, and Prabhjot Kaur felt, through her own head and into her toes, her sister's pleasure in life, her eagerness for the future, her happiness at leaving, at being gone, and yet Prabhjot Kaur felt only an inexplicable loss, and foreboding. And the rough, ashy sound of the pot being scrubbed mingled with her sister's pulse, which throbbed under her ear.

She covered her head with Navneet-bhenji's dupatta and tried to sleep. When Mani came in an hour and a half later, and flung her bag full of books on the floor, Prabhjot Kaur understood that she had seen Ram Pari and the children, who were still camped by the gate, and that she was incensed and ready for battle. But Mata-ji gave Mani such a look, all twisted brow and bulging eyes, that even she quailed, and quietly came and sat down next to Prabhjot Kaur. She picked furiously at a toenail. Then she said, 'We'll have to wait for Papa-ji.'

But Papa-ji was in no mood for struggles. He was exhausted, and he lay back against a masnad and combed his fingers through his beard, and Prabhjot Kaur could see that even though Mani had put her case squarely before him, and had done it well, in a few short, precise sentences, he was thinking of something else. 'That's difficult,' he said. And then he cupped his eyes. Mani was leaning forward, her fingers twisted and twisting in a kind of net. 'That's difficult,' he said, and then got up. He walked towards his room, and had already forgotten about Ram Pari and her difficulties, this was clear. Mani threw back her shoulders and raised her hands in defeat. Prabhjot Kaur drummed her heels on the floor. What to do, what to do? The silence continued, widened. Ram Pari came in at dinner time to make the phulkas, and the only thing that Prabhjot Kaur could hear were the slap-slaps of her hands on the atta. Her brothers were home, but even they ate quietly. Everyone looked worried, except for Navneet-bhenji. Finally, when the dishes had been cleared away, Mata-ji was nibbling on a little thimble of gur, which she held in two fingers above a cupped left hand. Ram Pari came and stood by the wall, leaning against it. She had a hand cocked on a hip, and one ankle crossed behind the other. 'Bibi-ji,' she said. 'I'm going.'

'Go,' Mata-ji said, and Prabhjot Kaur felt something twist and give in the exact middle of her chest.

Ram Pari was half-way across the courtyard when Mata-ji spoke again. 'Where will you go?'

Prabhjot Kaur could see how still Ram Pari was. Her shoulders were thin, dark rectangles, pinned against the moonlit white of the wall behind, against the sharp edge of the roof. She said nothing.

Mata-ji was looking at the tiny piece of gur left on her finger, as if she were weighing it, considering its possibilities. 'All right,' she said. 'You can stay for one night, behind the house.'

'Yes, Bibi-ji.'

'But only one night. Hear me?'

'Yes, Bibi-ji. One night.'

Ram Pari left quickly. Prabhjot Kaur knew that she was hurrying to get out of earshot before anything more could be said, and she herself couldn't bear the thought of any more talk. She felt suddenly limp, tired, as if she had walked all the way to school and back with a great bag hanging on her shoulders. She settled forward, slumped for a moment against Mata-ji's knees, then got up herself without being told to and got ready for bed. But in spite of wobbly knees and dragging eyes, she clambered up on a stool in the corner of the room where she slept with Mani, and craned her neck out of the window at an angle, so that she could see the busy crowd of dark figures bustling about at the back of the house. There was broken light from two windows, that was all, but Prabhjot Kaur saw how Ram Pari and her children were making their home. They had bundles, none of which Prabhjot Kaur could remember seeing during the long day, but from these bundles they now pulled sheets and rags, strips and tatters, which, arranged on the ground close to the house in a rough, jagged circle, became a habitation. Prabhjot Kaur saw how the shadow of a wall alone could be a shelter. She went to sleep filled to the brim with this new knowledge. She remembered all the drawings she had made of 'My Home' in her long life, and now she knew that all those simple boxy houses she had drawn were somehow a lie, and there was some satisfaction in looking back and thinking what a silly-silly child she had been.

The next afternoon, when Prabhjot Kaur got back from school, she went straight around to the back of the house, and there were two thick sheets nailed to the back wall at the upper end and weighted with broken bricks at the other, forming a kind of half-tent, under which the baby dozed. The other children were scattered in disarray around the garden, which wasn't quite a garden yet but mostly dusty earth, two forlorn trees and a wall at the far end. Prabhjot Kaur stepped close to the mouth of the tent and leaned in. Two poking-out bricks had been made into a little shelf, on which sat a bright picture of Sheran-walli-Ma resplendent on her tiger. From a nail hung a cloth bag which contained clothes. Another two nails held a gunny sack with grain in it. In the furthest recess, in the shadiest part of the tent, there was a small mountain of little bags, and against it the baby slept. Prabhjot Kaur thrilled violently, in the little green world behind the sheet, feeling newness jump up her arms in ecstatic little leaps. She was filled with admiration. How competently so little had been made into so much! How brave it was, all of it! She looked down at the baby. He had a thin bracelet on his right wrist, and a black string around his left arm with a taveez hanging from it, and a penis exactly like a little downturned water-tap. Prabhjot Kaur resisted the urge to pick him up and cradle him, and turned around instead. From a foot away the oldest of the girls was watching her, her hands behind her back. She had a dirty and very long plait that came down over her shoulder and hung in front of her, and alert black eyes, and one protruding tooth on the left side of her mouth. Prabhjot Kaur thought she must be about fourteen, but felt – instantly and without question – older than her. 'What's your name, girl?' she said.

'Nimmo,' the girl said.

'Do you know how to read, Nimmo?'

Nimmo shook her head. In half an hour Prabhjot Kaur had learnt, by heart, all their names – Nimmo, Natwar, Yashpal, Balraj, Ramshri, Meeta, Bimla, Nirmala, Gurnaam, in that order – and that none of them knew how to read, that not one of them, not even one of the boys, had ever seen the inside of a schoolroom. Prabhjot Kaur was horrified, because here was the illiteracy of our country, literally in her back veranda, but she was also secretly pleasured, because here was clear direction, a necessary task. She knew what she had to do. She would set about teaching them. But there was the question of how long they would be allowed to stay, whether or not Mata-ji would stick to her one-night policy and ruthlessly force them out into the wide world. Inside the house, Ram Pari was cutting onions, and Mata-ji had her hands slathered in besan, and there were pakoras sizzling madly in the karhai. They were gossiping about the widowed neighbour four plots down, who had a son given to bad ways and alcohol. They seemed quite content together. Prabhjot Kaur tiptoed around all evening, terrified, unable to bring up the one-night question for fear of reminding Mata-ji of it, and unable to forget it. But when bedtime came, and she stuck her head out of the window, the other family was still there, that round cluster of shiny heads in the dark. It was all quite baffling, Prabhjot Kaur thought as she waited for sleep, her head full of plans. People had stances, they threw out opinions, they made ferocious noises, but decisions were often made in a flurry of competing silences, and what was not said mattered more than what was. The world grew more complicated every day, she thought.

The next afternoon, which was Friday, Prabhjot Kaur lined the children in three columns of three, smallest to largest at the back, and started on the Punjabi alphabet. 'Ooda, aida,' she had them chant. For a blackboard she used the bottom half of a broken old carrom board. She drew the letters across the faded lines of the old game, precise as always, looking not just for correctness but also beauty. She immediately discovered that the younger ones were easier to teach. Meeta and Bimla eagerly took to the letters, and bent low over their pieces of paper, tongues curled between lips, and drew clumsy but correct shapes. Nimmo, on the other hand, mooned about, stared into the distance, lay down on her side and put her head down on her arm and drew letters that looked more like smashed kites or tangles of grass than the elegant, swooping, swan-like constructions Prabhjot Kaur wanted. As soon as Nimmo learnt the third letter, she forgot the first one, and when Prabhjot Kaur urged her to try again – 'Ooda, aida, Nimmo, ooda, aida' – she stuck out her tooth and twisted her face into a grin of such happy stupidity that Prabhjot Kaur felt her patience leaving her and wished she had the authority to give her one tight, biting slap on the ear, like the cracky ones the drawing mistress at school flung out with bloodcurdling suddenness. But Nimmo remained as thick as ever, as stubbornly gooey as old cartwheel grease. And Natwar disappeared altogether. On that very first Friday, Prabhjot Kaur turned from her carrom board, and her middle column was missing one student at the very rear. She stamped her foot, and ran to the corner of the building, but he was already outside the gate, running fast, and he didn't turn his head at her call. He never came back for lessons, but appeared regularly just when they finished.

'Never mind about Natwar. He's another one like his father,' Ram Pari said. 'You put something in their heads.' She appeared every afternoon, late, after she had finished the afternoon dishes and there was still time before chai, and she sat cross-legged with her back against the wall to watch the children being drilled. Prabhjot Kaur watched her watching, and after a week decided that she wasn't nearly grateful enough. Yes, Ram Pari rattled at the kids – 'Learn something, you ganwars!' – but she seemed to think it was a kind of game, and when she needed help with some task that Mata-ji had set her, she would march everyone away except the baby, as if hanging a set of dhurries and beating them free of dust was vastly more important than the three-times-table. Prabhjot Kaur's two brothers pretended serious admiration, but when they started calling her 'Adhyapika-ji', she understood that they were mainly amused and gave them a pert shoulder. Navneet-bhenji was too dreamy to care, and Mani didn't have time to discuss it, the exams were coming on. Only Papa-ji understood how important it was. By the time Prabhjot Kaur had got her class, or at least a part of it, to the nine-times-table, he was regularly drinking his evening chai while sitting on a high-backed chair set at an angle to her classroom, so that it squarely faced the garden, where there would be trees some time soon.

'You're doing a good thing, beta,' he told her one day. She was leaning against his arm, watching him pour the chai cleanly from the cup into the saucer. Like all things he did, the motion was parsimonious, without the slightest possibility of waste. His moustache, and the hair on his chin, was a silvery white, but his cheeks were covered with the softest black, and Prabhjot Kaur loved the way the white curved into the black. He drank, tilting the saucer and somehow not getting his moustache the slightest bit moist. He worked for a British company, and Prabhjot Kaur knew the English for what he did, 'Assistant-Regional-Manager' for a medical supply company, and that he had worked his way up from 'Salesman', but what 'Manager' really meant she had no idea. She knew that they also had dada-pardada land in the absolutely fast-asleep village of Khenchi, which despite its deliciously ridiculous name produced eleven quintals per acre of good wheat every year, and this grandfatherly bounty was a great help to them. She did know what a quintal looked like, because she had been to Khenchi once every winter ever since she could remember, to the broken-down yellow house squatting lonely in the middle of green fields. She knew that from the yellow house to this new one was progress, and that all of it had happened because of education, because Papa-ji had been the first boy in the village to pass his Inter and go to college.

'In another six months I'll have them all to class one level,' she said. 'In one year, to class two.'

He looked at her then, from under white eyebrows. 'One year?'

'Yes.'

He put the cup back into the saucer, even though it was still a third full, and handed it to her. She watched while he walked round and round the edges of their plot, brushing the wall with his sleeve. When Mata-ji called Prabhjot Kaur in, he was still out there, trudging in circles with his head low.

Why were old people sad? Mostly Prabhjot Kaur had no idea. Mata-ji had running feuds with aunts and cousins and neighbours, and sometimes she muttered about them and went on the whole day about some ancient betrayal or slight, but there were other days when, for no visible reason, she was just beset by sighs and a powdery sadness that paled her face. Even Navneet-bhenji had days when she seemed silenced by a shapeless melancholy, even after the engagement and the letters had made her languorous and lovely. So Prabhjot Kaur didn't think much of Papa-ji's mood. The next morning he seemed back to his normal sprightly self. There were workmen at the back of the house, and as she was leaving, Prabhjot Kaur gathered that they were to put grilles over the wooden shutters on the windows. What she found when she got home were more like bars, thick rectangular lengths of iron that sat squarely across the windows, and up and down. 'They'll be painted green when they finish,' Papa-ji said. 'Like the shutters.' But now Prabhjot Kaur's window didn't even open all the way, so that Ram Pari's family was hidden from her. She pointed this out to Papa-ji, this inefficiency in the construction, and incredibly enough all he said was, 'There's no time to fix it now, beta. And the window opens all the way, almost.' This was the same man who had had four cartloads of bricks taken back to the supplier because they weren't exactly what he had paid for. Prabhjot Kaur was going to talk about all this the next morning with Manjeet and Asha, but when she got into the tanga, she was amazed to find herself followed by Iqbal-veerji, who swung himself into the front seat and sat next to Daraq Ali, with his cricket bat between his knees and the handle held between two large-fisted hands. He didn't say a word all the way to school. And the three girls sat with their heads half-turned, and nobody in the tanga spoke. Only after they were inside the school gates did Manjeet snap her head and signal a conclave, and they found a corner to stand in, with their shoulders hunched and foreheads almost leaning against each other, and she whispered, 'In Minapur there were three murders last night. Three Hindus were killed.' She was trembling, Prabhjot Kaur could feel Manjeet's elbow twitching against her arm. 'One was a girl.'

Prabhjot Kaur couldn't learn even part of a lesson the whole day. She didn't write a word in her notebooks, and during recess the girls in the whole school stood around in huddles, and not one game of kidi kada was started. When the final bell rang and they all came to the gate, Prabhjot Kaur saw Iqbal-veerji standing by the tanga and felt a relief so gigantic that she ran forward to him, and stood a step away from him almost in tears until he put a hand on her head and walked her back around to the seat. Now there was that silence again, thick and uncomfortable as woollen blankets in the summer, and Daraq Ali didn't say one word to Shagufta, which frightened Prabhjot Kaur more than anything else. The streets seemed less crowded than usual, and Prabhjot Kaur could see that people weren't saying a thing to each other, nobody lingered on street corners or in front of shops to talk. When the tanga finally turned the corner, and she saw the famil-iar tall rectangle of the gate, Prabhjot Kaur exulted in a huge warm gush of safety which felt like a rising bath of honey, all cushiony and caressing against her skin. She ran inside, and hugged Navneet-bhenji, and sat close to her, and drank down an enormous tumbler of milk without even a squeak of ritual protest, gurgling it down in one long run of gulps. Only when the last drop was gone did she notice that Iqbal-veerji had gone on in the tanga, to escort Asha home. That night, she was glad of the bars, for the metal which at least held away dread, even though it couldn't make the fear vanish. She felt lucky she didn't have to sleep outside.

The light pressed on her face and she was awake. The courtyard was bright outside, and she knew it was late in the morning, very late. When she saw the time in the clock on the mantelpiece her heart thumped. The first assembly bell would ring in less than ten minutes. She threw herself out of bed and ran through the door. 'Why didn't you wake me?' she gasped at Mata-ji. 'It's so late.'

Mata-ji reached out a hand. 'It's all right, beta,' she said, her voice soft. 'There's no school today. Or college. Everything is shut.'

'Why?'

'There's some trouble in town. Go and wash your face and then eat.' She reached out further and touched Prabhjot Kaur's hand, held her by the wrist a little. 'Go.'

It was the quietest holiday Prabhjot Kaur had ever had. She stayed inside her room, arranging her books and cleaning out her school-bag, but at eleven she couldn't stand it any more and tiptoed through the house and slipped out of the front door. Standing by the gate, she could feel an absolute lack of motion in the streets, as if everyone had made an agreement and left town simultaneously. And yet she knew they were all there. She went back through the gate and walked around the house, and at the rear all of Ram Pari's brood were huddled together, even Natwar, who was usually bouncing about the lanes on filthy bare feet, rapt in some mysterious secret life Prabhjot Kaur knew absolutely nothing about.

'Go inside, Nikki,' Ram Pari said. 'You shouldn't be out here. Stay inside the house.'

'Why?'

'Bad things are happening, Nikki.' Ram Pari was looking straight at the rear garden wall, and Prabhjot Kaur saw that what had just been an untidy lane beyond, an insignificant ribbon of parched mud covered by a perpetual shifting mist of scraps of paper, was now even

189

in bright daylight a darkness from which danger came. Prabhjot Kaur studied the top of the wall, and wondered if it was high enough. She wanted to go and stand at its foot, to measure its height and so its protection. But now the garden seemed a foreign wilderness, and she couldn't make herself step off the brick on to the earth. She nodded and went back inside, and sat herself on her bed, cross-legged. She was waiting now, and didn't know for what.

Lunch was also a hushed affair, with everyone speaking in low tones, and Navneet-bhenji not saying a word at all. Papa-ji and the two brothers sat in a tight little circle and spoke with their heads lowered. Afterwards, it was back to the bed for Prabhjot Kaur, and more sitting, and then lying down with her heels drumming against the bedcover. 'Will you stop that?' Mani burst out. 'You're driving me mad.' Madness was what Prabhjot Kaur felt pooling behind her shoulder-blades, in that afternoon that passed like a slow procession of ants crawling up her leg. So when the chain at the front gate rattled, the metal sound of it echoed through the house and into Prabhjot Kaur's head and she felt a violent spasm of fear, but it was also a relief. Mani was twisted up on to her elbows, her mouth wide open and her neck a bunched bundle of thin ropes just under the skin. Prabhjot Kaur leapt from the bed and ran. She reached the door and swung out with a hand on a wall and saw Iqbal-veerji and Alok-veerji going through the gate and Papa-ji stepping out. She ran forward and saw Papa-ji standing at the other side of the lane, craning his neck, and there were running feet and the hubbub of voices. Now there was a quick panting next to her, and she saw that it was Natwar. They leaned together against the gate. He had eyes as bright as black agates. He slipped past her, and was out into the lane. Without a moment's hesitation she went after him, and was instantly in the shelter of a group of running men. She kept her eye on Natwar, and followed his dodges through the crowd, his sudden swerves and cuts amongst the huffing bodies. Now they came to a gathering halt, in a dense crowd. Natwar reached, without looking back, and pulled her through, bumping her head on hips and buttocks. She fell out of the jostle, and forward, stubbing her nose on Natwar's shoulder, and the way was clear before them. A tanga stood, tilted forward at an angle she had never seen. Tangled in the harness and traces lay a horse, its neck craning forward in a taut curve, as if it were trying desperately to inch along the ground, pull itself along. It was Shagufta. Prabhjot Kaur saw this straight away. Shagufta's lips were curled back, exposing the huge teeth in a rictus of effort. The front legs were curled together. The back ones were splayed out open, and between them and over them spilled fat blue coils from her belly. Prabhjot Kaur could see straight into Shagufta, into the cavity which was the colour of a very ripe winter jamun. The stuff from inside had come out as if with force, and even though it was not moving, Prabhjot Kaur felt it was still forcing itself out from the body, boiling over in oily billows. The road under the tanga was black and wet. On the other side of the tanga, as far away from it as Prabhjot Kaur, was a heaving crowd of men, Muslim men all of them, she knew this somehow, it wasn't the clothes alone, and at their front she could see Daraq Ali. He was shouting something and Prabhjot Kaur could see his teeth. All their mouths were open and she could see the white shine of teeth. That crowd was coming forward in small jerks and then going back. A shove in Prabhjot Kaur's back moved her forward, and she saw that Shagufta's eyes were wide open and moist. She thought now that Shagufta was still alive and was stepping up to her when she was lifted by her arm, twisted and lifted by it, and she cried out in pain. It was Papa-ji. He ran her back through the crowd, held against his side. He ran and ran. All through the lane she felt his fingers hard on her arm. Inside the gate, inside the courtyard, at home again, he took her by the shoulder and shook her, and his own head was moving back and forth and his face was sweaty, and pulled and pushed by his anger, Prabhjot Kaur saw only a blur. 'Why did you go out?' he said, and slapped her. 'Why did you go out? Haan? Why?' He slapped her again.

'Let her be,' Navneet-bhenji said, and took Prabhjot Kaur to her bed. She laid her down and then climbed on to the bed and held Prabhjot Kaur's head in her lap. She was stroking Prabhjot Kaur's face and shoulders, and Prabhjot Kaur could feel her fluttering heart. Mani was sitting on the floor, her knees up and her back against the wall. Mata-ji came in and shut the door quickly and put up the chain. She sat on the bed, her head covered with her dupatta. In the distance they could hear a confused and continuous shouting, like the steady crackle of a dim fire. 'Vaheguru, vaheguru,' Mata-ji said. They sat together until dark. And then it was quiet.

After that night none of the women went out. Prabhjot Kaur hardly even left her bed. She came out to eat and ran back to it, went out when called by Mata-ji, but then sidled away as soon as possible.

Papa-ji came and sat cross-legged with a pillow over his lap and teased her and made her laugh and tickled the soles of her feet, and she understood that he was apologizing for his moment of panic, and she was able to go out into the courtyard with her hand in his, but despite herself she grew anxious out in the open, she got a feeling in the middle of her chest as if a hard bubble was expanding to the size of an onion, making it hard to breathe. She came back fast, into her room. The white walls made her feel better, and the bars. She looked out of the window sometimes, to find Ram Pari and Natwar and all the rest huddled below, but she avoided raising her eyes to the garden, and what lay beyond. When she turned around, and she was securely in the room, on her bed, she was all right.

Outside, men and women were killed every night, and every day. Prabhjot Kaur knew what this was called: khoon. Prabhhjot Kaur held the word on her tongue, and to her it felt like a square metal apparatus with a gaping hole in the centre. Dripping with viscous fluids and sharp edges glinting. Manjeet had shown her this thing in a senior class history book once, this engine of death, and now it came back to Prabhjot Kaur. Khoon. Papa-ji and the brothers came into the house laden with the names of those who were already gone. A sardar named Jasjit Singh Ahluwalia on the corner where Pakmara Street ran into Campbell Road, near Tarapore Bakery, slashed to hanging bits by men with swords. Ramesh Kripalani, aged sixteen, found with his throat expertly cut around, head hanging into the gutter so that Ali Jafar Road was not sullied by a drop of blood. 'They say a butcher from Karsanganj did it,' Alok-veerji said. 'Caught him on the way home from his Chacha's house.' *Khoon*. There were more, many more. Mata-ji and her daughters listened to the lengthening list. On the day that final exams would have started, Ram Pari's husband was killed. He was one of three looters shot by the police on Larkin Road at six a.m. – Prabhjot Kaur heard about this the next day, first as a rumour, then as a certainty. A wailing rose behind the house, a blurred chorus that rose and fell, and there was nowhere to escape it, and Prabhjot Kaur learnt for the first time his name, Kuldish. All through the day they mourned Kuldish, the bad man who had never come to threaten Ram Pari, and the wails slid under Prabhjot Kaur's skin and made her shiver.

That evening Mata-ji told the brothers to stay at home, not to go out on to the street, and Iqbal-veerji laughed, and the sound fell into the room with a clank like iron. The brothers left anyway, and Alok-veerji glanced back as he shut the door, and Prabhjot-Kaur saw that he looked at her, all of them, his sisters and mother, with anger and something very much like contempt. Mata-ji began to curse Muslims. 'No one can ever live with these people,' she said. 'They are incapable of living peacefully with anyone.' Her face was suffused with blood, flushed and thickened by it. 'Dirty lying people,' she said. Prabhjot Kaur made lists in her mind, of the Muslims she knew. Daraq Ali, of course; Papa-ji's friend Khudabaksh Shafi, who came to visit always with baskets of strawberries or apples or mangoes, and all his sons and daughters and grandchildren; Parveena and Shaukat Shah, who owned the Excellent Store, from which Prabhjot Kaur and all her brothers and sisters had bought school uniforms and shoes all their lives; all the Muslim girls at school, especially Nikhat Azmi, who was a round-faced girl that the Trio played with whenever they went to Manjeet's house. The list went on and on, and once Prabhjot Kaur started, it seemed to her there was always one more person, one more face that she remembered late at night, before drifting into sleep. But Mata-ji cursed. And Pritam Singh Hansra wrote letters to Papa-ji. He had stopped writing to Navneet-bhenji, and instead wrote letters to Papa-ji begging him to come to Amritsar, to bring the family, all of it, but especially Navneet-bhenji. He had been in Amritsar for a month and a half already. 'You know yourself what is happening,' he wrote. 'And things can only get worse.'

But Papa-ji was paralysed. He shook his head in the morning at the newspapers' reports of flames and murder and ambushed trains full of refugees, and in the afternoon he was completely still. He sat crosslegged on an armchair in the courtyard, not even shifting in his seat, as if he were bound with tight chains that slowed even his breathing. He stopped changing his clothes then, and sat through the whole day in a banian and pyjamas, his hair loose under a patka and bare feet resting on the brick. Prabhjot Kaur knew he was waiting for something, and saw that he had been emptied of vigour, suddenly drained of volition like an upended bucket. She remembered how he had bounded from one side of the excavation to the other when the foundation was being dug, how he had not minded that his arms were muddied from grasping at the earth, how he had held up handfuls of mud from the bottom of the pit for her to test for moistness, how he had dusted his hands with great slappings of them, with wide sweeps to the sides and sharp cracks that she had jumped at. There was no more motion in him, and even the blinks of his eyes were slow, mournful sweeps, which Prabhjot Kaur could follow down and up. One day, she thought, I'll come out and even that will be stopped, finished, unmoving. She tried not to think this, but it came back as slyly as a persistent fly, this thought, and then its buzzing grew louder and louder until she hit at her forehead with the heels of her hands. I'll go mad, she thought. I will.

Finally Mata-ji took charge. It was now past summer and everyone they knew had gone, Manjeet and Asha and their families also. One evening a Pathan policeman rattled the gate. When Iqbal-veerji cracked the door an inch, the chain still firmly in place, the policeman flicked in an envelope that landed at Alok-veerji's feet. 'I'll be back in half an hour for an answer,' the policeman whispered, and went down the lane. Inside the envelope was an unsigned letter.

Sardar Saab, I will not sign my name, for this letter may be read. But you know who I am. I am your friend who brings fruits from the mountains. Now listen to me as your friend. You must go. You are being talked about, and today or tomorrow your house will be attacked. Understand what I am saying. Specifically your house. Your sons are known and there is talk about what they have done and they are in danger, much much danger. You must go. I will make arrangements. We have known each other for thirty years and I have sat in your house and you have come to mine. You must go, my friend. I will look after your house.

Papa-ji listened to Iqbal-veerji reading this out, and his face sat still as a lump of slack clay, blurry and softened. Mata-ji took the letter from her son's hand, and she put her dupatta over her head and wrapped it around her face. She waited by the gate, and when the small hollow knock came she put her mouth to the wood. 'Tell him we'll go,' she said.

'Be ready tomorrow night at nine,' the policeman said. 'A tempo will come. It will be a thousand rupees per person. No more, but no less. Understand?'

'Yes,' Mata-ji said. 'I understand.'

They packed all night and all day. Prabhjot Kaur was amazed at how many things were in a house. Papers, clothes, books, silver jars, photographs, chairs, more clothes, mattresses, expensive combs, shoes, each person had an array of things that were attached to them with tight knots of many-threaded time, each person had a heavy load of things that couldn't be left behind. Prabhjot Kaur looked at several ranks of dolls she no longer played with, threadbare heads that she hadn't petted in years, but then she tugged and strained at a paper sack trying to fit them all in, filled it with these long-ago companions until the paper gave way and tore with a single sharp rip. By late afternoon the courtyard and the baithak were full of tottering bundles tied in sheets, and staggeringly heavy suitcases, and iron trunks which took four people to lift. Prabhjot Kaur was trying to decide which books to take when Mata-ji came rushing in. 'Here, put this on.' It was a blue salwar-kameez with a square geometric print on rather thick cotton, which Prabhjot Kaur had decided three months ago was fit only for everyday house wear. But here was Mata-ji quite impatient. 'Take, take.' Prabhjot Kaur took it and wondered at the heavy tug of its weight. Mata-ji was gone already, out of the door. The salwar was what was heavy. Prabhjot Kaur turned it over and saw that there were little packets of cloth that had been stitched to the waistline, on the inside, just under the nada. There was metal in these little secret pockets, gold, she could feel the smooth, slippery density of necklaces and bracelets. When she walked out into the courtyard after changing, she saw that Mata-ji and all the sisters were wearing the same loose, rough clothing, ready for a strange kind of travel, and that they were all moving with a care-laden awkwardness, as if they didn't know the edges of their bodies any more. Mani clinked as she walked past Prabhjot Kaur, and yet Prabhjot Kaur was unable to be amused by her attempts to silence herself, her rolling heel-toe walk. Now nobody was saying a word. The sun was gone, sunk, and Prabhjot Kaur sat on a trunk and saw the surfaces of her home recede into dimness. Iqbal-veerji came in, his arms muddy, and washed his hands under the hand-pump. When the water fell on the brick it was very loud, the splatter like an explosion, and Prabhjot Kaur flinched. Then, again, silence.

'Bibi-ji.' It was Ram Pari. 'Bibi-ji.' She was whispering. Mata-ji said nothing. Ram Pari came in and squatted on the ground next to her, next to the charpai. 'What will we do?' she said. 'What will we do?'

'Here,' Mata-ji said. 'I'll give you some money.'

Prabhjot Kaur was glad of the darkness, because it hid her face. She had both hands to her mouth. For days now, or maybe it had even been weeks, she hadn't thought of them. She hadn't thought of Ram Pari, or Natwar, or Nimmo, or any of the others, the family just outside her window. They had been her students, and she had forgotten them completely. She had retreated to her bed and had given them up.

'Bibi-ji, where will we go? How?'

'I don't know, Ram Pari. Just take this.'

Prabhjot Kaur could see the long shape of Mata-ji's arm, held out. Ram Pari was the dark lump at the end of the charpai.

'Take,' Mata-ji said.

The shapes stayed the same, tilted slightly away from each other, the same distance with the same reaching between them, and a breath forced itself down Prabhjot Kaur's chest, pierced it, and in that sudden rough pain she had the certain knowledge that the world would never be the same again. She wanted to say something but there was nothing to say.

'You will leave us, Bibi-ji,' Ram Pari said. 'We will die.'

'Vaheguru will look after all of us.' Mata-ji held the hand out further, and shook it assertively. Ram Pari sank further into the tight huddle she had made of herself. Prabhjot Kaur thought they might all sit there for ever, under that huge, still sky. Then Alok-veerji came out of his room, loomed out tall above them all.

'Take it,' he said, and he took the money from Mata-ji's hand and lifted Ram Pari by the shoulder and walked her past Prabhjot Kaur. 'There is a kafila leaving two days from now. There will be thousands of people walking. You can go with them.' Prabhjot Kaur slipped off the trunk and walked close behind Alok-veerji, and though she couldn't see him doing it, she knew that he had thrust the money into Ram Pari's hand. 'We can't do anything now. Go.' He pushed her through the door and turned and went back to his preparations. Ram Pari stood in the passageway between the courtyard and the outside, stood very close to the wall. Prabhjot Kaur took a step forward and put both her hands against Ram Pari's side, clutched at her, leaned on her, she could feel the cloth against her face, against her eyes, and there was the living exhalation of another person, sweaty and sharp, bitter, Prabhjot Kaur breathed it in. Then Ram Pari forced her hands open. Down the passage she went, a shadow close to the wall, and Prabhjot Kaur watched her go.

The tempo, when it came, an hour late, was not the truck they were expecting but a creaky black car. The driver was a tiny bald man, and he was accompanied by the policeman of the afternoon. 'Hurry,' the policeman said. 'Hurry.' Iqbal-veerji and Alok-veerji loaded up the boot of the car and tied it down with rope. Two trunks and various bundles went on the roof, and inside the car, on the floor around the seats, they had bundles. But then the car was full.

'Come,' Iqbal-veerji said. As they slipped past the baithak, Prabhjot Kaur saw the figures clustered by the corner to the left, she couldn't see any faces but knew it was Ram Pari and Nimmo and Natwar and the rest. All the way to the gate she stumbled against packages that were being left behind. The engine of the car was already thumping. Papa-ji sat on the right in the back seat, then Mata-ji, then Navneet-bhenji and Mani and then Iqbal-veerji. Prabhjot Kaur sat in the front between Alok-veerji and the bald driver. The policeman patted the bonnet of the car.

'Go,' he said. 'Go quickly.'

As they went, Prabhjot Kaur twisted on the seat, came up on her knees to look back. But all she saw was the policeman, standing quite erect in front of the gate, and Mata-ji and Navneet-bhenji and Mani curled up in the back seat, heads low, like little children settled in to sleep on a long journey. 'Get down,' Alok-veerji said, and caught Prabhjot Kaur by the neck and yanked her low. His voice shook and now Prabhjot Kaur was very afraid. Her face was against his side and against the seat, but her eyes were strained open and she could see past the driver's elbow and through the steering wheel and through the glass, she could see the shape of homes and shops, the white of signs and the sudden deeper black when a street opened out, they turned and turned again and the engine grunted and choked and Prabhjot Kaur was completely unable to tell where they were. Then a series of pops sounded into the sky that Prabhjot Kaur could see through the dirty glass, pops like phap, phap-phap-phap as if a child had burst a balloon, and then a series of others very quickly. It was a happy sound. But the car jogged and twisted and came to a halt, sliding Prabhjot Kaur forward. And now it went backwards. Backwards and backwards so fast that Prabhjot Kaur twisted her hands around Alok-veerji's shirt and was now crying. She could hear men's voices, shouting and echoing. And Iqbal-veerji: 'Take this left here and then the Ravi Road.' The car moved forward now, turning to the left and throwing Prabhjot Kaur again. They were moving fast now, she felt it in the vibrations jolting her body. Orange light filled the inside of the car, spiralling through the glass and brightening every corner, and she could see the round silver rupee dangling from the key-chain, every detail of the King-Emperor's face. With a sound like a huge threshing watermill the flames towered up, for a moment filling the windscreen and the window and she shut her eyes. Another turn, this time to the left, and glass broke somewhere and then a sound so loud and so close and so ugly that Prabhjot Kaur knew instantly that it was a gunshot. The car lurched violently from side to side, a screech filled Prabhjot Kaur's head, she flew forward, and felt the impact of metal against her forehead, and a flowering, tinny echo inside which swallowed her up. Then she was lying on her side listening to a babble of voices, a continuous scream not very far away, and she could not tell where she was until the dark bar above twisted and receded and became one of the spokes of the steering wheel, and again that barking explosion, right above her head, this time she saw a flash, and she twisted herself and thrust herself further into the shadowed space under the wheel, and then again a shot and she shut her eyes.

She could hear Mata-ji weeping. Other than that hoarse gargling noise, it was very quiet. Prabhjot Kaur tried to still the movement of her knees, a shaking which grew from the convulsing of her stomach. She was convinced that this would give her away. She held her right hand against her right thigh and pressed it down hard. Metal scraped, and she knew it was the door of the car, and there was nowhere to go, and she wanted to scream but she held it in, fought against it with her muscles. 'Nikki, Nikki.' It was Iqbal-veerji. He drew at her softly and she came out of her coil and held on to his arms and cried. He got her out of the car and she wrapped herself around him. 'It's all right,' he said. But Mata-ji was sitting on the road, and Mani was trying to comfort her. And Papa-ji leaning against the back of the car, his head low and his hands on his knees, and spittle hanging from his mouth. Alok-veerji a little down the road, his body twisted to one side as he tried to see around a corner. Just beyond him there was a shape on the ground, like a bundle of clothes had come apart and scattered its contents haphazardly. It was a man's body. There was the head, and there was a hand. It was the driver.

Alok-veerji turned. 'We have to get out of here.'

'I don't know how to drive,' Iqbal-veerji said mildly.

They both looked stunned, as if this one skill they had forgotten to add to their sporting repertoire had suddenly revealed its hidden importance, its secret meaning.

And then Mata-ji stopped crying and said, 'Kill them.'

Her weeping had been so constant and so loud that when it stopped Prabhjot Kaur felt keenly how quiet it had become all over again, after all the bedlam. It was rather nice. But who did she mean? Mata-ji looked at her husband, and at one son and then at another.

'Kill them,' she said. 'Before they take them too.'

Prabhjot Kaur turned her head towards the car, and then to the street. Navneet-bhenji was gone. Prabhjot Kaur had not noticed until now, but now it was impossible to escape this fact. Navneet-bhenji had been taken.

Alok-veerji came towards Mata-ji, and Prabhjot Kaur saw that in his right hand he had a pistol, and in his left something long and curving. The front of his shirt hung down on the left side like a flap, revealing the inverted arc of his chest. There was blood on his neck, black and flowing, she could see it. And dangling not very far from her face, from Iqbal-veerji's hand, was a kirpan, no, a sword.

'Kill them,' Mata-ji said again. Mani's face was hidden from Prabhjot Kaur, darkened. Prabhjot Kaur could see only her unmistakable thin shoulders, her forearms as she held Mata-ji. Prabhjot Kaur stepped away from Iqbal-veerji, and raised her head, and saw that his pagdi had come off, his hair hung in a loose coil over his forehead. His mouth was shaking. He was looking at her and she saw him fight for control, bite down on his lower lip to stop it from trembling. Her fear now felt different, like a long, continuous fall from a great height, but in spite of this hurtling drop she felt embarrassment for her brother. She lowered her head and waited. She was waiting for death, a khoon ordered by her mother.

'I'll drive,' she heard Papa-ji say. 'I can drive.'

Of course, Prabhjot Kaur thought. He used to be a salesman. The car started on the first try, but then they had to push it back and up from the gutter it had dropped its front left wheel into. Prabhjot Kaur turned round and round on the dark street, unable to stay still, trying to face everywhere and afraid of what was behind her back. Then they were all in, and Prabhjot Kaur this time crouched down as far as she could get in the front seat. She pushed at the bundle in front of her with her legs, and when it gave way a little she forced her legs and hips into the little space she had made. She wished she could get under the bundle. She wished there was a little secret space under the seat that she could tuck herself into. She wished for a dark little metal hole which nothing would ever be able to get into, where she could get away from Mata-ji's horrible croaking sobs, her 'Vaheguru, Vaheguru' and her Japji Sahib which pierced all the clatter of the car and Prabhjot Kaur's own clamorous breathing, and Prabhjot Kaur clapped her hands hard and desperate over the ears.

She saw nothing. She kept her eyes closed. But there was a change in the sound of the road, a difference in the texture of the black under her eyelids, and she knew that they had left the city behind. Near dawn they came upon two trucks of soldiers, stopped by a well. Alok-veerji was afraid, but Papa-ji said there was no choice. They approached them slowly, and just before the car stopped Prabhjot Kaur opened her eyes. The sky was a neutral grey, the colour half-way between black and white. She had never stayed up all night before.

'These are Muslims,' she heard Mata-ji say. They were, and their leader was a major by the name of Sajid Farooq. Prabhjot Kaur read it on his breast pocket as she sat on a villager's charpai, shivering. Sajid Farooq put their car between the soldiers' trucks that morning, and by the afternoon they had a caravan thirty-one vehicles long. The next morning Prabhjot Kaur saw a line, a stream, a river of walking people that stretched to the horizon. The men and women and children walked behind each other in silence, trudging in the same direction as Sajid Farooq's trucks, and all the cars. They were moving very slowly, and the trucks and cars moved past each one of them with ease, but it took three hours to leave behind that whole lot. That evening they were met by other soldiers, in the same uniforms and the same trucks, but these were Hindus escorting a convoy of Muslims. Alok-veerji said the soldiers were Madrasis. This was the first thing Prabhjot Kaur had heard him say in two days. His eyes were red and sometimes tears ran down his face and he seemed not to notice them. Sajid Farooq took the convoy of cars and trucks that had come with the Madrasis, put his soldiers in front of them and behind them and drove away. Prabhjot Kaur watched the Muslims drive past, going to Pakistan. Then the Madrasis took the Sikhs and Hindus to India. The trip was uneventful. In two days they were in Amritsar.

Here they lived in a city of three thousand tents. People came from the city with clothes and food, to give to the refugees, and a politician came to walk through the filthy lanes that had been ploughed out by hundreds of feet between the walls of canvas. Prabhjot Kaur hid in their tent when she saw the photographers that came with the Congressman. She felt shame, a powdery burning that sizzled across her arms and shoulders. She saw it in Papa-ji's face when he took a half-sack of wheat from a bania who had brought a cartload of food-stuff from the city. She saw it in Mata-ji's crouch, how she sat with her dupatta pulled over half her face, and she saw it in Mani's long bouts of sleep, in the determined way that she lay herself down and turned away to one side, even when the sun burned on the canvas and the ground felt as if it were heated from underneath. They were all ashamed. Prabhjot Kaur felt it most when she looked at Mata-ji's face, her nose, her mouth, her lined forehead, and so she never looked at her. She cast her eyes up, or to the side, or examined her own hands, or sometimes, while walking by, just shut one eye or the other so that there was no chance of seeing. In Mata-ji it was unbearable, this shame, but it was in all of them, it hung around them like a bad, unwashed smell. It was shame that constricted Alok-veerji's throat, so that each word cost an effort of the muscles and emerged compacted and slow.

'It was an ambush,' Alok-veerji was saying. 'It was that Khudabaksh Shafi. He had it all planned.'

Prabhjot Kaur was standing outside the tent, holding a pile of damp clothes higher than her head.

'You mean for the house? He wanted the house so he scared us out?' This was Iqbal-veerji.

'Yes,' Alok-veerji said. 'The house. And everything else.'

Prabhjot Kaur's head hummed with an onrush of blood. This 'everything else' was something they never spoke about. Nothing was ever said, not one word. One name had disappeared from the world, taking with it a whole life.

'I can't believe that,' Iqbal-veerji said. 'I can't.'

'Believe it,' Alok-veerji said. 'They took the house, they took our land, but they weren't satisfied with that much. It was all planned. The driver drove us straight into an ambush, they were waiting. There were enough of them to – to take what they wanted. But they didn't expect us to be well-armed. So they got what they wanted, but they couldn't kill us all. So they ran. That is the truth about those people. I only wish I had done more. Instead of burning three houses I wish we had burnt a thousand. And killed a lakh of them.'

'Alok. Be quiet.'

'Why? Why be quiet? I'll shout it out loud. These Muslims are bhenchods and maderchods. If all their women were standing in front of me, I would hang them up and cut them open like goats. I would pull out their intestines with my own hands. With pleasure I would do it. Bhenchods. Maderchods.'

Prabhjot Kaur ran. She dropped the clothes and ran away. Her mother's words followed her: 'Kill them.' She tripped over tent-ropes and skinned her palms on the black gravel, and she ran past children kicking a piece of wood from one side of the pathway to the other, past women squatting in the doorways of tents repairing torn shirts, past bubbling pots on makeshift choolas of six bricks, past everything until she was finally at the edge, beyond all habitation. Ahead there was a brown path, and on the other side of that a bare maidan strewn with rocks, and then endless fields, green and thick. She stopped and held her sides, bent over until the sweat fell straight from her forehead to the ground, making dark circles on the earth. She straightened up. She wanted to go away. She wanted a place to go to, somewhere very far away, hundreds of miles from her family, thousands of miles from everyone. *Haven't you heard? A girl is born into a house, but her home is somewhere else. This house doesn't belong to you. Your home is elsewhere.* If I could keep walking, she thought. But she knew her geography too well, those lessons she had learned with the Trio, the ones she had written down in fair handwriting in books covered with brown paper. And now, now she knew more. There were seas to one side, mountains to another, nowhere to go, and fear everywhere. You would have to cross fear to get nowhere. The maidan was still, and the fields waited, silent. Prabhjot Kaur stood alone, at the edge of the city of refugees. Then she turned and went back to her father and mother and brothers and sister.

Finally they managed to go to Delhi. Mata-ji took out from underneath her clothes some of the jewellery she had carried, and this time they went by train. The two brothers deposited the rest of the family in the house of Gunjan Singh Parvana, who was not really a relative, but the son of a man from the village Khenchi. There was an ancient story about how Papa-ji's father had saved Gunjan Singh Parvana's policeman father from summary dismissal and unemployment, and so now he took them in. They had two tiny rooms and a veranda at the back of the house. Then the two brothers went to what was now the border, and beyond, to a foreign country. They had not wanted to go, but Mata-ji now said, for the first time, 'Go and find my daughter.' Prabhjot Kaur heard this while she pretended to sleep. Nowadays there were many discussions among the elders of the family that she and Mani were kept out of. Mani was really asleep, and even whimpering a little, but Prabhjot Kaur kept herself awake every night. She wanted to know, had to know. Staying awake got easier and easier. There were certain practices that kept you from an unknowing slide into yourself, from a feathery fall into the vacuum of rest: you paid attention to details, you kept the mind working and turning and racing, you listened. And Prabhjot Kaur heard Mata-ji's voice, low and full of phlegm and fierce: 'Go and find my daughter.' The other murmurs were all run together and powdery and hard to catch, but Prabhjot Kaur heard the command: 'Go and find my daughter.' It brooked no resistance. So they went. What Prabhjot Kaur couldn't understand was why they were reluctant to go. Of course they should go, she thought, why don't they want to go? and felt instantly a hurt in her stomach, a fist that grew upwards and twisted her heart so that she thought she would cry out loud. But she was silent, silent and awake, night after night, and she waited.

They returned a month and a half later, forty days and forty-one nights later, to be exact. Prabhjot Kaur, who now kept strict track of time, jerked out of a sleep that she was sure was only a few minutes old, and knew they had come back. The door to Mata-ji's room was shut, and the tones were very soft, but she heard them nevertheless, and she was certain. She got up and stood next to the door for a minute, and rested her head on the rough grey wood, and the voices passed into her forehead. She had no hope. Night after night she had imagined it, the happy moment, that sliding swish of salwar-bottoms over ground, that sound she knew so well, how she would cling to Navneet-bhenji, with her head buried in the soft comfort of home, and the beloved blood singing in the arms that held her. Now she knew this would not happen. She turned away, walked out on to the veranda. There was a wire fence, and beyond that a line of gulmohar trees, and in the distance a rising ridge. This was all the Delhi she knew. Next to the fence there was a woman crouching, and Prabhjot Kaur knew right away who it was: Ram Pari. She knew that squat, that comfortable ease so close to the ground, that position she could hold for hours.

'Is that Ram Pari?' Mani came out on to the veranda and ran down to the fence. She bent down to Ram Pari, and then Prabhjot Kaur saw Ram Pari's upturned face. She was an old woman. The skin hung off her cheekbones in limp whorls. She had a dupatta wrapped over her shoulders, a red one, and Prabhjot Kaur remembered it well from before. Now it was tattered and faded to a rusty brown. 'Where did you come from?' Mani said to Ram Pari.

'Iqbal-veerji, I saw him at the bus station,' Ram Pari said, and it was a shock to hear her husky voice, with the familiar village rhythms. 'We had come across the border. Walking.'

'And . . . and where is everyone?'

Prabhjot Kaur wanted to shout something at Mani. It seemed an unbearable question to ask, and she had no wish to hear it, or wait for an answer. But she stood absolutely still, unable to move.

Ram Pari shook her head. Slowly, she shook her head. To one side and then another.

There was the creak of the door, and Papa-ji came past Prabhjot Kaur, and then the brothers. The three men stood in the veranda, uncertain, it seemed, of what to do or where to go next. Mani had a hand on Ram Pari's shoulder. Prabhjot Kaur willed movement into herself, she turned and went into the house. In the small airless room to the right, her mother was weeping. She was sitting on the ground, next to a charpai, with her arms thrown over the sheets, and her head was down and she was sobbing. The sound was small and infant-like. Not angry, or outraged, just surprised. Prabhjot Kaur went in and stood next to Mata-ji, her knees feeling a small rattling from the bed, and sensed in herself a large anger, felt herself swell with it, become as hard as a rock, and also a sharp, cutting river of pity, a helpless overflowing of it. Her mother's head had grey hair, very dry and broken and ugly, and a balding patch at the back, and underneath, scalp as young and smooth as a baby's. Prabhjot Kaur shut her eyes for a moment, and then reached forward and put her hand on her mother's head. Mata-ji's body arced, and she came towards Prabhjot Kaur like a blind, nuzzling animal and held her around the waist with both arms, and leaned on her, and Prabhjot Kaur steadied herself, and patted her gently on the shoulders and neck, and tried to comfort the woman in her grief.

Burying the Dead

❧

Sartaj woke at seven. Ma was already sitting at the dining table, reading a newspaper through thick bifocals. She was bathed, dressed in a crisp white salwar-kameez, her hair neatly combed. He never in his life had managed to wake up before her, and sometimes he wondered if she ever slept.

'Sit,' she said. She brought out a plate, a cup. He read the paper: the cross-border peace process was picking up momentum. But twenty-two men had been killed in Rajouri by Kashmiri militants, maybe foreign mercenaries. The militants had stopped a State Transport bus on a main road, lined up the Hindu men on one side, and fired at them with AK-47s. One traveller had survived, under the bodies, with a bullet in his groin. There was a photograph of the corpses, lined up in a lumpy row. Sartaj smelt cooking eggs. He thought, why do we always line them up? Why not put them in a circle? Or a V? Or just anyhow, this way and that? It was one of the things you did when you had lots of victims, line them up, as if this controlled and contained the chaos of the event, metal exploding through living flesh. Sartaj had himself dragged limp bodies into ordered ranks, and felt better for it.

'These Muslims will never let us live in peace,' Ma said as she put down an omelette in front of him. It was the way he liked it, very fluffy with lots of chillies but no onions.

'Ma,' Sartaj said, 'this is a war. It's not like all Muslims are monsters or something.'

'I didn't say that. But you don't know.' She had taken off her glasses, and was polishing them now with her dupatta. When she looked at him, her face was absolutely expressionless, closed up like a steel-shuttered window. 'You don't know these people. They are just different from us. We will never let them live in peace either.'

Sartaj turned to his omelette. There was no arguing with her, she was set in her ways, and finally she would bring out heavy, simple assertions that she treated as unquestionable, and would hold to them like anchors. It was annoying and useless, any attempt to have this discussion, and it would just raise her blood pressure. Sartaj turned the page, and read a long human-interest story about a paan-wallah and his luxuriant moustaches.

In the crowded calm of the gurudwara, later, he watched his mother. She was sitting with her knees up, holding her arms around them in a way that he always thought of as girlish. As the massed voices rose and soared in a kirtan, she was lost in memory. He knew that look, soft, with half-drooped eyes gazing into the middle distance, that inwardness. She was very small, very fragile, and looking at her thin wrists he was full of fear and thought again that he should take her to live with him. How long do we have them, he thought, our parents? How long? But she was very stubborn, and clung to her house like a soldier fighting a war. The last time they had argued about this, she had said, this is my home. I will only leave it one way, when the time comes. And he had seen suddenly how alone one could be in this gigantic world, when time took your father and mother from you, and he had said, spluttering, don't talk like that.

'Tarai gun maya mohi aayi kahan baydan kaahii,' the singers sang. We are walkers on this journey, Sartaj thought, and we drop one by one. On the other side of Ma there was her oldest brother, Iqbal-mama, swaying from the shoulders to the hip. He was a very religious man, a trustee of the gurudwara, occupied always in good works and charity. Sartaj liked him, but found his constant piety stifling. There had been another mama, Alok-mama, who all the children had liked a lot more. Sartaj still remembered with awe how much that elephantine sardar used to eat, roasted chickens for breakfast, rogan josh for lunch with fresh jalebis afterwards, dinner was an epic struggle, with Scotch whisky added and Alok-mama's face glowing red. The children, all the cousins, used to joke that there was a trapdoor inside Alok-mama which led to an enormous cave where all the food disappeared, it was incredible that one man should eat so much. He used to wheeze going from one room to another. His wife found him dead one morning in the bathroom, with water from the tap falling on his face. This was when Sartaj was fourteen.

Iqbal-mama was very religious, and Mani-mausi was not at all so. There had been fights, shouted quarrels, when she had been sarcastic about Iqbal-mama's eternal worshipping. Ma always offered sisterly counsel to Mani-mausi, tried to keep her from baiting their brother. But nobody could rein in Mani-mausi when she was in one of her moods. She was quite the scandal of her family, with her divorce and her fiercely communist political beliefs and her vocal atheism. Sartaj didn't know how much he himself believed any more. He of course kept his beard, the hair, the kara, but he hadn't prayed of his own accord for years. There were pictures of the gurus in his house, but he no longer asked them for advice, or expected miracles from them, or even an easier day. The colours in the pictures seemed too bright to him now, the absolutely pristine whites of Guru Nanak's turban too far from dirty life. Still, Sartaj thought, it was good to come with his mother to this place. There was good light, and companionship in the aligned shoulders of the worshippers, and comfort.

Ma adjusted her salwar over her feet, and Sartaj thought then of the woman in Gaitonde's bunker, the long sprawl of her legs in her stylish pants. They had found no evidence of religion in her apartment, no cross or bible or rosary. So perhaps she was irreligious, or maybe just indifferent. But she had consorted with Gaitonde, whose long prayers and donations to religious causes were legendary. For a while during the late nineties, he had projected himself in the media as the Hindu Don, brave defender against the anti-national activities of Suleiman Isa. Sartaj remembered a *Mid-Day* interview in which Gaitonde had predicted the early demise of Suleiman Isa. 'We have teams active in Pakistan, looking for him,' Gaitonde had said. There had been an old file photograph at the top of the story, a very young Ganesh Gaitonde wearing a red sweatshirt and dark glasses. Sartaj had been impressed by the look. He had his own style, Ganesh Gaitonde did, but finally he had been the one who died, without any intervention – it seemed – by his old enemy. Why? It was an interesting mystery, somewhat pleasurable to contemplate, and Sartaj gave himself to theorizing about it for the rest of the morning.

He was still speculating when he and Ma finally got home, late in the afternoon. After leaving the gurudwara, they had spent two hours at Iqbal-mama's house, amongst a swirling welter of nieces and nephews. Sartaj had grown up an only child, and he rather liked – in small doses – the comfortable chaos of large families. Now Sartaj was pleasantly tired, but his mind was lazily ticking along, building stories about Ganesh Gaitonde. He was lying in bed, in a curtained darkness, wondering whether there had been a failed love affair between Gaitonde and Jojo Mascarenas, some tangled tale of fleshly desire and betrayal which had led to a murder-suicide. That was likely, he decided. Men and women did that kind of thing to each other.

'Sartaj, I want to go to Amritsar.'

Sartaj jerked up. Ma was standing in the doorway. 'What?'

'I want to go to Amritsar.'

'Now?' Sartaj rubbed his eyes, swung his feet to the floor.

'Arre, no, beta. But soon.'

Sartaj pulled back a curtain, letting in a spill of light. 'Why suddenly?'

Ma straightened the sheet. 'Not suddenly. I have been thinking about it for a while.'

'You want to see Chacha and all those people?'

'I want to go to Harmandir Sahib once more before I die.'

Sartaj stopped, his hand on the wall. 'Ma, don't talk like that. You'll go many times.'

'You just take me once.'

A heaviness had settled in Sartaj's chest, squeezing away his voice. He came around Ma, picked up his empty suitcase and touched her awkwardly on the shoulder. 'I'll see when I can get leave.' He coughed. 'Then we can go.'

While Sartaj packed, Ma brought in a pile of freshly ironed clothes. She sat on the bed and watched him. She had never done this, in all the hundreds of times he had prepared to leave home, and he felt her gaze slowing him. He had always been a neat packer, but now he tucked his socks into the rectangular slot between his shirts and pants with fanatical care. Ma told stories about Amritsar relatives, and by the time Sartaj had the suitcase closed, he knew he was late starting out for the station. Still, he lingered by the front door, and repeated his peri paunas, and tried not to think of the last time he had said goodbye to Papa-ji, at this same door.

Sartaj made it on to the train, but barely, and he was unable to sleep through to Dadar station as he usually did. Through dirtied glass, he watched the familiar darkening ridges slide by, outlined against the shape of his own face. He had made this journey many times, and loved it well, the long tunnel from Monkey Hill to Nagnath which had so excited him as a child, the steep inclines and the sudden turns that swept back hillsides like stage curtains to reveal the astonishment of plummeting green valleys, and you felt an exhalation and wonder in your chest, and were glad you were going somewhere. He got it still, that little puff of excitement, but now it had inside itself a little twinge of loss and nostalgia. Maybe this was why people had kids, so that when you could no longer travel with your parents, your children made all train trips new again. Then you could watch the lights of Mumbai appear, and be fully happy that you were home.

'Yes, bring in Bunty,' Parulkar said. 'By all means, bring him in, indeed.'

'I should do it, sir? Not one of your people?' Sartaj meant one of Parulkar's picked men who dealt with gangs.

'No, Bunty probably trusts you best. If I send one of my inspectors, he'll get frightened.'

'Right, sir.' They were sitting in Parulkar's car at Haji Ali. Parulkar was on his way to headquarters and had asked Sartaj to meet him on the way. Sartaj thought he was joyless, that he looked worn down. 'You have another meeting, sir?'

'Yes. I have nothing but meetings nowadays.'

'With DIG Saab?'

'Not only him. Everyone I can. The government is bent on pushing me out, Sartaj. So I have to see who can help me stay in. So I run from here to there.'

'Sir, you will take care of it. You always have.'

'I am not so sure. This time, even the money I am prepared to spend is making no difference. There is too much old history. They hate me personally, they think I am too pro-Muslim.'

'Because of Suleiman Isa?'

Parulkar shrugged. 'That, and other things. But mainly they suspect me of helping Suleiman Isa. They are fools. They don't seem to understand that to operate successfully against this gang, you have to exchange information with that one. They just know who they hate. They are politicians and gangsters themselves, but they see the world like this. Stupid.'

'That's why you will outsmart them, sir.'

'Don't be so sure, Sartaj,' Parulkar said, jabbing a hand towards the rising arc of buildings, 'nowadays, stupidity is what wins here.'

Behind him, the sea lay flat and quiet. His driver and bodyguards were standing close by, shading their eyes from the glare. 'The times have changed.'

There was no arguing with this simple truth, the times had indeed changed. 'If there's anything I can do, sir,' Sartaj said, 'please tell me.'

That was all the comfort Sartaj could offer to the old man. Sartaj watched Parulkar's three-car convoy edge away from the promenade, and thought that this was the first time he had ever thought of Parulkar as old. He had always seemed ageless because of his appetite for the job, his unflagging cheer and amusement at the absurdities of the policeman's life, his energy, and his steady and amazing progress. Maybe he had risen too far, maybe it was inevitable that at these high professional altitudes his sharp ambition would betray him, yes, it had twisted and cut him and emptied out his confidence and his joy. Perhaps it was better to stay at a respectable middling level, like Papa-ji had, to do one's job well and go home and sleep soundly.

But no, it was impossible to believe such a thing in these changed times, when a lack of passionate careerism was considered a fatal character flaw. Sartaj slung a leg over the motorcycle and kicked it into grinding life. He turned back along the causeway, coasted along and went past the entrance to Shiv Sagar Estates, where Harshad Mehta had once owned seven – or was it eight? – apartments. Sartaj had come there long ago, to support a huge CBI team which had searched Mehta's apartments for evidence of his multi-crore perfidy. Sartaj's contribution to the stockbroker's arrest had been crowd control, he had held back the rapidly growing crowd of onlookers and Mehta-supporters, and kept the building gate clear. That night and the next day, everyone he had met – policemen, friends, Megha – had asked eagerly, 'Did you see Harshad Mehta's house from inside? What was it like? It must have been great, no?' Sartaj didn't mind, at first, telling them that he hadn't seen anything except the outside of the building, but each enquirer had been so disappointed that finally Sartaj had felt obliged to make up a story about Harshad Mehta's extravagant living. There were indeed some fragments of fact in the mosaic he had built, little shiny nuggets harvested from constables who had been inside the building, but mostly Sartaj had thrown together pictures taken from television and films, he had talked about duplex drawing rooms with staircases that went coasting up to family quarters, doors that slid into walls, bedrooms as big as entire ordinary apartments, all floored with exquisite Italian marbles, and with an intercom tying it all together. 'Thirty thousand feet,' Sartaj had said. 'Can you imagine, he lives in thirty thousand feet?' And all those who could barely afford five hundred feet, or a thousand, had become a little wet-eyed and dreamed of a perfect life. Sartaj knew the admiration they were feeling, because he had felt it himself: Harshad Mehta was a thief, but he had dreamt big and lived large. He had been arrested, and then arrested again, and he had died of a heart attack, but in his own time, he had been a hero.

Sartaj gunned the engine, and liked the howl it made. Ambition had spread like an inescapable virus in those Harshad Mehta days, and there had been stock-market crashes and burst bubbles since, but the contagion had taken firm hold. Now these outsize aspirations were something like a universal condition. Maybe it was a form of health – after all, it gave you vim, zip, velocity. He had read an editorial in the papers not long ago, which had noted gratefully that the Indian cricket team had finally acquired some killer instinct. Yes, they had acquired cash and killer instinct. Very correct. Sartaj speeded up. It was time to go and hunt eve-teasers.

Wasim Zafar Ali Ahmad, of the lengthy name and the long political aspirations, had given Sartaj the names and address of the tapori brothers he wanted disciplined, and so Sartaj and Katekar went visiting. They had no hope of finding the two at home, but their intention was to cause terror and discomfort to the family, and thereby impel the brothers to give themselves up. So they went into the kholi with extravagant amounts of shoving and shouting. Sartaj kicked open the door and roared, 'Where are those two gaandus? Where are they?'

Katekar gathered up the family from the three cramped rooms. There was a tottering old man, a woman and a girl of eleven or twelve. The girl began to curse Sartaj in a steady monotone, and the woman clapped a hand over her mouth.

'What have they done?' said the trembling grandfather. 'What?'

Sartaj spoke to the woman. 'Are you the mother of Kushal and Sanjeev?'

'Yes.'

'Where are they?'

'I don't know.'

'You're their mother but you don't know where they are?'

'No, I don't know.'

She was a sturdy woman, short but big in the shoulders and bigger in the hips. She was wearing a bright red sari, the pallu of which she now wrapped tightly around her shoulders with one hand as she held her daughter with the other.

'What's your name?' Sartaj said.

'Kaushalya.'

'This is your father?'

'No, his.' Meaning her husband's.

'And where is he?'

'At his factory.'

'What factory?'

'They make mithai.'

'Is it near by?'

She jerked her chin towards her left shoulder. 'Next to the bus depot.'

Sartaj pointed at the girl, who had stopped muttering under her mother's hand. She was looking at him with an unblinking concentration. 'What's her name?' he said.

'Sushma.'

'Sushma, go and get your father.' Kaushalya removed her hand, but her daughter didn't move. Sartaj was used to being disliked by the public, but the little girl's hatred stung him. 'Go,' he growled.

'Listen to Saab,' Kaushalya said, and the girl ran out of the door.

Sartaj settled himself on the chair next to the door. He spread his knees wide and planted his feet firmly. Katekar turned to the small kitchen area on the left, and began to search, rattling pots and plates. He picked up a bottle from a shelf and sniffed at it loudly. Kaushalya and her father-in-law retreated to the other room. Sartaj could hear their urgent whispering.

Hunting apradhis should've meant car chases, sprints through crowded streets, motion and movement and pounding background music. That's what Sartaj wanted, but what hunting actually meant was intimidating a woman and an old man in their own home. This was a tried and tested policing technique, to disrupt family life and business until the informant sang, the criminal caved, the innocent confessed. Katekar spread himself over a couch covered with a bright blue sheet, and Sartaj called to Kaushalya and asked for chai and biscuits. She twittered angrily behind the wall, but went outside and asked a neighbour to walk down to the dhaba at the corner. She came back in, her head ducked down low, her jaw working, and stalked past them to her back-room refuge.

The walls were bare white, but on a single shelf there was a row of photographs, the record of Kaushalya's marriage and three children. Sushma laughed happily from a pink heart-shaped frame. Sartaj leaned his head on the wall and shut his eyes. But he was restless, too tense for a doze. He sat up, and Katekar was studying, intently, an old copy of *Filmi Kaliyan*. On the left corner of the cover, Bipasha Basu had her arms folded under the rolling expanses of her chest. Sartaj instantly resented her for the keen cut of desire that came up from his groin. He straightened up, rearranged discreetly and then had to lean forward to hide himself. The hell with you, Bipasha. The last time he had had sex was eight months ago, with a stringer for one of the Marathi afternoon papers. She had first come to him with tough questions about dance bars and bar girls, for a big lead story, and he had been impressed by her big shoulders, her loose green jeans, her cynicism and her rangy competence. They'd met three times, in three different restaurants, and she had each time carefully mentioned her husband, who was also a journalist, for another Marathi daily. But by the third afternoon, by the third cup of tea, she had run out of questions about bar-balas, and it was obvious that something else had to happen. They'd said goodbye awkwardly, and this time she'd not offered her hand for a hearty from-the-shoulder handshake. She called ten days later, and this time they'd walked on Chowpatty beach, brushing knuckles. He didn't think she was pretty, exactly, but he couldn't pause himself, cease short the impulse to rest his hand on the small of her back, under her loose, full-sleeved white shirt. They'd had weekly sex for four months, always in PSI Kamble's room in Andheri East, in the afternoons. Ghochi karo, boss, Kamble used to say. Had sex, made love, ghochi, whatever it was, it made Sartaj precariously alone, put an insoluble knot in his throat. To feel her skin against his was good, her crises tripped easily through her long body, and she was comfortably undemanding, relaxed and relaxing in her distrust of drama. And yet Sartaj felt no yearning for her, suffered none of the agonized need he had once endured for Megha, and this absence made unbearable those moments when he lay panting on Kamble's flowered sheets. He felt small and lost inside his own body, submerged far under the skin and drowning. Finally he had to stop, had to end it.

Now she was hurt, but she hid it under a journalist's shrug: *marad saala aisaich hota hai.*

Yes, men were like that. Before her, there had been other women. A call-girl, Kamble's gift on Sartaj's first post-divorce birthday: 'Fine high-class item, boss, total actress material.' Sartaj had been unable to perform, and the actress-item had patted his shoulder comfortingly. And there was a married friend of Megha's, who had waited to call until his divorce decree was final, so that it was all above board and incontestably moral. After sex, she loved to hear stories about murder, about gunshots on dark streets, about desperate and violent men, she lay next to Sartaj, plump and golden, a shine like metal hooks in her eyes, eddying little gusts of Obsession. And there had been a firangi even, an Austrian woman who had been pickpocketed on a local train and had come into the station to file a complaint. He had liked her blunt accent, all clangs and sudden stops, and the unreadable blue of her eyes, but she was so beyond his ken that he had no idea what to do, even when she stopped in two days later. He confessed to her that they had made no progress, that progress was unlikely, and then felt ashamed of Indian inefficiency. In Austria the thief would already have been convicted and sentenced. In that pause she asked if he would like to have some coffee. After three days of coffee he asked if she would like to see his house. At the apartment, she made him take off his turban. 'I want to see your hair open,' she said. 'You Amitabh Bachchan,' PSI Kamble had chortled when he had heard about this, squeezing Sartaj's hand, 'you bloody Rajesh Khanna, you're the King of all Sardar Studs.' Sartaj had recognized much of his own heady triumph in Kamble's exuberant thrill, that glad rush he had himself felt from the pornographic paleness of the Austrian's breasts, from the discovery of the light blonde hair under the white of her panties. As he had moved inside her, he was inside a thousand blue movies, and inside him were the impossibly unblemished glossy-paper phantoms of his adolescence, beckoning and very far. After they had finished she was quiet, and he had no idea what her silence meant. And the King of all Studs lay with his mouth open, terrified by the white vacuum of disappointment he was discovering inside his bones.

Sartaj shook his head and got up. Kaushalya's husband liked to be photographed. He sat squarely in the middle of every photograph, surrounded by women and children. Sartaj stood near the wall, his back to Katekar, and investigated the pictures. Here was the father of the two harassers. Did he have mistresses in addition to the wife? Looking at the belligerent thrust of his belly against his shiny white kurta, in the largest of the photographs, Sartaj was sure he did. He was a man, and so he had women. Sartaj had a long reputation as a policeman for the ladies, and he had told nobody that he had given up on sex. Kamble and Katekar and the others at the station crowed about ghochi, there were long stories that rose and fell and rollicked on about chut and khadda and tope and daana and hathiyar and mausambis, yes, she had mausambis so round and sweet you wept to look at them. Mausambis, grenades, dudh-ki-tanki, coconuts. And yes, maal, chabbis, chaavvi. Maybe I'm the only one, Sartaj thought, with stories about silent sex, far sex, aching sex, dull sex, doomy sex, stopped sex, needless sex, painful gloom-ridden bitter lonely sex. Sex. What a word. What a thing.

The chai and the father arrived together. Kaushalya's husband came in hard on the heels of the barefoot little boy who swung in with the cups of chai, which he carried in a special wire basket. The boy cocked an eyebrow at Sartaj, and getting the nod, he handed over the chai, very wristy and professional. 'Biskoot?' he said, and held up a pack of Parle Glucose. Sartaj paid, and fumbled in giving him a five-rupee coin. The boy picked it up from the floor with his toes, with his right foot, and then moved the coin to his left hand with a smooth dance move that lifted his shin parallel to the floor. For that Sartaj gave him a five-rupee tip, and the boy grinned and was gone.

Kaushalya had emerged, followed by the old man. Sartaj moved between her and her husband, took a sip of chai and said, 'What's your name?'

'Birendra Prasad.'

'You make mithai?'

'Yes, saab. Cham-cham, burfi and pedas. We supply to restaurants and shops.'

'You own the factory?'

'Yes, saab.'

'And your sons work with you?'

'Sometimes, saab. They are studying still.'

'That is good.'

'Yes, saab. I want them to move ahead. In today's world, you can't get anywhere without education.'

Birendra Prasad had seen the world, no doubt of it. Today he wasn't wearing a silvery kurta, he had on a green shirt and black pants, and his stockiness made him a good match for his wife. He was sturdy and determined and didn't like having policemen in his home, but he was making an effort to be calm and polite. His daughter was holding on to the back of his shirt and glowering at Sartaj. There were a lot of people now in a small room, and Sartaj could see the sweat pooling down Birendra Prasad's neck. Sartaj grinned, showing his teeth, and took a sip of chai.

'Saab,' Birendra Prasad said.

Katekar was moving around Prasad, to his left and behind him. Sartaj saw that it made the mithai-man very uneasy, his eyes twitched left and back and left again. 'Have you been in jail, Birendra Prasad?' he said.

'Yes, a long time ago.'

'What was the charge?'

'Nothing, saab. It was a misunderstanding . . .'

'You went to jail for nothing?'

Katekar moved in close. 'Saab asked you something,' he said, very softly.

The girl was crying now.

'It was for one year,' her father said. 'For theft.'

Sartaj put his glass down on the chair, and stepped close to Birendra Prasad. 'Your sons are going to jail also.'

'No, saab. For what?'

'You know what they are doing around here? You know how they behave with women?'

'Saab, that is not true.'

Katekar shoved the man gently, just a hand on a shoulder and a short push. 'Are you saying Saab is not telling the truth?'

'People spread all these rumours, and they are just boys. But . . .'

'You send your boys to see me tomorrow at the station,' Sartaj said. 'At four o'clock. Or I'll come and visit your family here again, and you at your factory. And I'll put your sons in jail.'

'Saab, I know who is doing this.'

Sartaj leaned in close and whispered in his ear, 'Don't argue with me, gaandu. You want me to take your izzat in front of your family? In front of your daughter?'

To this Birendra Prasad had no reply.

Katekar nudged at his shoulder, and he moved aside. Sartaj stepped around Sushma and over the sill. He and Katekar walked through the sunny lane, scattering a group of boys coming in the opposite direction.

'That Wasim Zafar is a deep one, saab,' Katekar said. 'The move is against the father as much as against the boys.'

'Yes,' Sartaj said. 'This Birendra Prasad must be a problem for him. He should have told us, the bastard.' Because it was quite possible that Birendra Prasad had his own connections. But Sartaj wasn't overly worried. Every man or woman you arrested or even touched was part of some web, and you couldn't spend your professional life worrying about who knew whom. You were a little careful, and if some problem came up, you dealt with it. Still, Wasim Zafar Ali Ahmad should have told them. 'Here,' he said, and gave Katekar the biscuits. He dialled on his mobile phone, and Wasim Zafar picked up on the second ring.

'Hello, who is it?' he said, very fast.

'Your baap,' Sartaj said.

'Saab? What is wrong?'

'Where are you?'

'I am near the station, saab. I came here for some work. What can I do for you?'

'You can tell us the truth. Why didn't you tell us you were moving against this Birendra Prasad?'

'The father? Saab, really, he's not such a problem. But he spoils his sons, and starts puffing up if anyone says anything to them. They are the ones who instigate him. He is a simple man, a dehati really, they are the haramzadas who think they are too smart. Once the boys are squeezed a little and become quiet, he will also sit down.'

'You have everything calculated out, don't you?'

'Saab, I was not trying to hide anything.'

'But you didn't give us all the information.'

'My mistake, saab. Saab, where are you?'

'In your raj.'

'Saab, where in Navnagar? I'll be there in five minutes.'

'Make it ten minutes. I'll see you in Bengali Bura, at Shamsul Shah's house.'

'Yes, saab. At their new kholi?'

'Yes, at the new kholi.'

'Okay, saab. I'm putting down, saab.'

Katekar was eating a biscuit. 'He's running to meet us?'

'Yes. He's very dedicated to justice.'

Katekar snorted. Sartaj took a biscuit, and they walked through the basti, towards Bengali Bura. Wasim Zafar Ali Ahmad was eager to be seen with the police. It would give him a chance to demonstrate his affinity with power, his ability to get things done. He would probably let it be known that he had summoned them himself, asked them not to forget the investigation into the murder of Shamsul Shah, urged them to keep working hard. In his telling, he would be the concerned community leader who was getting action from the police. Sartaj didn't begrudge him his spin. The man was revealing himself to be an adept politician, in spite of his error in not telling all about Birendra Prasad, the inconvenient father.

Sartaj paused at an intersection. The narrow lane directly ahead led to Bengali Bura, and the wider one to the right towards the main road. He brushed the crumbs from his fingertips, and said to Katekar, 'Let's go and see Deva first.'

Sartaj had an old contact in Navnagar, a Tamil named Deva. Sartaj had met him nine years ago, when he had arrested a gang of four tyre-thieves in Antop Hill. Deva had lived with the thieves, in the little closed porch at the entrance to their kholi. He had protested his innocence, said that he was just a tenant, he had nothing to do with the burglaries, he was just in from his village and new to the city, he had thought that having tyres stacked in the house was normal urban practice. Sartaj had liked Deva's cheerfulness, his humming of weird-sounding Tamil songs, his resolute nineteen-year-old attempt to muster up courage, despite the twitching in his skinny, pole-like legs. So Sartaj had decided to believe him, and looked after him, he had not put his name in the FIR and had spoken to a couple of people about a job for him, and now Deva was very respectable, settled, married, he had a son and another one on the way, and he had grown a small moustache and a paunch. He ran an ironworks in Navnagar, where a sweaty cadre of Tamils made enormous iron wheels for use in hand-loom mills, and fences and fittings, and all kinds of special-order items.

So Sartaj took the right-hand turn, and called Wasim Zafar Ali Ahmad as they walked, to tell him they would be delayed. The road had been recently tarred and maintained, and there was a constant traffic of cycles and scooters. The houses in this part of Navnagar were old and well-established, all of them had good water connections and electricity. Many of them were two and three stories tall, with shops and workshops on the ground floor fronting the street. A face floated above the staggered roofs, huge, luminous brown eyes that went and came from behind the parapets, larger than any of the windows, and there was a gleaming brow touched by blue light, half-open lips and swirling hair, all of it somehow completely weightless and paradisiacal. Sartaj knew that she was only a cunningly lit model on a vast billboard across the main road, but it was distracting to be watched so intently by her. He turned his eyes down and went on.

Deva called for refreshments as soon as he saw them, and wouldn't accept a refusal. A boy came around the corner with two Limcas, which Sartaj and Katekar drank standing near the door of the workshop, just outside it. There were no lights inside the workshop, just two livid streams of sunlight pouring through the roof, heating the glow of the molten iron as it slushed into the moulds and the faces of the nearly naked men who worked the bellows with their feet, stepping up high and then down in a slow and endless climb.

'Haven't remembered me for a long time, saab,' said Deva.

'The Tamils have been behaving themselves, Deva.'

Deva roared. He leaned in through the doorway and shouted a translation to his workers. There was a quick winking of gleaming smiles among the sparks. It was possible to live in Navnagar and never speak anything but Tamil. A shouted answer came back over the blaring rush and banging of work. 'He says,' Deva said, 'that we're so well-behaved now that even the Rakshaks love us.'

There had been a time when the Rakshaks had demonstrated son-of-the-soil Mumbai patriotism by hounding Tamil immigrants. Sartaj put his empty Limca bottle down, next to the door. 'Sure. They're chasing other people now.' Muscular chauvinism still won votes, but you had to be canny in your selection of enemies. So now the Rakshaks protested about the Bangladeshi menace, and told 'unpatriotic' Indian Muslims to leave the country. Same game, different targets. Sartaj motioned Deva away from the door and its exhalations of heat, and they walked down the lane a little, stepping over a gutter. Katekar followed close behind.

'You're investigating that murder,' Deva said. 'The boy who was killed by his friends.'

'Yes. Know anything about it?'

'No. I didn't know any of them.'

'Ever heard of a social worker named Wasim Zafar Ali Ahmad?'

'Yes, yes. That bastard. He's a sharp one.'

'How sharp? What are his dhandas?'

'His father is a local butcher. The son does mostly social work, I think. But he has a lot of cousins, these cousins have garages. Two around here, one somewhere in Bhandup. They are a well-settled family.'

'And these garages, are they crooked or straight?'

'Medium, saab. I hear they do business in second-hand parts.' Deva had an extraordinary smile, he thrust his jaw forward and his eyes narrowed and a bank of sparkling teeth split his face in half. Second-hand parts could come from anywhere, from legitimate sources or some poor fool's car. 'One or two of these cousins have been in trouble. Never arrested, saab, but little things here and there.'

'You know the names of these cousins?'

'No. But let's see.' Deva led Sartaj and Katekar around the corner, to a bakery, a large tin-roofed hall with towering ovens at one end and ranks of men kneading dough. At the very far end, there was a small cubicle, almost filled by a portly owner. He gathered up his lungi and his bulging stomach and walked amongst his workers while Deva used his phone. Sartaj listened to the nasal southern rhythms, which reminded him as always of Mehmood and childhood laughter, and tried not to breathe too deeply. The smell of the fresh loaves of bread was good but overpowering, too rich, too dense in the stifling heat. Deva made two phone calls, and Sartaj knew he was tugging at his Tamil connections across Navnagar, strumming them and listening to what came back. The Tamils had once been the feared newcomers into the city, the ones denounced and hated by the Rakshaks as the threatening outsiders who supposedly stole jobs and land. Now they were old Mumbaikars.

Deva sat back and settled into his chair. He held up his fingers in a little cone, and said, 'Ready, saab? Write down.'

He gave Sartaj five names, and their exact genealogies, how they were related to Wasim Zafar Ali Ahmad, and estimations of his involvement in their work, both legitimate and otherwise. It was solid intelligence.

'Good work, Deva,' Sartaj said. Katekar nodded benevolently. Sartaj put two five-hundred-rupee notes on the desk next to Deva.

They were old friends, but it was better in the long run that they conduct their business professionally. You could only do favours for each other for so long before resentment set in on both sides. Cash for information assured a future flow.

Sartaj and Katekar left Deva and walked over towards the Bengali Bura. Sartaj looked over his shoulder as they came up the slope, and the endless mud-brown and white roofs of Navnagar made a vast serried crescent, horizon to horizon, under the falling sun. The tableau impressed Sartaj as always with its gory reddish gigantism and melodrama, with the pressing energy of its very being, it was incomprehensible that such a thing should exist, this Navnagar. And yet here it was, astride Sartaj and towering, crimson-mouthed and real. He turned away. He noticed now that Katekar was carrying a large paper bag full of fresh pavs, to eat with his family over the next few days. Much of what Katekar and everyone else ate came from or through Navnagar, and other nagars like it. Navnagar made clothes and plastic and paper and shoes, it was the engine that pumped the city into life.

Wasim Zafar Ali Ahmad was waiting near Shamsul Shah's kholi, surrounded by a thick cluster of supplicants. His mobile phone glinted in his hand as he waved to Sartaj and Katekar. A woman tugged at his elbow, and he spoke to her in rapid Bengali, and extracted himself with many gestures of assurance.

'Saab,' he said. 'Sorry, these people, once they get hold of me, they don't let me go.'

'You speak Bengali?'

'A little, a little. Their Bengali has quite a lot of Urdu in it, you know.'

'And what other languages do you speak?'

'Gujarati, saab. Marathi, some Sindhi. You grow up in this Mumbai, you pick up a little of everything. I am trying to improve my English.' He held up a copy of *Filmfare*. 'I try to read one English magazine every day.'

'Very impressive, Ahmad Saab.'

'Arre, sir, I am younger than you. Please call me Wasim. Please.'

'All right, Wasim. Have you talked to Shamsul Shah's family already?'

'No, no, sir. I thought you would want to do that yourself. But one of these people said the father is not at home, he is working. The mother is here.'

'Inside?'

'Yes.'

'Keep these people away while I talk to her.'

The dead boy had purchased a better home for his family, you could tell that just from the substantial frontage of the property on the lane. Sartaj knocked. Standing at the door, he could see four rooms, a separate kitchen and cupboards finished with Formica. The dead boy's mother sent his sisters into the back rooms, and stood very straight and waited.

'You are Moina Khatun?' Sartaj said. 'Shamsul Shah's mother?'

'Yes.'

Moina Khatun's daughters were kept in strict purdah, but her own regime had been relaxed a little by old age, at least while she stood in the doorway of her own house. Sartaj thought she looked to be about sixty, although her real age could have been at least a decade less. She wore a blue salwar-kameez and a white dupatta over her head.

'This is a good kholi that your son got for you.' Sartaj couldn't tell if Moina Khatun's inscrutability was a tactic or a trait. He couldn't read her at all. 'He was a good boy. How did he get mixed up with those other two?'

She tipped her head to one side. She didn't know.

'Did you know this Bihari friend of theirs, this Reyaz Bhai?'

Moina Khatun slowly moved her head again.

There was a hush in the lane, and under that silence a vast chasm of loss. Sartaj felt like he had stumbled over an edge, and he didn't quite know what to do next, where to press, or whether pressing was a good idea. Into this quiet, Katekar spoke.

'It is against nature, that a son should die before his parents. It is impossible to accept. But He' – and here Katekar pointed upwards – 'gives and takes for his own reasons, he writes our destinies.'

Moina Khatun began to weep. She dabbed at her eyes, and her shoulders rounded. 'We must accept,' she said hoarsely. 'We must accept.'

Katekar had his hands clasped in front of him, and he tilted forward slightly from the waist, completely solicitous and not in the least bit threatening. 'Yes. How old was Shamsul?'

'Only eighteen. Next month he would have been nineteen.'

'He was a fine-looking boy. Did he want to get married soon?'

'There were already proposals for him.' Moina Khatun was animated now, brightened under her tears by the memory of past arguments. 'But he said he wanted to get all his sisters married first. I told him, the youngest is nine, you will be an old man by the time she has her mala badol. But Shammu, he said, getting married too young is a stupid thing we do. Let me get settled first, have a nice house. What is the use of getting married and lying at your parents' house, having fights between the wife and the mother-in-law? He wouldn't listen to us. First them, then me, he always said.'

'He was a good boy. He set up a good kholi for you.'

'Yes. He worked very hard.'

'Did you know what work your son was doing?'

'He worked for that company, taking parcels.'

'Yes. But he was doing some work with Bazil and Faraj also, no?'

'I don't know anything about that.'

Sartaj could see that Moina Khatun wasn't trying to hide anything, she really didn't know anything about her son's dealings with the murderers. This made sense, there was no reason for the boy to talk to his mother about his criminal activities. But Katekar didn't want to give up yet.

'They were good friends, the three of them. They grew up together, in this basti?'

'Yes.'

'Why did they fight?'

'That Faraj was always jealous of my son. He didn't have a job, he did no work. Even when they were young he was always fighting with Shammu.' Her face flushed dark, and she shook her fist, and spoke Bengali. The angry stabbing gestures she was making slipped the dupatta from her head, her voice cracked and rose, and now she was shouting. Her grief cut across Sartaj's throat, and he stepped back and looked for Wasim.

'She is cursing Faraj and his family, saab,' Wasim said. 'She is saying they are devils. Just everything like that.'

Moina Khatun's face had dissolved from its angular rigidity into something that Sartaj found difficult to look at directly. He cleared his throat. 'Nothing useful?'

'Nothing,' Wasim said.

'All right. Let's go.'

He walked away. Katekar raised a hand at the woman, and followed. They were almost around a corner when she called after them in Hindi. 'Don't let them escape,' she said. 'Get them. Don't leave them.'

Sartaj looked back at her, and went on. The lane widened as they came near the main road, and he could feel Katekar behind him. Sartaj slowed, let Katekar catch up and gave him a nod. They came down to the main road, towards the Gypsy.

'Wasim,' Sartaj said.

'Yes, saab.' Wasim scudded up beside them, unruffled and slick and brimming with sincerity.

'Okay, listen to me, bastard,' Sartaj said. 'About this Birendra Prasad . . .'

'Saab, truly, he will be no problem. Like I told you, the two sons make him the problem.'

On their left there was a wall covered with painted advertisements for cement and face powder. Sartaj stepped up to it and unzipped his pants. 'Listen, you said I was older than you. So let me give you a bit of advice. Don't think you are smarter than the people you want to work with. Don't hide things that they need to know.' Sartaj's stream spattered loudly against the bottom of the wall, and he only now realized how pent-up he had been. 'Don't surprise me. I don't like surprises. I like information. If you know anything, tell me. Tell me even if you don't think it's important. More information is better than less information. Understood?'

'Saab, really, I wasn't trying to fool you.'

'If you think I am a fool, then maybe I am the kind of fool who will have to look into certain businesses in this area, investigate certain people. Let me see, what were their names, your cousins? Salim Ahmad, Shakil Ahmad, Naseer Ali, Amir . . .'

'Saab, I understand. It will not happen again.'

'Good. Then maybe we can have a long relationship.'

'Saab, this is exactly what I want. A lasting association.'

Sartaj squeezed and shook, jogged his hips back, tucked and zipped. 'You can play the politician elsewhere. Not with us.'

'Of course, saab.'

Sartaj reached into his pocket for his handkerchief, and turned, and Wasim was holding up his copy of *Filmfare*.

'Please take, saab.'

'What?'

'There is good information inside this magazine, saab.'

Wasim's smile was very sly and small. Sartaj took the *Filmfare* and thumbed it open, and the pages fell apart naturally to a black-and-white picture of Dev Anand, partly hidden by a thin, paper-clipped stack of thousand-rupee notes, neatly staggered from right to left.

'It's just a small nazrana, saab. With hope for our future friendship.'

'We'll see about that,' Sartaj said. He rolled up the magazine and tucked it under his arm. 'I've told Birendra Prasad to bring his sons to the station tomorrow. In case he doesn't, keep track of the boys tomorrow, so we can get them if we need to.'

'No problem, saab. And saab, if you could also mention my name to Majid Khan Saab, and give him my salaam . . .'

'I will,' Sartaj said. 'But for four thousand rupees, don't expect to become the honoured guest of the station. This is only chillar.'

'No, no, saab. As I said, this is only a nazrana.'

They left Wasim there, and Sartaj was satisfied now that the man truly understood the nature of their mutual dependence. In the Gypsy, he unrolled the *Filmfare* and peeled off one note and handed it to Katekar, who tucked it into his breast pocket. Sartaj would also give some to Majid. He was under no obligation to pass any money upward, small amounts like this – under a lakh – were the field officer's prerequisite, and the senior inspectors and DCPs only shared if there was a respectable cake to cut. Still, he would give Majid the greetings from Wasim Zafar Ali Ahmad and offer a thousand, which Majid would laugh off. They had known each other for a long time, and a thousand – or even four thousand – was really only pocket change.

'Saab,' Katekar said. 'About this evening?'

'I hadn't forgotten.' Katekar had asked for an evening off, to take his family for an outing. 'Drive to Juhu now, I'll drop you and go.'

'Sir, there's no need . . .'

'It's all right. Drive.'

Sartaj felt a warm uprush of affection for stolid, dependable Katekar. Megha used to say that Katekar and he were like an old married couple, and maybe they were, but Katekar was still capable of springing surprises. Sartaj said, 'I thought you didn't like these Bangladeshis.'

'I like Bangladeshis in Bangladesh.'

'But that woman? Moina Khatun?'

'She lost a son. It is very hard to lose a child. Even if he was a thief. What was that dialogue from *Sholay*? Hangal's line? "The heaviest burden a man can carry on his shoulders is the arthi of his son."'

'Very true.' And true to filmi logic, this particular Bengali son had committed robbery to marry off his poor sisters. They went over a fly-over, over a clattering train with its late-afternoon crowds already swelling from the doorways. The dead boy had wanted more than marriage for his sisters, he had wanted a television set and a gas range and a pressure cooker and a larger house. No doubt he had dreamed of a brand-new car, one exactly like the brilliant silver Toyota Camry that was overtaking them now. What he had dreamed was not impossible, there were men like Ganesh Gaitonde and Suleiman Isa, who had begun with petty thefts and had gone on to own fleets of Opel Vectras and Honda Accords. And there were boys and girls who had come from dusty villages and now looked down at you from the hoardings, beautiful and unreal. It could happen. It did happen, and that's why people kept trying. It did happen. That was the dream, the big dream of Bombay. 'What was that song?' Sartaj said. 'You know, the one that Shah Rukh sings, I can't remember the film. *Bas khwab itna sa hai . . .*' Katekar nodded, and Sartaj knew that Katekar understood why he was asking, they had spent so much time together, on these drives across the city, that they followed each other's leaps and conceits.

'Yes, yes,' Katekar said. He hummed the tune, marking time with a forefinger across the steering wheel. '*Bas itna sa khwab hai . . . shaan se rahoon sada . . .* Mmmmm, mmmmm, then?'

'Yes, yes. *Bas itna sa khwab hai . . . Haseenayein bhi dil hon khotin, dil ka ye kamal khile . . .*'

And they sang together: '*Sone ka mahal mile, barasne lagein heere moti . . . Bas itna sa khwab hai.*'

Sartaj stretched, and said, 'This Shamsul Shah, yes, he had a big khwab.'

Katekar snorted and said, 'Correct, saab, but the big khwab took his gaand finally.'

They both burst out laughing. In the auto-rickshaw to Sartaj's right, two women turned their startled faces away and leaned back under the cover of the canopy. This made Sartaj laugh even louder. He knew it was frightening to other people, this furious, rasping mirth coming from policemen in a Gypsy, but that made it all even funnier. Megha used to say, 'You tell these horrible police stories and then you cackle like some bhoot, it's very scary.' He had tried, for her sake, to stop, but had never been completely able to. It felt good now, anyway, to be rolling across the city with Katekar, laughing wildly, and there was no need to restrain himself, and so he laughed some more.

They were quiet when they pulled up into the curve of Juhu Chowpatty, through the compacted clog of rush-hour traffic. Sartaj walked around the front of the Gypsy, feeling a faint brush of air from the ocean. The chaat stands were neon-lit already, and the customers were streaming in from the road. 'Tell the boys I said Salaam,' Sartaj said.

Katekar grinned. 'Yes, saab.' He put his hand on his chest for a moment, and then walked towards the beach.

Sartaj watched him go, the confident rolling walk, the heavy-shoul-dered sway, the clipped hair. An experienced eye would pick him out for a policeman in a moment, but he had a talent for shadowing, and they had made some good arrests together. As he rode through Ville Parle, Sartaj hummed *Man ja ay khuda, itni si hai dua*, but he could-n't remember the end of the song. He knew the tune would spin in his head all day, and the last antra would come to him very late, some-where between night and sleep. *Man ja ay khuda*, he sang.

Katekar found the boys and Shalini waiting, as appointed, near the stall called Great International Chaat House. He rubbed Mohit's head, poked him gently in the stomach. Mohit gurgled out a titter that made Rohit and Shalini smile.

'They're late again?' Katekar said.

Shalini twisted her mouth to the side. Katekar knew that look: what could not be changed had to be endured. And Bharti and her husband were always late.

'Let's go and sit,' Rohit said. 'They know where we sit.'

Katekar looked up and down the row of stalls, and across the road. There were two buses staggered behind each other, and it was hard to see. 'Rohit, go and see, maybe they're trying to cross.'

Rohit didn't like it, but he went, flapping his chappals angrily on the concrete. He had been stretched thin by his recent growth, but Katekar was certain that he would fill out once he hit his twenties, once he was married and settled. All the men in the family had attained an impressive thickness, shoulders and arms capable of intimidation, a respectable stomach. Rohit turned back, shaking his head.

'Papa, I want sev-puri,' Mohit said, tugging at Katekar's shirt.

'Let's go and sit,' Shalini said. 'They can find us.'

Rohit hadn't really gone far enough, but Katekar didn't need any more urging from Shalini. Bharti was her sister, and if Shalini thought they could go and sit, Katekar would sit.

They found two mats, as far right as possible, and arranged themselves. Katekar took off his shoes, sat cross-legged, sighed. The sun was still high enough to heat his knees, but there were the beginnings of a breeze against his chest. He opened his shirt, and mopped at the back of his neck with his handkerchief, and listened to Shalini and Rohit and Mohit place their orders with the boy who had shown them to their places. Katekar didn't want to eat yet. He was savouring the feeling of being at rest, of not having to shift from foot to foot like the waiter, who now sped off to his stall.

The boy hurried back, expertly balancing the food as he manoeuvred around and through the walkers. 'Eh, tambi,' Katekar said, 'get me narial-pani.'

'Yes, seth,' the boy said, and he was away.

'Narial-pani?' Shalini said, looking arch.

He had told her the previous month about an article he had read in an afternoon paper which asserted that coconuts were full of harmful fat. She had waved her hand at him and said that she didn't believe all these new-fangled things he read in papers, who had ever got ill from eating coconuts or drinking narial-pani? But she never forgot anything, and she wasn't going to let him get away with his backsliding from science. He tilted his head to one side, and smiled. 'Only today.'

She smiled back, and let him be. So Katekar sat and drank his narial-pani, and watched Mohit devote himself to his sev-puri, and Rohit watch the passing girls. A ship balanced on the gleaming horizon. Katekar watched it, and he knew it was moving but could not see it move.

'Dada!'

Katekar turned, and there was Vishnu Ghodke, waving frantically. He made his way over, followed by Bharti and the children. There was the usual flurry of greetings, and a lot of shifting about, and then the family was finally established on two mats. Shalini had Bharti close to her, and Vishnu was near Katekar. The children were hemmed in between Bharti and Vishnu. The two girls were typically beribboned and fancy-frocked, but the boy, who had been born last after much prayer and ritual, was dressed as if he were going to a wedding. He had on a little blue bow-tie, and a big red plastic wristwatch which he was winding and rewinding. Mohit and Rohit leaned over to push him about, and Katekar felt a surge of affection for the two, for wanting to mess up the prissy little brat's careful coif. He squeezed the cheeks of his two nieces as Shalini and Bharti launched instantly into an animated conversation about some ongoing family intrigue involving relatives of relatives. Katekar liked his older niece best, the girl who had quietly watched the boy become the centre of her parents' world with an increasing understanding and resignation.

'You've grown taller, Sudha,' he said. 'Already, so soon.'

'She eats like a horse,' said her father, with a guffaw and a hand on her head.

Katekar saw the angry squeeze of Sudha's jaw as she ducked away to whisper something in her sister's ear. Vishnu had a voice that didn't need any loudspeakers. Katekar said, 'She wants to grow up to be tall, like me. Sudha, you come here and sit next to me. I'm also very hungry. Arre, tambi.'

So Sudha sat next to Katekar, and they went over the menu together, and from that much-stained paper, chose a feast of bhelpuri, papri chaat and Sudha's favourite, pav-bhaji. They ate together, and now Katekar relished the break of sour into sweet on his tongue. Food was the greatest and most reliable of pleasures, and to sit on Chowpatty and eat it with wife and family, with the sea heaving gently, was as close to contentment as Katekar had ever been. So he sat and listened to Bharti go on. She was wearing a shiny green sari. A new one, Katekar thought. She had been a stocky little girl when he had first seen her, too shy to speak to him. A very few years later, Vishnu had given her a heavier mangalsutra than Katekar could remember from any wedding in the family, and she had never stopped talking since. She was wearing the mangalsutra now, along with a gold chain that went around her neck twice.

'That Bipin Bhonsle is such a haraamkhor,' she said. 'Before elections he told us that he would get a new extra water pipe to the colony. Now there is no new water pipe, but even the old one gets leaks every second week. Three children and no water, it is impossible.'

'Vote him out in the next election,' Katekar said.

'That is impossible, Dada,' Vishnu said. 'He has too many resources, too many connections. And the other parties have all gadhav candidates in that constituency. None of them can win. Putting a vote in for someone else is a waste of a vote.'

'Then find a good candidate.'

'Arre, Dada, who will stand against that Bhonsle? And where does one find good candidates nowadays? You need someone who is tough, who can give a jhakaas speech, who is attractive to the people. That type doesn't exist any more. You need one giant, all you get nowadays are crowds of small men.'

Shalini leaned to the side and brushed her hands off, then neatened her sari over her knees. 'You're looking everywhere but the right place,' she said.

Vishnu was very surprised. 'You know someone?'

Shalini pointed with both hands at Bharti. 'Here, here.'

'What?' Vishnu said.

Katekar pitched forward and back, shaken by laughter. It came more from the dismay on Vishnu's face, from his abject horror at his wife somehow becoming a giantess, than from Shalini's joke, but the children took it up and instantly they were all guffawing.

'See,' Shalini said, 'my sister Bharti is brave, she can impress anyone with her style, and nobody gives a speech like her. You should make her a mantri.'

Vishnu had understood by now that this was all humour, and he was grinning tightly, stretching his lip over his lower teeth. 'Yes, yes, Tai, she would make a good chief minister actually. She will keep everyone in control.'

Bharti had both hands in front of her mouth. 'Arre, devaa, I don't want any such thing. Tai, what are you saying? I have my hands full with these children, I don't want to sit on top of fifty thousand people.'

Katekar wanted to say something about her weight crushing fifty thousand, but then thought better of it and contented himself with a snort at the image of Vishnu's face compressed by her ample haunches. Vishnu looked uncertain, and then laughed along with him.

After Katekar finished eating, he and Vishnu walked along the water. Katekar had his pants rolled up, and he had left his shoes behind with Shalini. He liked to walk on the wet sand where it had been smoothed by the sea, feel it under his soles. Vishnu was walking a good five feet away, protecting his sandals. He hopped away now to save himself from an oncoming surge. 'Dada,' he said, 'one of these times you must let me pay. Otherwise we will feel embarrassed to come again.'

'Vishnu, don't start that whole argument again. I am elder, so I pay.' A bitter wash of irritation gushed up from Katekar's stomach. It was stupid, this pride of his that refused to eat meals paid for by Vishnu, but he could not stomach Vishnu's smugness, his satisfaction at his own success.

'Yes, yes, Dada,' Vishnu said, raising both hands. 'Sorry. You are doing well nowadays?'

'I am getting along,' Katekar said. Vishnu had of course noticed the thousand-rupee note that Katekar had used to pay the waiter. He never missed anything, the watchful Vishnu.

Vishnu stepped thoughtfully over a ragged branch from a palm tree. 'Dada, at this age, you should be doing much better.'

'At what age?'

'Your sons are growing up. They will need education, good clothes, everything.'

'And you think I can't give them all that?'

'Dada, you are getting angry again. I will stop talking.'

'No, say what you mean.'

'I'm saying only a little thing, Dada – this chutiya sardar inspector of yours will never make a decent income.'

'I have what I need, Vishnu.'

Vishnu lowered his head and became very meek. 'All right, Dada. But I don't understand why you stay with him. There are other postings you could have very easily.'

Katekar didn't answer. He turned and went back to the families. But later that night, lying in bed with Shalini next to him, he thought about Sartaj Singh. They had worked together for many long years. They were not friends exactly, they did not visit each other or go on vacations together. But they knew each other's families and they knew each other. Katekar could tell what Sartaj Singh was feeling from moment to moment, he could read his melancholy and his delight. He trusted the sardar's instincts. They had done some good detection, and when they had failed, Katekar always had the knowledge that they had tried hard. Yes, there wasn't as much money as could be made elsewhere, but there was job satisfaction. That was something that Vishnu would never understand. People like him wouldn't believe that a man could want to be a policeman for reasons other than money. The money was welcome, of course, but there was also the desire to serve the public. Yes, really, *Sadrakshanaaya Khalanighranaaya.* Katekar knew he could never confess this urge to anyone, much less Vishnu, because fancy talk of protecting the good and destroying evil and seva and service would elicit only laughter. Even among colleagues, this was never to be spoken about. But it was there, however buried it may be under grimy layers of cynicism. Katekar had seen it occasionally in Sartaj Singh, this senseless, embarrassing idealism. Of course neither of them would ever so much as hint at the other's romanticism, but perhaps this was why their partnership was so enduring. Only once, when they had rescued a trembling ten-year-old girl from a shed in Vikhroli, from her kidnappers, Sartaj Singh had scratched at his beard and muttered, 'Today we did good work.' That had been enough.

It was still enough. Katekar sighed, turned his head and stretched his neck, and went to sleep.

Sartaj saw the crowd first, a thick clutch of people pressed up to the front of a double-height glass window. The building was a new commercial complex, very beautiful with its expanses of grey stone and accents of polished steel. Sartaj had gone to the new office of his bank, to deposit some dividend cheques into his mother's account, and had come out dazzled by the sweep of the counters and the unprecedented cheer of the bank clerks. Now he peered over the collection of dark heads and saw a flash of deep red.

'Saab, come inside and see.' A blue-suited security guard was beckoning to Sartaj from the left.

'Ganga,' Sartaj said, and went through the door Ganga was guarding. Sartaj knew Ganga from the old bank building, where he had kept watch over a jewellery store with a long-barrelled shotgun and a baleful stare. 'Did your seth move here as well?'

'No, saab, I am working for a new company now,' Ganga said, pointing to his braided shoulder, where a blue-and-white patch announced his new allegiance: Eagle Security Systems.

'Better company?'

'Better pay, saab.' There were a lot of new security companies, and demand for ex-servicemen like Ganga was high. He shut the door behind Sartaj, and turned towards the window. 'Tibetan sadhus, saab,' he said, with proprietary pride.

There were five of them, five self-contained, serene men with very short haircuts and flowing scarlet robes. They were working around a large wooden platform, on which there was the colourful outline of a circle within a square within a circle.

'What are they doing?'

'They are making a mandala, saab. There were reports about it on yesterday's TV, you didn't see?'

Sartaj hadn't seen, but now he could see the apertures let into each side of the square, and the deep green that one of the sadhus was using to fill in the area just inside the innermost circle. Another sadhu was filling in the small figure of what looked like a goddess against the green background. 'What are they using, powder?'

'No, saab, sand, coloured sand.'

It was restful to watch the fall of the sand from the sadhus' hands, their sure and graceful movements. After a while, the general structure of the mandala emerged for Sartaj in dim white outline. Inside the final circle there were going to be several independent regions, ovals, each with its own scene of figures, human and animal and godly. Between these ovals, at the very centre of the entire wheel, there was a shape, Sartaj couldn't make out what it was. Outside these ovals there was the inner wall of the square, and outside the square there was another wheel, and more figures, and then a rim with its own patterns, all of it hypnotically complex and somehow pleasing. Sartaj was content to be lost in it.

'When they are finished, saab, they wipe it all up.'

'After all this work?' Sartaj said. 'Why?'

Ganga shrugged. 'I suppose it's like our women's rangoli. If it's made of sand, it won't last long anyway.'

Still, Sartaj thought, it was cruel to create this entire whirling world, and then destroy it abruptly. But the sadhus looked quite happy. One of them, an older man with greying hair, caught Sartaj's eye and smiled. Sartaj didn't quite know what to do, so he bowed his head, touched his hand to his chest and smiled back. He watched them work for a few more minutes, and then walked away.

'Come back tomorrow evening,' Ganga called. 'The mandala will be finished by then.'

Sartaj spent the day in the courts, waiting to give evidence in an old murder case. He had missed the last two dates, and the defence counsel had made a mighty noise, but today the judge himself was late, so the various parties to the case waited quietly. Sartaj read about the Tibetans in *Afternoon*, which described them as 'monks' and said they were making their mandala for the peace of the world. The judge finally arrived after lunch, and Sartaj gave evidence, and went back to the station. Birendra Prasad and his two sons were waiting under the portico.

'You wait here,' Sartaj said to Birendra Prasad. 'You two come with me.'

'Saab?' Birendra Prasad said.

'Quiet. Come on.'

The boys followed him inside. Sartaj took them through the front rooms, to his desk. He was tired, and he wanted a cup of chai very badly, but here were these two bastards. They were good-looking, strapping young men, both in bright T-shirts. 'Who is Kushal, who is Sanjeev?'

Kushal was the older one. He was chewing on his lip. He was only tense, though, not scared. He still had some confidence in his father and in himself.

'So you have eaten a lot of mithai in this life, Kushal?'

'No, saab.'

'That's why you have become such a hero with big muscles?'

'Saab . . .'

Sartaj slapped him across the face. 'Bastard, shut up and listen to me.' Kushal's eyes were wide. 'I know you have been bothering the girls in your area. I know you stand around the gallis and think you are the rajas of everything you see. But you aren't bhais, you aren't even taporis, you are little insects. What are you looking at, bhenchod? Come here.' Sanjeev cringed, and shuffled forward. Sartaj fisted him in the belly, not too hard, but Sanjeev doubled over and turned away. Sartaj thumped him on the back.

It was an old routine of violence and intimidation, and Sartaj performed it automatically. If Katekar had been there, they would have enacted the ritual with a practised co-ordination that approached a kind of beauty. But Sartaj was hot, and tired, and so he hurried up the sequence. He wanted to get it over with. The boys were amateurs, and required no great subtlety or skill. In ten minutes they were panting and stammering and terrified. Sanjeev had a stain down the front of his pants.

'If I hear about any trouble from you two again, I'll come and get you and give you some real dum. You understand? Maybe I'll bring in your father also. Maybe I'll string him up too.'

Kushal and Sanjeev shuddered, and had nothing to say.

'Get out of here,' Sartaj shouted. 'Go!'

They went, and Sartaj sat and leaned back and took out his hand-kerchief and found it already damp. It was disgusting, but he wiped his neck and shut his eyes.

His mobile phone rang.

'Sartaj Saab?'

'Who is this?' Sartaj said, although he knew the rough rumble of the voice. It was Parulkar Saab's old woman, the high-up contact in the S-Company he had spoken to a few days ago.

'It is your well-wisher, Iffat-bibi. Salaam.'

'Salaam, Bibi. Tell me.'

'I heard you are interested in a chutiya named Bunty?'

'I may be.'

'If you haven't decided yet, beta, it's too late. Bunty is dead, lurkaoed, finished.'

'Did your people arrange it?'

'My people had nothing to do with it.' She sounded completely convincing. 'The man was useless anyway, saala langda-lulla.'

'Where?'

'It will be on your police wireless in a few minutes. Goregaon. There is a building complex called Evergreen Valley, in the compound of that.'

'I know the place. All right, Iffat-bibi, I'm going.'

'Yes. And see, next time you want something, somebody, anybody, talk to me first.'

'Yes, yes, I'll come running to you.'

She guffawed at his sarcasm, said, 'I'm putting down now,' and hung up. Sartaj drove fast, accelerating through intersections and weaving across the lanes of traffic. There was already a police van in front of Evergreen Valley, and a crowd of plain-clothes officers in the car park to the rear. Sartaj saw several men he knew to be in the Flying Squad. As he walked up to the body, he saw their boss, Senior Inspector Samant, and then he was sure Bunty had been hit.

'Arre, Sartaj,' Samant said, 'what news?'

'Bas, sir, just work.' Sartaj pointed at the corpse, which lay face-down and twisted to the left. The wheelchair was on its side, three feet away.

'You know this maderchod?' Samant said, arching an eyebrow. 'What, Parulkar Saab has an interest in him?'

'Is it Bunty?'

'Yes.'

'I had an interest in him.' Sartaj squatted. Bunty had an interesting profile, very craggy and distinct, with a finely shaped nose. The back of his head was gone, and brain matter and blood spread in a fan-shape from him. His checked shirt was soggy too, in the back. 'One in the head, two in the back?'

'Yes. I think the back first, then the head. I didn't know you were working organized crime.'

'No, not generally. But I had contact with Bunty.' Sartaj stood up.

'After you got Ganesh Gaitonde I thought you might be on some special detail for Parulkar Saab.'

Samant was bald, pudgy and prosperous, and he was looking very hard at Sartaj. He was said to have killed at least a hundred men himself in encounters, and Sartaj had no trouble believing it. 'No, nothing like that,' Sartaj said. 'This Bunty business was just part of another case.'

'Bunty's business is finished,' Samant guffawed. 'Maderchod tried his best to get away. That wheelchair must have moved faster than a car.' He pointed at black skid marks that went across the car park, almost to Bunty's body.

'You thokoed him?'

'No, no. That would have been good, I've been after the bastard for a long time. But his own boys finished him. That's our theory at this time. Nobody saw it happen, of course.'

'Why would his own boys do it?'

'Arre, yaar, Gaitonde is dead, so poor lame Bunty's reach is lame also. On his own, he was not so much. Maybe his boys switched to the other side, maybe the other side paid them.'

'Suleiman Isa?'

'Yes. Or someone else.'

So Bunty hadn't managed to come in safe, after all. Sartaj walked over to the wheelchair. It was indeed impressive, with thick wheels that looked as if they belonged on a racing car. The machining of the body was solid, all in some sort of very modern, sturdy and precisely engineered steel. An engine pack and battery sat under the seat, which was thickly cushioned in black. A joystick and some controls on the right-hand armrest must have allowed for steering, and for raising the chassis on its hydraulic suspension and going up and down stairs and whatever else this sleek chariot did. All those foreign tricks hadn't managed to get Bunty away from his murderous friends, and so maybe now Miss Anjali Mathur's investigation had run into a dead end. Sartaj stood up. It wasn't really his case anyway. 'The wheelchair looks undamaged,' he said.

'Yes. The wheels were still running when we got here. There's one button there that switches it off. We'll keep it. Soon one of these gaandus will get shot and become a langda-lulla' – here Samant made a lolling face and let his arms go limp – 'and we'll use it to take him to court.'

'Very smart,' Sartaj said, touching his forehead. 'What was Bunty doing here?' Evergreen Valley was three massive buildings in a rectangular compound edged by small two-storey houses. The only green Sartaj could see were a few patchy hedges scattered at odd angles between the buildings.

'We don't know yet. Maybe they were visiting. Maybe they had an apartment here.'

'Please let me know if you find out anything, sir.'

'Yes, yes.' Samant walked with Sartaj towards the gate. 'If you are interested now in all this company business, Sartaj, we can work together. It is very good, you know, professionally and otherwise. We can exchange information.' Samant handed Sartaj a card.

'Of course.' What Samant wanted was that the next time Sartaj got a tip about a big catch like Ganesh Gaitonde, he should call Samant, the encounter specialist. Apart from professional praise and stories in the newspapers, putting a bullet in a big company bhai could make you a lot of money. Other companies would pay for a job well done. Samant was said to have single-handedly built a grand and very modern hospital in his village in Ratnagiri. 'I will call you if I learn anything.'

'My personal mobile number is there. Call any time, day or night.'

Sartaj left Evergreen Valley and Samant and Bunty and the wheel-chair, and went back to the station. Sitting at his desk, he examined Samant's card. Samant was actually 'Dr Prakash V. Samant', according to the elaborate gold lettering. He was also a 'Certified Homeopath', in addition to his achievements in the force, which included the Police Medal for Meritorious Service. Sartaj sighed at how undistinguished his own career had been, and then called Anjali Mathur and told her about the unfortunate demise of his source.

'So all we know is that Gaitonde was looking for a sadhu?'

'Yes, madam.'

'That is interesting, but not enough.'

'Yes, madam.'

'These things happen. Keep following up with the sister. You will get background, at least.'

'Yes, madam.'

'Shabash,' she said, and hung up.

Sartaj was glad that she understood that such things happened. You could never depend on a source, and even when they were talking, the information was always incomplete. You could only piece together a supposition about what had happened. And if your source was a bhai constantly dodging his occupational hazards, it was inevitable that he would one day end up with a bullet in his head. There was nothing that you, or he, could do about it. A policeman would fire the bullet, or an enemy, or a friend. If he hadn't spilled the information you needed by the time his skull compressed under the impact of flying metal and exploded, that was your very bad kismet. Bas. Bunty finished and your case finished.

But Sartaj knew he was only trying to console himself with this things-happen line. The truth was that he had never got used to violent death. He didn't know Bunty at all, he had only spoken to him for a few minutes, but now that Bunty had been shot he would stay with Sartaj for a few days. For a few nights he would show up, wagging his aquiline nose at Sartaj and waking him at odd hours. Sartaj had struggled with this weakness throughout his life, and it had kept him from making the professional choices that men like Samant grabbed eagerly. Sartaj had killed only two men during his career, and he knew he couldn't kill a hundred, or even fifty. He just didn't have the fortitude for it, or the courage. He knew this about himself.

Sartaj sat back in the chair, put his feet up on the table and dialled Iffat-bibi's number.

'So you have had Bunty's darshan,' she said.

Sartaj grinned. He was beginning to rather enjoy her abrupt pronouncements. 'Yes, I saw him. He didn't look too happy.'

'May he rot, and all his lineage too. He was a cowardly bastard all his life, and that's how he ended: running away.'

'So you know even that, Bibi? Are you sure your people didn't do it?'

'Arre, I said so, didn't I?'

'There is a theory that Bunty's own boys did it.'

'Did that fool Samant tell you that?'

'Samant is very successful, Bibi.'

'Samant is a dog who feeds on other people's leavings. You watch, he'll claim this as his own encounter. And the chutiya doesn't even know that Bunty's boys left him two days ago. He wasn't making enough income, so they went to other jobs.'

'You know everything, Bibi?'

'I've lived a long time. Don't worry, we'll know soon who took Bunty's wicket.'

'I would like to know.'

'Very good, beta – when you want to know, ask.'

Sartaj burst out laughing. 'All right, Bibi. I will remember that.'

Sartaj hung up, and thought about Bunty speeding around the city in his wheelchair, from hideout to hideout. He must have been very alone and terrified without his bodyguards, and sure enough, someone had found him and overtaken him. A small shudder of sympathy extended itself across the small of Sartaj's back, and he twisted angrily and stood up, bringing his feet down hard. Bunty had caused enough misery in his time, and the gaandu deserved whatever he got. Whoever had stamped him out deserved some money, or at least a medal. He hoped they had been well taken care of.

On his way home that evening, Sartaj took a detour to see how far the sadhus had come on their mandala. The crowds of the morning had thinned, but the sadhus were still working in the dusk, under a bright pool of lamplight. Sartaj stood by the window, and the older sadhu from the morning saw him, ducked his head and smiled at Sartaj's namaste. He was doing some fine work on one of the inset panels, colouring in the blond flank of a deer. The deer had impenetrable dark eyes, and sat against the deep greens of a forest glade. Sartaj gazed at the falling golden sand. The sphere was about half-done. It was inhabited now by a host of creatures, large and small, and a swirl of divine beings enveloped the entirety of this new world. Sartaj did not understand any of it, but it was beautiful to see it come into life, so he watched for a long time.

Ganesh Gaitonde Wins an Election

Kanta Bai died on a Friday in February. Just four days earlier, on Tuesday morning, she had woken up with a fever. She prided herself on her resilience, and cultivated a fine contempt for doctors. She had told me that more people died from going to hospitals than from their diseases. So she drank glass after glass of mausambi juice, and went out to her tharra-still as usual. She met her employees and sent out her consignments. By late afternoon she was very tired, and came back home and slept. She woke at eleven at night, shivering, with pain in her arms and legs, and loose motions. But still she – the fool who believed that she would survive anything, bacterial or human – she didn't call a doctor. She ate a plate of rice with curd, took two Lopamide tablets and sent her people away. At eight that morning her sister found her, eyes rolled up, torso twisted in soiled sheets. I learnt of this at nine, after they had already taken her to a private hospital in Andheri. She had malaria, the doctors said. I had her moved to Jaslok, and told the doctors that they should give her any foreign medicine, any treatment she needed. But she was dead on Friday afternoon.

We took her to the electric crematorium in Marine Lines. When she was laid out on the track that led into the fire, her cheeks were fallen, and her body under the sheet looked flattened, as if the quick sickness had shrunk her. Her skin no longer had that dark, reddish bloom, it was pale mud. I forced myself to look as the metal doors closed her off from us for ever. And then I stayed until they gave her sister the ashes. I could do nothing but sit quietly next to this sister as we waited, and then give her a ride home.

I had done nothing to save Kanta Bai – this thought tormented me that day, and over the nights that followed. I told the boys to pay attention to their health, and to seek medical advice as soon as they felt an illness coming on. I gave free physical check-ups to all my controllers, and started an anti-malarial campaign in the basti. I had the gutters cleaned, and took measures to remove pools of stagnant water. But I was only putting on a show. I knew I had been defeated.

It was at this time that they came to me. I want you to know that, Sartaj Singh. I never went to politicians, they came to me. I had Gopalmath, I had all the area that had belonged to the Cobra Gang, I had my hand in many businesses, money came in, and apart from the matter of Kanta Bai I was happy. I had dealings with corporators often, especially when we were arranging regular water supply to Gopalmath, but I had no liking for the breed, they were born lying. I had no love for politicians, and so I never tried to cultivate MLAs and MPs. But Paritosh Shah brought one of them to me. He said, 'Bhai, this is Bipin Bhonsle. He's standing for assembly elections next month and needs your help.' Now this Bipin Bhonsle, he was smartly dressed, good blue pants, printed shirt, dark glasses, he didn't look at all like those khadi-kurta bastards with their Nehru-topis who you see on television all the time. Bipin Bhonsle was young, my age and respectful.

'Namaskar, Ganesh Bhai,' he said. 'I have heard a lot about you.'

'This fat man has been telling you?' I said, waving Bhonsle to a chair. I took Paritosh Shah by the hand and made him sit next to me on the divan. He had grown and grown in the several years I had known him, so that the Paritosh Shah I first knew was disappearing slowly inside this cushioned mass. 'Look at him wheeze. I worry about his heart.' He was breathing hard from his climb up the two flights of stairs.

Paritosh Shah patted my arm. 'I am taking Ayurvedic medicine, bhai. No need to worry.'

He had told me about his new Ayurvedic doctor, who had five computers in his air-conditioned clinic. 'Better that you run a few miles every day,' I said. He made a running motion with his arms, pumping them up and down, and he looked so funny, with his jiggling breasts and his belly swaying from side to side, that I burst out laughing, and then he did. But Bipin Bhonsle only smiled, and not too much. I liked that. He had good manners. Meanwhile a boy brought out tea and biscuits. We drank and talked. The job was simple enough, I thought. Bipin Bhonsle was the Rakshak candidate for the constituency of Morwada, which bordered Gopalmath to the north. The voting population in his area was less than half white-collar Marathas, people who had lived there long before the building boom, before the developers had started building the posh colonies in the suburbs. Bipin Bhonsle was sure of these Marathas, of the office workers and Class II government officers and clerks, as he was of the pockets of Gujarati and Marwari shopkeepers and traders scattered here and there. The problem was the other half, the Congress voters and the RPI diehards who lived in the Narayan Housing Colony and around Satyasagara Estates and in the bastis of Gandhinagar and Lalghar. The Rakshaks had never been able to win an election in Morwada, mainly because of these bastards, who were all sorts, seths and professionals and airline crew and retirees, but Bipin Bhonsle was most resentful of the poor chutiyas who lived in the shacks of Lalghar. 'Bhenchod landyas,' he said. 'Of course not one vote for us from there. You put out a hand of friendship to them, they turn away.' Lalghar was a Muslim basti, so of course there were no votes for the Rakshaks from there. To expect votes from people you made a policy of hating was stupid, and typical of the Rakshaks, but I smiled politely at Bipin Bhonsle.

'So, Bhonsle Saab,' I said. 'What can I do for you?'

He put his teacup down and sat forward on his chair, very eager. 'Bhai, first we need help with the campaigning. They intimidate our workers when they go out to canvass, only yesterday they pushed around some of our people and grabbed our posters from them. They took two hundred and fifty posters. Later we heard they made a bonfire out of them.'

'And you Rakshaks are so helpless? I've never heard of you people needing to hire anyone. You have your own boys and your own weapons.'

He heard my sneer, and didn't like it. But he was still soft and polite. 'Bhai, we aren't scared of anyone. But I am very junior in our organization, this is my first election, and anyway this constituency is not considered that important. All the resources will go elsewhere. And I know those Congress and RPI bastards have brought in a lot of muscle. Even those Samajwadi fellows, I hear, are planning to strengthen up.'

'All right. So?'

'Once the campaigning stops, on the voting day, those are the crucial hours. We want to make sure that certain people don't vote.'

I laughed. 'Okay. You want the election given to you.'

He wasn't embarrassed. He smiled, and said, 'Yes, bhai.'

'I thought you Rakshaks wanted to clean out corruption in the country.'

'When the whole world is dirty, bhai, you have to get dirty to do any cleaning. We can't fight their money without tricks. Once we are in power, it will all be different. We will change everything.'

'Don't forget me then. Don't forget and clean me out with the general cleaning.'

He held out both his hands towards me. 'You, bhai? No, no, you're our friend, one of us.'

He meant that I was a Hindu, and a Maharashtrian. I didn't care for any of those things, not where business was concerned, but he was reassured that I was Ganesh Gaitonde. I shook his hand, and said, 'We'll meet in a day or two. We'll talk then about how much money will be needed.'

'Bhai, money can be managed. Please take your time to think about it, and just tell us what your requirements are. I think we will need fifty, sixty boys.' He stood up and folded his hands. 'Let me know when to come.'

After he was gone, I said to Paritosh Shah, 'Level-headed chutiya.'

'He's a little mad, like all those Rakshaks.'

Paritosh Shah believed fiercely in profit, and gain was his god, so anyone who let religion interfere in money-making was quite obviously crazy to him. The Rakshaks believed in a golden past, and blood and soil, and all such things, which made no sense to Paritosh Shah. I said, 'Not so mad. He's hiring us as much because he doesn't want us to work for one of his opponents as he is hiring us for our help.'

'That is true. I didn't say he was stupid. These Marathas are mad but cunning. You know that.'

'Where are you from?' I said. 'From Bombay?'

'I was born here. My great-grandfather came here from Ahmedabad, we still have relatives there.' He was puzzled. We had known each other for many years but I had never asked these questions. But now since I had asked, he did also. 'And you?' he said. 'Where are you from?'

I waved my arm over my shoulder. 'Somewhere.' I stood up. 'How much do we charge them for an election?' And so we talked about money. It seemed to me that to give somebody an election was to make them a raja, or at least a minor nawab, and so our help was worth a lot. But it seemed that this business of giving and taking elections was an old-established one, and there were already set rates, not princely ones. Twenty-five thousand to each boy, maybe fifty for the controllers. So for only twenty-five, thirty lakhs to us, Bipin Bhonsle would become a member of the Assembly. 'You can buy democracy for that much?' I said to Paritosh Shah.

'Now you want to become a politician yourself.'

'Not even if they were giving away seats.'

'Why?' He was smiling indulgently.

I shrugged. I had a congestion in my throat, a swelling of memory and anger, and I didn't trust myself to speak. So I spat out of the window, dismissed the whole filthy business of it, the lying posters and the whorish speeches and the pretended humility, and he knew me well enough not to ask more. Anyway, he was happy to talk about business.

After he left I turned to my English books. I was teaching myself, with children's books and the newspapers and a dictionary. Only Chotta Badriya knew, because he had bought me the books and the dictionary. I closed my door when I studied English because I didn't want anyone seeing me squatting on the floor, one uncertain and slow finger on the letters, which I had to laboriously knock together with moving lips until they adhered into a word: 'p-a-r-l-i-a-m-e-n-t . . . parliament'. It was humiliating, but necessary. I knew that much of the real business of the country was done in English. People like me, my boys, we used English, there were certain words we used with fluency in our sentences, without hesitation. '*Bole to voh edkum* danger *aadmi hai!*' and '*Yaar, abhi ek* matter *ko* settle *karna hai,*' and '*Us* side *se* wire *de, chutiya*'. But unless you could rattle off whole sentences without having to stop and struggle and go back and build them bit by bitter bit, unless you could make jokes, there were whole parts of your own life that were invisible to you yourself, gone from you. You could live in a Marathi world, or a Hindi colony, or a Tamil lane, but what were those hoardings speaking, those towering messages that threw their sharp-edged shadows over your home? When you bought an expensive new shampoo 'Made with American Know-how', what was that it said in red on the label? What were they laughing about, the people who skimmed by smoothly in their cushiony Pajeros? There were many like me, born far from English, who were content to live in ignorance. Most were too lazy, too afraid to ask how, why, what. But I had to know. So I took English, I wrestled with it and made it give itself to me, piece by piece. It was difficult, but I was persistent.

At four in the afternoon I closed my books and lay myself down on the floor and took a nap. I had a good bed, soft pillows, but of late I had been sleeping badly at night. An uncontrollable twitching in my limbs woke me as soon as I settled into slumber. I sometimes managed an hour in the afternoon, but today I thrashed about, full of plans, angles for the future, thoughts of expansion, suspicions about this man and sudden insights into that one. I ruled my corner of the island but couldn't still my mind. The cool pressure of the floor seemed to help, its rigid discomfort drew me to the surface of my skin and kept me there, in a hazy doze. When a boy knocked on the door at five, I jerked up with my heart squeezing hard. I washed my face, took deep breaths and then we went out. Once a day, at different times but always once a day, I took my boys and walked through my area. We took different routes, I wasn't stupid, but I wanted to show myself, to be seen. I won't tell you that there was no fear in me, but I had learnt to bury it, to layer it over with thick sheets of indifference. Ever since that bullet had hurled into me, I knew how real death was. I had no illusions. I had seen that a woman can be alive one day, eating mutton and sneering and joking and thrusting out her chest, her eyes humming with laughter and hunger, and then the next day can find her unconscious in a hospital bed, her mouth open and gasping. I knew I was going to die, I was going to be killed. There was no escape for me. I had no future, no life, no retirement, no easy old age. To imagine any of that was cowardice. A bullet would find me first. But I would live like a king. I would fight this life, this bitch that sentences us to death, and I would eat her up, consume her every minute of every day. So I walked my streets like a lord of mankind, flanked by my boys.

And so I maintained my grip, my reign. Fear was part of it, the fear the shopkeepers felt when they looked at me, the fear in the eyes of women who stepped back into doorways to let us pass. But that was not all, not at all. There is of course an excitement in the exercise of power, but there is also a safety in the bending to it. I tell you this is true. I felt it when they gave me chicken tika and bhakri, and asked me if I wanted a cold drink or tea, I knew it in the widening pools of their pupils when they dragged out their best chair for me and dusted it with their pallus. The truth is that human beings like to be ruled. They will talk and talk about freedom, but they are afraid of it.

Overpowered by me, they were safe, and happy. Fear of me taught them where they could live, it made them a fence, inside which was home. And I was good to them. I was fair, and didn't ask for so much money that it would hurt, and I taught my boys restraint, and above all I was generous. A factory worker had his leg broken under a tipping loader, and I supported his family for six months; a grandmother needed an operation to widen her veins and save her heart, and I gave her life, a chance to play with her children's children. 'Ganesh Bhai,' said a printer to me one afternoon, 'let me make a first-class business card for you.' But I didn't need any card. My name was known in my raj, and there were many who blessed it.

That evening, after my conversation with Bipin Bhonsle and my walk, I went to Paritosh Shah's house. His eldest daughter, first of four, was to be married in seven days. The house was sparkling already, three storeys of cascading lights, red and green and blue, blinking happily. It was a big house, finished only a year ago by him and his two brothers, and they lived in it all together, wives and cousins and countless visiting mamas and kakas, a whirling Gujarati chakkar. Dandia raas before weddings was definitely out of style, but for all his business innovation, Paritosh Shah was a firm traditionalist. So there were excited eddies of young girls in the courtyard, swirls of heady silk. They were waiting for me to start the dancing, and once I was seated in an armchair, all the men and women fell into four circles, the children in the inner two, and the singer raised a declamatory hand and began, '*Radha game ke game Mira*', and the circles whirled slowly, and then faster, and the steady clap-clap of hands echoed out the happy beat. When they brought out the sticks for dandia I stood up and asked for a pair. They laughed to see me tripping clumsily, unable to keep time inside the circles moving against each other, unable to find the clicking rhythm. I think at first this was equally the fault of the other dancers, especially the men, who were afraid to be dancing with me, stripped of their grace by my presence. They hesitated to knock their dandias against mine, they were scared of putting in too much force, they shrank from my strokes. But when they saw how I laughed at myself, and when my boys, who were leaning against the pillars, shook their heads and smiled, everyone relaxed, and the disco-dandia song tumbled on gleefully, and I found my hips loosening, and my shoulders were easy, and I was flowing, falling into step without effort, and the dandia rose and fell, a flourish here and click, another swing and click, a round face spinning to me and click, and I was dancing.

At home Chotta Badriya had a woman waiting for me. I was happy from the dancing, humming away and doing a step here, another one there. But she brought me down. There's nothing more depressing than a depressed randi. She was nicely plump and with a little round nose, and nineteen, but she lay there with a swollen batata-wada face, and I tried to liven her up with a few nips and pinches and squeezes, but she winced and set her jaw, so I took her by the hair and threw her out. Then I drank some milk, lay on my side wrapped around a pillow and tried for sleep, but it larked away from me and my head was full of the dandia and Paritosh Shah and the lights skidding down the side of his house and up again, and I turned to the other side, and now I thought of the men I had killed. I stood them in a row and compared them for character and strength and I decided I was better than any of them, and then I made plans to have the approaches to my house checked and tested, and to put more boys in place at the head of the lanes, just in case. It was late now, very late, and for the first time in many months, I used my hand on myself, and all the women I had known came and slid over me and also Rati Agnihotri with her malai skin. After I was finished I turned again, back to the other side, settled down into comfort and took regular, deep breaths. But finally I threw off the covers and cursed and reached for the clock. Three forty-five. I would have drunk then, anything, a bottleful of whisky or rum, but there was nothing in the house, and I would have got the boys to bring some, but the thought of what they would think and not say made me ashamed, and I lay on my back and decided to see it through. I would get up from bed at six and have an early day. I watched the fan gleam in its flight and then suddenly I was waking up and it was bright day, and I could hear the street fully alive outside. Noon. I had slept for six hours, maybe seven, but I was tired.

My exhaustion deepened as the days passed, as we fought the elections. My boys went out with the Rakshaks, and we pushed their campaign into every nook, their posters harangued the voters from every surface for miles. Two of my boys, armed with pistols, with a group of Rakshaks was enough to keep the peace and let them do their work calmly, no bhangad. A reputation for ruthlessness can do

248

wonders for peace. For us, it was easy money. Meanwhile, it was almost time for the wedding. Even before the ceremony I went to Paritosh Shah's house for the mehndi party, and I could see that he appreciated it, that I was so much a part of his joys and sorrows. Even in the midst of the thousand things he had to do, food and gifts and hotel arrangements for the groom's relatives, he noticed my wobbliness, how I was holding on to wakefulness with effort. 'Your doshas are out of balance,' he said. 'I'll set up an appointment for you with my Ayurvedic man.'

'I won't put myself in that bastard's clutches,' I said. 'It's just insomnia. It'll pass.'

'Nothing is *just* anything. The body is speaking to you. But you won't listen.'

Then he had to go and sit with the women, and the jewellers. There was some question of how many tolas of gold were to be used in the wide necklaces and bracelets and earrings for the dowry, how much payment for the making. I watched him step delicately down the steps to the courtyard and wondered what his body was speaking. How did one read those sheets of fat that surged and billowed on his frame? I rubbed my eyes. He had been good to me. He had never lied to me about money, he had never pretended to lay aside his self-interest, he had backed me as far as possible, to the risk of his life and then a little further, and he had shown me how in this world one thing connects to the next, where business comes together with politics and bhaigiri, how one must live. In this way we had been friends. He was a good man as far as he could be, he had grown fat with hard work, and so his bulk was his virtue. That was why his fat was light on him.

The whole house was fragrant from the cooking. I was hungry, but very tired, and eating would tire me more, I knew this. But to leave without eating would be an insult, so I took a thali and touched some food, and then pushed myself to my feet, and waved up the boys, and told Paritosh Shah to take care of his guests while he tried to see me to the door, and after a little argument, finally off we went. I was looking for my shoes in the great sprawl of footwear near the front door when Dipika came to me. Dipika was Paritosh Shah's second-oldest daughter, a serious-faced, quiet one with big-big eyes. She held out a thali piled with puris, and a glass, and said, 'But you haven't had any ras, Ganesh Bhai.' I had, but I was willing to take another puri from her, polite as she was. As I reached out she whispered, with her head still down, 'Can I please talk to you, Ganesh Bhai?' On the edge of the thali her thumbs were white.

So I took her, thali and glass and all, outside to the car and we talked. 'They're already talking about my marriage,' she said bitterly. 'And my sister's not married yet.'

'They're your parents,' I said. 'Of course they will. And you'll be happy, it's a good thing.' I knew that she was going to college, and I thought that she must have some modern-girl fashionable objection to marriage, some idea of job and career, all got from some silly magazine, so I started lecturing her on her duty, what real life was. She shifted about restlessly, rustling her red and green ghagra and gold chunni.

'But, Ganesh Bhai,' she said.

'Don't do but-this-and-that,' I said. 'Your parents are right.'

'But, Ganesh Bhai,' she said, with a little wail to her voice, 'I *want* to get married.'

And right then, from the small, painful furrowings on her smooth forehead, I knew this was going to be a lot more trouble than just girlish fantasies about a career. 'What?' I said. 'You have someone in mind?'

'Yes.'

'Where did you meet him? In college?'

She shook her head. 'NN College is all girls. His sister is my friend. She goes to NN.'

'What's his name?'

At least she still had the grace to be shy. Two tries, and a lot of blushing, and she got it out. 'Prashant.'

'What's the trouble? He's not Gujarati?'

'No, Ganesh Bhai.'

'What then? Maratha?'

A rapid shake of the head, and now she had her frantic grip on the thali again.

'Then what?'

She had her face almost in the thali now. 'Dalit,' she said. 'And he's poor.'

Her problem was gigantic, as elephantine as her father. I had always found the Gujaratis to be more advanced, more tolerant than other communities, but this would strain her father's understanding. He would do business with anyone, but marriage was another matter.

He had sent her to college, but not for this, not to marry some gaandu who was not only a Dalit but a poor Dalit. Maybe a very rich Dalit could have been approved, but I could hear Paritosh Shah saying it already, 'This is the family you want to marry us into?' Her mother and aunts would be harsher, more violent in their disapproval. Young Dipika had set herself to a hard battle. 'Why do you want to do this to your family?' I said. 'This is not some film. Your father will have this Prashant of yours torn to pieces.'

She looked directly at me then, and her back straightened, and her neck was graceful in its anger. 'I know it's not a film,' she said. 'I'll die, Ganesh Bhai. If anything happens to him, I'll kill myself.'

How little the young value life, they who are so full of it. How little they have seen of death. They think it's a mere pause in a drama, and they imagine the oppressing parents beating their breasts and wailing, and lost in that pleasure they never see the fall, the finality of one's own vanishing. I said as much to Dipika, and she laughed. 'I'm not a child,' she said, and I saw then how far she had gone with this Prashant, her young woman's splendid pride in the pleasures she had taken and given.

'What do you want me to do, Dipika?' I said.

'Talk to Papa. He will listen to you.' She took my hand and placed it on top of her head. 'Since I was a girl you have been kind to me. And I know you do not think in any old-fashioned way.'

What she meant was that in my company there were Brahmins and Marathas and Muslims and Dalits and OBCs, all working together, without difference or suspicion. We had OBCs who were controllers, and Brahmins who were foot-soldiers, and nobody gave it a thought. Muslims and Hindus were yaars who put their lives in each other's palms every day, every night. But this was not special to my company, it was true of many others. We who were bhais were truly brothers, we lived outside the law and were bound to each other. We were desperate men, and therefore free. But a company was a company, and marriage – especially in a joint family like hers – was something else. But how to tell this child, who now held my hand in both of hers, how?

'Go inside,' I said. 'Do nothing. Say nothing to anyone, not one person. Let me think about this.'

She was now dripping tears down her chin. I wiped her face with her pallu, and set her on her way with her wobbly thali. And I told Chotta Badriya that we were going to drive out to Film City.

'Now, bhai?' he said.

'No, next week, chutiya,' I said. 'Get in the car.' He was a funny boy, that one, built like a truck, not scared of swords, willing to play with flying bullets, but scared of Film City in the dark because someone had told him that leopards came down from the wooded hills at night. He sat next to the driver with his arm draped over the back of the seat and his fingers drumming nervously. Finally I clamped down his hand gently, and said, 'Okay, okay, stop shaking so much. You can stay in the car.'

He waggled his head delightedly. 'Yes, bhai. I'll watch the car.'

Every man in the car burst out laughing. I slapped the back of his head. 'Bhadwe, you guard it fiercely, okay? Make sure the mosquitoes don't steal it, okay? And if a big cockroach comes, you blow him to pieces with your gullel, okay?'

We laughed all the way to Film City. We slowed a bit for the guards at the gate, and then swept up the rising road, through the sudden darkness and quiet of the bushy slopes. It was already dusk, so the road was clear. There were the clustering shadows under the leaves, the flashing jigsaw of branches, and then suddenly in the clear there was a looming castle, high-turreted and fluttering with flags in the coming moonlight. It was made of wood and canvas, of course, but in this light it was absolutely real. We went past an entire Goan town square, capped by a high church holding up its crucifix, and also a fishing dock with boats asleep against each other in a leaning row. Here, in Film City, they made dreams of perfect love, they choreographed the songs that Dipika and her boyfriend no doubt sang to each other. The road curved sharply, and the engine whined, and we went up and up, to the helipad. The moon was low and close, hanging just above the lip of the high hills, and the valleys were cut sharply into silver and black, and a breeze slid up my neck. This was the deep quiet I craved, away from the city, that I came for again and again. I stepped to the edge of the helipad and the boys let me go, they stood in a distant arc and left me alone. I sat at the edge of the plateau, and looked for a leopard in the dappled patterning below. Come on, leopard, I said. Save me from this problem. I had promised the girl I would help, but how? She was a clever one, asking first and drawing me to her side. Otherwise, if her father had found out first, and asked me, without a thought I would have had her tattered Dalit boyfriend picked up and dropped off a cliff. Just like that. But now what? The daughter had asked for mercy, and I was Ganesh Gaitonde. But the father was my friend.

I sat until the moon had receded into the heights of the sky, and the leopard didn't come, and no easy answers. There was no solving this problem by killing anyone, and no amount of money would buy peace. There was love between the father and daughter, and so they would hate each other all the more, and wound each other, cutting nerves no assassin could ever reach. I got up and walked back through the boys, who sat in a dozing line. They staggered up and came after me, to the car. Chotta Badriya was fast asleep, his face against the window glass, lips plumped up and cheek flattened. I tapped the glass at his nose, and he came awake, groping under his shirt until he saw me. In that first waking clutch at the world, he had been afraid. I recognized the panic. We were all afraid. To walk out of the house, into a city street, into the air which hummed with the bullets of the next moment, to do this we cast aside fear, dropped it and pushed it into the deepest valley where the moon never shone. But the fear still moved, lived and fed, like an animal in the night. Chotta Badriya liked girls, very young ones. He even liked smallish women of older years who had no mausambis, who were flat before and behind and wore pigtails for him and sat on his lap and talked of dolls and held their heads to the side and giggled. He chodoed them sometimes, but I think only because the other boys would have laughed at him otherwise. For himself, he would have been happy just to hold them, to play at a dream of play, and so live a childhood which was free of the future. Now he was clearing his throat mightily and rolling down the window to spit.

'Bastard,' I said. 'What a fine guard you are.'

'Sorry, bhai,' he said. 'I was seeing leopards all over the place. So I thought I would never sleep. But then suddenly I must have fallen asleep.'

'You were, chutiya. Like a baby.' But I was rubbing the top of his head. He was a good boy. Brave and watchful, watchful for me, and intelligent. He noticed things, the look on people's faces, cars parked where they shouldn't be, and felt rumours on his nerve-endings. But he couldn't help me now, with my quandary, my delicate puzzle which could break hearts and heads. None of them could. It made me angry, this sudden slide down and back into the slithering mess of family. I had lifted away, I had left everything behind. I had been alone. But there was no escape. The wheels slapped at the road and we went back to the city.

The next day we waged the final battles of the elections. Bipin Bhonsle called again and again, polite as he had been during our first meeting, but nerve-racked and needing reassurance that we would give him his precious seat yet. The Congress incumbent had been going around the bastis, handing out hundred-rupee notes and rum and whole sheep to the citizens. Good fresh mutton is the basis of many a political career, I came to know. It made sense. A poor man fills his stomach, he takes pleasure in his dinner, he lubricates himself with two free pegs, maybe three, not too many because he has other plans, he rides his wife, in the morning they both go to the voting booth happy, in that uplifted haze their bodies feel light, and they forget all about how the khadi-wearing bhenchod politician has done nothing for them for years, how he has robbed and stolen and maybe murdered. All of that is gone, vanished, and the happy couple cast their votes, and the servant of the people is in once again, ready to serve them out of roti, kapda and makaan. Hungry, naked and without shelter, they have no memory after meat. So you feed sheep to sheep to herd them in the right direction, towards the slaughterhouse gate. Quite simple.

But I had my own schemes ready. For two days I had sent out rumours. My boys went into the markets and bazaars and restaurants of the Congress and RPI areas and whispered, 'The goondas are coming on election day, thugs have been hired.' A rumour is the most cost-effective weapon ever, anywhere, you start it for nothing and then it grows, mutates, has offspring. In the morning you plant a little red squirming worm in some shopkeeper's ears and by night there are a hundred skyscraper-sized gory Ghatotkachas stalking the land. So I had the enemy voters nicely primed, covered in a sticky marinade of fear. Now it was time to stoke the fire. I had thirty motorcycles ready, with licence plates removed. We put two boys on each, faces covered with dakoo scarves, with bags full of soda bottles for the pillion riders, a crate's worth for every bike. They went roaring out into the lanes. Through the enemy area they went, roaring and hooting. They cleared the streets with the bottles, gave each bottle a few shakes and lobbed it end over end at the few citizens brave enough to be still walking around. The glass flies like shrapnel, but really with soda bottles it's the shattering burst that does the trick, sends the trembling civilians scuttling back to their homes with their pants heavy with piss. The boys had a good time, riding around in the cool of the morning, exercising their bowling arms. Chotta Badriya came back home flushed red and singing. 'Any more, bhai?' he yelled up to me from the road. I was sitting on the water tank on the roof. 'Any more to do?'

'Bas, Badriya, bas,' I said. 'Calm down. That was enough. Now the police will come.'

'Phatak, phachak, the bottles burst, bhai.'

'I know.'

'Great fun, bhai.'

'I know. Now sit quietly, and maybe we'll do it again next year.'

Sure the police came, they came running to the affected areas. They came with their rifles and lathis all ready. Inspector Samant slipped around a corner and found a phone and called me. 'DCP Saab and ACP Saab are here, bhai,' he said. 'You got everybody moving. We are patrolling the streets. Preventing any disturbances, you see.'

'Good, good,' I said. Bipin Bhonsle had paid the policemen too, all the way to the top. They would organize the right kind of peace. 'No more disturbances must happen. But you see anyone on the roads?'

'Not one man, not one woman. I see only three dogs.'

'Good,' I said. 'Typical Congress voters. We'll let them go.'

So I laughed and put down the phone. Just this much was enough to keep the enemy at home, to make the battlefield ours. No booth-capturing, no ballot-stuffing, just this. Meanwhile the boys had fanned out in our areas, and were taking the voters to the booths. 'We are from the Fair Election Committee,' they said, and they took our voters, in tens and twenties, to the voting centres. 'All is peaceful,' they said. 'Come, come.' And the voters came, safe and escorted, and Bipin Bhonsle's men, wearing nice yellow party badges, smiled at them outside the booths. And the voters filed in, and were left all alone, and they made their little black marks on the ballot, and the folded pieces of paper fell into the slotted wooden boxes, making small rustles, and the lines moved efficiently along, and the day passed, and so the machinery of democracy moved and spun, with a little help from us.

In Gopalmath, I sat on my roof and did my daily business. In the courtyard below, and out on the street, the usual clusters of suppli-cants gathered. Money was brought in, and I gave it out. Lives were brought to me, and I mended them. I gave justice. I ruled. The sun puddled, hovered and died its daily death. I ate, and retired to my bedroom. It was another quiet, ordinary day.

Bipin Bhonsle won by six thousand three hundred and forty three votes.

I was dreading the wedding. Of course I had to go, but I didn't know how I would face Dipika, show her my face with no magic solution to grant her eternal happiness. I was angered by this feeling of helplessness, this paralysis of will. The problem stayed with me, gnawing with a thousand tiny teeth at the edges of my mind, like a flood of relentless ants. I was furious with Dipika. Who was she? What did she mean to me, that I owed her this? A little nothing of a girl, to come between me and my friend, to haunt and bother me with her huge staring eyes, she wasn't even pretty, why couldn't I just tell her to take her dirty mashooq and go to hell? Why? But I couldn't. She had begged me, and I had made a promise. There was no logic in it, but it was the truth, it had happened. So I had to act. But I still didn't know what I was going to do.

I took my gifts – gold bracelets, gold earrings and a gold necklace – and went to Paritosh Shah's house on the wedding day. I hardly had my shoes off when Dipika came running to the door, stopped herself from falling by clutching at the jamb. She swayed there, in her sari of gold, and I could sense my boys averting their eyes. I knew they were thinking: what is Bhai doing now? This much was all it took to start a story that would get longer and fuller as it went out across the city. 'Beti,' I said. I patted her head paternally. Then I took her by the shoulder and led her inside. In a corridor, while her aunts and cousins brushed past, all shiny and magnificent in their very best, I leaned close to her and pretended to give her something out of my wallet. 'Be calm, you fool,' I told her. 'If you act mad I can't do anything for you. Behave yourself now. When I want to tell you something, I'll tell you.'

'But,' she said. 'But.'

'Be quiet,' I said. 'If you want to do this big thing, be brave. Control yourself. Learn control. Leave fear behind. Look at me. Learn from me. You told me you were not a child, but you behave like one. Can you be a woman?'

She blinked away her tears, and wiped her nose with the edge of her pallu. Then she nodded.

'Good,' I said. 'Go and be a part of your sister's happiness. Be happy, or people will notice.' She was still tremulous, aflicker with thin bolts of emotion up her neck and into her cheeks. 'Listen to me,' I said. 'I am Ganesh Gaitonde, and I am telling you that everything will be all right. Ganesh Gaitonde is telling you this. Do you believe him?'

'Yes,' she said, and as she said it she started to believe it. 'Yes.'

'Go.'

She skipped off, and at the edge of the courtyard she took two little girls by the hand and whirled with them, and in their pealing laughter there was her happiness, as palpable as the breath of the hundreds of flowers hanging in the doorways, on the walls. She was happy. I had given this to her, and I didn't have it to give. I had no idea where to find it, how. And so in the mandap, sitting next to Paritosh Shah, as the priests sang and thick sacrificial smoke gusted from the fire and an elder sister's happiness was chanted into being, I was helpless before the younger sister's life. Yes, Dipika was happy now, sitting behind her sister, leaning on her mother's shoulder, her face flushed and perspiring a little from the heat of the fire, eyes gleaming wet from the sting of the smoke. Looking at her, I thought: what makes a woman so much a prisoner, why? Why is one man a Dalit and poor, and another not? Why does this happen, and not that? Why did this woman die, and not that one? Why are we not free? And the Sanskrit choruses moved under my skin and I felt them shiver my soul, and the question came to me: what is Ganesh Gaitonde?

After all the functions were over, after the eating and drinking and rituals of farewell, I said goodbye to Paritosh Shah and his wife and his parents and his entire battalions of Gujaratis, and he walked with me to the car, and even in the midst of all this, he noticed my distraction, and asked, 'What's the matter, bhai? You look tired. Still not sleeping?'

'Yes, I'm very tired,' I said.

'Listen to me, then. You can't go on like this. Take a Calmpose tonight, and tomorrow we will see to your health.'

'Tomorrow I need to ask you a favour.'

'Favour? What? Tell me now.' He bent towards me, and had his arm over my shoulder. There was the big red smear of the tika on his forehead, and I could see the tiny white grains of rice in it. 'Tell me.'

'No, tomorrow, Paritosh Shah. Not today.'

'All right, tomorrow then.' He came close to me, drew me into his soft, cushiony hug and thumped me on the back. 'I'll come to your place in the morning.'

'No, I'll come to you.' I squeezed his shoulder and drew away. 'Let me.'

'Fine, whatever you say, boss. Whenever you're ready. I'm here all day tomorrow.' But he was puzzled. He was not used to this Ganesh Gaitonde. In truth, it was a Ganesh Gaitonde I didn't know well, either. I had been struggling to get some sleep lately, but now I had been cut adrift, cast into some unknown, tossing waters by a mere slip, a sliver of a girl whom I hardly knew, owed nothing to.

'Tomorrow,' I said, raised a hand and went home. That night I didn't care about seeming weak, and felt my own shame like a distant irritation. I took a Calmpose, and slept, but I dreamt of a black sea, heaving its endless swells at me, and nothing else was alive, nothing lived under that flat white sky, and I was alone.

Bipin Bhonsle came to me the next morning, with gifts. He brought the cash he owed me, in four plastic bags, but he also brought a brand-new Sony video player, and four tapes, all of American films, and four big boxes of mithai. He said, 'My father told me, "Take him some good Scotch," but I told him, "Ganesh Bhai doesn't touch the stuff, and I can see why. That's why he's so efficient."' He was sitting at the edge of the chair, all serious and enthusiastic. 'You know what, Ganesh Bhai? I've made up my mind. From today, no more liquor for me also. I will learn from you. Now that we've won, there is a lot to do. No time now for drinking-shinking. We have to keep on winning.'

'Yes,' I said. I had woken up more tired than before, and my legs were heavy, unwieldy, as if the blood had become congealed and dense. But I roused myself to Bipin Bhonsle's eagerness. 'Good, Bipin, good. A sober man is focused, he is awake, he is watchful. No need for all this whisky and rum. Life is enough.'

It was a speech I had given many times before. For him it was all new. 'Right, Ganesh Bhai, of course: life is enough. But please, enjoy.' He held out the tapes. 'Each is an international hit, Ganesh Bhai. Action-packed. You will enjoy.' He was so grateful it took an hour to get him out, and that only when I told him I was already late for a meeting at Paritosh Shah's house. He left, but loudly protesting eternal loyalty, and anything I needed I should remember him, and of course he was only a small man but if there were anything I wanted I only had to call him, and on international pleasures he was an expert. 'Hot tapes, electronics, cigars, anything, Ganesh Bhai, anything,' he was saying even as he went down the stairs. He was wearing an orange shirt with a flower print, and brown gabardine trousers, and shoes of a deep reddish-brown hue, gold-buckled and glowing. When he turned to wave from the gate, the chain at his neck flashed fiercely in the sun. He was altogether a shiny man.

We sped over to Paritosh Shah's. I would rather have gone slowly, I still had no plan, no tactics of persuasion worked out. But I couldn't say it to Chotta Badriya, go slow, don't go, never go, because I am helpless. I was, after all, Ganesh Gaitonde. I had taken the role, now I had to play the part. So hero-like I got out of the car, walked to Paritosh Shah's door, which was auspicious still with flowers and vines, and into the house. By the time I was barefoot in the courtyard I had lost all my swagger and style. I entered Paritosh Shah's office quite humbly.

He was on the phone, in one of his interminable dealings, arranging for money to go from here to there, breeding the currency notes with each other as they swept past him, and keeping one subtle, careful hand in the stream. Money leapt to him, and he delighted in its antics. He started to put a hand over the mouthpiece, and I waved him on. Talk, talk, I signed at him, my hands at my mouth, and I sat down and watched him. Behind him there was a gold-framed painting of Krishna with his flute. The top of Paritosh Shah's desk was gold, and he had five phones on it. The walls were a darker gold. I looked at Krishna, at his easy, turning stance and his slanty smile, and I hated him. You are arrogant, god. I changed seats, but Krishna's eyes followed me. I couldn't get away from him.

Paritosh Shah put his phone down, all bright from the thrill of money. 'Namaskar, my friend,' he said. He rubbed his hands together and rocked back in his chair and looked happy with the world. And Krishna smiled at me from above his shoulder.

Paritosh Shah had remembered by now our conversation from the day before. 'So, bhai,' he said. 'What's the matter? What can I do for you?'

In that moment I realized what Krishna was smiling at. I realized the limits of my power. And I told Paritosh Shah everything I knew and had found out about Dipika and her lover, that his name was Prashant Haralkar, that his father used to work for the sanitation department, that the mother had taken the children and left this alcoholic father twenty years ago. And also that Prashant Haralkar had been a dedicated student, that he had studied by the light of street-lamps and had gone to night college, that he now had a permanent job with the BMC, and that he now lived in a small but good-enough house in Chembur and supported his mother and younger sisters.

Paritosh Shah covered his face with both of his hands.

I walked around the corner of the desk, and sat on the couch close to him. I put my hand on his knee, patted clumsily. He flinched away from my touch. 'Who will marry my children?' he sobbed through his fingers.

I had no answer. I had promised Dipika happiness, but what about Paritosh Shah's two other daughters and two sons, what were they to do? I could win elections, I could move men up the steep ladders of success and kill them in the next moment, I could burn down houses, seize land, bring half the city to a standstill with an arbitrary procla-mation of a bandh, if that was my pleasure. But who would fight the rows of meek matrons who had sat primly, heads covered, at the wed-ding of Paritosh Shah's daughter? Who would push their portly husbands into enlightenment? Paritosh Shah's natevaik would declare themselves busy in response to his invitations, they would forget to ask him to their functions, and their sons and daughters would be engaged and married elsewhere, no matter how much money he had or how close he was to me. And he would feel shame every time he saw some acquaintance, each time he walked in the street. Sitting next to Paritosh Shah, abased by his tears and unable to look at him, I knew how helpless I was. I would have beaten all his relatives, thrashed each of them with my shoes, broken all their smug, snug heads open to the modern air, if only that would have made any dif-ference. But custom floats between men and women, it hides in the stomachs of children and escapes and expands and vanishes in every breath, you cannot kill it, you cannot hold it, you can only suffer it.

'Have you met that bastard maderchod?' Paritosh Shah asked. He was angry now.

'No, I haven't. Listen, I didn't come to you for him. He matters less than an ant to me. But Dipika asked me.'

'Kill him,' he said. 'Just kill him.'

'Easily done,' I said. 'I'll give the order now. In an hour he'll be gone, no part of his body will ever be found, not one fingernail. But then what? He'll be gone and so she will be able to love him the rest of her life. And also hate you for the rest of her life.'

'She is young. This is foolishness. She will cry for a week and then she will forget him.'

'Is that how much you know your daughter?' His cheeks were burnished wet, and his jaw clenched and opened and shut, sending little rushes of torment up into his eyes and forehead. 'She told me she would kill herself, and I believed her. Do you understand? I believed her. You'll find her dead.'

'Then what?'

He was walking in small circles now. 'Let her marry him,' I said. 'Marry them quietly and send them away. Settle them in Madras, in Calcutta. Amsterdam, if you want.'

'That won't change anything,' he said. 'Everybody will still know. If she suddenly goes, disappears, they'll ask questions, they'll make up stories. Everybody always knows. You can't keep something like that a secret for ever. I am a well-known man.' That he was. 'Bhai,' he said, 'what do we do, bhai?'

'You won't marry her to this fellow?'

'No. I can't. You know that.'

So here we were. He was trapped, and I could do nothing. 'Marry her today to someone else,' I said. 'Marry her this hour. Find a boy and get a pandit and marry her off now. Then send them away. Somewhere. Maybe she won't kill herself. Maybe she will, but maybe she won't.'

He was panting. 'Yes,' he said, and picked up the phone.

I left by the back door to the house. I had betrayed Dipika, and I could not face her. They married her that afternoon, to a boy who was flown down from Ahmedabad. Dipika and her husband went by the next morning's flight back to Ahmedabad. The in-laws told Paritosh Shah that after a few days of gloom, she seemed to have adjusted, she began to smile and laugh. Paritosh Shah was satisfied that the reality of the marriage had already erased the silly illusion of romance. The boy's parents told him, over the phone, that Dipika was talking a lot to the younger girls in the family, and had been to the cinema twice with her husband and her devars and their wives. So, two months later, Dipika and her husband were sent on their honeymoon to Switzerland. On the fifth night of the honeymoon, in Bern, she left the hotel suite while the husband was sleeping. She walked out of the lobby, and out of the gates and on to the road beyond. She was hit by a car that came fast around a curve. The driver said later that she was walking in the exact middle of the road, on the painted dividing lines, and he never had a chance to swerve, he didn't even know what he had hit until he came to a halt and reversed. Dipika was killed instantly. The husband said she had seemed happy, that their relations were joyous, as between any new husband and wife. In the Swiss records they put it down as an accident.

Three months after Dipika's death, I was watching one of Bipin Bhonsle's American movies when Paritosh Shah came to me. I had been awake all night, so excruciatingly awake that I could hear the creaking of the settling joists, the click of a passing dog's toes on the concrete outside. I watched the red second-hand of my bedside clock scything smoothly around its eternal circle, and I felt it tearing at something inside my head. So I popped in one of Bipin Bhonsle's tapes, switched on the television and pressed buttons on the control, and where there had been black fuzz a lion appeared, stretching its mouth in a yellow-toothed yawn. I watched, and the first time I understood very little. But I used the rewind button, and by morning I understood the story, who wanted what, what was standing in the way, and who must be killed. It was a good story, but it was the words that were the pleasure for me. I ran one scene back and forth, and the hero raced backwards under fine white lines, jerky and clown-quick, and his mouth twisted, and sounds came out glistening with his anger, and I ran it back, and forward, and back, and the syllables fell on my ears like pattering drops, and suddenly they fell together and the sense came to me, he was asking, 'Where did he go?' He had his pistol ready and was asking, 'Where did he go?' And in that moment there was a humming joy in every part of me. 'There,' I shouted in English at the hero. 'He went there.'

When that film was over, I put in another one, and learned. Paritosh Shah came at nine o'clock, and sat on the bed and watched with me, watched another hero and his men move down a jungle river with water to their chests, their faces blackened. 'These are commandos,' I said. 'Their country's secret missile has been stolen by one bastard. So they are going to get it back from his jungle den.'

Paritosh Shah smiled. 'A jungle den? It would be expensive to supply and maintain. That's what I always wonder about. How do they get the oil and atta and onions to it, for so many henchmen?'

I switched off the tape. 'You're just too much of a bania,' I said, 'to appreciate a good story.'

'I just don't understand these foreign films.'

'I can see that. Everything all right at home?'

After Dipika's death, his wife had taken to bed with palpitations of the heart. She was still weak, and given to fits of crying. 'We are going along,' he said. 'And you? Did you sleep?'

He knew that I lay awake at night, that I watched television in the grey hours of the morning, that I fell fitfully asleep in the car on journeys. I shook my head. 'I'll take a pill tonight.'

He made a sweeping motion in the air between us, like a man wiping a window clean. 'That's what I wanted to talk to you about.'

'About sleeping pills? Your ved-maharaj has some new recipes?' I had tried his Dhanwantri's pills, had got indigestion and gas and no sleep, and had gone back to the allopathic doctor for his strongest medicines.

'No. Not that,' he said, very serious. 'Listen, bhai, I think you should get married.'

'Me?'

'Look at you. You're not happy. You can't sleep. You're distracted, you do this and that, nothing works. You're restless. A man needs to settle down. You have everything now, you need to become a grahastha, start a family, everything has a place and time.'

'Marriage doesn't bring happiness to all of us.'

'You mean Dipika. Bhai, she was my daughter. It wasn't the marriage that was wrong, it was the other thing. Once she had gone past all boundaries, where was the chance for happiness? But you need to get married. All the scriptures say a life has its stages. First you are a student, then you are a householder. But you, you live like you've given up the world already. Look at this.' He meant the room, the bare walls, the white sheets, the crusted thali from dinner on the floor. 'Chotta Badriya and the boys are all very well, but they can't be your life. You need a woman, she will make a home for you.'

'Who will marry me, Paritosh Bhai? Which respectable girl?'

'You worry too much, bhai,' he said. 'We have money. Everything is possible.'

Everything is possible. Yes, he and I had created possibilities, we had snatched dreams out of the air and snapped them into solidity. Everything was possible. And yet Kanta Bai and Dipika had died. Looking at Paritosh Shah, I was reminded of the smile of the god above his shoulder, the blue conjuror who had regarded me with his

sleepy eyes. He had had a family too, many families. Now he was trying to trap me into one. Yes, I now knew that certain things were
impossible, even for me, and it was true that money made marriages
possible. Most of our boys had chavvis, and some of these chavvis
became wives. Sometimes the parents objected, made a fuss about the
boy's profession, but always finally agreed. After all, the boy was
earning, and earning good money. 'Yes,' I said sourly. 'Money can
bring a bride. At least it can do that.'

'Do you have somebody to love-marry?' Paritosh Shah said with
the satisfaction of a player moving rapidly towards checkmate.

'No.' I had women aplenty, bar-girls, whores, would-be actresses.
Certainly no one to marry.

'Then don't refuse me, bhai,' he said. 'You came to me that day and
asked me for something. And I couldn't give you what you wanted.
But don't say no to me today. I am asking you for something. Say yes,
bhai.'

I knew in that moment that we are trapped for ever in the connections that wrap us from head to foot and bind us to each other, as
invisible as gravity but as powerful. From this net there is no escape. I
had come to this city alone, to be alone, but my solitude was illusion,
a story I had told myself to convince myself of my strength. I had
found a family, a family had found me. This Paritosh Shah was my
friend, and he was my family. All the rest of them, Chotta Badriya and
Kanta Bai and my boys, they were my family. I was a part of this family, and they wanted me married. I couldn't fight them. I was defeated.
I nodded. I said, 'All right. I'll do what you want.'

While we looked for a girl we fell into a war. Paritosh Shah wanted
my janampatri, he wanted to know about my parents and my gotra
and my village. 'Only by knowing a man's past,' he said, 'can you
settle his future.' And I said, 'Forget all that. I have none of that, I
have money. Past is passed. Future is future, so make it for me.' I
believed then that a man can become anything he wants. I wanted it
to be true: no past, any future. But Paritosh Shah, that fat bastard,
that slippery Gujarati schemer, that faithful friend of mine, he looked
at me as if I was crazy, and then dreamed a past for me. He ordered
up a janampatri, a long roll which unfurled across the room, sprinkled with stars and secret hatchings and vermilion Sanskrit and all
good things. 'But not too perfect,' he said. 'Otherwise no Papa will

believe it.' So, according to Paritosh Shah, there had been bad times in my early youth, poverty and danger and near-death because of a rising Shani, but I had overcome these malign inevitabilities, I had faced down fate itself through the strength of my will and my single-hearted devotion to Krishna-maharaj, I had turned destiny through the energies of my uncountable devotions. This too he invented, all this, my God-fearing daily poojas, my temple-building, my love of Krishna. 'It is good publicity, bhai,' he said. 'So give up your godless ways, nobody likes that stuff. People will think you are a communist, and anyway your children will need a good, God-fearing household.' His special-order janampatri predicted many sons for me, and a daughter or two, and a long life of rising power and stability and eminence. Only one or two periods of illness were foreseen, like beauty-marks on a perfect face, and even these were easily surmounted through wearing of the right stones. Paritosh Shah rolled up the scroll with quick, practised little twirls of forefingers and thumb, his underarms jiggling, and smiled at me. 'You are a very eligible boy. You'll get a queue of candidates, you wait.'

I had my doubts. We might have moved the planets to shine a golden light on my future, but the fact remained that men had died at my hands. The newspapers called me 'Ganglord Gaitonde'. I was hated and feared. I knew this. And yet, the photographs came in. The Papas sent in pictures of their daughters, through intermediaries and marriage-brokers. Paritosh Shah spread a sheaf of them on his golden desk, like a pack of playing cards. 'Choose,' he said.

I picked up the first one. She was sitting in front of a red backdrop, wearing a silky green sari with a gold dupatta, with her sleek hair pulled tightly back from a long forehead. 'This one looks like a schoolteacher,' I said.

'So don't choose that one. Make a shortlist. Then we'll consider family background, education, nature of girl, horoscope, and move on from there.'

'Move on?'

'See the girls, of course.'

'We'll go to her house? And she'll bring in tea while her parents watch?'

'Yes, of course. What else?'

I flicked the picture back on to the table, where it slid smoothly into the rest. 'This is completely mad,' I said.

'What, marriage is mad? Bhai, the world does it. Prime ministers do it. Gods do it. I mean, what else are you going to do with your life? What else is a man born for?'

What is a man born for? I had no answer to this, and so I took the photos back home and laid them out on the floor of my room in rows of ten. They shivered in the draught from the air-conditioner, these faces patted smooth with powder, softly gleaming with hope. It was April, and without the blast of frigid air, even with the fan on 'Full', I sweated into my mattress, left damp stains on chairs. My blood was hot, and needed wintry air, more cold than this city could ever exhale. Outside, under the sun, my trousers stuck to my thighs and drove me into rages of restlessness, my shoes left red rings around my ankles. In these moods I was capable of rash anger and carelessness, so the boys had special power cables laid, and they knocked a new window into my bedroom wall for the machine, and so I was cooled. I was now comfortable and calm, and yet those faces on the floor were all the same to me, each was as good or bad as the next one. They were pretty enough, not phatakdi beautiful –who would want that in a wife? – but pleasant and welcoming and shy. They were sufficiently educated, well-cultured, no doubt each knew cooking and embroidery, they were all qualified, so why pick this one, and not that one? I waited for a sign from one of them, a wink of the eye as they fluttered in the chill blast. And there I was, Ganesh Gaitonde, leader of my own company, master of thousands of lives, death-giver and generous benefactor, completely and wholly unable to make a decision.

'Bhai, there's trouble.' Chotta Badriya was knocking urgently at the door. I called him in and he said it again. 'Very big trouble.'

'What?'

'Tonight's shipment, bhai. The police have it. They were waiting at Golghat. They were above the beach, behind that line of trees. They waited until all the maal was loaded into the trucks, then they came out and arrested everyone and took it all.'

All of it was forty lakhs worth of computer chips, vitamin B-complex tablets and video cameras. The maal was brought to the coast off the fishing village of Golghat on a hundred-foot dhow, then put on neat little fishing boats for the trip to the beach, where three trucks were waiting with plastic sheets on the flatbed, all ready for my precious cargo. But now the police had it.

'They knew,' I said. 'They had information.'

'Yes,' said Chotta Badriya.

'It was only police? No customs?'

'Yes, only police.'

'Who was it?'

'Zone 13 officers. Kamath, Bhatia, Majid Khan, those fellows. Parulkar's boys.'

We both knew what that might mean. It was possible that the police had their own sources who had tipped them off, or it could be that one of our rivals had given them my maal. At the time, there were four other big companies in Bombay, the Pathan company down in Grant Road, the Suleiman Isa outfit in Dongri and Jogeshwari and Dubai, the Prakash brothers and their company in the north-eastern suburbs and the Ahir company in Byculla. Any of those four – no, five, if you counted the Rakshaks – could have thought us tiny fish, easy to feast on. It wouldn't be the Pathans, they were weak from their long war with Suleiman Isa, which they had barely survived. Any of the other companies could have thought of us as a tasty passing snack, we were by far the youngest, the most inexperienced, least connected, with the smallest money and weapons. Which was it?

Parulkar had just come in as Assistant Commissioner in Zone 13, and he was said to be close to Suleiman Isa. And Suleiman Isa and his brothers headed the most politically connected, best-armed, largest gang that Bombay had ever seen. Maybe they saw us as a growing threat, and maybe they were trying to eat us.

'Is that all we know?' I said.

'That's all, bhai.'

I was so angry that I felt it as a pain in my joints, a shifting throb in my stomach. I wanted to kill someone. But slowly, slowly. Suleiman Isa was big. I had to know for sure. 'Call Samant. Find him wherever he is. I need to speak to him.'

Who was hunting us? Samant investigated, inside the department, fielding rumours, giving out a little cash here, a bottle of Black Label there. He had friends everywhere, constables and clerks and peons, and through these hands the secret would finally slip. But it was taking too long. There was a spy in my company, somewhere close to me, some chutiya who had sold the secret of my shipment, and with every passing minute the danger to me loomed and grew, like a leaning hill. I had to pick up the mountain, or it would topple and crush me. I could lift this weight, I knew it. But first I had to find the snake in my house, I had to crush his head. Where was he hiding? How to get him out in the open? In my air-conditioned room I slid the heads of the girls into patterns, formations, and thought. On the last day of May, I went to Paritosh Bhai. 'I want to *do* something,' I shouted at him. 'I'm sitting here like a chutiya while a bunch of bhenchods laugh at me. My own boys are laughing at me.'

'Nobody's laughing at you,' he said. 'Be patient. It's a big matter, and nothing big gets done in a day.'

I was about to let loose at him again, but there was a knock at the door. Bada Badriya peered around the door, then let a timid little tailor into the room. Paritosh Bhai was getting fitted for new safari suits. The tailor stretched his tapes around him as Paritosh Shah kept up a rapid series of calls on his cordless phone. I sat and watched. He had been very busy recently, launching his airline. My fat man wanted to fly. He had dozens of businesses, he gloried in his construction companies, his restaurants, his rental properties, his plastics factories, his garments factory near Ahmedabad, but he dreamt of soaring high above the earth, and so he had been appearing recently in all the newspapers, beauteous and polished from his gleamy hair to his gold chain with Krishna locket and the gold Rolex which set off all the birth stones on his fingers. There was some comfort for me in the thought of him flying high above the stepped cliffs of Bombay's buildings, above the brown lowlands of its bastis, of him hovering like a smooth and rotund balloon over it all, shading the city's long-toothed silhouette in the benevolent umbra of his blue safari suit, more delightfully blue than the sun-bleached sky. Maybe one day his shadow would fall west and north, all the way to Delhi, and beyond. He had the intelligence, the ambition, and a clear cold eye. But for now the airline would extend its service from Bombay to Ahmedabad and Baroda. He was arranging the celebrations and formalities surrounding the maiden flight.

'Listen,' he was saying. 'Just listen. I knew that randi when she would suck a lauda for a whole night for five thousand rupees. Now she's become such a big star that she wants three lakhs to sit on a plane for an hour? To cut one ribbon? Be serious.' He was talking to Sonam Bhandari's secretary, negotiating a personal appearance. He listened, then settled into his no-nonsense negotiating voice. 'I can give one lakh. I'm starting an airline, not a fund for starlets who are already finished. One lakh.' The tailor was measuring from waist to floor now. 'How much? Okay. One-fifty. Done. I'll send over fifty thousand today. Okay.' He put the phone down. 'Done,' he said to me. 'A film star will come for the flight. We shall be on TV.'

'You be on TV,' I said. 'I'm not coming anywhere near your flight.'

'Not even with Sonam Bhandari on it?' he said. 'If you see her jiggle those coconuts, you'll forget all about your shipment.'

'No woman has coconuts good enough to make me forget that.'

He was quiet until the tailor gathered up his scribblings and samples and left. 'You've done everything that can be done,' he said. 'Now we just have to wait.'

And wait and wait and wait. Waiting was grindingly hard for me. 'Listen,' I said. 'I don't want to wait. We have to do something.'

'At times like these, we need help,' he said, looking crafty. 'Let's do a puja.'

'Fine.'

'What, really? You mean that?' That he was amazed was only natural: in all our years I had never said a prayer, never begged for divine favours, had eaten prasad only as a quick snack. But now he wasn't interested in my reasons, just in moving fast through this unexpected opening. He was picking up one of his phones already. 'We'll do a Satyanarayan Katha. I know just the pandit. You'll see, all his kathas bear fruit without fail. Not to worry. Before you blink we'll be on top of the situation.' He was smiling at me most benevolently. I could see the story he had in his head, hear the katha he was going to tell as resoundingly as if he was loud-speakering it into my ear: Bhai has come home, he was going to tell the boys, he has come home to the Lord, by the grace of God he has been woken up, in his heart devotion has come alive like a flame. The truth was that I didn't feel very lit-up, just inert. I had the sensation of drowning slowly, and as the water eased over my cheeks I had flung up a hand and clutched at whatever was floating by. This puja was a twig, and I grasped it.

I could see the heavy boat motionless on the shifting silver surfaces of the enormous waters. Paritosh Shah had picked a bhaiyya pandit for his puja, so I could understand the katha in Hindi without effort. This pandit was a very dramatic story-teller, and he was doing the Satyanarayan Katha with vivid expression, with different voices for the characters and full Dilip Kumar expressions, and now we were at the part where the trader and his son-in-law were on their way home with a boat laden with gold and pearls and perfumes and ivory, all the weighty profits of a long, windy voyage away from home. Then a dandi-swami appeared on the bank, crafty old Satyanarayan himself in disguise, to ask the simple question, 'Bachcha, what's in the boat?' And the businessman, afraid of having to give alms, greedy short-sighted bastard, said, 'Oh, nothing, Swami-ji, just some lata-pata,' and the dandi-swami nodded and said 'Tathastu' and the boat was indeed suddenly bobbing up like a cork, filled now only with fluffy grass and dry hay. The dandi-swami now went into a deep meditative trance, and exactly at that moment, before we could get to the busi-nessman's final comeuppance and regret, Chotta Badriya tapped me on the shoulder, and whispered, 'Come, bhai.'

Outside the room, he gave me a phone. I took the call with Paritosh Shah and Chotta Badriya and his brother Bada Badriya watching. It was our breakthrough. The night before, one of our landing agents from Golghat had spent the night with a girl named Simky in Colaba. This landing agent, one Konkani named Ashok Khot, had been on our payroll for four years. Last evening, he had come to Bombay to put his wife on a train to Delhi, where she was going for her brother's daugh-ter's wedding. She had gone off on the Rajdhani, well-settled with her two sons in the chair car, and then Khot had decided to partake of the delights of the city. He had called this Simky from the station itself, then picked her up an hour later in front of the Lido Bar, near Regal. Khot was flush with money. He had arranged for a private air-condi-tioned taxi with darkened windows, and he took her for dinner to Khyber, and then for a drive down Marine Drive. All during dinner he drank Johnny Walker Black and told her stories about men he had fooled and money he had made and high officers he had ruined, and in the car, between massaging her mausambis and laughing at jokes he never finished, he took sips from a silver glass attached to a flask by a silver chain. She lay back in the seat and listened, humming along with the songs on the cassette player. They ate kulfi at Chowpatty, and he staggered to the water and tried to sing a song, and then threw up into the sea, and then drank another peg just to show how much of a man he was. On the way back, he had the driver turn up *Makhmali and-hera* and opened fully Simky's choli and was nuzzling into her with small slobbering sounds and babbling softly, and under the music she heard it, 'Saali, you better be good to me, do you know who I am?'

Nobody can look cross-eyed at me in this city. Masood Meetha himself comes to my house.' In the hotel room in Colaba, Khot looked dully at her while he pawed at her skirt, and then he slid slowly to the side and fell fast asleep. Simky took his shoes off, and his socks, then tugged off his pants and Jockey underwear. She found twenty-four thousand rupees in five-hundred-rupee notes in his various pockets, of which she counted off five thousand, which she hid deep in her red purse. From this purse she carefully extracted a small paper pudi, and from it pinched a judicious nip of brown sugar and breathed it up her nostrils, sending a voluptuous shudder through her breasts. Then she lay back and slept. In the morning, Khot turned over and stretched, and she kept herself still despite the gutter-reek of his breath. When he tried to climb on to her, she turned her head and winced and in a little-Simky voice said, 'Raja, you made me so sore last night, I can't take any more, really I can't.' He laughed proudly, and magnanimously let her off. The next day she had lunch with one of our boys, Bunty Arora, from GTB Nagar. When Simky had first come from Chandigarh, Bunty had taken care of her, she had been his chavvi. Now he wouldn't touch her, she had a nasty brown-sugar habit, but still there was the feeling for an old mashooq, and occasionally when he was on that side of town, he looked her up. She told him about her night with Khot. Now, our Bunty had been the one who had introduced Khot to Simky. So he said, 'That bevda bastard, he's unbearable when he starts drinking.' And she said, 'Yes, he talks and talks, he won't stop! I'm this, I'm that, nobody had better look at me, Masood Meetha comes to my house. I wanted to hit him on the head with a cricket bat.' She tossed her hair, and for a moment she had that old Simky fire. Then she went back to her golden falooda and foggy humming. Our Bunty, he kept his face calm, and moved the conversation on, talked about films and stars and this and that, and when they had finished lunch, he saw her off and then walked to the nearest shop and made a phone call. Just as the dandi-swami was saying, 'Tathastu.'

So there it was. Masood Meetha was Suleiman Isa's number one man in the city, had been ever since Suleiman himself had taken off for Dubai. The enemy who had stolen our goods was Suleiman Isa, he and his bastard brothers. I put the phone down and said this to Paritosh Shah and Bada Badriya and Chotta Badriya. 'It's Suleiman,' I said.

'Are you sure?' Chotta Badriya said.

'Of course I'm sure. I was sure of it before, now we have proof. That bhenchod Parulkar and Suleiman have been close for years and years.' This was common knowledge, and Chotta Badriya's face showed it, he looked down and was quiet. Parulkar and Suleiman had risen together, or at least in parallel. Many of Parulkar's most famous arrests and encounters had been based on intelligence passed to him by Suleiman, and those who had gone to prison or bled out their lives in some lane had been the enemies of Suleiman, his rivals, or just those who had grown big enough to be seen by him as competitors. He and his clan had eaten up many in this city, they had grown fat on this daily diet, and they swaggered through the streets. Suleiman Isa and his many brothers, the Nawabs of Bombay. 'I am going to kill them all,' I said.

The fan was skipping above us, aslant in its fast circle and letting out a periodic creak. This was the only sound. This was very serious. The Pathans had fought a war against Suleiman, had killed one of his brothers and many of his boys, but he had struck back and bled them weak. Finally a truce had been called, and the firing had halted, no more pistols snapping away in restaurants and AK-47s at petrol pumps, but the Pathans were left crippled. It was madness to doubt Suleiman's will, or his brain, or his wealth, or his contacts in the police and in the ministries. So my friends were quiet. Finally Paritosh Shah said, 'There's no other choice.'

War comes upon us. We are led in leaning curves towards the battlefield. You may try to avoid it, but find that last flower-lined turn you chose was really an entrance into a blood-soaked arena. So we were here. 'Good,' I said. 'Let's start.'

We were victorious at first. We had the advantage of surprise. On that very first day, I had Khot picked up. His wife was still in Delhi, so some of the boys just went over to his house that night and picked him up from his bed, lifted him and brought him to me. I didn't want him in my home, so we dealt with him outside, behind the house. At first he tried to tell me that he didn't know anything about any Suleiman Isa, why would I think that he would even try anything as low and crazy as that, everyone knew he had been faithful to Ganesh Bhai for years and years, he swore on the heads of his children. Finally, the shameless bhenchod, he tried a religion angle. 'Why would I go with that kattu bastard?' he said. 'Ganesh Bhai, think about it. Like you

I'm a God-fearing man. Every week I give to the temple. This is only some Muslim plot to break our friendship.'

I hit him so hard I skinned a knuckle. 'Listen, you bastard,' I said, and then was too angry, I felt my blood swell up behind my eyes. 'Beat him' was all I could say. 'Beat him,' I said, and walked away.

He made coughing, gasping noises, and called on his father. 'Papa, Papa,' he wept. That was interesting. Pain makes babies of most men, and their mothers are usually who they cry out for. Maybe Khot didn't have a mother. I went back and watched, rubbing my hand. When I pressed at the second knuckle on my right hand a hot fan of pain bloomed into my hand. I pressed harder. Now it was a cold movement, quick and edged and stabbing into my wrist. It was a slippery tooth just under the skin, biting. Under the quick rain of kicks, Khot was convulsing on the ground. I pressed harder. He broke first.

He told us everything. There wasn't that much to tell. He and Masood Meetha had known each other since they were young men. The families were from adjoining villages originally, somewhere near the coast. Masood had approached him a year and a half earlier, in Bombay, had called and invited him for tea and biscuits in his Dongri office. Khot had refused to meet in Dongri, so they had chai at a cheap restaurant in Ghatkopar. All they had done that first time was talk about Konkani villages and the food and whatever happened to old so-and-so whose father was a postman. Then, a month later, late at night, Masood had casually stopped by Khot's house near Golghat, on the spur of the moment, he just happened to be near by, and he had asked for dinner, for all the traditional Konkani dishes that Khot's wife could make, and so then he had Bhabhi's cooking which was just like his mother's. After this dinner, there had been phone calls and gifts of watches and bottles of whisky, but never any face-to-face contact. Khot was no innocent, he knew from the very first sip of Meetha's tea during that first meeting what this whole game was about, why after all these years Masood Meetha had remembered him. And when it came time to make arrangements for my shipment, my forty-lakh shipment, it was Khot who picked up the phone and called Masood, 'Bhai, shall we have dinner?' He cried and told us all of this.

'Kill him,' I said. I turned and walked away, and before I was at the steps leading to the back door, it was done. Two flat thumps and Khot was done. Chotta Badriya followed me inside, and I heard the snick of the safety before he put his pistol back under his shirt. 'Don't dispose of the body yet,' I said. 'We'll send it back to Suleiman tomorrow. Afterwards.'

'Afterwards,' he said, and grinned. So we set to work. We had been preparing. We had our lists, our hand-drawn maps, our information. So we set up our fielding. The next day, between eight in the morning and four in the afternoon, we killed Vinay Shukla, Salim Sheikh, Syed Munir, Munna, Zahed Mechanic and Praful Bidaye. That same night Samant encountered Azam Lamboo and Pankaj Kamath, for which action he got big stories in the papers, 'Encounter King Guns Down Top Suleiman Shooters', and three lakhs from me. And that same night, actually at four-thirty in the morning, a car pulled up to the corner near the Imperial Hotel in Dongri and Khot slid out on to the pavement, his head wrapped in a crusted towel. So, we told them who we were. We wrote our answers in blood.

What I wanted was Suleiman's head, to kick around like a football. But he was safe in Dubai, where he had gone after the Pathans had killed his brother, after he had killed many of them. Bombay had become too dangerous for him, and so he had fled, the bhadwa, but still he ran his operations in the city, through Masood Meetha and others. We were braced for their assault, and for a day we waited, and then sure enough it came. They ambushed three of our boys as they left a relative's house in Malad. All three of ours died, all three before they could draw their pistols. Ajay Kumble, Noble Lobo, Amir Kenkda. The next day Parulkar's inspectors were waiting in ambush for our weekly collection run to Darya Mahal Bazaar, where the shop-keepers had their contributions ready. The police party, led by Majid Khan the muchchad, were dressed as labourers. They gave no warn-ing, and fired thirty-four bullets. Vinay Karmarkar, Shailendra Pawar, Ziauddin Qazalbash.

So we fought Suleiman Isa through the summer, and into the mon-soon floods. When we collected our bodies from the morgue, carried them through the white waterfalls of water, it seemed as if we had been fighting them for ever, that the war had always existed. They hurt us, but they couldn't kill us. And we ate away at them, we bled them a little every day. Meanwhile Paritosh Shah's Rajhans Airline flew, and he got hair implants because he decided he looked too old on television, and he gave me lectures every day on the power of his dandi-swami. 'You saw how he answered your need. You asked and he gave. Now how can you not believe?' I was tempted to believe. But early in my life, I had seen how belief was an inner rot that hollowed out a man and made him a eunuch. I knew faith was a convenient crutch for cowards and weaklings. No, I wanted no such disease inside me.

So I resisted, I argued coincidence to myself, that the fact that our information had come to us during the puja was clearly a trick of unconnected movements shifting past each other in a way that made sense only to me, random particles bumping themselves into an illusion that seemed like a shape. And what about the thousands of moments in every minute where there were no connections, no sparkling threads of meaning from one event to the next? Paritosh Shah saw Dandi-swami behind the flashing face of every second, he entreated him with gifts and bhajans, and pressured him with stones and charms and secret mantras, and quarrelled with him on occasion. And always he then apologized to Dandi-swami and flew on the wings of his blessings. He was convinced that if only I would let go of my resistance and fall into marriage, I would automatically slide into belief. 'Once you are well-settled,' he said, 'all this nonsense will settle itself also. One-two, like that it'll happen.' And he snapped his fingers, one-two. Every day he asked me for my shortlist of girls.

So the year wore on. September, October. In early November Samant called. We had been doing business all during this struggle and had profited mutually, him in cash, me in dead bodies. But it had become harder for us to meet face to face since we had both been written about in the newspapers. We were trapped by fame. Only Bombay-fame so far, not all-India, but it was enough to make us very careful. So we spoke on the phone, on numbers we changed every week.

What Samant had to say was simple enough. A month after the seizure of my shipment, the government had distributed monies worth almost a fourth of its value to various officers and a certain anonymous informant. We knew that this unnamed bastard was not Khot or his survivors – we had kept a careful watch on them. So who was it, this gaandu who had taken what was mine? Now Samant had a name: 'Kishorilal Ganpat'. I knew the name. All of Bombay did. He was a builder, for ten years now he had spread his constructions across the east of the city. From the highway you could see his buildings rearing their heads out of the green fields, above the villages and the old colonies. He was big. There had been talk of his dealings with Suleiman, but their interaction had been just ordinary, of the necessary sort, what any builder would have with Suleiman Isa in the normal course of events. Nothing close, nothing special. We ourselves had talked to Kishorilal Ganpat when he needed some help with clearing slums from four residential plots in Andheri. But if he had taken my money, if he had stolen from me, he was closer to Suleiman than anyone had known. This meant he was a banker for Suleiman, that he ate from the same plate as that maderchod.

I thanked Samant, and hung up. His reward would follow later, and we had nothing else to talk about. I had the option to swallow this news quietly, to forget that I had heard it, and I also had the option to act. I kept the information to myself, locked it away in my stomach. I wanted to think it over carefully.

Just before dawn the phone rang again. Another one of ours was dead. This was a boy from Gopalmath itself, a boy I had seen growing up in the lanes I had built. His name was Ravi Rathore, and he had come back on the bus from Aurangabad, where he had relatives. Suleiman Isa's dogs had picked him up in Dadar at the bus station. An ice-cream-wallah had noticed some pushing and shoving. There had been a black van parked near by. At one in the morning someone had noticed a body in a reeking pile of garbage near the highway in Goregaon East and had made an anonymous call to the police. There was a bullet hole in each of Ravi Rathore's thighs, and one in his forehead. We brought back the body, to his kholi, in the late afternoon. He had no relatives in Bombay, so I gave the fire to his pyre. The body in its white shroud was tiny under the wood, under the spray of flame. He had been very skinny, Ravi Rathore, with a chest bent inwards, and his favourite belt with heavy silver buckles used to wrap nearly twice around him. When the boys played cricket on Sundays on the sloping pitch close to the hill, running between the wickets made Ravi Rathore heave and pant. Now he was dead. We burnt him and came home. I sat on my chair, on the terrace, and watched the night come again. This valley we live and die in is a valley of light and shade. We flicker in and out of it. How easily Ravi Rathore gave up his small space in it. I turned away tea, and dinner, and remembered a monsoon long ago, and Ravi Rathore's skinny legs in shorts, paddling in a flooded corner between two twisting lanes. That was what I knew of him, that and his belt and his wheezing enthusiasm for cricket.

'What are you thinking of, bhai?' said Chotta Badriya. He was sitting on the floor, at the end of the terrace.

'Bachcha, what's in the boat?'

'What?'

'I'm thinking of Dandi-swami.'

Chotta Badriya ducked his head down low, rubbed at his ankles. He was trying to decide where my temper was, if he could risk another question. He picked at the roof, took up a flake with his fingernail.

'Leave my house alone,' I said. 'Here's what we're going to do. We're going to sink a boat.'

Kishorilal Ganpat was a great Shiva-bhakta. He thanked Bholenath every morning for all the crores he had swindled, for the bribes he had given, for sand-mixed cement, for shoddy wiring that spilt out of rough-finished walls, for illegal and unlicensed buildings, for encroachments, for extra floors towering far beyond FSI limits, for middle-class money desperate for homes, for starving labour, for slums, for tough, sword-swinging boys, for Suleiman Isa. Kishorilal Ganpat was properly careful in these bad times, so he had two sinewy bodyguards who were so tight-muscled that they walked wide-legged, like somebody had tweaked a rubber band around each of their golis. Kishorilal Ganpat also liked appearances to be just so, so he dressed the driver of his Mercedes in a white suit and a cap, and the two bodyguards in grey safari suits. Kishorilal Ganpat was also a hoarder of time. He collected short-cuts that saved two minutes or three in this jangling maderchod jam of a city, he gave speeches to his employees about Japanese punctuality, he came to the Shiva temple on Satyagrahi Jamunanath Lane every Tuesday morning at eight-thirty precisely, on the 'dot of the dot of eight-thirty', as he liked to point out to anyone listening. All of which made the game childishly easy for us. We set up our fielding. Six boys, six Star pistols. We knew where Shiva sat, on his pedestal, we knew the steps that led down to the lane lined with houses and hawkers, we knew where the Mercedes would wait for its master, we knew where the bodyguards would be. It went smooth, like an oiled lauda into a wet chut. Kishorilal Ganpat came down the steps, holding his prasad aloft on a special silver thali. He had positioned his shoes pointing outwards at the bottom of the steps, and he stepped into them efficiently, saving a good three seconds. The bodyguards were bent over still, their backs to their boss as they pulled on their sandals, and Kishorilal Ganpat was stepping high, skipping over a puddle of water, when my boy Bunty moved sideways and into his path, and Kishorilal Ganpat turned his head to look, and Bunty raised his right arm and blew out Kishorilal Ganpat's left eye. One of the bodyguards reached under his shirt and was cut down. The other sat down on the temple steps and never raised his hands from the stone, which he grasped with whitened fingernails. Meanwhile Kishorilal Ganpat staggered and stumbled at the corners of the lane, from door to door, looking for a way out, any way out. Bunty walked after him, squeezing rounds tenderly into his back and buttocks. Finally Kishorilal Ganpat knelt in front of a vermilion door, under an elegantly painted Om in white, his head down and gaand high in the air, his clothes soaked through with blood, quite dead.

Bunty and the boys walked away, not too fast, not too slow. The exit was as uncomplicated as the job, they got into two cars and left. They then left the two cars on a corner in Malad and got into a van. In three hours they were all out of the city. And those of us who stayed behind grew careful. We knew we had escalated, and so we were prepared. I lived now in three different houses, and went between them at unequal intervals. Paritosh Shah dreamed of flight in a lumbering Mercedes fitted out with armour plate and hardened windows. Chotta Badriya had boys taking strolls through far lanes, watching over our interests. The death of Kishorilal Ganpat moved from the front pages to smaller squares at the back of the newspapers, and then finally disappeared altogether. Apart from two encounters executed by Parulkar's people, which lost us three boys, life went on as ever before. Don't get complacent, I told my boys every day. Don't go to sleep. They aren't sleeping for sure, they're preparing something. It'll come: the axe, the bullet, the fall. It must. We are making war with Suleiman Isa. Suleiman Isa.

Ganesh Gaitonde: the name had a heft, a certain sturdiness. It stood up straight, it didn't back down, it was a strong name. In print it had a certain symmetrical solidity, and it rang on the ear like the double clash of a nagada. People trusted it, and people were afraid of it. And yet: Suleiman Isa. All those hissing 's' sounds, they spoke of cunning. Mean, twisty, rat-skinned cunning. Which caught up with us one morning in late November. I was phoned minutes after it happened. Paritosh Shah left the offices of Rajhans Airlines in his impregnable Mercedes. Security guards swung shut the double gates behind the car as it accelerated tank-like down the lane. In the front seat there was a driver, an old trusted employee, and a bodyguard, not Bada Badriya, who was on a week-long holiday in his village in UP, but a stand-in named Patkar. Paritosh Shah sat in the back, entering names into an electronic diary he had received that morning on special order from Singapore. He wanted to do business from the car, make even more money. The lane from Rajhans swung left on to Ambedkar Road. Just as the Mercedes approached the intersection, a van pulled out behind it, and pressed close. And a truck slammed across the lane, blocking the turn, trapping the Mercedes between its side and the van: no way forward, no way back. The van crashed against the back bumper, shoved the Mercedes forward into the truck. Bullets exploded the rear tires. Then there were two men swinging sledgehammers against the Mercedes' left rear window, which, for all its bullet-proof hardening, starred and curved concave under the blows. The bodyguard had his pistol out, but there was a man pointing an AK-47 at him through the window. To protect Paritosh Shah, Patkar had to lower the window, which would let in the AK-47. The bodyguard pointed his pistol, but the front window stayed up. Meanwhile the sledgehammers crunched on the back window. Paritosh Shah flopped about on the back seat and stabbed his car phone with scrabbling fingers. Then, at the top of a large inward bulge in the rear window, a small hole crumbled open under the sledgehammers, a hole about the size of a rupee coin. Enough for a muzzle to press in, a second AK-47. An entire magazine was fired into the car. The bodyguard tried to fire, to shoot at the braying blaze that sprayed into the inside of the Mercedes, but his bullets stopped nothing, and may themselves have bounced around on the inside of the car.

My boys tried to stop me from going there, from going to my friend. I shoved them aside and drove myself. I was there minutes after the police arrived, and they at least didn't try to stop me. The rear and side windows of the Mercedes were webbed crystalline, smeared on the inside with a dark jelly. The front left door was open. The driver had survived, and had crawled over the dead bodyguard to get out after the booming fire had stopped. I leaned into the car, rested a hand on the satiny leather of the front headrest, and looked into the leg-space at the back. There was no Paritosh Shah there. There was a mass of deflated flesh, punctured and holed and ripped. There was no face there. Under a broad forehead, a splintered bowl of uncooked meat, shards of sharp white bone. No Paritosh Shah. He could never have fitted into that small flume behind the seat, not Paritosh Shah, not my fat man. But there was a hand with rings, with shiny protective stones. Here was a foot, still in its new tasselled burgundy loafer. He had said that word to me, with much indulgent patience: 'Not red, bhai, that's called *burgundy*. Burr-gandy.' Here was a styled thatch of dark hair. But where was Paritosh Shah? Not here.

I went to his house, where the women said nothing to me. Yet I felt their hate. He had died because of me. He had died for me. I had killed him. Nobody dared say it, but it needed no saying. When his body lay in the courtyard, wrapped in white sheets, covered everywhere, while his daughters wailed, nobody said it. Near the heat of the pyre nobody said it. I went back to Gopalmath without hearing it said, and yet it echoed along each whistle of my breath, each squeeze of my pulse. I drank whisky. I told the boys to bring me something, anything, as long as it was here, right now. Now. My throat burnt from the whisky and I saw myself dying. I was knifed, sabred, shot, hanged. My body fell. And then fell again. Bullets separated my elbows, cut my torso in half. I welcomed each fall. Where was death? This life squeezed my head in its iron hoop. Paritosh Shah's plump flesh emptied of blood, of air. How life lets out. How it goes. Does the spillage make a sound? Or was there only the breaking crack of the bullets? I raised my hand, brought it close to my eyes, pressed my face into the springy growth of hair on the forearm, felt the life in it. Each follicle was alive. A turn of my other wrist broke the whisky glass on a bedpost. With a splinter shaped like a half-moon I cut at the ridge of muscle under my clenched fist. Through the serried stalks of the hair I went, and the blood seeped noiselessly. I turned the arm, and there was the bumping of the pulse on the wrist. Easy to cut, to cease. How easy.

And then I was disgusted with myself. Paritosh Shah had lived. He had lived fully, he had fed his women, his children, his hundreds of employees. He had fed the world, and even as he had died, he had fought to dial his phone, to say something. He had tried to call me. I knew this. Not his wife, not his children, it was me. What would he have said, through that miraculous leap of electricity, over the distance? Death was already on him, and I could not have saved him. He must have known that. What would he have said, at the end? To me, his friend? I looked into the broken curve of glass, speckled with my blood, and I knew. I crawled to the other end of the bed, found the pile of photographs. From the middle of the stack, without looking, by feel alone, I pulled one. And I called to the boys.

'That's the one I want,' I said to Chotta Badriya, who was sitting with half a dozen others, cleaning his pistol. They were all puzzled. They had been expecting a war meeting. Whenever we had lost someone in this fight, after the funeral we always gathered to pick our hits for the next day, the next week. Who to kill, and how, that's what we talked about. But now I wanted a woman.

Chotta Badriya picked up the photograph from the table, where I had dropped it. 'Now, bhai?'

'No, no, not like that.' I could see he thought I wanted a midnight ride, a quick relieving of my tensions, but this was a respectable-looking girl, and he was puzzled. I thumped him gently on the shoulder. 'Not that, dhakkan. Paritosh Bhai wanted this. And Dandi-swami. I want to marry her.'

Her name was Subhadra Devalekar, and I married her four days later. At first, her father thought it callous that I should marry so soon after my friend's death. I know most of my boys felt this also. But I explained, that this was my friend's last wish, and then they remembered all his lectures, his shortlist, his nagging. A rumour appeared out of nowhere, and hardened into a certainty, that he had actually called me from the Mercedes, as the hammer-blows had rung on his life, and managed to say to me, 'You must marry.' So by the time we walked around the fire, Subhadra and I, our marriage had become an act of adherence to a dead friend's last wish. The boys came out, in their dozens and dozens, from all over the city, and watched our austere ceremony at Gopalmath temple with moistening eyes, with ready pistols, with ferocious loyalty.

After the ceremony we sat in front of the house and the people of Gopalmath came to pay their respects. Subhadra's father collected envelopes. He was a bus conductor who had retired from the 523 route, and he had four daughters. He had been hesitant at first when Chotta Badriya had come calling, after all the afternoon tabloids were still publishing pictures of the 'Death Mercedes', but a stack of five-hundred-rupee bricks on his tea tray had persuaded him. Daughters are a care. Now the bus conductor stood to my right and took the gift envelopes from the line of well-wishers. Bada Badriya came forward with a fat red envelope. He had rushed back from his village as soon as we had contacted him, and was still ashamed at letting his boss out of his care, I could see that. But he hadn't been back to his village for five years, and what had happened was no fault of his. I told him that and hugged him.

And then I was sitting on a bed, a bed strewn with rose petals. A song played somewhere, a flute threaded through it. On a corner of the bed there was a huddled red tent of a sari, holding within it a trembling, skinny body. My wife. I was married. My head was floaty, as if I had just woken from a long dream. I asked: how did this happen? There was no answer.

Old Pain

Mary Mascarenas was ready to talk. Sartaj waited for her, alone, across the road from the Pali Hill parlour in which she worked. The road down the slope was alive with expensively dressed teenagers, boys careening through in sleek cars bought by their rich fathers, girls in swirling groups of three and four. Sartaj was waiting next to a cigarette stall, near a row of servants and drivers having their evening smoke and gossip. He had called Mary that morning, told her gently that he would like to speak to her. After work, she had said, and there had been no more anger in her voice, just resignation. So Sartaj was confident that he would get good information: she would need to explain now, to herself, what had happened, and why. He had come a little early, and now the drivers were talking about stock prices and the fortunes of companies. Drivers knew more than anybody else, they listened in on Saab and Memsaab's conversations in the car, they knew their movements, they carried documents and cash. Sartaj watched the flirtations between the boys and girls, and tried to keep an ear on the stock conversation, for Katekar's sake. Katekar didn't gamble, but he insisted that the market was logical, you only had to know the rules. If you could feel the rhythms, you could be king. All you needed was information and education. So Sartaj listened, but the drivers knew more than him, and he could make no sense of their lively arguments. Their very glossy memsaabs came out from the salon, and the little flock of drivers contracted and expanded, but their banter never flagged. They smoked cigarettes and ate from little packets of channa. They were well-paid, these drivers, and smartly turned-out, in keeping with the status of their employers.

It was past seven when Mary came through the blue glass door of the salon. She was wearing a black T-shirt, a slim black skirt to the knee and black flats. Her hair was pulled back into a ponytail, and

Sartaj was suddenly struck by her elegance. She was all quietness, and if you stood her in a row next to these teenage queens strutting past her, you wouldn't notice her. Not unless you were looking for that straight back, that symmetry of the shoulders with both hands on a black purse. She saw him, and he raised a hand.

He walked over to her side of the road, to the gleam of expensive shops, Gurlz, Expressions, Emotions. 'I'm late, sorry,' Mary said. 'There is some big party at the Taj tonight. I had three extra appointments.'

'Taj party definitely needs extra-fancy hair.'

'I have never been, so I don't know. But I can do the hair.'

Her Hindi was accented, functional and fluid, but improvised, it stumbled confidently past feminine possessives and tenses. Sartaj was sure her English was better, but his own English had rusted into awkwardness. They would get by in some knocked-together mixture, some Bombay blend. We're all right in these khichdi tongues, he thought. 'My car is over there,' he said. On the phone she hadn't wanted him coming to her place of work, and he had reassured her that he wouldn't be in uniform, he wouldn't be driving a police jeep, that he would be alone. He reversed out into the road as the drivers watched, and then waited for Mary to get in. 'We'll go down to Carter Road,' he said, and she nodded. She wouldn't want her neighbours wondering either, about visits from policemen, or strange Sikhs.

He found a curve far down on the sea-wall, a gravelly shoulder a little less occupied by hawkers and strolling lovers and beggars. 'That ship's gone completely,' he said. 'Not even a little bit left. What was it called?'

There had been a foreign freighter that had been forced aground with a dead engine by a monsoon storm. It had become something of a tourist attraction for a while, its hull far up out of the water. Very late one night, Sartaj had sat on a bench facing the ship and kissed Megha. They had separated not long after.

'It was the *Zhen Don*,' Mary said. 'They cut it up for scrap. It's been gone for years.'

'I thought they were going to turn it into an offshore hotel.'

'It was worth more as scrap.' The sky was the same indeterminate grey it had been for two days, and under it were the vague shapes of foreign ships, skimming the horizon. Mary turned her head towards Sartaj. 'I read in the papers you were supposed to have a policewoman present when you interrogated a woman.'

284

'I'm not interrogating,' Sartaj said. 'You're not a suspect. Nobody is a suspect. I'm just trying to understand what happened, why your sister was there. And I didn't think you would want to talk in front of more people. This is just a sort of private conversation. What you tell me remains with me.'

'I don't have anything to tell you.'

'You don't have anything to say about your sister?'

'I haven't seen her for a long time. Not talked to her for, for years.'

'Why? You had a fight?'

'We had a fight.'

'About what?'

'Why do you need to know?'

'It might show me what sort of woman she was.'

'Which will show you how she got to that place?'

'Maybe.'

'She was not a bad woman.'

She was anxious, squeezed up as far from him as she could get on the grimy blue seat. Looking at her little black bag, which she had placed between them, Sartaj realized that she was afraid of him, of the parking on the sea-wall, of what she thought he might demand of her. That's why she had asked about the policewoman. He was used to people being afraid of his uniform, but the idea that this woman thought that he might assault her sickened him. He fumbled for the ignition, and changed gears with a metallic scraping. He drove fast down the road and stopped near the thick of the evening walkers, right next to a boisterous group of teenagers eating ice-cream. Mary was watching him wide-eyed.

'I need some narial-pani,' he said. 'And understand, I'm not going to harm you. I just want to talk to you. Clear?'

She nodded, and watched him intently as he beckoned to a hawker and paid for two coconuts. She held hers in both hands and drank from it in great thirsty gulps until it was finished. Sartaj held out his. 'Want more?'

'No,' she said, and she was relieved, not quite easy yet but not cringing away from him any more.

Sartaj sipped at his narial, and watched her, and waited.

'My sister was fifteen when she first came to Bombay,' Mary said. She was looking out of her window, towards the slow rumbling of the sea. 'I lived in Colaba with my husband. She came to stay with us. We grew up on my mother's farm outside Mangalore. Our father died when I was eleven. I got married, moved to Bombay. So Jojo came to stay with John and me. She was young, but she said she wanted to be a nurse, and the school in our village was just a village school. She had passed her tenth exams, first class. She wanted to learn English and be a nurse. We had only a tiny place, but she slept on the sofa, and after all, she was my little sister. She was so small and thin, in those days. She used to wear three little ponytails. I thought she was watching too much television, I told John that. She used to sit in front of it, cross-legged, all day and night. But he said it was good for her, she needed to learn English and Hindi. He used to tease her and make her laugh, telling her that she knew only the jingles, Vico-Vajradanti! He said she could only talk about teeth and hair. But she was very intelligent, you know. Day by day she picked it all up. After a while she wasn't scared to do all the shopping. I had a full-time sales job at a leather-goods store, so having her there at home helped a lot. She was suddenly so confident. And she stopped wearing those print skirts, her hair changed, her walk became different. In six months she became somebody else. A Bombay girl. Then one day she started talking about acting. She used to imitate the heroines of the movies and serials, and the VJs. I can do that, she said. At first I just laughed and forgot about it. Then she said it again and again. John paid attention. He said, she's right, you know. Look at her. She's as good as any of them, better. Why shouldn't she be able to do it? He was right. She sparkled. I hadn't seen it, she was my little sister, but without her ponytails she was a star. She stood in front of the mirror on the cupboard, and she watched herself in the apartment windows. Now I saw how the neighbours watched her, when she ran down the stairs to get bread in the mornings. The boys from down the street waited for her in the evenings, just for her to walk by. I started to believe it too, that summer. Every heroine came from somewhere, after all. Nobody was born with the lights on their faces. This one was from Bangalore, that one from Lucknow. Some of them had come from very ordinary families. Now they had money, they had fame. So why not Jojo? Why not my sister? We were all caught up in it, in that fantasy. We had seen it come true for other girls. So why not Jojo? John had a friend who worked for MTV, as an accountant only. But this accountant knew people at the channel. So John took an afternoon off work and took Jojo to Andheri East, to meet some people at MTV. They caught the train, and then an auto-rickshaw. They came back all excited. The MTV executive, an Englishman, said that she was charming and beautiful. Imagine. She didn't get a job out of that, but just getting a meeting with somebody so important was thrilling. Such a huge distance, from our little flat to MTV, and they had crossed it all in one afternoon. The impossible was possible. So then the summer was over, and Jojo was enrolled in school, but school didn't seem that important. She was taking dance classes, and acting classes. She was talking to producers, directors. John took her sometimes, often, to these meetings in Bandra, in Juhu, in Film City. At his work they were concerned, then they were upset. I worried. But he said, big rewards need big risks. We need to see far ahead, and not be afraid. Don't be afraid. And I tried not to be afraid. But I was. I was afraid for Jojo. I saw how much she believed in her future. Everyone struggles, she said. You have to struggle. Aishwarya struggled, even Madhubala struggled. So I have to struggle, Jojo said. But finally I will win, she said. I will.'

A luxurious breeze came in from the sea, fluttered the sari of a walking woman in a swell of purple, stirred Mary's hair across her eyes. But she was far away, speaking not to him but to herself.

'We were all caught up in the struggle. I saved money for Jojo's lessons. John was always phoning his new MTV-type friends, keeping in touch. He was a new John also. I hadn't seen such excitement in him for a long time. I went with them, John and Jojo, to one or two of these filmi and television parties. Parties with the famous faces of television. Archana Puran Singh here, Vijayendra Ghatge there. I saw how John shook hands and laughed, how he hugged and thumped backs. That night in bed he held me and explained to me. This is how it works in this business. This is how you get jobs. It's all about contacts, it's all about goodwill. That's how it goes. That's how we spent that year, on the edge of something big. That's what it felt like. Jojo got one modelling job, and then a second. The first one was a small television ad for Dabur shoes, she was dancing with two other girls on a divider in the middle of a highway. We had the television on, waiting on a Tuesday night to see it. How we screamed when suddenly she was there. Jojo on television, dancing. We danced, and John had got a small airline bottle of champagne from his accountant friend, he opened it and we all drank straight from the bottle. After that dance on the highway, we were so sure. Nothing can stop us now. Only a matter of time. John said that all the time, only a matter of time. But nothing came. Jojo was tantalized by endless meetings, "Come back and see us again, we are still thinking," but then somehow it was always the other girl. She used to think and talk about it endlessly, why not me? She and John talked about clothes, make-up, attitude. Next time we'll do this. Next time it'll be like this. They planned and planned. Next time. And then I caught them.'

She stopped short, and wiped the hair away from her face. She was looking away from him, but she was with him now, no longer in memory.

'Caught?' Sartaj said very quietly.

She cleared her throat. 'I was at work. I started feeling very sick, weak. There was a viral fever going around at that time. Everyone had it. You could feel the temperature on my skin. The shop-owner said, go home. So I went home. They were in my bed.'

There was danger always in this moment, when the subject first revealed her or his humiliation. Too heavy a touch, even of sympathy, and you would lose them as they curled up around their exposed pain, closed up and hid all the essential detail. 'I understand,' Sartaj said. 'He must have tried to say it was all right, that nothing had changed.'

At this she was faintly startled, surprised by him, and now he could see the glisten of her pupils. 'Yes,' she said. 'I think he had some idea that we could all live happily together. That I would keep working for them, making the money to dress both of them and send them to their meetings.'

'And she?'

'She . . . she was angry at me. As if I had done something wrong. "I love him," she said. She kept saying that. I love him. As if I didn't. I finally said that. He's my husband, I said. And she said, no, you don't love him. You can't. She was screaming. And I was so angry. To hear my sister say that. To know what my sister and my husband had done. Get out, I said to her. Go away.'

'Then?'

'He left with her. He came back two days later to get their clothes.'

'Yes.'

'Then we divorced. It was very difficult. I couldn't pay the rent. I tried to get into the women's hostel, but they had no space. For a while I stayed at the YWCA. Then I had to live in a jhopadpatti, in Bandra East. All kinds of places I've seen.'

'You didn't want to go home?'

'To my mother? To that house I grew up in, with Jojo? No, I couldn't live there. I couldn't go back.'

So even a slum was better, better than that home left far behind. 'You have a good place now,' Sartaj said.

'It took a long time. I started in this salon cleaning the hair from the floor, washing the scissors and combs.'

'Did you see her again?'

'Two, three times. The judge makes you go to counselling before they let you get a divorce. She was there to meet him afterwards. I didn't speak to her. Then I saw her when the judge granted the divorce.'

'And after that?'

'I heard about them once or twice, from relatives and friends. They were living in Goregaon. Still trying to get her into films, anything. I saw her on television once, some advertisement for saris. Bas, that was it.'

'You never spoke to her again?'

'No. My mother was very angry at her also. Ma was sick, and Jojo tried to get in touch, but Ma said no, she didn't want to speak to her, to that sinful, shameless girl. She died without ever speaking to Jojo. And I didn't really want to know anything about Jojo.'

'So, not even a little news from somewhere?'

She shook her head. 'Once. Maybe two, three years ago. I have an aunt in Bangalore. My mother's sister. She said she saw Jojo at the airport.'

'Your aunty spoke to her?'

'No. She knew what she had done.'

'Jojo was getting on a plane?'

'Yes. She must have made money. I don't know how. I don't know anything about her. About what happened to her.'

What happened to her. How an ambitious, lovelorn teenager became a trader in bodies, how she ended up dead, murdered by a suicidal bhai. He didn't know how, but he could imagine it, the descent from filmi parties into many kinds of underworld. 'We also have very little information about her,' he said. 'She worked in television, produced some shows. There were some other activities.'

'Activities?'

'We are investigating. When we know more, I will tell you. If you hear anything, anything at all, please call me.' She would, Sartaj thought. She had a certain hope in him now. From these little scraps, these fragments, maybe she could reconstruct her sister, and forgive her, and herself. 'I'm glad you spoke to me,' he said.

'She was a sweet girl,' Mary said. 'When we were small, she was scared of thunder. She used to crawl into my side of the bed late at night and push her head into my stomach and sleep.'

Sartaj nodded. Yes, Jojo was also that scared little girl, holding on to her sister. It was a good thing to know. He drove Mary home. From the car, he watched her climb the stairs to her room. The light went on inside, and he reversed out into the main road. On the way home, as he veered left into the curve at Juhu Chowpatty, it began to rain.

Iffat-bibi called Sartaj just as he was finishing his dinner of Afghan chicken and tandoori roti from the Sardar's Grill down the road. 'Saab, I have an answer.'

'To my question?'

'Yes. Bunty was thokoed by two freelance shooters.'

'Working for whom?'

'Nobody. It was personal. Bunty took a girl from one of them some three, four years ago.'

'Took?'

'She liked Bunty's money better than the freelancer. This idiot free-lancer was in love with her.'

So Bunty had died for a woman, not land or gold. Or for anything to do with Ganesh Gaitonde. 'Okay,' Sartaj said. Bunty had wounded a lover, and the lover had waited and nursed his anger and been patient until Bunty's fortunes fell into steep decline. 'Okay.'

'You want them?'

'Who?'

'The freelancers. We know where they are right now, where they will spend the night. Where they will be tomorrow.'

'You want to give them to me?'

'Yes.'

'Why?'

'Think of it as just a gift between new friends.' Her Urdu was impeccable, and her voice could go cushiony and soft.

Sartaj got up, stretched and walked to the balcony. He leaned over the railing, and watched the treetops swaying in the damp breeze. The lamps threw the shadows of their leaves across the smooth surfaces of the cars.

'Saab?'

'Iffat-bibi, I am not worthy of such a gift. You have an old relationship with Parulkar Saab. Why don't you give it to him? I don't handle these bhai and company and shooter matters.'

'Is this true? Or do you think I am not worthy of giving you something?'

'Arre, no, Bibi. I am just afraid that when the time comes, I will have nothing equal to give you in return. I am a small man.'

She made a smacking sound full of exasperation. 'The son is just like the father. All right, all right.'

'Bibi, I meant no offence.'

'I know. But really, I used to tell this to Sardar Saab also, how will you get ahead if you don't make the big deals? And he always said, "Iffat-bibi, I have flown as high as I can. Let my son go further."'

'He said that?'

'Yes, he spoke about you often. I remember when you passed your twelfth, he distributed sweets. Pedas and burfis.'

Sartaj remembered the pedas, the saffrony taste of them that contained all the future. 'Maybe I am like him also, yes. Parulkar Saab moved ahead.'

'Yes, with Sardar Saab's help all the time. Parulkar was a sharp one from the beginning, see. Always thinking, thinking. There was this case, a robbery gang on the docks.'

She told him then about this gang, which had people on the inside and outside of the docks. They pilfered goods, of course, but they also took equipment and fuel, anything worth a little money. Parulkar had broken the case, with lots of Sardar Saab's help, his contacts and sources, all of which Sardar Saab was glad to give him. But when the time came for arrests, Parulkar let a senior inspector take the apradhis in and enjoy all the credit. 'It would have been a big case for Parulkar, but he saw ahead, see? Lose some heavy arrests now, but profit later.'

'He's fast like that.'

'How fast, you don't even know. But you haven't learnt much from him.' He knew she was smiling, and couldn't help smiling back.

'What to do, Bibi? We are who we are.'

'Yes, we are as Allah makes us.'

They said their farewells, and Sartaj went back to picking at his chicken. He was craving a peda, but it was late and he was tired. He comforted himself with another shot of whisky, and promised himself two pedas at lunch. He was sure it was going to be a good day.

By the next morning the rain had turned into one of those endless monsoon drenchings that felt as if the sky had collapsed under the weight of water. Sartaj ran from the car to the station, and by the time he was under cover his shoulders were drenched. He could feel the water inside his shoes.

'Your girlfriend's waiting for you, Sartaj Saab,' Kamble said from his perch on the first-floor balustrade above. He was leaning out, head close to the smooth fall of water from the roof, a cigarette in one hand.

'Kamble, my friend,' Sartaj said, 'you are full of bad habits and bad beliefs.' He had to raise his voice to be heard above the drumming of the water on the bricks. Kamble grinned back at him, very comfortable with his badness. By the time Sartaj got up the stairs, he was lighting another cigarette and he had his answer ready.

'Sometimes you need a bad one like me, Sartaj Saab,' he said, 'for all the bad work that has to be done in this world.'

'Since when have you become a philosopher, chutiya? You never needed any excuses before, so don't start blaming the world now. Who is waiting?'

'Arre, your CBI girlfriend, boss. You have so many you don't know which one is coming to visit?'

Anjali Mathur was at the station. 'Where?' Sartaj said.

'Parulkar Saab's office.'

'And is Parulkar Saab there?'

'No, he got a call, he had to rush to a meeting with the CM at the Juhu Centaur.'

'With the CM. Very impressive.'

'Our Parulkar Saab is a very impressive man. But I don't think he likes your chavvi very much, Sartaj Saab. I just see something in his look. Maybe he wants her also.'

Sartaj thumped Kamble on the shoulder. 'You have a very dirty mind. Let me see what this is about.' He walked down the corridor. Kamble was indeed dirty, but maybe it was just that he took more pleasure in the same dirt that everyone was swimming in. He certainly understood the politics of the station, and knew everything that went on in it. Sartaj nodded at Sardesai, Parulkar's PA, who waved him towards Parulkar's door. Sartaj knocked and went in. Anjali Mathur was sitting alone on the sofa at the rear of the room, at the end furthest from Parulkar's desk.

'Namaste, madam,' Sartaj said.

'Namaste,' she said. 'Please sit.'

Sartaj sat and told her what he had learned from Mary, which was very little. As usual, she took in the news, such as it was, and then stayed perfectly still. She was deliberating. Today she was in a dark red salwar-kameez. Wine-coloured, Sartaj thought. An interesting hue on her dark-brown skin, but it was loose, and covered her quite impersonally. There was no cut there, no personality. She carried her face the same way, shut off. Not hostile, just guarded, closed.

'Shabash,' she said. 'Every little thing is important. You know that. You never know what will open up a case. Now, I have two things to tell you. One, that Delhi has decided to halt this investigation. We were interested in Ganesh Gaitonde's return to Mumbai, the reasons for it, what he wanted here. But from what we have found out so far, Delhi doesn't think there's enough there to justify further enquiries. Frankly, nobody cares. They say, Gaitonde is dead, he's finished.'

'But you don't think he's finished.'

'I don't understand why he was here, why he killed himself, what he was looking for. Who he was looking for. But I have been called back to Delhi. There are more important things to work on, it is felt.'

'At the national level.'

'Yes. At the national level. But I would appreciate it very much if you would continue looking into the matter a little. I appreciate very much your hard work. If you could continue, maybe we would have some answers to our questions.'

'Why are you so interested in Ganesh Gaitonde? He was a common gangster. He's dead.'

She thought for a moment, considered her options. 'There is not much I am allowed to tell you. But I am interested in him because he was connected to certain very important people, to events at a national level. Whatever brought him back here, that could have an effect on future events.'

. And you want me to risk my head under these huge juggernauts, Sartaj thought. You want me to put my golis in the path of those oncoming, grinding wheels. You want to involve me in Research and Analysis Wing matters. International intrigue, derring-do in foreign

293

lands, desi James Bonds. He knew the agency existed somewhere, he had been told it did exist, but it was all very fantastic and very far from his very ordinary life. He had never really felt it was real, all that sinister spy stuff. And yet here was serious, small Anjali Mathur, in her dark red salwar-kameez, sitting on the sofa a few feet from him. And she was interested in the death and life of Ganesh Gaitonde.

The next question was obvious, but Sartaj kept himself from asking it: why does RAW have an interest in our friend Ganesh Gaitonde at all? Maybe some of the important people that Gaitonde had connections with were in RAW, maybe some mutual dealings had existed between the agency and Gaitonde, but Sartaj didn't want to know. He didn't want to be in this room any more, with quiet Anjali Mathur. He wanted to be back in his own life. 'Yes,' he said. 'Very true.' He was quiet. These RAW things happened far away from him, as they should. He didn't have any questions, he didn't want answers. He was done.

'I have to go back,' Anjali Mathur said finally. 'To Delhi. But I would be grateful if you would continue to investigate this issue. For you to do so would be completely logical, expected. If you learn anything, here is my number in Delhi. Please call me.'

He took the card, and stood up. 'I will,' he said.

She nodded, but he knew she saw his nerviness, his desire to be out of the room, away. Outside, Kamble was sitting on the visitor's bench, one leg crossed comfortably over the other. 'So what happened, boss?' he said with his customary leer.

'Nothing,' Sartaj said. 'Absolutely nothing. Nothing happened. Nothing will.'

Ordinary life had its own savoury pleasures. Sartaj was eating a very hot chicken Hyderabadi with Kamble when his mobile rang and began to skid slowly across the table. Sartaj nudged it back with a knuckle, and saw that Wasim Zafar Ali Ahmad was calling. 'Arre, tissue, tissue!' he called to the waiter and thumbed the phone. 'Hold,' he managed to get out before a cough caught at his throat.

'Saab, take a sip of water,' Wasim Zafar Ali Ahmad said paternally when Sartaj finally got the phone up to his ear.

'What do you want?'

'You are eating lunch, saab. I have your dessert.'

'The Bihari and the boys?'

'Yes.'

'Where? When?'

'They are coming tonight after midnight to collect money from a receiver.'

'After midnight, when?'

'I only know that the meeting is after midnight, saab. Maybe they are being careful. But I have an exact address.'

Sartaj wrote down the street and the landmarks and the name of the receiver. Wasim was very exact indeed. 'Saab, there are many kholis on the track side of the road, and there are always people moving around there, even late at night. So you must go in carefully, otherwise there will be trouble.'

'Chutiya, we have done a thousand of these arrests. This one will be nothing special.'

'Yes, yes, saab. Of course you are the master of these matters. I didn't mean . . .'

'All that matters is that the information should be good. Is the information good?'

'Saab, it is solid. You don't even know what I went through to get it.'

'Don't tell me. Keep your mobile on tonight.'

'Yes, saab.'

Sartaj put down the phone. He took up his tandoori roti and ate a large mouthful of chicken. It was delicious. 'What are you doing tonight?' he said to Kamble.

Sartaj and Katekar were waiting. They were in disguise, in tattered banians and dirty pants and old rubber-soled keds. Sartaj had an old patka draped loosely over his hair and tucked behind his ears, and thought that he looked like a rather debonair, dashing thela-wallah. They were sitting, reclining, under a thela pushed up on the pavement, across the road from a barred iron fence that edged the railway tracks. Katekar was complaining about the crowds on the trains. 'This country is hopeless,' he said. 'People push out babies with no more thought than street dogs making puppies. That's why nothing works, all progress is eaten up by new mouths. How can there be development?' This was one of his favourite themes. Any moment now he would start advocating a scientific dictatorship, universal registration and identity cards, and a strict birth-control policy. But now they were both silent as a train clattered by, going up the line, almost empty. During the day pods of men hung from the doors, swelling out over the rushing tracks, suspended by fingertips and toes. 'Almost one hour since the last train,' Katekar said. It was almost two-thirty. 'You watch. One heavy rain and trains will stop. This chutiya central line, if ten schoolboys stand in a row and piss on the tracks, bhenchod service is disrupted.'

Sartaj nodded. All this was true, and it was a restful pleasure to lie under a thela and complain. They had already complained about the municipality, corporators, transfers of honest civil servants and policemen, expensive mangoes, traffic, too much construction, collapsing buildings, clogged drains, unruly and uncivilized Parliament, extortion by Rakshaks, bad movies, nothing worthwhile to watch on television, American interference in subcontinental affairs, the disappearance of Rimzim from soft-drink stands, inter-state quarrelling over river waters, the lack of good English-language schools for children whose parents didn't have truckloads of money, the depiction of police on the movie screen, long unpaid hours on the job, the job, and the job. When you had complained enough about everything else, there was always the job, with its unspeakable hours, its monotony, its political complications, its thanklessness, its exhaustion.

Sartaj yawned. Near the iron fence, there was a rank of kholis with tin roofs. Some of the kholis were two-storeyed, and had leaning ladders, posts with pegs really, to allow access to the upper levels. There was a sturdy-looking pucca house about two-thirds of the way down the row, new and unfinished. A light burned behind a newspapered window in one of these upper storeys, and that room was where the apradhis were expected tonight. Not far from the lighted window, at the far end of the kholis, PSI Kamble and four constables were wrapped in sheets on the pavement, trying to look like tired labourers deep and fast in their sleep. Sartaj was quite sure they were complaining. On that side of the kholis, there was a sloping ridge of rubbish, its top higher than a tall man's head, banked up against a brick wall. Sartaj had passed it many times over the last few years, this noisome mountain, and it had grown and shrunk many times but never disappeared, and now at this far distance, he could see the bright neon blue, green and yellow of plastic bags winking from its archaeological layers. As senior officer on the operation he had the privilege of avoiding the gigantic stink, so Kamble and his fellows lay directly under its influence, and Sartaj knew they were cursing him. The thought of Kamble holding a perfumed handkerchief to his nose gave Sartaj a smile.

Now Katekar stopped in mid-complaint. Two men were coming up the street, leaning against each other's shoulders. 'Drunks,' Katekar said, and he was right. These men were only two, and it was unlikely that the actual apradhis would stagger drunk to a meeting with a receiver to collect money. Still, Sartaj stiffened, watched. The drunks went by, giggling. Down the road and three lanes to the left there was a country bar and a gambling den. Men went from one to the other and then went home. These two were happy, which only meant that they would wake up in the morning to find out what they had lost. Sartaj watched them go, feeling the warm tingle of anticipatory satisfaction moving up his shoulders. He would get the apradhis tonight. He would take the bastards in, and then he would sleep well afterwards. He had done well by Wasim Zafar Ali Ahmad, and now it was his turn to gain.

Katekar had, for the moment, run out of things to complain about, so now he was telling a police story. In the old days, he said, during the very early part of his service, he had known a hoary old inspector named Talpade. This Talpade was wizened and gnarled, stained not only by the paan he chewed incessantly, but also by the four corruption cases he had fought off and survived. It was said – and generally believed – that he had killed more than a dozen innocent men during his career, shot them dead during riots and encounters. He had once beaten an apradhi to death in the lock-up, and had been suspended for eleven months before he managed to extricate himself from the bloodspattered mess, mainly by scattering money up and down the chain of command until even his most ardent admirers and enemies marvelled.

Two years before his retirement, Talpade fell in love with a dancer. There was something admirable about a man that age gripped by a great passion. Of course he was ridiculous: he had new clothes tailored, his mehndi hair now was suddenly jet-black, his teeth gleamed an unearthly white. But you had to recognize and respect the completeness of his devotion. He went every night to worship at the altar of his beloved, he brought her home from the bar where she worked, he gave her messages from her lovers. Yes, she had other men, younger ones and more handsome, but Talpade accepted this pain as the price of his proximity to her, and suffered it with humble gratitude. He was transformed. There was something new moving under the age-old creases on his face, under the bitter valleys – you only had to spend a minute with him to know it was joy.

The force laughed at him. It was not his aged-rooster's walk or the new dark glasses he sported. The problem was that he loved Kukoo ('just like that actress from long ago'), and as Talpade told anyone who would stop and listen, Kukoo was as beautiful as a Kashmiri apple, and nobody could deny the fragile and fatal charm of Kukoo's nakhras. But she was a man. She said she was nineteen, but she had danced at various bars for the last five years, so it was more likely that she was twenty-five, at the very least twenty-two or so. She had luxurious straight hair to the small of her back, lightened to a striking almost-golden, a pert bottom of astonishing roundness, and opulent lips that deserved a poem of their very own. But there was never any doubt that Kukoo was a man. She never attempted to hide this. She had a slim, long chest, and her voice was husky. But she still accumulated a following as she moved from bar to bar, increasing her earnings each time.

So why had Talpade become such a majnoo for Kukoo? Was he, after all – despite his long marriage and three children – a gaandu, literally? Most of the men and women in the force believed so. But his friends, and those close to Kukoo, knew that Talpade never touched her. Not that she would have refused, no, Kukoo had a finely developed sense of how far you could tease a man, and above all she was practical. She knew when to be shy and when to be very forward. But Talpade didn't want to catch her and squeeze her and take her, he was content to sit at his regular table, just to the left of the dance floor, and look at her. On the sparkling silver of the dance floor, she was indeed something to look at, floating on the whirling lotus of her ghagra, her waist turning like a slender fall of water. Under those cunning black and red lights she was more beautiful than any other girl in the bar, more graceful than any woman on the street outside. Talpade sat and drank Old Monk and watched Kukoo. He gave her money just before he left, never called her to his table to take the cash like other men, never expected anything but an occasional glance and smile. He was happy to talk to friends who came into the club, he joked with the waiters, his concentration on Kukoo was not one-pointed or obsessive enough to be frightening, but it was obvious that he cared only about her.

His best friend, David, got sloppy drunk one night, grabbed Talpade's hand and said, 'Bastard, come, touch that thing between her legs. Then you'll know what she is.'

Talpade said, 'I know she's not a woman.'

'So then?'

'I like looking at her.'

'Tell me why.'

'It just feels good.'

And that's all he would say. David cursed Talpade for subjecting himself to open ridicule, for spending money and getting nothing, for plain stupidity. Talpade smiled and went back to watching Kukoo.

Two months later, Kukoo called David. She told him that Talpade was now weeping as he watched her. He had been doing this for the last three nights, watching her for hours as usual, and then, very late, crying without a sound or any indication that he was unhappy. 'Now he has finally gone mad,' Kukoo said. She wanted the friend to get Talpade away from her. He was depressing her with his big watery eyes, and offending the other customers, who came to have fun, not to mourn.

This time, David asked gently, 'Why?' And Talpade said, 'She reminds me of my childhood.'

They took him out of the bar, took him home, put him to sleep. The family brought in doctors, kept a careful watch over Talpade, comforted him and made him take his prescribed rest. He went back to work two Mondays later, and that same night he was at the Golden Palace, where Kukoo was dancing now. This time, when he began his usual tamasha, she had the bouncers take him out, followed them on to the road and screamed at Talpade, 'Don't follow me.' Once she had been afraid of him, but now she couldn't help herself. 'Bastard, making drama out of nothing. I don't want to see your face again.'

Talpade obeyed her. He never tried to see her again. He went about his life, but he was a listless man, emptied of all his ferocious force and energy. He died four months later, peacefully passing in his sleep.

Sartaj sighed. That was the end of the story. Like all the other police stories Katekar liked to tell, this one stopped suddenly and remained enigmatic, refusing to give up a moral or even a purpose. Sartaj had heard it before, from other people, and in its details he believed it was true. No doubt it had been embellished and changed in the telling and in the passing along.

'This is them,' Sartaj said. There were three figures throwing shadows across the pavement now, far up, too far to really make out, but Sartaj knew they were male, and that they were murderers. He felt it in his nostrils, in his teeth. He forced back the upper half of his body, which had risen in anticipation, back into the semblance of sleep. He waited.

'What are their names?' Sartaj whispered.

'Bazil Chaudhary, Faraj Ali and Reyaz Bhai.'

In the distance, there was a Fiat's particular whine as it turned a corner, and very faint, a flat electronic buzz from a light, and a metallic clinking down the tracks, all the silence of the city. The three men walked past Kamble's position, and then past the lit window. Katekar breathed out. And then the three stopped, turned and went back. One reached up, rattled the bottom of the second-floor door. 'Okay,' Sartaj said. Katekar slid out from under the cart, went right. Sartaj went left. 'Police,' Sartaj shouted. 'Put your hands up. Don't move.' Kamble's people were moving at the edges of Sartaj's attention, somewhere to his left. The three apradhis were twisted together, frozen in a clutching cartoon tangle, and then they broke, right and left. One ran up the road, and Sartaj let him go out of vision, out of sight. He was concentrating on the middle one, who had run forward, then back. He was skittering back and forth, holding a sharp, moving glint. 'Let it go, maderchod. Let it go. Hands up or I'll take your head off.' Something clattered on the road, hands went up and Sartaj risked a glance to his right. Katekar was aiming down a narrow gap between the shacks, a crevice that led to the fence.

'Out, bhenchod,' Katekar said. 'Throw it out.'

A square blade spun out into the light. A chopper, Sartaj thought. The stupid bastards are still carrying the choppers. He still had the high pulse of victory in his throat when a dark figure exploded from the shadowed cleft and collided with Katekar. Sartaj heard a snicking zip and then Katekar was sitting down and the apradhi was running. Sartaj took two steps back, steadied his arm, found the light polished smoothness of his sights, front and back, and then the kinescoped, flashing figure of the apradhi and he fired, two three four times. The apradhi slid into the ground. The flash subsided slowly from Sartaj's eyes. And Katekar was still sitting.

Sartaj knelt beside him. Dark fluid gouted from the nape of Katekar's neck in steady beats.

'Artery,' Kamble said from somewhere above Sartaj's head.

'Gypsy,' Sartaj shouted. 'Get the Gypsy.' He fumbled in his pocket, put his handkerchief on Katekar and the blood welled smoothly through Sartaj's fingers, swelled and billowed over his wrist.

'Here,' Katekar said calmly. 'Here.'

Three of them lifted Katekar into the vehicle. Sartaj struggled with his legs, and Kamble was whispering in his ears, so close that Sartaj felt his lips on his beard. 'All three apradhis died in the encounter. Yes?'

Sartaj heard the small sounds through the roaring of his own panic. He shook his head and ran around the car and pulled himself into the seat.

Kamble slammed the far door. The light fell on his face from above, dividing it into triangles of black and gold. 'All three,' he said. 'All three finished.'

There was no time to talk. Then they were careening past the blurring fence, and Sartaj was trying to hold Katekar steady and had a hand on the wound. Now the sense of what Kamble had said came to Sartaj. The jeep took a yawing left, and he heard the shots, mere pops, a rapid series of them.

At the Jivnani Nursing Home, at two forty-six a.m., Ganpatrao Popat Katekar was declared dead on arrival.

Sartaj felt old. From the paperwork he had learnt, remembered again, that Katekar was five years older than him. But he had always thought of Katekar as younger, young. Katekar had a complaint for every hour of the day, he had antic Marathi songs, he had obscure scientific facts, he had endless stories about the short lives of hard men. He took a paunchy pleasure in eating the aged-and-cured wickedness of the city, its piquant scandals, its bitter breakdowns, its ferociously musty unfairness, he made a meal of its resplendent and rotting flesh. Now, Sartaj had to write in a box on a form: 'Cause of death'. He shaped the letters carefully, convinced somehow that good writing on a departmental form was a kind of respect for the departed. He inked in, slowly, all the way to a full stop, and his hands started to shake. It was a vibration that started in the elbows, a pain drawn from the bone that went straight to his palms. Sartaj put his hands under the table, on his thighs, and waited for the shaking to pass. He clenched his fists, relaxed them. The shaking stopped, then came again. Sartaj looked about. Two constables sat just outside the door, he could see their shoes. The inspector on duty, Apte, was in the office across the hall to the left. He had left Sartaj alone out of concern, sympathy, given him his privacy. Sartaj breathed in, edged his chair back. The hands lay on the dirty white cotton, trembling. That was the word: tremble. Not twitch, not shake, but a small quivering that came from within to the skin. How melodramatic, Sartaj thought. He thought the word in English. *Melodramatic*. He remembered it. He made an effort and stopped the trembling. With a delicate, firm grip, he turned the form over. He picked up the pen again and poised the nib and then had to put it down. What strange things are hands. A belly cushioned by bulbous fleshy pads, fine fur patterning the back. Sartaj bent a finger back against the wood of the desk. If he leaned in with the weight of the shoulder, he knew the finger would break. The pain stood sharp against the humming haze of Sartaj's confusion, like a blue light in fog. Sartaj knew the sound a breaking finger makes. He had had Katekar do it once, break an apradhi's finger, a kidnapper's, the man had come to collect the money for a child, a businessman's daughter taken from her nursery school. The finger had been the kidnapper's little one, on his right hand. They had got the girl back, from a hotel in Bhandup. The sound of a finger breaking is not very large, but it is dry, sharper than you expect. It is a quick, creaky sound, a small firecracker bursting. Katekar had done it. Sartaj had made him do it, he had done it for the girl. Katekar had heavy hands. Sartaj remembered them and took the pressure off his own finger and stood up. This was self-indulgence, all of this, the hands, the memories, the form. He was avoiding what he knew he had to do next, what he had put off until morning: the visit to Katekar's family. He had said to Apte, let them sleep. Why wake them up now, in the middle of the night?

But light was inevitable. It was time to put his uniform back on.

Katekar's wife knew as soon as she opened the door. Sartaj saw this in her face. He had rattled softly at the hasp high up on the door, she had opened it still sticky-eyed and stumbling, and the sentence that Sartaj had prepared – 'Bhabhi, please forgive me' – vanished into the sickening knowledge of his own responsibility. She closed the door behind her, and folded her arms across the scalloped white lacy trim on the loose gown she wore. It had a rose pattern, the gown, complete with thorns on the green stalks. Sartaj had only seen her in slightly glittery saris, on very formal occasions. Maybe three, four times in as many years. She shut her eyes for a long moment, then opened them. Suddenly, she had changed. She set her bony face forward, like a prow, and reached out and touched his forearm. He realized then that he had been trembling again.

'What happened?' she said.

They brought the body home at two the next day. They laid Katekar on his bed, and took off the sheet in which he had been wrapped after the post-mortem. Then they sat him on a chair, and bathed him. The wound, low on his neck to the left, had been stitched shut. It looked too small to kill a man with a respectable belly, with heavy shoulders. The long post-mortem cut had been closed with thick black thread. Katekar's skin now had the colour and texture of cardboard that had dried fast after a soaking in monsoon rain, and Sartaj tried not to look at him. Sartaj pressed himself into a corner and averted his eyes from the men and women pushing in through the door, and tried to read the labels on the stacked cassettes next to the player, across the room. He listened to Katekar's wife speak to a relative about how many bottles of kerosene were needed, how many cow-dung patties, how much wood. Now they were putting new clothes on Katekar, his heavy steel watch on his wrist. His wife knelt and slid his chappals on to his feet. She had to struggle to get them on, she held Katekar's heel and pushed and then gently moved his toes apart to get one through the leather hoop. She stroked gulal on to his forehead, dabbed on a red tikka. She tilted her head back, was concentrated, serious. Another woman brought her a steel thali, a match sizzled and made a flaring arc in the air and Sartaj smelt incense, burning oil. She moved the thali in slow circles around Katekar's shoulders, his head. She was weeping.

They walked to the shamshan ghat. A man, another constable, carried a matka full of water. Sartaj could hear the rhythmic gulp of the water as he walked. The thali full of flowers and gulal was carried by another constable, close behind. From the thali, the constable threw grain and gulal as they walked. They entered the shamshan through a tall black metal gate. Standing under the towering open-sided shed, with its corrugated tin roof, Sartaj could hear the traffic over the high walls. He could hear voices, schoolchildren shouting, a vegetable-wallah's high cries. At the top of the wall, through drooping branches, he could see signs on the other side of the road, a tall commercial building. Katekar was laid on to the wood. A man stepped forward, this one Sartaj recognized, Potdukhe, a senior constable who had retired the year before. Potdukhe had a blade in his hand, a razor blade. He held Katekar's white sleeve with one hand, and with a swift motion cut the cloth from shoulder to wrist. Sartaj hunched his shoulders: the hissing pass of the blade came to him over all the sounds of the street. He swallowed and held himself still. Potdukhe slit the other sleeve, then opened the buttons on Katekar's pants: there must be no restrictions on the soul.

There was the distant mechanical growl of vehicles stopping, and a moment later Parulkar came into the shamshan ghat. He walked straight over to Katekar, stood for a moment over him, and then stepped back. He stood next to Sartaj, and put a hand on his wrist and squeezed. Then they waited.

The women stood at a distance, at the other end of the yard, near the wall. A rank of uniformed policemen turned, stamped, raised rifles to their shoulders and aimed high, at something far far above. Katekar's sons, who were still with the women, flinched under the roll of whiplash cracks. Then they were brought forward, through the cluster of men around the bier. Potdukhe put a hand on the older one's shoulders, and led him around his father, in a circle. The son – What was his name? His name? – carried the water-filled matka, and water dropped from a hole in it, spattered on the ground and danced up in quick, stammering splashes. A dhoti-clad priest now had a splintered fragment of wood in his hand, and it was flickering at one end. Sartaj suddenly wanted to see Katekar's face. He stepped to the left, but the wood was piled high, and what he could see was a coil of white cloth, a chin, the bridge of a nose. From this angle, close to the crown of Katekar's head, there was no Katekar, only some fragments. Sartaj shuffled to the right, it was important to see Katekar fully, but it was too late, the priest was holding the son's hand, showing him how to tap his father's head with a stick. It was a small tap, symbolic, but now the real blow, from the priest, would crack the skull. Sartaj swallowed. This was always the moment during funerals when he began to feel sick. It was necessary, he told himself yet again, or the skull would explode under the fire. But he felt the churning in his stomach begin. Somebody, it was Parulkar, took Sartaj's arm, and with the other men he moved back, three, four, five steps. Still, Sartaj heard the round crunch of the skull, when it came open, and Katekar was now open to the sky, completely and fully open. His son leaned forward, holding the burning wood. There was a small shifting inside the pyre, a series of tiny, rapid, racing convulsions. There was this movement and the gentle smell of ghee, that childhood smell from weddings and festivals. Then with an urgent gasp the fire took the wood, the body, Katekar. Now there was all motion, leaping up, up, and heat slid across Sartaj's face. He watched the fire burn, and did not look away.

After the friends and relatives had left, after the ashes had cooled, after the ashes had been collected and taken home and hung in a matka near the door, after everything, Sartaj went home. There was whisky, almost a bottleful, and Sartaj brought it out and put it on the coffee table, and a bottle of water, but after he poured out a drink the smell of it made him gag. So he shut his eyes, lay back on the sofa. Katekar was dead, the murderer was dead, the murderer's friends were dead, it was all over. Nothing to do, nobody to pursue. Katekar's death was a murder, an accident, an act of fate. It was a simple story, the way Kamble and others would tell it: three apradhis cornered, we should've fired first, encountered the bastards, but it was Singh's operation, Katekar got too close and didn't shoot, so he died. Case closed. These things happen. It's the job. But after everything, after all, Sartaj was unable to rest with this story, to be comforted by the neatness of it, by its clean forward velocity and its final rest. He was beset by questions: where was Bangladesh, what was it? Where was Bihar? How do three men travel thousands of miles, to one city, to a particular stretch of road, to a constable waiting under a thela? We are debris, Sartaj thought, randomly tossed about and nudging into each other, splitting each other's lives apart. Sartaj opened his eyes, and the room was still the old one, the shadows outside completely known to him, known a thousand nights over. This was his corner of the world, safe and familiar. And yet here was this question, sitting on his chest: why did Katekar die? How did this happen?

❧ INSET: *The Great Game*

'The purpose, the meaning, the intent and the methodology of intelligence is the discernment of patterns.' The students are waiting, eager for the revelation that will grant them understanding, hone their edges into preparedness, allow them to survive and triumph. 'The ability to sense method, orderliness, design, is the greatest talent an intelligence officer can possess,' K.D. Yadav proclaims, projecting to the back of the room. 'The old saying goes: once is happenstance, twice is coincidence, three times is enemy action. Remember that. If you can see the connections between data points, see the shape they make, read the story the data is telling, you will win. A patrol notices bootprints on a ridge in the Karakoram, a field officer on posting in Brussels writes a report mentioning the sale of miles of toughened communication cables. He who sees meaning in that, wins.' K.D. says 'he,' but there is a woman in the first row, a girl. He has known her for years, he has seen her grow from a child into a serious-faced young person, and one of the great pleasures of his life has been observing that very distinct personality that gazed up at him from the pram growing into the self-possessed, independent woman who sits before him now. He likes to think he had something to do with that growth, with the nurturing of that courage. But what is her name? How can he not know her name? How could he have forgotten, when he has voiced that name for years, decades?

And then he knows. He understands how he has forgotten. He has not forgotten her name in that room in the house in Safdarjung, in the classroom they have hidden away in a nondescript bungalow. He has forgotten it now, in this hospital room he is lying in. I am here, I am Karpuri Dwarkanath Yadav, known always as 'K.D'. I am in a small white room with drawn curtains. I am lying on a white metal bed. I am not teaching, not lecturing. I am ill, which is why I have forgotten her name. In the real classroom, years ago, I knew it. Now I don't.

She is sitting in front of him now, in the hospital room. She is reading a book. He remembers her as a child, always reading. She carried a book from one room to another, took a book to the dinner table and was always told to put it away by her mother. K.D. gave her books, he saw in her his own desperate childhood hunger for books to read, and was drawn to her by her precocity. He gave her Classics Illustrated comics, Enid Blyton and then P.G. Wodehouse. She still reads with that same one-pointed concentration, curved over the book she holds with both hands. He remembers that tense arc, that need, as if she wanted to eat the words. 'What are you reading now?' he says.

She looks up, pleased by the question, pleased that he is talking. 'It's called *A Search in Secret India*.'

'Paul Brunton.'

'Is there anything you haven't read?'

'I read it years ago.' He remembers exactly when he read it, in June of 1970 in an army mess in Siliguri. The book was an old leather-bound copy, with faded gilt lettering and three raised ridges on the spine. He can feel it in his hands now. He found it on a glassed-in shelf, above Ming vases from a long-ago punitive expedition to Peking. Outside the mess, there is a veranda which a lance-naik is sweeping. A barbed-wire fence. A cracking road and fields. But he still can't remember this woman's name, in this yellow hospital room. 'They must have reprinted it. What do you think of it?'

'Orientalist nonsense. White man looking for sadhus and enlightenment in a mysterious dark land. Same old fantasy.'

K.D. laughs. 'Just because it's somebody's fantasy doesn't mean it's not true.' This is an old argument between them. He always tells her she has to be weaned away from her JNU-bred fantasies of world citizenship and anti-imperialism and eternal peace. She always tells him that his realism is a fantasy too. But the argument has become over the years a formal exercise, a ritual which looks like a quarrel but which is really a demonstration of affection. And he is aware that he has the advantage. After all, he has recruited her into the organization. She is one of us now, one of the shadow soldiers. She has no choice but to be a realist. I trained her, I taught her tradecraft, analysis, recognition, action. I drew her into the secret world, into our troubles, into the web of secret causes. He smiles at her. 'Do you mean to say that sadhus don't exist? Or enlightenment?'

She puts her book down, draws her chair closer to the bed. 'I'm sure sadhus exist.'

'They do indeed. Real ones and fake ones. Both are useful.' She nods, and he is sure she understands, that she has not forgotten her lessons. He had insisted on a knowledge of the organization's history, of its antecedents, and so he had taught them about the Pandits, Nain and Mani Singh Rawat, and Sarat Chandra Das, and others, small and unsung men who had a century ago plunged into the forbidden northern lands disguised as pilgrims, who had walked north and west of the Himalayas, who had measured out thousand-mile routes by counting their strides as they walked. Prayer-wheels hid compasses, thermometers were snuggled into walking staffs, and the distances the walkers had measured had resulted in the first survey maps of these wild territories. And a map is a kind of conquest, the precursor to all other conquests. K.D. had told his students: remember those prayer wheels, one kind of knowledge can conceal another. Information nests inside information. Watch everything, listen to everything. Useful hides inside useless, truth in lies. And so this girl, his student, is now reading an Englishman's quest for peace, which she believes is nonsensical. Good. She is a good student. She is a good reader. She is holding his hand now. K.D. says, 'Why are you reading Brunton?'

'Uncle,' she says quietly. 'I need help. I need to know about Gaitonde. I need more. I need to know why he would be interested in sadhus.'

Ganesh Gaitonde is a bad man, but he was once an ally of the good men. K.D. had recruited him too. The organization needed bad men sometimes, for certain tasks, for specific missions. Only bad men had access to positive information in certain areas. So K.D. had found Gaitonde, in a jail, and recruited him. And Gaitonde had been a good source, his data had been cross-checked and corroborated and verified, and it had proved solid, and useful. He had executed commissions as well, performed jobs efficiently and with discretion. At the end he had gone renegade, he had betrayed the service and made up data and used their resources to expand his empire, but early on Ganesh Gaitonde had been a bad man on the right side, and K.D. had been his handler. To play this game well, you had to handle bad men, you had to have them do bad things which were finally good things. It was necessary. Only those who had never been on a real battlefield asked for unstained virtue and unblemished deeds. On the field, all actions were only provisionally moral, and the game was eternal. So was Ganesh Gaitonde a bad man? Was Nehru a bad man?

Hold on, cling tightly to lucidity. Don't think of Nehru, he is a distraction. Your mind is weaving, slipping. You are ill. K.D. clenches his fists, raises his head. The girl is intent, frowning a little. Just like her father. Her father's name was Jagdeep Mathur, and they had met each other early on a winter's day, in a conference room in Lucknow, on the campus of Lucknow University. The conference table has a green felt surface and is overlooked, from all four walls, by paintings of grand Europeans in academic gowns. There are seventeen men seated around the table, all of them in their early twenties, all of them sharp-eyed, intelligent, educated. K.D. has never seen any of them before, each has been told to report to this room at nine a.m. sharp. They are not talking to each other, they are waiting, they are practising discretion because they all know they are being recruited for secret work, in an agency which has not been named to them yet, which most of them have never heard of. K.D. has been interviewed twice already, after a very quiet approach by the vice-chancellor of his university in Patna. He thinks he knows why: he has a BA Honours in History and an LLB, and a National Cadet Corps 'C' certificate, and state-wide fame as a sportsman. He is tight, taut and very ambitiously educated. He has been thinking mainly of a career in law, but now he is vividly interested in this sequestered world, in these secret interviews and this promise of urgent and all-important work. So he waits at this table, with these other men who he recognizes as mirror-images of himself, from their strong forearms and alert glances he knows them to be sportsmen-scholars. The big double doors at the end of the hall swing open, and two men with military haircuts enter. Hard on their heels is an older man in a grey jacket, a professor perhaps, judging by his thick, wire-rimmed glasses. The professor walks towards the table, then turns back to the door, his neck bent forward expectantly. And Nehru enters. K.D. feels himself flush. It is unbelievable but it really is Jawaharlal Nehru. 'Gentlemen,' Nehru says, and his voice is hoarse, almost cracking. All the young men spring to their feet with a tremendous scraping of wood and shoes, and he waves them down impatiently. He sits without ceremony, leans forward and puts his elbows on the table. His hands are white, and K.D. can see how clean the nails are. But he looks tired, this Nehru. His eyes are yellowed, his cheeks are puffy. It is 18 February 1963. 'Gentlemen, you have all experienced the crisis India has struggled through recently. We live in dangerous times, we are struggling through an hour of crisis. Our borders have been invaded, our trust shattered. And that by the Chinese, who we thought were our friends. We must make sure such a thing never happens again. And so the nation must call upon its young men, its best and brightest. As I look at you I see the blessed light of an ancient past in your faces, and so I am confident again. I will ask much of you. In your work, your country will want the impossible from you. But you must endure. On your shoulders is our future. I trust in your strength, and in your unfailing dedication to your duty. Jai Hind.' He rises abruptly, and shakes hands with the man to his left. And then the next interviewee. K.D. has time to watch Nehru as he waits his turn to shake hands. He finds that he is breathing hard, as if he has just sprinted a quick mile. When his turn comes, Nehru reaches out and says something. K.D. is startled: 'Sir?' Nehru is already reaching for the next man's hand, but he says – without looking at K.D. – 'Do your best, son.' There is a trace of impatience in his voice at having to repeat himself, but K.D. treasures the words, and he watches carefully, but Nehru doesn't say a word to anyone else, not even to the professor. Nehru leaves, the doors shut behind him. Nehru has only spoken to K.D., only him.

The professor waves them back to their chairs. 'Gentlemen,' he says, 'as the PM said, you have been picked because you are the best. Welcome to the organization.' It turns out that the professor is not a professor after all, but an additional commissioner in the Intelligence Bureau, which – he informs them – is the oldest intelligence agency in the world. And they, if they choose to sign their recruitment papers, will be members, workers, soldiers for this venerable organization. They all sign eagerly, they are dazzled by Nehru.

Later that morning five of them celebrate at Yusuf in the Chowk Bazaar, where they have been taken by Jagdeep Mathur, a fellow-recruit who has grown up in Lucknow. They eat what he tells them are the best kakori kababs in Lucknow, and they discuss the magical appearance of Nehru in their midst. Mathur blames Nehru for the recent débâcle in the Himalayas, for all the defeats and all the dead, and K.D. cannot help but agree, but finds himself defending the old man's idealism, his belief in a future of peace and rationality. 'K.D., yaar,' Mathur says, 'you're just like my mother, always going on about how bloody good-looking Pandit-ji is, how he means well, how Gandhi-ji loved him like a bloody son, what a good good man Nehru-ji is. I say a good man shouldn't be our bloody prime minister. Good men are usually fools. Good men get people killed. When we live in a world with the bloody Chinese and the bloody Americans and the bloody Pakistanis we don't need good men, we need men who eat kakori kababs and carry big sticks.' K.D. nods, and says, 'Big lathis, actually.' Mathur laughs, he has a face like a perfect cube, with massive and ridged jaws, but he is quite striking with his fair skin and light-brown eyes. K.D. thinks he looks quite the Lucknow Kayastha, and he is aware that Mathur has noted his own surname immediately it was uttered, has perhaps filed him in some slot reserved for Yadavs and other backward castes, as no doubt every other of his new colleagues has already done. K.D. has noticed this, that the organization is old, and like other old organizations it is indisputably Brahmanical, with a light sprinkling of Kayasthas and Rajputs. And yet Mathur's grin is unfeigned, and there is not a moment's hesitation as he reaches across the table and thumps K.D.'s shoulder and chortles. 'Bloody big lathis,' he says. 'Exactly right. Bloody big lathis. Are you a lathait, K.D.?' 'I am,' K.D. says. 'I spent many years in shakhas.' It's true, he has spent many evenings in a starkly lit sandpit, whirling the lathi over his shoulders, learning defences and attacks from khaki-wearing instructors. Mathur approves of this, K.D. can see. He has passed some kind of test. Mathur likes him.

And after that kakori morning Mathur is known affectionately by his colleagues as Bloody Mathur, all the way until his disappearance two decades later. He leaves behind, on a road sixty-three miles north of Amritsar, a white Ambassador with two blown tires, one dead driver and one dead bodyguard and one dead informant named Harbhajan Singh, all killed by close-range AK-47 fire from at least three rifles. On that day, that year, K.D. is very far away, on the other side of the churning world, in London. He learns of Mathur's vanishing, is informed of it by the Europe desk in Delhi, puts down the phone and looks out of the window at the evenly ordered rhythm of staircases in an English square, at the white and grey fronts of the houses under a shadowed autumn sky. There is a six-hundred-year-old hospital on one side of the square, and a museum on the other. K.D. has a meeting in fifteen minutes, in a pub three squares down, with a Sikh militant he has been courting for six months. He has to be alert and careful, because he knows that this militant is also being run by a Pakistani officer, an ISI man named Shahid Khan, but all he can do is think of Anjali, little Anjali.

Anjali. Her name is Anjali. She is Bloody Mathur's daughter. She is sitting in front of me, now, in this hospital which is in Sector V of Rohini, in New Delhi. I am not in Lucknow, I am not in London. I am here. Anjali. Hold on to it. Don't mix up times, dates, places. Hold on to the sequence. There was Lucknow, where you met Mathur, and there was his disappearance in Punjab, but there were decades in between. There was NEFA, Naxalbari, Kerala, Bangladesh, London, Delhi, Bombay. Remember the dispositions, the distances, in the connections between the points is a shape. The shape is the meaning. In the shape of my life there must be a meaning. What is the shape? Apply analysis to the events, look for proximity, conjunction, repetition, similarity, find the impetus behind the momentum, the intent on the other side of the action. This is the business of intelligence. K.D. Yadav remembers teaching this, in a room in a house in Safdarjung. With this girl sitting in the first row. Anjali.

'Anjali,' K.D. says. 'Anjali.' His voice comes free of rust with a painful grinding, and he wonders how long it had been since he has spoken. 'Where have you been?' he says.

'Uncle, I need your help with Gaitonde.'

'Gaitonde is dead.' Gaitonde was dead. K.D. knows that, but doesn't know how he knows it. I am not in my right mind, he thinks. His greatest, his most secret and enduring pride has been in his memory, his precise eye for detail, his razor-edged logic, his capacity for analysis, his huge, humming, incandescent mesh of an intellect. In the corridors of the brahmins, in Nehru's royal gardens, he had walked proudly because of this famous mind. But what was my right mind? Was NEFA right, was London? In the ruin of his faculties, in the drifting, smoking aftermath of his collapse, there is a great lurking emptiness. It is an absolute vacuum, an utter absence, and K.D. flinches from it. And yet there it is, this loss, this suspicion that his whole life has amounted to nothing. He says to his little girl, his Anjali, he says, 'The spider weaves the curtains in the palace of the Caesars; the owl calls the watches in the towers of Afrasiab.'

She frowns. 'What does Sultan Mehmet have to do with Gaitonde?'

He is delighted, he has to laugh. What a mind she has! She has a doctorate in history. She understands his most obscure allusions, she has read the most esoteric and useless of texts, she needs them as much as he does, she is his inheritor, she is his daughter as much as Bloody Mathur's. Only she would have remembered, without a

312

moment's hesitation, that after Sultan Mehmet led his armies over the walls of Byzantium, after he and his men brought to a fiery end an empire which had lasted for 1,123 years and 18 days (Know the details! Remember the specifics!), after a day of killing and capture and rape and plunder, after everything, after Byzantium, the Sultan walked in the Palace of the Emperors, where the Byzantine rulers had endured lives of luxury and intrigue. He had won. And in the moment of his victory – the chroniclers tell us – looking up at the twilight sky, Sultan Mehmet whispered something to himself: 'The spider weaves the curtains in the palace of the Caesars; the owl calls the watches in the towers of Afrasiab.' But, K.D., control yourself, have discipline. Anjali needs you. What does Gaitonde have to do with Mehmet? What, indeed? 'Sorry,' K.D. says. 'I'm sorry. Gaitonde.'

'Yes,' she says. 'Gaitonde.'

'What was the question?'

'My latest information has Gaitonde, before his death, looking for three sadhus in Bombay. Why? Why sadhus? What's the connection?'

'Gaitonde was learning yoga in jail when I recruited him. The teachers were from some yoga school.'

'Abhidhyana Yoga. They're very old, very established, very respectable. I checked it out. As far as we know, Gaitonde had no contact with them after leaving the jail.'

The yoga teachers dressed in white, they taught yoga in the main courtyard of the jail, with discourses from the *Mahabharata* and *Ramayana*. The yoga was supposed to soothe the criminals, to make them better citizens. But K.D. always wondered why they believed this, the teachers. Why wouldn't yoga just produce better criminals, more centred, calmer thugs who were more efficient in their criminality? That master of villains, Duryodhana, was surely a yogi. They all were, those evil warriors. Gaitonde had looked quite calm, sunlit in his prison whites, in the superintendent's room. He was a bad man. Was Duryodhana a bad man? He had been killed through trickery and had risen to a warrior's heaven. Is there a soldier's paradise waiting for K.D. Yadav? I did my best, Nehru-ji, Pandit-ji, sir. No, no, think, think. Gaitonde. Why was he chasing sadhus? Help Anjali, help her. 'Gaitonde was religious,' K.D. said. 'He was always doing pujas, donating money for temples. He gave money to all the muths, we have pictures of him with the holy representatives. He knew some sadhus, surely, plenty of them. What's special about these three?'

'We don't know. All we know is three sadhus. They were important enough for him to break cover and come back to India. He knew we were displeased with him, he must have been afraid that we would sanction him. He must have been afraid of being killed. Still, he came back. Why? Do you know anything? Can you remember anything, Uncle?'

Yes, he can remember. She is looking for detail, for texture, for one or two particulars that will come together to unlock her conundrum, make sense of Gaitonde and his life and his death. That is what K.D. Yadav taught her. K.D. Yadav now has memory, but not sequence. He has elements, but not the distance between them. To him the past is no longer separated from the present by a distinct and comfortable boundary, everything is equally present, all things are connected and are here. Why? What's happened to me? K.D. can't remember. But he can remember. He is in a chopper flying up a valley. K.D. is laughing, grinning, because he can't help it, he hasn't ever been off the ground before, and now they are following the long mercury sliver of a river, they are curving and buffeting above the thick green, the shadows fall a deep black at the bottom of the ridges. There is a brilliant light, an early-morning gold that fills the rattling plexiglass, and the sky beyond is a colour that K.D. has never seen, a vivid, saturated hue that moves across his face, he can feel this blue in his skin. He's smiling, and one of the pilots turns and laughs at him. These are army flyboys, out of the base at Pasighat. The pilot is pointing down, at a patch of brown near the edge of the water, near the sprays K.D. can now see pummelling past the rocks. Then the river is spiralling up, and they are on the ground. The chopper takes off as soon as K.D. is out, and it is gone in a moment, invisible, drawing its thunder with it. Now there is another sound that K.D. can hear, a small but resonant chirping. It's not a bird he has ever heard, he's sure of that. Now there's another one, which sounds like a tin can full of stones being rattled. And one more, but K.D. isn't sure this last one is a bird, it's a whooping call with a click at the end, a snap. The tree-trunks at the other side of the clearing hold between them a blue-green light that is infinitely deep, a whole hazy world that K.D. knows absolutely nothing about: NEFA. He is alone in the North Eastern Frontier Agency, with a green army bag by his side, wearing a yellow bush-shirt and cheap Bata leather street shoes. He is suddenly afraid, completely afraid. Two bloody months of training, he thinks, only two months, and they did not train me for this, not for this jungle and for this unknown sky above.

A platoon of Assam Rifle boys arrive two hours later and explain they were delayed by a landslip three kilometres down the road, they had to detour. K.D. listens intently to the subedar's strange Hindi, and asks, how far are we going? The subedar grins, and says nothing. He has a pair of boots for K.D. The boots are too big, but that's better than too small. K.D. puts on three pairs of socks and walks. He walks for twenty-one days. On the third morning his legs are so tightly cramped that he can't squat to ease himself, and he leans against a tree and weeps. It's an oak tree, he knows this, and in that recognition he feels better. When he found out he was coming to these mountains, he bought a book about the flora and fauna, and studied it in spare moments. So he knows these are magnolias, and scattered poplars, and a chestnut. They have been following the line of the river, walking steadily upwards along a path that twists and backbends through the forest but always moves higher. In those early days of the walk, in that first week, they pass pairs and groups of stilted houses surrounded by patches of cultivation, rice and millet still surrounded by the charred ashes of burnt forest. Women sit in front of these houses, weaving, and the soldier-boys make sneering remarks about the nose-plugs they wear. The local men all wear straight blades at their waists, and the subedar tells him that they used these daos to take heads until not many years ago. These men look athletic enough to swing the daos and lop off limbs, but it's not them he's scared of, not their alien, slanting eyes under conical bamboo helmets. No. It's the breath of the forest that terrifies him, that creaking sigh of the bamboo that threads under the junipers. There is a belling and a booming that stretches through the long blue light under the canopy. The jungle speaks to itself, long calls and answers that surprise K.D., make him jerky, nervy. The soldiers laugh at him when a shrieking directly overhead makes him start, despite himself. 'It's only a monkey,' says the youngest one of them all, hitching his rifle to shoulder. His contempt is clear, and K.D. feels the justice of it. He knows it's only a monkey, and yet each night he huddles inside his blankets, pulling them over his head. He wakes up each morning more exhausted than the day before. In the mornings, the mountains hulk far above, black and engulfed by the thick cover, shoulder upon shoulder into the pinking sky.

They cross a ridge and descend, go down towards another thread-like river that fattens itself into a thrashing torrent. They wade across it, straining, and eat lunch on the far bank, the flank of a deer the subedar had shot two days ago. The mountains on both sides are precipitous, like walls, and the sky is a distant reflection of the river, a narrow twisting ribbon far above. Then they begin to walk again. They climb, and K.D. knows they are going much higher now. They hump through a forest of blue pines, their heads lowered against the weight of their packs, and K.D. is too tired to be amazed by the unearthly orchids that gleam up white and white from the grass, there is sweat in his eyes. In a long, sighing field of green bamboo the birds flutter above his head. Then they are edging through a last stand of poplars, and a meadow swoops out in a narrow crescent above them. Across it they walk, higher and higher, and looking behind him, to the south, K.D. can see the ridge they have crossed already, and ranged behind it, dozens of others, under the huge red sky. They camp that night in the meadow, and K.D. sleeps at an incline, asleep as soon as he pulls the blanket over his head. The next morning they eat a cold breakfast and walk on, and reach a saddle notched like a big V into the ridge. It has taken them two days, the trek up just this last immense slope. They come through the defile single-file, with K.D. exactly in the middle. He steps around a massive fortress of a boulder, watching his ankles against the cracks that run through the rock, and then he looks up and gasps. There are more meadows across the valley, but above those slopes, beyond them, the jagged white runs to the heavens, canopied by white clouds. The great silver peaks are very far away, and yet K.D. can feel their immense inhumanity, their indifference. He tries to steady his breath, and feels the frigid exhalations of the white crests like a claw in his throat. The next man in line nudges him, none too gently. 'What are you looking at, Raja Saab? That's Tibet over there.'

'China,' the subedar calls from below, without turning around. 'China.' The subedar is thirty-nine years old, the veteran of recent battles with the Chinese not far from here. He has skin the colour and toughness of old oil-paper. His name is Lalbiaka Marak, which is a name that K.D. has never known before. Among the jawans, there is a Das and a Gauri Bahadur Rai, but the rest of them have names like Vaiphei, Ao, Lushai and the exotically foreign Thangrikhuma. K.D. has no doubt that they find him oddly alien. They have taken to calling him Raja Saab, he doesn't quite know why. He doesn't feel very royal, with his stubble, his cracking lips, his blistered and oozing feet. Standing at the threshold of this great, deathly landscape, facing it with these men who are supposed to be his compatriots, K.D. Yadav feels completely alone. Ginzanang Dowara is standing very close behind him, and K.D. can smell the milky sweat on him. K. D. shrugs his pack higher, lowers his head and walks on. And after twenty-one days of walking, they reach their base.

A hundred and sixty men live in this little settlement of rough wooden cabins and tents, all of them from the Assam Rifles. There are two lieutenants and a captain on deputation from the army. 'We are a bit under-officered,' the captain tells K.D. 'But these are hard times.' The captain's name is Khandari, and he has grown up amongst other mountains, in Garwahl, but he hates these hills. 'In Garwahl the mountains have a soul,' he says. 'Here even the mountains are junglees.' K.D. laughs at him, points out that these are the same mountains, part of the same rippling chain that writhes over the subcontinent from east to west. But although he doesn't admit it, K.D. knows exactly what the captain means: these valleys which fall away from their feet are foreign in some profound way, they are very far away from anything he knows. Captain Khandari has seen combat in the recent war, in the far northern reaches of Ladakh, and he hates Nehru virulently, for all the men he says died fighting without ammunition, without support, without hope. Captain Khandari drinks mightily every evening, vast quantities of army-issue rum, and every evening he and the two lieutenants – Rastogi and DaCunha – play flush in the captain's hut. K.D. joins them, declines to join them in their wagering, in their violent throwing down of the cards, but he does share in their tippling. The rum takes away the awful feeling of isolation, that desolation of being cut off by mountains and impenetrable darkness. It feels cosy to be inside the firelit cabin, warm and woozy, telling stories. In four nights K.D. knows his new friends, his cronies, he knows of DaCunha's hopeless love for Sadhana, for her magnificent Technicolor behind, he knows Rastogi's love of obscure mathematical facts and riddles and tricks, and he has listened – very late at night – to Khandari's slurring and barely comprehensible accounts of terror-filled retreats across barren high plateaus. When K.D. leaves to pick and stumble his way back to his own cupboard-like hut, he can see the dying embers of campfires across the parade ground, the shadowy shapes of tents in orderly rows. And beyond them, the absolute black of immense rock walls under a cool, star-pierced sky.

On the fifth afternoon, K.D. feels recovered enough from the exhaustion of the long trek to make his way to the command tent, to face the impossibility of his job. He has been tasked primarily to investigate the Chinese presence in the area, to establish a network of informants and a fund of information, to make sure that the Chinese have in fact withdrawn and are engaging in no further incursions, to determine future Chinese intentions and the intentions of all and sundry in this sensitive border area. K.D. has no knowledge of the Chinese, or their language or history or politics, he has no experience or knowledge of this area or its peoples or geography. He is quite bewildered, but he makes his way to Captain Khandari. The captain, he is sure, will know where he should start. But the captain is very hung-over and surly, and finally K.D. is able to work out that only one patrol is sent out every week, they go four kilometres along the same route to the north-east, to an unoccupied bunker on a knoll. This constitutes the full effort of this unit to establish a presence in this area and collect intelligence. The shock is plain enough on K.D.'s face, but Captain Khandari shrugs and says, 'There's nobody out there, you know. Nobody at all. The Chinese are gone. It's all bhenchod empty.' K.D. is silent. He is trying to work up his courage to say something. Finally Khandari cocks his head and breaks the silence. 'Well,' he says. 'What do you want to do?'

Three days later two patrols leave the base, with routes that K.D. has picked out on one-inch maps. Now K.D. feels the hostility of men who have had their comfort disrupted, and he lives in silence. Even Marak – his friend the subedar – will not speak to him except in grunted monosyllables. K.D. finds a dead rat under his bed. Rastogi and DaCunha bring the patrols back earlier than expected, Rastogi by three full days out of the planned seven. Of course they report seeing nothing, absolutely nothing, and K.D. is sure they have gone around the next ridge and camped for a few days of rest and relaxation. The week after, he puts together another patrol for DaCunha and Marak and a platoon, and walks along himself. His feet twinge for the first mile, but he has a good pair of boots now, and after his muscles ease up, he enjoys the effort. He has lost weight, and he feels strong. There is pleasure in employing his new map-reading skills, and he examines the distant ridges through his binoculars at every halt. The men watch his binocularing with amusement, and DaCunha is barely civil. K.D. bears it quietly, he is doing his job, and he intends to do his job well. On their fourth day out they make camp in the lee of a rock wall that glitters in streaks of metallic silver, and K.D. opens his backpack and pulls out a book, hurrying because these are the last few moments of sunlight. He has been thirsting for books, for anything to read. He has long ago finished *The Riddle of the Sands*, which he brought with him into NEFA, and has been reduced to reading the labels on bottles of medicine, the fine print at the bottom of army requisition forms, and as even these have run out he has started to experience a kind of panic, as if he is slowly drowning. Then, just before they leave for patrol, in the corner of the command tent, behind a stack of food and supply files, he finds two books, left behind by some long-gone officer, who is now quite possibly dead. So he is now reading, within sight of Tibet, *The Benham Book of Palmistry: A Practical Treatise on the Laws of Scientific Hand Reading*. He is reading it very slowly, savouring each sentence, because it must last him. So he is lingering on the absurdities of each page, which find the shape of the future in the lines of the past, which locate meaning in these fleshy hieroglyphics of the palms. It must last, because in his backpack he has the other book, *Palmistry: The Language of the Hand* by Cheiro, and it is less than an inch thick, and to face these mountains with nothing to read would be unbearable.

Marak leans over him suddenly, cutting off the light. Marak is looking down at the open pages of the book, in which Benham is describing the proportions that obtain between the various mounts and the fingers. Marak is transfixed. He squats, with his arms resting on his knees, and faces K.D. squarely. 'You read the future?'

'Yes,' K.D. says quickly. 'Yes.'

Marak shoves his hand towards K.D.'s face. 'Read,' he says.

K.D. holds Marak's craggy hand in both of his own and tells a tale of the future. It's not so hard really. He uses some of Benham's strange prescripts, but mostly he lets Marak talk about his anxiety about his wife's health, his farmland struggles with his brothers, and from these he extrapolates and guesses. 'Your father was a very hard-working man, until the end of his life he worked every day from morning till night,' K.D. tells Marak, who looks at him with a new awe. Which is entirely misplaced, because there is no Benhamite reading involved in

319

this assertion, just simple deduction from the clues that Marak has scattered about in his very questions, in his eagerness to know the shape of his happiness to come, to have a talisman against the depredations that will come surely, by and by. K.D. leads him along gently, then senses that it will not do to give too much, that you must leave the subject wanting, pleasured and reassured but not satiated. 'Enough for today,' he says authoritatively. 'I am tired.'

'Yes, sir,' Marak says. 'I will bring you some tea.'

And he does. Meanwhile, K.D. has been studying the dramatic fall of light on the mountain that faces them, the deep swathes of red and black. He takes the mug of tea and says, idly, 'We will see Chinese.' He is not quite sure why he says it, except that he has been telling the future, and he is rather hoping they will see Chinese. Not that he is eager for confrontation, or fighting. He is not sure of his physical courage, and knows from his three brief training sessions with pistols that he is a very bad shot. But to see Chinese would make his training meaningful, would give substance to his inductions, make the enemy real. And since he hasn't talked to anyone in days, he lets this slip, 'We will see Chinese.' And they do. The next day, just past three o'clock, Thangrikhuma – who is on point – calls back, 'Dushman.' They edge up to the ridge line and peer across the dry valley at a scattering of grey dots on the grey rock. It is, yes, the enemy. Thangrikhuma has very good eyesight, K.D. can hardly see the dushman, but in his binoculars they become recognizably men, a section's worth of Chinese soldiers moving slowly west. The boys move up with K.D., and they lie close next to each other, watching. DaCunha is rustling a map, and now he declares, 'They're on their side. I think.' Their side is indistinguishable from our side: in this waste, here there are no markers, no fences. But there they are, and here we are.

For the next two days, K.D. and his men move along the ridge, paralleling the Chinese. They are careful to stay out of sight, and the Chinese lead them to what is clearly a new outpost, three bunkers built on a spur overlooking a pass, and a dugout for a heavy mortar. This is very good intelligence, but the men are more impressed by K.D.'s prediction, which they attribute not to sagacity, or training, or tactical knowledge, but to mystical insight. They each come to him along the route of march, one by one, and so he soon has an intimacy with their lives, and not just their public selves, but with their fears and hauntings, which he breathes in as they huddle in close to him. Even DaCunha succumbs, so that as they

320

head back to base, K.D. knows about his retarded sister, and about Violet who waits for him in Panjim. As they break their last camp before base, Marak helps K.D. roll up his sleeping bag, and smiles confidingly. 'Saab,' he says, 'on the first day out there was a big discussion. The common opinion was that it would be very easy to nudge you over a cliff. New officer fell off, he was inexperienced, what could we do?' Marak laughs as he tugs hard at straps. K.D. grins back, but he is terrified, and he spends the whole day edging away from the drop, brushing his left shoulder on rock and shale. The possibility of his own death has never occurred to him with any force, with any response in his flesh, which hasn't ever been able to imagine its own disintegration. In the stories of success he tells himself, he is always victorious, sometimes wounded but still alive. But here are these real strangers, who have contemplated his real death. Some of them have killed before, and will again, and it would have been of no great account to them, his demise. One quick push and he would have been gone. He lies in bed that night, in his cabin, and shakes. He is afraid to close his eyes.

He awakens in darkness. He raises his hand, but there is no watch, no luminous numbers. He must get up, shave, bathe, write up his report, raise Captain Khandari from his hung-over stupor, get him to radio the report in and up the chain of command. What time is it? There is much to do. K.D. turns the sheet aside and raises himself, and his head plunges with nausea, and he gags. Why is he so weak? He hadn't been tired enough last night for this fluttering of muscles in his chest, this quiver that lowers him to his pillow again. The white ceiling crushes him into the present again, and he knows with a terrified groan that he is not in his youth, in that first ecstasy of a job well done on the barren peaks of the north, he is in a hospital bed in Delhi, losing his mind.

He considers the phrase: to lose your mind. What would be left, if you misplaced your mind? If there is no mind, is there still a self? He remembers the parable, that to know the I there must be another I, an eye that watches the birds of the self feasting on the nectar of the world. But will there still be a watcher if you take these mind-structures away, these façades of language, these foundations of logic, these narratives of cause and effect? What will be left when it all comes crashing down? Bliss, or numbness? A presence, or an absence? 'The spider weaves the curtains in the palace of the Caesars; the owl calls the watches in the towers of Afrasiab.' He throbs suddenly with rage, with anger against the violence being done to him. I *did* my best. I *did* what was asked of me. The incensed tightening of his tendons becomes a spasm, and he thrashes for a moment, with a pulse dinning in his ear like a Mishmi drum. He gropes up through the darkness that is drowning him. I am lucid. I can remember my life, I can trace its histories. I learnt my trade in NEFA, by creating an intelligence network where there was none, by creating sources and cells and routes. I did this better than any of my colleagues anywhere else, I worked harder and riskier and more *sincerely* than any of them because I was a Yadav and they expected me to do otherwise, I knew some of them did. They were Brahmins, and they had their very certain opinions about OBCs. I never spoke of this to anyone, not even to Bloody Mathur. I just worked. After NEFA, there were the rice fields of Naxalbari where I travelled as a trader and drew out the killers of policemen and judges and district collectors, where I pursued the illusion-ridden boys who left behind their comfortable middle-class homes in Calcutta and came up-country to make revolution. I killed one of them, too, this would-be Maoist who was trying to kill me. I remember his name still, Chunder Ghosh, and the blood that pumped from his ears when I shot him in his forehead. I can recall, exactly, the operations in Kerala against the communist parties, against their electioneering and spread and scheming, against their very infrastructure. For Nehru's daughter we did this, quite illegally but gladly, because we knew from where these parties drew their ideology and direction, and we were on the ramparts, pushing back these hordes run by Peking and Moscow. And then I was in East Pakistan, debriefing the Bengali soldiers who had fled their Punjabi masters. The information I put together caused whole airfields to disappear into broken rubble under the precise fall of bombs. After Bangladesh, back to Delhi, to the manoeuvring with foreign diplomats, the lunches with embassy employees, the slow development of relationships that finally yielded sputters of information. Then London, Punjab, Bombay. My life, spent in this struggle. This constant long war, with its hidden and unsung victories. I did the work. I can remember every payment, every source, every attack by the dushman. I defended. And so this India still stands.

K.D. gasps for breath in the darkness. He had never married. 'K.D. is married to the job,' his colleagues said. Most of them had married and had families, children, grandchildren. He was alone, is alone. He has had women, has known respectable women and disreputable ones. He has been in love, and he has paid for sex, he has been introduced to relatives of friends with the clear intention of marriage. He sees that marriage is a good thing, and he cannot argue against its virtues. 'What else are we working for?' Bloody Mathur said once, exasperated, solicitous. 'If not for our children, for their future, what else is all this for?' There was nothing K.D. could say to this, no disagreement he could offer with his friend's paunchy contentment, his wife speaking in a soft murmur to the cook, his five-year-old daughter Anjali bending over a fairy-tale book on the carpet. Yet he is unable to offer a 'yes' to the proposals his friend brings him, or offer a satisfactory explanation, or an illuminating description of what he really wants. 'What do you want?' Mathur asks. 'What, what, what? Who is this heroine you're waiting for?' And K.D. is unable to name this woman, to reduce her to a list of ten qualities, to conjure up into words this inchoate refusal that rises from his bones.

K.D. lies in his hospital bed, and wonders what he had been waiting for. It is too late now, he will die alone. His father had also spoken about the comforts of companionship, but had Ma really been a companion to him? Simple Ma with her shyness, her perpetual ghoonghat, her quietness, her endless housework. She had supported her husband in his bruising climb out of poverty, and proudly talked about her husband's PT-master job to her relatives, and took him his hot lunch every day herself, all the way to his tiny office next to the school's football ground, his favourite dishes packed in a five-tier tiffin. But she had been unable to follow him into the foreign lands of the English language, and to the end of her life had been confused by phones and remote controls and the true distances of foreign countries, by the size of the world. They had married young, the future trainer of athletes Rajinder Prem Yadav and the simple Snehlata, in the barely formed shapes of adolescence, and had grown into the vividly distinct halves of young K.D.'s life: Papa's glossy-chocolate shoulders against the white of his banian, his voice blasting commands over the ranks of sweating boys, his awkward and hesitant English, his strictness, his envious fascination with athletic training in Russia, and Ma with her hands lathered with besan, her innumerable festivals and fasts and ceremonies which followed each other in endless cycles, her impressive laughter which she hid behind her pallu, her illiterate woman's pride in her son's academic achievements. They had been together for decades, Papa and Ma. What had they said to each

323

other, in their companionship, in their bedroom late at night? Had they saved each other from this early hour of the morning, from this ruinous absence of light? K.D. shivers, and remembers running home after a roadside scuffle with two boys from a rival school, with an aching jaw and his St Xavier's shirt torn at the pocket. Ma had clutched him close, and fussed with a haldi poultice until K.D. had held her away, physically made her stop. Papa had stood as straight as a steel pillar, his eyes narrowed, and told K.D. to find the boys and beat them up. 'From next term we will start boxing as a sport in school,' he said. 'You must learn to defend yourself.' That night, Ma had brought K.D. his glass of Ovaltine and had told him to ignore those hooligans, those government-school barbarians. 'They are just jealous that you are in such a good school. Forget them. Beta, work hard and you will advance. Don't get involved in all this nonsense, think about your future.' Ma expected K.D. to stand first or second in class always, despite his peasant ancestry, and she was full of hope, confident of his future.

And here is K.D. in that future, confident of nothing, uncertain even of the pain in his neck and head, pierced by it but unable to know absolutely, without doubt, whether it is in the present or merely relived memory. And now, in the breakdown of his body, K.D. understands that everything he has ever seen had been nothing but phantoms, that a rock held in one's healthy hand is only a ghost put together inside the skull, that illusions are the only reality. The future is an illusion, but the present is the most slippery illusion of all.

K.D. watches the sun crawl up the wall. He thinks about the colour, which is an orange flecked with red, shading into paler yellow as it climbs. There is no such thing as colour. There are photons bouncing around the world, and into and through a thin membrane on the surface of his eyes. There are electrical and chemical events triggering like novae. But there is no such thing as colour. A nurse moves through the room, prods at him and speaks to him, but he pays no attention. It's easy to ignore her, and the tiny bite of the needle she slips into his arm, they are merely discrete data flowing through the networks of his consciousness, as unreal as the hue on the plaster, which is now the exact tinge of the skin of a Kerala papaya around the aureole of the stem. It is a specific papaya that K.D. is seeing, one he ate in June of 1977, in a dak bungalow in Idukki. The papaya is present to him, with its slightly nauseating bouquet of rot, its flesh slipping, springing between his fingers.

It is as real as this wall, which is turning a dirty white. And then he sees that the lower half of the wall is still dark.

This is not the darkness of night, it is an absence of vision. The lower half of the wall is absent, as if somebody has attached blinders to K.D.'s eyes. If he tilts his head back, and then forward, he can move the edge between vision and non-vision up the wall, and then down. This loss of half his visual field persists if he turns towards the window, or the other way, towards the door leading into the corridor: half-window, half-door. It is a latitudinal loss, an equatorial one. The lower half of his world is gone.

When he tells a nurse about this new symptom, the staff spring into action. He is wheeled out of his room, examined, prodded, scanned by machines. Later that day, Dr Kharas is crisply factual. 'Your CT shows another lesion, a small one, here. We think there is damage to the visual cortex.' She is pointing to a cutaway diagram of a human brain, with the segments exploded out and labelled. The colours are brilliant, a primary blue for the cerebral cortex, a deep red for the thalamus. 'The damage from the tumour is causing a scotoma, a blanking out of part of your visual field. That's about all I can tell you. Did you feel anything last night? Nausea? Pain?'

K.D. wants to tell her, I felt icy air slicing at my throat as I struggled up a ridge, doctor. I felt blisters bursting on my feet, inside my boots. 'No,' K.D. said. 'Nothing.'

She nods, and writes on her notepad. She is thirty-eight, this Dr Anaita Kharas, married, two children. Dr Kharas and her husband were both born in Delhi, have grown up here. Anjali has run a little background check on her. They are wary of each other, Anaita and Anjali, a little prickly, but K.D. sees how similar they are, how alike in their efficiency, their sensible clothes, their assertiveness over the space they move in, the daily work they have to do against the scepticism and aggression of men to maintain their dignity and independence as women. 'I'm afraid there is not much we can do about your loss of function,' Dr Kharas says. 'There is no surgery that can reverse it, no treatment. There is much that we don't understand about the mechanics here.'

'I understand,' K.D. says. 'But will it get worse?'

'Again, this is hard to predict. A glioma is the least predictable of all tumours. Episodes of spontaneous remission have been reported. We will do our best. So, try not to worry.'

But he is not looking for sympathy, or comfort. He knows where he is going. What he would like are the percentages, the numbers. How long will his mind last, how fast will it fail? She has no answers. She lectures him a bit, sharply, about relaxation, about not getting depressed, not giving up. He smiles for her. He likes her. They had only one Parsi in the organization when he joined, and no Muslims, none, not one. He used to protest against this, pointing to the clumsy irony of protecting a secular state with a non-secular organization, to the rank unfairness of it. But the old men at the top thought it was too big a risk, not justifiable in light of the stakes that were being played for. Think, K.D. was always told, of who we are fighting. Yes. The dushman. They were there, and here we are. Them and us.

Away she goes, the good Dr Anaita, followed by a trail of interns and nurses. K.D. sits up in bed, watches pearls of clear liquid drip into a tube and into his forearm. He remembers Anjali's question now: why three sadhus, why was Gaitonde trying to find them? K.D. traces his association with Gaitonde, the first approach in jail, the conversations, the understanding reached, and then the jobs given, the favours traded. It was necessity. The world is shot through with crime, riddled with it, rotted by it. The Pakistanis and the Afghans run a twenty-billion-dollar trade in heroin, which is partly routed through India, through Delhi and Bombay, to Turkey and Europe and the United States. The ISI and the generals fatten on the trade and buy weapons and mujahideen warriors. The criminals provide logistical support, moving men and money and weapons across the borders. The politicians provide protection to the criminals, the criminals provide muscle and money to the politicians. That's how it goes. The dushman agency recruits a disaffected Indian criminal, Suleiman Isa, to plant bombs in the city of his birth, makes him a major player in the endless war. To fight their criminal, we need our own criminal. Steel cuts steel. Criminals have good intelligence on their rivals. It is necessary to deal with Gaitonde, for the greater good. And so there is Gaitonde, in a white T-shirt and white pyjamas and blue bathroom slippers, in the jail superintendent's office. K.D. tries to imagine himself back, relive the event. Maybe in the details he can find an explanation for the three sadhus. He closes his eyes and tries to slip into that afternoon, back into the room with its shelves of black files, its black-framed picture of Nehru. His breath is coming in short gulps, he doesn't know why. Stop it. Calm down. Calm, or you'll cause yourself more injury. Think. Why three sadhus? K.D. has no use for religion, and has always thought of Gaitonde's religiosity as a crutch for a terrified man incessantly afraid of assassins. Even strong men, hard men, men who are the bosses of companies, cannot face the blankness of death, the irreversible scissor-cut on the frail thread of awareness. One snip, then no more. Finished. This is unbearable, and so even Gaitonde, that blood-stained monster, dreamed fantasies about an after-life. We cannot bear this darkness. K.D. tries to examine his scotoma, to pay attention to it, but it is just nothing, a blank nothing. How dark it is, this loss under my eyelids, just under the red flutter of my pulse.

'Yes, that's Daddy's handwriting,' Anjali's mother tells her. Anjali has found an old university text that once belonged to her father, an ancient Indian history text, and she is pointing excitedly to the blue-penned notes in the margin, the underlinings. Bloody Mathur has been gone nearly a year now, but to his daughter he is a daily presence, a figure who looms larger because he is away, he is the romantically mysterious father who is not here. She has been told that he has 'gone away for a time', that he is 'on tour.' Within the organization, the generally held belief is that he was taken by the very same Sikh militants he was try-ing to recruit, that he was outwitted and ambushed, that he was probably tortured and then killed. A small minority believes that he was turned, that the ambush was a stage-play that he managed himself, that he has gone over the border, to the other side. But nobody expects him back, except Anjali, who has been told that he is 'travelling for work'. K.D. despises this lie because he sees expectation in Anjali's eyes every time the phone rings, a yearning in her knock-kneed sprint to the door when the postman rattles the gate. But she is eleven years old, and her mother thinks that a father who has gone away is what she can understand, or bear. K.D. knows that children face terrors every day, they walk through horrors that their elders deny and flinch away from. And what could be harder to bear than this expectation, this wanting? But he has no authority here. He has to be very careful. Rekha is pour-ing tea for him. She is formally hospitable to her dead husband's friend just returned from London, but K.D. knows there is no warmth here, no affection. She has always been polite, but distant, more than likely there is a hard armour of caste feeling under the good manners. If he says the wrong thing, he could get himself exiled, sent away from Anjali for ever. And he knows that this banishment would be something he could not bear. This would not be supportable. K.D. has no connections in the world. Papa and Ma are dead, and he doesn't have frequent communications with his relatives in Bihar. He has nobody. But Bloody Mathur has always welcomed him into his home, and K.D. has seen Anjali grow from infant to girl. She has always known him, he has been present through her entire life. K.D. understands that this small person sprang from Bloody Mathur and Rekha, but somehow she has become his daughter as well. Somehow he has become a father. He has no authority, but he has love. He understands that this little girl, in her blue school skirt, is his anchor in the world. She binds him together, with that long gaze of hers. He doesn't know how this happened, or when, but he knows it is true. She leans on his knee now, holding up the English doll he has brought her from London.

'She won't talk, Uncle.'

The doll is blue-eyed, flaxen-haired, with a puckered strawberry of a smile and a tinny voice. K.D. now realizes that he hasn't heard her saying 'Mama' for a few minutes. He turns the doll over, and under the pink dress, the panel in the small of her back is loose. He fingernails the panel up, and the wires inside are twisted around the battery, a green chip hangs loose. 'What did you do?' he says.

'I wanted to see how she worked,' says Anjali.

K.D. laughs, alight with pleasure and love. The feeling inside him is complete, unrestrained, without any of the holding back that he has felt in every other interaction in his life. She giggles. 'Uncle, I'm too old for dolls anyway,' she says, not unkindly. 'I stopped playing with them long ago. You don't know much about girls. I like reading now. You should bring me books.' They laugh together, sending each other into pealing outbreaks that spiral away. Anjali's mother watches, faintly suspicious. At least for that moment, K.D. doesn't care, and he carries Anjali's warmth with him into the next day, into the office where he sits at the Islamic Fundamentalism desk. In this enclosed, windowless cabin he collects reports from all over the world, he collates, connects, sifts, analyses. The beliefs and hatreds of men and women come to him in fragments, and he puts together the pieces. And then he writes his own reports, has them typed on crisp sheets of white rice paper, and through them information rises up, to the Additional Commissioner and then the Commissioner and then perhaps all the way to the prime minister. Information rises, and orders descend. Action is taken, and that produces results and new cascades of information. K.D. feels always that he is sitting at a node in a web, at the intersection of globe-spanning lines of energy that hum and spin and change shape. He can strum a thread here, and ten thousand miles away a man will slump in a doorway. He can write a paragraph, and two weeks later hear it paraphrased in a speech by the home minister. In this dusty room he sets strings of events in motion, he changes the lives of millions of people.

But he cannot find the men who took Bloody Mathur. He has a file, a thick one full of police reports and on-the-spot evaluations by teams of organization investigators, who evaluate the incident and also its investigation by the Punjab authorities. The facts are few and clear: Bloody Mathur had been cultivating a certain Harbhajan Singh, who had two years of college and no job, who was the son of a small farmer, who had been arrested twice for petty theft. This Harbhajan Singh had contacts in a certain militant group called the Punjab Liberation Army, and for months Bloody Mathur had fed money to Harbhajan Singh, who in turn had passed money to a close friend who had gone over to the militants. Good information had come back, verifiable material but none of it very useful. The source within the PLA asked for a face-to-face meeting, said he would bring another dis-affected friend. Bloody Mathur had a hunch, he went, and then was gone. Leaving a tilted, shattered Ambassador and three dead men. And there the trail stops, ceases. Bloody Mathur has disappeared, and that is all.

But K.D. won't let that be all, he refuses to allow matters to rest. He follows Harbhajan Singh's family, he follows his friends, he makes deals. Bloody Mathur used to say, 'If it's not money, it's lust. If it's not that, it's safety, his fear for his family. Any and every man can be bought. You just have to find out what the price is.' So Bloody Mathur ate tandoori chicken in roadside dhabhas with Harbhajan Singh, because the dushman had widespread operations in Punjab, it was their staging area, their haven, their easy entry into India. And so he vanished. Now K.D. pushes his field officers, he has Harbhajan Singh's brother followed and watched, he asks for backgrounders on known associates, listings of bank accounts. He manoeuvres men and resources and money, because they are in a battle, a war. K.D. fights back. He will not forget. So the great game is played in the streets and farmlands of Punjab.

The game lasts, the game is eternal, the game cannot be stopped, the game gives birth to itself. K.D. plays it, and plays it well. He has a vast memory, and a sensual feel for details: a pair of dark-lensed reading glasses glimpsed in a blurry photograph of preachers in Frankfurt stay with him for six years, so that he is able to spot the same man in another photograph taken on the other side of the world, in Peshawar, when Taliban commanders emerge from a meeting with an ISI major. These prodigious feats of connection and naming, this creation of meaning, give K.D. his reputation, his fame, his place in the organization. He advances. He is now an Assistant Commissioner, a junior one but a man with a future nevertheless. He is moving. Four years, and he moves on, this time to Berlin. In this divided city, he gives study visas to Iranian students, arranges scholarships for them, he gives sympathetic hugs to Afghan doctors and invites them to dinner. He sends parcels to Anjali, who is speeding through school, leapfrogging whole ranks of students with double promotions and impossibly high marks in final examinations. She reads up on Berlin, and asks for biographies of Hitler which she cannot find in Delhi, and books about generals with names as round and full as pink breakfast sausages.

'There are space-occupying lesions in the patient's frontal lobe.' Dr Kharas stands over K.D., surrounded by an attentive rank of interns. 'The effects of the glioma are interesting. The patient presents with reduplicative amnesia, during which he is quite literally somewhere else. Usually patients with this kind of amnesia imagine themselves to be at home, or in some place they like. This patient seems to range in his imagination to places where he has been in his life, all kinds of places all over the world.'

That's because I never had a home, fair Doctor Anaita. My home was a place in my imagination, a beautiful, prosperous land that doesn't exist yet. In all my journeys, that is where I was going, to this peaceful country of the future.

'Patients with this kind of impaired memory also usually present with confabulation. That is, they give incorrect answers in response to questions about remembered experience. Even questions about trivial matters, like details of past employment, dates, locations, elicit answers that seem coherent but are fantastic. The patients describe impossible, adventurous and gruesome experiences. Mr Yadav? Mr Yadav?'

Dr Anaita wants to demonstrate symptoms to her students. K.D. nods. He will give her that, he will give her whatever she wants. He owes her, he owes her because of her ardent curiosity, her skill, her passion for her job, he owes her because she gives him hope. Not hope for his own survival, but hope that he has lived a good life, that all the ugly things he has done might finally amount to something good. She is his hope.

'Mr Yadav, can you tell me your date of birth?'

He cannot remember. No matter, he mustn't disappoint her. He picks a number out of the air. '9 July 1968,' he says. There is a quick fizz of excitement among the interns, a tingle in their eyes. They like symptoms, symptoms demonstrate the inner workings of the defective machine. An abnormality in the organism, by inverse but impeccable logic, demonstrates some truth about its normal functioning. K.D. realizes that his 1968 date is many years too late, he is much older than that. But what happened on 9 July? The date is rough, it sticks and scrapes across his mind like a burr. Then he remembers. He sees it. In the lower half of his world, in the new half-darkness of his vision, K.D. sees a burning village. It is not fuzzy and indistinct like a remembered village, it is not a hallucination. It is a real village, and he can see it. He can see the flames moving under the wooden floors of the huts, a red-eyed sow grunting in panic through the orderly green rows of a turnip garden, he can hear the sharp pop of exploding bamboo. The colours are deep, incandescent, just like reality but more so, he can see the sparkle of saliva on the teeth of a black dog shot through the head, the hair on its splayed rear legs. It is more real than real, this dying village. He has never been to this village, but knows exactly what it is. This is the village of Chezumi Song, in Mon district of Nagaland, which on 9 July 1968 was visited by a unit of the Assam Rifles under the command of a Captain Rastogi, a Dakshesh Rastogi who was the very same mathematically-inclined friend of K.D.'s first field posting. Rastogi has grown, from lieutenant to captain, and he has grown thicker, he has grown into a fine man. He doesn't know it, but he is acting on intelligence that K.D. has collected and collated and passed down the chain of command, and he is after two Naga insurgent leaders, L.K. Luithui and M. Essau. They are known to be in the area, and they have relatives in this village. Rastogi's unit has lost six men to sniping and mines in the last month, and these two Nagas are the tacticians behind the attacks. The village is subjected to a search, and the villagers are interrogated. Captain Rastogi applies pressure. The village chief is beaten with rifle butts, along with the village notables. They all say they know nothing of the two insurgents. More pressure is applied. The chief's daughters, three of them, are dragged out of the square by the hair. Their names are Rose, Grace and Lily. They are raped. Twenty-two women are raped, and the village is burnt. Three of the village men are shot, and Captain Rastogi's report states that these three terrorists were cornered and killed in a running gunfight that resulted in the destruction of the village of Chezumi Song. L.K. Luithui and M. Essau, the two insurgents, are cornered three days later in a forest hideout eight miles to the north, and are killed. Captain Rastogi receives a commendation, and is thereafter a man on the rise. K.D. knows what was in the official reports, and he knows what really happened. He is, after all, an intelligence man. He knows that the tip-off about the hideout was given by a girl named Luingamla, who stuttered out the location because Captain Rastogi had a pistol pointed at her father's head. K.D. knows this. It is his business to know. He wasn't there, but he knows. He can see the village of Chezumi Song now, quite clearly. He can see it blazing. But where are the people? He can see none of the Nagas, and none of the soldiers. He hears screams. The birds are shrilling through his head. Now, a gunshot, and he knows it is a Webley-Scott .38, that is what Captain Rastogi carried that day. But there are no people in this real village.

'The village is burning,' K.D. whispers.

The interns lean close. Dr Kharas is listening intently. 'What village?' she asks. 'What village?'

K.D. says nothing. What can he say? That it was a village that you never knew of, that ceased to exist before most of you were born? It is gone, but it continues to burn. 'The village is burning,' he says again. Dr Kharas whispers to the interns, and finally they leave. The village continues to burn, but still without its inhabitants, or its invaders. K.D. listens to the crackling of the conflagration, the screams, the gunshots. By afternoon he is able to fall asleep, or into a dream of sleep. He wakes feeling exhausted, his joints ache. He slumps to the bathroom, one hand out to keep fingertips on the wall, all the way. Chezumi Song is no longer in his blind spot, in his half-band of darkness, but as he pisses, he sees a chess set. He tilts his head far forward to be able to see what he is doing in the pot, but where he is not able to see, where the square-tiled bathroom floor cuts off, there is now a chess set. He recognizes it, it is actually the top of a stone table, in a park in Berlin. He meets here, on scattered Friday afternoons, an Afghan engineering student named Abdul Khattak. This Khattak is very poor, with four

332

brothers and three sisters, all of whom live in a tiny apartment in Neukoelln, so the lunches that K.D. provides him are especially welcome, as are the small amounts of money that he is given when he performs. For the names of fundamentalist preachers and information on their movements and plans, K.D. hands him slim envelopes, and more envelopes for the names of anti-fundamentalist Afghans in Europe and at home, and perhaps introductions. K.D. and Khattak have talked about Indian visas for Khattak's younger brothers, and the possibility of scholarships at Indian universities and technological institutes. All this, naturally, for more information for K.D. But where is Abdul Khattak? He is not at the bench in the park, under the green canopy of oaks. K.D. can see the squares in the chess board, which are green and white tiles let into the cement. Khattak likes this rendezvous point because he loves chess. Following the international competitions is the one luxury he allows himself, this Khattak who runs between his classes and his laundry job and his siblings. Khattak doesn't like dead drops, although leaving notes under a park bench in a shopping bag, or taped to the back of a lamppost, would be much safer. Khattak likes to talk, after every two or three dead drops he insists on a meeting. Where is this Khattak, why is he not under this lightening March sky with its hint of spring? K.D. shuffles back to his bed, his arms held out, and he knows exactly why: Khattak is dead, lying in an alley between empty crates, behind a furniture store. His wrists are tied behind his back, his cheeks and chest are bruised from a beating, and his throat has been cut. His killers are never found, the police never have any clues and K.D. is not going to give them any. Khattak is dead, but much of his information is good, it is alive. K.D. uses it, he gains access to student networks that lead back to Kabul, and he gains a source in Jallalabad, a secretary to a mullah who is gaining political prominence. And now, in this Delhi hospital room, in his own half-blindness he can see the chess set, sunlit and waiting for the pieces, for the play. K.D. gets into bed, and wonders what happened to Khattak's brothers and sisters. They survived, of course. The survivors survive, that is what they do. And here is this chess set, green and white and glowing in his darkness.

'Who is the prime minister?' It's Dr Kharas, leaning in close to him, holding a bright light close to his eyes. 'Mr Yadav, who is the current prime minister?' It is night outside, and K.D. doesn't know how he got from morning to night. Anjali is standing at the foot of the bed, her hands clenched around the white metal rail.

K.D. smiles at her. 'My short-term memory is failing,' he says. He is trying to comfort Anjali: to have the apparatus to know you are failing is to have something, after all. But she is not comforted, he can see that. She knows that he has no idea who the prime minister is. He can remember the watch that Nehru was wearing, a commemorative HMT with small black numerals, and the fine hair on Nehru's wrist, but he doesn't know who the current prime minister is. It is gone, simply gone. Not here.

'Are you seeing any hallucinations now?' Dr Kharas wants to know.

He must have told her, during his lost day. He hadn't wanted to tell her, to not tell Anjali. He feels ashamed now. It is a shameful thing, to see things that are not there, to lose one's grip on what is, what is not. He could not stand Anjali pitying him, thinking of him as less than efficient. He has never suffered incompetence lightly. But no, she is pained but not commiserating, she will not condescend to him, he can see that. She can still see that he is present, within these ruins. He, K.D. Yadav, is still here, thinking, calculating, *understanding*. He looks at Anjali but addresses himself to Dr Kharas: 'No hallucinations now. Why am I seeing them?'

'It is the human brain,' Dr Kharas says, sitting back. She puts her hands together in her lap, rather like a priest imparting a moral lesson. 'The human brain does not like blanks. It does not tolerate empty spaces. Because of your structural damage, in the visual pathways, there is a gap in your visual field. So then the brain fills in this scotoma, this breach. The material it is finding is from your memories, from your stored sensations and concepts. It throws that material into the blank space. This happens all the time, actually, even in normal functioning. What data comes in is put together with what is already there, it all mixes together and changes and transforms and becomes a perception. This is how we experience everything.' She pauses to see if he is following, if he is absorbing all this information. She wants to be lucid, the knowledgeable Dr Kharas. He nods, and she continues. 'From the data from the outside, and from the material of memory, the brain makes up a story, and that story is what we think is reality. What makes it noticeable now is that you are completely losing half of your external data from the visual stream, and the brain is compensating for that loss. Otherwise what your brain is doing is completely normal. We are built like this only.'

334

'We are built like this only,' K.D. says, and bursts out laughing. It is funny, even though his Anjali and the good doctor are not laughing, no, they don't have even a smile, a twitch of amusement. We are built like this only, to see apparitions, to construct a vision of the world inside this lonely palace of bones, to live in this dream and be terrified of dying out of it, to suffer this nightmare made from impressions as if it were real. A rat's vision of reality is as real as mine, as yours, as ours. But we live and die and kill in this ghostly phantasmagoria of mirroring narratives. This is all dreadfully pathetic, or perfectly hilarious. K.D. cannot tell which, and he cannot stop laughing. He wheezes on. Finally he beckons Anjali to him, and makes her sit on the bed, close to him so he can hold her hand. 'Don't be gloomy,' he says. 'It's an interesting condition, at least. It is very educational.'

'There is a name for the syndrome,' Dr Kharas says, glad to provide structure. She is a great believer in empowering the patient through knowledge. 'It is called the Charles Bonnet syndrome, after the man who first observed it. It is common among people whose eyesight is failing. Often old people who are suffering from cataracts, for example, report seeing things: people, objects, ghosts.'

People, objects, ghosts. K.D. can see people and objects, but he is himself starting to feel rather like a ghost, a flickering network of electrical impulses encased in a leaky, creaky machinery of flesh. He feels himself dying and coming alive, his self fading in and out with every breath. Does Dr Kharas see this, that this self too is an illusion, thrown up by the pattern-seeking brain to fill in the void? He is filled with pity, for himself, for Dr Kharas, for his Anjali. What an agony of seeking and suffering is the unavoidable destiny of this drifting wraith. What convolutions of pain it must know and survive, from birth to death, this piece of nothing. Anjali is sad even now, and he pats her wrist. 'Don't worry,' he says. 'It's nothing.' But she is puzzled, and he knows he cannot make her understand that it is useless to mourn him, to grieve for something which was always a nothing. She is young, full in her flesh, engaged in her battles and hungrily alive. He cannot make her see, he should not. Perhaps only those at the edge of disintegration can understand this. 'The spider weaves the curtains in the palace of the Caesars; the owl calls the watches in the towers of Afrasiab.' But she is waiting to tell him something. Anjali waits for Dr Kharas to finish her instructions and her goodbyes, and gets up to shut the door. She returns to the bed, and sits close to K.D.

'Did you remember anything about Gaitonde, Uncle?'

'No. Nothing new. Only the things you already know.' Gaitonde was his recruit, his client. After K.D. had retired, Anjali had wanted to be his handler. There had been objections within the organization: she was too young, too inexperienced, and finally and most importantly, she was a woman. What kind of gangster would be handled by a female officer, what woman could handle the fearsome Gaitonde, that ruthless monster, that womanizer with no respect for women? This was old and accepted reasoning within the organization, that women couldn't be given field postings because they couldn't handle the kind of criminal elements that were the everyday providers and producers of intelligence, that women couldn't make deals and give instructions to sweaty smugglers, border-crossing petty criminals, drug-carrying mules, the illiterate and the vulgar and the desperate. So women were good at a desk, the reasoning went, they were fine analysts. Keep them there. But Anjali had chafed at her various desks, and struggled against this old-fashioned reasoning, and proven herself as a field operative in her foreign postings in London and Frankfurt. She was a fine analyst and also a good handler of women and men, a certain Pakistani immigrant-smuggler in Marseilles, a moustachioed and particularly brutal Pathan, had called her Bhen-ji and provided vital connections to carriers of Afghan heroin, with implications in Peshawar and Islamabad. So there were particular ways in which women could indeed handle men, but the organization had refused Anjali's request. They had given Gaitonde to one Anand Kulkarni, who was very masculine and very tough. Gaitonde proved finally to be unreliable, and Kulkarni had been criticized within the organization for his handling of him, but he – K.D. – was the one who recruited the bastard. It's his fault that Gaitonde went bad, if it is anybody's. K.D. asks, 'Why is it so important? Gaitonde is dead.'

'Yes, he is dead.'

'So, then? There will be a struggle to occupy his territories. Maybe his company will fall apart. Maybe they will kill each other. So what?'

She is evaluating him. She is trying to decide whether to tell him something, or not. He understands he is a risk now, that he cannot be trusted with information. He is not himself, he may tell Dr Kharas, the nurse, people passing in the corridor. And yet he wants to know. 'Tell me,' he says. 'If you tell me, maybe I can help. Maybe if you tell me, it'll help me to remember.' He is not sure whether this is true, whether the tatters of his once-vaunted memory hold together enough that results can be produced from small cues, from careful direction and prodding. But she has to gamble. Calculated risks are the everyday work of the game, and K.D. has trained Anjali in these small steps through danger: at that very last moment when you are walking towards a drop point, unsure whether you are under surveillance, do you keep walking or reach for the bag? You have come to know that one of your officers has been selling information to the other side, to many other sides, so a number of your sources may have been compromised, and you have a man in a defence research establishment near Islamabad, a physicist, do you call him in or not? Calculate the payoff, and the punishment that failure will inflict, and decide.

She has decided. She speaks fast and low. 'We found Gaitonde in a house in Bombay. The house was built like a very deep bunker, with hardened walls. We found the builder and the architect who built it for Gaitonde. They told us that it was done in ten days, from plans faxed in by Gaitonde. He told them not to worry about money, just finish it. They did. We have a copy of the plans. The title page and some other identifying labels had been removed or erased, but there was enough text to allow us to trace the plans to the source. They were downloaded from the internet, from a North American survivalist website entitled "How You Can Survive Doomsday". We examined the structure in Bombay. Gaitonde built a nuclear fallout shelter.'

Her eyes are silvery black and sparkling and frightened. Outside, night settles with the sigh of thousands of beating wings. The groaning rush of the city's traffic is still alive, far below. There is a certain formless vacuity to this nuclear threat, K.D. thinks, an ultimate white blankness which stops all thought, all motion. Anjali cannot think past it, he can see this. He prompts her. 'So Gaitonde broke cover, he ran?'

'Yes, he came back to Bombay. He was looking for three sadhus. He was found dead from a self-inflicted wound. In this shelter.'

'What was in the shelter? Did you find anything?'

'There was another body, of a woman. A woman named Jojo Mascarenas, a madam who had supplied women to him. Gaitonde killed her with the same pistol he shot himself.'

K.D. had known about the women, the girls that Gaitonde had consumed in a steady flow. He had never bothered to ask where the supply came from. Now he knew. 'And what else?'

'There was an album of photographs, of these girls. And money. One crore twenty-one lakhs, in new notes from the Central Bank.'

'You followed up on this woman?'

'Yes. We found her apartment, searched it. Found nothing interesting. There was some cash. Some of it must have been from Gaitonde, it was the same series of new notes, in plastic wraps. She operated on the fringes of the television and film industry, there is a lot of black money in that business. There were tapes, photographs of actors. Nothing else.'

She waits. She is allowing herself a little bit of hope, but K.D. has nothing to tell her. No explanations have become dislodged from the whirl of his confusion, no clues have come floating up from the drifting masses of his past. 'Let me think about it,' he says. 'I'll have to think about this one.'

She eats dinner with him, from a partitioned steel tray. He spoons up his khichdi and tries to think. The nuclear threat has been present on the subcontinent for decades, and they have dealt with it. The organization has run many ops to extract information about technologies, doctrines, tactics, locations, some of them very successfully. They have data, and they know the capabilities and intentions of the Pakistanis and the Chinese and the Americans. K.D. has seen some of these analytical reports and papers, and the reddish-brown satellite photos which show missile complexes and air bases, and knows there are real weapons at the ready, aimed at his cities, at him. And yet the reality of a nuclear explosion has always seemed unreal to him, very far away from the dirty night-time business of waiting in a freezing hut for a Pakistani informer, sitting on a broken crate with feet up to avoid snakes and scorpions. To put a man under a double barbed-wire fence, through shifting fields of wheat, under the night-scoped guns of Pakistani Rangers and past sleeping cattle, that was craft and labour and vocation, well-known and well-practised. But nuclear destruction, that belonged in the thrillers that K.D. read on long journeys and at bedtime, that he still reads. In the stack of books at his bedside, among the Roman histories and CIA autobiographies, there are these fictions that he reads for pleasure, often to laugh at the wild extremities of the scenarios that they create, the millions of dead and the dastardly plots and the brave, selfless heroes. In these books, and only in these books, bombs sometimes explode, taking whole cities. Only in these books is there the smoking aftermath, that silence without

338

birds. But you always shut the book, you put it back on the night-stand, you drink your little sip of water, you turn over and go to sleep. No need to build grim little bunkers in the middle of Bombay, no need for gangsters to run from their safe foreign refuges and into danger, no need to look for three sadhus. No need at all. But Gaitonde is dead. Why?

K.D. doesn't know. But he is thinking. Anjali is clearing up the trays and glasses and spoons. She looks exhausted. 'Go home,' he says. 'The ward-boy will do that.'

'I don't mind. Actually I asked them if I could stay here. They said they could bring in a cot.'

'Anjali, you don't have to. Really. You need your rest.'

'I can rest here. I just need to sleep, and I'll be very comfortable in their cot.'

He understands that she is concerned for him, but also concerned for her operation, her world which she believes is threatened some-how. She wants to stay close to him, to his fading memory and mind, in case he rants out a name, a place, a word, that will lead her into Gaitonde's bygone life. She loves her uncle, yes, but she is doing her job. She is following her training and her instinct, she is a good stu-dent. K.D. is dying, he knows it, she knows it. Most likely, the dying will lead her only to the country of the dead, but she is being careful – perhaps K.D. will give her something useful before he slips into silence. He smiles at her. 'All right, beta. As long as you are comfort-able.'

'I even brought my toothbrush,' she says, holding it up. She is again the little girl he knew once, and they grin at each other. It is cosy to have someone in the room, splashing in the bathroom. Anjali settles into the cot. They say 'Goodnight' to each other, and K.D. switches off the lamp above his bed. She sleeps, falls into long, even breathing almost immediately. He watches her, the shape of her shoulder. She doesn't have anyone to call, to tell that she will not be coming home tonight. She once had a husband, a Kannadiga boy she married against the wishes of the concerned parents, in the idealistic throes of a metropolitan Delhi love affair. The husband had studied economics at Zakir Hussain College, had gone on to a career in the IAS and had left her four years after the wedding, complaining of her incessant travel and obsession with her career. K.D. doesn't know if she has found anyone else, she certainly never speaks of it, even of the desire, of the longing. Has she come to prefer solitude, like K.D. himself? He has asked himself sometimes if solitude is preferable to boredom or betrayal, which seemed to be the inevitable end of all happy love affairs, of all happy marriages. People clung to one another out of fear. K.D. has preferred the integrity of being alone. He was a realist, he is. He has the strength to face death alone.

In the upper half of his visual field, his sight is sensitive and keen, he can see the fine shadow of Anjali's hair on the far wall, the slender, upstanding stalks thrown up on the grey. In the lower half, a man named Palash is walking on a bund between fields of rice. He is wearing a torn banian and a dhoti, and the skin on his neck is creased and dark. K.D. has watched the sweat sweep across it for ten miles. The man's neck is more real in this present, in this hospital, in this darkness, than it was on that afternoon long ago. It is a sheeny chocolate, and the grey hair that straggles over it is distinctly stranded, picked out by the failing sun into bright, glittering filaments. The path rolls down off the bund, and into the distance, straight as an arrow. The fields are flooded, and the young green shoots are mirrored in the still surface of the water. An elegant preying bird is making its slow, taut circles overhead, inflecting only the very last spread feathers at wingtip. K.D. can see its rich golden-brown belly, the white chest and head, and he knows it is a Brahminy Kite. He knows this bird, he knows this day. Ahead, there will be gunshots. By dusk, Palash will lead him to a hut on the outskirts of the village of Ramtola, where a young man named Chunder Ghosh is spending the night. Chunder Ghosh will say his name is Swapan, but K.D. will recognize him from Jadavpur University photographs, from birthday pictures at Kadell Road. That plump-cheeked boy is gone, but this gaunt revolutionary sitting cross-legged is Chunder Ghosh all right. Ghosh will ask K.D. many questions, probe K.D.'s cover, which is resilient and whole: K.D. is Sanjeev Jha, small-time jute trader and Naxalite sympathizer and possible provider of information about bigger, capitalist jute merchants who need to be eliminated in the class war. K.D. will answer questions about Patna, about the various qualities of jute, and a lantern will fuzz and flicker under Palash's pumping. K.D. will massage his right heel, where he has been bitten by some unknown insect, some slithering attacker. The flesh is raw, pushed up in a lump. Chunder Ghosh is a veteran of many bites, many fevers, but even he will spare a glance for this sudden wound. The questions will continue, go on. The questions will go on too long. K.D. will get up to relieve himself. He will take his hard-bottomed blue shoulder-bag with him, which has been searched and found to contain a thermos, a shirt, a packet of peanuts, two newspapers and one thousand six hundred rupees. Outside, K.D. will actually urinate. He will be able to, despite the constriction coming in steady swells through his belly. He will breathe, and reach into his bag, and find at the very bottom a fold of cloth which he will take up carefully with a small stripping sound. He will find a hidden compartment, and inside it a Polish .32 automatic, loaded and chambered. He will walk back into the hut, his hand by his side, the briefcase held before him. He will shoot Chunder Ghosh in the right eye, and Palash in the chest and in the back of his head. In his fast search through the hut, the only thing he will find is an ancient Colt .38 revolver, which Chunder Ghosh was holding cocked in his right hand, under his thigh. He will take it and flee. But all that lies ahead. What K.D. can see now is Palash walking ahead of him, the incandescent green of the rice, the kite swooping low overhead.

What lies ahead, in that first purple shimmer of dusk, at the far edge of the world? From different directions, K.D. Yadav and Chunder Ghosh are walking towards the same dismal hut, with its collapsing roof and cracked walls of mud. One is still doing his best for Nehru, the other has left behind his comfortable life of club and convent and theatre group for another vision equally grand and equally crazy. Both believe that somewhere on the other side of the hut, on the other side of the horizon, there is happiness. Just that, simply that: happiness. But K.D. sees clearly now, he sees from the great clarity of his illness that they were both betrayed, that they were betrayed before they ever began their journeys. A great knot of contempt uncurls in K.D.'s chest for those young men, so confident in their own health, in the rude heartiness of their dreams. What fools. What egotists. What could either of them have built that would not end in more murder, more loss, more sickness? 'The spider weaves the curtains in the palace of the Caesars; the owl calls the watches in the towers of Afrasiab.' And yet we schemed, and tore at each other, and killed each other. And we continue to do so, and we will never stop. We will lurch from massacre to pogrom, all in the name of some future heaven. K.D. feels a vast irritation, an exasperation at the entire species, at everything it has ever done. This life is a sickness, he thinks. Let it end. Let it all end. Gaitonde had been afraid of falling white

light, an explosion and a blasting wind that would tear away everything that had been built on the surface of the watery marsh. K.D.
Yadav turns himself on to his back and imagines it, the huge climbing
explosion, the sudden death, the silence afterwards. Finally there will
be quiet. A vanishing, like the blowing-out of a candle. He thinks of it
and he feels the peace of it, feels the necessity of such an end. He
smiles, contented, and sleeps.

Anjali is sitting by the bed, dressed, when he awakens. She smiles.
'Did you remember anything.'

'No,' he says. 'Nothing. Nothing at all.'

She nods. Behind her there is a young man, a sharp young fellow
with a foxy face, a clipped moustache. 'This is Amit Sarkar,' she says.
'He has just joined the organization, he is my trainee. He will stay with
you today.'

'Good morning, sir,' Amit Sarkar says, vibrating with the proper
enthusiasm of a recent inductee in the presence of a legend.

Anjali is keeping up the surveillance, going with her intuition on
this long shot. K.D. doesn't mind. He is finished with it all. 'Right,' he
says, settles back into his pillow. He wants to be easy, to float away,
but something is working at him. Gaitonde's money. There is something about Gaitonde's money that is nettling, the image of it sticks
and scrapes through his head, one crore and twenty lakhs of Central
Bank stacks. K.D. shoves the memory of the money away, he wants
none of it. He fixes on the wall, on the slight vibration of light across
it from the fan overhead. He passes into a comfortable drowsiness, a
light-feeling awareness that skips across memory and image and
thought without attachment. His mind feels weightless, freed of gravity. The lower half of K.D.'s vision is still visited by ghosts from the
past, soldiers long dead, informants, agents, victims. He watches it all
with a sublime detachment. And in the upper half, visitors come and
go, old colleagues with their grandchildren. Dr Kharas and her
interns. Nurses and attendants. Finally, in the evening, Anjali comes
back to relieve Sarkar. They whisper to each other, and then she comes
to sit with K.D. in the dusk. K.D. eats because she insists and he wants
no fuss. Or he would turn away from the food, also with no fuss. It's
all the same to him now. A night passes, and then a day. He watches
it all, life and the life inside his eyes, and they are all equally insubstantial, all phantoms, Dr Kharas and her pricking needles and diagnoses,
Anjali, the MIGs yawing and screaming down towards a Pakistani

airfield, two men walking through fields of rice. They are all illusions, these unreal men and unreal women, and they live by illusions and suffer for them and die because of them. Let it all end tomorrow, this meaningless cavalcade of ghosts, in an inescapable white flash of light. Tomorrow it is over. K.D. is content with this thought, and he is comfortable.

He dreams. He knows he is sleeping, and he knows he is dreaming. He is aware of himself as the sleeping watcher, and yet he feels the thumping impact of his feet through the thick bottoms of his keds as he runs. They are playing football on the high plateau they have levelled into the side of the mountain. Everyone is there: Khandari in his green Garhwali sweater with its sprays of rough wool, Rastogi on the far left, DaCunha with his incessant calls of 'Put-tru, put-tru, man!', and Ginzanang Dowara, who keeps trying to put through but always loses the ball. It is Sunday, and they have divided all the off-duty men into two teams, forty men to a side, and they play a hectic, savage football on what they think is the highest football ground on earth. They have hacked it out of the mountain in two months of high-altitude labour, widened a natural, almost level slope. This ball has come up all the way from Calcutta, through a chain of personal requests and favours called in. So now they play. Thangrikhuma has the ball, he is small and compact and very quick, he slips through a chain of half a dozen defenders with a leaning and a side-step that is so fast that it looks like some sort of cinematic flicker. K.D. gives a great shout of admiration and chases him. Thangrikhuma is fast, so fast. He knows K.D. is coming and doesn't care, he is grinning. K.D. runs hard. The valley beyond is green and grey, and the white clouds are puffy overhead. Thangrikhuma is running. Then Marak the subedar is in place, near the goalkeeper and the two rough stakes of wood which are the goal. Marak is old and slow, and he hangs back near the goal always, and then manifests himself at crucial junctures. He is experienced. He waits, he waits. Thangrikhuma is jinking and jiving, tempting him. Marak attacks now, he slides, our wily Marak. He misses Thangrikhuma but reaches back with an unerring hand as he falls and hooks a handful of jersey, and down goes Thangrikhuma. Foul, foul, but this is a man's game, and it's too late to cry foul, K.D. has the ball and is speeding it back into enemy territory. His boys are with him, shouldering aside the defenders, and K.D. has speed, such speed, he grins at the lovely jounce of the ball and it sits perfectly on his instep and comes back to him, he

343

has perfect control of it, he takes it past Rastogi easily, past the gasp of breath and the spray of sweat, and he is running free now, down the field, and he can hear DaCunha on his left, and Ginzanang Dowara is keeping up nicely on the right, and the ball glitters black and white in its bounce, K.D.'s chest pains him and he is happy and the air is cold in his throat, and the goal is ahead.

K.D. wakes, and he is weeping. There is a burning in his heel. Long ago, as he sat on the unfinished mud floor of a hut with Chunder Ghosh, sat cross-legged with his shoes off, he was bitten on the left heel by an insect. He remembers now, remembers how he rubbed the angry red stain with his thumb, and how Chunder Ghosh had for a moment stopped his questions and peered at the bite curiously. K.D. remembers and feels a sob come racking out of him. Anjali stirs, in her bed, and K.D. tries to hold down his convulsions, to make them stop. The men and women he is weeping for are mostly dead now, but he is crying for their lives, for the brevity of their struggles, for their brief agonies and joys. He is sobbing for the burning in their stings, for the momentary flaming of their desires.

'Uncle, what's wrong? Shall I call a nurse? Are you in pain?'

In the flaring of an electric bulb, Anjali is leaning over him. He shakes his head, and reaches for her hand. He is unable to speak, but he tries to smile at her, all the while shaking his head. She holds him. She sits on the bed and holds him in her lap.

'What is it?' she says. 'Don't be afraid,' she says.

K.D. is not afraid. He feels no fear at all, at least not for himself. But he can find no words for the great compassion that heats his body, this illusory carcass of damaged flesh. In his collapsing mind there is a fear for Anjali, for the life that surges through this strong young woman who holds him. She values her life, clings to it, as do her colleagues, her friends, her family. I must help her, K.D. thinks. I must. He casts back through his life, and through all that he knows and remembers, and now that he is thinking and has a purpose, his trembling stops. He lies still in Anjali's arms and thinks. Now there is that old joy of cogitation, and the information flows in an intertwining of streams, bright with colour and image and smell. It moves and he swims in it and changes angle and nudges it together in many and various arrangements: it feels like he is ambling through a kaleidoscope. There is that old pleasure. When the sky begins to grey outside, he stirs. 'The money in Gaitonde's bunker,' he says.

Anjali is leaning back against the headboard, and she comes out of her slumber. 'What?' she says.

'There was money in Gaitonde's bunker. You said something about wrapping.'

'The bundles were wrapped in clear, thin plastic. Like the kind that toys are wrapped in sometimes. Or chocolate.'

'Five bundles together? A stack like this?'

She looks at the shape he is making with his hands, the emptiness he holds in the air. Her eyes are sequined with pinpoints of early morning light. 'Yes,' she says.

'I want to see the money,' he says.

She runs across the room to her mobile phone, and he sits up to the fast blip of her dialling. She rattles out orders, and comes back to him. 'It's on the way,' she says.

But they both know it could take a while, to cut through the bureaucracy of the organization, to wake up people and have permissions given and safes opened. K.D. may not have time, he may forget. So he has her sit next to him and tells her, while he still has the facts. He tells her what he knows, what he remembers. 'Much of our Indian currency used to be printed in the Soviet Union. The Pakis ran an op after the Union fell apart, when everything was for sale. They tried to buy the original plates from the Russians. If they had got the plates, they would have been able to run a counterfeit operation that would have produced genuine notes, perfect money. But we got wind of it and got the plates from the factory. We killed their operation. But the Pakis did manage to get hold of very substantial amounts of original currency paper. We were too late to prevent that. With that paper, they've produced large-sum Indian currency, several series of big notes. They have some very talented technicians. The forgeries are brilliant. I've seen some of the notes, from seizures in Jammu and Amritsar. They are very good. They were completely wrapped in plastic, in stacks like this.'

Anjali nods, fast. 'Very good for transportation, in all kinds of conditions.'

'Yes, in any weather. The operation in Russia was run by an ISI man named Shahid Khan, who was a major at the time. He's good. I had known him before, from when he was with their embassy in London.'

'Shahid Khan,' Anjali says.

'Shahid Khan,' K.D. says. 'Very religious fellow. Hard worker. One of their best. Shahid Khan got the paper.'

She writes rapidly, on a white pad. He listens to the scratch of her pen, and when she is finished she waits for him, for more. But this is all he has.

They wait, together, for the money. Just after one, Amit Sarkar arrives, clutching a briefcase. Anjali holds up the stack for K.D. to look at. 'Yes,' he says. 'Yes.' He can feel himself smiling. The game, he thinks. It runs. He takes Anjali's pen from her and notches the point into the plastic and pulls. From this cut he pulls a note, and holds it towards the window, towards the brightness of the day. 'Yes,' he says. 'Yes. I think it's their money.' He has no idea what this means to Anjali, or whether it means anything at all. But they are all happy: it is something.

Anjali takes the money, takes her pad, hugs K.D. and hurries away. She must go, but she leaves Amit Sarkar with K.D., to listen, to watch over him. The organization still wants him to play, but it is too late. K.D. lies back in his bed, his arms spread wide. His pillows are very comfortable, good to feel against his cheeks. He is tired. It's time to rest. He shuts his eyes. He breathes, and sleeps.

Money

Put all together, Katekar's benefits and provident fund and small savings amounted to sixty-seven thousand and seven rupees seventy-four paise. The state government immediately announced a relief amount of two lakhs for his bereaved family, but it took nine and a half months for the cheque to wind its way through the convolutions of Mantralaya and the exacting attentions of many departmental clerks. By the time Shalini had the cheque cleared and the money deposited, it was almost a year to the day after her husband's death. She now spent her days speeding through six households where she washed clothes and dishes, did jhadoo-katka, and for this cleansing of homes was paid a thousand rupees by each. With two growing sons, this was not nearly enough, and it was a very steep drop from the days when her husband had brought home packets of cash. Now, finally, there were these two lakhs sitting in her account, and two lakhs seemed rather a lot to have at once, but Shalini knew well that sudden and fat chunks of money produced only an illusion of well-being. This is what she was now trying to explain to her sister.

'Bharti,' she said. 'Two lakhs seems like a lot. But how many days are there in a lifetime? How long will these two lakhs last, over three lifetimes? I have young boys. I have to pay for their school, all their books. And anything could happen. We could need the money at any time.'

Bharti was sitting cross-legged on a pillow she had taken from the shelf, with the table-fan full upon her. She wiped her face with her pallu, and ducked her head in that way she had when she was annoyed. 'Tai, if you are not going to spend it, what good is it doing sitting in that bank? We need it now, and he says the interest he will give you will be larger than the bank's.' Bharti's husband, Vishnu Ghodke, had two friends who were going to start a travel agency. He was to be the very smallest partner, but even for that he needed five lakhs, and he had less than three. Shalini was suddenly sitting on more than two. And so Bharti was here, on a Thursday evening, looking hot and angry. 'He says it's a sure business. People are travelling more and more. And both his partners have contacts in Bahrain and Saudi, and thousands want to go there. Thousands and thousands.'

Shalini shook her head. 'Bharti, even if crores and crores want to go to Saudi, I can't give this money. I am alone. I am alone and I have to take care of my boys.'

The thrust of Bharti's jaw was very bitter now. 'What about us? You have us. Don't you have any trust in us?'

'It's not a matter of trust or no trust.'

'Then?'

'Bharti, anything can happen. Anything.' It was life that you couldn't place any trust in. It was this life that fell out from under your feet, that left you falling and lost.

'But you are safe, tai. He'll pay you in monthly instalments, so there will be money coming in. In addition to what you are earning already. And you don't have any rent to pay. You will never be that badly off.'

Shalini and he had paid six lakhs for this safety over their heads, seven years ago. They had paid in four painful instalments, all in cash, all of it squeezed from thousands of washed plates and petticoats, from innumerable fifty and hundred-rupee bribes. So now she and her sons had a roof, two rooms, a kitchen, that was their own. That is what he had wanted, to own, to have a patch of earth that was not government property or a landlord's estate, he had wanted the safety of home. He had given them that. And then he was dead. The knowledge of his absence came to Shalini in a muscular twinge through her back and into her stomach, as it did now and again. She took a long breath, and then another. 'I can't do it,' she said. 'Bharti, I can't risk the money. Just think.'

'You are the one always thinking, tai. Thinking and thinking. But we people, we listen to our hearts. And so we thought we would ask you. We thought you would understand.' Bharti was getting up, gathering her purse and the folds of her sari about her.

'Bharti . . .'

'No, no, always you've been the smart one. Always you think three steps ahead. Always you get what you want because you think. But we are not like that.'

Shalini knew that to protest would immediately reopen and unreel a long and bitter discussion about a gold necklace that their mother had left to her and not to Bharti, and an incident at a family wedding when there had been an argument about the distribution of gift saris, and then exactly how much money had been spent on Shalini's wedding, and how much on Bharti's. They both knew completely the contours of these debates, and yet Bharti would finally weep and burn in righteous pain, her round face dissolving into soft infancy. So Shalini watched quietly as Bharti bent to pull the straps of her fancy green sandals over her ankles. Then she said, very gently, 'At least wait till the boys get back.'

'I left the children at Maushi's. It's been too long.'

Maushi was Vishnu Ghodke's maushi, who lived three buildings away from them. She was dependable but bad-tempered, and the children could not be left too long under her hard-handed discipline. Shalini thought the boy could use a few more slaps and pinches, but this was no time to criticize Bharti's son. As Bharti went out of the door, Shalini touched her above the elbow, just a little pat, her usual sisterly greeting and goodbye. But Bharti marched down the street, her head held high and rigid, and then Shalini lowered herself down, sat in the doorway. She allowed herself five minutes of slackness, of an exhausted lapse into complete relaxation. She watched the passers-by. It was almost seven-thirty in the evening, and the home-going rush was at its thickest. The shadows were long already, the days were getting shorter. Soon the nights would need an extra sheet, a blanket. The season was turning. The walkers passed in a steady flow, hypnotic in its even rhythm, the constant scissor motion of legs and ankles, the swing of bags laden with onions and potatoes and atta and soap and coconut oil. Some of the younger ones had smart office briefcases and a faster stride, all purpose and direction. They all passed.

Five minutes. Shalini knew when they were up. For as long as she could remember, she had had an unerring instinct for time, she could tell it down to the minute without ever needing a watch. She woke always without an alarm, and every day arrived at the station gate precisely six minutes before her train came in. She knew her rest was over, and so she got up. There was only a moment, a heartbeat or two, when her body was reluctant to leave its repose, its luxurious resting on brick and wood. Then Shalini gathered herself up, and got up. 'Ambabai,' she said gently, with a glance towards the deity on the shelf, 'rise, awaken. We have work to do.'

She had dinner ready when the boys came in. Rohit took half a bucket of water and led his younger brother out. Shalini could hear them murmuring under the splash of water. This was something that their father had insisted on, that when they returned from their games they had to wash their hands and feet before sitting in the house. In his presence they had always muttered against it, treated it as an unbearable fatherly burden, especially Rohit, who refused to do it if his father was not at home. Now that his father was really gone, Rohit performed the evening ablutions with a ritualistic seriousness, and led his brother through it with an unrelenting, police-like discipline. He had become very serious, Rohit had. He spoke to Shalini every morning about what was needed for the house, and went to the bazaar in the afternoon, after school. He brought back exact change, and showed her the lists of accounts he kept in a special notebook. He had a key to the house now, and wore it round his neck on a red string, and took it off only to sleep. As he ate now, he had it slung over his right shoulder, down his bent back.

'All homework is done, Mohit?' Shalini said.

Mohit had fast, stubby fingers. He was eating quickly, with his thali held in his lap and his head low. 'Mmmm,' he said. 'Mmmm.'

'Aai, he's got a maths test on Friday,' Rohit said, 'that he hasn't even started studying for.'

'Friday,' Mohit managed to get out between bites.

He had a smear of dal on his upper lip. He meant that Friday was three days away, Shalini understood this. He had done quite badly in his last exams, but that was only to be expected of a small boy who had gone to his father's funeral. Shalini had assumed, as had everyone who knew him, that he would adjust, cope, forget a little, and get back to his quiet, steady ways. But Mohit was still slipping, leaving his work undone while he sped through life on some secret mission. He hid himself behind his bed, in a nook filled with comics with lurid covers featuring moustachioed, pistol-clutching adventurers. He drew rifles in the margins of his notebooks, and muscular heroes firing enormous, blazing guns. He had a private life now, an inner world that Shalini could no longer reach. This happened with children, with sons, but not so soon. She patted the atta off her hands and reached out and tapped the top of his head with her forearm. 'Start studying tomorrow,' she said. 'Yes?'

'Yes,' he said.

'Want rice?'

'Yes,' he said.

Shalini fed them, washed up, slid the dishes into the rack on the wall, hung the pot and the pans and the spoons on their designated hooks on the roof. She took up her tooth powder and a glass of water and sat in the doorway. The lane held only a scattering of walkers, who stepped through the throw of light from each door. In another lane, long ago, he had said once that this repetition of light looked like a waterfall. That had been early in their marriage. Yes, she had said, like the cascade at Karla. They had been very poor then, and the trip to Karla and its caves had been a special treat a year after their marriage. He had walked inside the caves, marvelling at their roofs carved to look like wooden beams, and had stood before the stupas and become solemn, despite his scepticism, which even then was sharp and unrelenting. Now, in this lane, everyone was watching *Sabse Bada Paisa*, and the colours flickered in unison on the mud, up and down the street. She could hear the host's voice leaping from television to television, offering the chance of very large money. In her house there was a television, and usually there was no watching it this late on a weekday. That had been his rule. Study hard, he said to his sons, and when you have your own house you can watch television whenever you want. He made an exception for *Kaun Banega Crorepati*, though, because it was a knowledge-based show. Answer the right questions and you could win, you could own a crore, just like that. If you knew enough, you could be rich. Learn, learn, he told his sons, and they watched it together, seated cross-legged in a row. They used to shout out the answers. She used to call them the three monkeys, and they made monkey faces at her. Now Rohit was watching *Sabse Bada Paisa* intently, and its blues and greens moved across his face. Mohit was back in his nook, muttering out his secret stories to himself. He had lost interest in the show after the funeral. And Shalini sat in her doorway. On the television, the host asked, what is the name of the largest irrigation project ever built in India?

'Arre, Shalu.'

It was their neighbour, Arpana, with her man, Amritrao Pawar, both walking home in outing clothes. They seemed friendly enough tonight, so they must be going through one of the peace cycles in their lifelong war. Shalini made room for Arpana on the step. 'Out so late?' she said.

'My niece's Kelvan. In Malad.'

'Sudhir's daughter?'

'Yes. They are doing the wedding near his kholi itself.'

Arpana had two younger brothers, and she was close to the youngest. With the middle one, there was a feud of obscure origin. Shalini had heard the whole story when she had first moved into the house and met Arpana the feisty neighbour, but she couldn't remember the details. For many years she had known Arpana, and watched her quarrel with Amritrao Pawar, who had another woman and another family not so far away. At first Shalini had advised giving him up, sending him away. Then she had seen how they went from fighting to lifelong promises and opulent gifts, and one monsoon night, when she had herself been pregnant, she had gone late to ask Arpana for two onions. And standing outside their door she had heard how they made up, with what extravagant, moaning ecstasies they forgave each other. She understood then why the women on the street laughed when Arpana complained about her man's indifference and cruelty. He was standing facing them now, this Amritrao Pawar, with his hands in his pockets and a lordly smile of satisfaction teasing his mouth. Shalini didn't like him looking at her like that. Let him feast on his Arpana. She turned her shoulder to him. 'How was the boy?' she said to Arpana.

'Too thin,' Arpana said. 'He looked like that drainpipe, only not so black. But the family is good. He has a job at the airport.' She looked up from massaging her feet, at Amritrao Pawar. 'Why are you standing here like some lamppost?'

Shalini was afraid they would start a fight at her door. Sometimes all it took was a certain look. But Amritrao Pawar was happy tonight, and he only burbled into laughter. 'Waiting for you, rani. But I will wait at home.'

They watched him go, and Arpana snorted. 'They were drinking behind the house. He thinks I can't tell.' They nodded together at the foolishness of men, and then Arpana leaned in. 'Bharti came today?'

'Yes. How do you know?'

'That Chitra was on our bus.' Chitra was another neighbour, two doors down on the right. 'She said she saw Bharti at the bus stop.'

And other neighbours would have seen her at the road turning, and walking down the lane, and in the house, and noted her expression, and made their deductions. 'Yes,' Shalini said. 'She was here.'

'In the middle of the week? Did something happen?'

'Nothing, nothing. Just some money troubles.'

Arpana didn't look very convinced, or satisfied with just that much. But Shalini was not about to give in, and she turned the talk to Amritrao Pawar. That Arpana could never resist. She began her recitation of his recent sins, that he had gone to Mahabaleshwar with that randi and her whole brood – including the randi's Kaku – and therefore spent more money than he earned in two months, that he had fought with Arpana when she had remonstrated, when she told him that he had no ambition and was unwilling to take any risks, that he clung to his peon job like a fool scared of the world.

'Jobs aren't lying on the footpath,' Shalini said. 'Let him keep his job at least.'

'There's no income at all,' Arpana said. She meant apart from his salary. 'And they'll never promote him and never raise his salary. They are Muslims after all.'

'I thought his manager was a Brahmin? Some Bajpai, no?'

'Yes, yes,' Arpana said. 'But the company is owned by Muslims. And you know how they are.'

Shalini nodded. She had no arguments with this, but she doubted that Amritrao had anything in him worth promoting. Arpana settled back into her litany. She had tough, blocky shoulders and a thick neck, and she was nowhere near pretty, and over the last decade her cheeks had begun to droop. But still she and Amritrao Pawar returned to each other time and again, and tore at each other in rage and passion. The tragedy, of course, was that after all this, Arpana had no children. That is why she could never finally prove Amritrao Pawar in the wrong, and that was why he had another woman. All this painful need for each other, all this anger, and no children. Ambabai had her ways, her unknowable ways. 'Time for me to put the boys to sleep,' Shalini said.

'Yes. Are they all right?'

The women on the lane kept an eye on the boys, and Arpana especially took an interest in them, and sat with Mohit in the afternoons after school. 'Yes,' Shalini said. 'They are all right.'

They got up, nodded and went to the last chores of the day. Shalini tidied a little, chivvied the boys into bed, spread out the bedding and lay down. This was the hardest time of the day, when she missed resting her shoulder on his belly, when her bones could recall the curve her body made with his. In this waiting for sleep her mind moved sideways, twinkling-quick and unpredictable, his jokes and his laughter and little humiliations and joys from her own childhood came together and mixed up, bright, bright and painful. There was his filthy poem about Dev Anand and Mumtaz, and Shalini smiled, he had told it to her about a thousand times, all with the same glee. She drew in a deep breath, and then the hurt came. She wiped her face. At least she had his sons. His sons were sleeping close to her. She was drifting now. Muslims were like that. They killed my husband. One of them killed him, and now the murderer was dead. She sometimes wished the killer was still alive, so she could kill him again. But Sartaj Singh had shot the Bihari. Sartaj Singh was a killer too. They were all killers, and they had all killed her husband. The rage felt like iron pushing through her throat, and against every last shred of will, it forced itself out, making a low howl that scraped against the walls and frightened Shalini. She waited, but the boys were already sunk in their dense sleep, and outside the open door there was only the murmur of a distant conversation.

Shalini sat up. She took a glass of water and rinsed her hands, face and feet as quietly as she could. Then she sat cross-legged in front of Ambabai and Bhavani. Are you awake, Ambabai? Bhavani, no more of your ferocity – there is nobody to punish – but give me mercy. Give me peace. You failed him, Bhavani, I begged you every day for his safe return and yet you failed him. I won't call you bad names any more, I won't ask you why. You give me no reasons, and I will accept your silence. But give me a little portion of peace, give me relief from this deafening tumult of pain. I need to be quiet, for my boys. Ambai, are you listening? Give me this boon. I mourn him, but give me strength. Bhavani is blinding blue light, even her mercy comes like cool moonlight, but you, Ambai, are fruitful fields and overflowing water, rich mud and baby's breath and wide-brimmed lotus, you are my mother, bring me back from this exile, let me live under your shadow again. He was a good man. He walked to Pandharpur when I asked him to, even though he didn't believe that piety would cure his back. He lived in pain, I saw how he held himself upright with a hand on his hip at the end of the day, but he took care of us and he did his job. He was strict but never harsh, and Rohit and Mohit never feared him. He put a gold chain on my neck on the day of his first promotion and kept it there through our bad times. He never questioned me about money. When we fought he never hit me, only once he caught my elbow in anger and left a bruise. We were young, Ambai, he rubbed away the pain with phatkari and heated haldi, he gentled me with his sorrow. He smelt of coconut hair oil and Shiva-ji bidis then, but later for us he stopped taking tobacco in any form. Later he took women, I knew that, I fought with him, and he said he stopped, but I knew when he really stopped, when he knew truly what it meant to be a father. He wounded me, Ambai, and I him. I know I battered him sometimes with my cold quietness. But I did my duty as a wife, gave the embraces that men want. I fed him. He sustained me. We were companions, friends, not quite without quarrels but without rancour. Aai, I earn money, I go from day to day, but at night a rough rope pulls at my stomach, I twist to his side of the bed, I see things. I see him coughing in bed, he has a fever and I bring him a newspaper and he takes it, and his hand is hot and I feel a stab of worry. Then he is entering the kholi, and Mohit is crawling, his bottom wet. Him seated cross-legged, counting money. I am cutting onions, and the next day is Shayani Ekadashi. Ambai, where are you? Bhavani, are you here? I can feel you close, Ambai, but I am alone. Give me succour, Ambabai. I am alone.

'Aai?'

Rohit was standing behind her. She let him put her to bed, listened to his attempts to comfort her, let him go back to bed to comfort himself. She was remembering, again, that night when she went to Arpana's, to borrow the two onions, how she had stood outside Arpana's door, close to the wood to get away from the dripping rain, and listened to the sounds Arpana was making, somewhere between bitter and sweet. With a determined effort Shalini turned her mind away, made herself not think of it, of any of it. But still there was a small, dull pain that moved with every breath. She bore it, and whispered Ambabai's name again and again.

Anjali Mathur was following money. She did this in her spare time, what little there was at the end of the day or very early in the morning. She had managed to get to work early this Tuesday, so she was reading old files. She had run a data check for forged money, for the large sums of counterfeit currency the Pakistanis were known to have produced. Even with an arbitrary cut-off date of 1 January 1987, the database had given her a list of incidents, of mentions in reports, running to seventy-four single-spaced pages. So she had, over the last four months, been making her way through the original reports, one by one. It was tedious, and it was probably a waste of time, so she hadn't told anyone about her search. She had no idea of what she was looking for, other than detail, some pattern in the detail. A connection would reveal itself across the breadths of geography and time, a string of causes would unwind backwards and reveal a beginning, no, not a beginning but a node where many stories came together, and somehow the death of Ganesh Gaitonde would fit into the stream of events. Anjali didn't want an explanation, she was suspicious of explanations. Any explanation, any solution, always left out too much. But she trusted associations and correlations and rhythms, and the twistings and contractions of time. That was what K.D. Yadav had tried to teach them, to feel the beat and swing of the enemy's intention, that was what allowed you to predict. And this was why, after all the analysis, the cross-referencing and the computers and the mathematics, it came down to this, to reading old reports one by one. Finally it all depended on instinct. In her instinct, in her bones, Anjali felt a question about Gaitonde's return to the country, his death, about his bunker in the middle of Kailashpada, about the dead woman. None of it fitted together, none of it spoke a language that she could understand.

She had long ago learnt to decipher the particular vernacular of the reports, to imagine the event through the jerky telegraphese. She was reading one now, on plain unadorned paper.

TOP SECRET
Code Number of Source . . . 910-02-75P of . . . Unit Jammu Alpha
S. N. of report . . . 2/97 dated . . . 27.1.97

Particulars of source: Source Rehmat Sani is farmer, smuggler, w/family on both sides of border. Info was gathered from cousin Yasin Hafeez in Pak army.
Mode of communication: Personal meeting.
Reliability: II

Source conducted meeting with cousin in village Bhanni 13.1.97. Cousin is Havaldar in 13th Battalion, Punjab Regiment, at Mandi Chappar. His platoon was detailed to escort private three-tonne truck from known counterfeit printing press at 142 Shah Karnam Road (see report 47/96) to Lashkar-i-Azadi base at Hafizganj. Delivery was four crates, 4' x 4' x 4', received by Lashkar deputy commander Rashid

Khan. Source has no further info on contents. High probability contents are large amounts of medium denomination currency to be used in spring offensive in Valley and elsewhere. Source instructed to maintain observation.

Anjali knew the man who wrote this report. He had been her batch-mate during training. His name was Gaurav Sharma, he had been completely bald at twenty-six. In 1997 he had been posted in Jammu, and there was a little hint of him in that 'high probability'. He had been full of chaos theory during the training days and had tried to communicate to his fellow trainees, over chai and samosas during breaks, the rapture of fractals and strange attractors. In this report, as they had been trained, he had taken himself out of the language, tried to make it impersonal and objective. This was how it worked, as information moved upwards. The source was no doubt a sweaty vil-lain, a border criminal, a smuggler and murderer who had fatalism bred into him by the artillery shells that armies had fired over his head for the last fifty years, that fell into his village and fields to kill uncles and aunts. He was the sort of man who knew how to cross the border on a moonless night, who would think nothing of traversing the shrapnel-sharp dangers of no man's land. He knew how to lie motion-less for hours in a wheatfield under the probing, random fire of heavy machine guns, when to creep and when to stop. He had undoubtedly seduced his Pak army cousin into informing, tempted him first with easy loans for marriages and tractors, and then paid him outright. He made money at both ends, from his cousin and his handling officer. And no doubt the handling officer had given him cases of cheap rum, which he carried three at a time over the border into the ritually pure regions of Pakistan. The HO had met him in late January of '97, perhaps in some shack, some dhaba stinking of country liquor, paid him, and then reported to his supervisory office in Jammu, where Gaurav Sharma had prepared a report for the consumer desk in Delhi. The information would form the basis for reports that would go up the chain, and perhaps finally a chief secretary had been made aware that all data indicated that the enemy was planning an early offensive in the spring. Perhaps the prime minister had released funds, asked for budgetary changes. At every step up the ladder, the information was abstracted. Details were leached out. Here, in Delhi at the consumer desk, there were names and places and trucks and crates and Rehmat and Yasin. Up high, nobody wanted to know how it was done. Your job, K.D. Yadav had said, is also to shield the people on top from knowing too much. They shouldn't know. They need to be able to act, and shouldn't be bogged down in details. They need to preserve deniability. So keep it clean. Tell them what they need to know. Bas.

Anjali put the report aside, and turned to her everyday work. In the organization, within her professional circle in Delhi, her trip to Bombay had been finally regarded as quite frivolous. That man Gaitonde had bumped himself off, after a long career of bumping off other people, and so what? Thugs like that were unstable by defini-tion, and Gaitonde had had an up-and-down history of alcohol and women and much else. This was known. So he had built a safe house in Bombay. So what? The man was dead by his own hand, that was the only fact of any import. So what was the need for fact-finding, and what additional facts had been found? None. We told you so, the wise old men of the organization said, this is why you can't trust women in the field. This is, after all, why Kulkarni had been assigned to run Gaitonde in the first place. He had learnt his tradecraft in Punjab, he had run operations in Kashmir. He had been adjudged tough enough and Maharashtrian enough to deal with the foul-mouthed gangster, and he had – with a fine crusting of condescension – done Anjali the favour of clearing her to read his reports. 'I know you have an inter-est in the man,' he said, smiling toothily at her, 'and a good analyst can always help.' So she had followed Gaitonde's subsequent history, his use by the organization and his use of the organization, his escape from assassination attempts and his mounting paranoia, his lies to his handler, his instability and his sudden disappearance. When he had reappeared as a corpse in his old neighbourhood, smiling Kulkarni had been kind enough to allow her to go down and investigate.

She had found nothing useful, and so now she was back at her analysis. Her desk was Islamic Fundamentalism, and her beat was the world. Today she was following a Scotsman. He had been born Malcolm Mourad Bruce in 1964, in Edinburgh, to a Scottish carpen-ter and an Algerian hotel maid. The father had left when Malcolm was seven, walked out without a backward glance, and the mother had moved to Birmingham to live with her brother and his family. At seven-teen, Malcolm Mourad Bruce had become Mourad Chaker, passionate advocate of simple living, and had enjoyed a local celebrity in the

mosques as the boy-preacher with red hair. At twenty-two he had
appeared in Afghanistan, had fought the Soviets, had been wounded
seven times. Four years later there were reports of red-haired Mourad
fighting for the GIA in Algeria, killing journalists and bureaucrats and
army officers and civilians. He gained renown as the most intransigent
of the Salafist leaders, who refused to even speak to the moderate
Djazarists in his own group. For fierce Mourad, whose belief burned
in his eyes and in the flame of his hair, nothing less than a global
Islamic revolution was acceptable. In 1999, Indian military intelligence had reported a new band of militants operating in the valley of
Kashmir, led by a red-haired Mourad. It was of course the same man.
But did his appearance in the valley mean that the GIA was now insti-
tutionally involved in the fighting, that they were going to send money
and arms and men? Or was Mourad on his own, looking for another
war, another mission? This was the question. And so Anjali read
through the morning, through the afternoon, looking for connections,
for histories of men and women and their ideas and the associations
they formed, the journeys they made across borders. She read internal
organization reports from the Valley, think-tank papers from
Washington, shared intelligence from the CIA, funnelled through a
working group, three chapters of a book on the Algerian troubles by a
German academic, Xeroxed copies of articles from Algerian newspapers and magazines, with photographs of the dead turned by the
machine into flat black-and-white designs, and two years of field
reports from organization operatives in Morocco, Egypt and Algeria.
Her concentration submerged her like a diving-bell, and she was insen-
sible to the passing office chatter in the corridor outside, the mounting
glare of sunlight on the dusty window, the pigeon that stepped curve-
clawed through the bars and glared at her. Occasionally she tipped a
plastic bottle to the side of her mouth and drank water without a
pause in the velocity of her reading. In graduate school she had
acquired a note-taking skill that kept the lines steady and legible without needing more than an infrequent glance at the pad, and now she
filled up the pages. The day passed. At one-thirty there was a small
knock on the door, and Amit Sarkar tilted his head into the room.

'Come in,' Anjali said. 'You can come in, Amit.'

'Madam, lunch?'

Amit Sarkar was newly married, and every week looked a little
more prosperous from his wife's cooking. He no longer had that

359

hungry graduate-student leanness from the early days of his training, and had taken to bringing in a three-decker tiffin, to share. He was unfailingly polite, but she felt his disapproval of her bad eating habits, and his solicitude for her solitary divorcee life. She snapped at him sometimes, irritated despite herself by his presumptions. But today she was glad of the interruption. To live always between threat and counter-threat, from aggression to response, was suffocating. With his dal and bhat, Amit Sarkar brought her a whiff of normal life, of home and kitchen. 'What is it today?'

'Chingri macher curry, ma'am. It's Maithli's speciality.'

Maithli was short and round, with a chin-thrusting smile that made her eyes vanish. Anjali had met her twice and found her quite conventional and devoid of conversation. But her prawns were indeed good. Anjali ate, and Amit talked to her about his current project. She had him following the flow of foreign money, mainly from Saudi and Sudan, to radical Islamic organizations within India. He had unearthed, two days before, a link between a student group based in Trivandrum and a seminary in Nagpur, a thread of connections between a student leader and a middle-man trader and a fiery mullah. This was good work, and now Amit was developing the narrative. The student leader had a brother who worked in Dubai, and this brother was perhaps a conduit for money and information and ideology. Anjali ate, and listened. Maybe Amit had the makings of a good analyst: he was excited by detail, pleasured by conjunctions. He had a habit of assuming too much, of wanting his stories to work so much that he let his imagination produce texture and depth. But he could be worked out of that, that was her job, to wean him away from fancy. But he had the necessary fervour. She let him finish, and then took him down to bedrock, to the foundation of fact: the brother, Dubai, daily phone calls. That was all. 'Interesting, but not enough to suppose so much,' she said. 'We need more.'

'Can we request an operation?'

Anjali had to smile. He had all the enthusiasm of a puppy huffing after his first rat. She said, 'We can request, but we will never get. There are many higher priorities.' He nodded wisely, but despite his attempt at mature indifference, Anjali saw the small swallowing of disappointment. Every trainee had this fantasy, of moving a case from analysis to operations, of finding clues that would lead to a conspiracy so dangerous that it could only be tackled by desperate measures and heroic men and gunfights in the dark. That's what the trainees came in thinking, that's how they were recruited into the job. But the job was this, reading and reading, and finding fragmented stories, and understanding that some dangers might be fatal and yet not worth the allocation of resources. You watched some things, and let them go. So she tried to comfort Amit. 'But you never know. We'll keep them on a watch list. They may get ambitious and try something.'

Amit wasn't very mollified, but he put a good face on it and gathered up his tiffin. Anjali thanked him and gathered herself into her papers again. The pages smelt of haldi now, and adrak, and she wondered if years from now some other analyst would catch the scent, barely palpable, and be struck by a sudden longing for home. She read on. Amit's frown stayed with her. He chafed at the confinements of a Delhi desk, he wanted to get his hands mucky. Well, he would get action soon enough. Somebody, some dushman, always got ambitious and somebody always tried something. To sit in a small room in the bowels of the MEA and read reports all day was to be buffeted by the eternal agitation of humanity, by the ceaseless motion of desire and envy and hate. Nobody, it seemed, not one man or woman ever sat unmoving in the grove of contentment. Always, there was somewhere to go, someone to defeat, something to have. Well, it gave her a job, and a path in life. She read.

At six she gathered up her briefcase and purse, locked her safe and her filing cabinets, put her car keys in the outer pocket of her purse and walked briskly down to the garage. The two grandly moustachioed Delhi police constables on duty at the garage gate gave her an even stare as she drove past, that opaque and blankly belligerent gaze that was the routine burden of a single woman in Delhi. They didn't like the fact that she was a woman, that she was alone, that she had her own car, her own pay cheque. There was a time, when she had been younger, when she had looked back, when she had asked, what are you looking at? She had confronted businessmen, and bus drivers, and students, and labourers, and policemen. Policemen were the worst, protected by their authority and drunk on a daily diet of aggression and violence. But she had faced them too, goaded on by the memory of her father, who had laughed admiringly at her early tomboyishness, her courage, her refusal to back down ever. She still pushed hard, but somehow, one day, she had found herself too tired for confrontations. It wasn't the pace of her work alone. She felt worn down at her core, as if some steely metal spring had lost its early bounce. Let the young take their places at the barricades, these girls who traipsed around the college campuses with their bare midriffs and mobile phones. The pitted and weathered have other battles to fight.

Anjali took a wide turn down the boulevard, narrowing her eyes against the sunset, and grinned at herself. What an easy moderate age had made of her, all the early revolutionary fervour corroded away by – by what? – long hours, bills, this jangling traffic, the poisonous pollution that left films of black on her face and arms. And by professional defeats, a divorce and the abrupt amputation of love, a bone-deep realization that the future was not a limitless meadow, but only a narrow valley bounded by night. Looking at her mother's bow-legged, arthritic walk, her papery-skinned hands, Anjali felt the press of mortality. Her mother would die. K.D. Yadav would die, soon. Only her father was immortal, suspended somewhere in that endless youth of the missing. He was legally dead, but he was still alive. Anjali felt his presence in the very early mornings, when she was washing gently up through the wetlands of sleep. He came to her then, with that briny smell of sweat and Brylcreem, with his shoulder as solid against her cheek as the heating sunlight from the corner window. Then he was gone again, quite gone.

A silver Lexus came in close to Anjali's window, and then they all waited for the traffic to move. Behind the tinted glass of the Lexus, a teenage girl chewed gum steadily. She was flicking through a glossy magazine, fanning the pages fast from right to left. She looked quite bored, and she was beautiful. Her father was a minister, a tycoon, a famous doctor, one of those fixers who put deals together at the intersections of Delhi's many worlds. She lived in a Lexus climate, quite distant from Anjali, in a geography of Vasant Vihar and the Senso and farmhouse parties and teeny dresses. She felt Anjali's gaze and blinked up a glance and then went back to her magazine, quite indifferent. Anjali could see herself in the Lexus glass, sweaty and hot and very middlingly middle-class in her brown-red kameez and red chunni, unable to afford a replacement for her car's dead air-conditioning system. The traffic parted, and the Lexus slid away. Anjali mopped at her chin. How easy it was to be resentful, how easy it was to wish that a couple of angry policemen would stop the Lexus and ask for licence-registration, and make legalistic objections to the tinted glass, and accuse the gliding machine of unacceptable emissions. Anjali shrugged the thought away, sat up straight and brought herself back to facts, to what needed to be done, to work. Resentment was useless, all the more pointless because any hassling, sullen policemen would finally settle for a bribe of two or three hundred rupees.

At the clinic, Anjali dashed water over her face, her arms. When she emerged from the bathroom, K.D. Uncle's head was angled at exactly the same tilt she had left him in, towards the window. His profile stood dark against the brightness, that well-known arc of high fore-head and spare, bald skull, that prow of a nose. It had been five weeks since he had spoken a word. He was pliable and easy, he would walk with you if you held his hand, sit if you pushed him slowly into a chair. He ate slowly, but only if you fed him by hand, and he showed no pleasure in his favourite dishes. He was indifferent. He had gone away. Anjali knew this well, she recognized it when she sat directly in front of him and spoke to him. Behind those slow blinks there was neither happiness nor sadness. He was just absent. He had gone far beyond hate and desire, and so he could no longer love. Still, Anjali came as often as she could and sat with him. The nurses turned him over during the day, walked him to the bathroom and into the garden, but Anjali liked to turn him towards the window and the sunset. She had noticed, long ago in her childhood, how he liked the turning of colours. He liked mountains, and snow. He had told her about Himalayan peaks, about how at sunrise and sunset they turned a bright gold against blue.

The doctors gave him two months to live, maybe three. Anjali had seen how hard he had fought to come back to her, when he had told her about the counterfeit money. And after that momentary return, she had accepted, completely and without hope, the fact of his depar-ture. What was here was not K.D. Yadav. Still, she came and sat with him in the evenings. She would not, in any case, abandon him.

She settled herself down into the chair next to the bed and opened her sheaf of papers to the marked sheet. She was reading a Xeroxed journal article titled 'Warrior Ascetics in Indian History'. The infor-mation that Gaitonde had been looking for sadhus had led nowhere, and even Anjali now thought that it was a misrepresentation, a joke or an allusion to something else, or an outright lie. But her initial reading about sadhus had taken her headlong into one of her obses-sions. She called them her 'projects', but her ex-husband Arun had called them her manias: she would become fascinated by some obscure thing, some murky process that twenty people in the entire world cared about, and then she had to know all about it. Her projects had included the life cycle and social organization of the red ant, the history of terracotta sculptures on the subcontinent, the economy and organization of the Soviet gulags, the early history of the steam locomotive and railways. She had once spent four glorious months reading, in every spare moment, about the campaigns of Julius Caesar. None of this was of any practical use to her. She had tried to explain to Arun that the pleasure was in the little specifics, in finding out how something worked, how its components fitted together. When they had been courting, he had found these projects amusing, charming in their eccentricity. He had admired her curiosity and her memory. But later, after they were married, Arun grew tired of her endless reading and questioning. During one of their quarrels, he told her that he found her boring. Of course they had always known they were different, but once it had seemed that his gregariousness and her quiet calm would balance each other out. Later, afterwards, he liked to exchange visits with his ever-growing circle of friends, drink Scotch and watch Formula One racing, which he never missed, even when he was posted as a probationer in a backwater of Madhya Pradesh. He had taken a lift in a coal truck to get to a big-enough television, and some years later he had decided, also on a racing night, that Anjali was boring. She still thought he might not have thought her so boring if she had been willing to give up her career and move along with him on every new posting, like the other IAS wives did. Anyway, that was long ago, and it was all over. Anjali turned to her article and read about the Sanyasi Rebellion.

She was distracted, though. It was hard to read without being able to discuss the material with K.D. Uncle, without debate and exegesis and questioning. Even when he was travelling somewhere on the other side of the world, she had always talked to him about her reading, and now there was this absence which responded with lofty indifference. This silence made a hole inside her, a gap which threatened to expose that other, vaster chasm her father had left behind, and a shudder of panic started in her stomach. It was hard to be so alone, it was impossible. She stood up, walked away the anxiety, striding to the door and then back to the window. She was not alone. She had Ma to look after, and many friends, and good colleagues and essential, crucial work.

She was needed. And there was a man, perhaps a man, a professor of sociology, a little younger than her but very gentle. She could still hope for love, or at least companionship and compassion, unlike poor K.D. Uncle, who had truly lived like some sort of ascetic. She stopped short, tightened her shoulders and told herself to stop being ridiculous. It was heartbreaking to lose K.D. Uncle, but some part of him was here, she owed him at least the serenity and discipline he had inculcated in her. She sat next to him, squeezed his wrist, held on to it and began to read.

Working with hair had taught Mary Mascarenas the ephemeral nature of happiness. Sometimes, now and then, with a client, she would achieve a blazing moment of perfection in which the reigning style and ambition and physiology came together to produce beauty, pure and breathtakingly obvious. In these moments, when the hair emerged from wrappers and coils and heat, when the client turned towards the arrayed mirrors, there was a gladness, an ecstasy as real as love, or motherhood, or patriotism. But time passed. Styles changed, the client grew older and old, and hair grew, how it grew. It lengthened, and changed, it transformed its texture and curl, it fell, it greyed and grew thin. Happiness always passed. Sooner or later the happy client looked into her mirror and grew restless and wanted a new cut. The cuts came and went, and bangs were down one year and up the next and four years later descended again. What was in this season was sure to be out the next. Blonde came and went, and short efficiency was followed by long femininity. Mary was sure that the morning after the oldest profession was invented, the professional went looking for a stylist. She was popular with clients at the Pali Hill Salon, and so she had good job security, and a very decent income from commissions, and much information. Clients liked to talk.

Comilla Marwah was talking now, as Mary worked on her hair with a Yasaka cutting scissor and a comb. 'You don't know, Mary,' she whispered, 'how that woman went after Rajeev. Such drama about how miserable she was in her marriage to that horrible husband, and all of this delivered to Rajeev in little black dresses at Indigo. So of course something started. She used to go to the Oberoi, tell her driver that she was shopping: "Driver-ji, you go and have lunch, I'll take two-three hours." Then she would go in, through the hotel and to the other entrance, catch a taxi from there straight to

Rajeev's building, enter through the side gate and up to his apartment. So, nice afternoon bonk, then back in another taxi to the Oberoi, and ten minutes of shopping so she had some bags, and off to home looking like some Sati-Savitri. And telling Rajeev that she had made a terrible mistake, that she should have never left him in London, all this shit. Meanwhile she meets Kamal, who's rich, rich as in the industrialist type of rich . . .'

Comilla had to stop then, for a stylist to squeeze by with her client. Space was so expensive in Bombay that even the best salons always had too many chairs squeezed in, too much business. And every day the salons were full. There was a lot of money in the city, and Comilla had a fair bit of it, and she knew exactly who had how much. She went on, 'But then she meets Kamal. This is at the same time she's doing Rajeev on the side, on the side of the horrible husband I mean. Kamal is loaded, and socially he's completely connected, he's right in the centre. And let's face it, she's an attractive woman. So then she starts angling for Kamal. Right under her husband's nose, you understand. They move in the same circles, all of them. But again the same story, unhappiness, haay-haay, I'm so sad, all that. Men can't resist that. So stupid. So then she's doing Kamal and Rajeev at the same time. Can you believe that?'

Mary could believe it easily. She had believed reports about Comilla Marwah's own affairs, which affairs were – one had to admit – not simultaneous but serial. Mary made a properly shocked face, and whispered with exactly the right touch of titillation, 'And then?'

'Then what? That Kamal falls completely for her. She's got that chweet-chweet innocent face, you know. And, according to Rajeev, she gives a mean blow-job. So Kamal leaves his wife and three kids and ends up getting engaged to the bitch. Of course her poor husband is totally stunned, but imagine what poor Rajeev goes through. One minute he's her hero and lover who is going to take her away from her horrible marriage, the next he's one discard.'

'When is the wedding?'

'Next week.'

'Sounds like Rajeev is going to need some comforting.'

'Yes,' Comilla said. She was peering at herself moodily, in the moisture-clouded mirror. 'True.'

Mary patted her shoulder. 'You have lost weight. Going to the gym?'

'Five mornings every week,' Comilla said, but even the compliment didn't pull her out of her self-examination. 'And all for what? Men. And men are stupid. Want to know what the moral of this whole story is, with her and Rajeev and Kamal and all?'

'Tell me.'

'If you give a whore's blow-job with a saint's face, men will leave their wives for you.' And she burst into such grandly boisterous laughter that Mary laughed along with her. Comilla lay back in her chair and roared, and Mary had to put her scissors down and lean on the table. After a while the entire salon was laughing along with them, laughing at Comilla's guffaws. Comilla's mood was greatly improved, and she left Mary a hundred-and-fifty-rupee tip. Mary had given her a good cut, tight to the delicate bones of her head, revealing the long stalk of her neck. She looked wonderful, but not in a hundred years and a thousand haircuts would she look like a saint. She looked like a sleek woman in her late thirties, funny and experienced and brightly curious and wearing well, with that buffed gloss only money could buy. Mary knew too much about her, as she knew too much about many of her clients. Mary knew, for instance, that long ago, when Comilla had been in her early twenties, she herself had been made into the other woman, that her moneyed Marwari boyfriend had left her to marry a nice Marwari girl chosen by his parents. That this boyfriend had continued to meet Comilla in Goa for weekends through two children and many avowals of undying love and declarations that he cared nothing for his fat, boring wife. That he had always promised to leave the wife the next summer, and then the next. And that of course he never had. Comilla had finally managed to tear herself away from that disastrous love, but had found herself alone at thirty, an attractive professional woman with a good pay cheque, but quite disastrously single. There were many in Bombay like her, too many. She had flailed around for a couple of years, and had been lucky to land her husband, a widower nineteen years older than her. He was quite comfortable, had his fingers in real estate and travel and had been charmed by her style. He had married her, and they had had two children, and Comilla had found her stable, safe home and also, inevitably, certain discontents. After the children were born, she had taken two lovers. All this Mary knew.

Twilight was Mary's favourite time, and as she often did after work, she walked down Carter Road to the sea wall. She strolled slowly down the walkway, amidst joggers, crowds of teenagers and brisk, ked-wearing grandparents doing their evening constitutionals. There was a greenish tint in the sky this evening, shading from a foggy turquoise up high to a startling underwater jade at the horizon. This was what Mary loved about the dimming of the day, this mingling of colours and people. In this amiable mixing, to be alone in the city was to find companionship with a thousand strangers. Of course she had friends, and sometimes they walked the sea wall together. But often, to be solitary, and free, was the gift she wanted from Bombay. She had learned how to be alone, through dragging nights of terror and nostalgia, and now she prized her liberty. There was a certain temperate calm in being one's own person.

And yet there were women like Comilla, who, despite all their advantages, made their bargains for another kind of safety, full of lies and drama and half-understood and half-spoken compromises. Did Comilla's husband know of her affairs? Certainly half the world did, or at least the world that came in and out of the salon. Certainly there were enough women talking to each other about Comilla's adventures, and to Mary. Maybe he knew. Maybe he knew and looked away, maybe he understood. Mary thought she understood a little herself, but she never mistook this understanding for friendship. Comilla told her all kinds of things, but Mary knew she talked only because leaning back in a chair and offering her head to Mary's scissors drew them both into a momentary intimacy, a limited closeness that didn't need the darkness of the confessional box. But the thirty-five or forty thousand rupees that Mary brought home every month didn't make her a member of Comilla's social circle, not at all, even if it was more money than some white-collar briefcase-wallahs made. Comilla would sooner call in her driver to sit at her table than invite Mary to one of her dinner parties. Mary was a very good hairdresser, that was all. Mary had no illusions, no fantastic dreams about who she was and what she could become. She had found her place, and made her peace with it.

A trio of ragged girls passed Mary, their bare feet slapping the pavement, and they surrounded a tall, blond foreigner walking some ten feet ahead. Mary went past him, smiling at the patter of the girls as they held up their open palms to his face. 'How are you? Uncle, Uncle. Please, Uncle. How are you? Please. Uncle, hungry, hungry. Uncle, food.' They were jumping up, towards his beaky nose. He looked stricken. All this way he had come, to India, and now he was confronting its fabled poverty, and it had acquired English. The foreigner was shaking his head, no, no, but he had stopped, and Mary was sure that he would reach into his pocket in a moment. A band of little beggar boys streamed past Mary, heading for the foreigner. He'd have them all on his tail now, until he got into a taxi and fled. The privilege of his white skin and money cost him this minor trial, this swirling comet's tail of the needy. The kids on the sea wall were energetic and persistent, but they had long ago learnt to ignore Mary. She talked to them, but she gave no money, and they were professionals. This was work, and they had no time for idle chatter at this prime hour of evening.

Twenty minutes of walking had taken her to the far end of the walkway, almost to the Otter's Club bus stop. Under the deepening black, the low tide had pulled the waves far from shore, leaving a bare scrabble of rock and rubbish. Above it, facing the water, sat Sartaj Singh. Mary averted her face and angled to the left, away. She risked a single glance, quick, and he hadn't seen her. He was fixed on the stain of last light on the horizon. On she went, to the bus stop, where a bus was just drawing in. She ran the last few yards, and looked again only when she was safely on the bus, looked through the rear window. She could still make him out, alone on the edge of the walkway, his feet dangling over the rocks. She found a seat, and held her small grey purse tightly in her lap. Her pulse was racing, and she knew it wasn't just from the running. Why had she wanted so much to avoid a conversation with him? She hadn't done anything wrong. She was guilty of no crime. But he was a policeman, and policemen carried grief with them, like an infection. Better to stay away from them.

She held on to this relief all the way home, this sense of having escaped an encounter with something turbulent and dark. Even in the brief glimpse she had had of him, she had sensed a coiling sadness. He had been watching the sea and the sky with a questioning, pained tension in his shoulders and neck, as if he expected an answer. Better to run from such a man.

Mary shut the door to her room behind her, locked and bolted it. She switched on only one lamp, close and low to the wall, so that the shadows held her with a candle-lit cosiness. There was some fish curry left from last night's dinner, and she made a small bowl of rice with swift efficiency. She ate sitting on the bed, sipping from a large steel tumbler of water that she kept on the bedside table. She liked the animal shows on Discovery channel, the eternal round of birth and migration and breeding. Against the high dome of African sky, even the gory killings of deer and zebras by lions seemed only proper, a necessary link in an enormous cycle of harmony. Mary's friend Jana, who was addicted to the night-time serials about three-tier families and straying husbands, called her morbid and strange and made her change the channel when she came over. But the ceaseless longings and betrayals of the serials were offensive to Mary, she grew restless and upset and angry. Sharks at least were honest in their appetites, and beautiful besides.

She washed her plate, and the pots, and then reached to the back of the fridge for her chocolate. She had half a box of rum balls from Rustam's in Colaba, glorious in their individual gold-foil wrappings. She allowed herself one after dinner, and only she knew what a supreme act of self-control it was not to eat the whole box at once. She took the leftmost ball back to the bed, and turned up the sound on a leopard sliding through brush. The foil came off slowly under the very tips of her fingers, crinkling deliciously, so delicate. Then there was the golden waft of the cocoa, and she inhaled it deeply, and then tilted her head away so that she could come back to it anew. The first bite was always a small one, just a little nip so that her palate pinged from the clarity of the warm taste, and an ache started at the back of her jaws. Only after she had lost that first exhilaration did she allow herself a substantial chunk. And it was heaven. The dark taste of the rum swirled around her tongue, and she let out a little hiss of satisfaction at the leopard.

Then she was ready for sleep. She wore no make-up, ever, so her night-time ritual was short: a fast wash with a neem soap, and a good brush with Meswak toothpaste. She put on a faded pink caftan, softened by years of washes, and lay on her back, with her hands by her sides. When they were children, Jojo used to tease her about this pose of the dead, this corpse's motionless pause, but then Jojo even in sleep was a spiralling wind, and awoke often with her feet pointing at the pillow. She kicked and thrashed but wanted to sleep close, and Mary used to grumble about her lost sleep at breakfast.

Mary sat up, went to the bathroom, came back and lay down again. She tried breathing evenly, deeply. But her mind still turned and moved. Sleep, she whispered. Tomorrow is a long day. And, and. And

Jojo had loved rum balls from Rustam's, but they hadn't been able to afford them more than once a month. And today there was that Sartaj Singh, plonked like a squatting toad on her sea wall. The last time she had spoken to him had been in his car, when she had told him about John and Jojo. She had slept very badly after he had come to her with the news of Jojo's death, for a month she had walked around with a reeling heart, feeling dizzy through the day. Then finally the knowledge had settled in, become part of the structure of the new world: your sister is dead. That's how it was, when you confronted something impossible – your husband is sleeping with your sister – at first there was a nausea, a loss of all landmarks. Your own home became a hostile borderland. And then one day you knew that this raw wasteland, this garish alien light, was your home. You just had to have patience and will enough to survive the first terrors.

Mary sat up, propped a pillow against the wall and switched on the television. She found a documentary about space stations, and turned down the sound, and watched spidery white contraptions spin against stars. They were man-made, but soothing. It was always Jojo who had been the religious one, who at eleven had slept with a cross under her pillow, who had gazed up at the church altar with bright, sunlit eyes. Later, she had the same soaring love for celebrity, she had pursued its grail with the same marvellous faith. The closest Mary had ever come to this big-*big* feeling that Jojo told her about was when she watched wildebeest rumbling across a valley, or when she saw some unmanned spacecraft's pictures of the rings of Jupiter. She had been saving, for three years and five months now, for a safari holiday to Africa.

'Chutiya, you could go to Africa tomorrow if you claimed what is yours,' Jana had said, burning with real-estate lust for Jojo's flat, which she had never seen. 'That's a flat at Yari Road that we're talking about, not some smelly kholi.'

'It's not mine.'

'What, it belongs to me, then? Thank you,' – in English, with a bow – 'thank you.'

'You can have it.'

'Like they'll give it to me. Listen, gaandu, these are the facts: she was your sister. She is dead. There are no other living, immediate relatives. So it comes to you. All of it, flat and bank accounts and whatever.'

Jana had a gaali for every occasion and every other sentence, and she was a very good manicurist, an expert at fancy nails. She had a contemptuous bafflement for Mary's scruples. 'Listen, so your sister was a randi. Okay, so that's where some of the money came from. She also made television programmes, na? So you take the money thinking it's from television. What's the harm? After all she took your husband, na?'

This, to Jana's mind, was justice: good money for a husband. This was fair. There was no way to make her understand that this was exactly what Mary didn't want, to be paid off. She didn't want to take Jojo's dirty money, made from filth done on filthy hotel sheets with filthy men, she didn't want to take money in exchange for a husband, for happiness, for a childhood. Maybe Mary had never been able to believe quite wholeheartedly in heaven, but she had once believed quite naturally and easily that life on earth was good, that her future would be one long, gentle story of husband and children and grandchildren, marred just a little by scraped knees and fevers but always buoyant with love. Despite her father's early death, she had believed this, that she would find the contentment that had eluded her mother. Jojo had expelled her for ever and without possibility of return from this garden of innocence. Jojo had changed her world. For this, there could be no forgiveness, and no purchasing of indulgences. This Mary was sure of.

Mary clicked off the spaceships and lay back. She took a breath, let it out slowly, tried to find an easy, even rhythm. But Jojo came back tonight and bothered her, kept her awake as she never had during those nights of thrashing about and fast-asleep kicking. Even after Jojo's death, in that first week of shock, she had never lain awake like this. Of late, with days passing when she didn't think of Jojo once, Mary had started believing that she was rid of her at last. But the flat and the money were unfinished business. Mary didn't like slack ends, she had always been the responsible sister. That's why she would have been such a good mother. Again that upward stab of anger in the chest. Forget it. Breathe, breathe. Let it go. Let it be.

Mary woke the next morning to her alarm with a tired head, she felt the exhaustion even as her feet hit the floor. Four or five hours of sleep were nowhere near enough, not anywhere close to her usual nine, and still there was the day to get through, work to be done. So she went. Jana noticed it straightaway. In a break between her clients, she slid past Mary and whispered, 'So got a boyfriend at last, sleepy-jaan?'

Mary shook her head, but Jana grinned and made back-and-forth humping motions with her hips. Mary looked away quickly, and moved to the other side of her own client, afraid of provoking Jana into some further outrages. It was a small miracle that she hadn't been fired already. Over lunch, which they ate from tiffins outside the salon, Mary tried to convince Jana that she had just had a sleepless night. Jana wasn't having any of it.

'You sleep like a bear, even if someone is knocking down a building next door, okay? So try to make a mamoo of someone else. Something is going on.'

Something was going on, but Mary wasn't going to tell Jana about the annoying night-time return of Jojo. She knew well Jana's opinions on the subject, and didn't want to listen to them again. 'It was just a bad night, Jana,' she said. 'Nothing great. So how are Naresh-Suresh?' Naresh was Jana's two-year-old son, and Suresh was her husband, whom she had married against the loud objections of both sets of parents. She called the son and father 'my bachchas', and loved to tell long stories proving her affectionate patience and womanly wisdom and motherly firmness. Suresh was indeed five years younger than her, but Mary had always thought that his quiet forbearance in the face of Jana's temperament was simply heroic. They worked well together, one placid and one loud.

'Don't be too smart,' Jana said, inadvertently flicking mango pickle on to Mary's skirt with her jabbing finger. 'Tell me.'

'There's nothing to tell, idiot,' Mary said, holding off Jana's attempts to clean off the oil. 'Nothing at all. God promise.'

But the nothing kept Mary awake to the end of the week. Every morning she woke more tired. On Friday she declined a girls' night with movie and dinner, went home and took a Calmpose. At first there was a pleasantly dozy feeling in her arms, and she wiggled her head back into the pillow, anticipating the sleep as keenly as a mouthful of chocolate. But then the sweat gathered clammily under her shoulders, and she had to kneel up to switch the fan to its fastest. She lay under its whirl, and time passed. She tried to think of pleasant things, of Matheran in the rain, of *Kaho Na Pyaar Hai* and the song on the yacht, of happy clients. She turned her head to find the clock. An hour had passed. She groped on the table to find the papery leaf of

Calmpose, and thumbed another one into her mouth. That would knock her out, she never took pills, she took care of herself. Again, she waited. An auto-rickshaw putt-putted up the main road and took the corner into the lane, she could hear its gears grind. Loud, it was so loud. It stopped, very close, and she could hear the rattle of the meter as the driver put it up, and then the engine grunted and turned over again. In the pool of silence it left behind, an air-conditioner hummed and rattled. Mary had never noticed all these night sounds before. She turned on her side and put a pillow over her head. She could feel rage collecting in her stomach like a dead weight. Stop, don't raise your blood pressure. Relax, relax. But there it was, this gravity of accumulated anger.

Mary endured the night. In the morning, at first grey, she came off the bed covered in a cold sweat. She showered it off, but a buzzing remained in her head, a small, tinny drone that persisted past her chai and toast. She waited until nine-thirty, and then called the number that Sartaj Singh had given her months ago.

'Not here,' a constable snapped at her.

'Has his shift started?'

'Shift starts at eight. Bola na, he's not here.'

At ten Singh was still not at the station, and not at eleven either. 'Arre, he's out on some work,' a different constable told her, with exactly the same tincture of aggression and boredom. She had to spell her name for him very slowly, and she was convinced that he had tossed the note immediately into some rubbish pile.

Of course there was no call back, not by noon and not by one. How do the police in this country ever solve anything? Mary grew scathingly bitter by two. She felt perked up, revived. She called Jana, and met her at Santa Cruz station to shop. Jana bought little shorts with blue anchors embroidered on them for her son, and also three tiny T-shirts, and a pair of slippers for herself. Mary was distracted and suddenly very tired. Jana bargained ferociously with the thelawallahs, beat them down rupee by rupee. Mary slipped an arm through Jana's and dragged along with her through the shifting crowds. Jana gave her that old all-knowing sideways glance. 'You know what you need?' she said.

'Jana, don't start that boyfriend thing again.'

'What, yaar, you think I don't have anything more than boys in my head? I was going to say, you need to get out of the city for a while.

When you used to visit your Mummy, you always came back looking rested and fresh. This place, too long in it and you get ragdoed down.'

Mary held on tight to Jana's arm and nodded. The ragda that you were subjected to came from these streets, these shops, this noise, this air. Going shopping with a friend turned into this tiring trek, this weaving through hurrying throngs, this dodging of cars that darted at you from every side. Every minute you breathed in your dose of poison. But there was no Mummy any more, and no farm to visit. She had known, despite everything, that there was no escape for her from this labyrinth of hovels and homes, this entanglement of roads. She couldn't go back, not to live. So after Mummy had died she had sold the house and the farm, all its machines and instruments and furniture, and with that money had paid for her one room in the city, put some in the bank. The will had left everything to her, Mary, and had by name and specific mention removed the other daughter from the family and its inheritance. 'Where to go?' Mary said. 'You want to go to Matheran? Ooty?'

'Ooty would be good, no?' Jana said, full of longing. 'Blue hills.'

'Chal,' Mary said. 'Let's go.'

But a second was all it took for Jana to acknowledge this inevitable defeat. 'No, yaar. How to go?' Jana had many needs to save for. They both knew this, there was no need to discuss it further. But the blue hills were a good thing to think about.

The hills of the south stayed with Mary on the auto ride home. There had been hills on Mummy's farm too, not quite as high as the blue mountains, but hills nevertheless. Behind their property, to the west, Alwyn Rodriguez had a waterfall on his farm. It wasn't much of a waterfall, just a thin stream of water that fell over four feet of black rock. But it did curve in the sunlight, and there had been a time she and Jojo had been able to dance under it. Even later, as fresh novitiates, sitting on the bank with their feet in the water, they had the crisp fall of the water on the stone, and the comfortable settling of their insteps on its smooth, worn curve. Then, they had thought of the village as an awful place, small and stifling, with Alwyn Rodriguez and his endless feuds, and the murderous length of the afternoons when the radio stopped picking up All-India Radio and there was nothing, absolutely nothing to do. Mary pulled a chunni tighter over her hair, against the flapping wind and the fumes and the rush of the auto, and curved herself into a corner of the seat.

The auto came up the last curve towards Mary's house. Sartaj Singh was sitting on her steps, in that same forward-leaning squat from the sea wall. Mary got out of the auto, paid the driver. Her fingers were shaky, and she dropped a ten-rupee note and had to bend to pick it up. She was very annoyed. All she had done was call him on the phone, how dare he show up at her house like this? Just because these people were policemen they thought they could do anything. She took her change, and turned around determined to be stern with him, to get across to him that she paid his salary and understood her rights quite well. He was on his feet now. He had grown older. In the slanting light from the light-bulb above, Mary could see the flecks of white in his beard. He had been a handsome man, but now he looked like he had crumbled a little at all his edges. Once he had been all bite and confidence, but now all that sharpness had melted into a tempered exhaustion. His blue civilian pants were entirely lacking a crease. He had put on weight.

'Hello, Miss Mary,' he said.

'Since when have you been here?' Mary said, pointing with her chin at her step.

'An hour,' he said.

His voice was different too. He was altogether blurred. 'My neighbours,' Mary said, quite curt. 'You could have just called me.'

'I did. You were not here.'

'Still.'

'Yes. Sorry. But I thought it might be urgent. About your sister. Sorry.'

He was too tentative to fight with. Mary shook her head. 'Come.' In her room he stood by the door until Mary pointed to the chair. She didn't feel scared of him any more, of his authority or intentions, but she left the door ajar. He sat, and she saw that he still had that flat, unembarrassed cop's curiosity, he examined the room methodically, from left to right, and then came back to her. 'Water?' she said.

'Yes.'

'Chilled?'

'Yes.'

She opened the fridge, poured the water and walked across the room to hand him the glass. He watched her walk with that same frankness, and she was aware that although he was different, maybe tired and somehow dented, he was very much still a policeman. When

376

she bent forward to hand him the glass, she got a quick, sour whiff of his all-day sweat, of the trains and the crowds and the steady sun.

'Thank you,' he said in English, and drank. He drained the glass, and then stared abstractedly into it. 'I was very thirsty.'

'I need your help,' Mary said. It came out higher than she intended, shrill. She was not used to asking for help.

'Yes,' he said. 'Tell me.'

'My sister's property, you said you would help me.'

'You want to take possession?'

'Yes.'

'There are no other living immediate relatives?'

'No.'

'It shouldn't be too hard. You have to prove to the court that you are really the sister. That should not be hard, even if you had no recent contact. We will give a no-objection statement from the police, saying that there are no implications for our case. I will ask Parulkar Saab, my big boss, to expedite it. Bas, that's all. It might take a while, it is a legal process after all. You will need a lawyer for the papers.'

'I know one lawyer.'

'From your divorce?'

'Yes.'

'You know they say that in Bombay, you should have among your friends one politician, one lawyer and one policeman.'

'She has become my friend, my lawyer. But I don't know any politicians, or policemen.'

'You know me now.'

He was smiling. Mary knew that she was supposed to protest sweetly, to say that he was not her friend, and in turn he would argue that yes, of course he was. 'I'll ask my lawyer to get my papers ready,' she said. 'When can I come and get that statement from you?'

He lost the smile. 'You don't have to come,' he said. 'I'll bring it. No problem.'

'I don't mind coming.'

'All the way to the station. No need.'

A police station was no place for a woman was also what he was saying. 'Listen,' Mary said, 'I go up and down this city. I can come to your station. Just let me know when.'

'Okay.' He was quiet for a moment, quite serious. 'And . . . any more information about your sister?'

'I told you everything.'

'Yes. But. In all these months, something more may have come up. Something you remembered.'

'No, nothing.'

'Something even very little. It may not seem important, but it may open up the case for us. Please think.'

She had been thinking for these long weeks now, these months. How little could it be? How would telling him about Jojo's inexplicable love for fat Rishi Kapoor and his podgy, twinkle-toed dancing help him open up the case? There was everything to tell, and nothing. 'If I had anything, I would tell you. I don't even know what you want to know.'

He nodded, and seemed to come to a decision. 'The trouble is that we don't know exactly what we are looking for. We are still investigating the death of Ganesh Gaitonde. It is a matter of national security, and we don't know very much about why he came back to India, why he killed himself. So we are looking for any information connected to Gaitonde. We know your sister was close to him. We know she sent girls to him. Many girls, over a long period, to Bangkok, Singapore, places like that. So if we knew anything about your sister, what her movements were, who she was connected with, maybe it could lead to information about Gaitonde. That is why I keep asking.'

'Yes,' Mary said. 'Okay.'

He pushed himself to his feet. She could see the effort it took. 'All right,' he said. 'I will call you.' He nodded.

Mary was suddenly aware of how curt she had been. 'Thank you,' she got out. 'Thanks.'

'Don't mention.' He shut the door very gently behind himself, and Mary heard his progress down the stairs.

Don't mention. When Mary had first learnt English, she had said, 'Mention not.' She had said 'mention not' for years, until Jojo had corrected her. Jojo had learnt English very fast, and her English was faster and more natural and more correct, and incorrect in the right ways. She had been good at it. Sartaj Singh's English was ambitious but only half-successful, it stumbled now and then. He probably thought it was better than it actually was. There was that much arrogance left in him still.

Mary shrugged it all away. She took a long shower, stood under the flow and let it beat on her back. She liked the cold water, the thrill of it, even in winter. I grew up in a village, she'd told John when he'd marvelled. We didn't have running hot water like you city folks, and if you wanted it you had to carry it.

The memories came, but they didn't burden her, not tonight. She lay in bed and let them fly. Now that she had spoken to Sartaj Singh, she felt relieved. She had made a decision. Whatever she still owed to Jojo, she would do. Yes. She remembered now a show she had once seen about African elephants, and fell asleep thinking of baby elephants stumbling and tumbling after their mothers.

Ganesh Gaitonde is Recruited

I was impotent every day and every night of my honeymoon. As the floor tilted beneath us, I hunched over my wife, working at myself, cursing her, cursing the sea for a putrid whore, but in spite of all my efforts I was inevitably, astonishingly soft. We were on a boat, a ship called the *Peshwa*, pressing on to Goa. My boys had forced me to go on a honeymoon. After the death of Paritosh Shah, we had killed seven of Suleiman Isa's men in immediate retaliation, including Phul Singh, one of their top shooters imported all the way from UP. They had then got two of our boys, but their response had seemed less than full force, and I was sure more was coming. Meanwhile, as the days passed after my wedding, Chotta Badriya was increasingly horrified by my lack of interest in honeymooning. 'How can you stay here in this dirty hole on your suhaag-raat and most beautiful morning? You have to go somewhere beautiful. Everything has to start in beauty. Switzerland!' He kept up his Switzerland song until I threatened to send his golis to Switzerland ahead of me. It was madness for me to leave in the middle of a war. And yet Chotta Badriya's daily campaigning for rose-strewn nights and beautiful days had its gradual effect. This is the modern age, he said, you'll be in constant touch by phone. After all, even Suleiman Isa ran his operations by remote control from Dubai, he said, and you'll be gone for only a few days. Besides, Paritosh Shah had been a man of ritual and custom, who believed everything should be done the way it had been done yesterday and the day before, he knew every rite that marked a man's progress from conception to the feasts after his death. After Paritosh Shah's death, we had followed the accepted prescriptions in the tiniest details, fed a hundred Brahmins when a dozen would have done, and now Chotta Badriya pointed out that if I was marrying for Paritosh Shah, I had better honeymoon for Paritosh Shah. He tried to send me to Singapore on a plane, and I settled for Goa on a ship. Very romantic, he said, on a ship and all instead of some boring hotel. Yes, yes, I said. I disliked this plan the least because the trip was short, and I could always come ashore and speed back, if I was needed. Three days there, two days in Fort Aguada, three days back, honeymoon done. Except that I wasn't doing.

I couldn't talk to the boys, who were in the next cabin, of course I couldn't talk to them. On the second night it again became clear that nothing was happening, that all my pulling and stroking at myself, all my calling back to the swaying cabin of every woman, every girl, every whore I had ever bajaoed, and all my frantic imagining of every filmi star I had ever unbuttoned in my dreams, none of this was going to move the slightest flicker in my dead lauda. It curled up ashamedly against my thigh, raw from my rubbing. I curled up against the wall of the cabin. Finally I managed to get out, 'This has never happened before. It must be the boat, all this up-and-down-and-around like a mela-ride, it makes me sick.'

She was quiet. She lay with her back to me, her shoulder hunched up against the starlit round of the window. Her name was Subhadra. That much I knew about her. I looked at her arm, the bony narrowness of her shoulder, and in her turning away I was sure there was contempt, amusement. I sat up, and my ribs hurt from the deep breath I took then, such a furious gulp of rage I swallowed. When I turned my head more squarely to her, I had to force the muscles, they were so tight from anger. I wanted to say, it's you, you skinny chut, with your starving kutti's lean ribs. I wanted to grab her by the neck and shake her until her head snapped back and forth and shout, who could get it up for you? I would've killed her, thrown her into the water far from anywhere, and forgotten about marriage for ever, no matter what friends had said or wanted. My body wanted murder, there was a pressure down my spine that flexed and pulsed and wanted to cleave her in half. I would've killed her. But then she spoke.

'Have you ever been on a ship before?'

Yes, I had been on a ship. I had plunged down slatey valleys of water in a rattling boat, I had killed a man, a friend, I had taken his gold. I wanted, all at once, to tell her about my journey over the seas. 'Yes, I've been,' I said. 'Long time ago, when I was a boy, when I first came to Bombay. I went on a trip.' She turned over to face me now. She was surprised, I think, by the eagerness with which I spoke, I who hadn't said more than a dozen sentences to her in three days. 'That was my first time on ship, and first time out of the country,' I said. I told her about Salim Kaka, Mathu, but now that she was listening, her cheek resting on her two folded hands, I found that I couldn't tell her the end of the story, I couldn't tell her about the shots in the dark, about Salim Kaka's feet threshing the water, that true ending which was the beginning of everything for me. I had never told anyone, and I could hardly tell her, little Subhadra who was awestruck at my daring. I told her the alternative ending, the public ending: we set off for home, longing for safety and the smell of our own earth, and on the way we were ambushed by the police of that foreign country, who had been tipped off by Suleiman Isa, of course, and Salim Kaka fell in a running battle, he fell with his chest torn open by machine-gun bullets, but we left the ambushers far behind, and we made it home. With the gold. She sighed when I finished, let out the first small sound of satisfaction that I had heard from her. I touched her shoulder, and felt her stiffen. She thought I was about to start again with my pulling and pressing at her, but I hadn't the heart for it. I hadn't the courage to make another attempt. I kept my hand on her shoulder, and we rose and dropped together, and the long swirl of the water came to us, and slowly she grew safe under my palm, and relaxed. 'What about you?' I said. 'Have you been on the sea before?'

She told me about a childhood trip to Elephanta, about getting sick on the boat and trying to reach the edge but ruining her new yellow frock, about how unmercifully hot it was on the water, which lay still like a glittering mirror and hurt the eyes, about how her father's pocket was picked on the return trip. But I had profited from the sea. The sea could be both luck and disaster, maybe. I said that to her and heard her whisper a faint 'yes', and then we slept.

Once she got started talking, on and on she went. She woke up talking and never ceased. What she talked about was hard to know, because she talked about everything, her sister's stomach-aches, Indira Gandhi, going to the airport to watch planes take off and land, *Kati Patang*, a creaky table-fan her father refused to get rid of, the danger of malaria in the rainy season, the best bhelpuri-seller on Juhu Chowpatty, shipwrecks in swollen rivers. She went from one subject to another in a way that made perfect sense when you heard it, but which became madly incoherent and impossible to recount five minutes later. Hours would pass in this, the skipping flutter of her talk. I found it restful. We sat on the deck, under a blue-and-white striped awning, both wearing dark glasses and she still resplendent in her shining bride's jewellery, and I listened to the water singing against the side of the boat, and she talked. It was a pleasant hum that emptied my mind, that kept my nightly humiliation at safe distance. The boys kept at a respectful distance, within call but out of sight. I told myself that I was thinking, planning, analysing, that the hours which were passing were devoted to consideration of the problem of Suleiman Isa, the problem of further expansion of the company, the problem of future direction, but really I was lulling myself into a waking sleep. I was at complete rest. I was still.

Half a day out of Goa, my numb meditation was interrupted by Chotta Badriya. He came clattering up the metal stairs, and in his rapid clanking there was fear, I could feel it. I met him on the stairs, a third of the way down.

'What?' I said.

'The captain says they just heard the news. It's bad, bhai.'

'What is?'

'The masjid was torn down yesterday afternoon.'

He didn't need to say which masjid, for months there had been talk of only one masjid, one old faraway ruin of a building which was now the pivot for leaping political parties, the target for processions of thousands, the standing sign for ancient wrongs. I had thought it all quite silly, the whole question and the quarrelling nothing but politicians' tricks. But if it was destroyed, its falling would shake us all. That much was clear. 'And?' I said.

'In Bombay, bhai, things are bad,' Chotta Badriya said. 'Riots.'

In Goa, we drove from the dock to the airport, and flew back to Bombay the same afternoon. From the Goa airport, I tried to reach our controllers in Bombay, but all the dozen numbers I dialled were dead. 'The police must have switched off the phones,' Chotta Badriya said. That was likely, they did that sometimes when trouble started. The rumours at the airport were of burning buses, snipers shooting from rooftops into crowds below, men and women hunted down in lanes and killed. I wanted to get back to Bombay before Suleiman Isa took advantage, before those bastards came against us with everything they had under the cover of the chaos. During a riot, a war can come out into the open, and when a body falls or when a house burns, nobody is responsible. A riot is a free time for free murder. It was not a time to leave my company rudderless, headless, so we flew back. When we stepped on the plane I felt my golis sweat. The rows of seats were all empty, the passengers had all cancelled, only we wanted to fly into rioting Bombay. I sat shaking in my seat, and my crotch was damp – this creaky contraption would fly, this maderchod bus with wings? But I flew. I hurtled into the air, towards Bombay and my responsibilities. We rushed down the black asphalt, rattling and banging, and I said to Subhadra, 'Talk, talk.' With a grimace of panic she began, and her dread was not from the sudden upward arc of the plane, but from seeing me drenched through with a fear-sweat, her Ravana-husband become a vomit-spewing, snot-dripping hijra. I retched into a paper bag, and she sat up erect in her seat and put a hand on my shoulder. I knew she found it distasteful, the clammy, cold wet of her husband's fright. And what a husband, not the awesome rakshasa she had imagined entering her marriage bed, from whose reputation her mind had turned, overwhelmed, not that king but an impotent clown. But she was dutiful. She talked.

When the plane tilted over Bombay she stopped. I leaned over her and we both pressed our faces against the plastic, and from the muddy coastline emerged a scattering of islands, and then I could see clearly roads, buildings, the shape of colonies and the spreading brown patches of bastis. From behind us I could hear the boys arguing, 'That's Andheri there.' 'Maderpat, where Andheri? That's Madh island, can't you see?' Then they were all quiet. A thick black snake of smoke grew from a coastline settlement and twisted in towards the centre, towards another dark, curving fume – the city was burning.

All the way down not a word was said. The buildings fell towards us at a great velocity, but I was not afraid, I was trying to see what had been destroyed, what was on fire. All of us were quiet. The airport buildings were crowded with passengers huddled on the ground, sleeping with their heads resting on bags and suitcases. No taxis were moving, no autos. The phones were still dead, so there was not a way to call anyone in Gopalmath. For a while it seemed there was no getting out to Gopalmath, but Chotta Badriya went out on the road and wandered among the rows of taxis until he found the drivers huddled together near the police chowki. After half an hour of persuasion and much brandishing of thousands of rupees, one of them seemed tempted, and so Chotta Badriya drew him aside and told him not to be afraid, he was transporting Ganesh Gaitonde. This of course re-assured the driver, and so we jammed ourselves into the taxi, the six of us, and we drove out into the huge quiet. The straining engine seemed too loud, and as I told the driver to go faster, faster, I realized I was whispering. On all the roads that day there was no one, not one person, the bastis near the airport road were quiet, the hotels on the highway were silent, the windows of the apartment buildings were shuttered. I was afraid, we all were except the taxi driver, who gained confidence with each turn under my protection. But I knew we had no weapons, and if a crowd of hundreds had come howling over us, engulfed us with knives and stakes and bars and swords, we would all have died. In that silence trembling from murder, I could have shouted my name and the mob would still have torn out my throat. Against that blood-fed anger there was no name that was protection. Near Gopalmath we saw bodies, two bodies. They lay crabwise on the edge of the road, near a shoe shop. Blood had spattered on the corrugated iron of the shutter, over the raised lintel.

'Brain shots,' Chotta Badriya said.

He was right. Both of them were head shots. I was wondering if they were both Muslim. The board on the lintel said the shop was the Zuleikha Shoe Emporium. We crunched down the street, over splinters of glass, shoes, sticks, I saw a child's ruled notebook fluttering its pages. Subhadra had her eyes shut. Now we took the familiar turn to the left, down to the basti. This road had been smooth, I had had it rebuilt and resurfaced just two months ago. Now it was covered with loose stones, rocks, bricks. Somebody had fought a battle here. A burnt box of a car leaned its charred metal against a lamppost. There was a shout to our left, and from the first row of Gopalmath houses a man appeared, pointing an accusing finger at us. In his other hand he held a sword, a dancing curve of silver.

'Ey, Bunty,' Chotta Badriya called, and Bunty ducked his head in amazement, and ran up to the taxi, followed by the boys of Gopalmath. Bhai, bhai, they shouted. They were all armed, festooned with swords and lathis and spikes and rods and knives and pistols. I asked, what happened here? The landyas came, bhai, from the basti of Janpura over there, they said that one of our boys had stabbed one of theirs, so we showed them, bhai, we ran them back into that smelly dump of theirs. And those two on the turn at Naik Road, bhai, the policiyas did those, dhad-dhad two straight in the head, even the police know what is right and what is wrong this time. And they were thumping each other on the shoulder, all of them, shoving and falling and laughing like they had won a match, all their faces alive with sweat and youth and victory. And I asked, what about the Muslims in Gopalmath, what happened to them, are they all right? On the eastern side of the basti we had maybe sixty Muslim families, mostly tailors and factory workers, some of their sons worked for me. But when I asked about them my boys shrugged. What, I asked again, are they all right? They're gone, bhai, they said.

'Where?' I said. 'Where have they gone?'

Nobody knows, bhai. They're gone. They ran away. They fled.

'Did anybody do anything to them? What happened?'

They just went away, bhai.

'And their houses?'

Taken up, bhai. Other people are living in them now.

'Who? Some of you?'

Yes, some of us, bhai.

Chotta Badriya's face was rigid. He was immensely respected in our company, and until now his religion had never mattered. I took him by the arm, walked him away. 'Don't listen to these fools,' I said. 'Don't take it to heart. They're young and their heads have been turned by all this. They don't know what they're saying.'

But his eyes were full. 'I would have given my life for any of them,' he said. 'But now I'm only a landya for them? Bastards. Will they want my house also?'

'Badriya,' I said, 'this is a bad time. Don't get angry. Keep your wits, keep cold. Listen to me. Just listen to me, only me.'

I had my hands on his shoulder, and finally he let me hug him. I sent him to his home and family with four of my best boys, all armed, and told them if anything happened to Chotta Badriya or any of his family, I would shoot them myself.

Then I looked about, at the homes of Gopalmath. During a lull in my own war I had left my home, and came back to find my home the battleground for a larger conflict. They, somebody, had drawn borders through my vatan. My neighbours were now refugees, they had fled from unsheathed swords, from brain-shot bodies. Here was my Gopalmath, the habitation of my heart, the town that I had caused to be built, brick and brick, where I had walked with my friends, arms on shoulders, with the smell of gajras and falling water in the air, where I had found my manhood, my life. Here was the bright quilt of its roofs, stretching from the bowl of the valley up the hill, this vibrant spread of brown and blue and red knit together by the arcing, thread-like lanes, here were the numerous angular reachings of the television antennae, catching their fierce glints from the hovering sun. All of it lay desolate. And at the very edge of the horizon, to the south, a smudge of smoke. Under that unbearably bright sky I took my bride home.

The riots ended three days later. My impotence continued. We cleaned the streets, gathered up the wounded, I gave money to the families of those who were in hospital, and meanwhile Subhadra settled into my house and became 'Mummy' to my boys. Within days she was their confidante and sympathizer and whisperer and bringer to me of their problems, and mediator if I was angry. The house was suddenly clean, and gods and goddesses appeared in every room, and my stomach was suddenly lighter and happier from the food I ate, and all my shirts were in a neat ironed row in the cupboard, and still I was afraid all the time. When I heard her voice in the next room, kind and flowing and with a rhythm like bells, I feared that she was telling someone how useless I was, how I didn't even go near her, how I lay on my side of the bed with my arms over my head, how I told her to keep talking until I dropped into sleep. No, she wouldn't tell. But maybe it would slip out, some woman from the basti would make a remark, a teasing joke about Subhadra's happiness, some little pun with a little naughtiness in it, about marriage beds and nights and cruel men and aching limbs, and Subhadra would laugh, complete innocent that she was, and she would burble, but oh we don't do that. He won't, he can't. He can't, can't, can't. I fled from her voice, from can't, from danger, and spent the day being driven from meeting to meeting. I ate lunch in high and low restaurants, I sat in dance-bars and dully watched the girls pirouette. But I wasn't moved by any of them.

Chotta Badriya noticed this. He had been quiet, he had been upset by what had happened, by the masjid and the days that followed, I could see that. So I kept him close, I took him everywhere. And I could see that he was trying, that for my sake he was fighting himself. He tried to take care of me. 'Bhai, these dance-girls are second-rate finally. I have much better for you.'

'Much better? Where?'

'Actresses, bhai. Stars.'

'Every one of these wants to be a star, chutiya.'

'No, no, bhai. Really, actresses. Promise.' Those days, everyone was becoming a television producer. Oil traders and taxi-owners were suddenly making television serials. One of these was Chotta Badriya's cousin, and he had told Chotta Badriya about a woman who was a model and actor co-ordinator, and also trying to be a television producer. Naturally this woman came into contact with many young girls, all lovely and fresh and young and new in the city, struggling to make their fortunes.

'So she helps them to struggle a little with men, and make themselves and her some money?' I said.

'Exactly, bhai. Otherwise, you know how hard it is in this city. How can a young actress survive, alone in this city? She helps them, bhai, she helps them.'

'Well, we must help them too. And what is the name of this saint?'

'Jojo.'

Jojo. A strange name, but the girls she sent were indeed a cut above the common randi. They were educated, and some of them English-speaking. With them I was successful. With them I was easily hard, and profoundly able. With them I acrobated and strong-manned and warriored until they collapsed on the field. But at home I was nothing. I examined my wife closely, took in her slightly crooked smile, the straight slash of her eyebrows, the small powder-and-toothpaste smell of her, and found her to my liking. I wanted her. But there was no having her. My strength vanished when I was in the safety of my own bed, and I had no recourse. I read the advertisements for clinics on bill-boards and at the back of magazines, the promises of vigour from tablets and potions, but I was unable to tell anyone, not even Chotta Badriya. I was shamed. I picked up the phone and called one of the clinics, asked to speak to the Vaid, but they wanted money and they wanted to know my name, and the woman on the line was quick and brusque, and I called her a gaandu and slammed the phone down. Subhadra came in then with a glass of milk, and I drank it, and I thought bitterly, yes, that randi on the phone I could have ploughed, but drink my wife's milk is all I can do. So I went through Jojo's girls, one after the other.

But I found that when I was far away from Subhadra, unable to hear her talking, I was even more afraid. Perhaps being at home was the better thing, perhaps my near presence would constrain her a bit, keep her from telling somebody about my failures. So back I went. And I found her happy in her house. That was the truth, she seemed happy, she was happy. Her marriage was a joke, at its centre it had a limp nothing, but she bustled about with her keys in her pallu and rattled pots in the kitchen and ordered servants about and nagged me about eating, and seemed content. She bloomed as we worried about the ruins of the mosque, as the newspapers unfurled ancient histories of bitterness and the convulsing speeches of politicians. The magazines published maps of the country festooned with spiky outgrowths of little cartoon explosions, each tiny detonation representing a riot, bodies, bricks, swords, and meanwhile I was unhappy, and she was happy. One night, she bustled into our bedroom and sat next to me.

'I've been hearing about your friend,' Subhadra said.

'Who?'

'Your friend Paritosh Shah.' She sat next to me, held on to the sleeve of my kurta. 'All the boys keep telling me how he made you marry, what a good influence he was on you. Tell me about him.'

So I told her about carrying gold to him, about his enormous paunch, his feeling for money, his love for the game of gain, our adventures together, his pleasure in festivals and rituals and celebrations, his need for high flight. She listened to me, her hand on my sleeve, head down but eyes shining and blinking up at me, with stray strands of her hair lit up by the lamp behind, each filament aglow, making a small wheel of light above her head. 'And that motu friend of mine,' I said, 'he wouldn't do a thing without praying, if he had to go from Colaba to Worli he would pray, if he had to steal a crore he would pray. And then they killed him.'

'Did you kill them?'

'Kill who?'

'The ones who killed him!'

She spoke of killing men, this little virgin, as if she was speaking of cutting chickens. 'We killed some of them.'

'No, but the ones who actually did it?'

How to explain to her that finding out exactly who pulled the triggers and who swung the hammers was not exactly easy? What would she understand of intelligence-gathering, safe houses, double and triple bluffs, setting fielding and lurkaoing men? She had asked the simple question, did you punish the men who actually did it? There was no simple answer. And then it came to me, looking at the sindoor in her hair and the full trust in her eyes, that she had asked the only question that was worth answering. I had failed Paritosh Shah. I had killed some of Suleiman Isa's men, and considered that revenge. But to take random men and destroy them, that was no revenge. Paritosh Shah had worried about me, he had loved me, he had married and settled me down, and I had abandoned his memory, made excuses to his soul about the punishments I had exercised on his enemies, while his actual murderers ran free. This is why I was cursed within the marriage he had made for me. I could not consummate while his soul was unconsummated, while it searched for its rest. My incompleteness was a direct reflection of his. I laughed. It had taken Subhadra to show me this, Subhadra was also the name of the sister of the god Paritosh Shah had worshipped. It made a kind of sense, really it did. I jumped up. I bent over and kissed my wife. I was rejuvenated, reborn. I ran out to the meeting rooms, and called up my boys, woke up Chotta Badriya.

'What have we done lately to find out which shooters came after Paritosh Shah? Have we offered money? How much? Who have we asked? Who have we captured?'

In an hour I had made new plans, set new schemes into motion, doubled and tripled the flow of money that would ease men's tongues, talked to policemen and company-men and shooters and khabaris, collected names and half-names and the shadows of names, addresses, rumours of dissatisfactions and intrigues. The house hummed and sang and I felt my force extending across Bombay like electricity, because of me women and men were talking, running, moving in patterns that I had set in motion, I had thrown the net of my self wide, and in it I would gather the assassins, I would take them in. They could not escape. Watch me, Paritosh Shah, bhai, fat man. You will have to restore me to myself. I will give you your murderers, and you will give me Subhadra, my marriage, you will give me back to me.

And then the riots were upon us again. News of new murders came to us from the anguished lanes, from the roads still mourning old injuries: Muslim stabbed here, Hindu killed there, and then mathadi workers stabbed and killed, a family burnt to death, and the whirlwind took us again. Again the empty roads and the long silent afternoon and the rushing slap of many running feet on the ground and the sun rolling overhead, and screams, screams moving with tiny rattles up our windows, and news of men and women and children doused with petrol and burnt alive, and Subhadra huddled into a corner, and the abrupt tapping of gunfire lasting into the night. I put my boys on the peripheries of Gopalmath, in relays, and told them to sit tight, to watch, to guard. After three days Bunty came to me, bringing complaints. 'I can't control the boys, bhai,' he said. 'They want to *do* something.'

'Do *what*?' I snapped. 'Go out there and kill old women? For what? For an empty old building?'

He ducked his head. 'They are killing us.'

'And?'

'Bhai?'

'You look like you have something more to say.'

'The boys are saying . . . some of them are asking whether Bhai is with us, or with the Muslims.'

So, inevitably, here it was: us or them. Was I us or them? 'I'm with the money,' I said. 'And there's no profit in this. Tell them that.'

And yet the question stayed with me, through those nights of killing. Us or them? Who was I, who had always regarded the would-be attackers of the mosque and its defenders as equal fools? Now the mosque had come down, and everyone had become an attacker of that and a defender of this, you had to choose whether you were us or them. But what was I? I thought about it, waited for Paritosh Shah to tell me something, and held back from the bloodletting. Meanwhile some of my boys abandoned me. They were frustrated by my standing still, my doing nothing. Caught up in the frothy haze of rage that rose from the burning shops, from the bodies in the gutters, they went out armed with swords, and pistols. They took men from cars and slashed them to death, they raped women they found huddled inside hovels and then cut their throats, they used kerosene and kitchen matches and burnt stragglers alive, they shot children. So in those days of winter I lost my loyal soldiers to this massacre of us and them, this butchery that was not a battle. They left me and felt contempt for me, because I stood apart. I didn't need Bunty to tell me this. I was losing izzat, I was losing power, I was losing the company I had built and defended against so many predators.

Bipin Bhonsle offered me a way out. He drove up on a Sunday morning in a jeep festooned with saffron flags. He was followed by two Ambassadors, also packed with his Rakshaks, each variously armed. Bipin Bhonsle himself openly carried a sword, which he propped up on the side of his chair in my baithak.

'An armed MLA on the open road,' I said. 'How the world has changed.'

'Today we are going to change it back, bhai,' he said, rubbing at his face. He was puffy, exhausted, and he stank. His purple shirt was stained and crumpled, hanging out at the front, and I could see the sweaty folds of his belly. 'Enough is enough. We're going to show these landya bastards.'

I waited. But he seemed to have dropped off into an open-eyed sleep, with his chin on his chest. Lank strips of hair were plastered to his forehead, his usual puffy hairdo had been completely destroyed. What he wanted to show Muslims remained untold. Finally I said, 'Bipin Saab?'

He spoke without blinking, without moving from his statue-like sprawl. 'The word came from the top: show the maderchods. So we showed them.'

'The order came from the top?'

'From the very top top.' He yawned. 'I cut a head off. I mean clean off, sattack! like that. I had to use both hands on the sword. It bounced twice, the head. The funny thing is the blood. It goes far. Like from a pichkari, all over the place. The boys were all running, ducking away from the blood. The head didn't look surprised or anything. The head had no expression.'

'You showed him.'

'Yes. But you're sitting here, safe in your house, Ganesh Bhai.'

'The word didn't come from my top, Bipin Saab.'

'The landyas killed Paritosh Shah. And still you don't want to do anything.'

I could've pointed out that although Suleiman Isa was Muslim enough, he had plenty of Hindus working for him. And also that Suleiman Isa had nothing to do with the Muslim families who lived down the highway, and that cutting their heads off wouldn't make him bleed. But I said simply, 'There's no gain for me in doing this.'

He looked at me, flicked his reddened eyes at me. 'I'll bring you profit. I have much to do, so I'll make you a quick deal. There's a Muslim basti in Abarva. Know it?'

'Behind the white life-insurance building. Yes.'

'The land it's on belongs to an associate of mine. He bought it three years ago, good price, good area for development, but he can't get those slum maderchods off the land. Water connections, electrical, they have it all. They say they've been there for years, all that usual bhenchod nonsense. So, get them off. Burn it down. We'll pay twenty lakhs.'

'Bipin Saab, Bipin Saab. That land is worth four crores, easy.'

'Twenty-five, then.'

'I'll need a lot of boys.'

'Your boys can keep what they find.'

'Find in some miserable hut, while a fire is roaring over their heads?'

'Thirty.'

'One crore.'

He laughed. 'I'll give you sixty lakhs.'

'Done.'

'When?'

'Tomorrow.'

'All right. Do it fast. We'll keep this open season going as long as we can, but at some point they'll tell the army to start firing, not just do flag marches, and then things will become difficult.' He put his hands on his knees and pushed himself up, remained bent over for a moment, wriggling his back. 'Aren't you going to offer me a drink?'

'Bipin Saab, I should've asked.' I called out to the corridor, 'Arre, bring water, tea, something cold.'

Bipin Bhonsle grinned. 'I was thinking of whisky. Or rum. But you are the same, bhai. Water-water all the time.'

'Keeps me alert.'

'Whisky keeps me strong,' Bipin Bhonsle said, and picked up his sword. 'Water is bad for my heart.' He hefted the sword, pointed it at me. 'Good you are with us,' he said. And with that he went flouncing down the stairs, his heels clacking sharply on each step. The jeep spun in tight growling turns, and then they were gone. And I was now with us, I was against them.

This is the elegant way to burn a basti: you do it at night, you move a dozen cars full of boys to the east, to the life-insurance end of the basti, and there you launch a loud frontal assault. Your boys fire pistols and swing swords at the men of the basti, who emerge from their hovels to put up a despairing fight, their faces are maddened caricatures under the ranked headlights. Meanwhile at the far southwestern end of the basti another group of your boys is near the clustered shacks and houses. They are crafty and stealthy, your boys, they get in close and they can hear the screams and curses from the life-insurance end, and now they heave bottles filled with petrol, bottles primed with petrol-soaked rags. There is the crisp tinkle of glass and the small sparking flares now bloom into flowing rivers that run smoothly across rooftops, down walls, into windows. The fire speaks now, it makes a joyous, throaty grumbling as it eats, there is no stopping it. There are no phones, there is no fire brigade to come, no police. The defenders are no longer defending, they run, they dodge back into the corners, now illuminated by the bright glow above the roofs. Your boys chase them, kill some of them, the others flee to their women, their screaming children, and bolt away from the fire, they stagger and drop and get up and go, they disappear. They are gone. The flames swing easily from house to house, and our work is complete.

In the morning, the western façade of the life-insurance building was stained sooty grey, and where there had been a basti there was an empty field of cinders, spiked here and there by a blackened doorpost, a twisted pipe.

Two days later my payment was delivered in full. It came in stacks of crisp new plastic-wrapped notes, which I broke apart to distribute to the boys. By now almost all of them were back with me. Over the next four days we cleared two more plots of land. And we were all satisfied, me, the boys, Bipin Bhonsle. Riots are useful in all kinds of ways, to all kinds of people.

Finally, in the third week of January, the burning and killing stopped, under the bullets of the police and the army, and under orders from Bipin Bhonsle's bosses, and their boss. Finally there were too many dead bodies even for the very supreme top, and the reeling roar of the approaching chaos too deafening, and so it stopped. The city cringed and shook itself and began to clean up the debris, bulldozers swept up the emptied grounds and dug foundations, bodies were lifted from the gutters, from the rubbish heaps, and traffic churned through the lanes again. Here we were, slowly back to normal. And I was restored. Yes, I was able. I came home late one night from a meeting with Bipin

Bhonsle, to collect more monies he owed us from the riot-time work, to discuss new projects, and I took off my shoes and sat back on the bed, my head resting on Subhadra's new embroidered pillows, they were a deep red. She had rearranged the furniture in the room, so that we could look out of a double window as we lay in bed. I could see my darkened basti and the stars overhead. Subhadra brought me my milk, then sat cross-legged on the bed to watch me drink it. I sipped, and she rested her chin on her hand and hummed softly.

'What's that song?' I whispered. The night was so quiet, so fragile and cool, so shadowed, that I could only whisper.

Subhadra peeked up at me, and hummed on.

'What, saali? What's the song?'

She smiled, small and mischievous, and stuck out her tongue at me. And kept humming.

I grabbed her arm playfully, but she let out a theatrical little scream and twisted away. 'Let go,' she said. 'It hurts.'

'Don't act too much,' I said, releasing her. 'I hardly even touched you.'

'No,' she said. 'You're strong.' She rubbed her arm hard. 'See, you left a mark.'

'I can't see anything.'

'Even the boys say it.'

'Say what?'

'That you didn't know how strong you were. Yesterday they were saying, now finally he's showing his true strength. Now we know he's a true Hindu leader.'

'Hindu?'

'Yes.' She was looking down at her pale arm, where the skin showed a soft bloom from my fingers. 'They said, now he's showing those bastards what a Hindu bhai can do.'

There was a sloping river in the sky, a sinuous curve of light. There was the sky above, and us underneath. There were Hindus, and there were Muslims. Everything sits in pairs, in opposites, so brutal and so lovely.

'Close the door,' I said.

Now she spoke: 'What?'

'You heard.'

What happened to me then? Until then, all my life, I had felt like a ghost, a thousand ghosts roaming around inside my body, each equally possible and every one of them more lost than the other. I had come from nowhere and made a name for myself, but I had felt always that I was playing a part, many parts, and that I could switch from this name to another easily, that if I was Ganesh Gaitonde today, I could well become Suleiman Isa tomorrow, and then any of the men I had killed. I had felt anger, and pain, and desire, but I had held back always from allowing the fragments inside me to settle into a shape, a form. I had led men to believe in me, in Ganesh Gaitonde, and always secretly despised them for believing in me, because I was nothing. I had believed in nothing. I had committed to nothing. And so I was a phantom of a man, capable of frenzied couplings with whores, in whose sopping chuts I tried to make myself real, but I was not fit for marriage. Marriage is belief. Marriage is faith. Marriage is wholeness. I could see it now, I had been incapable of marriage, incomplete, imperfect and so impotent. But all the roads I had walked, thinking myself alone, all those broken paths had brought me inevitably to belonging, to the certainty of becoming something, one thing. I had burnt bastis, and so I had chosen, I had been forced to choose one side of the battlefield, wily old Paritosh Shah had had his way after all. I stood ready now. I knew who I was. I was a Hindu bhai. And so I hovered lightly above my wife, my wife, feeling the confident beat of my pulse along every length of my body. I went into her. Her scream thrilled over my shoulders. Afterwards there was blood, on the sheets, on my thighs. I was content. I said to Paritosh Shah, I haven't forgotten about you. I will find your killers. I slept deeply, sprawled in the evidence of my victory, late into the evening.

I had woken up, and for wakening to myself I was rewarded. This reward brought with it a curse. It was a videotape, and on it was a momentary glimpse of the man who had betrayed Paritosh Shah, who had delivered him to our enemies. The videotape came to me from one of our sources in Dubai, a man named Shanker who worked in an electronics store called Mina Television and Appliances. Shanker's boss, the owner of this Mina Television, had a side business of video-taping engagements and weddings and parties, and in November he had been called to a party at the revolving restaurant on top of the Embassy Hotel to tape a shaandaar party, to record for posterity a small but fantastically expensive birthday celebration, complete with Govinda flown in from Bombay to dance. The owner of Mina

Television busily taped, he caught the toasts drunk in champagne; the men standing in little semicircles in their glossy suits, their fists around stubby glasses full of Scotch; the women off in a great cluster by themselves around the sofas, their diamonds glinting, stabbing the lens with their quick flashes; and Govinda dancing, his twists and dips, his white shoes reflected in the black marble floor; and the birthday boy, Anwar, third brother to Suleiman Isa. And Suleiman Isa, yes, the bastard himself, swaying to Govinda's beat but with no expression on his face, no life. The Mina Television man brought his video back to the shop, he had been told to make three copies of it. He handed it to Shanker, told him to make the copies. Shanker made four. He kept one, and he brought it to Bombay when he visited in early February. He gave it to Bunty, and Bunty gave him money. And here it was, the tape, now on my television, in my office.

Suleiman Isa had a broad, flat face, with a sparse beard along the edges of his jawline, and a pencil moustache. In the tape he was wearing a white shirt with a round collar, and a dark grey suit with fancy embroidery on the lapels. I couldn't tell what he was drinking, but he ate kebabs from a plate and laid the toothpicks in a tidy row on the edge of the table. Neat, methodical. I watched the tape late into the night, running the Suleiman Isa bits back again and again. Chotta Badriya watched with me, and we counted four of the brothers at the party, we knew their faces from police file photographs. Finally Chotta Badriya started yawning about once every minute, and I sent him home to bed. I watched Suleiman Isa again, how he washed his fingertips in a little brass bowl, and patted them dry on a napkin. It was late now, and late in the party on the tape. Govinda had long gone, and even Suleiman Isa had left. Still the camera wandered, taking in men sprawled on the sofas, their shoes off, their ties twisted loose. One of them saw the camera, pushed himself up, three tries it took him, he raised his arms and attempted a Govinda twirl and fell, his legs kicking up against a table. A glass shattered on the floor. Much laughter. This was footage I hadn't seen before, we had always gone back to Suleiman Isa and the brothers. But now I watched it through, I wanted one look at all of it before sleep. The drunken man was picked up off the floor by two of his friends, and now all three of them stepped, skipped left-right-left, their arms over each other's shoulders. The camera panned left with them, overshot, and a man sitting on a chair ducked away from it, he slid off the chair and out of frame, his left shoulder raised high and face turned sharply away from the lens, from me. And then the camera twitched back to the right, and found the three dancing men.

But I went back. I scrabbled for the remote, pressed at buttons. There had been something about the man's big shoulder, something effortlessly fluid about his body even as he jerked out of sight, something so confident. He wasn't afraid, just easy, just making sure, he just didn't want to be seen by the camera. There it was, barely a second of blur, he was good, but not that good, not good enough – behind him was a sheet of blackish glass, a tall window with darkness outside, in one bottom edge of it I could see streetlights far below, but also in its flowing sheen I saw a face, a sharp blade of a nose, a long chin, strong neck, the quick undulating dangle of a gold chain with a shiny locket at the end: it was Bada Badriya. Our Chotta Badriya's older brother, Paritosh Shah's faithful bodyguard. It was him. It was him. It was so quick, barely a glimpse, but I was certain. And then I was unsure. When I slowed down the tape, pushed it forward frame by halting frame, the face broke up into blocks of light and slivers of dark, and became shapeless under my straining eyes. I pressed close to the screen. Was it a dull haze of shifting light, or was it him? In the still frames, there was only this vague cloud, this nothing. But when I ran it at speed, there he was, it was Bada Badriya, I was sure.

I stayed till morning, ignored Subhadra's sleepy summonings and went back and forth in that moment, from the chair to whatever lay beyond the camera's edge, until I felt his motion in my shoulders and hips, I knew what it was to move smoothly off a chair, to have reflexes that saw clearly a threat swinging close, a camera lens or a gun barrel, and muscles that stretched and sped with such grace, I was him, I knew why he did it. For the money, for advancement, for the anger of being forever a bodyguard, for the contempt he had for the man he was guarding, for his knowledge of his own big muscles, for his sense that he himself deserved something better. And Suleiman Isa had given him money, I knew, and promised him much more. Suleiman Isa had offered Bada Badriya a new version of Bada Badriya, bigger, better. And so Paritosh Shah had died. Looking at the tape, I knew this.

I ejected the tape, switched off the light and walked down the hall towards my bedroom. Half-way down I stopped, stood stunned, clutching the tape to my chest. I knew what I had to do with Bada Badriya, that was simple. It was as good as done already. But what about the young one, the younger brother, Chotta Badriya, my Chotta Badriya? What about him, the one who called me 'bhai' every day? Who was asleep this very moment in his house not fifteen feet from mine, from this house we had built together? I trusted him, I had not a second's doubt about him. What to do with him, the one who was loyal to me? When his brother died, when I killed his brother, he would know. Even if Bada Badriya was found decapitated in a ditch far away, in Thane, in maderchod Delhi, even if I told Chotta Badriya that Suleiman Isa had done it, finally he would wonder, he would look at my face and doubt me – Suleiman Isa would pass word to him, send him videotapes and photographs of Bada Badriya fraternally together with him in Dubai, and Chotta Badriya would remember Paritosh Shah and me, he would look at me and know I had no choice, that I had to do it, and he would loathe me. Maybe he would accept that his brother had done wrong, but for ever after he would stand next to me, behind me, and despise me. It couldn't be otherwise. This is how brothers are, this is what grows in the womb, this inescapable tie, this hate. Would he be loyal if I let his brother go? Would he stay with me if I forgave, forgot?

I closed the door to my bedroom. Subhadra said sleepily, 'Is it you?'

'Who else would it be, you idiot?' I snapped. 'Suleiman Isa?' I lay rigid next to her, unable to suppress the seething of my breath. She gathered herself in, timid, afraid. And I had the videotape under my fingertips, Govinda's dancing feet, and I knew in the pressured humming of my blood that all gifts are betrayals, that to be born is to be deceived, that nothing is given to us without something larger being taken away, that becoming Ganesh Gaitonde the Hindu bhai was itself an act of murder, it was the murder of a thousand and one other selves, and there was water in my ears, the moonlit bellow of churning water, and something came from my throat, a low groan.

'What's wrong?' my wife whispered.

I turned to her, I climbed on top of her, I yanked up her nightgown and I heard buttons pop and cloth tear, I forced into her. Her gasps, her cries were lost in the frantic exultation of my anger, in the growling grunts that came from my bitterness.

I had Bada Badriya brought to me the next day. My boys picked him up from his new petrol station in Thane. He had a reputation, he was known for his shoulders, for a trick he had of picking up a chair with a man in it and holding it over his head. So six of the boys went out. If he makes trouble, I told them, shoot him in the leg, but bring him to me alive. They waited for him in a little dhaba next to the petrol station, and he actually walked by them on the way to his car, with a bodyguard next to him. He had become a businessman, the bodyguard himself with a bodyguard now. Bada Badriya was bending down to get behind the wheel when my boys knocked down his gunman, laid him out with a three-foot pipe. And then they all had their pistols on Bada Badriya, at his legs, and if he had drawn he would have died then, his thighs chopped open by a dozen bullets. They were all trembling nervous. But he froze. The boys were cocky and contemptuous when they brought him in, very full of themselves, loud from the relief of having no bullets pass their way. Bunty, who had led them, clunked down a gun on the table and said to me in his Punjabi accent, 'Bhai, he had a Glock but he went nowhere near it. And the chodu called himself a bodyguard. He came quiet.'

Quiet he still was, Bada Badriya, sitting on a chair in the storage room where the boys had put him. He stood up when I walked in, and I had to look up at him.

'Why did you do it?' I asked.

'Do what?' he said, raising a hand towards me, palm up.

Until that moment I hadn't an exact plan. I had just wanted to look into Bada Badriya's eyes, and now, looking, seeing the shifty innocence he was trying to paste over his fear, this pathetic acting he was attempting, I grew huge with rage. It grew in my belly and my ribs hurt from it, and I shouted, I roared, 'I saw you. I saw you, maderchod. I saw you dancing.'

'Dancing? What, where?'

I couldn't stand him any more, his broad chest, his beefy life, his small boy's face. 'Kill him, Bunty. Kill him.'

And Bunty did.

Chotta Badriya was waiting for me in Alibag. I had sent him there the night before, to pick up four lakhs in cash that one of our controllers was holding for us. Go and get the money, I'd told him, and check on that controller, there's something slippery about him, I don't trust him. I have a feeling about that bastard, I'd told him. And I'd told him to stay in Alibag, I had a property there, a bungalow on the beach, I'd come to meet him there. I'd wanted Chotta Badriya out of the way, out of contact and touch, I didn't want somebody picking up a phone and calling him to tell him that his brother had been picked up. Stay at the bungalow there, relax, have a good time, I'd said. I'll come and join you. And he'd said, yes, bhai, come, you need the relaxation.

So I went out to the bungalow with Bunty, with three boys. We drove for three hours, through an afternoon thick with traffic and dust. I squeezed my eyes shut soon after we left Kailashpada. When I opened them, the fields had opened up, filled with new construction. I watched a hill roll through the powdery haze on my right. We turned to the east, along the highway, and then south again. I slept. And then the sea glittered ahead of us, a vast open plain shining with sharp, metallic points of sunlight.

Chotta Badriya called to us from the balcony of the bungalow. I got out of the car, stretched and grinned at him. He was wearing red swimming trunks, bright against the sloping white wall of the bungalow, and his stomach rolled gently over the red elastic. When had he become fat? When, in the last decade? We had seen each other so often and so closely that I had stopped noticing him. Do you really see the skin on your right hand? But now I saw his short hair, his belly, his marriage, his children, his love for the movies, his passion for good clothes, his loyalty to me.

Upstairs, he spilled the cash out on the bed. 'No problems, bhai,' he said. 'All of it is here. I don't think we have a problem with the fellow.'

'That's good,' I said. 'I need to piss.'

'Over there,' he said. And as I went into the bathroom, 'Do you want some chai?'

'Yes,' I said, and I shut the door. I heard him calling down the corridor, two chais, something to eat, quick, quick. The mirror over the washbasin was broken, one whole half of it gone, leaving only the raw wood underneath. I tried to piss, shook myself, but even after three hours there was nothing, I was dry. Still, I poured mugs of water down the toilet. Keep it normal, I told myself. Don't make him afraid. You owe him that much. I checked my pistol, then put it back under my shirt, in the small of my back. It had been years, literally many years, since I had used a gun. And my experience had been with revolvers, cheap revolvers, not the good Austrian automatic I now owned. Bunty had had to instruct me: this is how the cassette slides in, bhai, and then you pull the slide back. He'd said, with a look of sympathy, you don't have to, bhai, you know I can do it, bhai. And I'd said, no. No.

I opened the door. Chotta Badriya was sitting on the bed, putting away the money, stacking it neatly inside a blue travel bag. 'Everything all right, bhai?'

'All right?'

'You look a little . . . tired. Stomach troubles?'

'Yes. It's upset.'

'In our climate, you have to be very careful. There are too many germs everywhere, food gets spoiled fast. And we eat out too much, you know, all this greasy outside food. If you eat home food, keep a light diet, it's much better for your stomach.'

'All your light diet-shiet and you still have that,' I said, pointing to his stomach.

He threw his head back and laughed, and held the plump folds of his belly in both hands and lifted them up. 'Yes, bhai,' he said, smiling. 'That I have. What to do? We got rich.'

'We got old.'

'We're still young, bhai,' he said, and was about to go on, but then there was a rattle at the door, and Bunty backed in, carrying a tray. He put it down on the bed, handed me a cup of tea, and his pupils were small and spike-like in their questioning. I said nothing, and he shut the door very gently as he left, and there was a low drone of tension in the room now, which Bunty had stirred up with his cautious walk. Or maybe it was in my beating blood. Chotta Badriya was still looking at the door.

'What were you saying?' I asked, and my voice was too loud.

He looked back at me, and his mouth was small and concentrated as he searched for the thought, and then he relaxed into a big grin. 'I've completely forgotten, bhai.'

'Idiot,' I said. 'Drink your chai.'

'Now these are truly fattening, bhai,' he said, slurping from the cup. He held up a glistening brown bhajiya from the pile on the tray. 'There is more oil in one of these things than your body needs in a year.' He put it down carefully on the plate and took a long gulp of chai.

'Eat it.'

'What?'

'Eat it,' I said.

402

He had a kind of hatred for the pile of bhajiyas, a murderous attraction for them that knew exactly how much power they had over him. He pushed the plate away, sulky. 'They're bad for me, bhai. I have become fat.'

'Eat them, eat them,' I said. 'I'm giving you permission.'

'Yes?'

'Yes.'

He picked one up, held it up to the slabs of sunlight, examined the bhajiya's brown whorls and complicated branchings. He took a slow bite, and his eyes shut for a moment.

'Mmmm,' he said. 'Have one, bhai.'

'No, you eat. Can you eat the whole plate?'

'All of these?'

'All.'

'Easy. They're not that much.'

'Finish them, then.'

'No, all of them?' He really did look chotta then, with his shiny lips and surprised cheeks and boy's open face, all bright.

'It's an order.'

He began to eat, sitting cross-legged on the bed. He thumped shiny crimson sauce from a bottle on to the bhajiyas, and then held the plate up close to his chest and lowered his head to them. Now, I thought. But the pistol was tangled somewhere behind me, I could feel it cutting against my spine. I would have to get up, draw. No, no. Let him finish. When he finishes. Not now.

The pile was half-way gone now. I got up, walked to the window. The white top of my car sent up a glancing blaze of light into my eyes, and I turned and squinted. The sun was coming down, and the black shore stretched to right and left, all rocks and upthrusting edges. The trees were completely still, not a stirring of a leaf. Somewhere over there were other countries, millions of people sleeping. I saw them curled close to each other, naked, faces relaxed. Behind me was Chotta Badriya eating. I needed to turn around. Maybe he wasn't finished yet. But if he was finished he would look up, he would be looking at me. I took hold of myself, a breath, another one, and the faint swirl of the sea was close by, and I turned. He was still eating. He had two bhajiyas left. His cheek was full, plumped out and moving. Now there was one bhajiya left. The pistol came into my hand easily. It swung up. I swung it up, and I was careful, formal and correct. Get the balance right. Aim well. Hear nothing. See only the target, nothing else. That narrow space of brown skin just above and in front of the ear, just before the hair started.

His blood sizzled. The shot must have boomed, but from the long stifling tunnel of my aim I heard nothing, and in the next moment I knew that blood from a freshly broken skull froths, that it makes a small fizzling sound. It is a small, fast, stuttering hiss. It lasts for only a moment.

Bunty pushed the door open slowly, leading with his gun. He lowered it. There was no need for a second shot.

I was happy. I could understand now what Paritosh Shah had meant when he told me I needed to get settled, why he had always extolled the virtues of marriage. I *was* settled, I felt in place, rooted, held down to my soil in a way I had never experienced before. I knew who I was, I no longer felt that I was attempting at every moment to become Ganesh Gaitonde, that I was groping for the contours of Ganesh Gaitonde. With Subhadra next to me, and my acceptance that I was a Hindu bhai, that I was some kind of Hindu, I felt real. I was no bent-backed, harried husband – I still took Jojo's women – and I was no worshipper of gods and goddesses, but the boys understood me now, and came around me and felt comfortable. I was a leader they could identify with. Our rolls were back up to normal strength again. For the first time in my life, I experienced contentment. It puzzled me at first, this puddling of warmth inside my chest. Yes, Subhadra delighted in the everyday acts necessary to being a wife, she arranged and rearranged the utensils in the kitchen in graduated, gleaming rows, she danced about choosing my clothes in the morning and picked them up from the floor gladly in the evening. She walked efficiently about the house, her keys jingling at her waist. She was slim, not exactly pretty but pleasant-looking, and when I looked at her I was not beset by that angry desire that some randis brought forth from me. I wanted to sit with Subhadra, to watch the evening from our balcony, eat some ghavan and drink chai. Outside, our struggles and wars went on as before, but I was not consumed by these battles as before. We won, we lost sometimes, but we were still strong, and we were growing, and so I was happy.

But I was beset by bodily troubles. My stomach was keeping unwell, I had a bulging pain that came upon me often, late in the afternoons, a feeling of congestion in the lower abdomen, and then of expansion, as if something was trying to get out. Gas, the doctors diagnosed, and prescribed tablets and light food. But only Scotch whisky soothed it, made my tissues calm, took away the sudden pressures that threatened to tear. I couldn't let the boys see me drinking, so Bunty arranged another bungalow for me, this one within easy reach in Juhu, just down the lane from the Holiday Inn. I went every other day to this haven by the sea, where Bunty kept a bottle of Johnny Walker in a locked cupboard, and soda in the fridge. I sat alone on the terrace at sunset, and drank. Two small pegs was what I allowed myself. The drink was calming, but it brought on spasms of nostalgia. There were evenings when I cried for the early days with Paritosh Shah, when we were poor and young, when we had faced insurmountable odds and defeated monstrously strong villains. Where had those mornings gone, when we had gathered our weapons for good fighting? Where were our friends of those bright evenings? Where were the songs of our fleeting spring? I drank and listened to old numbers and remembered. '*Chala jaata hoon kisi ki dhun me, dhadakte dil ke tarane liye . . .*'

Meanwhile Bunty tried to learn everything he needed to, to manage our complicated affairs. He had started with us as a shooter, had been noticed early on in our war with Suleiman Isa, and now he was my trusted and main controller. He was full of confidence and vigour. 'Everyone knows what you did, bhai. From Matunga to Dubai, they've heard. They know that you found Suleiman Isa's bastards and tumbled them. Your partner is now fully paid for. You won this one too.' He said it to cheer me up when I was silent for long hours in the car. I knew that I had won. And I knew also that there was no victory in this world without another, larger loss hiding inside it, that in our triumph we were already hunted by some disaster. I knew something was coming. Suleiman Isa was coming. I told the boys to be careful, I increased security in Gopalmath, I forbade Subhadra from leaving the house. Not even to the temple, I told her. You are to stay at home. She looked glum but obeyed.

Twenty-one days from the day of Chotta Badriya's death, on a Friday, in the early afternoon, the bombs exploded. I heard about the first one minutes after it had happened, a phone call came in from one of our boys, he called from the city sobbing, bhai, there was a foot on the pavement, there was a sound, a huge boom, and I didn't know what it was and people were running and nobody knew what was happening and I ran around a corner with them and there was this foot on the pavement, bhai, it just lay there, sliced off at the shin, there was no blood, and then someone pointed around the corner, I looked, the stock exchange is gone, the stock exchange, it's blasted, burst. There was an exposion, bhai, a bomb, a bomb.

I calmed him down, told him to go home. Then more detonations came, at the Masjid Bunder grain market, at Nariman Point, and I had Bunty on the phone to the Goregaon police station, to headquarters, and I was dialling and there was the busy signal again and again, and then the phones went dead, and yet the news came in, an explosion near the Rakshak headquarters, now against the abrupt, numb quiet in the street there were quick flurries of shouting. Now there were boys hurrying up and down the street, and mothers gathering their children in, a car came to a halt, and there was the sound of running feet and Bunty ran in with yet more news, fishermen had died in Mahim from an attack, bombs had fallen from the sky, there were men wading ashore with machine guns. I told everyone to get indoors, lock down, and I put my boys on guard, armed them and stood them at the peripheries of Gopalmath. By evening we knew the shape of what had happened: there were no armed marauders from the sea, but there had been grenades thrown at the Fisherman's Colony, and twelve bombs had lifted up clouds of concrete through the length of the city, twelve times in two hours a blunt, cataclysmic ringing had torn at the heads of men and women and children, had killed hundreds of them, maimed thousands. On television the torn buildings stood eviscerated, all sags and twisted metal inside, and the ministers and policemen said an investigation was being conducted, they said it again and again. But in Gopalmath, my wife huddled against me, subdued and grateful, and I knew what they were whispering in the streets outside: Bhai knew, he knew something was going to happen. Yes, I had known. Yes. I had stood on this battlefield long enough to learn its rhythms, the falling drumbeats of its narratives. We were carried along in the story's surges, and many died, and I lived. I had dug deep holes for many, but I had survived because I had come to feel the subterranean sequences of cause and consequences, I knew in my flesh where the bone-white lightning would fall next. I was awake. I was playing the game.

It made perfect sense, it fell neatly like a wheel into a muddy groove, when it was announced by the police investigators that Suleiman Isa and his people had planned and executed the bomb blasts. Of course, of course. I knew it all from our paltu policemen before it was announced on television that in the simmering and swelling of anger after the mosque was pulled down, after the riots, young Muslim boys from Bombay had been flown to Dubai and then to Pakistan, that they had been trained by Pakistanis, that greasy packets of RDX had been brought in by sea by Suleiman Isa's vastly seasoned smugglers, that the trainees had made RDX bombs complete with timing devices and planted them in cars and scooters, that they had distributed these vehicles in the most crowded and best-known parts of the city, and then the massacre had followed. This was their revenge for the riots, for the many Muslims who had been killed.

There had been one small war, my inevitable war with Suleiman Isa, the war between our companies. This combat had been long, it was eternal. Now its connections to a larger war were becoming apparent. The game was many-tendrilled, webbed and seductive and infinitely dangerous. I heard about Suleiman Isa sending the bombs and I laughed, and I said, of course. And I asked myself, where next do I go? Where's the next move? What's coming for me?

It took a while, many months, but it came, sure enough. It came a day after my son was born. Gopalmath was bright and noisy with celebration, and my house was full of visitors. I was a bit shaky myself from the unfamiliar gusts of joy that came from my belly, from the quite unprecedented swelling of heated, helpless emotion that I felt when I looked down at my son's wrinkled little face.

In the middle of all this commotion Bipin Bhonsle called and asked for a meeting. He was now not only an MLA but a party leader, and so we had to take precautions and double precautions, and we met at a resort on Madh Island. They had rented a private bungalow, away from all the other cabins, and were waiting when we drove up at dusk. We sat under the palm trees, under the sky that out here seemed to be choked with stars. Bipin Bhonsle drank beer, which I turned down. With him was a man he introduced as Mr Sharma. This Sharma was one of those fair-skinned UP brahmins, very soft-spoken in fancy, All-India Radio Hindi. He was dressed in a long brown kurta and sat cross-legged on his chair, very poised, like he was practising yoga.

'Sharma-ji is an associate of ours from Delhi,' Bipin Bhonsle said. He wiggled his toes and tossed kajus into his mouth and drank. For a few minutes he talked about recent political struggles, rivals he had humiliated, profits he had made. Then he waved his boys back into the shadows, and jerked his creaking aluminium chair over to me, and leaned confidentially closer. His chest was plump and bulging under the shiny shirt.

'Sharma-ji needs your help, bhai,' he said. 'He is a very close friend of mine. Not in our party, of course, but we understand each other.'

'What kind of help?'

'These Muslims, you know.'

'Yes,' I said. 'What about them?'

'This war hasn't ended, bhai,' he said. 'They are here. They are growing. They will come against us again.'

'Or you will go against them.'

'After what this bastard Suleiman Isa has done, we will have to crush them. They live here but they're maderchod Pakistanis at heart, bhai. That's just the truth.'

'What do you want from me?'

This time Sharma-ji spoke. 'We need arms.'

'The Pathans move arms through Kutch and Ahmedabad. They'll sell you what you want.'

'They're Pathans, Bhai Saab,' Sharma-ji said, and under all the soft inflections there was iron. 'We can't trust them. We want our own pipeline. We want a steady supply.'

'There must be companies in the north.'

'Nobody has an organization like yours. We want to bring in the material by sea. We need someone to move the arms in. They have Suleiman Isa.'

'And you want me?'

'Exactly.'

I lay back in the chair, stretched. Suleiman Isa was the Muslim don, so I was the Hindu bhai. It was necessary. There was a low moon over us, plump and gentle. I breathed, and took in the fragrance of jasmine. So beautiful, I thought. It is a terrible world, I thought, and it is a perfect world.

'There's a lot of money in it, bhai,' Bipin Bhonsle said. 'And you know you should be with us. We have to protect Hindu dharma. We have to.'

'Relax,' I said. 'I'll do it. I'm yours.'

A Woman in Distress

On Tuesday morning there were five messages waiting for Sartaj from a Mrs Kamala Pandey. Sartaj shut his eyes, and through the smooth white plane of his headache tried to remember who Kamala Pandey was. It was a whisky headache, even and narrow and persistent. The morning sounds of the station house tapped at Sartaj's skull, the constables arguing in the corridor outside, the slushing of water on concrete and the steady rasping of a jhadoo, the insistent bluster of the crows, the anguished groans of a prisoner as he was led hobbling back to the cells from an interrogation. Sartaj wanted to go home to sleep. But the day was only beginning.

'Did this Kamala Pandey say what she was calling about?' Sartaj asked Kamble.

Kamble was rooting impatiently through desk drawers. He had spoken to his contact in the Flying Squad that morning, about an opening in the squad, and he was already acting as if the humdrum business and casual chaos of a mere suburban station was beneath him. 'No, she did not say. I asked. She said it was personal. And she left only a mobile number.' Now he looked up to grin. Kamble always had time to leer. 'She sounded like a real hot item, boss. Tip-top convent accent. Your girlfriend or what?'

'No. But I remember the name from somewhere.'

Kamble slammed the drawers shut. 'Definitely some trouble over there, boss,' he said, and turned to check the shelves behind his desk. 'A woman calls five times in one day, either she's in love with you, or she's in some ghotala. I asked if I could help her, but she insisted, no, only Inspector Sartaj Singh.' He turned back, and he had found the file he had been looking for. 'This maderchod station is like a bhenchod rubbish dump,' he said. His smile was huge and happy.

'But you're leaving us soon?' Sartaj said.

'I am, absolutely,' said Kamble. 'Soon, soon.'

'What's the delay?'

'Price has gone up. I'm short. Not by a lot, but by enough.'

'I am sure you're working hard to make it up.'

Kamble shook the file at Sartaj. 'A little here, a little there. I'm off to court,' Kamble said, tucking the file into a brown rexine briefcase. 'Come out with me tonight, boss. I'll introduce you to a couple of good girls.'

'I have an appointment. You go.' Kamble spent his evenings with a changing cast of bar girls. There was always one who was getting too old, one who was in her prime and a young one he was helping to get into the business. 'Have fun. Be careful,' Sartaj said. But he knew Kamble was not going to be careful in the least. He was bouncy with confidence and daring, content with how he was raising the money to get into the Flying Squad and hungrily looking forward to swathes of action and mounds of cash. He was young, he felt strong, he had a pistol in his belt and he knew he could take life and bend her to his will.

'You look after yourself today, Sardar-ji,' Kamble said, and he was quite healthily rosy in his twill shirt and new black jeans. 'Call me on the handy if you change your mind about anything. Or if you need help with anything.' And he strutted off, his briefcase tucked under his arm.

Sartaj sank down into his chair. He didn't much mind the condescension. He was himself getting used to the idea that he was washed up, that he had reached the crest of his career and that he wouldn't advance very far past his father's rank. He knew now that he wasn't going to be the hero of any film, even the film of his own life. He had once been the promising young up-and-comer, marked for advancement. Even the fact that he was a Sikh in a department full of Marathas had been an advantage as well as a burden, a marker of his separateness. He had stood out, and was known far and wide, and journalists had loved to write about the handsome inspector. But the years had worn away the shine, and he had become just like a thousand other time-servers in the department. He had his consolations, and he plodded through the day. Maybe even his memory was failing him, a little by very little. This was true. This was the truth that Kamble no doubt saw, as he went swinging up on his upward road. The Flying Squad had been very successful lately, as well. They had been killing Suleiman Isa's men rapidly over the last three months, and not just small-time taporis either. The newspapers had been publishing the life stories of important, highly valued shooters and controllers as they had fallen one by one to the bullets of the Flying Squad. Suleiman Isa, the chief minister had proudly announced just the week before, was in retreat. The Flying Squad was going to be an exciting place for Kamble, and he was sure he was in.

But this was Sartaj's life, stretching forward and inescapable. There was nowhere to go but here, to this daily trial, to this untidy mess of a station. Still, there was work. On his current roster of investigations he had three burglaries, two missing teenagers, one case of embezzlement and fraud and one domestic murder. All the usual desolations. And now there were these calls from Mrs Kamala Pandey. Who was she?

He dialled the number. She picked up on the first ring, and she was terrified. 'Hello?' she said. 'Hello?'

'Mrs Pandey?'

'Yes. Who is this?'

'Inspector Sartaj . . .'

'Yes, yes. I need to meet you.'

'Is something wrong?'

'Listen, please . . .' She stopped herself. 'I just need to meet you.'

She was used to getting her way. Sartaj remembered her now. Her husband had thrown a puppy out of a window. Sartaj remembered the dog, poor little white thing with her skull opened on the asphalt. Mr Pandey had suspected Mrs Pandey of infidelity, so he had murdered her dog. Mrs Pandey had refused to file charges against her husband, and the husband had refused to complain about her assaults with stick and knife. Sartaj hadn't liked either of them, and Katekar had liked them less. He had wanted to put them both inside for a night or two, on charges of disturbing the peace. Or at least shove them around a little, teach the spoilt little rich snots to keep it quiet, frighten them a little. Or one of them will end up dead, Katekar had said. Maybe that's why Mrs Kamala Pandey was calling now, maybe the husband was dead already, and had been tucked and bent until he fitted into a bedroom cupboard. It had happened before. 'What about, Mrs Pandey?' Sartaj said. 'What's the trouble?'

'Not on the phone.'

'There is trouble?'

She hesitated. 'Yes,' she said. 'I can't come to the station.'

'All right,' Sartaj said. 'Do you know the Sindoor Restaurant?'

On the way from the station to the underpass, Sartaj was flagged down by Parulkar, who was convoying in the other direction in a brand-new official car. Sartaj did a U-turn and followed Parulkar, who slowed down at the next patch of empty shoulder and stopped. Parulkar's security men sprang out alertly from their jeeps and made a perimeter and held their ferocious automatic rifles at the ready. Their number had increased over the last two months, or three, ever since Parulkar had pulled off yet another of his amazing feats of survival. Whatever the dispute had been with the Rakshak government, it had been settled. Suddenly Parulkar was their grey-eyed boy, the chief minister and the home minister were consulting him every two days. The enemies had become allies, and both sides were profiting. Organized crime was retreating, bhais and controllers and shooters were being killed at such a pace that soon there would not be many left to shoot, at least until the next generation showed up. All was right with Parulkar's world. He had made it so, and once again he had proved he was amazing. The rumour was that he had paid twenty crores to the chief minister alone, and much else to various functionaries. In any case Parulkar was back, glorious and jovial again.

'Come, come,' he called. 'Quick.'

Sartaj slid in beside him. There was a new fragrance inside the car, something quite delicate.

'You like it?' Parulkar said. 'It is called Refreshing Nectar. See, from there.'

A sleek aluminium tube with fins sat on the dashboard vent, blinking a red light that Sartaj assumed signalled the release of Refreshing Nectar. 'Is it from America, sir?'

'Yes, yes. Are you well, Sartaj?'

Parulkar had just come back from a two-week visit to Buffalo, where one of his daughters was a researcher at a university. He looked rested and contented and bouncy, very much like the Parulkar of old. 'You look very healthy, sir.'

'It is the clean air over there. A morning walk, over there, revives you really. You cannot imagine.'

'Yes, sir, I cannot.'

'I brought something for you also, a portable DVD player. It is so small' – holding his squared thumbs four inches away from each other – 'and the picture is sharp, absolutely sharp. You can take it anywhere with you and watch films, you see. Very good for a policeman.'

'That is a wonderful thing, sir. There was no need . . .'

'Arre, don't tell me about need. I know what you need. You come home, tomorrow, day after, and we will talk. The player is also at home.'

'Yes, sir. Thank you, sir.'

Parulkar thumped Sartaj on his shoulder and sent him on his way. Sartaj thought about the new DVD player, and worried. Now he would have to buy or at least rent DVDs and then watch them. Parulkar was sure to ask for reports on his viewing. But maybe that was all right. Maybe Parulkar really understood better than him what he needed. Some entertainment might be exactly what would fix him up, and revive him like a good morning walk in Buffalo. Where in America was Buffalo? And why was it called Buffalo? Sartaj had no idea. Some more of life's mysteries.

Sartaj sat at his usual booth in the Sindoor Restaurant and nursed a Coke. During a recent renovation, Sindoor had gained festive new red tables and a new menu which included Bengali and Andhra food. Sartaj was reading through the Bengali desserts when Shambhu Shetty walked in. 'Hello, saab,' he said and sat. They had last seen each other a week ago, when Sartaj had come in as usual to pick up the monthly Delite Dance Bar contribution to the station. Shambhu had complained as usual about the necessity of raids and rising prices, and had told Sartaj about his dream trek, through the forests of Arunachal Pradesh. Now Shambhu had auspicious news. He was engaged. He had sampled from the revolving tray of feminine delights that his bar brought to him every day, but now he said he wanted to settle. 'Those were only trailers, boss,' he told Sartaj. 'This is the main film.' The heroine of Shambhu's life-film was a nice girl that his parents had found, of course within the Shetty community. The two families had common friends in Pune, and had known vaguely of each other for decades. The girl had a B.Ed. but was content not to work after marriage. She was a virgin, that went without saying, or asking.

'Well done, Shambhu,' Sartaj said. 'When is the date?'

'May. The cards will be printed at the end of this month. I will send you.'

It was four-thirty in the afternoon, and the restaurant was almost empty. A pair of college lovers sat next to each other, on the same side of a booth, nursing their Cokes and pressing thighs against each other. Shambhu was relaxed but brimming with energy. He had marriage plans, and also plans for another bar, this one in Borivili East. This new bar was to have a filmi theme, pictures of film stars everywhere. There would be different halls for the dancers, each with a distinct decor. There was going to be a Mughal-e-Azam room, and a DDLJ room. 'You should invest,' Shambhu said. 'I guarantee good returns. Invest for your future.'

'I am a poor man, Shambhu,' Sartaj said. 'I'm sure you're not interested in investors who come with five hundred rupees.'

'Poor, you? Even after that Gaitonde hit?'

'That wasn't a hit, Shambhu. The man shot himself.'

'Yes, yes.' Shambhu was smiling, very wise to the ways of the police. 'And how did you happen to find him?'

'Anonymous phone call. Tip-off.'

'If you get a tip-off about some ready money, saab, come straight to me. This is a good time to invest.' Shambhu uncoiled himself out of the booth. His face sloped forward to the chin, and his eyes were too close-set, but he carried himself very well. He was at ease in the world. 'I'm expecting a beer delivery,' he said.

Shambhu shook Sartaj's hand and walked briskly to the door. He stood aside then to let Mrs Pandey through. She paused to take her sleek dark glasses off, and then marched straight up to Sartaj.

'Hello,' he said. Sartaj stood up, and pointed her around a partition, to a small table near the kitchen door. Here they were quite private, alone with each other.

She was wiping at her nose with a tissue, and Sartaj saw that she was strained, exhausted, but well turned-out. Her hair was glossy, in a sweep down to the shoulders, and she was wearing white jeans and a white top with very short sleeves and a cut that exposed a bit of her toned midriff. She was smaller than he remembered, but had a spectacular chest which filled out the white top very nicely. It wasn't exactly the outfit Sartaj would have recommended for a private meeting with a seedy policeman in a very middle-class suburban restaurant, but women had their own reasons. Maybe all the jhatak and matak made her confident. Maybe she liked the fact that men always looked.

She finally spoke. 'Thank you for meeting me,' she said. Her Hindi had just that little awkwardness that came from living her life mostly in English. 'Pani,' she said sharply to a waiter who had stepped up. 'Bisleri pani.'

Sartaj waited until the waiter had poured the water and walked away. Mrs Pandey's fingers had a clear gloss on them that Megha had worn sometimes. Megha would have described her as a 'hot little number' and steered Sartaj away from her. But Sartaj felt no desire now, only curiosity. 'It is my duty,' he said. 'But what is the trouble?'

She nodded. 'Trouble,' she said. Her eyes were her best feature, large and almond-shaped and the colour of a glass of good Scotch with one or two ice-cubes melted in. Megha would have said that she wasn't classically beautiful, but had worked and polished herself into hotness. She was in some very big trouble now, and it was difficult to talk about.

'You're an air hostess,' Sartaj said.

'Yes.'

'For?'

'For Lufthansa.'

'That's a good airline.'

'Yes.'

'They pay well.'

'Yes.'

'Has something happened to your husband?'

'No, no.' The sudden question made her shrink, fold her arms across her stomach. 'Nothing like that.'

But it had something to do with the husband. Sartaj was sure of it. 'Then what is it?' he said, very gently. He was quiet, and sipped slowly at his water. He was willing to wait.

She gathered herself, and then ground it out: 'Someone is blackmailing me.'

'Someone. You don't know who?'

'No.'

'How are they talking to you?'

'They call on my mobile.'

'Is it always one person?'

'Yes. But I hear him talking to someone else sometimes.'

'Another man?'

'Yes.'

'What are they blackmailing you with?'

Her chin came up. She had made her decision, and was not going to be intimidated, or shamed. 'With a man,' she said.

415

'Who is not your husband?'

'Yes.'

'Tell me,' Sartaj said. She hated having to explain herself, to justify anything. 'Madam,' Sartaj said, 'if I am going to help you, I need to know the details. Everything.' He poured her some water. 'I have worked for a long time as a policeman. There is nothing I haven't seen. Nothing you can tell me will shock me. In our country we do everything and say nothing. But you have to tell me.'

So she did finally tell him. There had been a man, her husband hadn't been so wrong in his suspicions. Actually he had been rather correct. The man was a pilot, yes. Only he didn't fly for Lufthansa, and there had been no fun on stopovers in London. Kamala Pandey's pilot flew for Sahara, his name was Umesh Bindal, he was single, she had met him at a party in Versova three years ago, the affair had begun a year after their first meeting, and she had broken it off six months ago. Their assignations had all taken place in Bombay and Pune and Khandala. The blackmailers had first called a month and a half ago.

'What do they have?' Sartaj said.

'They knew a lot of details, of a hotel. And when I had gone to his house.'

'That's not enough. They must have something else.'

She was flinching now, from what she had to say. 'Videos.'

'Of what?'

'Of us. Outside our room.' It looked as if the videos had been taken with a hidden camera at a guest house in Khandala. The lovers had used this guest house often, on a regular basis, and the staff had thought they were a married couple fond of quick hill-station vacations. The videos had them going into their room, and leaving it. And also holding hands and kissing and embracing as they walked to and fro, across the hotel courtyard. The blackmailers had left the video tape on the seat of Kamala Pandey's car, in a brown envelope. Then they had called her.

'How much did you pay them?' Sartaj said.

A small shimmer of puzzlement hovered over her taut cheeks. Sartaj laughed. 'It's not so unusual, madam. Everyone pays them first. The blackmailers send over the video or photographs or whatever. Then a month later they come back with new material. So what was the amount?'

'A lakh and fifty thousand. They wanted two lakhs, but Umesh told me how to negotiate with them. Now they sent a new tape.'

'How much do they want now?'

'Two lakhs.'

'And where is the tape?'

'I burnt it.'

'Both videos? Everything they had sent?'

'Yes.'

'Madam, that is not so good. We could have learnt something from the tapes. Even from the envelope.'

She nodded. The videos would have been too frightening to keep. The mention of them had made her a little watery, a little tremulous under the sheen. But now she showed some steel. She reached into her silver handbag and pulled out a folded piece of paper. She opened it out on the table, smoothed it down. 'I kept a list of their numbers,' she said. 'Each time they called, I wrote it down. With the times.'

'That is good,' Sartaj said. 'That is very good. And now if they send you anything, keep it. Try not to touch it too much.'

'Fingerprints.'

'Yes, fingerprints. You have to help us to help you. Where is Umesh today?'

'He's flying. He would have come with me, but you didn't return my calls till today.'

'I want to talk to him.'

'I'll give you his numbers.' She wrote on the paper. 'He wanted to go to the police the first time they called. I only didn't want to come.'

'You wanted it to stop.'

'Yes.'

'They never stop. Until we stop them.'

'That's what Umesh said. But I didn't want to tell anyone then.'

'Why did you break it off with Umesh?'

'Because I realized that he wasn't interested in me really. He is a nice man, but he has too many girlfriends. He just wanted fun, and I was giving it to him. But then it wasn't fun for me any more.'

'So he's very handsome, like a hero?'

'Very.' His handsomeness still evoked a fervour in her, tinged with an aftertaste of sadness. 'Very.'

'When did the blackmailers call you last?'

'Yesterday.'

'They will call today. Start listening to them carefully. I want to know exactly what they say. Take notes. Listen for sounds from near by. Anything at all. You have to start thinking like a police-wallah. A police-walli.'

That amused her just a little, that she could ever be a lowly police-woman. 'Police-walli,' she said. 'I will try.'

'Tell them you need time to collect the money, that you're getting it together. How was it delivered last time?'

'I had to put it in a bag, a shopping bag, and drive to Apsara cin-ema in Goregaon in the evening, at six o'clock. The afternoon show was just letting out, and there were lots of crowds. I was told to wait on the road across from the gate. Then they called me. They told me that a chokra in a red T-shirt was going to come up to me, and a sec-ond later he was knocking on my window. I rolled the window down, he asked for a package, and he took the money and ran off into the crowd. That was it.'

A crowded area, a street kid sent to collect the money – just stan-dard operating procedure for the average blackmailer. 'Umesh didn't come with you for the delivery?'

'No, they don't know that he knows. They told me not to tell any-one, not a single soul. They told me that they would hurt me.'

That was unusual, that blackmailers would threaten violence. There was no need for hurt if you had photographs. 'And the chokra, what did he look like?'

Kamala Pandey was confused. 'The kid? I don't know. He was just some urchin.' A barefoot boy was just exactly like any other street sav-age, despite his red T-shirt. You could find a dozen at any street corner in Mumbai.

'Try, madam. Can you remember anything at all about him? It's very important.'

'Yes. Yes . . .' She paused. 'His T-shirt. It was a DKNY round-neck T-shirt. It had the logo on it.'

'Deekay NY jeans?' Sartaj wrote in his notebook.

'No,' she said with the amused patience of somebody dealing with the lower classes. 'The letters D, K, N, Y and then "jeans". All capi-tals, one word. Like this.' She reached for his pen, and wrote in large letters: DKNY JEANS. 'The letters were very faded.'

Witnesses had to be praised for the slightest achievement, and cajoled into further discoveries. 'That is very good, madam,' Sartaj said. 'It will help us a lot. Anything else? Please try to remember. The smallest item can solve the case.'

She made a disgusted little pout, and touched a tooth, two behind her elegant, perfect right canine. 'His tooth, this one. It was all dirty-looking. Black, grey, instead of white.'

'Excellent. On that side?'

'Yes.'

'All right,' Sartaj said. 'It's good that you wrote down the numbers of the men who called. These are probably PCOs. Once you sign a complaint we'll put a watch on some of them.'

'I can't.'

'You can't what?'

'I can't sign a complaint.'

'Madam, without a complaint, without an FIR, how can I proceed?'

'Please understand. If any of this goes into writing, people will find out. People will know.'

'Madam, I understand that you are afraid that your husband will come to know. But will you please understand that without a complaint the police have no jurisdiction. We have no reason to interfere, no grounds to act on.'

'Please.'

She was leaning into the table, both hands up by her cheeks. A practised actress, this one. 'Madam, I can't do anything,' Sartaj said. He straightened his neck, loosened his tight shoulders. He was angry at her, had been angry for a while now. It burned through his chest. He didn't know why.

'Please,' she said. 'Think about it. I'll lose everything.'

'You should have thought about that a long time ago, yes?'

'Yes.' That stopped her, cut her off in mid-flow. 'Yes.'

She covered her eyes, and when she brought away her hands she was teary. A minute passed, then two. She dabbed away the tears. Sartaj was sure that an expert application of small pressure on her eyelids had helped start the tears, but now she seemed genuinely sad. There was a weariness that he recognized, an exhaustion from losing something built over long years. You had something that you valued very little, that you maybe had slighted and abused out of familiarity. Yet you then discovered that this thing itself, this connection, this very flimsy construction had spread its roots deep under your skin, and into the bone.

419

Kamala Pandey gathered herself again. In preparation for a direct attack, she levelled her shoulders and straightened up a bit. Sartaj remembered the walking stick she had broken on her husband's back, and he wondered if Mr Pandey had learned to recognize her cues and guard himself.

'Look,' she said. 'I will pay you.'

Sartaj said nothing. She reached into her bag, reached deep, and brought out a long white envelope. She paused, and waited for him to react. Sartaj said nothing. She slid the envelope across the table, left it next to his water, close to his hand.

Sartaj extended his index finger, nudged open the flap. Hundred-rupee notes. Two stacks. Twenty thousand rupees.

He was now very angry. He pressed the envelope shut. He pressed until the fingernail turned white and red. 'Listen,' he rasped. 'This is not enough.'

'Yes, yes, I know. This is just a token. I would rather pay you than them. Just help me. Just stop it from happening.'

'You have so much money of your own?'

'I work. My parents help me now and then.'

She kept separate bank accounts, and she had doting parents. 'Your parents live in Bombay?'

'In Juhu.'

'Brothers and sisters?'

'No.'

She was the single, spoilt child of well-off parents, suddenly in a lot of trouble. She believed, quite completely, that she was owed her privileges. It would be a pleasure to take her money from her. But Sartaj was very angry. 'Madam, I can't help you without a complaint.'

'How much do you want?'

He shoved the envelope across the table. 'I can arrest you right now, for trying to bribe a police officer.'

That shut her up. She put a hand on her mouth and began to weep. Sartaj could see that it was real this time. He stood up and walked away.

Why had he been angry at her? It wasn't just the money. He was quite used to taking money, to being bought. Things and people were bought and sold every day in this city. Sartaj bumped down the pitted lane to Katekar's place, keeping the motorcycle as close to the centre of the road as he could. The gutters were clogged, and occasionally the tides of rubbish hid serious holes in the asphalt. In this patchy dark, the khuds in the road came swiftly, and could take a man down. There was still a lingering aftertaste of indignation in Sartaj's mouth, a sour rancour that had nothing to do with what a spoilt, irritating little child she was. Was it only that she had been unfaithful, that she had done something a woman was not supposed to do? Men did it all the time, Sartaj knew this. Industrialists did it, and labourers did it. And sometimes women did it also. He knew this. He often saw, as he had done today, the aftermath. He had seen broken marriages and broken bodies, heard anguished sobs and screams. This was nothing new, in his job he had seen it all. So why had he been angry?

Sartaj coasted down the last few feet to Katekar's corner. The house was down an alley that narrowed and angled off to the left. Sartaj parked at the corner, and raised the rear seat to get at his packages. There was also a plastic bag crammed into the rear carrier. He shook away the anger, the question, and marched down the alley, turning his shoulders to slide by clumps of pedestrians. Some of them nodded at him. He had been a regular visitor for a few months, and they knew him now. He knew that some of them must still believe that he had got Katekar killed, but most of them were friendly now.

Katekar's sons were sitting near their kholi's door, studying. The tube-light inside threw their shadows out on to the road, and Sartaj knew their familiar shapes well before he saw them. Rohit sat always to the left of the doorway, his back flat against the wall and a book held well out in front of him. Mohit was always moving, his head jigging up and down even as he wrote. As Sartaj came up Mohit went from a cross-legged squat into a kneeling arc above his notebook. He was making a blue mess of the page.

'Hello, Rohit-Mohit,' Sartaj said.

'Hello,' Rohit said, grinning. Mohit kept his head down. He was writing furiously across drawings that slashed across the double spread of the notebook.

Sartaj lowered himself into the doorway and sat with his back hard against the jamb. 'Where's your Ma?'

'Aai is at her meeting.'

'What meeting?'

'There is a Family Welfare Group. She is a volunteer, so she has to go once a week.'

This was certainly new. It had been a little over two weeks since Sartaj had last visited, and Shalini had a new routine. Life moved along. 'Volunteer for what?'

'They give information. Aai goes and talks to women around here.'

'About health?'

'Yes. And I think about saving money. And cleanliness. They are planning to clean up the lanes. There are some pamphlets somewhere here if you want to see.'

'No, no.' Sartaj knew the groups, and the NGOs that worked with them, usually with government or World Bank funding. The groups were rackets for somebody or other, for the NGOs or the government or the Bank, but they did good work sometimes. And Katekar had been a great one for cleanliness, so Shalini's work was a fitting tribute. 'Here,' he said, and handed over the packets he had brought.

'Thank you,' Rohit said, in English. He had been working very hard on English recently, and planned to enrol in a beginners computer course in a month or so, immediately after his exams. Sartaj had made sure that a seat had been reserved in the Prabhat Computer Classes, which were reputed to be the best in the area. 'Learn Computer and Internet For Only Rs. 999', they advertised in multi-coloured advertisements pasted on every other wall. Rohit was going through the bags, laying down the plastic pouches of dal, and atta, and rice. 'Eh, tapori,' he said to Mohit, and tossed him two comics. 'Latest Spiderman,' Rohit said. 'Say thank you.'

Mohit couldn't take his hands off the comics, but he wouldn't say thank you. Sartaj wondered what his neighbours had told him about his father's death, who he had learned to blame. He was a strange boy, he had become a glowering little tyke, very opaque and very jerky, tightly sprung from within. 'Our Mohit likes Spiderman,' Sartaj said, 'but he is a patriotic Indian. He doesn't like saying thank-you-thank-you all the time, like those Americans.'

Rohit laughed. 'Yes, rudeness is our birthright.' He tweaked Mohit's nose, and Mohit made a spitting noise and ran past the partition into the other room. 'He really does want to be Spiderman though. For two days now he'll sleep with the books. Kartiya sala.' Rohit tapped his forehead.

Sartaj unbuttoned his breast pocket, brought out an envelope. 'Ten thousand,' he said. He handed it over, and scratched at his beard. It was getting hot, settling into the absolute grim stillness and dejection of the pre-monsoon months. His collar was soaked with sweat.

This time Rohit didn't say thank you. He got up, holding the envelope to his chest, and then Sartaj heard the metallic creak of a cupboard opening and closing. Rohit came back with a glass of water. Sartaj drank. He was a good boy, Rohit, and he was too young to be putting money in cupboards and thinking of how to raise his little brother. But then there were six-year-olds making a living on every street corner down to Colaba.

They sat for a while, talking about computers, the Middle East, and whether Kajol would do any more films. Rohit thought Kajol was the best actress since Madhubala. Sartaj hadn't seen a film for a long time, but he was glad to agree. When Rohit talked about Kajol, he grew intense and happy, and gestured emphatically with his hands at Sartaj's chest while he described Kajol's virtues. Kajol was not only a great actress, she was a good wife and mother. Sartaj found himself smiling, and was happy to listen, and agree, and let the night come on.

The next morning, Sartaj met Mary at her sister's apartment. As he had expected, it had taken several weeks to get Jojo's apartment handed over to Mary, her sole surviving relative. But now, he had been glad to report to her on the phone, he had the key, everything was ready. Tuesday was Mary's day off, and he had agreed to meet her first thing in the morning, before he went to the station. He had got himself up early, dragged himself into the shower, and was at the building punctually at six-thirty. She was waiting for him near the lift, as they had agreed. With her was a very tall, very thin woman, who was looking at Sartaj with mild amusement.

'This is my friend, Jana,' Mary said.

Sartaj had not expected friend Jana, but it certainly made sense that Mary would bring a friend. 'Namaskar, Jana-ji,' he said.

Jana took in the muted sarcasm, and grew more amused. 'Namaskar, Sartaj-ji,' she said.

Sartaj grinned, and quite unexpectedly Mary smiled. Her jaw thrust forward a little, and her eyes narrowed, and her face quite transformed. The dragging seriousness went from her, vanished. Sartaj wasn't quite sure exactly what she found funny, but it was a relief and a revelation to see that she could be diverted. 'Shall we go?' he said, pointing towards the lift.

'Yes, yes,' Mary said. 'Jana has come to look after me.'

Standing close to the two of them in the lift, Sartaj could see that Jana was very competent indeed. She wore a smear of sindoor in her carefully parted hair, and a dull red kurta over black salwars. Her shoes were sensible, and she carried a large, square shoulder-bag with wide shoulder straps. Inside it she carried a plastic bottle, no doubt full of boiled water. That was a mother's bag, nice-looking but capacious and hardy. It would carry lunch, chocolates, medicine, vegetables and school books. It was a trustworthy bag.

The lock to Jojo's apartment was tightly bandaged with coarse canvas that took in the latch as well, and the layers were secured by a drippy seal of red wax marked by the Mumbai Police. Sartaj handed Mary the key, and reached inside his gym bag for a pair of large black scissors. He had come prepared. The seal came off with a rip, and then Sartaj watched as Mary struggled with the key against the jammed lock. 'Let me,' he said, and Mary shook her head briskly and set her shoulders to the task. Jana gave Sartaj a rueful look over Mary's head: this is what she's like, let her be. They waited. Then the lock came open with a screech, and they were in.

Jana rushed around opening windows, revealing the drawing room in sections. Mary was still near the door. Sartaj reached behind her and ran his hand down the row of switches. No lights, no electricity. 'Yaar, this is a *nice* place,' Jana called from the kitchen, mingling surprise and a fat dollop of outrage.

Women were always outraged when officially bad women made money, had taste, enjoyed a little happiness, Sartaj thought. But Mary was unreadable. She walked through the apartment, paused in each room and took it in, and was very silent. Jana's commentary rolled on: in the bedroom, Jojo's lavish collection of footwear called up a moment of stunned silence, then two minutes of affronted references to Jayalalitha and Imelda Marcos, and then a long painstaking inventory. Mary was standing in the doorway, her hands by her sides.

Sartaj pushed a window open. 'There were some photo albums here,' he said. 'They must be somewhere in here.' The room was a mess, and the scattering of shoes and clothes and magazines lay under a thick slough of dust. 'Ah, there,' Sartaj said, and came around the bed to the dresser. He picked up the top album, and thumped it. A fine ash ballooned off the cover, and Sartaj was suddenly aware of how loud his voice had been, how triumphant. The direct light from the window didn't quite reach Mary, and he couldn't see her face. 'You should go to the BSES office, and have the electricity switched back on.' He put the album back on the dresser. 'There must be some outstanding bills. Okay, then, I must go.' He nodded, took a step and stopped.

Mary backed into the corridor to let him pass. Sartaj raised a hand at Jana, and she nodded, but she was watching Mary. Sartaj was all the way down the corridor when Mary spoke. 'Thank you,' she said.

'Yes, yes,' Sartaj said. 'Don't mention.'

'I haven't forgotten.'

'What?'

'About your investigation of Ganesh Gaitonde. I tried to think about Jojo, if I could remember anything.'

'Thank you.'

She smiled again, and again this time it came suddenly, without warning. She raised her left hand and did a curious little wave, holding out her hand towards him and turning it only from the wrist. Sartaj nodded, and shut the door.

An hour and a half of shifting and coiling had left Sartaj exhausted, but more awake than when he had got into bed. He had settled in just after midnight, feeling virtuous about the earliness of the hour, and clean from a long shower. But now a small and relentless agitation was working under his skin. He had drunk three whisky-and-waters. And still there was no sleep. He sat up. Shadows of wires swayed across the window-pane. He couldn't remember the name of the dog. There had been that small white dog that Kamala Pandey's husband had thrown out of the window. Sartaj remembered its stiff-legged sprawl in the car park, but he couldn't remember the name of the gaandu thing. He still had her number. He could call Kamala Pandey and ask her, what was the name of the dog your husband killed, that the two of you killed together, as you played your dirty games?

Sartaj swung his feet to the floor, rubbed at his eyes. He couldn't do that, it would be police harassment, persecution, something. But he knew who would be awake at two in the morning. He dialled, pressing at the lighted keys with a shaky finger. He listened to the ring and waited, holding up his hand. He was very tense. I need to get a blood-pressure test, he thought. There was a history in the family: Sartaj's father had struggled against hypertension and high cholesterol all his life. He had survived one heart attack, and died quietly in his sleep nine years later, of causes that the doctors said were natural.

'Peri pauna, Ma,' Sartaj said.

'Jite raho, beta,' she said. 'Did you just get home?'

'Yes. Casework.' Work was an acceptable reason for calling this late. Admitting to insomnia would occasion an enquiry into his eating habits, his consumption of alcohol and his health. He would be preemptive. 'Ma, you sound hoarse. Are you getting a cold?'

'A cold, me? I never get colds. Your father was the one who always got colds. He had that thin Bombay blood. We grew up in a good clean climate, we were used to good cold winters.' This was an old theme, that the north-western sardar was tougher than the Bombay sardar. The sisters were the toughest of all, and Navneet-bhenji was the eldest and the hardiest of the sisters. Here it came, the story of the stalwart and long-lost aunt. 'Navneet-bhenji used to bathe in cold water even on January mornings. At six-thirty in the morning because she had to get to early class at college. Even Papa-ji would tell her to put in a little hot water, but she never listened. And if you looked at her, you would think what a delicate, beautiful thing! She was a literature student, she looked like she should be counting pearls in a palace, but she was strong as some peasant. She used to paint really well also, you know. These scenes of the village fields, and houses, and cows. There was one she did of our new house that was wonderful, it was so exact.'

Now there was a pause. This halt was also a familiar one, as Ma mourned the dead sister. Navneet-mausi had been killed during Partition, but Ma had been talking about her for as long as Sartaj could remember. She was dead, but she had always been in Sartaj's life. All the children and grandchildren in the family knew her well, this absent mausi. They had lived with her, with the stories and the rigidity that would come over the faces of the elders as they spoke of her. Sartaj had tried now and then to press past that constriction of muscle and nerve, that freezing of emotion, to what exactly had happened during those bloodstained days. But all that Ma had ever said was, 'Those were bad days, very bad days,' and that was all. And that was what they all said, all the uncles and aunts and grandparents. That, and an occasional curse against Muslims: beta, you don't know, they are bad people, very bad people.

But tonight Ma was not angry about old hurts, or bitter, she was just quiet. So Sartaj finally said, 'I don't know how you remember

426

such old things. Exact paintings and things like that. I can't even remember the name of a dog.'

'What dog?'

So Sartaj told her the story: the husband, the wife, the dog thrown out of the window.

'What a horrible man!' Ma said. She liked dogs, and they liked her. 'Did you arrest him?'

'No.'

'Why?'

'The wife wouldn't file charges.'

'Arre, there was abuse of an innocent animal.'

'She wouldn't even say he had thrown it out of the window.'

'Maybe she was scared of him.'

'She's not so innocent either.'

'Why? You saw her again?' Ma had spent decades tussling with a policeman, two policemen, so she had developed her own skill at catching nuances and unvoiced truths. 'What's wrong with her?'

It was an ugly story to tell this late at night to his mother, but Sartaj told it. He made a quick little report on the wife, the pilot, the camera, the blackmail. He left out the bribe the wife had offered, and her tight little white top. Ma had severe opinions about shamelessness in any guise, and he didn't want to overly prejudice her against Kamala Pandey. The errant wife was surely condemned in any case. 'Of course I told her that I couldn't work on her case, without a complaint. She's a fool,' he said. 'A fool who thinks she can get whatever she wants, can do whatever she wants.'

'Yes,' Ma said. 'Her father must have done whatever his little daughter wanted, and given her no discipline. People spoil their children nowadays.'

Sartaj laughed out loud. This was why he called his mother in the middle of the night, for these sudden vaulting leaps of insight, these confirmations of his own hunches. She was quite amazing sometimes. 'Yes, she's a brat. Very irritating.' He sat up in bed, and drank a long draught of water. He was feeling better already, hearing her voice, listening to her breathing. 'Did you and Papa-ji talk much about his cases?'

'No, no. He didn't like to talk about work with me. He said a policeman's life meant that you couldn't escape from work until midnight anyway. Then to come home finally and keep thinking and

427

talking about work, that would drive you mad. So we talked about other things, and he said that relaxed him. That's what he said anyway.' She sounded dryly amused. He could see the tilt of the chin, that downward glance. 'The truth is that he was old-fashioned. He thought that I would be scared by all the murder and the dirty things they had to investigate. He thought women shouldn't be exposed to that kind of thing.'

'And you went along with that?' She loved action movies, and in recent years had developed an inexplicable taste for all the really bad, blood-dripping, moonlight-and-screams horror series on television. She read the crime columns in the papers every morning with relish and offered commentary, and the repeated observation that the world was a bad place, and getting worse.

'Beta, you adjust. *Adjust.* He didn't want to talk about work, so I didn't. That's how you go along. That's what this new generation doesn't understand.'

She meant Sartaj's generation, and Megha's. She knew that Megha was married, finally and completely out of Sartaj's reach, but occasionally she would revisit what had happened, what should have happened, what Sartaj should have done. Sartaj had long given up arguing, or even responding with anything other than the occasional 'Yes'. He lay back and listened. She was his mother, and he adjusted.

'Achcha, go to sleep now,' she said, 'or you'll be tired for your shift.'

'Yes, Ma,' Sartaj said. They said their goodbyes, and he turned towards the window so he could feel the air on his face. He fell into sleep easily, and dreamed. He dreamt of an enormous plain, a cloudless sky, an endless line of walking figures. He woke abruptly. The phone was ringing.

It was before seven, he knew that without opening his eyes. There was that stillness, in which a single bird was chittering. He waited, but the phone was not going to stop. He reached for it.

'Sartaj,' his mother said, 'you must help that girl.'

'What?'

'That woman from last night, the one you told me about. You should help her.'

'Ma, have you slept?'

'Where is she going to go? What is she going to do? She's alone.'

'Ma, Ma, listen to me. Are you all right?'

428

'Of course I'm all right. What would be wrong with me?'

'Fine. But why all this about that stupid woman?'

'I was just thinking this morning. You should help her.'

Sartaj kneaded his eyes, and listened to the bird. Women were mysterious, and mothers were more mysterious. Ma was quiet now, but it was her strict silence. It was a calm that tolerated no back-talk, no resistance. He wanted very much to go back to sleep. 'Yes, all right. Okay.'

'Sartaj, I'm serious.'

'I am too. Really, I will.'

'She's all alone.'

So was everyone else in the world, Sartaj wanted to say. But he mustered up obedience. 'I understand, Ma. Promise I'll help her.'

'I'm going to the gurudwara now.'

He had no idea what that had to do with calling him out of a perfectly good slumber, but he whispered, 'Yes, Ma,' and hung up the phone. Sartaj's bed was moulded to his body, the bird was not too loud, the morning was cool under his silent fan, but sleep was gone. He cursed Kamala Pandey. Saali Kamala Pandey, she is a kutiya, he said to the bird, bloody raand, and he got up.

Sartaj spent the morning writing redundant reports on small burglaries which would be perfunctorily investigated and never solved. His afternoon trickled away in court, between two magistrates and three cases. At five he drank a cup of tea in the restaurant across the road, and ate a greasy omelette. The restaurant was called Shiraz, and was full of gossiping lawyers. Sartaj hid himself away at the rear of the first-floor air-conditioned annexe, and tried to avoid meeting the lawyers' eyes as they walked to the washbasin. He chugged down a tall glass of chaas, wiped his moustache and started to feel better. He managed to get through the annexe without having to talk to anyone, and all the way down the stairs. But half-way to the entrance a weedy, pock-face rose up to intercept him.

'You're Sartaj Singh?'

This wasn't a lawyer. His grey shirt was sweat-stained, and he had the mean, foxy deference of someone used to people stepping around him. But he had a voice that made up for his build, brassy and deep. 'Who are you?' Sartaj said.

'You don't remember. I met you at the funeral. And two-three times before that.'

Of course. This voice. 'You're Katekar's . . . Shalini's sister's husband.'

'Vishnu Ghodke, saab.'

'Vishnu Ghodke, yes. Yes.' Sartaj remembered him from the funeral, but not before that. At the funeral he had been busy bringing things, organizing the mourners, directing the priests. 'Everything all right, Vishnu?'

Vishnu Ghodke touched his breastbone. 'By your blessings, saab. Although . . .'

Sartaj nodded. 'Yes. Katekar was a good man.' He waited for Ghodke to step aside. 'We'll meet again some time.'

Ghodke wasn't ready to leave Sartaj quite yet. He turned sideways to let Sartaj pass, and then followed him out on to the pavement. 'Have you seen Dada's boys?' he said into Sartaj's shoulder.

Sartaj was abruptly aware that he didn't like Vishnu Ghodke very much. He wasn't quite sure why, but he wanted to put a hand over his face and back him fast into the wall. 'Yes, I saw them yesterday. In the evening yesterday. Are they all right?'

'Of course, of course, saab. No, nothing like that.'

'Then like what?'

'Was their Aai there?'

'No, she was out.'

Vishnu Ghodke turned his head to the side, to look across the evening swell of cars towards the court house. Above his head was the red 'Shiraz' sign, with the lettering delicately arranged in four languages. 'This is what, saab?' he said, coming back to Sartaj. 'What is it? A woman should be at home. A woman should be with her family.'

'She has to work, Vishnu.'

'But this is not work, roaming about in the evening, leaving her children to go hungry.' He was making wide gestures towards the road and the courts beyond, as if Shalini was running wild among the black robes and the stained arches.

Sartaj's shoulders came up, he felt the dense throb of violence along his forearms. Maderchod. This bastard had to show up now, today. 'Those boys are fed and happy,' he said. 'Their home is well-kept. What is it that's tickling your gaand?' Vishnu Ghodke squirmed away, found the wall behind him. 'Haan? Tell me.'

'Saab, I was just saying . . .'

'Saying what?'

430

'She has started going to these meetings.' Vishnu was trying to find a quiet voice now, an intimate one. He wanted to be a man talking reasonably to another man.

'They talk about health. So?'

'Saab, health is one thing. But they tell them all these, these uncivilized things. All these things that are not fit for decent women. And they tell them to go about and talk to young girls and spread it into the community. Why does a young, unmarried girl need to know about pregnancy and nirodh and all? I have young girls, I am a father, and I tell you it is becoming very difficult. As it is, you never know what can be on television, right in the middle of the day. It is impossible for a family to sit together and watch. And then we have people like this, educated people who catch women like Shalini and turn their heads.'

Sartaj considered clouting this defender of the culture, once on each scrawny cheek. But that wouldn't smash any sense into his head, it would only make him more militant in his defence of his daughters. 'You don't worry about Shalini's head,' he said. 'And she's not talking to your daughters. If she says something to them you don't like, tell her to stop.'

'That woman won't listen to anyone, saab. Her husband is gone, so she thinks she can do what she wants.'

'So she won't listen to you. Is this why you are angry?'

Vishnu brushed at his shoulder, where the plaster from the wall had left a streak. He had grown confident as he had spoken, had forgotten some of his fear. 'Saab, I am not concerned about myself. I am only thinking of the boys, and that home. That home will suffer. We have a saying: *gharala paya rashtrala baya.*'

Sartaj reached out and put a hand on Vishnu's shoulder. He smiled. To the passing pedestrians, they were just two friends passing the time with friendly banter. But Vishnu was squirming already from the pressure of Sartaj's thumb just under his collarbone. 'So now you're worried about the country also?' Sartaj said. 'You listen to me, Vishnu. I don't like you going around talking, making trouble for her. You think you're some bhenchod saint? You wander around like some bastard loudspeaker, spewing lies.'

'But it's all true, saab.'

Sartaj squeezed, and now Vishnu was truly afraid. 'It's true that she's trying to take care of her boys. And do some good. You're a small man, Vishnu. Your brain is small, your heart is small, so you think small of people. You're a small, mean bastard, Vishnu. I don't like you. So shut up. Keep your mouth closed. Understand?'

Vishnu's eyes were sparkling with tears. He had a hand picking at Sartaj's wrist, but he couldn't get away from the pain.

'Understand?'

'Yes,' Vishnu said. But he had the persistence of a cornered rat, this Vishnu. He whispered, looking away, 'But I'm not the only one saying it. Other people are saying it as well.'

Sartaj let go of him, and leaned in close. 'Yes, other maderchods like you are always ready to say this and that about a woman who is alone. Especially when you are such a decent brother-in-law that you start these rumours yourself. So you'd better keep quiet.' Vishnu nodded, keeping his eyes down. Of course he wouldn't stop. Of course he would keep at it, add and embroider. But now he knew there would be consequences. 'If I hear you're making trouble, I'll come and look for you, Vishnu. She needs your help now. Live with her as a family should, Vishnu. Help her make that home strong, don't destroy it with your mouth.'

Vishnu was working his jaw, but was keeping his head down and his mouth shut, as instructed. Sartaj had no doubt he would open it as soon as he felt safe. Sartaj patted his cheek gently. 'I'll be watching you,' he said, and walked away.

Gharala paya rashtrala baya. So if the stability and prosperity of a house depended on its foundations, and that of a country on its women, what was Sartaj going to do about the glossy and very unreliable Kamala Pandey? He had his unambiguous instructions from Ma, and despite the distance, and his age, he did usually go along with what she wanted. For the most part. But she was a sentimentalist, wanting to rescue fallen women from their troubles. She was from another generation, and she had no idea what kind of trouble Kamala Pandey was. She could have no conception of how much Kamala Pandey annoyed Sartaj. It was easy to say, you must help that girl. Much harder to tolerate the bitch.

Sartaj let it sit in his stomach for three days. He went about his business, investigated, arrested, wrote reports, drank, slept. Kamala Pandey stayed with him, and it was pleasurable to think of her in trouble, of her wincing and cowering under the shower of abusive language that came in over her mobile phone, of her money being taken from her. Yes, she should learn that the world was not made for her delectation. Yes, she should know that she couldn't have just whatever she wanted. On the fourth day the relish ebbed, and by that evening it had been replaced by a dragging feeling of responsibility.

'What's the matter, Sartaj?' Majid Khan said.

They were standing on Majid's balcony, waiting for dinner. Sartaj was nursing his second glass of Black Label. Majid was wearing red shorts, and drinking fresh mausambi juice, and was speaking with the quiet authority of an old friend who knew exactly when Sartaj was being more morose than usual. He would press on until Sartaj talked. So Sartaj told him about Kamala Pandey, the whole story. 'She's one fancy item,' he said. 'Shows off her money. So some boys are taking some of it off her.'

Majid stroked his moustache upward. He had a spreading motion with thumb and index finger that he used when he was concentrating. 'Very interesting. I don't think there's a real problem with the case.' He meant that keeping it off the station books wouldn't be very difficult, or unusual. There was the possibility of good money, which always made discretion possible. Majid raised his glass. 'And, Sartaj, if she's so namkeen, investigating her could be fun.'

'Arre, Majid, I'm not interested in her.'

This made Majid straighten up, turn to Sartaj. 'Yaar, you said that she was sexy. She's giving it everywhere. She's got the chaska for it. So what does interest and no interest have to do with it? Take some.'

The logic was impeccable: if a woman was unfaithful once, she was therefore definitely available. Blackmailers sometimes used knowledge of an affair to take for themselves, to grab what was being distributed. Kamala Pandey's blackmailers hadn't tried that yet, but maybe they would, once she had run out of money. This was how the economy worked, there were many ways to pay. Sartaj spat over the railing. 'Ma said I should help her,' he said.

'Of course she would.'

'But . . .'

'You don't have interest in the money, you don't have interest in the woman.' Majid shrugged. 'So don't help her.'

'Yes. But what about those blackmailer bastards?'

They nodded at each other, grinning. They knew each other too well. Whatever he thought of Kamala Pandey, Sartaj was certain that he completely, unambiguously hated the blackmailers. He didn't like them operating in his zone, in his locality, in his area, in his mohalla. Maderchods, bhenchods, he wanted to squeeze their golis and see if they cried. Majid, who was scratching his thigh under his shorts, felt the same way. Sartaj could see it. Majid had a theory that all really good cops came from strong mothers. He had met Sartaj's mother, and his own Ammi was a tiny, wizened harridan who terrorized her daughters-in-law and still arranged marriages for her grandchildren without consulting anyone. Majid thought that a mother who kept an orderly house, who maintained cleanliness and had clear rules about what was right and what was wrong, actually ended up training her sons to be good policemen. He would list the names of department men he admired, and tell you about their mothers. Sartaj thought there was something to Majid's theory. Katekar's mother, for instance, had been a tough, massive-hipped matriarch. Years after her death, Katekar had spoken of her anger with awe.

'I think,' Majid said, leaning forward to clink glasses, 'Inspector Sartaj, that if your Ma tells you to, you have to put those blackmailers out of business.'

Sartaj had to agree. 'I'll call the Pandey woman,' he said. 'After dinner.'

At dinner Sartaj watched Majid and Rehana banter with each other. They argued about each other's parents, which set was more eccentric. Their own children giggled. Majid told stories about Rehana's mother that Sartaj had heard before, but he laughed again. Rehana was affectionate with her own children, with Farah and Imtiaz, and Sartaj thought that neither of these children would ever make good police. He had no doubt that Rehana was an efficient mother, and kind, but she didn't occupy her children's lives in the old-fashioned way that Majid had been talking about. She was their friend. And anyway, the kids were both too ambitious to consider a career in the force, which produced decrepit types like their father's sardar friend.

Sartaj drove home, burping loudly all the way. He went very slowly, quite aware that he was drunk. A perfectly round moon dodged behind buildings and darted out between billboards for next week's Shah Rukh Khan release, a grand love story. Sartaj tilted gently past a traffic circle, and thought that the posters had become a lot glossier than the hand-painted ones he remembered from his childhood, which had made

Dharmendra look like an alien with an inflated head. Love was altogether shinier now, or at least it had that appearance. Kamala Pandey was discovering how grimy it could be, how bare and bleak hotel rooms looked through a camera lens. Stopped at a traffic light, under another Shah Rukh poster, Sartaj considered the possibility of profits from her: did he want to take Kamala Pandey? Would he? Sartaj thought not. She was irritating, self-centred, spoilt. And anyway chodoing her would be dramatic, it would require an effort of will and force that would be exhausting, that would be anything other than pleasurable. No, if he helped her, it would be for the money, and only that.

Sartaj got home, took off his shoes and socks and dialled Kamala Pandey's number. She picked up on the first ring, and Sartaj could hear the panic in her 'Hello?'

'This is Inspector Sartaj Singh,' he said. He heard the breath that went from her then, as if someone had hit her hard under the breastbone.

'Yes,' she said. 'Yes.' Under her voice, there was conversation, music. A man was talking, close to her. They were in a restaurant, the successful young couple.

'I want to see you again. At the same place, at four o'clock.' She said nothing. 'Can you hear me?'

'Yes.'

'Don't worry. I am going to help you.'

'Okay. Thank you.' She was working hard to sound casual, as if she was speaking to a girlfriend about hair appointments.

'Did they call you again? Just say yes or no.'

'Yes.'

'We'll talk about it tomorrow. Relax. Bring that list of their numbers. Four o'clock, same place.'

'Okay, yes.'

Sartaj hung up. He put his feet up on the coffee table, loosened his belt. When he got paid on this job, maybe he would take Ma to Amritsar. He would take her to Harmandir Sahib, and watch her pray. It was comforting to feel the intensity of her devotion, it moved through him like a kind of familiar warmth. He wasn't sure if this was because he had grown up with the murmur of her prayers always sounding somewhere near, or whether within himself there was some forgotten, subterranean strand of belief that resonated into partial life when she hummed and sang. Anyway he would take her to Amritsar, and ignore her reckless remarks about this journey being her last one. If Ma wanted him to help the odious Kamala Pandey, let her profit from the job too. It was only fair, only fit.

Kamala Pandey wore a black outfit the next day at Sindoor. She was seated at the table near the kitchen when Sartaj came into the restaurant a few minutes after four. She had a bottle of mineral water in front of her, and an impossibly tiny mobile phone. Her hair was pulled back into a high ponytail, and Sartaj knew that the black blouse was definitely casual, but she still looked sleek enough to be on television, on some music channel.

'Hello,' she said. 'Thank you.' She had a way of tilting her head down when she smiled, so that she was looking up at you with very large eyes.

'Did you bring the money?' Sartaj said. He wanted short conversations with her, limited to professional requirements and concerns. She scrabbled in her bag, which was not the silver one she had carried earlier. This one was a black triangle, made out of some iridescent material. 'And the numbers?'

'The money is more today than yesterday,' she said.

There was thirty thousand in the envelope. Sartaj nodded. 'They called yesterday afternoon?'

'Yes. At one twenty-five. I told them what you said to say, that I need time to collect the money. They are not nice people.'

'They abused you?'

'They were saying very-very bad things.'

Her handwriting was full of curves and dashes and flourishes, but she had been meticulous about noting the dates and times of the calls in orderly columns with headings. 'When did you make the first payment?' Sartaj asked, and made a notation on the page. 'And when they called, did you hear anything interesting? Anything?'

'No. I tried. A car or a scooter passing by, now and then. But nothing else.'

'Keep trying. They will be very abusive, they will threaten you. Just delay. I need some time to look into this. I will call you soon.' Sartaj gathered up the envelope and pushed his chair back.

'Wait!' She held out an imperious hand, and then lowered it under Sartaj's glare. 'Please. You said you wanted to meet Umesh. He is coming.'

436

'Here?'

'Yes. He was supposed to be here at four. Sorry.' She was being deferential now, subdued.

'Okay,' Sartaj said. He looked at his watch, and then they sat. Sartaj had nothing to say to her. She played with her phone, pressed the keys, read a text message. Then she put it down, and looked through her bag. She peeped up at Sartaj, who kept himself very neutral, and then went back to her investigations. She was getting nervous and fidgety. This was not a woman who was used to men being silent around her. Sartaj was starting to enjoy himself. It was cruel, but he kept himself absolutely quiet, and the minutes passed.

When Kamala Pandey started to look slump-shouldered and forlorn, he took pity on her. It was too much to watch her droop. 'Is Umesh always late?'

That revived her like a bite of a tart lemon. 'He's on time for his flights, but for everything else he's late. He takes more time to get ready than me. You should see his bathroom, it looks like a chemist's shop. He has more shampoos and conditioners and scents than me and your wife and five other women put together.'

Sartaj let it pass, the little lure about his wife. He said, 'And he always calls and says he's on the way, he's in the car, he's rushing, he'll be here in fifteen minutes?'

'Yes, yes. And then two hours later he shows up, with some story. He used to drive me crazy.'

She was unable to help being just a little wistful. Sartaj was sympathetic: drama and craziness were painful, but you could miss that madness as you missed food or water. Until you settled into the dead calm of no hope, no disappointments. But Kamala Pandey still enjoyed talking about the sins of her ex, it revived her. 'Maybe he had other stops on the way?' Sartaj said.

She laughed out loud. 'Umesh always has two or three fools on his strings. He doesn't even hide it too much. He just makes you feel that he hasn't found the right one yet, that maybe you are the one where all the searching ends. He's honest enough that you believe him.'

'You saw the truth after all.'

'After a long time.'

And after all this knowledge she was still unable to cut away the yearning for him. Sartaj saw this as soon as Umesh walked in. Umesh shook hands firmly with Sartaj, and touched Kamala Pandey on the arm in greeting, on the bare skin. She kept herself stone-still, rigid. Sartaj abruptly remembered how he had fought down the vibration echoing up his arm when the estranged Megha had touched him lightly on the wrist, when she had bent towards him. He had strained with all his back and shoulders then to keep himself from tilting towards her in turn, and now he could not clench his throat shut against a warm pang of sympathy for this wandering wife.

'Hello,' Umesh said. 'I should make some excuse about being jammed in traffic, but really, I just got more and more behind this morning. Sorry.'

He certainly was beautiful. He wore dark red jeans, and a tight white T-shirt over pumped shoulders. The jeans were preposterous, but on Umesh they were perfect. He glowed golden, from his long arms up to the light brown eyes, which were very like Kamala's. She must have looked into them and seen herself. 'Sit,' Sartaj said. The man had an open, happy charm, and Sartaj wasn't going to give in to it.

'I'll just use the bathroom and come back,' Umesh said. 'It was a long ride.' He put his phone and a set of keys down on the table and hurried off. The phone was exactly the same model as Kamala's, satiny and small. His keys were attached to a model of a car, something low and fast.

'It's a Porsche,' Kamala said. 'Umesh likes cars.'

'Yes,' Sartaj said. 'And he drives too fast, right?' She nodded. That's how they must have gone up to the guest house, Sartaj thought, going too fast and weaving through the traffic, excited by the bursts of speed. 'What does he drive?'

'A Cielo.'

'A red one?'

'No, no. Those are just his pants. I told him red is not his colour, but he likes to be noticed. The car is black.'

Umesh came back into the restaurant and slid into the chair across from Sartaj. He was tall, an inch or two over six feet, and had the smallest waist Sartaj had seen on a man in a long while. He narrowed like an inverted triangle from the shoulders to the hips, and the quick travel from the gym-broadened shoulders to the absence of belly gave him the look of a cartoon figure. Kamala liked this superhero, though. She had tensed up again.

'Ah, Inspector saab,' Umesh said. 'Now I am totally at your service.'

'I know the main story,' Sartaj said. 'But I want to know about this guest house. What is it called?'

'Cozy Nook Guesthouse. On Frichley Hill, near that big Fariyas Resort. Cozy is a little place, not too crowded, nice view. It's just a cottage really, which the owners rent out. C-o-zed-y.'

He was looking at Sartaj's notebook, in which Sartaj had written 'Cosy Nook Guesthouse'. He was smiling warmly, and the joke was on the impenetrable English language, so it was impossible to be angry with him. He was altogether too pretty, but he was a good fellow. Sartaj could see how he would charm the ladies, he would tell them all his faults, and pay full attention with those sunlit eyes, and smile. You would have to be charmed. 'Yes,' Sartaj said. 'How did you find it?'

'A friend used to own a house near it, we used to drive past it. It's an old place.'

'Did you notice any new waiters? Any change in the staff?'

'No, not really. I wasn't paying that much attention, you see. But if I'm correct it's all the same people.'

'Any idea who could have taken those videos?'

'No, sir. There is the staff. But then also the other guests. I don't remember anybody specific, though.'

'You didn't ever recognize any of the other guests?'

'No, no. Never. If that had happened, I would have remembered.'

'Do you know which dates those videos were taken on?'

'No, you couldn't really tell. And I didn't note the dates we went up there.'

'How many times did you go to this Cozy Nook?'

'Over all those months? I don't know, maybe six, seven times?'

'More like eleven times, maybe twelve,' Kamala said. 'The last time was at the beginning of May.'

'I thought you broke up six months ago,' Sartaj said.

'We had.'

So they had gone all the way to the Cozy Nook for broken-up sex. They had probably argued all the way up there, and been silent on the way down. Judging from the bitter set of Kamala's lips, they had an argument coming now. Maybe more broken sex, although for Kamala's sake, Sartaj hoped not. There was little comfort to be gained from such transactions, especially when they involved a man like Umesh. Nice fellow, but not sturdy. Not at all like the decidedly unbeautiful but dependable Mr Pandey.

439

Now Sartaj asked Mrs Pandey, 'Who hates you?'

'What?' Kamala's shoulders hunched, and she curved in on herself and just a little bit towards Umesh.

'Who are your enemies?' Sartaj said evenly.

'Kamala is a very nice person,' Umesh said. He had his arm behind Kamala now, with fingertips resting on her shoulder. 'I don't think she has enemies.'

'Yes,' Kamala said. 'I mean, I've had quarrels with people, but enemies?'

'Everyone has enemies,' Sartaj said. 'It's better to know who they are.'

That silenced them for a moment, as they tried to calculate which friend or acquaintance might harbour enough secret loathing to qualify as a genuine foe. 'So you think this is personal?' Umesh said.

'Blackmail is usually about cash. But it may be worth thinking about friends and adversaries. Anybody who is in a position to have information, and who may be angry about something, or need money urgently.'

Umesh was shocked. 'Even someone connected to me? Wouldn't they have approached me as well?'

'You are not married. And you are a man.'

'And I support my parents and sisters. I don't have much cash flow. So they would go for the easy target.'

'So who can it be?'

Both the men looked at Kamala. Her cheeks were congested, flushed, and Sartaj wondered if she would weep. This time he would believe it, maybe. But she gathered herself and named her enemy. 'I had a friend named Rachel.'

'So you fought?' Sartaj said.

'Yes.'

'About what?'

Kamala laughed at his obtuseness. It was an ugly sound. 'What do you think?'

Of course. They had quarrelled over Umesh. There had once been sisterly love, maybe years of it, and then the beautiful Umesh had come between them. 'Rachel was your best friend?'

'Yes.'

'Then?'

'We met Umesh together. At a party.'

440

'And Rachel liked him?'

'Arre, boss,' Umesh interjected, a hand reaching across the table. 'I never even did anything with that woman. I met her a few times with Kamala, and God knows what all this Rachel assumed.'

What Umesh thought was not of any consequence, given the circumstances. 'What did Rachel feel?' Sartaj said to Kamala.

'She liked him.'

'From the beginning?'

'Yes. We talked about him after the first time at that party. She kept saying what a perfect man he was. Masculine, but sensitive.' This last with a roll of her eyes.

'And then?'

'What had to happen, happened.'

'When did you tell Rachel?'

She remembered exactly when. 'One Sunday two months later. I came back from a flight and went straight to her house. I just couldn't stand it any more.'

'And?'

'She told me to get out. She never spoke to me again.'

'She was that angry?'

'She had been divorced two years before that. And had never liked anyone.'

'Till Umesh.'

'Till Umesh.'

To his credit, Umesh wasn't smug about this, about his fatal charm that caused women to hate each other. He was anxious, and disbelieving. 'Still,' he said, 'it's hard to believe that someone like Rachel would come so low in the world. I mean, blackmail like this . . .'

'She is the only one who knows about us,' Kamala said dully.

Yes, Kamala knew more about anger, about the rotting remnants of friendship stored at the back of almirahs, old photographs and shirts given as gifts and souvenirs carried back from winter holidays in lovely Singapore, all of it curdling into black bitterness that burned through the day, morning and night, so that finally the only relief would be the blackmail. Not because it would yield money, but because it would cause humiliation and pain. Money was good, but healing and peace would come from elsewhere. Yes, Kamala understood. There was motive, and opportunity. Not enough to prosecute, but certainly enough to investigate.

'Give me Rachel's information, please.'

Kamala wrote swiftly, all from memory, in her pretty looping hand.

'All right,' Sartaj said. 'I will investigate. Your mobile number, please, Mr Umesh?'

'That's all?'

'It's enough for now.'

'I thought you would want to know lots of things.'

'If I have any questions, I'll call you. Number?' Sartaj wrote down Umesh's number, snapped his notebook shut. 'Remember what I told you,' he said to Kamala. 'Listen, just listen. And don't be afraid of them. They may act tough, but they need you. I'll be in touch.'

'So now you'll investigate those calls?' Umesh said. 'Follow them up at the calling numbers?' He was thrilled by the investigative process, by the potential pleasures of the story, even though it involved him directly.

'Something like that,' Sartaj said. 'You like detective movies?'

'Only Hollywood movies. Our Indian ones are so badly made.'

There was no denying that. 'That's true,' Sartaj said. 'But sometimes the Indian ones get things right also.'

Umesh plainly didn't believe this, but he let it pass. 'Why don't you just have Kamala tell them that she's going to pay, and then arrest them when they come to collect?'

'Because they expect that, and already are working against it. That's why they sent the chokra to get the money from her the first time. These boys are being careful. It's too risky. No use tipping them off.'

'They're that good?'

'Good, but not that good,' Sartaj said. 'We'll get them. Let us work on it.'

Umesh looked sceptical. Sartaj raised a hand in farewell, and left them sitting together, uncomfortable together but well-matched. Outside, he put his dark glasses on against the low late-afternoon sun. The glasses were quite out of style, he realized suddenly, by at least two years, maybe more. Maybe it was time to buy new ones. But he felt affectionate towards this old, battered black pair. They'd been through a lot together, and there was something to be said for the old and familiar and comfortable. Style was hard work, and expensive besides. He had got too old and too poor to work at it. Sartaj grinned at himself – what a boring, aged budhdha you've become – and drove on.

Kamala Pandey had a good head for detail, but the blackmailers had been very careful. The phone calls were spread out over the northern suburbs, both east and west, and there was only one call from each number. The only pattern Sartaj could pick out was that the calls came either early in the morning, between eight and ten, or after six in the evening. Which meant that the blackmailers had jobs. They were taking care of this business around the work of making a living.

'These are all PCOs,' Kamble said. 'I'm sure.'

'I know,' Sartaj said. He had recruited Kamble into the investigation that evening, once he had figured out exactly how much legwork was going to be involved. Kamble was quite willing to be recruited, for a price: forty per cent of the take. But working with Kamble also meant drinking with him at the Delite Dance Bar, and playing alibi for him with his girlfriends. Sartaj had already lied, as instructed, to two dancers about where Kamble had been earlier that evening. Sartaj said to him now, 'There's only one call from each place, so it's not likely that the operators will remember who made a call. But we'll cover the PCOs, starting with the most recent calls first. You want west or east?'

'West, boss.' Kamble was staring hungrily at the three dancers on the floor, who were spinning languidly to '*Aaja gufaon mein aa*'. The sequined blue and pink and green of their ghagras was gorgeous to watch, Sartaj had to admit. They were young. But it was early in the night, and the Delite was nearly empty, and they weren't being very energetic in their seductions. Kamble looked like he wanted to liven them up, by any means necessary. No doubt he would.

'All right,' Sartaj said. 'I'll take east. See you tomorrow.'

'Arre,' Kamble said, 'stay.'

'Tomorrow will be an early day. Extra work to do.'

'Every day is an extra-work day. Just have another drink with me.'

'Had my limit.' Sartaj got up.

'You need to get some sex in your life.'

'With whom?'

'Any of these.'

'No chance.'

'What, you think they won't like you? Boss, don't worry. They'll eat you up.'

'Exactly that.'

'Too easy? Then go for the one that doesn't want you. But you need to get back into the game, Mr Singh.'

'I do? Why?'

'What else is there?'

Indeed. What else was there? Retirement, or retreat? Ma had her religion, but that was only after a full lifetime with Papa-ji. Could you step out of the game at an early age, like some sanyasi who gave up everything and set off for the hills? No, Sartaj knew he couldn't do that. But he was going to get out of Delite for now. He was very tired, and he just wanted to go home. He raised his glass, emptied it. 'Thanks,' he said. 'Tomorrow, then.'

Kamble wasn't satisfied, but he gave in gracefully. He bared his big, toothy smile. 'Tomorrow,' he said. 'Tomorrow we'll see.'

Sartaj called Iffat-bibi that night, just before sleep. She had phoned him soon after Katekar's death, to express her condolences. She knew that they had been working together for a long time, but she also somehow knew about Katekar's young children, and had offered a nicely medium-sized sum of money to help the family. Sartaj had turned her down again, but after that they had spoken often on the phone. She was cunning, funny, and had endless stories to tell about apradhis and policemen from the past. She offered him little bits of intelligence, rumours and locations and names, and asked for nothing in return but that Sartaj make it easier, if he could, for any of her company's boys who went through his lock-up to meet their families. The information she provided was accurate and useful, but never concerned big cases or notorious apradhis. It was all comfortably small-time, and Sartaj felt their trade was fair, with no obligation left over on either side. And it was somehow restful to listen to her talk about Papa-ji. Papa-ji had talked to her about all his cases, it seemed, and Sartaj was getting a slowly emerging portrait of the old man that he could not have found anywhere else. Papa-ji, it turned out, was not so simply foppish as he may have looked, with his passion for double-breasted coats and custom-made shoes. He was vain, but without ego in the matter of his job. He knew his beat, and he had an instinct for what both apradhis and victims would do next. His arrests were not spectacular, but they were frequent, and they were steady and real, not fluff-jobs conjured up to bulk out an annual report. He was respected, despite his sartorial extravagances. But his vanity kept him mostly honest, at least in the big ways that made a difference to his career. He could not stand the thought that he, Sardar Tejpal Singh, was to be bought like a loaf of bread sitting on a shelf, like a packet of cigarettes. His pride kept him from being obsequious to his seniors: he was willing to ask for a favour, but he stopped at that. He found it impossible to persuade, wheedle, beg or bribe.

'Such a stubborn man,' Iffat-bibi said now, 'but he kept his head up like he wanted. Not that it did him much good.'

'Come on now, Bibi,' Sartaj said. 'Not everyone wants to earn a turnover like your Bhai's. How much is it?'

'Some newspaper said yesterday, eight thousand crores.'

'That's the newspaper. What do you think?'

She snorted. 'Bachcha, I'm an old woman, I don't do accounts. But it's enough.'

'Enough for what? What does anybody do with eight thousand crores?'

'Everyone needs a little extra. Not just for the things you need. For the things you want. Even your Sardar Saab.'

'What do you mean?'

'Arre, nothing, I was just talking like that.'

A shiver of unease moved over Sartaj's shoulders. He sat up. 'No, you were not. Tell me what you mean.'

'Nothing at all.'

'No, tell me. Iffat-bibi, don't try and fool me. What is it?'

'Beta, you are making a big noise about very little. I promised him I wouldn't tell anyone.'

'What is it? Was it a woman? Women?'

'Arre, you dirty-minded bastard, no!'

'Then what? Tell me.'

'You are making a big fuss over a very small thing.'

'What?'

'He liked to gamble.'

'Gamble?'

'Yes, yes. He loved horses. He liked to place bets on horses at the races.'

'He went to the racecourse?'

'No, never, someone might have seen and told your mother. I had one of my boys make the bets for him.'

Yes, Ma-ji, with her refugee's frugality, would never have stood for gambling in her household. She refused to buy lottery tickets because, she said, they were a complete waste of money, and anyone who

445

thought they could get a crore by putting in one rupee was a complete jhalla. And here was Papa-ji, a regular money-scattering, gambling fool. But then, he did love horses. One of his great regrets was that he had never learned to ride. At the breakfast table, he would smooth out the newspaper with great care and point to a sports-page picture of a horse and say, 'Look, how beautiful,' and Sartaj and Ma never commented or replied or even noticed, because he had been saying it for ever. So instead, outside home, he had had a secret life, or at least a secret side. Sartaj coughed, to clear the congestion in his throat, and asked, 'Did he lose much?'

'Lose? No, he never bet that much to start with. He had a limit of fifty rupees, and then later he raised that to a hundred. But he was good at reading the racing forms. He won more than he lost. Actually a lot more.'

Papa-ji won. He had this other universe, with its own rules and systems, its particular histories and tragedies and triumphs, and here he was a winner. He had beaten the chances, he had vanquished the game. A bittersweet flood of affection and nostalgia and regret came into Sartaj's mouth and nose and eyes, and he had to hold the phone away a bit, to keep the sounds of his sentimentality from Iffat-bibi.

'Sartaj?'

'Yes, Bibi. I was just thinking, the old man was quite a character.'

'Complete namoona. But, listen, don't tell your mother, all right?'

'I won't.'

Later that night, Sartaj wondered if Ma knew already. She and Papa-ji had had their difficulties, their silences which Sartaj could never decipher. He had heard raised voices behind closed doors, and one of their quarrels had lasted three days, but Sartaj never knew why it started and how it ended. All this was normal enough for any wife and husband, and these two had been devoted to each other for more than forty years. Maybe Papa-ji had his horses, and kept quiet about them, and Ma knew but refused to know. Maybe that's how they had been happy together. But did she wonder that day, Sartaj's birthday, when Papa-ji had brought in the biggest and most expensive Meccano set that anyone had ever seen? Papa-ji had put Sartaj on his shoulders, and Sartaj had echoed Papa-ji as he went around saying his Hello-jis, and everybody had laughed and been happy. Maybe one of Papa-ji's horses had won that day. He and Sartaj sat up late that night, building a red and green house with a big wall around it, and Ma had crouched next to them, showing them where a courtyard should go in, and the proper location for the main gateway. Papa-ji wanted to put a flagpole on the roof, but Ma said that would make it look like a government building, not a home. Papa-ji and Sartaj worked hard, putting in the final touches, an actual swinging gate, a small shed for the chowkidar, and Ma let Sartaj finish the whole thing before she took him off to sleep.

The next morning, there was a message waiting at the station house for Sartaj. It was from Mary: 'Come to the Yari Road apartment tomorrow evening.' And that was all. Sartaj turned the note over, puzzled, then folded it carefully in half and put it into his pocket. He was glad that Kamble hadn't seen it, or he would have had to endure at least half a day of smirking jokes about ghochi and merry Mary and private trysts.

Sartaj spent the afternoon driving from one PCO to another, reaping the expected harvest of blank looks and bafflement. An orange-haired, sixtyish owner of a shop near Film City put a paan in her mouth and gave it to him straight: 'Baba, I know the call was just the day before yesterday. But you see how many people I get making calls in one day. I don't sit here looking at their faces. They come in, they make their calls, they give me their money. Bas. I don't even remember the ones who came today.' She bent to the electronic meter on her desk, squinted at it. 'Already today there have been a hundred and thirty calls. And the busiest time is the evening.' Her hair was appallingly hennaed, but she was telling the truth.

'You have a good turnover,' Sartaj said.

'Everyone needs to ring home,' she said.

There was a small queue of carpenters waiting for her two phones, pretending that they weren't listening to the policeman's questioning. They were Punjabis, stubbled and brawny. They had walked over from the shop three doors down, where they were building shelves. They were interested in the fact of a Sikh policeman in Bombay, but they were too scared of police inspectors to talk to him. Their families were probably in Gurdaspur, or Amritsar, and they had learnt caution.

Sartaj went on to the next PCO. He went to nineteen in all, and at all of them there were the same men and women, making calls across the city and across the country. None of the owners or cashiers could remember two men among these thousands. At seven Sartaj called a halt and veered off to Yari Road. The traffic was dense, and by the time Sartaj got across the subway, the twilight was losing its fantastic range of orange hues. The bulb in the lift was fused, and Sartaj had to grope for the buttons. But Mary had light. She opened the door into a well-lit drawing room and grinned up at Sartaj. She had a duster in her hand, and a chunni tied around her hair, giving her something of a Rani-of-Jhansi air. 'Hello, hello,' she said. 'And sat-sri-akal. Come in.'

'Hello,' Sartaj said. The drawing room was crowded with cardboard boxes, but had been scrubbed clean. Mary had put in a day of work all right, but she seemed relaxed, buoyant. 'You have electricity.'

'Jana has a friend at BSES. I paid the past bills, and her friend got it all switched on.'

Jana was the kind of practical woman who would of course have a friend who could get electricity from BSES in a few days, instead of in a month or two. There was loud filmi music sweeping down the hall, from the bedroom. 'Jana's taking care of the shoes?'

Mary nodded, twinkling. 'And the clothes. She gets upset every two minutes because Jojo was too small for anything to fit her. Come on.' She stepped past Sartaj, calling, 'Jana! Jana!'

Jana also had a chunni tucked behind her ears, and the rapt look of a woman absorbed in her work. She greeted Sartaj with a quick nod and 'Hello,' and led the way into the study. 'We started cleaning in here first,' she said. 'Because mostly we were going to throw all these papers and files away.'

'We were throwing,' Mary said. 'And then Jana noticed one thing.'

They were pleased with themselves, for being able to tell Sartaj that they had noticed. But they were pleasured also by the knowledge itself, by the pleasure of detection. Sartaj said, with exactly the right degree of eagerness, 'What did she notice?'

From the top of the filing cabinet, Jana snatched up an envelope. From it she pulled out a photograph, and held it up with a flourish. 'This.' And another photograph. 'And this.'

Sartaj put out a hand to steady the picture she was holding up. A girl. A girl in a model pose, looking over her shoulder. She wasn't an especially attractive girl.

'The photograph was in the bottom drawer of Jojo's desk,' Mary said. 'Under some bills.'

'Yes.' Sartaj was trying to remember if he had examined these photographs himself when he and Katekar had searched the study. There was nothing distinctive about them, nothing to remember. 'And so?'

Jana was astonished. 'You don't recognize her?' She held up another photograph.

Sartaj took it from her. This one was a portrait, with the hair falling forward and a wistful look. He turned it over. The name was noted in a neat hand, 'Jamila Mirza'. Which meant nothing to Sartaj. 'Who is she?'

Both Jana and Mary were looking at him with that tolerant, motherly patience that women practised when faced with male stupidity. Jana held up another piece of paper. 'This is a list of monies. I think they're payments, and they go on over months and years. Copies of passport pages, see, same girl. And copies of plane tickets, to Singapore. She went lots of times, see, sometimes every month. This wasn't a casual thing. This one was a regular girlfriend.'

'But we know that Jojo sent girls to Gaitonde. This girl is just one of those.'

'But do you know who this girl is?' Jana said.

'Jamila Mirza?'

'She was that. Then she became Zoya Mirza.'

'Miss India? The actress?'

'Yes. That one.'

Sartaj could see a resemblance, but he was doubtful. He pointed to Jamila Mirza's waist. 'This one's too fat.'

'Liposuction,' Jana said. 'Maybe the last ribs were taken out.'

Mary ran her finger over the portrait. 'Definitely had her nose done. And the hairline's been taken up.'

'There was work on the chin too,' Jana said. 'See how it's longer. And the jaws have been narrowed. So now that we've found this early Zoya, we give you to her. You have to tell us what happens with her, okay? Whatever you find out, you have to tell us. Promise?' She was an old-time and very regular *Stardust* reader for sure, this Jana, she was ravenous for nippy star natter.

'But are you sure this is her?'

'Yes,' they both said together.

They spoke with the certainty of experts, and they were very sure. This was their work. Sartaj had to believe them. 'Amazing,' he said. 'I could never have seen it.'

Mary laughed, and touched his hand, near the wrist. She said, 'That's all right. Men never do.'

Ganesh Gaitonde is Recruited Again

I was arrested on a Thursday afternoon. They came for me in Gopalmath, at my home. Policemen were a familiar enough sight in my darbar, they knew very well my exact address, where I lived. I had never hidden away. They came sometimes to look for one of our boys, sometimes to ask me questions, sometimes even to ask for a favour on the quiet. I welcomed them always, gave them chai and biscuits and answers and then sent them on their way. This time it was the muchchad Majid Khan and three sub-inspectors I didn't know, and ten constables, all in plain clothes. 'Sit, sit,' I said. 'Arre, some cold drinks for them,' I called.

But Majid Khan didn't sit. His boys spread themselves about the room, and Majid Khan said, 'Parulkar Saab got a warrant issued this morning. I have to arrest you.'

'Your Parulkar Saab is mad, the maderpat,' I said. 'He doesn't have a single proof against me. Not one witness.'

'Now he does,' he said. 'We lifted that chutiya Nilesh Dhale from Malad last week. He had a pistol on him, and another one in his suitcase. So Parulkar Saab has you for harbouring criminals and complicity in criminal acts, and also for being in possession of illegal weapons. And it being in the suitcase means it was being transported, so movement and selling of armaments also. He'll add on anti-national activities. What else does he need? After two slaps across the face, Dhale is singing like a bird. By tomorrow Parulkar will have you involved in the conspiracy to kill Mahatma Gandhi.'

'I didn't hand any pistols to that bastard Dhale, did I? For this loose change you're going to arrest me? Parulkar can't make any of it stick.'

'There's no need to make any of it stick, you know this. All he needs is you inside for a while, you know that.'

I knew very well: I lived under TADA, and under TADA a while could last a decade. Under this act they could keep me inside for the entire duration of any trials, no bail, nothing, not even if it took six years, or ten. At the end of it all you could be completely acquitted, but you had still spent years behind bars. This is why Suleiman Isa and his main lieutenants had gone abroad, for fear of TADA and fake encounters. This Majid Khan was respectful enough, because he was a small inspector, and he knew my connections to the Rakshaks, who could be in power as early as the next elections, the next year. But right now there was a Congress government in the state, and his Parulkar Saab was close to them, and so I was to go in.

'Come quietly,' Majid Khan said very deferentially. 'I have ten more men in plain clothes outside, all armed. And two more vans around the corner, two minutes from here. Any trouble and we'll have a war neither of us wants.'

He was saying this because Bunty and two of the boys were standing at the door, facing off with the policemen. From my expression they could see something was wrong. I could hear anxious shouting from outside, and running feet. Bunty and the boys could resist, but I would be dead. Looking at Majid Khan I knew this. He was being careful out of concern for his future, but if it came down to it he was his boss's man, and he would draw his pistol. There were many who would be very happy if he shot me dead: Suleiman Isa, Parulkar and his friends in the police, a Congress administration filled with Isa's allies, a dozen industrialists who were paying us month by month. No, resistance was silly, and in this life, whoever I was married to, jail was my sasural. I would live through it, and with ease, because I was Ganesh Gaitonde. So I calmed Bunty down, and told him to take charge, and be careful. I said a quick goodbye to my wife and son, and went.

The police had a remand order for fourteen days, and they extended and re-extended it six times. For eighty-four days they kept me in the police lock-up in Savara, near Kailashpada. There was one room, ten by ten, a dirty mattress, a matka of unfiltered tap water, a bucket, a stinking hole in the ground for a latrine, and me. Parulkar kept me alone, away from any of my boys who might be passing through the lock-up on the way to jail, away from friends as well as enemies. They took me to court with a hood over my head, manacles on my feet and wrists, only me in a jeep with five riflemen. 'You're our special guest,' Parulkar told me. 'Our VIP guest.' The drives to court were the only time I felt the sun, and even then I was afraid because if they were going to encounter me, it would be during these trips. The story would run: Gaitonde's boys tried to rescue him, Gaitonde tried to escape, so we had to shoot him. I had spent years surrounded by my boys, by the comfort of their weapons, and now I learnt all over again what it means to be truly alone. Every day I awoke to the fizzing of the tube-light in the corridor outside my cell, and expected to die. Death had been close to me for a long time, but now I felt that I was walking, moment by passing moment, on the edge of an enormous chasm, that the difference between the sunlight and the abyss was just one quick nudge from one of Parulkar's men. Every night I was afraid to sleep, because I didn't know if I would wake up.

And every day, they interrogated me. On the days that it was Majid Khan or one of the other inspectors, the interrogation passed quickly, with rounds of tea and me making up stories about dead shooters. They pushed me, they asked quick questions, they tried to catch me out in contradictions and errors. 'But you said yesterday that Sandeep Aggarwal took the money to Bada Badriya in June, how could he have paid off his debts in April?' They were clever, but not as clever as me, I enjoyed telling them stories. I had a very good memory, I remembered all the connections between the tales I made up, and so I remained consistent, and I frustrated them and I intrigued them. It was better to be in the interrogation room with its windows and the treetops outside and the fresh air than in my stifling grave of a cell. And for all their policemen's curiosity, and their urgent desire to know everything I knew, they never laid a hand on me. They had lives to build, careers to worry about. If my Rakshak friends were to become tomorrow's ministers, and I remembered these small policemen with malice tomorrow, tomorrow itself they might be transferred to Aurangabad. So we were men together, and they brought me good food from the hotel across the road, and paan, and fresh clothes. For my stomach-aches, which had started on my first day in the lock-up, they brought me podhina tablets and jaljira.

But when Parulkar led the interrogations it was a different game altogether. It was always at night. He sat in an armchair, his shoes off, quite relaxed. He had me stand in the middle of the room, directly under the hanging light, and he always had two of his inspectors standing behind me. He asked his questions as if he was talking to a

452

friend about their trip to Lonavla next Saturday, easy and quiet. But then the blows would follow, sudden whipping gusts against my calves that staggered me forward, deep thumps on my back that emptied me of breath. I was driven to my knees time and again, and panting on the floor, I hated him. They lifted me up each time, and he started again. Questions, questions. His face hidden beyond the circle of light, his belly lifted up towards me. I endured. It was the insult of barking cuffs to the back of my head I could not bear, the slaps that stung tears from my eyes, the numbing flares that lit up my eyes from the inside. When Majid Khan was present during one of Parulkar's sessions, I felt his hate in his punches to the small of my back, all that anger he hid for survival's sake. When he was freed by Parulkar's direct orders, he hit me hard. During the fifth interrogation, that fat bastard Parulkar began to laugh at me. 'Look at the great Ganesh Gaitonde crying like a little girl,' he said. 'Look at him bawling.' I wasn't. I wasn't crying. I was wiping tears from my cheeks, but they were from the sharp cracks on my ears, which started the tears instantly. It was automatic, my body reacting like it would to coal-dust in the eyes, and had nothing to do with me weeping. But that maderchod Parulkar was sure. He leaned forward in his chair to laugh at me, and looking at his fat pig's nose, his little teeth, I knew he would kill me. He was Suleiman Isa's man, and he was bound to his political masters, and unlike his subordinates, he was quite willing to hurt me, he would snap my bones, he wouldn't stop at the slaps and the patta, he would beat my feet with lathis and attach electrodes to my golis. He was too far gone down his road with his allies to be afraid of me. Between him and me there could be no accommodation, and he would make me suffer.

So I decided to cry for him. I had to play it exactly right, he was an old, old khiladi, and he had questioned thousands of men, broken each of them. He had come up through the ranks because he was wily as an old crow, he had tip-toed through a lifetime of traps, watching with these squinty steel eyes of his. If I wept too hard, or too easily, he would see it, know it for fraud. So I acted the opposite, that I was ashamed, that I was trying to hold it in, that I was reaching for courage. That I was flinching despite myself from the blows, and splintering under them. I gave him his victory, an easy one but one that he worked for nevertheless. When I finally begged, he was burstingly greasy with pride and satisfaction. 'Give me something then,' he

453

said. 'Give me something and I'll send you back to your cell. Tomorrow you can even visit the doctor and get medicine for your stomach. Show him all your aches and pains.' I did. I gave him two shooters, small freelancers you could hire for three thousand rupees. They worked for everyone, for Suleiman Isa, for us, for anyone else, they were buyable. So I sold them to Parulkar for a little peace, for a radio in my cell, and for visits to the doctor. He was very pleased when I told him the three places they slept, and even more pleased when they picked them up that same night and encountered them before the sun was up. They must have had the reporters already tipped off that evening, because the story was in the next day's afternoon papers, complete with photographs of the dead men.

So then he trusted his power over me. The very next afternoon they sent me down to the doctor, a doctor who came to the station and met me in the room next to Parulkar's office. He prodded at my stomach, wrote out prescription slips, told me I had too much tension and left. I handed the slip to the constable who had brought me into the room and had watched over the examination. This was a man named Salve. I talked to Salve. I told him to get my medicine, and that my lawyer would give him the money. And that my lawyer would help him with anything that he needed, that Salve could depend on me. That we could be friends. That friends were a good thing to have in this world, in this kaliyug we lived in. Salve was scared, but he listened. My lawyer paid him for the medicines, and added about ten times more than that as a tip. Here, he told Salve, a gift from Bhai. A man like Salve, with his three children and wife and long and broad family of mother and retired father and widowed sister and her children, a man like that needs money. He must have it. So Salve took my money, and then I had a link to my boys outside. My lawyer had carried messages before this, and brought news, but it was good to have Salve. He was in the lock-up every day, he escorted me from there to here, he brought me food and water and batteries for the radio, and also reports from the company, and questions, and requests. We were wary of using him at first, but as he took more from us, he became ours. By the end of my remand days, between him and my lawyer I felt that I was leading my company again. I was connected, reconnected.

But all these passed messages didn't save me from the four walls of my cell, from the night-time quiet when footsteps on the far stairs walked across the back of my skull and made me twistingly uneasy and unable to sleep. In the afternoons I lay sweating on the stone floor, trying to cool my shoulders, my hips. I had forgotten how to be alone. I had lived for so long with my boys and my wife and my son, so close to them, that in this cell I felt that I was dropping through a void, drifting endlessly in a cloud of shadows. They had put me at the end of a blind turn in the corridor, behind an outer door that shut me off from the other prisoners. I was alone. The radio sputtered and caught, and I positioned its aerial with a thousand fine adjustments, I held it against a part of the wall that gave it greater voice. And then, when I could coax a song from it, I was eaten by nostalgia. To the thin, crackling warbles of sixties songs I relived my own days from a decade ago, from a month ago. And when the songs stopped, I felt questions come alive in my head, like a nest of parasites: what lies in the future? What had gone wrong in the past, to bring me to this? Why was I not more powerful than Suleiman Isa, more famous? Why was my company only third or fourth in power and prominence? Would my weapons-smuggling bring me more power, more connections? Would I grow bigger? Since I had started working with Bipin Bhonsle and his Sharma-ji, I had felt that I was participating in a very large game, a game so big that despite my recent growth I was dwarfed in it. I had become small again, and this was frightening and thrilling at the same time. In this huge, spinning battle, Bhonsle and Sharma-ji were my allies, and I had made my bonds with them, chosen them as they had chosen me. They were my side, my team. But what was the purpose? Where was the end of the war? Why? Why? This 'why' ran in my head, round and around, like a rat trapped in an iron box. Why? And in its wake this 'why' left behind a hole carved by its scuttling claws, an emptiness sharp and hurtful. The only thing that filled this cavity, that healed it until the next morning, was love.

Every week, Subhadra visited the station with my son. She would have come every day, but Parulkar used her visits as leverage. He only gave me these weekly visits after I began feeding him information, and said that he would let me see my wife and son more often if I co-operated more fully. But I wouldn't give him too much, he thought he was crafty, but I was his baap. So we played our game, Parulkar and I, and I waited from Monday to Monday for my family.

I loved my son. His name was Abhijaya, and he made me helpless. I thought I had loved other people before, but now I found that I had either wanted them, or had depended on them, that was all. I had never known what love really was. When they had talked about love in the films, gone on about how true love meant wanting nothing for yourself, desiring only the happiness of the other, I had dismissed all that as poetic babble put about by weak men and women who hadn't the strength to take what they wanted. But now, holding this squirmy little bundle in my arms, I knew it was all true. He was a year old, very confident, and he reached up for my face and rubbed his hands over my stubble and giggled. I felt an irresistible soft gushing force crack open my chest and reach into me, and a low laugh came out of me, a feeling up and down my spine: a man has a bond with his own blood that goes down to the beating core, to the nerve and the bone. I had become a father absently, in passing, but nothing I had known before was like this storm-like current of connection that passed from this tiny brat to me. I would let him do anything to me, and I would do anything for him. With him I had no statesmanlike grandeur to protect, no power to extend.

But I told Subhadra that she must be careful of her dignity in these filthy holes filled with police, that she had to learn to be strong, to be mother to the boys, that aside from our own Abhijaya she had these other hundred sons, hundreds of sons, the whole strength of the company. I told her that she had to protect my izzat both inside the lock-up and outside it, that she had to be strong. She looked more mature now, not older but now with layers of experience under that still-girlish face. There was just more of her there now, as if the floating particles of the flighty girl she had been had settled against each other, become more dense and strong, and now there was this Subhadra who listened quietly and gave good advice and would go out and tell my boys what to do. Bunty was my main support, but Subhadra was no less, and everyone knew this. The boys took this as somehow natural, but she had surprised me, I who took pride in never being surprised had been astonished by her and her son, and I didn't mind that somehow my wicket had been clean-bowled by these two frail creatures.

They were playing a game now. Subhadra was hiding her face behind her hands and revealing herself, and Abhi was laughing each time. I was content to watch them. 'How is your stomach now?' Subhadra said, from behind her hands. She was a good girl. She had been trying to get me to eat basketfuls of plums, which she insisted would get rid of all my aches. I bantered with her, and rocked my boy, and I was happy.

And when my wife and son were gone, when Parulkar had finished with his attentions to me, when Majid Khan had put away his poisonous politeness, when Salve had left with his cringing obedience, when I was alone and pacing my ten feet of space, I was haunted by that bastard Salim Kaka, who had once taken me on a boat to find gold. I had killed him so long ago, and had never worried about it, but now I couldn't get away from him. He was there in my cell, walking next to me, taking one of his huge strides for every two of mine, handsome in his red lungi. I had shot him, yes, and taken his gold to start my life, but what of it? He had been stupid to have me behind him if he didn't know enough about me to trust me absolutely. He had not implanted fear and loyalty carefully in me, as I did with my boys. He had been careless, and so he had died. Why was I remembering him now? I didn't know, but I kept remembering how he had taught me to shoot, and his filthy jokes, and his sudden gifts of money. 'Here's a hundred, bachcha, go and see a picture, get a woman,' he would say. And I would. But now I needed no money from Salim Kaka, but here he was.

Then the police let me out at last, and away I went to jail. I cared little for the long charge sheet they were putting together – murder, giving shelter to criminals, extortion, issuing threats – and was mostly glad to see my boys again. It was the solitary confinement that had addled my mind, I thought, and brought on this attack of useless memory. Because I had been taken away from my home, from my entire web of closeness, I had been driven into the companionship of Salim Kaka. Now I was to be held in judicial custody, and from the court itself I was taken to jail. They didn't keep me waiting in the car park in the basement, like they did with the hundreds of other prisoners on their way to prison. They had a special escort for me, and a vehicle all to myself. All through this, I dreamed of Salim Kaka. In the van, on the way to jail, I grinned and grinned at my own silliness. Majid Khan and the other escorting inspectors were puzzled. 'Don't be too happy,' the muchchad said, putting aside his carefulness for once. 'You're not getting out in a hurry.' What he didn't know was that I was getting out, getting out of myself. In solitary I had known my own prison too well. I was ready to be smothered by the proximity of my boys again, by their love. The jailers and Majid Khan took me through the big red double doors of the jail, through the small inset gate. They signed me into the jail, and then there was a long wait in the superintendent's

457

room until he showed up. He was a wiry old bandicoot named Advani who gave me a lecture on co-operative living. My boys were in Barrack Four, he told me, and the Suleiman Isa crowd was in Barrack Two. He was depending on me to keep the peace, he said. There had been too much trouble lately, too much fighting, even though he tried to keep old enemies apart as much as possible. Since we all had to make the best of our situation, he said, it was best to live in peace. And so he was depending on me.

I listened quietly. I agreed with everything he said. Despite all the stories I had heard about jail, this was a new world to me, and until I knew my ground I was quite willing to be a silent mouse. Advani was very satisfied with himself, the balding bastard thought he had impressed Ganesh Gaitonde by the force of his personality and the strength of his logic. 'If you have a problem,' he said, 'don't fear to come to me.'

'Yes, superintendent saab,' I said. 'Of course.' Of course he must have heard that the famous Gaitonde had been broken by Parulkar, that the fearsome don was really just a scared little roadside dog, dirty and scarred, who might run to him at the first outbreak of trouble. I bore his condescension, and lowered my gaze, and was led out by the warders into the jail. We passed through three great slotted metal doors, and then into the long inside court, where the barracks stood sparkling white inside their respective walls. Superintendent Saab had them painted recently, one of the warders told me, Superintendent Saab was keen on cleanliness. There was white trim along the paths, and flowerpots at the corners. In this late afternoon the prisoners were confined to barracks, and so there was nobody on the paths, or in the yards that lay between the barracks, or under the eight trees that marched up the expanse. But when we walked by Barrack Two, there was a great eruption of catcalls and cries and jokes. 'Please, please, Parulkar Saab,' they shouted. 'Don't make me dirty my pants, Parulkar Saab,' they called. They had heard, Suleiman Isa's bastards. No matter. I walked on.

In Barrack Four they were waiting for me, my boys. They had put together a garland from saved gulmohar flowers and neem leaves. I let them put the garland on me, I hugged them all and then I put them to work. Clean this place up, I told them, you're a disgrace. They grinned and laughed and set to work. Bhai doesn't put up with a mess, they said. They were glad to be ordered, to be directed. There were fifty-eight of them, known and accredited members of the company, out of a total of three hundred and nine in this barrack, which was one of the smaller ones, built originally to house a hundred. My boys ruled the barrack, owned the most space and all the best beds, ran the games, and controlled what went in and what went out. A small band of committed men loyal to each other will always rule a large, disorganized majority, and with me there, their force was increased tenfold. It is in the mind that cowards are overpowered, and the mass of men is always full of fear. My boys set about cleaning and straightening, and the whole barrack followed them, without having to be told. Soon the long room, with its double rows of thin blue dhurries lining either wall, was swept and ordered and clean. There wasn't much we could do with the shirts on the dangling wires, and the drying underwear strung on the walls, and the little piles of papers and photographs and magazines. But still, here was a place I could live in, that had my impress on it. The boys had a bed for me at the far end of the barrack, the furthest from the main door and therefore the safest. They arrayed themselves on all sides of me, in a protective series of rings, and in the centre they put three new dhurries piled on top of each other to make a mattress, and a pillow, and a little shelf made out of plywood taken from the jail workshop. They were good boys.

Their leaders were Rajendra Date and Kataruka, both of whom I knew from operations outside. Both had been senior shooters, and though I had been distanced from their activities by their controllers, I had spoken to both on the phone, and rewarded them. Both were serving murder sentences, and so both were jail veterans: Date had finished five years, and Kataruka seven. But neither had broken, or given up their controllers or anyone else, and they were doing their duty with honour. So we had supported their families outside with regular monthly salary packets, and bonuses, and had seen to weddings and hospital bills and property debts. Now they sat with me, knee to knee, and told me everything about the daily routine in this jail.

Date did the talking, mostly, with Kataruka nodding along and grunting occasionally. 'Inside the campus, bhai, inside the big wall, there are eight barracks, bhai, each with its own chotti wall. First barrack is for new prisoners, which you skipped. That's the most crowded, maybe seven, eight hundred men in it. From it they move prisoners into the other barracks. Number Two barrack is Suleiman

Company, bhai. Number Three is the baba room, all young boys, children. Four is us. Five has the old ones in it, all white-haired. There's one chutiya there who is eighty-four, he suddenly killed his wife, finally couldn't stand her snoring. Barracks Six and Seven is all the general lot, your average prisoner is put in there. Behind the barbed wire, over there, is eight, for women and girls. Very close, but no traffic goes from here to there.' He grinned. 'Only the maderpat jailers and inspectors exploit, not the common citizen. But here, in our barrack, we have settings for all other things. We can get oil, tea, masala, all kinds of food through the warders. We've already made the setting for you to get tiffin from home, bhai, so you don't have to eat this dirty jail food. In a day or two that should start. But if you're ever hungry, we can make a handi out of tin cans, burn coconut oil and cook with that. But if the constables see the fire they shout, bastards, and sometimes they put offenders in chains. But they don't trouble us, bhai, we can make you chai any time. Anything else you want, you let us know. The warders are all ours in this barrack, all doing life terms. And through the lawyers, we have a setting with many of the sessions court judges, we can usually get court dates moved around. Sometimes if a judge is paid enough, we can get emergency decrees for bail. But not for you, bhai.' My case was too heavy, too much in the news for quick bail. That we all knew. 'It's hot in here, bhai, in the summer, and cold in the winter. On the other end, close to Barrack One, there is a hospital, where there are actual beds with real mattresses, and fans. We have a setting with the doctors, for a small amount you can get admitted for a few days. The food is better there, too. If you want, you can go to the hospital for a holiday. That's easy.'

I didn't want a holiday. I wanted Suleiman Isa, or a few of his men. 'I want to hit those bastards in Barrack Two,' I said. 'They're happy that I'm in here. Let's show them what it means.'

'That's not so easy, bhai. They only let them and us out into the yard at different periods. When we're locked up, they're out. After a riot last year they started doing that. It's a jail rule, the warders can't go against it, or the staff. Or we would have done it already.'

They were both glad to see me ferocious, Date and Kataruka. Of course they had heard the rumours too, that I had broken under Parulkar's pressure. They were my men, pillars of my company, but I was sure a little doubt had seeped through their protective walls of faith. It was time to make things orderly again, set the world back to rights. I quizzed them some more, about jail procedure and customs, and then I told them to let me sleep. It was only early evening, hours still to go before the eight o'clock lights-out. But Date and Kataruka hushed the barrack, and I lay on my dhurries, and turned on my right side, and put an arm over my head, and fell instantly into black sleep. After weeks of trying to twist myself into rest, and thrashing awake from shallow dozing, I slept deep and long.

I awoke to the morning whistle, at five o'clock, feeling fit and fine, and ready for my war. The boys knew my need for cleanliness, so they had seen to it that the latrines had been rescued from their usual filth, and in the bathrooms full buckets of water were waiting, and a fresh towel. I was quick, and then Kataruka and Date came to get me. 'The mamus are here,' Date said. The constables were waiting by the door, and they led us outside in rows of two for the counting. Under the greying sky they walked up and down, counting, and while this ginti was going on, I discussed my plan with my two controllers. I had a plan already, the beginnings of a plan. Through the ginti and over breakfast we talked it through, and filled it in, and stretched it out, and I began to see it could really be done. After breakfast, the haval-dars saw us back into the barracks, where the mass of the prisoners now queued and quarrelled over the bathing and washing. A great hubbub arose under the rafters, a noise of men telling stories and arguing and playing cards and praying. At the north end of the bar-racks there was a makeshift temple, with bright pictures of Rama and Sita and Hanuman pasted on the wall, and here men sat in rows and sang bhajans. At the south end, the Muslims knelt in namaaz, facing a clean white wall. And through the long room men sat in clusters, and saw each other through the long hours until lunch. The warder and four of his assistants sat in pride of place, near a big radio turned up to full volume, and the songs trickled and floated to the far ends of the barracks: '*Mere sapnon ki rani kab aaye gi tu, aayi rut mastaani kab aaye gi tu . . .*'

In three weeks I was able to execute my plan. And in those three weeks, I learnt the rhythms of this new life: the whistle at five in the morning; the drowsy rows outside for the ginti; the rattling of alu-minium plates and bowls and the crackling of the tari on the dal, for which tari you paid extra; the long hours of the morning, and then the smell of cooking from the bissi where they kneaded the atta with their feet and threw rotting vegetables into huge bowls; after lunch at ten, the murmur of conversation and the snores and the smell of hundreds of men sweating; the smokers with their precious little balls of charas and their long rituals of burning and crumbling and rolling; the shifting games of chess, and teen-patti, and Ludo, and the curses and the laughter over the rattle of the dice; my boys ranged around the only two carrom boards in the barracks, feeding their passionate following of the championship league they had set up, complete with blackboards for singles and doubles ladders; the tussles and sudden enmities that flared between men packed together, that spread like winding fire through the rows of beds; the shouting and threats as two men faced each other under the eyes of a hundred, each too afraid of shame to back down; the brawny kalias from Nigeria selling tiny fifty-rupee packets of brown sugar in the yard; and their clients, hunched knee to knee in tight little circles over their chaser-pannis, breathing in the smoke with the devout expression of men who had seen another, better world. And the long wait for five o'clock and the dinner of the same watery dal, and the lumpy, coarse rice, and the rubbery chappatis, and then sleep at eight.

We lived this life, and dreamed of the outside. But this is the life we had to live, the only one. So I told Date and Kataruka something of my plan, and told them I needed two fresh men, two men unconnected to our company. But these needed to be two hard boys, capable of action, not the type who would boast and preen but then be paralysed by the sight of blood. Date and Kataruka complained, they shook their heads and said it was impossible to depend on men who had remained untested, untried. That's exactly why we make it hard to get into the company, they said, so we can see if the applicant has the belly for the job. That's why we send them on errands first, a minor beating or two, so they can prove themselves, make their way up in the proper manner. But no, I insisted. I want new faces, two with no earlier connection to us.

So they found me two, Dipu and Meetu. These were brothers originally from up north, they had come to Bombay with degrees from some college in gaandu Gorakhpur. They were twenty-two and twenty-one, real bhaiyyas, farmer's sons. They had stayed with some taxi-driving fellow Gorakhpuri, and tossed about from job to job. Dipu had sold detergent door to door, Meetu had worked as a salesman in a bathroom fittings shop. They were eager lads, full of energy, and they had gone up and down the length of the city, hanging from the trains, seeing all the sights. Just when they had been broken a bit, when they had begun to understand that all dreams didn't come true in this Mumbai, that not every fool from UP became Shah Rukh Khan, they got a call from a second cousin in Lucknow. He had a scheme, a project. He said he was going to start a business in Lucknow, with some buying and selling to do in Bombay. For that he needed to open a bank account in the city, have some funds available and ready there. So Dipu and Meetu were to start a joint account. He would send them the money to deposit in the account, and further instructions about who was to be paid and so on. A week later they received, by courier, a bank draft for a lakh and a half. The draft went through, and as instructed, they took forty thousand for expenses. A high time they had then, and a week later, another draft arrived, this time for two lakhs. The bank manager told them that the formalities would take a day, that the funds would be released the next morning. So back to the bank our two brothers went. They went to the counter, grinning, and the next second, they were down on the ground, with policemen's pistols pushing into their necks.

'Unmarked jeeps, bhai,' Dipu said. He was the one telling the story. 'And so we were trapped. The drafts were stolen, they told us while they beat us at the station. We had been betrayed by our own cousin.'

'Listen, bhenchod,' I said. 'You act innocent in front of the judge. If you tell me lies, I'll tear off your golis. You mean to tell me that you opened an account and deposited drafts out of innocence? What kind of business was it supposed to be?'

He swallowed. 'I don't know, bhai.'

'You didn't know, and you obeyed your cousin blindly? And you thought you were getting forty thousand for going to a bank in a clean shirt and pants? Maderchod, don't lie to me. You knew quite well those were stolen drafts.'

He and his brother had the same broad face, as homely as a shovel. He blinked, thought and then gave up. 'Yes, bhai. Only we thought one more draft wouldn't hurt.'

They were jumped-up peasants who thought they knew more than they did, and so they had fallen easily into the hands of the police. Dipu told me the rest of the story. The police had thrashed the name and address and phone number of the cousin out of them, but of course the cousin had flown his Lucknow coop. Then the policiyas beat them some more, on the bottom of the feet with pattas, on the

463

hands with canes, in the kidneys with fists. They threatened them with encounters, told them they were going to drive them to the seaside and put bullets in their heads. They told them they were going to send the UP police to their father's farm, to their mother's kitchen. 'Bataa re,' the inspectors said. 'Kaad rela.' But these brothers had nothing more to tell, and the cousin was gone, so finally the investigation was closed, and Dipu and Meetu were in jail, awaiting trial. The inspector on their case had told them that if they paid him a lakh, he would not object in court to them getting bail, and for fifty thousand, the public prosecutor would also keep quiet, and so then their lawyer's notice would sail through the court, and they would be out on bail. And even though they were in on serious charges, not just 420 for cheating, but also 467 and 468 for forgery, the inspector could manage bail for them. For a higher price, even, the whole case could be managed. But Dipu and Meetu had already spent whatever they had left of the forty thousand on their lawyer, and they had spent whatever little their father could come up with. So here they were, in judicial custody, waiting for their trial, waiting for their dates. They had been inside now for six months. There were men who had been waiting for a year. There were some ragged bastards who had waited for three years, and for four, and – so I heard – even a few for seven. So Dipu and Meetu, who had acted like fools but were capable of learning, had made approaches to my boys. And now they were talking to me, in the bathrooms of Barrack Four, long after nightfall.

I took them in. They told me they were capable of bloody work, that growing up in Gorakhpur had hardened them, that student union politics there meant canvassing with knife and lathi, that their district had produced several famous dakoos, that it was in their blood. I hadn't the opportunity of testing them, because they had to stay quiet, stay unnoticed, stay separate from my company. But they were mine.

Every week, I went to the special court for my bail hearings. The jailers always put other prisoners in the van, anyone who had a hearing at court that day. So Dipu and Meetu went to court in the same van as I did, we arranged it so with the lawyers and the judges. It was me, these two brothers, and either Date or Kataruka. We alternated these last two, and so it was always one of them sitting to my left, on the bench that ran down the side of the van. At my feet, on the ground, among the general ruck of prisoners, Dipu and Meetu. And opposite me, facing us, on the other bench, men from other companies. It was always like this in the van: the bhais sat on the benches, and the ordinary prisoners on the floor. Date and Kataruka would have preferred that I was not there at all when we executed the plan, they didn't want to expose me to danger. They tried to persuade me to leave it all to them, but I told them that it was crucial that I be there, that without me there was no need for this plan. Then I told them to shut up. And day after day, I waited in the van.

The first two weeks, on the facing bench were men from other companies, not Suleiman Isa's. The third week, Kataruka and I were already sprawling on our bench when the Suleiman Isa boys came into the van. There were four of them, none that I recognized, but Kataruka sat up to my left, flexing the rope on his wrists. We went to the courts bound like animals, roped to each other. But there was rope enough for what we had to do. The Suleiman Isa men arranged themselves, made themselves comfortable, and grinned at me. They were amused, and they were without fear.

'What are you laughing at, maderchod?' Kataruka said. He was very fair, my Kataruka, but very pock-marked. Quiet most of the time, but he spoke up then.

'No need for tension,' I said to him. I was very relaxed myself. I could feel my blood singing, but I felt calm. The Suleiman Isa boys were quite relaxed too, because they were four and we were two, because they had heard that I was really a coward.

'Is your gaand still sore?' one of them said to me. 'We heard that Parulkar took it every night for months. He said that you were a good gaadi to mount, that you moaned like a girl.'

I smiled back at him. 'Parulkar is an honest policeman,' I said. 'What he says must be true.' I shifted back on the bench and raised my knee, put my foot up on the bench, and scratched at my ankle.

They were laughing, all of them. The front doors of the van clanked shut, and the engine creaked itself up into a long vibration that drowned out their giggles, and the van jerked forward, and I said very quietly, 'Dipu.'

He was fast all right, this Dipu. I barely saw his hand move, it passed, and the Suleiman Isa boy on the right, for a moment he didn't even know he had been cut. He just sat, and then the blood sprayed across the van. And then we were on them, cutting. We were using blades, not the shaving kind but the heavier industrial ones that are used for cutting cardboard or tape, which we had smuggled from the jail workshop. We had split each blade in half, melted rubber on the broken side to make a kind of handle, and then we had slid the blades into the sides of our rubber Kitto chappals, into the heels. It took a second's knocking with a fingertip to find the blade in the chappal and pull it gently out. And then we were on them, cutting.

They were all sliced before any of them could raise a hand in defence. They were expecting two, and we were four. Make a man bleed and you will break his courage. And I had told my boys to go for their eyes. A razor blade will not kill, but it will put blood in the eyes and blind. So only two of them really fought back, the other two were shouting and panicking and trying to lose themselves in the howling mêlée of prisoners. I was calm. I dodged and waited and cut, and cut. There is a vast pressure of blood in a man's head, a quantity that you cannot imagine. It squirts like a pichkari, in quick jets with the beating of the heart. Our attack must have lasted barely a minute, but in the pleasure of my stabbing and slashing, time expanded into a long emporium of opportunities. I tell you I could see through the confusion and know the opening before it existed, I could wait and weave and then come through precisely and *cut*. In my calm I knew the van was stopped and the havaldars and the inspectors were struggling with the doors. I swayed back from the struggle, back towards the bench, let myself sit. 'Give me the lambi,' I snapped out to Meetu.

With a roll of his eyes he slapped it into my left hand, the lambi that he had carried inside his blue legal file, tucked behind the thick sheaf of papers and notices and reports. The lambi was actually a hinge from a bathroom door inside the barrack, carefully unscrewed and then shaped and sharpened on stone, given a handle by a wrapping of electrical wire. With it in my hand I went knee over knee, over the mass of men. I had seen the one I wanted, seen his face masked dark with blood. He put up his hands as I came towards him. There was a single twisting thrust, with my shoulder behind it, that I knew completely before I ever did it. I put the lambi in his neck. Then the policemen were on us.

They dragged us out with a great shouting and hubbub, there were dozens of them. We were grinning at each other. There was a cut on the back of Dipu's left hand. 'I cut myself, bhai,' he said. 'But I cut them more.'

'Chutiya,' I said, smiling.

466

Then they dragged us off to the anda cells. Into the high tanki-shaped building we went, and into the sunless cells. The others they shoved two by two through the low doors of the cells, but they took me down one level and made me bend and shoved me forward and then I was alone. It was dark, very dark. Finally I could make out two concrete slabs on either side of the circular room, and a hole in the ground between them. Two beds and a latrine. I was sweating. I felt my way around the walls, as high as I could go. No windows, not a shelf or a switch or a plug, nothing but the egg-smooth concrete. I sat on one of the beds for a long time. Then I took off my shirt and folded it and made a pillow. I lay down. Then I started laughing.

They kept me in the anda cell for two weeks. They shoved food and water through the door, and I lived alone in that stinking hell. The dark, it is the dark that cuts your heart, that slices through your brain. I tried to keep track of the hours, I tried to walk around the cell in fast circles, to keep healthy. I tried to sleep, and keep awake during what must have been the day. But soon I couldn't tell any more. I tried to calculate time by the meals, but they must have given me food when-ever they felt like it, it came to me cold and congealed, and I could swear that many days and nights passed before I heard the door scrape open again. And there was the rasp of my own breath, in and out, in and out, for centuries. I would open my eyes and know that only a minute had passed, or two. Yet I had been walking for an eter-nity along a swampy seashore. Another long minute waited, stretching its chasm before me. And then another one. I tried to imag-ine a clock, I hammered a nail into the wall and hung up a gold clock, with one of those swinging weights, I thought I could have it keep time for me. But my clock yawned and melted and vanished, and its hands curled and looped. I had heard that the anda cells could drive men into madness, and now this black room was testing me.

In this dark, women came to me. They walked through me with a cool tinkling of anklets. I lay flat on my back and they were floating above me, with their slim, red-patterned feet and dimpled ankles. The edges of their ghagras brushed softly across my cheeks, and I felt their footsteps on my chest, light as a blessing. In this indistinct dream, in the airy touch of their gauzes, I was delivered from my prison. They talked among themselves in a murmuring just under my understanding, in a whispering that became a faint music. I floated. I was gone.

When they took me out of the anda cell I didn't know how long it had been, two weeks or two thousand years. I shielded my eyes and asked nothing from the jail staff, or the policemen. Parulkar was there, abusive and puffed out in that strutting-cock way of his, and under his lead they dragged all of us through the compound and into the superintendent's office. Then there was of course more abuse and threats, and warnings of added charges and long sentences. But all of it was an empty show, because they knew and we knew that it had been our win. It was a small skirmish, but we had won. And however minor our conquest had been, it made a world of difference to my boys, and to me. Sometimes, that's how it is. So, standing straight under the fuss that the jailers and Parulkar were making, I came back to myself. On the desk there was a calendar that told me the date, 28 December. I had been inside the anda cell for thirteen days and one night. Time fell into place around me, with the sound of metal falling on to metal. I stood up straight. I kept myself quiet, kept my face straight and my eyes lowered, but I grew strong again. From the commotion they were making, it was clear that they were trying to fight me back from my moral victory. I knew that all my boys, in the barrack and outside, had heard of our battle, and they were strong again. I kept quiet. I was satisfied.

It was only back in the barrack that I learnt the details of our triumph. The bastard whose neck I had punctured was one of Suleiman Isa's top controllers, directly reporting to the boys in Dubai. Miraculously, the maderchod had lived, but he was still in the hospital, covered with long arcs of stitches. The doctors were expecting him to suffer lifelong nerve damage. The others had come back to their barrack with their heads shaved and swathed in bandages, and there was much comedy whenever my boys were within shouting distance of their windows: 'Anyone got a headache? Anyone need a champi?' Our injuries were trifling: there was Dipu's small wound, and Kataruka had a cut on his right calf, probably from Dipu or Meetu swinging wildly in the van. But they all looked dazed from the anda cell. Meetu was shivering, trying to keep it down but shaking nevertheless, despite the afternoon heat. I had to take command. 'All right,' I said to the boys clustering around. 'We'll celebrate later. Give us some tea. Then it's a bath for everyone, and rest. Arrange water.'

It was done. Finally we lay together in a circle, our feet pointing in, our bodies the spokes of a wheel, and the rest of the boys took turns to fan us. It was a pleasure to talk, to look up into the rafters and see light, to know the progression of a day. Dipu and Meetu were talking about women, about the prodigies of chodoing they were going to achieve when they got out. Kataruka was laughing at them. 'You ganwars,' he said. 'You think those Lamington Road whores are women? They're bhenchod worse than animals. You might as well chodo the next bitch you see nosing around in a garbage dump. You'll never know the true pleasure of a woman unless you woo her, until she falls in love with you and gives it of her own will. A convent-educated girl, who has been brought up well, who is shy, who is reserved – that's the true test of a man. But why tell you two about this, you'll never in your life come within sniffing distance of a girl like that.' So then of course they begged and whined to be instructed, my fine, dangerous dakoo brothers. I listened to Kataruka go on, and into the evening he imparted the secrets of seduction. 'When you are courting her,' he said, 'you must be Kishore Kumar. And I don't mean just that you sing Kishore songs to her, no. You have to let the voice of Kishore Kumar move through you, and become that effortlessly confident, that happy, that funny, that breezy. If you can do that, happily she'll come to you, boss. Then, once that happens, once you've got her, then you've to sing Mohammed Rafi, and only Rafi.'

'Why?' said our Meetu, yawning. 'If you've already peloed, why sing anything?'

Kataruka sat up, reached over and rapped Meetu on the head with his knuckles. 'Listen, gaandu. Listen carefully. You sing Rafi because otherwise you'll never get to pelo her again. Rafi is your royal return road to her chut.' He turned to me. I was laughing. 'What are we going to do with these farmers, bhai?'

I shook my head. 'And after Rafi, what do we sing next?'

'Ah, here's a man who knows life,' Kataruka said. He lay back again, stretched. 'When it is over, after she leaves you, or after you leave her – are you listening, chutiyas? – when you feel like your heart is being pulled out through your throat on a hook, then you sing Mukesh. Then Mukesh is your only way out, the only way you'll live to see another monsoon. Mukesh will heal you, so you can start singing Kishore again. So you have another chance. Understood, bastards? Kishore, Rafi, Mukesh.'

Meetu and Dipu nodded, but I knew they had barely understood anything. They were too young to know that you needed Rafi, much less Mukesh. They were grinning though, with their huge rabbit teeth. 'Let's have some Kishore,' I said. It was that kind of evening. We were all happy.

It turned out that Date was the one with the voice. '*Khwab ho tum ya koi haqiiqat, kaun ho tum batalaao*,' he sang. And then, '*Khilte hain gul yahaan, khilake bikharane ko, milte hain dil yahaan, milke bichhadne ko.*' The whole barrack grew quiet, and we listened to him. Each time he finished a song, there were calls for more, and requests for favourite numbers, and laughter. He acquired a team of backing singers and two tabla players, who used empty Dalda tins. When Date sang, he held his hand to his ear like a professional, and somewhere between songs I learnt that he had studied music as a child, that he came from a family of musicians, that his father played the trumpet in a wedding band until age took the power from his lungs, that Date's dream had been to be a playback singer. He sang '*Pag ghungru baandh Mira naachi thi*' and '*Ye dil na hota bechaara*', and then it was time for dinner.

Later that night Date came to me, nudged at my shoulder. 'Bhai,' he said. 'Can't sleep?' I had been turning and curling, trying to find a stretch in my body, a repose that would let me drift off. I was trying to breathe long, evenly.

'What, Kishore Kumar?' I said.

'The trouble is we need women, bhai.'

'Of course we need women, sala. You'll get me a woman, maderpat? From their barrack?'

'No, no, bhai. Impossible. The jailers won't risk it, there's too much risk. The warders don't have access. In any jail. Only once it's happened – you remember that woman Kamardun Khan?'

'Drug smuggler, yes?'

'Yes, she was an independent, ran brown sugar. She was in Arthur Road jail, and her boyfriend Karan Pradhan was in the men's barracks.'

'From the Navlekar company?'

'Yes, that Karan. Bhai, this Kamardun Khan was in love with Karan Pradhan. So she used to climb the nine-foot wall of the barrack, jump into the main compound. She bribed the sentries and the warders, and went to the men's barrack and spent many nights in every week with her chhava.'

'That's a woman.'

'Some say she gave the sentries a little taste too, just to get to Karan Pradhan.'

'That's love.'

'After they got out, she gave him a car. A brand-new Contessa.'

'He's dead now?'

'The Dubai boys got him, at his garage. They killed him in the Contessa.'

'And her?'

'She went crazy. Started trying to fight Suleiman Isa. She learnt how to fire a gun, got involved with a police inspector. She thought the inspector would help her get her revenge.'

'But?'

'The Dubai boys had her stabbed to death. Some say that the inspector sold her out to S-Company, told them where to find her.'

'That's tragedy.'

He sighed. For a moment I thought he would sing a Mukesh song. Then he gathered himself, and said, 'In this story there is drama, there is emotion, there is tragedy.' And we burst out into long cackles of laughter. We guffawed until the boys began to laugh at our laughter, at our frenzy.

'So,' I said, 'the Navlekar company has boys who are so handsome and so daring that women leap walls for them. What are my boys going to do for me?'

'I can't get you a woman,' Date said. 'But there is the other barrack.'

I knew of course which one he meant. 'The baba room?'

'There's one boy there, bhai,' he said, 'who has a bottom like you wouldn't believe, you see it and you'll swear it was Mumtaz's gaand.'

'How much?' I said.

'Three hundred for the warder, five for the sentry. A hundred or so for the gaadi.'

'Fine. Get five gaadis.'

'Five, bhai. One each for you and Kataruka and me?'

'And one each for the hero brothers.'

'But Mumtaz is yours, bhai. You just wait and see.'

Once I had counted out the money, it took less than half an hour to bring them over. Then there was a great huffing and humping in the darkness. Under my fingers the gaadi did feel like Mumtaz. In my early days in the city, when I had lived on the footpath and slept on cement, I had taken boys. But now I knew much more about women, and so I shut my eyes and saw Mumtaz. She moaned under me. Afterwards I was relaxed, and slept well.

The next morning, in my tiffin, wrapped in plastic and hidden in rice, there was a phone. It was like a small brick, but dense and heavy, and came with its own plug. Date and Kataruka sat close to me as I peeled away the plastic. There was a small quill of paper rubber-banded to the phone. 'PWR button makes it go on. Dial 022, then my number, then press OK,' was what it said, in Bunty's writing. We did, and he picked up on the first ring. 'Who is it?' he said.

'Your baap.'

'Bhai!'

'Where did you get this?'

'It's just off the boat, bhai. And very expensive. But fine, no?'

'Very fine.'

'You're the first man in the city to get one.'

'I am?'

'Okay, maybe second or third.'

He was exaggerating, of course. There were probably a few dozen rich bastards who already had mobile phones then, in those days long ago, but among the companies ours was the first to use them extensively. And this, in jail, was our first. I was very pleased with Bunty, and I told him so. He was the kind of man I liked, always looking ahead, moving with the times. We talked business. There was much to talk about. There was the ordinary business to take care of – our collections from various industries and businesses, our interests in real estate, our importing of electronics and computer parts, our cash investments in the entertainment industry. And then there was the uncommon project of arms smuggling, which took much care, we had to make the plans foolproof, pay much attention to detail. We moved only one shipment every six months or so, but each boatload ran into the crores, and the product itself was heavy and difficult to disguise and transport. Yet we had been completely successful so far, and our client was pleased. We used my old friends Gaston and Pascal, only their boat, and a minimal crew. And my company was better equipped as a result. We were confident in our strength. Bunty and I talked this back and forth, and were careful to code: AK-47s were jhadoos, and bullets were sweets, and a trawler was a bus. In all our dealings for these arms, our only client was Sharma-ji, who was always on time, always punctual with his substantial payments, always perfectly dressed in his perfect white dhotis. Bunty was satisfied with Sharma-ji, and so was I. And then there was also the matter of us providing support to a couple of small splinter companies in their movement of drugs through Bombay, to Europe and beyond. Bunty had in the past argued for us entering the drug-transit field directly, for the large money involved and to oppose the domination of the trade by the Pathans. But I had always resisted: since there was no local production here, the money wasn't large enough to justify giving up the publicity value of saying, 'We don't touch drugs.' And to oppose for the sake of opposing was a young man's foolishness. I was old enough to know that expanding too fast and too rapidly could make a company sick. Consolidate, consolidate, I often told Bunty. So now I told him to go ahead and provide logistics and muscle to the drug-traders. But be careful, I told him, keep our distance.

'Yes, bhai. Your battery's probably going to run out soon, bhai,' he said. 'Anything else?'

'I want a television in here,' I said. 'And a proper temple.'

'No problem. By this afternoon I can have them there. But the permissions might take time.'

'You don't worry about that,' I said. 'Just get the stuff to the main gate.' I switched off the lethal little phone, quite pleased with its sleek sides, its pulsating little line showing the strength of the signal. I beckoned Date over. 'Charge this up,' I told him. 'And tell the sentry I want to see the superintendent. This afternoon, no later.'

After lunch, I lay down for a rest and thought about Bunty. He was a modest man, not much to look at but intelligent and deadly cold in a crisis. He had been with me a long time now, and had risen until he was closest to me in all my company. He had come up fast, and yet I was not threatened by him. I knew he was ambitious, but I also understood that his aspirations extended only to living well and being respected, not to commanding his own company. I had no fear that he would want to supplant me, or break away to start his own operation. Why was he like that? Why was he content to be always second-in-command, while I had always to be the first? I was not stronger in my body, or more handsome, or more cunning. His appetite for women was as keen as mine, no more and no less. He had grown up with a widowed mother and two brothers and a sister, and the family had always balanced on the cliff-edge of destitution. But I too had survived with no money in my pockets. In most ways we were similar, and yet he was my trusted lieutenant, and I was his leader. Every morning he waited for my instructions, and was glad to receive them. Why? I conjured up Bunty's face, with its Punjabi nose and dangling forelock, his husky voice and his forward-leaning stance, and I could find no answer other than the simple one: some men were destined for greatness, and others to clear their path. There was no shame in being Bunty. He was a good man who understood his place. This conclusion was satisfying, and I relaxed into a doze. But then I settled and sank deeper, into memory, into blackness under which lay a looming bulk which spoke in many voices, and I was a fever-ridden child in a warm bed, a woman smiled at me and pulled a blanket to my chin, she touched my forehead, and I drew my knees up and turned on my side, towards her.

I willed myself awake. I sat up. I was a busy man, I had no time to waste on daydreams. I called to my boys, and reviewed plans for the coming weeks, and asked for suggestions to improve conditions in the barrack, and listened to complaints about lawyers and judges.

I met Advani the superintendent at three that afternoon, in his office. He sat under his picture of Nehru and lectured me in his elaborate Hindi. 'That was a very unfortunate incident,' he said. 'We need to work together to prevent such occurrences in the future. The consequences are painful for both of us.' I just looked at him. I let him talk and met his gaze and looked back at him. After a while he grew uncomfortable and looked away and kept talking. But I kept my eyes on the side of his wizened little skull, and then he slowed down and cleared his throat and stopped. The fan overhead kept up its tick-ticking and he tried to rise up to my glare, but then just gave up and lost. He was sweating.

'Can I do something for you, Advani Saab?' I said, very gently. 'Can I do something for your family?'

He slowly shook his head, and coughed. Then finally he could speak. 'What can I do for you, bhai?'

'I'm glad we are – what was it? – yes, co-operating. Here's what I need. The men in the barrack are bored, they need information and entertainment. So a television is coming, this afternoon. We need a new power connection for it, and a cable connection. And a temple.'

'But that's very good. Spirituality and information, both make better citizens. Permission can be given, of course. That is good thinking.'

He was trying to convince himself more than he was trying to flatter me. Looking at his long, twitchy hands on the desk, his watery half-smile, I was disgusted. Human beings are weak, pathetic. How had this man become a superintendent? No doubt he had an uncle who was in the service already, and a cousin who was close to an MLA. Men like these filled the public services. They were all the material we were given to work with in this world. 'It's your good thinking,' I said. 'You suggested it to me three weeks ago. You wanted to improve conditions for the prisoners. I am just the provider.'

It took him half a minute to understand that, the maderpat donkey that he was. 'Aah, yes, yes,' he said. 'Thank you, bhai.'

'Is there anything I can do for you, Advani?' I said, pretty sharp. 'Tell me.'

'No, bhai. Really.'

'Money?'

That made him panicky. He looked about his office as if someone was maybe hiding behind the cupboard. But this was too obvious and too direct a gambit on my part. Everyone wants money. He would take it, but I was a big name and an obvious connection to me could ruin his career. He would have to think about it, and be eased into it.

'What else? A recommendation to your boss? Admission of your daughter to a good school? An extra phone connection at home?'

'Nothing,' he said. 'For the smooth functioning of the jail, I am happy to co-operate. Nothing else.'

He had his hands in his lap now, and was keeping himself very straight as he said he wanted nothing, but in his eyes was that glisten of pain which came from suddenly being offered the secret wish of his heart, but not having the courage to take it. I had seen it before, that twinge of longing, the hesitation before desire. I had the power to give men and women whatever they wanted, to reach inside their guts and pull out whatever dirty little dream they had hidden in there for a lifetime, and make it real. This frightened them. I had helped men tell me they wanted to kill their fathers, women confess that they wanted their property-stealing brothers beaten up. So I knew what to do. 'Tell me about yourself, Advani Saab,' I said. 'Where were you born?'

All his self-control collapsed into a huge smile of relief. 'Myself, I was born in Bombay, in Khar. But my father was from Karachi. They lost everything in Partition, you know.' And he went on to tell me about his mother, also from Karachi, and how she was separated from

475

the father on a burning train, and their reunion on a Delhi railway platform. 'It was just like a film,' he said. 'They were on separate platforms, number three and number four, and the Amritsar Mail pulled out and they saw each other. Papa-ji went running across the tracks.' And he went on, all the way through their settling in Bombay, and the birth of the two sons and three daughters, and his own years at National College. His struggles until he was finally settled. Meanwhile I was walking around his office, looking into his cupboards, moving his files around. There were no photographs of his family, but one of himself with Raj Kapoor. He had been talking about his children, of his daughter's marriage to a US-settled boy, but now he had wound himself somehow back to his father, who knew film stars. 'Papa-ji knew Pran Saab in Karachi,' he was saying. 'They played cricket together.' So now Pran had been a langotiya yaar of Papa-ji's, and the whole family had gone to his sets many times. They had met many movie stars.

'Did you ever meet Mumtaz?' I said.

'Yes, I did,' he said. 'Twice. Arre, she was beautiful. With some of these filmi types, you know, it's all lighting and make-up. They look all fair and lovely on the screen, but when you see them in public, you realize it's all a sham, you wouldn't notice them on a local train if they didn't have that big name. But Mumtaz, let me tell you, she was something, fair as a rasgulla, what colouring, and juicy like an apple.' He was making little round motions with his hands.

I had him. I beckoned to him over the desk, and whispered, 'Advani Saab, have you ever eaten an apple like that?' He laughed, shook his head, threw up his hands, dismissed the notion. 'No, really, I mean it, there are plenty of these stars who can be arranged.'

'No,' he said. 'No, I don't believe that. Everyone says these things.'

'Are you saying I'm lying?'

'No, no. But.'

'Don't worry, Advani Saab. You wait and see. I'll bring you an apple.'

He hemmed and hawed and protested, like a guest making ritual refusals, but I was sure. I left him, went back to the barrack. I called Bunty, and told him we needed a film star for the jailer. 'But, bhai,' he said. 'Where am I going to get a film star?'

'Bastard,' I said, 'you're the king of Bombay, and you can't get a film star? Chutiya. Call that woman.'

'What woman?'

'Chotta Badriya used to get girls from her. Look in his diary, you'll find her number. If not there, he must have noted it down somewhere. Track her down. Some Jojo or Juju or something like that.'

'Yes, bhai. Anything else, bhai?'

I was quiet. There was something else, something that was sticky, that was bumping like a pebble between the gears of my brain. I had learnt to pay attention to these half-felt botherations. And Bunty had learnt to wait. I let it swim to the surface. 'Okay, Bunty. There is something else. This Sharma-ji, when he makes his payments, takes delivery, does he come with anyone else?'

'Drivers for the vans or trucks, loaders, a couple of guards. UP plates on the vehicles.'

'Do we know anything else about him, his backers?'

'No, bhai.'

'We need to know more. I don't like this, doing such business with people we know nothing about. Find out.'

'I will, bhai.'

'Be careful. Don't tip them off. Take your time, I don't care. Go very slowly but find out.'

'Understood, bhai.'

I took my afternoon nap. Shortly after I woke up, my boys brought in my temple, and the television set. It took eight of them to carry the temple. It was made of marble, and had a special granite base, to take the weight. There was a graceful statue of Krishna, playing his flute, his gold dhoti flaring behind him. He was poised on the balls of his feet, one foot behind and crossed over the other. He was dancing. The boys put up his temple, and installed him in it as the prisoners buzzed happily. Then we all sat down for our first puja. Meetu and Dipu sang a bhajan. Date put a big tika on my forehead, and Kataruka had a garland ready for me. I took the garland and put it at Krishna's feet.

Then we switched on the television. I had the seat of honour, directly in front of its high perch, in the exact middle of the room. The entire barrack arranged itself in a huge half-moon behind me, with the boys in the first row. We switched it on, and with perfect timing, *Deewar* was just starting on Zee. There were no arguments, we watched it. Every man in the barrack had seen it before, but there wasn't a whisper when the film was running, except when the lines were called out before the characters said them, and when great bursts of applause rang out. We were all with Amitabh, we were with him through his climb to the top, but when the inspector brother said, 'I have Ma with me,' the whole barrack said it with him. The film ran through dinner-time, but a quick consultation with my new friend Advani fixed that problem, and dinner was delayed, only for that day. On that day we were all together, all one.

That was how my days went, improving the condition of the inmates, managing the affairs of the company. The gaandu special court kept refusing my bail applications, and my lawyers kept making them. And so I languished in the raj of TADA, and my suffering continued. Every day, I spoke with Bunty. You cannot imagine how much work it is to run a company, all the things one has to think about: finance, accounts, law cases, pensions, distribution, publicity, benefits, equipment and transportation, inflows, outflows, discipline problems. But I had work, and my hands back on my company, so I slept well at nights. In the mornings, the television was going the minute we got back into the barrack after the count. The boys always switched it to a bhajan programme, and I would sit and listen for a while. Then we switched it to news. One morning, Date came to me, looking sour.

'These bastard landyas,' he said.

'What?'

'I hear they're complaining about the temple and television.'

'Complaining? Complaining how?'

'They're saying you're a Hindu don after all. Setting up big-big temples, and giving televisions to play bhajans.'

'I didn't hear them complaining when they were watching *Dewaar* again last night.' The channel had been playing it over again.

'Actually some of them did. They like the film and Amitabh. But they also say the story is really about Haji Mastan, but he had to be made into a Vijay because a movie about a Muslim don can't be made in this industry.'

'So it's the producer's fault that he has to worry about all the money he invests in the stars? These bastards will pay out of their pockets when the film doesn't recover?'

'Their jaat is like that, bhai. Ungrateful bastards. And if you do something for the Hindus, they always think it's against them.'

I was angry, but I was thinking. You can't change how people think by beating them up, and this was a problem of belief. And even after

478

the bomb blasts and the riots, I had Muslim boys working for me. I was, after all, publicly a secular don. Date was muttering curses. 'Find out what they need,' I said. 'See if they need copies of the Koran or something. Let's do something for them.'

'I tell you they won't change, bhai. Always complaining, complaining.'

'Just do it.'

He went off, his shoulders tight and head down, like a bull. The irritation stayed with me, under my skin. At nine-thirty, Bunty called with more irritation. He was upset about Jojo.

'Bhai,' he said, 'this Jojo bitch needs to be taught a lesson.'

'What did she do?'

'For weeks now she's been giving me trouble. She won't send any girl to the jail for Advani, she says. And she won't negotiate on price. But it's her whole attitude, bhai. Like she's some sort of big boss, not afraid of anyone. "If you don't want to do business, then don't," she told me. I asked her if she knew who she was talking to, and she said, "Yes, you're Gaitonde's little Bunty." It was the way she said it, bhai. I cursed her and she started laughing. She's mad. I wanted to go out and put two golis up her gaand, bhai.'

'But you called me instead. That's good, Bunty. Self-control always.'

'Only because you said we needed to deal with her, bhai. I don't know how Badriya put up with her. I told her to treat your name with respect, and she says, "Or what? He'll kill me?"'

'She said that? Then you said?'

'I told her that she was a screw-loose randi. And then I called you. Let me teach her. Let me beat her up, bhai.'

'What's her number?'

'You're going to talk to her yourself?'

'No, I'm going to have the barrack sing to her. Give me the number.'

So I called Jojo. She picked up on the second ring. 'Haan? Tell me,' she said, half in Hindi and half in English.

I came back in Hindi: 'That's how you say hello?'

'Who is this?'

'Your baap.'

'He died years ago, that weak bastard.'

'You don't have any respect for anything?'

'Men are worse than dogs. Especially men who waste my time. Like you.'

'You better listen to me.'

'Why?'

'People who make me angry suffer a lot.'

She burst out laughing, and she wasn't pretending: her laugh was wild and full, and hearing it I started to smile a bit.

'I don't believe this,' she said. 'Such big-big dialogues. I know who this is. The big Gaitonde himself, calling me.'

'Listen, saali,' I said. 'You want to end up in a ditch? I'll make you dig your hole yourself, before I put you in it.'

'That's a dhaansu line,' she said, and roared again. And then quietened down, and said, 'You want to kill me, Gaitonde?'

'It would be easy.'

'Fine. Come on, then.'

And she hung up.

I raised my hand to throw the phone, then very slowly lowered it. I pressed redial, and waited.

'Yes? Tell me,' she said. She was very calm.

'Are you completely mad?'

'Many people think so.'

'You're lucky to be still alive.'

'I think that every morning.'

I liked her. From that very first conversation, from the very first time I heard that voice, hoarse like a man's, I liked her. She laughed at me, and I liked her. But I made my voice hard, and spat out, 'You've always been off? You were born mad?'

'No, no, Gaitonde. I had to work very hard to get crazy. What about you, Gaitonde? What made your screws come loose?'

'Saali, control your mouth.' It was strange, I was furious at her, but somehow glad. 'My screws are fine.'

'Yes, yes. That's why you're sitting in jail and killing people on every side and behaving like Hitler.'

'You're lucky you're not here, in front of me.'

'I'm sure you can have me killed anyway, you big man.' And she burst out laughing again, with that baffling and hearty hilarity.

'Don't waste my time and my battery,' I said. 'Bunty said you were making problems.'

'Bunty is a chutiya. I won't send any girl to that jail. And a woman like you want is not going to come to any jail in the first place.'

'Bunty is an intelligent boy, and he would have listened to you if you hadn't sounded like a . . .'

'Like a what?'

'Can you get a woman like we want? A film star?'

'Maybe some television actress. And not at the jail.'

'Forget about the maderchod jail.'

'It'll cost money.'

'Everything costs money. Just be reasonable, and don't try to take advantage of us.'

'I do honest business.'

'Do good business with me, and you'll have a lot more business.'

'Good.'

'And don't call me Hitler again. You don't know how much I work for . . .'

'Yes, yes, you are a great benefactor of the poor. You give like a king. Listen, I need to go, I have work to do. I'll get in touch with your Bunty about arrangements.'

And she clicked off. Mad and maddening. But she was a good businesswoman – she got us a television actress, or at least an actress who was on television now and then, named Apsara. This Apsara was actually a film star too, a vamp who had been in a couple of movies with Rajesh Khanna during the downward slide of his career, when he started to look like a fat Gurkha. Apsara had been around ever since, one of those faces you remembered but couldn't quite put a name to. 'For this you're making me pay fifty thousand?' I told Jojo. She had set up the transaction with Bunty, but I had called her to argue over the price. It was an excuse, I admit. I wanted to talk to her. I told her, 'At least get us a real star from the period. You know, like Zeenat Aman or someone.'

'Gaitonde, that's the trouble with you men. In your dreams you think every famous woman is secretly for sale. From the period you want? Why don't I get you Indira Gandhi?'

'What? You're saying this to me? You're making a deal with me for this woman, and you're telling me that I'm imagining things?'

'The deal is happening because men imagine things. Poor Apsara. She needs the money.'

Poor Apsara turned out to be something of a drinker, but she was a happy drunk. We set it up: Advani showed up at the Juhu Centaur the next Saturday afternoon, to meet one of our boys who had a suite under the name of Mehboob Khan. Advani had a drink in the suite, my boy gave him a brown paper packet containing five lakhs, and then left him alone. A door opened, and Apsara floated in, wearing a white garara, very Meena Kumari. She had got heavy, but her skin was still luminous and light, and Advani must have thought he had gone to heaven. She asked him for a drink, and then sang songs to him. He told her he was her biggest fan. She acted out scenes for him, and he took the part of Rajesh Khanna in the scene from *Phoolon ki Rani* where the vamp takes the bullet for the millionaire playboy hero because she's so in love with him. Advani remembered every line of dialogue.

I got all this from Jojo the next day. I couldn't stop laughing. 'So they acted for each other?' I said. 'And then? Did he actually do anything?'

'The old man's got a lot of dum for someone that skinny and that old, that's what Apsara said. I think she liked him.'

'She thought he was Rajesh Khanna, saali drunken old buffalo. Women are crazy.'

'As crazy as men.'

And we laughed together. By this time we were talking every day. Somehow it had become a routine: at first it was me that called her, usually in the mornings, after I had finished my early call with Bunty. Then on a court day I didn't call her, and when I got back to the barrack I slept, and was wakened by the phone. 'Where were you, Gaitonde?' It was her. So we talked. After the Apsara deal, we did some more business – Advani needed more apples, as did certain other lawyers, and policemen, and judges. But Jojo and I talked, and business was only a small part of it. We talked of everything.

Thirteen months passed.

Thirteen months can pass just like that. The days slid into each other. I went to court, I took care of my company. Things changed, things remained the same. We got the charges against Dipu and Meetu dismissed. Date went off to Nashik jail to serve the rest of his sentence, Kataruka was released. Bunty was arrested, came into the barrack. The baba log in the children's barrack changed, and there was a new Mumtaz for me. Bunty was released. Our war with Suleiman Isa continued. The government changed in Maharashtra, the government changed in Delhi. I ruled over and mediated disputes in the jail. In the barrack, I had to set up a committee to make decisions over television-watching, since the Sunday mornings full of the *Mahabharata* and the *Ramayana* made the Muslims and Christians feel put down and want programmes of their own, and the Tamil and Malayali boys wanted to watch their Hot Songs programme at midnight, and then the Marathi lads demanded regular film-viewing. We provided whole goats to the Muslim prisoners on their festival days and told them that we would make any arrangements necessary on their fasting days, and see to it that the jail staff didn't interfere. So everyone was happy. Outside the jail, we fed Advani his apples, and inside he accommodated us, adjusted with us. My son grew, he walked, and on his weekly visits I played with him in Advani's office, and held him in my arms, taking in that dewy smell of the top of his head while he struggled and laughed and spoke to me in languages I couldn't understand. I changed also, inside this jail. Perhaps because of the time I had, I grew more quietly reflective, more interested in the world. I regularly read the news-papers, watched all the news programmes on television, and the political debates on Sundays, and the American movies in English. From television, I learned history. In jail I educated myself, I became a man aware of my past, my country's long story. But in spite of this thoughtfulness, or maybe because of it, I developed an embarrassing ailment: I suffered from piles. A minor indisposition, not an illness really, but how I suffered. I rose from the latrine trembling, dizzy with pain, nauseated by the bright red blood. I consulted doctors, changed my diet, took herbs prescribed by famed ayurvedic sages, but no, I still squirmed and squeezed and suffered, I suffered.

'You have too much tension,' Jojo said. 'Your life is entirely ten-sion. And your trouble is that you carry all the tension in your gaand. You need to relax.'

'Listen, my fine guru,' I said, 'I'm a don, I'm in jail, people are try-ing to keep me here, other people are trying to kill me. You want me to relax? How am I supposed to relax?'

'You think you have such a hard life.'

'Don't start that argument again. Suppose I agree with you, okay, I need to relax. How am I supposed to?'

So she got me to start exercising regularly, and two weeks later we brought yoga into the jail. Advani was quite happy with the idea. He got a story in the *Bombay Times*, with a full-colour picture and a blurb that described him as the 'most progressive jailer of our times'. Bunty and my boys were happy because two of the yoga teachers were women, and they got to look at them twist and reach and turn for a full hour. But I hushed their sniggers, and told them to concentrate and do what they were told. I had to trust and hope in yoga because my gaand was on fire. And I tell you, it worked. I felt calm, and relaxed. I relaxed not just in my muscles, but somewhere deep down in my soul. All that breathing in, breathing out, it eased some knot inside me. My piles got better. I won't lie to you and tell you that I was completely cured, but I was at least seventy per cent better.

'See, always listen to me,' Jojo said when I told her. 'Seventy per cent is large.'

'Yes. So I only feel like I'm passing large razor blades some of the time.'

'Gaitonde, for a hard man you complain a lot. Do you have any idea what it feels like to give birth?' And then she was off. This was one of her themes: that the world suffered, and in it women suffered the most, and the suffering of women passed unnoticed. 'Bastard men make suffering the duty of women,' she said. 'All those suffering mothers in the films. And women are also chutiyas for believing it.' Early on in our friendship, I had tried to argue with her. I'd said to her, do you think men don't suffer? Let me tell you a few stories of men torn up and dying and working all their lives for little pay and food a dog wouldn't eat. But she always had four stories for every one of mine, and I grew to enjoy listening to her, somewhere in all those woebegone tales there would be little tasty titbits about her. I knew that she grew up in a village, brought up by her mother – there was a sister somewhere, who she never talked to. The father had died early. When she had come to Bombay as a young girl, she had spoken only Konkani and some Tulu and Kannada, no Hindi or English or anything else. Jojo's sister's husband had run off with young Jojo, told her that he would make her a movie star, but after months and months of doing the rounds of producer's offices, he had prostituted her to one of them. He told her all the girls had to do this, compromise was the price of fame and part of the business, everyone compromised. She had understood this by now, and had done it, but the film had never materialized. Then there had been another producer, and then another. He began to beat her, this boyfriend. She spoke Hindi fluently by now, and some English. So she ran away. The boyfriend found her, beat her. She cracked his jaw with a pestle, so he left her mostly alone after that. But there was the question of making a living. So she struggled, starved, then went back to one of the producers and compromised, and then another. Now she kept their money for herself, and saved. She got into the dancer's union, and worked in a few movies, as a dancer in the big production numbers. For a while she held on to the dream, that she would some day be an actress, a Mumtaz who worked her way up from the chorus line to a star's gigantic close-ups. But she wasn't stupid enough to believe it for long. And she was smart enough to understand both demand and supply: she knew rich men, and she knew young girls who needed a way to survive in the city. So she began her business. But her business wasn't only sex. She did get some of the girls acting jobs. And she herself, finally, became a producer. With some of her money, and some of mine, that year she started planning the production of a television serial, about two young girls who became friends at school, where one was the rich darling of the teachers, and the other a poor foundling, and these two came together to the city and suffered and suffered. Jojo was very clear about our partnership. 'Listen, Gaitonde,' she told me. 'This is a business deal, nothing more, nothing less. I want all the money in white, by cheque. And no funny business. All I owe you is money, nothing more. You offered first, I didn't ask.'

'Achcha, baba,' I said. 'You don't owe me anything else. Business, that's all.' She sent me the script of the pilot episode, and I read it. And then never wanted to read one of her scripts again. Bunty was right. As he had said, what man could watch scene after scene of women crying over rubbish and then hugging each other? I told Jojo that I liked it. If this crying was what she wanted to make serials about, if that was what women wanted to watch, let them have it. I knew that despite Jojo's cheerfulness, her jaunty cursing, there were days when she didn't get out of bed, when she couldn't speak to anyone, when the entire world seemed to her a jungle of ash, a cremation ground filled with walking corpses. These black moods took her sometimes, and she lived through them only by promising herself death. That's what she told me one morning.

'I tell myself that if it gets too bad, I'll kill myself. And I have the pills ready. And then I count up the things in life that are good. The pain still hurts, but I know it isn't endless, because I have the pills. Then I can go through another day. And then another.'

485

She frightened me. I tried to make her see a priest, or a magician, or a doctor. I had seen shows on television about depression. She told me to mind my own business. 'Read my serial scripts,' she said. 'Maybe you'll learn something about women, Gaitonde.'

I didn't read any more, but I did keep talking to her. Right from the start, she refused to come to the jail to see me. 'The only reason we can talk this way is because we haven't met, Gaitonde. Don't you understand that?' I knew she wasn't shy of men or of sex. In fact she was quite the opposite, she had men, she chose them and took them. 'Why should men always be the ones who select and chase and take? I make my own money, I take care of myself, I want my own fun. I'm not ashamed of what I want.' So she chose men sometimes, and she took them to bed. She told me this after we had become frank friends, and she told it to me with no fear, no shame. When she told me this, a twist of alarmed excitement came up my throat, as if I had just run off the edge of a roof in the dark. 'That's, that's disgusting, Jojo,' I whispered urgently into the phone. 'Why?' she snapped right back. 'You can chodo those boys of yours in jail because you're a man and need relief? And that's not disgusting? But I am? You make me laugh.' Of course I told her that was different, that she was a woman. And she said, 'Yes, I'm a woman, and a woman can have ten times as much pleasure as a man. Don't you know that?' That was true enough. Everyone knew that. I said, 'That's why saali women need to be locked up, randis that they are.' And she burst out laughing, and said, 'But, my bhai, you're locked up and I'm not. I'm free.' She was free. She took men, and she called them her thokus. She made me laugh with stories about them, about how they cried when she left them, and the size of their parts, and their vanities. And she refused to meet me. 'Not now,' she said, 'and not later. I'm not going to be one of your thokus, and you don't want to be mine. We're bhidus, bhidu.' It was true. We were friends.

In May, TADA lapsed, but I remained in jail. The law was gone for the rest of the citizens, but since I had been charged under it, I still writhed under its heel. My case was still to be adjudicated under its rules, which were no laws but arbitrary edicts. I cursed my lawyers, and threatened to get new ones. Do we live in a dictatorship? I said. Have I no rights as a citizen? What are you, top lawyers or bhangis? Why am I paying you these truckloads of money?

Finally, finally, they got my case before the Bombay High Court and fought a good battle, all the way to a victory. The judge said he would let me out, on the condition that I should not threaten or even attempt to make contact with the government witnesses in the other cases pending against me, and that I was not to leave the city limits, and this, and that. Agreed, I said, agreed to anything and everything, your honour. And suddenly I was out. I was in court one morning, and then it was over, and I was in a car on the highway, on my way home. It was that simple. Suddenly I was sitting in my bedroom, with Subhadra to my left and my son running around the bed. It was stunningly quiet, and the rooms seemed immense, much larger than I remembered them. There were visitors, but Kataruka kept them at bay. He was an old hand at going into jail, and coming out. He insisted that a party and visitors and noise was the wrong thing, appropriate as it may sound. And a quiet evening is what I wanted, true. I ate the dinner that Subhadra served me, I put Abhi to bed. When the door was shut to Kataruka and the others, I reached for Subhadra. She came to me pliantly, and I truly went home.

After she was asleep, I got up, put on a kurta and slid open the door. I went up to the roof, to my old perch by the water tank. The night was hazy, no stars, just a low glow from the scattered lights. I was twenty-seven years old and I was home once again. There was that old smell, oil and burning and refuse, slightly stinging in the nostrils but alive, so full of life. I took it in, and I called Jojo.

She picked up on the first ring. 'Gaitonde.'

'I'm out.'

'I know.'

'Will you meet me?'

'No. How is Subhadra?'

'She's fine. Don't talk about her.'

'Okay. We won't talk about her.'

'So you refuse to meet me?'

'I completely refuse.'

'I could have you picked up and brought to me.'

'You could. Will you?'

'All right, no.'

'Good. I'll tell you what, Gaitonde – I'll send you a girl.'

'You'll what?'

487

'Don't act shy with me, Gaitonde. I know what you need. You'll like this one. High price, but good for you.'

'You know what I need?'

'See if I do.'

I did see. The next morning, she sent me the girl. Her name was Suzie, and she said she was eighteen, from Calcutta. She was half Calcutta Chinese and half Brahmin Bengali, and she had long straight black hair, long delicate arms that she crossed and folded when she laughed, and skin like thin white marble. I put her face-down and kissed the back of her neck while I was inside her. She moaned and drove back against me.

Afterwards, from the car, I called Jojo. 'What did I tell you, Gaitonde?' she said. 'Isn't she something?'

'Yes, yes, you were right.'

'In two years she'll have a show on MTV, you wait.'

'That may be. But I was thinking of you while I was on top of her.'

'You are on top of an eighteen-year-old, and you're thinking of an old woman like me? Gaitonde, you are an idiot, like every other man in the world.'

I had to laugh with her. I had waited for Suzie in a small hotel near Sahar, and now we were on the highway, going home. The traffic was moving fast, and the sun flashed off the roofs of the cars. I was free. 'I feel good,' I said to Jojo.

'Enjoy,' Jojo said. 'Enjoy, enjoy.'

We were home by eleven. In jail I had got used to waking up early, so already I had done my yoga, eaten, had Suzie. I was feeling light. But some of the boys were yawning. I set them to work. I played for a while with Abhi, who was now speaking in babbles of words and non-sense sounds, who held my face and tried to tell me things. He had little grammar, and no understanding of past and future, and still I could listen to him completely fascinated, my heart yielding in love. At noon Kataruka came into the hall where I was sitting with some petitioners. He leaned close to me to whisper, 'The nau-numberis are here. They say they have to take you to the station. Interrogation for another case.'

'Who is it? Majid Khan again?'

'No, I don't know these chutiyas. They say they are with Parulkar.'

'Bastards. Tell them to send whatever questions they have to the lawyers.'

'I did. They have an order from a magistrate.'

'Yes, and the magistrate chodos their mothers in the gaand every night. Tell them to wait. Tell them I'll come when I can. And get one of the lawyers down here.'

'Yes, bhai.' Kataruka was smiling. 'These maderchods have no manners. I don't feel even like giving them chai.'

'No manners?'

'They parked their van right in front of the house and refused to move it. Very pushy, bhai. Get him here now, like that they're speaking. They are some special commando types, two of them are carrying carbines, and one has a jhadoo. Think they are heroes.'

And he went off, humming a song. I turned back to my petitioners, parents who wanted a job for their son. But I was distracted, and thinking about this new nuisance. Commandos with Sten guns and AK-47s meant that there was some new task force maybe, some government initiative set up so that they could look serious about organized crime. Which would amount to nothing in the long run, but which would be a botheration. I made my promises to the petitioners, told them to check back in a week. When one of the boys opened the door for them, we all heard clearly the angry voices, a shout and then Kataruka's reply. He was hoarse and very loud. Bhenchod police, they were bellowing in my house. Maderchods. I got up, and walked down the long corridor, brushing past the family of petitioners, mother and father and uncles and son. Even in that anger, I was aware of that smell of home, that smell of onions and haldi and oil from the lunch they were cooking in the kitchen. I breathed it in. 'Get Gaitonde here *now*,' the policeman roared. Between him and me there was a scattering of my boys, and other visitors, all clustering around the argument, but through them I could see the policeman's shoulders and face, and behind him another one, and the long glint of an AK-47. 'When he is ready, he will come and see you,' Kataruka answered, as loud and as bloody-eyed as the policeman. I squeezed through the press. I wanted to get to shouting myself. I could see two policemen, but no more. In front of me was Dipu, grown city-smart and polished after his service with us, with a new haircut.

I asked Dipu, going past him, 'How many of them are there?'

Into my ear, he said, 'Four, bhai.'

I could see a third policeman now, standing to the left. He had his carbine shoulder-slung and ready, with a finger on the trigger. It came to me in the middle of my stride: four policemen, and only four, armed with automatic weapons and in a van, sent to fetch Ganesh Gaitonde. It made no sense. The shouting policeman leaned in even more towards Kataruka, and in that motion he saw me. Our eyes met. I turned and ran.

I went low through the blast from the guns, through and over the flailing bodies in the corridor, through the screams. Then I was in my bedroom, scrabbling and pawing behind the headboard for a pistol, and I had slammed the door shut behind me but the bullets fountained through the walls, scattering plaster, and I had less than a moment, and I went through the window to the right of my bed. I fell between the side of the house and the compound wall, and I knew I had broken something in my arm but I had to keep running. I ran out of the rear gate, and now two of my boys were with me, and they took me into the nearby lanes. We turned twice, and went into a house and the door shut behind us and we all three of us fell to the ground, dropped flat from exhaustion, as if we had run ten miles.

The firing was booming near by, but now with the hammering of the AK and the carbines, there were single shots in reply. Then, suddenly, it was over. No more shots, just screams now, desperate shouting flurrying across the basti. I was alive.

I came out into the lane holding my arm. Only now, when I started to walk, I felt a heated line of pain across my lower back, as if someone had drawn a molten wire across my buttocks. 'You're bleeding, bhai,' someone said to me. I pushed him aside, went into the house. 'We got one of them,' another boy said to me. We had got one, he lay near the front gate, his leg twisted up under his body. Inside the house, in the front hall, there was blood on the ceilings, smears of tissue on the walls. Dipu was dead, and so was Kataruka.

Seventeen men died in my house that day, and four women, and one child. But at the time, we had no count, only a tangle of bodies. It was only when we started picking them up, and carrying them out, that we found Subhadra and Abhi at the far end of the corridor, in the kitchen, curled up under the cover of her blue sari. They were both dead from the same AK-47 bullet, which had come through the door-jamb, and come through them. They were dead. My wife was dead. My son was dead.

I went back to jail. After I had my broken wrist plastered, and the graze on my backside stitched up, after we cremated our dead, we considered our options. We knew now that the policemen who had done the firing were not policemen, but Suleiman Isa's men, that the uniforms had been bought from Maganlal Dresswallah's, that the van had been stolen – or so the real police said – from Zone 13 headquarters. We knew, reliably, that the supari given for this suicide mission was two crores, so that the four maderchods who came to my house walked away with fifty lakhs each. But two of them didn't walk away, one died right there in my courtyard, another covered the inside of the van with the blood that he coughed up. He died the same day. But still, my enemies almost got what they wanted. They couldn't say that they had killed Ganesh Gaitonde in his own basti, in his own house, but they did say that they struck at me in my lair, that I had run from them, that I was a coward with a wound in my gaand. They were ashamed that they had broken the unspoken rule of the companies against hurting family members, but they could say that was an accident, and they could say that they had taken my gaand.

But I was alive. That was what mattered. Whatever the world said, I was alive. And that is what finally matters. Honour and pride are the dreams that men feed on, and will die for, but my boys understood that, even for them, it was better that I had stayed alive. I was still here, to recoup, to plan, to take revenge. And I had to stay alive. So I went back to jail. It was easy to arrange. I got into a car with some of my boys and went up to Mulund. We stopped the car at the Mulund check-post, and the boys picked a quarrel with the constables there. I came out and shouted too, and the boys conspicuously addressed me as 'Ganesh Bhai', just to make sure that the stupid mamus understood who I was. Then we all got back into the car and drove on, far beyond city limits.

So I had broken the conditions of my bail, and had to be put back in the one safe haven for me. I had understood that this time it had been fake police, but the next time it might be the real ones, come to take me for a ride in a black van, a ride that would end with a bullet in my head. Every door in the city hid an assassin, every day was a battle. I had become too big for them to leave me alive. And so jail was my impregnable castle, where the walls and the rules and the regulations made a home for me, where the jailers were responsible for keeping me from harm, and where I could continue to do business without hindrance.

I settled back into the old routine. There was a new set of faces in the barrack, but there was the same grouping of dhurries around my own, in order of seniority. Life went on as before. But I was alone, so very alone. My boys were my family, and they were kind as always, mindful of my losses and my injuries. They took care of me, and I did business. But in my heart I was alone. So many had died, not just in this last attack, but through my journey, in all the battles. And I was still alive. Why? For what? I waited for an answer. I practised yoga in the mornings, in the afternoons I practised pranayama. But all my hard-won calm was taken from me by Abhi's laughter, which I heard floating in the afternoon sunlight. At night, I went eagerly to my pillow because I knew he would come to me in my sleep, but my very waiting chased sleep away. I was light-headed. I walked through the world like a man sliding weightlessly through a dream.

'It feels so strange,' I told Jojo, very late at night, on the phone. 'I feel like, like a lost ghost. Like somebody else's story. Like there's a projector going chat-chat-chat somewhere and I'm moving around on a screen.'

'It'll pass, Gaitonde,' she said. 'Pain passes. It always passes.'

She sounded so close, as if she were in the next bed. I had made her buy a new mobile phone, and had a new handy myself, and we spoke only to each other on these new connections. I had two other phones for business. My enemies hadn't been trying to kill my family, that I knew, but still I was afraid for Jojo. I told her that our connection needed to become even more invisible to the world, that it was bad for her media-industry image if it became generally known that she and I were friends. This she understood, and she became even more discreet than she had already been. We spoke late at night, only on the special phones.

'Gaitonde?' she said. 'Hello?'

'Here,' I said. 'I'm here.' But I wasn't so sure I was there any more. A son roots a man in the world. Take away that connection and you cut him loose. 'You know what I miss? I miss the smell of his hair after a bath.'

'I know. What do you miss about Subhadra?'

I had trouble conjuring up her face, remembering what she looked like. But of course I didn't say this to Jojo. 'She used to bring me milk at night,' I said, but I knew Jojo had caught the hesitation. She kept quiet, though, and didn't read me one of her lectures about men and women.

'Gaitonde. You never talk about your father and mother.'

'I don't.'

'Your mother, who was she?'

'A woman, what else?'

'What else? What was she like?'

'She was my mother. Forget it. All this maderchod talk.'

Of course she caught the growl in my voice, and was quiet. I hadn't meant to cut her off, and I didn't want silence, couldn't stand it. 'Tell me about your mother and father,' I said. I could hear her breathing. 'Jojo?'

'I am trying not to curse you. Because you already have a lot of tension.'

'If I didn't have tension, you would give me gaalis?'

'Anybody who speaks to me like that gets gaalis.'

I was lying on the floor, in a corner of the barrack. I liked the cold concrete on the back of my neck. Through a window I could see the black rise of a wall, the sparkling shards of glass on its rim, keen in the moonlight. I had to smile a little. Somehow Jojo's recklessness, her anger, it made me smile. In life I would have hated her, I think. But on the phone, me here, she there, she had me smiling. 'Listen, madam,' I said. 'Tension I do have. So forgive me. Tell me about your mother.'

Jojo told me about her father, who was a sea captain. He drove small boats for a big company, and was away for months at a time. When he came home he wanted the house to be quiet. The parrots in the orchards behind the house drove him into a trembling rage, he threw firecrackers into the tops of trees and finally bought a shotgun. All his murdering of koels and swallows wouldn't banish the birds, and they sat on the heads of his scarecrows, and nested in their bellies. Finally he retreated to the armchair in his bedroom, put red earplugs in his ears and a black scarf over his eyes. His daughters tiptoed around him, and tried to stay awake late to listen for scraps of conversation between him and their mother. They never heard anything that would make sense of him, not even at meals, when all he said was that there was too much salt in the fish curry and that there was no money for Easter dresses. And so it went until he left, again for a few months. When Jojo was eleven, this big-beard father died of a heart attack on the bridge of his latest ship, on a rainy day in the Arabian Gulf. He died sitting in his captain's chair, with his black scarf over his eyes, so that his men thought he was sleeping. Finally he had quiet, Jojo thought. But there was no quiet for them, because when it came to the matter of his pension it turned out to be not so much. They were poor. But Jojo's mother refused to be downcast, or frightened. I have my land, she said, I refuse to live meekly and full of tears because my husband was taken by God. God is merciful and he will look after us. And so she brought them up, with hard work and hardships and hard discipline. You have to buy your own food in this world, she said, remember that.

'I asked her once about them, she the wife and he the husband, the two of them together,' Jojo said. 'About how she could stand to be with him all those years, through all that silence. Why.'

'And she said?'

'She said nothing. She used to do this thing with her mouth, make it all small like she was irritated, and wave her hand at you. Like you were a fool for asking. Then she would go on with her work. She was always working.'

'When did she die?'

'After I had my trouble with my sister. I didn't find out until a year after it had happened.'

The trouble had really been with the sister's husband, but I let that pass. When women talked about their troubles, it was best to let some things go by. This much I had learnt from my long talks with Jojo, the champion of women. If you argued, you got screaming argument, and then silence. And I wanted Jojo to talk, I needed her to go on talking. Late at night, she saved me with her talking.

In the mornings I read the newspapers. I started with the Marathi papers, then read the Hindi, and finally the English. My English reading was still very slow and halting, and often I had to stop and ask the boys about meanings and constructions. I had my English-Marathi dictionary, but still it was a dragging business, and I always grew annoyed by the end of it. 'Gaitonde Outfit Struggles to Recover from Losses,' the *Times of India* said, and by the end of the article I wanted to kill the anonymous 'special correspondent'. It wasn't just the errors in every other sentence, the carelessness of the reporting, but the tone, that slightly sneering implication that the writer knew everything, even what went on in the head of Gaitonde: 'As Gaitonde mourns his wife and licks his wounds in his cell, Suleiman Isa consolidates his power.' These English-wallahs were always superior, as if the world they lived in was some other one, far from my barrack, my streets, my home. When I grew angry, the boys grinned and said, if it aggravates you, bhai, why read this nonsense?

494

I didn't tell them, but I read the nonsense because it made me feel alive. In this pictured Gaitonde, caught between columns of newsprint, there was a vitality I didn't feel in my belly. He was hard-faced, confident, injured but ruthless, and plotting a comeback. Looking at him, I myself felt proud of him. Here was a man. So I didn't kill any reporters, but instead gave interviews. I sent bottles of Scotch to them, and flattered them with confidences. All of them wanted to know the story of my life, so I told them stories. They printed all of it. Our revenues grew, and more boys than ever wanted to join us.

It was in these days of my rising all-India fame that one of the warders came to me. 'Bhai,' he said, 'there's this mad chutiya in Barrack Five who keeps saying he knew you before you were Ganesh Gaitonde.'

'When I had another name? I never had another name. I have always been Ganesh Gaitonde.'

'I don't know what he means, bhai. He's crazy. But he keeps saying it.'

'Forget it, then. Why are you bothering me with it?'

'Sorry, bhai.' He turned away, ducking his head, and giggled. 'Sorry. He's a real vediya, he thinks he's Dev Anand himself. But he's always got his finger in his nose like this, crazy bastard.'

'Wait,' I said. 'Wait. This fellow. He's with the budhaus? He's old himself?'

'Yes, bhai. He's not so old, but he's got all white hair. He puffs it up, like Dev Anand.'

I opened my mouth, then shut it. I said quietly, 'Bring him to me.'

'I'll tell him you want to give him paper, bhai. He'll come running.'

'Paper?'

'He draws, bhai.'

'Draws? Never mind, just go and get him. Go, go. Now.'

There were some ten minutes of delay, as various guards were told what to do. But then there he was. I recognized him as soon as he came in through the door at the far end of the barrack, through all the hundreds of men. He was hunched over, and even thinner than before, but there he was, Mathu. Yes, the same Mathu who had been my fellow-shooter on that trawler long ago, who had travelled with me across the seas to bring back gold, who had been an equal partner in the destruction of Salim Kaka. He came up to me slowly, flanked by two of my boys, peering at me from under scraggy eyebrows. He had a stubble, and his careful grooming was all gone. Now he wore no talcum powder on that rodent nose, but he had his Dev Anand hair still, swept up into a suave curl. The hair was all white, complete white. There were crusts of dirt on his bare knees and ankles, and when he was up close I had to steel myself against his stink of old age and sweat and sadness.

'Mathu,' I said, waving the boys away.

He crushed a wad of paper between his hands, nodded his head from side to side and said, 'Yes, it is Ganesh.' Then he was quiet, and very still. He was still looking at me, like he was trying to measure me. He was not hostile, or afraid, he was just appraising. Then he seemed to be satisfied, and he lost interest in me, and worried his nose. He flicked away a fleck of green, and then he looked about the barrack, and then began to shuffle through the stack of paper he carried.

'Mathu, you bastard,' I said. 'Where have you been? What happened to you?' I had been annoyed by him then, long ago, but now I was stirred by affection and surprise and concern, I got up and thumped him on the back, and stopped because his shoulder blades cut into my hands. He was starved and he was trembling. 'Mathu, you want to eat something?'

That got his attention. 'Yes, Ganesh.'

So we got him some food. He hunched over his bhakri and garlic chutney and ate. His papers were carefully tucked under his right thigh. I called in the warder and questioned him about Mathu. 'He's been in here as long as I've been here, bhai,' the warder said. 'Which is almost five years. And I know he was here for a while before that, and he was shifted from Arthur Road, where he had been for at least a year.'

'Why?'

'As far as I know, bhai, the charges are that he killed his brother.'

'Then why has he not been tried?'

'His family is saying he is mentally unfit to stand trial, bhai. They've got some tame doctor to write that. So they keep having him moved from jail to jail.'

They would keep on avoiding a trial, and keep Mathu in jail for longer than his possible sentence if he were convicted of murder. Bastards. 'Who are these people who put him in here?'

'He has another brother, and one sister. It is all about property.'

It turned out that Mathu had taken his gold and gone home, to Vasai. He told his sister and brothers that he had been in Dubai, that he had had a windfall, and now he was back to take care of everyone. So of course they made him the big man of the house, even though he was the youngest. The gaandu spent his money on them: he bought them all houses, all within the same compound, and they started a business together. They got him married. Then of course the brothers and the sister and the sisters-in-law and the brother-in-law started fighting. They fought over land, and cash, and who was going to get how much profit from the business, and who was responsible for the losses. So finally the decision was made to split up the business, and split up the property. Mathu didn't want to, he saw all his gold flying away, but he had made the deeds out in the names of the siblings, and the business had many partners. The others made alliances and conspired against each other, and Mathu went from one side to the other asking them to be good to each other, and let go of their anger, and remember their father and mother. But the fighting got worse, and finally the eldest brother was murdered. He was found in his office one morning with a lamp wire wound around his neck, pulled tight till it cut the flesh, and he had thirty-two stab wounds. Nothing had been stolen, nothing had been disturbed. The only door into the room was locked. The investigating policemen decided that the killer must be someone known to the victim. A bloody knife was found behind Mathu's house. He had no witnesses who could place him anywhere the night before. His wife was visiting her parents. All his relatives said that he had been acting crazy recently, and that he had cursed and ranted against the dead brother, and threatened to kill him. So Mathu went away to remand, and then to jail to await trial, and he was still waiting. He had no money left, and anyway he couldn't have hired a lawyer. He was crazy.

'What is that on the paper, Mathu?' I said.

He cringed, and doubled over, and began to make a low whine.

'He is afraid you'll take it from him. In the general barracks, the prisoners used to make fun of him, and steal his paper and pencils and pens. That's why we put him in with the old men. He sits and draws all day long.'

'What, Mathu, what do you draw?' I rubbed his shoulder. 'Come on. You remember me. We went out on the boat together. See, you said you knew me. You know me. I am Ganesh Gaitonde.'

He turned to me then, and let me straighten him up and take the papers from under his leg. They were scraps of paper, old newspapers, envelopes flattened out and made wide, bits of receipts and jail documents. Every clear space on these scraps had been filled with tiny drawings of men and women and buildings and animals. He was a good artist, our Mathu. You could tell what a man was feeling, or if an animal was afraid. The trees bent to the force of a great wind, and there were streetlights on a dark lane. The people spoke to each other in little balloons, but the drawings were so crammed in and so tiny that you could hardly make out what they were saying, even when you had your eye an inch away from the paper. It was like some sort of gaandu crazy comic, it made you dizzy just to look at it, all those figures moving up and down the paper and spreading from one sheet to the next, every inch filled with some discussion or quarrel or love, but still you could tell that it was all connected, that it made some sense somehow.

'This is very good, Mathu. What is this you have been drawing?'

He was ecstatic that I had asked. For a minute I saw the Mathu I had known once, the Mathu who was faithful to his Dev Anand even in the days of Amitabh Bachchan, who liked to fly kites from morning till night all the way until Sakranti, who liked to wear navy blue because a friend of his sister's had once told him he looked handsome in it. He smiled wide, showing gaps in his yellowed teeth, and said, 'My life, Ganesh.'

I took that in. Now that he had said it, you could see that there was a little boy, about five or so, in shorts and chappals, who walked along the torn edge of an envelope, carrying a school-bag. 'This is you?'

'Yes.'

'And you're going to draw your whole life?'

'Yes, yes.'

'Why?'

That closed him up. He didn't have an answer to that. He hung his head down and after a while he began to cry. I hugged him and put him close to me, and got one of the boys to bring me a pad we had been using. 'Here, Mathu. Here's lots of paper. You want more paper?'

'Yes.' His nose was running, dripping on to the pad. He groped at the lined paper. 'And pens. With different colours.'

'I'll get you all that. Don't you worry.'

He nodded happily, and in that gesture I saw the young Mathu saying 'yes' to the idea of a movie, saying 'yes' to falooda and an outing. I had him cleaned up, and sent him back to the barrack laden with paper, escorted by two of my boys. Then I shivered, and pulled my knees up and thought. I could have him sent out into the world, of course, but the warder had told me he could barely get by without help even inside the jail. He gave his food to anyone who would give him a pen, and forgot to eat when he had food. All he wanted to do was draw his life. At the rate he was going at now – after seven, eight years of drawing he had reached his first day in class two – he would get to our trip with Salim Kaka in twenty or thirty years. He was no danger to me. So the next morning I gave orders, and deputed the warder who had brought Mathu to me to look after him in perpetuity. I gave Mathu a monthly pension, a sizeable one considering that his accommodation was free and all he really needed was paper and writing implements. He was to be fed and clothed and taken to the hospital once a month. And anyone who disrupted his drawing would have to answer to me.

So Mathu was drawing his life. I had time in jail to think about mine. Despite all my tragedies, my life had been a good one, I could see that. I had fame, I had power, I was still growing. I had suffered defeats, but I knew how to recover and respond. I learnt from my mistakes. I went on. But to what? Where was I going? If I were to draw my life, where would I send it after this meeting with Mathu?

Then, during my confusion, Bunty came to me with a report. He didn't want to give it to me over the phone, and he didn't want to send anything in writing. Our practice was that none of our controllers came to the jail. There were several cases pending against Bunty, but still he came to the warden's office. He shut the doors, and drew up a chair close to me. 'Bhai,' he said. 'It's about Sharma-ji.'

'So you finally found out who he's working for?'

'First we found him, bhai. A little money here, a few questions there . . . Sharma-ji's name is actually Trivedi. He owns petrol pumps in Meerut, and has old relationships with all the politicians there. He used to be a Jana Sanghi, but left the party in the early eighties. He and a cousin of his and a few others started a new party, Akhand Bharat. The party is still around, but they've only managed a few municipal seats, never anything in the state elections or for parliament.'

'And?'

'He lives well, bhai. He has a house called Janki Kutir, three storeys, big as a cinema house. All white marble. This Akhand Bharat party is still running, they spend too much money for how small they are. It's not all coming from petrol pumps. And there's not enough to pay for our shipments. So I looked a bit more. We followed him for a couple of months. Nothing. He has a very routine life, temple in the morning, petrol pumps, party office in the afternoon. Nine children, many grandchildren, big joint family. He has an office in the house, spends his evenings there.'

'Then?'

'We made a source in the telephone department, didn't have to spend too much. We got lists of all the outgoing calls from his office number. We tracked down most of the repeating numbers, but there was one mobile he calls every Saturday. Around the time of our last shipment he was calling it every day. So then we had to make a source inside the mobile phone company. That took longer, some more money.'

'Finally?'

'Finally the mobile belongs to one Bhatia, Jaipal Bhatia, who lives in Delhi, in South Extension. Nice bungalow also, this Bhatia has. His one and only job is that he works as personal secretary to Madan Bhandari.'

'Bhandari is who?'

'Bhandari is nobody. Just a businessman, has interests in plastics, textiles. Twenty, thirty crore turnover. He's only interesting because, outside his factories, he has one main love in his life, bigger even than his wife and children. He is the main supporter and bhakt of Shridhar Shukla.'

'Shridhar Shukla the swami?'

'That one. He is their boss. He's the top. I am sure of that.'

That certainly changed the whole game. Swami Shridhar Shukla was an international swami, he had lunches with presidents and prime ministers, and told fortunes for ministers, and had film stars by the dozen at his darshans. I had seen him often on television, sitting in a wheelchair and smiling. He had perfect northern Brahmin Hindi, and fast English. Very impressive man. Very connected.

'Maderchod,' I said. 'Maderchod.'

Bunty nodded. He saw our problem, which was that we didn't have the slightest maderchod idea of what our problem was. We didn't know this sea we were swimming in. I got up, walked around the room once. Nehru was looking down at me. I gave him back a stare: I've been learning about you, bastard, you weren't that great for the country. 'We act directly,' I said. 'You get on the phone to that, that bastard, what's his name?'

'Trivedi.'

'Yes, Trivedi. You tell him that I want to talk to this Shukla. Latest by tomorrow evening. No arguments, no this or that. I talk to Shukla, directly. Otherwise we have trouble.'

I hugged him. He had done good work. I went back to the barrack, and that night I was restless, agitated. Jojo noticed it. 'You sound different,' she said. 'It's been hard to talk to you. You've been all far away. Today you're different.'

'I'm not lying down.' I was walking the breadth of the barrack, one end to the other on my side, away from the disgusting heap of sleeping prisoners beyond our company's borders.

'That's not it. It's different. You're angry or something.'

It wasn't quite anger, but something. I was excited, like I was about to walk through a door. I talked to Jojo, then slept very lightly. At six the next morning my other phone rang, and I picked it up on the first ring.

'Ganesh,' a voice said.

I was quiet. I recognized the voice, but couldn't place it.

'Ganesh,' he said again. It was a round, deep voice. An expensive, expansive voice, and very kind.

'Swami-ji,' I said. I hadn't meant to add the 'ji', but it came out.

'Don't use my name on the phone, beta.'

'Did my friend give you this number?'

'Yes, it was passed to me.'

'We need to speak.'

'I agree. But not like this. Face to face.'

'That may not be soon.'

'Don't worry. I have looked at your charts. You have freedom in your future, beta.'

'How?'

'I don't know details, beta. I am always honest about that. But I can see it. You will be out of this jail very soon. Then, we will meet.'

'You have my charts?'

'I have been observing you. I was waiting for you. And now you have found me.'

'You were waiting?'

'Yes. Now you are ready. Life had to teach you its lessons, your yoga had to deepen your consciousness. Then you were ready. So you have come to me.'

It was impossible to argue with him. In the gentle flow of his voice there was an irresistible power. There was a tightness in my throat, and I blinked away the blurriness in my eyes. 'Yes,' I said. 'Yes.'

'Don't worry, Ganesh,' he said. 'Be calm, be quiet. Practise your yoga. Wait. Time will turn and switch its curves. Time will turn and turn. Be patient.'

And with that, he was gone. I watched him that afternoon on television. He sat cross-legged on a dais, leaning back against round white pillows, and spoke into a gleaming silver microphone. Out of focus, in the background, behind his head, I could see the metallic shine of the spokes of a wheel on his chair. I had never before noticed how good-looking a man he was, with his thick white hair sweeping back over his head but not too long, setting off the healthy springiness of his clean-shaven jaw. I couldn't tell at all how old he might be. His disciples sat in orderly rows, men on one side and women on the other. The discourse that day was about success. Why, he asked, does failure torment us so bitingly? And then, why does success sometimes leave us feeling dissatisfied all over again? Why does arrival let us down, even after we have dreamt of it for so long, have fought so hard for it along a cruel road? Why? The answer in both cases, Shukla-ji said, is because we believe in the illusion of the self. I am the doer, we believe. We shout this out at the world, I am doing this, I am doing that, I, I, I. Believing in this most slippery of all illusions, we think that our failures are our fault, that they flow from the shape of this self. We think we own our victories. And yet, when we find success, we discover that this self-illusion, this illusion of the self, can only live in the future, or in the past. It is eternally separated from the present, and so as long as we believe in it we know only loss. It is only when we transcend this illusion and laugh at it that we can know the pleasure of this moment, laugh because then you are truly alive. Swami-ji said, my children, give away your actions and discover your true nature. Know yourself.

I had to walk away from the television. It was as if he was speaking to me, to me alone. And yet I had to control myself, to be casual in my listening, to make jokes about gurus and swamis, and I couldn't stay with him too long. We had a secret connection, he and I, and because of that I couldn't make a public connection with him. It was too risky, too dangerous. Not only for me, but also for him. So I stood myself up and walked away. The boys switched channels to a filmi-song countdown.

I let them listen to their songs, but I followed Swami-ji's advice. I hardened my meditation, did it longer and with deeper concentration. The boys were impressed by my deepened calm, my improved memory, my larger love. I asked after their families, remembered the names of their wives and chaavis, asked after their children. We had arranged for Date to be brought back from Nashik Jail so that he could be with me in the barrack. He hugged me when he first saw me, embraced me for a long time. Then, the first thing he said was, 'Bhai, you even look younger. You look so fresh, like a boy.'

I felt weathered, like an old field that has been ploughed. But what he saw was the budding of the new shoots from a recent planting. Outside, the monsoons had just set in, and we sat near the windows and watched the water crash off the roofs. Business was good. The money came in, the money went out, more money came in. Our war with Suleiman Isa rumbled on. I knew the boys expected a decisive strike, a terrible retribution to be visited upon our enemies. I told them to be patient. When the crop is ripe, then cut it. Wait, wait. And so I waited. I was calm.

At the end of July I received a summons from Advani's office. 'Saab needs to see you in his office,' the warder said. 'It's very urgent.'

It was morning, still my prayer hour, and I knew a sudden dread. Advani would never disturb me at this time, and so something very bad must have happened for him to call me out. I put on my chappals, and we hopped from stone to stone along the yard, which was now a lake of rainwater. The clouds were black and low overhead, and it was quite still, the entire world filled only with the fall of water. Beside Advani's office, three men in white shirts stood in a row. I went past them, and Advani was at his desk, looking straight-backed and very official. He didn't get up.

'Saab,' I said, quite humbly. I was a good actor when my subordinates needed me to be one.

From Advani's right, a man was watching me intently. What I saw of him first was his dome-like head, quite bald and brown in the dark monsoon light. And then his eyes, watching me.

'This is Mr Kumar,' Advani said. 'He wants to talk to you.'

Advani got up and left, without another word or a glance at me. So this Mr Kumar was a powerful man. A senior official, maybe. 'Sit,' he said.

I did.

'I work for a certain part of the government, the central government,' he said. 'I have been following your fight with Suleiman Isa.'

Me, I kept quiet, didn't even nod. Let the man explain. He was very thin, with a sharp nose, and looked something like a statue of a starving Buddha I had seen on television. But there was power in him, a kind of certainty. Here was a man who knew who he was.

'I am aware of your present difficulties. But I appreciate the effort you have put in against this Suleiman Isa, and against his Pakistani friends.'

He was waiting for me to say something. I gave him a response: 'Yes, saab. That bastard is a traitor. He is a dog who lives on the Pakistanis' waste.' He nodded. 'He is anti-national,' I said.

'And you, Ganesh Gaitonde? Are you a patriot?'

'I am,' I said.

I am. It was as simple as that. In that moment, I realized that a patriot was what I am. I had once been an ignorant boy, interested only in money, in my dream of fame and luxury. But since then I had learnt much, understood much. In this world there is no man who can stand alone, and say I am free of everything but myself. I was a patriot. Looking at this Mr Kumar, I recognized in him a patriot, and knew myself to be one.

'I can help you,' he said. 'If you help us.'

'How do I help you?'

'If you stay in India, you will keep suffering violent attacks. Besides, all these legal troubles will continue. Now there is no TADA, but for you TADA will remain alive for ever. One day you'll arrange to get out, and then go in again. Maybe they will make a new, more ferocious law, and slap that on you as well.'

'Yes. No doubt.'

'So, go abroad.'

'I have thought of that. But my base is here. I do have some connections and facilities outside, but not enough, saab. It would take a lot of money and effort and time to set up operations anywhere else.'

'That is where we can help you. We can provide information, help.

Initial arrangements, of course, and logistics. Maybe money.'

The man was offering a lot. And he offered as if he had the ability to provide what he promised. But I needed to pin him down. 'And, saab, what do you want from me?'

'Your co-operation. You will give us information on anti-national activities. What they are doing, what they are planning. Sometimes we may have certain tasks that we may want you to complete. We need a partner who can do work of all types.'

Yes, work of all types. No doubt they needed someone to do the really dirty things that they could not get done legally themselves. They needed a strong arm, but one they could disown in public. It was time to let him know that he wasn't offering help to a fool. I leaned forward. 'But, Kumar Saab,' I said, 'you already have Chotta Madhav working for you.' Chotta Madhav had been one of Suleiman Isa's boys, but had split off and formed his own company after the bomb blasts. He operated now out of Indonesia, and fought against Suleiman Isa, and because he was an enemy of my enemy, we had maintained cordial relations, not hatred but not friendship either. And we knew he had some kind of relationship with the organization called RAW. This is what I wanted this Mr Kumar to know, that it didn't take very much thinking to fathom who he was.

Mr Kumar was amused. His smile was like a thin ripple that passed quickly across his skull. 'Is he working for us?'

'That he is. Just like Suleiman Isa is working for the ISI.'

'Maybe Madhav is working for us. But this is a time of extreme danger. We need more patriots.'

I nodded. 'What do you want me to do, saab?'

He told me. The rain fell outside. We made our plans. And so I became a warrior for my country and my people.

Meeting Beauty

❧❧❧

Zoya Mirza was a hard woman. She was hard to find, hard to speak to on the phone, hard to meet. Sartaj tried to explain this to Anjali Mathur, who seemed to think that a police inspector armed with the awful majesty of the law and incriminating photographs ought to be able to interrupt a film star's life of glamour and travel and subject her to an interrogation. 'Maybe I could do that,' Sartaj said, 'if any of this were official. Are we official yet?'

'No, I don't have anything I can take to my boss yet,' Anjali said. 'Just the vague possibility of a connection between a gangster and a film star. Nothing special.'

Sartaj couldn't argue with this. That filmi people were often connected to bhais was something that children in distant villages knew. This wasn't news. The information would damage Zoya Mirza's impeccable image of chaste sexiness if it got out, yes, and maybe twist her career out of its steadily rising arc, but there was no explanation yet as to why Ganesh Gaitonde had come back to Bombay. And not the faintest smoky beginnings of a story that would explain why he had built a concrete cube in Kailashpada, why he had shot Jojo and then blown his own head in half. 'You still want me to investigate quietly. So I can't ask my boss to call her to the station. You want me to go and talk to her privately, just go in and harass her. These film star types have high connections,' Sartaj said. 'If she calls some minister and gets me suspended, you won't be able to take that to your boss either.'

'She won't. You have the photographs.'

'It's a risk.'

'A small one.'

The risk is still larger than my profits from conducting this investigation, Sartaj wanted to say. He had called Anjali Mathur at the Delhi

506

number she had left him, and she had picked up on the first ring. Her telephone manner was brisk, and she had listened to his report and quietly suggested that he talk to Zoya Mirza. Very simple, very efficient. Sartaj took in a deep breath, let it out. 'Maybe everything looks small from Delhi, Miss Anjali. But I am truly a small man. And even small risks are big for me.'

She was quiet for a moment. She was a quiet woman altogether, restrained in her person and her dress. But now Sartaj could sense her making a decision, and when she spoke there was a decided urgency in her voice. 'I understand, but there is some background you need to know.'

'I need all the background. I have been told absolutely nothing.'

'I am telling you now. Listen. That house you found Gaitonde in, that was a nuclear shelter.'

'A what?'

'A shelter to protect from a bomb. An atomic weapon. The building was constructed according to a well-known architectural model. It is in books, and you can find it on the internet.'

'Why would he need that? Here?'

'That is what I want to know.'

The handset was warm against Sartaj's ear. He was sitting at the back of a small café in the main market street in Kailashpada, and the morning traffic was passing. A school bus lurched to the right and drew close to the footpath where a line of blue-uniformed girls picked up their book-heavy bags. An auto-rickshaw squeezed past the bus. Ordinary life, on an ordinary morning. Sartaj thought about Gaitonde's cube, on that plot two streets and three turns away, and felt dread settle into his chest, like a drip of cold water. He coughed his throat clear. 'Is there a threat? Do you know?'

'There has been a generalized threat perception, that some militant group could use a portable weapon in an urban area. One of the Kashmir groups. Or from the north-east. But no, there is no specific information. No particular threat.'

There had been a film. Sartaj hadn't seen it, but he had watched the advertisements on television. A militant group planted a nuclear bomb in Delhi. The hero warded off disaster by seconds, stopped the neon-green countdown timer just as it ticked down to zero. That was a movie, but Gaitonde's cube had been real. Sartaj had rested his hand on it. He sat up, eased his shoulders. He tried to think. 'Madam,' he said. 'Madam, if Gaitonde knew something about a threat, why didn't he tell your department? Our understanding is that there was a connection.'

'There was no connection.' She was curt, and quick. Sartaj understood that he had overstepped the bounds of departmental propriety, that she couldn't and wouldn't admit to running Gaitonde, especially not on an open phone line. 'We tracked his movements,' she said. 'We found out that he was running weapons into the country. And then we lost track of him. Then he showed up in Bombay.'

'In that house?'

'Yes. Talking to you. Maybe he was trying to tell you about the threat, before you went in.'

So maybe he was responsible if there was a real bomb in his city. A real bomb in this real city. Was that what Gaitonde had been trying to tell him at the end, when Sartaj walked away to send the bulldozer in? Sartaj had cut off Gaitonde in mid-sentence, had cut off his story and then found him dead. But it had been very hot, and Gaitonde had been very arrogant, behind his steel door. 'But it's been many months,' Sartaj said. 'Nothing's happened. You said there was no particular threat.'

'Yes. But I would still like to know what he was doing there. Why he built that house.'

Sartaj was starting to feel oddly cold. 'I'll talk to Zoya Mirza,' he said. 'I'll try.'

'Good. I'm sure you can do it. There is one other interesting point.'

'Yes?'

'The cash you found in Jojo's apartment is fake.'

'Those notes? All of them?'

'Yes. They are very good quality counterfeits. They are produced across the border, in Pakistan. They have been introduced into the country in sizeable quantities over the last eight, ten years. They are often used to fund operations that their people run here. And they are in widespread use.'

'Jojo had a lot of them. In unbroken packets.'

'Right. Interesting in itself. But we've also noticed that the inks and the paper are very much better in recent notes. Jojo's notes were all from one of these new batches, which are as yet not that common. One of the only other places where a big batch of these new notes has been picked up was during an IB and Meerut police raid on people

508

involved in arms smuggling. What happened was this: a Matador van was hit by a State Transport bus outside Meerut, the driver of the van was killed. The local police found one other passenger still alive, and twenty-three assault rifles in the back, under the floorboards. They interrogated the passenger the next day, and he told them he didn't know who he was working for, he was just supposed to pick up the van in Delhi and bring it to Meerut. He didn't know anything more. But he could give them the whereabouts of the men who had hired him in Delhi for the job. So, the police raided a Delhi house. They got three more men, a hundred and thirty-nine AK-56 rifles, forty pistols, almost eighteen thousand rounds of ammunition and ten lakhs in cash.

'Interrogation of all the apradhis revealed other names, other connections. When these leads were followed, and after several layers had been penetrated, it was finally revealed that the original supplier of the arms in Bombay was Gaitonde. That was the extent of that case, it led us to Gaitonde's arms smuggling. After his death, in my investigations, I was reading that case file. I thought of taking a new look at the seized cash. And yes, all ten lakhs were in these new Pakistani notes.'

'And who were these men who were arrested in Delhi?'

'They belong to an underground Hindu organization called Kalki Sena, which we had never heard of before. They are getting ready for a war, they said in their statements. I read some of the literature that was found on the raid. They are going to set up a Hindu rashtra, it seems. After the war, which will be the frightful end of Kaliyug, there will be a perfect nation, run according to ancient Hindu principles.'

'Ram-rajya.'

'Ram-rajya, yes.'

'And this war, who is it going to be against?'

'Muslims, communists, Christians, Sikhs. Anyone else who doesn't like this perfect nation. Militant Dalits also. The rifles were on their way to Bihar, to some right-wing private army run by landlords.'

'You think Gaitonde was part of this organization also? But he always presented himself as the secular don.'

'Yes. So maybe he was just doing business with these Kalki Sena-wallahs, nothing more, he had no involvement in their politics. The apradhis in Delhi couldn't tell us anything more, they were just one cell with a specific job. Whoever is running this is doing it well, putting in many cut-outs. So Gaitonde was maybe involved on an ideological level, or maybe he wasn't. I want to know. And I want to know, that nuclear shelter, why?'

'Yes. I'll talk to the actress.' Sartaj was now wanting to know as well, he wanted some answers to all these questions, some reason for that cube. If somebody was going to wage war against him and his family and his people, he wanted to know who the bastards were, and how they were connected to Ganesh Gaitonde.

'Good.'

Sartaj said a quick 'Okay, bye,' and walked out into the sunlight. It was good to be warm in the morning. He had an aching back from the night's sleep, a crimped shoulder, but even the discomfort was welcome. It was good to be alive. He felt a benevolence towards the shopkeepers with their handy calculators and their shrines to pot-bellied Ganesha, the billboards with their lists of goods and services, the sturdy Maratha women in bright greens and blues striding energetically to work, the three urchins playing cricket with a red rubber ball and a stick. Sartaj squinted, and tried to see the aftermath of a nuclear blast, what it would leave of this bazaar. He couldn't. He remembered the images from the bomb-thriller movie, the brown cloud they had shown in a film within the film, the deadly wind. But it was hard to make it real, here on this street. Impossible to imagine, impossible to believe. And yet, it was here. Here in Kailashpada.

The shops in the market on Rajgir Road were thronged by legions of young women buying clothes for the nine nights of Navaratri. Sartaj slowed down and tilted the motorcycle towards the left, where he drove at the road's edge, relishing the excitement and joy of the girls who dodged past him on their way in and out of the boutiques. Surely Devi would be pleased by all this youthful energy, this feminine happiness. It revived Sartaj anyway, delivered him from the bomb. Someone laughed, and the sound made a sudden song that floated above the grunting and heaving of the traffic. Sartaj turned to look for the laugher, and caught sight of enormous dark eyes reflected in a car window, a moving flash, just that, and then the motorcycle was inches away from the back of an auto-rickshaw and he swerved wildly towards the pavement. The engine died, and Sartaj came safely to a stop, and could see nothing on the roadward side but the long red side of a bus, and to his left a billboard rose some sixty feet above him, car-

rying the very foreshortened face of a blue-lit model up to the sky. He
sat still for a moment, grinning at his own idiocy, his heart thumping
a bit from the close call. A stanchion supporting the billboard made a
downward-pointing triangle with another metal post, and through the
triangle Sartaj could see the top of his own head in a shop window.
Oy, Sardar-ji, he said to himself, get control, yaar. What's wrong with
you?

He drove on, determined to think only professionally now, and
calmly, and logically. He was on his way to meet Rachel Mathias, the
Rachel who was an ex-friend of Kamala's and a potential enemy
armed with too much intelligence. He hadn't quite decided yet how he
was going to play the meeting. There was no official case, and he had
no evidence to accuse the embittered Rachel with, so the intent of the
visit was only to gather information, and to perhaps stir the muddy
waters a bit and see what came bubbling up. He could be an aggressive, frightening policeman, or he could be a discreet new friend trying
to serve Rachel's interests, not the crazy Kamala's. Detection was
often a matter of playing several parts, sometimes simultaneously. If
you could fit yourself into the suspect's prejudices, present yourself as
a solution to her problems, she would talk. Sartaj had done this often
enough, so he now didn't need to prepare too much, to think it all
through in advance. A quick run-through of the essential facts as he
drove was enough: two friends, one married, the other very lonely; a
man; a quarrel. Very simple. But Sartaj knew women's quarrels well
enough to know that they were never as simple as they might seem in
a summary. Maybe the beautiful Umesh had just been the flash-point
that set off this particular war, maybe tensions had been brewing for
years. Maybe the hostilities were really about something else altogether. Assume nothing, he cautioned himself as he parked. Stay alert.
Stop thinking about Navaratri and Durga and Lakshmi and
Saraswati.

But the goddesses were well-represented in Rachel Mathias's drawing room, which was crowded with what was clearly expensive art,
some of it antique. There were sculptures and paintings and, on the
wall furthest from the window, a gigantic wooden double door that
must have been taken from some great haveli. It leaned against the
wall at a sharp angle, cut out from its context but still breathtakingly
beautiful with its vibrant blues and reds and yellows and crossing
bands of dark iron studded with rivets. Sartaj knew that each of the

paintings on the wall, even the modern ones, would cost more than his annual income. Megha would have known the artists, all of them, but the only art that Sartaj recognized was a Raja Ravi Varma print of a bejewelled Lakshmi, graceful and voluptuous. A long time ago, on one of their first dates, Megha had taken him to an art exhibition and told him about the Raja and his works, and Sartaj had loved that Lakshmi ever since.

Now it was clear that Lakshmi had blessed this house, this duplex apartment in Juhu. It gave Sartaj an idea for the angle of his attack. When Rachel Mathias appeared, he introduced himself and said evenly, 'We are looking into people who seem to have assets disproportionate to income.'

'Black money, you mean? Tax matters?'

This Rachel was generously built, but did not give the impression of being lazy or indisciplined. Her bulk was honestly come by, from heredity and from age. She was rather attractive, with her short, efficient hair and well-groomed hands. She looked steadily at Sartaj, giving nothing away. Yes, this was a woman who would have self-control but also deeply felt emotions, this was a person who would feel an insult down to her bones, and then have the courage to avenge it. 'Yes, madam,' Sartaj said, 'these are just preliminary steps, you see. We give people a chance to clear themselves.'

'You're saying I have too many assets? That I spend too much money?'

Sartaj swept his arm around and up. 'This apartment, madam. All these paintings and objects. Your life-style.'

'My life-*style*? My ex-husband is putting you people up to this, yes? He's still trying to make me suffer because he had to give us this apartment. After leaving me and his two children for some twenty-year-old whore, he thinks I should sit at home every night?'

'Madam . . .'

'No, you listen to me. He doesn't give us enough to meet one-quarter of what his children need. Every other paisa I spend, I earn. All this furniture and art you see, this is for my business. I work hard.'

'Interior decoration?'

'Yes. And now I am going to open an art gallery with two other partners.'

'Very good. But there is still the matter of too much money, maybe. Questions have been raised.'

'Where? Listen, we do all our business in white. My accountant has every receipt, a copy of every cheque from every client. We can show you everything you want.'

Rachel was wearing a loose linen shirt in white, with grey pants of the same texture. The outfit brought out the rich brown of her very good skin, and the softer amber of her eyes. She had her hands poised elegantly on a knee, but she was worried now. Sartaj pressed on. 'Madam, there is no business that is done all in white. Especially interior decoration. It is all a matter of proportion. If we don't feel there has been enough co-operation, of course we will have to investigate properly.'

'What do you want?'

Sartaj stretched, and said very casually, 'Do you own a video camera?'

'What?'

'A video camera, madam. To take videos, you know, of marriages, prize-giving events, parties.' He mimed the action of taping. 'Nowadays very common.'

'Yes. We have two. One is old, and one is new. But, what . . .'

She was very confused now, and – Sartaj thought – a little afraid. It was time for a bit of the old police lathi. He leaned forward, and stared at her until she began to shift about on her pretty Mughal-style divan. The hostility in his eyes came easily when he summoned it, it swept from some endless reservoir of contempt for wrongdoers and rule-breakers, and he knew it was also tightening his shoulders and colouring his cheeks. 'Why two video cameras, madam? Why do you need so many?'

'I paid for the new one on a credit card, you can see . . .'

'That is not what I asked. What do you use the cameras for?'

'Like you said, celebrations. When we go on holidays. Like that.'

'Have you given a camera to anyone else? Lent it?'

'No. But why are you asking?'

'There is a case of blackmail I am investigating. A video camera was used.' He watched her carefully, and now he was sure that he had struck some potentially rich seam of fear. She was at the edge of the divan now, deportment forgotten. 'There is some indication that you may be connected to the case.'

'Me? How? What are you talking about?'

Sartaj shook his head. 'Madam, better that you do the talking now.'

Rachel wanted to, he could see that, but she grasped one hand over the other and swallowed and finally sputtered, 'I have nothing to say.'

He was sure she had heard the line in some TV serial. He stood up. He wasn't going to get a full confession just by showing up at a suspect's house. It had been known to occur, but it wasn't going to happen with this one. They would need to apply more pressure, perhaps with hard evidence picked up elsewhere. Meanwhile Rachel Mathias would worry herself into a nerve-racked condition of fear ripe for breaking. 'As you wish,' Sartaj said. 'Here is my card. Please call me if you change your mind.'

On his way to the door, Sartaj saw, on a marble-topped table, a picture of two boys laughing against a background of green mountains. 'Your sons,' he said. 'Very nice-looking boys.'

But this only seemed to frighten Rachel even further. She flinched. Sartaj was enjoying himself now. 'And not a bad frame either,' he said. 'Silver, and quite heavy. An antique, unless I'm mistaken. And even if I am, still expensive.' He ran a finger over the broad-leafed vine that ran around the edges of the frame, and then left her with, 'We will be watching your house.'

In the lift he felt quite victorious. This was an interesting suspect, this woman who had remade herself after being abandoned by her husband, who had constructed a new life. Who were the co-conspirators who were making the calls to Kamala? How had she found them, hired them? It would be interesting to find out.

Sartaj and Kamble were walking opposite sides of the street in front of the Apsara cinema, at rush hour. They were looking for Kamala Pandey's urchin, a boy of indeterminate age and appearance who wore a red DKNY JEANS T-shirt, who had been attired in red when he had picked up blackmail cash from her a month and a half ago, who carried a black tooth in his mouth. Kamble had been sceptical about their possibilities of success, and sulky, but they were out here looking. It was almost six, and the crowd shifted and swarmed over the pavements. The car horns made a fanfare that lifted Sartaj's heart. *Pyaar ka Diya* was the movie showing at Apsara, and it was a hit. Sartaj could feel it in the relaxed, post-climactic ease of the viewers coming out of the cinema, and in the happy eagerness of those going in. In this Apsara, on this evening at least, the flame of love still alight. Sartaj edged sideways through a gaggle of sharp-looking collegians dialling busily on their mobile phones. 'Jhakaas movie, yaar,' one of them said into his phone.

There were beggar boys and girls working the crowd, holding up their hands and trying out their patter. 'Hello, Aunty, give me something, only one rupee, aunty. One rupee, Aunty, I'm very hungry. Please, Aunty.' The chokras wore a variety of ragged shirts and banians, but no red T-shirt. Sartaj made his way down the road, all the way to the corner where the crowd thinned, and then he came back. He knew already the faces of the black-marketeers, who strolled the pavement with their own pitch: 'Bolo, balcony two-fifty, stall one-fifty.'

Kamble came across the road, dodging through the cars. He was in full black today, including new black shoes with some sort of silver lining on their complicated heels. He raised his chin at Sartaj, and Sartaj shrugged. 'No?' Kamble said. 'I saw three red T-shirts, but not on any chokra. One was a nice little round item, hair down to her gaand, and these . . .' He raised his cupped hands in front of his chest. 'Nice. You saw the blackies?'

'Yes.'

'There's also a toli of pocket-maars on that side. See the chutiya in the blue pants? He's the talker. Then over there on the left, the old man with the newspaper? No, no, there. He's the lifter.' There was a clean-shaven grandfather type in a very respectable and crisp white shirt moving inconspicuously along. 'Then, over there, that's the hand-off man.' This one was younger, slim and dashing in dark glasses and a loose grey shirt. 'Ah, there they go.'

Blue pants stepped up to a family party, mother and executive father and two children, and spoke to the father. Asked him directions, it looked like. The father was pointing up the road, making hand motions, go right, go left. Blue pants touched him on the shoulder, thank you. And at that very moment the grandfather made his move, stepped past the father and behind him.

'Got it,' Kamble said. 'Did you see it? He got the wallet.' His voice was tight with admiration.

Sartaj had seen a movement of the grandfather's hand between the bodies, that was all. 'Budhau is very good,' he said. 'Daddy doesn't know it yet.'

'He won't know until he tries to pay for ice-cream. I hope he doesn't have the cinema tickets in the wallet. Ah, there's the hand-off.'

The grandfather and dark glasses moved past each other, their shoulders brushed. Dark glasses strolled away, the wallet already under his shirt. 'Do we go?' Kamble said. 'Let's get the bastards.'

'No, leave it. We have other things to worry about.' An arrest or two was always welcome, but Sartaj didn't want to cause a commotion in front of the chokras. Any of them could be the boy in the red T-shirt. Sartaj didn't want to be revealed as a policeman until they had him.

'We're not going to get the red T-shirt boy like this,' Kamble said. 'Let's catch up a couple of his friends. There's a lot of the little bastards running around. We'll ask them. Two minutes and two slaps and they'll talk.'

'And maybe they won't. In any case, you'll send him running all the way to Nashik. Have patience, my friend. He's a poor boy who lives on the streets. He'll wear his red T-shirt tomorrow, if not today.'

'Maybe. Or maybe he bought a new blue one with the money the apradhis gave him. But how long do we stay?'

'Until the rush is over. Another half an hour. When the public leaves, we leave.'

'Fine.'

'Hold on for a minute.' Sartaj reached into his pocket and brought out his phone, now looking a little worn. He tapped at the tiny black keys. 'Hello, saab?'

'Sartaj. How are you?' Parulkar said.

'I'm good,' Sartaj said. 'I am following an investigation, sir, and I need some help.'

'Yes.'

'I'm in Goregaon, sir. At a cinema. There's a team of pocket-maars working the crowd, an old fellow with two boys. The lifter is the old one, maybe sixty-five, seventy. He's very good.'

Parulkar was quiet, for a moment. One of his many policing talents was that he had a memory like one of Yama's assistants, he never forgot a crime, not even the smallest one. He remembered apradhis from forty years ago, could tell you their family histories. A boy who stole a bicycle for a joyride found his misdemeanour written down permanently in the inescapable registers of Parulkar's recollection, to be brought up again when he was a grandfather. 'This pocket-maar,' Parulkar said now, 'is he bald? Heavy-set fellow?'

'No, sir. White hair, nice neat haircut. Very respectable-looking.'

'Ah, yes. Five seven, five eight? Stoops a little to the front, like he's about to collapse?'

'Yes, sir. He looks very harmless.'

'That's Jayanth. K.R. Jayanth. He's got great hands. We only arrested him twice, in seventy-nine and eighty-two. He lived in Dharavi then, used to work the trains on the western line, with a first-class pass. He wore very serious-looking glasses, carried a briefcase and everything. He got his son out to the US, through Mexico I think. The son worked as a taxi-driver, got a green card. Jayanth said he was making eighty thousand dollars a year, as a driver. He told me he himself had retired. This was in eighty-eight, eighty-nine. I haven't seen him since.'

'He's working again, sir.'

Parulkar chortled. 'It's hard to sit at home, you know, after retirement. And this Jayanth has a lot of skill. Not many like him left nowadays. Now they all want to do smash and grab. Nobody has that dedication any more.'

'That's true, sir.'

Sartaj thanked Parulkar and tucked the phone away. Kamble had figured out some of Parulkar's information from what he had half-heard, and Sartaj filled him in on the rest of it. 'Maderchod,' Kamble said, 'that Parulkar is good.'

'Yes. He is the best.'

'And on his way up again. He's like some circus jhamoora, you knock him down flat, he pops up straight.'

'He's very skilled, Kamble. Very experienced and very cunning.'

'Of course he's cunning, my friend, he's a Brahmin. He's a Brahmin and he's got cunning and resources and family in good places.'

Sartaj laughed. 'And you are just a simple dehati boy?' Kamble was a Dalit, and he never brought it up, but he sometimes had things to say about OBCs and Marathas and Brahmins.

'I am learning, Sardar-ji, I am learning from people like Parulkar only.' Kamble was grinning now. 'The word is that he's distanced himself from the Suleiman Isa company, and has aligned himself with the Rakshaks. After so many years of being close to the S-Company, he has completely defected to the other side. So that's why the Rakshaks love him suddenly. Is this true?'

Sartaj had heard this rumour also. He shrugged. 'You'll have to ask him.'

'Boss, no need to ask. He has taught me a lot already. I have already learnt that you get the money, you make the connections, you rise up, you make more money, more connections, you then get real power, then you make more money, then you . . .'

'I get it,' Sartaj said. 'I get it, guru.'

'No, no, I am nobody's guru, not yet. But Parulkar Saab is my guru, even if he doesn't know it. I am like Eklavya, except that I am going to keep my thumb and my lauda and every other maderchod thing.' Kamble's smile was now at its widest and most ferocious.

Sartaj couldn't help smiling back. Kamble had a way of being deadly serious and sunny at the same time. He was a self-proclaimed badmash, but he was a charming one. 'Let's get back to work.'

But Kamble hooked his thumbs into his belt-loops and rocked back and forth on his heels. He was looking down at his scientific shoes. 'Boss,' he said finally, 'do you really think there's a bomb in the city?'

Sartaj had told Kamble about Gaitonde's nuclear shelter on their way to Apsara. He had felt very afraid, in the slanting afternoon sun, and he had wanted to tell someone, and Katekar was dead. 'I don't know,' he said. 'Maybe Gaitonde thought there was some danger from a bomb.'

'But that was months ago. If they wanted to blow us up, they would have done it months and months ago. One day, phataak, just like that. We're still here, so that means there's no bomb.'

'Yes, that sounds logical.' It was good logic. Maybe Gaitonde had had an urgent threat perception. But time had passed, and Gaitonde was dead, and the threat hadn't materialized. So maybe he had been deceived, maybe he had gone mad. 'No bomb, yaar.'

'Crazy idea.'

Kamble nodded at Sartaj, and Sartaj nodded back at him. Then Kamble went back to his side of the street. Sartaj did another sweep up the pavement, edging diagonally to the wall and then back to the road as he walked. He knew they had been trying to reassure each other with all their nodding, and he knew that they both were afraid. They were both policemen, and they knew that disaster didn't announce itself and act in predictable ways, like in the movies. There was that woman who went to Bandra Reclamation with her family to a fun fair. The kids wanted to go on the Giant Wheel, so the doting parents went along. The mother was young, pretty and very proud of her perfect, long, deep-black radiant hair. On this

Sunday she had it open down to her waist, falling like a fragrant fountain. The wheel took them up, the wheel sped up, the wheel made the mother's hair fly, the wheel took the mother's hair around a turning spoke, and the wheel ripped the mother's whole scalp off. Or, you were a father close to retirement, you would be going about your business one day, quietly buying vegetables and chocolate, and an electrician's wrench would drop off the seventeenth floor of a new Daihatsu building, bounce through two layers of scaffolding, plummet and bury itself in your skull. That had happened in Worli, when Sartaj had been a two-month sub-inspector. Bombs went off as abruptly. You couldn't feel their presence before they exploded, they didn't give you a tingle on your forearms, they had no smell. There had also been that day, that long-ago Friday in 1993, when the phones had started to ring in the station at Worli. And Sartaj had sped out on his motorcycle, followed by a van, and had driven over pavements, past the stalled traffic, towards the Passport Office. There were men and women walking, running and then walking again. And a thick grey smoke ahead, a silence without birds. Sartaj kicked down the bike-stand, and ran down the road, past a green Fiat exposing its rusty innards like a tipped-over crab. Then his feet began slipping, and he looked down, and he was walking on blood, splashing through it.

Stop it. Just stop it. Sartaj cracked his knuckles, and the small pops brought him back to the pavement where he was walking now, to Apsara and *Pyaar ka Diya* and its posters, in which the lead pair paid tribute to the bent-back Raj-Nargis pose from *Awaara*. Concentrate on the problem at hand, Sartaj told himself. Do the job. Watch the crowd, look closely at the faces. Sartaj did that, but he was unable to rid himself completely of the memories, of the body parts which had been littered through the wreckage. An upper arm, a foot. Yes, bombs just went off. They exploded. Sartaj reached the end of his beat, and turned around and did it again.

Kamble came back across the road a little before the half-hour was up. The public had been mostly sucked into Apsara, or they had gone home, but some of the chokras were still hanging about. Sartaj watched Kamble stepping across the divider, and worried about his lack of patience. Strength was good to have, and courage was some-times necessary, but the main requirement of the job was to be able to spend countless hours completing small, boring, maybe meaningless tasks. Katekar, now, would never have wanted to leave Apsara so early. But Katekar was dead.

'Do you think the kattus did it?' Kamble said.

'What?'

'The bomb. If there's a bomb in the city, it's got to be the Muslims who brought it in.'

'Yes. That is true. It must be the Muslims.'

'So let's go and talk to this Zoya kutiya. Maybe she knows something. If we go straight to her house, she can't turn us away. After all, we're policemen.'

After all. That was true. 'Calm down. There's no use rushing in. We have time. You said it yourself, it has been months. If there is even a bomb, it hasn't gone off yet. It's not going to go off tonight. Or tomorrow morning.'

Kamble spat into the gutter. He stretched his shoulders back. 'Of course. I'm not saying that. But we could just go and talk to the randi. So what if she's acting like one big film star? That's all she is, one randi. Anyway, you page me and tell me when we need action.'

'I will. We can't summon her to the station, we have limitations. So we have to figure out an approach to her. We don't want to scare her.'

'Fine, fine. Are we finished here? I'm going to find myself a woman. Too much bomb tension, bhai saab.'

'Just one more minute. I have an idea.' Sartaj was watching, across the road, K.R. Jayanth the distinguished pocket-maar strolling towards the bus stop, licking at an ice-cream cone. Everyone, it seemed, wanted to give themselves a little after-work treat. 'Come on.'

Sartaj led the way across the divider, and he came up on Jayanth's right. He matched Jayanth's stride, and walked very close to him, just like a friend taking the evening air. Jayanth remained calm, Sartaj was pleased to note. He was an old hand, and likely to be reasonable. Jayanth just edged away slightly to the left, and kept at his cone. But now Kamble was on his other side, hemming him in.

'Namaste, Uncle,' Sartaj said.

Jayanth nodded. 'You're police,' he said.

Sartaj had to laugh, from the sheer pleasure of meeting a practised professional. 'Yes,' he said. 'Made good money today?'

Jayanth took a bite out of the cone. 'I don't know what you are talking about.'

Sartaj put a hand on his shoulder. 'Arre, Uncle. We have been watching you work all evening. With the two boys. You are very good.'

'What boys?'

'One in a blue shirt, one in dark glasses. Come on, Jayanth Uncle, don't annoy me now. You've come out of retirement, you're working hard. Nothing wrong with that.'

'My name is not Jayanth.'

Sartaj cuffed Jayanth in the face. It was a short blow, with the back of the hand that had been resting on Jayanth's shoulder, but there was some knuckle in it and it rocked Jayanth back. Kamble was staring in disgust at his right foot, which now had a long splatter of ice-cream along the front.

'Let's just take the bastard back to the station,' he said. 'He'll remember who he is there.'

On this busy street, only one woman had seen the blow. She was hurrying away from them now, throwing horrified glances back at Sartaj. She was carrying a netting bag full of vegetables and wore bright red sindoor in her hair. Sartaj ignored the impulse to explain to her, *this is just the language we speak, nothing really bad will happen to the nice old man*. He turned back to Jayanth. 'So, Uncle. You want to come back to the station with us?'

'All right.' Jayanth threw away his empty cone. 'I am Jayanth. I don't know you.'

'Sartaj Singh.'

'You don't work in this zone. How much do you want?'

'You have a setting with the local officers?'

Jayanth shrugged. Of course he had an arrangement with the local boys, but he wasn't going to give away information. 'We don't want to trouble you that way,' Sartaj said. 'Or arrest you. Not at all. But we need you to do some work for us.'

'I am an old man.'

'Yes, Uncle. But you don't really have to work. Just keep your eyes open.' Sartaj told him that he was to look out for a chokra in a red T-shirt with such-and-such logo, with a black tooth, that he was to discover the chokra's name, and if possible his habitation. That he was not to alarm Red T-shirt, or hint in any way that big, ugly, violent policemen were looking for him. That he was to call Sartaj or Kamble at this-and-this number as soon as he had a line on the boy.

'I can't go around looking into boys' mouths,' Jayanth said. 'They will think I am some pervert, they are very smart.'

'I know, Uncle. You just look for the right red T-shirt. Then you talk to him. Be patient. Don't rush anything. Just do your usual work, and keep your eyes open.'

'Okay,' Jayanth said.

'He'll be here,' Kamble said.

'Of course,' Jayanth said peevishly. Street chokras were very territorial, they had all their corners and areas marked out, down to borders drawn along the middle of streets. And they defended their regions as fiercely as generals battling over holy lands, everyone knew this. 'But you think he'll be here in the same T-shirt?' And then, to Kamble, 'What are you *doing*?'

Kamble was holding Jayanth's trouser pocket open and groping about in it. 'Don't worry,' he said. 'I'm not picking your pocket. Don't worry. And don't worry about the chokra. You just keep alert, keep looking. He'll show up.' He held up a brown leather wallet, worn down past the polish to the bare hide. 'You don't carry much money, Uncle.'

Jayanth didn't miss a beat. 'Too much crime on the streets nowadays,' he said.

Kamble chortled appreciatively. 'Six hundred rupees, and a picture of . . . What god is this?'

'Murugan.'

'No I-card, nothing at all.'

On the other side, in Jayanth's other pocket, something crinkled under Sartaj's gentle patting. Sartaj fished with his forefinger, and drew out an inland letter, folded twice over.

'Malad,' Sartaj said. The letter itself was in some incomprehensible southern script, but the address was in English. 'You're working very close to home, Uncle.'

'I'm an old man. Can't travel too far.'

Kamble gave him back the wallet. 'You moved out of Dharavi anyway. I bet it's a nice apartment in Malad. For an old man you make a good amount of money. Even if you don't carry it on yourself.' Jayanth flinched a little under Kamble's beady-eyed hostility, and looked down.

Sartaj wrote down the address. 'Why are you out here anyway, Uncle, at this age? Isn't your America-wallah son helping you any more?'

Jayanth waggled his head from one side to the other, and looked quite as sad as any filmi father who had endured a lifetime of family quarrels and ungratefulness and tragedies. 'He's got children of his own now,' he said. 'His own responsibilities.'

'He married an American woman?'

'Yes.'

Sartaj patted Jayanth on the shoulder, talked him through the assignment once again, and then sent him on his way. Kamble looked distinctly unhappy, and Sartaj knew he was thinking about the six hundred rupees in Jayanth's wallet. 'Woman?' Sartaj said.

'What?'

'I thought you were going to find an item. To help with bomb tension.'

'Yes, yes. There's too much tension nowadays. Even apradhis give you stories of their tension.'

'So maybe you should get two women. For the double tension.'

Kamble threw back his shoulders and rested his clenched hands on his hips, exactly like Netaji on a pedestal. 'You're right, my friend,' he said. 'I will take not two, but three women tonight. For the triple tension.'

Sartaj watched him swagger away, forcing the evening shoppers to step aside and leave him an emperor's way. Maybe when he was a bit older, and a little more defeated, he would make a good policeman. Right now, he was cocky and very afraid of this new danger he had learnt about today. Sartaj was also afraid, but he had spent a lot of time with fear, and he expected no relief from it. Quick, decisive action could maybe produce the illusion of comfort, but that would be only temporary. You had to learn to live with fear, with its red tongue and its garland of skulls. Sartaj turned to the left and strolled up the footpath. He was on the job, he would stay on it for another half-hour. The bomb could wait.

The science and art of approach was something that Sartaj had learnt at an early age, in his own home. People tried to approach his father the inspector, usually people in trouble, those who needed help. So they approached through friends and relatives and colleagues, through friends of friends and political connections. Once, a woman who had been threatened by her estranged husband approached through Sartaj's secondary-school principal. You found a connection

with the object of the approach, and then moved favour and obligation through this connection, so that the person being approached felt
that they had to help, or at least listen. Approach was how life
worked, getting through life meant strumming this web and moving
along its many pathways.

So approach was a skill Sartaj had, but the trouble was that he had
never before tried to approach a film star. Like everybody else in
Bombay, he knew one caterer who occasionally supplied food for film
shootings, two Grade-A extras and one distant cousin whose best
friend's uncle was a film producer. None of these connections would
get him into a room with Zoya Mirza without upsetting her. This is
what he told Mary and Jana late that night, in a maidan full of dancers
and bright lights. He had been unable to get away from the station till
very late, but they had insisted on an in-person report on the Zoya
Mirza situation. So he had met up with them in Juhu, at the Guru-ji
Patta Mandal's Grand Navaratri Celebrations. The gala posters outside promised 'Largest Dandia Raas Ever Seen', and although Sartaj
didn't believe that to be literally true, he thought there were at least
three thousand dancers on this field. Once he had got to the venue, he
had called Jana's husband on his mobile phone, and it had still taken
him fifteen minutes to find them, next to the Coca-Cola stand. Sartaj
had wandered, quite ravished, in a shimmer and a haze of red and blue
and green ghagras. The dancers wheeled with a great flickering of the
dandia sticks, and Sartaj was light-headed from the perfume and the
tinkling laughter, from the singer and her *Pankhida tu uddi jaaje*. Then
he saw tall Jana waving to him above the undulating river of jewelled
heads. He didn't see Mary until he was right next to her, and even
when he saw her he didn't know her, not for a full long glance. It was
only when she smiled and said 'Hello' that he knew her.

Jana was grinning. 'She really looks like a real Gujju behn, doesn't
she?'

'Yes,' Sartaj said. Mary was wearing a blue ghagra, and a deep-blue
chunni that shone with silver, and her hair was held up by some sort
of pearly clips. Her lips were a brilliant red. 'I didn't even recognize
you.'

'I know you didn't. But it's not really that complicated a disguise.'

Sartaj thought it was quite deep, but he nodded and shook hands
with Jana's husband Suresh, who was resplendent in a crimson kurta
and a jari half-jacket. Suresh held up little Naresh, who was dressed

exactly like him. Sartaj patted the boy's head, aware all the time that Mary was watching him.

'Here,' Jana said. She handed Sartaj a Coke, and then led the way to a sprawl of chairs to the left. She sent Suresh off with Naresh, seated herself comfortably, drew Mary down next to her and turned to Sartaj. 'Now tell.'

They both grew quite discontented when it became clear that Sartaj had nothing to tell about Zoya Mirza. 'Are you police always this *slow*?' Mary said. She had her back straight and her hands on her knees, like a schoolteacher.

'Of course they are, baba,' Jana said. 'Have you ever tried reporting something at a station?'

They were both giving him a bit of a tease, and Sartaj accepted the criticism with a smile. He held his hands out wide and said, 'It would be different if this was official. I have to be very careful.'

'Obviously we're going to have to manage this for you as well,' Mary said. 'Jana, didn't that Stephanie girl who used to work at Nalini and Yasmin's have a sister who did make-up for Kajol?'

'Yes, yes. But where is she working now?'

Sartaj sat back and watched admiringly as Jana cupped a hand over one ear and put a mobile phone to the other. There was now a garbaized version of *Chainya Chainya* pumping out over the loudspeakers, and under it Jana tracked down that Stephanie girl. She handed the phone to Mary, who followed a couple of leads. Sartaj was content to watch them, to admire them as they conducted their investigation. It was a peculiar kind of sideways spread, a questioning that moved not necessarily closer to Stephanie, but around her. Jana and Mary had a considered conversation about Stephanie's ex-best friend, who had also worked at Nalini and Yasmin's. They talked about this friend's boyfriend, and a shopping trip she had gone on, to that new mall in Goregaon, and her plan for a trip to Goa in the winter. As far as Sartaj could tell, this had absolutely nothing to do with Stephanie, or with Zoya Mirza. But Jana and Mary leaned close to each other and talked of the ex-best friend with great intensity and complete pleasure. Through the course of the several phone calls, they learnt about other women and their lives, other jobs and marriages and births. Mary was now talking to some woman about her grandmother's angioplasty. She hung up and said to Sartaj, 'It's too late at night, everyone's gone to sleep. But we'll have a connection to this Zoya Mirza by tomorrow.'

'A make-up connection,' Sartaj said.

'Are you making fun of us?' Mary said. 'Here we are, trying to help you, and you are making fun of us?'

'No, no, no fun. I'm admiring you two, actually. You're very impressive, how you find out things.'

'Suresh always says I talk too much,' Jana said. 'He says I go on and on about things that are completely irrelevant. He says if I want to go from A to C, I don't have to talk about L, M and Z.'

Mary drew herself back into a Suresh stance, full of superior distaste. 'You women, to get from Churchgate to Bandra you go to Thane.'

Sartaj and Jana broke into giggles. It was a very sharp Suresh imitation, it caught his posture and his quick, clipping speech exactly. Even after talking to Suresh for only two minutes, Sartaj could see that. Suresh emerged just then from the crowd, and said, 'I left Naresh with Ma,' and looked quite baffled as his wife and Mary and Sartaj collapsed into helpless laughter.

Jana stood up and put a hand on Suresh's shoulder. 'We're going to dance,' she said. 'Coming?'

Sartaj was relieved that Mary shook her head. It was a long time since he had dandia-ed, and he was sure he didn't want to wade out into this spiralling sea of experts.

'You go,' Mary said. 'I'm a bit tired.'

Jana and Suresh vanished into the whirling wheels of dancers, which were now four, one inside the other.

'Very beautiful,' Sartaj said. It was, in the halo of bronze spotlights, this sparking set of circles.

'They met here,' Mary said. 'Jana and Suresh. His father is one of the organizers.'

Sartaj remembered meeting Megha on garba nights, in a time so long ago that it was ancient. The music hadn't been quite so disco, then. 'Have you been coming for a long time?'

'Ever since I met Jana, four years ago. It's fun. I like dressing up and coming out.'

He had to grin back at her very pleased grin. 'Blending into the Gujaratis.'

'They're nice people.'

'Except when they're murdering Muslims.'

'That's true for everyone, no? Even the Muslims murder people sometimes. Christians do.'

'Yes. I didn't mean that . . . Sorry. Suresh seems like a good man.'

'It's okay.' She turned in her chair, to look directly at Sartaj. 'You think everyone is a murderer.'

'Anyone can become one. Sorry, sorry. This is not the talk to have at a garba. It's just the way policemen see things.'

Mary didn't look disturbed, not in the least. 'So what else do you see at a garba? Tell me.'

'Navratri nights are good for pickpockets, certainly. Chain-snatchers and that lot. And a lot of cash gets handled, you know. At five hundred rupees per ticket in some places, that's a huge amount. People get tempted, the people who are handling the money.'

'Life is like that, full of temptations.'

'True. That's the other thing. Boys and girls at these things. Even the very orthodox families, they bring their unmarried daughters out to these garbas. You can't watch them once they go out into that, that mess. So the boys find them. You know, every year, for the month or two or three after Navratri, all the clinics in town report a rise in abortions.'

'Really?'

'Really. Really, we police should take care over that kind of thing.'

'You want to have policemen watching the boys and girls at garbas?'

'If there were enough policemen, maybe that wouldn't be such a bad idea. It's getting worse.'

'Maybe the boys and girls think it's getting better.'

She was exaggeratedly serious, and Sartaj was suddenly aware that she was making fun of him. Amazingly, he found himself blushing. 'No, you are right,' he said, looking down and rubbing the back of his neck. 'It's very easy to become old-fashioned these days. I sound like my father. He was a policeman also.'

'Here in Bombay?'

'Yes. Here. Actually, you know, Suresh wouldn't have liked his stories. He was also one of those people who couldn't get to Bandra without visiting Thane.'

'I thought policemen were supposed to be brief.'

'Oh, he could be brief. But he always said that what was left out of the final case-report was actually the case. So he would be telling you about a robbery in Chembur, and suddenly you would be in Amritsar. My mother used to laugh at him.'

'Where is your mother now?'

So Sartaj told her about the house in Pune, and the advantages of having Ma close to family and gurudwara, and then he told her one of Papa-ji's interesting murder cases which had actually extended from Colaba to Hyderabad. Maybe not as far as Amritsar, but he thought she got the point. She didn't say much, but the two questions she asked went to the very heart of the bloody matter. It was only when Jana and Suresh came back – with their son sleeping on Suresh's shoulder – that Sartaj realized that more than an hour had passed. It was long past midnight. Sartaj walked them out, the little group, and saw them into an auto and waved them goodbye. He stood with his back to the ornate, flower-laden garba gate, his hands on his hips, and considered Mary Mascarenas. She was a quiet and complicated one, and surprisingly easy to talk to. She was intelligent, and she didn't like to reveal this. She had opinions, and she was stubborn. In a Gujarati ghagra she was glossy and somehow modest and small and lush. She was trouble, somehow. Or at least troubling. She was dangerous. She would bear watching.

Over his chai the next morning Sartaj decided that the whole bomb scare was ridiculous. He felt ashamed of having been afraid, for believing something that so obviously had been imagined by a credulous woman who just happened to be an intelligence officer. And these spies were from a paranoid tribe anyway, they were a caste of secret warriors who always saw a foreign hand in every crime, and a terrorist behind every corner. Sartaj had his chai, and he did not feel afraid. It was an unseasonably cool morning, for the very end of September, and he felt cheerful and energetic. He sat near the window with his second cup and the *Dainik Jagran*, and watched the birds wheel up out of the swamp into the opening light. The news was bad, or as bad as usual, there was further tension on the border, there had been a grenade attack in Jammu, the ruling coalition at the centre was shaky again and threatening to disintegrate. Things were falling apart, but Sartaj stood in the shower and soaped his chest and sang *Bhumro bhumro* along with the radio from the apartment below. He could hear children in the apartment above, laughing and singing along also. It was a good morning.

His mobile rang just as he was locking the front door. Today, he was confident. He was sure it was Mary, not somebody from the station. He thumbed a button and said, 'Hello, hello?'

'Hello,' Mary said, and Sartaj laughed out loud. 'You're very happy today?'

'Hello, Mary-ji,' Sartaj said. 'Sorry, sorry. I just heard a song on the radio, and some children singing it also.'

'That made you laugh?'

He could feel her smiling. 'Yes. It's a little crazy, I know. You know what they say about sardars.'

She giggled, then stopped herself short. 'It's not twelve o'clock yet, though.'

'You should see me then.'

'I have seen you in the middle of the day, and you were not happy at all. You were frightening.'

'I was investigating, I have to put on that face.'

'Put on another face for Zoya Mirza, okay? Otherwise she'll run from you.'

'Zoya? You found an approach?'

'Of course. And where she's shooting today and tomorrow. Write all this down.' Sartaj wrote, in his diary, the name of Zoya Mirza's make-up man and his pager number, and the name of the production in-charge and his mobile number. 'This make-up boy, Vivek, he's your main contact. He knows you are coming, and he has talked to the production in-charge. All they know is that you are a policeman and you are a big fan of Zoya Mirza, that you really want to meet her.'

'This is true.'

'You are a fan?'

'Yes.'

'You and every other Indian man. You just remember who made it possible for you to meet your Zoya. So phone us as soon as you get back from your meeting with her. Today, not tomorrow. Don't forget.'

'I won't. Thank you. It seems you are a fan also.'

'We just want to know. Everything.'

'Don't worry. I will call you.'

'I'll be waiting.'

Half an hour later, paused at a traffic light in Andheri, heated by a gushing of foul exhaust from a BEST bus, Sartaj was still thinking of Mary. She was eager to learn about the life of film stars. Everyone wanted to know about stars, about what they did and didn't do. Even those who professed to hate films and filmi people, these anti-filmis criticized the stars with a venomous intensity that revealed much knowledge, both current and historical. And Mary had a personal curiosity, she had lost a sister, and perhaps Zoya Mirza would reveal something essential and illuminating about Jojo. So Mary had lots of reasons to wait for his phone call. But he had a day of work to get through, thefts and bandobasts to look into, before he could get to film stars, even though he really wanted to ask Zoya Mirza some questions. He wanted the information. But film stars and Mary would have to wait. Sartaj was sweating now, and now he believed in the bomb a little, it had come back and it hovered at some distance from him, like a needle-toothed rat lurking unseen in thick grass. He could feel it was close, he could feel it on his forearms and his back just below the neck. He cursed it sincerely, at length, and went to his work.

As it turned out, Sartaj and Kamble were able to get out to Film City that evening, well before the end of Zoya Mirza's afternoon shift. They drove up past AdLabs, and up the hill to a huge palace. Zoya was the main lead in a multi-star period movie, one of the first big-scale swordfighting and swinging-from-chandeliers extravaganzas to be made in decades. Vivek the make-up man sat them down on fold-out chairs behind the palace and gave them cutting-chais and told them about the project. 'It's very different, this film. It's like *Dharamveer*, only it's fully up to date and modern. Huge special effects. This whole palace is going to lift into the air and then fly and be seen in the middle of a lake. They have huge battle scenes planned, they are going to have them all generated by computer. The hero has a big fight with a giant cobra with a hundred heads.'

'And what is Zoya playing?' Sartaj said.

'Madam is a princess,' Vivek said. 'But her parents, the Maharaja and Maharani, are murdered when she's young, and she grows up in the jungle with a chieftain's family. Nobody knows who she is.'

Kamble took a noisy sip of tea. 'A junglee princess?' he said. 'Very good. What does she wear?'

Vivek was bespectacled and thin and very serious, and he was now made distinctly uncomfortable by Kamble's frank leering. Of course he couldn't tell a policeman that he was a lewd gaandu, so he shrank a little and said, 'The costumes are very good, Manish Malhotra is doing them.'

Sartaj patted Vivek on the forearm. 'Manish Malhotra is the best. I'm sure Madam looks wonderful. How is it to work for her?'

'She is a very good person.'

'Is she? She seems so,' Sartaj said. Vivek regarded Sartaj through his very stylish blue-framed glasses, and Sartaj smiled innocently back at him. 'Of course she's beautiful. But I always thought that in her roles you could tell that she's a good woman.'

Vivek's wariness ebbed, and he sat up. 'Yes. She's very generous, you know.'

'She helped you?'

'She gave me a chance. We met when she was doing an ad film. When she became a star she didn't forget me.'

'You've been with her a long time, then.'

'Yes.'

'You have a good job, travelling all over the world with a movie star. I've never been out of the country.'

'Thirty-two countries till now,' Vivek said, bright and eager. 'Next week we go to South Africa.'

Kamble asked softly, 'You spent a lot of time in Singapore?'

'Yes, yes, Madam has done a lot of shooting there.' The question brought up no fear, no anxiety to mar Vivek's devotion to his Madam. 'It is a very beautiful place. We did a lot of fashion shoots there. Madam liked it very much, it's so clean and neat. We stayed for holidays also, sometimes.'

Sartaj finished his tea, and stretched. 'She must have friends there, then.'

Vivek was puzzled. 'I don't know. She and I didn't stay in the same hotel. What do you mean?'

Sartaj thumped his knee. 'Nothing, yaar. I go to Pune sometimes, so I have friends there. Do you think she can see us now?'

'I think her interview is still going on. But the shot is almost ready. I'll go and see.'

Sartaj kept up his expression of enthusiastic gratitude until Vivek disappeared round a corner of the palace wall. Three workmen were painting a portion of that wall an even gold. A dozen men sprawled on the grass next to them, and some women sat in a circle in the shade of a large van. Sartaj couldn't tell that a shot was being prepared for, much less that it might be almost ready.

'That chashmu bastard doesn't know anything,' Kamble said. 'He talked too easily about Singapore.'

'Yes. They would have been very careful, Gaitonde and her.'

Kamble scratched at his chest. On his wrist he had a copper bracelet. 'Gaitonde the great Hindu don,' he said. 'Of course he had to be careful about his Muslim girlfriend. Lying maderchod.'

'Having a Muslim girl doesn't hurt your reputation. And Suleiman Isa, he's had girls from every religion. They aren't marrying these girls, right? So maybe Gaitonde was trying to protect this Zoya. You can't become Miss India if your boyfriend is a bhai.'

'They're all chutiya liars, hiding here and hiding there,' Kamble said. 'I had a Muslim chavvi, you know, two years ago. We didn't hide anything from anybody. Yaar, she was beautiful. I would've married her.'

'What happened?'

'I didn't have the money to get married. A girl like that, she needs an apartment, good clothes, a good life. Her family found some chutiya who worked for a company in Bahrain. She's there now. One daughter.'

'She's happy?'

'Yes.' Kamble leaned forward and put his elbows on his knees, and looked out across the small valley to the rising hills. He was suddenly melancholy, lost in the memory of his lost girl.

'Eh, Devdas,' Sartaj said. 'You wouldn't have married her anyway. You had about a hundred other chavvis to get through.'

But Kamble refused to cheer up, and Sartaj thought he might break into a sad song at any moment. If you edited out the knocking carpenters, and the piles of wooden slats next to the palace, and the gossiping women, it was a landscape suitable for song, coloured a gentle saffron by the falling sun. There was grass, and trees, and hills that had been shot quite often to substitute for Himalayan peaks. Sartaj tried to think of a sad song suitable for Kamble, but could remember only lilting Dev Anand numbers: *Main zindagi ka saath nibhaata chala gaya.* He had the fear around him again, the fright from the bomb, it lurked somewhere under the palace wall. Maybe it was just the subterranean anxiety brought on by being in Film City, not so far from where a number of adults and children had been killed and eaten by the park's industrious complement of very wild leopards. Those were real leopards, yes, not filmi ones. Maybe that was why he was afraid. But he was also unaccountably cheerful. It was all rather curious.

'Come, come, please.' Vivek was waving to them from the gate. 'Madam will be on the set in a minute. You want to see the shot?'

Inside the palace, there was a buzzing stir of activity. Under the vaults and high-arched windows, men milled about and hammered and sawed. Sartaj stepped over nests of cables, and around thickets of metal stands. He had to bend low to step under a sheet of canvas, and a loudspeakered voice called 'Full lights,' and Sartaj came into a pillared audience hall ablaze with gold and green. There were life-size statues of warriors and maidens under the pillars, and the half-ceiling was covered with a dense latticework of sparkling crystal. There were two immense chandeliers, a crowd of satiny courtiers and a throne. Sartaj wound his way through yet another crowd of crew to a row of folding chairs, and then Vivek motioned: wait.

'That's Johnny Singh,' Kamble said.

'Who?'

'The director.' He meant a portly man who now sat in one of the chairs and peered intently into a monitor. 'And that's the cinematographer, Ashim Dasgupta.'

'You're a movie expert,' Sartaj said.

'The girls want to get into films, a lot of them.'

Yes, Kamble's bar balas would have wanted, many of them, to become Zoya Mirza. They would have done anything, risked everything to be here. Now that the glare of the lights had left his eyes a little, Sartaj could see that the statues were painted plaster, not stone. The gold paint on the pillars was thick, congealed. The crystal on the ceiling was probably some kind of cheap glass, or plastic. Above it, among the ranks of lights hanging from rickety catwalks, there were dangling legs, and peering faces. And yet, on the screen this would all crystallize into an unearthly glow, a perfect palace. Sartaj thought, Katekar would have loved this, he would have liked the dirty floor, and the cheap-looking diamonds on the noblemen's turbans.

'Silence! Silence!' the loudspeaker roared, and in the abrupt hush Zoya Mirza descended on the set. She strode in, actually, from the left, but she may as well have floated down from the Technicolor heavens in a rain of fragrant blossoms. She was very tall, slim and strong, but hidden in a shimmering gold wrap, and her hair was loose and very long, and the long sweep of her neck made Sartaj breathless.

'Baap re,' Kamble whispered. 'Mai re.'

Yes, Sartaj believed in the enchantment of cinema all over again. They watched as Zoya talked to the director and two assistants, as Vivek fussed over her hair and face. A woman knelt and did something to the lower edge of Zoya's skirt, which reached just half-way to the knee. Another pair of actors came up, an older couple in royal robes, and the director spoke to them and Zoya, making angular gestures with his hands. Kamble was whispering their names, the names of the actors and their pedigrees, their performances and their successes. Then Zoya shrugged off her wrap, and Kamble ceased altogether. It was the kind of jungli-princess outfit that Sartaj remembered seeing on calendars in his childhood, with a bikini top in some soft fawn leather held together by strings at the back, and a matching skirt which dipped far below her navel in front and swept back over her hips, really quite tight. The Maharaja and Maharani took up positions by the throne, and Zoya turned towards them and walked, and the endless curvature of her hip squeezed at Sartaj's throat. Yes. The set was fake, but Zoya Mirza wasn't. Of course Mary and Jana were right about the multiple procedures, the miracles of technology that had achieved her wondrous world-class beauty, but Sartaj didn't care. Zoya Mirza was artificial, and her lie was more true than nature itself. She was real.

This was the scene: the princess, who was unaware of her own royal descent, came to the grand capital city and the exalted court, in search of a mysterious warrior who had wooed her on the wild slopes of her own familiar mountains, and then disappeared. And here she was in the grand courts of the Maharaja, who was – unknown as yet to her – a usurper and the murderer of her own trusting parents. There were two lines of dialogue: 'Who are you, kanya?' and 'I am the daughter of the Sardar Matho, who rules the forest to the west of your borders.' The second line, which was shot first, took eight takes and forty-five minutes. Zoya said it striding forwards, up the shallow bank of stairs that led to the throne. She was quite heroic. Then there was a twenty-minute pause as the camera was shifted. Vivek offered more tea and biscuits. Madam didn't want to be disturbed, still. She was working.

'This story is like that show on television,' Kamble said. 'What was it? With all the rajas and ranis and double-crosses and spies?'

'*Chandrakanta*,' Sartaj said. 'Good show.'

'This is much bigger than *Chandrakanta*,' Vivek said, with considerable pride. 'The special effects in *Chandrakanta* were so cheap-looking. We have two Hollywood experts flying down for the climax. And anyway, the writers told me that they took much more from Bankim Chandra.'

'Who?' Sartaj said.

'Some old Bengali writer,' Vivek said. 'He wrote a novel called *Ananda Math*.'

'I thought that had already been made into a Bengali film,' Kamble said. He was crunching down the coconut biscuits.

'Never heard of it,' Sartaj said. It was pleasant to stand around a film set and discuss shots and special effects and dialogue and old Bengali novels. Even Kamble was no longer impatient. Looking at Zoya Mirza was more than time-pass, it was soothing in some deep way.

The reverse angle shot, on the Maharaja, took only two takes. Then there was a great movement and shouting again, and lights and reflectors were moved about. Vivek followed Zoya off the set, and came hurrying back ten minutes later. 'Come,' he said. 'Madam will see you now.'

In close-up, she was still extraordinary. The make-up was a little garish, but Sartaj understood that was for the lights and for the camera. Between the deadly keenness of her cheekbones and the plump fullness of her lips, there was a perfect tension that had nothing to do with make-up. Sartaj and Kamble sat next to each other in Zoya's trailer, on a deep leather couch built into the wall. She had emerged from a private dressing room, a pristine white gown wrapped around her, and was perched on a chair. Vivek stood next to the stairwell, quite rosy with his admiration for Madam.

'That jungli skirt looked wonderful,' he told her, but with an eye on Sartaj.

'Yes, very,' Sartaj said.

'Didi, they are big fans,' Vivek said. 'They came to me through Stephanie, you remember her? All because they wanted to meet you.'

Zoya wore the kind of smile that people used to attention and power put on to indicate humbleness. Sartaj had seen it a lot on politicians. 'I'm going to play a police officer next year,' she said, 'in Ghai-sahib's new movie. I am a fan of the police also. I appeared at a charity premiere for the Policeman's Association when I was Miss India.'

'I remember. We need your help again.'

'Of course I will try to help in any way possible. But I am very busy over the next six months . . .'

'We're not here to ask for a personal appearance,' Kamble said, very quietly. He didn't move at all, but his shoulders seemed to swell up a bit, and he was suddenly dangerous. It was all in the dull flat of his eyes, in the rigidity of his jaw. 'Or for a donation.'

Zoya caught the change of mood instantly, but Vivek laughed through it. 'They just want autographs, Didi,' he said.

Sartaj put a hand on Vivek's forearm, pulled himself up. 'We just want to ask you a question or two,' he said to Zoya, taking a step up to her. She didn't like him coming closer to her, but she refused to flinch. He whispered into her ear, 'About Ganesh Gaitonde.'

'Vivek,' she said crisply, 'wait outside.'

'Didi?'

'Wait outside. And I don't want to be disturbed.'

Sartaj nudged Vivek out of the door, shut it in his wide-eyed face and pulled the red curtain firmly over the inset window. Zoya had now figured out that she should be outraged, and she stood up. She drew back her shoulders, and looked very fine, but she had to duck her head, under the slope of the low roof. Sartaj thought it spoiled the effect a little.

'Why would you ask me anything about a man like that?' she said. 'What do you mean by this?'

'Don't bother,' Kamble said. He had his hands on his thighs, and his feet planted wide apart. 'We know everything. We know about that Jojo. We knew Gaitonde flew you out to various locations.'

'Madam,' Sartaj said, 'we just need a little co-operation from you.'

'Listen, I was a model, and I met lots of people –'

Kamble's sneer was magnificent, he looked to Sartaj like a cynical toad. He made a growling laugh that grated up Sartaj's forearms, and levelled a forefinger at Zoya. 'You listen,' Kamble said. 'You may think you are some big film star, you can get away with anything. We didn't want to embarrass you by having you come down to the station, so we came here. But don't imagine that you can escape us. Don't think we are idiots. We sent Sanjay Dutt to jail, you can end up there also. Six months in a little cell without all this air-conditioning, and all your charbi will come off.'

'Bas, bas, enough,' Sartaj said to Kamble. For Zoya, he had his gentle, understanding face. 'Madam, I know you are afraid. And you want to keep your life private. That is your right. But he's right, we know too much about your link to this Gaitonde for you to hide anything from us. We have records that prove he paid for your travel. We have copies of your old passport, under the name Jamila Mirza. We have copies of plane tickets.'

Kamble pulled a sheaf of copies out of a brown envelope and waved them at her. 'We know about Singapore,' he said. 'Here.'

She took the papers. She was very strong, she had – under that sinuous exterior – an inflexible will. Sartaj could feel it, he knew the imperious stride of the jungli princess was also Zoya's. But all her control over herself, all her skill at acting, couldn't keep the flare of anger and fear from her eyes. Something had indeed happened in Singapore. Kamble had scored a hit. This was the time for sympathy. 'Madam, believe me, we need nothing from you except some information. There is no case against you, no accusations. Please sit.' She stood, quite still. 'Nobody in our department apart from this officer here and me knows anything about your connection to Gaitonde. We will not reveal anything to anyone. We just need you to tell us about him, anything you know about Gaitonde's friends and connections and business. We have no need to know anything about you.'

'Unless you give us trouble,' Kamble said.

'We are under pressure to find information on Gaitonde's activities,' Sartaj said. 'If we can't come up with anything, we will be forced to tell our superiors of your links to him. That may become very embarrassing for you.' He took a deep breath. 'There is a videotape, madam.'

'A videotape?' she said. Her voice was very low.

'Gaitonde recorded his activities.' Sartaj could feel Kamble's stare on the side of his neck, and he resolutely kept his attention on Zoya. 'There is a videotape of you. With him. Doing things.'

She sat, sank down on the chair, without control and without grace. Her knees had twisted rubber-like under her suddenly, and she sat. She'd collapsed, they had her. Sartaj swallowed a taste like old glue in his mouth, and sat himself down, on the very edge of the couch, next to Kamble. Zoya had her eyes down, her ankles twisted. Sartaj leaned forward. 'It is a very explicit tape. It appears that you were not aware that you were being recorded, that it was taken with a hidden camera. It shows everything, just everything.'

Now she didn't hide her fury. 'Where is the tape?' she said. 'I'll pay you for it. How much do you want?' Her contempt was not only for Ganesh Gaitonde the treacherous boyfriend, but also for these two policemen who threatened the life she had won for herself.

'You know already we don't want money,' Sartaj said. 'Just information.'

'Then you'll give me the tape? And everything else?'

'Yes. Everything, madam. We have no panga with you. We wish you peace and lots of films. We are fans.'

Zoya wasn't much comforted by his fervour. She glared, and gathered up her limbs from her disarray, and became a film star again. 'Not here,' she said. 'My costume designer will be here in a minute.'

'Yes, madam. Too many people here.' Sartaj stood up. 'Tell us where to meet you.'

'My shift finishes at eleven-thirty. Come at twelve.' She gave them an address, a mobile number, and then dismissed them. 'Okay,' she said, 'now please go.' She shut the door behind them firmly.

'Randi,' Kamble said. 'Bitch. We should get some money out of her.'

Sartaj stretched. Their angle to the palace revealed the struts and the scaffolding under the walls. The spiky structure was weirdly beautiful in the half-light, like some sort of giant artificial cactus-like plant that had rooted itself on this hillside. 'Don't be greedy. Doing this is dangerous as it is. We should get out of here.'

Vivek was nowhere to be seen, and so they made their way through the set, past the inexplicable crowds of idle workers. Kamble waited until they were out by the motorcycles. 'Is it going to get more dangerous,' he said, 'when she finds out there's no video?'

'No,' Sartaj said. 'Already she's compromised herself, by admitting that a video may exist.'

'True. That was a good idea.' Kamble strapped on his green helmet. 'So after this is all over, when there's no more danger . . . Can we get some money out of her then?'

Sartaj kicked at his starter, ran up the engine and let it settle. 'This one survived Ganesh Gaitonde, my friend. You know a lot of women, but I'm older than you. Listen to me. If this one feels too badly attacked, she will attack back. Get your money somewhere else.'

'All right, all right, you be friends with her. You be kind to her.' Kamble's grin was very sly. 'I won't get money. Maybe you can get something else from her. I'll see you at the station.'

He rattled away, but not without turning his head to give Sartaj one parting guffaw. Sartaj tilted out into the road and followed. It was no use protesting about the accusation, Zoya was beautiful and stunningly so. And Sartaj had felt her beauty, but in a distinctly impersonal way. There had been no hope in his pleasure, and no pain, none of those cutting stabs of desire. But he had been struck by her resilience, her strength, how she had dealt with the problem of two hostile policemen, with this unexpected disaster that threatened her career, her possessions, her life. She had coped. This was impressive, very much so. Zoya Mirza was a problem-solver, she saw a difficulty, she bent under it for a moment and then she looked for solutions. It was best to be very careful around such self-possession, especially when you were yourself the problem.

Sartaj rode towards the highway. Kamble had already vanished from sight, among the trucks and the swarms of evening autorickshaws. Maybe he had a girl waiting for him, two girls. He was a great devotee of beauty, as Sartaj had once been. When Zoya Mirza no longer intoxicates you into lust, Sartaj thought, you are really getting old. You old man. You old, tired man. But he didn't feel sad, just strangely relieved. Time had visited him with its depredations, and worn him down, but he liked the feeling of being dilapidated. It was restful. He eased on to the highway, and rode into the twilight, humming *Vahan kaun hai tera, musafir, jayega kahan?*

At the station, Sartaj worked steadily on court paperwork and calls and reports. Just after eleven Kamala Pandey called. She had had no new phone calls from the blackmailers, but wanted to know about Sartaj's progress.

'We are working on it, madam,' Sartaj told her. 'Don't worry.'

'But what are you doing?' she said.

'We are following leads. We are pursuing some lines of enquiry. We are talking to our informants.' Sartaj said this quite smoothly, as he filled out a form on a burglary case. It was the standard line, and he had reeled it out a thousand and one times before. But Kamala Pandey wasn't quite satisfied with it. There was a murmur in the background, and then she came back at Sartaj, petulant now.

'But who? Did you have any breakthroughs?'

Breakthroughs. Sartaj sat back. 'Who are you talking to?'

'Where?'

'You are talking to somebody, madam. Who is it? You shouldn't be telling people about the case.'

'I am not telling anyone about the case. I am at a restaurant with friends, and one of them came out and asked me something. She's gone now. So you can tell me your details.'

'Madam, I can't reveal the specifics of an ongoing investigation,' Sartaj said, quite sharply. 'Please be assured that we are working very hard. In fact I am working on your case right now.' That wasn't exactly true, but he had put in some good hours on the matter, and he was tired, and about to get very angry.

There was again the murmur over the receiver, but Kamala didn't want to push any more. 'Sorry,' she said, 'I am just nervous.'

'No reason to be nervous,' Sartaj said. 'I will contact you as soon as I know something. And, madam, I need a photograph of you, to show to witnesses who might have seen the exchange of money. Don't worry, I will be completely discreet. I won't tell anyone who you are. Just have it delivered to me at my home address by courier. Today if possible, tomorrow latest.' She was reluctant, but Sartaj was very firm. He gave her his address, hung up and returned to his form.

Kamble was distinctly hostile when Sartaj told him about Kamala Pandey's call. They had met at twelve-thirty, as planned, across the road from Zoya Mirza's building in Lokhandwalla. Kamble was drinking a quick beer before they went up to Zoya's apartment. He had been working on two cases since they parted and was quite tired and peevish. He had insisted that he needed a bottle of beer before he went back to work. So they were sitting on a low boundary wall across the road from Zoya's gate, just two friends relaxing in the darkness. 'So the fancy kutiya is roaming around all over town, going to restaurants and bars,' Kamble said of Kamala. 'No doubt she will find another mashooq soon. They are all like that, these rich fast ones, they give it around for free. Once they start giving, you know, they can't stop.'

'I think she had love for this Umesh.'

'Then why stay with this gaandu husband? Just for his flat and his money?'

'She was trying to break off from Umesh.'

Kamble took a long, gurgling gulp. 'If she loves him, then why?'

'You don't always like who you fall in love with.'

'That is true, yes.' Kamble's broad cheekbones were splashed with moonlight and shadow from the palms they were sitting under. 'There was this girl, once or twice I thought she would die at my hands.'

'One of the dancer girls?'

'Yes. She was a dancer, that one originally from Rae Bareli. She nearly ruined me, that one. I was like a mad fool. And I tell you, she looked as innocent as some goddess. Cheeks like fresh malai.'

'So you didn't kill her?'

'No, I just let her go. And that after she had spent every last rupee I earned, for seven months. She and her bhenchod family. They were very good at taking my money. Some of these girls get it in their blood from birth, this talent for making money. Like this Zoya. I checked it out, flats on her floor cost one crore eighty lakhs.'

'Some of that must be Gaitonde's money.'

'Of course. But still. One-eight. And she's been in films for what, three, four years? These people are amazing.'

'Which people? Actors?'

'Arre, no, boss. Muslims. The Mughal empire is gone, Pakistan was made for them, but they live like kings here.'

'Kamble, saala, have you been to Bengali Bura recently? Or Behrampada? Those poor gaandus don't live in palaces.'

'They live here, na? And they take more land every day, and their population keeps growing. And in films, think about how many Khans there are, all the top heroes.'

'Because these Khans look good? And are good actors?'

'Yes, baba, they're good-looking. This Zoya is a real chabbis.'

'And your Muslim girlfriend?'

'She was a phatakdi, yes. I'm not saying that they are not handsome as individuals, or that they can't be good people. I know Majid Khan is a friend of yours. He's a good man. But, you understand, as a people . . .'

'What?'

'They won't live in peace with anyone. They are too aggressive, too dangerous. For a sardar, you're too soft on them.'

Sartaj was tired. It was late, and he had been up since six, and he had heard these arguments all his life. 'I think you are crazy, and quite aggressive yourself,' he said, getting to his feet. 'And I am soft on everyone.'

Kamble was happy to agree. 'Too soft for a policeman.' He tilted the bottle far back to his mouth, then tossed it into the bushes. 'Now I'm fit for Zoya.'

They went across the road and through the immense black-and-gold gates of Havenhill. The watchmen were expecting them, and waved them directly through. The building was an enormous pastel-pink block, looming thirty-odd storeys above the surrounding bungalows. Havenhill was newly built, newer even than the bungalows, which had been thrust out into the swamp just ten years ago. It was a fit abode for a towering film star, this Havenhill with its cavernous, Italian-marble lobby and its brushed-steel lifts. Sartaj and Kamble zoomed up in a miraculous whisper of up-to-date technology, all the way to the top, and as they got off an accented female voice told them it was the thirty-sixth floor. Zoya's door was simple, just plain black wood behind a black grill, but inside, the drawing room was vast. Two enormous chandeliers hung over two separate seating areas, and a long, glossy dining table was laden with white flowers. The old man who had let them in – Sartaj couldn't tell if he was Zoya's father or uncle or an aged retainer – seated them on a white couch and vanished. The gauzy curtains were white. Zoya's favoured colour scheme, it seemed, was white.

She swept in barefoot, but not at all a jungli princess now. She was wearing a loose, sheer white top and flowing white pants. Her hair was drawn back severely from a face completely devoid of make-up. And still she was grand, there was no other word for it. Sartaj felt Kamble tense beside him. Whatever your thoughts were about some collective notion of a people, there was no escaping the overpowering enchantments of this individual, especially if you were young and cocky and muscle-bound.

'Come,' she said. She led them into another white room, this one with two walls of glass windows that went from ceiling to floor. Sartaj sat in an inexplicably comfortable steel chair and felt that he was floating far above the sparkling lights and far sea. Kamble was very quiet, very subdued. Sartaj thought, yes, saala, this is how the rich live. A servant, a young woman this time, brought in a tray with glasses of water, and then shut the door. Zoya sat, perfectly poised and perfectly lit, her back to the night. 'I think,' she said, 'that there is no videotape.'

Sartaj kept himself wholly still. He kept his eyes on her, but he felt Kamble twitch. 'Listen,' he said, and he was harsh. 'Do you think we are fooling with you?'

Zoya was not intimidated. She evened out the fall of her pants. 'No, I think you are very serious. But I thought about it. If you had a tape, you would have shown me a little, like you showed me the photographs. *He* never showed much interest in making videotapes of us, and I know what he liked. He was never shy with me, he would have told me he wanted to make one. He wouldn't have done it with a hidden camera. So there is no videotape. Unless you're making one now. Are you?'

'No.' Sartaj allowed himself a glance to the right: Kamble was stunned, impressed at last by Zoya Mirza.

'No hidden video cameras?' Zoya said. '*Tehelka*-style? You are required to tell me, you know.'

'No, we're not recording anything?' Sartaj said. 'Are you?'

She laughed, and it was real, a full-throated amusement. 'I am not such a fool. I was surprised by you earlier, and I made the mistake of admitting a connection to that man. But I don't want any of this coming out, and I don't want to make enemies of you. What do you want? Money? How much?'

Kamble finally spoke. 'No, madam,' he said, very mellow. 'We don't want money. Just information. For an investigation into gangs. It has nothing to do with you.'

Smart boy, Sartaj thought. Peace is so very much better than war, especially when your antagonist reveals unexpected resources. 'Madam, we don't want to put you in any awkward situations. But we need help with our problem here.'

She let a thin rim of contempt show in her eyes. 'Don't be so polite. You are still policemen, and I don't really have a choice. If I talk to you, will you give me the material you have?'

'Yes.'

'And there is no more?'

'No.'

She didn't believe him, and she wanted him to know. But she was now ready to talk. She crossed her arms across her stomach, and sat back. 'What do you want?'

'When did you meet Gaitonde? How?'

'A long time ago. Eight, nine years ago. Through a friend.'

'Which friend?'

'Don't you know?'

'I may. I want to know from you.'

She gave him a beat of steady staring before she relented. 'Jojo,' she said.

'Okay,' Sartaj said. 'So what was the nature of your relationship with Gaitonde?'

She clearly thought this was a silly question, but she had understood she was supposed to provide even the obvious answers. 'He supported me. I was alone in Bombay.'

'Jojo had a cut?'

'They had their arrangement. Whatever he gave me was between him and me.'

'How did you meet him? Where? How often?'

Zoya had a precise memory, and now she gave them a good report: she had in the beginning seen him maybe once a month, always in Singapore. She had always stayed in the same hotel. A phone call late at night was her signal to take a freight elevator to the hotel garage, where a limousine would be waiting. She spent time with Gaitonde in a flat that belonged to one of his associates, Arvind. There was only Arvind's wife Suhasini in this flat, nobody else, not even servants. She had never met Gaitonde in Bombay, or anywhere else in India. The flat was huge, and Gaitonde and she stayed in the upper half, in the penthouse. Of Gaitonde's associates, she knew only Jojo and Arvind. After she had become Miss India, she had been quite busy and the frequency of their meetings had declined. When she had worked on her first film they had spoken frequently on the phone, after the film even that contact had declined, but yes, she had seen him a few times after that. They had never broken off their relationship, there had been no quarrels or disagreements, but there had been something of a slow unwinding. Gaitonde had seemed preoccupied towards the end, and then had disappeared altogether. Until he showed up dead in Bombay, with a dead Jojo. And that was all.

Sartaj took her back through the people she had met through Gaitonde, and she was sure – there was Jojo, Arvind, Suhasini. She had never even seen the driver of the limousine. Gaitonde had seen to it that the logistics ran efficiently, smoothly, exactly the same every time. 'We had to keep it private,' Zoya said. 'And he was very good at security.'

'Who did he talk about? He must have mentioned some names, some people.'

'He didn't talk to me.'

'How can that be? You spent all this time together. You were his secret girlfriend. He liked you. What did he say to you?'

'I told you, not much. I didn't talk, mostly. At first I didn't say much because I was afraid of him. Then I realized that he liked me silent, that was what he preferred. So I kept quiet.'

'So you must have listened a lot. What did he talk about?'

'To me? Not much. Make-up, my career. Films and the film business. What I should do next.' She was looking down at her hands now, and under the overhead light her face was a mask of gold. 'He thought he knew everything. I said yes a lot and nodded my head.'

'What was he like, this Gaitonde?'

'What do you expect? He was Ganesh Gaitonde. He was just like himself.'

'Madam, but you knew him. Really. You must know things about him that the rest of us don't. Some details.'

'He played the part of Ganesh Gaitonde even when he was alone with himself. I think he was the same when he was alone with me as he was when he was in his durbar with his boys. That voice, and sitting like this.' She slouched back in the chair, her shoulders came up, an aggressively cupped hand gestured towards Sartaj, as if wanting to squeeze his testicles. 'Ay, Sardar-ji. What, you think you can come on to my ship and push me around, shanne? Do you know who I am? I am Ganesh *Gaitonde*.'

At the orotund rolling of the name Sartaj and Kamble both burst out into laughter. She had that voice exactly right, the one that Sartaj had heard that long-ago afternoon, full of booming self-importance, even over a clangy speaker. 'Madam,' Sartaj said, 'you are too good.'

Zoya accepted the tribute as her proper due, with a slight inclination of the head. She was still Gaitonde, though. She picked up an imaginary phone, dialled with her little finger. 'Arre, Bunty! Maderchod! You sit in Bombay eating all the malai and getting fat, and take months to do work that should be done in one week. What happened with that khoka we were expecting from Kilachand this week?'

Sartaj gave her another appreciative laugh. 'Madam,' he said, 'so he talked to one Bunty in Bombay?'

'Frequently.'

'Do you remember any details?'

'Details of?'

'What they talked about.'

'No, I tried not to listen. It was all about khokas and petis and meet that one there and call that one. Mostly they did their business in Arvind's flat, downstairs. But at night, when I was supposed to be sleeping, sometimes Gaitonde would sit in the balcony and talk on the phone. I heard bits and pieces, but mostly it was boring. I can't remember details. I used to pretend I was sleeping a lot, just lie there and close my eyes and think about my career. He used to talk on his phone then.'

Gaitonde must have been planning murder, mayhem and extortion, but to a beautiful young woman dreaming of stardom, perhaps that was boring. Sartaj smiled encouragingly. 'So there was Bunty he talked to. Who else? Please think, anything can help us. Even any names.'

Zoya sat up, out of her Gaitonde sprawl. She put a hand on her chin and projected concentration. 'I can't really remember. There were always three or four phones. There was one phone for Bunty. Yes, yes, I remember. There was a Kumar on another separate one, a Kumar Saab or Mr Kumar.'

'Very good, madam,' Sartaj said. Kamble was writing on a small pad. 'That is very good. Mr Kumar.'

'I think there were other people in Bombay, in Nashik. Of course he talked to Jojo often. Sometimes he had me say hello to her. Then there was somebody in London, some Trivedi-ji or something like that. There were a few others. I can't remember. Then there was one phone only for his guru.'

'Gaitonde had a guru?'

'Yes, he talked to him almost as much as Jojo, I thought.'

'Who was this guru?'

'I don't know. He called him "Guru-ji".'

'Where was the guru calling from?'

'I don't know. All over, I think. I remember Gaitonde telling him once to go to Disneyland.'

'Disneyland?'

'Disneyland, Disneyworld. One of those. And another time this Guru-ji was in Germany.'

'What did they talk about?'

'Spiritual things. About the past and the future. God, I think. Gaitonde consulted the guru on shaguns and mahurats and when to start projects and everything like that.'

So Gaitonde had a guru. He had been famous for his piety, his four-hour pujas, his donations to religious festivals and pilgrimage centres, so it made sense that he had a guru. Of course he had a guru.

Sartaj took Zoya to the beginning, to her first meeting with Jojo, and then through Gaitonde and then again the days with him, and the nights when she pretended sleep and he phoned. The details were consistent, and the same names emerged: Arvind, Suhasini, Bunty. It really did seem that Zoya Mirza had built a connection to Ganesh Gaitonde solely through these meetings in an apartment in Singapore, and through phone calls. He had financed her rise as a model, and then her first film. How exactly Zoya had profited from her trips abroad emerged only very slowly, as Sartaj probed past her reluctance. She was reticent about her colleagues in the movie industry, but Sartaj could be relentless even as he was being polite. She was a worthy opponent, and he had a weak hand, and it was her house, so they went back and forth. But he finally had what he thought might be some approximation of the whole story. They looked at each other, Zoya and he, quite exhausted.

'Nothing more, madam?' he said. 'Anything at all about Gaitonde?'

'What else is there to say?'

'Nothing else about the great Ganesh Gaitonde? What he was like?'

'Great?' She shrugged. 'He was a short man trying to act like some big hero,' she said.

So are we all, Sartaj thought, and may Vaheguru deliver us from the judgements of our girlfriends. 'Okay,' he said. 'Thank you, madam.'

'You have the papers?'

Kamble stood up and held out an envelope, and then watched Zoya admiringly as she flipped through the sheets and the photographs. 'You are really very tall,' he said.

'Are these the originals?' she said, to Sartaj.

'They are what we found in Jojo's apartment, everything.'

It was a lie, and she knew it. But Sartaj was now standing up, not easy and pliable any more, and there was nothing to be gained from tussling with him right now. Zoya put the envelope down on a small glass table, and put her arms behind her back, and became suddenly tired and somehow girlish. 'I'll tell you something,' she said. 'I'm actually not six feet tall.'

'Arre, really?' Kamble said. 'You are, I'm sure.'

'No.' She walked behind them to the door, and into the hall. 'I'm really only five ten and a half. But Jojo told everyone that I was six feet, and everyone believed it. All the media made such a fuss about that. Now I can't get rid of it, this six-feet thing.'

Sartaj could see that Kamble was measuring himself against her shoulder. Kamble said, 'Why would you want to?'

'Some of the heroes, you know, they don't want to star with a tall girl. It makes them look small.'

'No,' Kamble said indignantly.

Sartaj could see down the hall, next to the kitchen door, the old man who had opened the door for them. He was polishing a silver dish and watching them.

'It's true,' Zoya insisted. 'I know I have lost very good roles just because of this. These men are just afraid, and they still dominate the industry.' She raised her shoulders and let them drop.

'We live in sad times,' Sartaj said.

'A real Kaliyug,' Kamble said, with a certain morose inwardness.

Zoya was amused. 'He used to say that all the time.'

'Who, Gaitonde?' Kamble said.

'Yes. He and his Guru-ji used to talk about Kaliyug all the time. About that and the end of the world.'

Sartaj was careful to let the moment pass, so as not to seem anxious. 'What else did they say about this?' he said, very gently.

'I don't know. He used that Hindi word for it, what is it? For qayamat?'

'Pralay?' Kamble said.

'Yes. Pralay. They talked about that.'

'Saying what?' Kamble was also very casual, but Zoya was now quite aware of the attention focused on her.

'Why? What is it?'

'Please, madam,' Sartaj said, 'we are just interested in everything Gaitonde said or did. Tell us.'

'I can't remember, exactly. I was supposed to be asleep. And it was all so boring. I didn't listen very much.'

'Still,' Sartaj said, 'you must have heard something. About pralay.'

'I don't know. I think they used to talk about how it was coming. Gaitonde used to ask if it was, and I think Guru-ji said it was. Something about the signs being all around.'

'They talked about how pralay was coming . . . What were these signs?'

Sartaj waited. Zoya shook her head.

'All right, madam. Thank you for your time,' Sartaj said. 'And if you remember anything else at all about this, or any other thing concerning Gaitonde, please call me. It's very important. And if we can be of any service, please call also. Any problems, anything, please call us.'

548

Zoya took his card, but she was troubled. 'Why, what are you worried about in all this? Why do you want to know about Gaitonde? He's dead.'

'We are just conducting an investigation into gang activities, madam,' Sartaj said. 'There is nothing to worry about. He is dead, yes.'

They left her worrying about her dead Gaitonde. In the lift they were both quiet, sweating suddenly after the uniform coolness of Zoya Mirza's white apartment. Her media image really was impeccable: there were no affairs and no scandals, and when other heroines said bitchy things about her in magazines she never ever replied. And all this she had built on a foundation provided by Ganesh Gaitonde. She's quite brilliant, Sartaj thought. The guards were dozing at the gate, and the moon had vanished, leaving behind only the orange circles from the streetlights. Near the motorcycles, Kamble finally spoke: 'We don't have any facts, really.'

'Just that Gaitonde had a guru, that's the only new thing. Nothing to bother Delhi with, really. I'll call in the morning.'

'Nothing to worry about.'

'I didn't know you were a religious man, Kamble.'

'What?'

'All that talk of Kaliyug.'

'You think this world we live in is anything but Kaliyug? Everything is upside-down, boss. That woman upstairs, living in that huge apartment, all alone. She has two policemen coming to her house, and she meets us alone in the middle of the night. She doesn't have a father or brother there, nobody.'

'I think she can look after herself.'

'That is my point, bhai. And yes, I am.'

'What?'

'Religious.'

'Buddhist?'

'Why do you assume that? No, I'm stubborn. I'm not going to give up anything, I'm going to take respect and whatever else I want from those Manuvadi bastards. Who are they to say what a man is, what level Hindu he is? Bhenchods. My father was like that also. For that, some people in our community fought with him.'

They left each other with a raising of the hand. Racing down an empty road in Goregaon, Sartaj tried to imagine pralay. He tried to see

549

a storm of fire take up the bodies sleeping on the steps and the pavements, a terrible wind crushing the buildings, crumbling them. The images wouldn't stay, the fear flickered out. Life was all around, too much of it. And yet, Sartaj couldn't fall asleep for a good hour and a half. He lay twisted in bed, uneasy. Gaitonde had a guru. There was something teasing at Sartaj's mind, something hiding just beyond his reach but touching him all the same. He drank some water and stretched and turned on his left side, away from the window. Pralay receded altogether, but left behind a void in which random fragments of Sartaj's past chased each other about, an emptiness in which his mind raced. Out of this twilight flurry came a face that stayed with him, and Sartaj held on easily to Mary Mascarenas and floated into sleep.

The next morning, Sartaj made two very early phone calls, the first to Anjali Mathur in Delhi. Anjali Mathur listened to his report about Zoya and Gaitonde's guru and pralay, and said a few encouraging words and a quiet thank you. She told him to continue investigating, and hung up. In the sparkling sunlight of early morning, pralay seemed quite absurd, and Sartaj felt contempt for the deluded Gaitonde and his deluded guru.

Sartaj sat back in his chair, cracked his knuckles and prepared himself for the next call. He wasn't nervous exactly, no. He wanted to call Mary, and he felt like a bear emerging from an over-extended hibernation into blazing, disorientating sunlight. Once he had been quite suave, capable of flirting with women at a moment's notice, and asking them out on a whim. Now he was sitting at his coffee table, trying to work out a script. He resisted the urge to write down some lines and thought, Sartaj, what a lallu you've become. Just pick up the phone and do it. But he didn't. He got up, drank a glass of water and sat himself down again. Now he had to admit that although he was not nervous, not in that way he used to be when he was thirteen, he was afraid. What was he afraid of? Not just of the possible disasters, of rejection or unpleasantness or betrayal, but also of good things. He was afraid of Mary's sudden smile, of the touch of her hand. It was better to live inside a cave, walled in and comfortable.

Gaandu coward, you should be ashamed of yourself. He shook his arms from shoulder to wrist, picked up the phone and dialled. Mary picked up, and he told her in a rush that tomorrow, the next day, he was going to drive up to Khandala for an investigation, and he wanted to tell her about his meeting with Zoya Mirza, and he thought that perhaps she might want to come up to Khandala, since tomorrow was a Monday and he knew that was her day off, and they could get out of the city, for a sort of picnic with Zoya Mirza spice. Even as he was saying it, he realized that it was all too elaborate, that what he had to tell her about Zoya Mirza didn't need a long drive and a meal in some mountain café. He stopped himself. He was expecting her to refuse, or want to be persuaded further, but she quite straightforwardly agreed and asked what time he would pick her up.

Sartaj hadn't driven the car for a couple of months, so that afternoon he gave it a quick going-over, and encouraged it with praise, and it rumbled into motion. He drove around the locality for half an hour, until he was satisfied that the old khatara was still able to rattle on. He cleaned the car out, had the oil and battery checked and by next morning felt quite prepared. They set off at seven-thirty. Mary wore black jeans and a white shirt. Sartaj was very aware of her hand on the seat beside him, not so far away, and the waft of her shampoo. They drove through Sion, relatively uncrowded that early. At Deonar, the dense press of buildings finally parted, and the sky suddenly appeared, vast and grey, and across the spreading panorama ahead Sartaj could see the mountains. He felt that childhood tingle in his stomach, and wanted to chant, we're going on a holiday, we're going on a holiday. But no, Mary would think he was crazy. He was smiling anyway, and Mary saw him and smiled too. They sped across the muddy water of the sea, arcing high above on the bridge, and then through clusters of apartment buildings, and then Sartaj saw the bright pastel buildings ahead, tall and very new, and knew they were almost at the expressway.

'They look like cakes,' Mary said. 'A building should look like someone lives in it, not like a cake.'

'It is the modern style,' Sartaj said. 'Are you hungry? Do you want to get something at the McDonald's?'

'No, no. I'm fine. Let's go.'

She made a soaring gesture, up and away into the Ghats, and Sartaj knew that she wanted to be on the hills as much as he. 'All right.' He paid the toll, and then they were away.

Traffic on the expressway was light, and it was good to be on the wide road, skimming against the wind. The khatara seemed to like it too, this unexpected, foreign-seeming sweep of smooth, wide road dropped on to the rough Ghati landscape. The car surged ahead, vibrating violently as Sartaj let it have its head.

'How old is this thing?' Mary said.

'Years and years. But she keeps on going.' He slowed, and changed a lane. Even changing lanes here was a pleasure, the drivers seemed to get a bit more civilized when they came on to the expressway. And there were so many lanes, all comfortably wide and perfectly arranged.

But further on, when they had reached the lower slopes, cars backed up behind a behemoth of a truck sprawled on its side, across the lanes. Traffic was still moving, and as they came past the blockage they saw that the rear end of the truck was buckled and ripped, and a sea of oranges had spilled out on to the tar. The car's wheels squished for a moment, and then they were past.

'Last time I came on the expressway,' Mary said, 'I saw five accidents.'

'These idiots have never seen an expressway in their lives, they've driven only in Indian conditions. So they see a big perfect road, they get excited, go too fast, don't know how to handle their vehicles. Bas, finish.'

'At least this one didn't close the entire road.'

There was that. Mary Mascarenas was an optimist, or at least she wasn't a pessimist. Sartaj felt a flush of well-being himself, sitting next to her. Yes, the road was still open. Now they didn't speak much, he was content to point out to her an inexplicable string of camels plodding down a side road, a fat girl walking on a bund between fields. They went through the tunnels and out into the sun, and there was the smooth drumming of the engine, the hiss of passing cars.

They reached the Cozy Nook at nine-thirty. The Nook was five cottages clustered together at the edge of a housing development, with a front office that was of brand-new concrete coloured an alarming pink. There were new houses on the slope on both sides of the Cozy Nook, so it wasn't really so cosy any more. No doubt they offered the hazy prospect beyond, dissected by electrical wire, as a fine river view. Khandala had filled up with new construction, and was no longer the leafy haven that Sartaj had made trips to with college girlfriends. But at least the hairy-eared, balding receptionist was reassuringly familiar in his jaded boredom and his rudeness.

'Write name,' he barked, spinning a register across the counter.

Sartaj grinned at Mary, and explained that he was a policeman, that he didn't want a room, that he wanted to ask some questions. Hairy-eared baldy was confused by Mary. 'She's my assistant,' Sartaj said. 'Now take out your registers.'

The investigation took half an hour. Sartaj found Umesh Bindal's name easily enough, he signed it with a flourish and two dots under the large curve. The other names on those dates were often illegible and, Sartaj was sure, mostly made up. 'S. Khan' gave his address as 'Bandra, Mumbai', and left no other information. If he had been the man with the camera, watching Umesh and Kamala in their satiated lover's walk down the pathway, there was no way to trace him. Sartaj had Baldy put away the registers and walk them around the cottages. Mary followed quietly.

She spoke when they were outside, back in the car and heading up the hill. 'Did you find what you wanted?' she said, her arm bumping against his as he took a sharp turn.

He shook his head, and waited until they were seated at a table in a restaurant, on the edge of a cliff. There was a breeze lifting up from the stepped floor of the valley, and Sartaj felt wonderfully relaxed and hungry. 'I wasn't expecting to find anything,' he said. And then he told her about investigations, about feeling your way along, groping your way along and coming up with half-understood clues, with evidence that wouldn't work as evidence but you knew was the truth. 'It's not like in films,' he said. 'Really, half of detection is accident. Like us missing the pictures of Zoya, and you knowing exactly what they were.'

'So you depend on random women to help you find gangsters by accident? That's not very comforting for the poor public.' Her eyes were prickling with amusement.

'Aaaah, but I have to be open to random women, you see. You have to be able to listen, to really see.'

'I can see you spend a lot of time listening to women.'

He knew she was teasing, but he couldn't stop himself from protesting, 'No, no, not like that at all.'

She began to giggle, and he laughed along with her. They ate over-sized neer dosas with a fiery sambhar. Sartaj wiped his plate clean and sat back. He was feeling quite content, at peace with the world. Gaitonde was dead and far away, and if there was a bomb it was unsubstantial, it was merely a horror-story device. Sartaj ran his eyes

553

up, over the scrubby green slopes and into the distance beyond the mountain tops, and said, 'It's so relaxing to be out of that city. It would be nice to live in a village, you know. Be close to the soil, the clean air. The stress would be so much less.'

Mary was leaning to one side, her chin propped on one hand. 'You in a village. That would be something to see.'

'Why, why? I might make a good farmer.'

She shook her head gently. 'I'm not saying it is just you. I grew up in a village, and I couldn't go back. Do you know what it's really like?' Then she told him about waking up in a red brick house with a tiled roof, to the dawning chatter of parrots, and stumbling out crumbly-eyed to the cowshed behind the house. The bathroom was a doorless enclosure attached to the cowshed, with water in a big copper baan embedded in the wall, over a fire. There were no toilets, just the fields of usal. Back behind the cowshed was also a well, and beyond that, a row of coconut trees and the paddy fields. A river edging down to the sea, glinting, and the smell of jasmine flowers. Coffee and appams at eight, paes at ten. The day at school, the chatter of Konkani and Kannada and Tulu on the winding dirt road. Lunch, and the eternity of the afternoon, skipping with Jojo on the red floor of the platform in front of the house. The rosary slipping through their mother's fingers, the hour-long evening prayer, the blessings from the elders. Dinner sitting on the polished floor, Mother on her monai bending low over her plate. The complete, stunning darkness when the lanterns were blown out. In bed by nine. And sleep.

'No electricity, no television, I don't think we even had radio till I was fourteen or fifteen.'

'You're right,' Sartaj said. 'It sounds very peaceful, but I don't think I could live there.'

'You couldn't,' Mary said. 'That village isn't there any more, to return to. It is all completely changed.'

Sartaj stretched his arms over his head, worked his spine, sighed. 'It is late. I have some work to do at the station. We should go,' he said. 'Back to Bombay.'

'You didn't tell me about Zoya Mirza. Jana will be angry if I come back with no news.'

So he told her about the meeting with Zoya Mirza as they drove down, not fast, not hurried. The city crept up, not dramatic, just inevitable. The scattered shacks and houses and buildings gathered themselves together into a dense mass. Sartaj had the feeling of being drawn in by a larger gravity, and he was glad of it. This was home. Mary sat comfortably, her knees drawn up, not quite as far along the seat as before.

At her house, they stood in front of each other, suddenly awkward. Sartaj had one hand on the car, the other awkwardly at his side.

'Zoya, is she pretty?' Mary said.

Sartaj shrugged. 'She's all right. Nothing much.'

Mary reached out to nudge his forearm. 'You're smarter about women than you pretend. But really, she's beautiful, isn't she?'

'Arre, I am not just saying that. She's okay, bas. Tall and all that, but just okay. You know she's not even really six feet. Jojo made that up. She's only a little above five ten.'

'Ooooooh,' Mary said, quite pleased by the detail. 'Jojo liked doing things like that.'

They looked past each other, and the silence grew long.

'I should go,' Sartaj said.

'Okay,' Mary said. 'I, I liked the drive.'

'Yes, me also.'

'Okay, bye.'

'Bye.'

She took a step up to him. He was quite stopped for a moment, and then he stuck out his hand. She smiled, shook it. I should kiss her on the cheek, Sartaj thought, but by then she had turned and was away from him. He watched her climb her stairs, waved at her and drove to the station laughing at himself. Where was all that smoothness gone, those old Sartaj-the-deadly-Singh moves? Absolutely vanished, leaving him an absolute bhondu. I am not ageing well, he thought. But he was very cheery, and he hummed *mehbooba mehbooba* all the way to work.

Anjali Mathur called him at eleven that night, while he was still working at the station. 'There's no mention of a guru in all our files on Gaitonde,' she said. 'Was this woman sure about this?'

'Yes. She mentioned several conversations.'

'Odd. He must have kept it hidden.'

'Very hidden. He kept Zoya hidden. He must have kept a lot of things hidden. He was good at it.'

'Yes. I did a search in our databases for the word "pralay". I came up with nothing. So then I looked for "qayamat". I found it three

555

times, all in literature from one outfit. This is a militant outfit called Hizbuddeen. They are very shadowy, we have never captured or killed any of their people. We don't even know where they are based, where they operate. But we've found their literature in raids on other Islamic groups in the Kashmir valley, in Punjab, in the north-east along the Bangladesh border. This Hizbuddeen has supplied money and arms to these groups, beyond that we don't know anything about them. They first seem to surface just around the time of the Kargil war. Now, their literature specifically promises "Qayamat", and talks about the signs of the last days. They quote verses from the Qur'an: "Closer and closer to mankind comes their Reckoning: yet they heed not and they turn away." Now, this is interesting. Mumbai is specifically mentioned, in each of the pamphlets.'

Sartaj could hear her leafing through paper. Through the open door, he could see the end of a bench, an empty hallway and a scrubby garden edged by a wall.

'Here,' Anjali Mathur said. 'It says, "A great fire will take the unbelievers, and it will begin in Mumbai." This line is repeated in the other pamphlets with minor changes. "A fire will begin in Mumbai and sweep across the country." But always, Mumbai is mentioned.'

Sartaj was outraged. 'What do these bastards have against Bombay? They don't mention any other cities?'

'No. They just talk about the nation of India as dar-ul-harb, and about its coming destruction. They insist on destruction. The name of the outfit comes from "hizbul", which is "army of", and "deen", which I think is used here in the sense of the Last Judgement. The word can also mean "religion" or "conduct", but in this case it refers to the third verse of the first chapter of the Qur'an, I think. So the Hizbuddeen is the "Army of the Final Day". Anyway, all this would be too little to propose a connection. But I thought the name of this organization sounded familiar. I had been analysing our records of counterfeit money which comes over the border, and I went back and did a cross-check in the databases. Hizbuddeen has been named five times as the source for large sums of counterfeit money. The samples we have from these incidents are exactly the same as the ones from the Kalki Sena, and the ones from Jojo's apartment, and what we found in Gaitonde's bunker.'

Sartaj's head was starting to hurt. What could be the connection between Jojo and rabid extremists promising annihilation? Between

Gaitonde and this Muslim militant outfit? Maybe there was no connection at all. He pressed his fingers hard into his forehead, and said, 'It is all still too vague.'

'I agree. There is no reason to conclude that this money indicates any connection. We have only possibilities. Nothing yet that holds together. Only more questions. Who is this guru? What was Gaitonde's relationship with him?'

'I will work on it.'

'Yes. I will keep looking here.'

So they were to keep on working. Sartaj worked another hour at the station, and then went home. He put his feet on the coffee table and drank his whisky, only one glass today, a light one at that. He was aware that he was still working, thinking about Gaitonde and Jojo and thick chunks of money. This was one of the things Megha had hated, that he was unable ever to stop the job from working inside him. He would drink tea, talk about relatives, go and see a film, and somewhere inside him the fragments of some murder would be fitting themselves together. He had always tried to tell her that none of this was voluntary, that he would stop it if he could. That, somehow, had made it worse for Megha, that it was impulse, or instinct. But instinct had taught him its inescapable lessons, and he had learnt to trust it. Now instinct told him that these pieces somehow made a whole. You knew that sometimes, you had the truth in your mouth but no evidence in your hands. And sometimes you acted on this knowledge, you planted evidence, wrote an FIR leaving out certain facts and putting others in. Justice had sometimes to be manipulated into being properly blind.

In this Gaitonde affair, there would be no justice, no redemption. There was only a hope for some partial explanation of what had happened, and this creeping fear. Sartaj was afraid now, he truly was. Now that he was at rest, the fear came back, amplified by English-movie images of disaster, of entire cities being obliterated by special-effects fire. Work, he told himself, work on it. Do your job. So Sartaj closed his eyes and rested his head on the back of the sofa and held his glass, and let the bits and shards of information fall through his head and body. He couldn't force anything, couldn't compel an answer. If he was easy enough, if he was fearless, if he opened his mind and heart and belly, a shape would form. He just had to be patient.

Ganesh Gaitonde Explores the Self

On the yacht we watched a lot of films. It was a hundred-and-thirty-foot boat (they had to teach me to call it a yacht) with three decks, and enough room for a sizeable separate drawing room. In that room I put the biggest TV we could fit, and a stack of movie players and a receiver. And in that room we watched movies, hundreds of videos and laser discs and DVDs. Not that we didn't work: I woke every morning at six and exercised and did my yoga and my puja and was at the phones by seven-thirty, eating my breakfast as I took my calls. Managing my company from a distance was at first a difficult education – I had to let go, to stop worrying about details, to give responsibility to others and not tell them how jobs should be done. I felt like a god, distant from the world but directing it from above. By ten-thirty or eleven I was usually done with the day's urgent work, and a little later Bunty called from Bombay with the news about collections and the added-up numbers from the day before. At noon I ate a light lunch with the boys, then took a half-hour nap. Depending on where we were, how close to a convenient shore, I sometimes had a girl to wake me up from the nap, Indonesian or Chinese or Thai. But in any case I was up by two, with the day stretching out in front of me.

So we watched movies: *Hum Apke Hain Kaun* and *Dilwale Dulhaniya Le Jayenge* and *Sholay* yet again, and *Dil To Pagal Hai* and *Hero No. 1* and *Auzaar*. And also *Mother India* and *Anarkali* and *Sujata*. And a thousand others I had never heard of, *Bahu Begum* and *Anjaam* and *Halaku*. I also liked to watch English movies, not just the bang-bang kind the boys enjoyed, but also more talky ones to improve my English. But the boys grew restless and bored by these, the ganwar bastards, and begged to go back to some bundal maderchod film where they could watch Raveena Tandon thrust and shove her hips like some sort of crazed machine. So we watched a lot of Indian movies, even Punjabi and Tamil ones. Mukund, one of the boys, was Tamil, and he translated *Nayakan* for us, and it was true, the Tamil version with Kamalahasan was a lot better. It was strange to see Bombay in Tamil, through Tamil, but the film had dum. It was true, just like life. We watched Vardarajan's life in complete silence, from his beginnings in the slums and his rise up to power and fame. When his son was killed, when that choking cry came from Kamalahasan's throat, we felt that pain, it was ours. We had also lost our loved ones. I had tears on my cheeks. All of us did.

The next day I told Bunty to have flowers sent to Kamalahasan and Mani Ratnam, no name on the bouquets, just a card, 'From a fan of *Nayakan*'. And that night when Jojo called I told her about how much we had all liked the film.

She burst out laughing. 'So there was a whole bunch of you tough bhais sitting around crying?'

'Kutti, it was a great performance. And a great story.'

'That last scene of the nayakan's funeral, I bet you cried all the way through that.'

'There were thousands and thousands of people at his funeral. Of course I cried. It was very touching.'

Off she went again. Finally she got hold of herself. 'Oof, you men are such sentimentalists. Don't worry, there will be thousands at your funeral.'

'Randi, you don't worry about my funeral. Whenever and however it happens, Parmatma has written it already. It has already happened, but we are fooled by the illusion of time. He has his plan. We are just actors in his play.'

'Vah. Actors in his play.'

'Yes. We dance along the lines of his leela. Birth, life, death, all has a shape, even if we can't see it.'

'What a philosopher you are today, Ganesh Gaitonde. You have changed, you go on and on about destiny and karma and bhenchod gandugiri like that. What has happened to you?'

'Nothing, except that I have started to understand a little of the truth of the universe.' Nobody but Bunty knew of my conversations with Guru-ji. I had to keep all these segments of my world apart, Jojo from Guru-ji, Guru-ji from Mr Kumar, and some of myself from everything.

'Chutiya, you've become one of those holy Hindus.' And she made a spitting sound, as if she was expelling something foul.

'Jojo, you should think about these questions also. Go to your church, maybe you will find some peace there.'

'Gaitonde, now you are turning into my mother. What mixed-up times we live in.'

'Exactly. This is why the spiritual search . . .'

'Arre, maderchod, you want me to go to the church so some smelly priest can pry into my head and tell me I am a bad woman and give me punishments? And what will his god, or your god, give me? Peace? I don't want peace. I want money, I want a flat, I want my business to grow. Peace! Why don't you give some peace to those girls you thoko every afternoon, my spiritual master?'

And she tumbled about her bed, laughing. I was smiling a little too. Then she stopped abruptly. 'Do you give them spiritual sermons also?'

'Arre, no.'

'Tell me the truth, Gaitonde.'

'Saali, how will I give them lectures if they don't speak Hindi?'

'And they don't understand your toota-phoota English.'

'My English is getting better every day.'

'Stay on the subject, Gaitonde. Have you tried talking to them about the path to, what did you call it, mokha?'

'Moksha.'

'Have you?'

'No.'

'Come on, Gaitonde. Tell the truth. You always have to me, even if you lie to everyone else.'

I was quiet. This was true enough, that I found myself telling her things about myself, my fears and my worries, that I revealed to nobody else.

'Gaitonde.'

'All right. Only once.'

'Tomorrow's *Mid-Day* headline: "International Don Ganesh Gaitonde Becomes the Great Teacher of Whores!"' She became incapable of coherent speech for a good five minutes. Then finally she came back on the line. 'See, I told you, something has happened to you.'

'It was only because . . . Listen, there was this Thai girl, she had a little statue of Buddha in her purse. So I tried to talk to her about nirvana. She understood the word nirvana, but nothing else.'

560

She had laughed herself almost out already, so this time she just chortled for a minute. Then she said, 'I know you better than anyone in the world. Admit it.'

'Admitted, yaar.' I was smiling now. When she was in a good mood, she made me feel light and happy like no one else. 'So if you know me this well, come and know me a bit better. Come and take a holiday on the yacht.'

'Gaitonde, don't start that again. The only reason you let me know you is because I don't let you near me.'

'Jojo, I won't touch you. I give you my promise. Kasam.'

'Touching is not the point, Gaitonde. You know that if we meet, the thought of touching will be there between us. And okay, not just from you but from me also. And that will ruin the whole yaari. I'm telling you.'

'Men and women can't have thoughts of touching and still be friends?'

'Maybe some men and women, on some other continent. But not you and me.'

'Haramzadi, it's not true.'

'It is and you know it.' She was smiling now, I could tell. 'It is written by your Parmatma. It's part of his plan.'

'You're my daily headache. I don't know why I put up with you.' But I was grinning now, and she could tell too.

'And I give you more good thokoing than any girlfriend ever could.'

'True.' Every month or two, she sent girls out from Bombay. The girls were flown out to Singapore or Jakarta on a performing artiste's visa, as part of some song-and-dance troupe. Most of them were really dancers, of a sort. After the shows were over, they were bussed out to wherever the yacht happened to be. There were some for the boys, and the best were reserved for me. Jojo knew my tastes by now. 'That's true. You're like a girlfriend who sends a new version every month,' I said. 'You're the most generous chaavi ever.'

'I am the most perfect chaavi in the history of man, Gaitonde. And after this special treat I'm going to send you next, you will remember me in your prayers to your Parmatma every morning.'

'What treat?'

'First say thank you.'

'For what?'

'You should say thank you to me every day for all I've done for you. But today say it specially, for what I am about to do for you.'

'A girl?'

'Not just a girl. This one is . . . This one is an amazement, Gaitonde.'

'So tell.'

'First of all, she's a virgin.'

'Yes, yes, like every other randi in Bombay.'

'Seriously. You have a doctor check her if you want. She's from a very orthodox family in Lucknow.'

'If she's that orthodox, what is she doing with someone like you?'

'Arre, baba, she wants to be an actress.'

'Of course.'

'Of course. She's six feet tall, Gaitonde.'

'You want to send me the Qutub Minar, saali.'

'You're a big bhai, you need a tall woman. And have you seen all those foreign models? Six feet is nothing.'

'She's beautiful like a model?'

'She will be.'

'Maderchod, she's ugly right now? And for this you want me to say "Thank you, thank you"?'

'Gaitonde, most men are stupid. But you don't have to be. Listen to me. Think about it. Here is this girl from a completely ordinary family in Lucknow. The father owns some little family restaurant, there is a mother who is a mother. A grandmother who lives with them. There are brothers, both older and younger. The parents managed to send all the children to English-medium schools.'

'Haan, so?'

'Imagine this girl, what her world is like in Lucknow. She goes to an all-girls school, she comes back to mother and grandmother. She doesn't talk to any boys, even the ones who make fun of her on the road for being five foot eight in the sixth. But this is one very intelligent girl. She reads, she watches. Somehow she makes up her mind that all this is not enough for her. Lucknow and marriage at eighteen is not what she wants.'

'Whole of India is full of idiots like her. Bad influence of films and television.' That made Jojo laugh, and for a few seconds she left off from her bhashan and laughed with me.

'Be quiet, Gaitonde. So, she decides this. She makes up her mind. At eighteen. Somehow she leaves. Somehow she makes her way into the world and shows up at my doorstep. Do you know what that takes?'

'Yes, she's a heroine. I should put her in charge of the boys in Bombay.'

'Gaitonde, you are a man after all. A man cannot understand what courage it takes to go against everything, to be a woman and to stand up and ask for just this much, that you can live out what you dream. All your boys put together don't have one-thousandth of that courage.'

'Okay, so she's the Rani of Jhansi. Then?'

'Then understand this. This girl wants everything. And she has the strength and courage to get it. She's not bad-looking right now, but because she wants it she will be beautiful. She wants to be a model and an actress, and she will. I'm telling you. I failed, I couldn't do it, but she will.'

'How are you so sure?'

'I'm sure because she reminds me of you.'

'Haramzadi, a woman reminds you of me?'

'Gaitonde, it's a compliment. You'll see what I mean. She reminds me of you because she's a little frightening.'

'I thought you weren't scared of anything. Including me.'

'Arre, I'm not scared of you. You know that, chutiya. What I mean is that she's so big and serious and one-pointed that she seems like one of those rakshasa women on those *Ramayana* serials. You're the only one who can handle her. I'm giving you a compliment.'

'You mean I'm the only one who can afford to pay for this giant virgin. How much?'

'A lot.'

'Of course a lot. Tell me the price.'

'But she doesn't want that much cash, actually.'

'Then?'

'It took me a while to understand, when she first talked to me. She doesn't want just a man. She wants an investor.'

'An investor in what?'

'In her. In her future.'

In that moment I felt the first warm stirrings of genuine interest in this creature of Jojo's. Maybe she really was as sharp as Jojo said. 'She said that?'

'Yes, she did. She understands this, Gaitonde, that a career in this modelling-acting game can't come out of nowhere. If you have rich parents, maybe they can pay for clothes and acting classes and dance classes and a gym and a mobile phone and a flat in Andheri and a car. If you're just a girl from Lucknow, with no fluid cash, you'll be just one more among thousands going from producer to producer by auto-rickshaw, and every photographer who agrees to take a picture for your portfolio will want to introduce you to his bed upstairs in the loft. And what you'll get out of all this in the end is a lot of bambooing and maybe a dance or two in videos. Bas. If you want to be a star, first you've got to have the ability to say "No," then you need money to sustain yourself and present yourself in a way that gets respect out of these bhenchod industry men. This is why all these children-of-stars dominate the industry, because they have not just connections but also resources.'

'So she needs resources to produce profits. Good that she understands.'

'Yes. But more resources than these also, Gaitonde. She wants to do a lot of work on herself. It's expensive.'

'Work?'

'Plastic surgery. She showed me her plan. She's researched it. She has a little chart of the body and she's got it all marked on that. With prices next to each part. And she knows exactly which doctor, what the procedures are. She's got photographs of actresses and models and rich women, Gaitonde, and she knows what each one has had done. You won't believe the kinds of operation all these famous people have had, Gaitonde, and how much this girl knows. This nose is good, she says, but that one's better. She's an expert. She has it all in a file marked "Body".'

Very interesting, I thought. A woman with a systematic mind. 'Fine,' I said. 'Let me see this amazement. How much?'

'Gaitonde, don't try anything funny with this one. If she thinks you're trying to give her a hool, she'll kill herself before she lets you do anything.'

'Yes, yes. How much?'

'Nothing for a meeting. You meet her and see. I'll pay for the air ticket.'

This was truly amazing. 'Jojo, you sound like you're in love yourself. In your old age you've become a chut-chattoing sixty-six. Bhidu, for you I'll pay. Take her, take her.'

'Gaitonde, stop talking like an idiot. If I liked girls, I would have told you. What I'm doing is also investing in her. Not just to persuade you. I believe this girl. She can sell herself.' Jojo used the English word 'sell'. It had a sexy *ssss* sound to it, on her tongue. Like that other English word 'sexy'.

'You've bought her stock? Before the IPO even?'

'Gaitonde, you buy too. If you're smart you will too. But there's one more thing.'

'What?'

'Are you as secular as you keep telling me you are?'

'I put up with you, don't I? That makes me secular and tolerant.'

'This girl is Muslim. Her name is Jamila Mirza.'

'Jojo, I still have some Muslim boys working for me in India. And when have I had a problem taking Muslim girls?' I took girls of all shapes and sizes and creeds. I was impartial.

'This is different, Gaitonde. Even your friend Suleiman Isa is secular like that, he doesn't have any problems taking Hindu girls, or Jain girls, or Christian girls. All men are secular down below. This is different. I'm telling you, investing in her means you have to really help her. You are connected to her. Not for a day or two or a week on the boat, but for the long run.'

'True. I see that. Let me think about it. When was she born?'

'You are going to do your astrology again?'

'Yes.'

'You're mad.'

'Tell me the date and time and place.'

She gave me the birth details, I wrote them down. She was the hardened sceptic that I had once been, but Guru-ji had shattered my defences. Now I was remaking myself.

Jojo said, 'What about for the boys?'

We discussed that for a minute or two, girls for my boys. Then Jojo had to get to a production meeting, and I went up on the deck. The boys were playing cards under a blue canopy. I had six of them on board, along with one accountant and one computer man, and one Maharashtrian cook and five Goanese crew (including three ex-Navy boys). The boys split the shifts, and there were always three of them awake and on guard, which meant playing interminable rounds of teen-patti for small stakes, as now. Arvind was taking his usual ten minutes to pick out his discards, and Ramesh and Munna were giving him gaalis. All was as usual. We were anchored within sight of the bright umbrellas on Patong beach.

The boys stood up as I came up to them. 'Bhai,' they all said, and touched my feet.

'Who's winning?'

'This crawling gaandu here. Because of him, one game goes on for years.'

This also was usual, that Arvind won. He was slow and steady. But their mood was sour this morning, I could see that. When they were back home, in Bombay, all the boys begged for foreign service. They wanted the foreign jeans, and the foreign girls, and the salaries in foreign currency. They had competed with each other to come to Thailand, to my yacht and my overseas operations, and demonstrated their eagerness and hard work and commitment every hour. But after a month or two or five in these alien waters, they always grew sour. They became sullen. Their bodies missed Bombay. I know, because after a year away from Mumbai I still got attacks of yearning, I craved the spittle-strewn streets of that great whore of a city, while waking up I felt that pungent prickling of auto-exhaust and burning rubbish at the back of my nostrils, I heard that swelling rumble of traffic heard from a high hotel rooftop, that far sound that made you feel like a king. When you were far away from the jammed jumble of cars, and the thickets of slums, and the long loops of rail, and the swarms of people, and the radio music in the bazaars, you could ache for the city. There were some afternoons when it felt like I was dying a little. Under the foreign sky I could feel my soul crumbling away, piece by piece. And I felt a loneliness I had never imagined, that I wouldn't have earlier believed could exist. Only after coming away from India did I realize that at home I had never been truly alone, that I had been secure in my web of family and company and boys. Even when I was by myself, I was still connected, still whole. Even when they had put me in the anda cell all by myself, I had been a part of this vast, invisible net, joined heart-to-heart. On Indian soil you couldn't be truly solitary, even when you were sealed in an evil-smelling tomb. Only after sailing away across these black waters had I known the meaning of this word: *alone*.

So we flew out these boys, and for these boys we flew out Indian girls, and Indian films, and Indian music, and gave them bi-weekly phone calls to India. Usually, in their first month, the new boys would be eager to mount every Chinki girl they could get their hands on. They spent all their cash on Thai and Indonesian and Chinese maal, and went mad for the German blondes showing their mangoes on the beaches. But once their first frenzy was quietened, they looked forward to the Indian girls like starving, flood-hit Biharis waiting for government food drops. It was comfortable to chodo a plump Ghaatan, it was comfortable to hum a Kishore Kumar song to a giggling Punjaban and have her understand, just understand without any effort. It felt like home.

So I told my three card-players about the girls coming in two weeks, and they brightened considerably. Now there was something to look forward to. 'Don't go mad over them,' I said. 'Don't become fools, these girls know how to take money out of a man. One chappan-churi will say, just buy me a few saris, won't that gold necklace look nice on me, and you'll be trying to act like a big bhai, and by the time they go home you'll have nothing in your pockets. Have fun, but keep a cold head.'

'Yes, bhai,' they said like schoolboys to a teacher.

'Chutiyas, however many times I say it, it is not enough. Let's see how smart you are four weeks from now.'

And four weeks later, slow and steady Arvind was married. In this lot of girls there was one Suhasini, who looked a little like Sonali Bendre, so she went by the stage name of Sonali and affected starry airs. We picked up the girls at the Phuket airport, and when the van arrived at the Orchid Seaside Hotel, our Arvind straightaway attached himself to this Sonali-Suhasini. It was quite usual for the boys and girls to pair up, these short, holiday-type attachments sometimes happened of course. This one was Mukund's girl, that one was Munna's. Ramesh always wanted to do them all, but even he backed away if he saw that one of the other boys was fida on one girl only. So at least for a few days Munna or Mukund could pretend he had a real chaavvi, and feel safe. So this we had seen, but we had never seen anything like Arvind with this girl. Sure, she had nice skin, and a big nose that at a certain angle, in a certain light, could suggest Sonali Bendre, but finally she was one lanky thing from Ghatkopar. And she was a randi. There was no getting around that. Arvind knew this well. After all, he was getting his lauda lasoon-ed every night.

When he and the girl came to ask my blessings for the marriage, this was the main theory that the rest of the boys had, that she had a talented mouth and Arvind was a full, poora, akha idiot. She was bathing his chotta bhai every morning and night, and the resulting short-circuit was happening in his brain. I quietened them down, told them to shut up and not cause quarrels. Arvind had his blood up, and once he got started in his dragging way, he was dangerous. That's why we had hired him. I sat him down alone and told him, 'Think about it. There are two types of girls, one type for mauj-maja and the other for marrying. It's one thing to have fun, even to go crazy over a girl for a week or two. That kind of thing happens to a man, the truth is that when you're getting it wet morning and evening, your brain does get hijacked by your lauda. But marriage is a big thing. You have to think about it with a level head. Think about your parents, society. You and your family have to live with your relatives after all. You can't keep this sort of thing secret for ever, who she is. Don't get carried away just because she looks like Sonali Bendre. Just have your aish and let her go.'

'Bhai, I don't care about Sonali Bendre. To me she looks only like Suhasini. And I have thought about it. I know this is the right thing to do.'

'How?'

'I just know it, bhai. I feel it here.' He held his hand to his chest, a very young man in love, and in love with big dramatic gestures. He had no idea that he might seem like a comedy. Even if he had known, I think he wouldn't have cared.

'After only, what, ten days, you know?'

'When you know you know.'

He was proud. He was one of that select group who knew. He counted himself now in the fraternity of Majnu and Farhad and Romeo. He was calm. 'All right,' I said. 'Let me think about it. What are her details?'

He smiled a huge smile, and yanked a piece of paper from his shirt pocket. 'I knew it, bhai. Here. All details are there, both hers and mine.'

I took the paper and sent him off. Being Guru-ji's follower, I had acquired a certain expertise in the science of astrology myself. Of course I was not one-thousandth of Guru-ji, but I had picked up some techniques here and there. Guru-ji himself had told me, 'You're a fast learner. You have an instinct for the science, a knowledge that is inside you. Through me you're just rediscovering it.' He told me that this was why I had survived for so long, while so many others had died. I had a feeling for the future, I could see through the spirals of time and so I knew when danger was coming. So I had lived. I was now learning to control this knowledge, to add to it whatever Guru-ji saw fit to give to me. I practised on the boys, and they trusted me. Looking at Arvind and Suhasini's birth-dates and times and places, it seemed to me that the two of them matched, that the influences of their respective stars paralleled each other and fitted snugly together where necessary. They had ricocheted through the world, driven by their destinies, and they had found each other on my yacht. Who could say that a perfect couple wouldn't or couldn't come together on my boat, which was after all called the *Lucky Chance*? I felt good about Arvind and Suhasini, and it would be auspicious to have a wedding. But I wouldn't give consent, of course, without consulting with Guru-ji. None of the boys except Bunty knew about Guru-ji, but he knew everything about them. These ones were my inner circle, and since they were close to me it was important that they be looked at and vetted by a superior mind. This little bit of care could maybe save my life some day.

I usually waited for Guru-ji's call in my office at five p.m., and he called when he could. I had a satellite phone especially and exclusively for him, with a built-in scrambler. He had a scrambler he travelled with, and so we talked in complete security. I had learnt all this new security technology from my baldy friend Mr Kumar from RAW, all this high carefulness. He had given me a secure satellite phone, and through my own people I had sourced two more, one for Guru-ji and one for Jojo. So I was triply secure: in my patriotism, in my spirituality, in my sex. The *Lucky Chance* was also designed to be secure. My old friends Gaston and Pascal had found me this old, falling-apart khatara that belonged to a Gulf sheikh, and because he was an old degenerate who we supplied with Scotch and young boys, and because it bored him to argue about such trivial sums of money, he let us have it for the throwaway price of seven crore rupees. Gaston and Pascal had hauled it to a shipyard in Cochin, and refitted it with gun lockers and security doors and special close-range radar, all under the technical advice of the mild-looking Mr Kumar. In Bombay everyone said that Gaitonde wanted a yacht because Chotta Madhav had had one for years, but that was completely untrue. I wanted to live on a boat because it felt safe. On a boat I knew who was coming, and when. A few men could make a boat secure. And Guru-ji had told me that on water I was safe, that my destiny grew and rolled on the waves.

Besides, Chotta Madhav had only an ordinary ninety-footer which he paddled around Malaysian waters. I took the ferociously-armed *Lucky Chance* wherever I wanted, through Indonesian straits if that's where we needed to go, and twice we had blasted pirate speedboats out of the water with heavy machine-gun fire. The stupid bastards thought we couldn't see them coming up in the dark. As long as I had technology and Guru-ji with me, nothing could touch me on the water. So I waited for Guru-ji's call.

As always, while waiting I spent time with my accountant. He was a full CA, my Partha Mukherjee, a good Bengali boy who had grown up in Bandra East. He had prospered with me, had moved his parents and sister into a flat in Lokhandwalla, and had already found a boy for the sister. The wedding was to be in November, with a five-star reception. I paid Partha Mukherjee well, with double bonuses, but that was exactly what he was worth to me. My company's annual turnover at that time was three hundred crores, and tracking that money and funnelling it from here to there, and investing it and expanding it, this in itself was a job and a half. Of course we still made money the old-fashioned way, from our taxes on businessmen and movie producers, from commissions earned from good middle-class householders who needed their retirement flats emptied of sticky tenants, from moving substances and materials across borders, from bookies and touts. But we had legitimate investments thrown across Bombay and into India, we had funds and stocks and real estate and start-up companies. All this Partha Mukherjee managed with his computers and his various assistants in various cities across Asia. I gave him half an hour every evening to summarize for me the worming of my money across countries. He showed me charts, and drew arrows on hand-drawn maps to explain to me where it was all going, from Kuala Lumpur to Bangkok to Bombay. I understood, and directed its flow. Fat old Paritosh Shah would have been proud of me.

When Guru-ji's call came I always threw Partha Mukherjee out. But that day it was not his phone that buzzed, but the other secure phone beside it. Mukherjee stood up without being told and gathered up his papers. All the boys knew, when the special grey phones rang they had to leave me alone. After the door had shut, with a small, reassuring, vacuum-sealing sound with a metallic click at the end of it, I tapped my code into the phone to start the scrambler. The phones were secure at both ends.

'Ganesh.' It was Mr Kumar, as stealthy and gentle as always.

'Kumar Saab.'

'The Bhavnagar information was good. We got four of them.'

'Including the local contact? All dead?'

'Yes. Shabash, Ganesh.'

'This is only my dharam, sir.' And there would be no publicity for me or for Mr Kumar. Perhaps the local Bhavnagar police would announce that they had broken a cell of ISI agents, and captured a stash of arms. But for us, who had engineered the entire operation, there was only this quiet shabash between colleagues, on a private phone. This was how the secret agencies worked. Mr Kumar had explained it to me: when we do our work properly, nobody knows. When we fail, everybody knows. This operation had succeeded, now he had plans for a new one.

He said, 'We are going to hit Maulana Mehmood Ghouse.'

'Saab, that's a very big wicket.' Mehmood Ghouse was a Pakistani mullah, a preacher who had been very active in the Kashmir valley. He boasted openly of how many kafirs he had killed with his own hands, and for a while every television channel had been showing a grainy clip of him at a jehadi prayer meeting in Multan, holding up the rotting, decapitated head of an Indian soldier by the hair.

'Yes, he's big,' Mr Kumar said. 'And he's getting bigger. He's standing for elections. Suddenly he's a politician, and he's saying the man in the Multan video is not him at all.'

'Who will believe that?'

'The British government. They're very impressed by the fact that he used to be an electrical engineer, that he uses computers and is a modern mullah. They've given him a visa.'

'Maderchod.'

'He's going to be there for a week. He will address public meetings, try to meet English politicians.'

'Nobody will meet him, saab.'

'Maybe, maybe not. But he's stepping out into the open. He thinks he's going to come back with bags full of pounds and new batches of chelas and an international profile. So we will make him international news. You get a couple of teams in place in London.'

'What is the timetable?'

'We think he arrives in London four weeks from now.'

'Four weeks. Easy.' We had a base in Cannes, and moved business through Europe routinely. We recently had taken an interest in Slovenia and the Baltics. We were learning and expanding.

'We will pass you information as we receive it.'

'We'll be ready, saab. But why now, saab?'

'It is a message. These people think they can strut about on television. Bas.'

'And the message is to be from?'

'It is to be anonymous, at this point. But let's see how the operation goes. Maybe we can send it from your address.'

'Of course, saab.'

'Bye, Ganesh.'

'Salaam, saab.'

He was always clipped and to the point, my Mr Kumar. Just so much talk as was necessary, no more. He was not my friend, despite our months of conversations. But this order today, this was a mark of trust. Everything I had done so far was minor compared to this, and I was glad. Not just because being given more sensitive jobs meant that I could ask for more in return, but because I felt genuinely involved in this war. Now I was fighting at a higher level. Chotta Madhav's men had some years ago hit a Nepalese politician, a main supporter of the Pakistanis in Nepal, but that had only been in Kathmandu. I was to do this work in the centre of Europe, in fancy vilayati London. I would not fail. I would do it despite battalions of bodyguards and all of Scotland Yard. I set about organizing the logistics.

I called in Arjun Reddy, my computer-wallah, and he sent out my commands through secure e-mail. He assured me, as he did every week, that we were using the most advanced encryption technology, that we changed our cipher every week, that even if the CIA and the entire American government spent a billion dollars and their entire computer force on one of our e-mails, it would take them two hundred years to break the code. But e-mail still made me nervous. No matter how much Reddy assured me of steel-clad protection, I couldn't get rid of the image of my words swimming through the stomachs of the planet's computers, alone and vulnerable. But anyway, I wrote to my people in Cannes: '*London mein fielding lagao. Do team bhejo, Sachin aur Saurav dono. Ready rehna, instructions baad mein.*' The op was four weeks down the line, but I had learnt from experience to have the elements in place early. Sometimes events speeded up, and in any case it was a good thing to have your boys learning the landscapes of the stalking ground, to get them used to the language and the buses and the neighbours, and to have the neighbours getting used to them.

Once the serious work was done, Reddy continued my own instruction in computers. I could handle Windows now, and knew in principle how to open a document and make a new one, how to slide through a spreadsheet and its layers, but I still got lost often. Sometimes I couldn't find the document I wanted, and sometimes I would get stuck in some box on the screen and nothing I did would back me out. It wasn't just the English that confused me, but the whole universe inside that screen, I couldn't reason out where the ground was, and which was the sky. Reddy drew diagrams on paper, but I couldn't grasp the geography, and it drove me crazy, especially when he tip-tapped with his twenty-three-year-old fingers and sped through the internet, and made the machine and the entire world-wide system do things, do what he wanted it all to do. I had thrown things at the computer a couple of times, coffee cups and dishes. But, still, I always calmed down and came back to the computer. This little box ran everything now, I could see that. I had to understand it. And I had to hire Reddy, and if necessary a hundred others like him.

That evening I made Reddy shut up and watch quietly as I started up the machine, typed in my password, connected to the net and found my way to a couple of websites. He was completely silent but vibrating with impatience at my slow clicking and laborious one-fingered hunting at the keyboard. Without looking away from www.myindianbeauties.com, which published a new actress or model picture every day, I said, 'All right, chutiya. You're making me nervous. Out.'

'Sorry, bhai.'

'Don't go far. If I need you I'll call you.'

'Of course, bhai.'

He shuffled off. He had big ambitions, and he had been trying to talk me into investing in a website with him and his brother. He had yet to show me how he would make money, since I had never once paid for an Indian beauty on the web. But he kept talking, and coming up with new ideas every two days. Once the door clicked shut again, I leaned back and locked it. Then off I went to Guru-ji's website, www.eternalsacredwisdom.com.

Guru-ji travelled all over the world, he travelled all the time. He had centres in a hundred and forty-two countries, with others being developed in twelve additional countries. But wherever he was in the world, whatever he was doing, there was always a new pravachan on his site every three days. You could read it in more than a hundred languages, including of course Marathi and Hindi. But of late I had been reading Guru-ji's words in English, under 'Discourse'. It took me a while, and some struggle and pain, but I always got through to the end. I kept the Marathi version open in another window for reference, but I stayed mostly with the English and so absorbed not only wisdom but also language. Guru-ji had praised me for my diligence, and had mentioned me in one of his summer discourses on time management, of course without mentioning my name. 'A successful man is one who never stops learning,' he had said. 'I have a bhakt who is very success-ful, who commands money and respect across the seas. But despite all his worldly achievements, he is not arrogant. He realizes what he does not know. A wise man said long ago, to realize that one is ignorant is the beginning of wisdom.' And then he had gone on to tell the story of my reading the discourse in a language I had not mastered.

Today the discourse was about sex. Guru-ji was never afraid of controversial topics, and never backed off from speaking about some-thing for fear of offending. He was fearless. I read on: 'Celibacy is held up as the ideal by all spiritual traditions.' I had to look up 'celibacy' in the English-Marathi dictionary. 'But to reach for celibacy when one is not ready is a mistake. Celibacy will come to you when you are ready for it. A celibacy that you enforce on yourself is itself a form of sensu-ality. The struggle with your body will become a passion. And desire will express itself, you cannot dam it, you cannot block it, you cannot kill it. Even the images you make of celibacy will be beautiful as a woman's hip, the hymns you sing to celibacy will be like a lover's kiss.'

These six sentences took me fifteen minutes to get through, and not only because of the English. I paused to reflect, to absorb, to admire. He said things so simply, in such direct, forceful language, and yet how deep the words went. I felt them in my heart, under my stomach. What an endless tug-of-war we fought with desire, I thought. How much we pulled, how much it pushed. What torments, and what ecstasy in our torments.

And yes, it was strange even to me, that I, Ganesh Gaitonde, who had once scorned all mention of gods, and regarded any talk of religious solace as weakness, was now a dedicated follower of a guru. How had it happened? It came about because Guru-ji and I started talking. After our first conversation, when I had compelled him to call me in jail, I had not expected to hear from him again. He had, after all, to protect his public image, his vast mission across the world. But ten days after I got out of jail and the country, he called me. He had asked his people to get the number from Bunty, and suddenly, there he was on my handset, Shridhar Shukla himself, with his solid bronze voice and his exquisite punctuation. This was a man who was eagerly sought after by millions, and yet he took the time to call me, to ask after my well-being. I was cynical, I waited for him to ask me for something, as every last caller did. But he had no matter to settle, no need for money or revenge, he just wanted to talk to me.

'I see, you want to talk to me,' I said. 'What do you want to talk to me about?'

He surely heard the sneer in my voice, but he answered calmly: 'About whatever is on your mind.'

'All right. I have a question to ask you.'

'Ask.'

'I don't believe that you are a true guru.'

He laughed. 'That's not a question. But that's fine. You don't have to believe anything about me.'

Then he was silent. It was infuriating that he was not provoked at all. I waited, and thought of slamming the phone down, and then finally spoke, because I was in fact curious. 'You can't be a true guru because of what you are having me do for you.' I meant, of course, the many weapons that I was bringing into the country for him. 'People who are truly spiritually advanced are peaceful. They are against violence.'

'Who told you that?'

'Everyone knows that.'

'So you think you yourself are not very spiritually advanced?'

I flushed, and sat up. 'We're talking about you.'

'All right, Ganesh, all right. But I was curious about where you got this idea about spiritual achievement and what everyone calls being peaceful. It's all over the place nowadays, everyone repeats it, nobody can say why they believe it.'

'It's obvious, no?'

'No.'

Then again he was silent. Bastard. 'Listen,' I snapped. 'Don't play games, just tell me. I'll ask, all right? So tell me, how can you be a true guru and do what you are doing?'

'Do you know what I am doing?'

'I know a little. I know my part, and it is not peaceful.'

'Yes, you know your part. You know the little you can see. And you have been told that to be a mahatma you have to be peaceful, whatever that means. But, Ganesh, can you imagine the whole picture?'

'Of course I don't know what your plan is.'

'But think of the picture that is even bigger than that. Think of life itself. Do you think it has no violence in it? Life feeds on life, Ganesh. And the beginning of life is violence. Do you know where our energy comes from? The sun, you say. Everything depends on the sun. We live because of the sun. But the sun is not a peaceful place. It is a place of unbelievable violence. It is one huge explosion, a chain of explosions. When the violence ceases, the sun dies, and we die.'

'That is different. It's not the same as killing a man. Or many of them.'

'All men die.'

'But they don't have to die because you blow their heads up with your bullets.'

'So by not killing you bring peace?'

I knew that wasn't true. I wanted to contradict him, but I knew that non-violence never brought peace. If anything was obvious, that was. He was a frustrating bastard, this guru. 'That's different,' I said. 'We live in Kaliyug, so we are doomed to fight. But you are supposed to be a holy man, so you should be telling us not to fight.'

'Why, Ganesh? Why? You are a very intelligent man, but even you have fallen into this trap. Even you. But it's not your fault, this propaganda is very popular in our time, all over the world. But think back on your own history, Ganesh. Have not holy men fought before? Have they not urged warriors to battle? Does spiritual advancement mean that you should not take up weapons when confronted by evil?'

He reminded me then of Parshurama, that great sage who took up his axe to cleanse the earth. And of Rama himself, most perfect of men, who took up his bow and fought against all odds. 'And what about the advice that Krishna gave to Arjuna on the battlefield?' this strange guru said to me. 'Arjuna wanted to be peaceful. He wanted to retire from the world. Should he have gone? Should Krishna have let him?'

I had to agree with him, no, it was clear that Krishna was correct. I said so, and then Guru-ji told me about the great Shankaracharya, and his defeat of Krakaca's kapalika army. And also about the Sanyasi Rebellion, during which sadhus and faqirs fought against the East India Company. 'We must resist this so-called peace which emasculates spirituality and makes it weak, Ganesh,' he said. 'We must see the big picture. We must know when we have to fight to bring peace. We must be strong in our faith. Our entire history, thousands of years of it, gives us examples of this. And if I am a holy man, Ganesh, so are you.'

'Me?'

'Yes, you.'

I was too dazed and exhausted – somehow this conversation had tired me out – to tell him that I believed in no faith, no spirituality. I hung up, and tried to work, and was plagued that entire day by this conundrum, me as holy man, myself as mahatma. I dreamt that night of the great akharas of naga sadhus who came to Nashik during the Kumbh Mela, about their naked bodies covered with ash, their matted brown jatas curling to their shoulders and below, their tridents and swords. I dreamt of the great roar that went up when the regiments of naga sadhus swept towards the holy waters for their bath, and the ferocious gleam on the sadhus' eyes as they ran. I saw a small man, a peaceful man, amongst these great and good sadhus, and I felt bitter contempt for him, and I woke up with my heart rushing. I turned my mind away from Nashik, but all night I was pursued by this question: what does it mean to be holy? Who is virtuous?

The next time Guru-ji called, we talked about God. I told him that I had no belief in such a thing, and no need for such a belief. I said that religion was a tool with which politicians whipped their constituents and drove them in herds towards the slaughterhouse. I said faith was for men who had no faith in themselves. He did not argue with me. He listened quietly, and said, 'Those are reasonable arguments. You are correct in your logic.'

He stopped me short with that. I had expected him to dispute and quarrel and hector, maybe to curse me for a fallen man. But he did none of those things. He listened to me quietly and gave me respect. Then he said, 'But, Ganesh, what about all the symmetries in the world?'

I had no idea what he was talking about, but then he explained. He showed me how for every fire there is water, for every predator there is prey, for every love there is a hate. He talked about electrons and their charges, and strange attractions and repulsions. There were parts of what he was saying that came to me only as a sonorous hymn, but I understood instantly, profoundly, what he was talking about. Yes, for every Ganesh Gaitonde there is a Suleiman Isa. For every victory there is a loss. 'Yes,' I said to him, 'I understand. Everything comes in twos, or repetitions of two and more. Everything clashes, and swings apart, and loops and comes around again.'

'Of course, of course, Ganesh,' he said, his pleasure booming through his voice, 'see, you already have it. I didn't even have to explain it. You already know. You already are on the path.'

'On the path to this God of yours? No, I don't think so.'

'You must not think that I am arguing for Vishnu, or any other creator, Ganesh. You know I am not that simple. Listen to me: through these symmetries, lift yourself even higher. Can you see the patterns of the world, of the universe? The waves below you, under the boat, they may seem chaotic, but are they? No, only in a minor sense. There is an order that we sometimes glimpse, sometimes lose. But the order is there. Beyond the local and the immediate, there is this grand order. Ganesh, go ashore and look at a field of grass. See how the sun feeds the grass, and the earth sustains it. Observe how the grass shelters other creatures, and feeds them in turn. Do you see how everything fits together. Finally, after everything, Ganesh, do you see the beauty?'

I tell you, my head was bursting then. I had my fingers on the skipping edges of his meaning, but it vanished from me with every breath. He knew this. He told me not to worry, but just to watch everything for the next week. 'Deal with everything as normal. But also, simultaneously, try to see beyond that. And next week, tell me what you saw, just randomness, or a shape. Chaos, or order.'

Five minutes after I got off the phone I was laughing at myself. I thought, you weakling, listening to the babblings of an old man. But he had planted something in me. I didn't want to, but I found myself looking for connections and mirrorings. And I found them. I thought about the ways in which men and women needed each other, and how the human race rolled on, despite all the quarrels and the heartbreaks. This was obvious enough, banal if you stepped away from it for a minute. But that led me to conception and birth, the minuscule pin-headed worm thrashing its way up towards the enormity of the egg, and the mixing of their smuggled pieces of instruction, all to form a new creature that would one day be whole, and producing emissaries himself. Commonplace, and yet so complicated and amazing. I felt foolish at the wonder that swamped my head, at being able to see these mundane surfaces that hid whole universes of complication. But I kept quiet and kept on looking, as he had told me to do. Towards the end of the week, my mind turned from things to sequences. I had watched programmes on television about the dinosaurs and their extinction, the rise of mammals (while the boys groaned and begged for another television set, so they could go back to their prancing heroines), I had watched long-ago hairy apes make their first kills on the African plains. That was the arc of life on the planet, all the way to humans, and to me. This curve had direction and velocity, it swept upwards and it was still going, towards the moon and then to the stars. But there was my life. Did it have shape? Was there beauty in its progress, if you only distanced yourself enough to see? I thought about this, and worried about it. Could it really be that I was randomly tossed about by the surging waves of events? That one day came next to each other just because it had to, because of nothing. I couldn't accept this. This buzzing blur of chaos caused me pain, I mean a stomach twisting and flexing, a headache, and again my piles caught at me and left me dizzy and shaking in the bathroom. My body was protesting against this assertion that my life meant nothing. No, my life had shape. I had started poor and alone, I had struggled, I had won, I had moved upward, I had found a home and many who loved me. And even now I was learning, I was progressing, I had a mission for my country, I had a teacher, I was going somewhere. I had a story.

This is what I told Guru-ji the next time we spoke, and he praised me. 'Your instinct is unerring, Ganesh. The atman knows the nature of the universe, it understands its intricate connections, from the smallest to the largest. The atman knows because it *is* the universe. But the mind interferes. This incomplete structure we call scientific logic blocks our view and, paradoxically, keeps us ignorant. Otherwise, how could you see this enormous network of connections, and not believe that there is an author?'

'You mean God, Guru-ji?'

'I mean consciousness.'

That was where we had started, and he had helped me on my journey to knowledge. No, he had picked me up and carried me up the mountain of wisdom. He bore my weight with ease, and as we ascended he showed me these unborn truths, these eternal facts. He pointed out to me the cycles of history, and beyond those, the rhythms of evolution, of stars being born and sliding towards their inevitable dissolution, of the universe expanding and then racing to a point to explode again.

And then, months after we first started talking, he revealed the power that these insights had brought him. He told me my future. I had read testimonials on his website from hundreds of people, that he could do this, and that he had done this for them. I had read through some of these pages, marvelling at the desperate need that humans have for reassurance and comfort. The testimonials were quite detailed, giving names and circumstances: here was a doctor from Siliguri whose daughter suffered from leucoderma and remained unmarried, and Guru-ji told him not to worry, that in the last three months of that year a solution to his problem would be found, and sure enough, in that very winter a German engineer came to work on an agricultural project, and was struck by the grace and white beauty of the girl, and he took her away to happiness in Düsseldorf. There was screen after screenful of this, and not only happiness had been predicted, Guru-ji was frank about bad times, about accidents involving water and divorces and business reversals. I decided that this was all nothing but the obsessions of small people who did not have the resources, internal or material, to fight with life and win. But then Guru-ji told me one evening, 'Watch out for the Thais.'

'What?'

'I see that you will attempt to close some deal with some Thai fellows in the next few days. Be careful. Do not trust them. They mean you harm.'

Now it was true that we were about to tie up a sale with some fellows from Krabi province, we had brought in four million tablets of methamphetamine for the Thais, but Guru-ji could just have made a guess: at any given time we would be making some deal or other with some group of Thais, nothing especially insightful in that. So I didn't take him too seriously, thanked him politely all the same and forgot about it until the morning of the exchange. Then, tickled uncomfortably by the recalling of Guru-ji's prediction, I woke up and called the boys – who had already left – and told them to be careful, and to keep a shooter in reserve. And the Thais, the idiots, tried the most hackneyed, the most boring grab and run that any of us had seen in fifteen years. They had brought some extra personnel and hidden them in a house up the beach, and they thought that was enough to overpower our unit. Of course we cut them down, our reserve shooter caught their back-up as they came blundering out of the house on cue, and that was that.

So it happened, leaving the question of Guru-ji's prediction entirely up in the air, hovering over my head like a bomb suspended in mid-fall. I was afraid to accept, to let it come down, lest it explode my mind. The long cycles of creation and destruction were all very well, but – maderchod! – how was a man able to look into the future? It was impossible. Time ran one way, from before to after, and physically you couldn't thrust yourself into what was to come.

Guru-ji heard me out patiently. Then he said, 'So you think you know what time is?'

'Guru-ji, what is there to know? Time is time. It goes from here to there, and we live inside it. The road is marked, and you can't do a U-turn.'

'But do you know, Ganesh, that scientists have discovered particles that travel backwards in time? And do you know that time is not constant, that it bends and stretches and compresses? If there is a jet plane passing above your head, going fast, its pilot is ageing a little less slowly than you? For him, time is passing more slowly compared to your time.'

'No. That can't be.'

'But it is. Even the scientists have known that for more than a hundred years. They have admitted that a travelling particle of light, which was born billions of years ago during the Big Bang, has not aged a second since then. So, Ganesh, if you could travel at the speed of light, you would be young for ever.'

I didn't understand any of this. I didn't understand the articles he e-mailed me, or the videos he had me watch, all his Einstein and relativity and black holes and the universe curving round on itself, it all made me as dazzled as a small child looking into the sun. But he convinced me that the world I thought I knew was only a shallow illusion, that how things looked and felt was a dream, not inconsequential but not substantial either. And he convinced me that some people, some men and women, even some children, could look through the spiral of time. 'It's an inborn ability,' he said to me. 'The horoscopes, the readings of the palm, all those are props that enable this ability, make it move and energize itself. If you have this ability, and you train it and discipline it and exercise it, make it supple and strong, you can read the narrative of the universe, and sometimes see where the story is going, catch glimpses of the future plot, because this future already exists. If you are a true master, then nothing is hidden from you. Me, I have a modest gift. And if it makes you uncomfortable to be paying attention to a jyotishi, if you feel like you are in the grip of some wicked fraud, then just think of me as a friend who offers advice now and then, with the best of intentions. Don't take me too seriously. I may be wrong now and then, I may misinterpret the scattered images and intuitions that I get. So take it for what it is worth, Ganesh. Maybe the information will be useful to you. Don't trust it without corroboration, treat it like any other intelligence you acquire.'

That's what he said. And then he grabbed pieces of what was to come and dropped them into my lap. He didn't do it every day, and he didn't always have crucial, life-saving information for me. He told me that a delayed shipment from Rotterdam would arrive on such-and-such a day, and it did. Or he said that one of my boys would face health problems in late July, and of course one dirty fool nurtured some monstrous fungal infection between his toes that finally kept him from walking. Guru-ji made mistakes also, twice what he said didn't come to pass. But the other fifty-two times it did. Yes, I counted, I made notes in a diary. The numbers taught me that what he was doing was true, that he had not lied. He had a talent. You can believe or not, as you wish, but I had resisted as long as I could. Now I believed.

Now the Guru-ji phone buzzed. I wiped my hands on my pants, and picked it up. I put in my eighteen-digit encryption code, and he spoke to me.

'I was thinking of you when I wrote today's pravachan, Ganesh.'

'Pranaam, Guru-ji. I was just reading it.'

'I know.'

He did that sometimes. He would know what you had been doing, what you were thinking, what you wanted but were afraid even to admit to yourself. Once, in long-ago days, I had been subject to fits of scepticism, but all my rock-like disbelief had been shattered and vanquished by the thunder of his insight. He knew you better than you, he saw into your life, he knew your future and your past, and he never made any judgements. That was the most amazing thing about Guru-ji, that he was himself the most sattvic man, more undesiring of the base things of life than the Buddha himself, but he never looked down on those of us who still thrashed about in the nets of wanting. I had asked him once whether my dhandas upset him, all the various businesses I ran to make a living. I asked him why he didn't try to have me give up those activities the world called criminal. A tiger is glorious as a tiger, he said, a tiger who tries to become a vegetarian sheep is a pitiful abomination. In Kaliyug, there are no simple acts, he said, and there has never been a clear path to salvation. 'So, Guru-ji,' I said now, grinning. 'You were thinking of me. What do you think? Am I ready for celibacy?'

He laughed his usual glorious burble, as free as a baby in his mother's arms. 'Beta, you are a warrior. You are my Arjun. You need not only your Draupadi, but also the other gifts of the earth as you wander. To block your own nature would be a crime, and would make you incapable of the work you must do.'

All this I had heard him say before, but I liked listening to him. There was something golden about the timbres of his voice, something dense, and they settled into my chest and comforted me. I grew calm listening to him, so sometimes I asked him questions just to hear him talk. But today I had a real question. 'Did you look at the papers, Guru-ji?' I meant six-foot Jamila's charts and biodata, which I had faxed to him in Denmark. He of course had no problem with the fact that she was Muslim, but wanted to consider her stars and her future.

I could feel him smiling. 'You are impatient, Ganesh.'

'No, no, Guru-ji. I know how busy you are. There's no hurry.'

'Ganesh, I understand. It has been a while. Too long.'

It had been a while since I had a woman. Of course I didn't partake of the common girls that were brought in for the boys. For me, Jojo only sent special cases, and all of those were approved by Guru-ji. But I wasn't so weak that I would grow impatient with him. 'Guru-ji, nothing like that. This one is more interesting than usual, that's all.'

'I agree with you, Ganesh. Her stars and signs and lines are very interesting indeed. This woman will go far. She has intelligence, but more than that she has luck. Every time she needs something, someone will come into her life who can provide. Her path will be smoothed and built for her.'

'But is she lucky for me?'

'I'm not quite certain yet. I've been looking at the charts, and in general they fit. But I am unable yet to get an image from them. Something is waiting to happen.'

'No hurry, Guru-ji,' I said. 'No problem.'

There were prime ministers and CEOs queuing up to consult with him, but he made time for me. He thought about me, he cared. Sometimes this realization caught at my throat, as now. He heard the thick emotion in my voice, and he said gently, 'So what's the news?' By news he meant the ongoing drama of the boys and their lives. He enjoyed hearing about them, about their amusements and their passions, and even about the problems of their mothers and sisters, and the law-suit that one uncle had filed against a brother. He was a realized master, but he was interested in all of it, in the common ordinariness of their problems. I always told him their tales, and he listened with relish, and offered comments and suggestions. 'Guru-ji, today I have a solid instalment. My slowpoke gadha Arvind has decided he's in love with one of the randis. He wants to get married.'

'Really? And what do you think?'

'I've checked the charts. No big problems.'

'Tell me.'

I read off the dates and times and places, and even as I finished he had seen deep into the case. 'This girl is very dynamic,' he said. 'This Arvind has strength and intelligence, but he is quite passive. A very tamasaic personality. This girl moves him, puts him in motion. You are right, there are no major problems here. But they will have only girls. And his liver will give him trouble. Otherwise the charts match. Let them do it, Ganesh. The other boys may make fun, but as leaders we must be forward-looking. This girl has paid her debts from her prior births, and it is time she is lifted from this life of selling herself. All of existence is a movement forward, from low to high, and it is our duty to help this evolution along. Marriage is an auspicious occasion, and this will be a good marriage.'

Once he said it, it was obviously and shiningly true. And it was the exact line I took with the boys. That very evening, after I said good-bye to Guru-ji, I called Arvind and his Suhasini in and gave them permission, and a talk. I told them that they were setting out on a great journey, and they had to be doubly strong and discreet because of the gossip that would follow them. I tried particularly to impress on her the duty she owed to her husband, what a good and great thing he was doing. This Suhasini had Sonali Bendre's slim height all right, those long legs, but her features were heavier, darker. She listened with her eyes downcast, but I could see in her what Guru-ji was talking about, this great energy. There was movement here all right.

So it was all arranged. In less than a week they were married. Of course I called Jojo before the marriage and told her what I had decided, and she said, 'Gaitonde, for once in your life you are doing a completely good thing.' She gave her blessing also, and sent a gift to the couple, diamond rings for both of them, with decent-sized stones set in white gold. We arranged a hall, and a pandit was brought in from Bangkok. I had given the boys a good lecture, and told them to respect the solemnity of the occasion, but I could see that they were themselves calmed by the chanting of the shlokas. The determined seriousness of Arvind and Suhasini as they bound themselves to each other quietened even the drunken Ramesh. They sat cross-legged, in a little circle, and watched. Me, I grew melancholy. The flames hummed and I sank away into them, into memory. My chest ached for my Abhi, and I remembered again how he used to bat at my cheeks with his little fists, and how he would kiss me when I begged him to.

This mood of mine persisted even after we had sent the happy couple off on their honeymoon, to a week in a cottage in Koh Samui. I meditated that evening, moved my breath in circles in my belly, and yet I was unable to shake off this shark-toothed bite of regret that swam just a little behind me, stabbing at my heels. I switched on the television and found an Indian channel. A blonde VJ spoke accented Hindi and introduced fast songs. I switched it off. I lay in bed awake, thinking that although my boys lived close to me, I was alone. They were feet away, separated from me only by lengths of metal and wood, and I was alone. With my boys I had to be strong always, to be their father, distant and powerful and sometimes wrathful. Those to whom I could tell the stories of my discontents and longings, they were all far away. I was close to them only in words, through broadcast and electricity. I was far from Guru-ji, and Jojo.

He called then. My Guru-ji called. I leapt out of bed, got the phone on the second buzz. 'Guru-ji?'

'Meet me,' he said.

'What?'

'You have been a good student, beta. I have meditated on it, and now I think you are ready for more knowledge. But to take you further on this path, towards the secrets of Paramatma, I need to initiate you. I am in Bombay from next week, for Ganesha Chathurthi. I'll be there for two weeks. I am conducting a very big yagna here, very important. The most important yagna of my life, actually. But after that I'll be in Singapore for a week. Come and meet me in Singapore.'

From our first conversation, through the months since, I had never met him. I had talked with him, maybe more than any of his other disciples, and I had seen him on television, but I had never sat with him, face to face. Now he was inviting me, and I was angry. Not at him, but at my life, myself. If he was doing the most important yagna of his life in Bombay, during Ganapati's festival, why should I not meet him there? Why Singapore, that hell of cleanliness that bored me more than any other place on earth? Bombay was the earth I longed for, and it was dangerous for me, but it was also my Kurukshetra. And he was my Guru-ji.

'Ganesh,' Guru-ji said quietly, 'can you come?'

And in that moment I understood, it hit me like a bullet in the belly. I felt the truth blow into me and it rose into my mouth as laughter. He was testing me. This was my last test. I laughed and said, 'Guru-ji, of course. I will see you, I will arrange it. In Singapore.'

'In Singapore,' he said. 'I will be expecting you.'

'Pranaam, Guru-ji.'

I hung up, woke Arvind out of his honeymoon bed and began to make plans. Only Arvind, and Bunty in Bombay, knew where I was going. The rest of the boys thought that I was setting off on an emergency trip to Jakarta. And Guru-ji thought I was going to meet him in Singapore. But I had made up my mind. I was going to Bombay, to take part in his yagna. It was all meticulously planned. I was sure Mr Kumar, my wily Mr Kumar, had his people watching me. I was forbidden to enter India. I had become very valuable to Mr Kumar's organization, and there was great risk to me inside the country, from Suleiman Isa and others. There was also risk to Mr Kumar and his people: if I was arrested inside India, maybe I would talk under police pressure, tell everyone of the deeds I had done for Mr Kumar. I knew these thousand-armed dangers, and so I planned with care. But even as I did, I was filled with admiration for Guru-ji, for his wanting to meet me. All I had to lose was my life. He was risking his great work, his position in the world, his connections with the small and the very large. If I was caught, if his relationship with me were known, he would lose his good name, his unstained honour. I was a gangster, and he was a saint. And yet he was risking everything for me, for my miserable, crawling worm of a life. Why? I wondered, and there was only one answer: he loved me. And so, even as Arvind and Bunty grumbled about the risk, about the police and my enemies and immigration officers and bullets, I was light-hearted. I was confident, I was fearless in the gentle cradle of my Guru-ji's love. Three days later I flew into Bombay on a Lufthansa flight from Frankfurt, with a newly shaved head, a stubbled jaw, steel-rimmed spectacles, a new passport and a suitcase full of baby clothes for a non-existent niece. I had business papers and invoices, and my cover was complete, and they stamped me through at immigration without pause or question, and I was out on the sweltering sidewalk before I could bring myself to believe that I was back in Bombay. I raised a hand towards Bunty over the crowds waiting for relatives, and then he recognized me with a start. We didn't say a word to each other until the car was out of the car park and we were zipping past the airport hotels.

'This is mad,' Bunty said. 'Bhai, there's nakabandi tonight. I was looked at pretty close twice on the way over here.'

I reached out and put a hand on his shoulder. 'At least say hello first,' I said.

He made a sound something like a laugh, full of nerves and edginess, and grabbed my hand. 'Sorry, bhai. I can't believe you're back, and like this.'

'How else would I come back, chutiya? On a magic carpet?'

He shook his head. 'This was too simple.'

He was scared of being by himself, without his bodyguards. I had told him to come unarmed and alone. 'Simple is best. What's the nakabandi for?'

'There were two big shop robberies over the last two days. I was told they have some information on the robbers, ex-employees. Small time, bhai.'

So, nothing to do with us. Still, there were policemen gathered near metal grilles at some of the crossroads. We had to go through two of the inspections by the time we got to the highway. They peered into the slowing cars, and at the second blockade one of the policemen shone a torch directly into my face. He waved us on. The breath came out of Bunty in a thin wheeze.

'Calm down, Bunty. They won't know me because they all know I'm far away.'

'You've lost weight, bhai, but still . . .'

On the boat I had a good diet and regular exercise, I enforced a regimen on myself to purify my body, and so I had shed the pounds from jail and marriage. 'And you've put it on,' I told him. He had. We passed a small party of devotees dragging a five-foot Ganesha on a cart. They were dancing in front of Ganesha, men and women and children, to the beat of two drums. They were happy. I could feel that old racketing drumbeat in my neck, in my shoulders. 'There are more jhopadpattis now,' I said. 'Look at this.' The swarms of shacks had crept up right to the highway, where I clearly remembered empty shoulders and scrubland.

'Really, bhai? Looks the same to me.'

I had been away for more than two years. Nothing looked the same to me. Under the orange light of the streetlamps the slums slept a convoluted sleep, browner and more numerous than I remembered. We passed a rank of hulking trucks painted bright red and green, and then went through a market with a hill of seeping vegetable rubbish at either end. The rubbish must have always been there, but I noticed it now. There was much new construction, taller buildings, one white one with gigantic concrete stilts built around it to support three new storeys on top of the already existing four floors.

'That's one of the new extra-FSI jobs, bhai,' Bunty said.

Some builders had oiled some bureaucrats, who had found a chink in the regulations to finger the Floor-Space Index, so suddenly there were these strange crane-legged contraptions all over the city. 'Three big new floors,' I said. 'That's a lot of money.'

'We know the owner,' Bunty said, grinning. 'He's become a friend of ours.'

He had contributed to my turnover, this FSI buyer, yet I was vaguely unsettled by this new trend. 'I wouldn't want to live on the ground floor of that thing,' I told Bunty. 'Those legs look like matchsticks.'

He grunted out a long laugh. 'If it goes down, bhai,' he said, 'all the better. Then you can build again, without that old building underneath. Maybe we should arrange it. He'll build it at double the selling price, better for us.'

'Chutiya,' I said, but I was smiling. The billboards were all announcing internet companies and websites in flashy, forward-tilting lettering that promised speed. Clusters of auto-rickshaws sat nose to nose like bulbous insects. I caught myself thinking that, *insects*, and thought, I've been away too long.

'Here,' Bunty said.

He had arranged a room for us at the back of a house in Santa Cruz. The street was very quiet, and the landlord was a furniture merchant with two school-age daughters, very orthodox and very respectable. We had two single beds, one coffee table and a clean bathroom. Bunty wrinkled his nose. 'All right, bhai?' he said, pretending concern for me. But it was he who had acquired high tastes, with his new incomes and his new stature.

'Fine for me,' I said. 'Let's sleep.'

I woke him the next morning at six. He groaned when he saw the time, but I was merciless. I got him up, and out, and we walked down the road to a restaurant. We drank chai from their first pot of the day, and ate idlis. A line of office-goers waited at the bus stop in the dust-haze raised by the buses and cars. Schoolchildren went past us, swinging their bags. I was content to watch the scene, it was like a pageant to me. But at eight-thirty I sent Bunty to bring me a scooter. He protested. 'Arre, why, bhai?' he said. 'I'll just drive you in the car.'

'You're not going to drive me,' I told him. 'And I want a scooter.'

He wanted to argue with me, but I gave him a look that shut him up. Off he went. Of course he was worried for his livelihood and his future, which would squeeze down considerably if I was jammed into a jail cell again, or killed. But he also loved me. We had walked together through many battles now, and I had made him a settled man, with a wife and two children and responsibilities and investments and money. So he hated me a little now, for making him risk it alone in a room in Goregaon with no guns and no bodyguards. But by nine-thirty he had a scooter for me at our room, a green Vespa with fancy silvered rear-view mirrors. 'I had to borrow it from someone,' he said apologetically.

'The mamus will stop me just for those mirrors,' I said. 'Your friend thinks he's on a racing motorcycle?' But driving even a Vespa was difficult for me, it had been so many years since I'd done it. I skidded even as I started off, and Bunty ran after me until I waved him away. The first ten minutes were terrifying, but I grinned at the rush of it, and sucked in the wind between my teeth. I went by three mandaps with towering Ganeshas, all of them a bright, radiant orange. By the time I got to Juhu I was fine, I was slipping between the cars with complete confidence, and changing gears smoothly. I was sleek. I saw myself in the rear-views, and I was a purposeful man having a good time in the morning. I was in Bombay, and I was fearless. I was going to my Guru-ji.

But once I got to the yagna-sthal in Andheri West I was stuck. They had police bandobast from two hundred feet away, and they weren't letting any lone scootering taklus through. I had to park, and walk with a few hundred other devotees towards the mansion. This house belonged to a film-producer devotee of Guru-ji's, a man with good political connections and lots of property in Bombay. The open ground in front of the house had been fenced and covered with a series of open-sided shamianas. The arrangements were all faultless, with wide, straight avenues between the shamianas and sadhus guiding the devotees to the proper seating places. There were television sets scattered through the shamianas, and good loudspeakers, so that you may have been seated far from the central dais – as I was – but you could see Guru-ji and what he was doing quite clearly. But he wasn't there yet, just a group of his sadhus arranging the materials of the yagna on the dais. He appeared precisely at eleven, wheeling strongly down the central aisle, followed by a group of sadhus. They had built a ramp up to the dais, and up he went. I found myself standing, dancing, elbow to elbow with my fellow devotees, shouting 'Jai Gurudev'. He let us fall into a chant, and then he raised his hands. We were silent. 'Sit,' he said, and all by himself went from the wheelchair to his seat in front of the microphones. He had strong arms, I could see that.

He told us about sacrifice, about the altar. The dimensions of the altar had to be based on a measure of the sacrificer: the length of the middle joint of the middle finger of the sacrificer was one angula, and one hundred and twenty angulas made one purusha. The sadhus needed to lay out a square equal in length to two purushas, or two hundred and forty angulas. Who was the sacrificer? Guru-ji asked, 'Who will be the sacrificer? We are merely the priests, but who will be the yajman?' He paused, and then answered his own question: 'In the old days, chakravartin emperors were the patrons of this sacrifice we are engaged in. But the day of the emperors is gone. Who is the emperor today? Who has power, who leads? It is you. You, the public.

Power flows from you, from your votes. So, today, you are the sacrificer, the yajman. The public is the sacrificer. Each and every one of you is the sacrificer. So we have taken a scientific average. From a sample of two thousand Indian men from all over the country, from every state, our doctors have taken precise measurements, and we will use the average as our angula. You, my friends, are our purusha.'

So, using cords and rods, and orientating by the sun, the priests laid out their square, and its peripheries, and its intertwining circles. Meanwhile Guru-ji talked to us about sacrifice. He told us how the universe was created through a sacrifice, how the gods sacrificed Purusha and from his limbs and his flesh all of creation was born. Everything that exists, everything that has ever been and will be is created by that first sacrifice. In any sacrifice, the sacrificer emulates that first great giving of the self, that first immolation. The sacrificer rehearses that sacrifice, and in doing so sustains the universe. 'In sacrifice the sacrificer becomes Purusha, he becomes the original being who divided himself to create all things. Since this is so, properly speaking, at the end of the sacrifice the yajman should immolate himself. If he is Purusha, he should die to give life. But we will not ask this of you, and this is not how sacrifice has been conducted for many years. Instead of the self, we put into the sacred fire certain objects that are worthy of sacrifice. Instead of humans, once cows were sacrificed, and horses, and goats and rams. We will use certain cereals, certain flowers, certain grasses. But remember, as we fling these into the fire, what is being sacrificed is the self. If you are the yajman, all of you, then what you are sacrificing is your own selves, your bodies, you. What we put into the fire are merely substitutes, which the gods accept. What is being sacrificed is you. You are Purusha. You must die, so that the universe may live.'

Meanwhile the priests built the altar. We watched them over the televisions. At a point on the precisely measured and orientated ground, they laid a lotus. Over this they put a golden disc. These were the first waters and the sun. On this they gently balanced a small golden figure, who was Purusha, who was the yajman, who was us. Over Purusha they built the altar, in five layers of bricks, in the shape of a great eagle. 'An eagle first brought the sacred soma from heaven to earth,' Guru-ji told us. 'And so, through sacrifice, we will drink of that divine bliss again. Through the flight of sacrifice, we will taste knowledge. We will know the self, and the universe.'

Under the coloured canvas of the tents there was a white, lucid light. It was a cloudy day, quite cool for a day far after monsoon-end. There was a quietness in the crowd. People came and sat, stepped around each other with a friendly hand on the shoulder, left when they had to. Holding us all was Guru-ji's calm voice, as deep as the sea, and the slow swells of the slokas, eternal and steady and unstoppable. Guru-ji translated and explained some of the slokas to us.

> Sacrifice is a loom
> Its many threads are these rituals
> The Fathers sit by the loom
> and weave the fabric
> They cry: 'Lengthwise! Crosswise!'
>
> This Man unreels the thread and sets it on the loom,
> he notches it on the bar of heaven.
> And the pegs are fastened to this altar.
> On this sky-spanning loom,
> the Sama hymns are the shuttles,
> blazing back and forth.

'Each god covered himself with a poetic metre,' Guru-ji said, 'and this metre became the source of their power as sacrificers. Agni was suffused by the Gayatri metre, and Savitar by the Usnih metre. Indra's energy came from the Trishtubh. The Jagati metre moved through all the gods. So from metre, through sacrifice, from this warp and weft, this weaving, this geometry, this form, this poetry, the universe was born.' Sitting cross-legged on the ground, anonymous and alone, I could see – in my mind's cinema screen – that moment of creation, the hymns sliding across each other like ghee and sandalwood, the heated sparks of the metres, the flames of the universe being born. 'When we sacrifice,' Guru-ji said, 'when we chant, when we allow the metres to move through us, we weave the world. We are creators. We sustain all that is, we hold it up, we make it. We are the universe.'

Back at our room, Bunty had a good dinner waiting for me, brought from his wife's kitchen. While I ate we talked business, and I gave instructions and answered queries. By now the boys on the yacht had probably figured out that I wasn't in Jakarta, that I wasn't available on the phone there, but nobody would imagine that I was here, sitting at a yagna in Andheri or eating parathas in Santa Cruz. They sent me reports, and Bunty took my orders to be passed back. With reference to our job for Mr Kumar, our boys were already in London, in safe houses, waiting for the mullah. I told Bunty to secure our communications with them, to see to weapons and logistics. Me, I slept a deep, outstretched sleep, a sleep as confident and happy as a well-loved and well-fed child's who knows that he will wake to care and love and laughter. I was smiling even as I woke.

Back I went, back to Guru-ji. On this second day I was early, one of the very first few people on the maidan, apart from the policemen and the volunteers. I made my way to the very first shamiana, and found myself a seat right behind the VIP section, very close to the altar. The sadhus were seated about the fire, which had not gone out, which would not go out for twelve days. The yagna had continued through the night, staffed by teams of priests. But now, in the morning, they were only beginning to switch on the loudspeakers. At eleven, on the dot and dash of eleven, Guru-ji arrived. Now I was able to see him up close. Sometimes, when he appeared on television broadcasts, he wore Nehru suits, exquisitely tailored but simple jackets in linen and silk. I myself had had some made, similar in line and cut. But today he was wearing a white dhoti, and a sheer white cloth thrown over one strong shoulder, leaving the other one bare. His hair swept up and back. He was handsome. He was sixty-four years old, but his skin was taut and clear, his eyes were alert and alive.

'This is a sacrifice that includes each type of person,' he told us that day. 'This is not a sacrifice for rishis or munis or emperors only. Whether you are from the highest sections of society, or from the lowest, you can participate in our Sarvamedha sacrifice. We invite you all. You are the yajman. But you must give. That is the meaning of the Sarvamedha sacrifice. You must give everything. Sarvamedha is the universal sacrifice, it is the all-sacrifice. In the old days, every type of animal was sacrificed to the gods during this sacrifice, and humans from every walk of life, from every profession, gave themselves to the sacred fire, they died during the Sarvamedha and were blessed. In the old days, brahmins and tailors, dhobis and warriors, all were immolated in the fire of the Sarvamedha. In the old days, the yajman of the Sarvamedha sacrifice gave all his possessions as the fee, everything he owned. When the father of Nachiketas hesitated at *everything*,

Nachiketas himself reminded the father that his son was his last possession. Nachiketas gave himself to death, and so achieved heaven for his father, and through his confrontation with death revealed to us the secrets of death, and life. Wisdom belongs to those who can burn themselves, and so discover the true self.' There was an absolute silence in the shamianas, a breath-stilled pause as we listened. And Guru-ji laughed. 'Don't worry,' he said. 'I won't ask you to give up your sons, and I won't ask you to jump into this fire.' The fire was leaping above the heads of the priests. 'The times have changed. We will complete the Sarvamedha, and we will sacrifice animals and humans, all that lives. But we will do it symbolically. We will substitute. You will burn, but only in effigy, only through a model of you. Like this one.'

He held up his hand, palm up, revealing a small model of a man. With the motion of his hand I noticed, across the flames and across the way, a policeman. I must have seen him before, in the bandobast outside and under the tents, but he caught my eye now. He was a sardar, wearing a tall khaki turban with a green patka underneath. He had just escorted someone to the VIP enclosure, and was backing away, but he turned back now to listen to Guru-ji. For a quick moment, the length of a snapping flame, the policeman and I held each other's gaze. And then we shifted back to Guru-ji.

As the priests chanted, Guru-ji gave the little figure to the fire. So, just like that, all afternoon and through the day, little casts of cows and bulls and men and women – made out of crystallized sugar or lime – were thrown into the sacred fire. The conflagration was fragrant and enormous. I was close enough to hear it. It had a steady rhythm, this music.

That evening, I waited late in a long queue for a meeting with Guru-ji. At eleven, he left the altar and retired to the film producer's house for the night. From eleven till midnight, he met members of the public in private audience. There was a queue that stretched from the gate of the house and wound around the maidan twice. I was somewhere in the middle. At midnight the policemen came through the maidan telling us that Guru-ji had to sleep, telling us to go home. There was a great groan, but people dispersed easily, without protest. We could imagine how tired Guru-ji was, how even his massive strength must be taxed by a full day of talking to us, of taking us along on his journey.

The policemen looked relieved. They were tired themselves, and they were used to the jostling, tumbling energy of the Ganapati processions, where thousands of young men in shorts and banians danced for Ganesha, drunk on sweat and brotherhood and surreptitious swigs of beer and bhang. But we went home in good order, all of us, Guru-ji's followers.

Bunty was waiting at our room, with food and his mobile phones. We took care of business. 'Bhai, my wife thinks I have a woman,' Bunty said when we had finished with the calls. 'I keep telling her it's just a busy time right now, special night-time jobs to do, but she saw me taking some of her adrak pickle for you, and now she's convinced that I feed my woman food from her kitchen.'

He was grinning, but I had met his Priya, who was a plump Punjabi with a convent-school education and the look of a Patton tank about her. Bunty had had his women on the side, of course, but in a very discreet way. Dealing with a raging Priya because he had to take care of me was evidence of his total dedication. 'I'll have to give you a double bonus on Diwali, beta,' I said. 'Buy her bangles.'

'Triple bonus,' he said. 'She was spectacular this evening. In the middle of the Red Fort, bhai. And she didn't hold back. I had to give her one on her ear, to shut her up.'

This year, for the festival, we had spent a crore and a half to build a replica of the Red Fort, complete with a glittering Peacock Throne, on which Ganesha sat. We had used real marble for the floors, and even the carving was exact, taken from photographs. People came from all over Bombay to Gopalmath, to see our Red Fort, it was a huge hit, bigger and better than any other pandal in the city. To imagine Bunty and Priya at it in the middle of the darbar hall was hilarious. 'Your Priya must have the Mughals rolling in their graves. We should send her to Pakistan, she'll finish off all those S-Company bastards.'

Bunty had to clutch at his stomach at the thought of Priya rolling over the border. When he could speak, he said, 'Everyone in Gopalmath remembers you, bhai. The boys think you are somewhere in Europe, but they all want to thank you, at least on the phone.'

I shook my head. 'Tell them I'm thinking of them. But no outside contacts, Bunty. This is my time with Guru-ji.'

It was true: I hadn't called Jojo even once, and I knew she must've been worried. She knew that I had gone on a trip, but from all my trips, I had called her. This time I hadn't called. It couldn't be helped.

I needed to concentrate, to purify myself. And so the days passed in prayer and contemplation. Every day I went early to the maidan, to get a good seat. Every night I stayed late, lining up in the queue to get a personal darshan of Guru-ji, just like any other follower. But there were too many of us, just too many, and there was never enough time before midnight to let us all in. But I was patient, and came back the next day. Guru-ji took us through the sacrifice, and my days passed listening to him, to his explications of the Vedas and the Brahmanas. I knew I was learning new things every day, and each day I felt lighter inside my body, as if some thick sediment was being washed away. Or, as Guru-ji put it in his discourses, some part of my karma was being burnt in the heat of the sacrifice.

'You even smell better,' Bunty told me on the eleventh morning.

'You mean I smelt badly before, bastard?' But I was smiling. I could whiff the improvement myself. Maybe it was just the smoke of the burning samagri from the sacrifice that had settled into my pores, or maybe this was how an unburdened soul was supposed to smell. I hugged him, and scootered off. I hummed a movie song, a Koli song: *'Vallavh re nakhva ho, vallavh re Rama.'* At the grounds, I settled myself into what had become my accustomed seat. At this time in the mornings, when the tents were empty, with the loudspeakers and the televisions turned off, I really did feel like the yajman, as if it were all for me.

'You're even earlier today.'

It was the sardar inspector. He was standing right behind me, his thumbs inside his belt, making his shirt neat. And yes, of course it was you, Sartaj. It was you in a crisp khaki uniform and a tall pagdi, and you were smiling. But then I only knew the sardar inspector. He was amused, friendly, this inspector.

'I have to come early,' I said. 'Otherwise I have to sit all the way back.' I kept my voice very mild.

'You can watch on these televisions even if you're far away,' he said. 'In the close-ups you can see each hair in their nostrils.' He tilted his chin towards the priests. He was a good-looking sardar, this one, and very stylish with his blue patka and matching socks.

'It's not the same thing at all,' I said, and even as I said it I realized I was being too sharp, too snappy. I had to be deferential, like a normal member of the public when faced by a policeman. It had been a very long time since I had been afraid of an inspector, but I had to act it now. 'What I mean, Sardar Saab, is that nowadays people think they can have darshan over television or phone. But you only get the full benefits of darshan if you come face to face, eye to eye. Guru-ji's glance has to enter you, his voice has to come into you. I've not seen him before, and I can tell you I have been changed over the last few days. All my television-watching from far away didn't add up to one moment of real darshan. Seeing the Golden Temple in a photograph is one thing. Going to Amritsar is another blessed thing altogether.'

'You're not from Bombay?' He had the policeman's trick of sudden questions, and that calculating glance. And under all that chikna film-star prettiness, the relentless brutality born of a thousand interrogations. I knew his type.

'Not originally. But I moved here some years ago.'

'What do you do?'

'I work in an import-export company.' He had turned it into a question-answer session after all, the suspicious bastard. Typical, typical. I very slightly turned back towards the yagna. But he wasn't going to let it go yet.

'I've seen you somewhere before,' he said. 'You look familiar.'

I stayed very still, didn't even let myself tense up. I looked at him over my shoulder and smiled. 'I have a very familiar face, saab,' I said. I had kept up with the shaving of my head, and let my beard grow in. I looked something like one of those Afghan mullahs myself. In my mirror I was most unfamiliar to myself. But this maderchod had a good eye. 'People always tell me I look like someone they know. My wife used to laugh about it.'

'She used to? Not any more?'

He was very attentive, this chikna inspector, and he was not at all the thick-brained sardar of all the jokes. You had to be on full alert with him. 'She's dead,' I said, very quietly. 'She was killed in an accident.' He nodded, looked away. When he came back to me he was the maderchod inspector again, but I had marked that small blink of sympathy. I could be sharp too. In my life I had learnt to read men also. 'You also lost someone,' I said. 'Who, your wife?'

He gave me back a hard glower. He was a proud man, of course, and in uniform. He wasn't going to tell me anything. 'Everyone loses somebody,' he said. 'That's what happens in life.'

'If you come into Guru-ji's protection, all this pain passes.'

'You keep your Guru-ji,' he said, but he was friendly again, with a very small grin. He raised his hand, and marched off to the back of the tents, to his duties. Guru-ji arrived at his usual punctual hour, and today he led us towards the end of the sacrifice, its fulfilment.

'We have come together on a great journey,' he said. 'For these many days you have walked with me. By participating in this great yagna, you have burnt away the inertia of hundreds of past lives. As the yajmans of this sacrifice, you will accrue its benefits, its powers. But remember what I told you about the Sarvamedha: the yajman gives away everything. To sacrifice yourself, you must sacrifice your attachments. So, today of all days, give. Give of yourself.'

It was a hot day, the last day of the Sarvamedha. After many muzzy days, the sun now burnt off the haze and slid across the tents, and moved bright strips of flame across our legs, our heads. The fragrant smoke gathered and thickened, and the slokas swept through us, and Guru-ji's voice gathered in my chest, and the crowd was packed in today, and the sweat dripped off my shoulders, and there were many who were weeping. Yes, I was crying too. I was not sad, I was not grieving. I was happy, and I was sobbing. I gave, whatever was in my wallet, and my watch. Throughout the days of the sacrifice, the devotees had given donations, had left money and valuables with the booths scattered among the tents. But today we gave everything. I saw women giving their jewellery, their mangalsutras, and men struggle with gold and diamond rings on swollen fingers. That afternoon, we truly became yajmans, and felt the power of the Sarvamedha.

Then it was over. At ten o'clock, Guru-ji put his hands together in a pranaam to all of us, and bowed his head. And then he went back to the house. This night, I was up close to the front of the queue for darshan. I had planned and made sure, and yet after an hour of waiting it became clear that I might not make it. Today all the VIPs came, there was a home minister and two actors and three actresses, and business tycoons and television news announcers and film producers and one general. Their cars came one after another and made a shiny cluster in front of the house, and our queue hardly moved at all. For the ordinary people darshan came very slowly, and tonight I stood among the ordinary. I waited. It was very close to midnight.

'Have you seen your Guru-ji yet?' It was the sardar inspector. He was tall, taller than me by a head. The black plate on his chest told me his name in white letters: 'Sartaj Singh.'

'No,' I said. 'Today, too many big people up there.'

I shrugged. I was calm, but quite drained, my legs felt like falooda, and I was a little dizzy. This inspector looked exhausted himself. There were dark stains on his shirt from all the sweat of the day, and under the white tube-lights he wasn't that chikna, just gaunt and long and tired. He was examining me with a policiya's impersonal suspicion. Then he said, 'Come on.'

He led me past the front of the line, through the parked Toyotas and BMWs and ranks of policemen and private security. He nodded at an inspector standing by the tall double doors of the producer's house, and then we walked through the crowded drawing room, and up a marbled corridor. Sartaj Singh talked to a constable, and then we angled down another corridor crowded with sadhus and devotees, out into a garden. We went to the front of the line. There were three sadhus ranged near the entrance, letting in devotees one by one. And beyond them, in the centre of the garden, the unmistakable profile of Guru-ji, seated in his wheelchair, talking to some woman.

'Okay,' Sartaj Singh said into my ear, 'I've brought you so far. Now you take care of yourself.' He barked at the sadhus: 'He's next.'

I felt his thump on my back, but before I could even turn to thank him, he was off. I would take care of myself, yes. I gazed calmly at Guru-ji's attendants, and took a step to the right and put myself squarely before them. I was going to be next. There was one tall, yellow-haired firangi sadhu who seemed to be the boss, and I smiled pleasantly at him and stared him down until he gave me back a dubious grin. I might stand in queues for Guru-ji, but I knew how to let little flunkies know I meant business.

After all the days of waiting, there was now a pause of only two minutes. The woman with Guru-ji stood up, turned away, and I slipped by the firangi sadhu. I was with Guru-ji in a moment, finally alone with him. I knelt in front of him, touched his feet, touched my head to his feet.

'Jite raho, beta,' he said, and laid a hand on my head. 'Come, come.'

He raised me up, motioned to the chair. I sat. I knew I was smiling like a happy infant, like a cheery, light-hearted madman. I sat, hands clasped in my lap, beaming at him.

'Tell me what you want,' he said, 'what you need.'

I burst out laughing. 'I need nothing now, Guru-ji. I wanted only to be with you.'

599

He knew me instantly. We had spent hours on the phone together, and he knew my voice as well as I knew his. He was supremely controlled, and there was no flinching, not a flicker of surprise, not a blink. Just a very long moment when he looked, took me in with hard eyes that cut through me, and I looked back at him. He tilted to one side, shifted in the wheelchair to catch me in the light, and I raised my face up so that it was open to him.

'Ganesh,' he said. 'Ganesh.'

'I came, Guru-ji.' I said it, but now I was nervous. He was very opaque then, completely still, hard as thunder. I could not say that he was pleased, and I was afraid that he was angry. I had risked myself, of course, but I had also endangered him. I had put everything to the test. 'I came because I wanted to be part of your yagna.'

'And you have been here all along?'

'Every day. From start to finish.'

Then he changed. He was warm, like a sudden sun. He had not moved, and yet I felt that I was enfolded. 'You are a fool, Ganesh,' he whispered, 'but a good fool.'

'You said it was the most important yagna of your life,' I said. 'So I had to come, Guru-ji.'

He reached out and slapped me, gently, on my cheek. 'Bachcha, you came because I called you.'

'Yes.'

'This Sarvamedha was a kind of initiation for you.'

'Yes.'

'I'm pleased you came, Ganesh. But now you must get out of here, out of the country. There is too much risk.'

'Yes.'

'But before you go, I have one question for you.'

'Ask, Guru-ji. I'll answer.'

'What happened to your father?'

His words were an inferno that started from a hard point deep inside me, and the red blaze grew and exploded and came into my eyes, and I was burnt empty. There were no ashes left even, no ashes to take away from the altar, I was simply combusted and where I had been there was a hollow. No more Ganesh Gaitonde. I had hidden something so deeply, so securely and behind impregnable barriers that even I had mostly forgotten it was there. How did this man in front of me dig through my flesh and find that tiny carapaced sphere, holding within it the huge energy of an exploding bomb? In that moment, I had no mind to ask, or answer, but I knew Ganesh Gaitonde had been simply destructed. He no longer existed. I had hidden my father for ever, even from myself, and I had forgotten my mother. But now Guru-ji was asking, he knew something had happened. And my usual answer – 'My father died, my mother died' – was no longer possible. He had cracked through, and there was no closing the fissure. So I was quiet.

He drew me close to him. I was limp, I had no strength to resist. I sat on the ground, my shoulder against his knee. He put a hand over my bald head, and I felt the breadth of his palm cradling me.

'I see a yellow wall,' he said. 'I see blood, a thin stream of blood running down the wall and dripping to the bottom.'

I was crying. He knew, Guru-ji somehow knew, and I could not hide from him.

'But that is all I see, Ganesh. Tell me. What happened?'

So I told him about my father, Raghavendra Gaitonde, son of a poor temple priest in Karwar, poor Brahmin himself, married to Sumangala. I didn't want to linger on the hapless man or the deceitful woman, so I told the whole ugly story fast. Raghvendra was starving in Karwar, trying to officiate at marriages and pujas, not finding many opportunities because he was very young and mild and ineffectual. So he went when his cousin Suryakant called him to Nashik. This Suryakant Shenoy owned some farmland, did some civil construction and also dabbled in local politics. He had served as the district secretary at the local Congress office for a while. He had recently finished some school building for the government in a village called Digadh, and after the project was finished he donated substantial money for a new Lakshmi-Narayan temple there. So Raghavendra was installed as the priest in this temple, and he had a small but tidy and pucca house, also courtesy of his cousin, and the living wasn't rich but it was enough, and Sumangala was happy at last. The conditions of the villagers slowly improved, helped by an irrigation project that Suryakant Shenoy had sanctioned, and so Raghavendra and Sumangala also experienced a bit of comfort, as the donations to the temple increased. Besides, Suryakant Shenoy came often to visit, always bringing a bag full of vegetables, ghee, butter, a good half potli of rice besides. He had lots of work in the villages in the area, and was glad to see his cousins, and there was no need for formality, it was his duty to help. Under his benign protection life went on, and a year and a half later, a son was born in the house. Of course there were celebrations and rituals, and Suryakant was a part of all this. The boy was named Kiran, on Suryakant's suggestion. Kiran grew up bright and energetic. He walked when he was eight months and one week old, he was speaking by the time he was two, and at four he was reading, not just tracing the letters over his father's shoulders, but managing to make out whole words. But it was also in this year the boy lost some of his natural cheer, he became inward and watchful. He was old enough now to see how the outside world saw his father. In the children who were his friends, and in their parents, he recognized a jokey contempt for the pandit, a dismissal of him as a negligible force, not quite a fool but hapless, a subject of pity, not sympathy. Kiran had no words for any of this, but he knew it as surely as he knew that his mother was regarded as beautiful. It was in this year that the Kumbh came around to Nashik again, after its absence of twelve years. Kiran went, of course, with his mother and Suryakant Kaka and neighbours, to take a dip in the waters of the sacred river, to be dazed and astonished by the unimaginable number of pilgrims, to marvel at the musk glands being sold by the gypsy women. Suryakant Kaka bought ice-cream for Kiran, and this unprecedented treat filled Kiran with a plump joy, and he hung off Suryakant Kaka's broad wrist. Finally they made their way to Ramkund, where Shree Ram was said to have taken his daily bath, and here, through a moving thicket of elbows and hips, Kiran saw his father. Raghavendra was standing on the slippery wet stone that led down to the water, holding a thali piled with white kumkum in one hand, and a small metal stamp in the other. He was offering to put tilaks on the pilgrims, like the one he had on his own forehead. A pilgrim stopped, and Raghavendra put the naamam on him, and as his father reached up, Kiran saw how thin he was, how the skin on his arm was loose, how his stoop signalled a deference, a humility that filled Kiran with anger. The pilgrim dropped coins into Raghavendra's hand, and for the first time ever, Kiran's throat filled with the bitterness of contempt, of disdain for his father. This man was a weak man, he was an incapable man. Now Kiran knew why the neighbours laughed at his father, why they called out 'Ay pandita' as they did, and the knowledge nauseated him. He refused to go down any further towards the river, despite anything anyone said, and after that it was known in the family that Kiran was afraid of water. This story stayed, and Kiran's contempt remained, until one afternoon when Kiran came home from the first day of class two, and found a crowd around his house. Something had happened. Hands grabbed at him, but he pulled himself loose and kicked and bit his way through to the door. Inside, there were the elders of the locality, frightened and yet titillated. One of them was pointing up. Then Kiran saw what at: a stream of blood running down the wall, a puddle at the bottom. He screamed, raced up the stairs, punched at the knees of a man who was blocking the door and burst out on to the roof. What was dead on the roof was not Kiran's father, but Suryakant Kaka. He was lying face down on a charpai, naked to the waist. Kiran knew the breadth of the back, the bulk of the shoulders. But the back of Suryakant Kaka's head was a pulpy mix of black and red and some other colour, creamy with shards of white. Another unsteady step, and Kiran saw that Suryakant Kaka was all intact in front, he was staring down at the ground below with a concentrated wonderment, as if the pitted brick contained whole universes of meaning. Suryakant Kaka had told Kiran about the names of stars, and the shapes of constellations. Now he was half-destroyed.

A neighbour took Kiran by the shoulders, tried to lead him away. Who was this man? Kiran knew his smell, this yellowed shirt, these long hands, but he couldn't remember his name. 'Who did it?' Kiran said, although – somehow – he already knew. The man shook his head, tried to lead him away. Kiran screamed, jerked free and asked again, 'Who? Who? Who?' A gravelly voice said, 'Tell him,' and still there was a moment's silence. Then the man holding Kiran said, 'Your father. He is gone.' And then, as an afterthought, 'Your Aai is below. With the women.'

The police came, and the women left, and the men left, and the body was taken away, and Kiran was alone with his mother, who sat huddled against the side of a wooden cupboard in the bedroom, her hair matted about her face.

'So,' Gaitonde told Guru-ji, 'my father killed that Suryakant, and he left. Nobody ever saw him again. I don't know where he is.'

'And your mother?'

'I stayed till I was twelve. Then I ran away. I came to Bombay.'

'You don't know where she is?'

'No.'

They had been shunned by the village. Shunned, that is, except by the men, who came around and assured Sumangala that she need not fear, that they were there to look after her, that she would have a comfortable life. These men brought – as that other man had – vegetables and saris and money. She could not go home to her maike because her parents wouldn't have her. So she stayed in that same house, with its new coat of whitewash which was donated by one of her new clients. That's what they were, clients. And now Kiran felt the full force of the village's contempt. They called him harami to his face, and the older boys made lewd jokes about his mother, about her body, about her practices and proclivities. There was no day when his body was not marked with bruises, some old, some fresh. He was always beaten in every fight, but after he picked up a large rock and sent it skimming past a tormenter's head, the gang saw that he meant to kill one of them, and after that they shouted their insults at him from a little further away. He began to carry a knife, and they called him mad. He waited, and one day when he could overcome his fear of the huge unknown spaces, when the heft of the knife under his shirt made him strong enough, he walked to the railway station eight kos away, and waited for a train. He already knew the name of the train, and where it went, and its timings. It came, and he squeezed himself into a crowded carriage. Nobody paid any attention to him. There was nowhere to sit, and he leaned against the side of a stack of big metal trunks in the corridor and waited. The edges of the trunks bit into his ribs and legs, but this was a good pain. He was going away. At every station, he asked, 'Is this Mumbai?' When a man said, 'Yes,' he hopped off. But the man had fooled him. He wanted to stab the man, but the train was already away. Kiran waited for another train. He arrived in the city at last, and waited until the buildings grew big and crowded against each other, and the roads were filled with cars. He did not ask anyone again. When he was sure, he got off.

'And you were home,' Guru-ji said softly. 'When did you become Ganesh?'

'The first time someone asked my name. I don't know why. I just said it.'

'Ganesh is the survivor. He always lives, no matter what. He overcomes.'

Then I sat for a long time, in silence, with Guru-ji's hand on my head. I was exhausted, as if I had climbed a mountain and come down the other side, but I felt calm. And with every pulse that beat through me, I grew stronger.

'Ganesh, beta,' Guru-ji said, 'you should go now. Otherwise my attendants will wonder.'

'Yes, Guru-ji.'

'You took a risk, but I am happy you came. Meet me in Singapore, as we planned.'

'Yes, Guru-ji.'

He hugged me close, held my bald head to his cheek. Then he sent me away. I touched his feet again, and left. But I left only his body, his crippled flesh. He had looked at me, into me. He had given me darshan, and he had had his darshan of me. He was in me now. He beat inside my heart. I took his great strength with me, and felt it throb through my arms, as real as my own blood. I whisked through the city, flew down the familiar avenues and through the packets of late traffic with an effortless ease. I could predict how the cars and auto-rickshaws would come close to each other, where they would part, I could see the geometry of their travel. I knew where they were going, the future of the streaking headlights. And I inserted myself into the gleaming stream, and I was fearless, my body knew the flow of this river. The waters came through me.

I got home, ate with Bunty and told him to book me on the first flight to Singapore. And then I had another short journey to make. I got back on the scooter, waved away Bunty's housewifely grumbling and sped away. Again, I found smooth roads and green lights, and was at Yari Road in twenty-five minutes. I had to ask two taxi drivers for directions once I got there, but once I turned the last corner, with the cigarette shop on the corner, I knew my way. I had had Jojo describe it for me a dozen times, so I could imagine her streets, her home. I took the curve to the left, and parked by her gate. Her blue Honda was parked in the second parking spot to the right, number 36A. I counted my way up the storeys, one two three, and found the corner apartment. Her lights were on. I dialled.

'Ganesh?' she said. 'Ganesh?'

'Who else would it be on this phone?'

'Don't act smart. Where have you been?'

'I had to travel.'

'Travel means you can't call? What is wrong with you?'

'Everything is right, Jojo. Why are you so angry?'

'Because you are a careless idiot.'

605

I had to laugh. Nobody else in the world spoke to me like this. 'I think you like me, Jojo.'

'Very little. And even that, I don't understand why. I must be mad.'

A shadow crossed the second window. I could imagine her, stamping about and jabbing with her free hand at the idiot far away. 'If you like me a little, Jojo, I have a suggestion.'

'What?'

'Let's meet.'

'Gaitonde, I thought we had been through that.'

'This is different.'

'Why?'

'Because I'm different now.'

'How?'

'You just have to meet me and see. Otherwise you'll never know.'

She thought about it. The shadow crossed the window again. She said, 'Gaitonde, I'm still the same.'

'So you don't want to meet?'

'I don't want to meet.'

'Last chance.'

'Don't argue with me, Gaitonde. I'm too tired.'

I didn't argue with her. I talked to her for ten more minutes, about her work, her new thoku, her girls. It was good to speak to her, to fall back into our banter and our friendship.

'You sound happy,' she said.

'I am,' I said. 'I am.' I raised my hand at her building watchmen, two of them, who finally, after all this time, had noticed I was there, and had roused themselves to come to the gate from their comfortable chairs. 'I have to go, Jojo,' I said. I hung up.

'What, hero?' one of the watchmen said through the gate. 'You're blocking our gate.'

I wasn't blocking anything, and they were being bothersome, but I was feeling kindly. 'I'm going,' I said quietly. I turned the key in the ignition, and switched on my headlight. She came to her window then, Jojo did. She must have seen the single weak shaft of yellow in the dark. I saw her, the touch of light on her head and shoulders. But I'm sure she didn't see me.

I was in Singapore when we hit the mullah in London. 'Maulana Mehmood Ghouse Assassinated in London,' the *Straits Times*

606

announced at the bottom of the front page. The BBC World Report devoted a full segment to the killing, and then had a panel discussion with two reporters and one professor. They discussed the implications of the killing, and listed the possible assassins: rival militant organizations in Pakistan, revolutionary Afghan groups, various intelligence agencies, the Israelis, the Indians, the Americans. The consensus was that it was probably the Israelis.

The date for the mullah's visit to London had been moved up, and Mr Kumar had moved up the date of the operation, to the mullah's first day in London. 'If you can, get him before he opens his mouth to the media,' he had said. And we had. Despite all the hurrying up, we did it clean. It was difficult. He had two layers of security, his own men and the British police. We had been told not to use a big bomb, there was to be no massacre of civilians in a friendly capital. So we did it with a small bomb. His hotel room had been swept, and the car he used also. All very tight. Mr Kumar knew far in advance the name of the small and exclusive hotel he would stay in, and also that in this hotel there were only two suites on the top floor. The detailed brief that Mr Kumar had sent us emphasized the fact that the mullah had once been an electrical engineer, that he travelled with a laptop that he used for reading the newspapers around the world and – probably – exchanging encrypted e-mails with his people. Mr Kumar's file told us that he liked to do this in bed, at night, while munching on pistachios. So we had rigged the outlets on both sides of the bed, in both suites. The security teams checked for bugs and bombs, but the outlets passed. On his first night in the hotel, the mullah plugged in his laptop, and fried his power supply and the machine itself. He cursed, ranted and had his people call reception. The woman at reception apologized, and offered to open the business centre downstairs so he could use the broadband connection there. The mullah cursed some more, picked up his bowl of pistachios and went off to the business centre. His security people went over the room, but he was fuming and angry and talking to them from just outside the door. The computer inside was already up and running, and the mullah wanted the broadband very badly. He was impatient. In he went, and sat at the machine. For ten minutes he skimmed from newspaper to newspaper, and littered the floor with pistachio shells. Then a certain man, a white European who was sitting in the lobby, made a call on his handy. And then another man, an Indian man sitting in a parked car outside the hotel, pressed at something in his pocket. And the keyboard under the mullah's hands exploded, and blew off both arms at the elbow. And sent little plastic keys marked with English letters dashing into his brain.

It was sleek and brilliant, our operation. Even Mr Kumar said so. 'Nobody will ever believe this is an Indian operation,' he said.

'What, they think that my boys aren't smart enough to pull something like this off? We're too dehati to do anything involving computers?'

'Not just you, Ganesh,' Mr Kumar said. 'The entire world, including our very own, very free Indian press, will refuse to believe this is ours.'

'Saab, I can provide positive proof . . .'

'Let it be, Ganesh. Let them think it was the mighty Israelis. Let them underestimate us. A confused enemy is always better than an impressed but careful enemy. Let it be. I told you, we are the invisible soldiers, we win no medals.'

So we let it be, we let it go. It was frustrating not to take credit for a great victory, but I saw Mr Kumar's point. He had spent a lifetime not taking credit, but I can tell you it was hard for us. I gave a triple bonus to everyone involved in the operation, and sent them off to holiday in Bali. And of course I restrained myself from talking about the operation to Guru-ji, who was fascinated by the particulars of the event. 'These Israelis really observe the psychology of the target,' he said. Sometimes I was glad his clairvoyance was not total. But Guru-ji did see images of a group of violent men looking for him, hunting him, so he tightened his own security. I advised him on what he needed. After all, in Bombay, I had been able to get physically close to him without once being searched.

I didn't even begin to understand the psychology of Guru-ji, but here's what I knew about him: he was born near Sialkot, on 14 February 1934, at nine forty-two in the evening. He grew up all over western Punjab, transferring from one air-force base to another with his aircraft-technician father. They were thrown eastwards by Partition, but they made their journey safely, under the protection of the services, and settled first in Jodhpur, and then in Pathankot. Guru-ji soon became a famed sportsman, the captain of every cricket team he played for from the eighth class upwards. There were hopes, expectations, that he would play for the country. In Pathankot, on the day before his eighteenth birthday, he had borrowed his father's motor-cycle to go to the cinema, to meet his friends. He spun off the road near the main entrance of the army cantonment, near the captured Pakistani tank with the drooping cannon. It was a bright sunny day, there was no water or oil on the road. Nobody ever knew why it happened. The military police picked him up and took him to the nearby military hospital, and they gave him immediate attention. But there was an injury to his lumbar vertebra, and he lost function in the lower part of his body. 'I woke up on my first day as a man,' he told me in Singapore, 'to find that I was only half a man. But then, Ganesh, there was the other thing.'

The other thing was his visions. Before the accident he had been a normal Punjabi boy, interested in cricket, fast motorcycles, good food, his yaars, his exams. He had a kind of general belief in fearless Hanuman, and he went to the temple with his mother, and gossiped at weddings while the priests chanted. That was the extent of his spirituality. But after his accident, he was visited by visions. He saw the past and the future. These were not dreamlike images, confused and fuzzy. He saw details, he could see the colour of a man's tongue, the embroidery on a woman's handkerchief. He could smell cooking oil, hear the splash of water on brick. Two days after recovering consciousness, he told a nurse, 'That man – Fred, Phillip? – who gave you a gold necklace is still thinking of you.' Hospital staff are used to dealing with raving patients. But this nurse had been in love with a much older cousin by marriage, and they had never told anyone, and she had certainly not told this injured boy. From that moment his reputation grew and unfurled across the city and beyond. And from that moment he began his great journey inward, his attempt to understand the nature of the self, of time and the universe. 'I had to try to understand what was happening to me, Ganesh,' he said. Right from that hospital bed he began his meditations and his reading, his meetings with philosophers and sadhus and tantrics and pandits. It had been a long, ceaseless search. 'In my injury I found myself,' he said. 'From the outside I was brought to the inside.'

Which didn't mean that he wasn't interested in the outside. He had a passion for science, for the new knowledge of today. He read every scientific magazine he could find, and thick books about what walked on earth before humans ever existed, and what would fly in the spaces of the future. He keenly followed all the latest inventions and innovations in computers, and talked to me about medicine, and lasers, and cloning. He had a wheelchair that could climb stairs by itself, and turn corners on two wheels, and balance on one. His eyes burned when he talked about gyroscopes and software and non-polluting power generation. He sat on the board of three universities. He was a secular man. He didn't have that unreasoning hatred for Muslims that I had encountered so often in India and abroad, that disgust for burkhas and beef-eating and dirty personal habits. Guru-ji welcomed them at his sermons, was glad to have them in his following. What he didn't like was a certain Muslim tendency to expand, to grasp, to want to rule always. He pointed out that they were the cause of societal trouble in whatever country they lived in, and said that they grated against the grain of time. He told me this only in private, of course. In his public speeches, he was circumspect. But when we were alone, he told me, 'After the fall of the masjid, and after the riots, Ganesh, they have been importing weapons.' This was true. I had confirmed it from my own sources. Huge shipments of automatic rifles had come in, and grenades. There were even stories about anti-tank weapons, and Stinger missiles. If they only lived as co-operative members of our culture, Guru-ji said, if they only knew their place, and tried to blend in, then there would be no problem. But there is a tendency in their religion that makes them dangerous. 'So,' said Guru-ji, 'we too must be prepared. We must arm ourselves too, despite the cowardice of our politicians.' So we prepared. We armed, and he continued to fund this secret work, and also his effort to inform and prepare the world for the coming cataclysm, the end of Kaliyug.

We were sitting on a rooftop in Singapore when he told me about his work with his universities, about his educational hopes for the future. This was Singapore, so I kept having to restrain my urge to spit past the railing, on to the street and the orderly Singaporeans below. But Guru-ji loved the place. He liked the hygiene and the rules and the strictness and the Singaporeans, and used the city as a hub between his travels. He had another rich devotee here, a property magnate, and Guru-ji had the use of a large penthouse apartment on Tanglin Road. The penthouse had a sizeable balcony, with full-sized trees and a thick carpet of turf. From this balcony we looked out at the sparkling skyline. Guru-ji enjoyed this high garden. 'If only our country was managed well, Ganesh,' he told me, 'we could have all this. What don't we have? We have the resources. And we have more than enough talent.

But we don't have political will, and we don't have the right structure. We don't have discipline, external or internal.'

'You will bring us to Ram-rajya, Guru-ji.'

'Are you flattering me, Ganesh?'

He was crunching on carrot sticks and crinkling his eyes at me. 'Of course I am not, Guru-ji.' I was sprawled on an armchair next to him, my bare feet up. I had used a different passport and name to leave India, from Delhi, and I had shaved off my beard. I came every evening to Guru-ji, as a business consultant, and we had dinner in the garden. We talked of everything – the world, my life. I told him about the early days in Gopalmath, the death of my son. He knew me as well as anybody ever had, better than anyone.

'Are you getting impatient?' he said.

'Impatient, me?'

'It has been five days. You want to get through the initiation, go home to work.'

'No, Guru-ji, not like that. My work is always going on, and it's all over the phone anyway. And my time here with you is a peace that I have never had. But I am concerned.'

'About what?'

'Security. The longer I stay, the more risky it is. For me, for you. If someone recognizes me . . .'

'Yes.'

'And people are always looking for me.'

'Your enemies.'

'I don't want to expose you to danger, Guru-ji.'

'I understand. And I agree. But this is necessary.' He ate another carrot stick. 'Do you have any idea what the initiation is, Ganesh? What we will do?'

'Some sort of puja. Some secret mantra. Some rite.'

He was grinning at me again. 'Some ritual involving human sacrifice? A baby killed at the altar of some unspeakable goddess?'

'If that is necessary . . .'

He threw up his hands. 'Arre chup, Ganesh. No, it's nothing like that. Ritual is very powerful, but you have already been through a ritual with me. You came with me through the sacrifice. No, ritual is not what you need right now. No. You want to know what your initiation is? Here it is: these past five days were your initiation.'

'Guru-ji?'

'You sat here and told me about yourself. You gave me every part of yourself. You told me things you had never confessed before.'

It was true. I had told him about my fear of bullets, my longing for women, the gold I had started my career with and how I had got it. I had told him everything, except that I worked for Mr Kumar. That was another me, and I could not give that self to Guru-ji.

I left Singapore the next day. On my way to the airport, I met Guru-ji one last time, just for five minutes. He was preparing to travel also, to South Africa this time. We met in the kitchen of a convention centre where he was giving a lecture to a Hindu historical studies group. I touched his feet. 'I feel light, Guru-ji,' I said. 'I feel like some curtain has been drawn. Like a window has been opened.'

He was proud of me, he had that gladness about him. He was full of joy, just looking at me. 'I know,' he said. 'You are truly a vira. The journey inside is what takes most courage. And you have been fearless. Now you are ready to move on.'

He had a plan, I could tell. I knew him better now, too. That is what comes from darshan. We had looked into each other. 'Move on to what, Guru-ji? Where am I going now?'

'That girl.'

'Which girl?'

'Forgotten already? That girl you spoke to me about, you had sent me her details.'

'Ah, the big girl.'

'The Muslim virgin, yes. Send for her, Ganesh.'

'Our stars match up, Guru-ji?'

'You've slanted the stars, Ganesh. You are a brave man. Get the girl. Now we are going to move this world. Get that girl. And from now on, you must have only virgins.'

'Virgins?'

'You are a vira, and virgins will give you the greatest power. You will know they have been pure, and that will feed your strength. And you will need power in these coming times.'

Then he had to go back to his historians. So we said goodbye to each other, embraced closely under that smell of cooking food and flowers. I went home, to my castle floating on the waters. And I sent for the big virgin.

Investigating Love

K.R. Jayanth the pocket-maar called Sartaj late on a Saturday night. 'I have the red T-shirt chokra,' he said. He didn't actually have the boy with him, but he had his whole name, the names of the boys he worked with and the location of the stoop on which they slept. Jayanth explained at great length how he had kept a vigilant lookout for a red T-shirt, how he had been ceaselessly alert, how he had stayed beyond his usual working hours at the cinema. Then, on this Saturday night, after the late-show rush, he had noticed Red T-shirt skipping about near the car park, begging from the late arrivals. Jayanth had been canny, he had kept his distance. When the lane and the car park had quietened down altogether, he had motioned Red T-shirt over. The boy had been suspicious, but he had come, flanked by his two yaars. Jayanth contrived to be in the right position, at the right angle, and as soon as Red T-Shirt talked, Jayanth saw the black tooth. He had the right chokra. They were a tough little crew, barefoot and hardened and wary. But he had charmed them, mostly by giving them money. He had told them that he had a friend who was looking for some likely boys to do some work for him. 'What kind of work?' said Red T-shirt, stabbing his middle finger through a circle he made with his other hand. Jayanth had reassured them that there was no chodoing to be endured, that the friend in question was in fact a dealer in various interesting goods, and he needed some sharp lads to fetch and carry and messenger. And he had given them a hundred rupees, and he had told them that more cash would be forthcoming, fat reams of it.

'You told them I was a bhai?' Sartaj said.

'No, no,' Jayanth said. 'Just an import-export kind of man, you know. Otherwise I could never have got anything out of them. As you can see, it worked very well. We have the little bastards. I'll bring them to you tomorrow.'

Informants liked to be praised even more than witnesses, so Sartaj praised Jayanth. Some of them fancied that their informing made them part of a crime-fighting team, that it was them and Sartaj against the other criminal bastards. Sartaj had heard it all a thousand and one times, and it never ceased to give him a little thrill of amazement, how even the lowest of thieves could fancy himself a detective, how easy it was to gild one's own misdeeds in the cheap gold of morality. We all stink, he thought, but not one of us likes to smell our own stench. And he said, 'Yes, we have the little bastards. Well done.'

Sartaj wrote down the names of the chokras, and set a rendezvous with Jayanth for the next afternoon. He hung up, feeling the small stir of excitement at a case moving, at finding a very precarious purchase on the steep cliff of the unknowable. But then, instantly, the worry about bombs and gurus and annihilation descended on him like a monsoon fever. He felt foolish for being pleased with Jayanth, for working on his other cases. What use was it to be concerned with the everyday matters of blackmail, thievery, murder, when this enormous fear billowed overhead? It was an abstracted danger, this grim notion of a sweeping fire, it was unreal. But with its cold drip of images, it crowded out the mundane. Sartaj blinked. He was at his desk, in his dingy little office with the weathered benches and untidy shelves. Kamble was hunched over a report. Two constables were laughing in the corridor outside. There was a little pool of sunlight from a window, and a pair of hopping little sparrows on the sill. And all of it was dreamlike, as gauzy as the wafting of early morning. If you let yourself believe in that other monstrous thing, even a little, then this ordinary world of bribes and divorces and electricity bills vanished a little. It got eaten up.

Stay with the details. Sartaj rubbed his eyes, shook his head. Stay with the details. The specifics are real. It was important, somehow, to care about Mrs Kamala Pandey and her sordid adultery and the chokra in the red T-shirt. Sartaj felt a loyalty to the ordinary, a sudden affection for Mrs Pandey and her glossiness and her made-up face and her greed for glamour. But the question kept coming back: who was Gaitonde's guru? Sartaj had no idea. There were gurus at every corner, and in every locality. There were Mohameddan gurus, and Vedic gurus, and gurus who had been born in Hawaii to Japanese parents, and gurus who denied the existence of God. There were gurus who sold herbal powders, and others who cured cancer by having the patients swallow magic goldfish. Gaitonde could have been devoted to any of these. Maybe he had a guru who was not a guru to others, maybe he was a chela to a private guru. Sartaj had known a pharmaceuticals executive in Chembur who lived only on fruit, who accepted no disciples other than his sons and daughters and close friends, who took no gifts, who was said to glow with a golden sheen on Guru Purnima. Gaitonde's secret guru could be an unknown guru. People found spiritual connections in odd and unexpected places, they found succour and consolation in farmers and postal clerks. There were police constables who told fortunes and practised left-handed tantra. Where to look for Gaitonde's guru? Sartaj had no idea.

'Do you have a guru?' Sartaj asked Kamble on Sunday afternoon when they met near Apsara. They were waiting at a restaurant down the road from the cinema, sipping at Cokes. Kamble had turned out in his Sunday best, a grey bandhgalla suit with an edge of silver to the cloth. He was going to a wedding later.

'Of course I have a guru,' Kamble said, taking off his jacket. Underneath, there was a silvery shirt with a stiff Nehru collar. 'He lives in Amravati. I go once a year to take his darshan. Here.' He leant forward, and pulled at one of the two gold chains he wore around his neck. In a hexagonal pendant he had a small picture of his guru, a round-faced man with a bushy beard. 'His name is Sandilya Baba. He's a devotee of Ambadevi. She has given many darshans to him.'

Sartaj had to work hard to flatten the irony out of his voice. 'She comes and talks to him?'

'Yes, she talks to him. He is the most content man I have ever known. Happy all the time.' Kamble tucked the pendant back under his shirt. 'You sardars have gurus, or not? Apart from the original ones?'

'Yes, we have babas of various sorts. Some people follow them.'

'Not you?'

'No, not me.'

'You don't have a guru. Why not?'

It was a perfectly reasonable question, and Sartaj had no answer. He tapped his watch. 'It's almost time,' he said. 'Better get ready.'

Kamble edged himself out of the booth, and picked up his bottle. 'You should find a guru,' he said. 'No man can get through life without a guide.'

He walked away from Sartaj, sat at a table near the door and busied himself with a newspaper. He was now supposed to be a stranger to Sartaj, to work as a hidden tactical reserve in case the boys ran. He would have been more useful as a fielder if his suit and shirt hadn't been quite so spectacularly showy, but then that wasn't Kamble's style. Sartaj wiped the pitted formica of the table with a tissue, and wondered what Sandilya Baba thought about shiny suits, and money taken in bribes, and encounters. Maybe it was just his job to get misdemeanours fixed in the larger justice system of the sky, maybe he wasn't so personally strict about rules bent here and there. He was a guide for Kaliyug, this Sandilya Baba.

The owner of the restaurant was standing on a chair, fiddling with the knobs on the radio tucked away into the little shelf above a cupboard. He got the reception right, at last, and a song dropped into the small whirring clatter of the ceiling fans, '*Gata rahe mera dil, tuhi meri manzil*'. Sartaj finished his Coke, and asked for another. So Kamble had faith in Ambadevi, through the agency of Sandilya Baba. It must be good to have faith, Sartaj thought. He had never had it himself. Even as a child, when he had stood next to Papa-ji in the gurudwara, and shut his eyes and prayed as instructed, he had to make an effort to conjure up a proper feeling of devotion. Papa-ji had known Vaheguru as a living force, present in every day of his life, he prayed to Vaheguru every morning, and whispered his name when his toe swelled with gout. But for Sartaj, Vaheguru had always been a distant, fuzzy concept, an idea that he would have liked to believe in. When he reached for Vaheguru, what he found was an aching loss. Still, he went to the gurudwara with Ma, he kept his hair long, he wore a kara and carried a little miniature kirpan in his pocket. He did this for the comfort the tradition brought him, for the affection he bore for his parents, for his pride in being a Sikh. But he carried this secret loss, this absence of Vaheguru inside himself. Yes, it would be nice to have a guru, an intermediary who had personal conversations with the Almighty. But Papa-ji had disapproved of all new-fangled babas, all these charlatans: the khalsa has the Guru Granth Sahib, he said, and that book is the only guru a Sikh needs. He was very strict about it.

Three boys came into the dhaba, followed by Jayanth. They came past Kamble, and Sartaj nodded at Jayanth. 'Sit,' he said.

The chokras sat on one side of the booth, elbow to elbow. The very smallest one sat last, on the right, and reached for a spoon and began to turn it over and over. Jayanth edged in next to Sartaj and did the introductions, from left to right. 'This is Ramu, Tej, Jatin. This is Singh Saab, who I told you about.'

'What's the work?' This was Ramu, who was oldest and clearly the ringleader. He was wearing a black T-shirt with silver stars on it, not the red one that Jayanth had seen him in. He was as skinny as the other two, with the same layering of grime and the same dust-stiffened hair, but he had style and unblinking black eyes and he wasn't scared. He was just wary. Sartaj would have picked him to get a package, too.

'Want a Coca-Cola?' Sartaj said. 'Something to eat?' Ramu shook his head. The other two kept still, following his lead, but Sartaj felt their hunger like a shimmer of heat coming across the tabletop. He raised his hand. 'Eh,' he called. 'Four Cokes, three chicken biryanis. Fast.'

Ramu didn't like this delay in talking business, but he wasn't ready to bolt yet. He kept quiet, and the other two once more followed his lead. They were all twelve, thirteen maybe, roughened up and full of precocious wisdom. Tej had a scar that ran up his neck, into the hair. They all three dug into the huge mounds of rice and chicken as soon as the plates were put on the table. Jatin, the little one, ate as fast as the others, but was now fascinated by his glass of water. He turned it in quick circles between bites, and never looked up. Over their bobbing heads, Kamble tapped at his watch. He had a wedding to get to.

'Who is that?' Ramu said, twisting around. He had caught Sartaj's glance. As he turned back, Sartaj saw the blackened tooth. Kamala Pandey had done well to spot the cosmetic defect in the seconds she had had Ramu near her. Yes, that one was a slim churi, sliding through an affair under her husband's nose. But here was Ramu, holding a chicken leg, and looking very nervous.

'He's a friend of mine,' Sartaj said.

'Why isn't he sitting here?'

'He likes to sit there. Listen to me, Ramu. You know who I am?'

Ramu put down his chicken.

'Saab asked you a question,' Jayanth said. He had emptied his Coke, and was now patting the corners of his mouth with a clean white handkerchief. 'Do you know who Saab is?'

Ramu and Tej were reading Sartaj now, eyes wide, food forgotten. Then Ramu looked over his shoulder. Kamble was now sitting on the seat behind him, his arm along the back of the booth.

'Bhenchod,' Ramu said to Jayanth, with a hard-edged bitterness. 'You gaandu old man, you brought us to the police. Bhenchod, I'll see you some time. I'll take care of you.'

'Eat your food,' Sartaj said. 'Nothing's going to happen to you.'

Ramu wanted to run, but Kamble had his hand on his shoulder, gently rubbing. 'Listen to Saab,' Kamble said. 'Eat.'

Tej and Jatin were waiting for instructions from their leader. Ramu took his elbows off the table, and sat back, his jaw set. He was very stubborn. Sartaj liked him.

'All right,' Sartaj said. 'Let's make a deal.' He put a fifty-rupee note on the table, smoothed it out. 'This is yours just for listening to me. I am not interested in bothering you, I am not going to take you to the remand home. I just want some information from you. I am not going to force you or anything. I'll give you this now, you just listen to me. Yes?'

Sartaj slid the money across the table, left it near the far edge. Ramu gave him another half-minute of steely hostility, then picked up the note. He examined it, held it up to the light, turned it over. Kamble was grinning over his head. Ramu put the money in his pocket. 'Talk,' he said.

Sartaj nudged the edge of Ramu's plate. 'Just relax, don't take tension. I have no reason to pick on you. Come on. Your chicken will get cold.' Ramu nodded, and the other two boys set to. But Ramu was concentrating on Sartaj, and he wasn't interested in chicken. 'What I want is this,' Sartaj said. 'About a month, five weeks ago, you did a little job outside Apsara. You went to a car, and picked up a package from a woman in a car. You delivered the package. You remember this?'

Ramu shook his head curtly. 'I don't remember anything like that.'

'Are you sure?'

'Of course I'm sure. Even if I had done something like that, I do ten jobs a day. How can I remember something from long ago?'

Tej and Jatin had their heads bent over their plates, but Sartaj was sure he had seen a very small stiffening in Tej's shoulders, a barely discernible break in the steady rhythm of his chewing.

'Think hard,' Sartaj said. 'You were wearing a red T-shirt. It was in the evening.' Ramu was very good, with his impenetrable glare, but Sartaj was sure that Tej had been along that evening too. He was twitchy now, working hard to keep up the eating.

'No,' Ramu said.

'Why don't we just take them out behind the dhaba?' Kamble said. 'And give them a lathi up their gaand? They'll remember then.'

Sartaj slid a photograph out of his pocket and put it on the table, between Ramu and Tej. 'This was the woman you took the package from,' he said. 'Remember now?'

'I told you,' said Ramu with exaggerated patience. 'I didn't do anything like that.' He was getting into the part now. He raised his hands, let them drop.

But Tej had stopped eating, and was staring at the studio glamour shot of Mrs Kamala Pandey.

'Maybe you don't remember,' Sartaj said. 'But Tej knows her all right.'

Tej tried his best now, his chin sticky with rice and grease. 'No, no, I don't know her,' he said.

Sartaj put a fifty-rupee note next to his plate. 'Yes, you do. I saw you look. She's like a film star, isn't she?'

'Be quiet,' Ramu said to Tej, who had a dreamy fix on the money as he gathered up another large chunk of rice in his fingers.

'Ramu,' Sartaj said. 'Why do you want to fight with me? Are the men who hired you to get the package your friends? You think you have to protect them? Or are you scared of them? You think if you tell me, you'll get into trouble?'

'I'm not afraid of anyone.'

Ramu had his head down, and his shoulders up, and his voice low. Sartaj recognized the anger: it was Amitabh Bachchan in *Deewar*, or Shah Rukh in any of his films. 'I don't mean to insult you, boss,' Sartaj said. 'You have information I need. You name your price.'

Ramu leaned back, rubbed at his nose with the back of his hand. He was very thoughtful. Sartaj thought he had a price in mind already, but he was being the businessman for the benefit of his followers. He announced it finally. 'Five hundred rupees.'

'Too much,' Sartaj said. 'I'll give you two hundred.'

Ramu came forward now, his eyes sharp. He put his elbows on the table. 'Three-fifty.'

'Let's settle at three hundred,' Sartaj said. 'Not yours and not mine.'

'Fine. Let's see the cash.'

Sartaj suppressed a smile, and put the money on the table. 'Let's see the information,' he said. 'So who were they?'

Ramu took the currency notes, riffled professionally through them, put them away. 'I don't know who they were. They just found us near the cinema.'

'How many of them?'

'Two.'

'Old, young, what?'

'Old.'

'How old? Like Uncle here? Or like me?'

Ramu stabbed a contemptuous thumb towards Kamble. 'No, old like him here.'

Kamble knuckled the top of Ramu's head, crisply enough to make him wince. Tej and Jatin grinned. 'Careful, chutiya,' Kamble said. 'I'm not as nice as Saab over there. So, these two men, you got names?'

'No. They didn't give names.'

'So how did it work?' Sartaj said.

'They came up to us just before the evening show. They said they would pay us to get a package.'

'Then?'

'We walked with them.'

'Down the road?'

'Yes, a little bit. They showed us the car. They stayed on one side of the road. I went across. I knocked on the window. The woman rolled down the window. She gave me the package.'

'Did you say anything?'

'Yes, I said, "Give me the package." They had been speaking to her on her mobile. She was expecting me.'

'So you brought the package back?'

'Yes. And gave it to them. One of them made a call on his mobile. They walked away, they went. Bas, that was it.'

'You ever saw those two again?'

'No.'

'What did they look like?'

'Nothing special. Just ordinary.'

'Ramu, your information is not worth the money. Come on. Try again.'

'There's nothing to tell you. They were wearing shirts and pants. Bas, what else to tell you?'

'Something useful, Ramu. Something useful. How tall?'

'Not like you. Like him,' Ramu said, jabbing a thumb towards Jayanth.

That was all Ramu had. 'Tej, did you notice anything?' Sartaj said.

Tej shrugged. 'No, they were like he said.'

'Tell me anyway. What did you see?'

But prompting Tej elicited nothing but the same vague impression of two average men wearing average clothes.

Jatin, the little one, hadn't said a word so far. He didn't look up now, and kept turning his glass.

'Jatin, you also tell me. What were these men like?'

'They were both wearing black jeans,' Jatin said. Kamble blinked, and leaned over the back of the seat, trying to get a look at Jatin. And Jatin went on steadily, 'One of them was half-taklu, no hair over here. The one who had the phone, that one, he was this taklu.' Jatin tapped the front of his head. He spoke without looking up, in a quiet, small voice, and said 'jins' for 'jeans', but he was very sure about the two men.

'That's good,' Sartaj said. 'Now, this taklu one, what kind of shirt was he wearing?'

'White T-shirt. And the other one, he had a blue shirt with long sleeves.'

Jatin was smaller than the others, with a malnourished mouse-face. He tilted his head when he spoke, towards Sartaj's breast pocket, and in that quick glimpse Sartaj saw that he had a bit of a wandering eye. He wouldn't look at you if you were looking at him, and so he passed unnoticed, with his bony shoulders and his drooping head. Sartaj took a tissue and began to fold it, over and over, and he kept his eyes on it. 'Yes, Jatin,' he said, 'so what else did you notice?'

Jatin was shy now. He turned his head away from the table, and twisted his arms together. But Ramu, with the money in his pocket, was feeling magnanimous. 'Ay, Jatin,' he said. 'Tell him if you know anything. It's all right.' And then, to Sartaj, with a little twirling motion of the forefinger at his temple, 'He's always like this. But he remembers everything.'

Sartaj unfolded his piece of tissue, and then began folding it again. 'Jatin, were they driving a car? How did they come?'

'We didn't see them driving anything,' Ramu said confidently. 'They weren't the type who would have a car. Maybe they came in a bus.'

Kamble shook his head at Sartaj. Jayanth was starting to look sceptical, now not quite as enthusiastic about the possibilities of successful detection. Sartaj felt the let-down himself: maybe this was all the boys had. Maybe this was a dead end. 'Were they carrying anything, Jatin?' he said. 'A book, a newspaper?'

Ramu shook his head patiently. 'I told you, his bheja is fried.' He tilted his head to one side, and hammed up a cockeyed impression of Jatin. Tej giggled. And Jatin sat very still, not flinching.

'All right,' Sartaj said. 'Want a falooda, Jatin?'

Kamble held up a hand. 'I'm going to go,' he said. 'Okay, boss?'

'Yes,' Sartaj said. 'I'll see you tomorrow at the station.' He motioned at a passing waiter. 'Three Royal Faloodas over here, quick.'

Jatin reached across the table for a tissue. Kamble unfolded himself out of his booth and walked towards the entrance. He was pressing keys on his mobile phone. Jatin was folding his tissue.

'Bip-beep-beep-bip,' Jatin said, and his tissue was a triangle now.

'What?' Sartaj said.

'Bip-beep-beep-bip-*bip*.' Jatin balanced the triangle on one side. It stayed in place, balanced.

Ramu reached behind Tej and batted the back of Jatin's head. 'He's my brother, but he's a yeda.'

Jatin started to fold another tissue. 'Bip-beep-beep-bip-*bip*-bap.'

Sartaj watched Jatin's fingers on the tissue. The other triangle stayed miraculously upright. 'Kamble!' Sartaj shouted, startling the owner, the waiters and the three other customers. 'Kamble!'

Jatin had finished his triangle by the time Kamble got back to the table, looking distinctly annoyed. 'What?'

'Give me your handy,' Sartaj said. He took the phone, cleared the display and put it flat on the table in front of Jatin, in front of his triangles.

Jatin reached out, and with a very skinny and very dirty finger pressed keys on the phone. When he got to the top of the keypad, the phone began to connect. Sartaj pressed 'End.'

Kamble was leaning over Jatin's shoulder. 'It's a mobile number,' he said, with the awestruck voice that he usually reserved for a new sixteen-year-old dancer at the Delite Dance Bar. 'It's the number I was just dialling.'

Sartaj nodded, and pressed 'End' again to clear the numbers. 'Jatin, do you remember the number that Taklu dialled that day?' he said to Jatin. 'What was it?'

'Bip-beep-beep-bip-*bip*-bap,' Jatin said. He continued, with more bips and beeps, varied in pitch and tone. Then he nodded, and pressed keys on the phone, moving without hurry and with absolute confidence from one to the next. He finished with a little flourish and went back to folding yet another tissue.

'This is the number that Taklu dialled, Jatin? After you gave him the package?' Sartaj said, turning the mobile phone around on the table.

'Yes,' Jatin said, and put another triangle on the table. Along with the other two, the triangle made a perfect larger triangle.

Kamble put his hands on his hips. 'Maderchod,' he said. 'Amazing. Give the man a falooda.'

'Very often,' Sartaj told Mary, 'detection is nothing but luck. Mostly it's like that. You sit around, and something drops into your lap. Then you pretend that you knew what you were doing all along.'

'That is *not* true in this case,' Mary said. 'You were not sitting around. You found the pickpocket. You made him find the boys. You gave the boys lunch. You were kind to them, instead of beating them like that fool wanted.'

'Kamble,' Sartaj said. They were sitting on a bench on the Carter Road seafront, under a truly spectacular sunset full of feathery circles of reddened cloud. The walkers were coming by briskly, and now, for a moment, a passing puppy on a leash nuzzled at their ankles. 'He was just playing his part. And anyway, getting the apradhi is not going to be that simple. I'm sure of that. We tried calling the number, from two different PCOs, and he didn't pick up. This bastard is careful. I can feel it.'

'You'll get him. And this Kamble, he would have tried to be rough with the boys if you had let him, and that little one would never have given you that number. You got that success in your detection because you were prepared for it. You were listening for it. You know that.'

Sartaj did know this. He had believed it for years, had learnt it from his father even before he had entered the force, and he had said as much to many a trainee. But still, it was nice to have Mary telling him this, reassuring him with a hand on his wrist. The puppy came back now, tripping in the other direction, and she bent to scratch its ears, and Sartaj felt her hand on his skin even after it was gone, even more acutely. 'Yes,' he said absently. 'Yes.'

'Yes, what?' The puppy was paddling away on its oversized feet, and Mary was looking at Sartaj with a sort of teasing amusement.

'That only,' Sartaj said hurriedly. 'You have to be listening, but sometimes the trouble is that you don't know what you're listening for. Like there's a song, but you don't know what the tune is. So you just have to wander around, looking and listening. It can make you feel like a fool.'

She was very direct now, her eyes locked on to his. 'You are not a fool,' she said.

It was a declaration, and Sartaj didn't hesitate now. He reached out and took her hand, and they sat together, holding hands. He very much wanted to kiss her, but there were walking grandmothers, and babies, and sprinting urchins. So, they sat. Sartaj thought of what Mary had just said: 'You are not a fool.' If he told Kamble about it, Kamble would mock Sartaj for the smallness of his romance, for the small, back-handed compliment that had finally brought them together. But Kamble was very young. Yes, no ghazal ever declared fervently that the beloved was not a fool, no Majrooh Sultanpuri love song had ever felt it necessary to claim this. Kamble believed in big romance and big tragedy, properly so. But Sartaj was content: to be rescued from one's foolishness was the greatest tenderness. We are all fools, he thought. I know I am. To find one person who forgives you for this, that is big. That is great.

They stayed on the seafront as dusk thickened and the sea receded into darkness, as the waves became uncurling ribbons of white. Mary squeezed his hand suddenly, and said, 'What will become of those boys?'

'Which boys? Little Red T-shirt and his gang?'

'Yes.'

'They'll survive.'

'Yes, but how?'

Sartaj shrugged. 'Like everyone else does.'

She nodded. But Sartaj could see that the boys stayed with her, that she was thinking about them still. He put an arm around her shoulder. He didn't want to tell her what Kamble had said when they had finally left the boys and Jayanth the pocket-maar and the restaurant. They had been talking about the amazing little crazy kid, and then Kamble had said, 'That Ramu is quite a leader, the bastard. Ten years from now he's going to give us trouble, you'll see.' Sartaj had agreed. Ramu was sharp and brave and hungry. He would be a good apradhi, maybe a shooter. And then Kamble had said, 'We should take him into the gali and encounter him now. Save us the trouble later of chasing him down, and save him the trouble of growing up.' And Sartaj had laughed and thumped Kamble reprovingly on his back, but he had known that Kamble was probably right. With some kids, you could see their future written on their foreheads. You could see how badly they wanted the good life, and how that life was going to run away from them. But he didn't want to think of Ramu and his troubles and his coming misfortune, not now. So he held Mary, and told her about his own childhood, and how he had never wanted to become a policeman like his father, but had become one anyway.

Now they were quiet. Sartaj could hear, even across the broad expanse of the road, the trills and laughter and hoots from a group of teenagers, boys and girls, sitting near the bus stop. They were sitting on car bonnets and sideways on the seats of motorcycles, and they were young and confident and happy and well-off. They were flirting, and later that evening some of them might try to find a hidden nook to touch in, to reach hungrily for each other. But Sartaj was content to hold Mary's hand, and later, to have the weight of her leaning against his back as he drove the motorcycle towards her house. He stopped at an intersection, and from the auto to his left came the well-known refrain from an old song: '*Tu kahan yeh bataa, is nasheeli raat mein.*' Mary hummed it against his shoulder. 'You know this song?' Sartaj said.

'Of course,' she said. 'It's Dev Anand, right?'

It was indeed Dev Anand, it was Dev Saab walking through a foggy night in an old black-and-white film, Sartaj couldn't remember the name. But he remembered that it was a cool night – maybe Mussoorie or Nainital, no, Shimla, it was Shimla – and Dev Saab was as weightless as the melody, light on his feet and limber, and lovely Nutan was waiting for him. The lights changed, and Sartaj drove slowly next to the auto, followed it away from Mary's home, so that they could listen to the song. '*He, chand taaron ne suna, in bahaaron ne suna, dard ka raag mera, rehguzaron ne suna.*' The wind moved smoothly over Sartaj's cheeks, and Mary sang into his ear, and he laughed and thought, this is happiness, just this much: to be driving through these unruly, well-known streets, with an old song, with a hand on your hip, and with a new love. Just this much, suspended between past and future: this woman, this song, this dirty and beautiful city.

The song ended, and with a swerve and sudden speed Sartaj left behind the auto. At Mary's house, he kissed her twice, and then once more. It was very easy. She got off the bike, and put a hand on his shoulder. She was very close to him, and he leaned forward and kissed her. She closed her eyes, and he kissed her again. She was looking at him from under long lashes, and she smiled wide, and he kissed her. 'Go,' she said, and pushed him gently in the chest. He went, and he sang – badly, he knew – all the way home.

The kisses stayed with him the next morning, as he drove to Katekar's house. He parked the motorcycle, and stepped over the gutter. It was quite early, before seven, and the narrow lane was quiet. But Shalini was sitting in her door, picking pebbles and waste out of a pile of rice grains. She got up when she saw him, nodded and went into the house. Rohit brought out a chair for Sartaj. He had a moustache now, a few straggly strands that made him look even younger, but he was trying his best. 'Hi,' he said.

Sartaj stopped a smile at the hip English, and said his hi too. 'How are the classes going?' he said. He sat, and tugged an envelope out of his hip pocket. Rohit had started evening computer classes and had told Sartaj on the phone about e-mail and Linux and other things that Sartaj didn't understand.

Rohit took the envelope and riffled through the hundred-rupee notes inside. 'Thank you. The classes are going well,' he said. 'It is all very interesting.'

But he was pensive. He was wearing new blue jeans and a banian, and there was something new about his hair. Sartaj could see that he was dressing to be a new person, a person who said '*Hi*' and '*Thank you*' and who found computer classes very interesting. But it wasn't quite working. The jeans were flimsy, with a loose orange stitch that fell far short of international sophistication. There were a pair of blue sneakers just inside the door, and they had the same look of bedraggled hopefulness. There would be boys and girls in that computer class who spoke this language fluently, who would know the nuances of T-shirts and dark glasses. They would be hard on Rohit, and Sartaj

626

felt twinges of sympathy as Rohit leaned against the wall and talked about how busy the classes were, and how some of its graduates had got work in Bahrain.

Shalini brought out a glass of tea. Sartaj sat up: she looked new. He sipped at his tea, and listened to her, and tried to puzzle out what exactly it was about her. She was talking about her work, not the jhadoo-katka work she did to make money, but the volunteer work she did with her organization. The group was called SMM, which stood for Shakti Mahila Manch, and they went out into the bastis to educate women. 'We talk to them about hygiene, and family planning,' she said to Sartaj. 'But the thing that upsets the husbands is when we tell the women that they should open their own bank accounts.'

Sartaj laughed. 'The husbands think you are taking away their cigarettes and their drink. You'd better be careful.'

Shalini laughed. 'They make a lot of noise. But they don't do anything to us. They beat their wives. Brave men.'

'There was that one incident,' Rohit said. 'In Bangalore.'

'Yes,' Shalini said. 'Our team leader told us. This was last month. The Bangalore branch had a group in a basti there. They were threatened by some men from a religious organization, some parishad or the other. The branch complained to the police, but the locals wouldn't do anything. They had to get the local MLA to intervene. But there'll be trouble yet.'

Sartaj was thinking of Mary, of how her upper lip had felt under his. He got it suddenly: Shalini's eyebrows had been plucked. Where there had been straightforward, rough brushstrokes, there were now delicate, precise arches. The change brought out her cheekbones, her eyes. Sartaj had never much noticed Shalini before, she had always been Bhabhi, Katekar's wife. Now he looked at her. She was wearing a dark blue sari, and a blouse of the same material, but with blue stitching at the collar and sleeves. She would never wear red, yellow or green again, not unless she remarried. She wore no jewellery, and her hair was tidily taken back into a bun. She was far from pretty, but there was a spare elegance about her that Sartaj had never noticed before. 'There is always trouble,' he said, his heart suddenly full of his dead friend Katekar. Did Shalini have a boyfriend, a lover? She seemed calm, even as she spoke about men and their anger, and possible violence.

'We have to keep working,' she said with an air of finality. 'Let them do what they want.'

Mohit appeared in the doorway, rubbing his eyes. He was wearing a pair of brown shorts, and that was all. His chest was narrow, with a black birthmark under his left nipple. He had a black thread around his neck, with a silver amulet on it. Sartaj remembered how Katekar had objected to that amulet, how he had cursed ignorance and superstition. But Shalini had insisted on it, to protect Mohit from sorrow and misfortune. 'Eh, Mohit,' Sartaj said.

Mohit started. He came out of his sleep, and in that fragmented moment, between his muzzy half-consciousness and full waking, Sartaj saw his anger. His loathing for Sartaj was full and fierce, a child's hatred as vast as the sun. Sartaj was the only one who saw it, and he flinched. Then Rohit, who was leaning against the jamb, tapped Mohit on the head and said, 'Wake up, Kumbhkaran. Sartaj Uncle is here.'

Mohit ducked his head, and when he looked up again he was sweet and harmless. 'I'm hungry, Aai,' he said.

'Go and get ready for school,' Shalini said. 'You're late. I'll give you something.' There was an edge to her voice, an undertow of sorrow.

'I am late also,' Sartaj said. 'I should go.'

Rohit walked with Sartaj down the lane, towards the corner. 'He keeps getting into fights,' he said suddenly. 'And twice this month already he's skipped school.'

'Mohit?'

'Yes. I try to watch him as much as I can. But both Aai and I have so much to do. He was never like this before.'

Before the event, before the death, before a fleeing apradhi trapped against a fence. Before everything. Mohit would measure his life before and after. And he would know who to blame. 'He'll grow out of it,' Sartaj said. 'It takes time. It's all so soon after. It takes time.'

Rohit nodded. 'Aai says that too. She prays every morning, especially for him.'

'How is she?'

'Aai?' Rohit said absently. 'She's fine.'

She couldn't be all fine, Sartaj thought. She and Katekar had spent years together, they had brought up two sons. Yet, this morning, she had seemed strong. There were those eyebrows, and her work with SMM. Was this a new Shalini, or had he never seen her clearly before?

Women were resilient, he knew that. Ma had survived Papa-ji's death, after two days of weeping she had decided that the house had become unacceptably dusty. And then she had cleaned, not only the inside but also the little patch of garden in front and the courtyard at the back. She had called in workers to scour the wall at the back, and white-wash it. She had lived on, a little more austere than she had been before, but ever more capable, more sinewy. A time or two Sartaj had thought – with a slight queasiness arising from the observation – that she seemed more calm after Papa-ji had gone, more steady and self-possessed.

Sartaj kicked the motorcycle into life, and tilted it around. Then he had to wait. A man with a long white cast on his leg was trying to manoeuvre the down-sloping turn to the left. He had to position his crutches exactly right to get the cast over the gutter, but the lane was troughed through and uneven and very narrow. There was a woman next to him, picking at his arm to position a crutch. The man cursed at her. His face was dense with fury, and his crutch scraped at the side of the gutter and slipped.

'Here,' Rohit said.

Sartaj watched him get the man and his broken leg over the gutter and down the lane a bit. Rohit was a good boy. He was responsible, and steady, and he loved his mother. He came back now to Sartaj.

'That's our neighbour Amritrao,' Rohit said. 'He was drunk one night, fell off the fast train as it came into Andheri station. He was lucky he didn't get his legs cut off. But he fell on the platform, smashed into the cement, *phachack*. So now he hobbles around.'

'And curses his wife.'

Rohit grinned. 'They curse at each other, actually. They're famous for their fights. And our Arpana, she has better curses than him. She told him once that you could drive a double-decker bus into his father's gaand, it was so wide from being bambooed by all the money-lenders he had borrowed from. She's just being nice to him right now because he's hurt. Just give it a couple of days, he'll get better and she'll be giving it to him.'

But right now, Arpana was being the dutiful wife, with a hand under her husband's elbow. He was tottering and swaying at the bottom of the lane, just before the slight rise that led to Katekar's house. 'He's going to fall and break his other leg,' Sartaj said. 'She should get him a wheelchair.'

Rohit was full of doubt. 'A wheelchair in these lanes, up and down? It wouldn't get through this last part. And imagine pushing it up the slope, over all these tilts and angles. A wheelchair wouldn't work.' He was looking down at the ground, measuring its slant and its condition. He really was a very serious boy.

Sartaj pumped his engine. 'A computerized wheelchair would,' he said over the bike's metallic thumping. 'I saw one once, that thing could race up this rise like a racing car. You wouldn't have believed it.'

'A computerized wheelchair?' Rohit was stunned by the possibilities. 'So it had to be motorized with a strong electric motor. Was there processing for each wheel?'

'I don't know,' Sartaj said. In this shining young face, he saw again Katekar's great faith in science, that trust in the greatness of technology, and he felt affection turn through his chest with the aching tug of a pulled muscle. 'But it worked all right. That fellow who owned it, he said he could go up and down stairs on it.'

'Was the wheelchair foreign? I've never seen anything like that here. That is so amazing.'

'Yes, it was imported. But I don't think it was built for Indian conditions, for dirt and monsoons. The poor bastard couldn't get spare parts. It was very hard to maintain.'

Rohit shook his head. 'Our country really is primitive.' And as he said it, he looked so like his father that Sartaj threw his head back and laughed.

'Study hard, guru,' Sartaj said, and patted him hard on the chest, and edged the bike up the lane, towards the main road. There were more people walking about now, on their way to the day's work, and he had to go slowly. The walls still had an early-morning glow about them, and the small houses were spilling children in uniforms into the path. Sartaj had to stop often, and his calves began to ache from pedalling at the ground to make way. What will become of those boys? What will become of Mohit? Sartaj was thinking now of Mohit's fights, his anger, his hatred. Where would he be ten years from now? What would he be?

Sartaj was finally at the intersection. He bucked the motorcycle out on to the wide asphalt, turned to the left and gratefully sped away. It was good to be out of the basti, out of the twisty mess. He went faster. But dread followed him, an image of an older Mohit lying in a dirty lane, his back bent across a gutter. Sartaj couldn't quite see his face, there was a blankness there, but he knew it was Mohit, and he was bleeding from gunshot wounds, and he was dead. Sartaj shook his head, and tried to think of the investigation at hand. No, no. Mohit would grow out of his trauma, he would forget, he would get better. He wouldn't become a tapori, a thug, a bhai. No. Kamble wouldn't have to encounter him, no, not ten years from now and not ever. Sartaj would see to that, he was certain of it.

Sartaj went south along the highway. He drove fast, weaving in and through the morning traffic. All his speed and his cutting close between buses couldn't rescue him from Mohit's revulsion, and from the certain knowledge of Mohit's future. Mohit in a checked shirt, bleeding from three close-range bullet wounds in the chest, Sartaj could see the powder burns on the cotton. It was all very real. You're being superstitious, he told himself, this is very silly. Mohit will be all right. Mohit will be all right. He drove on.

Parulkar was waiting for Sartaj in his niece's apartment in Santa Cruz. The deliveries of his money to Homi Mehta, his consultant, had slowed for a while, but now the pace was picking up again. He had no doubt spent untold sums of money as he engineered his way back to political favour, and now he was recouping. Sartaj had made a delivery less than a month ago, and now he was marvelling once again at the green marble in the lobby of the niece's apartment building. The stone seemed to increase its lustre each time Sartaj came back. Perhaps that was one of the virtues of Italian marble. The steel in the lift was still unmarked, so that Sartaj could see his face and tend to his moustache. He decided he was looking better than he had in a long time, and then wondered how this could be so, given all the recent stress. And perhaps he was imagining it anyway.

But Parulkar noticed it too. 'You are looking smart, Sartaj. Good, good.' He thumped Sartaj on the back and led him inside the apartment. The glass-topped dining table had dishes laid out on it, on lace-edged white place mats. 'Have some poha and chai. The poha is especially very good.'

'I've already eaten, sir.'

'Try some anyway, beta. Once in a while it is good to enjoy the small things in life. I'll have a cup with you.'

The poha was indeed spectacular. Sartaj ate a small helping, then heaped his plate again. Parulkar drank chai and looked on benignly.

They spoke about current cases and about Parulkar's family. The renovations on Parulkar's house were at last complete, and now his daughter Mamta – whose divorce was proceeding through the family courts – and her children could live comfortably with Parulkar. Life was getting on. Parulkar seemed content, and all his old vigour had returned, redoubled. 'We will begin some new community interaction projects next month,' he said, 'after Diwali. New work for the new year.' And he listened to Sartaj's tales about the Gaitonde affair, and was confident that it would all amount to nothing. He shook his head and said, 'This is all just unnecessary fear, based on very little real evidence. That woman is connecting things from here and there, making up a case for herself to pursue. People do that when their career is just sitting. Gurus and bombs! Nonsense.'

Sartaj wasn't completely reassured, but Parulkar's confidence was comforting. After all, Parulkar was the man with the unerring instincts, whose record of arrests and successful investigations was unequalled. 'Yes, sir,' Sartaj said. 'It is all just a story based on rumours, nothing more.' He pushed back his plate. 'That was very good.'

'Come on,' Parulkar said. 'I have something for you.'

Sartaj was expecting the usual load of cash to be transported, but Parulkar led him to the bedroom and offered a grey box.

'Open, open,' he said.

Sartaj lifted the lid – bearing an embossed logo he had never seen before – and found tissue paper, very soft paper that individually wrapped the most glossy, elegant shoes he had ever encountered. They were simple, but sleek, and every stitch around the sole spoke of care and quality. The colour was perfect, brown with a hint of red, not flashy but eloquent. These were ideal shoes.

'They are Italian, Sartaj,' Parulkar said, 'straight from Italy. You wear a nine wide, yes?'

Sartaj had to make an effort to break out of his trance. 'Yes, sir.'

'Come on, try them on. I had a friend bring them in from Milan, told him the size and everything. Let us see if they work.'

Sartaj sat on the bed, pulled at his laces. The moment he slipped the new shoe on his right foot, he knew it would work. 'It's good, sir.' He put on the second one, and stood up. 'Perfect fit, sir.' He walked from one end of the room to the other, and shook his head in wonder. It was not just the hold of the shoe, which was close without getting snug, but its weight and mechanism. Sartaj walked. This was an Italian shoe which lived up to its foreign billing.

'Right,' Parulkar said. 'So let's throw away those old ones. I was surprised that you wore them so long.'

'Wear these on the street, sir?'

'Of course, Sartaj. Good things are not for keeping in the cupboard. Life is uncertain, one must enjoy. Wear them.'

Sartaj looked down. Yes, it would be possible to wear these on duty. They were not conspicuous, and only a discerning eye would be able to recognize their true quality. 'Thank you, sir.'

'Mention not,' Parulkar said, waving an expansive hand. He nodded, very satisfied. 'Now you look like Sartaj Singh again.'

Homi Mehta was counting the stacks of Parulkar's money at his usual unhurried, precise pace. Sartaj leant back in an office chair, his arms behind his head and his legs straight out, feeling quite relaxed. It was amazing that a pair of shoes should give him such an oasis of serenity, but then it was the small things in life that really mattered. Let global events do their worst, good craftsmanship was still possible and, yes, necessary. Sartaj wriggled his toes and let out a sigh, surprising Homi Mehta and himself.

'Twenty. All complete and correct,' Homi Mehta said, and patted the cash. 'You are happy today.'

Sartaj shrugged, but couldn't hold back a smile. 'Just comfortable.'

'Did you bring any money of your own?'

'No. Not today, Uncle.'

'Arre, how many times to tell you? Save when you are young.'

'Yes, I know, I must think of the future. Maybe next time.'

'Next time, next time, like this your life will pass. Let me tell you, one day you wake up and you are old. And where is your security? And how will you support your wife?'

'I'm not married.'

'Yes, yes, but you will be. You don't want to depend on your children, I tell you. Especially nowadays.' Homi Mehta stood up and began stacking the money into a black plastic bag. The snowy white of his linen shirt was exactly the tint of his neatly clipped hair. 'No doubt your children will be good children, but it is a shameful thing to have to ask them.'

'Uncle, you have me married and having children already. Anyway, I'm not so close to retirement yet. There is time left.'

'Yes, yes, exactly what I am saying. Use the time fruitfully, Sartaj. Lay out a strategy. Establish your targets, and make a scheme. I can help you.'

Sartaj could see that Homi Mehta was completely baffled by his obtuseness, that he was a man who lived by long-term plans and intricate outlines. 'Okay, Uncle. You are completely correct. Next time I come in we will sit down and discuss everything. We will write down goals, and make . . .' Sartaj made motions, a series of steps.

'Charts.'

'Yes, charts. Don't worry. We will do everything. Everything will be taken care of. We will prepare.'

In the lift, hedged into a corner by a sabji-walla and his basket of tomatoes and onions, Sartaj watched the wrinkled neck of the liftman. The lift stopped at many floors, and the liftman clanged back his doors and let in servants and saabs, mothers and dhobis. Sartaj was thinking about how uncanny an animal this life was, that you had to seize it and let go of it at the same time, that you had to enjoy but also plan, live every minute and die every moment. And what of disasters? Suppose the cable broke, and the lift plummeted, carrying its load of men and women into the dark chasm below, would they all grieve within that drop for the days and years missed, or worry about the ones left behind? The light that came between the bars of the door flashed white and dark across Sartaj's eyes, and he felt light and insubstantial, and yet full of blood and muscle and movement.

The lift heaved and shifted and settled on the ground floor, and Sartaj shook off all questions and suppositions and imaginings and stepped out into the hard daylight. There was work to do. He had almost reached the building's gate when his phone rang.

'Sartaj Saab, salaam.'

'Salaam, Iffat-bibi. Everything is well?'

'Yes. But you could brighten my day.'

'Tell me.'

'I hear you are down in the city, near us. Why don't you give us a chance to extend our hospitality?'

Sartaj stopped short. 'How do you know where I am?'

'Arre, saab, we are not following you. No, no. It is just that we also do business with the man that Parulkar Saab makes you take his money to. One of our boys saw you, he told me, that is all.'

Sartaj was on the road now. He turned in a quick circle, but there were only the ordinary pedestrians passing by, nobody who looked like a fielder. 'Your boys are everywhere.'

'We have many employees, that is true. Saab, you know we are in Fort, not so far away. Come and eat with us.'

'Why?'

'Why? I am your well-wisher, and I hope you are mine.'

'Why do you suddenly want to meet me?'

Iffat-bibi let out a long breath. When she spoke again, she was no longer the kindly old woman. 'I have a big proposal for you,' she said, and her voice had smoothened and tightened into stone. 'A proposal that I would prefer to give to you face-to-face.'

'I am not interested.'

'At least listen to what I have to say.'

'No.'

'Why? We have dealt with each other before.'

'On small things, and I am a small man. I have no capability for big proposals.'

'You are content with remaining small?'

'I am happy.'

Her laughter was straightforwardly mocking. 'That is a coward's happiness. How long will you run Parulkar's little errands? That man makes crores, and you, how much? Your promotion is overdue, and does he help? He is not your well-wisher, Sartaj Saab.'

'Don't say anything about him.' Sartaj's hand was trembling, and he had to make an effort to keep his voice down. 'Don't say anything. Understand?'

'You are very loyal to him.'

Sartaj waited. He could believe now that this old kutiya helped run a company, that she sent out murderers and extortionists.

'But he is not loyal to you,' Iffat-bibi said. 'He was not even loyal to your father . . .'

'Bhenchod, shut up.' Sartaj hung up. He strode down the road, then realized he had gone past the Gypsy. He came back, heaved himself into the driver's seat and sat with his hands on the wheel, trying to calm himself. There was no need to get angry. That randi

635

was just trying to manipulate him. Yes, and she had succeeded. Calm, calm.

Sartaj finally started the vehicle and pulled out into the traffic. Now he was able to think. The question was, why was Iffat-bibi saying these things about Parulkar to him, to him of all people? When, and why, had Parulkar become distasteful to her, and to her company? It was probably true that he was now close to the present government, but that was only survival. Iffat-bibi and her people would have to understand that. So why was Suleiman Isa now Parulkar's enemy?

Sartaj had no answers, and he did not want to ask Parulkar. He had always kept himself clear of Parulkar's big business, away from knowledge of Parulkar's intricate network of patronage and money and connections. He did not want to know because he wanted no part of it. He was afraid of the gravity of that vast constellation of ambition and wealth and power, he was afraid that he would be sucked, helpless, into it. Yes, maybe Iffat-bibi was right, maybe he was a coward. He had not courage enough for that spinning circle, he was frightened – as frightened as a child – of being shattered by its velocity.

By the time he passed through Mahim, one question still bit at him: had Papa-ji been afraid, too? Maybe Papa-ji's integrity, and what little of it Sartaj had himself, came really from fear. Maybe they were both not big enough to ask for too much. Small rewards for small hearts. But there was no way around this thorny blockage. Sartaj did not want to deal with Iffat-bibi. He did not want to know more about Parulkar, and that was that. He drove faster, and tried to leave it all behind.

Sartaj met Kamala Pandey in a coffee shop on S.V. Road. She was going shopping in Bandra that afternoon, she had said, and the coffee shop was a convenient place to meet. She was sitting at the back of the shop, with two full shopping bags and Umesh next to her. Sartaj wasn't expecting Umesh, but he was there, glorious and beautiful in black jeans and a white T-shirt. He was sitting close to Kamala, arm to shoulder, and Sartaj wasn't sure that they weren't secret boyfriend and girlfriend again, but he was certain there had been some haramkhori recently. Some pushing-and-pulling, as Kamble would have put it.

'Hello,' he said.

Sartaj pulled out a chair and sat. He nodded, and said nothing. Kamala shifted about, and then said in a very small, girlish voice, 'I told Umesh to come. I thought he may be able to help.'

Sartaj kept his voice soft, and very neutral. 'If you want to keep this case private, then keep it really private.'

Umesh smiled, and leant forward across the table. 'Inspector saab,' he said, 'you are absolutely correct. But Kamala is alone in this, you see. And she needs some support. I am the only one she can talk to about this. A woman needs support, you see.'

He really was very charming, in a confidentially boyish sort of way. His hair fell over his forehead and he had a very sweet smile, a young one. Sartaj couldn't deny any of this. 'Yes,' Sartaj said. 'But . . .'

'Will you have a coffee, inspector saab?' Umesh said. 'Do. It's very good here.'

'No,' Sartaj said. 'I'm in a hurry.'

'Try the cappuccino,' Umesh said. He raised a pointing finger, and called to the boy behind the counter. 'Harish. One cappuccino here.'

Sartaj let it go. He had only a vague idea of what a cappuccino was, and he knew he didn't want one. But it wasn't worth the effort to argue with charming Umesh. 'We are making progress on the case,' he said to Kamala. 'There have been some breakthroughs. Let's see if something comes of them.'

'What breakthroughs?' Kamala said. She was eager, excited.

'I can't talk about details, madam. The case is still under investigation.'

'Please,' Kamala said. 'What is it?'

Sartaj shook his head. 'I'll let you know when we have something more concrete. This is just a connection.'

'Is it something to do with Rachel?'

'Perhaps.'

'Surely you can tell Kamala,' Umesh said. 'Given the conditions that exist.'

'What conditions?' Sartaj said.

Umesh shrugged. He tilted his head towards one of Kamala's shopping bags. A brown envelope was sticking out of it, from among the rich squares of boutique tissue paper.

'Ah, those conditions,' Sartaj said. He reached across the table, took the brown envelope between thumb and forefinger. Inside, there

637

was the unmistakable square bulk of money. Sartaj dropped the envelope into its cushion of Kamala's packages and stood up.

'Where are you going?' Kamala said.

'Please understand one thing,' Sartaj said, looking at Umesh. 'I am not your employee. You are not my boss. I do not report to you. Keep your money.' And then, in English, 'Good luck.'

'Wait,' Kamala said, frantic.

'Arre, boss,' Umesh said. 'You took offence. I didn't mean anything like that.' He was on his feet now. 'Sorry, sorry.' He put a hand on Sartaj's arm, then took it away quickly.

Sartaj knew that he had on his fearsome face, and that Kamala was quite afraid. She had never seen his flat policeman's eyes, this jagged promise of violence. Sartaj felt a flicker of regret, for frightening the fair Kamala, but Umesh had withered under this hostility, and Sartaj was enjoying his befuddlement. Then there was someone standing at Sartaj's elbow. 'Cappuccino,' the boy said brightly, quite unaware of the tension at the table. Sartaj looked down at the foamy cup, and when he came back to Umesh, the man's charisma was back in place.

'Inspector saab,' Umesh said. 'Truly, I am sorry. I am a fool. I am a fool. Please. I'm an idiot. Kamala mustn't suffer because of me.'

Harish the cappuccino boy was taking in the drama, wide-eyed. Sartaj felt foolish himself. He had been frightened this morning by Mohit's anger, by his own apprehensions over Mohit's future. Then he had been unsettled by Iffat-bibi. And here he was, taking it all out on Kamala. And Umesh really was drooping with regret and sadness. There was a vulnerability to him that Sartaj hadn't seen before. Sartaj shook his head, and took the cup from Harish. 'Okay,' he said. He sat, and waited until Harish was safely away. 'All right,' he said to Kamala. 'When there is something concrete to tell you, I will tell you.'

Kamala nodded rapidly. 'Yes, yes,' she said. 'That is fine.'

Umesh was sitting back in his chair, far back from Sartaj. 'Try your cappuccino, sir,' he said. 'It is really very good.'

Sartaj took a sip. It was rich and full, like its foreign name. He looked around at the shop, at its glossy pastel walls and pictures of European streets. Harish was serving a gaggle of eighteen-year-olds at the counter. The tables towards the front were all occupied by students, resplendent in their chunky shoes and carefully tousled hair. We never had places like this in college, Sartaj thought. Megha and he had huddled together in Irani restaurants, drinking stale chai, enduring stares from balding businessmen.

'Sugar?' Umesh said.

'It's sweet enough,' Sartaj said. There was a little green car sitting next to Umesh's cup, attached to his keychain. 'What's this one?'

'It's a Ferrari,' Umesh said.

Sartaj turned the car around with the tip of his finger, moved it back and forth on the table. It was a perfect little working model, with a steering wheel and little letters and numbers on the sides. 'Wasn't it a different one last time? A red one?'

'Yes. That was a Porsche.'

Sartaj nodded. 'So you like the Ferrari better now?'

Umesh raised both his hands, miming a baffled astonishment. 'Arre, inspector saab,' he said. 'What, a man should have only one gaadi? A man needs more than that.' The irony was as heavy as the innuendo. But he was very aware that he was being the naughty boy, and he was very beautiful, so it was impossible to be annoyed with him. Even for Kamala, who rolled her eyes but couldn't keep the amusement from her eyes.

'So you actually have these cars?' Sartaj said. It was a mean question, but Sartaj had to ask it. Umesh made him feel old. Once there had been a Sartaj who had wanted flashy women and flashy cars, many of them, and thought he deserved them.

'You see,' Umesh said. 'Actually . . .'

Kamala slapped Umesh's shoulder. 'Shut up,' she said. And then, to Sartaj, 'In his dreams he owns them. He buys six car magazines every month. He has posters on his wall.'

'It's my hobby,' Umesh said, quite pious. 'They are amazing machines.' There was a low-slung fervour in his voice, the hushed kinetic energy of the true fanatic. 'And anyway, you are quite wrong. On my wall there are no posters any more. There is a screen.'

'Oh, yes,' Kamala laughed. 'The new film theatre.'

'You have a film theatre in your house?' Sartaj said. 'With a projector and everything?'

'No, not a *film* projector,' Umesh said, with a tolerant smile for Sartaj's ignorance of the new. 'It's a very high quality Sony DVD player, attached to an LCD projector. You get an image that is about fourteen feet across.' Umesh held his arms out wide. 'And it's a better image than most of the cinemas have in this country. I also put in a

639

new Sanyo amplifier, and Bose speakers. You turn up the sound on that, you can feel it here.' His hand thumped on his chest, and his eyes were soggy with passion. 'You should come over some time, watch a movie.'

'He'll bore you with some American racing movie,' Kamala said. 'Cars going around and round for two hours.'

'No, no.' Umesh dismissed her with a manly chopping motion of his right hand. 'We can watch a police film. I told you, I like detective stories.'

Sartaj was still trying to imagine a fourteen-foot screen and a projector in a Bombay apartment. 'You have a special room for this screen?'

'No, yaar, in my bedroom only. You don't need a lot of space, the projector is only this big, like this. You just come and see.'

'Maybe some time,' Sartaj said. He stood up. 'Too much work right now. How much does a thing like that cost, projector and sound and everything?'

'Oh, not so much,' Umesh said. 'Of course it's all specially imported, so you have to be prepared for some cost. But not as much as you think.' He patted at his face with the tips of his fingers.

'What?' Sartaj said.

Umesh said affectionately, 'My friend, you have foam on your moustache.' He held up a paper napkin in one hand, and the brown envelope in the other. 'Take.'

Sartaj took both. 'Don't worry,' he said to Kamala, wiping at his face. 'We are on the case.' Kamala tried to look reassured, but her doubts swam just under the lovely lustre of her cheeks. Sartaj hesitated, then added, 'And yes, some of the progress has been with Rachel. As I said, don't worry.'

Kamala's back straightened, and she smiled and nodded. Umesh was gratifyingly pleased as well. Maybe he loved Kamala in his own way, Sartaj thought. A pretty fellow, but likeable. 'Okay,' Kamala said. 'Thanks.'

Sartaj left her with Umesh murmuring into her ear. Endearments, maybe, or whispered memories of their shared past. No, Sartaj was sure that Umesh was talking about the uncertain competence of the investigator she had acquired. Sartaj got a fragmented glimpse of himself in the glass door of the coffee shop as he slung a leg over the motorcycle. It was a stylish move, but the man doing it was out of shape, dressed in a sadly out-of-date checked shirt and blue jeans. The turban was still tight and just so, but the face under it had been broken down by time. The detectives in Umesh's foreign movies were no doubt better-looking, better-dressed, better men altogether. That much was undoubtedly true.

On the road north, past the Santa Cruz airport, Sartaj thought about other truths. He was, in fact, Kamala's employee. He was paid by the great Government of India, at skimpy GOI rates, but it was nevertheless true that his salary cheques came in part from Kamala Pandey, citizen in good standing. Her cash payments in brown envelopes made him doubly her subordinate, and yet he had stood up, and had proclaimed that he was not her worker, her peon, her coolie. A light plane took off to the left, and Sartaj watched it soar past him, into the blue. The traffic was moving quickly now, and for a few seconds Sartaj had the illusion that he could keep up with the plane. Then it was away. He had thought he was past competing with people like Umesh and Kamala, that he had stumbled away from the siren call of success and victory, but apparently his pride was still alive. He could still get angry over being reminded of what he really was, a civil servant, a servant, no more, no less. Bloody sardar, Sartaj thought. Bloody policeman.

Kamble was enjoying being a policeman this afternoon. He had solved a burglary case – it was the building watchman and his two friends – and he had made money from an embezzlement case, from the defendant. He was writing up a report in the detection room when Sartaj found him. 'Saab, come, come,' he said. 'Please sit.' Then he wrote with one hand, drank noisy slurps of chaas with the other and told Sartaj all about his triumphs. After he had finished and filed his report, they walked to the back of the station, and took a stroll around the interior of the compound wall, around the temple. They stood under a droopy sapling and talked.

'The phone number that Taklu called is registered in the name of –,' Kamble said. 'But wait – you won't believe it. Tell me who you think it is.'

Kamble had contacts in the mobile phone company. He had made much noise about how difficult it was going to be to get any help and information, this being an unofficial investigation, and how he was going to need more cash to move things along. Now he was very satisfied with himself, with the quickness of his sources and their reliability. 'Come on, Kamble,' Sartaj said. 'It's hot out here.'

The saplings that Parulkar had planted had grown, they had got taller but they were sadly shredded-looking, stripped of leaves and branches. They gave no shade. There was a splattering of sunlight across Kamble's shoulders, and he was sweating. 'Boss, really you won't be able to tell,' he said. He ceremoniously took out a wad of folded paper from his pocket, computer forms with the holey strips still attached. He shook out the sheets. 'Try once.'

Sartaj shrugged. 'Minister Bipin Bhonsle?'

Kamble bent forward and hacked out a laugh. 'Yes, he'd want to lock up all the loose women in India. But no, it's not him. Listen. The address is a made-up one in Colaba, it doesn't exist. But the name is . . . Kamala Pandey.'

'No.'

'Yes. That's what it says here. Kamala Sloot Pandey.'

'Let me see.' Sartaj took the top printout. 'That's not "sloot",' he said. 'That's "slut".'

'Which is?'

'An English word. It means like a randi.'

'A raand?' Kamble ran a hand over his head, backwards over the clipped hair. 'Taklu is calling his boss, that kutiya Rachel, and that saali is laughing at us.'

'At Kamala, I think,' Sartaj said. 'I don't think that Rachel expected anyone to get to the number, really. She thinks she's real smart. This is all a joke to her.'

'Bhenchod. Now I want to catch her,' Kamble said. 'Not even for the money.'

Sartaj handed Kamble the brown envelope, which was now lighter by half. 'We'll catch her. What else did you get?'

'One month of calls to this phone, incoming and outgoing. They're all from the same mobile, and all to this same mobile. That's got to be Taklu's handy, the one he used at the cinema.'

So Taklu and his partner had a mobile phone, and they used it only to call this number, to reach their boss. And their boss – who, judging by this extra bitchery of 'slut', was Rachel Mathias – used her mobile phone only to call them. Very efficient, very careful. 'The other phone, Taklu's phone, is in what name?'

'Same name, also hers. Same to same, sloot and everything.'

642

So Kamala was a slut twice over. Now Sartaj wanted to catch Rachel too, and not for the money. But the two mobile phones calling each other presented a problem. The addresses they were registered to would be fake, and the payments would be made in cash to add phoning minutes to the SIM cards. It was a closed system.

But Kamble had a feral stretch in his jaw, like a wolf that had just eaten a gulp of fresh flesh. 'Don't look so worried, my friend. Someone made a mistake. There is one call from Taklu's phone, to a land line. This was three weeks ago, just one call, one and a half minutes long. It is a residential line. I have the name, and the address. And it's all real.'

They went out to the real address that evening. It was a long drive, with rush-hour traffic all the way to Bhandup. Kamble rode behind Sartaj, and Sartaj felt his weight and his impatience. Every now and then Kamble pointed out openings between the jammed vehicles, and urged him on, faster. Sartaj kept up his usual steady pace, refusing short-cuts that he knew would finally slow them down. They stopped behind a long line of brilliantly coloured trucks at a crossroads, and Sartaj turned his face from the steady heated flow of foul exhaust. There was an orange bubble of light that hovered over the road, from the streetlamps, and above it the hard black of the sky. To the right, across and above the moving cars, Sartaj could see the low sprawl of lights, spreading densely to the east and north. Beyond the lights, barely there, the rise of hills. Out here, you could see the city spreading, working itself out into the soil and through the earth. Maybe there were still some tribals in those hills, hanging on to their little patches of land and quaint customs. These trucks would bring out cement and machines and money, and long legal documents, and the tribals would sign and sell, or be moved out. That's how it worked.

Kamble was laughing. Sartaj twisted to look, and Kamble was squinting at the back of the last truck. 'Gar ek baar pyaar kiya to baar baar karna,' the fancy white Hindi script proclaimed under the usual Horn-OK-PLEASE, 'agar mujhe der ho jaye to mera intezaar karna.' The mudguards had been painted red and orange, with an edging of a leafy pattern in green. 'There's four spelling mistakes,' Kamble said. 'In two lines.'

There were indeed. 'Poor poet,' Sartaj said.

'Not bad lines, either,' Kamble said.

The lights changed, and the trucks came to life with a great roaring of horns and engines. Sartaj rode behind the last poetic one, and thought about the troubles of poets and clever lawbreaking master-minds. You could carefully turn out the most elegant crime, and hide behind layers of mobile phones, but the trouble was that you had to work with idiots. It was hard to hire good help. Somebody always disobeyed the simplest of instructions, and made a mistake, many mistakes. Detection made detectives look clever, but often solutions were gifts from fools. Sartaj now remembered Papa-ji holding forth on the general decline of the criminal classes, expounding his theory that the newer boys were all muscle and no subtlety, that using an AK-47 instead of a sleek Rampuri blade made you a lesser villain and a smaller man. Papa-ji always had examples – reaching back to the nineteenth century – of legendary burglars and conmen who worked crimes of wit and bravura. A generation always gets the apradhis it deserves, he used to say.

It was deep evening by the time they came to their apradhi's two-room kholi at the back of the Satguru Nagar basti, at the end of a winding lane. They had followed an inspector named Kazimi, who had mehndi-coloured hair and a stiff walk. Kamble rolled his eyes at Kazimi's pointy-toed prance, his high step as they went over a clutch of water pipes. Kazimi was a friend of a friend, and Satguru Nagar was part of his beat. He hadn't asked any questions about their investigation, and a thousand rupees had made him very flexible about accommodating their schedules. This was not a policeman in a very profitable posting, and Sartaj was sure that he had children, almost-grown children who needed to be settled. He had that harried air, those slumping, burdened shoulders. Kazimi was efficient, though. He had recognized the name, Shrimati Veena Mane, right away, and now he was leading them through nameless alleys without hesitation.

'How much more?' Kamble said. He had stopped, and had a hand out on a post, and was scraping the bottom of a shoe against an angle of a wall. 'I hate coming into these places. Bhenchod.'

'Not so far,' Kazimi said. 'One, two more minutes.' He was rubbing at his hip.

'What happened?' Sartaj said, meaning the hip.

'I got shot,' Kazimi said. 'During the riots. It hurts after a day of walking. Even after all this time.'

Sartaj didn't need to ask which riots, and he didn't want to ask how and why Kazimi had been wounded. Kamble was upright now, and they were moving.

'This basti has grown a lot in the last two years,' Kazimi said, his profile lit up from the doors they were passing. 'There are now almost five hundred kholis.'

Five hundred cramped little homes, brick and wood and plastic and tin making small spaces for many bodies. Kamble was probably one generation away from a home just like these, maybe two, but he had the superiority of the escapee, the emigrant. He was on his way to somewhere else, and he didn't like being drawn back. Sartaj was trying to be careful about his own Italian masterpieces, but if your shoes got dirtied, you had to accept the smear and deal with it. People lived here, and this was their life. Actually, this basti was better than many Sartaj had seen. Its inhabitants had progressed, they had escaped the tattered lean-tos that new immigrants built, the temporary arrangements made out of discarded cardboard boxes. Here, there was pumped water, and bricked-up gutters, and electricity in most of the kholis, and Shrimati Veena Mane had a phone. Sartaj had even seen a rank of five toilets near the front of the basti, with a blue NGO placard over them. These were people moving up, slowly but surely.

But they didn't like policemen, these inhabitants of Satguru Nagar. Two teenage boys sat on a ledge between two kholis, their arms intertwined, and they glared at Kazimi, and Sartaj caught the rest of their hostility as he walked past them. A balding grandmother sitting in a doorway, a thali laden with rice grains held between her knees, called out to them, 'What sin are you going to commit today, inspec-tor?' There was enough stinging contempt just in her 'tor' to curdle the milk that she had boiling on the stove inside.

'I'm not after your son today, Amma,' Kazimi said, without looking back. 'But tell him I said hello.'

She had more to say, but Sartaj lost it under the tinny blare of *Yeh shaam mastani, madhosh kiye jaye*, which came from a television to the left, turned up very loud. They were almost at the end of this lane, which stopped abruptly at a grey concrete wall. There was broken glass on top of the wall, and curls of barbed wire. There was empty space beyond, trees and empty land.

'There,' Kazimi said. 'Second door before the end, on the left.'

'All right,' Kamble said, edging past Kazimi. 'Let's go.'

'Slowly,' Kazimi said. 'Slowly.'

Sartaj put a hand on Kamble's back, to restrain him, and then drew it back from the sweat. 'He's right,' he said, wiping his hand on his jeans. 'We don't know who the apradhi is. Or if he's one of the taporis we passed on the corner. Go gently, Kamble. Gently.'

Kamble wasn't convinced, but he let Kazimi go on ahead. This second door on the left was freshly painted a gay orange, and had a Ganesha in white above the lintel. The door was open just a crack, and a faint electronic babble came through. Kazimi ambled up the lane, looking as if he was headed towards the very end. Then he turned abruptly, and put a hand on the orange door, and shoved.

There was a sharp crack, of wood on flesh, and a grunt of pain. Sartaj could see, past Kazimi, a hand clutching a knee, a bare back, skinny calves. There was a man on the floor. He had been sitting with his back to the wall and the door, watching TV. He came up to one leg, hobbling, and said, 'Who? Who are you?'

Sartaj, who was half-way through the door, felt Kamble's warm exhalation on the back of his neck. 'Bastard,' Kamble said. 'It's Taklu.'

This was certainly possible, that this lean, hollow-chested specimen was the Taklu that little Jatin had described. He was of the right age, the right height, and his hair had retreated up to the very dome of his head. Kazimi had him backed up against a shelf.

'You are new here,' Kazimi said. 'Otherwise you would know me. What's your name?'

'Who are you?' Taklu insisted.

'We're your baaps,' Kamble said from the door. 'Don't you recognize us?'

Sartaj moved past Kazimi, to the back of the kholi. There was another room there, with two wooden cupboards, and three steel trunks stacked on top of each other. A fuzz of grey light came through a thickly-barred ventilator high up on the brick wall. Altogether it was a fair-sized home, well-kept and clean. The kitchen area, in the front room, had a suspended grill with rows of utensils, and a stove with two burners. To the left, near the door, a green phone sat resplendent on a white lacy cloth, on a small wooden stool.

Taklu was now quiet. He had let go of his knee, and he had his arms across his chest. Under his blue knit underwear, his legs were shaking, right next to the Sunil Shetty movie on television. 'My name

646

is Anand Agavane,' he said. He knew now that he had three police-men in his house, and his voice was shaky.

Kazimi took a step up to him. 'Who are you, Anand Agavane? Why are you here, in Veena Mane's house?'

'She is my aatya. This is my aatya's house. I come and stay here sometimes. I drive an auto for a seth who has his garage near here. Sometimes I have to return the auto late at night, so I come and sleep here.'

'Your aatya is rich, eh?' Sartaj said. 'She's got a phone and every-thing.' He was squatting next to the stool. The phone had a guard-lock on the dial, and a box full of coins and small notes next to it. Veena Mane took money from her neighbours, to let them make calls and receive them. 'What's the number for this phone?'

'The number?'

'Yes, the number. You don't remember your own aatya's number? What is it, Kamble, the phone number?'

Kamble was in the back room now, and Sartaj could hear him tip-ping over trunks and flinging cupboards open. He called the number back, singing out the digits.

'Is that it, chutiya?' Kazimi said. He was standing very close to Anand Agavane now, nose to nose. 'Is that your aatya's number?'

'I haven't done anything.'

Kazimi slapped him. There was a moan from outside, from the row of faces that now crowded the lane. Anand Agavane hunched against the television, holding his face.

Sartaj thrust his head out of the door. 'Get away from here,' he snarled. 'Or I'll take you bastards in as well. You want a lathi up your gaand? This is not some cinema show.' Veena Mane's neighbours retreated, and then turned away. But Sartaj knew that they would be listening, that what went on in one kholi was loud in the next. He came back into the room, turned up the television. A model in a green sari sang about exquisite coffee.

'Look at this,' Kamble said as he came through the narrow passage-way from the back room. He held up a cubical black plug and a dangling wire. 'This looks like it should plug into a mobile phone. How many phones does your aatya have, after all? What is she doing, calling the Ambanis every ten minutes?'

Sartaj took the plug from Kamble. He put a comforting hand on Anand Agavane's shoulder, close to the neck. 'Listen to me,' he said.

'We're not after you. We know about the calls to the woman, we know that you sent those chokras to pick up money at Apsara.' Sartaj could feel Anand Agavane's pulse under his fingers, as high and fast as a bird's. 'We just want you to tell us your boss's name yourself. Who do you call? Just tell me. It'll be all right, nothing will happen to you.'

But Anand Agavane was in a stupor, with knotted eyes and rigid jaw. Sartaj had seen it before, this cornered conjuring-up of courage. Anand Agavane was going to try to be honourable, he wanted to save his friends. He would break, but it would take some effort, questioning, a beating or two. They would have to take him somewhere, work on him.

Kazimi nodded at Sartaj, then slapped Anand Agavane again, a lazy backhand. It was only a punctuation mark, with not much force behind it. 'He asked you something,' Kazimi said. 'Answer.'

'I don't know anything about any money,' Anand Agavane said.

'What about the mobile?' Sartaj said. 'Where is it?'

Kamble took a white shirt from a hook, dropped it. Then he dug into a pair of white pants and came up with a wallet. 'An auto driver's packet, with so much money? And you don't even own the auto, bastard.' He flung the pants at Anand Agavane, bounced them off his face and on to the floor.

Sartaj tipped boxes from a kitchen shelf. On the far side of the stove, a black shelf held images of the Tuljapur Devi and Khandoba, and a framed black-and-white marriage picture, a man and a woman with a vague resemblance to Anand Agavane. That must be Veena Aatya, bejewelled and shy for her wedding. Sartaj swept the metal clean, and glass crunched on the floor. Kazimi planted a foot on Agavane's pants, and reached down and pulled the belt loose. He doubled it over, and slashed at Agavane's shoulders, his hips.

'If you make me angry,' he said, 'you'll have to spend the night with me, bhenchod. Not with your aatya. And I tell you, I will have a lot of fun, but you won't. Where is it, this maderchod mobile?'

Sartaj turned away from the shelves, back to the room. The kholi looked as if it had been suddenly destroyed, as if a hard wind had taken the bright calendars off the wall and gashed them in half, and spilt a canister of good rice across the floor. Sartaj tried to think across the thwacking of leather on skin, and Kamble's steady cursing. Anand Agavane had been sitting on the floor watching television, right there. He would not be far from his mistress's voice, the phone must be near the door. Somewhere over there. There was a shuttered window, but the scarred, twisted wood left only space enough on the sill for a packet of Wills and matches. Sartaj shook open the folded mattress that Agavane had been sitting on, and that yielded nothing but a musty smell and a faint sprinkling of fuzz. Sartaj stepped over the phone and its stool, and then there was nowhere to go. That was the room, this much was the kholi.

In the corner, at the height of Sartaj's head, a wire basket hung from a white rope. The basket was empty. Maybe Aatya was off buying atta, and potatoes, and mutton, which she would hang in the basket, away from the inescapable rats. She kept a neat house, even if her nephew was an apradhi. Anand Agavane was crouched over now, his head between his knees and arms wrapping around tight. His shoulders were flushed red now, and his head was bald and sweaty. Stubborn bastard. Sartaj knuckled the basket, and it swung gently against the wall. The rope went up to a hoop on a rafter. There was a picture on the wall, a recent studio portrait, all bright colours and dramatic lighting for a young couple. Aatya's daughter, maybe, in a red sari, with dark glasses pushed back on her head. Her husband stood next to her in a leather jacket, hands on hips, in a sleek model stance. The jacket was probably rented from the photographer, who had posed them as a modern young couple in front of a night-time city. The lights swept up and down, and sparkled on water. It could be Marine Drive, or New York. The black-framed photograph hung from a protruding brick. All down this front wall, a foot above Sartaj's head, there were paired bricks that angled out into the room. Aatya must have had them built in, every two feet or so. A practical woman. Sartaj reached up to the first one, and ran his hand over the top, and found only the rough surface and the twine that held up the photograph. He did the second one, and then kicked aside the mattress, took a step. He reached up, and felt the rush of confidence even as he did. Yes. He felt the smooth plastic at the tips of his fingers. It was the phone.

'I have it,' he said.

Kamble flung aside a tin biscuit box he had been investigating, and buttons and spools and needles rattled against the far wall. 'Show, show,' he said, holding out a hand.

But Sartaj held on to the phone, it was his, for the moment at least. This was that moment when a case opened up, when he felt he was ripping through a dark curtain, when there was that sharp rush of triumph and further appetite. He let it rush through him, and he could feel the grin on his face. He pressed keys on the phone, then held it up to Kamble. 'Last ten numbers dialled,' he said. 'All the same number, the other mobile.'

'Got you,' Kamble crooned. 'Caught you, bastard.' He took the phone, tapped the screen with his forefinger. He was as happy as a little boy with a softie cone.

But Kazimi was disgusted. He kicked Agavane, and then tottered away and sat on an upturned crate. 'Maderchod,' he said to Agavane. 'For this you made me work this much? You think we wouldn't have found the gaandu phone up there? You're sitting in a kholi as big as a mouse's hole, bhenchod. Stupid. Now we've got you.' He flapped out a big blue handkerchief, and wiped his face and the back of his neck. 'Finished now, hero? You ready to talk?'

Agavane's face came up to the light. He was weeping. 'Saab,' he said. 'Saab.'

It was eleven when Sartaj got to Mary's. He pulled up, suddenly aware of how loud the motorcycle was. The staircase was far from the single flickering light bulb at the end of the lane and very dark. Sartaj toed his way up, noticing for the first time the creepers on the wall to his left, the thick cushiony covering of leaves and vine. He knocked on the door twice, and was just starting to think of going down the stairs when it creaked open. Mary was fuzzy-eyed and very slow. She mumbled something, and shuffled backwards to let him in.

'I fell asleep,' she got out finally, through a huge yawn. There was a mother duck and little ducks on her very large yellow T-shirt.

'Sorry,' Sartaj said. 'I couldn't get out until now. I can go.'

'No, no.' She shut the door. 'I was just watching television, I closed my eyes.'

On the screen, a line of zebras, brilliant black and white, went leaping over a ridge. Sartaj reached out and touched Mary's cheek.

'Sartaj Singh,' she said, 'you are smelly.'

Sartaj stepped back. 'Sorry,' he said. 'A whole day of work, you see.' He was aware suddenly of his own reek, of the awful petroleum-tinged seams of dirt and sweat that had settled over his body, forehead to ankles. 'I should go. My plan was to go home first, but it got very late.'

Mary laughed. 'You're blushing,' she said. 'I didn't know that policemen could blush. Listen, you don't have to go. Why don't you take a bath?' She tipped her head towards the door behind Sartaj.

'A bath?' She was right, he had blushed, Sartaj could feel the flush on his chest and neck. He had never been shy, but now the thought of taking his clothes off behind that thin plank of wood made him feel unbearably exposed.

But Mary became brisk and efficient. 'Go,' she said. 'I'll get a towel. I'll warm up the food, it'll be ready when you finish.'

Sartaj bent over near the front door to take his shoes off, and then changed his mind and took them off outside, on the landing. He tucked the brown socks far back into the shoes, and smiled back at Mary.

'Do you take off your, your . . .?' she asked, holding out a green towel.

'Pugree. Usually.'

'So?'

He sat on the chair at the foot of her bed and unwound his pug. She watched him intently. It had been a long time since he had done this in front of a woman. His heart was squeezing fast, and his face felt warm.

'It's very long,' Mary said. 'That's a lot to carry on your head.'

'You get used to it.' Sartaj was wrapping the long swathe of blue cloth from elbow to hand as he took it off his head. 'Like a woman with a sari, no?'

Mary nodded. 'So did you catch her?'

'Who?'

'The woman who was blackmailing that girl.'

Sartaj froze. Anger and an inexplicable tincture of shame burned through his belly. Men are bastards, he thought, rakshasas. He didn't want to tell her who the apradhi was, but knew he had to. He took up another turn of cloth around his arm, and drew in a breath. 'No, we caught one of the low-level boys. But now we know who the black-mailer is. The bastard we caught, he told us everything.'

Mary clapped her hands, once, twice. 'Come on, tell. Who is it?'

Sartaj shook his head, and unclamped his jaw. 'It's the boyfriend,' he said.

'Which boyfriend? Whose?'

'Kamala's old boyfriend. The pilot. Umesh.'

'Wait, wait. The good-looking one? The one you met?'

'That one.' Sartaj stood up, ceremoniously laid his folded-up turban on the chair. 'This fellow we found today, his mother used to work for the pilot's family before she died. So the pilot recruited him for this job. To make the calls, to get the money.'

Mary's face had settled into an opaque blankness. 'Blackmailing this woman who,' she said, 'who . . .' She turned towards the wall, and her neck was taut.

'Umesh has expensive tastes,' Sartaj said. 'I think he saw too much cash in Kamala's purse, decided he needed some of it.'

'What are you going to do?'

'I don't know. We can't arrest him. There's no official case. We haven't decided yet.'

Mary picked a fragment of thread from her T-shirt, flicked it aside. 'Beat him,' she said. 'Beat him.'

'Yes,' Sartaj said, and then he didn't know what to say. Mary's shoulders were hunched under the fine yellow cloth.

'You can use my shower cap,' she said. 'If you want.'

'Yes.' Sartaj was glad to be able to escape to the bathroom now. He had trailed the sewer-smell of crime into Mary's home, and had upset her. In her anger there was the pain of her own history. He wasn't being a very successful suitor, he thought as he shut the door to the tiny bathroom. On the sill, under the ventilator, there was a row of shampoos and lotions and soaps. There were two hooks on the back of the door, both laden with towels and clothes. He didn't want to put his clammy shirt on top of her nightie. He moved the gown – soft, very soft – to the other hook, and the towel underneath, holding by the very tips of the fingers. He unbuttoned his shirt. Kamble had wanted to beat the pilot also, when Anand Agavane had told them who the blackmailer was. Kamble had been furious. He had wanted to pull the bastard pilot from his cockpit right then, or go to his house and beat him in the middle of his bhenchod movie-theatre room. Kazimi and Sartaj had both been surprised by Kamble's vehemence, and Kazimi had finally said, 'Why do you want to beat, bhai? The bastard has lots of money.' And Sartaj had nodded.

Sartaj put Mary's shower cap over his patka, and turned on the tap. There was no shower. Sartaj waited for the red plastic bucket to fill, watched the water froth. Kamble was very young. Under that cynicism, which he wore like armour, there was a romantic after all. 'Arre,

I have lots of girls,' he had said to Kazimi and Sartaj, 'but I don't make money from them. I spend maderchod money on them, as much as I can, more than I have. This pilot is a badhwa.' It had taken a while before they could calm him down, before they could convince him that beating was only a temporary pleasure, that it was no real punishment for a man like the pilot. He was still muttering when they had left each other. 'She had *love* for him,' he said, using the English word 'love' and stabbing at them with a forefinger, 'and he just exploited her. Bastard.'

Sartaj dipped mugs of water from the bucket, over his shoulders and belly. He was sitting cross-legged on a white aluminium stool, facing the tap. They had been so sure the apradhi was Rachel Mathias, scorned and insulted and vengeful. But it had turned out to be the beautiful lover himself who had wronged his beloved. Kamble, the amazing man, believed in the unspotted ecstasy of unadulterated love, in the dreams they sang about in the songs. '*Gaata rahe mera dil, tu hi meri manzil.*' Sartaj hooked the mug on the edge of the bucket, and sat with his hands on his thighs, eyes closed. Was it possible to come back to belief again, to leave behind too much knowledge and the comfortable distances of exile? Sartaj thought of the woman on the other side of the door, just so close, and how strange and unexpected it was that he was in her home, in her bathroom. He rubbed a bar of Lux over his shoulders, and thought of that other woman, the woman who had loved the pilot. Umesh was not a good man, but Kamala wasn't so good either. But Sartaj didn't want to remind Mary that Kamala had a husband, that she was selfish and frivolous and unfaithful, he didn't want to argue the point. Not here, not now. He wanted, just now, only quiet, and Mary close. There was always the possibility of arguments in the future, of betrayal and pain and damage, but this evening he needed a small enclosing circle of faith. The future wasn't here yet, and the past was gone. He turned the tap to full, and splashed large mugfuls of water on to his head, his chest, his thighs. He was grinning. He hummed the song: '*Kahin beetein na ye raatein, kahin beetein na ye din.*'

He was towelling himself dry when Mary knocked on the door. 'Here,' she said. He opened the door a crack, enough so that she could put her arm through. 'You can wear this.'

'This' was a well-worn white kurta. He shut the door, and held it up. It was a little short in the sleeves, but it fitted him quite well at the shoulders and chest. He wondered if it was her ex-husband's, or a boyfriend's, but he put the thought away. What did it matter? The kurta was clean, it had that crisp laundry smell of starch and ironing. He rolled the sleeves up his forearms, pinching down the edges of the folds to get them sharp and straight. His patka was easily retied, but there was nothing he could do about the hollows under his eyes, and the gaunt fall of his cheeks. He patted his beard down, and nodded at himself in the mirror, and went out.

Mary had dinner waiting for him on the small table near her bed. This was what they had originally decided on the phone, that he would eat her machchi kadi and rice after work. 'I hope you ate,' he said. 'I was very late.'

She had a small stove lit, and steam burbled from a pot. 'I was too tired to eat,' she said. 'Sit down.'

They ate sitting cross-legged on the floor, with the table between them. Mary's machchi kadi was fierce, but not malicious. Sartaj gasped as he ate, and drank a lot of water, and told her stories about his childhood. He told her about eating so much chole-bature at a roadside shop in Shimla that he had to be carried home by Papa-ji, and about his teenage passion for Royal Falooda from a particular Irani restaurant in Dadar, and about Gokul in Santa Cruz, where you could get a mango ice-cream so creamy that it took you back to long-ago summer mango-eating debauches, when you dipped for Dussheries in big buckets of cold water. He told her about afternoons when the June heat pressed through schoolroom walls, and seventy boys in white uniforms grew surly and restless, and the most dashing and popular of them – Sartaj and his friends – just had to jump through a window to eat kulfi on the street corner. She laughed at his stories, and filled his plate with more rice.

'I didn't know you had such a weakness for sweet things,' she said. 'I don't have any kulfi. Maybe some old toffees. I had some chocolate, but it's finished.'

'That's all right,' Sartaj said. 'No, no more.'

But he ate some more. After he had finished, after he had washed his hands and discreetly scrubbed his teeth with a dab of Mary's neem toothpaste, he sat with his back against the bed, sucking at an orange-flavoured sweet. This was one of three she had found far back on a shelf. She was washing dishes and pans, and the clanky music of it was comforting. Sartaj sighed, settled his shoulders, swallowed the last sliver of the sweet and closed his eyes. Just a minute or two, he thought, of rest.

He woke to a darkened room and Mary's hand on his face. 'Sartaj,' she whispered. 'Get into the bed.'

He had been dreaming, dreaming of Ganesh Gaitonde. The story of the dream fled from him as he pushed himself up on an elbow, but the last image remained with him: Gaitonde talking to him through a wall. *Listen, Sartaj.*

He had been curled on the floor, next to the bed. There was a cushion under his arm. 'I fell asleep,' he said, feeling quite foolish.

'You were tired too.'

He couldn't see her eyes or her face, but he knew she was staring at him. He got up, and sat on the edge of the bed, next to her. She moved, and lay on the far side of the bed, next to the wall. 'If I am here too much,' he said, 'and stay, won't your neighbours say things? Your landlord?'

She reached out, pulled gently at his wrist. 'Don't worry. You're a big Punjabi policeman. They're too scared of you to open their mouths.'

He arranged himself next to her, and they were still, shoulders touching. Sartaj took a breath, and turned on to his right side, and found her facing him. They kissed. In the darkness her lips were full and supple, different from before. She settled into the arch of his arm and collarbone and pressed her mouth to his. There was the tip of her tongue, an agile prickle that pierced him. Her breath moved through him.

A sound came from Sartaj, a low rasp, and he was hard against her. He spread his hand over the small of her back and brought her to him, her hips and belly. He had half-rolled on to her when he knew she had retreated, gone away somewhere. Her arm lay stiff against his back. He moved back.

'Sorry, I,' she said, 'I . . .'

Sartaj could feel her agitation, her anxiety. He tried to gentle her, stroked fingers through her hair. He was painfully erect, and there was a hunger in him that wanted to take her, but he was somehow content to lie close with her. Their breathing came together, and after a while he could see the gleam of a smile. He smiled also, and they kissed. He thought now she was different from the other women he had been with, not inexperienced exactly, but shy. She nuzzled tentatively at his chin, as if she was testing out something she had learned recently. He held her lower lip between his teeth, played with the corners of her mouth. She laughed, and he with her. They lay together. The baby-shampoo smell of her hair was the last thing Sartaj knew, and he settled gratefully into it.

In the delicious cool of first morning, Sartaj knew he was dreaming. He was walking down an endless twisting lane in a basti. The corrugated tin roofs were glistening with black rain, and there was a man stretching a torn piece of polyethylene over his shack. Sartaj walked. Katekar was walking next to him. They were talking about the riots. 'Those were bad days,' Katekar said. They were both walking behind Kazimi. Kazimi was walking in front of them. They walked. Then they spoke of the bomb blasts. Sartaj told Katekar about the severed foot he had seen on the road, about the tree stripped of all its leaves. 'He was lucky,' Katekar said, pointing with his chin at Kazimi. Katekar looked sad. I am dreaming, Sartaj thought.

Then Sartaj was awake. Mary was asleep next to him, and she was holding on to his forearm. Her breathing was slow and easy in the calm. Sartaj's hip was stiff, but he didn't want to turn over, the bed was narrow, he didn't want to wake her. Kazimi was lucky, he thought. Those were bad riots. Those endless nights with the burning bastis, the fleeing Muslims, the men with swords. The screams. The gunshots echoing from the buildings, back and forth. Who had shot Kazimi, a Hindu or a Muslim? Or another policeman, shooting wild? Anyway, he was lucky. He was lucky, and he was lucky only to be limping, he was lucky that he was not in a wheelchair. If he had been crippled, he wouldn't be able to walk down those bumpy lanes. Not unless he had a wheelchair like Bunty's.

Sartaj sat up. He was quite awake now, blood thudding in his head. Mary stirred beside him, he had jolted her.

'What?' she said.

Sartaj was remembering Bunty's wheelchair, the slick foreign styling of it. And he had a voice from long ago in his ear, a man preaching. A golden voice, confident of the truths it was telling. He couldn't see the man directly, but there he was, on a television monitor. He was a great guru, a famous guru, and he had done a yagna. Mary's television was dark. In it, Sartaj could see his own face. There had been a wheel on that other television screen, a wheel behind the guru's head. A shiny wheel, long ago. The guru had been on a wheel-chair. A fast wheelchair, an unusual wheelchair. Sartaj remembered the low electronic hum it made.

'I have to go,' he said.

'What happened?'

'Nothing, nothing. I have to get to work. I will call.'

He kissed her, tucked a sheet high about her shoulders and gathered up his things. The landing was dark, and there was the slightest begin-ning of light at the sliver of horizon he could see between the buildings. He shut the door behind him, and then sat on the top step to pull on his shoes. His fingers were twitchy, nervous, as he tried to hurry. He took the steps in three loping leaps, and as soon as he was on solid ground he reached for his mobile phone. The screen was a dead grey. Maderchod, he hadn't charged it last night. And then he was on the motorcycle, speeding down the empty roads. He knew of an all-night PCO near Santa Cruz station, and he was there in less than ten minutes. He knocked at the window, got up the boy dozing behind the counter. Come on, come on. Then he was listening to clicks on the line as the call went through. On the green partition that sepa-rated the booth from the counter, a large heart had been scratched into the wood. There was an arrow through it, and 'Reshma' and 'Sanjay' in flowing script on either side. The heart was bleeding little drops of blood, a whole line of them arcing down towards the ground. Sartaj ran a finger over the arrow.

'Hello?' Anjali Mathur's voice was low and rough, but alert.

'Madam,' Sartaj said. 'This is Sartaj Singh calling from Mumbai. You are sleeping, sorry.'

'What happened? Tell me.'

'Madam,' Sartaj said, 'I think I may know Gaitonde's guru.'

Ganesh Gaitonde Makes a Film

'You dab the eye-shadow on, darker at the corners of the eyelids.'

I was lying across a silver-framed, satin-sheeted bed, watching Jamila put on make-up. She had the lights on in a blazing circle around the mirror and was sitting up close to it, assaying her face with the calm detachment of a doctor. She was bare-chested, but when she worked on her face even I could only pay attention to her eyes, her cheeks. 'Then you put the eyeliner on, Lakme charcoal black. You make a little tail on the outside of the eye. See? Like a little fish. It balloons up at the end. Which gives a false contour to the eye. Okay, so. If your upper lid is highly eyelined, you don't want to go heavy on the lower lid. You would lose definition on the upper lid. If you want your eyes to look big, you go a bit high on the outer edges of the lower lids. Use a pencil that you can smudge, and push it up a bit.'

She was speaking loudly, over the disco music with its strutting beat, but enunciating very sharply. She practised clear speaking. She checked on me to see if I was paying attention, and I smiled. I was nicely tired, I had taken her twice that evening, once on the floor. There were six feet of her, all of it smooth and young and resilient and yielding, and I had explored the entire territory, every last bit of it. 'Your eyes look huge,' I said.

'Okay, then. Cheekbones. You use blush on the cheekbones, get a shine. I like Bronze Blitz. See? Then you have to decide, do you want a soft look or a hard look? Where are you going, what's the impression you want to make? If you're going to be under lights, with cameras clicking, you might want a hard look, to stand out in the photographs. But we're not going anywhere. So, soft. For a soft look, I like using this MAC lipliner, it's German. You outline the lips. I'm using the Plum Preserved colour today. Now, you only want to outline the lips. If you used the lipliner on the whole lip surface, it would be too sharp. So, I use blush-on for lipstick.'

'Very clever,' I said. 'You are one sharp Jamila.' She didn't even give me back a thousandth of a smile. About her work she was as serious as a pandit. Or a mullah, in her case.

'You dab in the blush-on, then spread it with a finger. Like this. So, lips done. Now, mascara.' She opened her mouth further to put on the mascara. I had noticed this every time I had watched her do her face, just as I had noticed it with every woman I had been with. They would reach towards their eyes with the mascara, but would open their mouths wide. They were a strange tribe, women. 'With mascara, linger on the roots of the eyelashes as you go up. As you go up, shake the applicator a bit, do a little twist. See? Linger, shake, twist. And what do you get? Thick, lovely lashes. That's what. Okay, now we're getting done. But not finished. The secret is: blend, blend, blend! Everything has to blend. No sharp edges.'

She blended. I watched.

'Let's see. What else? Okay, today, for the sultry look, I'm going to use some lip-stain. It gives a stained effect, sort of smoky. I'm going to use a purple MAC lip-stain. You should even out the stain. If you don't have a brush, you can use the end of a pencil. Like this.' Then she turned to me, held out her hands wide. 'Finished. See? I'm done.'

And yes, yes, she was done. She was transformed, from an interesting and stretchy piece of unpolished Lucknow steel into a translucent, weightless blooming of light. She stood up, to her full long height, and slipped a blue dressing gown over the delicate angle of her shoulders. Underneath, she wore only black thong panties and slim pumps. I had paid Jojo an unprecedented amount for this tall virgin, and then given lakhs to Jamila herself afterwards, and every time she stood straight and tall like this, I thought, paisa vasool. She walked away from me, down the length of the suite, hip-tilting against the Singapore skyline. At the end of the carpet, she struck a runway pose and gave me a long gaze over her shoulder. There was a little flash of upreaching nipple, erect and clearly silhouetted. And in that moment, with the bright blue behind and she all gold and darkness in front, we could have been on television, on Fashion TV or Star TV or Zee TV. She came back to me, doing that walk, and I felt that tearing pull in my chest that you get from rich, glossy, beautiful women. There was that mingled longing and hopelessness, of seeing something that swam in the heavens far above. The difference was that I could have this one kneeling before me in a second. Mine, I thought, she is mine. So there was the pain, but also this pleasure. So I let her walk. She knew I liked to watch her, and she gave me a show. When I could stand it no more, I had her pose on all fours near the window, in the bronze waning of the light, and I knelt in front of her, at her mouth. This was the third time that day, I hurt and shuddered and finally found release.

Afterwards we ate. I was hungry all right, but to watch her eat was frightening. She ate politely enough, with knife and fork and little pats of the napkin to the corners of her lips, but she put away enough food for three men. If you insisted on speaking to her, she would of course make good conversation, about the topics of the day. But left to her preferences, at mealtimes she was completely quiet. She ate her way through plates of chicken, followed up with a dish of lamb, or two, and finished with goblets of ice-cream. Instead of tea or coffee, she drank a glass of lassi, or milk if that was all that was available. The first time we'd eaten together, she had told me she didn't need caffeine, that every cell in her body ran and sprinted by its own nature. She needed only five hours of sleep a night to look rested and rosy, and could get by perfectly with four.

I, on the other hand, was exhausted from the day's exertions, all within the confines of this flat. So I ate quietly, and then bathed. When I came out of the bathroom, Jamila had the covers turned down and a glass of warm milk on the night-stand. I had trained her well. While she showered, I sipped at the milk and talked to Arvind on the intercom. He was just downstairs from us, in the bottom half of this double duplex apartment with his Suhasini, who no longer looked like Sonali Bendre. Guru-ji had been right about their marriage: they had each become stronger in it. Arvind was still thoughtful, but he was now decisive and pragmatic. Suhasini had given up her flashy, trollopy ways, and was now placidly happy, and her energy fuelled her husband. I had made Arvind a controller in our eastern operations, and had established him in this fine apartment on Havelock Road, which was really two apartments. I met Jamila only here, in this upper penthouse, only in this one place. Our interaction was most secret, and not only because of the risk to me. It was obvious to all of us, to me and Jamila and Jojo, that a girl who wanted to be Miss Universe had better not be easily connected with an international lord of crime. So we kept it quiet. Just as the tall Jamila was quiet. Even when she showered she never sang, when she watched movies she never laughed or cried or clapped. Now, from the bedroom, I could hear the splashing of the water, and that was about all. I talked business with Arvind, and asked after the pregnant Suhasini. Then I hung up, and called Bunty in Bombay. More business talk, and by the time we had finished Jamila was done with her long evening ablutions. Her washbasin in the bathroom looked like a chemist's shop, with ointments and lotions and shampoos arranged neatly in rows. Yet when she came to bed, with her hair up, she managed not to have that clammy, creamed-up look that so many women brought with them to sleep. She just looked clean, scrubbed and healthy.

I switched off the light, and we lay next to each other. I knew she wouldn't sleep for a while, for an hour or two at least, but she deferred to my schedule and was courteously pliable. She ate and slept and woke when I wanted. And I wanted to sleep now. But her body kept me awake.

It was not only appetite that tickled and teased my mind into movement. I was sated, for the moment. What I was thinking about was the form of her body, its lines and arrangements and proportions. We had remade that form. Jamila's bottom had been realigned. That is, the cheeks – which are naturally asymmetrical on all human beings – had been lined up. The fat inside the small rolls on her hips had been sucked out and inserted into her gaand, to make it properly plump and perky. The lower end of her thighs, the sides and the upper rear portions, just under her bottom, had all been liposuctioned. Her waist had been liposuctioned. As had her upper arms and the area behind her chin. She had new saline implants in her breasts, natural-shaped ones we had examined and handled and discussed at length. We had done all this at Dr Langston Lee's house of wonders on Orchard Boulevard. He had a peerless reputation, a clean and very modern clinic and extravagant rates. But he was a master, that small-eyed and funny-speaking man, he was a maha-magician of flesh, he could move it and transform it and make it vanish and have it reappear. Jamila had found him through her extensive world-ranging research, and he had not disappointed. Even I, who had been a thoughtless consumer of bodies, a mostly undiscriminating chodu who knew what he liked but not why, even I had learnt from listening to their discussions. I understood now this language of beauty, its grammar and its sublime syntax. Listening to these two poets, I understood how a well-made song of curves and textures and spaces could effortlessly enchant the stoniest heart. It was magic that they had created together, this doctor and his subject. There was no defence against the cunning spell they had made out of her.

This process had cost a lot of money already, and unimaginable pain. I hadn't ever visited Jamila in the clinic, but I had spent time with her after the surgery, in our flat. She had never let out a groan, or complained, but I knew what effort it cost to make one journey from the bed to the bathroom when the tissues under her thighs had been ripped and assaulted by a probing nozzle. I saw the grinding strain in the sweat on her forehead. I felt it in her bruises, in the yellow-green welts across her breasts, in her clutch on the bed-cover. So much pain, so many days of it. And it was not over. We were going to do her face next. Dr Lee was going to carve hollows in her cheeks. He was going to put fat in her lips. He was going to work on her nose, sharpen it with an implant. He was going to raise her hairline. And the chin was to get an implant too, to lengthen it, to make it strong, shapely, exactly the right counterpoint to her brow. He was going to make her harmonious, flawlessly balanced, perfect. She was then going to be – according to her calculations – complete.

'How did you begin?' I said.

'Saab?' she said. Her reply was instant, and she was not sleepy, not fuzzy. But my question, it must be admitted, had been vaguely phrased.

'When did you first think you wanted to be a star? When did you make a plan to come to Bombay? How did you manage it?' There was no change in her breathing, or movement in her body, but she came into full alertness now. I could feel it on my forearms, at the back of my neck.

'That is a boring small-town story, saab.'

'Tell me.'

'Yes, saab,' she said. She was a good girl. She always called me 'saab', and was quiet and obedient. Now she spoke, in even tones. 'The first time I saw models was when I was six years old.'

'Yes,' I said. And as she spoke, every other minute I made a sound, a 'yes' to let her know that I was listening. And she went on.

'I mean, I had seen them before in magazines and newspapers, and actresses in the films, but that time I saw models in real life, in our Lucknow itself. My mother had taken me to my chacha's house, and on the way back we walked through Hazratganj. The models were walking out of a department store, they had come to Hazratganj for the grand opening. They walked out of the store, across the pavement, through a crowd held back by policemen, and climbed into an air-conditioned bus. That was it, thirty seconds, maybe a minute. With me standing squeezed between my mother and some man, looking up at them. They passed so close that I could have reached out and touched a skirt, a hand. But I didn't. I held on to my mother's burqa and looked up at the models. They were there, right there. In Hazratganj. But they looked like they were from another world. Like they were fairies. They were tall. Taller than me, taller than my mother. Thin and tall. Two of them spoke as they went past, in English, and I understood none of it. But even their voices had that feeling, that mood which was there on their red cheeks, their dark eyes. They were fairies. After that when anyone told me a story about princes and djinns and magic, I always saw the models. I never forgot them. That evening, I asked my mother who they were. She didn't know. She was a pious woman who always wore a burqa, what did she know of models? I tried to tell my father when we got home, and he laughed and asked my mother what I was talking about, and she shrugged. Some shameless cut-haired foreign girls, she said.

'They weren't foreign, they were Indian enough, a troupe of top models from Bombay. But that was foreign enough for my mother. We found out the next day who they were. My father was a small man, he owned a small restaurant in the Chowk Bazaar, and he was pious. He thanked Allah every day for the success of the restaurant, which was famous even beyond Lucknow for its kakori kababs. But he was also progressive. In the restaurant he took not only two Urdu papers but also the *Times of India*. He couldn't read English himself, but he hoped that his children would learn, move up in the world. Actually, his hope was mainly for his sons, my elder brothers. But I – who was the youngest and his pet then – also used to flip through the papers and magazines that he bought for them, and listened to his discussions with them. That morning my eldest brother, Azim, who was most fluent in English in the family and was preparing for the UP State Services exam, he laughed and said, here are Jamila's foreign women. And there they were, in a photograph on the third page of the paper, floating down a long raised walk. I recognized the one right in front, she had been part of the conversation I had heard. Azim explained to my father that they were models who had come from Bombay for a fashion show at a five-star hotel, which had been attended by all the rich people of Lucknow, and also the DIG and the collector. That was the first time I think I had heard the words "fashion show". I hardly knew what they meant. I imagined a crowd, like that on the pavement in Hazratganj, and the beautiful models walking above them all. Nothing else, just drifting by. And all the people looking at them.

'This was all I knew then. And this was all I clung to for a long time, for many years in my world, which was my street, my home and my school, and my father and mother and brothers and aunts and cousins. Every night I had that walk, every night I slept at last seeing only the beautiful models of Bombay, walking by me on a footpath where the crowd was gone, which had somehow been lifted up out from Lucknow. I wanted to know more, but by instinct I did not ask, I didn't let anyone know. I knew women shouldn't hanker after such things, that good girls memorized surahs and hadiths and were modest and quiet, not just while awake, but even when sleeping. Just sitting next to my mother, when I ate after the boys had finished, I knew this. So I kept quiet, and learned by listening, whatever bits and pieces I could. I tried to read the *Times of India*, with Azim, until it became something of a joke in the family. Come, Azim said every morning, as he opened the paper. So I knew a bit more. I knew that models lived in Bombay, that most of them were English-speaking girls who grew up there, that they made wonderful amounts of money and moved with high-high people. But it was only after we got a colour television at home, and cable, that I really understood anything.

'This was just after I had turned eleven. That year, after we got cable, I began to watch television in the afternoons, and grow. Until that summer I had been an ordinary girl, only my father paid me any special attention, everybody else thought I was plain, quiet, good. But then I began to grow. I grew, and grew. My mother had been a little tall for her times, maybe five-five. My father was maybe an inch taller. Azim was the tallest in the family, five-eight. But then I began to grow. While I watched the fashion-based shows on MTV and V, I lengthened. On Zee they did interviews with fashion designers, and choreographers, and photographers. I watched. At night I ached. My joints hurt, and my tendons pulled and stretched. I watched *Fashion Guru*, and practised my English, and grew. By the time I was fourteen

I had overtaken all my brothers except Azim, and the next year I was taller than him. I was thin, so thin. The mohalla girls said unkind things to my face, and my mother muttered. My father's explanation was that he had a great-uncle who had been five-nine-and-a-half, and I had gone on him. But at the end of my sixteenth year, I was taller than even this uncle, and still growing.

'My family was worried. Where were they going to find a man taller than me? And even if they did, would this tall man want a wife who was long and stretched? But I wasn't worried. I knew where they wanted tall girls. I knew who I was. I had studied not only fashion, but myself. Even if nobody around me could see it, I knew I had potential. Two years after Aishwariya and Sushmita won, a beauty parlour had opened right by our mohalla. The young girls and wives used to go there, to get eyebrow plucking and facials and wedding make-up. But still, the girls who were considered pretty, who all my brothers mooned after, they were all fair and a little plump and demure-looking. I knew my colours and my lines, and I was nothing like them. I was considered ugly, I was dark. But I knew. In my mirror I could see what was there, and what needed to be done. I had read all about deportment and training and walking on the catwalk and that model look and plastic surgery. I knew where I could go. I knew where I had to go. There was only one place for me: Bombay. So I came.'

I had never heard her speak so much before, never this long at one stretch. I think it was the darkness, and my unexpected question, and my whispered affirmatives – finally she hadn't even been telling her story to me, but to herself. The rest of her journey I knew, Jojo had told me. Jamila had waited until the day after her eighteenth birthday. Late that afternoon, she left her house wearing a burqa, carrying only her purse in which she had seven thousand four hundred rupees, some of it saved painfully over the years, most of it stolen from her mother's almirah. She had three gold bangles, and some silver jewellery of no account. She caught a rickshaw to Nakkhas, via Kashmiri Mohalla, where she bought a cheap suitcase. She kept her face covered and walked hunched over, becoming a pious old woman to all who passed her. Even then her acting skills were unmatched. She carried this suitcase to a friend's house, where she had – over the past few weeks – carried articles of clothing to make a stash. Then she went to the railway station, where she waited for the Pushpak Express. She already had a ticket and a reservation for a sleeper berth, made two weeks before under an assumed name. She sat quietly in the train, and watched the miles slide by. All she left in Lucknow was a note, which her mother would find late at night in the kitchen. It said, 'I am going of my own free will. It is my choice. Please do not try to find me.' She wrote nothing about where she was going, and why, and what for. Since she had never said a word to anyone about her ambitions, about her direction, nobody knew where to look for her. Even the friend who had helped her thought she was aiding Jamila towards a secret, married boyfriend. But there was no man, no boyfriend, only her dream. In Bombay she had discarded the burqa, changed her name again and stayed at a little women's guest house near Haji Ali, a dormitory where every woman got one bed and a small table and a two-foot shelf. I knew how she had suffered the first few months, the little sales jobs, the grasping bosses, the three-hour bus rides to meet photographers, the indecent suggestions and the passes and the humiliations. I had heard all this, and yet I had never understood the strength of this Jamila until that night, when she told me how she had come to this understanding of herself, of what she was and who she could be. Jojo had been right, this Jamila was like me. There are some minds that can change the world. I had learned from Guru-ji that this earth we walk on, this sky that we huddle under, all of this is a dream. Those with tapas and enough willpower can move this universe, he had said. I had written my own life. Now I knew that Jamila also had this ability, this desire. We, those few who have this grand vision, can rewrite ourselves. Some time between sleeping that night and waking the next morning, in sleep or maybe out of it, I decided to make a film for her.

'So you have really fallen for the Egotistical Giraffe,' Jojo said decisively when I told her about my plan to produce a movie. I had made my usual afternoon call to her, in Bombay.

'Why do you assume that I've fallen for anything?' I said. 'I have been wanting to make a film for a long time.'

'Maybe, perhaps. But now is when you choose to make it. You are fida on her. Admit it. The Egotistical Giraffe has you hooked.'

Nothing would budge her from this belief, this certainty, and from referring to Jamila each and every time as the Egotistical Giraffe. This despite the fact that Jamila was her protégé, that she, Jojo, was the girl's best sponsor, that Jojo herself had brought her to me. 'Jojo, you are jealous of the poor girl.'

That got a big Jojo laugh out of her. 'Jealous that she has to put up with you sticking it to her every two minutes, Gaitonde?' I had, in a foolish moment of satisfied relaxation, told her how much I liked to arrange Jamila in aesthetic poses, how I took her in various positions and exotic locations. Giving a woman any information is a foolishness that I counselled my boys against. Whatever you tell will always be one day used against you. But with Jojo somehow I broke my own rules. We had known each other too long, we knew each other too well. Sometimes even during the act – chodoing Jamila in a limousine on the way to a restaurant, say – I was aware that I was looking forward to telling Jojo about it. That the telling was crucial, that the act was for the telling. I had to tell Jojo. And so she knew too much, including how much I enjoyed riding the Egotistical Giraffe. 'I have better things to do with my time than giving my gaand to you, Gaitonde,' she said.

'But Jamila's gaand is going to be on a big screen,' I said. 'And that burns yours.'

'Ten years ago it would have. Maybe even five. But now I am happy, baba. Do you understand that? Happy. I like my work, I like what I have. I have success at what I do. And I realize now that even if I had got a film, I wouldn't have lasted long in that business. I was just a little girl playing big games. I didn't know anything.'

'This Jamila has been studying the business since she was a child.'

'Yes. She worked very-very hard for a long time. That's because she is an Egotistical Giraffe.'

There it was again, that sting at the end of the unwinding compliment. 'Don't be a kutiya,' I said. 'You live off bachchas like her. And their studying and hard work.'

Jojo accepted this gracefully. She could be sharp as a Japanese chef's knife, but she was honest. 'That's true,' she said. 'And I send some of them to you, Gaitonde. For your enjoyment.'

'Yes,' I said. 'Read me a letter.' This, too, was one of my pleasures. For the last two or three years, Jojo had been receiving letters. They came in those brown envelopes they sold near post offices and in bazaars next to postings about government jobs and stacks of application forms.

'Yes, yes,' Jojo said. 'Just hold on. I got a really good one on Friday. I was saving it for you.'

I could hear her rooting about through her shelves. The letters came from all over the country, but especially from the north, from places like 'Azadnagar, Maithon Farm, Dhanbad', and 'Asabtpura, Moradabad', and 'Mangaon, Dist. Raigad', and 'Mallik Tola, Banka, Bihar'. Some Hindi paper out of Delhi had plagiarized a *Times of India* Sunday article about modelling, complete with pictures of a couple of women who had come to Bombay from small towns and had become successful models and actresses. In this article, the paper had listed Jojo as one of the model co-ordinators who worked with new people. And the letters had started arriving. They came in a steady trickle that grew into a gush as the article was copied and duplicated and stolen by other papers. The letters were mostly from men, and Jojo and I had speculated about why women didn't write more often. Jojo thought that the girls were probably afraid of receiving a reply at home. Jojo said, what if the father opened a letter from me telling the girl to come to Bombay? She said, the girls just run away. Or sometimes they win a local beauty contest and talk one of the parents into coming to Bombay with them. Nowadays even the parents hear the lakhs jingling in their dreams, so they come.

'Okay, Gaitonde,' Jojo said. 'Here it is. This one is from village Chhabilapur, post office Gobindpur, district Begu Sarai.'

'Where?'

'Bihar, baba.'

'What is it with these Biharis?'

'They're good-looking people, they're intelligent, they're ambitious and they're survivors. Now be quiet and listen.'

'Yes, yes. Tell me.'

Her reading of Hindi was slow and painful, she had only learnt to speak it after she had reached Bombay. And she had learnt to read – what she could – even later. She'd got better at Hindi from reading letters to me. Before she had told me about these letters, she used to stack them up unopened behind a cupboard and throw them away once a week. But after she had told me about them, I had made her read one to me, and then another. Now she cast an eye over each one, and saved the best for me. 'This one,' she said, 'starts with the usual opening. He read about the Mr International contest in a paper, and my company was mentioned in the article. He wants to know how he can enter the world of modelling.'

'Arre, read it, Jojo.'

'Gaitonde, his Hindi is really difficult and northern, full of *hum* and *humara pata* and *kasht karein* and all that.'

'Just read it.'

'Okay. I liked this one because he makes lists. Languages known: Hindi, English, Magahi, Maithili. His name, by the way, is Sanjay Kumar.' The amusement was already gurgling in her voice. 'Sanjay Kumar does not want to send an ordinary biodata. So he has added a "Favourites List". Favourite flower: Rose. Favourite heroes: Anil Kapoor, Salman Khan, Aamir Khan. Favourite heroines: Rani Mukherjee, Kajol, Aishwarya Rai.'

'Why does he think you need to know this?'

'Who knows? Listen, Gaitonde – favourite films: *Karan Arjun*, *Sholay*, *Dilwalle Dulhaniya Le Jayenge*, *Pardes*. Favourite foreign places: London, Switzerland, New Zealand.'

'The bastard has never left Chabillapur.'

'He's seen New Zealand in the movies, Gaitonde. His father bought a VCD player for the family, they watch films every day. Favourite creams: Fairever, Pond's Cold Cream. Favourite perfume: Rexona. Favourite soap: Lux, Pear's and Pear's Face Wash. Favourite shampoos: Clinic All-Clear and Nyle Herbal Shampoo. Favourite hair oil: Dabur Mahabrahmraj Hair Oil.' She was laughing so hard now that she could barely read. 'Favourite powder: Denim and Nycil. Favourite shaving set: Denim and Old Spice. Favourite toothpaste: Colgate Gel Blue and Aquafresh. Favourite jeans: Levis. Favourite cars: Cielo, Tata Safari, Maruti Zen, Maruti 800, Ferrari 360 Spider.'

'This little maderchod has not even smelt a Ferrari in bhenchod district Begu Sarai. They don't even have chutiya roads there which are worthy of being called roads.'

'He's done his research, Gaitonde. Listen, listen.'

Listening to Sanjay Kumar's lists gave me a queer feeling in my belly, a soft, slipping panic in my veins. Of course he was funny. Jojo read out his lists and we laughed. I listened to her laugh and I laughed some more. But still there was this unnameable, endless plummeting in my chest. I didn't want to tell Jojo about it, but even if I had wanted to, if I had tried to, I wouldn't have known what to call it. I had never been to Bihar, but I knew exactly what sort of district Begu Sarai was, what village Chhabilapur looked like. There was one ruptured road winding through the fields, and muddy little kachcha lanes leading off to the clumps of huts and houses. There was something called a primary school, which was really a bunch of children sitting on the patio of the local Shiva temple, with a teacher – when there was a teacher – calling out the alphabet. There was a long wall bordering the sarpanch's orchards, and advertisements for engine lubricant and seed on this wall. There was a family of labourers squatting by the pond, waiting to be paid for the day's work. There was a three-storeyed college, with ranks of loafing students in the stained corridors. Outside, the motorcycles of the rich boys, the merchants' sons, the landowners' sons. Overhead, a vacant sky. Somehow, in this village, in this district, Sanjay Kumar had gathered the elements of his lists, he had put them together. He had written it all down. How? From borrowed newspapers, from second-hand magazines? From television, watched at a friend's house between power cuts? He had prepared his letter, then copied it out in fair, and sent it off to Bombay. Thinking of Sanjay Kumar bent over his letter, under a lantern, this is what made me queasy.

'At the very end of the letter,' Jojo said, 'after he signs off, he adds a request.' She snorted. 'He lists English as one of his languages, up front in his letter. But at the end, he writes, "I await your speedy and kind response. Please answer my letter in Hindi only." This Sanjay Kumar is not very smart. Or he thinks model co-ordinators in Bombay are chutiyas.'

'Who would dare to think you are a chutiya, Jojo? No, no. The poor boy is just trying to move ahead in the world. Remember, you were there once.'

'I was never such a gaandu as this. Sending letters to Bombay. Wanting replies in Hindi. Listen, I've been in the business for a while now. I have a feeling for people now, for who moves ahead and who doesn't. And I'm telling you, this one doesn't have a chance. Even if he looks like Hrithik Roshan, he doesn't have a chance. If he comes to Bombay, he'll be eaten up.'

I couldn't argue against that. 'Yes,' I said. 'Yes.' Sanjay Kumar didn't have a chance. He probably didn't have a chance even if he stayed in that rotting, choking village of his. But whether he stayed or left, he was going to keep watching movies, making lists, continue writing letters. Stupid bastard. But there were crores and crores like him, up and down and across the country. They were there, and they were our audience. I was going to make my film for them.

Of course I consulted Guru-ji before I put any cash into play. I wanted to see Jamila on the screen, and I was sure she would succeed as a star, but I wanted direction. I wasn't about to rush into a game I knew nothing about without some knowledge about what was to happen. But Guru-ji could see nothing, he couldn't see into the future of my movie with any specificity. 'I have a good feeling about the project, beta,' he said. 'But that's all. It happens sometimes, it's like trying to see through a warped lens. Some things get blanked out, some things come into sharp focus. I can't see anything bad.'

'But you can't see anything good,' I said.

'No, not that either. But it's a minor risk, compared to some of the things you've done. And are doing.'

He was absolutely correct, as usual. I had risked my life many times, and this was just money. I remembered then what Paritosh Shah used to say, if you let Lakshmi go, she comes back to you multiplied, if you try to imprison Lakshmi she will escape you and never come back. For Jamila, I had to let my Lakshmi out into the world, to move as she pleased. It was only appropriate.

So I made a movie for Jamila. Getting the production team together was easy enough. I had the money, so I hired the best. Actually, I had Jojo find me a producer, a man named Dheeraj Kapoor, and this Dheeraj did the hiring. Dheeraj had made three hits in a row, all in the four to six-crore budget range, with respectable actors and strong scripts. Now he was hungry for a chance to jump into a higher league, to play the game with twenty-odd crores and real stars. I liked hungry men to work for me. You had to watch them closely, but they performed well. And this Dheeraj was a coming man, I could feel it. He would succeed.

Meanwhile the new Jamila went from triumph to triumph. We had given her a new name, a name to fit that star she was becoming: she was now 'Zoya Mirza'. It was a good modern-sounding name, short and easily written and pronounced, it had that hip Z sound at the beginning and towards the end. It was a new name that could live in this new world. And once the work on her face was complete, she was more than new. She was the future. What Dr Langston Lee had done to her cheeks, her hairline, her chin, her nose, was not radical. It was just a little bulk taken off there, a hair's breadth of length added there. She was the same, and yet she was completely different. Before, she was striking. Now, she was dazzling. Sometimes it was hard to look at her, it was as if she were far away, even when she was sitting right next to me. Her beauty made me yearn, and it was hard to bear. She was complete, and she made me feel that big raw hole somewhere deep inside me, a wound that ached when she was far, and even more when she was near.

And she succeeded. She got more ramp work than anyone else in town, and two glossy covers in a month. There was a buzz about her even before she won Miss India, and more afterwards. She won the contest easily, and without having to compromise in the usual ways. She stayed tantalizingly out of the reach of the photographers and the judges and the publishers, and collected her crown. She made the chief editor of the sponsoring newspaper believe that he would get between her legs if she won the crown, and slipped away from him altogether. She was able to do all this because of my support. Not that we applied pressure, or bribed anyone, or used any of our other techniques. No, I just provided the resources that let her become the unearthly Zoya, that let her say 'No'. Cash creates beauty, cash gives freedom, cash makes morality possible. Cash makes films. So I started work on my movie with Manu Tewari.

This Manu had already written three small films, the last of which had won the National Award for best picture. I'd seen it, and thought that for an art movie about hijras it wasn't so boring, and that the writing was actually quite powerful. So we flew Manu Tewari out to Thailand. I was willing to let Dheeraj and his team make many other choices, but I wanted control over the story. I had an idea or two myself, and I had watched a lot of films recently, and followed the weekly collections in India and abroad. I knew what I wanted in my movie. But this Manu turned out to be a socialist, and full of rules besides. For the first three days he was with us, he was as quiet and still as a rabbit who looks up and finds himself in a den of tigers. Dheeraj Kapoor had told him only that he was flying out to Bangkok to meet the financier of the film, nothing else. And in Bangkok, Manu had been picked up, put on a flight to Phuket, and suddenly he found himself on a yacht with Ganesh Gaitonde and lots of mean-looking boys with big guns. Of course he was paralysed, he didn't know where to sit, when he was allowed to stand, or whether he could piss without permission. The boys amused themselves the first couple of days by being especially bloodthirsty in front of him, by reloading their pistols and waving them about and generally terrifying the wits out of the poor writer.

Finally I shooed them off, and sat Manu Tewari down with a glass of Scotch, and calmed him down. I praised all his movies, and told him that the last one had made me cry, and that too for hijras, which was a far greater compliment to him than any bhenchod National Award. He settled down a bit then, and took a sip of Scotch, and began to grin a little. Writers are pathetically susceptible to praise. I have worked with politicians, and gangsters, and holy men, and let me tell you, none of these can compete with a writer for mountainous inflations of ego and mouse-like insecurities of soul. I anointed Manu with large helpings of his own glory, and he relaxed. Of course, coming from Ganesh Gaitonde, the admiration was ten times as delicious. Manu Tewari slowly relaxed back into the sofa, and took another Scotch, and told me stories about the making of his hijra movie, how they had to persuade their hero that playing a lauda-less, skirt-wearing, hand-clapping hijra was not going to cripple his career for ever. Manu Tewari was himself a medium-sized piece, medium in every way. You could have taken him as a blueprint for all that is average in the world, he was not short but not too tall, he had grown up in Bandra East as the son of a Class II employee in the state Ministry of Finance, and he had gone to college at Rizvi and had had a totally undistinguished academic career. I knew all this about him from Dheeraj's background report, but no report could have contained the madness that he hid somewhere deep inside that unremarkable body, that he let out only when he talked about movies.

'*Naajayaz* was good, bhai,' he said. 'The scenes between Naseer and Ajay Devgan were very good, but somewhere in the second half it began to drag a little. That's Mahesh Bhatt's problem in his later movies, he either moves everything too fast, or he drags it out. So the poor public is either confused or bored.' I had quite liked *Naajayaz*, but I let it pass and listened to him. Manu Tewari certainly knew his movies, he even knew details about some obscure underworld movie which had been under production from 1987 to the summer of 1990 and had come and disappeared in 1991, without anyone noticing. Except Manu Tewari. He knew who the music director was, and what ad films the cinematographer had done after that movie, and who the director had been chodoing during the song schedule in Australia, and how the film had done average business in Bombay and Hyderabad, but had been totally rejected in the Punjab circuit. He went on, 'But the best crime-and-gangster movie of the early nineties was *Parinda*. It moved our films in a new direction, in terms of texture and realistic atmosphere. Clearly, Jackie Shroff found himself as an actor in that film, and he was a different Jackie afterwards. And it introduced Nana Patekar to a national audience. And Binod Pradhan's cinematography set a new standard altogether.'

He spoke of *Naajayaz* and *Parinda* with the seriousness of a man talking about the nature of God, or the history of the world. Actually, movies were his entire world. He had grown up in his quiet little flat, with his one sister and one brother, and he had led a colourless and blameless life. But through it all he had grown this thing inside himself, this worm, this python that ate films to survive, that swallowed them whole and kept them for ever. You had to give him the merest excuse to talk about *Mughal-e-Azam*, and he would go on for an hour. But to get him to talk about his own mother took some severe nudging from me. And even then he only said, 'What to say about her, bhai? She's a housewife. She looked after us.'

For all his bright-eyed curiosity about the details of other people's adventures and agonies, that was all he could find to say about his mother. But I had only been trying to make family chat, a management technique I had learnt from Guru-ji. This Manu Tewari was comfortable enough now. It was time to get down to business. 'All right. So,' I said, 'let's talk about the story.'

He sat up straight then. When it came to work, he was instantly focused, that first time and always afterwards. 'Yes, bhai,' he said. 'Please tell me.'

We were sailing from Kata beach to Patong. In the late afternoon grey, the glassy sea slid beneath us. A towering cloud-bank hung over us to the east, still and perfect and unreal. I took a deep breath. 'I was thinking of a thriller,' I said.

'Yes, yes, bhai,' Manu said. 'Excellent. A thriller.'

'I like those films where there is some danger, and the hero has to avert the threat.'

'A suspense story. I like it, bhai.'

'The girl helps the hero, and they fall in love.'

'Of course. And we'll do an international thriller, so that the songs can be shot abroad with justification.'

'International thriller, yes.' I was starting to like the boy.

'Did you have any ideas about the hero, bhai? Who is he? An ordinary man? A policeman? A secret agent?'

'No. He's one of us.'

'You mean . . .?'

'It's a crime thriller.'

'Okay, okay. I see the story. The hero is on the wrong side of the law, but he was driven into the underworld by circumstances.'

'Yes. I want to start with him coming to Bombay.'

'Right, right,' Manu said.

But he was looking doubtful. 'What?' I said.

'In a thriller, bhai, there may not be enough time to develop his entire history.'

'Why? You have three maderchod hours.'

'True, true, bhai. But you'll be surprised how quickly three hours fill up. You have five, six songs, that itself is close to forty minutes. Then, you have space for maybe forty scenes before the interval, thirty, thirty-five afterwards. And a thriller has to start with the danger, tell the audience what they're supposed to be scared of, what is at stake, and then it should race to the finish. And also . . .'

'What?'

'The boy coming to Bombay, becoming a criminal. It's been done, in *Satya*. And *Vaastav*, that also had the introduction-to-the-underworld theme.'

'I don't care if it's been done. It's still true. Look at all these boys who are with me.'

'Of course, bhai. They have been telling me their stories. But, you see, the audience gets used to things. First time, they love it. Second time, they love it less. Third time, they say, "It's too filmi, yaar," and they reject the truth altogether. You see?'

I saw. I had done the same myself. 'The audience is a bastard,' I said.

At this he jumped up and clasped my hand. 'Yes, bhai, yes, the audience is a gaandu, it is a madman, it is a monster of a baby that must be fed.' He realized then that he was perhaps being a bit too familiar, so he let go of my hand and backed away. But his eyes were brilliant with sudden sympathy, and he couldn't stop himself from going on. 'Nobody knows what this maderchod audience wants, bhai. Everyone pretends, but nobody really knows. You can make a big film, spend and spend on publicity, and in the cinemas you won't even hear crows calling. Meanwhile, some B-grade, shoddily made film with no story to speak of will make a hundred crores.'

'But you still try to predict what they want. And you have all these rules. Why only forty scenes before the interval? Why not sixty?'

'Can't be done, bhai. The audience is unpredictable, but it is also very rigid. It wants only what it wants, in the way it is used to getting it. Even if you have a really dhaansu story, if you change the shape of the story the audience will throw things at the screen, and tear up the seats, and riot. That's the thing, bhai. You have to do new things in old ways. Or old things fitted out in new clothes. Your film has to be hatke, but not too hatke. The art-film types keep saying they're doing new-new things, but they also have to obey the rules. It's just a different set of rules, and a different audience. You can't get away from the rules.'

'We're not going to make a maderchod art film,' I growled. I was going to spend thirty crores on this film. We had two big heroes signed up already, and Dheeraj had an appointment with Amitabh Bachchan's secretary the coming Tuesday. I had told Dheeraj also that I wanted fultu special effects, and first-class costumes and locations. I wanted the film to look glossy and big, it was going to be huge. And huge costs money, lots of it. I was doing this for Zoya, but I wanted my money back, at least that. 'You forget art,' I told Manu. 'You write one fast-moving thriller. Put something in every scene that makes this public feel like it has an electric wire connected to its golis. Keep them awake and excited. Give it to them, hard and fast.'

He nodded, up and down, fast. 'Yes, yes, bhai. I understand. Action and spectacle and big-big glamour.' He held his arms out wide. 'The emotion of *Mother India*, the scale of *Sholay*, the speed of *Amar Akbar Anthony*. That's what we want.'

That's what we wanted all right. So we got to work.

I continued my work for Mr Kumar's people. Mr Kumar had retired the year before, despite my protests. 'Saab, why do you have to go?' I'd said. 'In our business, there is no retirement except going upstairs.'

'Ganesh, my business is not your business.'

He was always like that, short and blunt. But he was not unkind, this wily old bowler who had played the game for so long. We were not friends, but over the years we had come to understand each other, and our mutual need. He needed me to extract threads of information from Kathmandu, and Karachi, and Dubai, and sometimes make certain people disappear, and I needed him to put pressure on policemen in Delhi and Mumbai, and supply me with information in turn, and help occasionally with logistics and resources. We had no illusions about each other, but we were comfortable, like neighbours who had grown older together. And I tried to tell him he was not old enough yet to take sanyas. 'Saab, if the government makes you retire just when you are at the top of your form, a fabulous khiladi like you, then the government is mad.'

'It's not just the government, Ganesh, I also want to sit and rest.'

'All right, saab, then sit in one place, and talk to me on the phone. Like a consultant, you know.'

He said, 'Work for you?' I could tell he was amused.

'Work with me.'

'No, Ganesh. I have done enough, and I am feeling tired.'

He was not being rude, and I did not feel insulted. 'But what will you do?'

'Read. Think. As I said, sit in one place.'

I knew from long experience that he would not be persuaded by arguments or temptations, and so the discussion was closed. 'All right,' I said. 'It has been good to work with you, Mr K.D. Yadav.' I wanted to let him know that I knew his real name, but I had respected him enough to call him Mr Kumar, as he wanted, for all the time we had co-operated.

'Very good, Ganesh. I had no doubt you would investigate me, and find out.'

'I learnt from you, saab.'

And so he passed from my life, this faraway teacher of mine. He introduced me to his successor, a Mr Joshi, and for about a month he stayed in touch, to help with the transition. I soon knew this Mr Joshi's real name – Dinesh Kulkarni – and I told Mr Kumar exactly what I thought of him. 'This man's a fool, saab. He sits in Delhi and wants to tell me where to send money, and how much, and how many men to send on an operation. He doubts me and my sources, and speaks to me as if I'm his servant.'

'Be patient, Ganesh,' Mr Kumar said. 'You will take time to adjust to each other.'

So I was patient, but that bastard Kulkarni did not adjust to me or to anything else. It was amazing to me that the country's security was being handled by such a gaandu, but then I had seen gaandus rise to the top in every profession. I had to deal with this particular gaandu.

Meanwhile, Mr Kumar finally slipped away into his retirement. I worked on.

We wrote the screenplay for my film between Ko Samui and Patong. I preferred the long quiet of Samui, but the boys wanted the jostling chaos of Patong. I let them have one week out of every three in the bars and on the beaches, and then turned our bows again towards peace. With Manu Tewari on board, they had something else besides endless card-playing to occupy their hours, even on the sea runs. It was exciting for them to see a story form, to feel it take on contours and characters. They discussed the narrative endlessly, badgered Manu for new scenes, and offered opinions and suggestions, and told him their own adventures. They were passionately involved with the hero of the film, and each sulked in turn when Manu refused to incorporate some turn or twist which he had thought up for this hero. A few times I had to intervene and put down a final veto on a suggestion before Manu got beaten up, or thrown off the boat. Of course our normal work and play went on as usual: I talked to Kulkarni every week, and ran his intelligence operations, found information and killed a bastard here and there for my country; I consulted Guru-ji and moved his shipments; I spoke to Jojo and laughed with her; I met Zoya and took her. But in those six months, no matter what else we did, that story threaded through our brains and bodies and obsessed each one of us. We talked about it morning and evening and night, and discussed the casting, and listened avidly to the songs as they came in from the recording studios. And we hovered over Manu Tewari.

He was middling in size, and not hard at all, but that Manu was stubborn. He would eat whatever you put on his plate, and not complain at all if you changed television channels while he was watching the news, but if you tried to interfere with his scenes, he was fierce as a yellow-toothed sow with her threatened piglets. I was his financier, and his paymaster, and after all I was Ganesh Gaitonde, but even with me he argued back and defended his decisions and debated. Sometimes the boys winced when our story sessions heated up, and our voices rose, and Manu Tewari risked rudeness. But I tolerated him, because he was a good writer. He was writing me a strong story. And besides, I was learning from him. As the weeks passed, as I argued with Manu Tewari, I began to see what he was talking about.

He taught me about cinema, how a simple cut from a blown-out matchstick to a blazing desert could explode in your chest and rock you back in your seat. We watched DVDs with him, and learnt the language of extreme close-up and long shot, the release of space and the compression of time, how the simple movement of a camera down a pair of fixed tracks could say more than a thousand books. I learnt these tools, and I watched *Mughal-e-Azam*, and *Kagaz ke Phool*, and I watched them dozens of times, and I learnt how a small group of master craftsmen, a gang of purposeful madmen, could wield light and sound and space to make shimmering monuments that materialized on cloth screens, on dirty village walls, on a yacht in the southern seas. I could start to see how a good story had a certain geometry, a succession of curves, a billowing rise of crests and plateaux that led to the final explosion, and satisfaction. If you made a story that was lopsided, that was blemished, this ugliness would bring only boredom and emptiness. In beauty there was bliss.

'Exactly,' Guru-ji said to me one afternoon. 'But not only bliss. Also terror.' He had taken an unexpected delight in the slow birth of our story. I had expected he would think the whole project too cheap and childish, but yet again he surprised me. He listened to our ideas and innovations attentively, and gave advice without being domineering. And here he was, finding not only beauty but also terror in our half-finished script.

'Terror, Guru-ji?' I said. 'How?'

'Anything that is truly beautiful is also terrifying.'

I thought about that. Was Zoya terrifying? No. I felt a craving for her, and sometimes a flutter of disquiet at how strong this longing was, but I was not scared of her. Of course not. But I wouldn't argue with Guru-ji. Instead, I said, 'Guru-ji, but you said the world is beautiful because it is ordered and symmetrical. Does that mean it is frightening?'

'Yes, it is. For the ordinary person, who sees only randomness, the world is just depressing. When you move along a little, you start to see its real loveliness. Then you realize that this exquisite perfection is terrible, it is frightening. When you conquer this fear, you know that beauty and terror are the same thing, and this is as it should be. There is no need for fear. For the world to be beautiful, it must finish. For every beginning, there is an end. And for every end, there is a beginning.'

'Symmetry?'

'Yes, Ganesh. Precisely that.'

It started to make sense to me. This is why the screenplay had to move in its cycles of sequences, but inevitably towards a climax, after which there would be nothing. Or, as Guru-ji was implying, maybe something, but only after the world of the screenplay had vanished. But I was still grasping – as I often did – at the entirety of his meaning. 'I don't fully understand, Guru-ji, sorry. I see the necessity of order. But I like beauty, I don't fear it.'

He laughed, but kindly. 'Don't worry, Ganesh. You are a vira. You will climb to the top of the peak, and see the abyss. You will see both beauty and terror. But for now, what you are doing is very good. You will seduce the audience, and make lots of money.'

Yes, there was the money. And cash was what Manu argued with the boys about. He worked in the most money-minded business in the world, but he wanted the rich to give their money to the poor. He believed in state ownership of essential industries, high taxes on the middle classes and even higher taxes on the upper classes, and protection for Indian industries against multinationals and imports. The boys all came from low-income families, but every last one of them was a diehard capitalist. 'You think I'm a chutiya to give my money to the poor?' Amit said. 'You know how many bastards I had to kill to get it?' And Nitin said, 'Fifty years of state control and what do you get? Cottage industries that have been making straight losses for fifty years, a population that spends all its time and energy trying to get around the stupid rules, and massive corruption.' And Suresh said, 'Where is your precious Soviet Union now, sala? Tell me where?' And Manu Tewari argued back, and told them that capitalism would collapse because of its internal contradictions, that the march of history was inevitable, and that they were an ignorant lot who didn't and couldn't see the forces working under the surface of events. 'Our story can only have one end,' Manu said. 'The proletariat will finally rule.' To which Amit said, 'Exactly. Boss, I am the proletariat. And what I want is three Mercedes cars, three lund-lasoons a day, and lots of good butter chicken. When I get all this, who will I be? The ruler of some poor proletarian bastards.'

So Manu Tewari's political lectures didn't gain him a following of fierce comrades on my yacht. But we all listened attentively to his rules for making a good movie story, and there were a lot of rules. The boys began to call him Manu the Rule-giver. He had a rule for every occasion, for every scene and situation, and examples for support. He told us the villain must be stronger than the hero, and also somehow attractive. And that two songs must never be put next to each other, except when Sooraj Barjatya does it. And the heroine must be very sexy, but she can never have sex. And the first one or two scenes after the interval must be unimportant throwaway scenes, because your viewers take a few minutes to come back in from the lobby, with their samosas and drinks. And once you're at the climax, move it along fast, because the audience is going to get up and start leaving so that they can beat the traffic jam outside. And the hero's mother must be introduced early, and our love for her must be total. At this last one, I had to object. 'Why do we have to have a mother cluttering up the film?' I said. 'The screenplay's too long anyway, and we have to cut scenes. She'll just eat up screen-time.'

'Bhai, we have to have a mother. It's a basic requirement. Otherwise, who is this hero? Where does he come from? He won't make any sense then.'

'I don't know a thing about your mother. But you make sense to me, bastard. Why do we have to show her? A mother is implied.'

'For the sympathy, bhai, for the sympathy. A hero without a mother, and without love between them, feels incomplete. A good mother makes him good, even if he's bad.'

'And if he's got a bad mother? Does that make him better?'

Manu grinned. 'In films, bhai, there are no bad mothers. Only evil stepmothers.'

There were bad mothers in the world, but I couldn't argue with the fact that there were no bad mothers in films, so this one stayed in the film. She had two scenes at the beginning, one immediately after the interval, and then she appeared in the closing shot, smiling benignly in the background as the boy and girl sped away to happiness in a speed-boat. This much I could live with.

Once the screenplay was finished, complete with dialogue, we did a full reading. We did it in the early morning, off Patong. In the calm of the morning Manu told us the story, from the hero's introduction as he robbed a diamond store, and his betrayal by his underworld partners, to his discovery of a terrorist plot, and his falling in love with the girl who was his link to the terrorists, and his discovery of his own patriotism through his love for the girl, and his struggle with the terrorists and the traitor bhais, and then the climax. It took three hours, and the sun came up flaming hot on our backs, but none of us noticed. We were caught up in Manu's storytelling, in his expressions and his acting-out of the scenes, and his descriptions through which he made us see the boy and the girl and their desperate run through India and Europe. When he finished, we all sat back drained and happy, almost as if we had actually seen the film.

'That is good,' Arvind said. He had flown in two days early from Singapore especially for the story session, leaving behind the precious Suhasini. 'I think that works. I think that will make a great film. It is very exciting but also very sensitively written.'

'And who are you, Basu Bhattacharya?' I said amidst general laughter. But I was grinning. The story was good, and all the major objections I had raised earlier had been addressed. I knew exactly what was going to happen in the story, but still it had made my stomach tighten, and the scene where the boy said goodbye to his mother and went off to fight his war had brought forth a painful constriction of my throat. I turned to Manu. 'Okay,' I said. 'I think we're ready to shoot.'

He pumped his fists and jumped up and down three times and then clasped my hands. 'Yes,' he said. 'I agree, bhai. We are ready. Let's start. Let's begin.'

I was impatient to start shooting, and Zoya was more than ready. She had gone to the Miss Universe contest in Argentina, and had come in as fourth runner-up. We had been certain that she would win, that she would be occupied with Miss Universe duties for a year, but the judges had made their inexplicable decision, and she was now free and impatient. 'We will start immediately,' I said to Manu. 'But today I want you all to celebrate. I'm giving you two nights. And everyone gets a bonus. Take the launch and go. You can stay at the bungalow.'

I gave them each twenty thousand baht and sent them away. I kept back only Arvind and a skeleton crew of three, and the screenplay. I read the whole thing over, I pored over Manu Tewari's fanatically neat handwriting, his orderly lines in which he had contained so much shooting and kissing and car crashes and tears and torn hearts. I read it all twice, and then I called Jojo and read the whole thing to her. I intoned, 'Fade to black,' and then I asked, 'Does it work?'

'Yes,' she said.

'Yes and what?'

'Arre, what do you mean, what? I said it works.'

'I know you, saali. You can say yes, and have it mean exactly no. So, tell me.'

'I did tell you. It works for what it is.'

'What is it exactly?'

She took a dragging breath. 'Gaitonde,' she said, 'I didn't mean anything. It's a great script. It'll be a hit.'

I breathed in myself, and took a moment to press down my anger, and said in as reasonable a voice as I could, 'No, no, Jojo. We have to know if anyone has any doubts. We have to know now so we can fix it.'

She knew I wasn't going to let her retreat, so she gathered herself and came forward. 'Fine. What I was saying was, that it is good enough for what it is. And what it is . . . It's one of those movies in which men blow up things and fight a lot and cry over each other.'

'My boys and I fight and cry on this boat. What's wrong with that?'

'Nothing. I told you, your film is going to be a hit.'

'But?'

'But nothing. It's just not the kind of film I enjoy too much myself.'

'You're saying that women won't come? You wait, with the stars we have, and the way we shoot the songs, every woman will come with her children and her grandmother. And they'll all want to see Zoya.'

'Baba, I said it'll be a hit, no? All I'm saying is that it's a certain kind of film.'

'Yes, it's not the kind where you have three women jabbering at each other about how sad and put-down they are for one and a half hours, and then another two women ranting about how bad men are for another hour. Gaandu, you make a dozen television shows like that if you want, but you're not going to shove my film down that smelly path.'

The slow ripples of her laughter calmed me down. 'Gaitonde,' she said, 'I'm not trying to shove your maderchod film into anything. You are going to stuff it down the whole of India's throat anyway, including the women. We won't escape. So don't worry. Just tell me, what are you calling this bastard?'

'Don't abuse my film,' I said. 'You abuse me relentlessly, but don't you dare call my film names.' I was smiling. 'I was thinking of calling it *Barood*.'

'That was used in the seventies.'

'I know. But I still like it. You don't?'

'Not too much. It doesn't suggest the international angle.'

'So, you want to call it *International Barood*?'

I lay back on the bed and waited for her to stop laughing. I was laughing a little myself. 'Be serious. This is important, a title can really help a film's sales.'

'Yes, yes. It's too bad *International Khiladi* has been used. That would've been perfect.'

That would indeed have been perfect. But it had been used, and not too long ago, so we went on to other ideas, from *Love in London* to *Hamari Dharti, Unki Dharti*. It was quite a pleasure, to cast about in old, half-remembered titles, and to find words and little pieces of language, and play with them and put them together like pieces of a puzzle, trying to find the words that would express the feeling of the screenplay, of life itself. But then my pleasure was interrupted by my own band of international khiladis. A phone call came in on the local line: Manu Tewari and three of the others had been arrested.

'What? Where? How?' I snarled at Arvind. The boys had clear instructions to keep a low profile, to stay out of trouble, to be invisible. All of us had come into Thailand by sea, and had never gone through any kind of immigration, and as far as the Thai authorities knew, we did not exist.

'It's that bastard writer, bhai,' Arvind said. 'He got into a fight with an American sailor at the Typhoon bar.'

'That little chodu?' I was amazed. Manu wrote good violence, but he wasn't a fighter. He watched, and waited, and considered, and then usually wrote. 'He fought over what?'

'There's a girl at the Typhoon bar he likes.'

'So?'

'She was with an American sailor from the carrier.' There was an American aircraft carrier at the head of the bay, accompanied by two smaller ships. The carrier was grey and vast as a mountain, and had two days ago disgorged three thousand sailors on to Patong beach. 'This sailor had bought her out of the bar for the last two nights. She was sitting on his lap. The sailor was saying rude things about her in English to his friends, how she sucked his lauda. The girl didn't understand, but Manu did. He said something to the sailor. The sailor said something back. Manu broke a Heineken bottle over his head.'

'Bhenchod.'

'So then the sailor knocked Manu over the table. And the sailor's friends came into the conversation. And the boys jumped them in turn. So they're all in jail.'

I felt like leaving them all in jail, but I needed Manu. So I got them out. Of course I couldn't get directly involved in the mess, but I sent off Arvind with the necessary money, and I got on the phone and made calls. Three days, two lawyers and a hundred and twenty thousand baht in bribes later, I had them back on the yacht. There was a furious green welt across the left side of Manu Tewari's face, and he was as tottery as a collapsing socialist state. The boys told me he hadn't slept for three days. For all his sympathies with the oppressed, it turned out he had never been inside a jail before, and the Thai cells had affected his nerves very badly. I sent him off to bed, and gave the boys a good talking-to.

'Bhai,' Amit said. 'What were we supposed to do? We were just sitting there drinking. All of a sudden this bastard Manu stands up and hits the American with his beer bottle. And the American was one of those huge goras, as big as a truck. So he shook his head and slugged Manu across the room. And his friends jumped in. So we did.' He shook his head. 'All over some whore. And he's never even taken her gaand.'

So then they told me. At the Typhoon bar there was this Thai whore who called herself Debbie. Six months ago, Manu had gone to the bar with the boys and had bought Debbie a drink and started asking her where she came from, how many brothers and sisters she had, what sort of house they lived in. Debbie was a sharp little churi, she saw her opportunity, and gave Manu Tewari enough material to write four tragedies – she told him, in very broken English, about her crippled farmer father, and her silent, hard-working mother, and their rickety wooden house in the hills above Nong Khai, and her barefoot, wormy brothers and sisters, and all the rest of it. So for the last six months, each time we had come into Patong, Manu Tewari had taken this Debbie out for lunch and dinner, and bought her dresses and belts and perfumes, and maybe – even though he wouldn't admit to it – had given her cash to help send her little siblings to school in the far-off hills of Nong Khai. He had done all this without touching her mountains and valleys even once. But she was, after all, a working bar-girl. The American sailor had paid in good dollars for Debbie's chut and

685

her lund-lasoons and for the right to talk about it, and so the big maderchod had set off Manu Tewari's socialist notions of honour. And cost me a lot of money.

'Bastard writer,' I said. Only a rule-giving Manu Tewari type could sail around Thai waters for six months and not get his lauda wet. I gave my instructions. The next week, the boys went back into Patong and took Manu Tewari along. That night, while he slept, they slipped two girls into his room. The girls were both seventeen years old, both had long silky black hair down to their tight little behinds, both had creamy little breasts, and both were naked when they went into Manu's bed. He woke up gasping, but they didn't give him time to ask any of his questions, one put something into his mouth, and the other put something of his in her mouth. His socialism failed completely, but his lauda stood up, and he exploited both of them mercilessly until the next morning. Then he slept, and when he woke he was full of regret and a bad conscience and started telling them he was sorry. So the girls started playing with each other's chuts and pushed their nipples into his lips. He groaned a little, but he stopped talking, and then oppressed them well into the evening. He didn't mention beautiful Debbie from the Typhoon bar even once.

That's what you have to do with writers sometimes: shut them up. They get so caught up in language and stories and rules that they can't see the simplest facts. Or all the beautiful warm curves that cash buys. But the lauda feels, it knows. You have to give the lauda a chance.

We made the film. It was shot in Bombay, London, Lausanne, Munich, Tallinn and Seville. I watched weekly rushes in Bangkok, and gave my reactions and advice, but always through Dheeraj Kapoor and Manu Tewari. All the other crew, and especially the actors, had no idea who they were really working for. I knew I had to protect Zoya and her future, and so I kept security very tight. And as I watched her, week after week, I knew her future was going to be very-very big. I knew she was beautiful, but to see her on a big screen was to feel like a child in the face of a golden combustion of light. She was thirty feet high, weightless as a dream, and when she smiled your heart slammed into your spine and staggered you back like a bullet. Her cheekbones were as sharp as falling swords, and as she stalked away from the camera, there was a serpent slide to her back that shivered up your neck. It wasn't just me, Arvind watched the rushes with me and was also awed and silenced. After listening to us rave about the girl for six weeks, Suhasini came along and watched a rough cut of the song shot in Estonia, and all her sarcasm and competitiveness vanished, and she turned to us as the lights came on, and said, 'Okay, I'll admit it. The girl looks good.'

'Just good?' Arvind said. 'Come on. Tell the truth. If not to me, at least to Bhai.'

Suhasini put an arm under his, and leaned across him. 'Fine, fine. Bhai, the girl was definitely the right choice. She's going to be a huge success. Stupendous.'

Even the women saw it, Zoya *was* stupendous. Her fame grew as the production rolled on, as the carefully timed press releases were sent out, as her photographs began to appear on the covers of film magazines, as flashes of the songs appeared on television. She was very busy now, and was able to fly out to Singapore only intermittently, and much less often than before. And I must confess that I was glad about this. To admit this to myself was gratingly hard back then, it felt like two stones grinding against each other just under my navel. But the stinking truth that came bobbing up my throat was that as Zoya grew bigger, I felt that I grew smaller. Oh, I was powerful, I was feared, I was rich, I could give life, or take it. I supported families, and generations of children had been born in the homes that I had built, that flourished under my protection. I was not afraid of her success, after all I had built it, I had created her. And yet. It was hard to admit, hard to know, and it is hard to tell now: as Zoya grew into the nation's goddess, my lauda shrank.

I am not lying, and I was not deluded, I was not crazy. The thing grew smaller. Not so much in length but in its circumference and heft. I remembered it being hard and muscled and healthy, and now it seemed apologetic and wan. Once it needed no excuses, now it was weakened by constant doubt. No, not that Zoya ever said anything. She was still as energetic in her sucking, as compliant as always and as expressive of her pleasure. She moaned when I took her, she shut her eyes, she flung her arms over her head – as always – when the shudders spread from her chut. Once, pounding on her daana, taking her to that edge, driving her over it into the fall of joy, had made me feel righteous and victorious. I was the ruler of her rich brown expanses. But now I had seen what an artful actress she was. On screen, she had made me believe completely that she was someone else. But then, how was I to know that the Zoya I knew, who I thought I knew, was not actually someone else? Was my Zoya only a performance? Were those moans only acting?

This is the ache, if you are unfortunate enough to care what a paid woman feels and thinks. This is the fatal squeeze of that paradox. The more she shrieks from the press of your pleasure, the more you suspect that her sighs are overstated, that you are not pleasing her at all. And you can never know the truth. If you ask, she will tell you what she thinks you pay her to say. If you don't ask, you will get angry. You will get angry enough so that the only reaction you will accept from her as true is the evidence of her pain. I grew rough in my handling of Zoya. I pulled at her hair, I bit her breasts and tugged at her nipples, and she winced and writhed but never tried to stop me. I understood why. After all, I gave her money. I had paid for parts of this perfect physique. And yet I could never be sure that it was not invulnerable to me, that this body did not escape me most precisely at those moments when I took it most deeply. I grew angry. One morning I took her in a way that I had rarely done before, I took her like I took the boys in jail, like I had taken Mumtaz of the luscious gaand. I ploughed into Zoya from behind, I held her by the hair and took her hard. She screamed and gave way before me. My fingers left scarlet clusters on her sides. 'Saali,' I spat out at the flexing camber of her back, 'randi, take it, here, here. Take it.'

She turned her head against the pull of my fist, and her sweat slipped against my knuckles, and she said, 'Yes, yes, give, give,' and she laughed. She *laughed*. 'It's good, saab. Give. Yes, give.'

The delight in that hoarse laugh chilled my golis like a shivery splash of iced water. At once, immediately, I was unable to give. I was incapable. I slipped out of her, and I went in a stumbling rush into the next room. I sat on the sofa, and Zoya followed and curled in next to me. 'What happened?' she said. 'What's wrong?'

I sent her away. I had nothing to say to her, and in no way could have explained to her what was wrong, what I needed from her. The trap I was in was immaculate. I didn't trust her joy, and it seemed I couldn't even hurt her. I was so small. I sat in the dark. I kept thinking of Zoya's co-star, Neeraj Sen. That bastard was six foot two, with grey eyes and biceps like hand grenades. Yes, he must have a lauda that matched up to the rest of him. I shut my eyes and saw Zoya and Neeraj standing in a doorway, symmetrical and matched and equal to each other. She had an arm around his neck, and a leg raised up to his right shoulder, and she was taking his enormous machine, and she was transported. Her ecstasy was real, I knew it. I could tell. They were coloured red by a rising dawn, and they were happy.

I jumped up, rattled at the side of my head with an open palm. Wake up, bastard. Come back to your senses. Zoya would never do that. Zoya knows what she owes you. Zoya understands that you have made her. Zoya comprehends your power, your reach. Zoya would never offend you. Zoya is a good girl. Realize this.

I apprehended this, I had it locked up in my fists. I knew exactly how much I frightened men, how I overpowered women. Nobody would dare offend me. If there was a fool somewhere in the world who insulted me by mistake, I could have him erased the next day, he would vanish as if he had never existed. I could have Neeraj Sen taken up and vanished. He would cease, he would desist, he would go. He would not exist any more.

No, no, I needed him. I had already spent sixteen crores on this film, and the budget was inflating itself, surging up to reel in all those helicopter chases, those location changes in the songs. I had invested in Neeraj Sen? Why was he so big, the bastard Bengali? Six foot two and bulging? Who had ever heard of a six-two Bengali? Ah, yes, his grandmother had been a film actress, a Shakira Bano, one of those dancer-prostitutes who had become actresses in those black-and-white days. She had been a minor success, and under the screen name of Naina Devi she had played Madhubala's sister in a couple of films, and had done a famous bar dance with Dev Anand. She had married a Bengali cinematographer and had retired from the filmi game. But her sons had gone into distribution, and now this grandson Neeraj Sen was a hero, three films old and rising. Moving up and high and higher, with his six foot two height inherited from his grandmother, that's where he got those Pathan muscles. Bastards, I should kill them both, Neeraj and Zoya. There was a Glock in my bedside table, with a round in the chamber, and two extra clips. I could walk in, sweep it up and blow her head off. I could put two bullets in every limb, one in her belly, one in her chut, one in that unreachable heart.

I sent her home instead. I made some excuse about a sudden phone call from Thailand, some urgent work that required my presence. She knew something was wrong, but she was also intelligent enough not to press me. She kissed me (she had to bend low to do that), and then she went back to Bombay and work. I went back to Thailand, and took the yacht out to Ko Samui. And then I tested myself on several girls. I followed Guru-ji's advice to take only virgins, and paid extravagantly for them. Jojo sent me a girl from Andhra, and another one from Kerala, and a Bengali one. This last one was a Muslim, with hair down to her knees and slanty brown eyes. She wasn't as tall as Zoya, in fact she stood eye to eye with me. When I laid her down she covered her face with her hands, and I was instantly hard. When I released with one final thrust, she screamed. And in that instant I had the title for my film: *International Dhamaka*. I lay on top of her, laughing, and called Dheeraj Kapur and Manu immediately afterward. They agreed that it was a dhaansu title that would attract the masses and the classes. 'We are going full speed now, bhai,' Manu said. 'Like your title says, we will explode internationally.' And he did not know how correct he was. With these girls, I was full speed. With all of them I was capable, confidently competent and more. They were too young and inexperienced to fake their reactions. Their pleasures were as real as their pain. I had no doubt, I was so very sure.

But I was also sure that my own pleasures were halved. The sensations that came buzzing up my spine were as high-voltage as always, and the hum in my head that came from seeing a beautiful Bengali novice clumsily tonguing my lauda was still heated, still high. But somewhere in this circuit between my high and my low, between my head and my crotch, there was a missing connection, and this fissure broke the current and damped it. I felt the excitement, but from a great distance. Of course I understood why this was so. I was Ganesh Gaitonde, and I had lived long enough and seen enough of the world to understand it a little, and understand myself even more. I knew why I could be confident and strong with these girls: they were trivial, I cared nothing for them, or for what they felt. When I took the Bengali at night, when I bent her like a bow over the railing of the boat, the water plunged against the prow and the crouching winds rushed the clouds over our heads, and I raced into her but my heart was quite still. It did not move.

Zoya shook me, she shuddered me directly into ecstasy. When I was with her, there was a constant agitation that pierced me through, a vibration, a friction, a warmth that was both joy and pain. When I was away from her, this stirring subsided, but never quite vanished.

Zoya had disturbed me, and I hated her for it. And I loved her. I admitted it, I had to admit it to myself: I was in love with her. It was shameful, that I had fallen into the very trap that I warned the boys against, but I could not deny it. There was this word 'love', and now I understood what it meant. Suddenly I didn't want to fast-forward all those love songs in the movies. No, I wanted to soar for four and a half minutes with *Ke kitni muhabbat hai tumse, to paas aake to dekho*. In my cabin I sang along with:

> *Abhi na jao chhhod kar, ke dil abhi bhara nahin*
> *Abhi abhi to aai ho, bahar ban kar chayi ho.*
> *Hawa zara mahak to le, nazar zara bahak to le*
> *Ye shaam dhal to le zara, ye dil sambhal to le zara . . .*
> *Main thodi der jee to loon, nashe ke ghoont pee to loon*
> *Abhi to kucch kaha nahin, abhi to kucch suna nahin*
> *Abhi na jao . . .*

The boys noticed my new affection for swooningly sentimental music and made little jokes about it. I laughed back at them, with them, but I told them nothing. I could tell nobody, the very thought of revealing my love made me flush and tingle like I had a fever, like I was a little boy caught by a sudden glance of light from an opening door. I shut away my love in a bunker, I hid it and held it safe. I didn't tell the boys, I didn't tell Guru-ji, I didn't tell Jojo. I didn't even tell Zoya. I just gave her diamonds, and a new car, and sent her regular shipments of cash.

I am sure she understood. We spoke every day, even as the pre-release madness of dubbing and photo-shoots and interviews took her from one end of Bombay to the other. I followed her on her special pink late-model Nokia mobile phone which I had given to her, which of course she used only to talk to me. On that phone, she called me 'Bill', and told me stories of her day, and her meetings with magazine editors and producers, and her excitement for the future. I listened, and gave her advice, and dreamed with her. In those days, just before the release, everything seemed possible. Even a bigger lauda.

I loved Zoya so much that I was determined to be bigger for her. In Bangkok I could have bought a tiger's penis, and had it pounded into pills that promised me potency and stamina. But I was long past such superstitions. I already knew how to take care of potency and stamina:

I ate food with little oil in it, I exercised every day, I had a new stair-climber installed next to the engine room, so I could get a rigorous aerobic workout. No, all I needed was size. And in this age of research and development, I could expand scientifically. By now I was more fluent in my handling of the computer, and could navigate my way to a search engine. I told the boys I didn't want to be disturbed, closed the door, and I searched. I had trouble with the language, at first. Typing in 'lauda' found a site for an airline named exactly that, and a site about some racing-car driver, and another one about a drug called 'laudanum'. You stupid bastard, I said to the half-face I could see in the screen, of course use English. I knew the English, I knew it from the X films that the boys brought on board, from the tangled acrobatics of those images, from the close-ups. I typed in 'big cock'. Now I got listings of dozens of sites offering pictures of enormous laudas in every colour. I didn't want that. I had to struggle for a few minutes, until I remembered 'penis', from an article in the *Times of India* about elephants and their mating habits. I tried 'penis size', which gave me surveys of average size of penises, but also, lower down on the page, http://www.100percentpenisenlargement.com and http://www.big-penis-enlargement-size.com and http://www.betterpenis.info. Much better.

So, I read and learnt and thought, I took many days to make my decision. This was no trivial decision. I was trying to grow and structure my future and myself. I was trying to anchor my love, to make my beloved happy, happier. I studied, and I thought. I learnt the physiology of the penis. Cross-section drawings showed me the mechanisms under the surface, the branching pipes of blood that made it rise and made it strong. Very early, I ruled out the use of penis pumps as obviously harmful to the capillaries, causing tiny tears in the tissue as the penis expanded in a vacuum. Weights, I thought, would work. Hang enough weights on a tissue and it will lengthen, that was obvious enough. I had seen, back home, tribal women whose ear lobes were stretched from the earrings they wore. But the elongated ears had always seemed hideous to me. A stretched penis may be longer, but it would be thinner, like a piece of rubber pulled out of shape. No, not acceptable. I wanted length, but I also had to have girth. It had to be steel-hard, a sleek, tireless engine that Zoya would love.

And then I found Dr Reinnes. A week after I began weeding out the thickets of penis sites, I came upon http://www.scientificpenis.com.

The name itself was an attraction, and I clicked on it right away. When I saw the page, I was impressed by its simplicity. There were none of the lurid colours of the other sites here, no huge flashing fonts in green and red that made tall claims. No, just clean, even black lettering on a white background. The whole site was reasonable and neat, it was clean. There was a sobriety about the page, and in Dr Reinnes's whole approach, that came from him being a medical doctor. As he explained on the site, he ran a regular medical practice in California. His techniques for enlargement had been developed over years of research and experience, and they were based on a deep scientific understanding of the functioning of the human body. And all this was offered discreetly over the internet for the low price of 49.99 US dollars. A simple credit-card transaction would enable the user to access the locked pages which contained the Reinnes Method, and to begin the seeker's journey of self-improvement.

I had six credit cards, all in different names. And what was 49.99 in good US dollars, for such knowledge? I used my Platinum Visa, in the name of 'Jerry Gallant', which was an alias based in a Belgian PO box address. And two minutes of typing later, I had access. I skimmed past the multicoloured diagrams, and the advice on hormonal dysfunction and nutrition. I wasn't sick, and my intake of protein was already balanced. I only wanted size. Here was the secret: pump more blood into the penile arteries. And this was achieved through a daily programme of exercises, first an application of a hot compress, a towel soaked in hot water and then moulded around the penis. And then the main exercise, which was a milking motion with thumb and forefinger ringed, from the base of the lightly lubricated penis to the head. I tried it right then, in front of the computer, the milking I mean, not the hot towel. Yes, it was true, if you drew the finger-ring down the length of a semi-erect penis, you could see the blood being forced to the head. There were other exercises also, a pulling one for length benefits, and an internal pelvic one for stamina. I could see the sense of the routine, its basis in what lay underneath, the logic of its sequences. Of course you could exercise the penis as you exercised every other muscle in your body, and make it strong and big. The genius of Dr Reinnes was that he gave you a system. I printed out the charts that allowed you to track your daily progress, all the way until you moved to the 'Advanced' section six months and many added inches later. I began that very evening.

After forty-seven days of regular and sustained penis exercise, I registered a growth of half an inch. Zoya came to visit me in Singapore four days before the release of *International Dhamaka*. This was necessarily a lightning visit, she flew in on a Thursday morning and flew out that same evening. Keeping her visit to the city secret was now impossible, since the stewardesses knew who she was now, and little girls came up to the first-class cabin to ask for autographs. So the official story was that she was coming in to do some shopping before the premiere, to pick up some jewellery and dresses. We put her in the Ritz-Carlton and had her go down a private elevator to a waiting limousine. She called me from the car, 'I'm on my way, saab.'

She was as respectful as always, as careful of my time and feelings. Me, I was nervous. I had on a new black Armani suit, and a tailored gold shirt. My shoes were polished, and my fingernails were shiningly manicured. I sat in an easy chair facing the door, not at all easy. I drank from a glass of Evian, and I was ridiculous, and I knew it. I heard her coming up the stairs. I stood up. The door flung open, she came in, flinging off her hooded coat, shaking back a tidal ripple of hair. I had a bare glimpse of fawn-coloured pants and a little top, and then she *ran* to me. In the squeeze of her embrace, in the balm of her breasts, all my doubt vanished. 'I missed you,' she said. 'I missed you so much.'

And this was the girl Jojo called the Egotistical Giraffe. She was kissing my neck, coming back up to my lips and then going down to my chest again. With a drawn-out sigh she went to her knees, and nuzzled at my zipper, her arms still reaching up to my shoulders. I put a hand on her forehead and tipped her face up to me. 'No, wait.' She was worried, she looked up at me like a reprimanded child. This was our usual ritual when we first met, this frantic first sucking. I loved to see her mouth opening to me. But today I held her chin delicately. 'We will, we will,' I said. 'In two minutes. But first I want to hear about what's been happening.'

Up she jumped, laughing and happy. We sat on the easy chair, her back and legs sprawled over the arms and on my lap, and she put her arms around me and told me everything. Instead of two minutes it took two hours. She told me about the problems of shooting, the artificial lake that was supposed to be Switzerland, that began to stink because the bastard light-boys kept pissing into it. Then there was the beautiful white horse that gave eight shots in complete calm, it was a long-time filmi horse. Then, in the lighting break before the ninth shot, an electrician was dragging a power cable through the grass, and this white horse panicked, and bucked, and backed itself off a cliff and dropped thirty feet. They had to shoot it. With a real revolver.

'It's a dangerous business, this shooting,' I said.

'And tiring. And so slow, so very long, saab,' Zoya said. 'I feel like I've been doing this film for ever. But it's been a lot of fun. There are such specimens on that set.'

Then she got up and imitated Dheeraj Kapur exhorting the cinematographer to go faster with his lighting, 'Please, sir, already we are thirty-four per cent over budget, and thirty days over.' She had him exactly, his paunchy walk and his Punjabi heartiness, his delicate way of holding a cigarette with his middle finger and thumb, and even the shortness of his upper lip, which gave him the look of a mildly ferocious dog. She came alive when she was acting, my Zoya. When she was Dheeraj Kapur, there was none of that distance that usually separated Zoya Mirza from the outside world and those of us who lived in it. She was not deep behind the black shine of her eyes, unreachable. She was there, in the downy surfaces of her forearms, in the large, ambling gait of the producer. Her life sparkled and sparked, here, here, for me. I laughed and pulled her down into my lap, until she got up to do someone else. She could do a perfect Manu Tewari. She made me see his square, communistic beard, the way he fingered it when he was trying to appear impressively thoughtful. I don't know quite how, but she made me feel his labouring seriousness, his hair-dissecting scalpel of a mind, his eager belief in fairy tales about the future. I suppose that is what a great actress should do. She made you want to believe, and so you did.

When I finally took her to bed, I had no doubt. I was whole. In our talking, and the laughter that had passed between us, I found my strength again. I went into her four times that day, and she came into me. I did not distrust her pleasure, or mine. It was all one. And my penis was heroic. I did not point out my growth to her, there was no need. Her moans as she took her satisfaction were all the proof I needed.

International Dhamaka flopped. After all that publicity, after all the money pumped into MTV song clips and gigantic six-sheeter hoardings and *Dhamaka* lunch boxes in bright red plastic, nobody came to see it. On the first day itself, collections were sixty per cent in Bombay, and lower outside. The critics were cruel to the film, but we had half-expected that, and nobody in the film industry really cared what the critics had to say, if the people came. If the public paid for tickets. But, by the middle of the second week, ticket sales were lower than forty per cent nationwide. The foreign markets, where we had expected the film to be a full-speed hit, treated us only slightly better. The mader-chod NRIs didn't come either. I was on the phone to Dheeraj Kapoor day and night, we put up new hoardings in the metros, we increased the frequency of the TV spots, with added titles that invited the public to see 'Superhit *International Dhamaka*'. We told them to be part of the magic. We tempted them to see the world.

But the gaandus wouldn't come. We cut seven scenes, edited down fourteen others and shot a new song, with not one or two but three top models wearing hardly more than fluorescent bikinis and some gauze. We had this item song in the cinemas in Bombay and Delhi in a record thirteen days, but still the bastard public wouldn't come. By the end of the third week, the trade papers fearlessly and unanimously listed *International Dhamaka* as a flop. I couldn't deny this. It was a flop.

Until now Dheeraj Kapoor had counselled patience, faith, stamina. He had told me stories of how G.P. Sippy had kept *Sholay* in the cinemas for a month, while the industry mocked him, while he lost money. Finally, word of mouth about Gabbar Singh had made the difference, and the audience had packed into the cinemas, and kept *Sholay* showing for five continuous and enormously profitable years. But now, even Dheeraj Kapoor admitted that *International Dhamaka* was a flop. It was his film as much as mine, but in that fourth week he let it go. 'No more, bhai,' he said to me on the phone late one night. 'You've spent too much already. We have to accept. We have to adjust.'

So I let it pass out of the cinemas. I had to confront the truth: *International Dhamaka* was a flop. I couldn't put a pistol to the audience's head and make them sit in the cinemas, so *International Dhamaka* was a flop. But it was a good film. I had seen it so often that I think I could hardly see what was on the screen any more, I was so sunk in the details of framing and sound and pacing. Now I watched it again. Yes, it was a good film. You couldn't doubt that. It had action, love, patriotism and unforgettable songs. It was beautiful and perfect. So why had it been rejected? Why was the public flocking in to see *Tera Mera Pyaar*, which was a nonsensical, badly shot little piece of romantic boy-loses-girl-and-cries-and-cries rubbish, made with three crores and unknown actors? 'We can't know,' Dheeraj Kapoor said. 'You can't ever know, bhai. The audience is a bastard. Every chutiya in the industry will now give you thirty-six reasons our film didn't work, but during the preview shows they all loved it. All the analyses after a film is released are useless. You can't tell the future. And you can't really tell the past. We can't know.'

I wanted to know, I had to know. I asked Guru-ji. He was in South Africa at the time, giving a series of lectures, but he made time to call me. He knew I was in trouble, he knew how sad and helpless I was. He understood that I had never been this helpless, so he took care of me. He was more than a father, he was motherly. I knew he had been unable to see into the future of this film, but I asked him to look into its past. 'It had everything, Guru-ji,' I said to him. 'It had every element that a viewer looks for. So why didn't it work?'

'You want a reason?'

'Yes, I want a reason, Guru-ji.'

'That is the trouble, that you want one reason.'

'But, Guru-ji, you are the one who keeps telling me that the world is not chaos. You gave a lecture yesterday to seven thousand people about the cycles of time, and how we are moving steadily towards a new age.'

'I said that?'

He had that roomy grin on, I could tell, that flash in his eye that just ate up your confusion. 'Yes, you said that. I read your lecture on the website. You said that what we do has a purpose.'

'I did say that, beta. The fault is in your question. When you ask for a reason.'

I stopped, I thought. I still couldn't grasp what he was moving me towards. 'I don't understand, Guru-ji. Please tell me.'

'You ask for a reason, for one reason. But there are hundreds of reasons, thousands of them. There is not only one immediate cause. There are many. All these reasons meet each other and cross each other, and flow forward in the service of the grand purpose. And you stand at the place of the crossing of these thousands of reasons, and ask for one.'

'So maybe the reason was not in the film at all.'

697

'Yes. Maybe the time needed something else. Maybe the flow was moving in a certain direction when your film released.'

'Was it? Was it?' My mind was too small to see this intermingling of velocities, to encompass all of it without rupturing like a bulging paper bag. But he was Guru-ji, and I needed this from him. He could see all of it, and I wanted him to give me some faith in this flow I was being tossed by. 'Please, Guru-ji. Tell me.'

'Yes, Ganesh,' he said. 'There were many reasons which had nothing to do with the film itself. You told the truth, but right now the public is comforting itself with young love. They will wake up to your truth, but not now. And, Ganesh, why do you worry only about reasons? There are many purposes. Attracting an audience into the cinemas and making money exist as purposes only in the immediate sense. Your film will find its dharma in the long future, in the net of consequences that grow from its release. You have succeeded, you just don't know it yet.'

I could see the web of action and purpose and effect that he was talking about, or at least a pale ghost of it. He was Guru-ji, he could see this vast story that was so much larger than my story, he had gone beyond the limitations that I had, that Manu Tewari wrote within. We believed that a hero saw his goal in the first act, and his enemies, and so his quest went in a lovely arcing line towards the climax, and towards his victory. We believed that because this hero was fearless and strong, he would gain his prize in the eighteenth reel. But I saw now that we were not to know our causes, or our effects. Only the enlightened ones knew what that story was. Only Guru-ji could shatter the prison of time, and look directly into the blazing confusion of creation. 'Guru-ji, it is good of you to tell me that,' I said. 'I thought I had been defeated.'

'You are not defeated,' he said. 'Have faith, and do your work.'

I tried. I kept up with my meditation, and my exercises, and I buried myself in work, of which there was plenty. I ran three operations for Kulkarni, and of course found ways to sweep up a few of my own personal enemies in the minor bloodletting these entailed. That was pleasing. But I was distracted. I had discipline enough to keep to my routine, but I found no joy in it. Zoya, on the other hand, called me every other day with exuberant tales of her acting triumphs on various sets. She had signed six films with top banners, three of them after *International Dhamaka* had been released and declared a flop.

Of all of us, she was the only one who emerged from this disaster unscathed. In fact, she was stronger, she was more beautiful than ever, and she was on television every half-hour. The industry and the public had somehow decided that she wasn't responsible for the soggy *Dhamaka* of our film, and so she thrived. Meanwhile, my half-inch gain had withered down to a quarter, and even that slight advantage depended on how I held the ruler against my lauda. Sometimes, very late at night, I caught myself thinking that I had somehow deceived myself earlier into believing that I had grown, that Dr Reinnes had helped me with his science. And then the white chasm of despair beckoned temptingly. But no, I persevered. I remembered Guru-ji and I went on. And yet, I was despondent. Sometimes I woke up early in the morning and opened a certain black file and went through our reviews. The Hindi and Gujarati papers had been the most enthusiastic about *International Dhamaka*, and the Punjabi magazines only slightly less so. The *Dainik Samachar* had loved the music, and said that 'Zoya's debut is the most promising in years'. But without a single exception, the English newspapers and magazines had been unkind to us. *Times of India, Indian Express, Outlook*, bastards all. I had kept the bad reviews as well, and was sometimes compelled to read them, even the snobbish English ones. '*International Dhamaka* is too loud, too long and too witless to make much of a dhamaka,' said the critic for *India Today*. Kutiya, randi. 'All the international stunts and empty patriotism add up to boredom.' That was *Outlook*. Bastards.

There was one who worried me like a burrowing insect under my skin, like a speck of coal in my blood-ridden eye. His name was Ranjan Chatterjee, and he wrote for *The National Observer*, had written weekly film reviews for thirty-two years. He was always described in the magazines as 'veteran movie critic Ranjan Chatterjee', and he poured out his accumulated frustration and rage on us. 'One falters in the face of such arrogant carelessness,' he wrote. 'One quails.' I had to get Manu Tewari to explain who this 'one' was, and why Ranjan Chatterjee was writing about this disembodied number. 'Forget that maderchod, bhai,' Manu Tewari told me. 'He's a bitter old budhau, nobody reads him any more.'

I did, though. I read him through to the end, and then read him again, months later. And then again. '*International Dhamaka* strains one's credulity even more than the usual Bollywood film,' he wrote. 'It

699

is a string of tired film clichés strung together. These bhais live in unreal gilded luxury and fly around the world as if they are catching the morning train to Nashik. They are more slick than James Bond, and more suave than Casanova. One has long since given up hope that the commercial cinema would be concerned with realism. But the superficially glossy *International Dhamaka* makes one wonder if the filmmakers have ever met a real gangster.'

I caught myself thinking about this Ranjan Chatterjee during meetings, and in the mornings, I shook out of a fragile sleep with his 'one' rattling in my head. I had to do something about him. So I gave my instructions. The wrinkled old chutiya lived in Bandra East, in a block of flats that the government had built for journalists and writers. The very evening I gave my orders – it was a Friday – Ranjan Chatterjee was coming home from a first-day first show, with dinner afterwards paid for by the producers, who hoped to mollify him. He was walking fast, up from the garage towards the lift. The bastard was no doubt eager to get to his flat and put together a poisonous little garland of insults for the film he had just seen, to slap the entire crew of a hundred and fifty people with his abuse on Sunday morning. He had that spring in his step, the codger. But he never made it to his typewriter: Bunty and four of his boys were waiting at the corner of the building. They put a hand under each of Ranjan Chatterjee's arms and carried him to the back of the compound. He was making little squealing noises. They stood him up against the wall, and then they broke both of his legs. They wielded those bars that road workers use to pry up chunks of cement. When the first crisp tap landed on his right thigh, Ranjan Chatterjee shook to the ground and began to scream. The windows up the side of the building lit up, and the chowkidars came running around the corner, and stopped short as soon as they saw a drawn pistol. After his other leg took a blow, Ranjan Chatterjee screamed some more, screamed enough to wake up the entire housing society. Bunty waited for him to stop.

He settled finally into a slobbery wet sobbing, and Bunty slapped him lightly on the cheek. 'Hello,' Bunty said. 'Arre, listen to me. Listen.'

Ranjan Chatterjee raised his head and began vomiting. Bunty flinched away in disgust, and then reached down and grabbed a handful of hair and raised up the bastard's head. 'Does it hurt?' Bunty said. 'Tell me, does it hurt?'

Ranjan Chatterjee blinked his watery, wide-open eyes, and finally he was able to find Bunty. He began to wail, to make a small sound like a lonely kitten. 'Yes,' he said. 'Ah, ah, ah. Yes, it hurts.'

'Good,' Bunty said. 'Then you know this is real. And that you have met a real bhai.'

He slammed Ranjan Chatterjee's head down, and walked away. He and the boys got into their waiting car, and away they went, no trouble, no fuss. In the car they all sang the theme song from *International Dhamaka*: '*Rehne do, yaaron, main door ja raha hoon.*' I know all this because one of the boys had been shooting it all, taping it on a little Canon digital camera with an attached spotlight. Even in that one harsh light, the detail that Canon caught was amazing, and the resolution was like nothing I had seen before on video. I could see the snot sliding out of Ranjan Chatterjee's nostrils, and his tiny little pupils. They brought the tape to me the next afternoon, it was hand-delivered to Bangkok and on to Phuket. I watched it fourteen times that first evening, and then I took a Chinese girl, and that night I slept deep, long and hard. I was relaxed, I had expelled Ranjan Chatterjee from my system. Yes, maybe life had a higher order that only the enlightened ones could see. Maybe the stories that we ordinary mortals told were only small lies, convenient explanations for what we couldn't understand. But still, breaking Ranjan Chatterjee's legs gave me what Manu Tewari would have called 'closure'. I had done it, and I felt better, the story was complete. I was finally free of *International Dhamaka*, and I could get on with my life.

I sank into my sleep like a deep-sea diver seeking calm water under a storm. Every night, I slept long at night, and I woke up and then I slept again. Three months had passed, and I had settled back into my routine of exercise and work. I made money, I discussed intelligence and tactics with Kulkarni, I talked to Guru-ji and Jojo, I flew to Singapore twice to meet Zoya. I also slept a lot. I found that I needed nine hours at night, instead of my usual six, and also I took naps during the day. I curled up on sofas, and retreated to my bedroom after lunch. Once, in the middle of a web-surfing session, I even lay myself down under the desk for a quick quarter-hour doze. I just needed to sleep.

Jojo said I was depressed, and Guru-ji said I was just exhausted from the added strain and stress of a year and a half of filmmaking. Whether it was despair or anxiety or something else altogether, I slept.

That evening in September, I had fallen asleep on deck, in the arm-chair that was placed in the bow of the boat for me. We were anchored off Ko Samui. I was reading some spreadsheets, and then I was asleep. In my sleep I knew I was sleeping. I knew I was on the *Lucky Chance*, that I was floating on quiet water, that the sky was vanishing away from me into the dark. I was asleep but not restful in my sleep. I wanted rest but I could not find it.

Then Arvind was patting me awake. 'Bhai,' he said. 'Come. You've got to see this.'

'What?'

'On television, bhai. It's amazing.'

'Gaandu, you're waking me up to watch a television show? How late is it?'

He was already half-way down the stern, and this was Arvind the ever-respectful. There must be something truly astonishing on televi-sion, I thought. 'A few minutes till eight o'clock, bhai,' he said, and hurried towards the door to the main cabin. I shoved myself up and followed, dizzy and reeling, through a dislocation of time. I felt unhinged from the day and night. The evening was unreal to me, even though I could feel the wood under my passing hand.

On the television, a building was burning. There was a city skyline, and a building was burning. I sat down. 'What's this?' I said.

'New York, bhai,' Arvind said. He was perched on the edge of a chair, crouched forward. The others were crowded into the room. A Thai voice spoke excitedly over the images.

'A film?'

'No, bhai. It's real. A plane flew into the building.'

It looked like a film, I thought. One of those big American disaster-and-adventure-and-terrorism movies. 'An accident?' I asked. Arvind didn't know, he raised his hands. 'Get to an English channel,' I said. My blood was humming.

Every channel we found was rolling the same images, of the smoul-dering tower and its twin. Then we found a Hong Kong channel which was running a Fox satellite feed. 'The North Tower continues to burn,' the reporter said. The smoke spilled out of the side of the building. Then another slim silver shape came skimming in at camera right. I was on my feet, breathless. The airliner disappeared behind the burning skyscraper, and then a spiky gout of flame grew out of the other tower. All in silence.

We were quiet. I knew then what this was. I just knew. 'It's not an accident,' I said. 'This is terror.'

I was in front of the television until three in the morning. I had food brought to me, and had the boys turn the sound up when I went to the bathroom, which I used with the door open. I watched until I could no longer keep my eyes open. Then I told the boys to stay awake in relays, and call me if there were further attacks or new revelations.

In my cabin, my solitude was unbearable. Water slapped at the boat, and I flung my clothes off and tried to breathe. Why was I so agitated? Yes, a lot of people had probably died, but people died every day. What was it then, that whipped me into this frenzy of agitation? The boys and I had decided that the attack had to be engineered by Muslims, yes, maybe Arabs. But so what? Yes, this was an escalation, and now America would attack with its giant strength, and make more enemies, but that was an ongoing affair. I had no answers, and I needed to sleep. I forced myself into the shower, and then I lay down and took a pill.

I kept falling into a light doze filled with smoke and dust, and gasping out of it. I saw, again and again, the true line that the plane made as it went to its meeting with the elegant vertical of the building. I turned on my side, tried to think about work, women, but that shape kept coming back to me. Yes, this was terror.

I sat up. Where was Guru-ji now? In Europe somewhere. Prague. Yes, I could call him. I picked up the phone.

He picked up on the first ring. 'Ganesh? Are you all right?'

'Guru-ji, did you see on television today?'

'Yes.'

'It was terrible.'

'Yes.'

'I mean, those bastard Americans act like they own the entire world, someone was going to hit them sooner or later. But still, that was . . .'

'Yes, Ganesh?'

What I wanted to ask was spinning in my head in a thousand fragments. I worried at my chin, rubbed my eyes and tried to bring it all together. 'You said the world was beautiful.'

'Yes.'

'It had a beginning.'

'Yes.'

'And that means . . . that it will have an end.'

'It must. Before it can be born again.'

So the tensions and struggles of the world would rise, in an exquisite arc, and then a stunning explosion, a culmination would follow, and then, nothing. I had heard people talk about the end of the world before, and had seen films about many disasters, but none of it had seemed real to me, ever. But here was that end, sitting in my belly as hard and heavy as a diamond. It was real. 'This will happen,' I said.

'It is inevitable. This is why all the great religious traditions speak of the destruction that must come. Pralay, qayamat, apocalypse. But, Ganesh, don't be frightened. This fear comes from the small ego that traps you. You are infinitely larger than that. From that larger perspective, there is no need for fear.'

I knew he meant well, but this was no comfort to me. Yes, I could maybe think of myself as a distant, dispassionate eye hovering far above the ground I walked on, reading – with pleasure – everything that lay beyond my body's knowledge and over the horizon, but I couldn't feel this. No. I said goodbye to Guru-ji and lay down, and imagined this great web of ricocheting events sweeping always forward, always towards fire and water, towards dissolution, and my mouth was dry. I propped myself up on an elbow, reached for my water. When I put the glass back down, it made a small clink against the gold coaster, and this ringing boomed through my head. I felt my hands shaking. All motion flowed together, every action drove the next one, and a ripple became a wave, and then a torrent hurtling over the unavoidable chasm. Maybe even that tiny jangling of the glass had in some way led us a small way towards echoing doom. A sound crashed into me, maybe my pulse, or maybe some resonance made of everything else, containing beginning and end, birth and life and all-consuming death.

🦎 INSET: *Five Fragments, Scattered in Time*

I

Suryakant Trivedi is drinking a cappuccino in a café near the British Museum. He has been in England for almost two years now, and this is the only vilayati vice he has acquired. He has not given in to any other temptation or pressure. He dresses exactly as he did in Meerut, in long starched kurtas and sober pyjamas. In the winter he sometimes makes a concession and wears thermal underwear, which his America-based son sent him from St Louis. His eldest son, the one he lives with here in Hounslow, worries about him riding on the tube in such flagrantly foreign clothes, but Trivedi knows that putting on some fancy jacket is not going to make him look less Indian. And if he is attacked by some hooligans, well, he is not afraid of injury, or death. Guru-ji has asked him to live in London for a while and do what needs to be done, and Trivedi owes everything to Guru-ji. Even here, watching the tourists walk by in the bright May sunshine, he feels the presence of Guru-ji. This constant support is not just a comfort, but the basis on which he has built his whole life. Only one who has had such a guru can understand how this preceptor is also father and mother and friend, how merely thinking of him flattens obstacles and vanquishes dread. But right now there is no fear, the cappuccino is very hot, exactly the way Trivedi likes it, and the froth is delicious, with its little sprinkling of mocha. He savours it on the tip of his tongue, then lets it swirl back. He feels lazy and content, and allows himself to think of his wife, who died in 1987 of congestive heart failure, who gave him many children and suddenly left. With Guru-ji's help he was able to look past the illusion of death and the haze of hurt that descended, and now he is able to think of her with only fondness and joy.

So Suryakant Trivedi is somewhat fuzzy and absent when Milind enters. Milind is twenty-two, handsome and open-faced and tall. He greets Trivedi effusively, and puts down a bulky gym bag on the floor between them.

'All peaceful?' Trivedi says.

'Yes, sir. No problems.' Milind was born in London, and has only been back to India five times, never for more than two months. But his Hindi is orthodox and flawless. He comes from an old Jana Sanghi family, his grandfather was an eminent professor of Sanskrit at Benares Hindu University. He has grown up in an environment of learning and piety, and he is fiercely patriotic. He knows Trivedi as a leader of the small but fervent political party Akhand Bharat, and he thinks Trivedi is in London to expand the organization and spread the message. He is very willing to do the clandestine work that Trivedi tasks him with. Milind is really quite thrilled to pick up a bag from the Left Luggage office at King's Cross station, to bring it to Trivedi-ji with care and dispatch, to be careful and watchful.

Trivedi understands all this, and therefore invents carefully calibrated dangers for Milind to be afraid of, and stories to be titillated by. He tells Milind that the bag contains military documents from a certain eastern European country, to be passed on to his own governmental contacts at home. Trivedi also pays Milind for his trouble in good English pounds, and buys him an occasional gift, a watch, or a medium-expensive pen. 'Have some coffee,' he says today. 'This is good.'

Milind drinks a Coke instead, and then another one. He has been warned never to speak of their work while doing the work, so he talks about local politics. Trivedi doesn't follow English elections, so he has only the barest idea of what the boy is talking about, but he nods and occasionally interjects, and lets Milind talk his excitement away. He drinks another cappuccino, and savours the irony of what he has pulled off – yet again – for Guru-ji. The gym bag contains money, ten lakhs in five-hundred-rupee notes. The origin of this crisp new money, where it comes from, is what makes this triumph particularly tangy. Trivedi has three cut-outs between himself and the source. There is Milind, there is another delivery boy named Amir and finally there is a clandestine and very extreme Muslim group called Hizbuddeen. Setting up the Hizbuddeen was Guru-ji's idea. The name, though, was Trivedi's. His Urdu is quite good actually, and the name came easily to him:

Hizbuddeen, the Army of the Final Day. Guru-ji loved the name instantly, and had praised Trivedi for his quick, precise thinking. Such an organization would, yes, have such a name. A fake Islamist extremist group is essential to Guru-ji's future plans. But accepting money through the Hizbuddeen was completely Trivedi's contribution. After all, raising funds is one of the primary objectives of any such outfit. So of course the Hizbuddeen collected funds for their activities, and when it transpired that the Pakistanis wanted to contribute, the irony was by far one of the best rewards for all Trivedi's work over the years. At the Pakistani embassy in London, there is a man named Shahid Khan who is listed as a First Secretary, who is quite obviously an intelligence officer. Eight months ago, this Shahid Khan initiated contact with Hizbuddeen, cultivated them, offered them training, resources, money. So, earlier this week, the Pakistanis gave money to Hizbuddeen, who gave it to Amir, who left it for Milind to collect, and now it is with Trivedi. And Trivedi will use it to fuel Guru-ji's activities. He will pass some of it down to the Kalki Sena, which needs much money for arms, for recruitment, for the laying-in of resources. They must be ready for the final day. Trivedi thinks of the Kalki Sena as the operational arm of Akhand Bharat, and he likes the fact that it is small and fleet and well-armed. Sometimes, despite his age, he can't help thinking of himself as a modern version of Shivaji or Rana Pratap. Trivedi takes another sip of his cappuccino. Quite completely delicious.

'When do we meet next, Trivedi-ji?' Milind says.

This was usually Milind's first question after he had cooled down from all the tension of the current job. Trivedi always answered it the same way: 'I don't know yet. I will be in touch.' The boy was useful, but somewhat irritating. Given a choice, Trivedi would have liked to use someone quieter, and perhaps more intelligent, but you worked with what was at hand. He sends Milind off, pays the waiter and shoulders the gym bag. It is satisfyingly heavy. The Pakistanis are good paymasters for their people. Every month their man meets a representative of the Hizbuddeen and hands over the money. Every month Trivedi collects their contribution and sends it off to Guru-ji's people. Every month he experiences these moments of sublime satisfaction. Let the bastards pay for their own defeat, which was sure to be final and conclusive.

Trivedi walks past the museum. He has been in it only once, and has never gone back. He had been amazed and appalled by the corridors of splendid plunder that the British Empire had looted from all over the world and put in this mausoleum for idiots to gawk at. It nauseated him, to think of the British flag fluttering over Delhi. Never again, he had said to himself, and he swears it again. Trivedi has learned the Great Game. He knows now about cut-outs and false-flag operations, and he has tamped down his distaste and interacted with bad men, disgusting men. He has shared meals with drunkards, shaken hands with criminals. He has called himself Sharma and listened for hours to the foul-mouthed Ganesh Gaitonde and his company of brutes, he has pretended laughter at their obscene jokes. Yes, Trivedi has demeaned and dirtied himself. But he has done it all for Guru-ji, he has done it for the future. He is doing what needs to be done. He is tired now, his feet ache and he feels his age. By the time he gets home, his shoulders will hurt as well. He will be a little afraid during that last walk home from the station in the dusk, when the sky will turn into a very foreign blue-grey, and the responsibility that he carries on his shoulder will weigh more than ever, but he will whisper to Guru-ji, and he will walk on. He is confident. He turns his mind to the present, to maintaining his brisk pace which he has practised since he first met Guru-ji almost three decades ago. He passes an English family and smiles at the little boy who walks between his parents, holding their hands. The unblemished innocence of children is a good thing to see, it has always been a fount of hope to him. Trivedi thinks of the money, and what lies ahead, and he is happy.

II

Ram Pari scrubs a pot. She is squatting in the courtyard of Bibi-ji's house, in front of the hand-pump, scouring the blackened pot with ash. She likes the skid of her palm across the curved side of the pot, but her shoulders are beginning to twinge with the pain that will stay in them until the end of the day, until she sleeps. She is getting too old for this work, but then what other work is there? Her nose itches, and she rubs at it, not very successfully, with the back of her forearm. She is watching Navneet, Bibi-ji's daughter, who is lying face down in the baithak, writing a letter. The girl is moony, as usual, and she has been working on the same piece of paper for the last hour. Ram Pari knows that she is writing a letter to her fiancé. Ram Pari thinks that the girl is shameless for doing this, and that her parents are fools. Such laxity can only end in disaster. Ram Pari can recall many a scandal, among rich and poor, to prove her point. But it is useless to say anything to Bibi-ji, she is a stubborn and proud woman who will brook no criticism from those she thinks of as her inferiors. And anyway there is no reason for Ram Pari to be concerned, it isn't her business what these people do. She realizes that she has stopped rubbing, and that any moment Bibi-ji will hear the pause, and come out and snipe at her, so she settles back and sets to scrubbing again.

Navneet sits up, yawns and then gets up and walks across the courtyard. She goes into the room that she shares with her two sisters, and then emerges, wearing her going-out chappals. She must be going to that college again. Ram Pari doesn't know what use it is to educate a girl so much, but she respects reading and writing. She herself can't do either, and knows she is too old to learn. But she knows that men who read and write have an advantage. She has her own bitter experience to prove that. But she doesn't want to think about such disasters, and her illiterate husband's failures, so she whispers, 'Rabb mehar kare,' and pumps water, and the splash fills her ears.

Navneet is standing near her. 'Ram Pari,' she says absently, 'your eldest daughter is very pretty. When she's old enough, you should find a handsome boy for her.'

Ram Pari feels irritation swirl in her throat. This vain cow with her white skin thinks that everyone has time to look at themselves in the mirror all day long, and think about handsome lafangas. 'She's already married,' she says shortly.

'What, that little thing?'

'She's not that small. She will go to her sasural soon.'

'How old was she when she got married?'

Ram Pari moves a flat hand in the air, less than the height of the hand-pump. 'Among our people it is like that.'

Navneet puts a hand over her mouth and sits on the stool near the pillar, which her father uses every morning when he puts on his shoes. 'And she has never seen her husband since then?'

'No. Why should she?' Ram Pari says this and then is afraid that she is being too curt. But she doesn't know how to demonstrate now that she is appropriately docile and respectful, so she picks up a karhai and puts it under the pump. She scoops up a fistful of ash, and as the karhai rattles under her scrubbing, she understands what Navneet wants. So she turns, and smiles sweetly, and says, 'But, you talk to *him* all the time, no?'

'No, no. I don't talk to him, I only write letters once in a while.' The girl has a shadow of darker pink on her cheeks, and she does have the grace to look somewhat embarrassed.

Ram Pari is confident now. She laughs, and says, 'Maybe, but he writes all the time, every day.'

Navneet shrugs shyly, and Ram Pari – despite herself – feels a kinship with her. Yes, it is good to be very young, to be full of anticipation and longing and a little dash of delicious fear, to hover on the edge of a new life. She decides to be generous. 'Is he very handsome?'

'You want to see a photo?' Navneet is on her feet already, and even before Ram Pari can get out her yes, she is half-way across the courtyard, and even Ram Pari recognizes – without a trace of envy – the unconscious grace in her youthful run. Let the girl be happy. It is her time to be happy.

Navneet comes back and squats next to Ram Pari. She opens a notebook filled with indecipherable marks, flips a page, and there is her man. He wears a very high-pointed turban, and stares at Ram Pari with insouciant arrogance, a hint of a smile playing over his lips. He is indeed very good-looking. The photo has been tinted, and the red of his cheeks stands out against the blinding brilliance of his teeth. 'Vah,' Ram Pari says, 'just like some hero.'

'Yes, I tell him all the time that he could easily be an actor if we went to Bombay. But of course he doesn't want to shave his beard, and of course I don't want him to. He used to act in college, and a lot of his friends say he looks like Karan Dewan, but I think he really looks like Ashok Kumar.'

Ram Pari nods.

But Navneet wants more. 'Don't you think so?'

'I don't know Ashok Kumar.'

'What? Haven't you seen *Kismet*?'

A great burst of raucous laughter bursts out of Ram Pari. All her rancour is swept away. 'No, I haven't seen *Kismet*.' She now feels only tenderness towards this child who believes that everyone has the money and the time to go to some *Kismet*, who sees her future unfolding before her on a screen that glitters with romance and promise. Ram Pari feels in her stomach, in her groin, the heartbreak that awaits Navneet, which will come only because she hopes for so much. Ram Pari does not know what the catastrophe will be, but she knows it will arrive. She says as kindly as she can, 'Maybe I will see *Kismet* some day.'

Navneet is beginning to realize that she has said something maybe a little silly, and is confused. She stutters, and blushes again. Ram Pari wants to reach out and touch her, but she doesn't. She knows that Bibi-ji may come in at any moment, and shout at her for wasting time. But she can shrug off Bibi-ji's bellowing for all eternity, and just now, just in this moment, she loves this Navneet. She says, 'Tell me what *Kismet* is about,' and she settles down to listen.

III

Rehmat Sani watches the night sky emerge from the fading bloom of a flare. He is comfortable and dreamy, settled into a hollow in the earth he has come to know well after using this route for almost three months. He is sixty yards from the fence, on the Pakistani side, and he is in no hurry. He has five hours before first light, and he has patience. The first time he crossed the border was when he was a boy, and back then you could just walk across, being careful to avoid the patrols and the minefields. Then, the bribes for the Rangers and BSF men had been smaller, and the mines more scattered, and the fence hadn't been put in. But no matter. Rehmat Sani knows every inch of ground for a hundred miles south and north, and the border is many thousands of miles long. Even if it is all fenced, he will still get across. He has business on both sides, and of course family.

He has done well this trip. Instead of the usual quarters of rum, this time he had carried two big bottles of foreign whisky for his cousin on the Pakistani side. Mushtaq has a captain who wanted the whisky, and a captain could be very useful, so Rehmat Sani had acquired the whisky from Aiyer and taken it across. Aiyer is small and dark and wears very thick glasses and looks quite unlike an intelligence man, but he is no fool. He knows when to be flexible. So Rehmat Sani has profited from the captain, from the money he has carried for his cousin the havaldar, and also from a bottle of rum he took across for his own private gain. He has no new information for Aiyer, but Aiyer will wait until the captain can be developed. Aiyer is young but he is learning well. Rehmat Sani has high hopes for him.

Rehmat Sani stretches, easing his muscles. Maybe he is getting too old for this. He can smell the damp from the deep, watery nullah which he will use to get to the fence. The crawl through the twisting defile will leave him soaked and cold, and it is this last bit of this route that makes him wish, every time, that he had sons who were earning already. But his first wife had given him only four daughters, and the younger wife had become pregnant only after three years, after he had gone to Ajmer Sharif and tied a thread and wept and appealed to Khwaja Sahib. Only then had Khalid been born. He is in school now, in the fifth standard, and Rehmat Sani intends to educate him fully. Rehmat Sani understands the demands of the time, he knows that a man without education – like himself – will not get far, or live well. But it is hard to bear the burden of two daughters married, and two still sitting at home. When Rehmat Sani was Khalid's age, he had already travelled with his father as far as Lahore. He cannot remember much before that first journey, but he remembers the rooftops of Lahore glowing in the morning sun.

Rehmat Sani shakes off the nostalgia and readies himself for the descent into the nullah. It is dark again, and the singe of the flare has faded from his eyes. He does not need to raise his head to check for threats. He can tell from the loud silence of the night, from the steady pinging of insects, from the ease of his own body. Against his chest, he can feel the plastic packet he has tucked away under his banian. The Pakistani captain paid for his whisky in crisp new Indian notes, which is convenient for Rehmat Sani. At home, he will take the money out of the plastic and give it to his senior wife to deposit in his bank and get his passbook updated. He cannot read the passbook, but he likes looking at the notations when she returns from her half-day trip to the bank. The scribbling makes him feel safe. Now he wonders where the Pakistanis get so much new Indian money. It's strange that the freshly minted notes are taken over the border one way and then come back the other way with him. But this has been his whole life, going one way and the other, over this immense line in the ground, under the fence and around it. He doesn't think much about why it winds its way across the fields, but it exists, so he has made his living from it. He yawns, and turns over. Time to go. It will take him two hours to get to the fence, another two hours before he is over to safety on the other side. Then he will stand up, shake off the mud and go home.

Dr Anaita Kharas is squatting, emptying vermiculite into a pot. She has already put in the soil and the sand and the peat moss, in carefully measured proportions, and now she sifts the mixture through her fingers and enjoys its roughness. She could use a trowel – her sons tell her that her hands look like a labourer's, not a doctor's – but the weight of the earth on her palms settles her every morning before she sets out to work. She comes up here every morning, to the terrace of her house in Vasant Vihar, and works on her garden. She grows ficus and bottle-brush plants, bougainvillea and herbs, yellow champa and juhi. The December cold is biting into her fingertips, but even that is good. She has found that she needs this time alone, and putting suva seeds in a pot prepares her for the day of patients and disease. She is thinking, as she finishes her planting, about K.D. Yadav, who died three days ago. He was a good patient, even before his tumours turned him silent and unmoving. He suffered his loss of ability and comprehension with dignity. Only once she found him weeping, standing next to the window, and then he accepted her usual doctorly exhortations with a smile. He was much older than her, and very old-fashioned with his namastes and standing up when she entered the room, or at least wanting to, but he always listened to her intently. A time or two she found herself telling him things that had nothing to do with medicine and everything to do with her own life. He had that way of asking questions, of probing without seeming to, so that you gave him information without knowing you were. Days later, he would say, 'Yes, I must have been in Calcutta when your father was posted there,' and then you would remember that you had told him about living in Calcutta for a year at the age of eleven. He was a smart man, K.D. Yadav, for someone who had worked many undistinguished decades in the Ministry of Human Resource Development.

Anaita stands up, flexes her knees. She walks around the periphery of the roof, examining the plants closely. She had fought an infestation of powdery mildew two months ago, and had lost two gulmohars, and had decided to be more vigilant in the future. Disease comes fast, and takes everything. But today her plants look well. They sweep in a conflagration of colours across the terrace, and the vines climb to the top of the water tanki a full floor higher. It is a large house, one that she and Adi would never be able to afford to buy or build today. Adi's parents had bought two big plots in the sixties, when Vasant Vihar was still a wilderness beyond the Ridge. They had sold one plot twenty years later, and built a house on the other, and so now Adi and Anaita and their sons live in this colony of plenty. They are very lucky, but still prices are crazy in this locality. The boys don't realize how expensive it is to put the food they love on the table, the meat and good bread and fruits. They are at that age when it is very important for them to keep up with their friends, and their friends – many of them classmates at Modern School – are the sons of industrialists and businessmen. Anaita thinks back to her long-ago days of ten rupees a week pocket money, and worries yet again for her sons. People have too much money nowadays, and they throw it about as if it meant nothing. Their children wear sunglasses worth thousands of rupees, and birthday parties cost lakhs. Many of their neighbours in E-block have three and four cars parked in their driveways, and maybe one more outside. So the boys sometimes resent Anaita and Adi, and think of them as stingy parents.

Anaita has finished her inspection, and she walks to the middle of the terrace, near the stairway, and looks down into the courtyard. Adi's father had insisted on building a small open space in the centre of the house, and no argument from his wife had persuaded him for even a moment. 'I want to see light,' the old man had said, and after the house was built, he had put an armchair in the gallery abutting his precious courtyard and read the paper there every morning, no matter whether it was June or the chilliest of Januaries. Anaita had rather liked him for that. Now she can see Adi carrying a tray out of the kitchen. Any moment now he will call out for her, and then go and wake the boys. She will go down and drink the chai that he's made, joke with the boys and eat some eggs. Adi is a good man. They have had their quarrels, sometimes severe ones which left both of them feeling ragged for weeks, but they have persevered and have survived. Adi says sometimes that they have worn the sharp edges off each other. He makes her laugh often, he takes part in the daily drudgery of raising a family and they are content together. She needs to go down now, she doesn't like to leave the house too late, the traffic starts to congeal along the avenues, but she is still thinking about that K.D. Yadav.

Why? She isn't sure. She liked him, but she has liked other patients and has lost them. Death is nothing new to her, she deals with it every day, she is familiar with its onrush, with the sound of it, and the inertia and smells of its aftermath. She knows it is coming for her, for Adi, and she can even imagine – almost without flinching – the death of her children. Why, then, does K.D. Yadav stay with her? She strokes the leaves of a tulsi plant and breathes, and the chill is almost painful against her nostrils. How terrible it would be to lose the distinction between cold and hot, between inside and outside. At the end, when K.D. Yadav had gone completely still, he had looked neither happy nor sad. Had he still been able to tell whether it was day or night, whether he was alive or dead? Anaita had told his young friend or colleague, whatever she was, that Anjali Mathur, 'Don't worry. It's all quite painless, he is not suffering.' But now, she thinks of what it must be like not to suffer, to exist in some kind of vast void, and she shudders. Poor man, she thinks. He had liked so much to read, and finally the letters and the page must have melted together, become one thing that was nothing. Poor, poor man.

'Anaita!'

Adi is standing in the courtyard, holding a frying pan. Anaita giggles at the sight of him, completely ridiculous in that tacky Chinese dressing gown with the dragon curling its claws, which he absolutely refuses to give up.

'What are you doing, yaar?' he says. 'Please go and take a bath, otherwise you'll make me late.'

'Coming, baba, coming,' Anaita says. She takes one last look around her garden, and goes down to her life.

V

Even as he savours his victory, Major Shahid Khan worries about defeat. He is clipping his beard, and in the mirror he can see that none of this anxiety shows on his face or in his eyes. He has trained himself to be impassive. He has his Ammi's clear Punjabi skin, but none of her easy expressiveness. His wife sometimes wonders how two closely related people could be so unlike. But Shahid Khan knows that he has inherited all of Ammi's melancholy, her gargantuan rage, her sudden, bitter sarcasm. But he has learnt to control himself. He gives nothing away, ever. For all her sadness, Ammi sometimes laughs until her face goes red and you have to worry a little about her, but are unable to warn her because you have to hold on to yourself to keep from falling over. Her love for Shahid and his brother and their sister is so openly all-consuming that other mothers joke about it. Her sacrifices for these children are legendary. But Shahid Khan has tamped down all this emotion which swirls up from his genes, he has learnt early – in the ragged lanes of his childhood – to wear the armour of impassivity. This ability has served him well in his profession. He has this ability, and his faith, which stands him on unshakeable bedrock, which gives him the strength to endure anything.

But today he is worried. He is in London, and late last night, just before leaving his office at the Pakistani embassy, he learnt about a death on the other side of the world. One Gurcharan Singh Bhola had been killed by the Indian police in Gurdaspur District, in a village called Veroke. Gurcharan Singh Bhola was the commandant of the Khalistan Tiger Force, which had been relentlessly whittled down by the Indian forces over the last year. And now Gurcharan Singh Bhola is dead. Shahid Khan had met him once, in those days when he was a lieutenant and cutting his teeth in the fields and villages of Punjab. Gurcharan Singh Bhola was a tall man, impressive with his muscular wrestler's build and his burning commitment to his Khalistan. But Shahid Khan had only met him once, on a night when Bhola had passed through his picket, and it is not grief for the sardar that weighs Shahid Khan down this morning. He is now very far from Punjab, but it is obvious that the Indians are crushing the Khalistan movement. They are brutal, ruthless. With support from the central and state governments, their army and the paramilitary forces are hunting down the revolutionaries one by one. Shahid Khan knows exactly how much it cost – in money and effort and lives – to build up and support the movement. Now, it is finished. This reverse is humming in Shahid Khan's veins. He has been trained to accept losses. He believes in ultimate victory like he believes in the fact of this mirror in front of him, as something that just exists, but the humiliation of loss is something that has always maddened him. He knows it is weakness, this anger. It clouds his judgement. He had hoped that with age he would learn equanimity, but passion lingers. He tries to think of his successes, in particular the recent operation in the ruins of the USSR, which operation he resuscitated and rescued after the Indians almost succeeded in killing it. For decades, during the years of cosy allegiance between India and the USSR, the Indians had had much of their high-value national currency printed in the Ukraine. After the fall of the Soviet empire, Shahid Khan's agency had sent operatives into the Ukraine, to probe at the press where this currency was printed. These operatives had succeeded in setting up a deal – for a substantial sum paid in hard currency, the Ukrainians would give them the original plates for the Indian notes. That would have been a triumph indeed, to be able to print counterfeit Indian money from the original plates. But the Indians had got wind of the deal – everything was rotten in the Ukraine – and had claimed the original plates, and had got hold of them. Out of this complete disaster, Shahid Khan had brought a kind of victory and some dignity. He had come in after the fact and acted fast. The plates were gone, yes, but the paper was still there, sitting in huge warehouses, lightly guarded. Shahid Khan moved quickly, he made deals, he arranged logistics, he had a minor Indian embassy official picked up by local thugs and held for two days. And while the Indians were distracted, he stole their currency paper. Now the notes printed on this original, completely genuine paper – which Shahid Khan had obtained at some personal risk – are in circulation throughout India, and Shahid Khan knows that he is well on his way to becoming a lieutenant-colonel. Yes, there is that, even though the personal triumph cannot rescue him entirely from the national failure.

He shakes himself out of his reverie, puts the scissors down and runs the water. He bathes efficiently, and as he towels himself dry he can't help thinking, yet again, that the huge fluffy length of cloth is an absurd luxury. He has been able to afford such things for a while, and doesn't begrudge his family these conveniences, but he has been shaped in a harder school. After he prays and eats, he straightens out his papers and pays some bills. It is a Sunday, and the women in the household – his mother, his wife, his daughter – have gone to East Ham to visit relatives. He is alone, and finally, after all responsibilities have momentarily been discharged, he feels that he can take an hour off. He goes to his bedroom and shuts the door. The front door is locked, and he knows nobody will disturb him, but he is compelled to make sure that his privacy is secure. Until now, only his wife knows he does what he is about to do.

He sits in his favourite armchair, which faces the window. Good light is essential. He puts a pillow over his lap, the balls of yarn to his right. Then he begins to knit. He is making yet another scarf. His wife donates them, usually to a madrassa or an orphanage back home. The needles click, and click, and Shahid Khan's shoulders ease and drop. He has been doing this for the last two years, since a doctor in Karachi told him that he had better learn to relax, or his ulcers were going to kill him. 'Learn how to really take a holiday,' the doctor said. 'Get a hobby.' At first Shahid Khan played squash. He had always wanted to learn, and it looked like a good workout. But he found that he needed to win. He took extra coaching lessons, and began reading books on technique. When he found that he was dreaming of rematches, he gave it up. He was then sent to Ukraine, and there he took up chess. Wary of playing against another person, he invested in a handheld chess machine. The cleverness of the thing was delightful, how it folded out and clicked softly into a complete board, the recessed compartments for the pieces, the little red lights with which the machine told you which piece it wanted to move, and where. While he was learning to use it, his insides felt better. But then he wanted to play it at the harder levels, and the pains flared up. Anyway the martial metaphor was too obvious, its viziers and its pawns and black-and-white battleground made him think too much of the real world. He gave the machine to a friend, and suffered for a while in silence. Then he tried riding, but that lasted only until he met a recalcitrant horse.

He called the Karachi doctor from Moscow, and almost hung up when he heard what the man had to suggest. It took him two months to buy the yarn, and another three weeks to begin. But he found, even that first time in the hotel room in Tallinn, that his hands fell naturally into the rhythms. He understood the taut opposition of knit and purl, and did not need to think. He did not need to knit faster, or better, or even competently. He just made something, something red and oddly shaped and large, and decided later that it was a scarf.

So Shahid Khan sits facing the noontide sun. His eyes are wide open, and there is only a small burning within his belly, and he does not mind it. In a little while it too will be gone. He is breathing. The white yarn stretches against his skin, and then relaxes. The needles sound against each other. The warp and weft form, and flow. His mind, his heart fills with the radiant glow of Allah's mercy. The fabric grows, and he is at peace.

Ganesh Gaitonde Remakes Himself

I gave myself a new face that winter. I had been worrying for a while about the many photographs of me that had been published in the newspapers and magazines in India. Television programmes regularly ran video clips of me leaving the law courts in Bombay. I was too recognizable, too well-known. Once, on the beach at Ko Samui, a group of young Indian tourists had turned to stare at me, and had whispered nervously to each other. I had left India not only to avoid jail, but also to elude my many enemies. I needed to change. I had seen Zoya transform herself, so I understood how it could be done, what it cost in pain and money, what its possibilities were. I needed to be new.

I knew I wanted this transformation, and not for security reasons only. There was a dissatisfaction working under my skin, a discontent. Every morning I looked at myself in the mirror, and the face I saw was not the man I knew myself to be. I knew myself to be sculpted lean, as if the terrors and triumphs of my life had carved me a new shape. But the years had sagged my cheeks, thickened my nose. My chin sank into a bulge of flesh, there was a droop at the corners of my eyes. The blurring of my features was unbearable. I wanted to alter the outside to match the inside.

I went, of course, to Zoya's Dr Langston Lee. I gave him two months and a lot of money, and experienced more pain than ever before in my life. He gave me a long, elegant nose with a sharp bridge, new cheekbones, a narrower chin that balanced the nose, and a complete absence of jowls. He did some subtle things with my eyebrows, and put a dimple in each of my newly taut cheeks. And I was a different man. The first time I looked into a mirror, after the surgery was complete, after the bandages had come off, I wanted to hug Dr Langston Lee, the little Chinese bastard. Even past the remaining swelling and the stitches I could see that he had understood what I wanted to become. His talent was not only in his fingertips, it was in his eyes and in his imagination. He could share your dream, and cut through skin and fat to make it come alive. I looked nothing like the Ganesh Gaitonde that had been. I was the Ganesh Gaitonde that I wanted to be. I was myself.

'Zoya is not going to know who you are, bhai,' Suhasini said when she and Arvind visited that afternoon. 'I can hardly tell who you are myself. This Langston Lee is a genius.'

It hurt to smile, but I did. I liked the idea of Zoya not knowing who I was, of her being baffled by this new man. I wanted her confused and jittery, unsure of herself. She was shooting two films in America, in Detroit and Houston, and I had not told her about my plans for a new look. My surgery had been kept a secret, from her and anyone else who did not need to know. 'Let's surprise Zoya,' I said.

'She's going to jump like a cow with a stick jabbed up its gaand,' Arvind said. 'If it wasn't for the voice, bhai, I wouldn't have recognized you.' He peered at me, leaning over the foot of the bed. 'It's not like anything has changed that much. But somehow all the changes together have completely changed you.'

I healed fast. As soon as Dr Langston Lee gave me the go-ahead, I flew to America. Zoya couldn't get much time off from her shoots, and I really wanted to see her. Or, rather, I wanted her to see me. So I went. Our operations in the US were very limited, so there were no teams of boys to set up the logistics for me, and no bodyguards. I travelled alone, under an impeccable Indonesian passport, and I was sure I would be safe. I was protected by my new look. I had new clothes as well, a suitcase full of light linen suits and cotton shirts in pastel colours. Arvind had been nervous about sending me off alone, but I'd told him that I was safer on my own, that I would attract less attention without an entourage. More so because this broke the pattern that my enemies expected and watched for, they knew that for years I had always been surrounded by my boys. They would never look for me by myself.

I said all this, and believed it. Yet, when the plane took off from Bangkok, and I was soaring off to this new world, I dipped headlong into terror. I was alone. On the *Lucky Chance*, I could hear my boys walking on the deck, their laughter was the first thing I heard in the morning. Now, in this little bubble of first-class air, in this cabin hurtling far above the earth, I couldn't reach them. They were gone. I touched my chin, my nose. Under my handsome new skin there was only me. I felt that I was far away, far from everyone and everything I knew. I calmed myself, told myself that this was an unexpected but natural response to a situation I was not used to, that my body was anxious in its new form. I asked for water, and shut my eyes. The perspiration rolled off my neck, and I knew I was making myself conspicuous. But I couldn't fight down the panic, and finally I gave in and used the airline phone to place a call to Arvind. He was quite agitated when he picked up and heard my voice, we had agreed to maintain an emergency-call-only policy over this trip. 'Bhai,' he said. 'What's wrong?'

Of course I couldn't tell him what was really wrong, about the steely taste of longing and loneliness at the back of my throat. I couldn't say, I just wanted to hear your voice, you bastard. I spoke to him about some investments we had made the week before, and the movement of money from an account in Hong Kong to funds in India. It was all trivial stuff, not material for an emergency call at all. He was puzzled, but he knew his manners, and so he asked no questions, just listened to my instructions. I hung up, and then called Bunty in Bombay. I had nothing to discuss with him that was even vaguely urgent, so I talked to him about Suleiman Isa and our latest intelligence on S-Company's activities. I left Bunty as confused as Arvind, and then I called Jojo. 'I'm in the middle of a meeting,' she said. 'I'll call you back.'

'You can't.'

'Why not? I'll be free in half an hour.'

I hadn't told her about my trip to America, or my surgery. And I certainly couldn't tell her now, sitting next to a Thai grandmother with stern, steel-rimmed glasses and very sharp ears. 'I will be in meetings myself,' I said. 'Tomorrow. I will call.'

'Is something wrong, Gaitonde?'

She knew me too well, this Jojo. 'No, no,' I said. 'Go back to work. Tomorrow, we'll talk tomorrow.'

'Okay,' she said. 'Tomorrow.'

I thought about Jojo as I lay back in my seat. She was my friend, and she could tell more than anyone else what my mood was, whether I was generous or angry, hard or heated or just sad. I trusted her, but I had to keep certain facts from her for reasons of my security. I lived in constant and unrelenting danger, and I had to keep secrets. I had to be

721

careful. I had to assume that this grey-haired Thai woman in the next seat, who was now eating peanuts with the very tips of her glossy fingers, this harmless old lady may also be a spy capable of hurting me. Maybe she understood the Hindi that I spoke to Jojo, maybe she worked for Suleiman Isa and his allies. It was impossible, but I had to allow the possibility.

No wonder I felt lonely, I thought. I lived a life of secrets and suspicion. I had necessarily to separate myself from even my friends, and this was the price I paid for power. I was a ruler, a king, so I could never relax. Even a new face couldn't completely liberate me from fear. I was compelled to walk alone. But this solitude that I felt on the flight to America, this was new. I had never felt anything like it. I felt like I was a whirling ball floating in immeasurable space. I was suspended in a complete vacuum, quite free. Yes, this was freedom, I was independent and alone. And I was terrified.

I broke my rule of years and asked for a Scotch. I held my breath and drank the bitter brown medicine. Then I drank two more, and finally I was able to sleep.

I woke up to Los Angeles spreading like a long stain to my right. It was vast, and I felt very small. I couldn't shake it off, this feeling of my own littleness, this childlike apprehension. It stayed with me in the limousine to the hotel. The streets were wide and clean, and the cars moved in orderly rows, and it all seemed very foreign. I had never felt so apart in Thailand, or even in Singapore, so unlike the drivers who sped past me. I saw an Indian man parking his car next to a market, and I watched him as he walked to a phone. He was bald, paunchy, and he could have walked down any gali in Bombay without attracting any attention. His name was probably Ramesh, or Nitin, or Dharam. But still I felt very far from him. Maybe it was an effect of this huge, hazy sky above, and this clear, colourless light. Space was different here, and so was gravity. I felt weightless.

My suite at the Mondrian floated twelve storeys above Sunset Boulevard. The traffic slid along below in silent ribbons of metal. The silence was unsettling. I switched on the television, turned it up, took a quick shower, and then called Zoya. She was in a room on the seventh floor. She had caught an early flight from Houston that morning and had checked in under the name of Madhubala. I had to spell the name out to the operator twice, finally the call went through, and there was Zoya. 'Hello?' she said. She had picked up an American accent.

'It's me,' I said. 'I'm in Room 1202. Come up. The door is open. Come in.'

'Yes,' she said. 'I'm coming.'

She was a good girl, she didn't need any more instructions than that. I had drawn the curtains, so that there was only a single sweep of light across the room. I sat in an armchair, backlit. It was a very dramatic shot, from her point of view. I wanted a full impression on her, a total high-impact moment that would stop her short. And then the revelation of my face.

It worked just as I had planned. She came in, paused, then shut the door. 'Saab?' she said. She was wearing a white skirt, very short, and a white blouse that tied high. There was that oppressive curve of her waist, that cutting jut of her hip. She knew just what I liked. Saali, she was smart. But today I had her. I switched on the lamp next to me, and she said quickly, 'Who are you? Who are you?' She was afraid.

I wanted to laugh, but I kept it in. The bafflement and the fright on her face were too delicious. She crossed her hands in front of the long slot of her belly button, and got as far as 'Where is he? Where is . . .?' before she stopped herself. She set her jaw, and said, in English, 'I am in the wrong room. Sorry.' I was proud of her. She had maintained security. I had taught her well. She turned and stepped smartly towards the door.

'Zoya,' I said.

She stopped, came around. 'Allah,' she said. That was the only time I ever heard her call on her god. 'Is it you?'

'It's me.'

'But how can it be?'

'What, only you can change?'

She came up to me, knelt at my feet. She reached out and touched my cheek with the very tips of her fingers. The wonder moving through her slack jaw slowly ebbed as she narrowed her eyes and calculated, considered. She turned my face gently towards the light. She whispered, 'Dr Langston Lee?'

'Yes.'

'Oh, he is a master. This is excellent work. It is very subtle, and very effective.'

'Do you really like it?'

'Dr Langston Lee is really too good.'

723

That was enough about Dr Lee. I grasped Zoya's wrist with my left hand, and took her chin with the other. 'Do you think it suits me? Do you think it is me?'

She lost that model's measuring look instantly, and smiled at me, her eyes instantly afire with admiration. 'You look very handsome, saab,' she said. 'Even better than before. You could be a star in a film, you know.'

'What, me?'

'Yes, yes. You should make one. With me as the heroine. *International Dhamaka Part Two*!'

'Sequels never work in India,' I said. 'And anyway the first one was a flop.'

'With the new Ganesh Gaitonde as hero,' she said, 'it would be a superhit.'

She leaned into me and kissed me then, and in that moment I really was a hero. I led her into the bedroom, and we came together in a true international dhamaka. This one was a hit, at any rate. There was no time to take off our clothes, even. She tugged up her skirt, and I grabbed the tiny stretch of cloth underneath and twitched it off, and then I climbed on to her, and into her. We were stretched diagonally across the bed, and behind her head the undraped windows gave me the city of Los Angeles. I was laughing like a madman, with my new face, and that was how I came to America.

We went to Universal Studios the next morning. I was reluctant, but Zoya insisted that with my new face nobody would know me, that there was no danger. 'And what about you?' I told her. The rides were sure to be full of maderchod Indian tourists, who now flocked about the world with their cameras and their kids and their new money. Her fans were everywhere. She assured me that she could look very different, that nobody would recognize her if she chose not to have them recognize her. She was quite certain, and she really wanted to go, so we went. And we had a fine time. For me, the pleasure came from watching Zoya's pleasure – she was like a child at her first village fair. She sped from one ride to another, and screamed louder than anyone else when the big shark lunged its open mouth towards us. I hadn't seen many of the films the rides were about, but Zoya knew them all, and she told me their stories. She was wearing spectacles – very plain, large ones – on the tip of her nose, a blue cap, a large white T-shirt with long sleeves, and black jeans. Her hair was in two long ponytails, and she wore no make-up at all. People stared at her, she couldn't hide her height, but nobody recognized her. Not even the teenagers from Delhi who sat in the next car on the Jurassic Park ride and called me 'Uncle'. So Zoya could transform herself into ordinariness as well. With her eyes and face and body, she was capable of anything. She was an actress.

She took me twice through the Terminator ride. 'Once is not enough,' she said. 'I just love Arnold.' I knew who Arnold was, one of the boys had brought a pirated DVD of one of his films on to the boat the last year. I liked the special effects, of course, but on the whole the film had bored me. Like many of these American films, it had one good idea and clung to it so hard that it seemed poor in emotion and range. The scenes seemed flat because even in the most dramatic moments the American actors spoke quietly to each other, as if they were discussing the price of onions. And there were no songs. Finally, ultimately, most American films were sparse and unrealistic, and did-n't interest me very much. But here was Zoya, staring up at the shining steel skeleton of the Terminator, at his beady red eyes, in the same way she had looked at me the day before. Even through her glasses, I could see the fire in her eyes, matching his. She saw me look-ing, and kissed me on the cheek quickly. 'You know,' she said into my ear, 'I dream sometimes of winning an Oscar. Of standing up there. But best of all, maybe I'll get to meet Arnold.'

Arnold. She said the bastard's name as if she already knew him, as if she had shared pani-puri with him at Chowpatty. We went on with the rest of the rides and the exhibits, and she finished the day glowing and giggling. I was exhausted. We left Universal at five, and in the lim-ousine she told me stories of more American films, and stories about their stars. I listened, and finally said, 'Saali, how many of these films do you watch?'

'Usually one a day. I have a little portable DVD player, you know. I can take it on shoots also. Sometimes I watch more than one movie, even on shooting days. It's a good way to improve my English. You should do it also. You know Suleiman Isa watches English films every day.'

I pinched her lower lip. 'How do you know that?'

'Arre, everyone knows that.'

This was true. Everyone who knew something about the under-world knew something about Suleiman Isa's film habits. 'And everyone is wrong,' I said. 'He doesn't watch movies. He watches just three films, again and again. Every evening, he sees one. Then the next, and the next. Then he starts again.'

'What?'

'It's true. We have good intelligence on this, from the inside. He watches *The Godfather* series again and again.'

'No! Really?'

'It's true.'

'Why?'

'Ask the bastard. He's crazy.'

She nodded. 'And have you seen the films, saab?'

'I saw the first one.'

'Didn't like it?'

'It was okay. I thought *Dharmatma* was better. Even *Dayavan*.'

She burst out laughing, and wrapped her arms around me. 'You travel all over the world, bhai, but you have such desi tastes. You are so *ch-weet*.' She kissed me then, and put a hand down the front of my jeans, and showed me how sweet I was, and I forgot about Suleiman Isa and his chutiya *Godfather*. But later that night, after she was asleep, I lay awake thinking about American films. My boys watched American action movies all the time. They said they liked the stunts, and the special effects. Why did Suleiman Isa watch the *Godfather* pictures all the time? I had never thought about this before, but now, lying in a bed under this alien sky, held up by the city's sprawling constellations of lights, it occurred to me that his reasons for watching were maybe the same reasons I had for making *International Dhamaka*. He wanted to understand what had happened to him, what he had become. And for the first time, I felt a kinship with him.

What had I become? I had become someone else, something else. As I tried to grasp how exactly I had changed, what had happened to me, a burrowing little worm of doubt moved through my belly, and up around my heart. Zoya said I was handsome now, that I could be a film star if I wanted. I knew I looked better, that I was younger than ever and sharp-featured. But, but if Arnold was who she dreamed of meeting, could I ever be as large-muscled as the Terminator? If the Terminator came to her in her dreams, even as she slept next to me, could she truly love me? I told myself that the Terminator was a fiction, that I was more powerful than some cheap American actor. I told myself, you have killed more men than some pretend Terminator. A word from you moves money and arms across continents. If anyone should be called the Terminator, it is you.

And yet, when Zoya stirred in the early morning, and nuzzled sleepily at my side, what met her from within me was still that wriggling parasite of disbelief. I looked at the arm that was holding her, my arm, and all I could think of was that it was so scrawny, compared to Arnold's. Actually, even the hero in the film she was shooting in Texas was more of an Arnold than me. He was short, but he had a bulky, steroided chest, and worked-up arms. I knew I could afford the best steroids, and build a gym for myself, and hire trainers, but would I ever be close to the vision that Zoya carried around in her head, this man that she could truly love? Did she love me, this Zoya, this Egotistical Giraffe?

The question was ridiculous, and I knew it, and yet it stayed with me. We ate breakfast sitting at the dining table in the main room, and as usual it was a wonder to watch her eat. She drank a jug of orange juice, and put away three omelettes. I watched her, and she was beautiful again, she was Zoya Mirza the film star herself. Be happy, I told myself. She is with you. And then the phone rang. Not the hotel phone, and not my mobile, but the secure satellite phone which was on the bedside table. I hurried to it. Only Arvind and Bunty had that number, and they would use it only under extraordinary circumstances.

It was Arvind. 'Bhai?' he said. 'You should come back.'

'Why?'

'Our potato business,' he said. The 'potato trade' was our phrase for our armament-smuggling operations, which we ran for Guru-ji. We had been doing this for years now, bringing shipments of arms and ammunition to the Konkan coast and handing them over to his people for transportation. 'They have found out about it. They have one of our shipments.'

'Who has found out?'

'The Delhi people.' Which was Dinesh Kulkarni, otherwise known as Mr Joshi, and his organization, and therefore the maderchod Indian government.

'I will be on the next plane,' I said.

'Please come fast, bhai,' he said. 'They are very angry.'

What he meant was that he was afraid for my safety, exposed as I was in this foreign country, out here in this grand hotel suite without any bodyguards. This is why he was being so careful and cryptic, even on a secure line. 'I understand,' I said. 'Don't worry. I'm on my way.'

I said goodbye to Zoya, and I went.

'Why did you do it, Ganesh?' This was Kulkarni, who was now being sternly schoolteacherish. 'Why?'

'We needed samaan for our own people.'

'Don't lie to me. In the shipments the police caught, there were one hundred and sixty-two AK-56 rifles, forty automatic pistols and eighteen thousand rounds of ammunition. That's not personal use, Ganesh. That's armament for a war.'

'We might have sold some. It's good business, and income is down from all other sources. The whole economy is down. As you know, saab.'

He came back sharp and quick, 'Are you working with someone? Are these weapons intended specifically for someone? For some group, some party?'

'No, no, saab. We just need the cash, and this was a good market. You know how the situation in the country is nowadays, everyone wants insurance against everyone else. We were just distributors, to everyone.' I was sweating. I was back on the yacht, in Phuket waters, and I was covered and guarded on every side, but I knew our situation was very serious. We had a problem. And Kulkarni was letting me know exactly how bad our problem was. I was wishing now that K.D. Yadav had not retired, and that he was still handling my business with his organization. He was a practical man, he understood our necessities. This bastard Kulkarni was talking to me like some little boy he had caught with stolen goods.

'We overlooked your other projects and businesses,' he said. 'But this . . . I don't know if we can overlook this. Even with the organization, those who objected to having a relationship with you are now completely justified.' He was certainly very angry himself. 'How many shipments were there?'

I knew he wouldn't believe that there had been just the single shipment, so I told him that there had been one more, a much smaller one. I told him that there would be no more. I tried to talk him out of his anger, and told him how loyal I was. I reminded him of all the operations I had run for his organization, all the hard and completely reliable intelligence I had fed them. I made allusions to our many conversations, and the years of my work for Mr Kumar. He remained grim, and unyielding, and kept burrowing for more information on our arms business. I warded him off, gave him as little as I could and finally put the phone down feeling harried and afraid.

Arvind had come down from Singapore, and he was pacing around on the deck outside. He was on the phone to Bombay, trying to track the police case as it developed, following tips from our sources inside the department. I waited. There was no moon out that night, and the water shifted its silver-black surfaces at the corners of my eyes. Someone was watching me. I was sure of it. They were out there. Maybe they were listening to Arvind's conversation on his phone. The instrument was supposed to be secure, but whatever was secure could be cracked. Mr Kumar had taught me that.

Arvind thumbed off his phone. 'Nothing new, bhai,' he said. 'They're holding a press conference tomorrow morning at ten. Maybe something new will come out then.'

We still didn't know how the police had found our shipments. We didn't know how they had connected the shipments to us. They had had some good intelligence. Who had given it to them? Suleiman Isa and his boys? Or did the police have their own informants high up in our company? Quite possible. We would have to investigate. But I had an urgent, immediate worry. Our potato operation was compromised. I had to alert our client. I had to go to Guru-ji.

Guru-ji once again foretold my future, and this time he saved my life. I met him in Munich, where he was conducting a five-day workshop and a yagna. I flew alone. Arvind and Bunty tried to keep me from going, and then they tried to send half a battalion of shooters with me. I told them I was much safer alone, that I was protected by my new face. I demonstrated this to them: I walked past boys who had worked for me for years, and none of them recognized me. As long as I kept a low profile, I would be protected.

Guru-ji's security was of course paramount in my thoughts, and I had no wish to taint his reputation in any way. I didn't trust our usual methods of communication any more, I didn't know whether the technology we used was still safe. Our experts were getting new machines, new software, new methods. But I needed to talk to Guru-ji. So I took this risk, of being alone in a foreign country. I used the same approach

I had earlier, in Bombay. I attended the Munich yagna and waited afterwards for an audience. Only this time he knew I was coming.

I got to Munich at five in the evening and found the hall where Guru-ji had been holding his workshops. The yagna was a miniature of the one he had done in Bombay, and as the flames leaped and danced he spoke about the cycles of history. I sat at the back of the hall and watched him over the orderly ranks of firangi heads. There were television screens hanging from the roof of the hall, but I only looked at Guru-ji straight-straight, I strained my eyes and focused on him. After all these months of his voice over the telephone and his eyes in fuzzy newspaper photographs, I wanted a direct darshan. And I felt his presence, his great atman and the peace it brought to me. I was soothed, I was healed, I was revived. Only those who have seen him in person know what a light pours from him, what a glowing sweep of clarity comes from his darshan. I sat up like an eager child, and was instructed by him. He was speaking about our times, about the turbulence that was churning our world. 'Do not be afraid,' he said, in his rumbling Hindi, with simultaneous German translation. 'In the last few centuries, you have heard people speak of "progress", but you have seen only suffering and destruction. You have been terrified of science itself, of its rapaciousness and amoral power. You are told by your politicians that things are getting better, but you know they are getting worse. And you are seized by fear. I say to you, do not be afraid. We are approaching a time of great change. It is inevitable, it is necessary, it will happen and has to happen. And the signs of the change are all around us. Time and history are like a wave, like a building storm. We are approaching the crest, the outburst. You can feel it, I know you can, it is a build-up of emotion in your own body as well. The events are mounting in their intensity, they come one after another. But in this maelstrom is the promise of peace. Only after the explosion, we will find silence and a new world. This is sure. Do not doubt the future. I assure you, mankind will step into a golden age of love, of plenty, of peace. So do not be afraid.'

I listened to him and I was not afraid, although I had reason to be. I had come to him with a nervous stomach full of troubles, a spirit that was tired, and courage that was being tested. I had come to him, leaving behind my boys and my protection, because I needed to be in his presence. And already, in a few minutes, I was calmed. I had grown up sceptical of sadhus and sants, I had always thought they were charlatans and tricksters and confidence men, but here was a man who cracked through the shield of my doubt with his ineffable power. You may indulge yourself in the bitter satisfactions of scepticism, you may think me weak-headed, a paralysed fool looking for comfort, a tottering man wanting a crutch. All these thoughts – and I had had them too – are blinders against the truth, against reality itself, which was simply the peace I found sitting in the same room with him. Of course it wasn't just me who gained this tranquillity, but also all those Germans in the room. And thousands of others all over the world, who responded to him, his call, his teachings. He had that effect. Call it 'charisma', if that eases your mind, your desire for a certain limited logic. That was exactly the trap of reason that Guru-ji spoke about at the end of his sermon that night.

'Listen with your heart,' he said. 'Reason can stand on the path to wisdom, like a watchman with a lathi. Logic is good, it is powerful, we use it every day. It gives us control of the world we live in, it enables our daily living. But even science tells us that everyday logic cannot finally describe the reality of the world we live in. Time contracts and expands, Einstein told us this. Space curves. Below the level of the atom, particles pass through each other, a particle exists in two places at the same time. Reality itself, the real reality, is a madman's vision, a hallucination that the small individual human mind cannot hold. You must explode the ego, recognize everyday reason for the small and limiting jailer it is. You must walk past it, into the boundless expanse beyond. Reality waits for you there.'

I waited for him patiently, after the sermon was over. He had the usual line of devotees waiting to talk to him. I sat on a chair in the emptying hall, as the sadhus let the Germans one by one into a private room to the side. I wasn't worried that they would halt the audiences before they reached me, this time Guru-ji knew I was coming. So I was content to sit and watch the firangis emerge from their personal darshans, smiling, transformed.

'You are Indian?'

It was one of the Germans. She was wearing a deep red sari and had her blonde hair caught up in a jooda on the back of her head. There was a mangalsutra on her neck, and sindoor in her hair. She was young, maybe in her mid-twenties, but she looked like a traditional Indian mother from thirty years ago, from a small town at that. 'Yes,' I said.

'From where?' she said. Her English was clear and clangy. I had heard this accent on the beaches of Phuket.

'From, from Nashik,' I said.

'I have not gone,' she said. 'But Nagpur, you know Nagpur?'

I nodded.

'Guru-ji married me there, and gave me a new name.'

'Guru-ji married? You?'

'No, no, married me to my husband. To Sukumar.'

'Sukumar, he is Indian?'

'No, also German. After I met him I became Guru-ji's disciple. Then Guru-ji married us.'

'And gave you a new name.'

'I am Sita.'

'A very good name.'

'Guru-ji says it is a high ideal.'

'What?'

She gestured up, up towards the heavens. 'Sita is a good woman.'

This Sita had bright blue eyes, and a happy, beaming countenance. I smiled back at her. 'Sita was the best woman.' One of the sadhus waved at me then. It was my turn. 'Bye,' I said to Sita.

'Namaste,' she said, with an elegant folding of the hands and a deep bow. 'It is always nice to meet someone from home.'

I stood up, and fought off a sudden dizziness. I was tired, yes, too much travel in a short time. I stood by the green door to the private room, flanked by two sadhus, both firangis with bushy brown beards. They were both completely calm, quite silent. Then the door opened, and I was in.

Guru-ji was seated on a gadda near the fireplace, and his hair was a silver halo. The chairs and couches – it must have been a meeting room – had been moved to the sides, leaving the open space that he liked. He watched me come to him. I knelt in front of him, and touched my forehead to the ground, clutched at his feet. He put his right hand on my head, and said, 'Jite raho, beta.' He took me by the shoulders and raised me up.

I kept quiet. I should have said something, in gratitude for his blessing, but I held myself back.

'What is your name, beta?'

I hadn't planned this silence on my part, I had no intention of testing Guru-ji. But suddenly, I wanted him to know me. Not one other man or woman had seen through the disguise of my new face. But Guru-ji knew my soul, he knew even the small, hard, cinder-like fragment at the centre, which I had never shown to anyone. He knew the softness and yearning which lay under that black surface. He was waiting now, expectant.

'Are you dumb?' he said. 'Can you not speak?'

A smile came slipping across my face. I was being very silly, but the fact that he thought me mute amused me greatly. I knelt there, smiling.

'Ganesh?' he said.

I was amazed. I had wanted him to recognize me, but I hadn't expected him to. It was merely a wish, from the deepest core of who I was. There are many longings that float close to the surface of our skin, and I had achieved many of these: power, money, women. But there are needs so deep that they are not named, not even to oneself. They operate like subterranean flows of molten liquid, on which the continents move. They burst up sometimes with the fury of volcanoes, and then vanish, gone to the underground again. This is the true underworld, where desire boils eternally. I had wanted, like a child, to be named and known. And Guru-ji had done it.

'How?' I said. 'How did you know?'

'Do you really think you can hide from me?' He patted my cheek, then hugged me close.

'Guru-ji.' I was laughing. In one touch, I was rescued from my exhaustion, my anger, my fear. This is why I came to him, across the world and alone. I held his hands. 'Guru-ji, I know seeing me is . . .'

He shook his head. 'Not here.'

So he called up one of his sadhus, told him that I was a bhakt named Arjun Kerkar, that I had a very personal problem that would require a long consultation. His staff seemed used to this. Guru-ji climbed into his wheelchair in one powerful movement, and I followed him down into the garage. There was a flight of seven stairs down from the elevator lobby to the floor of the garage, and he took it easily in his wheelchair. The fat black wheels made little whirring and clicking noises, and the wheelchair danced down the stairs, perfectly balanced.

'Excellent, Guru-ji,' I said.

'Latest model, Arjun,' he said to me, with a flash of teeth over his shoulder. 'Everything is computerized. I can balance on two wheels. Look.'

733

And he did, whirling slowly on his two wheels. I clapped. There was a special van waiting in the garage, with a ramp to let the wheelchair in, and we skimmed off to the house where Guru-ji was staying, a devotee's mansion just outside the city. Everything was efficiently organized, and the sadhus spoke to each other on little walkie-talkies, and there were no delays or wasted motion. In fifteen minutes we were in Guru-ji's suite, which had been set up exactly the way he liked it, with fresh flowers in every room, and fruits on the table, and his CDs of sitar music and devotional chants by the bed. I took my shoes off, and found a comfortable chair in a little anteroom. I waited. Guru-ji took a bath, dictated some essential letters to his aides and then dismissed them. He called me in, and I found him seated on his bed in the centre of the room, wearing a white silk kurta and a dhoti.

'Come,' he said, pointing to a chair by the bed. 'Sit. Tell me, when did you do this to your face? Why?'

So I told him. Of course he agreed with the security concerns I had, but he also said that I had felt the urge to renew myself because of the coming change. 'A new world needs a new man. And you have renewed yourself. You felt the need to do so, you listened to the calling of the times, Arjun. I think that is the correct new name for the new you. I shall call you "Arjun" from now. You shall be Arjun who fooled me.'

'Only for ten seconds, Guru-ji. You are the only one who recognized me.'

'It's a good face, Arjun. Nobody will know it. Now tell me why you wanted to meet.'

He followed me closely, as I told him about the recent disaster. I told him that of course no operation is ever completely foolproof, that I had insulated myself from the arms smuggling with several levels of delegation through the company, and used semi-independent groups. And we had fed the UP police some arrests, low-level men that we thought would satisfy them, cool them down. But they had more information than we thought they did, and they had pursued further investigations, and I had been finally implicated. My thought was that some of this relentless zeal was being funded and informed from Dubai and Karachi, by Suleiman Isa and his fellows. They were using their people in the police to prosecute a new campaign in their war against us. And so the police – both UP and Maharashtra – were pushing us hard.

'Yes,' said Guru-ji. 'Yes, Arjun.' In the face of all these calamities, he was still as a statue in a temple. 'Do they know about me?'

'You – no, no, Guru-ji. Never. You have been kept completely out of the operation, your name has never ever been mentioned. Nobody in my company knows about you, even. I have maintained full security. I have come only by myself on this trip, no boys, no cover. There is no threat to you from my side, I have made sure of that. But I think we must pull back on the arms movements. It is too hot right now.'

'Yes, Arjun. In general, I agree. But let me meditate on that.' He reached out, put a hand on my shoulder. 'You look tired. Sleep now. We will talk in the morning. There is a bed for you in the small room.'

He was right. It had been a journey across the world, and many days of conflict and bad news before that. I felt drawn out, thinned out, as if I was barely hanging on to wakefulness. He cupped my head with his hand, in blessing, and I felt as if I was sliding safely into sleep. His eyes were dark, opaque, huge. He raised me up, and embraced me. 'Go to sleep. I will think about it. In the morning we will decide how we will act.'

I staggered into the room to the side of the suite, collapsed into the bed. I barely had the strength to turn on to my side, and then I was asleep.

I woke up to the sound of mantras. I sat up, and was instantly awake. As I padded through the suite, I was suddenly aware of how hungry I was, how alive. My shoulders were strong and relaxed, I felt the blood moving in my chest, there was sandalwood in my throat. I laughed. I felt like I had been reborn. One night of sleeping close to Guru-ji and I was young again.

The big windows on the eastern side of the suite opened up on to a garden, and I could see Guru-ji and the sadhus performing a puja. They were seated in a hollow square, with Guru-ji at the centre facing a small fire. I sat cross-legged near the window, far from them, and watched. It was very early, and under the deep grey of this foreign sky a small glow lit up their faces. I didn't know the mantras. It must be some ceremony for sadhus only, I thought, and I was content to sit and listen.

But, afterwards, Guru-ji explained the ritual to me. At the moment of dawn, he said, they meditated on change. Through this small yagna, he said, they were working to bring about a change in the world. The universe was consciousness itself, in interaction with matter, which itself was just energy. The combined consciousness of the monks and Guru-ji's own tremendous spiritual power were moving the universal consciousness towards transformation. 'History has a shape, Arjun,' he said. 'The universe is a miracle of design. We have talked about this before. Look at this garden. For every insect, there is a predator. For every flower, there is a function. Some scientists still look at all this beauty, but insist that it is the result of mere random selection, of chance and nothing else. They are blind. They are afraid. Pull back from chance, look at it with the right vision, and chaos reveals patterns. The question is, are you able to read its signs, understand its language? The question is, can you look through the surfaces? You and I are sitting here, Arjun, talking to each other in a garden. The sun is coming up. Is all this just random, without meaning? Is there no *direction* to everything?' With a wide motion of his arm he took in the earth, us and the sky. 'Look into yourself, Arjun. Feel the truth inside you. And tell me, who is the creator of this direction?'

I knew the answer to this. 'Consciousness.'

'Undoubtedly. And do you know where this consciousness is? Where it lives?'

'Everywhere?'

'Yes. And in us. You are He, Arjun. Your consciousness *is* the universal consciousness. There is no difference. If you can know that, really know that, then there is nothing you cannot do. You can shape history itself. Leaving the mind behind, the vira can direct events. He can move time towards transformation.'

I nodded. 'I understand, Guru-ji. What do you want me to do?'

'We have to do one more run, Arjun, one last one.'

He wanted to do one trip, one consignment. The cargo wasn't very bulky, or heavy. There was some cash – rupees mostly, but also some dollars – which had been collected abroad and now needed to be transported into the country. There was some laboratory equipment, which Guru-ji's people needed to run some agricultural experiments in Punjab. These they could have brought in through normal channels, but customs clearance would take weeks, maybe months, and important work would be held up. And finally there was some computer equipment, which again was urgently needed. No arms, no ammunition. Very simple, and even clear of the specific activities that Kulkarni was raging about. 'I wouldn't ask this of you, Arjun,'

Guru-ji said, 'if it was not vital. Without this cargo, our work of several years remains undone, incomplete. Of course I could easily move it through other channels. But you and I, we have a history. We have trust. I trust only you to do this for me. And in this shipment, there must be no mistakes. Arjun, I know there is great danger for you. So I will not tell you that you must do this for me. But I ask it of you, and leave the decision to you.'

Of course I agreed. I was bound to, as his disciple. And I owed him much, he had saved me time and again, in many ways. I told him I would do it, that I would begin to plan it as soon as I got back to Thai waters. Then I asked to spend another day with him. It was a risk for both of us, but I was compelled to beg this of him. I had a foreboding, a dense certainty that I would not see him again. I told him this, and he calmly agreed. 'Yes, that is true,' he said. 'I know it too.'

'You can see this?'

'Yes.'

'Why? What happens?'

'I don't know. I can't see that, but I do see this. That this is our last meeting.'

'How can we both know this? Has it already happened, whatever is going to happen? But how can that be?'

'Our small minds think that time is like a single railway track, Arjun, going forward always into the future. But time is much more subtle than that.'

'Are we already parted, in the future?'

Guru-ji shook his head. 'Every moment contains a number of probabilities. There are choices we can make at every minute. We are not machines moving along a track, no. But there is no such thing as full freedom. We are bound by our pasts, by the consequences of our actions. We can lean towards this choice or that, at the criss-cross of events. And sometimes the probabilities converge at a node, into something approaching a certainty. And then, if you are capable of listening, of seeing, you know.'

So we both knew. I had no pretence of being a seer like Guru-ji, of having his spiritual powers or his insight. But I knew. 'All right, Guru-ji. I remember you said in one of your pravachans that in every meeting there is already the beginning of loss.'

'Yes. We find each other only to lose each other. Loss is inevitable.'

'So there is no need to grieve. Perhaps we will find each other again.'

'Perhaps. But Arjun, even if we are not going to see each other face to face, I don't want to lose you in this life too soon.'

'Guru-ji?'

'I see danger for you in the east. I see great danger.'

'From where, Guru-ji? From whom?'

'I can't tell. But there is danger to your life. Be very careful.'

'I will. As always. I'll be even more careful. Even more.'

'I will watch over you.'

So, we took a walk. There was nothing else to say or do. I lived in danger, I had done it for years now, and now Guru-ji had given me a warning. I would be even more vigilant, if that was possible. Guru-ji liked greenery, he loved flowers and trees, he had spoken of this often in his sermons, about the need to save the environment. In the centre of Munich there was a park, and we went to it, just Guru-ji and I and two of his sadhus. The sadhus walked some distance behind us, out of earshot. Guru-ji and I spoke of ordinary things, about the price of gold, and the increasing number of overweight children in the middle class in India, and the next generation of computers, and the world-wide changes in weather and the implications for the monsoon. After the cosmic conversations that we had had recently, it was a relief to come back to the ground, to this summer day with strolling families, and children who stared at Guru-ji, and leaping dogs. The braver kids came up to Guru-ji, and he talked and laughed with them. Looking at them, I thought of what a perfect shot this was: the rolling grass, the heavy-headed trees moving gently in the breeze, the generous sun, Guru-ji's great bent head, and the slender, pale necks of the children as they clustered about him. Remember this, I told myself, witness this and remember it always.

I tried to see Guru-ji clearly. He was so enlightened, so far advanced that he was somewhat removed from the world of men and women. I knew that he valued cleanliness, that he liked gardens and greenery, that he had vast amounts of knowledge about arcane subjects, that he liked to learn about the latest advances in technology as soon as they happened. But still he hovered a little above the earth, I couldn't know him like I knew Arvind, or Suhasini, or Bunty. I knew them like I knew myself, I knew the shape of their desires, what they were afraid of, how they thought. I could predict what they would do, and I could make them want certain things, I could direct them and control them. I had them.

But Guru-ji, when I tried to think about him, when I imagined him, he appeared in my thoughts like one of those pictures from calendars of Vivekananda or Paramhansa, vivid and unforgettable but not quite human, more than human. I couldn't quite grasp him, my Guru-ji. Even when he was sweeping along in his wheelchair a few feet in front of me, leaning back so he was only on two wheels, followed by a comet's tail of laughing children. I had asked him once about his family, and he had told me quite openly about his air-force father, who kept the country's fighter planes running and had a drinking problem. And about his mother, who suffered from asthma and wept copiously when his motorcycle accident happened, but who was his main supporter in his quest for spiritual knowledge, and his first devotee. I knew about his tastes in food, that he was vegetarian but not at all fussy, that he would share a poor farmer's meagre lunch and enjoy it with the same gusto as he would a prime minister's fancy tea. I knew all this, and yet I knew that I knew him not at all. He remained hidden behind that steady gaze of his, that taking-in which gave back love and peace and certainty. Maybe I was being presumptuous, I thought as I walked along behind him, to hope that I could understand him as I understood other men. He had left the ego behind, and become something divine. And I was not yet close enough to divinity to comprehend this godliness. To attempt to do so was itself an act of ego, a movement of pride. All I could properly hope for was this moment of darshan, a fleeting connection. But still, I had an urge to try. I stepped up to him, past the children, and said, 'Guru-ji?'

'Yes, Arjun.'

'I have a question. Perhaps it's impertinent.'

'All the better. Ask it.'

'Have you ever been in love, Guru-ji?'

'All the time, Arjun.'

'Not like that, Guru-ji. I know you love me, and them –' I pointed at the children '– but with a person. Ishq, pyaar, muhabbat, Guru-ji. Have you ever been a deewana?'

'I was very young when this happened,' he said, pointing at his legs.

'So, never?' I thought I knew the answer already. A man who had realized his own supreme essence loved all creation equally, he would have no need for this partial, fragmented blindness that was love for another person. If you were Brahman itself, why would you need to become Majnoon? But he surprised me.

'A deewana? Yes, maybe once. Before the accident. When I was very young.'

'No, really?'

'Yes, really. We saw each other every day because we lived in neighbouring houses, and yet the hours apart were torture.' He smiled. 'Is that what you are talking about, Ganesh?'

'Yes, Guru-ji,' I said eagerly. 'And when you saw her, you were afraid of each minute because it was passing.'

A grinning blue-eyed boy spoke to Guru-ji in German, and Guru-ji answered him very seriously. He nodded at me – over the boy's little shoulder – and said, 'Yes. Like the other half of you is near you for a moment, but will be taken away.'

I struggled down the choking in my throat. So he was a man after all, an ordinary mortal who had suffered these pangs, and had felt loss. 'What was her name, Guru-ji?'

He patted the boy on the shoulder, sent him away. He was looking towards me, but seeing something else, someone very far away. 'What does it matter, Arjun? Names are lost in time. All infatuation leads to loss.'

'Then what happened, Guru-ji? Was she sent away?'

'This happened. And I went away, into injury and then into myself.'

Then he had become our Guru, and now he loved us instead of her, whoever she had been. No doubt she remembered their love also, but perhaps she was consoled by the fact that he loved her still, in a manner much more profound than the mere love of one small, ignorant mortal for another. I was nevertheless comforted by the knowledge that he had once been something like me. 'Thank you,' I said, 'Guru-ji, thank you for telling me.'

'It's nothing much,' he said, and he was looking over his shoulder at the group of children, who had angled off, and were now running across the fields in a flashing of golden legs, with that boy leading.

The sadhus came up now, and I fell behind, carrying my knowledge of a young man in love like a new treasure in my breast. We walked on.

One of the sadhus was speaking to Guru-ji in French. This sadhu was Swiss, a balding, red-headed fellow, who had been given the name 'Prem Shantam'. Guru-ji had all sorts in his following, and he spoke bits and pieces of many languages. He turned back to me now. 'Arjun!'

I stepped up. 'Guru-ji?'

'Prem here tells me that up ahead there is a section of the park where these Germans give up all modesty. They lie around without any clothes on. He is suggesting that we do not go that way.'

'Maybe we should avoid it, Guru-ji.'

'Why? Are you afraid of seeing their bodies?'

'Me? No, not at all. I am used to it, Guru-ji, from Thailand and all that.'

So we went ahead, down by a sparkling river. And there were the naked Germans, mostly men, lying on the grass and walking about naturally, quite without embarrassment. I had seen them on beaches far away, I was familiar with their white skin, their wrinkled behinds. But here I was vaguely disquieted. Here, in this city of churches and tall spires, this exhibition made no sense.

Prem said something, and Guru-ji translated for me, still gazing down at the river bank. 'He says they call it "Free Body Culture". I don't think it's free, or cultured. They are deluded. There is a time and place and an age for everything. There are stages in life when certain things are proper. A sadhu who meditates naked in a jungle is truly naked. He has left all culture behind. These people are still clothed in the traps of language. They think they are free, but they are bound by their rebellion against proper shame. Truly we live in Kaliyug, when everything is upside down.'

There were a few women among the naked, and two of them were watching us now. One was light-haired, typically German, but the other had thick, curly black hair, and she was very tall. She was a German all right, but her skin was tanned brown.

'Come,' Guru-ji said. He folded his hands in a namaste at the girls. 'They will think we are looking out of some dirty curiosity.'

He spun his wheelchair around. As we moved away, away from the river, I looked back and the dark item was watching us still. Guru-ji was right, she was shameless, fearless. Kutiya. But by the time we were back at the entrance to the park, I had forgotten about her. I was with Guru-ji, and I was much easier in my temper than usual. The irritation came and went. We went back to the mansion, and we ate a quiet lunch in the great hall, the sadhus and Guru-ji and I. And afterwards we sat in the garden next to the bedrooms again, enjoying the

741

sunlight. I was sleepy and relaxed, content, not sad at all. If this was a node in time, the probabilities had all counted down to this silence. I was at peace.

'There is something you haven't spoken to me about, Arjun,' Guru-ji said suddenly. 'Is there something else?'

Of course there was. I should have known better than to keep it from him. He always knew. And not just with me – on his website there were testimonies from dozens, hundreds of devotees from all over the world that spoke of his ability to sense their troubles, to see through their hesitations. Somehow, he knew. 'It's something very small, Guru-ji. After all the big things we have been talking about, it seems silly to even bring it up. That's why I kept quiet.'

'Arjun, nothing is small if it bothers you. A small grain of sand can stop a mighty machine. Your consciousness controls the world you make, and if your mind is crippled, your world is broken down as well. So, tell me.'

'It's the girl.'

'The Muslim girl?'

'Yes.'

'What is wrong?'

'Nothing exactly. I mean, I don't see her as often nowadays. She is very busy with her films and work. And I have much to do also. When we do meet, everything is good. She is beautiful. She is obedient.'

'But?'

'But sometimes I get afraid. I don't know. I don't know if she really loves me. I look at her and I watch her eyes, but I can't tell. She says she does. But does she love me?'

Guru-ji shook his head. 'That's not a small question, Arjun. That is a big question. Even the sages can't look into a woman's heart. Vatsayayana himself wrote, "One never knows how deeply a woman is in love, even when one is her lover." That is exactly what is happening here, to you.'

'But you, Guru-ji, do you know?'

'No, I do not. And even if I did tell you, that "Yes, she loves you," what of it? Are you sure the same will be true tomorrow? Women are fickle, Arjun. They cannot control their emotions, they are changeable as prakriti itself. Would you try to love the weather for its constancy, or a river for staying in one place for all eternity? This bodily love is not love. It is only a momentary infatuation. It passes.'

'Why then does she come back to me? And pretend?'

'She is ruthless, Arjun. As long as she gains from you, you will feel that she might love you. That is the skill of the whore. It is a skill that comes naturally to women. It is not their fault, they must act from what they are made of. They are weak, and the weak have these kinds of weapons: lies, evasions, acting.' I must have looked sad, or exhausted, because he moved over closer to me, so that he could rest a hand on my wrist. 'You can only know this truth by experiencing it, Arjun. If I had told you not to be with her, you would have obeyed me. But you might have thought that I was a grumpy old man, suspicious of pleasures. But now you know. You have seen through maya. We have to go beyond this.' He pinched the flesh on my wrist between a thumb and a long forefinger. 'This is useful, but it also blinds us. The pain you feel now is the gateway to wisdom. Learn from it.'

I knew he was right. And yet my flesh fought against it, against this decision I knew I must make. My stomach bubbled with hopelessness. Was there to be only this great bleakness, left behind by the vanishing illusion of love? I felt like I was standing on an endless open plain, every dead brown yard of which was lit by some strange, equalizing light. I saw this, and I winced away from its emptiness.

'Yes, Arjun,' Guru-ji said. 'Everything has been burnt up, and all that is left for you right now is ashes. But this grey desolation is also an illusion, just a step on your path. Trust me. Keep walking with me. Beyond this charnel house of romance, there is peace and a larger love.'

And he kept me close, for the rest of the day. We were together until I left, late that evening. He held me tightly, and the last words he said to me were, 'Have faith, Arjun. Don't falter in your faith. I will be watching over you. Don't be afraid, beta.'

I wasn't afraid. I drove through the night, to Düsseldorf, and caught a plane to Hong Kong. I followed all procedures and protocols, my own tricks learnt over a lifetime, and also K.D. Yadav's tradecraft, to make sure I wasn't being followed. I did it out of habit, but I knew I was safe. I had Guru-ji's protection over my head. On the plane, I leaned my seat far back and went to sleep. I was very tired. In two days I had been reborn. Something had died in me, and now there was a newness in its place. Guru-ji had remade me again. Throughout that long flight, I dreamed of Guru-ji's hands. That was the one part of him that I took with me, this one close-up shot. He himself may have been divine, but his hands were of this world. They were small, and they were very white. His nails were absolutely clean. When I woke up, I wondered why I kept seeing these hands in my sleep, why they were so vividly real, so present, so human. He had given me a new name, and a new vision. And together we would set in motion a new cycle of time.

An ambush was waiting for me in Singapore. I went first to Phuket, to the yacht, and organized Guru-ji's shipment. In two weeks, our new channels of communication were in place and working and impervious to breaches. No doubt that bastard Kulkarni was watching me closely, but he wasn't going to hear anything. I called Pascal and Gaston, my very old comrades. We had been using their ships and their expanded resources (yes, they had grown with me), but now I told them that they had to make one journey for me themselves. They had to become crew and captain, just like in the old days. Gaston complained, and grew as truculent as a moody child. He had diabetes, he said, and he had an old slipped disk that would bounce around at the slightest bump. I told him to stop whining like an old woman, put on a truss and get his boat ready. He grumbled, but he did as he was told. He owed me. It took us three weeks to put everything in place, and then they set off, Gaston and Pascal, along with two of their best men. The pick-up, off the coast of Madagascar, went cut-to-cut and smooth, and the journey back was peaceful, over calm waters. They dropped the cargo off near Vengurla, and went home. Guru-ji's people took delivery and carried it further, wherever they needed to. I paid Gaston and Pascal triple their usual rate, and that was that. No problem, no fuss.

It was time for a trip to Singapore, I thought then. I wanted to see Zoya one last time, to break my connection with her. I had grown past the need for her, I had gone beyond love. I wanted to settle with her and to say goodbye. I had no more bitterness or anger left, and I wanted to finish honourably, with no confusions or resentments. I had not seen Arvind face-to-face for a while, and I didn't like to let too much time pass without sitting down with my main managers. Useless though this flesh was, there were things you learnt only from it. So I flew into Singapore, two days in advance of Zoya. I caught a night flight in. Arvind picked me up as usual, and we drove to the apartment, observing the usual security procedures on the route. We doubled back, looking for followers and watchers, and we changed cars midway. This tradecraft had become second nature to us by now, and we did it without having to think about it. There was a plump moon hanging low over us. We talked about business, and investments, and personnel problems. And we gossiped a little, about one of Suleiman Isa's lieutenants, Hamid. This Hamid lived in Karachi, and he had had an affair by e-mail and phone with the wife of his top Bombay controller while the poor maderchod was rotting in jail. Arvind had recently heard one of the tapes from the police taps on the wife's phones, and he imitated the randi panting and moaning as she told Hamid how she would lick his pole. 'Bhai,' he said, 'we live in amazing times. Her husband is sitting in jail. And she is e-mailing pictures of herself to Hamid, photos of herself in a bikini.'

'It's good for us, this management technique of theirs. Gives a new meaning to telling the boys, "We'll take care of the wife and kids if you have to go to jail for us."'

'Yes, bhai. After all, the husband had been in jail for five years at this point. And a woman has needs that have to be taken care of.' Arvind was reaching out of the car window to insert a card into a slot in the wall, so that we could get through the double security gates of the apartment building. 'You know, bhai, at the end of the call, Hamid says to her, "I have never said this to anyone in my life." Then he says, in English, "I love you." And she says, in English, "I love you."'

'I suppose he never said it to his three wives, the bastard.'

Arvind grinned. 'Maybe not in English.'

His own wife looked fat and happy, so I knew he had been telling her that he loved her in many languages. The children were asleep, but I stopped by their separate rooms to take a look at them, the boy and girl. I told Suhasini that they had grown since I had seen them last, two months ago. I wasn't just flattering. Even with them lying down, I could see the monster length of their legs. They were only seven and five. They would both be six feet tall before they stopped budding, these freakish flowers from Arvind's garden. I ate some rice and dal, and spoke to their proud parents about the speedy little brats.

'It's all the protein, bhai,' Suhasini said, wiping her heavy chin with the end of her pallu. 'In our time, in India, we didn't get enough. We were all malnourished. Now, if you have the knowledge, you can give your children what they need. This growth looks unusual only to us.

Really, it's just normal.'

All her Singapore protein was making her grow into a perfectly round football, but I didn't tell her that. I praised her children, and then went to bed. Just as I was about to fall asleep, Zoya called from Bombay. 'I'm so sorry, bhai,' she said. 'I've been delayed.' She had finished her shooting on time that day, they had been on location, and on the way back to the city, on the highway, they were stopped by a seven-mile traffic jam. Three speeding trucks had wrapped themselves around each other. It took six hours to clear the tangled mess. She was very sorry, and very scared. She had never missed an appointment with me before.

But I truly was beyond passion and anger. I told her quietly to get a good night's rest and catch the flight the next day. And then I closed my eyes and was at rest.

I was bored the next morning. Arvind and I had our morning conference, I called Bunty. I took care of business, but I had scheduled the day for Zoya. I had expected solemn discussions, maybe some tears. Now, I had nothing to do. I watched some television. I played with the bachchas. Then it was time for lunch, and the big question under discussion was where we were going to order food from. Arvind wanted Indian food, but he was outvoted.

'There's a new Cantonese restaurant in the Singapore Shopping Centre, bhai,' Suhasini said, palpitating with greed. 'Their food is fantastic. But they don't deliver. Tell *him* to go.'

'It's not so close,' Arvind said. 'And there's three Chinese places down the street here.'

'I'll go,' I said.

'What?' Both of them said it, both with the same bafflement.

'I need to get out,' I said.

'But, bhai?' Arvind said.

He didn't need to say any more. I had never gone out in Singapore, not once. In Thailand, I rarely left the yacht. I had emerged to take the trip to Germany, but that had been understood to be a unique, emergency procedure. And here I was, offering to go and get Chinese food. 'I need the outing,' I said.

He knew me well enough not to argue. 'I'll send a couple of boys with you.'

'Arre, no, baba.' I pointed to my face. 'I'm protected completely by this. Nobody knows me any more.'

So I went. Once I was out on the main road, I let the car lunge ahead. I sped, I weaved and I felt free. It was good to be a simple man with an unknown face going out to get Chinese food. There was real pleasure for me in this servant's errand, in walking into the restaurant and ordering the food, in paying for it, in thanking the little Chinese receptionist. I tried to imagine what she saw: an Indian man in his thirties, clean in a sparkling white T-shirt and grey shorts and white Nikes, quite handsome but nevertheless ordinary. Did she see something of who I really was in my eyes? But I was wearing sunglasses with tinted grey lenses. I was safe.

I settled back into the car and switched on the air-conditioning, and it came on fast and strong, and the thought came to me that it was a very expensive car. The leather under my thighs was as soft as a young girl's cheeks. The car was a new-model Mercedes, fitted out with all the latest gadgets, including a GPS system. That bastard Arvind. Why did he need a GPS system in this chutiya little city? How did he afford all this? Was he keeping back too much money, were his percentages too large? Or was he lying about his various incomes? All the way back I was bothered by these questions. I listened to the *International Dhamaka* CD, and worried.

I was still thinking about money as I parked and went up in the lift. My company was doing well, but our expansion had slowed. Maybe I needed to introduce austerity measures, to impress upon the boys the need for financial restraint and resource management. I realized suddenly, then, that I was very hungry. The packages of food I held in both hands were wafting up spice and meat. The lift stopped at our floor, and I tapped at the door with my toe. Open, gaandu.

I stepped through. There were two men in the corridor, flanking the door of the lift, facing it.

I didn't know them. One was Chinese, one Indian. They both had short hair, clipped close at the sides in military style.

'Where you going?' the Chinese said.

What's it to you, maderchod? is what I wanted to say. It rose from my gut, but I was thinking. In that eternity which nestled inside that fraction of a moment, I was thinking. Thanks be to Guru-ji. I said instead, 'Food.' I held up the bags, in both hands. 'Delivery,' I said. 'Penthouse.'

'They don't need it,' the Indian said, in Hindi. 'They have gone out.'

My body wanted to turn and run. Into the lift, down the stairs, away. But I was thinking. *Don't make them suspicious.*

'Money,' I said. 'They have to pay.'

'Get out,' the Chinese said.

'Go,' the Indian said.

I muttered quiet curses, turned back into the lift. I pressed a button, and then cursed some more.

The Indian stepped forward, put a hand on the door. 'You work for the people in the penthouse?'

'No. For Wong's Garden.'

'Your name?'

'Nisar Amir.'

'Take your glasses off.'

I was still wearing my Guccis. I put down one bag, and took them off. He scanned my face, gave me that policeman's look that riffled through thousands of remembered apradhis for a match. I didn't look away, and I tried not to hate him. I was thinking, be a delivery boy.

'Okay,' he said, and let go of the door.

A small thunk of rubber and metal hid me from them, and I collapsed back against the mirror at the back of the lift. My legs were trembling. I took the bags of food with me into the basement, holding them like shields against my chest. I got into Arvind's fancy car, and I drove away.

It took me three days to get out of Singapore, and it was difficult. I didn't know who those men were, who had found me in my penthouse. But after they searched the apartment, they had my new passports, so they had my new face. I had only two mobile phones, and three hundred and seventy-three Singapore dollars. But I could talk to my boys, and I had my intellect. I left finally in a very small rowing boat, which took me to another, bigger boat, in which I lay under slats of wood, under fish-smelling darkness. This boat took me across the Straits of Johor to another small boat, which finally dropped me off on a Malaysian beach. The next day I was in Thailand.

I was safe, but Arvind was dead. The day after my run for Chinese food, the Singapore police announced that they had found him dead, in the penthouse. He had been shot three times. Suhasini had been shot once, in the head. The children were dead too. The story, according to the Singapore authorities, was that a gun battle had taken place in the penthouse. Suhasini had opened the door to some unknown assailants, and had been killed immediately. Arvind had fired at the attackers, who had retaliated, and in the crossfire both children had perished. And then Arvind had fallen, under the volleys of the assassins.

That was it. The Singapore police expressed outrage at this unprecedented outbreak of savage gang warfare in their garden city, and announced a tightening of immigration controls. It took them four days to get through Arvind's alias, to work out who he actually was, and then the newspapers in India published front-page articles about the massacre, and theorized about the identity of the killers. They gave the credit to Suleiman Isa and his lieutenants, and praised their plan and the audacity of executing it in strict Singapore, and printed diagrams of all the rooms in the apartment, with little stick figures shooting at each other. And they asked, 'But how did Ganesh Gaitonde get away?'

I had got away, yes. But who from? It was easy to believe that it had been the boys from Dubai once more. That was too easy, too pat. I kept remembering those haircuts. Those two men in front of the lift, hadn't they held themselves like policemen, like soldiers? Maybe it wasn't Suleiman Isa who had put this hit in place, maybe it was a government. Kulkarni and his organization were very angry at me, maybe they had decided that it was time to end this particular operation, to close out this account. Maybe they had decided to finish Ganesh Gaitonde. I had run missions exactly like that for them myself, when they had gone after assets who were compromised. Retire this man, they had said, he was once ours but he is now against us. Or at least he is not with us. And I had done it, I had found some poor chutiya, in Kathmandu, in Brussels, in Kampala, and I had killed him. Whoever they had named, wherever. I had done it. And now they were after me.

No, no – I stopped myself from believing this. Don't jump to conclusions, I told myself. Don't hurt yourself like this, don't believe that your own country despises you enough to want you gone, wiped, finished. I spoke to Kulkarni three times that week, and he was always courteous, concerned about what had happened. He said he was conducting a thorough investigation at his end, and promised that information forthcoming from Singapore would be passed instantly to me. After a conversation with him, I always got off the phone feeling reassured, revived. But five minutes was all it took for me to find the subtle poison in all his honey. Yes, he was reassuring, but maybe he was setting me up for another attack. Maybe they had the observers already in place, maybe the fielding had already started, and they were about to tumble my wicket. Yes. Who had given me away in Singapore, who had the address of the penthouse, and the security codes for the building gate and the elevator, and knowledge enough to cut off the video cameras which lined every corridor? Where had the intelligence come from? Had Zoya betrayed me? Why had she missed her flight? Yes, there had been a traffic jam on the highway that day, I had checked, but why had she left so late from the set? Or was it Arvind, had he made a deal with someone, and then been betrayed himself? Had the killers been instructed to thoko their source as well, to make a clean sweep of it? It was possible. It was all possible.

Under the full Thai moon, I lay awake struggling with the possibilities. And when I rose in the morning, I was afraid. Guru-ji had said there was great danger to my life, and I knew it had not passed. Once again, after years, I started carrying a gun. After two days, I started carrying an additional pistol, strapped to my ankle. I had the world's best body armour flown in from America, and I wore it under my shirt through the day, comforted by its IIIA protection, which would hold back .44 Magnum bullets before they reached my chest, my back. I increased the number of armed sentries on the yacht, and rotated them in teams three times a day. I slept sometimes on the boat, and sometimes in various houses on land, and varied my routes. I took all possible precautions.

Meanwhile, the calamities kept coming. Bunty called one afternoon, quite subdued, not his usual cheery self at all. 'Bhai,' he said. 'I'm in a clinic.'

'What's wrong?' I imagined a dozen tragedies all at once: syphilis, bullets, his children ravaged by malaria.

'It's Pascal and Gaston. They're both in here, bhai. Both admitted.'

'What, only Gaston had diabetes, right? The other one caught it from him as well?'

This got a little laugh from him, a very small one. 'No, bhai. It's something else. They're both sick. And both the boys who went with them on the boat on that last run are also. They're all vomiting, again and again.'

He meant that trip we had made for Guru-ji's shipment, that final and very special one he had asked for. I said, 'They ate some bad fish, the stupid bastards.'

'Gaston's hair is falling out, bhai.'

'It has been for years.'

Bunty said nothing. He was very grim. That he had taken the time to go to the clinic was in itself quite unusual. He was a busy man, I made sure of that. And now he wasn't laughing, this Bunty who made jokes every day about men getting shot in the golis. Gaston's condition must indeed be serious, too serious. 'Okay,' I said, 'listen, get them good doctors. If money is needed, give it. Take care of them.'

'That's what I thought, bhai. They've been with us a long time.'

He hovered over them for the next two days, pushing the doctors to cure our friends. Meanwhile, I called Inspector Samant in Bombay and organized two encounters for him, gave him two Suleiman Isa controllers in Bombay. He killed these controllers on the same night, one after the other. The Dubai bastards hadn't claimed credit for the hit on Arvind, but I wanted them to know we weren't sleeping, that we were very capable of replying in a language they understood. The encounters gave satisfaction, especially because Samant e-mailed me morgue photographs of the dead bastards, with their heads split open by bullets. But the comfort passed quickly, and the fear maintained its steady, muffled drumbeat.

'Shall I send you a girl?' Jojo asked that Sunday evening. 'I have one or two new ones that may entertain you.'

'Arre, I'm finished with all that.'

'I don't believe you, Gaitonde. You don't believe that yourself. You're never going to take a girl again? In your entire life?'

'Maybe I will, maybe I won't. But it isn't an important concern any more. I have gone beyond all that.'

She made a squeaking groan, like a puppy in piercing pain. I thought she was maybe suddenly ill too. Then she erupted into a helpless torrent of laughter. I held the phone away from my ear, and said, 'Jojo, maderchod, listen to me.' She was far beyond listening, and I put the phone down and waited. I let a minute pass, and two, and then I picked up the phone. She was giggling now, but as soon as I said her name she was off again. 'Crazy chutiya,' I said, and hung up. At that moment, I wanted her in front of me so I could put my hand on her throat and choke off that dirty sound, I wanted her to rattle into

751

red-faced silence while I squeezed and squeezed. I strode around my cabin, went out on to the deck and came back again. Kutiya. I had let her become too familiar, too informal with me. Maybe she needed to be taught a lesson. Right from the start I had let her get away with too much.

I was thinking this when she called. 'Saali,' I began.

'Sorry, sorry,' she said. 'Truly. Gaitonde, you have to forgive me. It was just such a surprise. You of all people. You who enjoy women so much. It is hard to believe, that you are saying this.'

'Gaandu, you are just afraid of losing my business. You want me to spend money on another Zoya, build her up, so you can get your cut.'

'I'm just trying to calm you down, Gaitonde. You have never been like this. And you told me once that to run a company you have to be calm and cold. You are not calm now.'

She was right. I was not calm. I was agitated, afraid, angry. 'A girl isn't going to cool me now,' I said. 'Try something else.'

'Want to hear some letters?'

We hadn't amused ourselves with her application letters for a long while. 'Yes, yes,' I said. 'That's good. Read one.'

She had a few ready, right there at her desk. They came in a steady drizzle, ebbing and flowing with the Face of the Year and International Man contests on television. 'Okay. Listen. Do you want to hear one from village Golgar, post office Fofural, district Dhar, Madhya Pradesh? Or do you want one from Kuchaman City, district Nagaur, Rajasthan?'

'Fofural? No, I don't believe it.'

'Maybe it's Fofunal. His English writing isn't that clear. The address is in English. Shall I read his postcard?'

So they were writing English in village Golgar, post office Fofu-maderchod-something. The thought made my head whirl. 'No, leave the bhadwaya in Golgar. We don't hear that often from Rajasthan. Let the Rajasthani speak.'

'Yes. His name is Shailendra Kumar. He writes . . .' She slowed down now, as she ploughed through the Hindi. 'He's got one of those things at the top of the postcard, *Om evam saraswatye namah*. With little curlicues underneath.'

'So, our Shailendra is a pious boy. Very good.'

'He writes "Dear Sir/Madam". That's written in English. Then he switches to Hindi. "My name is Shailendra. I am currently a student in the twelfth class. I am choosing modelling as my career. I am eight-een years old. My height is five foot eleven. I have an impressive personality. I have taken part in many school plays."'

Jojo paused. I knew what she was waiting for: I was now supposed to say something cutting, something funny about Shailendra the gaon actor who dreamed of walking a ramp in the big city. Then we would laugh together, we two who had escaped our own gaons, and then we would read some more. But today I just felt sad, at the thought of Shailendra the hero of the district, with the personality that the girls talked about as they walked through the fields, maybe he even rode a motorcycle sometimes, his uncle's motorcycle. He was tall, and so he thought he should come to Bombay. To become bigger. 'Jojo,' I said. 'I'm feeling quite tired. I think I should try to sleep.'

'This early?'

'Let me see,' I said. 'Maybe I'll feel better in the morning.' I hesi-tated, then asked, 'How are you, Jojo?'

It silenced her for a moment, my asking. I never had done that before. 'Arre, Gaitonde, I'm tip-top. Business is down a bit, but then the economy is down, nobody has money. I am surviving.'

'Do you have a thoku?'

'Of course. I have two. You may be finished with women, but I have one or two uses for men still.' She laughed her laugh, and this time she raised a small smile from me. 'Although they are so much trouble, Gaitonde. Always wanting this and that. Sometimes I wonder why I bother. No man can satisfy me like my vibrator, anyway.'

Now I had to laugh. 'You are shameless.'

She was. Later that night, I thought of my friend Jojo. Others had come and gone, they had died, they had left, but Jojo – the one I had never met face to face, the one I had never eaten a meal with, the one I had never touched, had never taken – she was still with me. Sometimes days passed without my talking to Jojo, but always she was there with me, in me. She was fearless, she told me what she thought of my actions, she advised me, she listened to me. She knew me, and in these recent days of my terror, she was the one person who I never suspected of betrayal. It just never occurred to me to think that she may have passed information to the shooters, even though it was true that she knew my life more intimately than many. I forced myself to think objectively of Jojo now, to remove her from myself and look at her as I would at a stranger: she was a businesswoman, a producer, a madam, a woman loose in her ways and thoughts. Untrustworthy by any logical evaluation, but I trusted her. Nothing that I could imagine – she did it for money, she gave me up under threats from my enemies, she did it on a whim, she did it by mistake – nothing could shake the rock of my trust. I gave up the attempt. She was Jojo, and she was in my life, threaded into it like sinews looped through bone. I didn't know how this had happened, or when exactly, but I knew that without her I would collapse into an arid, rattling heap. She had to stay, she had to be with me.

I couldn't sleep that night, and called her twice. She told me more about her thokus, and made me chortle. Then it was four in the morning, and I was awake, and it was too late to call her again. Guru-ji was travelling, and unavailable. I thought of going up to the deck, but I was exhausted, so tired that I could trace each twitching of my calves up into my thighs. The clock at the bedside had slowed its blinking to a slow, leisurely pulse, and then paused altogether. Time had dissolved itself into a gummy deep of moonlight, and I floated in it, a transparent, lifting form swayed back, and back, by its billows. I am walking fast behind Salim Kaka, through a clicking swamp. Mathu is to my right. We have the gold, and we are away. We are happy. There is water ahead of us, a small stream that cuts through the mud. Salim Kaka is at the edge. I am glaring at Mathu, trying to see his eyes. Salim Kaka has a foot down, into the water. There is a pistol in my hand.

Up, I flung myself up out of bed. I threw open the door and went down the corridor, knocking. I woke up the boys, and took them upstairs. 'Let's watch a picture,' I told them. They were confused, and sleepy, but they didn't ask any questions. In ten minutes we were seated in front of the television, and they were arguing about what to watch. They offered me *Company*, which I still hadn't seen. But I knew its story already, its betrayals, and I knew the real players, Chotta Madhav and his old friend in Karachi. This morning, I didn't want any of its bullets, its blood. So they rummaged around, in the boxes of tapes and DVDs, and finally we settled on *Humjoli*.

We watched Jeetendra and Mehmood bounce around the screen, thrashing their enemies as they sang *One, two, chal shuru hoja*, and I was nicely distracted by the laughter that filled the room. The vivid seventies colours were restful to look at, and even the tightness of Jeetendra's white pants was comforting. This past was a foreign country that I could escape into, a haven that had already happened and that nothing could disturb. Over the next two days we watched *Dil Diya Dard Liya*, and *Anand*, and *Haathi Mere Sathi*. When the call came in from Mumbai, I was watching that scene near the end of *Guide*, that scene where Rosie comes to see the guide as he fasts to death. 'Bhai, it's Nikhil, from Mumbai. Bunty's assistant.' I wiped the tears from my face, and took the phone. I rarely spoke to this Nikhil, who had worked with Bunty for four years now. Nikhil reported to Bunty, and Bunty reported to me, that was the chain.

'What?' I said.

'They shot Bunty, bhai.'

'Who?'

'I don't know.'

He was swallowing again and again, hiccuping into my ear, and I knew he was about to vomit. 'Nikhil,' I said. 'Sit down. Are you sitting down? Sit. Don't worry. I have boys on the way. Just tell me what happened.'

It took me twenty minutes, and he did dribble up twice, but I got the story out of him. Bunty had gone that morning to the Juhu Maurya, where he got a massage from a specialist in the Thai temple technique. He then had a breakfast meeting in the coffee shop, and got some chocolate cake packed for his children. He waited in the lobby for his car to pull up, and then walked down the stairs to it, flanked by three bodyguards. In the driveway, there were three tall, turbaned and liveried gatemen, opening and closing doors, and also four hotel security guards in grey safari suits. The four security guards now reached under their shirts and pulled out Glocks, and they shot Bunty and his boys, two bullets for each target. It was deadly efficient, and crisply done. The bodyguards were blown down, dropped to the road and dead. Bunty had bent to get into his car, and he was knocked through the open door. That was what saved him, the bending, and his driver. The bullets hit him in the back and neck, instead of the back of his skull, and when he fell face forward on to the seat, his driver stepped on the accelerator and skidded away. Bunty dangled and dragged along, and he lost four toes on his right foot, but he lived. The driver got him out of the hotel gate, even as blasts blew through the rear window and the left-hand windows. One of the Sikh gatemen charged the shooters, and got a bullet in his belly for his troubles. But by then the real hotel guards were running up to the front of the building, and there were police constables lumbering up from the chowki at the intersection, and the shooters had to go. They went.

They got away, and Bunty was alive. They had him in the Lilavati Hospital, tubed and wired. He was hanging on. He was fighting. But my boys were afraid, they were angry and confused and lost. I tasted their panic in the air, the promise of it like the first faint tinge of rot. I did what I had to, I managed them. I moved people around, I moved in money, I moved influence. To give my boys the illusion that we were fighting back, I organized two encounters over the next two days. The Suleiman Isa boys who were killed were low-level functionaries, riff-raff, but morale depends sometimes on the necessary deaths of small men. So it was done.

But I knew the truth, that we didn't know who we were fighting against. Even if the Suleiman Isa bastards took credit – which they did – there was no reason to believe that it was actually their operation. No, they were maderchod liars, and if they said they had shot Bunty, it was definite that they hadn't, that someone else had watched him, learnt him and his habits, and had tried to execute him. But who? Who?

I knew who. I spoke to Nikhil the next day, and then directly to one of the investigating police officers on the case, who read to me from the eyewitness testimonies. Every last one of them reported short haircuts on the shooters. One of the Sikh doormen used the word 'fauji' when he described the bastards. And I remembered the two in the corridor in Singapore, the ones who stopped me and questioned me even as their friends did their bloody work in Arvind's apartment. They were the same crew, I knew this, I could tell. Maybe they were even the same men, flown from Singapore to Bombay by their bosses, by an organization which watched me and knew everything about me. They knew where I lived and where I went and what I did, they were hunting me. They wanted to eliminate me. They had used me, I had served a function, and now – because I had served my own interests in a manner that they disliked – they wanted to wipe me away, rub me out so that there wasn't as much as a small stain left on their files. I would cease to be, and they would pretend I had never been.

I was sure, almost sure that I knew my killers. To be absolutely certain, I needed to consult Guru-ji. I needed him to see the truth and tell it to me. But he was travelling, I was told, he was unavailable, even to me. I left urgent messages, asking and beseeching that he get in touch.

756

But he didn't call, and I was left to myself. I was astonished. I had always been able to reach him, even just to ask him if the next Tuesday was a good day to start a new diet. Now, in the hour of my greatest crisis, when my allies were hunting my men and me, Guru-ji was gone. I was patient as long as I could be, and then I cursed the sadhus I spoke to on the phone. 'Do you know who I am?' I said. 'Do you know how close I am to him? I will have you thrown out, exiled to an ashram in Africa, bastard.' But they insisted that they did not know where he was. Ten days after he first became unavailable, a message appeared on Guru-ji's website explaining that he was in retreat at an undisclosed location, that he was deep in meditation, that he could not be disturbed, but he would be back soon, that he would bring back new and deeper wisdom to his disciples, who were his beloved children.

But I am your eldest son, gaandu, and where are you? Yes, I cursed him directly. I needed him, and he had vanished without a word to me. He knew everything, he must have known that he was going even as he said goodbye to me in Munich, a sign would have sufficed – a hand on my shoulder, a single touch on my cheek. But he was gone.

Four days after Bunty was shot, I became even more alone: Gaston and Pascal died, one in the morning, one in the night.

'The doctors said they know what it was now, bhai,' Nikhil told me. 'They know what they died of. The doctors say it was radiation sickness, bhai.'

I had to ask what it was, this 'radiation sickness'.

Nikhil explained it to me, what he had learnt from the doctors. 'They wanted to know if Gaston and Pascal had visited an atomic power plant recently, bhai. Like maybe Trombay. Or if they had drunk water from a well near Trombay, or eaten fish caught in Thane creek. Or gone anywhere close to the Tarapur plant. I told them, of course not. Why would Gaston and Pascal visit Tarapur?'

'Did you tell them anything, Nikhil?'

'No, no, nothing. Nothing at all, bhai. I told them the truth, that Gaston and Pascal are respectable businessmen and family men. That they haven't been anywhere dirty like that.'

But they had been on a trip recently, into the open sea. The ocean was not dirty, but maybe you could catch radiation sickness from what you brought back from the waves. I called Guru-ji again, and this time when there was no reply I had boys go to his offices in Delhi, and his homes in Noida and Mathura. His servants didn't know where he was, his sadhus didn't know, his mother said she didn't know. He was gone, vanished, as if he had suddenly transcended his body and become one with the universe. But the sadhus closest to him had gone too, Prem Shantam and all the others in the inner group, the ones who travelled with Guru-ji and tended to him and took care of him. They were travelling. Guru-ji had not left this earth, he was going somewhere? But where? Where did his journey end, and when?

I tried to reason this out, to remember my conversations with Guru-ji and deduce my way into his intentions. But even as I tried, I knew my attempts were useless, that my ordinary mind was incapable of holding – even for a moment – his extraordinary understandings. And my thoughts felt ragged, frittered away by fear and the thousand concerns of my reeling company. My attention was shredded, there were too many problems to address, too many matters of reorganization to think about and implement, too many wounded men and widows to take care of. I couldn't keep focused on any subject, and found myself floating in fuzzy dreams during the day, and unable to sleep at night. I knew I was in bad shape, and there was nothing I could do to make myself better. Guru-ji was gone. I was afraid. I dreaded going to the bathroom because I winced and writhed and left streamers of blood on the porcelain. Pascal had bled from ulcers around his mouth, I had seen photographs of his face, his glazed eyes. I spent more and more time in the computer room, getting the boys to help me find information on radiation and burns and death. I had of course read in the newspapers that our country had incredible new weapons, and missiles that would deliver them, but I had never known much about Trombay, or uranium, or Nagasaki, but now I learnt, I learnt fast. I spoke to Jojo about all this, about the danger in the world, at our borders.

'Arre, Gaitonde,' she said. 'Nobody is going to fire off those things. Nobody is that crazy.'

'You never know. Somebody may not be crazy and they may set one off. They may have their reasons.'

'What reasons could those be, Gaitonde?'

She was really being quite patient with me, talking to me about this without cursing or slamming down the phone. I think she knew how tattered and tired I was, and she was trying to be kind. Usually, she had no patience with fear, or fantasies, or what she called men's terrors. I didn't want to tell her about my crawling panic about Guru-ji and what he may have had us smuggle and his disappearance, mainly because I understood very little of it myself. I just had a dread, and fragmented images of fire, always fire. I wanted her to leave Bombay. 'You never know,' I said. 'Pakistan might do something. And then we might do something. Some general may decide this is a good time for an attack. Bombay is the first place that would get hit.'

'We are all friendly with the Pakistanis right now, Gaitonde. And even when we are shouting at each other, it's all show. They always make noise, and then we make noise, bas. Don't worry so much, Gaitonde.'

I tried to get her to take a holiday in New Zealand, to go to Dubai even, for shopping. But no, she had work in the city, she was produc-ing and managing, and there was money to make and people to see, she was just too busy. 'And if it happens, Gaitonde,' she said finally, 'so what? We all have to die some day. And if Bombay is gone, then where will I live anyway? I can't go back to my village.' She laughed. 'Or do you want me to go and stay with what's-his-name in Kuchaman City? Listen, baba – if this city is gone, my office is gone, my home is gone, all my work is gone, what I know is gone. Then there's nothing to stay alive for anyway.'

And she dismissed my attempts to send her to Australia, and burst into wild laughter when I told her that she should expand her business to London maybe. She said, 'Don't worry so much, Gaitonde. I saw this in an American picture last month, somebody sets off a big atom bomb in an American city. I was scared during the film, then after-wards I was all right. This happens only in films. It's too filmi. If it happens in a film, it won't happen in life. Nobody's going to set off a dhamaka. You've already made that film. Don't take on so much ten-sion about nothing, just relax. Go to sleep.'

I let it go, I let her have her way and spoke of other things. But I had an idea. I kept it to myself, I didn't tell her, and I got my boys work-ing. This is our top priority, I told them. I threw money into the project, I moved material from Thailand and Belgium into the very heart of Bombay. I followed the construction closely. I had photo-graphs e-mailed to me every hour, and I watched the immensely thick walls rise out of a precise square of darkness in an empty plot in Kailashpada. That dimness came from an immense excavation, down into the earth. I built a safe house, a shelter. I built walls that would hold back fire, a profound deep that would keep the poison from Jojo's skin. I made this house for her, in case of emergency she could descend into it. But I found that if I thought of this small white house at night, I was able to go to sleep. On my yacht, this is what I did every night: after I had made sure that the sentry teams had been set up, and the motion detectors and the short-range security radar had been tested and adjusted and activated, I locked myself into my bedroom. I settled into a comfortable seat on the floor, and meditated. I tried to keep my mind still, concentrated into a point, and tried to experience the consciousness that was the universe, that was me. I went beyond gods and goddesses, beyond blue-skinned Krishna and his bloody open mouth with its threats of dissolution, I journeyed beyond all form, to the essence that lay beyond language. Then I got into bed. I curled myself almost round and then I was in Bombay, in Kailashpada and inside my white cube, I was far under the surface, I was sheltered and held by good thick steel and the best, hardest cement in the world. In this imagined embrace, I at last found peace. I was secure.

The End of the World

Kamble was still heartbroken about the conclusion to the Kamala Pandey case. He said it again, 'That maderchod bhenchod pilot, he is lower than the bhadwas, even. They take money from women, all right, I can understand that. You put a randi to work, you help in bringing customers, you put in time and effort, you get something back. But this Umesh, this bastard, he didn't even have the guts to stand face to face with Kamala and demand, "Give me money." He hid and took photos of this woman, and he used other men to extract money from her. And she *loved* him.'

'Shocking,' Sartaj said. 'Just shocking to think that a man may do such things to a woman.'

Kamble threw off Sartaj's sarcasm with an angry shrug. 'Arre, boss, okay, yes, I have lots of women. Maybe I hurt them too, but I give everything to them, they also hurt me. I am not talking about money only. I give this –' He thumped his chest. '– and anything else they ask for. Money? I shower money, I throw it away. I give it away and delay my own plans because I am ready to let them hurt me. You understand?'

He was ridiculous and he was completely serious, and Sartaj reached across the table and patted his arm. 'Yes, this pilot is a complete bastard,' he said gently. 'We will take care of him, don't worry.'

Sartaj then told Kamble about waking up that morning with a memory of a guru preaching, and remembering that he had once been part of the bandobast for a big public ceremony in Andheri West, a religious ritual that had gone on for days, that had been conducted by a deep-voiced guru who had used a very sophisticated foreign wheelchair. 'This was many years ago,' he told Kamble, 'but more recently I went to see the body of an apradhi named Bunty, who had been thokoed by some small-time chillar shooters after his own company fell apart.'

'Bunty, bole to Gaitonde's man?'

'That one. I had talked to this Bunty on the phone just a few days before he was killed. And he was talking about his fancy wheelchair, which could go up and down stairs and do all kinds of tricks. And he said that Gaitonde gave him the wheelchair.'

'So you think . . .'

'I'm telling you, Kamble, that guru had the same wheelchair as Bunty. I remember very clearly. Maybe not the same model, but the same make.'

Kamble looked very sceptical, and in the hard light of afternoon Sartaj had to admit that the link looked very tentative and fragile. But he tried to sound cheerful, and told Kamble about jumping on to his bike in the very early morning and speeding to the PCO near Santa Cruz station and calling Anjali Mathur in Delhi, waking her up. And how she had called back later in the morning to say that her organization was investigating the guru.

'Now they are looking into it,' Sartaj said, 'and they will find everything out. They have lots of resources. If there is really a threat to the city, they will find out about it, and fix it.'

But Kamble refused to be cheered up, even by the thought of an all-powerful national organization saving the city and himself from possible thermonuclear destruction. Sartaj had invited him to the Mughal-e-Azam Restaurant in Goregaon, for a celebratory lunch, to mark their breaking of the Kamala Pandey blackmail case. But Kamble was still scowling darkly. He shook his head and waved his hand at the window, towards the city and the world beyond. 'Boss, you want to save *this*?' he said bitterly. 'For what? Why?'

They were sitting in the air-conditioned first-floor cabin, amidst a half-hearted attempt at Mughal splendour. There was a brass surahi on the window-sill next to each booth, and two faded paintings of princesses in long-nosed profile on the wall. But you could see the pile of dirty dishes in the washbasin next to the bathroom, and the glass on the window was stained and spotty. The city that Sartaj could see – in the direction of Kamble's contemptuous gesture – was equally dusty and shabby on this furious October day. They were protected from the dense swirl of exhaust and road rage by Mughal-e-Azam's wheezing air-conditioner, but that was only temporary. Soon they would have to emerge from this dirty haven into the dirt of the untidy streets, into the random and endless excavations by PWD crews, the

762

jiggling and lawless streams of traffic, the sullen and sweaty walkers. None of it was pretty, but was it so bad that it all deserved to die? 'Come on,' Sartaj said. 'You're getting too emotional about all this.' Sartaj was amused by Kamble's romanticism, his anger at the pilot, but to wish for a final collapse was much too excessive.

'No, I'm very serious,' Kamble said. 'Better if it was all destroyed.' He moved his hand flat above the table, in a cleaning gesture. 'Then it can all start again, fresh. Otherwise, nothing will change. Like this, just like this, we'll go on.'

It was astonishing to Sartaj that Kamble still believed in change. How insidious and indestructible hope was if it refused to vanish from the breast of this corrupt, greedy, violent man. 'But if something happens, if the bomb goes off, we all go. Not just you and me. Your parents, your sisters, your brother, all, everything. You want that to happen?'

Kamble shrugged. 'Arre, bhai, if we go, we go. Everyone has to die. Better to all go together.'

Sartaj had to laugh at the grandiosity of Kamble's disillusionment. Kamble was very young, after all. His disappointment demanded a complete cleansing, a new start, nothing less. 'Don't be silly,' Sartaj said. 'Eat your chicken.'

A waiter put down a gloriously red tandoori chicken, and a plate laden with rumali rotis. 'Raita,' Kamble said, 'bring the raita, yaar.' He tore off a big hunk of breast and chewed it thoughtfully. 'Bastard, it's good.'

That was the trouble with the bedraggled Mughal-e-Azam. It was incapable of cleaning itself up, and its waiters were slow and sullen, but somehow the establishment produced spectacular tandoori chicken. Sartaj took a leg, and savoured the plump moistness, tinged slightly by clay. Kamble wielded a handful of rumali roti and took in another long strip of chicken, and closed his eyes in ecstasy.

'At the very least,' Kamble said, 'what we need in this country is a dictator. You know, to organize everything.' He chewed noisily. 'With that you have to agree.'

'If he organized everything, then he would catch you, right? And all your activities?'

'No, no. No, saab. If everything was good, I wouldn't need to engage in any of my activities. You see? I only do what I have to do, to live in this Kaliyug.'

It was an unassailable argument, quite perfect in its circularity. Kamble was enraptured by perfections: if there was no perfect world, he wanted a perfect destruction, or at least a perfect dictator. Sartaj felt his stomach churn, and waited for the raita. He tried to remember if he had ever believed in such unadulterated ideals, if he had ever been so young. Certainly, he had once believed that Megha was utterly and wholly beautiful, and that he was the most handsome sardar in all of Bombay, if not in the entire southern half of the country. But that was a long time ago. 'Since we live in Kaliyug, my friend, let's decide what we are going to do about the pilot.'

'You know what I want to do.'

'You can't thrash him. A couple of slaps, maybe. But nothing else. Think about it, Kamble. There's not even a FIR, and this isn't some road labourer from Andhra. This chutiya could be big trouble if you leave him with a broken leg or something.'

'I know some other fellows who could do the breaking.'

'No,' Sartaj said.

'All right, all right.' Kamble waved a bone morosely. 'Let's take his money, then.'

'And his toys.'

'The film theatre?'

'Yes.'

Kamble chortled. For the first time that day, he got that ferocious, beady exuberance in his eyes. 'DVDs,' he said. 'I want all his DVDs.' He split a chicken breast in two, and pulled at a morsel within. 'Did you tell her yet?'

Sartaj shook his head. He hadn't told Kamala yet, and he wasn't looking forward to it. He was sure that she would weep, and maybe there would be hysterics. Maybe she would curse the pilot, and then herself. 'You want to tell her?'

'Are you crazy, boss? Me? I spend my life dealing with angry women. I'll go and talk to the pilot, read him his punishments. I'll tell him all the fines he has to pay. But her? No, no.' Kamble seemed restored, with his lips wet from the chicken. 'Anyway, you are the one she likes,' he said, grinning, and waved for more roti. 'You take care of her.' He turned his head towards Sartaj abruptly, his hand still in the air. 'Boss, why Santa Cruz station?'

'What?'

'You said you drove to Santa Cruz station to make the call. Why?'

'I was passing by.'

'At six in the morning you were passing by Santa Cruz?'

'I didn't say six.'

'You said you woke up the Delhi woman.' Kamble put both elbows on the table, leaned forward. 'My friend,' he said, 'where did you sleep last night?'

'Nowhere.'

'Nowhere?'

'At home.'

'At home. Home. Home.' Kamble puffed up his cheeks, and looked quite like a benign bulldog.

'Home-home what?'

'It is nice to find a home, Sartaj Saab. Especially a home that is near Santa Cruz.' Kamble twisted in his seat, and roared, 'Arre, have you gone to Aurangabad to get our rotis?' He came back to Sartaj, and beamed. 'What, did I say something? Eat, eat.'

'I need to go,' was all Kamala Pandey said when he told her who the blackmailer was. They were sitting at their usual table in the empty Sindoor Restaurant, towards the back and to the left. It was late in the afternoon, and the low sun through the frosted windows made a golden glow in which the white-clad Kamala had looked very pretty. Now, after hearing about the pilot and his perfidy, she clamped her jaw and a vein vibrated across her forehead, and she said only, 'I need to go.'

She swept her keys off the table and got up even as Sartaj said, 'Wait, wait.' He followed her towards the door, then came back to get her purse. When he got outside, she was sitting in her car, staring past the paan-wallah and the pedestrians. 'Madam?' he said.

Her hand was shaking against the side of the steering wheel, scraping the key against metal. She looked down, collected herself and tried again. This time she managed to fit the key in.

'Madam,' Sartaj said gently. 'Don't drive right now. Please.'

He opened the car door, and she let him take her by the elbow and draw her out. She stood with her hands straight by her side while he leaned into the car for the keys, and then he had to turn her around and walk her back into the restaurant. He seated her first, then sat himself down across from her. Her eyes were a translucent amber, and she was looking straight through him. 'Madam,' he said. 'Madam, would you like some water?' He slid a glass towards her, and then reached out and took her hand and curled it around the bottom.

She began to weep. She withdrew her hand, put it into her lap, and the sharply defined lines of her face seemed to blur, and a sound came out of her and shivered down Sartaj's spine. He had heard it many times, this guttural, child-like cry. He had heard it from parents whose children had been murdered, brothers who had lost sisters in accidents, old women who had been made into paupers by their relatives, and yes, from lovers who had been betrayed. This low bawling was always hard to confront when it started because you knew there was nothing you could do. Sartaj had learned to wait it out. Kamala was quite unaware of him, and she howled without shame, or reserve. A waiter poked his head out of the kitchen door, and then Shambhu Shetty looked through. Sartaj raised a hand, just slightly, and shook his head. Then he waited.

Kamala cried herself out, and then she pressed both hands to her face. Sartaj took a sheaf of tissues out of a glass on the table and held them out. She dabbed at her face, and took a deep breath. 'I love him,' she said in English.

'Madam, he is a very bad man. He has stolen from you. He has used you.'

'No, not *him*. My husband. I was talking about my husband.'

That paused Sartaj. He fumbled for more tissues to hide his incredulity, and he cleared his throat. 'Yes, madam, of course.'

She leant forward, and she was fierce now. 'No, you don't understand. I know you think I am a bad woman.' Her make-up had been smudged away, and Sartaj had never seen her face so bare, not even on that first morning when she had been quarrelling in her nightclothes. 'But you don't understand. I want to be married to my husband. I don't want to leave him, I don't want a divorce. If I wanted to leave, I would have left a long time ago. I don't want to leave. I want to stay. Do you understand?'

She had the apradhi's need to explain herself, even after the danger of punishment had been extinguished. 'Madam?' Sartaj said.

'Are you married?'

'No.'

'No?'

'No.' Sartaj had no intention of explaining himself to Kamala Pandey, of trying to explain his own failures to this failed woman.

'Then you can't know.'

'Know what, madam?'

'Marriage is very hard. Falling in love, getting married, that is easy. But then you have a whole life left. You have years and years. And you want to stay, you want to. To stay, sometimes you need something. I know it sounds like a lie, like an excuse. But it is true. Having him there, he, you understand . . .'

She didn't want to say the name, Umesh, on her tongue, it was too bitter. 'The pilot?' Sartaj said.

'Yes, the pilot.' She shook her head from side to side, marvelling at herself, her life. 'He made it possible for me to stay with my husband. I swear. Otherwise I would have gone. I have my own job, I have a house to go to, with my parents. But I love my husband.' Her shoulders shook, and she cried a little, and blew her nose into tissues. She looked very young now, with strands of hair sticking to her cheeks. 'You have a bad opinion of me and my husband because you saw us fighting and all that. But really we are better than that. We are good together. You didn't have a chance to see that.'

Sartaj was sure that this was right, and true, that Kamala Pandey and Mr Mahesh Pandey were happy husband and wife, when they were not hitting each other. In marriage, as elsewhere, nothing was simple. Maybe Kamala needed the pilot, as her husband needed her, as she needed her husband. Somewhere within this tangle of need and loss and lies, there was the truth of love. 'Madam,' he said to Kamala Pandey, looking straight into her eyes, 'I understand.'

'I won't do it again, though. Not anything like this again, with some other man. It's not worth it.' She was troubled still, of course, guilty and unsure of herself and the future. She touched her hair, smoothed it behind an ear. 'How I must look. Are the bathrooms here clean?'

'Only medium-clean,' Sartaj said. 'And sometimes there is no running water.'

'I'll wait till I get home. I'll go home.' She began to gather up her purse and keys.

'Madam, we will get the pilot and talk sense into him. But please, don't you do anything. Don't talk to him, don't confront him. If he tries to get in touch with you, you refuse any calls or anything like that. And let us know.'

'I don't want to talk to him. I don't ever want to see him again.'

'Good. If there was an FIR and a case, we could have thrown him into jail. But we'll teach him. We will get any tapes and information he has, don't worry. And we will try and recover your money from him.'

She shuddered. 'I don't want anything from him. Just keep him away from me.'

'We will, madam.'

Then there was nothing else to say. She slid out of the booth, and tottered a little in her high heels. She was still shaky, but she would be all right. She would make it home. Women were strong, stronger than they looked. Even fancy women like Kamala Pandey.

'Oh, your money.' She rummaged in her purse, handed him a brown envelope.

'Thank you, madam.'

'Thank you,' she said. She straightened up. He saw her pull herself together and take command of her surfaces, put them together bit by bit, and now she was almost the Kamala he had known before. She turned sharply and walked away, very decisive and crisp.

Sartaj watched her go, her pert, gym-conditioned bottom and her confident walk, and thought that if she was very lucky he would never see her again, or hear from her. If, that is, she managed to hang on to the regret and fear that she had suffered for the past few weeks, and to all the anger against the pilot that would come in a day or two. But it was her confidence and self-possession that would lead her down ambiguous alleys, sooner or later. She would forget the hard lessons she had just learnt. She would believe that nothing like this would happen to her again. She would need to live with her husband, and to live a little apart from him. Life was long, and marriage was hard. She would maybe make mistakes again, because she loved her husband. Love, Sartaj mused, was an iron trap. Caught in its teeth, we thrash about, we save each other and we destroy each other.

Anyway, the case was closed. It was none of his business now, unless she called him again. He put his money in his pocket, and went back to the station.

Parulkar had just finished watching a demonstration of a new laptop when Sartaj knocked at his cabin door. 'Come in, come in,' he called. He acknowledged Sartaj's salute with a wave, and pointed him at a chair near the desk. Then he folded his hands over his belly and watched benignly over the young salesman, who was wrapping cords and cables and tucking them away into a carrying case.

'I will wait for your call, sir,' the salesman said.

'I will not call, someone from the technology committee will call,' Parulkar said. 'But be positive. You have very good technology.' He waited until the salesman was out of the room with his various brief-cases, and then grinned at Sartaj. 'They have good machines, but very expensive. And they are not willing to compromise on price, to con-tribute to the strengthening of the police department and the country. So they will suffer.'

He probably meant that the company was not willing to contribute nearly enough to the strengthening of Parulkar's own financial devel-opment, but Sartaj didn't want to know about any of that. So he told Parulkar about Kamala Pandey's suffering and its resolution, and the punishment that was to be meted out to the pilot.

'Interesting case,' Parulkar said. 'Well done. What is the payoff from the pilot?'

'We don't quite know yet, sir. Kamble and I are going to talk to him tonight. But it should be at least a few lakhs, in cash and kind. The bastard has a lot of money.'

'Very good.' Parulkar was pleased. Sartaj would pay Majid Khan, who would kick something upstairs to the ACP, who would pass something on to Parulkar. By the time the money got to Parulkar, the amount would be small. But he collected many small amounts, which added up to big amounts.

'You look very healthy, sir,' Sartaj said. It was true. Parulkar's hair was swept back from his forehead into a Brylcreemed wave. He had lost a little weight, and he looked young.

'The secret is a strict diet, and good exercise, Sartaj. You must maintain yourself. Without health nothing is of any use. I have stopped eating any non-veg at all, and my cholesterol is down. There may be all these temptations in life, but one must plan for the long run.'

'Yes, sir.' Sartaj knew how much Parulkar loved his chicken pand-hara rassa, very tikhat, and soonti, and mountains of biryani. If he was willing to give up all those, he must be planning for a very long life, and a career almost as long. It was good to see him back in the game, all confident and crafty. Sartaj smiled, and lobbed him the obvi-ous question, 'So what are you eating nowadays, sir?'

Parulkar sat up, called for chai and told Sartaj all about bajra rotis, and high-fibre fruits, and the dangers of refined sugar. 'Sartaj,' he said, 'one must balance the body for the soul to thrive.' Then he had to leave for a meeting at police headquarters. Sartaj walked him out to his car, and watched the little convoy leave. Parulkar's white Ambassador was escorted by two Gypsy-loads of armed policemen and an unmarked car carrying yet more policemen in mufti. He was well protected.

Sartaj walked around the zonal headquarters and back into the station. He had paperwork to do, cases to work. It would be another late night, another inevitable dose of the bad restaurant food that he lived on. Eating well, eating for a long life, was not so easy. You needed time, you needed money, you needed a certain position, maybe you even needed bodyguards. Anyway, Sartaj thought, I am not so old, my body is still working. I will worry about it next year. He cleared a desk, and sat down to work.

Sartaj and Kamble had planned to confront Umesh later that night, but at six-thirty Sartaj received a call from Anjali Mathur. 'I will be arriving at the domestic airport at eight o'clock sharp. Meet me there.'

She came out of the airport building surrounded by a knot of men. There was another group waiting at the end of the walkway for them, and from this hectic confluence of safari suits, she emerged to raise a hand at Sartaj. She was wearing her usual efficient shoes and a dark green salwar-kameez, and she looked very tired.

'This is my boss, Mr Kulkarni. Please come in the car with us.'

Sartaj followed them to a white Ambassador in the parking area. The boss, who was a studious-looking bureaucrat with thick glasses, pointed Sartaj at the front seat. He and Anjali slid into the back. The air-conditioning inside the car was on, and the driver was standing by outside, but apparently they were not going anywhere. Kulkarni folded his arms over his chest and said, 'Go ahead, Anjali.'

The briefing was thorough and precise. Anjali had followed up on Sartaj's tip about Gaitonde and the guru. This guru himself – one Shridhar Shukla – had disappeared the previous year, or 'gone into retreat', according to his people, who were unable to provide current contact information. The organization itself had fallen into disarray after the Guru's disappearance, with furious infighting and struggles and even murders, all of which had been widely reported in the

national press. The first of these unpleasant episodes, a double murder, had taken place in the ashram outside Chandigarh, and the police
had been summoned. One òf the officers who had responded, an IPS
probationer on his first operation, had found some money in the room
where the murders had taken place, a sum of ninety thousand rupees
exactly. He had turned it in at the station, where the senior inspector
had spotted the notes as counterfeit. The ashram authorities, when
interrogated, had said that the money had probably come in as part of
an anonymous cash donation, and they were unable to provide further information. And there the matter had rested, with a couple of
notations in a couple of forgotten files, and a stack of counterfeit
notes in an evidence room.

Six weeks later, an armed party of the Jullunder police raided a flat
in a residential building, after a tip-off from a disgruntled dhobi. The
dhobi had delivered ironed shirts for the three male inhabitants of the
flat, had got into an argument with one of them over a damaged shirt
and had been paid less than his due. The dhobi had then tipped off the
local beat constable, alleging that the three men – one of whom was a
blond foreigner – were engaging in drug dealing out of the flat, that
suspicious characters were going in and out all the time. The raid by a
special operations group followed. No drugs were found. No arrests
were made, although a bowl of rice was still boiling in the kitchen
when the police entered the flat. The three men who had rented the
flat had apparently fled through a concealed rear staircase, which the
raid party had failed to discover and secure. In the flat, the police
found three suitcases and assorted clothing, a few books, a laptop and
ten thousand rupees in cash. On closer examination, the money was
found to be counterfeit. The ThinkPad laptop was examined and
found to be password-protected. The hard drive was then removed
from the laptop, and connected to another computer and scanned. All
the data files were found to be stored on a logical drive encrypted with
a 256-bit cipher, using a commercially available program named
DeepCrypt. The local computer consultant tasked by the police tried
extended dictionary attacks, but failed to break the encryption.
Although it was curious that the men had fled, the Jullunder police
had no special reason to pursue the case, and no means of doing so.
So the case was filed and forgotten. Forgotten, that is, until a mention
of the counterfeit money had bubbled up through the channels and
multiple layers into a database containing all mentions of such

counterfeiting, which had been tapped by Anjali Mathur in Delhi. And she had noticed, in her careful and slow and relentless querying through the lists of counterfeiting cases, that this Jullunder file contained a mention of Guru Shridhar Shukla. The browser on the confiscated laptop had stored its cache on an unencrypted portion of the hard disk, and only three sites had been visited in the three weeks recorded in these history files. One was Hotmail, the other was a pornography site called *www.hotdesibabes.com* and the third was this Guru's website.

Anjali Mathur had taken this admittedly vague connection to Mr Kulkarni, told him that there was in both cases counterfeit money of the same type, on the same paper, from the same plates, and also both times the Guru was involved. Mr Kulkarni, in his wisdom, had allowed her to requisition the organization's computer department, to attempt to crack the encryption on the Jullunder laptop. But this laptop had by now disappeared from the police station concerned. The station officer apologized profusely, and promised that in future the evidence room would be guarded more securely, and that he would institute an enquiry, and punish all the policemen responsible for the loss. This halted all enquiries, until Anjali remembered that the hard disk had been removed from the laptop by the consultant, and called the SHO back. The hard disk was finally found at two a.m. on Tuesday night, in a brown envelope secured by a rubber band, on the top shelf of a bookcase in the consultant's office. At which point it was couriered to Delhi, to Anjali Mathur. And, in two days and seven hours, the encrypted logical drive was unencrypted, unlocked and made available.

'We have capabilities in the area of encryption,' Anjali Mathur said, with a certain pride, 'that are even ahead of the western countries. And that DeepCrypt encryption program they used was not very good.'

'That's good luck for us,' Sartaj said.

'Very good luck,' Kulkarni said. 'As it turns out.'

Anjali nodded. 'What we found on the encrypted drive were blueprints, technical documents and progress reports. From analysis of all this, we are convinced that there is indeed a device, that this device has been made with materials brought into the country and that it is technically sound. They bought spent nuclear fuel on the international black market and brought it into the country. They then used converted mass spectrometers to separate and extract enriched weapons-grade material from this spent fuel. Mass spectrometers are machines that are routinely used in academic institutions and laboratories. They can be legally bought on the open market. A mass spectrometer converted to work as a calutron will only produce tiny amounts of enriched weapons-grade material over weeks and months, but if you are patient enough you will ultimately have enough for a device. And we know they were using a number of calutrons, maybe as many as a dozen, fifteen. So they had the material and they had the knowledge and expertise. We know they made a device. And we know that the device has already been brought into this city. This is clear from e-mails and documents that we found on the hard disk.'

'Device,' Sartaj said. 'You mean a bomb.'

'Yes.'

'Where? Where is it?'

'That is the problem,' Anjali said. 'We do not know.'

'Nothing else? No clues?' Sartaj felt detached from himself, as if it were somebody else having this bizarre discussion in the back of a car in front of Terminal Two, on a muggy night like any other, with travellers and their relatives hefting suitcases into dickies. He tried to focus, to bring his usual hunger for details to bear on the problem at hand. It was important to keep working, to be professional in the face of this bad fantasy made worse by reality. 'There must be something.'

'No, there is not much. There is a reference to a house in Mumbai. The exact sentence is, "I hope Guru-ji is enjoying the terrace at the house," and the implication is that this house is inside the city. That is all.'

'Why are they doing this?'

Kulkarni took off his glasses and polished them. 'We are not sure. On the hard disk,' he said, 'there are also files from a publishing programme. These include the text and images and fonts for three pamphlets. The pamphlets are supposed to be the product of an extremist Islamic organization named Hizbuddeen.' He put his glasses back on, with the air of an absent-minded professor. 'We ourselves have collected printed copies of these pamphlets during raids on various banned organizations. Our impression was that Hizbuddeen was a fundamentalist organization with Pakistani links. We knew Hizbuddeen funded other such organizations, and was perhaps planning a big terrorist operation. Now, this new information would suggest that Hizbuddeen is actually a false front, a fake organization created by this Guru Shridhar Shukla and his people. Our theory now is that their plan is to set off this device and blame it on Islamic fundamentalism. So, the evidence we have so far collected on Hizbuddeen is a false trail, laid by this man Shukla and his organization. The idea being that, after a nuclear incident, Hizbuddeen would claim responsibility, and would be believed.'

'But why? What do they hope to gain?'

The light fell flat on Kulkarni's glasses, making little half-moons of them. He shrugged. 'We are not sure of the intended consequences, or the motives. Perhaps they want heightening of tension, escalation, perhaps retaliation.'

Sartaj didn't want to think about what retaliation might mean in this instance, but he couldn't stop himself from asking about the first looming disaster. 'If they set this, this device off,' he said, 'what will happen? How big is it?'

Kulkarni deferred to Anjali with a tilting of his glasses. Apparently she was the detail person on their team. 'From what we can gather,' she said, 'it is not a small device. The construction may actually have taken longer because they wanted to deliver a larger payload. And they don't care about miniaturization at all. It was probably driven into the city in the back of a truck. If it goes off . . .' She swallowed. 'Probably much of the city.'

'Everything?'

'Almost. If they plan carefully and place it well.'

Sartaj had no doubt that they would place it extremely well. They had calculated the instrument, and their purpose, and they would make sure of the destruction. There was only one question left. 'What do we do?'

Kulkarni had something like a plan. 'We are setting up a working committee right now,' he said, 'at the Colaba police headquarters. We will issue an alert in the next two hours. But there will be no mention of the device. We will just say that there is a reliable tip on a big terrorist operation. Any mention of the device may cause widespread panic, people rushing to leave the city, that sort of thing. We don't want that. It would be impossible to control.'

Sartaj could well imagine the rush, the highway clogged with cars and trucks, the desperate shoving to get on to trains, the screams of lost children. And he could also feel the need, in some other corridor of his mind, to warn Mary, to get Majid Khan's children out of the city. But he nodded, and said, 'Yes, yes.'

'If information about the device leaked to the general public,' Anjali said, 'then the people in charge of the device might also learn about it. They may set it off then, to prevent discovery and prevention. The whole investigation has to proceed with that in mind. It has to be very tight.'

'Fully tight,' Sartaj said. 'But what are they waiting for?'

'We know nothing about their timetable,' Anjali said. 'We would like to continue what you have been doing for us. You have done very well. Use your resources to investigate.'

And with that, they let Sartaj out and left him swaying in the exhaust of their several Ambassadors. He felt completely alert, but quite dazed. There were orange lights burning over the terminal building. A trickle of sweat, released by the gathering heat, moved down his collarbone. Review the information, he told himself. But there was very little: the apradhis maybe included a famous guru in a wheelchair and a yellow-haired foreigner, they were maybe in a house that had a terrace, the house was maybe large enough to hold a large machine, maybe there was a truck near by. That was it, that was all. On this, everything depended. Don't worry, Sartaj told himself. Just go to work. Just work.

So he hurried to his motorcycle, slung a leg over it. Then he was unable to move. Had the last few minutes really happened? In his memory now, everything that had happened in the car had the feeling of jerky, speeded-up film. Sartaj tried to slow his breathing and parse the conversation, recall it bit by bit, but all he could find was a jumble of sentences and words: 'It is not a small device'; 'intended consequences'; 'payload'. How were Anjali and her boss able to speak so calmly and efficiently of such things? Maybe people like that were used to speaking of unspeakable things. Maybe international spies used that language all the time. Sartaj had thought of this thing before, this device, he had encountered it in fictions and newspaper reports, but now that it was inside his city, in his home, he was unable to imagine it. He tried to see it, some sort of machine in the back of a truck, but all he could see was an absence, a hole in the world. What came out of this void was an avalanche of regret, a knifing pain in his gut for everything left undone and for all the memories of the past. He bent over. In the bulge of the silvered handlebar there was the shine of the streetlamp and a thousand faces, a boy he had fought with in Class Three and humiliated in front of the whole school, Chamanlal the paan-wallah from the main road corner, a beautiful girl that Katekar had once told him about who worked for Gulf Air at the international terminal, that lame beggar who worked the crossroads at Mahim Causeway. Everything would be gone, not just loved ones and enemies. Everyone. This was the unbearable promise of this device, now made real. It was ridiculous but it was true. Sartaj sat in the car park and tried to comprehend this, to hold it in his head so that he could think about it, and decide what to do next. Finally – he did not know how much time he had passed, just sitting – he gave up. Better to leave it as a blank, and think around it. At least then you could work. Yes, work. Go to work. He started the motorcycle, and began.

Three days of work brought no breakthroughs, no revelations, no arrests. The alert had gone out, but there was too little substance. There was not enough to ask informants, only this: have you seen a group of three, maybe four men? One blond foreigner, one guru in a wheelchair, maybe, maybe? Leads had come in, hundreds of them, but they led inevitably to innocent old men in creaky wheelchairs, and to outraged foreign executives with hair just a shade lighter than brown. There was no progress. And life went on. On Tuesday evening, Sartaj visited Rohit and Mohit and Shalini. He gave Shalini an envelope, ten thousand rupees, and sat in their doorway and drank a cup of chai.

'You look very tired,' Shalini said. She was sitting inside the house, near the stove, starting dinner for the boys.

'Yes,' Rohit said. He was leaning against the wall, next to Sartaj. 'You do.'

'I have not been sleeping well,' Sartaj said. 'Too much work.'

Rohit brushed at the collar of his sparkling white T-shirt. 'But you are very thin, also.'

'I still haven't found a good cook.'

Shalini smiled. She was wearing a glossy green sari, and she looked well. She gave Sartaj a sly, knowing look. 'What, that Christian girl doesn't cook for you? Or you don't like her food?'

Sartaj started, splashed his chai all over his chest. 'What girl?' he sputtered, brushing at his shirt.

Rohit clapped his hands and laughed. 'Don't bother, don't try,' he said. 'Her spies are on all four sides, really. She knows everything.'

Shalini's shoulders shook. Sartaj couldn't remember when he had seen her laugh like this, even back when her husband had been alive. 'Yes,' she said. 'You don't even know how I know.' She waved a powdery belan at him, looking supremely satisfied. 'And don't think it was the easiest way. No policeman told me.'

Shalini was not about to entertain any denials of the Christian girl. Sartaj gave in, with what he hoped was a modicum of grace. He ducked his head and asked, 'So who told you?'

'I can't give away my khabaris. No, no.'

Sartaj tried to think who it could be, who would know about Mary, who would have talked. Kamble knew about her, and he may have told somebody at the station, who may have told a civilian. Or maybe Shalini had a friend who worked near Mary's house, who would have seen Sartaj coming and staying and going. Or maybe it was somebody at Mary's salon. There were a thousand and one ways that Shalini could have heard the story of Sartaj and Mary, countless connections that slipped through the city and bound each person to everyone else. Sartaj had used this inescapable network many times himself, and now he was found out. 'Your mother is really a pucca professional,' he said to Rohit. 'The department should hire her.'

Shalini laughed and flung a handful of some brown spice into a pot, and there was a great hissing and fizzing. 'So tell us about this girl.'

'But you already know everything,' Sartaj said. He was about to say more, something general about how men could never hope to escape the vigilance of women, when he saw Mohit come stumbling down the end of the lane. There was blood on his shirt.

'What happened?' Rohit said, and knelt to take his brother by the shoulders. 'Who did this?'

There were rings of crimson around Mohit's nostrils, and a blackish smear across his chin. In a swirl of sari, Shalini came past Sartaj. 'Beta,' she said, 'what happened?'

But Mohit was grinning. 'Don't worry,' he said. 'We did much more to them. It was those bastards from Nehru Nagar.' He was triumphant, satisfied. 'We showed them, they ran away.'

Shalini was holding Mohit's shirt at the shoulder, where it had been ripped at the seam and into the back. 'You fought with those boys again?' She grabbed his face, tugged it up towards hers. 'I told you not to go near them. I told you not to go even near that side.' Her anger forced her teeth back, and Sartaj could see her nails digging into the boy's cheeks. But Mohit was not afraid. 'I'll tell Saab to take you to the remand home,' she said, turning him towards Sartaj. 'He'll beat you.'

Sartaj stood up. 'Mohit, you shouldn't –'

'Maderchod sardar,' Mohit said, and his hatred squeezed past his mother's fingers. 'I'll kill you. I'll cut you.'

Shalini gasped, and then slapped Mohit on the back of the head, hard. She dragged him into the house, past the already gathering audience of neighbours and slammed the door. But Sartaj could still hear Mohit's low growl, grim and unrelenting.

'I need to go,' Sartaj said to Rohit, and took him by the elbow and walked away. 'I have an appointment.'

'Sorry,' Rohit said. He fingered, nervously, the key that hung from his neck. 'Mohit is getting spoilt, in spite of everything we do. He is keeping bad company. He has a gang of four, five boys. They keep fighting with these other, older taporis from Nehru Nagar. I have even beaten him myself, but he keeps getting worse. His marks in school are terrible.'

'He is young,' Sartaj said. 'It's just a bad time. He'll come out of it when he gets older.'

Rohit nodded. 'Yes, I think so also. But very sorry.'

Sartaj thumped Rohit on the chest, said, 'Don't worry, there is plenty of time, he'll realize sooner or later,' and kicked the motorcycle into heaving life. As he edged up the pitted slope, it came to him that perhaps Mohit would never come out of this blood-flecked spiral, even if there was plenty of time. Maybe he was lost already, lost to his brother and his mother and to himself. Sartaj had played his part in pushing Mohit towards this hard path, into this pit from which there was no return. Every action flew down the tangled net of links, reverberating and amplifying itself and disappearing only to reappear again. You tried to arrest some apradhis, and a policeman's son went bad. There was no escaping the reactions to your actions, and no respite from the responsibility. That's how it happened. That was life.

Rachel Mathias was waiting at the station for Sartaj. She was sitting in the corridor outside his office, squeezed up at one corner of a bench next to a row of impassive Koli women. She was hot and unhappy, but when she rose he was impressed by the elegant fall of her blue sari and the simple silver bracelet on her right wrist. She was not at all crumpled by the squalor of the station, and now she stood very straight and looked him directly in the eye.

'How long have you been waiting?' he said.

'Not very long at all. This is my son Thomas.'

Judging from how sullen Thomas was, they had been at the station at least a couple of hours. 'Come,' Sartaj said, and led them into the office and sat them down. Thomas sprawled back in the chair, and then straightened up after a cutting glance from his mother. He was fifteen or so, good-looking and confident and muscled. All the boys were lifting nowadays, and Sartaj was sure that Thomas had been an early starter.

'About what we talked about the other day,' Rachel said.

'Yes?' Sartaj said. He knew now that she was not guilty of black-mailing Kamala, but everyone was guilty of something. It had happened before in his career, that the threat of a policeman's pressure had made people confess to something that he wasn't looking for.

'Thomas has something to tell you.'

Thomas didn't want to say anything, he had his eyes down and his fists clenched, but his mother was implacable. 'Thomas?' she said.

Thomas worked his jaw, cleared his throat. 'What happened was –' he began, and then was unable to go on. He wiped his hands on his jeans, and flushed, and Sartaj felt a surge of sympathy. Thomas had built his biceps and gelled his hair, but he was a child still.

'Maybe,' Sartaj said, 'Thomas can talk to me alone.'

Rachel nodded. 'I will wait outside.'

She swung the doors shut behind her, and Sartaj tapped the table. Thomas managed to look up now. 'Tell me,' Sartaj said.

'Sir, about our video camera . . . I'm sorry.'

'Sorry for?'

'For making the video.'

Sartaj felt a daze settle over his shoulders like a fine mist. 'The video. Yes.'

'It wasn't my idea.' Thomas managed to tell it all now, in fits and starts. It wasn't his idea. It was Lalita's idea. Lalita was his girlfriend, a year older than him. They had been in a relationship for a year. When Thomas had got his new video camera they had taken it out and shot footage of all their friends, and of the city, and of random people on the streets. For a few days they had shot a short film written by Thomas, but they abandoned it half-way because they were bored. Then Lalita wanted to shoot them, the two of them together, just hanging about in Thomas's room. Then once the camera was on, they forgot it was on.

'Forgot?' Sartaj said.

'Yes.' For a while they forgot. When they remembered, Lalita didn't want to switch it off. So there was a shot of them kissing.

Sartaj rubbed his eyes, and pinwheels spiralled and disappeared. He dropped his hands, and Thomas was still there, young and handsome in his tight white T-shirt, with his string of small beads around his neck. Still there, and inexplicable and yet real and present. 'Only kissing?' Sartaj said.

'Yes, yes. Our clothes were always on.' So their clothes had stayed on, but still his mother had been furious when by chance she had picked up the camera and switched it on and seen them on the LCD. Yes, one or two of Thomas's friends had seen the video, but that was all. And Rachel Mathias had immediately destroyed the footage. And that was the end of it, until Sartaj showed up, asking questions about video cameras.

Sartaj knew he should say something, maybe shout at the boy, terrify him. He was certain that shooting the video had been Thomas's idea, not Lalita's. Or maybe not. Maybe the Lalita that Thomas was describing did exist. Yes, Sartaj was sure she did. What did Sartaj know about the world these boys and girls lived in, with their video cameras and their internet and their relationships at fifteen? Who were these people? He lived next to them, along with the thousands of other lives in the city, and he knew them and didn't know them. All of it existed together somehow. Sartaj made an effort, and finally managed to be stern with Thomas. 'If you do this kind of thing at this age,' he said, 'you will ruin your whole life.' He went on, but he didn't know if he believed any of it himself. As he walked Thomas to the door, a hand on his shoulder, Sartaj surprised himself. 'Listen,' he said, 'look after your mother. She's all alone, and she works very hard for you and your brother. Be good. Don't give her trouble.'

He hadn't planned on asking for virtue for Rachel Mathias's sake, but Thomas seemed to be affected by it, more so than by the warnings and admonitions that Sartaj had just delivered.

'Yes, sir,' Thomas said, his eyes wet. 'Sorry, sir. I will.'

Sartaj woke up from a deep, dreamless sleep, to a fan making a hazy white circle over a green ceiling. With a great effort, he turned his head. Mary was sitting on the floor, flipping through a magazine. The sound was down on the television, and a great, silent herd of gazelles leapt over a rise and vanished into yellow grass. 'What time is it?' Sartaj said. It was dark outside.

'Nine-thirty. You were very tired.'

'I was. What are you reading?'

'It's a travel magazine. There is an article about diving in the Andaman islands. It's so beautiful under the water. Look.' She got up and sat on the bed next to him. Orange and red fish swam in water that was so blue that it jumped from the page.

Sartaj propped himself up on an elbow. 'Why don't you go?' he said. 'You should take a vacation.'

'Will you come?'

'Me? No, I don't even know how to swim.'

'I am saving for Africa anyway.'

'Yes. But, meanwhile, take a vacation. How about Kodaikanal?'

'I've been there.'

'Then go to your village.'

'There's nothing there to go back for. Why are you trying to send me away?'

Sartaj sat up. He took the magazine from her, and held both her hands in his. 'It's very dangerous here in the city, right now. We are expecting a big terrorist action. They are going to do something, we know that. So maybe you should go away.'

Mary's shoulders hunched. 'Will you come?'

'I have to stay here.'

'Why?'

'It's my job.'

'To find them?'

'Yes.'

'What are they going to do?'

'Something, something very bad, very big.'

She burst out laughing. Then she stopped herself, and was very serious. 'Sorry. I believe you completely. That's why I'm laughing. What else can you do but laugh?'

'You are very brave.'

'No. Not brave at all. I'm afraid. But it's too crazy to think about.'

'So will you go?'

'No. Not alone. What is the point? Everything I have is here.'

Her eyes were moist. He kissed her then, and she curled into him. She kept her lips on his, and her tongue was warm and supple, and she moved up over him. They laughed together as he winced and moved his thigh from under her knee. She kissed him, on the corners of his lips, and then she reached down and took his hand. She drew it up, put it on her breast. For a quiet moment, they were still, and Sartaj saw how the flecks in her eyes moved in the lamplight, and behind those there was a soft, unknowable darkness. They smiled at each other. Sartaj began to undo the buttons on her blue shirt, one by one. The buttons were very small, and he had difficulty with each one. He felt quite clumsy. Mary chortled at him, and arched her back as he went lower, to help him. He imitated her giggling, and she came back to him, her cheek against his beard, and they laughed together. She drew the shirt off her shoulders, revealing a lustrous sweep of brown skin, and slipped down beside him. Sartaj leaned over her. She put a palm on the back of his neck, and drew him to her.

Lying with Mary under a sheet, skin against skin, Sartaj told her about his childhood. She wanted to know his life from the beginning. 'Tell me,' she had said. They were now up to his teenage years. It was very late, long past midnight, but Sartaj felt alert and strangely content. His body was relaxed, the pleasant ache in his muscles was the memory of their sex. He had been clumsy, and insecure, and too solicitous afterwards, but somehow none of that mattered. It had been good to be embraced by her, to feel the living pulse inside her. It was good to lie with her, to move her hair behind her ears, and answer her questions. Now she wanted to know, 'So what was her name?'

Sartaj had been telling her about his first girlfriend. 'Sudha Sharma. She lived two buildings down, and her brother was my best friend at the time.'

'Later he found out about you and his sister and beat you up?'

'No, no, he never found out. He would have killed me. But we were very careful.'

'How old were you?'

'Fifteen.'

'Fifteen! At fifteen I knew nothing about sex, absolutely nothing. You were so bad at fifteen?' Mary pinched the skin on his shoulder, hard.

'Arre, I didn't say we had sex. Where was there to have sex? In her father's bedroom? There were so many aunts and grandmothers in that house you couldn't turn around without having some woman ask you what you were doing.'

'But you corrupted that poor girl anyway.'

'Me, corrupt? Ha. I wouldn't have had the courage to look at her, even. She was three years older, and she was the one who gave me extra aam-papad to eat every time I went over there. And held my hand under the table. I was so scared I couldn't drink my glass of water.'

'These Bombay girls are too fast. So then?'

'We used to meet after her tuitions in the afternoon.'

'And then you kissed her?'

'She kissed me.'

'Yes, yes. Where?'

'Why, here, of course,' Sartaj said, pointing to his lips.

'Not that, you silly man.' Mary made a mock-angry face, but kissed him anyway, a quick peck where he had pointed. 'I meant, where? In her father's bedroom?'

'The first time, in the family room of a restaurant in Colaba. She had two girls with her, but they left us alone. Then, after that, you know, on the rocks in Bandra.'

'On the seafront? Really, she was shameless.'

'Sudha? No. She was just Sudha.'

His smile must have been a little too fond, because Mary pinched him again. 'So what happened? Did you marry her?'

'I was too young. She married someone a couple of years later. All arranged by her parents. I went to the wedding.'

'Oh. Poor boy.'

'No, it wasn't like that. We never thought we would get married. I was too young. And not from her caste either.'

'And still she seduced you. My God.' But Mary was teasing now, and stroking at his chest. 'But I suppose she just couldn't resist Sartaj Singh.'

'Yes. I was already almost my full height, you know.'

'And almost as handsome as you are now. A full hero, almost.'

She was mocking him now, gently, and he scooped her up and over himself. 'Are you making fun of me? Are you?' He had discovered already that she was very ticklish, and now she shrieked and twisted under the tips of his fingers.

'Only a little fun,' she finally got out.

Her breasts flattened against him, hiding and then revealing the dark rounds of her nipples. She saw him looking and reached for the sheet. She was strangely shy for a woman her age, one who had been married and divorced. Maybe that is what village girls were like. Sartaj had never been with one before. This particular one was now lying on her side, the sheet pulled up to her chin, gazing intently at him. 'What?' Sartaj said.

'What what? Don't think you're going to distract me just like that. Okay, so this fast girl got married to some unfortunate man. Then what happened? Who did you marry?'

So he pulled her close and told her about Megha, about the thrill of their impossible college romance, which went across class and the impenetrable boundaries of accent and clothing and music. He told her about how Megha had found his affection for old Shammi Kapoor numbers quite incomprehensible, and how she had trained him not to wear flared pants. And how, finally, they had married and failed. Or maybe they had succeeded in some small way, in not hurting each other too much.

Mary murmured sympathetically as he told the story, and then she sighed and her breathing evened out. Her body made small twitches, extensions and contractions of her arms and legs, and Sartaj smiled. Her hair brushed across his nostrils, and he remembered those long-ago days of walking with Sudha on Marine Drive, of being maniacally excited and terrified as he pressed his thigh against hers in the back booth of an Irani restaurant. He had thought a lot about sex and love in those days, sometimes it seemed that not a minute passed without some overwrought image of sex skittering through his brain. And there had been that anguished longing for an imagined someone, a hazy and yet incandescent woman who was beautiful, and good, and understanding, and sexy, and supportive, and everything else. He had once thought that Megha was all these things, and Vaheguru only knew what Megha had imagined him to be. They had disappointed each other. He had thought he might never recover from the disillusionment, and for a while he had fancied himself a cynic. Then

784

he had discovered that he was still very much a sentimentalist, that he wept late at night over Dilip Kumar in *Dil Diya Dard Liya*, that he felt a huge lump in his throat when he read newspaper stories about poor boys who had studied by the light of streetlamps and made it through the IAS exams. Now there was this woman, this Mary resting against him. This was not illusion, or heated filmi romance, or cynicism, or sentiment, this was something else. Love had turned out to be something altogether other than what he had imagined it would be, at fifteen.

Sartaj moved his shoulder from under Mary's head, and settled her on a pillow. He turned towards her, rested his fingers on her thigh and tried to sleep. But now he couldn't help thinking of the bomb. He was feeling safe now, so he tried again to imagine what it must look like, this device, and could only come up with some silly image of a tangle of wires against steel, inset panels that displayed racing neon numbers. Maybe this device would take Mary away from him, just as he had finally found her. He knew this to be true, and yet he didn't feel the strong emotion that he expected, some rage, or black melancholy, or despair. He touched Mary's cheek. We are all already lost to each other, he thought. In the moment of our possession we lose those we love, to mortality, to time, to history, to themselves. What we have are these fragments of generosity, these gifts of faith and friendship and desire that we can give to each other. Whatever comes later, nothing can betray this lying in the dark, this breathing together. This is enough. We are here, and we will stay here. Perhaps Kulkarni was wrong about the people of Bombay, perhaps they would stay in their city even if they knew that a great fire was coming. Perhaps they would wait for the bomb in these tangled lanes, grown out of the earth without forethought or plan. People came here from gaon and vilayat, and they found a place to sit, they lay down on a dirty patch of land, which shifted and settled to take them in, and then they lived. And so they would stay.

Still, of course, the search for the guru and his men continued. Sartaj followed leads, went to apartment buildings in Kailashpada and Narain Nagar, where people had reported their suspicions about their neighbours. And also bastis in faraway Virar. On the Friday afternoon, Sartaj stopped in at the Delite Dance Bar. Shambhu Shetty gave him a Pepsi and asked, 'Boss, what's going on? I'm getting two visits from the constables per day, at least. They come thumping in, and ask my staff about some wheelchair man and some foreigner. And why would sadhus come into a bar anyway? But your people barge in every day. It's not good for business, you know.'

'It's just one of those alerts from Delhi, Shambhu,' Sartaj said. 'There is some information, so we have been told to follow up on it. That is all. It is very urgent, so we have to look everywhere. You never know where you can hear something. The constables have their orders.'

Shambhu was still irritated. 'Why do they disrupt work like that? They come in during busy times also, it really affects our collections. As it is, our whole business is in danger. There are rumours that if the government changes in the next elections, those Congress bastards may ban dance bars altogether. If it's not one gaandu trying to protect Indian culture, it's another one. Bastard politicians. You know how many times I get MLAs and ministers asking me to send girls for private parties?' Shambhu was complaining, but he looked prosperous and well-fed. Marriage seemed to agree with him.

'Yes, Shambhu, I know. But right now, let the constables do their job. This is an emergency. Could be serious. Really, if you know anything you should let me know. Okay?'

Shambhu stretched and scratched his belly. 'What, is it those bastard Muslims again?'

'No,' Sartaj said. 'It's not Muslims. Not at all. Just look out for a wheelchair and a foreigner, Shambhu. It's very important.'

But Shambhu wasn't convinced. He slouched off, muttering. He had recently made a contact at MTNL who arranged free long-distance calls on the red phone in his office. So he had invited Sartaj in to share the bounty, and had taken the opportunity to make his complaints about the constables. Sartaj picked up the phone and dialled. If Shambhu was getting irritated by the questioning, and his customers were noticing it, it was likely that the apradhis also knew that they were being pursued. A big investigation left a big footprint, and subtlety wasn't something that came easily to tired constables at the end of their shifts.

'Hello?'

'Peri pauna, Ma.'

'Jite raho. Where have you been, Sartaj?'

'Work, Ma. There is a big case going. The biggest.'

She chuckled. 'That is exactly what your Papa-ji used to say. Every case was the biggest case in the history of the Bombay police.'

Sartaj could hear the pleasure in her voice, the affection for old spousal dodges. 'Yes, Ma. He used to tell me that also. But this case, it really is an important case. Really really important.'

But Ma wanted to talk about Papa-ji. 'He once investigated the theft of a dog, an Alsatian puppy. He told me that was also a really really important case. He stayed out whole nights, investigating leads. And it wasn't for the owners, even. I mean, they were rich, they would have got another dog after a week or two. But your Papa-ji kept on telling me, "Imagine how that poor little thing feels, taken away from home like that." He found it, a week later.'

'I know, Ma.' Sartaj had heard the story many times before, from both Ma and Papa-ji. When Papa-ji told it, the case became an object lesson in careful investigation and the cultivation of informers. He had never mentioned the puppy's feelings. But Ma, as she was doing now, always had Papa-ji stalking the streets, worried about the dog, and the puppy whining incessantly at her kidnapper's home. Papa-ji had found the dog in four days, through a widening series of neighbourhood interviews and some careful pressure on the shopkeepers at the corner of the street. The apradhi, when he was discovered, turned out to be the nephew of the owner of the general store one lane away. This nephew was addicted to the new craze for video games, and he had sold the dog to his neighbours on Nepean Sea Road, so that he could play Missile Command endlessly at a brand-new parlour down the street, the first in that part of the city. So the dog was duly brought back, and the nephew jailed and disciplined.

'And, you know, Pinky was so glad to be back at her real home,' Ma said, as she reached the end of this well-rehearsed family tale.

'Who is Pinky?'

'Sartaj, really, sometimes you don't listen at all. Pinky was her, the puppy.'

'Pinky was the puppy?'

'Yes, yes. What's so difficult about that?'

'No, no, Ma. I remember now.'

After Sartaj said his goodbyes and hung up, and thanked Shambhu, he stood outside the door of the Delite Dance Bar and thought about Pinky. In all his recountings of the case, Papa-ji had never mentioned that the animal in question was called Pinky. He'd probably thought it didn't matter, one way or the other. But somehow it did. Knowing that she was Pinky made the whole matter of the missing dog more poignant. It was impossible that Pinky was still alive, but maybe her children and grandchildren were thriving somewhere in the city. Maybe Sartaj had himself petted some of them. He could think of at least three, no, four quite handsome Alsatians with whom he had an acquaintance. Two of them were nervous neurotics, but Sartaj put that down to them having to live in small flats all their lives. It was enough to drive anyone a little crazy.

He slung a leg over the bike, and then sat still for a moment. The evening sun blazed off the office windows across the road and threw a haze over the traffic below. The roadside hawkers were doing good business, selling clothes and cards and footwear to passing pedestrians. To the left, three buildings away, there was a cluster of chaat-wallahs, on the crowded landing of the Eros Shopping Centre. Sartaj could smell the heated pav-bhaji, and suddenly he was hungry for papri chaat. He had been addicted to it as a kid, and finally Papa-ji had rationed him to one plate a week, on Fridays. Today was a Friday, he thought, and he got off the bike and walked down.

Amidst the sizzle of the concoctions on the tavas, Sartaj queued up behind a giggly group of collegians. The girls were sleekly dressed in short tops and tight jeans, and they all wore bright red and blue bracelets around their wrists, some version of bangles made out of rubber. One of them saw him looking at her friend's arm and turned away haughtily. They whispered together. Sartaj turned away to hide his smile. No doubt they were complaining to each other over this lecherous uncle, this cheap roadside Romeo. But he just felt kindly towards them, and was amazed that it had been so long since his college days that flared pants had made a comeback.

He got his papri chaat and walked around the ring of white plastic chairs that edged the patio until he found an empty one. Then he gave himself to the pleasure of the papri chaat, to its crunch and the lovely sourness of the tamarind. He must have made a low sound of satisfaction because the three-year-old boy peeking at him from behind his mother's knee laughed and pointed. Sartaj wrinkled his nose at the boy and took another bite. 'Mmmm,' he said.

His mobile rang. Sartaj fumbled with the paper plate, wiped his hand on a napkin and finally got to the phone. It was Iffat-bibi.

788

'What, have you forgotten your old friends?' she said. She was as coarse-voiced as ever.

'Arre, no, Bibi,' Sartaj said.

'Then you must still be angry with me.'

'Why do you say so?'

'Because if you need something, and you don't ask those close to you, then you must be angry.'

'Do I need something?'

'Maybe you don't, but your department has been flailing its arms all over Mumbai.'

'About what?'

'Maybe you don't want those men, if you want to play all these childish games.'

'Which men?'

'The man in the wheelchair. The foreigner. And the others.'

'You know where they are?'

'I may know.'

'Iffat-bibi, you have to tell me. It's very important.'

'We know it's important.'

'You don't understand. Do you know their location? It's very urgent.'

'Has this guru escaped with a lot of money? That's very bad of him.'

'All right. What do you want?'

Iffat-bibi sighed. 'Now you're speaking like a sensible man. But not like this, not over the phone.'

'Where are you right now?'

'In the Fort area.'

'It'll take a long time for me to get to Fort. And here every minute matters. You don't know what might happen, Iffat-bibi.'

'Then you had better catch the train, no?'

'Just tell me what you want. I promise I'll do it.'

'What I want, I can't ask for like this. Come. My boys will meet you at the station.'

So Sartaj went. He caught the fast train to VT, where two young men were waiting for him outside the terminal. They came up to him out of the crowd, and one of them said, 'Sartaj Saab. Bibi has sent us.' Sartaj followed them to the gate, and then up towards the *Times of*

India building, where a nondescript black Fiat was waiting. Everyone got in, Sartaj at the rear left, and they drove on. Nobody spoke. The driver circled around, past Metro, and back towards D.N. Road. Sartaj watched the familiar streets slide by. Papa-ji had spent considerable chunks of his career down here. He had taken the young Sartaj for walks down his beats, pointing out places where crimes had been perpetrated and apradhis apprehended. The car now turned left into a U-turn, and then right, and Sartaj saw the small Technicolor temple he had loved as a child, its walls covered with brightly painted sculptures of gods and goddesses. Papa-ji and he used to meet there, 'next to the temple,' no need to say which one.

But the old shops were gone. Sartaj didn't recognize any on the lane they turned into, although the haphazard clusters of scooters and cycles were the same. And the crowds were thicker, even at six o'clock in the evening. The driver said, 'Here,' and they stopped.

Bibi's boys led Sartaj around a seafood restaurant, through a narrow alley, to the back of the building. They went up a staircase smelling of rotting fish, and then a door opened. They were inside a very small office, some sort of accountants, it looked like. There were ledgers on the shelves, which went all the way up to the ceiling. The desks were crammed in tight next to each other, and there still half a dozen employees bent over the computer screens. To the right, the space had been doubled by putting in a mezzanine, which contained three whole workstations thus suspended in mid-air. One of the men pointed Sartaj to the end of the office, where a cabin had been wedged into the triangular end of the room. Sartaj opened the door, and bent to get through.

Iffat-bibi was seated cross-legged on a red executive chair at the point of the triangle. She had her burqa thrown off her head, revealing a youthful thickness of hennaed hair. 'Come, come,' she said. 'Arre, Munna, get some chai for Saab.' She waved Sartaj into a chair almost as magnificent as the one she was sitting on, and closed the ledger that she had been perusing. 'Do you want the air-conditioner higher, saab? They keep it so cold in here that it freezes my bones. But you are a young fellow, you people like it like that.'

'No, no need. It's cold enough.'

The room pushed them close together, and Sartaj thought that Iffat-bibi looked exactly as he had expected. She was large and craggy, with a square-cut jaw and youthful skin. The toothless mouth was startling, under the alert eyes and sharp nose. He couldn't imagine her as a young woman. Maybe she had been the same age for the last hundred years. She certainly looked as if she could go on for at least another hundred.

'Saab, what will you eat?'

'Nothing, Bibi. Please, we need to discuss your information. There is great danger, and those are very dangerous men.'

'Danger is always there, saab. If you miss the chance to eat, danger will still come.' There was a knock at the frosted glass door, and then a boy put a steaming cup of chai in front of Sartaj. 'Get some tandoori machchi for Saab. And that special jhinga.'

Sartaj sat back in his chair and gave himself up to the rituals of hospitality. The end of the world would wait, it had been coming for months and forever. Iffat-bibi was implacable in her courtesies. Arguing would get you nowhere, better to co-operate and enjoy. 'So, Bibi,' he said, 'what is the news?'

Iffat-bibi shifted her bulk on the chair, from one haunch to another. 'Saab, I am just an old woman, I don't get out much. I just came here today to check some accounts.' But then she told tales about minor taporis, and shooters from rival organizations, and bar girls. The food arrived, and Sartaj ate a symbolic bite of each dish. His head was throbbing. The cold air streamed across his cheeks and curled across his neck, and he was assaulted by a foreboding that settled in his thighs and made them cramp. He settled himself in the chair, and tried to relax, and make conversation.

Finally Iffat-bibi was ready to come to the point. She slurped the last of her chai from a saucer, put it down and said, 'You want these men.'

'Yes.'

'We know where they are.'

'How?'

'They have rented a house from one of our associates. Of course they didn't know that this landlord was one of our friends. They paid cash up front, quite a lot of it, for two months' rent and the deposit.'

'How long ago was this?'

'Almost two months. The lease is almost ended.'

Sartaj felt his stomach lurch. 'What kind of house? A flat? A bungalow?'

'Don't be smart with me, beta. We'll just say a house. And no, you won't find them. Only one of them ever goes in or out. The rest are there, the wheelchair man, the foreigner, but they never show themselves, not to anyone. Only the landlord saw them go in. And nobody thought about it till now, when all you policiyas started chasing all over for them.' Iffat-bibi extracted a silver box from somewhere inside her voluminous coverings, and began to arrange herself a paan. 'What have these fellows done?'

'Nothing yet.' Sartaj was very still, he had his palms resting on the table.

Iffat-bibi spread a silvery paste over the leaf, and then deftly folded it small. She popped it into her mouth. 'I know you think you can maybe find them. You think you have some information, a house, a house with a garden and stairs. But believe me you won't find it. Don't be a foolish boy, don't even try that.'

'Yes.' Sartaj took a sip of his tepid chai. The walls pressed in around him, and he blinked at Iffat-bibi, at her reddened, chewing mouth. 'Yes,' he said. 'What do you want?'

This pleased her, this mature understanding he had demonstrated of what was required. She beamed at him. 'We want Parulkar.'

'Saali, don't you dare go near him. If you touch him, I'll . . .'

'Sit down.' Iffat-bibi did not flinch from his anger, she sat as immovable as a mountain. 'Sit.'

Sartaj let go of his painful grip on the table, and let himself back down into his chair. 'Don't go near him.'

'Arre, baba, who said anything about touching him? We're not fools, we are not going to thoko him, nothing like that. We don't want the entire police force of Mumbai on our backs.'

That made sense, Sartaj thought. No policeman of that rank had ever been killed in the city. 'But why do you want to do anything to him?' he said. 'He is close to you, he is close to your superiors. So why?'

Iffat-bibi spat red into the rubbish bin at the side of the desk. 'Yes, we thought he was close to us also. And we have been friends with him for a long time, we supported him in his times of trouble. But now he is secure, he has new friends.'

'You mean the new government? But a man has to live. He has to work under them, so he has to accommodate them a little bit.'

'Yes, yes. Of course. We understand that. We've never begrudged anyone their work, their livelihood. Arre, Parulkar Saab has kept back money from us that was ours, full khokas of it. We said, let it go. The relationship is more important than just money.'

'So now, what is it? What happened?'

'Over the last four months, seven of our boys have been killed. These were not some chillar, you understand. All were top shooters and controllers. All were intelligent, good at hiding, good at moving. But the police, this Flying Squad, knew exactly where to find them. So they encountered them. And the government puts it all over the papers, and say they have crushed crime. And we ask, how are the police suddenly so good at tracing our best boys?' Iffat-bibi leant forward into the lamplight. 'We did our own investigation. Now we know. Parulkar gave our boys to this government.'

'Iffat-bibi, the intelligence for the encounters could have come from a thousand places. Your boys were killed, that's bad, but it doesn't mean . . .'

'We have our own intelligence. We are sure. He switched sides, and he is killing our boys.'

Despite the cold, Sartaj's hands were sweating. He wiped them on his pants, and tried to keep them still. 'He will come back to you. If you want, I will talk to him myself.'

'No, he won't talk to us now, even. He doesn't take my phone calls. He won't take Bhai's phone calls. Can you imagine?'

Sartaj couldn't imagine. To refuse phone calls from Suleiman Isa himself meant that Parulkar had really made the switch, that he had taken years of his life, packed them up and walked across a very dangerous border. Sartaj didn't want to believe it, but it all made sense: Parulkar's rehabilitation with the current Rakshak government, this government's sudden success in hunting down members of the S-Company. Parulkar had done it, he had made the move. 'Let it go,' Sartaj said. 'Forgive him. Like you forgave the money.'

'It's too late. He has caused too much damage.' She pointed straight up, towards the ceiling and beyond, and shook her head. 'The order has come from upstairs. Bhai is very angry, Bhai feels insulted. Bhai said so. Parulkar has to be removed from his job, from the police. Bas.'

So that was it, Parulkar was to go. He had emerged the triumphant survivor once again, in this last battle, and he had done it by turning against old friends. Now they would finish him. 'Why are you telling me this?'

'You are very close to him.'

'Yes. So?' Sartaj knew the answer, and all this talking was just a play for time, a slight and foolish manoeuvre against the unyielding levers that were moving against him, that were squeezing him into a very small and dark place.

'You can help us.'

Sartaj shut his eyes. Here, within the thunderous churning of his blood, he was a child again, waiting in the dark for monsters to retreat from his skin, for someone to come and save him from grief, for sleep to take him from terror. He tried to calm himself, but a confusion of memories flung itself through him, here was Papa-ji flying a kite against a clouded sky, Parulkar hunched over a dead body during Sartaj's first murder case, a motorcycle ride through monsoon rain with Megha, Ma striding through a market in Delhi. Sartaj rubbed his face, opened his eyes. What should I do, what should I do? 'You don't understand,' he said. 'You don't understand that we could all be dead tomorrow. Everything could be finished. Believe me.'

'I may believe you,' Iffat-bibi shrugged, 'but they won't, Bhai and them. They will think it's a trick. They want Parulkar.'

'Then forget them, forget your Bhai. Forget all of them. You tell me where that house is.'

'I cannot.'

Sartaj fumbled at his holster. 'Tell me,' he barked. 'Tell me.'

Iffat-bibi clapped her hands, and chortled. 'What are you going to do with that thing, you madman? Shoot me?'

Sartaj had the pistol in his hand now. His thumb slipped on the safety catch, and then he steadied himself and aimed at her face. 'Tell me.'

'Do you think I am afraid of dying?'

'I'll shoot. Tell me.'

'I can't tell you because I don't know. They gave me only that much. Shoot then. My boys will come from outside, and you will also be dead in a second, and khattam shud.'

I can shoot, Sartaj thought. It would be an action. He would blow a hole in this floating white visage, above the gaping mouth, and then he would be dead himself. Whatever happened afterwards, he wouldn't know, it would be somebody else's business. Whatever happened, whatever happened to Parulkar and Anjali Mathur and Ma and Kamble and everyone else and Mary, it would happen.

He put the pistol down on the table, and unclamped his fingers from it.

'Wipe your face,' Iffat-bibi said curtly. She slid a box of tissues across the table.

Sartaj blew his nose. 'All right,' he said. 'What do you want me to do?'

The train had just pulled out of Dadar station when Kamala Pandey called. 'Umesh has called three times in the last two days and left messages on my mobile,' she said. 'He wanted to know how the case was progressing. You have not talked to him?'

'Actually, madam, I have not. I got very busy suddenly. There is a very big matter that needs to be taken care of.'

'I see.'

She understandably believed that Sartaj had taken the money and shirked his responsibilities, and she was not pleased. 'Don't worry, madam,' Sartaj said. 'We will take care of it tonight.'

'Okay.'

'No, really. I'm very sorry. But we will fix him tonight.' He meant it: Umesh would be a welcome distraction. He had read every advertisement he could see on the walls of the compartment, and then he had taken out his notebook and read scribbles from two months ago, trying to avoid thinking about what he had to do for Iffat-bibi. Yes, he would consider the pilot, and deal with him. 'There was an unavoidable delay, madam,' he said, 'but now we will get him.' And he watched the buildings skim by, and the abrupt gaps that exposed a yellowing sky.

Sartaj and Kamble thumped and banged on the pilot's door at nine-thirty, and found him eating dinner with his parents and his three sisters. There were children running about, and the smell of rice and dal in the air. The pilot's father was a portly old gent dressed in a banian and blue-striped pyjamas. He came up behind the servant who opened the door and asked angrily, 'What's the matter? Who are you? Why are you creating this hungama?'

'Police,' Kamble growled, and shoved past the father and the servant.

Sartaj followed, at a more leisurely pace, taking in the happy tableau. Two sisters were older than Umesh, and they wore elegant salwar-kameezes and looked very respectable and married. One sister was younger, maybe college age. The looks in the family definitely

795

came from Umesh's mother, but had been unevenly distributed in the next generation. One sister, the oldest, was passably pretty, despite the extra weight she carried in her arms and hips. The other two were quite ordinary. Definitely, the pilot was the star in this plot, the shining hero of his mother's affections, and she herself was quite beautiful. The mother had a long, narrow face, and smooth white hair she had wisely left uncoloured, and now she was frantic. 'What police?' she said. 'What?'

'Don't worry, Ma,' the pilot said, reaching out and stroking her wrist. 'They're friends of mine.'

Kamble laughed a laugh so theatrically evil that the youngest sister started and crossed her arms across her chest. 'Yes,' Kamble said, 'we're very-very good friends of Umesh's. We're his langotiya yaars. We know all about him.'

Umesh was up now, trying to herd them away from the dining table, away from his family. He clapped Sartaj's shoulder and smiled. 'Good to see you, Sartaj Saab. In here.' He didn't give away the slightest whiff of nervousness, he was relaxed and confident.

Inside his film theatre, he shut the white door and latched it. The room was large enough to hold a white bed and half a dozen black leather armchairs in a semicircle. And of course there was a screen which stretched across one entire wall. 'What do you want?' Umesh said. He was too smart to be rude, but he was curt.

Kamble had his hands on his hips, his head forward. 'Is that door sound-proof?' he said, very softly. The agitated talk from the table had been cut off cleanly, and now it was completely quiet, not even any noise from the cars moving their headlights over the curve below the window.

'Yes, yes.' The pilot was confused, and very curious. 'I like to listen to films very loud. I have a top sound system. If a plane crashes on the screen, you can *feel* it.' He tried one of his little smiles now, one of the sweet boyish ones.

Kamble slapped him. 'Did you hear that?' Kamble said. 'Han? Did you hear it?'

The pilot had a hand on his cheek, and the other balled into a fist, close to his chest. He was very offended. He had probably never been slapped, never even by his mother. Kamble was waiting, ready and eager, wanting an aggressive move, a curse, anything. But Umesh was too smart, he was too much in control. 'What do you mean by this?'

he said. He lowered his hands, puffed out his chest in righteous indignation. He asked Sartaj, 'What has happened to him?'

Sartaj had been looking up at the tiny white speakers mounted high up near the ceiling, many of them no doubt positioned to give full surround sound. He grinned. 'I think he's very angry with you. Because you were trying to fool him.'

'Fool him? I never did anything to him.'

Kamble took hold of the pilot's white T-shirt, and pulled him close. 'But you did everything to Kamala, bastard.'

Umesh plucked at Kamble's hand. Now Sartaj could see the first beginnings of fear, the schemes spinning behind his beautiful eyes.

'We know everything,' Sartaj said. 'We have your Anand Agavane. We have his mobile phone. He has told us everything. He told us how you had him calling Kamala, how he collected the money from her. We know you were blackmailing your girlfriend.'

'No,' Umesh said. 'No. I don't know . . .' His fair skin was flushed, his voice was whispery.

'Don't try it, Umesh,' Sartaj said. 'You want us to put you in handcuffs and take you out there, in front of your family? We'll search the whole house, we'll turn it all upside down, and we'll find the mobile phone you were using to call Anand Agavane. Then we'll take you to the lock-up. So don't try it. Otherwise we'll have to tell your mother everything.'

The pilot sagged. His mouth contorted, and a little wet sob came out of it. He gasped rapidly, in and out, and spittle flecked out on to Kamble's wrist. 'Bastard,' Kamble said, and let go of him.

'Can I sit down?' Umesh said. Kamble stepped aside, and the pilot walked unsteadily to one of the big black chairs and sat on its edge, his head hanging down and his arms on his thighs.

Kamble pulled another chair up close and leaned back in it. He nudged Umesh's knee with the toe of his shoe, and said, 'What, you think you watch a few American movies and learn everything? You think you're some maharathi? Arre, cheap bastards like you, we catch them every day. And we bamboo their gaands. But you are worse than any maderchod, blackmailing your own girlfriend. Taking money from her.' Kamble leaned to the side, and spat on the ground. 'Bhenchod, I've seen many chutiyas who sold their own sisters for money, but they're better than you.' He spat again.

'Sorry,' the pilot said. 'Sorry.' He was crying now, and wiping at his eyes with his hands and his tight-biceped T-shirt.

Sartaj noted that Kamble had been careful to miss the white carpet with his expectorations, which meant that he had marked it for himself. Which was fine with Sartaj. A white carpet was a foolish bit of showiness in this city. You'd have to keep the windows closed, and run the air-conditioner day and night to keep the dust out, the grime from settling. 'Umesh,' Sartaj said. 'Here. Look at me. Look at me. Now tell me. Why did you do it?'

The pilot shook his head, stroked at his reddened eyes again. 'Daddy had an angioplasty,' he said. 'So much money. And Chotti, she's got to get married.'

Kamble cracked his knuckles. His sneer was ferocious. 'You're very poor, no? And your girlfriend, she just has too much money, no?'

Umesh was too emotionally wrought to catch the sarcasm. 'Arre, what expenses does she have? She lives with her husband, and he even pays for her petrol. Every month she puts away her' – and now he stretched his arms wide – 'this big pay cheque, and her parents give her money. And still she had me spending money on her. I bet she didn't tell you that. She wants gifts, she wants the best hotels. I tell you, that woman is expensive.'

Sartaj inhaled and said very softly, 'Yes, and besides you have to buy all this expensive equipment, so you need money. Good carpets cost a lot of money. How much a set of seven foreign speakers must cost, I don't even know.'

Umesh retreated into the chair, and when he came back up he had decided to be charming. He shrugged insouciantly, gave Sartaj a bit of roguish twinkle, one man of the world talking to another. 'Everyone has necessities, boss. Everyone. I am sure we can come to some understanding.'

'What?'

The pilot pushed himself up, rising out of the chair. The smooth rims of his teeth made perfectly resonant arcs with his curving lips. 'Kamala really has too much money, yaar. We could all share . . .'

Something like a sob came out of Sartaj's throat, and he smashed his fist into Umesh's mouth. A jolt of pain arced up into Sartaj's shoulder, and the hard crack of bone on bone was immensely satisfying. Sartaj swung again, and Umesh was falling off the chair, the chair was tipping over, Sartaj stepped around it and followed Umesh. He carefully aimed his kicks, and the third one flipped Umesh on to his back, and the pleasure of it throbbed in Sartaj's head. There was a screaming in his ears. A white-haired woman was huddling over Umesh, there was red smeared and speckled across the carpet, and Kamble had his arms tight around Sartaj's arms and chest, he was dragging him back. Sartaj tore himself loose, turned and shoved his way through a knot of shrieking women, through the door and then he was out. He was out on the road in front of the building and his chest hurt and his hand, he held it up to the light, a gash oozed black across his knuckles. He wanted somebody else to hit, something, but the cars swept by, out of reach, and he could only hold the edge of a crumbling boundary wall, and curse and curse.

Ganesh Gaitonde Goes Home

'If it happens in a film, it won't happen in life,' Jojo had said to me. When I'd told her about my fear of radiation burns and bombs and buildings being swept down by a roaring wind, she'd said, 'It's too filmi.' But I knew better, I knew more. I had seen scenes from my own life in two dozen films, sometimes exaggerated and sometimes reduced, but still true. I was filmi, and I was real.

I had known Jojo for years, and I knew that I was still slightly unreal to her. I was her friend, but I was also Ganesh Gaitonde, the crime lord, the ruthless international khiladi, the crorepati and arab-pati who lived in palaces. For the overwhelming majority of people, gangsters and spies only existed as figures of light, as glittering and temporary notions thrown up by electronics and celluloid. But I was in fact a gangster and spy, and so I knew well what was possible. My own life had taught me what was real, and I knew that what men can imagine, they can make real. And so I was terrified.

I told myself every morning that there was no reason to be frightened. After all, perhaps Gaston and Pascal and the others on the boat had been exposed to radioactive material by accident on the docks or elsewhere. All kinds of materials passed through, some belonging to government agencies. Maybe something had leaked on the way to one of the big atomic power plants. And even if we had brought in some harmful material on the boat, it may just have been inside one of those machines meant for the agricultural work that Guru-ji was conduct-ing. Yes, no doubt that was the case. It was an accident anyway. Then why was I so scared? No need to be like this. Maybe I had lived so long with the fear of my own death that it had fed on itself and grown larger and stronger until I had this monstrous dread inside me, this lurking, poisonous thing that threatened the death of the whole world.

All would be well, though. Guru-ji would come back from his secret meditation or journey or yagna, whatever it was, and he would tell me exactly what had happened to Gaston and Pascal, and that would be that. He would calm me, and life would settle into a routine again. I remembered all our conversations, I made an effort to trace – in my imagination – our history together. I brought out the files in which I had stored all his pravachans and read them again, and was once again entranced by his wisdom, soothed by his compassion. I watched recordings of his speeches and wept. I spent hours paging through Guru-ji's website, reading the hundreds and thousands of testimonials written by his disciples, and looking at the happy faces of those saved from despair and madness and disease. Every morning I felt that all would be well, that a man who cared for so many – orphaned children, destitute women, the aged and the abandoned – must be a dharmic man. If Guru-ji brought guns into the country, it was to protect morality, to strengthen right and hold off wrong. I was his disciple and I was protected under the umbrella of his love. I was safe. I laughed at myself, and berated myself for my lack of faith. I set to work. But soon I was again awash in horror, surrounded by flayed, stinking corpses, oppressed by a wind that whistled inside my head and left emptiness.

Like a worm, fear grew out of this void and fattened. I was afraid of assassins coming at me over water and under it. Arvind and Suhasini had been killed in Singapore, Bunty had been shot in Mumbai, many others had died. I knew that Suleiman Isa was trying to kill me, and I suspected that Kulkarni and his organization wanted me dead, and some mornings I thought they were running their operations co-operatively. But under these fears there was always this other thing, a quiet terror as bright as the blue on a morning wave. In the afternoons it lapped at the sparkling glass on the portholes as I tried to take a nap, as I shoved my face into white sheets and tried to find my way to oblivion. Food seemed a waste of time to me, dining with the boys a long tribulation, and women gave me no satisfaction. Yes, I turned virgins from my bed because the one final spasm of pleasure didn't seem worth all the work that went into the ridiculous act. I felt old, and empty. It took hours for me to find sleep, and when I did, I slept lightly, racked by dreams of empty wastelands, of burning cities.

In the early morning hours, sometimes, I was able to dream of Mumbai. In that light half-sleep, I put myself into those lanes, and I was young and happy again. I relived my victories, my narrow escapes, my triumphs of tactics and strategy. And not only these grand moments – these historical landmarks the whole city remembered – I also recalled small details and passing conversations. A neer dosa shared with Paritosh Shah at a roadside udipi stall near Pune, Kanta Bai dealing cards on top of an upturned carton. A game of carrom with the boys on the roof of my house in Gopalmath, with monsoon winds swaying the wires on the rooftops of the basti. On these mornings, I awoke happy. I was confident that everything was all right, no reason for worry. And by evening I was trembling again.

If only I could talk to Guru-ji. I couldn't find him. The months passed, and Guru-ji was still gone. Of course I had my boys looking for him, but I knew that they were beginning to resent this intrusion into their time, which they preferred to spend making money. They were all polite, of course, and did as they were told, but I knew that their efforts were less than enthusiastic, and that their constant reports of 'Nothing found, bhai' glossed over the fact that they hadn't actually looked. Bunty was barely out of the hospital, still alive but crippled, deadened from the waist down. Of course we were providing the best medical care for him, the best technology. I spoke to him every day, and he was taking on work and responsibility, but he hadn't the energy to push the boys, to make them devote themselves to the search. It didn't help that I couldn't tell them exactly why we were searching for Guru-ji. I had only my insane imaginings, and I didn't want to sound crazy, and I didn't want to start a panic. Life had to go on, work had to continue, money had to be earned. Also, I couldn't announce my reasons without exposing my whole connection with Guru-ji, without giving away everything I had kept secret for so long. So I said only that we needed to find Guru-ji, and that was all. But there was no motion on this mission, no success, not even a lead.

So I went to Bombay.

I flew in from Frankfurt with a best-quality German passport in the name of Partha Shirur, and walked easily through immigration and customs. An hour later I was in a bungalow in Lokhandwalla. My cover was that I was an NRI businessman based in Munich, that I was returning to India after a very long time abroad, that I was investigating business opportunities. So here I was, suddenly sitting in a cane chair on the roof of the house, which was called 'Ashiana'. I was sweating through my shirt, but I was enjoying myself. I asked for a glass of coconut water, and sipped it, savouring that particular Bombay stink in the thick air, of petrol fumes and pollution and swamp water. Behind me, a stack of flat buildings made a wall for my back, and in front there was a dirt road edged with streetlights, and then a leafy darkness. I felt reinvigorated, and the aircraft exhaustion dropped away from me as I listened to the crickets sing. A pack of dogs skulked around the corner, yipping at each other. I was content.

There was a commotion at the staircase, and then I heard that low whirr and whine of a wheelchair. But it wasn't Guru-ji, it was Bunty, navigating his way over the little step in the roof. We had of course got him a wheelchair exactly like Guru-ji's, despite the cost. He deserved at least that.

'Bunty,' I said. 'Bastard, you're like a racing driver in that thing.'

'Bhai,' he said. 'It's a good machine.'

He looked lost inside his own skin, as if he had shrunk into himself. I had to bend to hug him. 'It's the best, my friend. Did you drive it up the stairs?'

'No, no, bhai,' he laughed. 'I'm not as good with it as our other friend. I had them carry me up.' He angled a thumb at the three young lads near the doorway on the other side of the roof. I could see their faces in the light from the stairs, and they were all new. I knew none of them.

'Tell them to go away,' I said.

He waved at them, and they retreated. 'They don't recognize you,' he said. 'If I passed you on the street, I wouldn't have known you.'

'Best surgeon, he gave good results,' I said.

'Yes. But we have to be careful, bhai. One meeting.'

'One meeting.' That was our plan. I was going to be in the city, but I was going to stay undercover. The government was using MCOCA to throw our boys in jail, the encounter specialists were killing them faster than ever. It was a very dangerous time. As far as my company knew, I was still in Thailand, or Luxembourg, or Brazil. I was going to communicate with Bunty through our secure communications equipment and e-mail. We were going to be near, but act as if we were far. But we had to meet once, at least once. I had told him that, I had ordered it even though it was a risk for me. I had told him I didn't care if he was being watched not only by the police and Suleiman Isa's people, but also by the CIA with all their satellites. He had taken bullets for me, and I wanted to see him face to face. We had been together for a long time. I pulled up my chair close to his, sat shoulder to shoulder with him. 'Here,' I said. 'For you, chutiya. All the way from Belgium. It's a genuine platinum Rolex, with diamonds on the dial and the strap. I got it through our friends there, but it's still twenty-two thousand dollars.'

'Bhai.' He was holding it with both hands cupped, as if it was a blessed idol I had brought back from a pilgrimage. 'Twenty-two thousand yu-ess. That is just too good. It is so masst. It is beyond masst, I don't know what to say.'

'Don't talk, bastard. Put it on.'

He put it on, and held his arm up and away so that he could admire the Rolex. He had a young girl's delight in his smile, that pleasure in unexpected jewellery. He was afraid of scratching it, though, of bumping it and losing a diamond. He held his arm carefully across his lap as we spoke, resting on his withered thighs. We talked then, of business and his family, of export and import and investments and stocks, and who had died and who was still alive. It was good and necessary conversation, but I realized even as we gossiped and joked and theorized that it was not the talk that mattered, but the sight of the paan-stained teeth on this loyal little gaandu, the ability to reach out and slap his shoulder. You can listen to the sounds that a phone makes, but it is not the true voice of a man. It was good to sit next to him, and talk until the birds began their morning clamour. It was like old times.

He left after eating breakfast with me. I walked down to the garden gate with him, and watched as he went jauntily up a folding ramp into the back of his van. He turned the wheelchair within its own axis, so that he was facing to the front, and held up a hand to wave at me. I raised a hand, marvelling again at the wheelchair and the spirit of Bunty, who had learned to manoeuvre in such tight quarters. The van pulled away in a swirl of dust – always this dust in this city, already this grimy, polluted sweat – and I went back into the house. I was tired, but I felt confident, because I was Ganesh Gaitonde and men sacrificed their limbs and their potency for me, they suffered pain and paralysis, and yet – even after the embarrassment of pissing into plastic bags – they offered to serve me again. They were happy to work for me, to be my boys. A watch from me was worth as much to them as a medal from the president. Yes, I would find Guru-ji. I was sure of it. He couldn't escape me. This city was mine, this country belonged to me. I had the guns and the money, and I would find him. I went inside, drew the curtains tight against the glare, turned up the air-conditioner and went to sleep.

Bunty's boys hadn't recognized me, and I had no trouble convincing the rest of the company that I was still in foreign waters. But Jojo, that sharp kutiya, was suspicious right from the start. I called her that first afternoon, and even before I could say 'Hello' she was at me.

'Gaitonde,' she said. 'What's happened?'

'Nothing has happened. Why would something be happening?'

'You never call me this early in the afternoon.'

'I got free today and decided to call you. Are you going to prosecute me in court now?'

She shut up, but only for a moment. Then she was back, dangerously soft. 'So where are you, Gaitonde?'

'Where would I be? I'm in my room. I'm at home.'

'But where?'

'Why do you want to know?'

'I'm just asking. Just like that.'

'In your whole life you've never done anything "just like that".'

'So where are you?'

'In Kuala Lumpur.'

A car came around the corner outside.

'That sounds just like an Ambassador. They drive Ambassadors in Kuala Lumpur?'

Somebody should have made her a spy, this Jojo. She was absolutely correct, an Ambassador had just turned the corner near the gate, and it was rattling down the road now. 'That's a Japanese jeep, idiot,' I said.

'So the Japanese are making noisy khataras now. Okay. But Malaysian birds sound like that? And the kids play cricket?'

I was in an exclusive, expensive bungalow, but of course there was no escape from the noise. There were the crows and there was the cricket game down the street, and there were also labourers working on the construction site two streets away, shouting at each other in Telugu. There was filmi music somewhere, a radio, but very low and far away. I cupped a hand over the phone and turned towards the corner. 'There are lots of Indians in this building,' I said. 'Don't argue with me. I'm not in the mood.'

'All right, all right, Gaitonde. So how is life?'

How was my life? I felt old, I was alone and I was afraid. 'My life is fit,' I said. 'It is absolutely top-class. You tell me about yours.'

So she told me about hers: problems with girls who thought they deserved more money than they were worth, a leaky wall in her apartment that seeped beads of water even after it had been waterproofed twice, a television-show deal that had slipped through her hands. I listened to her and thought how well I knew her, and how well she knew me. With Jojo, distance made no difference, whether she was near or far I felt her presence, as if she were sitting next to me. We had learned each other's breathing, so that now when we spoke and joked there was an easy rhythm to it, like a boy and girl on a seesaw pushing each other off into air, like circus acrobats turning and finding each other in mid-flight.

Jojo was real to me, and distance made no difference. I was barely a mile and a half from her apartment, less if I went directly across swamp and sea. I could be there in ten minutes. I could have walked up her stairs, knocked on her door and asked her for a cup of chai. But I had no desire to go, no need to see her. She was with me, even when she was away. I could feel her inside me. She was more real to me than myself. Me, I had faded and broken into pieces. This was true. I could hardly admit this to myself, but it was true. The thing I called me, myself, it felt to me like an old brown blanket, tattered and patched and barely holding together. I, who had once been Ganesh Gaitonde, who had been glorious and whole to the entire world, I was now gone from myself. I felt like a small boy walking alone through an endless plain lit by funeral fires, afraid and lost. In this ashy haze, in which I no longer knew what was good or worth having, I clung to Jojo. She was my strength and my only pleasure, my anchor and my only friend. I listened to her, and laughed, and collected myself for my search.

'Gaitonde,' she told me, 'it sounds just like you're sitting at a corner in Tardeo. But you move around so much that you confuse me also, not just yourself. You should stay in one place for a while now. Even if it's this Kala Langur.'

I told her what she could do with her Kala Langur, which made her giggle, and then she told me a story about a woman who had gone to Nepal for a holiday and had been abducted by a bear which fell in love with her. 'Really, Gaitonde, it happened. Bears take women all the time.' Which I think, in some roundabout way, was meant to be an

806

argument for staying at home. I didn't tell her that I couldn't stay in one place, that I had no choice, that I had to travel. I just listened to her, and left the next day for Delhi. Five of my boys met me there, all the main crew from the yacht. They had flown into airports all over the country, from Sydney and Singapore and Mombasa, and had rendezvoused at two hotels in Greater Kailash. They were to be my special squad, my undercover commandos. Bunty's assistant Nikhil had come from Mumbai to head this contingent. He hadn't been exactly happy to leave behind his good money-making operations and his family in Mumbai, but I had insisted, and he had packed his bags. He knew me well enough not to argue. He was completely bald already at thirty, and he had an older man's stolid patience. He had managed the details: the boys had good cover stories, new documentation that had been dirtied for a properly aged look, and sober clothing and decent haircuts. I brought money and weapons, and we were ready to go.

We started in Chandigarh. Guru-ji had suffered his crippling motorcycle accident in Pathankot, and he had been brought to a hospital in Chandigarh, and during his recovery he had formed an attachment to the city. It was here, among these broad avenues and circles, that he had finally settled his parents, and it was here that he built his first ashram and headquarters. The ashram complex had been large to start with, but now it sprawled over a hundred acres on the outskirts of Sector 43. We got to Adarsh Nagar in the late afternoon, with the setting sun on our shoulders. The massive blue gate at the entrance was manned by white-clad sadhus, the usual mix of Indians and foreigners. Nikhil had called ahead and set up a meeting with Sadhu Anand Prasad, who was the governing head of Adarsh Nagar and the top sadhu in the national organization. The sentry sadhus made phone calls, and Nikhil chatted with them, and as we waited I got out of the car and strolled down to the barrier. The gate was actually a monument by itself, like one of those gigantic guardhouses that you see at the front of castles and fortresses, with rooms and chambers and armouries inside. Guru-ji's gatehouse was a glorious shimmering blue, it had delicate rounded turrets and pointed spires and little balconies, and despite all its bulk it sat lightly on the earth, as if it had been transported in from another era. It could have guarded the palace at Hastinapur, or stood before Ravana's golden fortress. Inside the compound, there was a thick covering of green grass, cut straight and even, and long boulevards, and widely dispersed buildings, all in blue and white. There were clipped trees, and flapping orange and red flags along the roads. The shaded archway of the gate was suffused with fragrance from neat blocks of yellow flowers that lined the steel fences.

'Okay, bhai,' Nikhil said to me. 'We can go in.'

We drove along, past sadhus walking purposefully in small groups. There was an infinite hush over these gardens, a quiet removed from time, so that even the gathering flocks of evening birds spoke only in mild tones. There were children strolling in the meadows, but they walked in orderly columns and bowed their heads with a namaste when an elder passed. I had seen this ashram on video, but now in life it looked a little smaller than I had imagined it. But it was perfect in its shape, it was quite balanced and square. At the other end of the campus there was another blue gate, and two more at the east and west, and exactly half-way between all of them, at the geometrical dead centre of the grounds, there rose a massive stepped pyramid of white marble, a pillar pointing at heaven. This was the main administration building. We parked in front of it, and went through another cordon of secretary sadhus. Then we were shown into a lounge lined with low couches, and here we waited.

It was Nikhil who finally said what we were all thinking. 'Bhai,' he said, 'there's a lot of cash here. Maybe we're in the wrong game.'

'It's never too late,' I said. 'You want to start a religion?'

'Let's do it.' He scratched at his golis. 'You be head godman. I'll manage the finances.'

'Meaning I do all the work and you get the largest cut, you greedy maderchod. At least come up with the rules for this new faith. What is our philosophy?'

The chutiya didn't have any trouble coming up with a creed. He sprawled back on his sofa, folded his hands over his comfortable little belly and put his feet on a table. 'There's only one rule. You gain grace by giving Bhai money. The more you give, the more karma you get rid of. Give everything you've got, and you are granted moksha.'

The boys all grunted and rattled with laughter, and I smiled too. But it hurt me in my heart, this smooth cynicism, this easy sneer. Guru-ji had no doubt made a lot of money, but I didn't believe that money alone was his objective. I knew this. I didn't pretend to understand how his mind worked, but I knew there was a plan beyond the cash, that there was a further coherence behind the faultless order of the ashram. I just didn't know how to read the meaning of this mantra, I couldn't speak this tongue, I couldn't grasp what this square with its circles inside was trying to tell me.

As I grappled with these conundrums of religion and aesthetics, Anand Prasad's secretary summoned us into his office. I let Nikhil go ahead, and came in last behind the others. Nikhil did the talking, he was supposed to be the head of an NRI association interested in donating money to Guru-ji's charities. As I listened, I was struck by how comely this Sadhu Anand Prasad was. His skin was a polished chocolate, agleam against the white robes he wore, and although he must have been at least fifty, his long dark hair fell over an unwrinkled forehead. He had a slight southern accent, and in all my life I had never seen such a handsome Tamil. His secretary was a very tall Dutchman, blond and sharp-featured enough to be an actor. The secretary stood behind Anand Prasad's chair, and together – in that airy office full of silk-covered furniture – they were like an advertisement for Guru-ji's methods. They were beautiful.

Nikhil was pushing for a meeting with Guru-ji. He told Anand Prasad that his organization had millions to give, that our members were Indian businessmen and computer programmers and doctors spread out all over the world, and that they were eager to contribute. But they were followers of Guru-ji, and to give to him they must necessarily meet him. If not in person, then why not a video conference? Or at least a phone call to start with.

'I'm very sorry,' Anand Prasad said. 'But Guru-ji is in retreat. Even before he left, he gave strict instructions. He is not to be disturbed, not even for emergencies. In fact, I can't even get in touch with him. I don't know where he is, or how to communicate with him.'

'He calls you, then?' Nikhil said.

Anand Prasad's shrug was as elegant as a dance. 'No, no,' he said. 'He has really gone.' He made a magician's gesture with both his hands. 'You could say he has vanished. He will only come back when he wants to.'

'He won't even come back for a million dollars?' Nikhil said. 'Even for poor children? And starving women?'

He was trying hard, but I could see that it was useless. Anand Prasad didn't know, and what he did know he wasn't going to tell. 'Forget it,' I told Nikhil. 'This maderchod is a flunky. He doesn't know anything.'

Anand Prasad was shocked. He was full of his holiness and his exquisite good looks, and nobody had ever spoken to him like that. 'What?' he said. 'Who are you?' he said.

I took two steps up to his desk. Next to an elaborate pen-holder and three phones, there was a golden model of an altar in the shape of an eagle, the size of two hands across. I picked it up. It was quite wonderfully detailed, down to the bricks and the samagri inside the altar, ready for burning. And it felt profoundly weighty in my hand, it fitted into my palm with an impressive density. The smoke of sacrifice was in my nostrils, that fragrance that signals both life and death. I was suffocated by yearning, I was drowning in it. Where was Guru-ji? Why wouldn't he speak to me? What had I done wrong?

'What is this?' I said. 'Gold?'

'You listen,' he said.

He puffed up from his chair now, very righteous and indignant. I took another step, and in that motion I swung the altar and cracked his forehead. 'No,' I said. 'You listen.' The metal rang like a bell, and a sprinkle of blood appeared on the clear glass of the window. 'It's hard,' I said with satisfaction. 'It's not gold.' Anand Prasad was jerking about on the floor next to his chair, his robe up around his hips. I straddled the bastard, took hold of his shoulder and raised him up, and went to work with the altar. I found a calm in the hitting, a concentration that came into me like a wash of clear water. The blows came out of me in an even rhythm, with my breathing, as if I were meditating. I was lost in the relief of it, nights of fear and anger all gone into this satisfaction. Then the altar was covered with blood, and Anand Prasad was dead.

I let go of him, and his skull clunked softly on the marble. The boys were watching me, wide-eyed. Nikhil had his ghoda pointed at the Dutchman, who was crouched in a corner. 'No,' I said. 'No bullets. This is a message. Do it like this one.' I let the altar drop.

The Dutchman had time to scream only once before they were on him. I opened a door, and inside there was a sparkling toilet, a full-fledged executive bathroom. These upper-echelon sadhus didn't begrudge themselves any of the benefits, no, they surely didn't. I clicked on the light, and saw myself in the mirror: blazing eyes, blood on the face. I washed, and in the other room the Dutchman died in a flurry of thumps and moans. When I came out, the boys were straightening themselves up.

'Better wipe down that thing, bhai,' Nikhil said, his chest heaving. 'Fingerprints.'

The altar had hair stuck to it, and little pieces of flesh. 'Bring it,' I said. 'We'll get rid of it.'

When the boys were cleaned up, we left. We walked out, cool and easy and slow, and went down to the car and got in and drove at an even pace to the gate. We waved at the sadhus and we were away.

We had our exit route already laid out. At our safe house we had a change of clothes and a black Sumo waiting. I had trained the boys well. In less than fifteen minutes we had the rooms swept clean and the Sumo loaded. We wiped down the Maruti Zen that we had driven to the ashram, and then we left. We went south, towards Delhi. We passed columns of passenger buses and laden trucks, and for a while we drove behind a marriage party. I felt very calm now, in this twilight. Now Guru-ji would have to talk to me. I had done something very wrong, and he would have to punish me. He would have to call me to scold me. I would of course apologize, but I would tell him why, and he would understand. He would forgive me.

We had left behind the industrial estates and the shops and the dhabas, and now the fields of sarson and wheat stretched to the blackening horizon. The electricity posts rushed up, raising and lowering their cables over our heads. When I was a child, travelling on a rattling bus from Digadh to Nashik, I used to imagine these posts calling out to me as I left them behind, as they swept behind me into the past. But in those long-ago days I had never seen so many prosperous farms, these pucca houses with the TV dishes and antennae reaching towards the sky. Everything had changed.

But nothing had changed. I observed this truth all over the country. Over the next many weeks I travelled with Nikhil and the boys, and we did a zigzag bharat-darshan. We went to Guru-ji's ashrams, his offices and his places of business. We followed clues, rumours, hunches and whim. So we went from Chandigarh to Delhi to Ajmer, from Nagpur to Bhilai to Siliguri. Then back to Jaisalmer, and then to Jammu and Bhopal and Digboi. Then we stopped for a week in Cochin, so Nikhil could dose himself with antibiotics to ward off a watery flu that had him groaning at the toilet every half-hour. We rented a tourist bungalow near the waterfront and watched the Chinese fishing nets rise and fall out of the water. Meanwhile Nikhil struggled, and the doctor prescribed test after test. After eleven of these tests, I told the bastard that I was on to his cut-practice. 'What is cut-practice, saar?' he said in his Malyali accent.

'Maybe you call it something else down here,' I told him, 'but it's the same thirty per cent cut you get from the laboratory. I'll bet you a lakh on that. You want thirty per cent? I'll give you thirty per cent.' And I showed him the back of my hand. After that he became quiet and compliant as a whipped randi, he gave his capsules and bowed his head and went away. I couldn't resist showing the bastard his place, but it was bad tradecraft. We needed to keep a low profile, I knew this. But the gaandu had annoyed me. He wore jeans, and drove a Capri, and kept talking about how he was dispensing the 'latest-latest' medicines, but he conducted business just like any village doctor giving water injections to illiterate shepherds. It was the same all over India – we met farmers who carried mobile phones and murdered their daughters and sons for marrying out of caste, we bought bottles of mineral water from scabby, bare-footed chokras whose arms were covered with ringworm. Nikhil had been complaining bitterly every night about the scratchy phone connections he got when he tried to have his laptop dial in and collect e-mail, and finally in Coimbatore an unearthed power plug roasted his sleek Sony Vaio and killed it quite dead. And now he was shitting twelve times a day, and he said he was very afraid he was going to keep huggoing until he died on this bhenchod white throne in this maderchod Malyali city in this harami cesspool of a country.

Even Guru-ji's ashrams were infiltrated by confusion. I had seen this. Chaos seeped in past his steel fences, his blue gates, his protective mantras. All over the country, the ashrams were laid out according to the same exact plan. Whether it was big or small, in a city or in the countryside, each ashram had the same north-south layout, and the same four blue gates. The buildings and distances increased in size, or decreased, but the layout remained precisely the same. Once we had been to a couple of the ashrams, we knew how to navigate them, we knew that the first building on the left after the main gate was the arts and crafts shop, that the laundry was always hidden away in the north-east corner. And always, always, there was the pyramid at the centre, which was always the most sacred, the most powerful, the headquarters. As we went from one identical ashram to the next, looking for information about Guru-ji's whereabouts, I began to see the sense of the geography, the meaning of the design. It was like having a conversation with Guru-ji, looking at these sites that had been blueprinted in his mind, and created wholly by his insight and imagination. The whole landscape focused always on the marble pyramid, which resembled our old Indian temples but wasn't quite like them. Here, in this building completely devoid of images, there was the work of the mind, and what lay beyond the mind. Here there was administration and meditation, dharma and moksha. Far from this central point, at the very outskirts, there were the menial buildings, the laundries and the generating plants, the public toilets and the arts pavilions. Arranged in the middle there were the schools for the children and the dormitories for the married couples, and the medical clinics and the communications facilities. Closer to the centre, away from the buildings where ordinary lay devotees could freely enter, there were the curving residences and viharas and halls of the sadhus, of those who had given up the world. These made a precise circle around the white pyramid itself, beyond which there was only liberation.

I could see the logic and progression here, the movement from the outside to the inside. The relationships of these points and angles, the architecture of these constructions, this was the geometry of time and life itself. I had heard, many times, Guru-ji speaking of the ages of man, the proper affiliations of castes and groups, the place of women in a just society, the education of children – and here, in these ashrams, it was all laid out for the discerning eye to see. There was an order here that was the order of Guru-ji's intellect. Reading these landscapes was like listening to a sermon, and I could now see very clearly his vision, his idea for what the country should be, then the whole world. He wanted to transform and uplift all of India into this green-gardened peace, to move it into perfection. Some parts of Singapore had the cleanliness that he wanted, but there was no city on earth that had this symmetry, this internal consistency that exactly balanced shops and meditation centres, and let you see the central temple through the precisely aligned arches of the library and the laundry. These buildings and the blue gates looked like the past, like the golden sets on the mythological television serials, but they were Guru-ji's future. This was the tomorrow that he wanted to bring to us, the satyug he wanted to create.

But the present was resisting. In Coimbatore, near the east gate of the ashram, an ancient banyan tree had tipped over one morning and crushed eleven metres of the fence, and so let in a flock of goats that ate through three gardens of roses before they could be rounded up and expelled. In Chandigarh, there was a sex scandal involving the head sadhu, three teenaged girl devotees and a local assistant police commissioner. I saw, myself, the condition of the administrative offices at Allepy, which had suffered a persistent infestation by both termites and red ants. And then there was the matter of our handling of the haughty Anand Prasad and his Dutchman, which had sparked off a power struggle in the hierarchy of Guru-ji's organization. The *Asian Age* had headlined its story 'Brutal Double Murder in Guru's Mysterious Absence', and had gone on to speculate that Anand Prasad had been eliminated by a rebel coterie of sadhus. Now we noticed hired guards at the ashrams, and even more stringent security procedures, and rumours reached us of arguments and scuffles between the leading candidates for Anand Prasad's position. The *Asian Age* had got it half-right: the sadhus were innocent of Anand Prasad's execution, but there was now indeed ferocious squabbling and infighting within the organization. None of the sadhus knew who we were, so each group thought my reappearing and disappearing search party were goondas hired by another faction, and accused each other of murder. So we pressed on in our quest, using money and intimidation impartially. We killed no one else, but in Bangalore we had to break one computer programmer's arm, so that the other programmer – his girlfriend – would give us the password for an e-mail system. And so it went on.

We found nothing. There were rumours aplenty about what had happened to Guru-ji. Some really believed that he had gone into samadhi, if only temporarily, and others said that he was dying of cancer. Everyone had something to say, but nobody could give us the smallest bit of hard information. My boys grew despondent. The travelling was hard work, and they were away from their normal money-making activities. They hadn't seen their wives and chavvis in weeks. The boys in Mumbai were complaining of police pressure each time we called them, and our shooters and operatives were getting encountered with a distressing regularity. And then Nikhil got his own smelly dose of chaos, and so I called a rest halt in Cochin. I told the boys to rest up, I told them that we would set off soon. But I was starting to think that we would never find Guru-ji, that he had escaped me after all.

After ten days in Cochin, Nikhil finally shook off his illness. He was fully ten pounds lighter, and looked exhausted. The locals had a carnival that night, and we sat on the second-floor balcony of our bungalow and watched them pass in an endless parade of tableaux and noisy re-enactments. There was an elephant, a real one, wearing a gold headdress. He was followed by a group of men wearing pink satin dresses and false breasts and garish make-up. Then there was a truck with a representation of the products and people of Kerala, including a Hindu, a Muslim, a Christian, a Jew and a blonde tourist on a beach chair. A little while later, on another truck, there was a scene out of the *Mahabharata*, with the heroes wearing shiny armour and dancing to a disco beat. My boys were out there somewhere, in the watching crowd of thousands. Nikhil sipped at a beer, and I drank pineapple juice, and we watched.

'Bhai,' he said. 'Not to question you or anything, but I am thinking of the boys. They are getting a little restless. Why are we searching so hard for this Guru-ji?'

'You *are* questioning,' I said.

'Not with any disrespect, bhai. But, you know, Bunty said you always told him that morale is important. And the boys . . .'

'Your morale is down also? You miss your wife that much?'

'I miss the children, bhai. And business . . . If we're here, we aren't concentrating on business.'

I had told them nothing, but now I could see that some explanation might be necessary. If Nikhil, who owed everything to me, was willing to say these things to my face, then a morale-boost was necessary. 'Okay,' I said. 'Listen to me carefully now. I'll only say this once.' On the truck passing below us now, there was a circle of some sort of tribals, dancing around a fire made out of a red spotlight and fluttering red ribbons. They were all wearing dark glasses. I said, 'I can't tell you much, but I can tell you this. We are searching for this Guru-ji because of business only. He fooled us. He ran a double-cross.'

'He owes us money?'

'Yes. He owes us lots of money. He betrayed us.'

'Bastard,' Nikhil said. He looked satisfied. I made sense to him now, and the world made sense to him. 'Then we must find him.'

'Tell the boys that for as long as we are here on this mission, wages are doubled. And there will be a bonus at the end.'

That cheered him up considerably. I left him on the balcony and went into my room. I turned up the air-conditioner to full and lay on the bed with the lights off. Nikhil would call his wife soon, and talk

815

to his children. I thought of calling Jojo, but I was too shaky. I had been having trouble sleeping ever since I came back to India. At first I thought it was jet-lag, displacement, the barking of the dogs and the creaking of the crickets. But then a week passed and I slept only in snatches. Three nights running I knocked myself out with sleeping pills, and woke up feeling more tired each morning. Now weeks had passed and each night was a long, hard journey, and I walked weight-lessly through the days like a ghost. Nikhil hadn't said it, but I knew he was also concerned about me. I sometimes fell asleep during the day, seated upright during a business conversation with Mumbai, or after lunch while waiting for the sweet. I woke always startled and ter-rorized by the same dream, the same horizon of ash and darkness. I had to work hard to be able to concentrate on sums of money, on problems of tactics and management.

I needed to sleep, but tonight there was certainly no sleep. Even over the roar of the air-conditioner, the music of the carnival crashed into my head. There were three songs, or maybe four, in different languages, all bouncing off each other and sometimes mingling into an unbearable throbbing loudness. Under this, there was the murmur of the crowd, which swelled up now and then into a cheery bellow. I cursed them, the over-populating bastards of India, milling about in their lakhs and crores. I wished then that they all had one head, so I could shoot them all dead at once. But no, no silence for me. How many men had I shot dead? Not as many as these. I could kill one every second for the rest of my life, and still there would be plenty left to drum on my skull with their bleating little voices, their mewling enjoyments. They were as many as the motes of silver dust in the yel-low bar of light that crossed over my head from the glass of the window. They were inescapable.

Why did the room smell of mogra? That was the attar that Salim Kaka wore, that he had on that night when I killed him for his gold, that he sprayed over his beard and chest from a green glass bottle before he went off to one of his women. I remembered the way he would tilt his head back and shake the bottle over his neck, and then the thick oily smell of the attar. And his underarms, shaved clean, and the pink of his gums and his great white teeth.

The room was sealed shut, there were no flowers near by, I knew that. And yet, there was this fragrance, dense and inescapable. I propped myself up on an elbow, took a sip of water, lay down again.

And there it was, at the back of my throat and deep in my head, this mogra. I opened my eyes.

But what was that in the corner, caught by the edge of the window's glow? A silky red sleeve, a shoulder. Yes. A beard. Long hair, down to the thick nape of the neck. It was Salim Kaka. I had shot the bastard in the back and he had come back. My hands were shaking, and a hum rose in my head higher than the din outside. It was Salim Kaka, it was him. I could see his eyes. Gaandu Pathan. 'You think I'm scared of you, bhenchod?' I said. He said nothing. But he wouldn't blink, and his contempt for me was bright and hard and unwavering.

Then he was gone, and there was only a window, and a red curtain. I got up and staggered over, I put out a hand and touched the wall with the tips of my fingers. I could see how the curtain, viewed from the bed and in this uncertain light, might have twisted and transformed into an arm. But I had seen his face, those paan-stained lips, and I had seen those deep collarbones. Those huge hands.

No, no, no. You are going crazy, Ganesh Gaitonde. It is lack of sleep and exhaustion that has made you weak, that has reduced you to madness. I pulled my shoulders back straight, and walked rapidly from one side of the room to the other. Breathe, I told myself. I sat cross-legged on the ground, at the foot of the bed, and practised the breathing that Guru-ji had taught me. I let the anxiety flow out with each exhalation, I took in energy. Slow, slow. It was only a hallucination. Yes. But I could still smell the mogra.

He had been here, in my room. It was lunacy to believe this, but I knew it was true. Salim Kaka had been a great believer in magic himself, and he had visited a malang baba in Aurangabad every two or three months. The malang baba had given him a red taveez to wear around his neck, and a blue one for his right arm, all to protect him from knife and gun. But Salim Kaka had fallen to my bullets, and I had stolen his gold, and now I was madder than Mathu. I knew myself to be deranged, and yet I knew Salim Kaka had visited me. Maybe the malang baba had sent him back, to make that doglike leer at me.

We left the next day, for Chennai. As the plane took off over the low green hills, the business-class cabin reeked sweetly of Salim Kaka. He was coming with me, wherever I went. Now that Guru-ji had abandoned me, the malang baba could work his spells on me. He could send Salim Kaka thousands of feet up into the air, and across the ocean. I tried to ignore the smell, and concentrate on my planning. For a while I had thought that our disruption of Guru-ji's ashrams and their functioning would bring him out of hiding, that he would emerge to punish me and protect his people. But now, in the air, looking down on the fields far below, it became clear to me that a man who saw into the past and future, who conceived of time in yugas, who saw how the centuries whirled according to some secret plan, who had detached himself from his own desires and ego, such a man would care nothing if a mere organization fell apart, if one or two men were killed. He didn't care what I did. Whatever gestures of affection he had made towards me, he did not care for me. I was nothing to him. He flew far above the highest flight of any jet, and looked down on us as if on ants. By the time we landed, I was sure that our strategy had been a failure. But I had no alternative scheme, and so I kept quiet. We went to our safe house, we waited for nightfall, we executed our break-in at an administrative office. But we found nothing, as I expected. And Salim Kaka stayed with me, back to the house and into the dawn. I gagged on my morning milk, which under its almonds had that syrupy stink of flowers.

The boys looked dejected. They were draped over the sofas and the beds, looking bleary. Bonus or no bonus, it was hard on them to fail miserably time and time again. I was acting the cheerful leader, but my own feeling of hopelessness was bound to infect them. I knew I should be talking to them about our next operation, but my eyes were bloodshot and scratchy, and an ache had seized the left half of my head, and I just didn't have the energy. Nikhil was leaning back in his chair, his feet up on a balcony railing, leafing listlessly through an old Tamil film magazine that someone had left in the bathroom. He didn't seem very impressed by the round-faced southern starlets, or the incomprehensible advertisements with bicep-baring men. He put down the magazine on the table, and I picked it up and flipped it open at random.

Zoya looked up at me from a full-page picture. She wore white and was lit with a silvery glow that made her look very fair and completely innocent.

She must have been shooting a southern film recently. She was doing films everywhere, actually, and I could see why. She was beautiful. But, oddly enough, I didn't want her. I no longer felt that agonized twist in my stomach that she once had called forth by merely sitting still. I looked at her now and I saw that she was perfect, that she had achieved the proportion we had worked so hard towards, that balance of top and bottom, that fine play of light and dark. Even on the cheap paper of the magazine, through the blurry printing, I could see this. And I felt nothing. I didn't want her, I didn't love her or hate her. I was indifferent.

A longing for a talk with Jojo rose through my chest. I felt myself flush, and I got up. 'I have to make a phone call.' I left them all behind, and shut the door to my bedroom, and dialled Jojo. She woke from sleep, husky-voiced and bad-tempered.

'What do you want, Gaitonde?' she said. 'In the middle of the night?'

'It's eight in the morning. And I want to talk to you.'

'Talk about what, Gai-ton-de?' she said, with a little wail at the end.

I didn't really have a subject that I wanted to talk to her about, I just wanted her voice, her breath. But Jojo's mornings were just suffering until she had had her three cups of tea, and I knew that if I didn't give her a good reason for waking her up, she would slam down the phone and curse me besides. I needed to make something up. 'I am looking for a woman,' I said.

'Bastard,' she growled. 'So call me in the evening.'

'Wait, wait,' I said. 'I don't want a woman, like that. I mean we're looking for a missing woman. She stole some of our money and ran. We can't find her. For months we've been looking.'

'I know her? What's her name?'

I had to come up with a name. The Tamil magazine was lying on the table, fluttering its pages under the swirling fan. 'Sri,' I said. 'Sridevi.'

'What? Sridevi ran away with your money?'

'No, no. Not Sridevi the film star. This is another woman. With that name.'

'So why can't you find her? You watched her family?' Jojo yawned.

'She doesn't have any family. Not married, nothing. We've been everywhere she worked, but there's no sign.'

'So you are stuck, Gaitonde.'

'I am.'

'So then you turn to me.' She was very smug. 'Did you try kidnapping her boyfriend?'

'She doesn't have a boyfriend. Or even a girlfriend.'

'What kind of monster is this? No friend, boy or girl.'

'We've interrogated people she worked with. No use.'

Jojo was rattling about now, she was up and moving. I knew her routine, she was shuffling into the kitchen where the maid had put a pot of water on the gas the night before. Jojo would light the gas without opening her eyes hardly, and reach for a mug of milk that was kept ready on the top shelf of the fridge. There it was, the click of the gas-lighter. 'Okay, so you have no other information about this Sridevi. After all this searching, your entire company has found nothing.'

'Nothing.'

'I told you your employees are fools.'

'Yes, yes. Many times.'

'Give a boy a ghoda, doesn't make him smart. Just makes him a chutiya with a gun.'

'Saali, this is how you help? Get back to Sridevi.'

'Okay.' She was leaning on the counter, I knew, waiting for the water to boil. She was cracking elaichis now, three of them. 'What is her native place?'

'She doesn't have one.'

'Everyone has a native place.'

'Hers is gone. It's in Pakistan. But why?'

'Your brain is also turning into falooda, Gaitonde. People are fools, you know that. They all want to go home. They always do it, even when they know they shouldn't.'

This was true. Keep an eye on a man's village, and sooner or later you got him. Plant an informant in his locality, and one day you could put a round in the back of his head. The police did this all the time, and I had done this. Jojo was right, human beings were stupid, they circled round and around and finally came back to where they started, as if pulled back by the steady tug of an inescapable cord. But what if your home was gone, if there was nowhere to go to? Where would you go? 'I'll think about it,' I said. 'That's not a bad idea. It's a possibility.'

'Fine,' she said. 'You think about it. Now let me drink my chai in peace.'

But I didn't let her go, not yet. I kept her on the phone and talked to her about her production troubles, and her bai who had an alcoholic husband, and the increasing pollution in the city. 'I'm hanging up,' I finally said a full half-hour later, by which time she had finished her chai and was ready to bathe and work. I was feeling more settled, now that I had a direction. I called Nikhil in, and we got to work. We had accumulated papers and documents during our raids, and had seized two laptops. We had information. There was too much of it, actually, two suitcases full and whatever else was on the computers. I explained to Nikhil, and instructed him, and we began to sift through everything. The problem, of course, was that we didn't know what we were looking for. 'Home,' I told Nikhil, 'any place where he would go home to.' He looked puzzled, but only as much as I was myself. Where would a man like Guru-ji go? Chandigarh? But we had already been there, and had found nothing. So where would he go? And for that matter, where would I go, or Jojo? Where do you go when home has become impossible? I had no answers, but we kept looking. It took us five days of searching, and then Nikhil found it.

In Guru-ji's personal account ledgers for the current year and the year before, there were entries for 'Bekanur Farm'. Eighty-four thousand and one lakh thirty-four thousand, on the credit side. We didn't have the records for the five years before that, but there was another entry in the one prior year we could find, for a cheque written – again on Guru-ji's personal account – for a 'Tractor for Bekanur Farm'. And there was a letter on one of the computers, from the current year, to the Punjab State Electricity Board about arrears for Bekanur Farm. This letter was signed by none other than Anand Prasad, our recent sadhu friend. What was a high-up in the organization, a supremo like Anand Prasad, doing writing to PSEB about a matter of two lakhs and some odd thousand? What was this farm anyway? We searched all the public literature available about Guru-ji, and found nothing. There was no mention of a farm fifty miles south of Amritsar, not a word about any farm at all. Certainly he had never said anything to me about owning a farm. There was of course his interest in rural development, in agricultural progress, but that was handled by another sub-division altogether. Their agricultural department had a separate organizational structure, a separate chain of command and separate bank accounts. This Bekanur was something else altogether, it was handled by Guru-ji himself and his very closest associates. And it was kept, as much as possible, a secret.

We went to take a look at this farm. I told the boys that this was our last leg on this journey, that whether we found success or not, we would call a halt to the mission afterwards. They were cheered and relieved, and we landed in Amritsar energized and ready to go. We followed our usual procedure and proceeded to the prearranged safe house in two groups, had a late breakfast, and collected our car and were ready to go. The morning was bright and hot, and I was dozy in the front seat of the car. Nikhil was driving. Behind us, the boys were arguing about the gold in the Golden Temple, how much exactly there was and what it was worth. Jatti, who was a Punjabi but who had only been to Punjab once before, was telling them with authority that the gold was worth arabs, not crores. The others were scoffing, and Chandar wanted to go to Jallianwalla Baug. 'Since we're here anyway,' he said.

We're not tourists, I wanted to tell him, but it would have taken too much energy to make the words emerge from my half-sleep. Besides, I was being a bit of a tourist myself. I found myself entertained by the handsome swagger of these Punjabis, their aggressive stares, and their loud voices. There was a sardar outside a garage that was on our left now, his hair piled up into a big uncovered knot on the top of his head, talking into a mobile phone. He raised his kurta to scratch at his navel as we passed, revealing a full and hairy belly. He was smiling. Maybe that was his garage, and the big pink-and-green house behind it was his, complete with satellite dish and Toyota in the driveway and a watchman with a rifle. Amritsar was a dingy little provincial town, but there was money here, and a lot of guns. A police jeep overtook us, and the three constables in the back all cradled jhadoos in their laps, with double magazines taped together. I hadn't seen so many automatic weapons on the street, on any street, not ever. In my car there was the smell of mogra. I closed my eyes, and opened them to find us racing through sarson fields, behind a truck brimming with steel rods. There were tigers painted on its back panels, and a goddess in the middle.

'We're almost there, bhai,' Nikhil said.

He turned off to the left, down an embankment. The road narrowed now, and we bumped and swayed over a flowing canal. 'We're in the proper dehat now,' Chandar muttered. 'Look at the dehatis.' There were two men walking in the middle of the road, leading a bullock. Nikhil honked, and very slowly they moved aside to let us squeeze past. They bent a little to stare into the car as we went by. Villagers all right, and prosperous ones. The land here was lush and ripe, and I could hear a water-pump thumping not far away. We drove on. We had to ask for directions once, at a fork in the road, from a young couple on a motorcycle. The wife kept her red dupatta tight on her head by biting down on one end of it, but I could see she was a fine, strapping piece. The boys thought so too, I could tell from the strained, attentive silence behind me. The husband was stringy and unkempt and altogether unimpressive, but his directions were good. We got to Guru-ji's farm just after two.

There was no steel fence around these fields, and no gates. Just green swathes of wheat, and well-kept bunds lined with trees. A house glimmered white through an orchard. 'Mango,' said Jatti as we neared the orderly rows. The road was smooth now, unfinished gravel that crunched under the tires. A peacock called, and I saw a hint of its sudden rush through the trees. Then we turned around a thick, ancient neem, and we were at the house.

It was a single-storey building, sprawling and wide. There were no windows along the front wall, which was broken only by a tall archway that led into a small open veranda. The doors in the archway were green and massive and heavy, with a smaller portal let into the one on the left, only wide enough to let a single man through. This was open, and Nikhil rattled the lock-chain hanging next to it. 'Arre,' he called. 'Koi hai?'

But the only reply came from the pigeons walking along the rafters in the archway. I leant in through the door. A cow and her calf munched happily in a stall to the left. Straight ahead, four brick steps led to a landing, which faced a single room. I could see an old-fashioned takath and two chairs, and a big round clock. The air was fresh and heavy with that old smell of cow-dung and bhoosa. The plaster on the walls facing the landing was cracked, and the bricks in the veranda were worn smooth. This was an old house, old and also old-fashioned. Near the cow-stall, water dripped from a hand-pump and tapped steadily on the iron drain-cover below.

'Are you sure we're in the right place?' I said to Nikhil.

He pointed to the far end of the landing. Behind a pillar, a ramp went up the stairs, just wide enough for a wheelchair. So yes, this was maybe Guru-ji's place, but it was nothing like anything else that he had built, that we had seen. What was it, exactly? Nikhil rattled the chain again.

A blast from the car horn made us jump. Jatti was standing next to the car, grinning. He sent up a series of blaring honks, and I shouted at him. 'Enough, maderchod,' I said, and he stopped with a hurt look on his face. The quiet was astonishing, after that din, and the pigeons fluttered nervously in the veranda. Then we heard a shuffle, and a man turned the corner of the building.

He was old, at least seventy, this I could tell straightaway from his stiff-kneed gait. When he came closer I realized he was eighty, if anything. He was wearing baggy white pyjamas, a tattered orange sweater and a grey scarf wrapped tight up to his ears. He peered at us through thick, black-rimmed glasses. There was a crack straight through the middle of the left lens.

'Hain?' he said.

'Namaskar,' Nikhil said. 'Namaste. Are you the malik of the house?'

That was obvious flattery, this budhau was far from being the owner of anything. But the old man took it in with a smile. 'No, no,' he said. 'I am the manager.'

'The manager,' Nikhil said, mocking the man's Punjabi – 'munay-jer' – but only gently. 'Yes. Can we have some water? We've driven all the way from Amritsar.'

He gave us steaming hot chai. He took us inside, seated us in the room next to the veranda, and emerged fifteen minutes later with brass tumblers and a big, blackened pot. He poured us the chai, half a glass each, and only then asked us who we were. Nikhil gave him some story about how we were businessmen from Delhi, and how we were looking for good farmland to purchase. And that someone on the main road had told us about this mango orchard, and the farm, so we had come to take a look. And, by the way, who is the owner of this fine property?

'Saab comes from Delhi,' the man said.

'And his name?'

'My name is Jagat Narain.'

'Yes, Jagat Narain. You make good chai.' Nikhil took a long slurping gulp, and looked wholly appreciative. 'And Saab's name is?'

'Which Saab?'

This was going to take a long time. I got up and edged out of the door. At the side of the landing there was a door leading into a dark passageway. I groped through the hall, and came out on the other side into a large brick-lined courtyard. There was a tulsi bush at the exact centre, and rooms along all four sides. I walked along the periphery, pushing doors open. They creaked open to reveal bare floors, old wooden cupboards, simple shelves built into whitewashed walls, saggy charpais covered with rough blankets. In one room there was a black table-fan on a wooden desk, and bottles of blue and red ink and a green fountain pen. I walked on. Along one entire side of this inner square, there was a large hall, open to the courtyard. The floor was covered with chatais, and there was a row of round pillows against the far wall. In little alcoves, there were pictures of Ram and Sita, and Hanuman, and a bespectacled, grandfatherly man in a turban. I stooped closer to this last black-and-white photo, and saw a clear resemblance to Guru-ji. Who was he, Guru-ji's father or grandfather? An uncle?

I turned to the right, to the kitchen and three other rooms. A sparrow walked along the edge of the little platform where the tulsi grew, and the sun came into my eyes. The kitchen was dark, hung with brass utensils, and had two blackened chulahs on the floor. No stoves, no gas range. There were two more rooms with beds, and a storeroom that contained only three empty steel trunks. I came back out into the sunlight. I was shivering a little, and my mouth was dry. What was this place? In a corner behind the kitchen there was another hand-pump, the bricks beneath it smeared wet. I put my weight on the handle and pumped, and with a couple of tinny creaks a shiny rope of water dropped and splattered. I drank, leaning down into the flow. The water was chilled and pure.

Nikhil came through the passageway now, feeling his way with a hand on the wall.

'There's nothing back here,' I told him. 'Empty rooms, everything is old. This place barely has electricity.'

'But it was only built twelve years ago, bhai.' He was uneasy and excited too. 'His saab lives in Delhi, goes by the name of Mrityunjay Singh. They bought the farm at the height of the Punjab troubles, got it cheap. Then they broke down the perfectly good house that was already here, dug up even the foundations. Then some years later they built this thing. This saab visits maybe once a year. I asked about the ramp outside. He said that was for a friend of Saab's who comes in a wheelchair, who has come here maybe two, three times. He doesn't know the wheelchair-wallah's name, everyone just calls him Baba-ji.'

So Guru-ji had built this house, and then visited it only three times in more than a decade. Why this house, why here? It must have cost more to make it look old than just to build a new and modern house.

Nikhil pumped some water, drank and wiped his mouth. 'That tastes very good,' he said. 'The manager said this Baba-ji liked to spend time on the roof. The manager's gone to get the keys, he'll show it to us.'

Jagat Narain came into the courtyard, followed by the boys. He was rattling an iron ring hung with large keys. He led us – slowly – up a staircase that angled up from a corner of the courtyard, a staircase also equipped with a ramp. It took him five minutes to find the right key, and then he scraped with it at the door. I stood, feeling my toes on the edge of a stair, taken back suddenly to childhood, to a holiday morning and running up to the roof with a new kite crisp under my fingers. 'Maderchod,' I said. 'Nikhil, take the keys.'

But then the ancient bastard managed to get the lock open. We scattered out into the bright sunlight. There was one room on the roof, again with the sparse furnishings and the bare shelves. The flat roof went all around the courtyard, with no railing at the inner edge. I walked around to the other side, trying to get my mind to grasp something that endlessly fell just beyond its reach. It was like I had forgotten something I had just known. I could hear Nikhil talking to the manager on the other side of the courtyard.

'We have one thousand one hundred and eleven acres,' Jagat Narain said. 'All the way to the main road and beyond it. We go all the way to the fence.'

'What fence?'

'It's the border fence, boss,' Jatti said.

'A very long fence,' Jagat Narain said, nodding. He made a big gesture with both his arms, to take in the entire horizon.

Jatti explained the fence to Nikhil, with proprietary Punjabi pride. It was thousands of kilometres long, it went all the way from Rajasthan to Punjab and up beyond, into Jammu. Jatti had seen it on his last and only visit to Punjab, at Wagah. It was a double fence, much taller than a man and electrified. There were bells hung on it, to warn of infiltrators. Jatti's chacha had seen a Pakistani infiltrator who had been shot as he tried to cross one night. The machine-gun bullet had taken his face off. Jatti made a clawing motion in front of his face. 'Do you understand?' he said. 'The bastard had no face left.'

I leaned on the parapet, trying to see this deadly fence. But there was only a soft white haze beyond the arc of the earth, far on the other side of the trees. Jagat Narain lumbered over to stand beside me. 'Baba-ji looks also.'

'Looks at what?'

'Out there. He likes to sit here in the evenings. Watch the sun going down.'

What did Guru-ji see when he looked? It was pretty enough, even now. At sunset it must be beautiful. But there were beautiful sunsets elsewhere. Why come out here, to the middle of nowhere, and spend good money on all this land, and on an old house that was new? I half-shut my eyes and tried to see as he did. Here was an endless blur of green, the smell of earth, the sound of running water, and I saw the house of my childhood, and for a moment I was happy. My eyes snapped open, and I found that I was smiling.

Why?

But there was no time to ponder this mystery: a man was pedalling his bicycle furiously up the road towards us. As he came closer I saw that he was young, thirty maybe, and he was tall. 'Who is this?' I said to Jagat Narain. The bicycle man was glaring up at me as he pumped away, and he was not happy.

'That's only Kirpal Singh. He was at the Tupa Nahar fields today. We are spraying there for Karnal Bunt.'

Kirpal Singh was now at the front of the house. He flung down his bike, and a few moments later we heard him pounding up the stairs. He came out on to the roof already shouting, 'Jagate! Who are these people?' Nikhil began his looking-for-farmland-to-buy story, but Kirpal Singh wasn't having any of it. 'Saab,' he said, his chest heaving, 'you must leave. Nobody can come on to this farm without permission from our saab.' He gave Jagat Narain a bitter look.

'They are from Delhi also,' Jagat Narain said, as if that explained everything.

Close up, this Kirpal Singh was a big, rough-cut ruffian, with hair that spiked straight up into a big bush, and he gestured with dirty, cracked hands at least double the size of mine. He was wearing a worn grey Pathani suit, and despite the layers of grime on him, he had the bearing of a policeman, or a jawan.

'Listen, my friend,' Nikhil said. 'Calm down. Call your saab on the phone and we'll talk to him.'

'There is no phone here, saab.' He was very direct and firm and aggressive, under his thin politeness. 'Now you go.'

'I have a phone. I have a good signal.' Nikhil held up his handy. 'See? We can talk to him. What is his number?'

'The farm is not for sale. You go now.'

Kirpal Singh was crouched a little now, his shoulders hunched up. He was ready for a fight. I gave Nikhil the nod. 'Fine, yaar, fine,' he said. 'We will go. No problem. Thank you for the chai. Here is my number, give it to your saab if he's interested.'

He offered a card, and held it up until Kirpal Singh reluctantly took it. Then we filed down the stairs. I could feel the big lout looming behind me, breathing heavily. He was agitated, but about what? Why was he so nervous? He followed us all the way out, through the passageway and into the front veranda, and through the gate. Nikhil started the car, turned it around, and I waited, standing close to the wall. To my right, Kirpal Singh's bicycle lay on the ground, where he had thrown it. A large square can of pesticide was tied to the carrier with rope. There was a skull and crossbones on the can, in red. And a red rat, dead, upside down with his tail curled over him. 'They eat the crops?' I said to Kirpal Singh. 'The rats?'

He looked relieved, now that the boys were getting into the car. 'Yes, saab.' He was trying to make up for his rudeness. 'Not only the wheat. They eat everything. Plants, rubber. The cables for electricity also, they eat the plastic from them. Very hard to stop them.'

'Kill them all,' I said, and he finally smiled. I got into the car and we drove away.

Nikhil was looking into the rear-view mirror. 'What do you think, bhai?'

'There's something there.'

'Yes. If it was just a farmhouse, that bastard wouldn't be threatening to bite us like that.'

We'd given the farmhouse a cursory going-over, and found nothing. Was it worth going back, and worth dealing with Kirpal Singh, to search it thoroughly? I felt strangely dispirited. The road rolled on, and maybe it was better to take it all the way back to Amritsar, and then catch a plane to Delhi and on to Bangkok, and go back to my life. But that was unbearable. I had no life to go back to, not until I had found Guru-ji. Even now, even after all my rage at him, all I wanted was to sit at his feet again. I knew this. I might curse him and call him a fraud, and say that I was done with him, but what I really wanted was to feel his hand cupping my head, and the blessing of his voice. I had questions, yes. I wanted to ask him why he had left, why Gaston and Pascal had died, what he had had us transport for him, what he was doing, what his plan was. The meaning of my life was somehow hidden in these questions. But if he refused to give one single answer, I would accept that, as long as he came back to me. As long as he didn't leave me like this, just me, without him, without guidance and care. I had to find him. But Guru-ji was too advanced for me, too realized. With all my lifetime's worth of learned lessons, and my cunning, I would never find him. I could let it go, and ride on, and away. But why was I afraid? If I had learnt anything from my life, it was to trust my fear. And yet: I was so tired. The road raised itself above the fields, and the deep waves of green came one after another. I could sleep. The power cables swept gently up, down. They came towards me, carrying diamonds of light from the dropping sun. The rats ate them. The rats ate cables.

'Stop,' I said.

'Bhai?'

The car was halted now, near the canal. Above the gurgling of the water, I could hear a very soft wind as it stirred slow waves through the bending stalks of wheat. I twisted in my seat and looked back down the road, at the electricity posts that disappeared into the distance. There was a string of them that angled off from this road towards Guru-ji's farmhouse, that marched through the fields and past the mango orchard. On the roof, yes, on the roof of the house there was a pole above that single room, a pole at which three power lines terminated. If the house was so old, with its creaky table-fans, why did it need so much power? I hadn't seen any power cables anywhere in the interior of the house, so what were those rats eating?

I turned to Nikhil, and told him all this. 'Yes, bhai,' he said. 'But maybe they need the electricity for irrigation. Water pumps and all that, you know.'

Maybe. Maybe. But there was this new house which only looked old. 'Turn around,' I said. 'Let's go back.'

So we went skimming back past the mango orchard, as evening came on. Kirpal Singh came out to meet us, this time. He stood in the middle of the road, legs apart. Nikhil stopped the car, and I got out. I heard the other doors clicking open behind me. 'Arre,' I said, 'did you find my spectacles? Black ones.'

'No,' he said. 'No spectacles.'

'Let's look,' I said. 'They may be on the roof.'

Kirpal Singh was confused. He didn't want us back here, but he didn't like the idea that something of mine was maybe in the house he was guarding. He was a nice brute. I took him by the arm. 'I can't see without my glasses, yaar. I'm half-blind.' I turned him back towards the gate. 'Just let's take a look.'

He was stupid, but he was fast. Chandar had come up on his right, and our timing was exact. We had done this so many times in the past weeks that we had practised it to perfection. I would talk to the mark, and distract him just enough so that Chandar could lay his iron-loaded leather cosh along the back of the head. But Kirpal Singh anticipated it, and flinched away from me and turned, so that the blow took him on the kanpatti and half-tore his right ear off. He fought like a demon then. There were five of us on him, and he took us down and gave us pain. He broke three of Chandar's fingers, knocked Nikhil back and almost out with a single punch that cracked his nose. Jatti stayed on the ground, hacking and coughing and clutching his neck. We fought him. I found myself sitting on the road, empty of breath and hurting in the abdomen, scrambling back away from the heaving welter of bodies. I got my pistol out, but couldn't get a clear shot. Then Kirpal Singh was coming at me. I had time for one squeeze of the trigger, and that knocked his collarbone and twisted his lunge to the side. He still got his right hand on me, though, and I felt his weight on me and his mouth was gaping, terrible and crimson. I felt the shots hit his body, the impact through the muscles, and he was lying on me.

They lifted him off, and I staggered to my feet. 'How many shots?' I said.

Jatti was wheezing, his face wet with tears. 'That gaandu was a commando or something.'

'Four shots, bhai,' Nikhil said. His white shirt was stained all the way to the waist with blood from his nose.

Four was a lot of shots, but it was a big farm. Maybe nobody had heard us. Maybe nobody would pay attention. 'Jatti,' I snarled, 'get into the house and keep the old man quiet.'

'Bhenchod,' Jatti said, his eyes going wide. He ran to the house.

The rest of us took hold of Kirpal Singh and dragged him through the gate. He weighed on all of us, weakened as we were by our sudden injuries. I could hear the shudder in Chandar's breathing as each step jarred his broken bones.

'Hold on, beta,' I told him. 'We'll be out of here soon.' We threw the body down by the cowshed. I told Chandar to kick some gravel over the blood on the road, and keep a lookout from the gate. Then the rest of us began our search of the house. Jatti had found Jagat Narain in the courtyard, blithely washing dishes next to the pump. He must have heard the shots, but apparently they didn't make much of an impression. We locked him inside one of the empty rooms, and told him to go to sleep. Then we looked.

I told the boys that we had to follow the power. From the roof, from the pole, we traced the in-wall connections that went down to the junction box on the ground floor. There was a separate small room at the back of the house that contained this junction box, with two steel locks on the door. We had to extract Jagat Narain from his cell, get him to give us the keys for the locks. By now he had understood that he ought to be scared. He was co-operative, and made no arguments, but his hands were shaking, and he whispered, 'Where's Barjinder? Don't leave Barjinder behind.'

'Who is Barjinder, kaka?' Nikhil said, patting him on the shoulder. 'What are you going on about?'

Jagat Narain shook his head. 'We have to get to Amritsar,' he said. 'Our house is burnt. We have to get to Amritsar.' He was still saying it when Nikhil shut the door on him.

I was shaking a little myself when we emerged again into the twilight, thunderous with calling birds. I thought, I am wound up from the excitement of the chase. I knew I was on to something, and I was even more sure when we opened this back room and saw the junction boxes and the circuit breakers and the meters. All the technology was up to date and beyond, clean and shining and working flawlessly. The numbers on the meters were moving, slowly but steadily, no doubt of that. Something was sucking up electricity.

We followed the cables. There had been an attempt to disguise the paths that they followed under the plaster and through the brick, so we had to arm ourselves with picks and shovels. We dug. There was one circuit that fed the house, but there were two others that looped off outside, two feet under the surface. It was hard, slow work, chipping at the packed soil under the gravel. We crawled slowly into the shadows under the mango trees. Nikhil went back to the house and

831

came out with two Petromax lanterns, and we went forward in that dancing light. It was full night when we found the underground complex. There was an empty square in the middle of the grove, a shape that you only saw as an absence of trees. It was very innocent, unless you traced the PVC-sleeved cable that led to a T-junction and then went straight down. We padded about in circles. Jatti found a ventilator first, guided by the small hiss of air. Then, under an adjacent patch of thatch, a small metal panel painted in camouflage brown and dull green. Nikhil put his ear to it.

'The air-conditioning unit is under here,' he said.

I put a hand down, and the hum came into my shoulder. Now we knew we were right. The boys scraped at the ground, clawed at the grass, calling for the lanterns. I went out beyond the light, unmindful of the sting in my knees as I went over roots and rocks. The secret was underneath, I could feel it close. The gold was close. I had searched it out always, the prize, the advantage. And so I found it.

There was a length of the same metal as the air-conditioning panel. It lay between two old trees, making a slight rise in the earth. There was a thin covering of leaves and twigs, and under it the riveted steel. 'Here,' I shouted. 'Here.'

We cleared off the top of it, and now in the lamplight I could see that it was a trapdoor. Five feet by five, with slots let into one side to allow for lifting. Jatti caught hold and gave it an experimental tug. 'Locked,' he said, pointing at a keyhole between the handles.

'Look on the dead chutiya,' I said.

I was shooting deadly straight that night, no misses. They found the key on a dirty nada around Kirpal Singh's neck. It was a big, heavy, three-inch slab of steel, one of those computerized keys, now stained with blood. But it turned effortlessly in the lock, and we were in. A ladder angled down. A light-switch conveniently positioned next to the door provided clean, even, blue-white illumination. There were three large rooms, decreasing in size. The first two were efficiently filled with bookshelves, filing cabinets and computer tables. But the shelves were empty, and there were no files, and no computers. The extension cords were still in place, though, and there was a mess of other computer cables behind the desks. On the white surface of the desks, we could see faint outlines where the computers had rested. Nikhil ran his finger around the brown outline of the bottom of a cup on one of the keyboard trays, where someone had put down his chai.

There was one very large printer that sat in a corner of the second room, and that was all the equipment that they had left behind.

The third room was a storage space, now completely empty. A wire rubbish bin held only the wrappers from two reams of computer paper. Jatti went down the room, opening cupboards. He stopped at the last one. 'Bhai.'

There was a steel trunk on the bottom shelf, not one of those tinny things that you can buy in any bazaar, but a sleek silver cube of foreign make. You could tell that from the locks alone, which were built into the shape of the trunk itself. 'Bring it out,' I said.

It was heavy. It took two of them to drag it out into the central room. 'That key was the only one on the commando, bhai,' Nikhil said.

So Jatti got out his ghoda, leant close to the first lock and squeezed one off. There was a whine that sped around the room and went by my head, and we all dropped, cursing. 'Maderchod,' I said. 'Everyone all right?'

They nodded. But there was a hole in the printer. And only a small dimple in the lock on the trunk.

Our blood was up now. We looked at each other, and then at the shiny, plump curves of the trunk. 'Get me a rod,' I said, 'or something.'

It took us forty minutes of hacking at the locks with picks and shovels to open a crack in the trunk, to get it to reveal the seam that ran around its circumference. Then we inserted two crowbars into the split and heaved in opposite directions. It flew open finally with a shriek of tortured metal, and all of us fell to the floor. And then we were silent.

The trunk was three-quarters full, and what it contained was dollars. I reached out – and I noticed that my hand was skinned and bleeding and trembling – and picked up one of the little stacks, wrapped around with a paper band. The denomination was hundreds.

'How much, bhai?' Nikhil said.

'A lot.'

I moved the boys fast, then. We took the trunk, closed the trapdoor, went back to the house. I had everyone wash under the pump in the courtyard before we went out to the car. We were going to be on the road, near the border, early in the morning, and if we were stopped I didn't want to get into a shootout because of a blood-stained shirt.

There wasn't much we could do about Chandar's hand, which was swollen into a football. He had a fever now, besides. So we wrapped him up in a blanket and put him on the back seat. Then we were ready to go. But not quite yet. There was one more item of business, and we all knew it. Jatti was the one who finally spoke.

'What about the old man, bhai?'

Yes, the old man. He was senile, he was half-mad, but he had seen our faces. There was a dead body in the house, and the old man could perhaps connect us to it. I had taught the boys what needed to be done in such situations. 'I'll do it,' I said. I went back in, past the snuffling of the cow, through the corridor – towards the slow tapping of water – and into the courtyard. I opened a door, and Jagat Narain was sitting on a bed, his hands resting on his thighs, watching. He was waiting for me.

'Come,' I said. 'We're leaving now. You can come out.'

He didn't move. I went in, took him by the arm, and he stood up easily enough. I walked him out, and as we stepped over the high sill, he whispered, 'What time is it?'

'It's going to be five.'

'Morning or evening?'

Now, under the starlight, I could see his big thatch of white hair, and his high forehead. In his cracked lens, there was my face, broken in half. 'Morning,' I said, overcome by a sudden tenderness for the helplessness of old age. He didn't know whether it was day or night, where he was or where he was going. It was all the same to him. 'Look, there is the moon.'

He raised his face and blundered away from me, his arms up. 'Yes,' he said, pointing with both hands.

There was a small sliver of moon, a piece of an arc, rising or setting – I didn't know. I took a step back, raised my ghoda, levelled it and fired. The flash filled my eyes, and then he was lying on the brick, his hands extended. I leaned over him, and gave him another in the head.

And then I ran. I don't know why, but I ran all the way to the car, and jumped in, and Nikhil didn't need to be instructed. He turned the wheel, and we were moving. But even through the spray of gravel, and over the sudden reek of exhaust, the smell of mogra followed me all the way to the canal. We raced through the dawn, and reached Amritsar safely. We paused only for a short visit to a doctor, and then I split up the team and sent them on their various ways. I understood well that this was the end of our mission. We had not found Guru-ji, but what we had found was something finally valuable enough to attract a lot of attention. There were, in that trunk, exactly nine hundred and eighty-four thousand, three hundred and twenty-two dollars. The boys called it a million, but the true amount was a little less. So Nikhil and Jatti caught a train to Delhi, and Chandar a plane to Bhopal, and that evening I flew to Bombay with the money. There was a car waiting for me at the airport, and a new safe house ready in Juhu. But I wasn't yet safe when my satellite phone began to ring. We were ploughing through traffic on the highway when I heard the ring, muffled but distinctive. It was my Guru-ji phone, my latest encrypted satellite one. I shouted at the driver to pull off to the side, hit the back of his head when he was slow to batter his way across the weaving streams of cars, and then I dragged him out to open the boot. I knew exactly where the phone was, in the outside pocket of my shoulder bag, and then I had it out and up to my ear.

'Hello?'

'You took my money.'

'Yes.' Yes, it was Guru-ji. Yes, it was that familiar voice, that chesty, resonating boom which was so reassuring, so comforting. Yes, there was the precise enunciation of every word, especially the last. Finally, after all this searching, I had found Guru-ji, I had brought him back to me. 'Where are you?'

'Why did you take the money, Ganesh?'

'Why did you go away?'

'I told you that we would never see each other again.'

'But not that you would vanish.'

'Ganesh,' he sighed. 'Ganesh. After all this time you haven't understood that fundamental teaching I tried to give you. We are all lost to each other already. To cling in love is to betray love itself.'

'Big words,' I said. 'Big-big words.' There I was, Ganesh Gaitonde, standing on the side of the highway, within sight of hundreds of men and women as they went to home and work, stamping my feet. There were passing gaggles of blue-skirted schoolgirls who could see the tears I was wiping from my eyes. But I didn't care. 'I was calling you, and there was no reply,' I said. 'But it was only when you lost some dollars that you cared to call me.'

'It's not the dollars, Ganesh,' Guru-ji said. 'It's the inconvenience. I am in the middle of a big project. I need the cash to make certain payments. I don't care about money, but the rest of the world wants hard currency.'

'What is this project?'

'I will tell you that it is a big project, Ganesh.'

'Did you make me a part of it?'

'Everyone has a part in it.'

'Don't play games with me. Answer me. Answer me.' I fought for control over myself, lowered my voice. 'You had us bring in some kind of nuclear material. Don't tell me you didn't. My men died.'

He sighed. 'Yes, Ganesh. That is true enough.'

'What are you going to do with it?' I said. He was silent. 'Tell me, and I'll give your money back.'

'Will you, Ganesh? Will you really if I tell you the purpose?'

'Yes,' I said. 'I will.'

'I wonder if you will have the courage. But why do you ask me, Ganesh? I think that perhaps you already know.'

I felt a stab of outrage, that this old man was questioning my courage. Me, who had risked so much for him. But I stopped myself, I said nothing. For what would I not have courage? I turned, and looked at the untidy roofs of a basti stretching away below the raised road, and the clustered buildings beyond. This man had first come to me wanting weapons. He was preparing for war. I wasn't afraid of battles, I had thrown myself into combat all my life. But if his war came, it would be a big one, it would burn through every corner of India. It would be painful, he had said to me, but afterwards we will be better. We will find peace. And then I remembered standing on the roof of the house he had built close to the border, and seeing a sea of green, and glimpsing – for only a moment – a perfect happiness, everything fresh and completely new and unstained, and me, I was young again and full of hope, and the world was again newborn and vast, and I was smiling.

And in that moment, I knew.

I heard myself say, against the living roar of the city, 'You want a bigger war.'

'Very good, Ganesh. A war bigger than the one you thought we were getting ready for.'

'You built . . . a bomb?'

'Don't ask me such questions, Ganesh. I can't answer those. I told you, you know already. What would I do with such a thing?'

'Set it off. In a city somewhere. In Mumbai.'

'And who would be held responsible?'

'You would make sure it was some Muslim organization.'

'Very good. And then what?'

Then? Bloodshed. Murder everywhere. If there was tension on the border, maybe some kind of retaliation. Maybe even if there wasn't tension, war would come, a real war, a war that would eat millions, a war unlike anything we had ever heard of. But these were only words. I tried to imagine it, but I couldn't. I could only feel a hole inside myself, an emptiness so deep that it could swallow Mumbai, the country, everything.

'Listen,' I said. 'You shouldn't do it.'

'Why not?' he said. 'Are you afraid of dying? You've been so close to death so many times, you can't be afraid of it. And you know you will die, if not today, then tomorrow. You have dug holes for so many, someone will dig a hole for you. You told me that, once.'

'I don't care about my own death.'

'But you care about the death of many? A few thousand, or a few million? Why, Ganesh? You have killed a few hundred in your life, at least. What does it matter, a few more?'

I didn't have an answer for him. I didn't know why it mattered, but it did. I imagined this crawling ants' nest of a city eaten by fire, all of it crumpled and black and twisting and finally gone. They led miserable, small lives, these scuttling millions. After they were gone, after the great cleansing wind that would take not only this city but every other one, there would be space for a new start. From all the sermons I had listened to, from fragments of lessons and from wisps of Sanskrit, came this certain knowledge: this is what Guru-ji wanted, this complete erasure of everything I knew. And I was scared. I couldn't speak.

He understood this. 'You are weak, Ganesh,' he said. 'Despite my best efforts you lack strength. You are wilful and violent, but all that is only a thin covering for your frailty. Underneath you are as sentimental as a woman. But it's not your fault. This is the general condition of the human race in this Kaliyug, Ganesh. All these United Nations, these dreamy-eyed do-gooders who rush to stop conflicts, they don't understand that some wars must be fought, that killing must happen. They think they have stopped war, but all they ensure is a state of constant, smouldering war. Look at India and Pakistan, bleeding each other for more than fifty years. Instead of a final, glorious battle, we have a long, filthy mess. These well-meaning idiots always chatter on about the progress of the human race, but they don't understand that progress cannot occur without destruction. Every golden age must be preceded by an apocalypse. It has always been so, and it will be so again. But now we have become too cowardly to let time move on. We stop up its wheels, we clog it up with our fears. Think of it, Ganesh. For more than fifty years we have put off the fight on our borders, and suffered small humiliations and small bloodshed every day. We have been dishonoured and disgraced, and have become used to living with this shame. We have become a whole race of quailing Arjuns fleeing from what we know to be our duty. But enough. We will fight. The battle is necessary.'

'But everything will be finished,' I said, in a child's quavering voice. 'Everything.'

'Exactly so. Every great religious tradition predicts this burning, Ganesh. We all know it's coming.'

'Why? But why?'

'You told me yourself, when you were making that film. What was it called?'

'*International Dhamaka*.'

He gurgled with glee again. 'Yes, *Dhamaka*. You told me that every story needed a climax, and a big story needed a big climax. Read the signs in this world, the signs all over this life we lead, and see what it needs. It wants an ending, Ganesh. It needs a close, so it can start over again. You're only scared because you're seeing it from the inside. Step outside and take a look, and you will see how it cannot end any other way.'

'I'll stop you.'

'How, Ganesh? I've learnt security from you. And you have taught me well. You found me once, long ago, because my people were careless. But you won't find me again. You haven't found me after all these months of searching. You can't do anything. Nobody can do anything. Time will move on. The inevitable will come. You took my money, and all you did was delay what must happen, what has to happen. That is all.'

' 'So what do you want from me, then?'

'Don't fight me. Don't go against the mechanism of history. Give me back my money.'

'No. I won't be part of this.'

'You are already a part of it, Ganesh. You made it possible, you ran part of it, and whatever you do now, you will help it to happen. Whether you act or don't act, the war will come, the blood will flow. You can't stop it. You can't stop yourself, Ganesh.'

'I will tell . . . I will tell the authorities.'

'And they will believe you, Ganesh? A gangster who has told a hundred lies to them, killed a thousand men?'

'I'll kill more of your sadhus.'

'They all must die some day. What difference is a few days?'

I had nothing more to threaten him with.

'What difference is a few days for any of this, Ganesh?' he said. 'The sooner the end comes for this filth we live in, the better. Think of the future, Ganesh. The future. What comes afterwards.'

And then there was a click, and he was gone.

The cars sped by me, bleeding their trails of light in the dusk. I felt as if I was falling. Then, in that moment, I didn't think of my boys or millions of people or the country or the world. I thought only of me. That faint metallic snap in my ear sliced through my neck and into my stomach, and left me alone. I knew he wouldn't come back. I wouldn't find him, and he would not call me again. I was alone. Once again, I was Ganesh Gaitonde setting out into an unknown world, a knife hidden under my shirt. There was bile rising into my mouth. I turned my head and spat, and brownish liquid trickled down the low white wall that ran along a pavement. I watched it flow, and again there was a rupture inside me, an endless, raw-edged chasm, and I was falling into it. I was alone. Across the road, smoke drifted up from a pile of rubbish. I was seized by a violent shaking, a trembling in my legs and arms and shoulders. I stumbled to the car, and got in. The driver carefully avoided looking at me, and we went on. I lay in the rear seat, holding myself.

The new safe house in Juhu was an apartment on the top floor of a two-storey bungalow overlooking the beach. Bunty had put a team on guard, and the place had been swept and secured. The boys took me on a tour of the place and showed me the two rear exits, down separate staircases, which were also watched over. I went up to the top floor, and I shut two doors and let myself collapse on to the bed. You're exhausted, I told myself. All that travelling for weeks and weeks, the anxiety of the hunt, the changes in water and food. You need to rest. But I was still shaking, I was full of a wild energy that raced under my skin and made it itch and twitch. And there was that smell. Not just mogra this time, but something smouldering underneath, the heavy bulk of burning flesh. Some bastard must have tossed a dead rat or something into a bonfire on the beach. I'd send the boys out and get the maderchod fixed. I staggered over to the window. No, there was no fire, nothing but the waves drumming evenly on the sand. But these windows. There were windows along the entire sea-facing wall, from floor to ceiling. And more windows along the other wall, facing another building across the road. What sort of safe house was this? Suleiman Isa and his entire organization could watch me from that other roof. The police could station a battalion of snipers on the beach, to take off my head. I called down to the boys. Bastards, come close these windows.

I had them close and bolt the windows, and draw the curtains. Still there was that funereal stench of flowers and flaming meat. I shouted for the boys again. I had them bring up electrician's tape and seal all the edges of the windows. They were baffled, and despite their fear of me, and the years of respect, there were some who couldn't hide their scepticism, and their amusement. I didn't care. I told them to go out on the beach and look for a bonfire, and to look in the compounds of all the buildings around us. Extinguish any fire you find, I told them, stamp it out. They nodded, yes, bhai, yes, bhai, and they shuffled out. I shut the door and put wide black swathes of tape over all the chinks and gaps and the keyhole. Then I dragged an armchair over to the exact centre of the room and sat, holding my ankles. No question about it, the smell was still in the room. Give it some time, I thought, let the contamination in the room die out, and you will be delivered from it. So I let the minutes sag by, and took in slow breaths. I shut my eyes and practised my pranayama. I wanted calm, all I wanted was a small portion of peace. But there was light pressing up against my eyes, flares of carroty orange against a lighter background of saffron. It was dark in the room, the curtains were golden and thick, some kind of brocade. Where did this light come from? And then I thought of how fragile this building was, how brittle was the glass in the windows. I may as well be sitting cross-legged on top of my funeral pyre, waiting to be blown back into death by my enemies, by whatever disaster was just now heaving itself over the horizon. I had to protect myself.

Bunty had his handy switched off. I must have called him thirty times over the next two hours, only to get the same bhenchod voice with its purring foreign accents. He finally called back, in a panic. 'Sorry, bhai, sorry. I just had it on vibrate, and it was under a shirt and things. Sorry. Really sorry.'

The bastard's legs didn't work, but another piece of him was still half-functional. It turned out that he had been with a sixteen-year-old girl, and needed to concentrate so much that he forgot his job and his obligations. I educated him again in the requirements of his position, gave him a run-down on the sort of careless chutiya he had become, and told him what I wanted. And then he became even more of a cringing dog. He confessed that he didn't have the keys for my underground shelter, for the safe house I had built for Jojo in Kailashpada. He had some long story about how the builders had needed the keys because they had to finish the electrical connections, and they had given it to so-and-so, and this and that. I cut him off, and told him that I wanted to be in my shelter by nine in the morning, and if I wasn't he would lose something else besides his legs.

'But, bhai,' he said, 'don't you want to go home?'

'Home? What home?'

'Thailand, bhai. The yacht. Now that the mission is over.'

I told him to mind his own business, and slammed down the phone. Should I go across the waters again? Far away, to safety. But where was safety? I could go to New Zealand, or to some rocky island beyond, yes, sure. But when the burning came, when Guru-ji's great destruction swept along the seas, what would be left?

I walked the perimeter of my room, clenching and unclenching my hands, trying to take the cramps out of my shoulders. Where would home be when home was gone? Could you have a home away from home when there was no home? What would you long for, what would you dream of when you settled into sleep? When somebody asked, where do you come from, what would you say? No, I couldn't go anywhere, I couldn't leave. I would stay right here, close to the field of battle, in it, and I would stop Guru-ji. He was confident that I couldn't stop him – 'You can't stop it' – but I was Ganesh Gaitonde. He could see forwards and backwards in time, but I had escaped fate many times. I had beaten what was written, I had changed it. I had survived. Now I would survive again. I would save my home. And to do that I needed to be completely safe.

Bunty beat his deadline by three hours. He called at six, and had me picked up at six-thirty. I hadn't slept at all, but I felt strong and alert as we drove through the stirring, stretching city. I watched as an auto driver uncurled himself out of the back seat of his rickshaw, as a mother hurried her stumbling son towards a public toilet. Elderly people walked in a garden, swinging their arms briskly. There was sun on the very tops of the trees. A bhajan was playing on some radio channel, and we heard scattered snatches of it from a long row of kholis as we passed.

Then we took a left turn and drove up to a market square. The shops were still mostly shut. One yawning seth and his boy assistant struggled with a shutter, and they paid us no attention as we parked next to the white cube in the middle of an empty plot. I ran a hand over a faultless white wall as we went up to the door, and felt better already. I remembered the specifications, the exact hardened thickness of its walls, and the cost of the cement we had used. One of Bunty's boys rattled the key in the door, until I grew irritated and took it from him. It was a computer-cut key, with little dimples on both sides, and once you slid it in half-way you had to give half a turn to the left. Then with a little push inwards, it turned like silk. 'Right,' I said. 'Tell Bunty I'll call him.'

'Bhai, if you need anything else . . .'

I shut the door – I had to lean into the weight of it with my shoulder – and stood in complete, welcome darkness. There was a low hum of well-tuned machinery in my feet, but the squawking of crows outside was gone, cut short. From the blueprints, I knew exactly where the light-switch was, to my right on the wall, but I didn't want to reach over. For the moment, I was content to swim in this safety, to know that nothing could reach me here. My mind stilled, and I stood.

I jerked out of my reverie suddenly. I didn't know how long it had been, a minute or half an hour. I hadn't quite slept, but I had rested somehow. I willed myself into movement, switched on the light and pulled up the metal trapdoor in the middle of the room. A short ladder led down into the control room. Everything was as I had planned, the multiple video screens and the computers, the radios and the gas masks. The builders and technicians had followed the instructions precisely, down to the dry fruit stores and sealed bottles of water. There was a small gymnasium, and a shelf of DVDs, of old Dev Anand and Dilip Kumar films. A steel cabinet contained ranks of weapons, AK-56s and Glocks. A man could live here.

So I did live in my home, my house beneath the earth, for two weeks. I communicated with Bunty and the boys, and took calls from Nikhil in Thailand every morning and evening, and conducted business with Brussels and New York. The boys brought my files over, and all important incoming documents were handed over to me as they arrived. Everything was as before, except that I was not floating about on some foreign sea, or flying from one alien city to another. I did my work, safe in Mumbai's belly. Not that I was complacent about being back home. I followed all security procedures, and I wore a comfortable nylon shoulder holster always, with a readied Glock 34 in it. I was in a combat zone, and I protected myself.

But I couldn't sleep. I lay in bed, or on the ground, or on a special body-conforming mattress that Bunty's boys brought me, and none of these gave me a moment of slumber. I ate handfuls of Calmpose and Mandrax, and a bottle of Ambien was specially flown in from New York. But even the American pills couldn't drag me down into unconsciousness. All I could fight my way to was a twilight between wakefulness and sleep, a suspended paralysis in which my body was heavy and unmovable, but my mind was still awake and aware. Through half-open eyes, I watched driblets of fire crawl up the wall. I knew there was no fire, that what looked like sparks were reflections from the computer monitors and the little red lights on the disk drives, but even when the effects of the chemicals wore off, I could still smell – yes – the mogra and the burnt bodies. I consoled myself with the thought that the air-exchange systems couldn't completely scrub the city odours away. After all, the carbon filters weren't creating new air, they couldn't get out what was already in, at the very deepest levels. What I was smelling was the pollution of the millions above me, the effluvium of their living. From this there was no escape, there couldn't be, and I taught myself to get used to it. It was only a sharpness at the back of my throat, a small irritation in my eyes. I was Ganesh Gaitonde, I had suffered greater pains.

I couldn't get used to the worry, though. Being awake through the day and the night gave me time to sit around and think. Long after business had been taken care of, after I had gone through my to-do list and my accounts and my planning, I sat in my swivel chair in front of the computers and screens and thought. I was of course trying to debrief myself about my recent search for that bastard who called himself a guru, I painstakingly went through the files and papers we had taken from his offices, I tried to remember exactly each sentence he had uttered during our last conversation. Maybe there was some clue somewhere that I had missed, maybe there was some opening that I could squeeze through. I would turn the thing over, our entire history together, and go back and forth, and finally withdraw defeated. I was beaten. So then I worried. I would distract myself with simultaneous channels of television, news and a film and music all together, and yet the worry welled up from the maps behind the newscasters, and from the dances that the heroines and heroes threw themselves into, and the peace of Lata's voice.

'What are you worrying about now, Gaitonde?' asked Jojo. She now finally believed that I was back in some foreign country, because of the quiet I phoned her from. And as always, she could tell my mood from the moment I began to speak, and even before, from my silence.

'About you,' I told her. It was true. If the war came, I would survive in my shelter. But if Jojo was outside, I would lose her. But how would I live without this voice in my ear, without the knowledge that Jojo knew me? I was feeling alone now as I never had before. I had been by myself in my youth, I was then desperately poor and ignorant and quite alone, but the loneliness had hung lightly on my shoulders, like the swirling, streaming cape of a dashing hero. The screenplay of my life had arced upwards in a single continuous movement, and I had left lovers and yaars and enemies behind without regret. It was necessary. It was an essential part of my character, and without it I could never have become Ganesh Gaitonde. But now Jojo was inside me, and without her I would shatter. I knew it. 'I worry about you only, Jojo,' I told her. 'Kutiya that you are. I don't know why.'

'You've gone senile,' she said. 'If you don't know why, why are you worrying?'

'No, no. I know why I am worrying. Only I don't know why I'm worrying about you. You're such a rude, shameless, bad-tempered kutiya.'

She roared out her laughter, like the beast she was. 'Arre, Gaitonde, after all these years you still don't know? You really don't know? All right, all right, never mind. Let it go. But tell me what the worry is.'

'You need to live in a safer place.'

At this she became unreasonable, as she always did. She spewed abuse, and told me I needed to get my head checked, or my golis, or maybe both. And then that her life was just fine, her business was good, and she wasn't scared of anything. And that I needed to get my train off this annoying track or she would have to drive it up my gaand.

I, by contrast, was completely reasonable. I started to point out the rising crime rate in the city, the worrisome incidence of random robberies, the rapes, and also the aggressive posturing of governments and militant groups, leading to bomb explosions in restaurants, and what this might mean for the situation at the border. At this, she whispered fiercely, 'I wish they would put one of their bombs inside your head,' and hung up.

These days, ever since I had entered the bunker, our conversations seemed to be ending this way more often than ever. We had our usual discussions about the girls Jojo was representing, or the television shows she was producing, and trends in the business climate, but finally I would bring the talk around to the nature of the world we lived in, the mortal dangers it was planning to throw at us. Then, with a groan or a curse or a shout, she would hang up. And I would go back to my worrying.

Today, I began to consider alternatives for Jojo. I could present her with a shelter that looked like a house, and fool her into safety. But how would I guarantee that she kept the doors closed, and keep her from asking where the windows were? No, no. I flipped channels, and saw an advertisement for exotic foreign holidays. A happy couple walked on a beach. I could send her off to remote locations, give her free first-class tickets to some island in the southern oceans. Yes. Fly her off to some resort with plenty of muscular beach-boys and fancy shopping. Yes, here she was, buying a pair of high-heeled boots. I could see her. She was dressed in a tiny red skirt, and her legs were young and muscular. She had a row of shopping bags behind her, and she was happy. Next to her was a little black handbag, very soft leather. And in the handbag there were two phones, one ordinary mobile that she used for her life, and a red encrypted phone that was her link to me. She was safe and happy, and thinking about this made me content. Even if something happened, if fire rumbled behind the horizon, she would be protected.

But, but if something happened, if that thing happened, the phones wouldn't work. There would be no flights, no planes perhaps. All the systems that ran the planes and the phones would crash. I knew enough now, from the films I had seen and the television shows I had watched, I knew that this complete breakdown was what I should expect. Even the machines that were still working would die from lack of power. That was why we had installed a triple set of generators and batteries for the shelter, in addition to hardened power lines from the mains, and made arrangements for solar power. So Jojo would be on her island, and I in my underground rooms. And between us there would be vast oceans, and merciless sun. In all the years we had been together, I had never minded the distance, because I knew that even if I were walking down some street in Belgium, or flying over an Arabian desert, Jojo was with me. She was always nestling close on my hip, two presses of a button away. I could send her away now, but how would I bring her back? I paced the control room, from end to end, thinking of the effort it required to walk a mile. For years now, distance had meant nothing to me, and I had cared only about time. I had located cities by the number of hours it took to fly a jet from one to another, and had learnt to subtract a day from the date, or add half a night to the morning hour. Now, on the ground under my feet, I saw the long lines of longitude and latitude, I saw them stretching out beyond the walls, I saw the awful arc of the earth, and the rocky void that gaped between Jojo and me. We were so small, and this world was so vast. Without her voice in my ear, I was smaller still.

I had to bring her in. Yes. She would resist, she would be angry at first, but finally she would understand. I would lay out for her the magnitude of the problem at hand, I would convince her of the danger, I would show her the evidence and she would understand. We had always been able to talk, right from the start. She was a stubborn harridan, but she was also reasonable. She was interested in her own interest, and I would show her that it was impossible to remain outside. She would agree.

I picked up a phone, called Bunty and gave instructions. 'Get her over here,' I said.

She would be frightened and angry when they got her, but I had no choice. If I had issued her an invitation to meet me, she would have refused, no matter how much I pleaded. So the boys did what they had to do: they waited until morning, outside Jojo's building. She drove out at ten-thirty, alone in her blue Toyota. They followed her down Yari Road, and north towards Goregaon. They were in two cars and a van, and it took them just ten minutes to neatly box her in and drive along, with the van on the rear. Then the car in front of Jojo braked hard, and the van clanged on her rear bumper and pushed her forward for a gentle three-vehicle accident. They were travelling slowly, there was no danger of anyone getting hurt, but Jojo got out of her car spitting maderchods and bhenchods. She was too angry at the girl driving the van to notice the three men who got out of the car in front, and the other two in the car to the side. I'd told them all that Jojo was not to be hit, and I wasn't sure the sight of a ghoda would be enough to keep her from fighting and screaming, even if it was held to her head. So they used an Omega stun gun. As Jojo ranted at the girl, one of the boys pressed the stun gun into her hip, just above her belt, and let her have a thirty-second shot. There was a crackling sound, and Jojo gave out a little scream that turned into a whine, and then she went to the ground. Using a stun gun is a risky business: you can give some people a jolt, and they feel the ferocious snake-bite, and they just get angrier and break your skull. I had been afraid that Jojo would start kicking the boys in the golis, but she collapsed and twitched and rolled her eyes back and was out for a good ten minutes. By which time she was in the back of the van, hands and feet gently roped, too jangled to do anything but slobber on to the seat. The other cars – including Jojo's – followed, and so this little procession brought her to me.

I took delivery at the door – shielded from the shopkeepers' eyes by the bulk of the van – I took her and shut the door, and carried her down the staircase. I laid her on the bed, propped her head on a soft pillow and brought her some cold water. I held the glass to her lips, and then wiped up the slabber from her chin and neck. She mumbled something, all thick-voiced and wet. Her mouth was rubbery and out of control, I could tell, but by now her eyes were concentrated and very alive. She looked at me, she glanced right and left to take in the room.

'Relax, Jojo,' I said. 'A few minutes and everything will be all right. Here, drink some water.'

But she clamped her chin and gave me a spiky glare, sharp enough to take my head off. She tried to speak, and again it turned into a saliva-dribbling slur. I cleaned her up, and then I sat back and looked at her. She was thinner than I remembered from the photographs, a little pinched around the lips. In the pictures she had always had a luxurious red mouth, and for the last many years I had always imagined her like that, every day. But that was all right. This was the early morning for her, she had just woken up and was heading to her gym, she hadn't had time to put on her lipstick. I understood about women and their make-up. Jojo looked a little older than I had expected, I hadn't known about the lines on her neck, or the wrinkly skin on her hands. But she was attractive all the same, a taut, well-maintained item with thick, highlighted brown hair and a slim body. I could see her flat stomach where her top had ridden up a bit, over the low-slung jeans.

She saw me looking, and she raised her head from the pillow. This time, she paused before each word, and formed it with exacting, laborious precision. She said, 'Who. Are. You?'

I clapped my chin, and laughed. 'Arre, Jojo. Sorry, yaar. I never told you. I changed my face. For security reasons. I am Ganesh. Ganesh Gaitonde. Gaitonde.'

She shook her head. 'Zo-ya said.'

So Zoya had told her about my surgery. Never trust a woman with your security. Maybe I should have had that kutiya Zoya shot after I had discarded her. But never mind that randi, here was Jojo still quite scared and suspicious and hostile. I had to convince her that I was me, that I was the Ganesh Gaitonde who spoke to her every day. Was my voice that different, was it so altered by distance and electricity? But no matter. I had to become Ganesh Gaitonde for Jojo in this face-to-face meeting, even though both our faces were changed from those we had imagined during our long friendship. I told her about how we had first spoken to each other, so long ago, and how we had become yaars. I told her about the girls that she had sent to me, and the jokes we had made afterwards. I told her about the virgins I had taken, and the payments that I made to her for their freshness. I told her about the projects I had funded for her, and about the problems I had talked to her about. I told her how she had cursed me, and called me 'Gaitonde'.

By the time I had finished with my little history, she was sitting up on the bed, her arms hugging her knees tightly to her chest. And she knew who I was. But I had no idea whether she was curious or angry, afraid or puzzled. I couldn't read her. I knew her voice, but I didn't know her body at all. She had to say something for me to know what she was feeling. I waited.

She opened her mouth, shut it. She was testing her ability, her tongue and lips, and finally she decided she was recovered. 'What has happened to you, Gaitonde?' she said.

848

I had been expecting an angry curse or two, and a demand to know why I had shocked her, and brought her here to my shelter without her permission. I had my explanation ready, and now it came out in a great rush, and I told her about yagnas and bombs, and dollars and sadhus, and fire and the end of a yuga. As I talked, she got up from the bed and edged around the room. She was still a bit unsteady on her feet, and had to put a hand out to the wall to balance herself. But she was quite alert, and she was examining the room, what was in it, where the doors were. Even as I babbled, I felt a surge of pride in her. She was doing what I would have done myself. She looked at the mini-gym, opened the doors to the toilets. Then she made her way to the doorway leading to the control room. I followed her through, still talking.

'Where are we?' she said. 'Why do you have that gun?'

I could see why she was confused. I had four of the monitors on, American and Indian and Chinese news on three of them, the internet on the other. She was disorientated, she had blacked out and didn't know how much time had passed. She thought she was maybe in Malaysia, or Spain. It could be anywhere.

'Don't worry, Jojo,' I said. 'We're still in Bombay. But we're safe. Don't worry.'

Now she turned to me. She was shorter than I was, but she stood very straight and drew her shoulders back and threw her hair back over her shoulder with a swaying toss of the head. Watching that one little movement gave me an instant understanding of why she always had a queue of men waiting to be her next thoku. I noted this objectively, as a fact about Jojo. In that moment, in the condition I was in, there was no stirring of physical desire in me, least of all for Jojo. All I wanted was for her to talk to me.

'Gaitonde,' she said, 'you're insane.' She spoke to me in the voice she used for scolding her servants, which was low, decisive and unrelenting. 'You need to have your bheja checked by a doctor. Forget that, it's too late for that, you should just march to a madhouse and admit yourself. Tell the nurses to put chains on your hands and feet so you won't go bothering other people . . .'

'Jojo, listen to me.'

'No, you listen to me. Who do you think you are? You think you're some king, you can just kidnap people? You can just *shock* somebody like they were some animal and have them dragged down to you? You bastard, just because everyone in the world is afraid of you, you think you can do anything? I'm not afraid of you, maderchod.'

She had her face thrust up into mine, her fingers jabbing towards my eyes. She cursed me again, and a burst of spit stung my cheek, and then another.

I wanted to hit her.

But this was Jojo, I wanted to take care of her. I pulled myself away, I put up my hands, I took a breath. 'You're disturbed right now. I understand. But let me explain to you, Jojo. We have been friends for many years. Think how long it has been. I could have done this at any time, I never did. So just calmly listen to me. Afterwards, if you don't agree, you can do whatever you want.'

She tilted her head down and watched me. I could see that she was calculating and weighing, taking in me and the room and her chances. But I couldn't tell whether she was going to give in or give me a slap. I should have set her up with a video-conferencing camera, so I could have watched her neck and her angry shoulders all these years. I thought I knew her, but I should have known more of her.

'Okay,' she said. 'But talk fast. I have lots of work to do today.'

I sat her down in an armchair in the control room, and got her a fresh glass of water. I asked if she was cold, and turned down the air-conditioner. Then I gave her the reality of what was happening. I told her everything, point by point. I showed her a chart in an old edition of *India Today* in which they had printed the possible numbers of dead and wounded in Mumbai after a nuclear blast. I found her a website which showed actual footage of explosions and trembling survivors. I showed her recommendations for safety procedures, and lists of materials necessary for survival.

'Wait,' she said. 'Wait.'

'What?'

'You want me to stay down here? You mean, *live* in this thing?'

She was incredulous, disbelieving and then contemptuous. Now I had no difficulty in deciphering the furrows on her forehead, the quality of her scowl. And suddenly, this hardened haven on which I had lavished untold suitcases of money seemed small and inhospitable. 'It's not so bad,' I said. 'It's very comfortable, actually. You've got the best beds, everything is air-conditioned. There is a gym, you can exercise. There is filtered water. Communications are excellent. You can work easily from down here.'

'Till when?'

'What?'

'How long are you going to stay down here?'

I was surprised. The answer was obvious. The Jojo on the phone had always been smarter than this one, she had never needed so many explanations. 'Till it's over,' I said. 'Or not over.'

Now Jojo disappeared. She vanished behind that incomprehensible face, and I couldn't tell what she was thinking. But when she spoke, I recognized her again. She was very soft now, she was the gentle, generous-hearted woman who spoke to me about my problems and my stress and what kind of food I should be eating. 'Gaitonde, why don't you sit down? You need to relax, or you'll give yourself piles again.'

She had a grin on her face, and I thought, this is what she looks like when she gives out that gurgly chuckle. I hadn't realized I was standing. 'Yes, yes.' I sat.

She drew up her chair close to me, pulled up her feet and sat cross-legged. I laughed, because this I knew about her – she had told me that sometimes during official meetings with important types she forgot where she was and sat like that, like a proper Konkani bai straight from the village. She nodded, and gave me a smile. I felt better instantly. This was the Jojo I knew. 'Okay, Gaitonde,' she said. 'Tell me – till what's over?'

'Haven't you been listening? The whole thing,' I said. 'If I find him, then I can stop it. Then it's over. If I can't find him, then it doesn't stop. Until it all stops.'

'Okay,' she said. 'There's this Guru-ji. You need to find him. Right, right. And how long will that take?'

'I don't know. It could happen at any time.'

'Today, you mean?'

'Or tomorrow.'

'Or a few days?'

'Months, maybe. But if I can't find him, it has to stop sometime. It's inevitable. You can see that.'

'But Gaitonde, I can't stay here for that long. I have a business. I can't run it from here. I have to meet people, I have to see girls. I have to run around everywhere.'

'You can call them from here. We can set up the room upstairs like a reception room. A sofa, a desk. Very easy.'

'But,' she said, 'but, Gaitonde.'

She wasn't fighting me any more, but of course she thought that the task ahead was impossible. Anybody would who hadn't led my life, who hadn't achieved my level of understanding, who hadn't left behind so many certainties that turned out to be illusions. I knew the truth, that finally safety was a room on a yacht, or a cave under the earth. I had to bring her along slowly. 'Jojo,' I said, 'just try it for a day.'

'Just a day?'

'One day and one night. Tomorrow if you want to go, you go home.'

'Promise?'

'You need me to promise? When Ganesh Gaitonde says he'll do something, he does it. But for you, Jojo,' – I touched my throat – 'I swear.'

I showed her the treadmill, and the weights. She didn't want to exercise, though, said it was too late in the day now and she was going to miss some phone calls and appointments. So I cleared a desk for her – swept away newspapers and maps, magazines and financial charts – and gave her a phone for herself. I did my own work as she made her calls. At two o'clock – precisely her preferred time – I brought her lunch. It was the Konkani food that she loved, all kokum and fiery fish. She picked at her plate, and I watched her. Somehow it was hard to speak to her. We had had lunch together before, with me on the yacht and her at her house. Then, we crunched and munched into each other's ears, and talked and talked. Jojo called this our gazali sessions, during which she would give me the latest gossip about friends of hers, and I would make her laugh with the new idiocies committed by my boys. There was no reason why we couldn't have those easy jokes again, that laughter. I had collected new escapades, I wanted to tell her about an idea I had for a new television serial. And yet the silence sat between us, like a great black dog on the table. But I was Ganesh Gaitonde, I wasn't scared of anything, I tossed aside the discomfort. 'Jojo,' I said, 'you want to watch a film tonight? We can get pre-release prints, the very latest ones.'

She slid her plate to the middle of the table. 'Whatever you want.'

'I know that,' I said. 'But I am asking what you would like.'

'I don't care. We can watch what you want to watch.'

'But you must have an opinion.'

'I told you, I don't care.'

She had her knees drawn up again, and her hair fell like a curtain, hiding her face from me. I reached out and turned her chair to me, but I could see only her jeans, and the tight clutch of one hand around the other. 'Arre, baba,' I said softly, 'of course you care. There's never been an upcoming film you haven't loved or hated in advance.'

She bayed at me, 'Maderchod, Gaitonde, I told you I don't care!' Her cheeks were dark with blood. 'Get whatever chutiya film you want!'

Nobody spoke to me like that. Nobody shouted at me. I wanted to hit her.

But I got up and walked away. Without looking at her, I told her, 'I'm going to rest. For a while.'

I lay down on the bed, curled my arm over my eyes. I could hear Jojo moving around in the other room. There was a click, plastic against plastic. Was she going to make a call? Who was she calling? Would she call my enemies? Or the police? Tell them where I was, so she could get out of here? No, she wouldn't do that. She couldn't. However upset she was, despite the nervousness that was moving through her body and making her tremble, she would never do that to me. She was Jojo, and I was Ganesh Gaitonde. We were together, we needed each other. She was going from one end of the room to the other. What was she doing? Wood ground against concrete. Was she moving a table? Why? Now she was quiet. Where was she? A narrow creak of metal. Ah, she was climbing the stairs. She wanted to get out. She was going to try. No matter. I had shut the steel trapdoor. You couldn't open it without pressing a nine-key combination, or – in case of electrical failure – you had to snap out a panel and then turn two wheels simultaneously. She must be pulling at the handle at the bottom of the door. Let her.

'Gaitonde,' she said. She was standing in the doorway. 'Gaitonde, do you want women?'

'What?'

She came out of the shadow. 'I have two new, fine items. Fresh from Delhi.' Her face and shoulders were shiny with sweat. 'I swear, they're better than anything you've had before. Once you have these, you'll think that Zoya was some third-class randi working behind Andheri station.'

'I don't want any items.'

'But, Gaitonde, they'll come down here and live with you. Both of them. Think about that. One is sixteen, and the other is seventeen, and you can have them both. They'll be happy to be here. Really. They'll stay with you as long as you like.'

'I don't want them.'

'Gaitonde, the sixteen-year-old, I'm going to have her hair dyed golden. She looks just like some foreign model, she's got skin like malai.'

'No.'

When she was trying to persuade you of something, she tilted her head down and looked up at you through her eyelashes, and her hair fell in smooth curves around her jaw, like a dark helmet. 'I don't want to be here.'

'Just try till morning . . .'

'Gaitonde, I'm telling you now, I don't want to be here.'

'Just try for a few hours at least.'

'I know now what I want. And I'm telling you, I need to get out of here.'

'Why?'

'Because it's driving me crazy. It won't get better, only worse.'

'We can change everything, bring in whatever you like.'

She screamed. Her whole body clenched towards its centre, she hunched over, and out of her came a long tearing squall that knocked me upright. 'Shut up,' I said. But her eyes were watery and blank, and she took a breath, and again made that haggard wail that fell against my face like a slap.

I took her by the shoulders and shook her. She fought me, turning inside my arms and jabbing sharp elbows into my ribs. Something burned against my chin, and I let go of her and touched my face with the tips of my fingers. They came away with a slick covering of pink. The bhenchod kutiya had claws.

She was circling her hands in the air, in front of her chest. 'Don't you understand? I can't stay like this. I can't. I have to go out. You can't keep me in this jail.'

'Don't you understand? Up there you'll die.'

'So what? I would rather die than stay in this hole.'

I turned away in disgust. 'That is complete nonsense. You're crazy right now. You know that's not the truth. You don't want to die.'

She came after me. 'Shall I tell you the truth, Gaitonde? You are a coward. You used to be something, you used to be a man, but now you are a trembling little madman hiding in a pit.' She was standing right behind me, and I could feel her sour breath on my shoulder, the smell of her panic.

I turned, and in the same motion I gave her the back of my hand. It landed hard, and I felt her teeth snap and she reeled back. 'Ah,' she said, 'ah.' Blood pumped from her nose.

'Randi.' I followed her around the room as she staggered back. 'You want to see what kind of man I am? Let me show you. No, come, come. Here, you want some more? Who's trembling, han? Who's shaking?'

Her teeth shone white through a mess of dark blood. 'You, you're not a man,' she said. She spat laughter at me, and stood her ground. 'You bought women, so you think you're a great hero. None of them even liked you, you bastard. Without your cash, you wouldn't even have been able to come near them.'

'Bas,' I warned her. 'Enough. Be quiet. Understand – I am trying to help you. I am trying to save your life.'

'They laughed at you, gaandu. They made jokes together, about what a pathetic, weak little rat you are. You think you're anything in front of a woman like Zoya? She told us that she never got one good night in bed out of you.'

'That's a lie. Zoya liked me.'

She threw her head back and howled. 'Zoya liked me,' she crowed. 'Zoya liked me.' She bent over and put her hands on her knees. 'Zoya *liked* me.' Blood slipped and dripped on to the ground, but she was only amused. 'Zoya liked *me*.'

'She did.' The voice coming out of my throat was strange to me, small and forlorn. 'The first night we were together, she told me that. She said I was amazing. She did. We did it all night. That's the truth.'

'Gaitonde, you idiot.' She was triumphant now. 'You fool. She made a chutiya out of you. It wasn't you, you simpleton. She gave you a glass of milk and badams. And in that she gave you one crushed-up Viagra, one full big blue tablet. She was going to give you two, but I was afraid we'd kill you. I told her, it's okay to want to get ahead, you want to go to the moon, I understand, but don't burst the rocket that's going to get you there. And it worked. It wasn't you, saala. It was the Viagra.'

A blue haze of rage came across my eyes. Through it I saw her, standing straight up, laughing. She was not afraid of me.

'*Zoya* liked me,' she said. 'Gaitonde, you fool, you think she was some virgin you impressed with your huge manliness. You chutiya. She had had a dozen men before you, and many afterwards, and you were the most pathetic. You were, you were smallest.'

'Liar. She was a virgin. You told me. She told me.'

'A virgin?'

'Yes.'

'You idiot. How do you think she survived in this city before she came to you? You bhenchod men always pay more for virgins, so she became a virgin for you.'

'No. I saw the blood.'

She laughed so hard she had to hold on to the side of a table. 'Gaitonde, of all the pompous, gaandu men in the world, you are the blindest. Arre, inside ten miles of here there are twenty doctors who will make any woman a virgin again. The operation takes half an hour, it costs twenty-five, thirty thousand rupees. And in three weeks the renewed virgin can be ready to spread her legs on a white sheet, so some tiny little Gaitonde can see all the blood and think he's big.'

I shot her.

The Glock was in my hand. There was the smell of some flower in the air, some leaf with bitterness underneath. I didn't remember the sound, but my ears were stunned.

She had fallen in the doorway leading to the beds. I looked down at the comforting black metal in my grip, then came up to her. Yes, she was dead. There was blood, still moving. A flutter in her eyelashes, from the silent breeze of the air-conditioning. Her pupils were quite still. And there was that hole in her chest. I had not missed.

I sat. I let myself down, and sat next to her. Jojo. Jojo. In front of me, there was the back of a computer, a white cable dangling. Beyond that, a white wall. I shut my eyes.

When I awoke, I was on the floor, her foot was in front of my face. There was no respite for me, no avoiding what I had done. I came into consciousness suddenly and cleanly, and there was no gap of knowledge. I knew that I was lying next to Jojo, on the hard ground, and that I had killed her. But what I noticed all new, all keen and fresh and as if for the first time, was how complicated a thing a human foot is. It has little pads, and arches, and a convoluted network of muscles and nerves, it has bones, so many bones. It flexes and moves and walks and endures. Its skin takes on the colour of the years it passes through, until the cracks in it form a net as complicated as a life itself.

I held Jojo's foot. I cupped its ankle and held its cold inertia. On my wrist, my watch blinked out the hour at me. Six thirty-six. We had had lunch at two. Had I only slept for a few hours? But I felt rested, and my head was clear. Then I saw it, I saw that the day had changed. I had slept for more than twenty-four hours.

Get on with it. But get on with what? More money-making, more women, more killing. I had already lived that, I had no appetite for more. So, get on with what? Lying on the ground, next to Jojo, I asked myself that. I felt whole again, delivered from fuzziness and distraction and exhaustion by this long rest on this bloodstained ground. In this clarity, I could see that Shridhar Shukla – Guru-ji – had been right. I couldn't stop it. I couldn't stop anything. I was defeated. He had beaten me, because he knew me better than I knew myself. He knew my past, and he knew my future. What I did, or didn't, do was irrelevant. Or worse, it was entirely relevant. Whatever I chose to do would contribute to his plan, would end in fire. The world wanted to die, and I had helped it along. He had set up the sacrifice, and every action of mine was fuel. I couldn't stop it.

I softly rubbed the fissures on Jojo's heel with the very tips of my fingers. Was her death also foretold? She had not had an easy life, I thought. She had tried to take care of her feet with lotions, but the skin had cracked from all her walking. So much effort, so much striving, and to come to this. To be brought to this sudden end by her friend. But yes, I thought, this is what we can choose. You can't stop it, Guru-ji had said, you can't stop yourself.

But I can. I can stop myself. This is the only and last thing I can choose. In this, I can defeat even you, Guru-ji. I can stop myself.

Okay, Jojo. Okay. I sat up. Where was the gun? Here. Loaded and ready. One bullet is all it would take. I didn't want to look at her face. I kept my eyes on her feet and turned around, until I could rest my back on the wall. Okay.

But I couldn't do it. Not yet. Not yet. But why not? I wanted to. I wasn't afraid, I was eager. Maybe Jojo was waiting for me on the other side. Maybe she would curse me and hit me, but finally she would understand. I would talk to her and she would understand, as she always had. It was just a matter of talking, and time. And I would curse her for betraying me, for lying to me. But finally I would forgive her. We would forgive each other. But I couldn't do it yet, put the gun up to my mouth. Why? Because, because simply this: what would they say about me after I had gone? Would they say, Ganesh Gaitonde went mad in a secret room in Mumbai, he killed a girl and then himself? Would they say, he was a coward and a weak man? If I didn't tell them, they wouldn't understand. They would spread rumours, and lies, and invent reasons, and speculate about causes.

But who would listen to me? Jojo was gone, and Guru-ji was absent. I could call any reporter, and he would come running. But reporters were devious bastards, they wanted headlines and action, scandals and tales. There was that fellow at *Mumbai Mirror*, who was very good, but even he would think of me as Ganesh Gaitonde, crime lord and international crook. No, it had to be somebody good, somebody simple. Somebody who would listen to me as a man might listen to another man on a railway platform, with sympathy and kindness, just for an hour or two until the train came. Somebody who had seen me not merely as Ganesh Gaitonde, but a human being.

So that was when I thought of you, Sartaj Singh. I remembered my first meeting with Guru-ji, the first time I had sat with him, face-to-face. I remembered how you had helped me to that meeting, how you had talked to me and – on the very last day – taken me in, to my fate. I remembered that generosity, unusual for anyone, incredible in a policeman, and I remembered you. You have a policeman's cruelty in your eyes, Sartaj, in your swagger, but under that studied indifference there is a sentimental man. Despite all your sardar-ji preening, you were moved by me. Our lives had crossed, and mine had changed for ever.

So I knew what to do. I got up smartly, went to the desk and made some calls. In fifteen minutes I had your home number. I called, and listened to your sleepy mumble. And I said, 'Do you want Ganesh Gaitonde?'

You came. I looked at you, peering up into the camera. You were older, harder, but still the same man. And I told you what had happened to Ganesh Gaitonde.

But you haven't listened to all of it, Sartaj. You too are not free of ambition. You want to take me in, to have my arrest added to the list of your triumphs. You sat in front of the steel door to the bunker, and you listened, but you called in a bulldozer. You've broken through the door, the second monitor on my right shows you edging forward, pistol ready. You are coming in. I'm still talking, but you aren't listening to me any more. Your eyes are afire. You want me, you and your riflemen. But listen to me. There is a whirlwind of memories in my head, a scatter of tattered faces and bodies. I know how they skirl through each other, their connections and their disjunctions, I can trace their velocities. Listen to me. If you want Ganesh Gaitonde, then you have to let me talk. Otherwise Ganesh Gaitonde will escape you, as he escaped every time, as he escaped every last assassin. Ganesh Gaitonde escaped even me, almost. Now, at this last hour, I have Ganesh Gaitonde, I know what he was, what he became. Listen to me, you must listen to me. But you are now in the bunker. I have left the trapdoor unlocked for you. Under each step of yours, I can see dozens of my years pass. I can see it all together now, from the very beginning to the first house I built for myself, my first home in Gopalmath. I remember it all, from a village temple to Bangkok. But you are already inside, in the shelter.

Here is the pistol. The barrel fits snugly into my mouth. I think of what Jojo would say: *Bastard, you're scared or what? You want me to do it for you?*

No, Jojo. I'm not afraid.

Sartaj, do you know why I do this? I do it for love. I do it because I know who I am.

Bas, enough.

Safety

Parulkar was late the next morning. Sartaj sat on the bench outside his office and watched a quartet of sparrows fly through the rafters and around the pillars. They went from one side of the corridor to the other, and then out over the courtyard and to the wall beyond. Then back they came. One of them executed a lazy roll and sat at the end of the bench, dipping his head down and bobbing it back. He – or she? – fluffed his wings, hopped to the left and flashed tiny brown eyes at Sartaj. Then he was away. They are wary of us, Sartaj thought, and otherwise wholly indifferent. Our tragedies matter nothing to them. The thought was oddly comforting. So that bastard Ganesh Gaitonde had blown half his head off in a white bunker, so maybe there was a bomb in Bombay, so what? Life would go on. Sartaj tried to concentrate on this thought, and to follow the sparrows as they came to the ground and plummeted upward.

Parulkar's PA came through the doorway to the left, a sheaf of papers in his hand. 'Saab's escort radioed ahead. They'll be here in twenty minutes.'

'Good, Sardesai Saab,' Sartaj said. 'I'm here only.'

Sardesai nodded, and went down the staircase. Parulkar had a long list of appointments, all of whom were waiting on the other side of the staircase in a long queue that Sartaj had blithely walked past. Sartaj had called Parulkar at home, early in the morning, when he knew Parulkar would be sitting in an old armchair with his papers and his chai, and he had presumed on old acquaintance to wangle himself an early meeting. 'It is very urgent, saab,' he had said. And so here he was, ahead of the queue. He was trying to practise his operational readiness techniques, which mainly consisted of trying not to think of what was to come shortly. After all, how hard could it be? He had lied to suspects, and to apradhis, to his parents, to Megha, to other women, to

860

himself, to his superiors, to journalists, to many policemen. He was a master of lying, a veritable adept at it. But he had never lied to Parulkar. This is what tensed him up, and it was exactly this nervousness that Parulkar would pick up on. Parulkar was the guru who had taught Sartaj how to lie, and when to lie. He had given him the craft. Would he detect Sartaj's hesitations, his over-eagerness? This is how you catch a suspect in a lie, he had once taught Sartaj, you watch not only for contradictions, but also if the story sounds too similar each time he tells it, if the language is the same, if it has been rehearsed. Sartaj had seen him reduce hardened men to tears in half an hour.

The four sparrows sat in a row on a power line loosely tacked above the pillars and shook their tails at Sartaj. Relax, Sartaj told himself. Don't over-think it. He jiggled his arms and loosened his shoulders. It's a job, it's just a job. Think about something else. He thought about Mary, about her small hands and the gathering of age at her knuckles, and a small swell of tenderness carried him into a vivid recollection of their love-making, her exhalation as he first went into her. Then he was afraid again: why wouldn't she leave the city? How stubborn she was in her fatalism. Now he was afraid again. Parulkar would know, like every other senior officer, about the details of the high-status alert from Delhi. He would be alert himself, and sceptical, and hard to fool. The anxiety sang in Sartaj's veins and drummed into his forehead. He felt weak and incapable.

But Parulkar, when he came bouncing up the staircase followed by his three bodyguards, was at the top of his game. 'Sartaj Singh,' he boomed, 'come in, come in.' He led the way into his cabin, ordered two cups of chai, karak and with adrak, and had the floor-to-ceiling curtains at the back of the room swept back so they could look down on the garden he had built in the years of his tenure. The air-conditioner was adjusted, a spray of air-freshener was squirted into the corners of the room, two vases of fresh flowers were brought in, and finally they sat, Parulkar and Sartaj, facing each other.

'Okay, tell me,' Parulkar said. 'What is so urgent?'

'Saab,' Sartaj said, 'yesterday Iffat-bibi asked to meet me. Actually, she insisted. She said it was top priority. She wouldn't tell me anything on the phone.'

Parulkar was looking down into his chai. He frowned, reached into the cup with a teaspoon and removed the film from the surface. 'So where did you meet her?'

This was Parulkar at his most dangerous, when he was apparently casual and uninterested. 'In Fort, sir,' Sartaj said. 'Behind a seafood restaurant called Kishti.' This he had also learned from Parulkar, that when setting up a big lie it was important to be truthful in the small details. You wanted to give the interrogator a lot of specifics to check and cross-check and find correct. 'In an accountant's office.'

'Yes, yes. That's Walia's office. He handles a lot of their legitimate business for them. What did she want?'

Sartaj leant closer. Of course there was nobody in the office, but somehow it was necessary to whisper. 'Sir, Suleiman Isa wants to talk to you.'

Parulkar put down his teacup, edged it back on the table. 'Can't be done. My position is too sensitive. And nowadays you never know when and where the Anti-Corruption Bureau is listening.'

'I told her that, sir. But she insists. I mean, she said that he insists. They said you choose when and how. By phone or satellite phone or however. You choose everything.'

'Even if I choose my end of the connection, the other side is not safe. Who knows what agency is listening to them?'

'They thought of that, sir. If you don't want to call Suleiman Isa in Karachi, you can talk to Salim in Dubai.' Salim was Suleiman Isa's top controller and long-time friend, he ran the day-to-day business of the company from Dubai. 'They said you can have someone bring a fresh phone to Salim at a place you both agree on, and he will call from that phone to whatever number you designate in India. So there will be safety at both ends.'

'So I should talk to Suleiman Isa's errand boy? These bastards have become too arrogant.'

'If you have a contact in Karachi who can bring a phone to Suleiman Isa, sir, then you can talk to him directly. Whatever you want, Iffat-bibi said.'

'Dubai or Karachi, that is not a problem. The problem is these gaandus who think they are masters of the world.'

'I understand, sir. Shall I tell Iffat-bibi no, then?'

Parulkar rubbed his stomach, picked up his cup again. 'What else did she say? Tell me the whole thing.'

So Sartaj told him the whole thing, from the summons on his mobile phone, the journey to the accountant's, finding Iffat-bibi in the tiny cabin, how she had asked for a conversation with Parulkar Saab, how Suleiman Isa was growing anxious to talk to Parulkar, how they understood Parulkar's delicate position with the current government but there was an unavoidable need to talk. 'She said it was a matter of some money, sir, that Suleiman Isa wants to discuss.'

'That bastard,' Parulkar said. 'I have always given them a complete and clean accounting.'

'Of course, sir.'

A gang of labourers were working on a renovation of the Hanuman temple behind the station. They were stripped down to their banians and blue-striped underwear, and were scrambling over the white dome of the temple. Parulkar watched them, scratching at his nose. 'Do you have any ideas?' he said.

'You want to talk to Suleiman Isa, sir?'

'He is a cranky man. He has become almost crazy now, after all those years abroad. Better to talk to him, clear up whatever confusion he has. Bas, finish it, you know. No need to make him more suspicious than he already is. So, okay, I will talk to him. On a new phone, which can be delivered to him personally in Karachi a few minutes before he calls. My man will watch him dial on that phone only, and will confirm to me that security has been maintained. The question remains of where to receive the call.'

'Yes, sir. Sir, I was thinking. Are you still going to Pune on Thursday?' Parulkar had a meeting with senior Pune policemen planned for that morning.

'Yes, yes.'

'Then, sir, why not after your lunch, you come to our house there? Don't tell anyone till the last minute, just say then that you want to go and visit Ma. I will be there, I will reach there on my own that morning. At two forty-five, I will call Iffat-bibi from my mobile and tell her to have Suleiman Isa call on Ma's land line at three. They can ask for me, I'll give you the phone. No problem, no fuss, and both ends safe. You can talk.'

Parulkar put down his teacup and wiped his hands on a napkin. He smoothed back the short hair above his ears, in a gesture that he must have acquired as a young man. It reminded Sartaj of some fifties film hero, but he couldn't think of which one. Parulkar nodded. 'There is just one phone there?'

'Yes, sir.'

'Only your Ma uses it?'

'Yes, sir. I have even stopped using it since I got my mobile, sir, it is cheaper to make calls on the mobile than on the land line. But Ma, sir, she doesn't like mobiles. She says they're too small and have too many buttons.' Sartaj was suddenly aware that he was saying 'sir' too much. Calm down, he told himself. Look at the man. But don't stare at him. Drink your chai. Don't shake the cup.

'All right,' Parulkar said. He always made decisions that suddenly. He weighed the alternatives, ran down the moves as far as he could and then he jumped. He had the courage and faith of a good gambler, and the confidence that he would win. 'All right. But tell Iffat-bibi that the call comes in at three precisely. If they are two minutes late, I leave. And we will keep the conversation short. Ten minutes maximum.'

'Yes, sir.'

'And Suleiman Isa is not to use my name during the call, or his.'

'I will inform them, sir.'

'Right. Shabash, Sartaj. Let us get this over with. And don't tell your mother I am coming. We will surprise her as well.'

'Of course, sir,' Sartaj said. He stood up, saluted. He could feel his shirt wet against his lower back. The stain would be huge, despite the humming air-conditioner. He moved the chair aside, awkwardly, and backed away. He was almost at the door when Parulkar called.

'Sartaj?'

'Yes, sir?'

'You look very tired. What is the matter?'

'That alert from Delhi, sir. They have us all running around.'

'All nonsense. Their intelligence is too vague, there is nothing specific. It is all very ridiculous. There is no bomb-vomb. You take some rest.'

'Yes, sir.'

Outside, Sartaj nodded at Parulkar's guards and walked towards the staircase. He wanted very much to sit down on one of the benches and rest his wobbly legs, but he made it downstairs and kept walking, out of the station, past the crowds and the guards, through the high gate with its curving sign overhead, and stumbling along the street, through the preoccupied pedestrians and the swooping cars and the stray dogs with their scabied flesh. He stood at a corner, blinking. He did not know where he was. He turned to peer up at shop windows and street signs, and he realized he had somehow crossed a busy road. It was as wide as a black river, and the hungry eddies of vehicles swept by unceasingly. He did not know how he had come across, at the risk of his life, but here he was. His mouth was painfully dry, but he did not want a drink. He just wanted to get back to work. Far down to the left, there was a traffic light with a crossing. The bright circles flashed orange and green, green and orange. Sartaj made his way back to the station.

On Thursday, Sartaj drove out early. He told himself that he wanted to get to Ma's and prepare, that he wanted to travel in the cool of the early morning. But he had been unable to sleep, and finally it was easier to get up and start the car and drive than toss about in the musty sheets. It was good to be up in the mountains, to twist and loop along the old road. If he went fast and recklessly, the danger pushed everything out of his head, and he roared through Matheran and Khandala with only a thin skirl of memories trailing behind him, Megha and college picnics and walking up a domed hill. And then he was in Pune, and there was nothing to do but go home to Ma.

She was squatting in the front room, surrounded by open trunks. 'Look at these old sweaters,' she said to Sartaj. 'I forgot I even had them.'

Sartaj bent low to her. 'Peri pauna, Ma.' He lowered the battered lid of a black trunk and sat on it, his calves against the almost faded stencilling of Papa-ji's full name. 'What are you doing?'

'Beta, there are too many things here. If you also don't want them, what is the use of keeping them here?'

Ever since Papa-ji had died, she had gone on these cleaning binges every six months. She had given personal and household effects to cousins, aunts, uncles, servants, neighbours and beggars. She had shocked Sartaj sometimes with her ruthlessness, her detachment from old chairs and walking sticks and blue blazers. The only things that had seemed safe were old photographs and letters, but maybe even those would disappear in this round of vetting. Ma had an old photo close to her, on the floor. Sartaj knew it well, that blackened silver frame, as long as he could remember Ma had kept it in her cupboard, nestled close to her dupattas, where she would see it every morning. He picked it up, and there she was, held for ever in blooming youth, Ma's lost sister. She was lovely, she flung a flow of jet-black hair over her shoulders as she laughed, turning back to the camera, and her body was a taut curve leaning into the far horizon. Sartaj knew every detail of the picture, he knew her name was Navneet, and that was about all he knew. Ma hadn't liked to speak about her. Now, perhaps, beautiful Navneet would also vanish. Sartaj didn't like it, this slow erosion of the home that he remembered, that he carried within himself. It was terrifying sometimes to come back to Pune and find another few pieces of it gone. One day, he thought, all that will be left will be these white walls. And then, not even that.

But he couldn't stop Ma. How could you argue with generosity? And in old age she had become stubborn and independent. She did what she wanted. 'Yes, Ma. That's true. But do you really want to give that cardigan? You really liked that one.'

She held up a green cardigan by its shoulders, and then ran a finger along its red border of flowers. 'Where will I need this? All these Maharashtrians come out in heavy coats in December, and it doesn't even feel like winter to me.'

She prided herself on her northern love of low temperatures, and her Punjabi hardiness. 'If we go up to Amritsar,' Sartaj said, 'you will want it.'

'When? For months you've been telling me that, beta.'

'Soon, soon, Ma. Promise.'

She didn't seem at all convinced, but she did put the green cardigan on the right, in the small pile of items that were to be retained. Sartaj didn't want to watch any more, this patient excavation and disposal of their life together. 'I'm going for a walk,' he said.

She nodded, working at the stubborn lock on another trunk.

'All this will be scattered about all day?' he said.

'I have to do the work. Why?'

To warn her of Parulkar's visit was impossible, so Sartaj shrugged. 'Do you want anything from the market?'

She didn't. She seemed entirely more self-sufficient than he remembered from his childhood, when Papa-ji and servants and sometimes neighbours had been required to fetch and carry, to run errands and escort her from here to there. Sartaj couldn't decide whether she had actually changed, or whether she had whittled down her needs and desires so much that the only person she really required was herself. He had no doubt of her love for him, and of her faith in Vaheguru, but even these attachments now sat lightly on her. She wanted only to go to Amritsar, and maybe she was readying herself for another journey. Sartaj shivered, and walked faster.

The lane to the market was busy with white-haired women and men carrying jholas full of vegetables and fruit. Sartaj greeted some of them, the ones he knew from the gurudwara or from walks with Ma. In this locality of many retirees, the morning shoppers had time to stop and chat, and Sartaj was glad to listen to their reports about their sons and daughters, their thoughts on crime and their complaints about politicians. But finally there was no way to avoid going home, to what was to happen, and he trudged back. He was laden with packages himself now. It was hot, even under the rain trees and the gulmohars, and his feet sweltered and ached inside his shoes.

'What have you brought?' Ma said. Next to her, the pile of things to keep was just about the same size as when Sartaj had left, and the other stacks had grown.

'Just some few bananas, Ma.' Sartaj went into the kitchen, stepping over red bedcovers. He took the little Chini bananas out of the paper packet and put them on the counter.

'Is that beer?' Ma said. She was standing in the doorway. 'Why?'

'Just like that.'

'I thought you didn't like beer.'

'Now I do. Can we eat? I'm hungry.'

So Sartaj opened a bottle of Michelob and sipped at it and picked at his food. Afterwards, he lay on the bed in his room and shut his eyes hard against the glaring afternoon light that seeped past the curtains. At two, he got up and went back to the kitchen. Standing next to the washbasin, he opened another bottle of beer and forced down the thick bitterness of it. Then he padded past Ma, who was still at work among her trunks, and groped in the bathroom shelf till he found his tube of Vajradanti. He brushed his teeth twice, then sat on the bed to wait. He watched the clock.

He heard the knock on the door at two-thirty. He let Ma get up and shuffle over and open it, and then he listened to Parulkar greeting her effusively. 'Bhabhi,' he said, 'you look completely fit. After retirement I too will come to Pune. The air here is so much better.'

'Arre, Sartaj didn't tell me you were coming. Sartaj? Sartaj?'

But Sartaj didn't want to get up off the bed, not yet.

She called again, 'Arre, Sartaj, Parulkar-ji has come. Beta, where are you? I don't know what he's doing.'

Sartaj knew what he was doing, yes, he did. So he forced himself up and went out and pretended surprise at Parulkar's visit and welcomed him in and cleared the sofa for him and offered him beer and little Chini bananas. Parulkar drank with his usual gusto, and asked for Ma's special spicy pakoras to go with the beer. He stood in the doorway and talked to Ma as she brought out her pans. 'So then Sardar Saab said, "I need to go home, I have a new wife I haven't seen for three days." And only then I realized he hadn't slept for four days.'

Parulkar's story was about Papa-ji, who had been famous in the department for being able to go for long days and nights without sleep, and also for his prodigious naps. Despite Ma's ambiguous feelings about Parulkar, she was charmed by this talk of her dear departed, of his talents and his dedication to his work. She cut vegetables with new enthusiasm, and laughed, and told Parulkar that she remembered that week, and the kidnapping case they had been working on.

'That was when the baby boy was stolen by his uncle,' she said. And then they talked on about the long-ago past.

Parulkar glanced at his watch, and Sartaj nodded. It was two forty-five. He walked into the bedroom, picked up his mobile and called Iffat-bibi. Of course she already knew the number, but the play had to be acted out. 'Tell me,' Iffat-bibi said, and Sartaj recited his lines.

In the kitchen Parulkar was now telling stories about Sartaj, flattering ones about his successes in sports, and Ma was smiling. These were two of Parulkar's great talents, this immense memory and this easy charm. It was impossible not to respond to his concern for your well-being, his intimate knowledge of your history and your hopes. So now they stood, all three of them, in a little family group, near the kitchen door. Parulkar asked Ma about her health, and the upkeep of the house, and Papa-ji's pension payments. 'Any problem you have, Bhabhi-ji, you call me immediately. Sartaj of course has my direct mobile number always.'

Ma was distinctly chatty. She asked about Parulkar's daughters, and their children. Parulkar proudly told her of their various achievements and joys. Even the divorced one (and she was well rid of that spendthrift, drunkard husband) was doing well now, she had started her own clothing business. At first it had been just modern salwar-kameezes and fancy ghagras for the women in the colony, but now she was getting customers from as far away as Shivaji Park. 'All this,' Parulkar said, 'she did with only little support from me. She did it all alone. She used to be such a home-caring type, you know, always with the children, didn't even know how to write a cheque. Now she is handling thousands of rupees, and she has four tailor-masters sitting for the whole day in our house. And is talking about buying a shop near by.'

'The world has changed,' Ma said. 'All these young girls have become very brave.'

'Yes, yes, Bhabhi-ji, what a change in our very lifetimes.'

Ma pointed at sliced onions and cauliflowers. 'These won't take too long.'

'No matter how long, Bhabhi-ji,' Parulkar said. 'I must have them. I am trying to avoid oil and fried foods, but for your excellent pakoras I must make an exception. But only today, and only since I am here in Pune.'

Ma took in the gallantry with a pleased little nod. 'Once in a while fried food is all right. But this Sartaj, he eats so badly all the time. All that greasy restaurant food, this is why he looks so tired.'

'Yes, yes, Bhabhi-ji,' Parulkar said. 'I tell him all the time, this is no way to live. Whatever has happened, a young fellow cannot be alone. A man needs a family.'

They both assayed Sartaj expectantly, like benign doctors looking for signs of improvement in a particularly intractable patient. Sartaj knew he should say something, but he felt very distanced, separated from the both of them by some fissure in the air, by a fracture that had flung him far away. They had the look somehow of an old photograph, as if they were made already unreal by the orange glow of nostalgia. 'Yes,' Sartaj said.

'Yes what?' Parulkar said.

The phone churred out its old-fashioned ring.

'Phone,' Sartaj blurted, full of relief and terror. He got up, picked his way across the trunks. 'Hello?'

'Give it to Saab.' The man's voice was confident, aggressive.

'Sir,' Sartaj said, 'the phone is for you.'

'Oh,' Parulkar said, 'okay.' He was in no hurry. He took a long swig of his beer, wiped his hands on a handkerchief.

'Sir, you could take it in there, sir. In the bedroom.'

Parulkar nodded, and went. Ma didn't like this, Parulkar going into her room, but she couldn't stop him now. The bedroom door snapped shut, and she shook her head at Sartaj. He waited for the click on the handset, and Parulkar's 'Hello', and put the phone down. 'It's an important call, Ma,' Sartaj said. 'Very important. From the central government.'

She still didn't like it, but she was still enough of a policeman's wife to know that calls from the central government couldn't be avoided, and sometimes had to be taken in private. She cleared the table and wiped it clean. Sartaj drank another beer and watched the clock. Fifteen minutes passed, and then twenty. Parulkar was going over his limit, but maybe they were arguing about money. Maybe they were fighting about the deaths of Suleiman Isa's shooters and controllers. Maybe they were threatening each other.

'What is that man doing in there?' Ma said. 'I'm tired. His pakoras are ready, they will get cold.'

She had missed her afternoon rest, and had been distracted from her work. 'Ma, it's not his fault the call came.'

She shrugged, and sat down decisively on the floor, back at the trunks. 'He should think himself, coming to people's houses in the afternoon. But he was always like that.'

Sartaj tried to hush her down from her old woman's loudness. 'He will hear you, Ma. You don't worry, he'll be finished soon.'

But it was a full ten minutes before Parulkar emerged. He was triumphant. He winked at Sartaj and picked up his glass from the table and took a swig of beer. He sat down, in what used to be Papa-ji's chair, and ate pakoras with deliberate, unhurried enjoyment. He was calm and confident and clearly victorious. He knew he had vanquished Suleiman Isa and all his henchmen. He talked to Ma about old times, when they had all been young, when Papa-ji had been renowned for the mirror gleam of his shoes. Finally Parulkar said, 'Achcha, Bhabhi-ji. Now I must go. But I will come back for your pakoras soon. No, no, please don't get up.'

Ma didn't get up, but she mustered up enough politeness to say, 'Yes, you must,' and wish Parulkar's children well. Sartaj walked out on to the veranda with Parulkar, who was polishing a pair of shiny silver-and-black dark glasses.

'Did it go all right, sir?'

'Yes, yes. The man just needed some sorting out. He is quite reasonable, if you know how to handle him.' Parulkar put on his glasses with a flourish. 'Anyway, it is settled now. Finished. Good work, Sartaj. Thank you.'

'Sir, no need . . .'

Parulkar patted his arm. 'Your mother looks healthy. You have good genes. You will live long, Sartaj, if you take care of yourself. Okay, chalo, I will see you back in Bombay. Have a good rest. Relax. Go and see a film or something.'

He turned smartly and trotted off to his car. The bodyguards got into their jeeps with a clanking of weapons and doors, and the procession went on its way in a festive cloud of dust, followed by two yelping dogs.

Ma was standing by the door. 'The bananas and the beer,' she said. 'You knew he was coming.'

'Yes.' She hadn't listened to all those policemen's tales for all those years for nothing. She knew how to take apart motives and actions, consequences and causes.

'Are you all right?'

'Yes.'

'Is there any trouble? Did you do something?'

'No.'

'Go and rest.'

As he went by her, she laid a hand on his wrist, in an action as familiar and old as childhood. She was checking him for fever, for anything out of balance and in need of care. But today, this afternoon, there was no sickness in him, no particular bodily reason for his exhaustion and his reddened eyes. As he slumped by the open door to Ma's room, he saw something glint and glimmer on the table next to her bed. So Ma had decided to keep the photograph of her beloved Navneet. Ma's attachment to things was fading, but she still cared for people. He could still feel her hand on his wrist. How small her hands were, and her feet. She was altogether a small person, so tiny in her childhood that Navneet and the rest of the family had called her 'Nikki'. It was hard to imagine her as a giggly girl, but little Nikki had somehow grown into Ma, who took care of him even as she slowly loosened herself from the world's grip. In his room, Sartaj put the fan on full and stripped down to his underwear. The sleep came fast, and when he woke up it was quite dark. He lay still, listening to the night. He could hear Ma, moving things about in the kitchen, and beyond her, the neighbours and a slight shifting of wind and cars and a small squall of children's voices. We are still here, he thought, we are still alive. We have survived another day. But the thought did not make him feel any better.

Sartaj called Iffat-bibi four times that night, and then every hour the next morning, while he drove back to Bombay. Each time she said the same thing, 'When they are ready, they will tell me. And then I will tell you your sadhu's address. You will get your information, saab. Don't worry. Just have a little patience, a little more.'

But Sartaj, who had practised patience his entire career, found it hard to find any now. Back in Zone 13, from the patio of the station, he watched Parulkar come into work that morning, and the man seemed as jovial and energetic as always. So he was still unaware of the trap that already had him in its teeth. And he didn't know, yet, who had set him up. He would know soon.

Sartaj left the station and halfheartedly pursued leads on a burglary case until noon. He then decided he needed an early lunch, and made his way to Sindoor. He asked for some papad, and chicken tikkas, and gave the waiter a bottle of Royal Challenge whisky in a plastic bag. By the time Kamble joined him an hour later, Sartaj had managed to soften the light inside Sindoor into a gentle haze. Kamble sat, and watched as the waiter put another full glass of tawny liquid on the table.

'Boss,' Kamble said, 'do you want to eat something also?'

'I'm not really hungry. This is enough.'

'Bring some naan,' Kamble told the waiter. 'Lots of naan. And some vegetable raita. And some daal.' He settled back into the booth, squared his shoulders and said softly, 'What happened? Trouble with the girl? Tell me.'

Sartaj laughed, then stopped himself, and laughed again. Kamble was sympathetic, he wanted to give advice about women. Kamble the man about town. Kamble was a good fellow. Kamble was a dirty bastard, had his fingers in every filthy deal, but he was also generous. He was kind. He was a good man. 'Kamble,' Sartaj said, 'you are a good man.'

'Yaar, I am as good as I should be. Here, drink some water. What are you doing?'

'What am I doing?'

'Yes.'

'I am eating my lunch. I am sitting in Sindoor eating my lunch with my good friend.'

'That's all?'

'I am also waiting for some very important information.'

'From who? About what?'

Sartaj shook a finger at Kamble. 'That I can't tell you. Sources must not be revealed. Even to a friend. Not this source. But the information is good. I tell you it is good. And we need it, it is for the big case. The biggest case. You know.' Sartaj pointed at the patterned ceiling, and made the sound of an explosion.

'Yes, I know. Here, eat.'

Kamble put a piece of chicken on Sartaj's plate. Sartaj nodded, and picked it up and chewed. Kamble fussed over him through lunch, and made him eat far too much, and drink a glass of chhass. Still, Sartaj managed to keep up his intake of alcohol to match, despite Kamble's dodges of handing half-emptied glasses to passing waiters. So he was still nicely fuzzy when Shambhu Shetty came into the restaurant and pulled a chair over to the booth.

'The boys said you were here,' he said. He had the pudgy look of a very content man.

'Shambhu, you have to start exercising more,' Sartaj said. 'It's not nice to see you like this.'

Kamble whispered something to Shambhu, and Shambhu whispered back. Then he unfolded a paper and slid it on to the table. 'Saab,' he said. 'I get *Samachar* early at the bar. I thought you would want to see.'

There was a triple-height banner headline spread across the page: 'Senior Police Officer Caught in Conversation with Anti-National Don.' And a picture of a uniformed Parulkar underneath. The sub-heading ran: 'Opposition Demands Suspension and Probe.' Sartaj turned his head away. He didn't want to read further.

'They say that the ACB has a half-hour recording of Parulkar talking to Suleiman Isa in Karachi, and this recording has been leaked to all the newspapers,' Shambhu said. 'It is already on several websites, you can listen to the whole thing. Parulkar discusses money payments with Suleiman Isa, specific jobs, things like that. And – where is it? – here. "Independent voice experts have already indicated to this newspaper that in their opinion the recording in question is of the voices of DCP Parulkar and Suleiman Isa."'

'Bhenchod,' Kamble said. 'Let me see.' He grabbed the paper, read rapidly, threw over the sheet and skimmed down the page. 'Maderchod. The man is finished. This saala is gone.'

'I can't believe it,' Shambhu said. 'Such a mistake from him.'

'Everyone makes mistakes,' Sartaj said, 'sooner or later. Tomorrow if not today.'

They both were quiet. Then Kamble pointed to the newspaper. 'You want to read it?'

'No.'

'All right. I have to go back to work. What are you going to do?'

'I will sit here and wait for my information.'

But Kamble seemed to think that was a bad idea. He objected and argued until Sartaj grew furious, and then Kamble argued some more. The other diners in the restaurant, the tables of executives and house-wives, risked uneasy glances over shoulders, and began to mutter, and so finally Sartaj gave in. He went with Kamble on his very boring rounds of a matka den and a shoe factory, and of the Nehru Nagar basti in Andheri in search of a tadipaar who had reportedly crept back into Kailashpada and exited again. Sartaj stumbled through the lanes behind Kamble, his head reeling from the fanfare of smells, good and bad. He was not drunk any more, but the walking and the unceasing surge of faces pressing close to him kept him occupied and comfort-ably numb.

At six, his phone rang. 'Bhai was pleased,' Iffat-bibi said.

'Yes.'

'He said to give you a gift. Just a token. Five petis.'

'I don't want the maderchod's money. Just give me the address.'

'Are you sure? Turning down a gift from Bhai is rude.'

'You tell him exactly what I said. I want the address, okay? The address.'

Iffat-bibi sighed. 'All right,' she said. 'You young people are very foolish sometimes. Do you have a pen?'

The address was for a two-storey bungalow at the western edge of Chembur, set back from a middle-class neighbourhood by a well-maintained ten-foot wall. After Sartaj wrote down the address in his notebook in very careful block letters, he made Iffat-bibi repeat it three times. Then events moved very fast. He called Anjali Mathur, and he and Kamble met her and her people on a street near Vrindavan Chowk in Sion. Then they went north to Chembur, accompanied by an IG and a gaggle of very senior policemen and some tough-looking military officers who offered no job descriptions. Some local Chembur cops – none of whom Sartaj had met before – offered local information, and led them to the immediate neighbourhood of the bungalow. A discreet perimeter was set up, and a command post was set up over a dairy sixty metres away, behind a screen of trees. Sartaj never saw the bungalow. He and Kamble sat to one side of the very busy room, and watched it fill with radios and unrecognizable equipment and competent, confident men. Anjali Mathur huddled in conferences with her boss and others, and remembered to send chai to Sartaj and Kamble when it came around.

Kamble nudged Sartaj. 'Boss,' he whispered, 'go over and stand near them. They may want your advice. Or to ask you something. You found this maderchod house for them. You are the hero of the day. Go and behave like you deserve the credit, or one of those gaandu IPS officers will steal it.'

But Sartaj didn't particularly want to give advice to anyone. He was content to sit in the glow of the laptop screens and watch the skies change colour outside the window to the rear. Someone had once told him, he didn't remember who, that the fantastic colours in Mumbai's evening came from all the pollution that floated over the city, from all the incredible millions who crowded into a very small space. Sartaj had no doubt it was true, but the purples and reds and oranges were still beautiful and grand. You could watch them change and deepen and lose themselves in black.

At ten that night, Anjali Mathur came over and sat next to them. 'It is confirmed,' she said. 'There are seven men in the house. We have two distinct radioactive signatures, and there are two three-ton trucks in the back, behind the bungalow. We think they were going to drive the bombs to their ground zeros.'

'Two bombs? Now what happens?' Kamble said. He was rigid with excitement and anticipation.

'There is a team already here, in place. They will go some time in the night. That decision will be made by the operational commander.' She tilted her head towards the front of the room, to a military man leaning over a radio. She seemed to be waiting for a response from Sartaj.

He cleared his throat. 'I am sure your team will win.' Sartaj felt, inexplicably, like laughing. He restrained himself, of course, but she gave him an appraising glance as she got up.

Kamble followed her past the tables, and came back a few minutes later even more nervous and anxious. His eyes flared and he leant over and thumped Sartaj on the shoulder. 'The Black Cats are here, boss. With those black commando hoods and guns and everything.'

Sartaj tried to discover some enthusiasm within himself about the Black Cats, but he just felt sleepy. He noted his own curious lack of excitement about the prospect of being saved, and thought it was probably just exhaustion. It is the insomnia, he thought, and all the recent ups and downs, all the stresses coming together. Probably I will feel something tomorrow. But right now I think I will just sit here and feel nothing. Probably it is all the beer and the whisky, making up the weight that is crushing my thighs like black iron. Probably I am just very tired.

He awoke to a rough jostling, to insistent and heavy hands against his cheeks. 'Sartaj, wake up.' It was Kamble. 'Gaandu, you are the only man in the world who would snore through his own best moments. The climax is about to happen, boss. They are about to go in. Wake up. Wake up.'

Sartaj sat up, ground the sleep from his eyes. 'What time is it?'

'Four-thirty.'

A single bird hooted in the pre-dawn stillness. Inside the command post, there was an expectant silence, an absolute immobility that was filled with waiting. Sartaj wanted to ask Kamble how they would know that the team had gone in, that the command had been given, but Kamble had his hands over his mouth, his thumbs hard over his cheeks. He looked like a little boy waiting for exam results to be announced.

Nothing changed in the room, but then, from far away, came a series of pops, and then another, phap-phap-phap, phap-phap-phap-phap. And then a last little boom. A moment passed, and then from the front of the room, a cheer grew and spread. Anjali Mathur came running through the clapping crowd. 'We're safe,' she said. 'We're safe.'

Sartaj nodded, and made himself smile. He was surrounded suddenly by police officers and RAW men and Black Cats, all of whom jostled each other and hugged each other and shook hands with him. Apparently Kamble had made sure that they knew where the credit was due. Sartaj turned through the crowd and was able, slowly, to peel through it and get down the stairs. He walked away, to the back of the compound behind the dairy, which was crowded now with police vehicles and other unmarked cars. But it smelt mostly of milk, and Sartaj thought he caught the faint, good edge of gobar. But that was doubtful, how many dairies in the city really had cows any more? But it was rejuvenating to breathe in. His head was clearing.

So, with those little banging sounds far away, apparently the world had been saved. Sartaj didn't feel any safer. Inside him, even now, there was that burning fuse, that ticking fear. He leant against a post in a wire fence and tried to feel satisfaction. Our team won. Sure. Kamble had been dancing inside, he was happy. But Sartaj couldn't keep the question at bay: You want to save *this*? For what? Why?

It took three weeks for Sartaj's promotion to come through. Nobody knew about his work on the Gaitonde affair, on the bombs, so there was no reason given for the extraordinarily expedited order and paperwork. At the dairy itself, that morning, Anjali Mathur had told him that the bombs did not exist officially, and that they never would. The decision had been made at the very top, she told him, for reasons of national security. And she had shrugged, and he had understood, because he was a policeman and he knew that successful operations sometimes could not exist officially so that some higher-up's reputation could be protected, so that some politician would not have to acknowledge how close disaster had wandered.

Sartaj wouldn't have minded the invisibility of what they had done that morning, except for the fact that rumours rushed in to fill the vacuum left behind by the lack of facts. The general understanding in the department was that Sartaj had somehow rolled over on Parulkar, that he had engineered Parulkar's astonishing downfall. In the version of the phone call between Parulkar and Suleiman Isa that was on the ACB tapes and the websites, the first few seconds had been clipped off. Sartaj's 'Hello?' had been cut, and the conversation only began with Parulkar picking up the phone and saying, 'I am here.' Nobody knew that the call had been taken at Sartaj's mother's house, and yet there was a tacit understanding throughout the force that Sartaj had had something to do with the circumstances of the call. It was known that the promotion was his reward, along with a gift of one full khoka from Suleiman Isa. There were rumours also that Sartaj had beaten up an innocent man, injured him very badly, and a belief that even this matter was squashed in return for the destruction of Parulkar. In the department, there was no bad feeling towards Sartaj about this, and in fact there was a renewed respect from many quarters. Parulkar was an old player, and he had made many enemies along the way. Many were not unhappy to see him fall. Even those neutral towards him felt that he had maybe tried to grab too much. Parulkar's friends and enemies now thought of Sartaj as a formidable strategist, someone to be cultivated.

Meanwhile, Parulkar was on the run. On the second day after the phone call was made public, questions were asked in the legislative assembly and also in parliament. That same evening, a warrant was issued for Parulkar's arrest. But his application for anticipatory bail had already come in, and he was already absconding. His lawyer told the papers the next day that the proceedings had been hasty and unprofessional, that the voice on the tapes was not Parulkar, who had dedicated many years of selfless service to the nation. Furthermore, there was no proof that the other voice on the tape was indeed one Suleiman Isa. And also, that the conversation which actually took place on the tape was in no way demonstrative of criminal malfeasance or anti-national activity.

But that same day the chief minister announced a massive reshuffling of senior police officers, and in response to questioning by reporters stated categorically that there was no question of himself or anyone from his cabinet interfering with the due process of the law. 'The enquiry is going along. We will have results very fast. You will see. DCP Parulkar should give himself up. We will be strict but fair.'

Sartaj himself had no idea where Parulkar was. He had some idea of how to get word to him, and so he left discreet messages with a couple of khabaris, and with Homi Mehta the money manager. But there was no response. Twice that fortnight, his mobile had rung late at night. Both times, the caller had not spoken. Sartaj could hear slow exhalations, an old man's laborious inhalations. The second time he had said, 'Sir? Is that you, sir?' But there had been no response, and no caller's number on the display. The morning after Sartaj's promotion was formally announced, his mobile rang while he was in the bathroom. He felt his way out, soap still on his face, and found the phone vibrating on his bed. 'Hello?' he said.

Again, there was the same breathing. This time, Sartaj felt that this silent man was very angry at him. 'Sir,' Sartaj said. 'Sir, you have to listen to me. It was very important, I will tell you everything about it.'

But the caller put down his receiver. There was a click, and then nothing. That evening, Sartaj was just finishing his shift when Kamble came into the detection room. 'Boss,' he said.

'What?' Sartaj snapped. He had been overseeing the interrogation of an armed robber. Since his promotion, he no longer found it necessary to third-degree the prisoners himself. He merely instructed, and watched. The room smelt of sweat and piss.

'You'd better come outside,' Kamble said. And then, in English, 'Please.'

Sartaj followed Kamble outside, into the hallway that opened out into the compound. Kamble took him by the elbow and walked him to the edge of the pond. There were birds wheeling overhead. 'They found Parulkar this afternoon.'

'Good. Where did he give himself up?' Because if Parulkar didn't want to be caught, he wouldn't be.

'No, not like that. They found him.'

Kamble said that just forty-five minutes ago, the detail watching Parulkar's home had been alerted by screams coming from inside the house. They had gone in and found two of Parulkar's granddaughters in hysterics. It turned out that Parulkar had been inside the house all along. In that ancestral abode, under a staircase, there was a wooden panel that hinged away to reveal a small ten-foot room wedged in behind the kitchen. Parulkar had been safely ensconced inside, and he could have stayed indefinitely, since food and other resources could have been easily provided to him, and the main thrust of the investigation was elsewhere, as far away as Pune and Cochin. But this evening, Parulkar had emerged from his hiding place and gone into his bedroom, without care for the daylight which he had been avoiding. He had shaved, bathed, changed into a fresh kurta. He had taken off his watch and placed it on the table by his bedside. Then he had taken the keys to the Godrej cupboard next to his bed, opened it and the locker inside, and had extracted his service revolver. He went into the bathroom, took off his chappals, stepped into the bathtub. The girls had heard the report of the pistol and had run in and found him.

'Bas,' Kamble said. 'That is all I know so far.'

Sartaj stepped away. Shadows moved over the water, and ripples moved from opposite sides of the pond and ran across each other. This is all we know so far, Sartaj thought. And this is all we will ever know. We die for things we don't understand, we sacrifice those we love. 'I should go there,' he said.

'To his house? Boss, right now, no. Do not go there.'

879

'Yes, you're right. Of course I shouldn't go there. Okay. I think I will stay here for a while.'

Kamble went back into the station. Sartaj stayed outside. He listened to the flapping of the flag on the temple, and watched the water. He had the sense that something was about to change. He was waiting. But he wasn't sure it ever would.

❦ INSET: *Two Deaths, in Cities Far From Home*

I

The Ansari Tola in Rajpur was on the eastern side of the town, on the other side of the nullah from the crossroads and behind a line of khajoor trees. There were just eleven huts, clustered together in an untidy circle. A muddy track went down from the culvert to the Tola, and the first hut, on the highest land, belonged to Noor Mohammed. He owned seven katthas of poor land, on which he grew potatoes and makkai, and he drove an ikka drawn by a rickety brown nag. His wife was named Mumtaz Khatun, and they had three children, one boy and two girls. Noor Mohammed was the least poor man in the Ansari Tola, which meant that he and his family just barely scraped by, and that his children hardly ever needed to go to sleep on a stomach-filling diet of chillies and water. Noor Mohammed and Mumtaz sent their sons to school, but intermittently, depending on the season and the work to be done in the fields. They did not have much to spare, not time and not food and not money. Still, they gave thanks to Allah when another son was born to them. They named him Aadil.

Aadil was curious and adventuresome from the very start. When he was two, he disappeared one rainy afternoon from under the noses of his two sisters. His mother came home to the Tola to find the whole community in an uproar, and the sisters weeping. Everyone searched in the fields, and a boy cousin was lowered down into the well. Noor Mohammed clenched his fists, and walked the near edge of the nullah. Finally, Noor Mohammed's brother Salim found Aadil where nobody had thought to look, on the road on the other side of the nullah. 'He was just walking along,' Salim said of his nephew, 'all naked but not tired or afraid at all.' Aadil had decided to explore the world, it seemed, and had just gone off on his own. His mother squeezed him close and asked him, 'Where were you going? What were you looking for?' Aadil didn't say anything at all. He patiently suffered all the fuss, and looked around with big black eyes. He was a very serious boy. 'If I hadn't been coming back from Kurkoo Kothi just then,' his uncle said, 'our young adventurer here would have gone all the way to Patna.'

The distance to Patna was only one hundred and twenty-eight kilometres, but it took Aadil eighteen years to get there. Until then, he struggled against the limitations and confinements of Rajpur, a town of one and a half lakh citizens that lay untidily sprawled on the southern bank of the Milani river. The Milani was a minor watercourse which split from the Boorhi Gandak sixty kilometres before it emptied into the Ganga. A medieval Kali temple stood on a rocky outcrop next to the Milani, facing a white mosque on a nearby hill. During the summer, and late in the winter, the water in the river receded, revealing grey rocks covered with carvings of curving-limbed gods and goddesses from some ancient, forgotten time. To the south and east, on the highest hill in the immediate surroundings, the haveli of Raja Jadunath Singh Chaudhury crumbled quietly into a ruin that was haunted – according to the entire population of Rajpur – by mad ghosts and cackling chudails. Raja Jadunath had lost most of his land, and he could not compete in splendour or munificence with the local MLA, Nandan Prasad Yadav, who during Aadil's childhood built Kurkoo Kothi into a magnificent blue and pink extravagance, surrounded by a twelve-foot wall and armed guards. Noor Mohammed always said that the Raja had no head for modern politics, and Nandan Prasad Yadav was a past master at that dirty game. So one grew small, and the other big. Noor Mohammed was sometimes hired by the Raja, to drive his children to the railway station in the Raja's ancient buggy, and most of the men from the Ansari Tola worked as labourers on the Kurkoo Kothi.

Some of the boys in the Ansari Tola could read a little, and one had studied till the eighth. None of their fathers could read, and in the whole history of the settlement no member had finished high school. But Aadil, it was clear from the very beginning, was fascinated by the written word. Even before he could read, he traced the shapes of letters on old newspapers. At the two-room primary school near Prem Shanker Jha's mango orchard, Aadil paid attention with such rapt intensity that the other children noticed it right away. One of the

Yadav boys said, 'Eh, this Aadil looks like such a dibba when the teacher's talking,' and he made a deathly serious face with big eyes. 'Aadil-Dibba,' he said, and puffed out his cheeks, and the three classes gathered on the chabutra of the schoolhouse all burst out laughing. From that day on, Aadil was known as Dibba, and became famous as a padhaku boy. Even the teacher – when he was in school and teaching, and not off trying to make a little money selling onions wholesale – noted Aadil's dedication and quietness, and tried to keep the school bullies off him. This resulted, of course, in groups of strapping lafangas paying extra attention to Aadil on the way from and to school. Still, he persevered. He passed the fifth, and then went to the Zila High School. To make it into the sixth had been very hard, because Aadil's mother and father had no money for books or slates or pencils. Now it was harder, and not only because more books were needed, and pens, and a geometry set. There were many days that Aadil had to work in the fields, especially when there was planting or harvesting to be done, and there were other days when he laboured at brick kilns with his uncles and cousins. He was old enough to earn now, and so he did. There were mouths to be fed, and homes to be mended, and marriages to be paid for. But he was assiduous about his learning. Despite everything, he stuck it out. He read borrowed books, and spent evenings under the flickering bulbs of the Shivnath Jha Sarvajanik Pustakalaya. The library had been endowed by a renowned local Brahmin landowner, and named after his very learned father. There was a little discomfort evinced by the library staff at first, at having a Muslim boy come and sit so boldly under the garlanded picture of the old man who had spent his whole life bathing, purifying and sanctifying. But they soon grew used to the sight of Aadil sitting at a wooden bench, bent over a book or a newspaper. Times were changing, and the two rooms and dozen shelves of the library were after all supposed to be sarvajanik, and Aadil was definitely one of the people, if only a grimy and somewhat unpalatable one. So Aadil learned about Rajpur and what lay beyond. He located himself not only in space, but also in time. I am, he thought one day, part of the twentieth century.

Rajpur, though, stubbornly remained in some other time, in some era that wasn't quite the present and definitely not the future. The potholed main road that led out of town looked nothing like the Soviet highways that Aadil saw in black-and-white magazines, and the sight of whole villages in America with electricity and phones filled him with wonder. There was one phone now in Rajpur, at Nandan Prasad Yadav's house, but Aadil had never seen it. He had seen three films, two in a temporary outdoor cinema set up by an exhibitor who rode up in a jeep and unfurled a dirty white screen which turned a blazing Technicolor after dark. Then Prem Shanker Jha built a cinema house he named Parvati, in which Aadil saw *Bobby*. He sat on the ground, up front near the screen, and what he dreamed about afterwards was not Rishi Kapoor's sleek motorcycle, or Dimple Kapadia's glistening, almost naked body, but the clean, two-storeyed pucca houses, the phones, the roads, the water that fell magically from taps. Aadil now began to recognize how dirty Rajpur was, with its open drains and lanes built to no plan, its wandering tribes of spindly dogs. The fields wandered to the horizon, a long, marching column of electricity poles stripped of their copper and wire stopped abruptly in the middle of a cracking wasteland, and the crows made their relentless clamour over the eaves of the Ansari Tola. Babies were born, marriages were made, old men and women died, but everything remained the same. Near Prem Shanker Jha's orchard, Aadil played football and gilli-danda with Brahmin and Yadav and Bhumihar boys, but he had never visited their homes, and they had never set foot in the Ansari Tola. No Paswan would ever enter the inner courtyard of a Brahmin or Bhumihar house, and even outside, the poor man would squat on the ground to talk to his upper-caste patron, who lounged comfortably on a khattia. The lowly were allowed no chairs, no pride, no dignity.

When Aadil was in class nine, his chachu, the gentle Salim – who had found him wandering down the road to Patna so long ago – died of a wrenching stomach ailment that emptied him out in torrents of diarrhoea. His mourning relatives laid out the frail body, cleansed it, wrapped it in its white shroud and carried it to the Muslim graveyard at the western end of Rajpur. But the maulvi who lived in the mosque there wouldn't let them in, and soon the Sayyids and Pathans who lived near by came running. You cannot bury anyone here, they said, you have your own graveyard. The men from the Ansari Tola protested in the name of Allah, and then they beseeched the mighty Maqbool Khan, who was the wealthiest Muslim in Rajpur, the son of a zamindar and the descendant – it was said – of amirs and nawabs. The dead man's relatives asked for sympathy, for compassion, for reham. They told Maqbool Khan and the Pathans and the Sayyids that their own graveyard was lost, that it had been covered by water when the river changed course after the monsoon. But there was no mercy that day in Rajpur, not even for the dead man, who had been a five-time namaazi and the most generous of men. Maqbool Khan gave the mourners five rupees, and told them that they had to construct a new graveyard. It took two days to bury Salim, because there was no free land lying around in Rajpur, even just a few feet of hard earth, enough to hold a man. Aadil's father found a scrubby slope, a rough triangle of sour, barren soil between the nullah and the road, and the men cleared and levelled this and made a graveyard, and buried Salim.

Aadil began to wake up with anger in his head. It was there, ready to greet him with its insistent monotone, even before he opened his eyes and saw the muddy brown of the wall, before he heard his mother's sighs as she struggled through the constant pain in her back. The low grinding of the anger stayed with him through the day and burnt the flesh from his bones, so that he became very thin. He was tall now, and nothing like a dibba, although the nickname stayed with him. His mother began to joke about finding a girl for him. For Aadil, this early talk of marriage was another torture. The other boys his age in the Tola had flirtations with girls, and Anwarul – who had a broad chest and a dangerous walk – had an ongoing affair with a married woman from the Chamar toli. But Aadil's passion was his books, and he wanted nothing else but the swooning pleasure of learning. For this it was hard to find support in the Tola, even from the very few men and women who had travelled a little outside Rajpur. Noor Mohammed and Mumtaz Khatun had never been further than Alagha, which was forty-four kilometres from Rajpur. For them, Patna was a place out of legend, and they knew only vaguely of Delhi, and nothing of Peking. To be born, to labour in Rajpur, to survive – this was what they knew of life and expected from it. To persuade them that it was possible for Aadil to finish high school was a struggle, to convince them that it was desirable took a long, relentless campaign which was never quite won. There were many in the Tola who told them, educate this boy too much and he won't want to work on the land, so be careful. Somehow, despite all this, Aadil fought his way through to the tenth, and passed the finals. He missed a first class by two marks, but then no other student had studied with borrowed texts, without notebooks and pens and lamplight. There was no celebration in the Ansari Tola, but Aadil's parents were proud of him, and much of Rajpur now knew of him as something remarkable, like the five-legged calf that had been born to a cow in the Raja's stables. Aadil understood that he was being patronized when Brahmins and Yadavs and Pathans called out to him in the streets, and called him 'Professor saab'. He shrugged it off. The laughter fed his anger, and his anger kept him moving.

But now he wanted to attend intermediate and college, and it was going to take more than anger to get him there. The fees were manageable, but there was a lot more to be paid for. He knew something now about education, and he understood that it required a lot of ready cash. You had to buy books, pens, application forms, you had to pay special fees for exams and graduations, you had to have a bicycle to go to the Lala Chandan Lal Memorial College on Jawaharlal Nehru Road, which was on the far side of Rajpur from the Tola. You had to pay for clothes, for two pairs of pants and two shirts, so that you could sit on the benches alongside boys who wore jackets and shiny shoes. And still there were all the other things you couldn't pay for, for kachoris from Makhania the chat-wallah who set up his stall across the road from the college gate, for films at Parvati, for camaraderie and carefree laughter. The intangibles that were never named, but were education also, these you could never pay for. Aadil knew all this, and yet he wanted to go to college. He refused marriage and insisted on intermediate and then college. No argument by the elders in the Tola could sway him in the slightest. Aadil had told them that fees and books and exams alone would require seven hundred rupees, maybe more, every six months. They asked, where will that come from? But Aadil was adamant. He was not rude, but he put his head down and repeated one single sentence: 'I want to go to college.' Finally Noor Mohammed took him to see the Raja.

Aadil had never been to the haveli before. He had seen the surrounding brick wall on top of the hill, and he had seen the Raja's children in their sparkling-clean clothes. He was surprised now by the headless statue in front of the house and the rows of broken windows, the splintered railings on the balconies. Still, it took his breath away, the haveli with its sheer size and expanse, the overgrown gardens that must have once needed a staff of fifty gardeners, the empty stables tall enough to have harboured elephants. The Raja met them on a patio behind the house. He took a long draw on his hookah and gazed out at the distant glint of the river. He was wearing a white shirt and a blue lungi, and seen up close he looked most unlike the pictures of royalty that Aadil had seen in his history books. Even the hookah was quite threadbare, with a cracked cup. Noor Mohammed squatted next to the Raja's arm-chair, and tugged at Aadil's sleeve until he lowered himself also. The Raja listened to Noor Mohammed, and said, 'Noora, the boy is quite right. He should be educated. These are times for education. But my condition is very bad. Now those bastards have taken my land up to the orchard.' He made a gesture over his shoulder.

The bastards he was referring to were the Gangotiyas, who had lived near the confluence of the Milani and the Boorhi Gandak until last year, when they had been dispossessed in one disastrous week by changes in the course of the waters. They had shown up in Rajpur en masse, some six hundred and fifty ragged men, women and children, and a settlement had appeared overnight on the Raja's land. They had occupied some thirty bighas, around two large ponds, and proclaimed it their own. They said they had been given the land by the Raja's deceased father, who – according to them – had been transformed by a meeting with Acharya Vinobha Bhave, and had converted instantly to the Acharya's idealistic ideology of land redistribution. The proof of this was a bequest on a ragged-edged sheet of paper, supposedly signed by the Raja's father and dated two weeks before his death. The Gangotiyas were supported by the opposition politicians, and all the declining influence and contacts of the current Raja were not enough to get them off his land. He was in court, of course, but a ruling might take ten years, or twenty. Meanwhile the Gangotiyas planted crops, had built many huts and seven pucca houses, a school and a temple.

'Raja-ji, the times are very bad,' Noor Mohammed said. 'But our family has been yours for generations. You have looked after us.'

This was true. By tradition, men from the Ansari Tola had worked in the stables at the haveli, but the horses and elephants had disap-peared after independence. Once, all the land from the haveli to the river, including the shifting soils of the diara closest to the water, had belonged to the Rajas. But the haveli no longer had hundreds of lathis to wield, so the Yadavs had taken the fertile diara fields, and the Gangotiyas had taken the fields near the ponds. The Raja was pressed from both sides. He took a pensive draw of his hookah, and squinted into the distance. Aadil noticed that his rubber chappals, under the armchair, were both splitting at the toes. Aadil's father then said the same thing again, 'Raja-ji, our family has been yours for generations.' They sat with the Raja through the afternoon, watching him puff and sigh and look out over the fields. When it grew dark he gave Noor Mohammed fifty-one rupees, and told Aadil to work hard. And they came back to the Tola.

The next morning they went to Maqbool Khan's house. 'Mir saab,' Noor Mohammed said to him, 'our family has been yours for generations.' Maqbool Khan was sitting at a desk, talking on three phones simultaneously. His land holdings were much reduced, but he now owned seven trucks and three tempos, and had interests in the dusty trades of gravel quarrying and brick-making. He wore a spotless white kurta, though, and sported a luxuriant, up-curling moustache worthy of his lordliest ancestor. Noor Mohammed had taken up his squat next to the desk, and Aadil hunched beside him and listened to Maqbool Khan make deals. Other men came in and sat on chairs and talked to Maqbool Khan and left.

After an hour Maqbool Khan leaned back in his chair, smoothed back his hair, and looked down at Aadil and said, 'Boy, so you want to study? What will you read?'

'Biology.'

For some reason Maqbool Khan found that very funny. He burst out laughing, showing red-stained teeth. 'Horses and cows?' he said. 'Noora, your son will go to college to learn chickens. Why don't you teach him at home?'

Noor Mohammed stayed quiet. After a few minutes, when Maqbool Khan seemed to have forgotten them, he whispered out his old refrain, 'Mir saab, our family has always been with you.' They stayed until Maqbool Khan got up for his lunch. As he walked past them, without looking, he put some notes into Noor Mohammed's cupped hands. Noor Mohammed thanked him with many a 'Mir saab', and tucked the money inside his shirt, and did not count it until they were out on the road, shaken by the turbulence of passing lorries. Maqbool Khan had given eighty-one rupees.

The next day they went to Kurkoo Kothi. Nandan Prasad Yadav was too busy to see them. In fact, Noor Mohammed and Aadil didn't even get inside the house. They waited with a herd of supplicants at the freshly painted rear gate. Workmen had erected scaffolding to repair the tops of the walls, and put new coats of blue and white on the brick. Four guards armed with fearsome rifles lounged by the gate and spat occasionally into the grass. After Noor Mohammed and Aadil had waited for three hours, a secretary emerged from inside the house and sat on a chair in the shade and took requests. When Noor Mohammed and Aadil got up to him, he listened to what Noor Mohammed had to say, and interrupted him brusquely: 'Write a request.' That was all. Father and son retreated to the back of the queue. Aadil had a pen, and a small notebook, but Noor Mohammed thought that such a request should be written on a grander paper. The next morning, he delayed going to the fields, and watched Aadil write a letter on a clean sheet of foolscap paper. Of course Noor Mohammed couldn't read what was being written, but he made Aadil read the whole letter to him three times. Then he told Aadil to take it immediately to Kurkoo Kothi, and give it to secretary saab. Aadil set out, past the nullah and on to the road. The sun burnt his shoulders and thighs. He squinted, and plodded on, fighting against the reluctance that weighed him down. He went past the left turn that led up to the haveli, and now there was a beat inside his head that matched his feet, a steady pulsation of self-loathing. Aadil walked through the bazaar, and down to the right, near the railway station, he could see Maqbool Khan's office. His stomach heaved, and he wanted to stop, to vomit. But he made himself go on. He exercised his will again, this instrument he had honed since childhood, and conquered his body. He went all the way to Kurkoo Kothi, and sat in the crowd until early evening, and handed the letter to the secretary, and came back.

Noor Mohammed went to Kurkoo Kothi once a week after that, to ask after his letter. Aadil had already started attending college, without new clothes and without a bicycle, and he despised himself for needing the money, and despised his father for asking for it. At Diwali, Nandan Prasad Yadav himself appeared at the gate, and Noor Mohammed – at last – came back with a hundred and one rupees. So Aadil made his way through intermediate first year and second year and then the three years of his BSc in zoology, with money earned and scrounged and begged, with debts trailing behind him. Zoology was his consolation. To think about two thin metres of DNA tucked into the infinitesimal space of a single cell was to vanish into wonder. Aadil prayed, he believed, but the only times he now felt an absolute balm of consolation and healing and Allah's love was when he contemplated the beauty of phyla and classes, when he studied photographs of phagocytosis and pinocytosis. Five years slipped by, five hard years that were very long and yet fleeting. Aadil knew he had to keep doing zoology. He would complete his BSc, and he wanted an MSc, there was no question about it. There was also no MSc to be had in Rajpur, not in zoology and not in anything else. Sixty kilometres away there was a zoology department at Nav Niketan University, but Aadil wanted to go to Patna. The city was very far away, but the distance was precisely what Aadil wanted. He needed to go far away from Rajpur, and he imagined Patna as a sprawling criss-cross of lighted boulevards, a haven of anonymity where nobody would know him or his family. He had no doubt that he could get admission in Patna. He had worked hard, and his professors were pleased with him. His marks were not spectacularly good, but he had managed low and middling first divisions all along. The question, as always, was money. From where was it going to come, the two hundred rupees a month, maybe two hundred and fifty, which it would take to survive and study in Patna? There were no scholarships available to him. No high-level contacts were going to exert their influence to get him funding from Patna Science College, no politician was going to give him an education as a gift. Aadil would have to do it on his own.

Aadil went to Maqbool Khan. 'Make me a driver,' he said.

Now Maqbool Khan suddenly wanted to defend the dignity of Aadil's learning. 'How can an educated boy like you be a driver?' he said. 'Why don't you give tuition or something?'

'The Hindus won't hire me to teach their children,' Aadil said. 'And there are not enough Muslims in Rajpur, not enough who can pay.'

Maqbool Khan scratched at his chest thoughtfully. 'I have need of an assistant. I can't keep all these numbers in my head. You are honest, help me with sums and bills.' But Aadil asked who got paid more, a truck driver or a number-adding assistant. 'It's not that simple,' Maqbool Khan said. 'You have to apprentice as a cleaner first. Only later you make more money.'

'I will be a cleaner,' Aadil said simply. 'When do I start?'

So Rajpur was treated to this new spectacle, the great brainy Dibba as a truck cleaner. The day after he got his BSc, he started working for Maqbool Khan. 'Arre, what else did you expect?' the knowledgeable ones of the bazaar said. 'Noora's son, was he going to be the prime minister?'

Aadil wore his new uniform of grime and grease with equanimity. His parents were hard to console, though, and he had to persuade them that this work was only a temporary condition. Education made you unfit, it seemed, for work done by hand. Aadil felt twinges of this distaste himself, but he told himself that this work was also a kind of education. Maqbool Khan's trucks plied the rough roads around Rajpur, and Aadil saw all these hundreds of kilometres. He rode along with loads of gravel, and came back with timber and cement. Once a week he helped Maqbool Khan with accounts, and made sense of his bank passbooks. By the end of the first year he was allowed to drive, and sent on trips that lasted as long as a week.

Aadil's hair, on the left side of his head, began to turn grey. His mother blamed his education, the long nights spent peering at books in flickering lamplight, his unmarried state, the stress of driving week after week. His father advised him to colour in the grey flecks with mehndi, or even some of the expensive new dyes that were just starting to become available in the bazaar. Aadil liked his grey. He thought it gave him the mature look of a great scientist. Still, it was startling sometimes to catch glimpses of himself in a cracked rear-view mirror, and wonder who the lined face belonged to. At the end of two years, by which time he had collected enough money to go to Patna, his whole head, front to back and left to right, was silver-flecked. He came to Patna University prematurely whitened, and full of renewed energy.

Patna was not as he had expected. It was large, bigger than any town or city he had ever seen. It did have wide roads here and there, and some gardens, but there were parts of it that looked like villages clustered together, or Rajpur compressed and made more expensive. There were the same untidy shacks, the winding lanes, the piles of rubbish. The area around the university, though, had some impressive old buildings, some built in colonial times and others given by later benefactors. There were old trees, and Aadil liked sitting on the ghats in the evenings and watching the far shore of the river. The number of students, at the university and in the neighbouring colleges, was staggering. There was a kind of relief in going to some large function, a rally or a lecture or a commemoration, and seeing the rows and rows of faces, in knowing that there were hundreds and thousands of others who had followed the same path, that at least there were some others who had endured the same hungers. Far from his family and the Ansari Tola, Aadil felt a loneliness he had never known, but he welcomed it as a growing pain. I am in the city now, he thought, and I must learn to live in a modern way. This is necessary.

Amidst the laboratories and the cheap restaurants of Patna, Aadil tried to remake himself, but his other selves kept catching up with him. Somehow, his classmates knew about Dibba, his ancient nickname. Maybe one of his old professors from Rajpur had mentioned it to a Patna friend in the zoology department, maybe some Rajpur boy had come up to another college and seen him in the streets. However it had happened, Patna knew who Aadil was, who his father was. They knew he had driven trucks, and cleaned them. There was some praise for this unusual history, and one of Aadil's professors said to him – privately, in the professors' common room – that he should be an inspiration to aspiring scientists everywhere, that such a poor boy should go so far, but Aadil felt an inexplicable undercoating of contempt in the remark. After delivering his high-minded compliment, the professor offered him no other attention, no help, no advice, no grant money or fellowships. Aadil worked on alone. Three times, after completing his own namaaz, he went to meetings of Muslim student organizations, but he was stifled by the constriction of their discussions, which narrowed everything down to the faith and its history. So he kept to his work, and stayed in the laboratories until late into the evening, and read while the hostel rang with raucous laughter, and then settled into sleep.

In the first month of his second year, Aadil met Jagarnath Chaudhury. Jaggu, as he was known, was a Bhumihar Brahmin from Gopalganj, far north and west. He rode a motorcycle and wore dazzling red and yellow jackets, and he sang film songs in a mellow baritone as he swaggered down the halls. He was sitting, that afternoon, on the pillion of his motorcycle, one foot up on the wall that ran around the hostel. With a great deal of shouting and banter with his cronies, he was making plans to see a play put on by the Kala Manch that evening. Aadil edged past them, holding a stack of books to his chest, and he was almost at the stairs when Jaggu called, 'Arre, what's-your-name, you come too.' Aadil tried to decline, but Jaggu dismissed his protests about studying to do and preparation to complete. 'Don't be such a sadial,' Jaggu said. 'The tickets are already bought. You're coming, harami.' Being affectionately cursed by Jaggu was somehow persuasive, and Aadil quietly went along. The play was disastrously bad, even Aadil, who had never seen a play before, could see that it was a badly acted melodrama about persecuted daughters-in-law with a hammered-on happy ending. And yet, it was delicious to sit in a darkened room on hard wooden benches, and pass witty remarks and chortle and eat greasy samosas. Afterwards, they went to a restaurant and ate chicken and tandoori rotis. Aadil turned down the offers of beer, but he allowed himself a Coca-Cola. The astringent taste of it relaxed him somehow, and he laughed at Jaggu's jokes, and told a story himself, about old Ramdas, a farmer in Rajpur who refused to accept that anyone had landed on the moon. They stayed out late, and walked home through empty streets, and yet Aadil woke up refreshed the next morning. He went to his day with an inexplicable lightness in his heart, and the work went easily. When he came back to the hostel, he sat near the gate with Jaggu and the others for an hour.

This became Aadil's daily routine. He was disciplined about getting out and to classes early every morning, but in the evenings he sat with the boys and talked about politics, corruption, films, international events, the changing climate, women, cricket. The conversation moved fast, in a mixture of Hindi and Bhojpuri and Magahi with English sprinkled over it all. Sometimes Aadil kept quiet, when the allusions escaped him, or when the slang flew so fast that it left him quite behind. During and through these sessions, because of the nights at restaurants, he was realizing how much there was that he didn't know about the lives of his new friends, about people who didn't live in the Ansari Tola. Despite all his reading, his world had been limited, and not only because of the smallness of Rajpur. Now that he was friends with boys who had grown up with televisions in their homes, who took motorcycles and trips to Calcutta for granted, whose parents subscribed to newspapers and magazines, Aadil understood that poverty was a country of its own, that he was a foreigner stepping clumsily through unknown landscapes. But he was a good learner, and he applied himself. He had a terror of embarrassing himself, and so he was shy, and always reluctant to assume familiarity. But Jaggu always knocked on his door, and included him in all the group's plans. 'Wake up, Dilip Saab,' he would say, 'time to go.' Jaggu insisted that Aadil was an exact duplicate of the young Dilip Kumar, down to the soft voice and the tragic mumbles. 'Put a rifle in your hand,' he had said, 'and you're straight out of *Ganga Jamuna*.' Aadil understood that this, in Jaggu's lexicon, was high praise. But since Jaggu thought that he himself was the spitting image of Jackie Shroff, and modelled himself with nitpicking precision on his namesake, Aadil didn't take the compliment too seriously. Jaggu's generosity was exactly equal to his self-deception. He believed sincerely that he had fully repudiated his Bhumihar medium-sized-zamindar ancestry by studying history and getting involved with theatre and poetical circles in Patna, but he lived on fat monthly money orders from home. He said he didn't believe in caste or creed, but he once confessed to Aadil – late at night, after many bottles of beer – that he thought people from the lower castes were unclean. 'They don't bathe,' he whispered confidentially. 'It's not in their sanskars, you see. That you can't deny.' He never told Aadil whether Muslims bathed or not, but he especially favoured patriotic films about combat with Pakistan. He ate tandoori chicken avidly, and believed that the narrative of history must be deduced from corroborated facts and archaeological evidence, but he grew wildly furious when he read in the paper about a professor who had published a book proving that Vedic Indians ate beef. 'This is all a plot,' he had muttered, his face crimson, 'a maderchod plan.' He didn't say whose plan it was, and Aadil didn't ask. It was understood.

And yet Jaggu was an affectionate and faithful friend. He went out of his way to help Aadil and his other hostel-mates, he organized outings, he went on his motorcycle and fetched medicines when someone was sick. Even though he wasn't in Aadil's department, he collected gossip about Aadil's professors, and advised him on the subtleties of academic politics. He was a constant support, and Aadil was glad to have him as confidant. It was impossible to admit, even to Jaggu, but university was very hard for Aadil, and getting more difficult. It wasn't just the studies and the research, which took hours and effort and the energy from Aadil's body. This he could manage, even though he was now competing with boys who were truly gifted, and not just the ragged lot of Rajpur louts. It was the chronic shortage of money that wore him down. How could you read, and concentrate on what you were reading, when your stomach twitched and ached from hunger? As the weeks passed, Aadil's small reserve of cash in the bank was being whittled down. There were always unexpected expenditures, fees and hostel collections and antibiotics for a sudden fever. There were books that were not on the curriculum but which professors casually declared to be essential pre-exam reading. And there were new hungers, for a play, for dinner at a restaurant and maybe a Coca-Cola. But the rupees vanished rapidly, and Aadil struggled, and tried to reduce his spending. But there was no excess to trim away, and he felt as if his discipline were cutting into his own flesh. He suffered, and he hid his suffering.

'Beta, what is happening to your hair?' Jaggu said to Aadil one evening, tugging him down by the shoulder so he could peer closely at Aadil's head. They were sitting on top of the wall, outside the hostel, waiting for the group to gather for an expedition to the Ashok cinema.

'My hair? Nothing,' Aadil said. He patted down his parting, and was reassured of the fullness of the growth.

'Yaar, it's going completely white.'

'No.'

'I'm telling you.'

'It's the same. It has been like this for a long time.'

'No, no. Full white, I'm telling you. Come and look.'

They went back into the hostel, upstairs to Jaggu's room, which had many mirrors. Jaggu positioned Aadil in front of one on the wall, and held another one behind his head. 'Look,' he said.

Aadil looked, and he saw that the back of his head was indeed quite white. From behind, he was an old man.

'I think it's spreading from back to front,' Jaggu said. 'But listen, it's nothing to worry about.' And he proceeded to list hair dyes, and pronounce on the virtues of different brands, and instruct Aadil in their usage. He was outraged when Aadil shook his head, and refused to colour.

'Why, bhai, why? I ask you, why?' Jaggu said. 'Nothing could be easier. It's not like you have to do it every day. You need to take care of yourself, and you refuse to do even this little thing.'

Aadil held Jaggu's wrist, and smiled, and shook his head, and led him down, back to the gate and the others. It was impossible to explain to Jaggu that hair dye even once a month could be an unbearable expenditure, a luxury reserved for people not like Aadil. Jaggu, who threw away his toothbrush every second week because he thought it looked worn and tired, couldn't know what it really meant to live without a thick fold of rupees available at all times. He didn't lack intelligence, or sympathy, or insight. He was just different, he couldn't understand. Aadil couldn't blame him personally. Aadil couldn't tell him, either, that there were many days now when he felt like an old man. Maybe Aadil had aged prematurely, which was why there was this debilitating weariness seeping through his veins. He fought to rouse himself from bed every morning, struggled through fatigue to get through lectures, studying, exams. The exhaustion was not just in his muscles or cells, this he could have perhaps isolated and controlled and defeated. He had somehow been eroded, ground down until only a thin sliver of will was left, steely and brittle. He was on the verge of breaking, and yet he had to go on. He survived. He kept at it, and by the end of the year, by the time that exams were done and plans were being made for the future, Aadil had had enough. He wanted to go home.

'Why?' Jaggu said. 'Go back to what? You have to get a PhD, that's the only thing you can do.'

Getting a doctorate was the only possible choice if you wanted to teach, which Aadil did want to do. But paying for another degree, for three or maybe four years, was something he was not capable of, not any more. Maybe a human being could only expend so much effort, he thought, and he had been trying so very hard from class one onwards, he had no strength left to exert. He knew that he couldn't drive trucks any more, or miss another meal, or borrow books and make fervent promises that he would return them before dawn. He tried to explain to Jaggu. 'I am just very tired,' he said.

Jaggu grew angry. 'What is this, this laziness? I thought you had more guts than that. You are just throwing away years of education. At least try.'

For the first time, Aadil felt a sullen rage towards Jaggu, his friend who had so easily finished one degree and was going on to another one, who would no doubt complete this one with a song on his lips, who would have a PhD and a teaching job dropped into his lap. He would think he had really tried so hard to earn these prizes, he would believe that he had sacrificed and sweated. No doubt, one day, seated with his fellow professors in some cosy common room, he would tell the story of his friend Aadil, a poor rural boy who hadn't had the fortitude to finish his education. *Those people*, he would say, and sigh and take a sip of his chai. And here he was, generous Jaggu, righteous and indignant. Aadil wanted to slap him.

Instead, Aadil turned away. He withstood Jaggu's impassioned entreaties and gibes for the next three weeks, and then he went home to Rajpur. Here, in the bazaar, there were debates and arguments about what had happened to Dibba in Patna. Some thought he had failed, others believed that he had not even gone to Patna. Otherwise why would he come back, with all his supposed education, and work on the land? This was the puzzle that Rajpur tried to solve, and some even went out to Ansari Tola, to see Aadil in the fields, wearing a lungi and sweating next to his father. Aadil shrugged off all questions and taunts, and kept to himself. He came into town rarely, to get seed and fertilizer, and went straight back out. The months passed, and the bazaar wits grew tired of Dibba, and moved on to other topics. Interest was suddenly revived when it became clear that Dibba was going to produce a spectacular crop from that little patch of patli earth near Ansari Tola. After the spring harvest, there was much sage nodding of heads in Rajpur. 'That Dibba boy is earning all that Patna money back for his father. From his ekfasli land, Dibba's going to produce two harvests. Old Noora must be happy.'

Noor Mohammed wasn't happy. He was very afraid. During the cutting of the crop, Aadil had noticed that their land had shrunk. The farm next to theirs belonged to Nandan Prasad Yadav, and during the harvesting, it expanded six inches all down the length that abutted Noor Mohammed's land. Nandan Prasad Yadav's men cut their crop, and when they were done, the addah that separated the two properties had somehow shifted six inches to the west. One farm grew, the other lessened. When Aadil pointed this out, at first Noor Mohammed denied it. Then Aadil grew angry, and walked him down the boundary, and pointed out where it was closer to the babul tree on their side, and further from the pump on Nandan Prasad Yadav's land. Noor Mohammed could deny it no longer. He admitted that their land had been taken, but begged Aadil to do nothing, say absolutely nothing. 'We are very small people,' he said. 'They are elephants.'

Aadil was quiet. The yellow flowers of the babul blazed against the distant haze over the river. 'How much have they taken?' he said.

'You said this much, kya?' Noor Mohammed said, holding up a callused hand, fingers stretched out.

'No,' Aadil said. He took his father's hand. 'I mean in all, everything, in all the years.'

Noor Mohammed looked over at Nandan Prasad Yadav's holding, which went all the way into the high land and to the road. He wasn't measuring, he knew already. 'We used to own almost one and a half bighas. One bigha they took when I was a boy. My Abba, he borrowed some money and signed a paper.'

'What paper?'

'Who knows? He couldn't pay, so they took the land.'

Noor Mohammed didn't know who had the paper now, either, or where it could be found. 'Beta,' he said, 'the land belongs to them now. It's theirs.'

Aadil pointed down at the new addah. 'And this?'

Noor Mohammed had no sorrow, no anger. His brow and cheeks were as hard as carved black stone. 'This also,' he said, 'is theirs.' He turned and walked back to the Tola at his usual even pace, not slow and not fast.

Noor Mohammed grew afraid the next day, when it became clear that Aadil was not willing or able to stay quiet. Aadil went that morning to Kurkoo Kothi and demanded to see Nandan Prasad Yadav. After being kept waiting for four hours, he went to the Rajpur police thana and tried to file an FIR, and when the constable on duty laughed at him, he came back to Ansari Tola, took a spade and tramped out to his fields. An hour later a labourer on Nandan Prasad Yadav's land saw him, digging furiously. He had moved fifteen feet of the addah back over. Another hour later, two men with lathis and two with shotguns came out to Ansari Tola, and spoke to Noor Mohammed. He and two of his cousins ran out to the field, and talked and then struggled with Aadil. They had to wrestle the spade away from him. He cursed them all, and Nandan Prasad Yadav's men laughed. Aadil walked away. Noor Mohammed and his cousins moved the addah back to where it had been that morning.

Aadil went to the land records karamchari the next day, and from there to the circle inspector. Both seemed impressed by his sophisticated manner of speech, and advised him to file a land suit, and they would take it up with the circle officer, who was actually a deputy collector, who would take it up with the collector. Neither the karamchari or the circle inspector knew anything about a promissory note signed by Aadil's grandfather, but the karamchari promised to look up the number for the plot of land in the registry, and see if there was anything to be found there.

Aadil understood that nothing would be found, and nothing would be done. He had no money to bribe the karamchari, and no influence to bring to bear on the circle inspector. The Ansari Tola didn't have the numbers or the will to beat back Nandan Prasad Yadav. The land that had been lost would never be regained. He knew this as surely as he knew that the Milani flowed from west to east, and yet he was unable to reconcile himself to it. He knew that in Rajpur the rule of law was an illusion that not even children believed in, but he could not find the fortitude that his parents practised. He was no longer silent. When he went into the bazaar, he spoke angrily against Nandan Prasad Yadav. He called him a thief and a bastard. He had not drunk beer in Patna, but now he began to drink tadi. His relatives now often found him staggering down the road to the Ansari Tola. He sat on the culvert, talking to himself and darting red-eyed glares at all who walked by. His mother and father pleaded, threatened, got the maulvi to speak to him, but nothing could assuage Aadil's despair. His mother insisted that he be married now, that a wife and responsibility would calm him down, but no parents were willing to give their girl to such a known madman, all his education notwithstanding.

Aadil still worked assiduously in the fields, every day. Every day, he walked the length of the addah, making sure it had not moved again. One evening, that August, he found two men waiting for him at the end of the field. One was tall, with enormous muscled forearms and a belligerent air. But it was the other one, short and dark and round-faced, who was clearly the leader. 'Are you Aadil Ansari?' he said, holding on to the ends of his gamcha and bouncing on his heels.

'I am.'

'Lal Salaam. I am Kishore Paswan.'

Aadil didn't quite know how to react to Kishore Paswan's upraised fist. He had never been the recipient of a red salute before, and he fumbled and put his hand on his chest. Kishore Paswan didn't seem to mind. He was grinning up at Aadil.

'I heard you are having lots of trouble.'

'Who are you?' The Naxals had never been very active around Rajpur, and Aadil had never heard of Kishore Paswan.

'I told you who I am. I am Kishore Paswan Jansevak. Come. Tell me what's been happening.'

Kishore Paswan took Aadil by the elbow and led him to the side of the field, where they all squatted in the shade of a tree. Paswan had a very soft voice, and a soothing manner. Aadil found himself telling his whole story, not just about the stolen land, but about his struggles in primary school, and his times in Patna. Paswan listened, and then told Aadil about himself. He was from near Gaya, the son of daily-wage labourers. His family had been active in the anti-feudal movement, and his Naxalite father had worked with the great revolutionary Chunder Ghosh. When Kishore Paswan was three, both his father and Chunder Ghosh had been shot and killed by a police agent disguised as a businessman. So Kishore Paswan had been politically active since youth, working against the oppressions of the upper castes and the state. History had remade him into Kishore Paswan Jansevak. He was now a functionary in the People's Revolutionary Council, which was an above-ground, legitimate organization dedicated to the betterment of the poor. 'We are dedicated to justice, my friend,' Kishore Paswan said. 'If you are politically aware, you are with us. If you are intelligent, you have no choice but to be with us. We want to unite the proletariat. We have in our membership every caste, every religion. Some of our leadership are even Brahmins. It does not matter. If you understand the structure of oppression, then you cannot help being with us.'

As Kishore Paswan went on to describe this structure, Aadil saw that his logic was impeccable. That feudalism still existed in Rajpur was obvious, that the reactionary classes oppressed the proletariat went without saying. But now, as Paswan instructed Aadil in the subtleties of Marxism-Leninism-Maoism, Aadil saw how precisely the theory fitted the facts. Of course Aadil had heard of Marx before, he had discussed Lenin with his hostel-mates, but he had been too pre-occupied with zoology to delve into the works of Mao, to read or investigate, to understand the Great Helmsman's long march and the spring thunder his party had once proclaimed over India. Now it seemed to Aadil that what Paswan was telling him had a scientific elegance about it. Of course, of course. The institutions of the state were reactionary by nature, defined by the class positions of those who controlled them. The police and other executive arms of the state were used to destroy, to exterminate the developing class struggle of the landless peasants. What was always referred to as a 'law and order problem' in the reactionary newspapers was actually the natural outcome of a socio-political system which generated poverty, unemployment, illiteracy and all-round underdevelopment for more than ninety per cent of the toiling population in mostly rural areas, while producing immense wealth and extravagance for a handful of parasitic classes in the villages and the cities. The aim of the class struggle was to eliminate feudalism and bureaucratic capitalism. The contradictions of the present class-divided society would result in its destruction, leading to a truly classless society on earth. The dialectic itself would produce the necessary next stage, the workers' paradise. This could not be denied. It was inevitable.

Paswan spoke rapidly, without pause. His words fell like scouring medicine on Aadil and burned away the last vestiges of bourgeois illusion from his mind and his heart. He knew then how ridiculous it had been of him to invest hope in a rotten system. To trust the reactionary classes in any way was a sign of weakness and ignorance. Aadil wanted to participate, to somehow take part in the revolution.

'That's easy to say,' Paswan said, 'hard to do.'

'I will do anything.'

'Good. Mind you,' Paswan said sternly, 'the first battle that a revolutionary must win is against his own ignorance and bad habits. We expect nothing less than ideal social behaviour, worthy of a revolutionary. You must take control of yourself. You must examine yourself and your actions ceaselessly, and dedicate yourself completely to the struggle. No less is acceptable.'

So Aadil immediately, from that day on, gave up tadi. He never drank again. He applied himself to the struggle. Comrade Jansevak instructed him to educate the poor in and around Rajpur, to raise revolutionary consciousness, and to keep farming, to not lose heart. Fortified, Aadil continued. With the backing of the PRC, accompanied by Comrade Jansevak, Aadil revisited the karamchari, who was now exceedingly co-operative and productive. A land suit was promptly filed against Nandan Prasad Yadav.

A week later, Aadil had no water. The irrigating water that fed his fields came from the river, to the east, and through Prem Shanker Jha's land. This had been the arrangement for decades, for generations. Now Prem Shanker Jha closed the narrow channel and declared that he needed the land for cultivation, that the movement of water across his fields was a burden that he was unwilling to carry any more. He refused to listen to any arguments. Aadil was no longer willing to plead. Prem Shanker Jha and Nandan Prasad Yadav were not on the best of terms. They were rivals for influence and money and land, the political candidates they backed sometimes clashed with each other. And yet, they were now colluding. As Comrade Jansevak observed, this is the way of the capitalist world, bitter enemies will become brothers to protect class interests. Don't worry, Comrade Jansevak told Aadil, we will struggle.

But that Monday, Aadil was arrested. At five in the morning, he was pulled out of a bitter, thrashing sleep, and taken to the thana. The FIR had already been prepared: one Aadil Ansari, acting in collusion with a group of eleven unknown men, had surrounded two constables at the Garhi chowki and overpowered them. The intruders had then broken into the armoury in the chowki, and decamped with nine .303 Lee-Enfield rifles and four hundred and sixty rounds of ammunition. The two constables had been tied up and blindfolded, but they had clearly seen the ringleader, whom they recognized as the notorious Naxal leader, Aadil Ansari.

On the basis of this lie, Aadil was remanded to custody for ten days. The policemen beat him every day, with straps, and with lathis on the soles of his feet. Noor Mohammed made frantic outcries at Nandan Prasad Yadav's gate, and sat whole days outside the thana and wept. After ten days, Aadil's bail request was refused, on the grounds that he presented the risk of violence to society at large, and to the two witnesses of his crime in particular. He was sent a hundred kilometres south to the Hasla Aadarsh Kara to await trial. Aadil spent the next two years and three months in this jail, through a series of trial dates and postponements, all because the two constables were unable to come to court and testify. First both were ill, then they were posted along the Nepal border, then they were ill again. They were simply unavailable. The trial, of course, had to happen, and so Aadil was kept in jail. He surprised himself with his patience, his good spirits, in this fetid, crumbling edifice that crushed so many men. It had been built fifty years before, to house six hundred prisoners, and it now held two thousand. The food smelt of rot, and fevers and dysenteries took a steady toll. But Aadil was never depressed or afraid. He did not pray any more, not even once a day. He dedicated himself to the study of Marxism-Leninism-Maoism and the campaigns mounted by peasants and workers in every part of the world. Aadil read the pamphlets and books sent to him by Comrade Jansevak, and educated every man he came into contact with. In Hasla jail, Aadil was soon known as the Professor, and this was the sobriquet that he took with him to the outside.

Aadil and four others escaped one bright December morning when the chief minister was visiting the district. Many from the jail staff had been assigned to duty on the roads and for the minister's bandobast, leaving only a skeleton force in the prison. Aadil and his fellow prisoners overpowered two guards behind the jail laundry, and then climbed a wall, using wooden racks and cords from the laundry to construct makeshift ladders. Two days later, Aadil was in Rajpur, in conference with Comrade Jansevak. 'I want those bastards,' he said.

'Are you sure?' Comrade Jansevak said. 'If you kill two policemen, you will run for ever.'

'I am already running. Don't worry. I've decided. I have left everything behind.'

Aadil killed the two constables named in the FIR four days later. Five policemen were actually killed in the blast, but Aadil was concerned about his two accusers. The others were just accidental profit. Comrade Jansevak had put Aadil in touch with the People's Action Committee, which was the military arm of the PRC. The PAC had the necessary intelligence and the matériel for the job. They knew that an inspector and four constables would be travelling in a jeep to the village of Ganti, to investigate a clash between rival groups in a land dispute. For three days the PAC had hidden scouts watching the dirt road that the police would have to drive down to Ganti. On the fourth day, the police jeep was seen approaching at eleven in the morning. It was confirmed that Aadil's two constables were in the back of the jeep. The jeep passed, and as soon as it was out of sight, the PAC platoon and Aadil went to work. Aadil watched the PAC men lay the landmine in the road. They were using sticks of RDX, which they called gelatin. The platoon leader grinned as he lowered the Dalda tin containing the explosive into the hole they had dug. Aadil had not been told any of their names, for reasons of operational security.

The platoon leader said, 'Professor, do you know what this is?'

'I do.'

'And you still stand so close by?'

'Comrade Jansevak told me that you were an expert.'

The platoon leader grinned. Then Aadil helped him unreel a black wire back from the road, up the side of an addah and then behind it. Two men from the platoon went along the wire, kicking dirt over it. Then they all lay behind the rise, the PAC men cradling their rifles. The sun came over them and they waited. Aadil's head was pounding. The platoon leader told him about the raid on a mine in Singhbhum that had netted them twelve hundred gelatin sticks. They waited. At two-thirty a scout signalled from the east.

'The jeep is coming,' the platoon leader said. 'You want to do it?' He held up the end of the black wire, separated out into two strands. In front of him there was a red car battery. 'You have to do it with exact timing. Too soon or too late and it won't hit.'

Aadil shook his head. He wanted to do it, but he wanted to be sure. His hands were shaking and he wasn't sure that he could manage the calculation, of moving object and distance and the near-instantaneous speed of electricity. The jeep bumped along the road and came closer and now Aadil could hear it. It appeared that it had passed the spot which Aadil had marked as the location of the mine, but then it vanished in a white and brown spasm of the earth that shut Aadil's eyes. When he blinked them open there was a gout of black dust and smoke and then a blackened metal hulk crashing far from the road, on the near side towards the PAC platoon. The men cheered and hooted.

'Forty feet,' the platoon leader said. 'It flew at least forty feet.'

Aadil ran behind them, his ears still ringing, as they went forward. A small shower of paper came drifting down, and the air smelt of petrol. Then Aadil saw a policeman's body, but only half of it. The boots and the legs were quite intact, and the brown leather belt still held its polish. But above the waist there was a dirty tangle of innards, and nothing else. Aadil's throat clutched, and he had to turn away. Control yourself, he told himself. You have performed many dissections. This is nothing new.

'First time is always hard,' the platoon leader said. He kicked away a smouldering metal strut and bent over to get a look at another body underneath. The chassis of the jeep, behind them, was covered with a fine layer of lapping blue flames. 'Don't worry. The habit will get into you. Some day you'll do it yourself.'

'I'm not worried,' Aadil said. The nausea he had just suffered was just a spasm of the body, his mind knew better. The policemen were class enemies, and they had to be executed. There wasn't really a choice.

As he expected, Aadil got used to the killing. He operated mainly in Bhagalpur and Munger. Comrade Jansevak thought he was too well-known around Rajpur, and there were now too many informers and enemies who would take a personal interest in doing him harm. So Aadil fought his war far from home. He carried a rifle and a Rampuri knife, but his main work was education and indoctrination. He went from village to village, moving mostly at night and never crossing an empty field during the day. He conducted classes for the peasants, gathering them at midnight by the light of a single lantern. He taught them their own history, and offered them a vision of the future: equality, prosperity, no landlords, no debt, each person the owner of his own fate.

With each passing week, Aadil became more depended on by the commanders of the PAC. Since he was the Professor, he never commanded a squad, but he rose rapidly through the ranks and became a trusted tactician. The landlords had their armies, and the police their power and brutality, and so the game was played out across the hills and the riverine mazes of the diara. Aadil planned the operations, the executions in response to massacres, the ambushes of police convoys and kidnappings of engineers and doctors. He discovered an instinctive feeling for feint and counter-blow, for subterfuge and evasions. He delighted in the success of his schemes, and he was not impervious to the admiration of his comrades, and so he trained himself to be a good soldier. He was no longer sickened by the smell of human blood. He took part in a few operations, most notably the ambush of an eight-vehicle police party that was returning from an investigation of the killing of a sarpanch. There was a hot exultation in the firing of an SLR at the khaki-clad figures scuttling about the road below, confused and terrorized by the mines which had blown their three lead trucks. The plan had been entirely Aadil's. The sarpanch, who had been an informer and a reactionary right-winger, had been executed in a particularly public way, by beheading in the middle of the village market on a busy Tuesday. Since the sarpanch had been close to the local MLA, Aadil knew that the police would send out a substantial convoy to investigate and reassure. So Aadil and two squads had waited for them on the road, and found them. The final bag was thirty-six policemen killed, many injured, for not one PAC casualty. The Professor again won high praise, but what Aadil valued the most, afterwards, was the memory of the rifle jumping against his cheek, the smell of the powder. The sensations told him that he was not useless, discarded. He had tilted his shoulder against the leaning of the world, and he would shift it on its axis.

The years passed. The battles came and went, one after another. Aadil's parents passed, one after another in less than a month during one cold winter. His mother died content, knowing that her son was at last married. Aadil's wife was much younger than him. Her name was Jhannu, and she was a Musahar girl educated until the tenth class, a fiery ideologue of the party and a canny, experienced fighter. Aadil met her when he outlined an operation for her squad in Singhbhum. She pointed out the flaws in his plan, but was moved by his white hair and his reputation for dedication to the cause. They married, and he was overwhelmed by the heat in Jhannu's lean, brown body and his hunger for a certain soft place at the bottom of her throat, just next to the hard muscle of her shoulder. But in less than two years they drifted apart. She was assigned to lead a squad in Hazaribagh, and seeing her required an elaborate passing of messages and risky journeys. Aadil wondered also if she had begun to question the quality of his commitment to the struggle. He worked as hard as ever, but he found that knowledge had lessened his ability to indulge himself in simplicities. He was not quite a cynic, but in bed, maybe a little relaxed by the feel of her hair against his cheek, he had let slip a remark or two about the leaders of the party. For instance, he had complained to Comrade Jansevak when Jhannu was being sent away from him, and Comrade Jansevak had said, 'A worker of the party must take such things in his stride. Aadil, my friend, maybe marriage itself is not such a good idea for soldiers. We must sacrifice everything.' But Aadil knew that Comrade Jansevak himself had not one wife but two. There was one he had been married to long ago, in his childhood. And there was another, barely out of childhood herself and renowned for her blossoming beauty. Comrade Jansevak kept her in a house in Gaya, in a three-storeyed pink mansion equipped with a satellite dish and a television in every room, and two Kirloskar generators. Aadil knew this, and maybe he said something to his own wife. And once, only once, very late at night, he had whispered to Jhannu about all the killing, the executions and the retaliations. She quoted Chairman Mao. 'The country must be destroyed and re-formed,' she said, and grew stiff against him.

Aadil also knew where the money for Comrade Jansevak's mansion came from: it was taken from the levies and taxes the PAC extracted from farmers and businessmen. Aadil had learnt the business of revolution. Much of the money passed through his own hands, as it went from bottom to top. He appreciated that the logistics of war demanded funding, he knew the price of an AK-47 and the cost – per thousand – of bullets. There were other expenses, for salaries and pamphlets and travel and medicine. He knew all this, but there were times when he couldn't help thinking of what he was doing, of what he was directing, as nothing less or more than extortion. He took money. He gave guns to boys and girls and told them to bring back money. He tried to teach history to his soldiers, but he knew that many of them mouthed his lessons exactly as they had chanted religious hymns, without curiosity and without understanding. Jhannu quoted Chairman Mao in every conversation, and practised dialectical materialism every day, but for every one of her there were ten boys to whom Chairman Mao was only a hazy yellow god who gave them weapons. Some bastard zamindar had taken their land with the force of his lathaits, and so now they had a rifle and much ammunition. That was all they knew and all they wanted to know.

So Aadil knew all this, and spoke about it briefly to his own wife, and so lost her. And yet, he was no counter-revolutionary, no recidivist. His ideology was as clear as mountain water. He believed sincerely and completely, he trusted still in the promise of the future. The revolution would chip away at all forms of exploitation, until a truly classless and stateless world communism was achieved. This was inevitable. The revolution would continue. There was no liberation without revolution, and no revolution without a people's war. What could look like an imperfect practice of Marxism-Leninism-Maoism was often merely practicality. Perfection was to be sought with imperfect means. The virtues of the oppressed were cunning and subterfuge and deception. The duty of the cadres was to obey the dictates of the party. All this Aadil accepted and believed. He had no doubts about the purity of the party's aims – no matter how many green sofas Comrade Jansevak bought for his wife – and he would continue to serve with the utmost enthusiasm and vigour. He would give his life to the party, to the workers of the coming years. He had known only struggle, but they would know happiness. For them, and their future lives, he was willing to live with Comrade Jansevak's perks, with the burdens that were placed on peasants and small shopkeepers, he would put up with the executions of backsliders, and all the blood.

Killing was commonplace to Aadil now. Keeping score through the chaos and noise of ambushes was hard, but Aadil calculated that he himself had killed a dozen men, maybe twenty, maybe a few more. No more than that. He had seen many more than that killed, by bullet and explosion and axe and lathi. He couldn't remember all the dead bodies he had seen, the small piles of flesh and rags that he had stepped over. He had gone on, face always to the front, leaving the dead behind. At first, each death that Aadil had witnessed had been a momentous event, a change in the world that struck him with the force of a revelation. He had paid close attention to the symptoms, a twitching arm, an open eye with the shine gone off the sclera, leaving it blackish-yellow. The retina gone grey. Then, long ago, each of these transfigurations had promised a great transformation tomorrow, each dying had presaged the coming light of the worker's dawn. Now the corpses fell, and Aadil did not count them. Death was the ground he stepped on, the country of his existence. Aadil lived inside death, and so no longer noticed it.

It was life, finally, that unhinged him and sent him fleeing from the revolution, from Comrade Jansevak and the PAC, from Bihar. The platoon leader who had taken Aadil on his first ambush was now an area commander, and Aadil was allowed to know his name, Natwar Kahar. Natwar Kahar operated in Jamui and Nawada mostly, aided by a second-in-command named Bhavani Kahar. This Bhavani, who was just twenty-four, was a distant relative and special protégé of Natwar Kahar's. Natwar Kahar had inducted Bhavani into the party when he was a young boy, and groomed him as a soldier and potential party leader. The boy had charisma, and he was fearless. On Diwali night, young Bhavani was picked up by the police in the village of Rekhan. Bhavani was deep in a drunken sleep in the house of a woman, a widow, when the police found him. And so handsome Bhavani disappeared into the grinding jaws of justice, and Natwar Kahar was left raging. The police had obviously received a tip-off, a very specific one. Natwar Kahar examined his suspects, all the villagers, and he finally settled on Bhavani's woman. She was the only one who knew that Bhavani would come to her bed that Diwali night, that he had a weakness for good rum. She had sent her two children to her mother's house, and that on Diwali night. So Natwar Kahar had her seized and brought up to his camp. He asked for her name – which was Ramdulari – and then he asked her for a confession. Ramdulari protested, she was innocent, she would never do such a thing, and especially she would never betray Bhavani. She was a tall woman, Ramdulari, not beautiful but with a long, lush body and a fast walk. Her husband had died of kalazar during a flood some eight years ago. She had raised her two boys, and maintained her house and survived. When she spoke to Natwar Kahar, she had her head covered but she looked very directly at him and did not beg, or tremble, or look afraid. Natwar Kahar insisted on a confession, and she shook her head, and spoke back at him impatiently, saying that Bhavani was dear to her, as much as he was to Natwar Kahar.

So Natwar Kahar convened a people's court that very same evening. Ramdulari was tried, the evidence was examined and she was convicted. She again refused the chance of confession and self-criticism. The sentence was, of course, death, as it always was for betrayal. But Natwar Kahar wanted to make an example of Ramdulari. Instead of proceeding with the customary beheading, he cut her a little at a time. The next morning he called the squad together, and in front of them he cut off all her toes and fingers. He did it with a small kulhadi which was kept about the camp for stripping poles and saplings. She screamed, and bled, and Natwar Kahar laughed and had the camp doctor attend to her. 'Keep her alive,' Natwar Kahar said. The doctor was not really a doctor. He had once been a compounder, and he had never encountered multiple amputations. But he had some experience with bullet wounds and cuts, and Ramdulari survived. She was very strong. They kept her in a pit behind Natwar Kahar's shack. She was given food regularly, and it became something of a camp amusement to watch her try to eat with the pads of her hands, and bend double to lick up grains of rice from the dirt.

Aadil saw Ramdulari three weeks after her trial. He hadn't believed the story when he had first heard it, about Natwar Kahar's punishment of the informing whore. He thought it was good propaganda, effective in preventing the Bhavani Kahar situation from occurring again. Even when Aadil came to Natwar Kahar's camp, to pick up a delivery of cash, he did not think to mention the woman. He thought she was dead and the matter closed. He had finished putting the plastic-wrapped stacks of notes in his jhola when Natwar Kahar asked, with a grin, 'Do you want to see Ramdulari?'

Aadil didn't know whose name that was, and Natwar Kahar explained with a proprietary pride. Aadil followed him, the bag heavy over his shoulder. The stench from the pit pressed at Aadil's face, but Natwar Kahar walked on, unconcerned. They stood overlooking the sloping hole. At the bottom, in the moist yellow and brown mess, there was a large moving object. Aadil couldn't make out what it was. It was neither human nor animal, nothing that he had ever seen before. It moved in sideways jerks and spasms, something like the little crabs that popped up from the sand on the river's edge. Then Aadil's head swam softly and lifted, and the sun shifted its arc, and he saw that below him was a woman, but strangely attenuated. She was not complete.

'We cut her at knees and elbow four days ago,' Natwar Kahar said, chopping at his arm with the edge of his hand. 'I thought for sure she was gone. There was too much blood. But the bitch won't die.'

Ramdulari was looking at Aadil. He felt himself swaying, unable to look away. Her eyes were enormous and dark and remote, and he could read nothing in them, not pain or sorrow. The dark hair wrapped around her face and her lips drew back. She was saying something. But what? He was sure she was speaking. He couldn't hear her, not past the roaring that came from inside his body, everywhere, his arms and legs and stomach, like the flapping of a thousand wings. Natwar Kahar was saying something. What?

'If we put food and water on the other side, over there, she crawls. It takes hours, but she gets there. She just won't die.'

Hearing Natwar Kahar's voice, hoarse and low, broke Aadil's trance. He was able to look away. Natwar Kahar was watching Ramdulari, and he was almost admiring, almost respectful. He was rubbing his chin. Aadil heard the scrape of his fingers over his white stubble. Natwar Kahar said, 'She's as strong as a horse.'

Aadil reeled away. He found the support of a tree, and vomited at its roots. He finished, and Natwar Kahar was waiting for him, one arm folded across his chest, the other smoothing out his moustache.

'It was the smell,' Aadil said. 'Very bad.'

'Arre, Professor,' Natwar Kahar said, smiling widely, 'after all these years you're just the same.'

Aadil didn't assert his toughness, his many ambushes, his operations, he did not argue. All he wanted was to be out of Natwar Kahar's camp. He left within the hour, even though it was long before darkness. He took his bodyguards and left, and pushed hard all night, down the paths and across the nullahs. They reached their safe house in Jamui town early. The boys slept, but Aadil sat by the window and watched the road. He was afraid to shut his eyes, because when he did so a crawling began under his skin, a jerky sliding that terrified him. He wondered whether he had remained the same, or whether he had changed. At two in the afternoon, when the heat came off the ground in billowing breaths, he slipped out of the door. He left the bag of cash he had collected from Natwar Kahar on the floor of the front room, and took nothing with him, not even a pistol. In his pocket he had eight thousand rupees, his Rampuri knife and a driver's licence in the name of Maqbool Khan. He went to the station, bought a second-class sitting ticket for an express train, and was in Patna at a little past six-thirty. He went straight to the ticket counter, paid four hundred and forty-nine rupees, and sat on the platform until his train got in at eleven-twenty. He did not have a reservation, so he squatted in the corridor in an unreserved coach, squeezed in tightly amongst a wedding party. At Jhansi, he got out of the coach, and bribed a sleeper berth out of the ticket collector. Then he slept. The motion of the train somehow countered the agitation in his body, and he was able to doze whole afternoons away, getting up only to use the bathroom and drink water. In a little more than fifty hours, he was in Mumbai.

Mumbai was very far from Jamui, from Bhagalpur and from Rajpur, and it was vast and anonymous, and Aadil wanted to hide in it. But it frightened him. This city was more of an unknown wilderness than any jungle ridge. That first day, he got off the train and walked along the railway tracks, and a heavy odour seeped down his throat, and he had no idea where he was. There were makeshift homes along the tracks, and children playing just feet from the rails. They laughed at him when he flinched at passing trains. The taller buildings behind the huts were stained grey and black, and festooned with wires. Aadil passed an enormous pile of rubbish flecked with plastic bags, and then a very old man sitting against the iron fence that bordered this section of track. The old man had a white beard, a sunken chest under a torn kurta, and a little white bag on the ground next to him. He was staring at something far away, even further than the far fence and the buildings behind it, further than the dim hills. Aadil shuddered as he walked past the old man. He walked faster. He was very hungry. He stopped, counted the money he had, then found a gap in the fence and went through. He was afraid to cross the wide road with its endless stream of traffic, but finally he found his way across and plunged into the city.

Aadil lived first in Thane, then in Malad, then Borivili, and then near Kailashpada. He avoided bastis with settlements of Biharis, and he moved often. A glance of recognition made him anxious, and at night he dreamed about Natwar Kahar and a band of riflemen hunting him down in the streets of Mumbai. Two months after he arrived, on a street corner in Andheri, Aadil saw somebody he knew from Rajpur, a boy named Santosh Nath Jha – otherwise known as Babloo – who had been three years junior to him through school and college. Babloo was counting out coins to pay a paan-wallah, and he didn't see Aadil start and back up behind the wall, into a lane. Aadil looked once again, to make sure it was Babloo, to satisfy himself that such a long coincidence could and did happen, and then he hurried away, staying close to the side of the road and ducking his head. He moved kholis again the next day, to a smaller room in Borivili. His kholi was at the end of a very narrow lane, butted up against the wall. Aadil breathed in the miasma of refuse, from a dump on the other side of the wall, but he felt safe here for a while. He recognized the appalling squalor of his surroundings, compared to which a PAC camp was luxurious, but he had nowhere else to go. Within a month he moved again, because his Tamil neighbours were too curious, and because they had friends and visitors from everywhere, even Bihar. This time he found a kholi in Navnagar, in the Bengali Bura. Here, the inhabitants were all Bangladeshis. Here, finally, Aadil felt safe. These Bengalis were all illegals, with purchased documents and falsified places of birth. They were careful, and they kept to themselves. They were slow to trust Aadil, they fell into silence when he passed by, and he felt comfortable within the wariness. Inside their alien Bengali, he was safe.

He did not like to leave the basti, so sometimes he gave money to the boys who lived down the lane, to bring him food and razor blades and medicines for his headaches. He now suffered from pain in his temples, agony so intense that for two or three days on end he would lie inside his kholi, newspaper taped over every crack and chink, sweating and naked and shaking. The boys brought him packets of Advil from the chemist near the highway, and gave him cups of chai. There were three of them, Shamsul, Bazil and Faraj. They were eighteen years old, all of them, uniformly equipped with tenth-class educations and dreams of wealth. Shamsul and Bazil worked as messengers for a courier company, and Faraj hung around the basti and occasionally did odd jobs for merchants in the market. They were all keen film-fans, and each had a personal favourite hero he tried to emulate in his speech and cadences. They had all come to Mumbai at about the same time, and now, some fifteen years later, they were quite citified, and regarded their parents with the tolerant affection of urban sophisticates for well-meaning bumpkins. Aadil listened to the boys talk. They liked to sit on the ledge next to his door, holding hands and holding forth on the world, paying attention to the citizens passing by, especially the girls. They knew Aadil as 'Reyaz Bhai', and his kholi was a nice little establishment for them. Faraj hid his cigarettes there, and all of them appreciated the small money he gave them, for running his errands. They had tried to cheat him only once, in the beginning, but then he had taken up Bazil by the throat, and his flat, whispery voice had frightened them, and they had returned the few rupees they had kept back from his payment for rice and cooking oil. They had kept away for a few days after that, but he had beckoned them over and given them another task, a request for onions and a newspaper. Since then they had treated Aadil with a careful respect, and he let them come and go into his small room.

It amused him how they hankered for cars and mobile phones and convent-educated girls, and how they spoke endlessly about what big apartments they would buy when they had made their fortunes. They were full of desire and they had no viable plan. Sometimes they whispered, and Aadil knew they were trying to talk themselves into some petty crime, some pilferage to afford them money for cinema tickets or hair cream. Their parents were quiet, hard-labouring people who were terrified of the police, but the boys had ambition. They told stories to each other, excitedly, about the great gangsters of the city, about Suleiman Isa and Ganesh Gaitonde and Chotta Madhav. They enacted the plot of *Company* for Aadil, all of it from Africa to Hong Kong, in the four feet of muddy lane before his door. But Aadil knew they had never stolen anything more than some scrap metal from a dealer in Kailashpada, and that they were never going to get to Singapore. Not without him leading them.

'Stop babbling,' he told them, 'and listen. If you want to make money, you need discipline. And four choppers.'

Aadil had called them in one April night when the heat lingered long after sunset. They sat on his floor in a row, like wide-eyed, damp puppies. When they understood he was talking about a robbery, they shrank into themselves and became very quiet. Aadil had seen this, of course, in new recruits who had just realized that the combat they were about to go into was real. He outlined his plan, and finally Faraj said, 'You have done this before?'

Aadil let them know that he had, many times, and he gave them no details. But they were satisfied. He had been a mystery to them, and now they knew just enough about him to make up more stories. Like most young men, they wanted to be led, and they slipped easily under his command. He gave them tasks, and praised them, and they were his. They needed no ideology, because they were already convinced that they needed money, and it was theirs to take. They had no need to believe in a future workers' heaven because they believed in a present paradise of cash. In any case, Aadil had no ideology left to give. He felt all higher purpose had been burned out of him, leaving behind a purity of vision. His money was running out, and he needed to eat, and to have a small place to live. He could work, perhaps as a driver, or as a labourer, but he would not. He was incapable of it. He did not trouble himself with anger at the enormous hoarding of wealth in this city, or the daily violence of poverty visited upon millions and millions. All that was as it was. Aadil only wanted this much – food, room to sleep in, and to be left alone, and he would take these necessities.

Two weeks later, Aadil and his boys mounted their first operation. The target was a third-floor apartment in Bandra, near Hill Road. Shamsul had three times delivered packages there, addressed to the daughter of the house, a thirty-year-old woman who was an executive in an advertising agency. During the day only her parents were at home. The father was a frail man, much troubled by asthma. The mother was the one who opened the door of the apartment to Bazil, who was wearing a courier service uniform especially commissioned from a tailor. Bazil held up a large brown package. Faraj and Aadil were waiting in the stairway. Aadil had told the watchman at the building gate that he was an electrician, and Faraj his assistant. The old woman opened the door, Shamsul gave her a piece of paper to sign and then Aadil was at her side, the chopper held up for her to see. They pushed her inside, woke the husband from his sleep. Faraj reached into his electrician's bag and handed Aadil a thick loop of rope. As Aadil tied the parents to chairs, he talked to them. 'Don't worry, Mata-ji,' he said. 'Nothing will happen. I will look after you. No noise, no trouble, and I will look after you.' He had told the boys that the threat of violence was always more effective than the practice of it. Terror, he had told them, gives you power. Their choppers had cost them only nineteen rupees each, but they were effective. Aadil put one on the table in front of Mata-ji and Papa-ji, and said, 'See, if you are good, I won't have to use my patra. Just give us twenty minutes, and we will be gone.'

Aadil sent Shamsul down first, with his courier bag stuffed with jewellery. In precisely twenty minutes, he and Faraj left with the cash, both Indian rupees and an unexpected roll of dollars recovered from the back of a godrej safe. Faraj wanted to kill the old couple before going. 'They have seen our faces,' he said. 'It would be safer.' Aadil cuffed him on the back of the head, and pushed him to the door. He spoke quietly to Mata-ji again, and then loosely gagged her and Papa-ji.

'Don't forget,' he said, 'that we know where your daughter works. Be quiet.' He had no idea where the daughter worked, but he was sure that was enough to keep them quiet until he and Faraj were down the stairs, past the watchman and out on the road. And so it went. They all got out safely, and there was no noise, no fuss and no killing.

The boys were overjoyed with the takings, which amounted to sixty-seven thousand in cash, two hundred dollars and the jewellery. Shamsul knew a receiver, and he had the transaction all set up. They moved the jewellery the same day, for a lakh and forty thousand. The dollars were in small bills, ones and fives and tens, so they got a low rate. But after all, the boys had never seen so much cash before all in the same place, in their hands, and they were suddenly kings. Aadil tried to convince them that they must be careful, that to be suddenly flush with cash and new clothes and sunglasses and shoes might invite suspicion, maybe a visit from the local beat constable. They agreed, and promised to be careful, but Aadil could see that they were little children with new toys, making promises that they could not keep. The next day, he moved again, to a room on the far side of Navnagar. His room here had a smooth tiled floor, which had been put in by the prior tenant, and running water. He forbade the boys from coming to see him, and met them only outside the basti. They protested at first, Bazil especially, but Aadil explained to them the need for security and discretion. 'If you want to continue,' he told them, 'you must be invisible, you must move like fish in the sea. And do what I tell you, if you want to continue.' The boys did want to continue, even then, when their pockets were heavy with money. They needed more.

Aadil wanted very little. He had his room, he cooked his own food, he drank cups of very sweet chai through the day. This was his only luxury in his new life, apart from books. He spent his days reading zoology. The books were second-hand university texts, mostly, bought from pavement dealers. He was surprised by how much of the material he remembered, and how easily it all came back to him. There was no direction or purpose in his reading other than the comfort it gave him. To follow the species to the phylum, to trace the structure in one direction and then back again, this provided meaning enough. There was no need for politics. So Aadil lived on, and lived quietly, and every month he and the boys planned and executed another job. Shamsul wanted to do more, but Aadil counselled patience and stealth. The boys wanted not only to rebuild their kholis and buy new stoves for their mothers, they now dreamt of cars. But for the moment, at least, they obeyed. One good job a month, the target carefully selected, based on good intelligence, brought in enough to satisfy them. For seven months they worked. Aadil was now occasionally reading chemistry, interspersed with the zoology. He had gone through many books on organisms and cells, and now he wanted to watch substances act against each other and make something new. There was an obscure pleasure in the elements coming together, making heat and fire and life. As far as he could see, there was not any grand purpose in these interactions. They happened, that was all. This fitted perfectly with his sense of his own life now. He had thought sometimes of suicide, in a distanced, theoretical manner, but had discovered that he wanted to live. He was not quite sure why, other than the sweetness of chai and the palliative effects of facts. Probably the reason for wanting to go on was very simple, he thought. A virus wanted to reproduce, and an insect ran from danger. So Aadil wanted to live.

So Aadil survived, in quiet and in hiding. He was, apart from his headaches, quite content. He was surprised that he did not feel lonely, after the camaraderie of the camps, but the books were consolation enough. He felt a tenderness towards himself, towards his prematurely aged body, and sometimes he allowed himself little luxuries: a new mattress, two sets of sheets, a bottle of shampoo. He did not worry too much about the future, although he had the sense that somewhere close by, disaster lurked under the deceptive ease that Mumbai had given him. He was sure of this, but when the catastrophe finally came, it was from a flank that he had grown complacent about. The boys, he thought, had settled down nicely. During operations, they were no longer jittery, they conducted themselves with professionalism and calm watchfulness. After their first big extravaganzas of spending on clothes and televisions and women, Shamsul, Bazil and Faraj had grown into careful businessmen, and invested their money in small businesses run by cousins and aunts, and took in high rates of return. They all gained weight, and looked generally prosperous. Aadil began to believe that he had, all by chance, collected a good and reliable squad. The boys were friends, bound to each other by shared interests and experience and danger.

Then Faraj and Bazil killed Shamsul. Aadil was in his room that afternoon, sleeping, when Bazil knocked. Aadil was shaken out of a dream of childhood by Bazil's frantic thumping, a dream in which he walked over a culvert and the roofs of low huts swam in the evening haze. Then he was awake, his hand on his chopper.

'Bhai,' Bazil said. 'Bhai?'

Aadil opened the door and found Bazil shaking against the wall, spattered with blood. Aadil pulled him in. 'What?' he said.

Bazil told him. For many weeks, months actually, he and Faraj had been suspicious of Shamsul and his dealings with the receiver who bought their goods. Shamsul always did the buying and selling by himself, and was reluctant to discuss exactly what prices had been paid for specific items, and he wouldn't discuss what the buyer said during a meeting, or even what the buyer said he might be able to move easily. It was all very strange. Bazil and Faraj had observed for months that Shamsul had more money than either of them, more – yes, it was true – than both of them put together. Faraj had joked with Shamsul, and had even asked him if he saved more than anyone, but Shamsul had always ignored the implications. He refused to defend himself, which made Faraj even more suspicious. Then last week Shamsul had bought a second kholi, a perfectly new place with four rooms and a double-sized water tanki. He hadn't told them, the bastard, about this grand new house, but Bazil had found out because his mother sometimes took in embroidery work from the builder's wife. Bazil told Faraj, and Faraj got very angry. Faraj had made a plan. They would get Shamsul drunk, and take him out near the nullah, behind the big water pipes, and confront him. They would use threats if necessary. But they would find out what was going on. Enough was enough. Bazil was to come prepared. So they invited Shamsul, very casually, to share a bottle of excellent vilayati rum. He was eager, of course. Shamsul had a liking for drink, and after some rum he always grew sentimental and sang. But this time the session was awkward from the very beginning, with Faraj fairly vibrating with tension from the moment he welcomed them into his new kholi. He had boiled eggs and salt and pepper all ready, and a plate of tangdis, and he poured them tall glasses as soon as they came in. After that everything blurred into a confusion of loud talk and lewd jokes and anger. Shamsul started to sing but then wanted more tangdis. Faraj told him, you pay for your own, you have too much money. Shamsul laughed it away, and for a while Bazil and he talked about girls. They talked about Rani Mukherjee and Zoya and Zeenat Aman, and then Shamsul mentioned Faraj's younger sister, whose name was also Zeenat and who was said – in the basti – to have a resemblance to beautiful Zeenat from the seventies. What he said was very innocent, that our Zeenat was ready for her first starring role now. But Faraj had been sitting silent in the corner, drinking glass after glass. 'You bastard,' he said, 'you have our money.' Bazil now realized that he was himself drunk, probably more drunk than Shamsul. He tried to stand up, to get in front of Faraj and remind him of the plan, of the walk out to the nullah. But it was too late. Faraj and Shamsul were shoving at each other already. Then Bazil was flabbergasted to find Shamsul shouting at him, who had done nothing and said very little. Shamsul refused to confess, and Faraj pulled out his chopper from behind the bed, and Bazil grabbed his own, and Shamsul was hitting out at them, thrashing his hands, trying to get out of the kholi. There was blood on his chest now. Then he was running down the lane, and they brought him down once, and again. He tried to get into someone's house. Maybe he thought it was his own. They hit him again and he fell. And it was done.

Aadil wiped Bazil's face clean of the tears, gave him a clean shirt and shoved him out. 'Go,' he said. 'Run.' But Bazil stood as helpless as a blind ox in the lane, and Aadil had to give him instructions: go home, get money, get out, find a lodge far away and stay there, and we will meet on Sunday at the Maharaja Hotel in Andheri East, at one o'clock. Being told what to do got Bazil into motion, and he went. Aadil cleaned out his own kholi. He took cash, two shirts, two pairs of pants and a pair of shoes. He was out in ten minutes, and he walked at an even pace, never looking back.

Aadil stayed at a lodge near Dadar station that night, and then moved again to Mahim the next day. He had no intention of going to the Maharaja Hotel on Sunday, and he knew well that he should leave Mumbai. But where else was there to go? There were other cities, other huge masses of men and women in which to lose himself, but he was here in Mumbai and it had taken him in. He did not have the vigour to stir himself again into motion, to journey again to some new place, to find new languages and new people. This was home, and he was here. This was decided. In two days he had a room near Film City, and on Sunday he did go to the Maharaja Hotel. Maybe it was a mistake, but the boys were his team. They brought in his living. Finding others would be work, and take time, and the end of the month was near. Almost time for another job. So he found a corner near the Maharaja Hotel, and he watched. Faraj and Bazil came just before one, in an auto-rickshaw. They went in, and Aadil waited. He had been trained in patience by his instructors, and then by all his ambushes. An hour passed, and then another. There was no sign of lurking policemen, but still Aadil waited.

Just after three, Faraj and Bazil walked down the steps of the hotel, looking disheartened. They walked down the road, and Aadil followed. He let them get far ahead, then crossed the road and closed in again, on the other side. No policemen, as far as he could see. But Faraj had his arm over Bazil's shoulders, and Bazil seemed to be crying. Aadil came back over to them, took Bazil by the elbow. 'Be quiet,' he said to Faraj. 'Walk.'

Aadil took them to a little patch of garden in the middle of the road, on a traffic circle. There was a single tree in the circle, and he squatted under it. The boys sat uncomfortably, cross-legged and shifting from side to side. Aadil let them sweat in the sun and told them what idiots they were. He didn't let them talk, and told them that there were no excuses for what they had done. They had jeopardized him and the entire unit and their operations. Their actions had been irresponsible, and their drinking irreligious. They had understood nothing of what he had taught them about the use of force.

Bazil began to weep again. Faraj swallowed, and said, 'I know it was wrong.' Aadil let them talk, and extracted promises that they would never touch alcohol again. Then he led them from the circle, through the rings of cars, and bought them a water-melon juice each. They discussed the next job. Their best source of intelligence had been Shamsul, who people had trusted because of his mildness and reedy body. Householders and chowkidars had thought him harmless, and talked to him. Now the team was handicapped, but there was nothing to do but adapt. In less than a week they had a target, and a plan. The address this time came from Bazil, for a family near Sahar Airport. They had a son working in Dubai, who sent them frequent parcels. Aadil delayed the job by four days, just so that they could make sure they had their information right. They walked the area, penetrated the building compound and came out again. The operation went smoothly, the boys were calm, they walked away with sixty thousand in cash and a bagful of gold jewellery, including biscuits. The Dubai boy had been preparing for his sister's wedding. Aadil was pleased.

Faraj had been detailed to find a trustworthy receiver, and had located one along Tulsi Pipe Road. The contact had been made over the phone, and arrangements finalized, and they were now on their way to make the delivery. Aadil had decided that all of them were to go, to prevent future misunderstandings. They walked along the railway tracks, skirting the shacks that had been built along the fence. The meeting had been set up for the late evening, but Aadil had been hit by a headache that swirled up his spine like a storm. He had been unable to see past the bursts of sharp fire that arrived in his eyes. Even now, when midnight had long passed, and he was recovered, the streetlights burnt hotly with a spectral glow of orange around them. A train sped by, and each rattle and knocking stood out against the darkness and hurt Aadil's ears. The boys were quiet and solicitous, and they walked on either side of him.

Aadil felt alive, awakened by the pain. The crunch from the ground under his feet recalled to him some far memory, something that came to him and retreated, came to him and went. The earth was breathing, he could feel it.

The shouts came from behind and ahead, and they were very loud. A flare from a flashlight came at Aadil, and with it, 'Police'. Aadil twisted to the left and ran, crouching low. There were men ahead of him. Directly against his right shoulder there was a tin shack, a closed door. Then a small gap before the next shack. Aadil went into the hole, and brought up against the bars of the fence. The tracks were on the other side, but the fence was high. Aadil reached up, and his hand slipped against the iron. He turned. His chopper was in his hand.

'Out, bhenchod. Throw it out.'

The policeman had a pistol. Aadil could see the barrel, the line of light along it, and the heavy shoulders of the man behind. He threw the chopper out low, on to the road. A small clang. The policeman was waiting, and the barrel of the pistol lowered just a little. Aadil inhaled a long, sweet swig of air, and had the absurd thought that maybe they could stay like this for ever, at bay and at peace. But his hand had already found his knife, swirled it open, and then his body was moving. The policeman never fired, maybe he lost Aadil in the shadow. Aadil went at him, and he struck as he had been taught, as he had learnt, as he had practised.

Aadil was running. The policemen were behind him and he was running. He still had the knife in his hand and he wanted to let go but he couldn't. He ran. Then he was no longer moving. He shut his eyes, opened them, and knew that he was on the ground, face down. The surface of the road arced away from him, and a trickle of water shone softly. There was no pain, but he felt very dreamy and soft, as if he were just waking up. I think I killed that man, he thought. Then it occurred to him that he was himself dying. He was not afraid, not afraid at all. But he felt enormously sad, but he did not know why, or what for, and he wondered and waited. Then he was dead.

II

Sharmeen defended her hero loyally. 'The trouble with you, Aisha Akbani,' she told her friend, 'is that you change your opinion every five minutes. One day Chandrachur Singh is everything to you, one week later you say you wouldn't even look at him if he showed up under your window with roses. You know what you are? You are *fickle*.' Sharmeen had read the word 'fickle' recently, in one of her eighth-grade texts, and she used it with huge satisfaction.

Aisha tilted her admittedly very pretty nose and dismissed Chandrachur Singh with a decisive wave of her hand. 'Sharmeen Khan, if it was a matter of one week or one month, then okay, you would have a point. But that guy is so over. It's been so long since *Maachis*, and not a single good film. Okay, maybe one or two. And it's not about films anyway. I keep telling you, I just don't *like* him.'

Sharmeen and Aisha were lying on Sharmeen's bed, in her bedroom on the second floor of a house in Bethesda. Sharmeen loved the sharp drop in the Maryland countryside outside her window, which caused a medium-sized oak to hang over what she called a 'cliff' and what

Aisha described as a 'little drop'. Aisha was sometimes infuriatingly contrary, she would argue for the sake of argument, but Sharmeen adored her anyway. She had been her first friend when Sharmeen had arrived in America nearly two years ago, when she still in her half-Punjabi, half-London accent had spoken of 'Amrika'. Aisha – who hadn't been quite as pretty then – had been sympathetic and kind, and now, even when she had blossomed, even in eighth grade, she still stuck to Sharmeen. They were best friends, and they were inseparable. Aisha liked to pretend that she was an anti-romantic, a cynic, and so she refused to admit that the view from Sharmeen's window was really quite dramatic, especially when it was all covered in January snow, as now. There was the oak, the cliff and a long, rolling meadow that ended in a snarl of tall bushes. On full moon nights it all sparkled and looked quite wild, and Sharmeen lay with sleepy, half-open eyes and imagined Chandrachur Singh on a white horse, galloping through the brambles and up the cliff.

'You're dreaming again,' Aisha said, and pinched Sharmeen's arm.

Sharmeen pinched her in turn, and said, 'Turn the page.' They were sprawled face down on the flowered bedspread, heads away from the pillows, chins leaning on the very bottom rim of the bedstead. They had a new issue of *Stardust* open on the floor, where it could be slid speedily under the bed at the first warning creak on the stairs. Sharmeen's parents were strict about what she read, and *Stardust* was so not allowed that it had never even been mentioned in this house. Sharmeen's father especially had disciplined and encouraged her from an early age to guard her values and family izzat. His name was Shahid Khan, and he was a colonel, and he had been posted at the embassy in London, and he had travelled all over the world, but he had never slackened in his observances and prayers, and he was known among his friends and colleagues for his piety and simple living. So Sharmeen didn't talk or read about Pakistani films and actors, much less the hideously shameless industry across the border. But Sharmeen and Aisha read *Stardust* anyway. They were mildly interested in home-grown talent like Noor and Zara Sheikh, but they were passionate about Indian films. A three-page article about Chandrachur Singh, with colour photographs, had sparked off this last argument, which had gone exactly the way it had the time before, and the time before that. Sharmeen was always steadfast in her devotion to Chandrachur Singh, she defended him against Aisha's unfair accusations and attacks, and finally she drifted off into a Chandrachur Singh reverie. There she would stay, until Aisha jolted her out of it with a pinch. Aisha turned the page, and now they were looking down at a double-page spread of Zoya Mirza.

'Wow,' Aisha said, 'she's beautiful.'

There was no doubt she was. She was curled up on a red divan, wearing a red satiny mini-dress that left her long, golden legs quite bare, and her chest pressing against a low-cut neckline. Sharmeen said, 'Um.' She had a complicated reaction to Zoya Mirza. She liked Zoya's height and some of the roles she was so good in, like the crusading lawyer she had played in her second film, *Aaj ka Kanoon*, but she thought that a Muslimah showing her body like this was not a good thing. It made her uncomfortable. There had been a time when she would have thought it was a very bad thing, she would have agreed wholeheartedly with Abba and Ammi that this was unquestionably an evil. But she had spent a lot of time with Aisha, and Aisha thought Zoya Mirza was cool. So Sharmeen said, 'She's all right,' and left it at that, and tried to turn the page.

But Aisha put her hand down, over Zoya Mirza's very flat stomach. 'Why?' she said. 'She's as good-looking as Chandrachur Singh. Much more. You can't say she's not.'

Sharmeen didn't want to talk about this, because she knew where the discussion would go. Aisha's parents prided themselves on being modern. Her mother worked as a real-estate agent, and her father ran a software company. Aisha's eldest brother had married a white American girl, who hadn't converted even after the marriage. And Aisha's sister and she both went about with their heads uncovered. Aisha was very proud of her long brownish hair, and Sharmeen knew that she pitied her, Sharmeen, for having to wear such conservative clothing outside the house. She refused to accept Sharmeen's assertion that she felt safer with her hair covered, and closer to Allah. Aisha said that was all social conditioning, and Allah had never said anything about covering yourself head to toe. So arguing with her was useless, but an argument was going to happen anyway. Sharmeen could see that. So she sighed, and said, 'She just always looks so cheap to me.'

Aisha rolled over, clapped her palms over her eyes and burst out, 'Cheap? *Cheap*? Sharmeen Khan, after all this time in America, you're still such a fundoo.'

'I am not a fundoo.'

'Yes, you are a fundoo.'

This time around, they had reached their customary impasse with unusual swiftness. Before leaving Pakistan, in Rawalpindi and Karachi, Sharmeen had never been called a fundoo, not by a friend or an enemy. She had always gone to army schools, where many of her classmates had dressed like her and the older girls had worn hijaab and mostly everyone had agreed about what was proper and what was not. But that had been an eternity ago, when she was eight and nine. Now she was almost fourteen and on the other side of the world and Aisha was her best friend and everything was different. Now she had to defend herself, and deny that she was a fundamentalist. 'Being modest,' Sharmeen said, 'doesn't mean that you are a fundoo.'

Aisha came back instantly with, 'And being proud of your body doesn't mean you're cheap.'

Sharmeen felt her own body contract into itself. She hated this eternal argument which set off this constriction centred at her belly. 'Fine,' she said, and tried to turn the page.

'Fine what?'

'Fine, she's not cheap. Oof. Can we move past Zoya Mirza now?'

Aisha turned the page, to another two pictures of Zoya Mirza. It was her *Stardust*, and she'd brought it in her black bag, so she had proprietary rights. She was allowed to read *Stardust* at home, in front of her parents, who no doubt thought of Sharmeen's parents as fundoos. Sharmeen waited patiently for Aisha to finish reading the article about Zoya Mirza, and thought about her father and mother and their religiosity. Abba was the more observant, the more rigorous. His forehead was marked with a namaaz ka gatta, the testimony of his five kneelings and five prayers daily, and every time Sharmeen had flown in an aeroplane with him, she had been comforted by his readings from a small, exquisite Koran during take-offs and landings. He had told Sharmeen about how his faith had sustained him, how it had made it possible for him to rise despite all the difficulties. He had battled poverty and dispossession, family troubles and discrimination, and had studied hard and prayed and come up through the ranks of the army. Now he was attached to the embassy in Washington in a, very important position, and Sharmeen admired and loved him very much. Despite anything Aisha or her emigrant parents might think of him. Sharmeen didn't care.

'Okay,' Aisha said. She'd finished the article, and was ready to go on to the next. But she couldn't let Zoya Mirza go without a last admiring, 'I tell you, she's so smart.'

Sharmeen held her tongue, and they settled into a long perusal of an article about Anil Kapoor's career, and then an analysis of older heroes. Sharmeen watched films only at Aisha's, on DVD, and so her knowledge of heroes and heroines and their histories wasn't as wide and deep as Aisha's, but she had an astute sense of what was going to be a hit and what wasn't, and she could remember entire songs after hearing them only once. Of the black-and-white heroes, from long before either she or Aisha had been born, Sharmeen liked Dev Anand. After that she had a partiality to Amitabh Bachchan. Aisha was quite agreeable about these two preferences, it was only over Chandrachur Singh that they parted company. Sharmeen had often wondered why it was that modern times divided them more than olden times. Now they agreed about Feroz Khan – both thumbs down – but disagreed about Fardeen, whose first film hadn't been released yet but whose photographs were suddenly everywhere, who Aisha thought was cool but Sharmeen pronounced a dork. 'Dork' was one of Sharmeen's new words.

'Sharmeen,' came the call. 'Beta?'

They had plenty of warning. When Ammi opened the door, the *Stardust* was safely deep under the bed, and Sharmeen and Aisha were seated in the middle of the bed, facing each other. Looking, Sharmeen hoped, like two obedient girls having a respectable discussion about something suitable.

'Salaam alaikum, Khaala-jaan,' Aisha said. She was adept at these sudden transformations. She suddenly had her hair tucked behind her ears, her arms wrapped around her knees, and she looked as sweetly innocent as one of those forties heroines simpering at an approving elder.

And Ammi did approve. 'Waleikum as salaam, Aisha,' she said, dabbing at her mouth with the end of her chunni. 'Are you well?'

'Yes, Khaala-jaan, very well.' Aisha did a little side-to-side nod of the head that she brought on when she was being good for aunties and uncles. 'You look very pink. The cold weather brings out your cheeks.'

The flattery wasn't strictly necessary. Ammi had been at first surprised and then charmed by Aisha's good Urdu and modest manners.

She didn't approve of Aisha's family, but was quite comfortable with letting the sweet girl into her own house and being her daughter's sweet friend. Aisha was quite safe, but she never missed a chance to lay on the butter. Ammi smiled, and succumbed once again to Aisha's acting. 'It is just the heat in the kitchen,' she said. 'Sharmeen, go and watch Daddi for a while. I can't keep running up there.'

'Now, Ammi?'

'No, next year.'

'Ammi, we were just talking about exams.'

'So go and talk up there. That poor old woman is not going to stop you.'

Sharmeen couldn't tell Ammi that she hated the musty smell of that room, that it scared her to be in the presence of that supine, wizened body that had once been her Daddi. She made a face, and then winced as Aisha pinched her toe.

'We'll just go, Khalla,' Aisha said. 'Two minutes.'

Ammi left, but not without a warning glare at Sharmeen. Aisha gathered up her things, and herded Sharmeen through the kitchen and up the stairs to the back room. Even the heavy smell of Ammi's cooking couldn't hide the grim reek of old age, that shut-off closeness which smelt of camphor and bitter medicine and however slightly – this is what made Sharmeen gag – of urine. Though the room was warm, from the heating ducts and the kitchen just down the stairs, Daddi lay under a thick covering of quilt and blankets. Sharmeen sat on the chair next to the door, and tried to breathe very lightly. Aisha marched up to the bed, and plonked herself down on the couch next to it. Even though Daddi was by now little more than a lump under the blankets, Aisha professed an interest in her. She said Daddi changed every time she visited the house, got smaller and more creased and pickled. Sharmeen thought this was true, that what was left in this room was not the tall, loud, sarcastic woman with huge dark eyes that she remembered vaguely from early childhood, but she preferred not to look. She would prefer to leave this smelly body alone, at the back of the house.

'She's got two more hairs on her chin,' Aisha said. She leant in, closer. And then, in her hip-hop voice, whispered, 'Hey, Dadds, how you doin'?'

She jumped back.

'What?' Sharmeen said.

'She spoke.'

'So what? She does sometimes. She thinks she's in Rawalpindi. Talking to the butcher.'

'No, idiot. She spoke in English. She said, "I am very well, thank you."'

'She must have heard it somewhere. Come *here*.'

But Aisha pulled the couch closer to the bed, and turned her face sideways to look into the opening in the quilt. Sharmeen had seen her get this way before – when Aisha got obsessed with something, she focused so hard that she really couldn't hear somebody trying to talk to her from two feet away. It was very annoying, and if she got fixated on Daddi they would have to come up here every day for the next week. Sharmeen got up, went around the bottom of the bed and put a hand on Aisha's back. 'A-isha,' she said.

'Quiet, na. She's talking.'

'She jabbers all the time.' Daddi muttered away morning, noon and night, she spoke to the walls of her room and told stories and occasionally cursed, which made Ammi laugh and Abba frown. All this frightened Sharmeen, these purblind eyes, this stringy white hair and the flaky flesh underneath. She could hear a voice under the quilt, reedy and brittle. She wished she was somewhere else, outside in the crisp American frost.

'It's English,' Aisha said.

'Don't be silly. Daddi doesn't know English. And Dadda couldn't even read anything. They didn't speak English, that's certain.' Daddi's husband had been illiterate, and Daddi could read Urdu, everyone in the family knew this. But Daddi had sacrificed and scrimped to educate Abba, she had said her youngest son was going to be a professional man, not a tempo-driver like his father. And Dadda's first wife and her children had laughed at her, and thrown her out of the house right after Dadda's early death. Daddi had been out on the street, with three children and no money, nothing, and she had still managed. She had managed to make Abba something other than a tempo-driver. All this was the family history, which Sharmeen had known ever since she could remember, but through her own life nobody had ever mentioned Daddi speaking English. That was just absurd.

'Come here,' Aisha said, and reached behind and pulled Sharmeen down. 'Listen!'

Sharmeen found herself face to face with Daddi. The pale skin was blotchy now, disfigured by spots, but Sharmeen knew that once it had been legendarily glorious and resplendent. Dadda had married Daddi because he had been dazzled by her Punjabi beauty, and his first wife had despised her, had called Daddi a prostitute, had hated having her in the same house, had fought against it. Dadda used to call Daddi a rose, a zannat ki hoor. Looking at Daddi, this was hard to believe, but this is what everyone said. Daddi's breath was now rank, like old adhesive. Sharmeen was sure that she would never ever let herself become so repulsive. She would rather die first. Sharmeen made a face. 'That's not English.'

'Now it's not. Now she's saying something in Punjabi. What is it?'

What Daddi was saying had the cadence of a chant, a prayer, but it was unfamiliar. 'I don't know,' Sharmeen said. 'Let's go.'

'I've heard it somewhere. It's a song.'

'Yes, yes, now she's singing some Daler Mehndi song for you.'

Aisha wasn't about to rise to Sharmeen's weak sarcasm, not while she had this new mystery to investigate. She had her head cocked close to Daddi's. 'She stopped.'

'Good. So come over here. Then after five minutes we can leave.'

But Aisha insisted on sitting next to Daddi and waiting for her to speak again. There was no budging her. She watched Daddi intently. Sharmeen turned away from that wet, wrinkly mouth, and tried to talk to Aisha, to get back to some other subject, anything. She tried Chandrachur Singh, Brad Pitt, school, strict teachers. Aisha remained distracted, and answered only in haans and naas. Sharmeen, as hard as she tried, couldn't quite push away the chip-chip sound that Daddi made with her lips every few seconds. Finally she fell silent, and they both waited for Daddi to say something.

Sharmeen jumped when she did, even though she knew it was coming. This time Daddi's voice was louder, stronger, but it still sounded as if it was coming from somewhere else, from somewhere far away. It was the chant again, '*Nanak dukhiya sab sansaar*,' and this time it was familiar to Sharmeen too. 'What is it?' she whispered.

'I don't know,' Aisha said.

Daddi broke off. In that terse silence the Punjabi words fell together in Sharmeen's head and she knew what they were. She didn't want to react, but she stiffened against Aisha's side and Aisha instantly knew that she knew.

'What is it?' Aisha said.

Sharmeen didn't want to say. None of it made any sense. She shrugged. 'It's Punjabi.'

'I can hear that also. But your Punjabi is pretty good. What is she *saying*?'

Aisha wasn't going to let it go. Sharmeen whispered, 'It's some kind of song. Like those sardars sing at their temple or whatever.'

Aisha shook her head. 'Your daddi is saying a Sikh's prayer?'

Sharmeen nodded. 'Nanak, that's from the sardars, no?'

'Yes,' Aisha said. She was holding Sharmeen's hands very tightly, and now she asked the crucial question. 'But why?'

'I don't know.' Sharmeen had no idea. Dadda was a Punjabi, and Daddi was a Punjabi refugee from the other side. Her family had all been killed by Hindus. Dadda had rescued her and brought her home. He had married her, and his first wife had raged, and after Dadda died the chudail first wife had thrown her and Abba out. Dadda had loved Daddi, and if he had lived, everything would have been different. But Daddi and Abba – who was then only a boy – had suffered, and finally Abba had triumphed. Nowhere in all this old history was there any reason for Daddi to say Sikh prayers.

'Find out.' Aisha was all aflush with the drama of the moment, with the possibilities of the mystery.

'How?'

'Ask questions.'

Ask questions. That was easy for Aisha to say. Sharmeen didn't want to ask her parents questions about Sikh prayers. Aisha wouldn't quite understand, but Sharmeen knew in her bones, in her very blood, that asking about this would be a disaster. Abba hated Sikhs only a little less than he hated Hindus. He said the sardars were a barbarous, uncultured people, full of violence and hate. Hindus were worse, of course, they were unscrupulous liars and cowards and idolaters, but Sikhs were half-way to Hindus. Abba had spent his life fighting against both, and had been decorated and promoted for his dedication and his successes. Sharmeen wasn't going to start talking to him about Sikh prayers in his own house. She loved him, but he was an austere, disciplined man with an unforgiving temper. He went to work at the embassy and spent long hours, and the home he returned to had to be clean, quiet and peaceful, and full of godly grace. Sharmeen knew better than to provoke an upset with stupid questions about the mutterings of senile old Daddi. So she finally managed to get Aisha packed off home, and retreated to her own room, and tried to calm herself down. But she was restless, and after lunch she went back to Daddi's room.

Daddi was still curled up in exactly the same position, with her head to the left. Sharmeen knew that Ammi got her up in the mornings and evenings to feed her, and give her medicines, and sometimes Daddi was even carried down by Abba to the drawing room, to sit with everyone. But mostly she spent her whole life here, in this one room, dozing and talking to herself. Sharmeen shuddered, and swore to herself again that she would never be this horribly old, and waited for Daddi to say Sikh stuff again. Daddi was mumbling and muttering now, though, and it was hard to make anything out, and although it was Punjabi, it wasn't any kind of prayer. Sharmeen sat patiently. She had a maths textbook with her, and she made herself comfortable on the low green chair and read. She was curious now herself, not as excitedly as Aisha, but with a strange, uneasy flow of anticipation and dread and nausea through her abdomen. She wanted Daddi to say that thing again, that prayer, but she didn't.

Sharmeen came awake slowly, her cheek against the wooden arm of the chair. A faint smog of snow drifted against the window, and the light had changed to a luminescent slate that reminded Sharmeen of a dream she had once had, of walking across a vast plain, towards high mountains. When had she had that dream? She couldn't remember. She pushed herself up and rubbed her face. There must be a nasty pattern there, from the wood. Sometimes, when she and Aisha napped in the afternoons, they giggled with glee over the impressions left on their faces and arms, and pretended that these were permanent marks, scars. Aisha hated sleeping too long in the afternoons, though. She said that waking up after a long daytime sleep made her feel lost, like she didn't know where she was, or who she was. Sharmeen liked to sleep any time, day or night, and she slept when she felt like it. Although she would never say it to Aisha, she thought that despite all her outrageousness and her risk-taking, Aisha was peculiarly delicate in some ways. She got really nervous about tests and papers, and was afraid of lizards. Sometimes Sharmeen felt like she was protecting Aisha, not the other way around.

Sharmeen started. Daddi was sitting up in bed. The covers had fallen around her waist, and under the white sweater her collarbone was very fragile. She was looking at Sharmeen. 'Nikki,' she said. 'Take me home.'

'What, Daddi? What?' Sharmeen gathered herself up and knelt next to the bed and held Daddi's hand. It was as light as nothing. 'Daddi, what did you say? Who is Nikki? Which Nikki?'

Daddi said, 'Nikki, where is Mata-ji? Take me home, Nikki.'

'Which Mata-ji? Do you mean your Ammi?'

But Daddi had retreated into her customary absence. She was looking through Sharmeen now, through the window and out beyond. Sharmeen wasn't sure now if she saw the snow, or the trees, or anything at all. She sat with Daddi for a while, then made her lie down and covered her with quilts. At dinner that evening, Sharmeen asked Ammi, 'Where did Daddi come from?'

Ammi shrugged, 'Ask Abba.'

That was as much as Sharmeen was able to get then, much to the frustration of Aisha, who had been appraised over the telephone of Daddi's command to Nikki, whoever that was. But Abba wasn't at home that night, he was working late again, and all questions had to wait until the next morning. 'That's so bizarre, that you can ask only him,' Aisha said. 'My mother can tell you everything about Papa's whole family.'

Sharmeen protested only mildly. She didn't like thinking of her parents as bizarre, but now it did seem odd that Amma talked so much about her own family and their ancestry, but never about Daddi. There was no getting around her silence, though, so Sharmeen waited until morning, waited for Abba to finish his bath and fajr prayers and breakfast. They had a little chat before she went to school, every day, and mainly he liked to talk to her about her studies. They discussed the proper religious view of many of the topics that came up in the classroom, and he gave her his opinions on events in the world. He was an expert on international affairs, and had been nearly everywhere – or so it seemed to her. She loved to hear him describe the jungles of Myanmar, and the steppes of Ukraine. He stroked his greying moustache, and told her in his deep voice about the tigers he had seen in Nepal, and the horses in Sweden.

Today, they talked about Afghanistan and Iraq, and then, gathering up her books, Sharmeen asked, 'Abba, where is Daddi from?'

Abba straightened the mats on the table. 'From Punjab. Other side of the border now.'

'Yes, but from where exactly?'

'Near Amritsar.'

Abba was very relaxed, but Sharmeen knew that asking anything else right now would seem too curious. She went to school, pacified the impatient Aisha and bided her time. Over the next three days, she asked Abba what she hoped were innocent, casual questions about family, natural for a young girl to ask. She learnt that before her marriage, Daddi's name had been Nausheen Sharif; that yes, Daddi had brothers and sisters who were all lost as they tried to flee towards Pakistan; that there were no living relatives on her side, at all and anywhere; that she had gone to school but did not have a college degree; that she liked jalebis and khari lassi. 'And,' Sharmeen finally asked, 'who is Nikki?'

'Nikki?' Abba said.

'Daddi said something about some Nikki, when I was sitting with her.'

'You spend a lot of time with her nowadays.'

Sharmeen and Aisha had been going up to Daddi's room every afternoon, maintaining a vigil for more Sikh prayers or English or mentions of this Nikki. Ammi had been very pleased by Sharmeen's new devotion to homely duties, but Abba seemed very neutral. It was hard, a lot of the time, to tell what he was thinking or feeling. He would say something, make a statement in a voice that gave nothing away, and then a quiet would descend. He could outwait you or anyone, and when you spoke you felt like he was seeing right through you. Sharmeen felt anxiety rise through her spine like lava, and she said as calmly as she could, 'She's so old. She must be lonely.'

He softened then, and made Sharmeen sit beside him, even though she was running late, and told her about the moonlight on Himalayan peaks.

'But he didn't tell you about any Nikki?' Aisha said later that afternoon. 'No yes, no no, no nothing?'

'He said nothing.'

'This "Mata-ji" stuff is from sardars also, I think. You have to find out about this Nikki.'

'I am *not* going to ask him again.'

'Yes, yes. He can be quite scary, your Colonel Shahid Khan, with that big moustache and that voice. Even when he says, "Good night, beta," he makes me feel all shivery.'

There was a lurch inside Sharmeen's head, a quick, dizzying movement of perspective – she had always seen Abba as Abba, who was tall and strict and baritone and smelt of leather and Arnolive hair oil, who was as permanent as the sea. Now she saw him suddenly as Aisha saw him, or others might see him, dour and dangerous and with his own secrets. She felt suddenly older, as if something about herself had really changed, and she didn't like it. 'He's not scary,' she said quietly.

Aisha had had one of her sudden shifts of attention, and wasn't listening to Sharmeen any more. She was peering at Daddi. They were in Daddi's room, poised close to her in case she said anything mysterious or shocking or revelatory. But Daddi was talking in chaste Urdu and Punjabi – as she had been for days – of nothing but butchers and horses and long-ago journeys. 'She's being very boring,' Aisha said. 'Nothing new, no?'

'Yes,' Sharmeen said, 'nothing new.' There had been no Nikki, no prayers, nothing. If there even was a mystery, they were no closer to solving it. Maybe there was nothing to be found out. Sharmeen wasn't even sure she wanted to find out anything any more. The wall of Abba's evasiveness – and yes, it was that – held back a gigantic, crushing weight, something that threatened even him. Sharmeen couldn't explain this to Aisha because she didn't know how she knew this, but she was frightened by this and wanted to leave it alone. Looking at Daddi now, at the sharp arc of her nose, which both Abba and Sharmeen herself had inherited, Sharmeen wished that Daddi would just stay quiet, that she would shut up and not say anything surprising or dramatic or explosive. She wanted Aisha to come away, leave this room and whatever broken memories it contained, but she knew better than to say anything. Telling Aisha not to do something often meant that she did it anyway, even if she didn't want to in the first place. So Sharmeen made herself wait, she had patience and endurance. It was only a matter of time.

Aisha's interest in Daddi lasted longer than Sharmeen expected. Through the winter holidays, she kept dragging Sharmeen up to that dim room every other day, made her sit next to Daddi while they talked about actors and music and boys and school. Daddi had lapsed into an almost constant silence now, broken only occasionally by sniffles and coughs and a deep gargling sound at the back of her throat. Over three weeks, she spoke only once, and that was to ask someone when the train would leave. This became something of a joke between Sharmeen and Aisha, for some reason it was very funny to randomly say to the other, in a strong Punjabi accent, 'Arre, listen, when does the train go?' By the time school began and their bags were full again, and Aisha was shocking Sharmeen with her shameless talking to boys, even this one Daddi line was forgotten. And now Sharmeen had to go up to Daddi's room only when Ammi reminded her. Aisha no longer insisted on afternoon visits, and Sharmeen was glad of this.

Daddi died at the beginning of spring, on a day when the newspapers were full of the early blooming of the cherry blossoms. Sharmeen came home from school and found Abba seated at the table in the kitchen, holding a cup of steaming chai. Ammi stood at the counter, her hands held over her stomach. Sharmeen knew instantly that something bad had happened. Abba was never home this early.

It was Ammi who spoke. 'Beta, your Daddi passed this afternoon.' Now Sharmeen saw that Abba had tears on his face, and her legs shook and she trembled. Ammi rushed forward and held her and helped her to a chair. Both Abba and Ammi fussed over her then, and made her drink chai, and hugged her. During the funeral, and afterwards, the story went around that Sharmeen had almost fainted when she heard about her Daddi, and people she didn't know came to her and talked to her about acceptance and Allah's will and a long, long life and eternal love. Sharmeen never told anyone that what had frightened her that day, what had driven a spike of abject terror through her chest, was not the news about Daddi but the child's sadness on Abba's face, the wounded yearning and loss and uncertainty she had never seen before and never wanted to see again. Sharmeen kept her head down and kept very quiet and waited for all of it to stop.

There was one other thing that Sharmeen never told anyone, not even Aisha.

For the month after Daddi died, Sharmeen's sleep was broken several times each night. She slid into wakefulness flushed and sweating, and her head reeled from a torrent of thoughts about Daddi, a song that she had sung, and the time she had gone three times to exchange sandals at the Crystal City Mall and the saleswomen had started to shake their heads as soon as they saw her hobbling down the corridor. Sharmeen would sit up in bed, drink water, lie down and try to get back to sleep. But it felt as if there were thin black hooks in her heart that pulled her awake with tiny pinpricks of guilt. The gritty little scrapes of pain didn't just come from the feeling that she, Sharmeen, had not spent enough time with Daddi ever since she had turned thirteen, that she had been too preoccupied with her studies and Aisha and Chandrachur Singh. No, not that only. There was also this bitter realization for Sharmeen, that now Daddi was really gone and now she would never know all there was to know about Daddi. Not so long ago Sharmeen had felt bored by Daddi's talk, by her accounts of lighting laltens in monsoon storms. Now it seemed like a whole world had blinked out on that Tuesday afternoon in the American spring, a whole universe extinguished just like that, so easily. And Sharmeen had no chance to get it back.

It was a Tuesday night again, one month to the day from Daddi's death, and Sharmeen woke up. She tried not to open her eyes, not to think about being awake. Lately she had decided that it was the uncertainty about falling asleep that actually kept her awake. So she tried to remain still, and breathed deeply. She tried to think good, pleasant thoughts, and against the rush of memory she built the bulwark of an imaginary landscape, a forested hillside, no, a beach and a green-blue sea stretching away. Then, with a sigh, Sharmeen gave up. She was awake. She opened her eyes, and Daddi was sitting on the bed, at the very foot of it. She had on her favourite dark blue pashmina shawl, the one she had got just three years ago, but she was very young and beautiful. Her forehead was high and the black hair tumbled down in luxuriant, old-fashioned curlicues. I am dreaming, Sharmeen thought. I can wake up. Wake up. But she couldn't, and it was unmistakably Daddi still sitting there, with the window and the moonlight behind her. Sharmeen thought, if I sit up and drink some water, this will stop. But her arms and legs lay against her sides as heavy as white stone, and despite all her straining she could not move. Now it occurred to her that she should pray, but then she felt a twitch of guilt in her heart, for being afraid of Daddi. She looked directly at Daddi and felt terribly sad, for Daddi and herself. And then Daddi said, in a low voice, not unhappy but brimming with tenderness, 'Nikki, take me home.'

Then Sharmeen was awake. She could move, and she sat up and cupped her face with her hands. She felt relieved and ridiculous all at the same time. She thought, tomorrow I will tell Aisha about this funny, filmi dream, and how real it felt. Maybe I will tell Abba and Ammi too. She could imagine herself telling them, and the expressions of wonder and concern they would have on their face. She could see herself telling them, and Aisha, and other people in the future.

But she never told anyone, not ever. In a few months, her own memory of the dream began to fade, and the vivid, living black of Daddi's hair and the blue of her shawl became dusty and indistinct. On Sharmeen's next birthday, Aisha gave her a pink diary with a small golden lock. Late that night, Sharmeen remembered her dream about Daddi, and thought she should write it down. But she couldn't remember what Daddi had said, exactly, in the dream, and after a few minutes she gave up and wrote about Aamir Khan instead. She wrote about his films, and his acting, and when she had finished she locked the diary and tucked it under her mattress. Then she slept, and never dreamed of Daddi again.

Mere Sahiba

❧✦❧

The lilting voice over the speakers asked, '*Mere sahiba, kaun jaane gun tere?*' Sartaj had no answer to this question. He was sitting cross-legged in a veranda of the Golden Temple, at the edge of the parkarma. To his right was the shrine of Baba Deep Singh, and straight ahead, the Harimandir Sahib flushed a delicate, reddish gold in the early sun. Sartaj and Ma had arrived punctually at the temple gate at three in the morning, and had come in and watched the procession that carried the Guru Granth Sahib over the water, to its seat. Sartaj had made his way through the crowd, and for a few seconds he had put his shoulder to the palki and had helped carry the holy book, and then he had come back to Ma, longing for the surges of excitement and certitude that he had once felt on this holy ground. Now they were sitting shoulder to shoulder, and the sun had come up, and the parkarma was busy with people, and the singer asked his question.

Sartaj and Ma had arrived in Amritsar the day before. She had been very tired when they reached her mausa-ji's son's house, and they had stayed up late, for a long dinner with many cousins and aunts and almost-forgotten distant relatives. But still she had told him to set the alarm for two-thirty, and they had set off for the Harimandir Sahib in the darkness. Now she had her hands folded in her lap, and she rocked back and forth gently as her lips moved.

'Are you hungry, Ma?'

'No, beta. You go and get something to eat.'

'No, I'm all right.' Sartaj was all right, more or less, but he was worried about Ma. She was closed off in some private world of memory and grief and prayer, very far from him. Her eyes were wet, and she dabbed often at the corners of her mouth with her chunni. And she prayed, so softly that he could not make out what shabad she was reciting. He did not know what or who she was

937

mourning, or how to make her feel better. 'Are you remembering Papa-ji?' he said.

She slowly raised her head and turned to him. Her eyes were brown and enormous and surprised, and he had the sense suddenly that he was looking at someone he didn't know.

'Yes,' she said. 'Papa-ji.'

But she was not telling him everything, there were things she wouldn't speak of. Sartaj knew this, and was embarrassed, as if he had intruded into some dark room he was not meant to see. 'I am hungry,' he said. 'You'll stay here?'

'Yes. Go.'

So he left her, and walked around the rippling pool, along the parkarma. There were pilgrims sitting in the verandas, and two little boys ran out ahead of Sartaj, chased by their mother. She held them by the shoulders and walked them back to their father, and the older one grinned at Sartaj, revealing a missing front tooth. Sartaj smiled, and strolled on. The stone was warming under his bare feet. His earliest memory of Harimandir Sahib was of cold toes, of Papa-ji holding his hand and guiding him swiftly through the foot-bath just outside the complex. He had skipped down the chilly marble stairs, dazzled by the gold reflection in the water of the sarovar. He knew he had been brought here earlier, as an infant, but that was what he remembered now, that winter morning, walking between Papa-ji and Ma, holding their hands. He had then been unable to read the names of martyrs and fallen soldiers on the marble plaques set into the walls and the pillars. Now it was hard for him to avoid the names of the dead, to look away from the lists put in place by Indian army regiments and grieving families. Here was a plaque, on the wall just next to the causeway that led to the Harimandir. A captain from 8 JAK Light Infantry had fallen at Siachen. Two years after his death, his wife – also a captain – had donated Rs 701 and put up the plaque in his memory. Now more than a decade had passed, and Sartaj wondered if the wife still grieved. He was sure she did. Sartaj imagined the husband, far above jagged peaks, climbing a mirror-like wall of ice. The husband was very young, and brave, and he was far higher than any human habitation, and he was climbing towards death. And Sartaj could see the wife, in her military uniform, her face turned up to the rising sun. Sartaj walked, and wept.

What was he crying for? He was mourning the dead, the captain, but also his enemies, who had waited for him on that frozen battlefield, gasping for air and wasting away their lungs. He was crying for all the names on all the plaques, and for the Sikh martyrs in the paintings in the museum upstairs who had stood in defence of their faith and had been tortured and mangled and executed. He cried for the six hundred and forty-four names on the list in the museum, for the Sikhs killed when the army had besieged the temple in 1984, and he cried for the soldiers who had been knocked down by bullets on these very stones. Sartaj walked. He wiped his face, and came in a full circle around the sarovar. Ma was still there, her back against a pillar, her eyes shut. He went past her, and started around the parkarma again. An old man looked at him curiously, gently, and Sartaj realized he was weeping again. There was no calculation that could determine exactly how much had been sacrificed or what had been gained, there was only this recognition of loss, of pain endured and absorbed. The heat came into Sartaj's feet now, and he welcomed its sting and walked on. In this circling around the Pool of Nectar, there was a kind of peace. He did not expect Vaheguru to forgive him, or even if his fragmented, doubting belief in Vaheguru entitled him to ask for forgiveness. He did not know whether he was a good man or a bad man, or whether his actions were rooted in faith or fear. But he had acted, and now this walking hurt him and comforted him. So he walked on, in a circle, past the Dukh Bhanjani Ber, which cured all afflictions, and past the platform of the Ath-sath Tirath. He came around, and then again. He forgot how many circles he had taken, and that he was walking, and there was only the movement of his body, the shining water and the song.

'Sartaj?'

Ma had a hand on his elbow.

'I was just walking,' Sartaj said. He wiped at his face with his sleeve, and led her back to the shade of the corridor.

'What happened?' she said. She reached up, straightened his collar. She was his mother again, with her little worried frown and her desire to see him completely neat and smart. That stranger he had seen in her a while earlier was gone. Hidden, perhaps.

'Nothing, Ma. Are you ready to go?'

She was, and they walked along the parkarma towards the exit. But then Sartaj stopped. That winter morning long ago, when he had come here with Papa-ji and Ma, Papa-ji had wanted him to take a dip in the pool. Papa-ji had taken his own shirt and trousers off, and in his blue-striped kachchas had gone into the water. 'Come, Sartaj,' he had beckoned. But Sartaj had hidden behind Ma, and refused to go. 'A sher like my son doesn't mind a little cold,' Papa-ji had said. 'Come.' But it wasn't the cold Sartaj had been afraid of. He had become suddenly shy. He was aware of the bulk of Papa-ji's brown shoulders, and he felt skinny and small, not a sher at all. He didn't want all those people looking at him. So he shook his head and clung to Ma, and she'd indulged him, 'Leave the boy alone, ji, he'll catch cold.' And Papa-ji had laughed and emerged from the pool, cascading water on to the steps, his kara bright against the width of his wrist.

It was summer now, and Sartaj had no shyness left in him. 'I think I'll take a dip,' he said to Ma.

She was pleased, but practical as always. 'You don't have a towel or anything.'

He shook his head, and shrugged. She waited by the Dukh Bhanjani Ber for him, holding his clothes neatly folded over her forearm. He went down the steps, turning his feet sideways on the wet stone. The water was surprisingly cool, and it pressed up against his sides. There were many men in the water about Sartaj, and the murmur of prayers. He folded his hands and lowered his face into the water, and the sounds softened. Far underneath, there was an ancient spring that led to the breathing centre of the world. A long swell, a slow shifting in the water, came up against his chest, picked him up and held him. A gentle rumbling was in his ears, a rustle, like waves on a beach heard from very far away. It was inside him, this sound. For a moment, all of Sartaj's weight receded, he felt his ageing arms and his slackening stomach lift, and he was floating. He came up, and the sparkling drops fell from his eyelashes, and he smiled at Ma.

She raised her free hand, palm towards him, and smiled back.

In the compartment on the way back to Mumbai, their travelling companions were two sisters, one eighteen and the other twenty, and their parents. The girls both wore elegant salwar-kameezes in red and green, and played Kishore Kumar songs on a portable cassette player. They were very polite, though, and asked Ma first if she would mind. She didn't, and so they all sped across the Punjab countryside to the cadence of *Geet gaata hoon main* and *Aane waala pal*, with the steady drumming of the wheels underneath. Ma was soon in a deep conversation with the girls' mother, about everything from how much

Amritsar had changed to a jeweller they both knew in Andheri. Sartaj talked to the father.

'I came to Bombay twenty-three years ago,' the man said. His name was Satnam Singh Birdi, and he was a carpenter. He had come to the city with only his skills and the name of an acquaintance of his father's on a piece of paper. The village connection hadn't worked, his father's friend had been indifferent, so in those early days Satnam Singh had slept on footpaths and gone hungry. But he was a good worker, he had found jobs working for other carpenters and interior decoration companies. His speciality was fancy cupboards, ornate tables, executive rooms. After seven years he had left to form his own carpentry service with two of his brothers, and they had prospered. The youngest brother had spent half his life, nearly, in the city, and he was always well-dressed, he carried a mobile and spoke English. He was their front-man, he brought in business and negotiated the contracts. They had expanded, and hired many carpenters themselves. Vaheguru had blessed the family, and now Satnam Singh and his wife had a nice apartment in Oshiwara. The girls had grown up, and they were top students, first-class students.

'This one,' Satnam Singh said, 'wants to be a doctor. And the young one says she wants to fly planes.'

The young one reacted immediately to the tolerant sigh in her father's voice. 'Papa,' she said tartly, 'lots of women are pilots nowadays. It's nothing unusual.'

And they plunged immediately and happily into what was obviously a long-running family argument. Ma – Sartaj's mother – took the young one's part, to the surprise of her new friend, the other mother. 'This is very good,' Ma said. 'Why should girls be kept back?'

Sartaj listened to them all talk, to Satnam Singh Birdi and his wife Kulwinder Kaur and their daughters Sabrina and Sonia, and he was surprised by an infusion of joy that spread like warm syrup through his chest. He resisted, because there was no basis for this hope. This was just one family, one story. And yet, here it was: this man and woman had travelled far, and they had worked, and they had made a life. Now their daughters looked forward to more. It was not so much. No doubt there had been tragedy and tribulation already, and Sabrina and Sonia would come, in time, to their own disappointments and defeats. But Sartaj could not keep a smile from his face, and he laughed aloud at Sabrina's sallies at her mother.

941

They all ate lunch together, shared paraunthas and bhindi and puris, and fruits bought from the stations. After lunch, the elders slept, and the girls wanted to hear policing stories about famous people. Sartaj told them a few suitable to their age, about film stars and tycoons, and grew drowsy. He had to accept, finally, that he was one of the elders, and he climbed up to his berth and slept heavily, lulled by the rocking of the train.

The smell of chai woke him, chai and pakoras. He lay still for a few minutes, luxuriating in the promise of the moment, in the pleasure of his own rested body, in the rising urgency of the whistle and the speed, in going home and Mary waiting for him. Then he clambered down, and ate. The girls brought out two packs of cards, and dealt out a hand of rummy, including everyone. Ma said she hadn't played in years, that she was too old to play well, but then revealed herself to be an adept and wily player. She took in the hands she won with a gleam in her eye, and trumped ferociously, thumping her card down.

'Vah, ji,' Kulwinder Kaur said, 'you are a complete expert. What cards you throw every time!'

Much later, after dinner and when the Birdi family was asleep, Sartaj sat at the end of Ma's bottom berth. He knew she wouldn't sleep till much later. She was lying back, her knees drawn up. Behind her head, the fields sped by, uncanny and beautiful in the wash of moonlight.

'Ma?' Sartaj said softly.

'Yes, beta?'

'Ma, there is this girl . . .'

'I know.'

'You know?'

She giggled. Sartaj couldn't see her face, but he knew the look, when she bent her chin down and nodded her head from side to side.

'I am a police-walli also,' she said, 'I have friends who tell me things. I know a lot of things.'

'That's true. You do.'

She shifted over on to her side, with a hand below her cheek. 'This is good, beta.' Now she wasn't joking at all. 'A man should be with a woman. That is how it is. You can't get through life alone.'

'But you like being alone,' Sartaj said. Perhaps it was the darkness which made it possible for him to speak to her so bluntly, to point to how diligently she guarded her own independence.

'That is different,' she said. 'I have seen all of life, Sartaj. I have done my duty.'

She used the English word *duty*, and Sartaj remembered Papa-ji calling out, '*Arre chetti kar, dooty par jaana hai.*' It was strange to think of love as duty, to imagine that Ma's salwar-kameez and red paranda had been a kind of uniform, that maybe her assiduous care of his and Papa-ji's health and cleanliness and nutrition had not been natural, but somehow cultivated and consciously sacrificed. So this familiar figure resting next to him had led her own private life in all the homes they had shared, she had her own history of every birthday, every journey. Again Sartaj had that unsettling feeling that this woman, his own mother, Prabhjot Kaur, was also someone he did not know. It wrenched his heart, just slightly, but out of that hurt came a new affection for this stranger he had lived with all these years. She had worked very hard, without recognition, without recompense. So maybe she was more like an underpaid police-walli than she knew. He smiled, and asked, 'Are your feet hurting?'

'A little.'

Sartaj massaged her ankles, pressed her feet. The train picked up speed, and went over a long bridge with that booming rattle which mixed exuberance and nostalgia. Whoever she was, this woman, Sartaj did not feel alone sitting at her feet, or lonely. She had been many things to him. They had been mother and son, but they were also Prabhjot Kaur and Sartaj Singh, they had been each other's support for many years, and they were friends. Outside the window, the river rose to the horizon in a vast spill of icy silver light. Sartaj held his mother's foot, and with the fragile weight of her bones against his hand, he thought, she is old. He allowed himself to think of her death, and he shivered suddenly, but he was not sad. Every connection came freighted with loss, every attachment with the possibility of betrayal. There was no avoiding this conundrum, no escape from it, and no profit from complaining about it. Love was duty, and duty was love.

Sartaj caught himself thinking these philosophical thoughts, and he grinned at his own fatuousness. I must be tired, he thought. He patted Ma's feet, then silently went up to his berth. He curled over under a clean-smelling white sheet, and a song from the afternoon came from under the rolling wheels. Was it a Kishore Kumar song, what was it? He could hear the tune, but what were the words? He pulled the sheet up to his chin and, very softly, hummed the song and tried to remember.

943

Mary wanted to put mud on Sartaj's face. 'It's not mud,' she said indignantly, but that's exactly what it looked like, mud in a small pink pot.

'Yes, it is,' Sartaj said. 'You went downstairs and got it from under one of the plants.' They were sitting facing each other, on his bed. This was the first time she had visited his apartment, and he had spent the afternoon tidying up and cleaning away the dust that had accumulated during his Amritsar trip. She had arrived at six-thirty, carrying a small blue backpack over her shoulder. He had teased her about how young she looked, like a stylish college student, and then they had made love. Afterwards, he told her about the journey, and told her about how grimy he had felt, despite being inside an AC compartment all the way. At which point she'd jumped off her bed and rummaged inside her backpack and come up with the jar of mud.

'It is a very expensive facial treatment, Sar-taj,' Mary said. 'At the salon, people pay how much for it, you don't know. Look, it has fruits and essences in it. It will rejuvenate your skin, take out all the impurities from the train, all that dust and grit. It's like multani mitti, only better.' She shifted forward, so that her thighs straddled his. She was wearing a sheet around her waist, and her hair fell to the curve of her bare shoulders. 'Arre, don't move, baba.' She dipped two fingers in the pot, and painted the stuff over his forehead. It felt cool going on, cool and smooth. 'Pull your hair back.'

She worked carefully and slowly, her tongue between her teeth. He craned up, and she laughed and let him kiss her, but only for a moment, and then she pushed him back with the heel of a hand on the shoulder. He leaned back against a pillow and watched her eyes, the shaded brown of her skin. There were shallow rimples in her lips, and he examined the curve of her eyelashes. When she had finished, and nodded with satisfaction, he took the pot from her and scooped up a dab and smoothed it along the line of her cheekbone. The stuff was red and softer than ordinary mud, very even and fine-grained, and it went on easily. He painted her face, working from the top down. When he was at her neck, he leaned his head back, feeling the clay pull at his own skin already, and there was a moment of astonishment when he saw her whole, because it was Mary but not quite Mary. The red made a mask on her, so that the features were those he knew well but the face was still and opaque and unknown. 'You don't look like yourself,' he said.

She nodded. 'We have to let it dry now,' she said. 'Fifteen-twenty minutes.'

So they sat, with her hands on his chest, and him holding her around the waist. He watched the red change colour, become lighter, and seams appear in it. It was like looking at an ancient stone statue, except there were her eyes at the centre, bright and glowing. It was disquieting somehow, this abstraction of Mary into something else, something impersonal, so he glanced away, over her shoulder. The door to his cupboard was open, and on the outside of it was the long mirror he had nailed up long ago, to check his style before he set out each day. He could see himself and Mary in it now, silhouetted and symmetrical, and part of his own face, the red cheeks under the loose flow of hair. There was a stranger there, a man equally unknown. He breathed, and he turned back to Mary, very calm, and held her very close.

Their breathing swirled in the silence and was louder than the streets outside the window, and the cries of birds fell faintly into their respirations. Mary had told him the treatment would rejuvenate his skin, but quite apart from the tightening of his skin, the mud seemed to be working its effects deeper. He was here with Mary, and he was not afraid of either the happiness or the heartbreak that lay ahead. He was newly alive, as if he had been freed of something. He did not understand why this should be so, but he was satisfied with not under-standing completely. To be alive was enough.

'It's dry,' Mary said. 'Let's take it off.'

He led her into the bathroom by the hand, and took the sheet from her and tucked it behind the towels. She twisted at the knobs on the wall, and a jet of water frilled out across the narrow room. She laughed, turning to him, and her smile cracked through the clay. He laughed too, for no good reason. They washed it off each other's faces, and the mud ran down their bodies and they were covered with a glaze of it, and Sartaj saw Mary – the Mary he knew something of – emerge from the layer of red, and he wanted to touch every part of her, and he did.

A party of Municipal men were working on a hole in the road. They weren't actually working, they were standing around the hole looking at it, and apparently waiting for something to happen. Meanwhile, a vast funnel of traffic pressed up against the bottleneck. Sartaj was somewhere towards the front, on his motorcycle. He was hemmed in by a BEST bus and two autos, and there was nowhere for anyone to go, so they all waited companionably. The bus was crammed full of office-goers, and the autos were taking college students to their classes. Young boys were working the stalled traffic, selling magazines and water and gaudy Chinese statues of a laughing man with his hands above his head. A pair of maimed beggars went from car to car, tapping their stumps on the windscreens. There were two radios playing somewhere close, mixing channels. Sartaj drank it all in, incredulous that he had missed all this while he had been away, and that he was glad to be back. Even this particular stench of exhaust and burning and heated tar, even this was delectable. I must be mad, he thought. And he remembered Katekar, who had been crazy in the same way, who had complained endlessly but had confessed to yearning for the city when he went to his in-laws' village. 'Once the air of this place touches you,' Katekar had said, 'you are useless for anywhere else.' And he had twirled his finger at his forehead, and laughed, his shoulders shaking.

The bus moved, and Sartaj swerved ahead, risking a meeting with tonnes of metal, and then he was past the Municipal men and through the gap. He sped ahead. A curve festooned with bright new film posters brought him near a beach, and the sea lay flat and brown. There was new construction near the Kailashpada naka, a hulking steel scaffold thrust itself out of the ground. The labourers had built their red and blue tents in its shadow, and naked babies crawled over the piles of gravel. Sartaj slowed for a pair of rangy white dogs which crossed the road full of purpose, looking exactly as if they had an important meeting in five minutes. A breeze blew against Sartaj's chest, and he was happy.

He coasted easily through the gates of the police station, and parked in front of the zonal headquarters. From where he was sitting, he could see through the reception area to the gallery that led to the senior inspector's office and the detection room. Kamble was sitting at the desk directly in front of the main door, bent over and writing something in a register. A man and a woman sat across from him, leaning towards each other, their shoulders huddled. A constable led a shackled prisoner past. The scrape of a jhadoo against stone came from the balcony above, slowly repeating itself. Majid Khan called out to an inspector, and the booming curl of his friendly abuse made Sartaj grin.

Sartaj got off the bike. He put his shoes up on the pedal, one by one, and buffed them with a spare handkerchief until they shone. Then he ran a finger around his waistline, along the belt. He patted his cheeks, and ran a forefinger and thumb along his moustache. He was sure it was magnificent. He was ready. He went in and began another day.

Custom Edition for University of Maryland University College

ALGEBRA
& TRIGONOMETRY
BEECHER | PENNA | BITTINGER

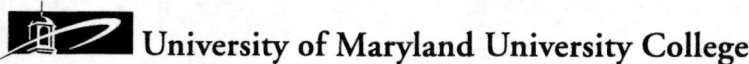 University of Maryland University College   **MATH 107, MATH 108, AND MATH 115**

Taken from:
Algebra and Trigonometry, Third Edition
by Judith A. Beecher, Judith A. Penna, and Marvin L. Bittinger

Note to Students: The material included in this book has been specifically selected by your instructors. They have chosen to eliminate some material which is not critical to your course, and in doing so, the price of the book has been adjusted to reflect the content removed.

PEARSON

Custom
Publishing

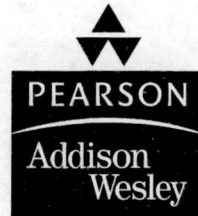

PEARSON

Addison
Wesley

Taken from:

Algebra and Trigonometry, Third Edition
by Judith A. Beecher, Judith A. Penna, and Marvin L. Bittinger
Copyright © 2008 by Pearson Education, Inc.
Published by Addison Wesley
Boston, Massachusetts 02116

This special edition published in cooperation with Pearson Custom Publishing.

Printed in the United States of America

10 9 8 7 6 5 4 3 2 1

ISBN 0-536-48004-4

2007360571

MH

Please visit our web site at *www.pearsoncustom.com*

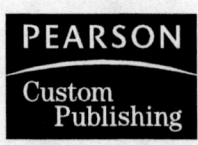

PEARSON CUSTOM PUBLISHING
501 Boylston Street, Suite 900, Boston, MA 02116
A Pearson Education Company

For Our Children

Michelle and Matthew
Tony and David
Lowell and Chris

Contents

3 Polynomial and Rational Functions   253

4 Exponential and Logarithmic Functions   347

5 The Trigonometric Functions   433

Trigonometric Identities, Inverse Functions, and Equations

6

533

Analytic Geometry Topics   **767**

Preface

Our challenge, and our goal, when writing this textbook was to do everything possible to help you learn the concepts and skills contained between its covers. Every feature we have included was put here with this in mind. We realize that your time is both valuable and limited, so we communicate in a highly visual way that allows you to focus easily and learn quickly and efficiently.

Take advantage of the side-by-side algebraic solutions and visualizations, the Visualizing the Graph and the Connecting the Concepts features, the Vocabulary Reviews, the Classify the Function exercises, and the Study Tips. We included them to enable you to make the most of your study time and to be successful in this course.

In an effort to encourage you to observe and interpret the mathematics that appears daily in the world around you, we conducted a vigorous search for real-data applications during our writing process. These applied problems connect the mathematical concepts in this course with your everyday life.

Best wishes for a positive learning experience,

Judy Beecher
Judy Penna
Marv Bittinger

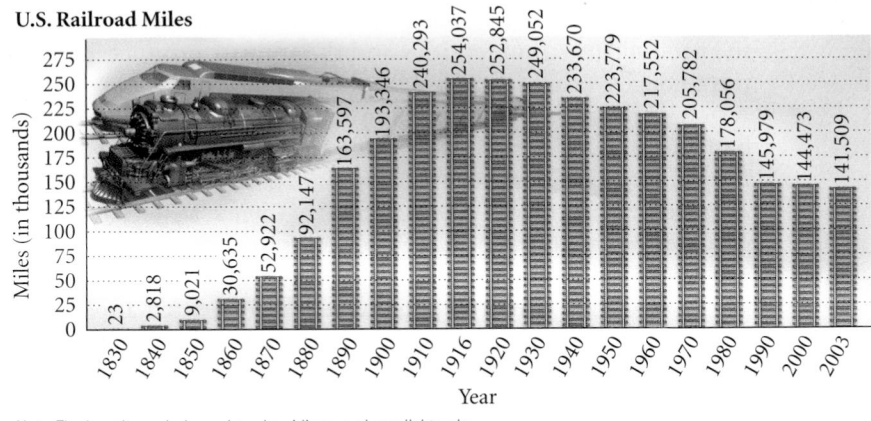

U.S. Railroad Miles

Miles (in thousands)

Year	Miles
1830	23
1840	2,818
1850	9,021
1860	30,635
1870	52,922
1880	92,147
1890	163,597
1900	193,346
1910	240,293
1916	254,037
1920	252,845
1930	249,052
1940	233,670
1950	223,779
1960	217,552
1970	205,782
1980	178,056
1990	145,979
2000	144,473
2003	141,509

Note: The lengths exclude yard tracks, sidings, and parallel tracks.
Source: Association of American Railroads

CONTENT FEATURES

Algebra and Trigonometry, Third Edition, covers college-level algebra and trigonometry and is appropriate for a one- or two-term course in precalculus mathematics. We introduce functions earlier than most precalculus texts, and our approach is more visual as well. Although a course in intermediate algebra is a prerequisite for using this text, Chapter R, "Basic Concepts of Algebra," provides sufficient review to unify the diverse mathematical backgrounds of most students.

✦ **New in the Third Edition**   In this edition, we have reorganized and expanded the content and features of the text.

- ✦ Section R.7, *The Basics of Equation Solving,* has been added to the optional review chapter. As the name suggests, this section provides a review of fundamental equation-solving techniques from intermediate algebra that will be used in Chapter 1. It can be taught in class or the student can refer to it independently as needed.
- ✦ Section 3.1, *Polynomial Functions and Models,* has been divided into two sections: Section 3.1, *Polynomial Functions and Models,* and Section 3.2, *Graphing Polynomial Functions.* Each of these two shorter sections is designed to be taught in a single class period, eliminating the need to carry the discussion of a section over from one class to the next.
- ✦ An additional objective on graphing damped oscillations, functions found by multiplying trigonometric functions by other functions, has been added to Section 5.6, *Graphs of Transformed Sine and Cosine Functions.*
- ✦ Section 6.4, *Proving Trigonometric Identities,* now includes using the product-to-sum identities and the sum-to-product identities to derive other identities.
- ✦ A new objective on graphing nonlinear systems of equations has been added Section 9.4, *Nonlinear Systems of Equations and Inequalities.* Also new to this edition are Section 9.5, *Rotation of Axes,* and Section 9.6, *Polar Equations of Conics.* Material on parametric equations, which was formerly in an appendix, is now placed in Section 9.7.
- ✦ Also new to this edition are many new and updated applied problems that contain real and relevant data. These applications help answer the question, "What is all this math good for?"
- ✦ To encourage students to put pencil to paper and practice skills at the time they are presented in the text, we have added a "Now Try" feature. At the end of nearly every example, the student is given the number of an exercise that corresponds to that example and is directed to "Now Try" doing the exercise.
- ✦ To help build test-taking skills, we have added true/false and multiple-choice exercises in each chapter review.

✦ **Function Emphasis**   Functions are the core of this course and should be presented as a thread that runs throughout the course rather than as an isolated topic. We introduce functions in Chapter 1, whereas most traditional precalculus mathematics textbooks cover equation-solving in Chapter 1. (See pp. 74, 82–84, 184, 200, 255, and 491.) Our approach introduces students to a relatively new concept at the beginning of the course rather than requiring them to begin with a review of what was previously covered in intermediate algebra. The concept of a function can be challenging for students. By repeatedly exposing them to the language, notation, and use of functions, demonstrating visually how functions relate to equations and graphs, and also showing how functions can be used to model real data, we hope that students will not only become comfortable with functions but will also come to understand and appreciate them.

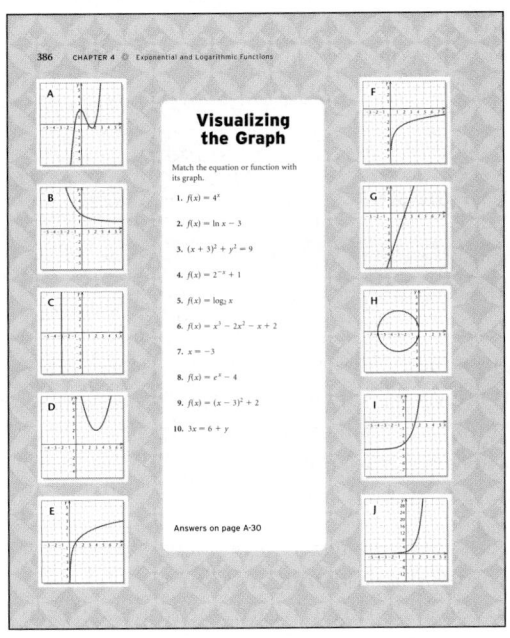

◆ **Visual Emphasis** Our early introduction of functions allows graphs to be used to provide a visual aspect to solving equations and inequalities. For example, we are able to show the students both algebraically and visually that the solutions of a quadratic equation $ax^2 + bx + c = 0$ are the zeros of the quadratic function $f(x) = ax^2 + bx + c$ as well as the x-intercepts of the graph of that function. This makes it possible for students, particularly visual learners, to gain a quick understanding of these concepts. (See pp. 209, 212, 255, 320, and 386.)

◆ **Emphasis on Graphing** To further enhance the visual aspect of the material, there is an increased emphasis on graphs and graphing in this edition, again reminding students how important and informative visualization can be in the discipline of mathematics. (See pp. 62, 79, 216–221, 273–274, 362, 382, 497, and 507.)

◆ **Visualizing the Graph** This feature provides students with an opportunity to match an equation with its graph by focusing on the characteristics of the equation and the corresponding attributes of the graph. This feature appears at least once in every chapter. (See pp. 114, 225, 315, 386, and 522.)

In addition to the full-page feature shown at left, many of the exercise sets include exercises in which the student is asked to match an equation with its graph or to find an equation of a function from its graph. (See pp. 165, 166, 265, and 370.)

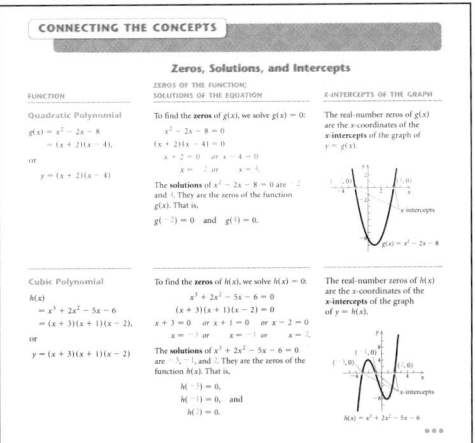

◆ **Connecting the Concepts** This feature highlights the importance of connecting concepts. When students are presented with concepts in a visual form—using graphs, an outline, or a chart—rather than merely in paragraphs of text, comprehension is streamlined and retention is maximized. The visual aspect of this feature invites students to stop and check their understanding of how concepts work together in one section or in several sections. This concept check in turn enhances student performance on homework assignments and exams. (See pp. 186, 212, 364, and 570.)

◆ **Zeros, Solutions, and x-Intercepts Theme** We find that when students understand the connections among the real zeros of a function, the solutions of its associated equation, and the first coordinates of the *x*-intercepts of its graph, a door opens to a new level of mathematical comprehension that increases the probability of success in this course. We emphasize zeros, solutions, and *x*-intercepts throughout the text by using consistent, precise terminology and including exceptional graphics. Seeing this theme repeated in different contexts leads to a better understanding and retention of these concepts. (See pp. 202, 212, and 581.)

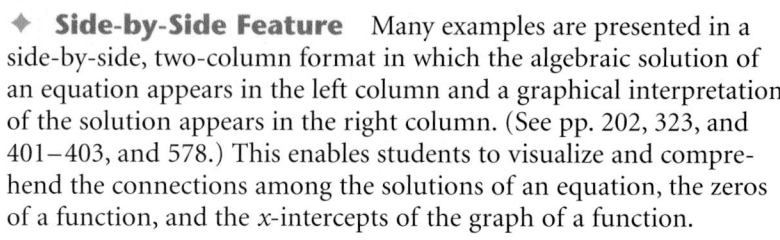

◆ **Side-by-Side Feature** Many examples are presented in a side-by-side, two-column format in which the algebraic solution of an equation appears in the left column and a graphical interpretation of the solution appears in the right column. (See pp. 202, 323, and 401–403, and 578.) This enables students to visualize and comprehend the connections among the solutions of an equation, the zeros of a function, and the *x*-intercepts of the graph of a function.

◆ **Now Try Feature** Now Try exercises are found after nearly every example. This feature encourages active learning by asking students to do an exercise in the exercise set that is similar to the example the student has just read. (See pp. 201, 362, and 679.)

◆ **Classifying the Function** With a focus on conceptual understanding, students are asked periodically to identify a number of functions by their type (for example, linear, quadratic, rational, and so on). As students progress through the text, the variety of functions they know increases and these exercises become more challenging. The "classifying the function" exercises appear with the review exercises in the Skill Maintenance portion of an exercise set. (See pp. 300 and 711.)

◆ **Vocabulary Review** This feature checks and reviews students' understanding of the vocabulary introduced throughout the text. It appears once in every chapter, in the Skill Maintenance portion of an exercise set, and is intended to provide a continuing review of the terms that students must know in order to be able to communicate effectively in the language of mathematics. (See pp. 246, 319, and 489.)

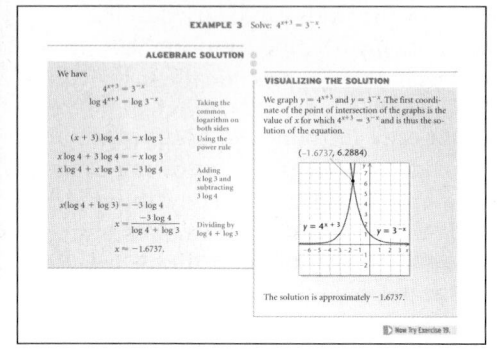

World Trade with China

Source: U.S.–China Business Council

◆ **Real-Data Applications** We encourage students to see and interpret the mathematics that appears every day in the world around them. Throughout the writing process, we conducted an energetic search for real-data applications, and the result is a variety of examples and exercises that connect the mathematical content with everyday life. Most of these applications feature source lines and frequently include charts and graphs. Many are drawn from the fields of health, business and economics, life and physical sciences, social science, and areas of general interest such as sports and travel. (See pp. 97, 100, 117, 180, 191, 264, 372, 450, 614, and 689.)

YEAR	NUMBER OF SALADS SOLD (in millions)
2003	133
2004	179
2005	173

Source: McDonald's

◆ **Technology Connections** This feature appears throughout the text to demonstrate how a graphing calculator can be used to solve problems. The technology is set apart from the traditional exposition, so that it does not intrude if no technology is desired. Although students might not be using graphing calculators, the graphing calculator windows that appear in the Technology Connection features enhance the visual element of the text, providing graphical interpretations of solutions of equations, zeros of functions, and x-intercepts of graphs of functions. (See pp. 178, 204, 402, and 582.) Exercises that are designed to be worked using a graphing calculator are grouped together in the exercise sets under the heading Technology Connection so that they can be easily identified. A graphing calculator manual, providing keystroke-level instruction for five models of graphing calculators, is also available. (See Supplements for the Student.)

◆ **Study Tips**   Appearing in the text margin, the Study Tips provide helpful study hints throughout the text and also briefly remind students to use the electronic and print supplements that accompany the text. (See pp. 121, 146, and 284.)

◆ **Review Icons**   Placed next to the concept that a student is currently studying, a review icon references a section of the text in which the student can find and review the topics on which the current concept is built. (See pp. 301 and 348.)

◆ **Optional Review Chapter**   Chapter R, "Basic Concepts of Algebra," provides an optional review of intermediate algebra. Section R.7, *The Basics of Equation Solving,* is new in this edition. Some or all of the topics in this chapter can be taught at the beginning of the course, or they can be used as a convenient source of information throughout the term for students who need a quick review of particular topics.

◆ **Appendix Covering Basic Concepts from Geometry**
This appendix covers basic concepts from geometry that students need to know in order to work with topics pertaining to angles and triangles. Formulas from geometry are also listed near the back of the book.

PEDAGOGICAL FEATURES

◆ **Chapter Openers**   Each chapter opens with an application relevant to the content of the chapter. Also included is a table of contents for the chapter, listing section titles. (See pp. 253, 435, and 767.)

◆ **Section Objectives**   Content objectives are listed at the beginning of each section. Together with subheadings throughout the section, these objectives provide a useful outline of the section for both instructors and students. (See pp. 74, 200, and 491.)

◆ **Annotated Examples**   We have included over 590 examples designed to prepare the student fully to do the exercises. Learning is carefully guided with the use of numerous color-coded art pieces and step-by-step annotations. Substitutions and annotations are highlighted in red for emphasis. (See pp. 205 and 392–393.)

✦ **Use of Color**   The text uses full color in an extremely functional way, as seen in the design elements and numerous pieces of art. The use of color has been carefully thought out so that it carries a consistent meaning that enhances students' ability to read and comprehend the exposition. (See pp. 160, 348–349, and 351.)

✦ **Art Package**   The text contains over 1170 art pieces including photographs, situational art, and statistical graphs that not only highlight the abundance of real-world applications but also help students visualize the mathematics being discussed. (See pp. 70, 130, 312, 361, and 419.)

✦ **Five-Step Problem-Solving Process**   The basis for problem solving is a distinctive five-step process established early in the text (Section 2.1) to help students learn strategic ways to approach and solve applied problems. This process is then used throughout the text to give students a consistent framework for problem solving. (See pp. 178–180, 182–183, and 210.)

✦ **Variety of Exercises**   There are over 5550 exercises in this text. The exercise sets are enhanced with real-data applications and source lines, detailed art pieces, tables, graphs, and photographs. In addition to the exercises that provide students practice with the concepts presented in the section, the exercise sets feature the following elements.

Collaborative Discussion and Writing Exercises can be used in small groups or by the class as a whole to encourage students to talk and write about the key mathematical concepts in each section. (See pp. 215 and 389.)

Skill Maintenance Exercises provide an ongoing review of concepts previously presented in the course, enhancing students' retention of these concepts. These exercises include Vocabulary Review (see pp. 132–133, 246, 319, and 424–425) and Classifying the Function (see pp. 300 and 711). Answers to *all* Skill Maintenance exercises appear in the answer section at the back of the book along with a section reference that directs students quickly and efficiently to the appropriate section of the text if they need help with an exercise. (See pp. 166, 280, and 360.)

Synthesis Exercises appear at the end of each exercise set and encourage critical thinking by requiring students to synthesize concepts from several sections or to take a concept a step further than in the general exercises. (See pp. 289 and 319.)

Technology Exercises are to be done using a graphing calculator. They are set apart from the non-calculator exercises, making it convenient for the instructor to avoid assigning them if graphing calculators are not being used in the course. (See pp. 89 and 408.)

✦ **Highlighted Information**   Important definitions, properties, and rules are displayed in screened boxes, and summaries and procedures are listed in boxes outlined in black. This organization and presentation provides for efficient learning and review. (See pp. 293 and 376.)

✦ **Summary and Review**   The Summary and Review at the end of each chapter contains a list of important properties and formulas covered in that chapter followed by an extensive set of review exercises. A section reference is provided for each exercise. This directs the student to the appropriate place in the chapter to find help, if needed, in doing the exercise. To help students build and/or polish test-taking skills, we have added true/false and multiple-choice exercises to the review exercises. The chapter summary and the review exercises provide excellent preparation for chapter tests and also for the final examination. Answers to *all* review exercises appear at the back of the book. (See pp. 247–250 and 426–430.)

✦ **Chapter Tests**   The test at the end of each chapter allows students to test themselves and target areas that need further study before taking the in-class test. Answers to *all* Chapter Test questions appear in the answer section at the back of the book, along with corresponding section references. (See pp. 173 and 431.)

STUDENT SUPPLEMENTS

Graphing Calculator Manual
ISBN-13: 978-0-321-46538-2;
ISBN-10: 0-321-46538-5
- By Judith A. Penna
- Contains keystroke-level instruction for the Texas Instruments TI-83, TI-83 Plus, TI-84 Plus, TI-84 Plus Silver Edition, and TI-89
- Teaches students how to use a graphing calculator using actual examples and exercises from the main text
- Mirrors the topic order in the main text to provide a just-in-time mode of instruction

Student's Solutions Manual
ISBN-13: 978-0-321-46644-0;
ISBN-10: 0-321-46644-6
- By Judith A. Penna
- Contains completely worked-out solutions with step-by-step annotations for all the odd-numbered exercises in the exercise sets, with the exception of the Collaborative Discussion and Writing exercises, for all the odd-numbered review exercises, and for all the chapter test exercises

INSTRUCTOR SUPPLEMENTS

Annotated Instructor's Edition
ISBN-13: 978-0-321-47194-9;
ISBN-10: 0-321-47194-6
- Includes all the answers to the exercise sets, usually right on the page where the exercises appear
- Readily accessible answers help both new and experienced instructors prepare for class efficiently

New! Insider's Guide
ISBN-13: 978-0-321-46645-7;
ISBN-10: 0-321-46645-4
- This guide includes resources to help faculty with course preparation and classroom management, such as helpful teaching tips specific to chapter objectives; useful outside resources for teachers; helpful tips for using supplements and technology; black-line masters of grids and number lines for transparency masters or test preparation; and a correlation guide from the second edition to the third edition.

New! Adjunct Support Center
- Offers consultation on suggested syllabi, helpful tips for using the textbook support package, assistance with content, and advice on classroom strategies
- Available Sunday through Thursday evenings from 5 P.M. to midnight
- e-mail: AdjunctSupport@aw.com; Telephone: 1-800-435-4084; fax: 1-877-262-9774

(continued)

STUDENT SUPPLEMENTS

Video Lectures on CD with Optional Captioning
ISBN-13: 978-0-321-46463-7;
ISBN-10: 0-321-46463-X
*   In these section-specific videos, author Judy Penna leads an engaging team of lecturers who provide comprehensive lessons on every objective in the textbook using consistent methodology and terminology throughout. Many of these lessons are staged as an office hour during which a student poses questions and works through the problems with the instructor. Available for purchase with the text at minimal cost, these lessons provide an easy and convenient way for students to watch video segments from a computer, either at home or on campus.

Addison-Wesley Math Tutor Center
*   Staffed by qualified mathematics instructors who provide students with tutoring on examples and odd-numbered exercises from the textbook
*   Free tutoring is available via toll-free telephone, toll-free fax, e-mail, or the Internet through a registration number that can be packaged with a new textbook or purchased separately.
*   White Board technology allows tutors and students to actually see problems worked while they "talk" in real time over the Internet during the tutoring session www.aw-bc.com/tutorcenter.

INSTRUCTOR SUPPLEMENTS

Instructor's Solutions Manual
ISBN-13: 978-0-321-46481-1;
ISBN-10: 0-321-46481-8
*   By Judith A. Penna
*   Contains worked-out solutions to all exercises in the exercise sets, including the Collaborative Discussion and Writing exercises, and solutions for all end-of-chapter exercises

Printed Test Bank
ISBN-13: 978-0-321-46341-8;
ISBN-10: 0-321-46341-2
*   By Laurie Hurley
*   Contains four free-response test forms for each chapter following the same format and having the same level of difficulty as the tests in the main text, plus two multiple-choice test forms for each chapter
*   Provides six forms of the final examination, four with free-response questions and two with multiple-choice questions

TestGen Computerized Test Bank
ISBN-13: 978-0-321-46322-7;
ISBN-10: 0-321-46322-6
*   Features a computerized bank of questions developed to cover all text objectives
*   Enables instructors to build, edit, print, and administer tests
*   Available on a dual-platform Windows/Macintosh CD-ROM

PowerPoint Lecture Presentation
*   Classroom presentation software correlated specifically to follow the sequence of this textbook, with presentations for each chapter
*   Available within MyMathLab or at www.aw-bc.com/irc
*   Active Learning Questions also available

Technology Supplements

MyMathLab®

MyMathLab is a series of text-specific, easily customizable online courses for Addison-Wesley textbooks in mathematics and statistics. MyMathLab is powered by CourseCompass™—Pearson Education's online teaching and learning environment—and by MathXL®—our online homework, tutorial, and assessment system. MyMathLab gives instructors the tools they need to deliver all or a portion of their course online, whether students are in a lab setting or working from home. MyMathLab provides a rich and flexible set of course materials, featuring free-response exercises that are algorithmically generated for unlimited practice and mastery. Students can also use online tools, such as video lectures, animations, and a multimedia textbook, to independently improve their understanding and performance. Instructors can use MyMathLab's homework and test managers to select and assign online exercises correlated directly to the textbook, and they can import TestGen tests into MyMathLab for added flexibility. MyMathLab's online gradebook—designed specifically for mathematics and statistics—automatically tracks students' homework and test results and gives the instructor control over how to calculate final grades. Instructors can also add offline (paper-and-pencil) grades to the gradebook. MyMathLab is available to qualified adopters. For more information, visit our Web site at www.mymathlab.com or contact your Addison-Wesley sales representative.

MathXL®

MathXL® is a powerful online homework, tutorial, and assessment system that accompanies Addison-Wesley textbooks in mathematics and statistics. With MathXL, instructors can create, edit, and assign online homework and tests using algorithmically generated exercises correlated at the objective level to the textbook. All student work is tracked in MathXL's online gradebook. Students can take chapter tests in MathXL and receive personalized study plans based on their test results. The study plan diagnoses weaknesses and links students directly to tutorial exercises for the objectives they need to study and retest. Students can also access supplemental animations and video clips directly from selected exercises. MathXL is available to qualified adopters. For more information, visit our Web site at www.mathxl.com or contact your Addison-Wesley sales representative.

MathXL® Tutorials on CD
ISBN-13: 978-0-321-46462-0;
ISBN-10: 0-321-46462-1

This interactive tutorial CD-ROM provides algorithmically generated practice exercises that are correlated at the objective level to the exercises in the textbook. Every practice exercise is accompanied by an example and a guided solution designed to involve students in the solution process. Selected exercises may also include a video clip to help students visualize concepts. The software provides helpful feedback for incorrect answers and can generate printed summaries of students' progress.

ACKNOWLEDGMENTS

We wish to express our heartfelt thanks to a number of people who have contributed in special ways to the development of this textbook. Our editor, Anne Kelly, encouraged and supported our vision. Kari Heen, our executive project manager, deserves special recognition for overseeing every phase of the project and keeping it moving. We are very appreciative of the marketing insight provided by Becky Anderson, our marketing manager, and of the support that we received from the entire Addison-Wesley Higher Education Group, including Ron Hampton, production manager, Joanna Doxey, assistant editor, and Ashley O'Shaughnessy, assistant editor. We also thank Christine Stavrou, media producer, for her creative work on the media products that accompany this text. And we are immensely grateful to Martha Morong, for her editorial and production services, and to Geri Davis, for her text design and art editing, and for the endless hours of hard work they have done to make this a book of which we are proud. We also thank Daphne Bell for consulting with us on the graphing calculator material and Laurie Hurley, Patty LaGree, Dawn Mulheron, and Jennifer Rosenberg for their careful accuracy checking and proofreading of the text.

The following reviewers made invaluable contributions to the development of the third edition and we thank them for that:

Stacie Badran, *Embry-Riddle Aeronautical University*
Sherry S. Biggers, *Clemson University Department of Mathematical Sciences*
Christine Bush, *Palm Beach Community College, Lake Worth*
Walter Czarnec, *Framingham State College*
Joseph De Guzman, *Riverside College, Norco Campus*
Douglas Dunbar, *Okaloosa-Walton Community College*
Wayne Ferguson, *Northwest Mississippi Community College*
Joseph Gaskin, *State University of New York, Oswego*
Dauhrice K. Gibson, (retired), *Gulf Coast Community College*
Jim Graziose, *Palm Beach Community College*
Joseph Lloyd Harris, *Gulf Coast Community College*
Susan K. Hitchcock, *Palm Beach Community College*
Sharon S. Hudson, *Gulf Coast Community College*
Jennifer Jameson, *Coconino Community College, Flagstaff*
Susan Leland, *Montana Tech of the University of Montana*
Bernard F. Mathon, *Miami-Dade College*
Debi McCandrew, *Florence-Darlington Technical College*
Barry J. Monk, *Macon State College*
Darla Ottman, *Elizabethtown Community College*
Vicki Partin, *Lexington Community College*
Kathy V. Rodgers, *University of Southern Indiana*
Lucille Roth, *Tech of the Low Country*
Abdelrida Saleh, *Miami-Dade College*
Rajalakshmi Sriram, *Okaloosa-Walton Community College*

J.A.B.
J.A.P.
M.L.B.

Algebra and Trigonometry

Basic Concepts of Algebra

APPLICATION

I n 2005, airlines worldwide lost a record 30 million pieces of luggage (*Source*: SITA). On average, how many pieces of luggage were lost each day of the year? (Use 1 year = 365 days.)

This problem appears as Exercise 82 in Section R.2.

R.1 The Real-Number System

♦ Identify various kinds of real numbers.
♦ Use interval notation to write a set of numbers.
♦ Identify the properties of real numbers.
♦ Find the absolute value of a real number.

✦ Real Numbers

In applications of algebraic concepts, we use real numbers to represent quantities such as distance, time, speed, area, profit, loss, and temperature. Some frequently used sets of real numbers and the relationships among them are shown below.

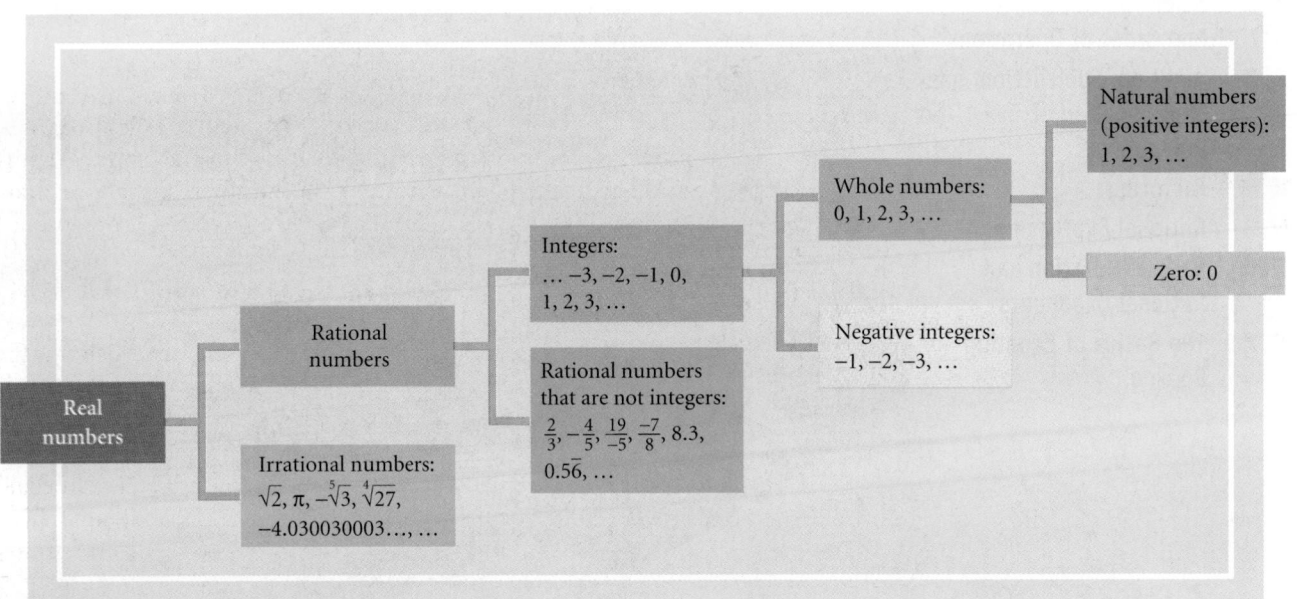

Numbers that can be expressed in the form p/q, where p and q are integers and $q \neq 0$, are **rational numbers**. Decimal notation for rational numbers either *terminates* (ends) or *repeats*. Each of the following is a rational number.

a) 0 $0 = \dfrac{0}{a}$ for any nonzero integer a

b) -7 $-7 = \dfrac{-7}{1}$, or $\dfrac{7}{-1}$

c) $\dfrac{1}{4} = 0.25$ Terminating decimal

d) $-\dfrac{5}{11} = -0.\overline{45}$ Repeating decimal

The real numbers that are not rational are **irrational numbers**. Decimal notation for irrational numbers neither terminates nor repeats. Each of the following is an irrational number.

a) $\pi = 3.1415926535\ldots$ There is no repeating block of digits.

$\left(\frac{22}{7}\right.$ and 3.14 are rational *approximations* of the irrational number $\pi.$)

b) $\sqrt{2} = 1.414213562\ldots$ There is no repeating block of digits.

c) $-6.12122122212222\ldots$ Although there is a pattern, there is no repeating block of digits.

The set of all rational numbers combined with the set of all irrational numbers gives us the set of **real numbers**. The real numbers are *modeled* using a **number line**, as shown below.

Each point on the line represents a real number, and every real number is represented by a point on the line.

The order of the real numbers can be determined from the number line. If a number a is to the left of a number b, then a **is less than** b ($a < b$). Similarly, a **is greater than** b ($a > b$) if a is to the right of b on the number line. For example, we see from the number line above that $-2.9 < -\frac{3}{5}$, because -2.9 is to the left of $-\frac{3}{5}$. Also, $\frac{17}{4} > \sqrt{3}$, because $\frac{17}{4}$ is to the right of $\sqrt{3}$.

The statement $a \leq b$, read "a is less than or equal to b," is true if either $a < b$ is true or $a = b$ is true.

The symbol $\in$ is used to indicate that a member, or **element**, belongs to a set. Thus if we let $\mathbb{Q}$ represent the set of rational numbers, we can see from the diagram on p. 2 that $0.5\overline{6} \in \mathbb{Q}$. We can also write $\sqrt{2} \notin \mathbb{Q}$ to indicate that $\sqrt{2}$ is *not* an element of the set of rational numbers.

When *all* the elements of one set are elements of a second set, we say that the first set is a **subset** of the second set. The symbol $\subseteq$ is used to denote this. For instance, if we let $\mathbb{R}$ represent the set of real numbers, we can see from the diagram that $\mathbb{Q} \subseteq \mathbb{R}$ (read "$\mathbb{Q}$ is a subset of $\mathbb{R}$").

✦ Interval Notation

Sets of real numbers can be expressed using **interval notation**. For example, for real numbers a and b such that $a < b$, the **open interval** (a, b) is the set of real numbers between, but not including, a and b. That is,

$$(a, b) = \{x \mid a < x < b\}.$$

The points a and b are **endpoints** of the interval. The parentheses indicate that the endpoints are not included in the interval.

Some intervals extend without bound in one or both directions. The interval $[a, \infty)$, for example, begins at a and extends to the right without bound. That is,

$$[a, \infty) = \{x \mid x \geq a\}.$$

The bracket indicates that a is included in the interval.

The various types of intervals are listed below.

Intervals: Types, Notation, and Graphs

TYPE	INTERVAL NOTATION	SET NOTATION	GRAPH
Open	(a, b)	$\{x \mid a < x < b\}$	
Closed	$[a, b]$	$\{x \mid a \le x \le b\}$	
Half-open	$[a, b)$	$\{x \mid a \le x < b\}$	
Half-open	$(a, b]$	$\{x \mid a < x \le b\}$	
Open	(a, ∞)	$\{x \mid x > a\}$	
Half-open	$[a, \infty)$	$\{x \mid x \ge a\}$	
Open	$(-\infty, b)$	$\{x \mid x < b\}$	
Half-open	$(-\infty, b]$	$\{x \mid x \le b\}$	

The interval $(-\infty, \infty)$, graphed below, names the set of all real numbers, $\mathbb{R}$.

EXAMPLE 1   Write interval notation for each set and graph the set.

a) $\{x \mid -4 < x < 5\}$ b) $\{x \mid x \ge 1.7\}$

c) $\{x \mid -5 < x \le -2\}$ d) $\{x \mid x < \sqrt{5}\}$

Solution

a) $\{x \mid -4 < x < 5\} = (-4, 5);$

b) $\{x \mid x \ge 1.7\} = [1.7, \infty);$

c) $\{x \mid -5 < x \le -2\} = (-5, -2];$

d) $\{x \mid x < \sqrt{5}\} = (-\infty, \sqrt{5});$

$$-5 \ -4 \ -3 \ -2 \ -1 \quad 0 \quad 1 \quad 2 \quad 3 \quad 4 \quad 5$$

> Now Try Exercises 13 and 15.

✦ Properties of the Real Numbers

The following properties can be used to manipulate algebraic expressions as well as real numbers.

Properties of the Real Numbers

For any real numbers a, b, and c:

$a + b = b + a$ and $ab = ba$	Commutative properties of addition and multiplication
$a + (b + c) = (a + b) + c$ and $a(bc) = (ab)c$	Associative properties of addition and multiplication
$a + 0 = 0 + a = a$	Additive identity property
$-a + a = a + (-a) = 0$	Additive inverse property
$a \cdot 1 = 1 \cdot a = a$	Multiplicative identity property
$a \cdot \dfrac{1}{a} = \dfrac{1}{a} \cdot a = 1 \ (a \neq 0)$	Multiplicative inverse property
$a(b + c) = ab + ac$	Distributive property

Note that the distributive property is also true for subtraction since $a(b - c) = a[b + (-c)] = ab + a(-c) = ab - ac$.

EXAMPLE 2 State the property being illustrated in each sentence.

a) $8 \cdot 5 = 5 \cdot 8$ **b)** $5 + (m + n) = (5 + m) + n$

c) $14 + (-14) = 0$ **d)** $6 \cdot 1 = 1 \cdot 6 = 6$

e) $2(a - b) = 2a - 2b$

Solution

SENTENCE	PROPERTY
a) $8 \cdot 5 = 5 \cdot 8$	Commutative property of multiplication: $ab = ba$
b) $5 + (m + n) = (5 + m) + n$	Associative property of addition: $a + (b + c) = (a + b) + c$
c) $14 + (-14) = 0$	Additive inverse property: $a + (-a) = 0$
d) $6 \cdot 1 = 1 \cdot 6 = 6$	Multiplicative identity property: $a \cdot 1 = 1 \cdot a = a$
e) $2(a - b) = 2a - 2b$	Distributive property: $a(b + c) = ab + ac$

> Now Try Exercises 49 and 55.

✦ Absolute Value

The number line can be used to provide a geometric interpretation of *absolute value*. The **absolute value** of a number a, denoted $|a|$, is its distance from 0 on the number line. For example, $|-5| = 5$, because the distance of -5 from 0 is 5. Similarly, $\left|\frac{3}{4}\right| = \frac{3}{4}$, because the distance of $\frac{3}{4}$ from 0 is $\frac{3}{4}$.

Absolute Value

For any real number a,

$$|a| = \begin{cases} a, & \text{if } a \geq 0, \\ -a, & \text{if } a < 0. \end{cases}$$

When a is nonnegative, the absolute value of a is a. When a is negative, the absolute value of a is the opposite, or additive inverse, of a. Thus, $|a|$ is never negative; that is, for any real number a, $|a| \geq 0$.

Absolute value can be used to find the distance between two points on the number line.

a b

$|a - b| = |b - a|$

Distance Between Two Points on the Number Line

For any real numbers a and b, the **distance between a and b** is $|a - b|$, or equivalently, $|b - a|$.

EXAMPLE 3   Find the distance between -2 and 3.

Solution   The distance is

$$|-2 - 3| = |-5| = 5, \quad \text{or equivalently,}$$
$$|3 - (-2)| = |3 + 2| = |5| = 5.$$

▶ Now Try Exercise 69.

R.1 EXERCISE SET

In Exercises 1–10, consider the numbers $-12, \sqrt{7}, 5.\overline{3},$
$-\frac{7}{3}, \sqrt[3]{8}, 0, 5.242242224\ldots, -\sqrt{14}, \sqrt[5]{5}, -1.96, 9,$
$4\frac{2}{3}, \sqrt{25}, \sqrt[3]{4}, \frac{5}{7}.$

1. Which are whole numbers?

2. Which are integers?

3. Which are irrational numbers?

4. Which are natural numbers?

5. Which are rational numbers?

6. Which are real numbers?

7. Which are rational numbers but not integers?

8. Which are integers but not whole numbers?

9. Which are integers but not natural numbers?

10. Which are real numbers but not integers?

Write interval notation. Then graph the interval.

11. $\{x \mid -3 \le x \le 3\}$ 12. $\{x \mid -4 < x < 4\}$

13. $\{x \mid -4 \le x < -1\}$ 14. $\{x \mid 1 < x \le 6\}$

15. $\{x \mid x \le -2\}$ 16. $\{x \mid x > -5\}$

17. $\{x \mid x > 3.8\}$ 18. $\{x \mid x \ge \sqrt{3}\}$

19. $\{x \mid 7 < x\}$ 20. $\{x \mid -3 > x\}$

Write interval notation for the graph.

21.

22.

23.

24.

25.

26.

27.

28.

In Exercises 29–46, the following notation is used:
$\mathbb{N} =$ *the set of natural numbers,* $\mathbb{W} =$ *the set of whole numbers,* $\mathbb{Z} =$ *the set of integers,* $\mathbb{Q} =$ *the set of rational numbers,* $\mathbb{I} =$ *the set of irrational numbers, and* $\mathbb{R} =$ *the set of real numbers. Classify the statement as true or false.*

29. $6 \in \mathbb{N}$ 30. $0 \notin \mathbb{N}$

31. $3.2 \in \mathbb{Z}$ 32. $-10.\overline{1} \in \mathbb{R}$

33. $-\dfrac{11}{5} \in \mathbb{Q}$ 34. $-\sqrt{6} \in \mathbb{Q}$

35. $\sqrt{11} \notin \mathbb{R}$ 36. $-1 \in \mathbb{W}$

37. $24 \notin \mathbb{W}$ 38. $1 \in \mathbb{Z}$

39. $1.089 \notin \mathbb{I}$ 40. $\mathbb{N} \subseteq \mathbb{W}$

41. $\mathbb{W} \subseteq \mathbb{Z}$ 42. $\mathbb{Z} \subseteq \mathbb{N}$

43. $\mathbb{Q} \subseteq \mathbb{R}$ 44. $\mathbb{Z} \subseteq \mathbb{Q}$

45. $\mathbb{R} \subseteq \mathbb{Z}$ 46. $\mathbb{Q} \subseteq \mathbb{I}$

Name the property illustrated by the sentence.

47. $6 \cdot x = x \cdot 6$

48. $3 + (x + y) = (3 + x) + y$

49. $-3 \cdot 1 = -3$ 50. $x + 4 = 4 + x$

51. $5(ab) = (5a)b$ 52. $4(y - z) = 4y - 4z$

53. $2(a + b) = (a + b)2$ **54.** $-7 + 7 = 0$

55. $-6(m + n) = -6(n + m)$

56. $t + 0 = t$

57. $8 \cdot \dfrac{1}{8} = 1$

58. $9x + 9y = 9(x + y)$

Simplify.

59. $|-7.1|$ **60.** $|-86.2|$

61. $|347|$ **62.** $|-54|$

63. $\left|-\sqrt{97}\right|$ **64.** $\left|\dfrac{12}{19}\right|$

65. $|0|$ **66.** $|15|$

67. $\left|\dfrac{5}{4}\right|$ **68.** $\left|-\sqrt{3}\right|$

Find the distance between the given pair of points on the number line.

69. $-5,\ 6$ **70.** $-2.5,\ 0$

71. $-8,\ -2$ **72.** $\dfrac{15}{8},\ \dfrac{23}{12}$

73. $6.7,\ 12.1$ **74.** $-14,\ -3$

75. $-\dfrac{3}{4},\ \dfrac{15}{8}$ **76.** $-3.4,\ 10.2$

77. $-7,\ 0$ **78.** $3,\ 19$

Collaborative Discussion and Writing

To the student and the instructor: The Collaborative Discussion and Writing exercises are meant to be answered with one or more sentences. These exercises can also be discussed and answered collaboratively by the entire class or by small groups. Because of their open-ended nature, the answers to these exercises do not appear at the back of the book. They are denoted by the words "Discussion and Writing."

79. How would you convince a classmate that division is not associative?

80. Under what circumstances is $\sqrt{a}$ a rational number?

Synthesis

To the student and the instructor: The Synthesis exercises found at the end of every exercise set challenge students to combine concepts or skills studied in that section or in preceding parts of the text.

Between any two (different) real numbers there are many other real numbers. Find each of the following. Answers may vary.

81. An irrational number between 0.124 and 0.125

82. A rational number between $-\sqrt{2.01}$ and $-\sqrt{2}$

83. A rational number between $-\dfrac{1}{101}$ and $-\dfrac{1}{100}$

84. An irrational number between $\sqrt{5.99}$ and $\sqrt{6}$

85. The hypotenuse of an isosceles right triangle with legs of length 1 unit can be used to "measure" a value for $\sqrt{2}$ by using the Pythagorean theorem, as shown.

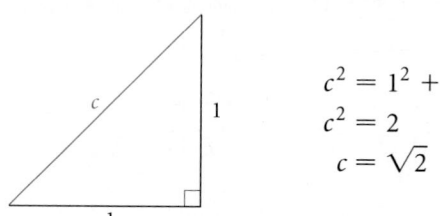

$$c^2 = 1^2 + 1^2$$
$$c^2 = 2$$
$$c = \sqrt{2}$$

Draw a right triangle that could be used to "measure" $\sqrt{10}$ units.

Integer Exponents, Scientific Notation, and Order of Operations

R.2

♦ Simplify expressions with integer exponents.
♦ Solve problems using scientific notation.
♦ Use the rules for order of operations.

♦ Integers as Exponents

When a positive integer is used as an *exponent*, it indicates the number of times a factor appears in a product. For example, 7^3 means $7 \cdot 7 \cdot 7$ and 5^1 means 5.

> For any positive integer n,
>
> $$a^n = \underbrace{a \cdot a \cdot a \cdots a}_{n \text{ factors}},$$
>
> where a is the **base** and n is the **exponent**.

Zero and negative-integer exponents are defined as follows.

> For any nonzero real number a and any integer m,
>
> $$a^0 = 1 \quad \text{and} \quad a^{-m} = \frac{1}{a^m}.$$

EXAMPLE 1 Simplify each of the following.

a) 6^0 b) $(-3.4)^0$

Solution

a) $6^0 = 1$ b) $(-3.4)^0 = 1$

▷ Now Try Exercise 7.

EXAMPLE 2 Write each of the following with positive exponents.

a) 4^{-5} b) $\dfrac{1}{(0.82)^{-7}}$ c) $\dfrac{x^{-3}}{y^{-8}}$

Solution

a) $4^{-5} = \dfrac{1}{4^5}$

b) $\dfrac{1}{(0.82)^{-7}} = (0.82)^{-(-7)} = (0.82)^7$

c) $\dfrac{x^{-3}}{y^{-8}} = x^{-3} \cdot \dfrac{1}{y^{-8}} = \dfrac{1}{x^3} \cdot y^8 = \dfrac{y^8}{x^3}$

▶ **Now Try Exercise 1.**

The results in Example 2 can be generalized as follows.

For any nonzero numbers a and b and any integers m and n,

$$\dfrac{a^{-m}}{b^{-n}} = \dfrac{b^n}{a^m}.$$

(A factor can be moved to the other side of the fraction bar if the sign of the exponent is changed.)

EXAMPLE 3   Write an equivalent expression without negative exponents:

$$\dfrac{x^{-3}y^{-8}}{z^{-10}}.$$

Solution   Since each exponent is negative, we move each factor to the other side of the fraction bar and change the sign of each exponent:

$$\dfrac{x^{-3}y^{-8}}{z^{-10}} = \dfrac{z^{10}}{x^3 y^8}.$$

▶ **Now Try Exercise 5.**

The following properties of exponents can be used to simplify expressions.

Properties of Exponents

For any real numbers a and b and any integers m and n, assuming 0 is not raised to a nonpositive power:

$a^m \cdot a^n = a^{m+n}$	Product rule
$\dfrac{a^m}{a^n} = a^{m-n} \ (a \neq 0)$	Quotient rule
$(a^m)^n = a^{mn}$	Power rule
$(ab)^m = a^m b^m$	Raising a product to a power
$\left(\dfrac{a}{b}\right)^m = \dfrac{a^m}{b^m} \ (b \neq 0)$	Raising a quotient to a power

EXAMPLE 4   Simplify each of the following.

a) $y^{-5} \cdot y^3$

b) $\dfrac{48x^{12}}{16x^4}$

c) $(t^{-3})^5$

d) $(2s^{-2})^5$

e) $\left(\dfrac{45x^{-4}y^2}{9z^{-8}}\right)^{-3}$

Solution

a) $y^{-5} \cdot y^3 = y^{-5+3} = y^{-2}$, or $\dfrac{1}{y^2}$

b) $\dfrac{48x^{12}}{16x^4} = \dfrac{48}{16}x^{12-4} = 3x^8$

c) $(t^{-3})^5 = t^{-3 \cdot 5} = t^{-15}$, or $\dfrac{1}{t^{15}}$

d) $(2s^{-2})^5 = 2^5(s^{-2})^5 = 32s^{-10}$, or $\dfrac{32}{s^{10}}$

e) $\left(\dfrac{45x^{-4}y^2}{9z^{-8}}\right)^{-3} = \left(\dfrac{5x^{-4}y^2}{z^{-8}}\right)^{-3}$

$$= \dfrac{5^{-3}x^{12}y^{-6}}{z^{24}} = \dfrac{x^{12}}{5^3 y^6 z^{24}}, \text{ or } \dfrac{x^{12}}{125y^6 z^{24}}$$

▷ **Now Try Exercises 15 and 39.**

✦ Scientific Notation

We can use scientific notation to name very large and very small positive numbers and to perform computations.

> ### Scientific Notation
> **Scientific notation** for a number is an expression of the type
> $$N \times 10^m,$$
> where $1 \le N < 10$, N is in decimal notation, and m is an integer.

Keep in mind that in scientific notation positive exponents are used for numbers greater than or equal to 10 and negative exponents for numbers between 0 and 1.

EXAMPLE 5 *Business Travel.* In a recent year, Americans made about 151,700,000 business trips that took them at least 50 mi from home (*Source:* Travel Industry Association of America). Convert the number 151,700,000 to scientific notation.

Solution We want the decimal point to be positioned between the first 1 and the 5, so we move it 8 places to the left. Since the number to be converted is greater than 10, the exponent must be positive. Thus we have

$$151{,}700{,}000 = 1.517 \times 10^8.$$

▷ **Now Try Exercise 51.**

EXAMPLE 6 *Mass of a Neutron.* The mass of a neutron is about 0.0000000000000000000000000167 kg. Convert this number to scientific notation.

Solution   We want the decimal point to be positioned between the 1 and the 6, so we move it 27 places to the right. Since the number to be converted is between 0 and 1, the exponent must be negative. Thus we have

$$0.00000000000000000000000000167 = 1.67 \times 10^{-27}.$$

▷ **Now Try Exercise 59.**

EXAMPLE 7   Convert each of the following to decimal notation.

a) 7.632×10^{-4} b) 9.4×10^{5}

Solution

a) The exponent is negative, so the number is between 0 and 1. We move the decimal point 4 places to the left.

$$7.632 \times 10^{-4} = 0.0007632$$

b) The exponent is positive, so the number is greater than 10. We move the decimal point 5 places to the right.

$$9.4 \times 10^{5} = 940,000$$

▷ **Now Try Exercises 61 and 63.**

TECHNOLOGY CONNECTION

Most calculators make use of scientific notation. For example, the number 48,000,000,000,000 might be expressed in one of the ways shown below.

4.8E13

The computation in Example 8 can be performed on a calculator using scientific notation.

4.22∗5.88E12
            2.48136E13

EXAMPLE 8   *Distance to a Star.*   The nearest star, Alpha Centauri C, is about 4.22 light-years from Earth. One **light-year** is the distance that light travels in one year and is about 5.88×10^{12} mi. How many miles is it from Earth to Alpha Centauri C? Express your answer in scientific notation.

Solution

$$
\begin{aligned}
4.22 \times (5.88 \times 10^{12}) &= (4.22 \times 5.88) \times 10^{12} \\
&= 24.8136 \times 10^{12} \quad \text{This is not scientific notation because } 24.8136 > 10. \\
&= (2.48136 \times 10^{1}) \times 10^{12} \\
&= 2.48136 \times (10^{1} \times 10^{12}) \\
&= 2.48136 \times 10^{13} \text{ mi} \quad \text{Writing scientific notation}
\end{aligned}
$$

▷ **Now Try Exercise 79.**

✦ Order of Operations

Recall that to simplify the expression $3 + 4 \cdot 5$, we first multiply 4 and 5 to get 20 and then add 3 to get 23. Mathematicians have agreed on the following procedure, or rules for order of operations.

Rules for Order of Operations

1. Do all calculations within grouping symbols before operations outside. When nested grouping symbols are present, work from the inside out.
2. Evaluate all exponential expressions.
3. Do all multiplications and divisions in order from left to right.
4. Do all additions and subtractions in order from left to right.

TECHNOLOGY ·················
CONNECTION

Enter the computations in Example 9 on a graphing calculator as shown below.

```
8(5−3)^3−20
                    44
(10/(8−6)+9*4)/(2^5+3²)
                     1
```

To confirm that the parentheses around the numerator and around the denominator are essential in Example 9(b), enter the computation without using these parentheses. What is the result?

EXAMPLE 9   Calculate each of the following.

a) $8(5 - 3)^3 - 20$

b) $\dfrac{10 \div (8 - 6) + 9 \cdot 4}{2^5 + 3^2}$

Solution

a) $8(5 - 3)^3 - 20 = 8 \cdot 2^3 - 20$ Doing the calculation within parentheses

$\qquad\qquad\qquad = 8 \cdot 8 - 20$ Evaluating the exponential expression

$\qquad\qquad\qquad = 64 - 20$ Multiplying

$\qquad\qquad\qquad = 44$ Subtracting

b) $\dfrac{10 \div (8 - 6) + 9 \cdot 4}{2^5 + 3^2} = \dfrac{10 \div 2 + 9 \cdot 4}{32 + 9}$

$\qquad\qquad\qquad = \dfrac{5 + 36}{41} = \dfrac{41}{41} = 1$

Note that fraction bars act as grouping symbols. That is, the given expression is equivalent to $[10 \div (8 - 6) + 9 \cdot 4] \div (2^5 + 3^2)$.

▷ **Now Try Exercises 87 and 91.**

EXAMPLE 10   *Compound Interest.* If a principal P is invested at an interest rate r, compounded n times per year, in t years it will grow to an amount A given by

$$A = P\left(1 + \frac{r}{n}\right)^{nt}.$$

Suppose that $1250 is invested at 4.6% interest, compounded quarterly. How much is in the account at the end of 8 yr?

Solution   We have $P = 1250$, $r = 4.6\%$, or 0.046, $n = 4$, and $t = 8$. Substituting, we find that the amount in the account at the end of 8 yr is given by

$$A = 1250\left(1 + \frac{0.046}{4}\right)^{4 \cdot 8}.$$

TECHNOLOGY ·················
CONNECTION

The TVM Solver option in the Finance APP on a graphing calculator can be used to do Example 10.

```
N=32
I%=4.6
PV=−1250
PMT=0
FV=1802.263969
P/Y=4
C/Y=4
PMT: END BEGIN
```

Next, we evaluate this expression:

$A = 1250(1 + 0.0115)^{4 \cdot 8}$ Dividing

$\quad = 1250(1.0115)^{4 \cdot 8}$ Adding

$\quad = 1250(1.0115)^{32}$ Multiplying in the exponent

$\quad \approx 1250(1.441811175)$ Evaluating the exponential expression

$\quad \approx 1802.263969$ Multiplying

$\quad \approx 1802.26.$ Rounding to the nearest cent

The amount in the account at the end of 8 yr is $1802.26.

▷ **Now Try Exercise 93.**

R.2 EXERCISE SET

Write an equivalent expression without negative exponents.

1. 3^{-7}

2. $\dfrac{1}{(5.9)^{-4}}$

3. $\dfrac{x^{-5}}{y^{-4}}$

4. $\dfrac{a^{-2}}{b^{-8}}$

5. $\dfrac{m^{-1}n^{-12}}{t^{-6}}$

6. $\dfrac{x^{-9}y^{-17}}{z^{-11}}$

Simplify.

7. 18^0

8. $\left(-\frac{4}{3}\right)^0$

9. $x^9 \cdot x^0$

10. $a^0 \cdot a^4$

11. $5^8 \cdot 5^{-6}$

12. $6^2 \cdot 6^{-7}$

13. $m^{-5} \cdot m^5$

14. $n^9 \cdot n^{-9}$

15. $y^3 \cdot y^{-7}$

16. $b^{-4} \cdot b^{12}$

17. $7^3 \cdot 7^{-5} \cdot 7$

18. $3^6 \cdot 3^{-5} \cdot 3^4$

19. $2x^3 \cdot 3x^2$

20. $3y^4 \cdot 4y^3$

21. $(-3a^{-5})(5a^{-7})$

22. $(-6b^{-4})(2b^{-7})$

23. $(5a^2b)(3a^{-3}b^4)$

24. $(4xy^2)(3x^{-4}y^5)$

25. $(6x^{-3}y^5)(-7x^2y^{-9})$

26. $(8ab^7)(-7a^{-5}b^2)$

27. $(2x)^3(3x)^2$

28. $(4y)^2(3y)^3$

29. $(-2n)^3(5n)^2$

30. $(2x)^5(3x)^2$

31. $\dfrac{b^{40}}{b^{37}}$

32. $\dfrac{a^{39}}{a^{32}}$

33. $\dfrac{x^{-5}}{x^{16}}$

34. $\dfrac{y^{-24}}{y^{-21}}$

35. $\dfrac{x^2y^{-2}}{x^{-1}y}$

36. $\dfrac{x^3y^{-3}}{x^{-1}y^2}$

37. $\dfrac{32x^{-4}y^3}{4x^{-5}y^8}$

38. $\dfrac{20a^5b^{-2}}{5a^7b^{-3}}$

39. $(2ab^2)^3$

40. $(4xy^3)^2$

41. $(-2x^3)^5$

42. $(-3x^2)^4$

43. $(-5c^{-1}d^{-2})^{-2}$

44. $(-4x^{-5}z^{-2})^{-3}$

45. $(3m^4)^3(2m^{-5})^4$

46. $(4n^{-1})^2(2n^3)^3$

47. $\left(\dfrac{2x^{-3}y^7}{z^{-1}}\right)^3$

48. $\left(\dfrac{3x^5y^{-8}}{z^{-2}}\right)^4$

49. $\left(\dfrac{24a^{10}b^{-8}c^7}{12a^6b^{-3}c^5}\right)^{-5}$

50. $\left(\dfrac{125p^{12}q^{-14}r^{22}}{25p^8q^6r^{-15}}\right)^{-4}$

Convert to scientific notation.

51. 405,000

52. 1,670,000

53. 0.00000039

54. 0.00092

55. 234,600,000,000

56. 8,904,000,000

57. 0.00104

58. 0.00000000514

59. One cubic inch is approximately equal to 0.000016 m^3.

60. The United States government collected $1,137,000,000,000 in individual income taxes in a recent year (*Source*: U.S. Internal Revenue Service).

Convert to decimal notation.

61. 8.3×10^{-5}

62. 4.1×10^6

63. 2.07×10^7

64. 3.15×10^{-6}

65. 3.496×10^{10}

66. 8.409×10^{11}

67. 5.41×10^{-8}

68. 6.27×10^{-10}

69. The amount of solid waste generated in the United States in a recent year was 2.319×10^8 tons (*Source*: Franklin Associates, Ltd.).

70. The mass of a proton is about 1.67×10^{-24} g.

Compute. Write the answer using scientific notation.

71. $(3.1 \times 10^5)(4.5 \times 10^{-3})$

72. $(9.1 \times 10^{-17})(8.2 \times 10^3)$

73. $(2.6 \times 10^{-18})(8.5 \times 10^7)$

74. $(6.4 \times 10^{12})(3.7 \times 10^{-5})$

75. $\dfrac{6.4 \times 10^{-7}}{8.0 \times 10^{6}}$

76. $\dfrac{1.1 \times 10^{-40}}{2.0 \times 10^{-71}}$

77. $\dfrac{1.8 \times 10^{-3}}{7.2 \times 10^{-9}}$

78. $\dfrac{1.3 \times 10^{4}}{5.2 \times 10^{10}}$

Solve. Write the answer using scientific notation.

79. *Distance to Pluto.* The distance from the earth to the sun is defined as 1 **astronomical unit**, or AU. It is about 93 million mi. The average distance from the earth to Pluto is 39 AUs. Find this distance in miles.

80. *Parsecs.* One **parsec** is about 3.26 light-years and 1 light-year is about 5.88×10^{12} mi. Find the number of miles in 1 parsec.

81. *Nanowires.* A **nanometer** is 0.000000001 m. Scientists have developed optical nanowires to transmit light waves short distances. A nanowire with a diameter of 360 nanometers has been used in experiments on the transmission of light (*Source: New York Times*, January 29, 2004). Find the diameter of such a wire in meters.

82. *Lost Luggage.* In 2005, airlines worldwide lost a record 30 million pieces of luggage (*Source:* SITA). On average, how many pieces of luggage were lost each day of the year? (Use 1 year = 365 days.)

83. *Chesapeake Bay Bridge-Tunnel.* The 17.6-mi-long Chesapeake Bay Bridge-Tunnel was completed in 1964. Construction costs were $210 million. Find the average cost per mile.

84. *Personal Space in Hong Kong.* The area of Hong Kong is 412 sq mi. It is estimated that the population of Hong Kong will be 9,600,000 in 2050. Find the number of square miles of land per person in 2050.

85. *Nuclear Disintegration.* One gram of radium produces 37 billion disintegrations per second. How many disintegrations are produced in 1 hr?

86. *Length of Earth's Orbit.* The average distance from the earth to the sun is 93 million mi. About how far does the earth travel in a yearly orbit? (Assume a circular orbit.)

Calculate.

87. $3 \cdot 2 - 4 \cdot 2^2 + 6(3 - 1)$

88. $3[(2 + 4 \cdot 2^2) - 6(3 - 1)]$

89. $16 \div 4 \cdot 4 \div 2 \cdot 256$

90. $2^6 \cdot 2^{-3} \div 2^{10} \div 2^{-8}$

91. $\dfrac{4(8 - 6)^2 - 4 \cdot 3 + 2 \cdot 8}{3^1 + 19^0}$

92. $\dfrac{[4(8 - 6)^2 + 4](3 - 2 \cdot 8)}{2^2(2^3 + 5)}$

Compound Interest. Use the compound interest formula from Example 10 for Exercises 93–96. Round to the nearest cent.

93. Suppose that $2125 is invested at 6.2%, compounded semiannually. How much is in the account at the end of 5 yr?

94. Suppose that $9550 is invested at 5.4%, compounded semiannually. How much is in the account at the end of 7 yr?

95. Suppose that $6700 is invested at 4.5%, compounded quarterly. How much is in the account at the end of 6 yr?

96. Suppose that $4875 is invested at 5.8%, compounded quarterly. How much is in the account at the end of 9 yr?

Collaborative Discussion and Writing

97. Are the parentheses necessary in the expression $4 \cdot 25 \div (10 - 5)$? Why or why not?

98. Is $x^{-2} < x^{-1}$ for any negative value(s) of x? Why or why not?

Synthesis

Savings Plan. *The formula*

$$S = P\left[\dfrac{\left(1 + \dfrac{r}{12}\right)^{12 \cdot t} - 1}{\dfrac{r}{12}}\right]$$

gives the amount S accumulated in a savings plan when a deposit of P dollars is made each month for t years in an account with interest rate r, compounded monthly. Use this formula for Exercises 99–102.

99. Marisol deposits $250 in a retirement account each month beginning at age 40. If the investment earns 5% interest, compounded monthly, how much will have accumulated in the account when she retires 27 yr later?

100. Gordon deposits $100 in a retirement account each month beginning at age 25. If the investment earns 4% interest, compounded monthly, how much will have accumulated in the account when Gordon retires at age 65?

101. Gina wants to establish a college fund for her newborn daughter that will have accumulated $120,000 at the end of 18 yr. If she can count on an interest rate of 6%, compounded monthly, how much should she deposit each month to accomplish this?

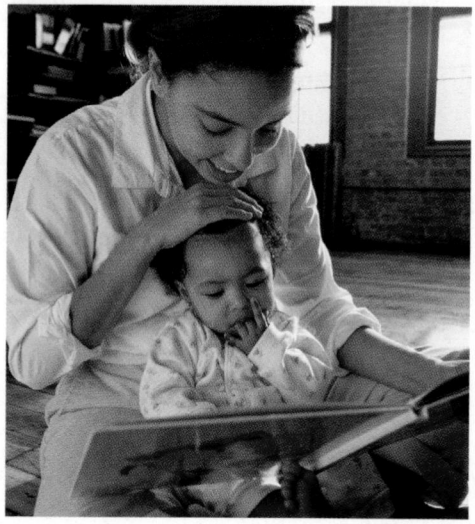

102. Liam wants to have $200,000 accumulated in a retirement account by age 70. If he starts making monthly deposits to the plan at age 30 and can count on an interest rate of 4.5%, compounded monthly, how much should he deposit each month in order to accomplish this?

Simplify. Assume that all exponents are integers, all denominators are nonzero, and zero is not raised to a nonpositive power.

103. $(x^t \cdot x^{3t})^2$

104. $(x^y \cdot x^{-y})^3$

105. $(t^{a+x} \cdot t^{x-a})^4$

106. $(m^{x-b} \cdot n^{x+b})^x (m^b n^{-b})^x$

107. $\left[\dfrac{(3x^a y^b)^3}{(-3x^a y^b)^2}\right]^2$

108. $\left[\left(\dfrac{x^r}{y^t}\right)^2 \left(\dfrac{x^{2r}}{y^{4t}}\right)^{-2}\right]^{-3}$

R.3

Addition, Subtraction, and Multiplication of Polynomials

✦ Identify the terms, coefficients, and degree of a polynomial.

✦ Add, subtract, and multiply polynomials.

✦ Polynomials

Polynomials are a type of algebraic expression that you will often encounter in your study of algebra. Some examples of polynomials are

$$3x - 4y, \quad 5y^3 - \tfrac{7}{3}y^2 + 3y - 2, \quad -2.3a^4, \quad \text{and} \quad z^6 - \sqrt{5}.$$

All but the first are polynomials in one variable.

> **Polynomials in One Variable**
>
> A **polynomial in one variable** is any expression of the type
>
> $$a_n x^n + a_{n-1} x^{n-1} + \cdots + a_2 x^2 + a_1 x + a_0,$$
>
> where n is a nonnegative integer and $a_n, \ldots, a_0$ are real numbers, called **coefficients**. The parts of a polynomial separated by plus signs are called **terms**. The **leading coefficient** is a_n, and the **constant term** is a_0. If $a_n \neq 0$, the **degree** of the polynomial is n. The polynomial is said to be written in **descending order**, because the exponents decrease from left to right.

EXAMPLE 1   Identify the terms of the polynomial

$$2x^4 - 7.5x^3 + x - 12.$$

Solution   Writing plus signs between the terms, we have

$$2x^4 - 7.5x^3 + x - 12 = 2x^4 + (-7.5x^3) + x + (-12),$$

so the terms are

$$2x^4, \quad -7.5x^3, \quad x, \quad \text{and} \quad -12.$$

A polynomial, like 23, consisting of only a nonzero constant term has degree 0. It is agreed that the polynomial consisting only of 0 has *no* degree.

EXAMPLE 2   Find the degree of each polynomial.

a) $2x^3 - 9$ **b)** $y^2 - \tfrac{3}{2} + 5y^4$ **c)** 7

Solution

POLYNOMIAL	DEGREE
a) $2x^3 - 9$	3
b) $y^2 - \tfrac{3}{2} + 5y^4 = 5y^4 + y^2 - \tfrac{3}{2}$	4
c) $7 = 7x^0$	0

▶ Now Try Exercise 1.

Algebraic expressions like $3ab^3 - 8$ and $5x^4y^2 - 3x^3y^8 + 7xy^2 + 6$ are **polynomials in several variables**. The **degree of a term** is the sum of the exponents of the variables in that term. The **degree of a polynomial** is the degree of the term of highest degree.

EXAMPLE 3   Find the degree of the polynomial

$$7ab^3 - 11a^2b^4 + 8.$$

Solution   The degrees of the terms of $7ab^3 - 11a^2b^4 + 8$ are 4, 6, and 0, respectively, so the degree of the polynomial is 6.   ▶ Now Try Exercise 3.

A polynomial with just one term, like $-9y^6$, is a **monomial**. If a polynomial has two terms, like $x^2 + 4$, it is a **binomial**. A polynomial with three terms, like $4x^2 - 4xy + 1$, is a **trinomial**.

Expressions like

$$2x^2 - 5x + \frac{3}{x}, \qquad 9 - \sqrt{x}, \quad \text{and} \quad \frac{x + 1}{x^4 + 5}$$

are not polynomials, because they cannot be written in the form $a_nx^n + a_{n-1}x^{n-1} + \cdots + a_1x + a_0$, where the exponents are all nonnegative integers and the coefficients are all real numbers.

✦ Addition and Subtraction

If two terms of an expression have the same variables raised to the same powers, they are called **like terms**, or **similar terms**. We can **combine**, or **collect**, **like terms** using the distributive property. For example, $3y^2$ and $5y^2$ are like terms and

$$3y^2 + 5y^2 = (3 + 5)y^2$$
$$= 8y^2.$$

We add or subtract polynomials by combining like terms.

EXAMPLE 4   Add or subtract each of the following.

a) $(-5x^3 + 3x^2 - x) + (12x^3 - 7x^2 + 3)$
b) $(6x^2y^3 - 9xy) - (5x^2y^3 - 4xy)$

Solution

a) $(-5x^3 + 3x^2 - x) + (12x^3 - 7x^2 + 3)$

$\quad = (-5x^3 + 12x^3) + (3x^2 - 7x^2) - x + 3$ Rearranging using the commutative and associative properties

$\quad = (-5 + 12)x^3 + (3 - 7)x^2 - x + 3$ Using the distributive property

$\quad = 7x^3 - 4x^2 - x + 3$

b) We can subtract by adding an opposite:

$$(6x^2y^3 - 9xy) - (5x^2y^3 - 4xy)$$

$$= (6x^2y^3 - 9xy) + (-5x^2y^3 + 4xy) \qquad \text{Adding the opposite of } 5x^2y^3 - 4xy$$

$$= 6x^2y^3 - 9xy - 5x^2y^3 + 4xy$$

$$= x^2y^3 - 5xy. \qquad \text{Combining like terms}$$

▷ Now Try Exercises 5 and 9.

✦ Multiplication

Multiplication of polynomials is based on the distributive property—for example,

$$(x + 4)(x + 3) = x(x + 3) + 4(x + 3) \qquad \text{Using the distributive property}$$

$$= x^2 + 3x + 4x + 12 \qquad \text{Using the distributive property two more times}$$

$$= x^2 + 7x + 12. \qquad \text{Combining like terms}$$

In general, to multiply two polynomials, we multiply each term of one by each term of the other and add the products.

EXAMPLE 5   Multiply: $(4x^4y - 7x^2y + 3y)(2y - 3x^2y)$.

Solution   We have

$$(4x^4y - 7x^2y + 3y)(2y - 3x^2y)$$

$$= 4x^4y(2y - 3x^2y) - 7x^2y(2y - 3x^2y) + 3y(2y - 3x^2y)$$

$$\qquad\qquad \text{Using the distributive property}$$

$$= 8x^4y^2 - 12x^6y^2 - 14x^2y^2 + 21x^4y^2 + 6y^2 - 9x^2y^2$$

$$\qquad\qquad \text{Using the distributive property three more times}$$

$$= 29x^4y^2 - 12x^6y^2 - 23x^2y^2 + 6y^2. \qquad \text{Combining like terms}$$

We can also use columns to organize our work, aligning like terms under each other in the products.

$$
\begin{array}{r}
4x^4y - 7x^2y + 3y \\
2y - 3x^2y \\
\hline
-12x^6y^2 + 21x^4y^2 - 9x^2y^2 \\
8x^4y^2 - 14x^2y^2 + 6y^2 \\
\hline
-12x^6y^2 + 29x^4y^2 - 23x^2y^2 + 6y^2
\end{array}
$$

Multiplying by $-3x^2y$
Multiplying by $2y$
Adding

▷ Now Try Exercise 13.

We can find the product of two binomials by multiplying the **First** terms, then the **Outer** terms, then the **Inner** terms, then the **Last** terms. Then we combine like terms, if possible. This procedure is sometimes called **FOIL**.

EXAMPLE 6   Multiply: $(2x - 7)(3x + 4)$.

Solution   We have

$$
(2x - 7)(3x + 4) = 6x^2 + 8x - 21x - 28
$$
$$
= 6x^2 - 13x - 28
$$

▶ Now Try Exercise 15.

We can use FOIL to find some special products.

> **Special Products of Binomials**
>
> $(A + B)^2 = A^2 + 2AB + B^2$ Square of a sum
> $(A - B)^2 = A^2 - 2AB + B^2$ Square of a difference
> $(A + B)(A - B) = A^2 - B^2$ Product of a sum and a difference

EXAMPLE 7   Multiply each of the following.

a) $(4x + 1)^2$ **b)** $(3y^2 - 2)^2$ **c)** $(x^2 + 3y)(x^2 - 3y)$

Solution

a) $(4x + 1)^2 = (4x)^2 + 2 \cdot 4x \cdot 1 + 1^2 = 16x^2 + 8x + 1$
b) $(3y^2 - 2)^2 = (3y^2)^2 - 2 \cdot 3y^2 \cdot 2 + 2^2 = 9y^4 - 12y^2 + 4$
c) $(x^2 + 3y)(x^2 - 3y) = (x^2)^2 - (3y)^2 = x^4 - 9y^2$

▶ Now Try Exercises 23 and 33.

R.3   EXERCISE SET

Determine the terms and the degree of the polynomial.

1. $-5y^4 + 3y^3 + 7y^2 - y - 4$

2. $2m^3 - m^2 - 4m + 11$

3. $3a^4b - 7a^3b^3 + 5ab - 2$

4. $6p^3q^2 - p^2q^4 - 3pq^2 + 5$

Perform the operations indicated.

5. $(5x^2y - 2xy^2 + 3xy - 5) + (-2x^2y - 3xy^2 + 4xy + 7)$

6. $(6x^2y - 3xy^2 + 5xy - 3) + (-4x^2y - 4xy^2 + 3xy + 8)$

7. $(2x + 3y + z - 7) + (4x - 2y - z + 8) + (-3x + y - 2z - 4)$

8. $(2x^2 + 12xy - 11) + (6x^2 - 2x + 4) + (-x^2 - y - 2)$

9. $(3x^2 - 2x - x^3 + 2) - (5x^2 - 8x - x^3 + 4)$

10. $(5x^2 + 4xy - 3y^2 + 2) - (9x^2 - 4xy + 2y^2 - 1)$

11. $(x^4 - 3x^2 + 4x) - (3x^3 + x^2 - 5x + 3)$

12. $(2x^4 - 3x^2 + 7x) - (5x^3 + 2x^2 - 3x + 5)$

13. $(a - b)(2a^3 - ab + 3b^2)$

14. $(n + 1)(n^2 - 6n - 4)$

15. $(x + 5)(x - 3)$

16. $(y - 4)(y + 1)$

17. $(x + 6)(x + 4)$

18. $(n - 5)(n - 8)$

19. $(2a + 3)(a + 5)$

20. $(3b + 1)(b - 2)$

21. $(2x + 3y)(2x + y)$

22. $(2a - 3b)(2a - b)$

23. $(y + 5)^2$

24. $(y + 7)^2$

25. $(x - 4)^2$

26. $(a - 6)^2$

27. $(5x - 3)^2$

28. $(3x - 2)^2$

29. $(2x + 3y)^2$

30. $(5x + 2y)^2$

31. $(2x^2 - 3y)^2$

32. $(4x^2 - 5y)^2$

33. $(a + 3)(a - 3)$

34. $(b + 4)(b - 4)$

35. $(2x - 5)(2x + 5)$

36. $(4y - 1)(4y + 1)$

37. $(3x - 2y)(3x + 2y)$

38. $(3x + 5y)(3x - 5y)$

39. $(2x + 3y + 4)(2x + 3y - 4)$

40. $(5x + 2y + 3)(5x + 2y - 3)$

41. $(x + 1)(x - 1)(x^2 + 1)$

42. $(y - 2)(y + 2)(y^2 + 4)$

Collaborative Discussion and Writing

43. Is the sum of two polynomials of degree n always a polynomial of degree n? Why or why not?

44. Explain how you would convince a classmate that $(A + B)^2 \neq A^2 + B^2$.

Synthesis

Multiply. Assume that all exponents are natural numbers.

45. $(a^n + b^n)(a^n - b^n)$

46. $(t^a + 4)(t^a - 7)$

47. $(a^n + b^n)^2$

48. $(x^{3m} - t^{5n})^2$

49. $(x - 1)(x^2 + x + 1)(x^3 + 1)$

50. $[(2x - 1)^2 - 1]^2$

51. $(x^{a-b})^{a+b}$

52. $(t^{m+n})^{m+n} \cdot (t^{m-n})^{m-n}$

53. $(a + b + c)^2$

R.4 ▷ **Factoring**

♦ Factor polynomials by removing a common factor.

♦ Factor polynomials by grouping.

♦ Factor trinomials of the type $x^2 + bx + c$.

♦ Factor trinomials of the type $ax^2 + bx + c$, $a \neq 1$, using the FOIL method and the grouping method.

♦ Factor special products of polynomials.

To factor a polynomial, we do the reverse of multiplying; that is, we find an equivalent expression that is written as a product.

✦ Terms with Common Factors

When a polynomial is to be factored, we should always look first to factor out a factor that is common to all the terms using the distributive property. We generally look for the constant common factor with the largest absolute value and for variables with the largest exponent common to all the terms. In this sense, we factor out the "largest" common factor.

EXAMPLE 1   Factor each of the following.

a) $15 + 10x - 5x^2$ **b)** $12x^2y^2 - 20x^3y$

Solution

a) $15 + 10x - 5x^2 = 5 \cdot 3 + 5 \cdot 2x - 5 \cdot x^2 = 5(3 + 2x - x^2)$

We can always check a factorization by multiplying:

$$5(3 + 2x - x^2) = 15 + 10x - 5x^2.$$

b) There are several factors common to the terms of $12x^2y^2 - 20x^3y$, but $4x^2y$ is the "largest" of these.

$$12x^2y^2 - 20x^3y = 4x^2y \cdot 3y - 4x^2y \cdot 5x$$
$$= 4x^2y(3y - 5x)$$

▶ Now Try Exercise 3.

✦ Factoring by Grouping

In some polynomials, pairs of terms have a common binomial factor that can be removed in a process called **factoring by grouping**.

EXAMPLE 2   Factor: $x^3 + 3x^2 - 5x - 15$.

Solution   We have

$$x^3 + 3x^2 - 5x - 15 = (x^3 + 3x^2) + (-5x - 15)$$ Grouping; each group of terms has a common factor.

$$= x^2(x + 3) - 5(x + 3)$$ Factoring a common factor out of each group

$$= (x + 3)(x^2 - 5).$$ Factoring out the common binomial factor

▶ Now Try Exercise 9.

✦ Trinomials of the Type $x^2 + bx + c$

Some trinomials can be factored into the product of two binomials. To factor a trinomial of the form $x^2 + bx + c$, we look for binomial factors of the form

$$(x + p)(x + q),$$

where $p \cdot q = c$ and $p + q = b$. That is, we look for two numbers p and q whose sum is the coefficient of the middle term of the polynomial, b, and whose product is the constant term, c.

When we factor any polynomial, we should always check first to determine whether there is a factor common to all the terms. If there is, we factor it out first.

EXAMPLE 3   Factor: $x^2 + 5x + 6$.

Solution   First, we look for a common factor. There is none. Next, we look for two numbers whose product is 6 and whose sum is 5. Since the constant term, 6, and the coefficient of the middle term, 5, are both positive, we look for a factorization of 6 in which both factors are positive.

Pairs of Factors	Sums of Factors
1, 6	7
2, 3	5 ←

The numbers we need are 2 and 3.

The factorization is $(x + 2)(x + 3)$. We have

$$x^2 + 5x + 6 = (x + 2)(x + 3).$$

We can check this by multiplying:

$$(x + 2)(x + 3) = x^2 + 3x + 2x + 6 = x^2 + 5x + 6.$$

▶ Now Try Exercise 19.

EXAMPLE 4   Factor: $2y^2 - 14y + 24$.

Solution   First, we look for a common factor. Each term has a factor of 2, so we factor it out first:

$$2y^2 - 14y + 24 = 2(y^2 - 7y + 12).$$

Now we consider the trinomial $y^2 - 7y + 12$. We look for two numbers whose product is 12 and whose sum is -7. Since the constant term, 12, is positive and the coefficient of the middle term, -7, is negative, we look for a factorization of 12 in which both factors are negative.

Pairs of Factors	Sums of Factors
-1, -12	-13
-2, -6	-8
-3, -4	-7 ←

The numbers we need are -3 and -4.

The factorization of $y^2 - 7y + 12$ is $(y - 3)(y - 4)$. We must also include the common factor that we factored out earlier. Thus we have

$$2y^2 - 14y + 24 = 2(y - 3)(y - 4).$$ ▶ Now Try Exercise 21.

EXAMPLE 5   Factor: $x^4 - 2x^3 - 8x^2$.

Solution   First, we look for a common factor. Each term has a factor of x^2, so we factor it out first:

$$x^4 - 2x^3 - 8x^2 = x^2(x^2 - 2x - 8).$$

Now we consider the trinomial $x^2 - 2x - 8$. We look for two numbers whose product is -8 and whose sum is -2. Since the constant term, -8, is negative, one factor will be positive and the other will be negative.

Pairs of Factors	Sums of Factors
-1, 8	7
1, -8	-7
-2, 4	2
2, -4	-2 ←

The numbers we need are 2 and -4.

We might have observed at the outset that since the sum of the factors is -2, a negative number, we need consider only pairs of factors for which the negative factor has the greater absolute value. Thus only the pairs 1, -8 and 2, -4 need have been considered.

Using the pair of factors 2 and -4, we see that the factorization of $x^2 - 2x - 8$ is $(x + 2)(x - 4)$. Including the common factor, we have

$$x^4 - 2x^3 - 8x^2 = x^2(x + 2)(x - 4).$$

▶ Now Try Exercise 27.

◆ Trinomials of the Type $ax^2 + bx + c$, $a \neq 1$

We consider two methods for factoring trinomials of the type $ax^2 + bx + c$, $a \neq 1$.

The FOIL Method

We first consider the **FOIL method** for factoring trinomials of the type $ax^2 + bx + c$, $a \neq 1$. Consider the following multiplication.

$$\begin{array}{cccc} F & O & I & L \\ \downarrow & \downarrow & \downarrow & \downarrow \end{array}$$

$$(3x + 2)(4x + 5) = 12x^2 + 15x + 8x + 10$$

$$= 12x^2 + 23x + 10$$

To factor $12x^2 + 23x + 10$, we must reverse what we just did. We look for two binomials whose product is this trinomial. The product of the First terms must be $12x^2$. The product of the Outside terms plus the product of the Inside terms must be $23x$. The product of the Last terms must be 10. We know from the preceding discussion that the answer is $(3x + 2)(4x + 5)$. In general, however, finding such an answer involves trial and error. We use the following method.

To factor trinomials of the type $ax^2 + bx + c$, $a \neq 1$, using the **FOIL** method:

1. Factor out the largest common factor.
2. Find two First terms whose product is ax^2:

$$(\ \ x + \ \ )(\ \ x + \ \ ) = ax^2 + bx + c.$$

FOIL

3. Find two Last terms whose product is c:

$$(\ x + \ \ )(\ x + \ \ ) = ax^2 + bx + c.$$

FOIL

4. Repeat steps (2) and (3) until a combination is found for which the sum of the Outside and Inside products is bx:

$$(\ \ x + \ \ )(\ \ x + \ \ ) = ax^2 + bx + c.$$

I   FOIL

O

EXAMPLE 6   Factor: $3x^2 - 10x - 8$.

Solution

1. There is no common factor (other than 1 or -1).
2. Factor the first term, $3x^2$. The only possibility (with positive integer coefficients) is $3x \cdot x$. The factorization, if it exists, must be of the form $(3x + \ \ )(x + \ \ )$.
3. Next, factor the constant term, -8. The possibilities are $(-8)(1), 8(-1)$, $-2(4)$, and $2(-4)$. The factors can be written in the opposite order as well: $1(-8), -1(8), 4(-2)$, and $-4(2)$.
4. Find a pair of factors for which the sum of the outside and the inside products is the middle term, $-10x$. Each possibility should be checked by multiplying. Some trials show that the desired factorization is $(3x + 2)(x - 4)$.

▶ Now Try Exercise 35.

The Grouping Method

The second method for factoring trinomials of the type $ax^2 + bx + c$, $a \neq 1$, is known as the **grouping method**, or the *ac-method*.

To factor $ax^2 + bx + c, a \neq 1$, using the **grouping method**:

1. Factor out the largest common factor.
2. Multiply the leading coefficient a and the constant c.
3. Try to factor the product ac so that the sum of the factors is b. That is, find integers p and q such that $pq = ac$ and $p + q = b$.
4. Split the middle term. That is, write it as a sum using the factors found in step (3).
5. Factor by grouping.

EXAMPLE 7   Factor: $12x^3 + 10x^2 - 8x$.

Solution

1. Factor out the largest common factor, $2x$:
$$12x^3 + 10x^2 - 8x = 2x(6x^2 + 5x - 4).$$

2. Now consider $6x^2 + 5x - 4$. Multiply the leading coefficient, 6, and the constant, -4: $6(-4) = -24$.

3. Try to factor -24 so that the sum of the factors is the coefficient of the middle term, 5.

Pairs of Factors	Sums of Factors
1, −24	−23
−1, 24	23
2, −12	−10
−2, 12	10
3, −8	−5
−3, 8	5 ← $\quad -3 \cdot 8 = -24;\ -3 + 8 = 5$
4, −6	−2
−4, 6	2

4. Split the middle term using the numbers found in step (3):
$$5x = -3x + 8x.$$

5. Finally, factor by grouping:
$$6x^2 + 5x - 4 = 6x^2 - 3x + 8x - 4$$
$$= 3x(2x - 1) + 4(2x - 1)$$
$$= (2x - 1)(3x + 4).$$

Be sure to include the common factor to get the complete factorization of the original trinomial:
$$12x^3 + 10x^2 - 8x = 2x(2x - 1)(3x + 4). \quad \blacktriangleright \text{ Now Try Exercise 45.}$$

✦ Special Factorizations

We reverse the equation $(A + B)(A - B) = A^2 - B^2$ to factor a **difference of squares.**

$$A^2 - B^2 = (A + B)(A - B)$$

EXAMPLE 8 Factor each of the following.

a) $x^2 - 16$ **b)** $9a^2 - 25$ **c)** $6x^4 - 6y^4$

Solution

a) $x^2 - 16 = x^2 - 4^2 = (x + 4)(x - 4)$

b) $9a^2 - 25 = (3a)^2 - 5^2 = (3a + 5)(3a - 5)$

c) $6x^4 - 6y^4 = 6(x^4 - y^4)$
$$= 6[(x^2)^2 - (y^2)^2]$$
$$= 6(x^2 + y^2)(x^2 - y^2) \quad x^2 - y^2 \text{ can be factored further.}$$
$$= 6(x^2 + y^2)(x + y)(x - y) \quad \text{Because none of these factors can be factored further, we have } factored\ completely.$$

▶ Now Try Exercise 49.

The rules for squaring binomials can be reversed to factor trinomials that are squares of binomials:

$$A^2 + 2AB + B^2 = (A + B)^2;$$
$$A^2 - 2AB + B^2 = (A - B)^2.$$

EXAMPLE 9 Factor each of the following.

a) $x^2 + 8x + 16$ **b)** $25y^2 - 30y + 9$

Solution

$$A^2 + 2 \cdot A \cdot B + B^2 = (A + B)^2$$
a) $x^2 + 8x + 16 = x^2 + 2 \cdot x \cdot 4 + 4^2 = (x + 4)^2$

$$A^2 - 2 \cdot A \cdot B + B^2 = (A - B)^2$$
b) $25y^2 - 30y + 9 = (5y)^2 - 2 \cdot 5y \cdot 3 + 3^2 = (5y - 3)^2$

▶ Now Try Exercise 57.

We can use the following rules to factor a **sum** or a **difference of cubes**:

$$A^3 + B^3 = (A + B)(A^2 - AB + B^2);$$
$$A^3 - B^3 = (A - B)(A^2 + AB + B^2).$$

These rules can be verified by multiplying.

EXAMPLE 10   Factor each of the following.

a) $x^3 + 27$ **b)** $16y^3 - 250$

Solution

a) $x^3 + 27 = x^3 + 3^3$
$$= (x + 3)(x^2 - 3x + 9)$$

b) $16y^3 - 250 = 2(8y^3 - 125)$
$$= 2[(2y)^3 - 5^3]$$
$$= 2(2y - 5)(4y^2 + 10y + 25)$$ ▶ Now Try Exercise 67.

Not all polynomials can be factored into polynomials with integer coefficients. An example is $x^2 - x + 7$. There are no real factors of 7 whose sum is -1. In such a case, we say that the polynomial is "not factorable," or **prime**.

CONNECTING THE CONCEPTS

A Strategy for Factoring

A. Always factor out the largest common factor first.

B. Look at the number of terms.

Two terms: Try factoring as a difference of squares first. Next, try factoring as a sum or a difference of cubes. Do *not* try to factor a *sum* of squares.

Three terms: Try factoring as the square of a binomial. Next, try using the FOIL method or the grouping method for factoring a trinomial.

Four or more terms: Try factoring by grouping and factoring out a common binomial factor.

C. Always *factor completely*. If a factor with more than one term can itself be factored further, do so.   ● ● ●

R.4   EXERCISE SET

Factor out a common factor.

1. $2x - 10$

2. $7y + 42$

3. $3x^4 - 9x^2$

4. $20y^2 - 5y^5$

5. $4a^2 - 12a + 16$

6. $6n^2 + 24n - 18$

7. $a(b - 2) + c(b - 2)$

8. $a(x^2 - 3) - 2(x^2 - 3)$

Factor by grouping.

9. $x^3 + 3x^2 + 6x + 18$

10. $3x^3 - x^2 + 18x - 6$

11. $y^3 - y^2 + 3y - 3$

12. $y^3 - y^2 + 2y - 2$

13. $24x^3 - 36x^2 + 72x - 108$

14. $5a^3 - 10a^2 + 25a - 50$

15. $a^3 - 3a^2 - 2a + 6$

16. $t^3 + 6t^2 - 2t - 12$

17. $x^3 - x^2 - 5x + 5$

18. $x^3 - x^2 - 6x + 6$

Factor the trinomial.

19. $p^2 + 6p + 8$

20. $w^2 - 7w + 10$

21. $x^2 - 8x + 12$

22. $x^2 + 6x + 5$

23. $t^2 + 8t + 15$

24. $y^2 + 12y + 27$

25. $x^2 - 6xy - 27y^2$

26. $t^2 - 2t - 15$

27. $2n^2 - 20n - 48$

28. $2a^2 - 2ab - 24b^2$

29. $y^4 - 4y^2 - 21$

30. $m^4 - m^2 - 90$

31. $y^4 + 9y^3 + 14y^2$

32. $3z^3 - 21z^2 + 18z$

33. $2x^3 - 2x^2y - 24xy^2$

34. $a^3b - 9a^2b^2 + 20ab^3$

35. $2n^2 + 9n - 56$

36. $3y^2 + 7y - 20$

37. $12x^2 + 11x + 2$

38. $6x^2 - 7x - 20$

39. $4x^2 + 15x + 9$

40. $2y^2 + 7y + 6$

41. $2y^2 + y - 6$

42. $20p^2 - 23p + 6$

43. $6a^2 - 29ab + 28b^2$

44. $10m^2 + 7mn - 12n^2$

45. $12a^2 - 4a - 16$

46. $12a^2 - 14a - 20$

Factor the difference of squares.

47. $m^2 - 4$

48. $z^2 - 81$

49. $4z^2 - 81$

50. $16x^2 - 9$

51. $6x^2 - 6y^2$

52. $8a^2 - 8b^2$

53. $4xy^4 - 4xz^2$

54. $5x^2y - 5yz^4$

55. $7pq^4 - 7py^4$

56. $25ab^4 - 25az^4$

Factor the square of a binomial.

57. $y^2 - 6y + 9$

58. $x^2 + 8x + 16$

59. $4z^2 + 12z + 9$

60. $9z^2 - 12z + 4$

61. $1 - 8x + 16x^2$

62. $1 + 10x + 25x^2$

63. $a^3 + 24a^2 + 144a$

64. $y^3 - 18y^2 + 81y$

65. $4p^2 - 8pq + 4q^2$

66. $5a^2 - 10ab + 5b^2$

Factor the sum or difference of cubes.

67. $x^3 + 8$

68. $y^3 - 64$

69. $m^3 - 1$

70. $n^3 + 216$

71. $2y^3 - 128$

72. $8t^3 - 8$

73. $3a^5 - 24a^2$

74. $250z^4 - 2z$

75. $t^6 + 1$

76. $27x^6 - 8$

Factor completely.

77. $18a^2b - 15ab^2$

78. $4x^2y + 12xy^2$

79. $x^3 - 4x^2 + 5x - 20$

80. $z^3 + 3z^2 - 3z - 9$

81. $8x^2 - 32$

82. $6y^2 - 6$

83. $4y^2 - 5$

84. $16x^2 - 7$

85. $m^2 - 9n^2$

86. $25t^2 - 16$

87. $x^2 + 9x + 20$

88. $y^2 + y - 6$

89. $y^2 - 6y + 5$

90. $x^2 - 4x - 21$

91. $2a^2 + 9a + 4$

92. $3b^2 - b - 2$

93. $6x^2 + 7x - 3$

94. $8x^2 + 2x - 15$

95. $y^2 - 18y + 81$

96. $n^2 + 2n + 1$

97. $9z^2 - 24z + 16$

98. $4z^2 + 20z + 25$

99. $x^2y^2 - 14xy + 49$ **100.** $x^2y^2 - 16xy + 64$

101. $4ax^2 + 20ax - 56a$ **102.** $21x^2y + 2xy - 8y$

103. $3z^3 - 24$ **104.** $4t^3 + 108$

105. $16a^7b + 54ab^7$ **106.** $24a^2x^4 - 375a^8x$

107. $y^3 - 3y^2 - 4y + 12$

108. $p^3 - 2p^2 - 9p + 18$

109. $x^3 - x^2 + x - 1$ **110.** $x^3 - x^2 - x + 1$

111. $5m^4 - 20$ **112.** $2x^2 - 288$

113. $2x^3 + 6x^2 - 8x - 24$

114. $3x^3 + 6x^2 - 27x - 54$

115. $4c^2 - 4cd + d^2$ **116.** $9a^2 - 6ab + b^2$

117. $m^6 + 8m^3 - 20$ **118.** $x^4 - 37x^2 + 36$

119. $p - 64p^4$ **120.** $125a - 8a^4$

Collaborative Discussion and Writing

121. Under what circumstances can $A^2 + B^2$ be factored?

122. Explain how the rule for factoring a sum of cubes can be used to factor a difference of cubes.

Synthesis

Factor.

123. $y^4 - 84 + 5y^2$ **124.** $11x^2 + x^4 - 80$

125. $y^2 - \frac{8}{49} + \frac{2}{7}y$ **126.** $t^2 - \frac{27}{100} + \frac{3}{5}t$

127. $x^2 + 3x + \frac{9}{4}$ **128.** $x^2 - 5x + \frac{25}{4}$

129. $x^2 - x + \frac{1}{4}$ **130.** $x^2 - \frac{2}{3}x + \frac{1}{9}$

131. $(x + h)^3 - x^3$ **132.** $(x + 0.01)^2 - x^2$

133. $(y - 4)^2 + 5(y - 4) - 24$

134. $6(2p + q)^2 - 5(2p + q) - 25$

Factor. Assume that variables in exponents represent natural numbers.

135. $x^{2n} + 5x^n - 24$

136. $4x^{2n} - 4x^n - 3$

137. $x^2 + ax + bx + ab$

138. $bdy^2 + ady + bcy + ac$

139. $25y^{2m} - (x^{2n} - 2x^n + 1)$

140. $x^{6a} - t^{3b}$

141. $(y - 1)^4 - (y - 1)^2$

142. $x^6 - 2x^5 + x^4 - x^2 + 2x - 1$

R.5 ◆ Rational Expressions

- ◆ Determine the domain of a rational expression.
- ◆ Simplify rational expressions.
- ◆ Multiply, divide, add, and subtract rational expressions.
- ◆ Simplify complex rational expressions.

A **rational expression** is the quotient of two polynomials. For example,

$$\frac{3}{5}, \quad \frac{2}{x - 3}, \quad \text{and} \quad \frac{x^2 - 4}{x^2 - 4x - 5}$$

are rational expressions.

✦ The Domain of a Rational Expression

The **domain** of an algebraic expression is the set of all real numbers for which the expression is defined. Since division by zero is not defined, any number that makes the denominator zero is not in the domain of a rational expression.

EXAMPLE 1   Find the domain of each of the following.

a) $\dfrac{2}{x-3}$

b) $\dfrac{x^2-4}{x^2-4x-5}$

Solution

a) Since $x-3$ is 0 when $x=3$, the domain of $2/(x-3)$ is the set of all real numbers except 3.

b) To determine the domain of $(x^2-4)/(x^2-4x-5)$, we first factor the denominator:

$$\frac{x^2-4}{x^2-4x-5} = \frac{x^2-4}{(x+1)(x-5)}.$$

The factor $x+1$ is 0 when $x=-1$, and the factor $x-5$ is 0 when $x=5$. Since $(x+1)(x-5)=0$ when $x=-1$ or $x=5$, the domain is the set of all real numbers except -1 and 5.   ▶ Now Try Exercise 3.

We can describe the domains found in Example 1 using *set-builder notation*. For example, we write "The set of all real numbers x such that x is not equal to 3" as

$$\{x \mid x \text{ is a real number } and\ x \neq 3\}.$$

Similarly, we write "The set of all real numbers x such that x is not equal to -1 and x is not equal to 5" as

$$\{x \mid x \text{ is a real number } and\ x \neq -1\ and\ x \neq 5\}.$$

✦ Simplifying, Multiplying, and Dividing Rational Expressions

To simplify rational expressions, we use the fact that

$$\frac{a \cdot c}{b \cdot c} = \frac{a}{b} \cdot \frac{c}{c} = \frac{a}{b} \cdot 1 = \frac{a}{b}.$$

EXAMPLE 2   Simplify: $\dfrac{9x^2 + 6x - 3}{12x^2 - 12}$.

Solution

$$\dfrac{9x^2 + 6x - 3}{12x^2 - 12} = \dfrac{3(3x^2 + 2x - 1)}{12(x^2 - 1)}$$

$$= \dfrac{3(x + 1)(3x - 1)}{3 \cdot 4(x + 1)(x - 1)}$$

Factoring the numerator and the denominator

$$= \dfrac{3(x + 1)}{3(x + 1)} \cdot \dfrac{3x - 1}{4(x - 1)}$$

Factoring the rational expression

$$= 1 \cdot \dfrac{3x - 1}{4(x - 1)}$$

$\dfrac{3(x + 1)}{3(x + 1)} = 1$

$$= \dfrac{3x - 1}{4(x - 1)}$$

Removing a factor of 1

▷ Now Try Exercise 9.

Canceling is a shortcut that is often used to remove a factor of 1.

EXAMPLE 3   Simplify each of the following.

a) $\dfrac{4x^3 + 16x^2}{2x^3 + 6x^2 - 8x}$

b) $\dfrac{2 - x}{x^2 + x - 6}$

Solution

a) $\dfrac{4x^3 + 16x^2}{2x^3 + 6x^2 - 8x} = \dfrac{2 \cdot 2 \cdot x \cdot x(x + 4)}{2 \cdot x(x + 4)(x - 1)}$

Factoring the numerator and the denominator

$$= \dfrac{2 \cdot 2 \cdot \cancel{x} \cdot x(\cancel{x + 4})}{2 \cdot \cancel{x}(\cancel{x + 4})(x - 1)}$$

Removing a factor of 1:

$\dfrac{2x(x + 4)}{2x(x + 4)} = 1$

$$= \dfrac{2x}{x - 1}$$

b) $\dfrac{2 - x}{x^2 + x - 6} = \dfrac{2 - x}{(x + 3)(x - 2)}$

Factoring the denominator

$$= \dfrac{-1(x - 2)}{(x + 3)(x - 2)}$$

$2 - x = -1(x - 2)$

$$= \dfrac{-1(\cancel{x - 2})}{(x + 3)(\cancel{x - 2})}$$

Removing a factor of 1: $\dfrac{x - 2}{x - 2} = 1$

$$= \dfrac{-1}{x + 3}, \text{ or } -\dfrac{1}{x + 3}$$

▷ Now Try Exercise 11.

In Example 3(b), we saw that

$$\frac{2 - x}{x^2 + x - 6} \quad \text{and} \quad -\frac{1}{x + 3}$$

are **equivalent expressions**. This means that they have the same value for all numbers that are in *both* domains. Note that -3 is not in the domain of *either* expression, whereas 2 is in the domain of $-1/(x + 3)$ but not in the domain of $(2 - x)/(x^2 + x - 6)$ and thus is not in the domain of *both* expressions.

To multiply rational expressions, we multiply numerators and multiply denominators and, if possible, simplify the result. To divide rational expressions, we multiply the dividend by the reciprocal of the divisor and, if possible, simplify the result—that is,

$$\frac{a}{b} \cdot \frac{c}{d} = \frac{ac}{bd} \quad \text{and} \quad \frac{a}{b} \div \frac{c}{d} = \frac{a}{b} \cdot \frac{d}{c} = \frac{ad}{bc}.$$

EXAMPLE 4 Multiply or divide and simplify each of the following.

a) $\dfrac{x + 4}{x - 3} \cdot \dfrac{x^2 - 9}{x^2 - x - 2}$ 　　　　**b)** $\dfrac{y^3 - 1}{y^2 - 1} \div \dfrac{y^2 + y + 1}{y^2 + 2y + 1}$

Solution

a) $\dfrac{x + 4}{x - 3} \cdot \dfrac{x^2 - 9}{x^2 - x - 2} = \dfrac{(x + 4)(x^2 - 9)}{(x - 3)(x^2 - x - 2)}$

　　　　　　　　　Multiplying the numerators and the denominators

$$= \frac{(x + 4)(x + 3)(x - 3)}{(x - 3)(x - 2)(x + 1)}$$ 　Factoring and removing a factor of 1: $\dfrac{x - 3}{x - 3} = 1$

$$= \frac{(x + 4)(x + 3)}{(x - 2)(x + 1)}$$

b) $\dfrac{y^3 - 1}{y^2 - 1} \div \dfrac{y^2 + y + 1}{y^2 + 2y + 1} = \dfrac{y^3 - 1}{y^2 - 1} \cdot \dfrac{y^2 + 2y + 1}{y^2 + y + 1}$ 　Multiplying by the reciprocal of the divisor

$$= \frac{(y^3 - 1)(y^2 + 2y + 1)}{(y^2 - 1)(y^2 + y + 1)}$$

$$= \frac{(y - 1)(y^2 + y + 1)(y + 1)(y + 1)}{(y + 1)(y - 1)(y^2 + y + 1)}$$

　　　　　　　　Factoring and removing a factor of 1

$$= y + 1$$ 　　　　　　▶ Now Try Exercise 19.

✦ Adding and Subtracting Rational Expressions

When rational expressions have the same denominator, we can add or subtract by adding or subtracting the numerators and retaining the common denominator. If the denominators differ, we must find equivalent rational expressions that have a common denominator. In general, it is most efficient to find the **least common denominator (LCD)** of the expressions.

> To find the least common denominator of rational expressions, factor each denominator and form the product that uses each factor the greatest number of times it occurs in any factorization.

EXAMPLE 5 Add or subtract and simplify each of the following.

a) $\dfrac{x^2 - 4x + 4}{2x^2 - 3x + 1} + \dfrac{x + 4}{2x - 2}$

b) $\dfrac{x}{x^2 + 11x + 30} - \dfrac{5}{x^2 + 9x + 20}$

Solution

a) $\dfrac{x^2 - 4x + 4}{2x^2 - 3x + 1} + \dfrac{x + 4}{2x - 2}$

$= \dfrac{x^2 - 4x + 4}{(2x - 1)(x - 1)} + \dfrac{x + 4}{2(x - 1)}$ Factoring the denominators

   The LCD is $(2x - 1)(x - 1)(2)$, or $2(2x - 1)(x - 1)$.

$= \dfrac{x^2 - 4x + 4}{(2x - 1)(x - 1)} \cdot \dfrac{2}{2} + \dfrac{x + 4}{2(x - 1)} \cdot \dfrac{2x - 1}{2x - 1}$ Multiplying each term by 1 to get the LCD

$= \dfrac{2x^2 - 8x + 8}{(2x - 1)(x - 1)(2)} + \dfrac{2x^2 + 7x - 4}{2(x - 1)(2x - 1)}$

$= \dfrac{4x^2 - x + 4}{2(2x - 1)(x - 1)}$ Adding the numerators

b) $\dfrac{x}{x^2 + 11x + 30} - \dfrac{5}{x^2 + 9x + 20}$

$= \dfrac{x}{(x + 5)(x + 6)} - \dfrac{5}{(x + 5)(x + 4)}$ Factoring the denominators

   The LCD is $(x + 5)(x + 6)(x + 4)$.

$= \dfrac{x}{(x + 5)(x + 6)} \cdot \dfrac{x + 4}{x + 4} - \dfrac{5}{(x + 5)(x + 4)} \cdot \dfrac{x + 6}{x + 6}$

   Multiplying each term by 1 to get the LCD

$= \dfrac{x^2 + 4x}{(x + 5)(x + 6)(x + 4)} - \dfrac{5x + 30}{(x + 5)(x + 4)(x + 6)}$

$= \dfrac{x^2 + 4x - 5x - 30}{(x + 5)(x + 6)(x + 4)}$ Be sure to change the sign of *every* term in the numerator of the expression being subtracted:

$= \dfrac{x^2 - x - 30}{(x + 5)(x + 6)(x + 4)}$ $-(5x + 30) = -5x - 30$

$= \dfrac{(x + 5)(x - 6)}{(x + 5)(x + 6)(x + 4)}$ Factoring and removing a factor of 1: $\dfrac{x + 5}{x + 5} = 1$

$= \dfrac{x - 6}{(x + 6)(x + 4)}$

▶ Now Try Exercises 37 and 39.

✦ Complex Rational Expressions

A **complex rational expression** has rational expressions in its numerator or its denominator or both.

> To simplify a complex rational expression:
>
> *Method 1.* Find the LCD of all the denominators within the complex rational expression. Then multiply by 1 using the LCD as the numerator and the denominator of the expression for 1.
>
> *Method 2.* First add or subtract, if necessary, to get a single rational expression in the numerator and in the denominator. Then divide by multiplying by the reciprocal of the denominator.

EXAMPLE 6   Simplify: $\dfrac{\dfrac{1}{a}+\dfrac{1}{b}}{\dfrac{1}{a^3}+\dfrac{1}{b^3}}$.

Solution

Method 1. The LCD of the four rational expressions in the numerator and the denominator is a^3b^3.

$$\frac{\dfrac{1}{a}+\dfrac{1}{b}}{\dfrac{1}{a^3}+\dfrac{1}{b^3}}=\frac{\dfrac{1}{a}+\dfrac{1}{b}}{\dfrac{1}{a^3}+\dfrac{1}{b^3}}\cdot\frac{a^3b^3}{a^3b^3}\qquad \text{Multiplying by 1}$$
$$\text{using }\frac{a^3b^3}{a^3b^3}$$

$$=\frac{\left(\dfrac{1}{a}+\dfrac{1}{b}\right)(a^3b^3)}{\left(\dfrac{1}{a^3}+\dfrac{1}{b^3}\right)(a^3b^3)}$$

$$=\frac{a^2b^3+a^3b^2}{b^3+a^3}$$

$$=\frac{a^2b^2(b+a)}{(b+a)(b^2-ba+a^2)}\qquad \text{Factoring and removing a}$$
$$\text{factor of 1: }\frac{b+a}{b+a}=1$$

$$=\frac{a^2b^2}{b^2-ba+a^2}$$

Method 2. We add in the numerator and in the denominator.

$$\frac{\dfrac{1}{a}+\dfrac{1}{b}}{\dfrac{1}{a^3}+\dfrac{1}{b^3}}=\frac{\dfrac{1}{a}\cdot\dfrac{b}{b}+\dfrac{1}{b}\cdot\dfrac{a}{a}}{\dfrac{1}{a^3}\cdot\dfrac{b^3}{b^3}+\dfrac{1}{b^3}\cdot\dfrac{a^3}{a^3}}$$

←— The LCD is ab.

←— The LCD is a^3b^3.

$$=\frac{\dfrac{b}{ab}+\dfrac{a}{ab}}{\dfrac{b^3}{a^3b^3}+\dfrac{a^3}{a^3b^3}}$$

$$=\frac{\dfrac{b+a}{ab}}{\dfrac{b^3+a^3}{a^3b^3}}$$

We have a single rational expression in both the numerator and the denominator.

$$=\frac{b+a}{ab}\cdot\frac{a^3b^3}{b^3+a^3}$$

Multiplying by the reciprocal of the denominator

$$=\frac{(b+a)(a)(b)(a^2b^2)}{(a)(b)(b+a)(b^2-ba+a^2)}$$

$$=\frac{a^2b^2}{b^2-ba+a^2}$$

▷ Now Try Exercise 57.

R.5   EXERCISE SET

Find the domain of the rational expression.

1. $-\dfrac{3}{4}$

2. $\dfrac{5}{8-x}$

3. $\dfrac{3x-3}{x(x-1)}$

4. $\dfrac{15x-10}{2x(3x-2)}$

5. $\dfrac{x+5}{x^2+4x-5}$

6. $\dfrac{(x^2-4)(x+1)}{(x+2)(x^2-1)}$

7. $\dfrac{7x^2-28x+28}{(x^2-4)(x^2+3x-10)}$

8. $\dfrac{7x^2+11x-6}{x(x^2-x-6)}$

Simplify.

9. $\dfrac{x^2-4}{x^2-4x+4}$

10. $\dfrac{x^2+2x-3}{x^2-9}$

11. $\dfrac{x^3-6x^2+9x}{x^3-3x^2}$

12. $\dfrac{y^5-5y^4+4y^3}{y^3-6y^2+8y}$

13. $\dfrac{6y^2+12y-48}{3y^2-9y+6}$

14. $\dfrac{2x^2-20x+50}{10x^2-30x-100}$

15. $\dfrac{4-x}{x^2+4x-32}$

16. $\dfrac{6-x}{x^2-36}$

Multiply or divide and, if possible, simplify.

17. $\dfrac{x^2-y^2}{(x-y)^2}\cdot\dfrac{1}{x+y}$

18. $\dfrac{r-s}{r+s}\cdot\dfrac{r^2-s^2}{(r-s)^2}$

19. $\dfrac{x^2-2x-35}{2x^3-3x^2}\cdot\dfrac{4x^3-9x}{7x-49}$

20. $\dfrac{x^2+2x-35}{3x^3-2x^2}\cdot\dfrac{9x^3-4x}{7x+49}$

21. $\dfrac{a^2 - a - 6}{a^2 - 7a + 12} \cdot \dfrac{a^2 - 2a - 8}{a^2 - 3a - 10}$

22. $\dfrac{a^2 - a - 12}{a^2 - 6a + 8} \cdot \dfrac{a^2 + a - 6}{a^2 - 2a - 24}$

23. $\dfrac{m^2 - n^2}{r + s} \div \dfrac{m - n}{r + s}$ **24.** $\dfrac{a^2 - b^2}{x - y} \div \dfrac{a + b}{x - y}$

25. $\dfrac{3x + 12}{2x - 8} \div \dfrac{(x + 4)^2}{(x - 4)^2}$

26. $\dfrac{a^2 - a - 2}{a^2 - a - 6} \div \dfrac{a^2 - 2a}{2a + a^2}$

27. $\dfrac{x^2 - y^2}{x^3 - y^3} \cdot \dfrac{x^2 + xy + y^2}{x^2 + 2xy + y^2}$

28. $\dfrac{c^3 + 8}{c^2 - 4} \div \dfrac{c^2 - 2c + 4}{c^2 - 4c + 4}$

29. $\dfrac{(x - y)^2 - z^2}{(x + y)^2 - z^2} \div \dfrac{x - y + z}{x + y - z}$

30. $\dfrac{(a + b)^2 - 9}{(a - b)^2 - 9} \cdot \dfrac{a - b - 3}{a + b + 3}$

Add or subtract and, if possible, simplify.

31. $\dfrac{5}{2x} + \dfrac{1}{2x}$ **32.** $\dfrac{10}{9y} - \dfrac{4}{9y}$

33. $\dfrac{3}{2a + 3} + \dfrac{2a}{2a + 3}$ **34.** $\dfrac{a - 3b}{a + b} + \dfrac{a + 5b}{a + b}$

35. $\dfrac{5}{4z} - \dfrac{3}{8z}$ **36.** $\dfrac{12}{x^2 y} + \dfrac{5}{xy^2}$

37. $\dfrac{3}{x + 2} + \dfrac{2}{x^2 - 4}$ **38.** $\dfrac{5}{a - 3} - \dfrac{2}{a^2 - 9}$

39. $\dfrac{y}{y^2 - y - 20} - \dfrac{2}{y + 4}$

40. $\dfrac{6}{y^2 + 6y + 9} - \dfrac{5}{y + 3}$

41. $\dfrac{3}{x + y} + \dfrac{x - 5y}{x^2 - y^2}$

42. $\dfrac{a^2 + 1}{a^2 - 1} - \dfrac{a - 1}{a + 1}$

43. $\dfrac{y}{y - 1} + \dfrac{2}{1 - y}$
(*Note:* $1 - y = -1(y - 1)$.)

44. $\dfrac{a}{a - b} + \dfrac{b}{b - a}$
(*Note:* $b - a = -1(a - b)$.)

45. $\dfrac{x}{2x - 3y} - \dfrac{y}{3y - 2x}$

46. $\dfrac{3a}{3a - 2b} - \dfrac{2a}{2b - 3a}$

47. $\dfrac{9x + 2}{3x^2 - 2x - 8} + \dfrac{7}{3x^2 + x - 4}$

48. $\dfrac{3y}{y^2 - 7y + 10} - \dfrac{2y}{y^2 - 8y + 15}$

49. $\dfrac{5a}{a - b} + \dfrac{ab}{a^2 - b^2} + \dfrac{4b}{a + b}$

50. $\dfrac{6a}{a - b} - \dfrac{3b}{b - a} + \dfrac{5}{a^2 - b^2}$

51. $\dfrac{7}{x + 2} - \dfrac{x + 8}{4 - x^2} + \dfrac{3x - 2}{4 - 4x + x^2}$

52. $\dfrac{6}{x + 3} - \dfrac{x + 4}{9 - x^2} + \dfrac{2x - 3}{9 - 6x + x^2}$

53. $\dfrac{1}{x + 1} + \dfrac{x}{2 - x} + \dfrac{x^2 + 2}{x^2 - x - 2}$

54. $\dfrac{x - 1}{x - 2} - \dfrac{x + 1}{x + 2} - \dfrac{x - 6}{4 - x^2}$

Simplify.

55. $\dfrac{\dfrac{x^2 - y^2}{xy}}{\dfrac{x - y}{y}}$ **56.** $\dfrac{\dfrac{a - b}{b}}{\dfrac{a^2 - b^2}{ab}}$

57. $\dfrac{\dfrac{x}{y} - \dfrac{y}{x}}{\dfrac{1}{y} + \dfrac{1}{x}}$ **58.** $\dfrac{\dfrac{a}{b} - \dfrac{b}{a}}{\dfrac{1}{a} - \dfrac{1}{b}}$

59. $\dfrac{c + \dfrac{8}{c^2}}{1 + \dfrac{2}{c}}$ **60.** $\dfrac{a - \dfrac{a}{b}}{b - \dfrac{b}{a}}$

61. $\dfrac{x^2 + xy + y^2}{\dfrac{x^2}{y} - \dfrac{y^2}{x}}$

62. $\dfrac{\dfrac{a^2}{b} + \dfrac{b^2}{a}}{a^2 - ab + b^2}$

63. $\dfrac{a - a^{-1}}{a + a^{-1}}$

64. $\dfrac{x^{-1} + y^{-1}}{x^{-3} + y^{-3}}$

65. $\dfrac{\dfrac{1}{x - 3} + \dfrac{2}{x + 3}}{\dfrac{3}{x - 1} - \dfrac{4}{x + 2}}$

66. $\dfrac{\dfrac{5}{x + 1} - \dfrac{3}{x - 2}}{\dfrac{1}{x - 5} + \dfrac{2}{x + 2}}$

67. $\dfrac{\dfrac{a}{1 - a} + \dfrac{1 + a}{a}}{\dfrac{1 - a}{a} + \dfrac{a}{1 + a}}$

68. $\dfrac{\dfrac{1 - x}{x} + \dfrac{x}{1 + x}}{\dfrac{1 + x}{x} + \dfrac{x}{1 - x}}$

69. $\dfrac{\dfrac{1}{a^2} + \dfrac{2}{ab} + \dfrac{1}{b^2}}{\dfrac{1}{a^2} - \dfrac{1}{b^2}}$

70. $\dfrac{\dfrac{1}{x^2} - \dfrac{1}{y^2}}{\dfrac{1}{x^2} - \dfrac{2}{xy} + \dfrac{1}{y^2}}$

Collaborative Discussion and Writing

71. When adding or subtracting rational expressions, we can always find a common denominator by forming the product of all the denominators. Explain why it is usually preferable to find the least common denominator.

72. How would you determine which method to use for simplifying a particular complex rational expression?

Synthesis

Simplify.

73. $\dfrac{(x + h)^2 - x^2}{h}$

74. $\dfrac{\dfrac{1}{x + h} - \dfrac{1}{x}}{h}$

75. $\dfrac{(x + h)^3 - x^3}{h}$

76. $\dfrac{\dfrac{1}{(x + h)^2} - \dfrac{1}{x^2}}{h}$

77. $\left[\dfrac{\dfrac{x + 1}{x - 1} + 1}{\dfrac{x + 1}{x - 1} - 1}\right]^5$

78. $1 + \dfrac{1}{1 + \dfrac{1}{1 + \dfrac{1}{1 + \dfrac{1}{x}}}}$

Perform the indicated operations and, if possible, simplify.

79. $\dfrac{n(n + 1)(n + 2)}{2 \cdot 3} + \dfrac{(n + 1)(n + 2)}{2}$

80. $\dfrac{n(n + 1)(n + 2)(n + 3)}{2 \cdot 3 \cdot 4} + \dfrac{(n + 1)(n + 2)(n + 3)}{2 \cdot 3}$

81. $\dfrac{x^2 - 9}{x^3 + 27} \cdot \dfrac{5x^2 - 15x + 45}{x^2 - 2x - 3} + \dfrac{x^2 + x}{4 + 2x}$

82. $\dfrac{x^2 + 2x - 3}{x^2 - x - 12} \div \dfrac{x^2 - 1}{x^2 - 16} - \dfrac{2x + 1}{x^2 + 2x + 1}$

R.6   Radical Notation and Rational Exponents

◆ Simplify radical expressions.
◆ Solve applied problems involving radical notation.
◆ Rationalize denominators or numerators in rational expressions.
◆ Convert between exponential notation and radical notation.
◆ Simplify expressions with rational exponents.

A number c is said to be a **square root** of a if $c^2 = a$. Thus, 3 is a square root of 9, because $3^2 = 9$, and -3 is also a square root of 9, because $(-3)^2 = 9$.

Similarly, 5 is a third root (called a **cube root**) of 125, because $5^3 = 125$. The number 125 has no other real-number cube roots.

> ### nth Root
> A number c is said to be an **nth root** of a if $c^n = a$.

The symbol $\sqrt{a}$ denotes the nonnegative square root of a, and the symbol $\sqrt[3]{a}$ denotes the real-number cube root of a. The symbol $\sqrt[n]{a}$ denotes the nth root of a, that is, a number whose nth power is a. The symbol $\sqrt[n]{}$ is called a **radical**, and the expression under the radical is called the **radicand**. The number n (which is omitted when it is 2) is called the **index**. Examples of roots for $n = 3$, 4, and 2, respectively, are

$$\sqrt[3]{125}, \quad \sqrt[4]{16}, \quad \text{and} \quad \sqrt{3600}.$$

Any real number has only one real-number odd root. Any positive number has two square roots, one positive and one negative. Similarly, for any even index, a positive number has two real-number roots. The positive root is called the **principal root**. When an expression such as $\sqrt{4}$ or $\sqrt[6]{23}$ is used, it is understood to represent the principal (nonnegative) root. To denote a negative root, we use $-\sqrt{4}$, $-\sqrt[6]{23}$, and so on.

EXAMPLE 1 Simplify each of the following.

a) $\sqrt{36}$
b) $-\sqrt{36}$
c) $\sqrt[3]{-8}$
d) $\sqrt[5]{\dfrac{32}{243}}$
e) $\sqrt[4]{-16}$

Solution

a) $\sqrt{36} = 6$, because $6^2 = 36$.

b) $-\sqrt{36} = -6$, because $6^2 = 36$ and $-\left(\sqrt{36}\right) = -(6) = -6$.

c) $\sqrt[3]{-8} = -2$, because $(-2)^3 = -8$.

d) $\sqrt[5]{\dfrac{32}{243}} = \dfrac{2}{3}$, because $\left(\dfrac{2}{3}\right)^5 = \dfrac{2^5}{3^5} = \dfrac{32}{243}$.

e) $\sqrt[4]{-16}$ is not a real number, because we cannot find a real number that can be raised to the fourth power to get -16. ▶ Now Try Exercise 11.

We can generalize Example 1(e) and say that when a is negative and n is even, $\sqrt[n]{a}$ is not a real number. For example, $\sqrt{-4}$ and $\sqrt[4]{-81}$ are not real numbers.

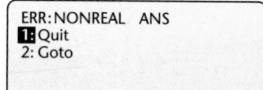
◆ Simplifying Radical Expressions

Consider the expression $\sqrt{(-3)^2}$. This is equivalent to $\sqrt{9}$, or 3. Similarly, $\sqrt{3^2} = \sqrt{9} = 3$. This illustrates the first of several properties of radicals, listed below.

Properties of Radicals

Let a and b be any real numbers or expressions for which the given roots exist. For any natural numbers m and n ($n \neq 1$):

1. If n is even, $\sqrt[n]{a^n} = |a|$.
2. If n is odd, $\sqrt[n]{a^n} = a$.
3. $\sqrt[n]{a} \cdot \sqrt[n]{b} = \sqrt[n]{ab}$.
4. $\sqrt[n]{\dfrac{a}{b}} = \dfrac{\sqrt[n]{a}}{\sqrt[n]{b}}$ ($b \neq 0$).
5. $\sqrt[n]{a^m} = \left(\sqrt[n]{a}\right)^m$.

EXAMPLE 2   Simplify each of the following.

a) $\sqrt{(-5)^2}$ b) $\sqrt[3]{(-5)^3}$

c) $\sqrt[4]{4} \cdot \sqrt[4]{5}$ d) $\sqrt{50}$

e) $\dfrac{\sqrt{72}}{\sqrt{6}}$ f) $\sqrt[3]{8^5}$

g) $\sqrt{216x^5y^3}$ h) $\sqrt{\dfrac{x^2}{16}}$

Solution

a) $\sqrt{(-5)^2} = |-5| = 5$ Using Property 1

b) $\sqrt[3]{(-5)^3} = -5$ Using Property 2

c) $\sqrt[4]{4} \cdot \sqrt[4]{5} = \sqrt[4]{4 \cdot 5} = \sqrt[4]{20}$ Using Property 3

d) $\sqrt{50} = \sqrt{25 \cdot 2} = \sqrt{25} \cdot \sqrt{2} = 5\sqrt{2}$ Using Property 3

e) $\dfrac{\sqrt{72}}{\sqrt{6}} = \sqrt{\dfrac{72}{6}}$ Using Property 4

$\qquad = \sqrt{12} = \sqrt{4 \cdot 3} = \sqrt{4} \cdot \sqrt{3}$ Using Property 3

$\qquad = 2\sqrt{3}$

f) $\sqrt[3]{8^5} = \left(\sqrt[3]{8}\right)^5$ Using Property 5

$\qquad = 2^5 = 32$

g) $\sqrt{216x^5y^3} = \sqrt{36 \cdot 6 \cdot x^4 \cdot x \cdot y^2 \cdot y}$

$\qquad = \sqrt{36x^4y^2}\,\sqrt{6xy}$ Using Property 3

$\qquad = |6x^2y|\sqrt{6xy}$ Using Property 1

$\qquad = 6x^2|y|\sqrt{6xy}$ $6x^2$ cannot be negative, so absolute-value signs are not needed for it.

h) $\sqrt{\dfrac{x^2}{16}} = \dfrac{\sqrt{x^2}}{\sqrt{16}}$ Using Property 4

$\qquad = \dfrac{|x|}{4}$ Using Property 1

▶ **Now Try Exercise 25.**

In many situations, radicands are never formed by raising negative quantities to even powers. In such cases, absolute-value notation is not required. For this reason, **we will henceforth assume that no radicands are formed by raising negative quantities to even powers**. For example, we will write $\sqrt{x^2} = x$ and $\sqrt[4]{a^5b} = a\sqrt[4]{ab}$.

Radical expressions with the same index and the same radicand can be combined (added or subtracted) in much the same way that we combine like terms.

EXAMPLE 3 Perform the operations indicated.

a) $3\sqrt{8x^2} - 5\sqrt{2x^2}$

b) $\left(4\sqrt{3} + \sqrt{2}\right)\left(\sqrt{3} - 5\sqrt{2}\right)$

Solution

a) $3\sqrt{8x^2} - 5\sqrt{2x^2} = 3\sqrt{4x^2 \cdot 2} - 5\sqrt{x^2 \cdot 2}$

$\qquad = 3 \cdot 2x\sqrt{2} - 5x\sqrt{2}$

$\qquad = 6x\sqrt{2} - 5x\sqrt{2}$

$\qquad = (6x - 5x)\sqrt{2}$ Using the distributive property

$\qquad = x\sqrt{2}$

b) $\left(4\sqrt{3} + \sqrt{2}\right)\left(\sqrt{3} - 5\sqrt{2}\right) = 4\left(\sqrt{3}\right)^2 - 20\sqrt{6} + \sqrt{6} - 5\left(\sqrt{2}\right)^2$

Multiplying

$$= 4 \cdot 3 + (-20 + 1)\sqrt{6} - 5 \cdot 2$$
$$= 12 - 19\sqrt{6} - 10$$
$$= 2 - 19\sqrt{6}$$

▶ Now Try Exercise 45.

✦ An Application

The Pythagorean theorem relates the lengths of the sides of a right triangle. The side opposite the triangle's right angle is called the **hypotenuse**. The other sides are the **legs**.

The Pythagorean Theorem

The sum of the squares of the lengths of the legs of a right triangle is equal to the square of the length of the hypotenuse:

$$a^2 + b^2 = c^2.$$

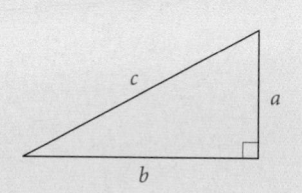

EXAMPLE 4   *Surveying.*   A surveyor places poles at points A, B, and C in order to measure the distance across a pond. The distances AC and BC are measured as shown. Find the distance AB across the pond.

Solution   We see that the lengths of the legs of a right triangle are given. Thus we use the Pythagorean theorem to find the length of the hypotenuse:

$$c^2 = a^2 + b^2$$
$$c = \sqrt{a^2 + b^2} \quad \text{Solving for } c$$
$$= \sqrt{25^2 + 47^2}$$
$$= \sqrt{625 + 2209}$$
$$= \sqrt{2834}$$
$$\approx 53.2.$$

The distance across the pond is about 53.2 yd.

▶ Now Try Exercise 59.

✦ Rationalizing Denominators or Numerators

There are times when we need to remove the radicals in a denominator or a numerator. This is called **rationalizing the denominator** or **rationalizing the numerator**. It is done by multiplying by 1 in such a way as to obtain a perfect nth power.

EXAMPLE 5 Rationalize the denominator of each of the following.

a) $\sqrt{\dfrac{3}{2}}$

b) $\dfrac{\sqrt[3]{7}}{\sqrt[3]{9}}$

Solution

a) $\sqrt{\dfrac{3}{2}} = \sqrt{\dfrac{3}{2} \cdot \dfrac{2}{2}} = \sqrt{\dfrac{6}{4}} = \dfrac{\sqrt{6}}{\sqrt{4}} = \dfrac{\sqrt{6}}{2}$

b) $\dfrac{\sqrt[3]{7}}{\sqrt[3]{9}} = \dfrac{\sqrt[3]{7}}{\sqrt[3]{9}} \cdot \dfrac{\sqrt[3]{3}}{\sqrt[3]{3}} = \dfrac{\sqrt[3]{21}}{\sqrt[3]{27}} = \dfrac{\sqrt[3]{21}}{3}$

▶ Now Try Exercise 65.

Pairs of expressions of the form $a\sqrt{b} + c\sqrt{d}$ and $a\sqrt{b} - c\sqrt{d}$ are called **conjugates**. The product of such a pair contains no radicals and can be used to rationalize a denominator or a numerator.

EXAMPLE 6 Rationalize the numerator: $\dfrac{\sqrt{x} - \sqrt{y}}{5}$.

Solution

$$\dfrac{\sqrt{x} - \sqrt{y}}{5} = \dfrac{\sqrt{x} - \sqrt{y}}{5} \cdot \dfrac{\sqrt{x} + \sqrt{y}}{\sqrt{x} + \sqrt{y}} \qquad \text{The conjugate of } \sqrt{x} - \sqrt{y} \text{ is } \sqrt{x} + \sqrt{y}.$$

$$= \dfrac{\left(\sqrt{x}\right)^2 - \left(\sqrt{y}\right)^2}{5\sqrt{x} + 5\sqrt{y}} \qquad (A + B)(A - B) = A^2 - B^2$$

$$= \dfrac{x - y}{5\sqrt{x} + 5\sqrt{y}}$$

▶ Now Try Exercise 85.

✦ Rational Exponents

We are motivated to define *rational exponents* so that the properties for integer exponents hold for them as well. For example, we must have

$$a^{1/2} \cdot a^{1/2} = a^{1/2+1/2} = a^1 = a.$$

Thus we are led to define $a^{1/2}$ to mean $\sqrt{a}$. Similarly, $a^{1/n}$ would mean $\sqrt[n]{a}$. Again, if the laws of exponents are to hold, we must have

$$\left(a^{1/n}\right)^m = (a^m)^{1/n} = a^{m/n}.$$

Thus we are led to define $a^{m/n}$ to mean $\sqrt[n]{a^m}$, or, equivalently, $\left(\sqrt[n]{a}\right)^m$.

> **Rational Exponents**
>
> For any real number a and any natural numbers m and n, $n \geq 2$, for which $\sqrt[n]{a}$ exists,
>
> $$a^{1/n} = \sqrt[n]{a},$$
> $$a^{m/n} = \sqrt[n]{a^m} = \left(\sqrt[n]{a}\right)^m, \quad \text{and}$$
> $$a^{-m/n} = \frac{1}{a^{m/n}}.$$

We can use the definition of rational exponents to convert between radical notation and exponential notation.

EXAMPLE 7 Convert to radical notation and, if possible, simplify each of the following.

a) $7^{3/4}$ **b)** $8^{-5/3}$ **c)** $m^{1/6}$ **d)** $(-32)^{2/5}$

Solution

a) $7^{3/4} = \sqrt[4]{7^3}$, or $\left(\sqrt[4]{7}\right)^3$

b) $8^{-5/3} = \dfrac{1}{8^{5/3}} = \dfrac{1}{\left(\sqrt[3]{8}\right)^5} = \dfrac{1}{2^5} = \dfrac{1}{32}$

c) $m^{1/6} = \sqrt[6]{m}$

d) $(-32)^{2/5} = \sqrt[5]{(-32)^2} = \sqrt[5]{1024} = 4,$ or
$(-32)^{2/5} = \left(\sqrt[5]{-32}\right)^2 = (-2)^2 = 4$ ▶ Now Try Exercise 87.

EXAMPLE 8 Convert each of the following to exponential notation.

a) $\left(\sqrt[4]{7xy}\right)^5$ **b)** $\sqrt[6]{x^3}$

Solution

a) $\left(\sqrt[4]{7xy}\right)^5 = (7xy)^{5/4}$

b) $\sqrt[6]{x^3} = x^{3/6} = x^{1/2}$ ▶ Now Try Exercise 97.

We can use the laws of exponents to simplify exponential and radical expressions.

EXAMPLE 9 Simplify and then, if appropriate, write radical notation for each of the following.

a) $x^{5/6} \cdot x^{2/3}$ **b)** $(x+3)^{5/2}(x+3)^{-1/2}$
c) $\sqrt[3]{\sqrt{7}}$

Solution

a) $x^{5/6} \cdot x^{2/3} = x^{5/6+2/3} = x^{9/6} = x^{3/2} = \sqrt{x^3} = \sqrt{x^2}\sqrt{x} = x\sqrt{x}$

b) $(x+3)^{5/2}(x+3)^{-1/2} = (x+3)^{5/2-1/2} = (x+3)^2$

c) $\sqrt[3]{\sqrt{7}} = \sqrt[3]{7^{1/2}} = (7^{1/2})^{1/3} = 7^{1/6} = \sqrt[6]{7}$ ▶ Now Try Exercise 107.

TECHNOLOGY CONNECTION

We can add and subtract rational exponents on a graphing calculator. The FRAC feature from the MATH menu allows us to express the result as a fraction. The addition of the exponents in Example 9(a) is shown here.

```
5/6+2/3▸Frac
                3/2
```

EXAMPLE 10 Write an expression containing a single radical: $a^{1/2}b^{5/6}$.

Solution $a^{1/2}b^{5/6} = a^{3/6}b^{5/6} = (a^3b^5)^{1/6} = \sqrt[6]{a^3b^5}$

▶ Now Try Exercise 117.

 R.6 **EXERCISE SET**

Simplify. Assume that variables can represent any real number.

1. $\sqrt{(-11)^2}$

2. $\sqrt{(-1)^2}$

3. $\sqrt{16y^2}$

4. $\sqrt{36t^2}$

5. $\sqrt{(b+1)^2}$

6. $\sqrt{(2c-3)^2}$

7. $\sqrt[3]{-27x^3}$

8. $\sqrt[3]{-8y^3}$

9. $\sqrt[4]{81x^8}$

10. $\sqrt[4]{16z^{12}}$

11. $\sqrt[5]{32}$

12. $\sqrt[5]{-32}$

13. $\sqrt{180}$

14. $\sqrt{48}$

15. $\sqrt{72}$

16. $\sqrt{250}$

17. $\sqrt[3]{54}$

18. $\sqrt[3]{135}$

19. $\sqrt{128c^2d^4}$

20. $\sqrt{162c^4d^6}$

21. $\sqrt[4]{48x^6y^4}$

22. $\sqrt[4]{243m^5n^{10}}$

23. $\sqrt{x^2 - 4x + 4}$

24. $\sqrt{x^2 + 16x + 64}$

Simplify. Assume that no radicands were formed by raising negative quantities to even powers.

25. $\sqrt{10}\,\sqrt{30}$

26. $\sqrt{28}\,\sqrt{14}$

27. $\sqrt{12}\,\sqrt{33}$

28. $\sqrt{15}\,\sqrt{35}$

29. $\sqrt{2x^3y}\,\sqrt{12xy}$

30. $\sqrt{3y^4z}\,\sqrt{20z}$

31. $\sqrt[3]{3x^2y}\,\sqrt[3]{36x}$

32. $\sqrt[5]{8x^3y^4}\,\sqrt[5]{4x^4y}$

33. $\sqrt[3]{2(x+4)}\,\sqrt[3]{4(x+4)^4}$

34. $\sqrt[3]{4(x+1)^2}\,\sqrt[3]{18(x+1)^2}$

35. $\sqrt[6]{\dfrac{m^{12}n^{24}}{64}}$

36. $\sqrt[8]{\dfrac{m^{16}n^{24}}{2^8}}$

37. $\dfrac{\sqrt[3]{40m}}{\sqrt[3]{5m}}$

38. $\dfrac{\sqrt{40xy}}{\sqrt{8x}}$

39. $\dfrac{\sqrt[3]{3x^2}}{\sqrt[3]{24x^5}}$

40. $\dfrac{\sqrt{128a^2b^4}}{\sqrt{16ab}}$

41. $\sqrt[3]{\dfrac{64a^4}{27b^3}}$

42. $\sqrt{\dfrac{9x^7}{16y^8}}$

43. $\sqrt{\dfrac{7x^3}{36y^6}}$

44. $\sqrt[3]{\dfrac{2yz}{250z^4}}$

45. $9\sqrt{50} + 6\sqrt{2}$

46. $11\sqrt{27} - 4\sqrt{3}$

47. $6\sqrt{20} - 4\sqrt{45} + \sqrt{80}$

48. $2\sqrt{32} + 3\sqrt{8} - 4\sqrt{18}$

49. $8\sqrt{2x^2} - 6\sqrt{20x} - 5\sqrt{8x^2}$

50. $2\sqrt[3]{8x^2} + 5\sqrt[3]{27x^2} - 3\sqrt{x^3}$

51. $\left(\sqrt{3} - \sqrt{2}\right)\left(\sqrt{3} + \sqrt{2}\right)$

52. $\left(\sqrt{8} + 2\sqrt{5}\right)\left(\sqrt{8} - 2\sqrt{5}\right)$

53. $\left(2\sqrt{3} + \sqrt{5}\right)\left(\sqrt{3} - 3\sqrt{5}\right)$

54. $\left(\sqrt{6} - 4\sqrt{7}\right)\left(3\sqrt{6} + 2\sqrt{7}\right)$

55. $\left(1 + \sqrt{3}\right)^2$

56. $\left(\sqrt{2} - 5\right)^2$

57. $\left(\sqrt{5} - \sqrt{6}\right)^2$

58. $\left(\sqrt{3} + \sqrt{2}\right)^2$

59. *Distance from Airport.* An airplane is flying at an altitude of 3700 ft. The slanted distance directly to the airport is 14,200 ft. How far horizontally is the airplane from the airport?

60. *Bridge Expansion.* During a summer heat wave, a 2-mi bridge expands 2 ft in length. Assuming that the bulge occurs straight up the middle, estimate the height of the bulge. (In reality, bridges are built with expansion joints to control such buckling.)

61. An *equilateral triangle* is shown below.

   a) Find an expression for its height h in terms of a.
   b) Find an expression for its area A in terms of a.

62. An isosceles right triangle has legs of length s. Find an expression for the length of the hypotenuse in terms of s.

63. The diagonal of a square has length $8\sqrt{2}$. Find the length of a side of the square.

64. The area of square $PQRS$ is 100 ft^2, and A, B, C, and D are the midpoints of the sides. Find the area of square $ABCD$.

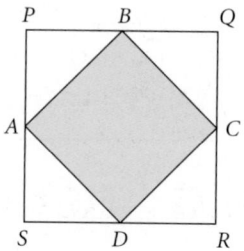

Rationalize the denominator.

65. $\sqrt{\dfrac{2}{3}}$

66. $\sqrt{\dfrac{3}{7}}$

67. $\dfrac{\sqrt[3]{5}}{\sqrt[3]{4}}$

68. $\dfrac{\sqrt[3]{7}}{\sqrt[3]{25}}$

69. $\sqrt[3]{\dfrac{16}{9}}$

70. $\sqrt[3]{\dfrac{3}{5}}$

71. $\dfrac{6}{3 + \sqrt{5}}$

72. $\dfrac{2}{\sqrt{3} - 1}$

73. $\dfrac{1 - \sqrt{2}}{2\sqrt{3} - \sqrt{6}}$

74. $\dfrac{\sqrt{5} + 4}{\sqrt{2} + 3\sqrt{7}}$

75. $\dfrac{6}{\sqrt{m} - \sqrt{n}}$

76. $\dfrac{3}{\sqrt{v} + \sqrt{w}}$

Rationalize the numerator.

77. $\dfrac{\sqrt{12}}{5}$

78. $\dfrac{\sqrt{50}}{3}$

79. $\sqrt[3]{\dfrac{7}{2}}$

80. $\sqrt[3]{\dfrac{2}{5}}$

81. $\dfrac{\sqrt{11}}{\sqrt{3}}$

82. $\dfrac{\sqrt{5}}{\sqrt{2}}$

83. $\dfrac{9 - \sqrt{5}}{3 - \sqrt{3}}$

84. $\dfrac{8 - \sqrt{6}}{5 - \sqrt{2}}$

85. $\dfrac{\sqrt{a} + \sqrt{b}}{3a}$

86. $\dfrac{\sqrt{p} - \sqrt{q}}{1 + \sqrt{q}}$

Convert to radical notation and simplify.

87. $x^{3/4}$

88. $y^{2/5}$

89. $16^{3/4}$

90. $4^{7/2}$

91. $125^{-1/3}$ **92.** $32^{-4/5}$

93. $a^{5/4}b^{-3/4}$ **94.** $x^{2/5}y^{-1/5}$

95. $m^{5/3}n^{7/3}$ **96.** $p^{7/6}q^{11/6}$

Convert to exponential notation.

97. $\left(\sqrt[4]{13}\right)^5$ **98.** $\sqrt[5]{17^3}$

99. $\sqrt[3]{20^2}$ **100.** $\left(\sqrt[5]{12}\right)^4$

101. $\sqrt[3]{\sqrt{11}}$ **102.** $\sqrt[3]{\sqrt[4]{7}}$

103. $\sqrt{5}\,\sqrt[3]{5}$ **104.** $\sqrt[3]{2}\,\sqrt{2}$

105. $\sqrt[5]{32^2}$ **106.** $\sqrt[3]{64^2}$

Simplify and then, if appropriate, write radical notation.

107. $(2a^{3/2})(4a^{1/2})$ **108.** $(3a^{5/6})(8a^{2/3})$

109. $\left(\dfrac{x^6}{9b^{-4}}\right)^{1/2}$ **110.** $\left(\dfrac{x^{2/3}}{4y^{-2}}\right)^{1/2}$

111. $\dfrac{x^{2/3}y^{5/6}}{x^{-1/3}y^{1/2}}$ **112.** $\dfrac{a^{1/2}b^{5/8}}{a^{1/4}b^{3/8}}$

113. $(m^{1/2}n^{5/2})^{2/3}$ **114.** $(x^{5/3}y^{1/3}z^{2/3})^{3/5}$

115. $a^{3/4}(a^{2/3}+a^{4/3})$ **116.** $m^{2/3}(m^{7/4}-m^{5/4})$

Write an expression containing a single radical and simplify.

117. $\sqrt[3]{6}\,\sqrt{2}$ **118.** $\sqrt{2}\,\sqrt[4]{8}$

119. $\sqrt[4]{xy}\,\sqrt[3]{x^2y}$ **120.** $\sqrt[3]{ab^2}\,\sqrt{ab}$

121. $\sqrt[3]{a^4\sqrt{a^3}}$ **122.** $\sqrt{a^3\sqrt[3]{a^2}}$

123. $\dfrac{\sqrt{(a+x)^3}\,\sqrt[3]{(a+x)^2}}{\sqrt[4]{a+x}}$

124. $\dfrac{\sqrt[4]{(x+y)^2}\,\sqrt[3]{x+y}}{\sqrt{(x+y)^3}}$

Collaborative Discussion and Writing

125. Explain how you would convince a classmate that $\sqrt{a+b}$ is not equivalent to $\sqrt{a}+\sqrt{b}$, for positive real numbers a and b.

126. Explain how you would determine whether $10\sqrt{26}-50$ is positive or negative without carrying out the actual computation.

Synthesis

Simplify.

127. $\sqrt{1+x^2}+\dfrac{1}{\sqrt{1+x^2}}$

128. $\sqrt{1-x^2}-\dfrac{x^2}{2\sqrt{1-x^2}}$

129. $\left(\sqrt{a^{\sqrt{a}}}\right)^{\sqrt{a}}$

130. $(2a^3b^{5/4}c^{1/7})^4 \div (54a^{-2}b^{2/3}c^{6/5})^{-1/3}$

R.7

The Basics of Equation Solving

  ✦ Solve linear equations.

  ✦ Solve quadratic equations.

An **equation** is a statement that two expressions are equal. To **solve** an equation in one variable is to find all the values of the variable that make the equation true. Each of these numbers is a **solution** of the equation. The set of all solutions of an equation is its **solution set**. Equations that have the same solution set are called **equivalent equations**.

◆ Linear and Quadratic Equations

A **linear equation in one variable** is an equation that is equivalent to one of the form $ax + b = 0$, where a and b are real numbers and $a \neq 0$.

A **quadratic equation** is an equation that is equivalent to one of the form $ax^2 + bx + c = 0$, where a, b, and c are real numbers and $a \neq 0$.

The following principles allow us to solve many linear and quadratic equations.

Equation-Solving Principles

For any real numbers a, b, and c,

The Addition Principle: If $a = b$ is true, then $a + c = b + c$ is true.

The Multiplication Principle: If $a = b$ is true, then $ac = bc$ is true.

The Principle of Zero Products: If $ab = 0$ is true, then $a = 0$ or $b = 0$, and if $a = 0$ or $b = 0$, then $ab = 0$.

The Principle of Square Roots: If $x^2 = k$, then $x = \sqrt{k}$ or $x = -\sqrt{k}$.

First we consider a linear equation. We will use the addition and multiplication principles to solve it.

EXAMPLE 1 Solve: $2x + 3 = 1 - 6(x - 1)$.

Solution We begin by using the distributive property to remove the parentheses.

$$2x + 3 = 1 - 6(x - 1)$$

$2x + 3 = 1 - 6x + 6$	Using the distributive property
$2x + 3 = 7 - 6x$	Combining like terms
$8x + 3 = 7$	Using the addition principle to add $6x$ on both sides
$8x = 4$	Using the addition principle to add -3, or subtract 3, on both sides
$x = \dfrac{4}{8}$	Using the multiplication principle to multiply by $\frac{1}{8}$, or divide by 8, on both sides
$x = \dfrac{1}{2}$	Simplifying

We check the result in the original equation.

Check:

$$2x + 3 = 1 - 6(x - 1)$$

$$2 \cdot \tfrac{1}{2} + 3 \; ? \; 1 - 6\left(\tfrac{1}{2} - 1\right) \qquad \text{Substituting } \tfrac{1}{2} \text{ for } x$$

$$1 + 3 \quad \Big| \quad 1 - 6\left(-\tfrac{1}{2}\right)$$

$$4 \quad \Big| \quad 1 + 3$$

$$4 \quad \Big| \quad 4 \qquad \textbf{TRUE}$$

The solution is $\tfrac{1}{2}$.

Now Try Exercise 1.

Now we consider a quadratic equation that can be solved using the principle of zero products.

EXAMPLE 2 Solve: $x^2 - 3x = 4$.

Solution First we write the equation with 0 on one side.

$$x^2 - 3x = 4$$

$$x^2 - 3x - 4 = 0 \qquad \text{Subtracting 4 on both sides}$$

$$(x + 1)(x - 4) = 0 \qquad \text{Factoring}$$

$$x + 1 = 0 \quad or \quad x - 4 = 0 \qquad \begin{array}{l}\text{Using the principle of}\\\text{zero products}\end{array}$$

$$x = -1 \quad or \quad x = 4$$

Check: For -1:

$$x^2 - 3x = 4$$

$$(-1)^2 - 3(-1) \; ? \; 4$$

$$1 + 3 \quad \Big|$$

$$4 \quad \Big| \quad 4 \quad \textbf{TRUE}$$

For 4:

$$x^2 - 3x = 4$$

$$4^2 - 3 \cdot 4 \; ? \; 4$$

$$16 - 12 \quad \Big|$$

$$4 \quad \Big| \quad 4 \quad \textbf{TRUE}$$

The solutions are -1 and 4.

Now Try Exercise 29.

The principle of square roots can be used to solve some quadratic equations, as we see in the next example.

EXAMPLE 3 Solve: $3x^2 - 6 = 0$.

Solution We will use the principle of square roots.

$$3x^2 - 6 = 0$$

$$3x^2 = 6 \qquad \text{Adding 6 on both sides}$$

$$x^2 = 2 \qquad \text{Dividing by 3 on both sides to isolate } x^2$$

$$x = \sqrt{2} \quad or \quad x = -\sqrt{2} \qquad \text{Using the principle of square roots}$$

Both numbers check. The solutions are $\sqrt{2}$ and $-\sqrt{2}$, or $\pm\sqrt{2}$ (read "plus or minus $\sqrt{2}$").

Now Try Exercise 47.

R.7 EXERCISE SET

Solve.

1. $6x - 15 = 45$

2. $4x - 7 = 81$

3. $5x - 10 = 45$

4. $6x - 7 = 11$

5. $9t + 4 = -5$

6. $5x + 7 = -13$

7. $8x + 48 = 3x - 12$

8. $15x + 40 = 8x - 9$

9. $7y - 1 = 23 - 5y$

10. $3x - 15 = 15 - 3x$

11. $3x - 4 = 5 + 12x$

12. $9t - 4 = 14 + 15t$

13. $5 - 4a = a - 13$

14. $6 - 7x = x - 14$

15. $3m - 7 = -13 + m$

16. $5x - 8 = 2x - 8$

17. $11 - 3x = 5x + 3$

18. $20 - 4y = 10 - 6y$

19. $2(x + 7) = 5x + 14$

20. $3(y + 4) = 8y$

21. $24 = 5(2t + 5)$

22. $9 = 4(3y - 2)$

23. $5y - (2y - 10) = 25$

24. $8x - (3x - 5) = 40$

25. $7(3x + 6) = 11 - (x + 2)$

26. $9(2x + 8) = 20 - (x + 5)$

27. $4(3y - 1) - 6 = 5(y + 2)$

28. $3(2n - 5) - 7 = 4(n - 9)$

29. $x^2 + 3x - 28 = 0$

30. $y^2 - 4y - 45 = 0$

31. $x^2 - 8x = 0$

32. $t^2 - 9t = 0$

33. $y^2 + 6y + 9 = 0$

34. $n^2 + 4n + 4 = 0$

35. $x^2 + 100 = 20x$

36. $y^2 + 25 = 10y$

37. $x^2 - 4x - 32 = 0$

38. $t^2 + 12t + 27 = 0$

39. $3y^2 + 8y + 4 = 0$

40. $9y^2 + 15y + 4 = 0$

41. $12z^2 + z = 6$

42. $6x^2 - 7x = 10$

43. $12a^2 - 28 = 5a$

44. $21n^2 - 10 = n$

45. $14 = x(x - 5)$

46. $24 = x(x - 2)$

47. $x^2 - 36 = 0$

48. $y^2 - 81 = 0$

49. $z^2 = 144$

50. $t^2 = 25$

51. $2x^2 - 20 = 0$

52. $3y^2 - 15 = 0$

53. $6z^2 - 18 = 0$

54. $5x^2 - 75 = 0$

Collaborative Discussion and Writing

55. When using the addition and multiplication principles to solve an equation, how do you determine which number to add or multiply by on both sides of the equation?

56. Explain how to write a quadratic equation that has solutions -3 and 4.

Synthesis

Solve.

57. $3[5 - 3(4 - t)] - 2 = 5[3(5t - 4) + 8] - 26$

58. $6[4(8 - y) - 5(9 + 3y)] - 21 = -7[3(7 + 4y) - 4]$

59. $x - \{3x - [2x - (5x - (7x - 1))]\} = x + 7$

60. $23 - 2[4 + 3(x - 1)] + 5[x - 2(x + 3)] = 7\{x - 2[5 - (2x + 3)]\}$

61. $(5x^2 + 6x)(12x^2 - 5x - 2) = 0$

62. $(3x^2 + 7x - 20)(x^2 - 4x) = 0$

63. $3x^3 + 6x^2 - 27x - 54 = 0$

64. $2x^3 + 6x^2 = 8x + 24$

CHAPTER R SUMMARY AND REVIEW

Important Properties and Formulas

Properties of the Real Numbers

Commutative:	$a + b = b + a;$ $ab = ba$
Associative:	$a + (b + c) = (a + b) + c;$ $a(bc) = (ab)c$
Additive Identity:	$a + 0 = 0 + a = a$
Additive Inverse:	$-a + a = a + (-a) = 0$
Multiplicative Identity:	$a \cdot 1 = 1 \cdot a = a$
Multiplicative Inverse:	$a \cdot \dfrac{1}{a} = \dfrac{1}{a} \cdot a = 1$ $(a \neq 0)$
Distributive:	$a(b + c) = ab + ac$

Absolute Value

For any real number a,

$$|a| = \begin{cases} a, & \text{if } a \geq 0, \\ -a, & \text{if } a < 0. \end{cases}$$

Properties of Exponents

For any real numbers a and b and any integers m and n, assuming 0 is not raised to a nonpositive power:

The Product Rule: $a^m \cdot a^n = a^{m+n}$

The Quotient Rule: $\dfrac{a^m}{a^n} = a^{m-n}$ $(a \neq 0)$

The Power Rule: $(a^m)^n = a^{mn}$

Raising a Product to a Power: $(ab)^m = a^m b^m$

Raising a Quotient to a Power:

$$\left(\frac{a}{b}\right)^m = \frac{a^m}{b^m} \quad (b \neq 0)$$

Compound Interest Formula

$$A = P\left(1 + \frac{r}{n}\right)^{nt}$$

Special Products of Binomials

$(A + B)^2 = A^2 + 2AB + B^2$

$(A - B)^2 = A^2 - 2AB + B^2$

$(A + B)(A - B) = A^2 - B^2$

Sum or Difference of Cubes

$A^3 + B^3 = (A + B)(A^2 - AB + B^2)$

$A^3 - B^3 = (A - B)(A^2 + AB + B^2)$

Properties of Radicals

Let a and b be any real numbers or expressions for which the given roots exist. For any natural numbers m and n $(n \neq 1)$:

If n is even, $\sqrt[n]{a^n} = |a|$.

If n is odd, $\sqrt[n]{a^n} = a$.

$\sqrt[n]{a} \cdot \sqrt[n]{b} = \sqrt[n]{ab}.$

$\sqrt[n]{\dfrac{a}{b}} = \dfrac{\sqrt[n]{a}}{\sqrt[n]{b}} \quad (b \neq 0).$

$\sqrt[n]{a^m} = \left(\sqrt[n]{a}\right)^m.$

Rational Exponents

For any real number a and any natural numbers m and n, $n \geq 2$, for which $\sqrt[n]{a}$ exists,

$$a^{1/n} = \sqrt[n]{a},$$
$$a^{m/n} = \sqrt[n]{a^m} = \left(\sqrt[n]{a}\right)^m, \quad \text{and}$$
$$a^{-m/n} = \frac{1}{a^{m/n}}.$$

Pythagorean Theorem

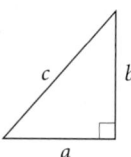

$$a^2 + b^2 = c^2$$

Equation-Solving Principles

The Addition Principle: If $a = b$ is true, then $a + c = b + c$ is true.

The Multiplication Principle: If $a = b$ is true, then $ac = bc$ is true.

The Principle of Zero Products: If $ab = 0$ is true, then $a = 0$ or $b = 0$, and if $a = 0$ or $b = 0$, then $ab = 0$.

The Principle of Square Roots: If $x^2 = k$, then $x = \sqrt{k}$ or $x = -\sqrt{k}$.

REVIEW EXERCISES

Answers for all the review exercises appear in the answer section at the back of the book. If you get an incorrect answer, restudy the section indicated in red next to the exercise or the direction line that precedes it.

Determine whether the statement is true or false.

1. If $a < 0$, then $|a| = -a$.   [R.1]

2. For any real number a, $a \neq 0$, and any integers m and n, $a^m \cdot a^n = a^{mn}$.   [R.2]

3. The domain of an algebraic expression is the set of all real numbers for which the expression is defined.   [R.5]

4. If $a = b$ is true, then $a + c = b + c$ is true.   [R.7]

In Exercises 5–10, consider the following numbers: [R.1]

$$-43.89, 12, -3, -\tfrac{1}{5}, \sqrt{7}, \sqrt[3]{10}, -1, -\tfrac{4}{3}, 7\tfrac{2}{3},$$
$$-19, 31, 0.$$

5. Which are integers?

6. Which are natural numbers?

7. Which are rational numbers?

8. Which are real numbers?

9. Which are irrational numbers?

10. Which are whole numbers?

11. Write interval notation for $\{x \mid -3 \leq x < 5\}$.   [R.1]

Simplify.   [R.1]

12. $|-3.5|$ 13. $|16|$

14. Find the distance between -7 and 3 on the number line.   [R.1]

Calculate.   [R.2]

15. $5^3 - [2(4^2 - 3^2 - 6)]^3$ 16. $\dfrac{3^4 - (6-7)^4}{2^3 - 2^4}$

Convert to decimal notation.   [R.2]

17. 3.261×10^6 18. 4.1×10^{-4}

Convert to scientific notation. [R.2]

19. 0.01432   **20.** 43,210

Calculate. Write the answer using scientific notation. [R.2]

21. $\dfrac{2.5 \times 10^{-8}}{3.2 \times 10^{13}}$

22. $(8.4 \times 10^{-17})(6.5 \times 10^{-16})$

Simplify.

23. $(7a^2b^4)(-2a^{-4}b^3)$ [R.2]   **24.** $\dfrac{54x^6y^{-4}z^2}{9x^{-3}y^2z^{-4}}$ [R.2]

25. $\sqrt[4]{81}$ [R.6]   **26.** $\sqrt[5]{-32}$ [R.6]

27. $\dfrac{b - a^{-1}}{a - b^{-1}}$ [R.5]   **28.** $\dfrac{\dfrac{x^2}{y} + \dfrac{y^2}{x}}{y^2 - xy + x^2}$ [R.5]

29. $\left(\sqrt{3} - \sqrt{7}\right)\left(\sqrt{3} + \sqrt{7}\right)$ [R.6]

30. $\left(5x^2 - \sqrt{2}\right)^2$ [R.6]

31. $8\sqrt{5} + \dfrac{25}{\sqrt{5}}$ [R.6]

32. $(x + t)(x^2 - xt + t^2)$ [R.3]

33. $(5a + 4b)(2a - 3b)$ [R.3]

34. $(5xy^4 - 7xy^2 + 4x^2 - 3) - (-3xy^4 + 2xy^2 - 2y + 4)$ [R.3]

Factor. [R.4]

35. $x^3 + 2x^2 - 3x - 6$

36. $12a^3 - 27ab^4$

37. $24x + 144 + x^2$

38. $9x^3 + 35x^2 - 4x$

39. $8x^3 - 1$

40. $27x^6 + 125y^6$

41. $6x^3 + 48$

42. $4x^3 - 4x^2 - 9x + 9$

43. $9x^2 - 30x + 25$

44. $18x^2 - 3x + 6$

45. $a^2b^2 - ab - 6$

46. Divide and simplify: [R.5]
$$\frac{3x^2 - 12}{x^2 + 4x + 4} \div \frac{x - 2}{x + 2}.$$

47. Subtract and simplify: [R.5]
$$\frac{x}{x^2 + 9x + 20} - \frac{4}{x^2 + 7x + 12}.$$

Write an expression containing a single radical. [R.6]

48. $\sqrt{y^5}\ \sqrt[3]{y^2}$

49. $\dfrac{\sqrt{(a + b)^3}\ \sqrt[3]{a + b}}{\sqrt[6]{(a + b)^7}}$

50. Convert to radical notation: $b^{7/5}$. [R.6]

51. Convert to exponential notation: [R.6]
$$\sqrt[8]{\frac{m^{32}n^{16}}{3^8}}.$$

52. Rationalize the denominator: [R.6]
$$\frac{4 - \sqrt{3}}{5 + \sqrt{3}}.$$

53. How long is a guy wire that reaches from the top of a 17-ft pole to a point on the ground 8 ft from the bottom of the pole? [R.6]

Solve. [R.7]

54. $2x - 7 = 7$

55. $5x - 7 = 3x - 9$

56. $8 - 3x = -7 + 2x$

57. $6(2x - 1) = 3 - (x + 10)$

58. $y^2 + 16y + 64 = 0$

59. $x^2 - x = 20$

60. $2x^2 + 11x - 6 = 0$

61. $x(x - 2) = 3$

62. $y^2 - 16 = 0$

63. $n^2 - 7 = 0$

64. Calculate: $128 \div (-2)^3 \div (-2) \cdot 3$ [R.2]

   A. $\dfrac{8}{3}$ **B.** 24   **C.** 96   **D.** $\dfrac{512}{3}$

65. Factor completely: $9x^2 - 36y^2$.   [R.4]

A. $(3x + 6y)(3x - 6y)$
B. $3(x + 2y)(x - 2y)$
C. $9(x + 2y)(x - 2y)$
D. $9(x - 2y)^2$

Collaborative Discussion and Writing

66. Anya says that $15 - 6 \div 3 \cdot 4$ is 12. What mistake is she probably making?   [R.2]

67. A calculator indicates that $4^{21} = 4.398046511 \times 10^{12}$. How can you tell that this is an approximation?   [R.2]

Synthesis

Mortgage Payments.   The formula

$$M = P\left[\dfrac{\dfrac{r}{12}\left(1 + \dfrac{r}{12}\right)^n}{\left(1 + \dfrac{r}{12}\right)^n - 1}\right]$$

gives the monthly mortgage payment M on a home loan of P dollars at interest rate r, where n is the total number of payments (12 times the number of years). Use this formula in Exercises 68–71.   [R.2]

68. The cost of a house is $98,000. The down payment is $16,000, the interest rate is $6\frac{1}{2}$ %, and the loan period is 25 yr. What is the monthly mortgage payment?

69. The cost of a house is $124,000. The down payment is $20,000, the interest rate is $5\frac{3}{4}$ %, and the loan period is 30 yr. What is the monthly mortgage payment?

70. The cost of a house is $135,000. The down payment is $18,000, the interest rate is $7\frac{1}{2}$ %, and the loan period is 20 yr. What is the monthly mortgage payment?

71. The cost of a house is $151,000. The down payment is $21,000, the interest rate is $6\frac{1}{4}$ %, and the loan period is 25 yr. What is the monthly mortgage payment?

Multiply. Assume that all exponents are integers. [R.3]

72. $(x^n + 10)(x^n - 4)$

73. $(t^a + t^{-a})^2$

74. $(y^b - z^c)(y^b + z^c)$

75. $(a^n - b^n)^3$

Factor. [R.4]

76. $y^{2n} + 16y^n + 64$

77. $x^{2t} - 3x^t - 28$

78. $m^{6n} - m^{3n}$

CHAPTER R TEST

1. Consider the numbers
$$-8, \tfrac{11}{3}, \sqrt{15}, 0, -5.49, 36, \sqrt[3]{7}, 10\tfrac{1}{6}.$$

a) Which are integers?
b) Which are rational numbers?
c) Which are rational numbers but not integers?
d) Which are integers but not natural numbers?

Simplify.

2. $\left|-\dfrac{14}{5}\right|$ **3.** $|19.4|$ **4.** $|-1.2xy|$

5. Write interval notation for $\{x | -3 < x \le 6\}$. Then graph the interval.

6. Find the distance between -7 and 5 on the number line.

7. Calculate: $32 \div 2^3 - 12 \div 4 \cdot 3$.

8. Convert to scientific notation: 0.0000367.

9. Convert to decimal notation: 4.51×10^6.

10. Compute and write scientific notation for the answer:
$$\frac{2.7 \times 10^4}{3.6 \times 10^{-3}}.$$

Simplify.

11. $x^{-8} \cdot x^5$

12. $(2y^2)^3(3y^4)^2$

13. $(-3a^5b^{-4})(5a^{-1}b^3)$

14. $(3x^4 - 2x^2 + 6x) - (5x^3 - 3x^2 + x)$

15. $(x + 3)(2x - 5)$

16. $(2y - 1)^2$

17. $\dfrac{\dfrac{x}{y} - \dfrac{y}{x}}{x + y}$

18. $\sqrt{54}$

19. $\sqrt[3]{40}$

20. $3\sqrt{75} + 2\sqrt{27}$

21. $\sqrt{18}\,\sqrt{10}$

22. $(2 + \sqrt{3})(5 - 2\sqrt{3})$

Factor.

23. $y^2 - 3y - 18$

24. $x^3 + 10x^2 + 25x$

25. $2n^2 + 5n - 12$

26. $8x^2 - 18$

27. $m^3 - 8$

28. Multiply and simplify:
$$\frac{x^2 + x - 6}{x^2 + 8x + 15} \cdot \frac{x^2 - 25}{x^2 - 4x + 4}.$$

29. Subtract and simplify:
$$\frac{x}{x^2 - 1} - \frac{3}{x^2 + 4x - 5}.$$

30. Rationalize the denominator: $\dfrac{5}{7 - \sqrt{3}}$.

31. Convert to radical notation: $t^{5/7}$.

32. Convert to exponential notation: $\left(\sqrt[5]{7}\right)^3$.

33. How long is a guy wire that reaches from the top of a 12-ft pole to a point on the ground 5 ft from the bottom of the pole?

Solve.

34. $7x - 4 = 24$

35. $3(y - 5) + 6 = 8 - (y + 2)$

36. $2x^2 + 5x + 3 = 0$

37. $z^2 - 11 = 0$

Synthesis

38. Multiply: $(x - y - 1)^2$.

Graphs, Functions, and Models

APPLICATION

Lucie Mays-Sulewski, from Westfield, Indiana, won the women's division of the 2006 Indianapolis 500 Mini-Marathon race. The first American woman to win this race since 1993, she reached the 5-mi point after 31 min 10 sec and arrived at the 10-mi point after 1 hr 1 min 38 sec. (*Source*: www.500festival.com) Find Lucie's speed in miles per minute (average rate of change) from the 5-mi point to the 10-mi point.

This problem appears as Exercise 47 in Section 1.3.

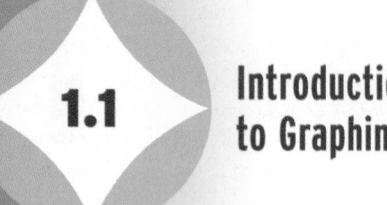

1.1 Introduction to Graphing

◆ Plot points.

◆ Determine whether an ordered pair is a solution of an equation.

◆ Find the *x*- and *y*-intercepts of an equation of the form $Ax + By = C$.

◆ Graph equations.

◆ Find the distance between two points in the plane and find the midpoint of a segment.

◆ Find an equation of a circle with a given center and radius, and given an equation of a circle in standard form, find the center and the radius.

◆ Graph equations of circles.

◆ Graphs

Graphs provide a means of displaying, interpreting, and analyzing data in a visual format. It is not uncommon to open a newspaper or magazine and encounter graphs. Examples of bar, circle, and line graphs are shown below.

Source: Ipsos Insight

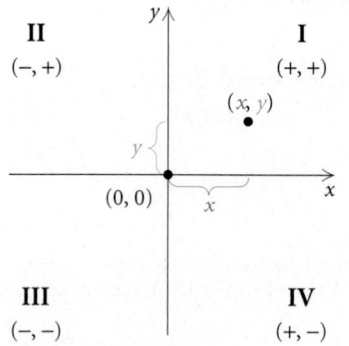

Many real-world situations can be modeled, or described mathematically, using equations in which two variables appear. We use a plane to graph a pair of numbers. To locate points on a plane, we use two perpendicular number lines, called **axes,** which intersect at $(0,0)$. We call this point the **origin.** The horizontal axis is called the **x-axis,** and the vertical axis is called the **y-axis.** (Other variables, such as *a* and *b*, can also be used.) The axes divide the plane into four regions, called **quadrants,** denoted by Roman numerals and numbered counterclockwise from the upper right. Arrows show the positive direction of each axis.

Each point (x, y) in the plane is called an **ordered pair.** The first number, x, indicates the point's horizontal location with respect to the y-axis, and the second number, y, indicates the point's vertical location with respect to the x-axis. We call x the **first coordinate, x-coordinate,** or **abscissa.** We call y the **second coordinate, y-coordinate,** or **ordinate.** Such a representation is called the **Cartesian coordinate system** in honor of the French mathematician and philosopher René Descartes (1596–1650).

In the first quadrant, both coordinates of a point are positive. In the second quadrant, the first coordinate is negative and the second is positive. In the third quadrant, both coordinates are negative, and in the fourth quadrant, the first coordinate is positive and the second is negative.

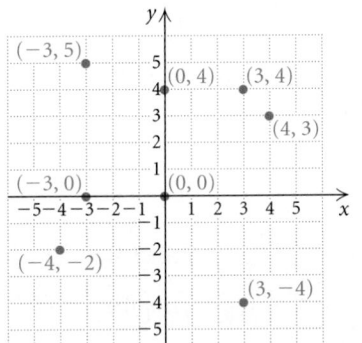

EXAMPLE 1 Graph and label the points $(-3, 5), (4, 3), (3, 4), (-4, -2), (3, -4), (0, 4), (-3, 0),$ and $(0, 0)$.

Solution To graph or **plot** $(-3, 5)$, we note that the x-coordinate, -3, tells us to move from the origin 3 units to the left of the y-axis. Then we move 5 units up from the x-axis.* To graph the other points, we proceed in a similar manner. (See the graph at left.) Note that the point $(4, 3)$ is different from the point $(3, 4)$.

▶ Now Try Exercise 1.

✦ Solutions of Equations

Equations in two variables, like $2x + 3y = 18$, have solutions (x, y) that are ordered pairs such that when the first coordinate is substituted for x and the second coordinate is substituted for y, the result is a true equation. The first coordinate in an ordered pair generally represents the variable that occurs first alphabetically.

EXAMPLE 2 Determine whether each ordered pair is a solution of $2x + 3y = 18$.

a) $(-5, 7)$ **b)** $(3, 4)$

Solution We substitute the ordered pair into the equation and determine whether the resulting equation is true.

a)
$$2x + 3y = 18$$
$$2(-5) + 3(7) \;?\; 18$$ We substitute -5 for x and
$$-10 + 21$$ 7 for y (alphabetical order).
$$11 \;\mid\; 18 \quad \text{FALSE}$$

The equation $11 = 18$ is false, so $(-5, 7)$ is not a solution.

---

*We first saw notation such as $(-3, 5)$ in Section R.1. There the notation represented an open interval. Here the notation represents an ordered pair. The context in which the notation appears usually makes the meaning clear.

b)

$$2x + 3y = 18$$

$$2(3) + 3(4) \ ? \ 18 \qquad \text{We substitute 3 for } x$$
$$6 + 12 \qquad\qquad\quad \text{and 4 for } y.$$
$$18 \ \big| \ 18 \ \ \text{TRUE}$$

The equation $18 = 18$ is true, so $(3, 4)$ is a solution.

▷ **Now Try Exercise 7.**

✦ Graphs of Equations

The equation considered in Example 2 actually has an infinite number of solutions. We cannot list all the solutions, but we can make a drawing, called a **graph,** that represents them. On the following page are some suggestions for drawing graphs.

> ### To Graph an Equation
>
> To **graph an equation** is to make a drawing that represents the solutions of that equation.

Graphs of equations of the type $Ax + By = C$ are straight lines. Many such equations can be graphed conveniently using intercepts. The **x-intercept** of the graph of an equation is the point at which the graph crosses the x-axis. The **y-intercept** is the point at which the graph crosses the y-axis. We know from geometry that only one line can be drawn through two given points. Thus, if we know the intercepts, we can graph the line. To ensure that a computational error has not been made, it is a good idea to calculate and plot a third point as a check.

> ### x- and y-Intercepts
>
> An **x-intercept** is a point $(a, 0)$. To find a, let $y = 0$ and solve for x.
> A **y-intercept** is a point $(0, b)$. To find b, let $x = 0$ and solve for y.

EXAMPLE 3 Graph: $2x + 3y = 18$.

Solution The graph is a line. To find ordered pairs that are solutions of this equation, we can replace either x or y with any number and then solve for the other variable. In this case, it is convenient to find the intercepts of the graph. For instance, if x is replaced with 0, then

$$2 \cdot 0 + 3y = 18$$
$$3y = 18$$
$$y = 6. \qquad \text{Dividing by 3}$$

Thus, $(0, 6)$ is a solution. It is the *y-intercept* of the graph. If y is replaced with 0, then

$$2x + 3 \cdot 0 = 18$$
$$2x = 18$$
$$x = 9. \qquad \text{Dividing by 2}$$

Thus, $(9, 0)$ is a solution. It is the *x-intercept* of the graph. We find a third solution as a check. If x is replaced with 5, then

$$2 \cdot 5 + 3y = 18$$
$$10 + 3y = 18$$
$$3y = 8 \qquad \text{Subtracting 10}$$
$$y = \tfrac{8}{3}. \qquad \text{Dividing by 3}$$

Thus, $\left(5, \tfrac{8}{3}\right)$ is a solution.

We list the solutions in a table and then plot the points. Note that the points appear to lie on a straight line.

x	y	(x, y)	
0	6	$(0, 6)$	← *y*-intercept
9	0	$(9, 0)$	← *x*-intercept
5	$\tfrac{8}{3}$	$\left(5, \tfrac{8}{3}\right)$	

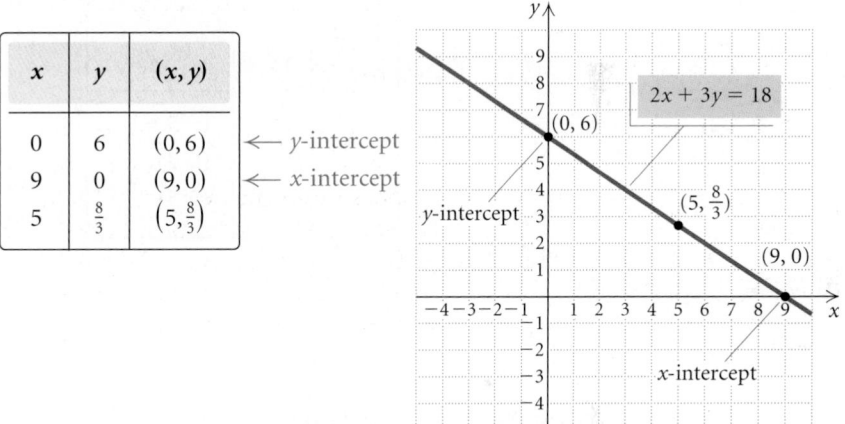

Were we to graph additional solutions of $2x + 3y = 18$, they would be on the same straight line. Thus, to complete the graph, we use a straight-edge to draw a line as shown in the figure. This line represents all solutions of the equation. Every point on the line represents a solution; every solution is represented by a point on the line.

▷ **Now Try Exercise 15.**

Suggestions for Drawing Graphs

1. Calculate solutions and list the ordered pairs in a table.
2. Use graph paper.
3. Draw axes and label them with the variables.
4. Use arrows on the axes to indicate positive directions.
5. Scale the axes; that is, label the tick marks on the axes. Consider the ordered pairs found in part (1) above when choosing the scale.
6. Plot the ordered pairs, look for patterns, and complete the graph. Label the graph with the equation being graphed.

When graphing some equations, it is easier to first solve for y and then find ordered pairs. We can use the addition and multiplication principles to solve for y.

EQUATION SOLVING
REVIEW SECTION **R.7.**

EXAMPLE 4 Graph: $3x - 5y = -10$.

Solution We first solve for y:

$$3x - 5y = -10$$
$$-5y = -3x - 10 \qquad \text{Subtracting } 3x \text{ on both sides}$$
$$y = \tfrac{3}{5}x + 2. \qquad \text{Multiplying by } -\tfrac{1}{5} \text{ on both sides}$$

By choosing multiples of 5 for x, we can avoid fraction values when calculating y. For example, if we choose -5 for x, we get

$$y = \tfrac{3}{5}x + 2 = \tfrac{3}{5}(-5) + 2 = -3 + 2 = -1.$$

The table below lists a few more points. We plot the points and draw the graph.

x	y	(x, y)
-5	-1	$(-5, -1)$
0	2	$(0, 2)$
5	5	$(5, 5)$

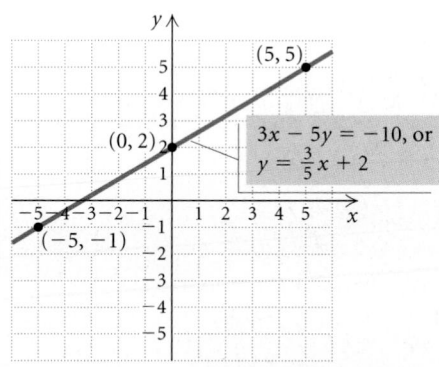

▶ Now Try Exercise 27.

In the equation $y = \tfrac{3}{5}x + 2$ in Example 4, the value of y *depends* on the value chosen for x, so x is said to be the **independent variable** and y the **dependent variable**.

TECHNOLOGY
CONNECTION

```
Plot1  Plot2  Plot3
\Y1 ■(3/5)X+2
\Y2=
\Y3=
\Y4=
\Y5=
\Y6=
\Y7=
```

```
WINDOW
Xmin = -10
Xmax = 10
Xscl = 1
Ymin = -10
Ymax = 10
Yscl = 1
Xres = 1
```

We can graph an equation on a graphing calculator. Many calculators require an equation to be entered in the form "$y = .$" In such a case, if the equation is not initially given in this form, it must be solved for y before it is entered in the calculator. For the equation $3x - 5y = -10$ in Example 4, we enter $y = \tfrac{3}{5}x + 2$ on the equation-editor, or "$y = $", screen in the form $y = (3/5)x + 2$.

Next, we determine the portion of the xy-plane that will appear on the calculator's screen. That portion of the plane is called the **viewing window.**

The notation used in this text to denote a window setting consists of four numbers $[L, R, B, T]$, which represent the **L**eft and **R**ight endpoints of the x-axis and the **B**ottom and **T**op endpoints of the y-axis, respectively.

(continued)

$y = \frac{3}{5}x + 2$

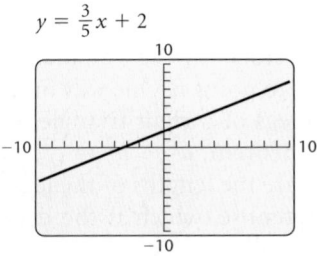

The window with the settings $[-10, 10, -10, 10]$ is the **standard viewing window.** These settings are shown in the window at left. On some graphing calculators, the standard window can be selected quickly using the ZSTANDARD feature from the ZOOM menu.

Xmin and Xmax are used to set the left and right endpoints of the x-axis, respectively; Ymin and Ymax are used to set the bottom and top endpoints of the y-axis. The settings Xscl and Yscl give the scales for the axes. For example, Xscl = 1 and Yscl = 1 means that there is 1 unit between tick marks on each of the axes. In this text, scaling factors other than 1 will be listed by the window unless they are readily apparent.

After entering the equation and choosing a viewing window, we can then draw the graph.

TECHNOLOGY CONNECTION

A graphing calculator can be used to create a table of ordered pairs that are solutions of an equation. For the equation in Example 5, $y = x^2 - 9x - 12$, we first enter the equation on the equation-editor screen. Then we set up a table in AUTO mode by designating a value for TBLSTART and a value for ΔTBL. The calculator will produce a table starting with the value of TBLSTART and continuing by adding ΔTBL to supply succeeding x-values. For the equation $y = x^2 - 9x - 12$, we let TBLSTART = -3 and ΔTBL = 1. We can scroll up and down in the table to find values other than those shown here.

EXAMPLE 5 Graph: $y = x^2 - 9x - 12$.

Solution Note that since this equation is not of the form $Ax + By = C$, its graph is not a straight line. We make a table of values, plot enough points to obtain an idea of the shape of the curve, and connect them with a smooth curve. It is important to scale the axes to include most of the ordered pairs listed in the table. Here it is appropriate to use a larger scale on the y-axis than on the x-axis.

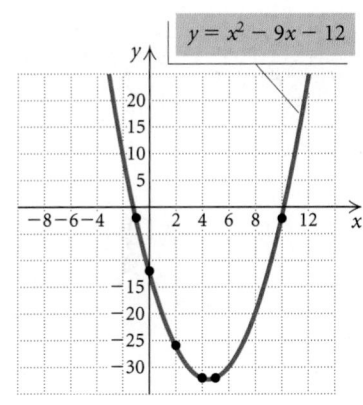

x	y	(x, y)
-3	24	$(-3, 24)$
-1	-2	$(-1, -2)$
0	-12	$(0, -12)$
2	-26	$(2, -26)$
4	-32	$(4, -32)$
5	-32	$(5, -32)$
10	-2	$(10, -2)$
12	24	$(12, 24)$

① Select values for x.

② Compute values for y.

▶ **Now Try Exercise 37.**

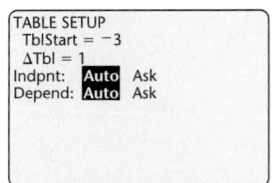

TABLE SETUP
  TblStart = -3
  ΔTbl = 1
Indpnt: **Auto** Ask
Depend: **Auto** Ask

X	Y1
-3	24
-2	10
-1	-2
0	-12
1	-20
2	-26
3	-30
X = -3	

◆ The Distance Formula

Suppose that a photographer assigned to a story on the Panama Canal needs to determine the distance from point A to point B. One way in which he or she might proceed is to measure two legs of a right triangle that is situated as shown below. The Pythagorean theorem, $a^2 + b^2 = c^2$, where c is the length of the hypotenuse and a and b are the lengths of the legs, can then be used to find the length of the hypotenuse, which is the distance from A to B.

Photographer

A similar strategy is used to find the distance between two points in a plane. For two points (x_1, y_1) and (x_2, y_2), we can draw a right triangle in which the legs have lengths $|x_2 - x_1|$ and $|y_2 - y_1|$.

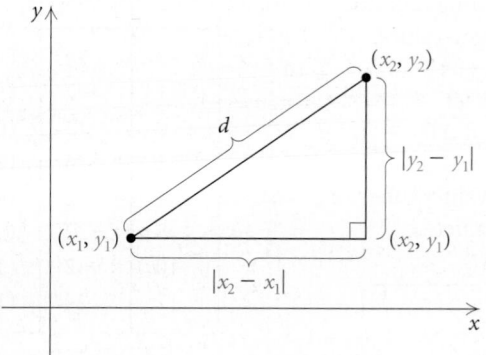

Using the Pythagorean theorem, we have

$$d^2 = |x_2 - x_1|^2 + |y_2 - y_1|^2.$$

Substituting d for c, $|x_2 - x_1|$ for a, and $|y_2 - y_1|$ for b in the Pythagorean equation, $c^2 = a^2 + b^2$

Because we are squaring, parentheses can replace the absolute-value symbols:

$$d^2 = (x_2 - x_1)^2 + (y_2 - y_1)^2.$$

Taking the principal square root, we obtain the distance formula.

The Distance Formula

The **distance** d between any two points (x_1, y_1) and (x_2, y_2) is given by

$$d = \sqrt{(x_2 - x_1)^2 + (y_2 - y_1)^2}.$$

The subtraction of the x-coordinates can be done in either order, as can the subtraction of the y-coordinates. Although we derived the distance formula by considering two points not on a horizontal or a vertical line, the distance formula holds for *any* two points.

EXAMPLE 6   Find the distance between each pair of points.

a) $(-2, 2)$ and $(3, -6)$ b) $(-1, -5)$ and $(-1, 2)$

Solution   We substitute into the distance formula.

a) $d = \sqrt{[3 - (-2)]^2 + (-6 - 2)^2}$
$= \sqrt{5^2 + (-8)^2} = \sqrt{25 + 64}$
$= \sqrt{89} \approx 9.4$

b) $d = \sqrt{[-1 - (-1)]^2 + (-5 - 2)^2}$
$= \sqrt{0^2 + (-7)^2} = \sqrt{0 + 49}$
$= \sqrt{49} = 7$

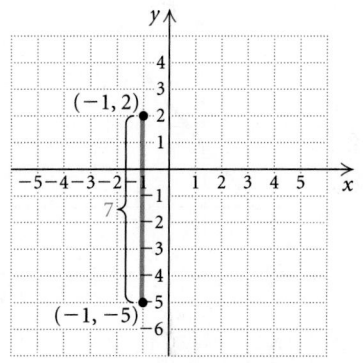

▶ Now Try Exercise 39.

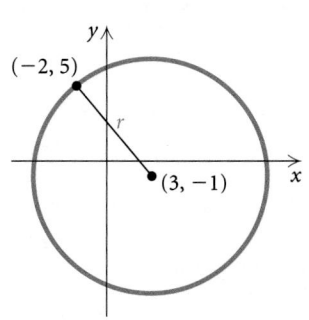

EXAMPLE 7   The point $(-2, 5)$ is on a circle that has $(3, -1)$ as its center. Find the length of the radius of the circle.

Solution   Since the length of the radius is the distance from the center to a point on the circle, we substitute into the distance formula.

$$d = \sqrt{(x_2 - x_1)^2 + (y_2 - y_1)^2};$$
$$r = \sqrt{[3 - (-2)]^2 + (-1 - 5)^2}$$ Substituting r for d, $(3, -1)$ for (x_2, y_2), and $(-2, 5)$ for (x_1, y_1). Either point can serve as (x_1, y_1).
$$= \sqrt{5^2 + (-6)^2} = \sqrt{61} \approx 7.8.$$ Rounded to the nearest tenth

The radius of the circle is approximately 7.8.   ▶ Now Try Exercise 51.

✦ Midpoints of Segments

The distance formula can be used to develop a way of determining the *midpoint* of a segment when the endpoints are known. We state the formula and leave its proof to the exercises.

> **The Midpoint Formula**
>
> If the endpoints of a segment are (x_1, y_1) and (x_2, y_2), then the coordinates of the **midpoint** are
>
> $$\left(\frac{x_1 + x_2}{2}, \frac{y_1 + y_2}{2} \right).$$

Note that we obtain the coordinates of the midpoint by averaging the coordinates of the endpoints. This is a good way to remember the midpoint formula.

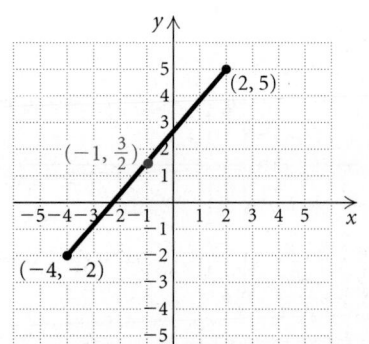

EXAMPLE 8   Find the midpoint of the segment whose endpoints are $(-4, -2)$ and $(2, 5)$.

Solution   Using the midpoint formula, we obtain

$$\left(\frac{-4 + 2}{2}, \frac{-2 + 5}{2} \right) = \left(\frac{-2}{2}, \frac{3}{2} \right) = \left(-1, \frac{3}{2} \right).$$

▶ Now Try Exercise 57.

EXAMPLE 9   The diameter of a circle connects two points $(2, -3)$ and $(6, 4)$ on the circle. Find the coordinates of the center of the circle.

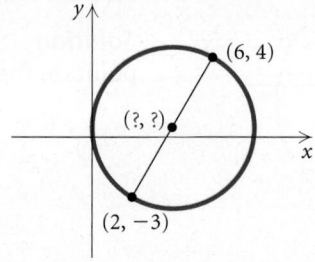

Solution   Since the center of the circle is the midpoint of the diameter, we use the midpoint formula:

$$\left(\frac{2 + 6}{2}, \frac{-3 + 4}{2} \right), \quad \text{or} \quad \left(\frac{8}{2}, \frac{1}{2} \right), \quad \text{or} \quad \left(4, \frac{1}{2} \right).$$

The coordinates of the center are $\left(4, \frac{1}{2} \right)$.

▶ Now Try Exercise 69.

✦ Circles

A **circle** is the set of all points in a plane that are a fixed distance r from a *center* (h, k). Thus if a point (x, y) is to be r units from the center, we must have

$$r = \sqrt{(x - h)^2 + (y - k)^2}.$$ Using the distance formula, $d = \sqrt{(x_2 - x_1)^2 + (y_2 - y_1)^2}$

Squaring both sides gives an equation of a circle. The distance r is the length of a *radius* of the circle.

> **The Equation of a Circle**
>
> The equation of a circle with center (h, k) and radius r, in standard form, is
>
> $$(x - h)^2 + (y - k)^2 = r^2.$$

EXAMPLE 10   Find an equation of the circle having radius 5 and center $(3, -7)$.

Solution   Using the standard form, we have

$$[x - 3]^2 + [y - (-7)]^2 = 5^2$$ Substituting
$$(x - 3)^2 + (y + 7)^2 = 25.$$

▶ Now Try Exercise 71.

EXAMPLE 11   Graph the circle $(x + 5)^2 + (y - 2)^2 = 16$.

Solution   We write the equation in standard form to determine the center and the radius:

$$[x - (-5)]^2 + [y - 2]^2 = 4^2.$$

The center is $(-5, 2)$ and the radius is 4. We locate the center and draw the circle using a compass.

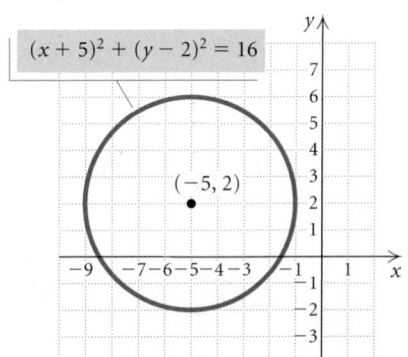

$(x + 5)^2 + (y - 2)^2 = 16$

$(-5, 2)$

▶ Now Try Exercise 83.

TECHNOLOGY ··
    CONNECTION

When we graph a circle, we select a viewing window in which the distance between units is visually the same on both axes. This procedure is called **squaring the viewing window.** We do this so that the graph will not be distorted. A graph of the circle $x^2 + y^2 = 36$ in a nonsquared window is shown in Fig. 1.

$x^2 + y^2 = 36$

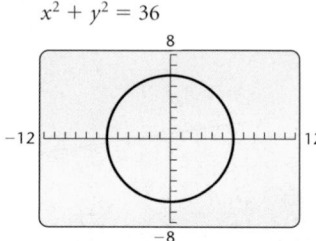

$x^2 + y^2 = 36$

Figure 1   Figure 2

On many graphing calculators, the ratio of the height to the width of the viewing screen is $\frac{2}{3}$. When we choose a window in which Xscl = Yscl and the length of the y-axis is $\frac{2}{3}$ the length of the x-axis, the window will be squared. The windows with dimensions $[-6, 6, -4, 4]$, $[-9, 9, -6, 6]$, and $[-12, 12, -8, 8]$ are examples of squared windows. A graph of the circle $x^2 + y^2 = 36$ in a squared window is shown in Fig. 2. Many graphing calculators have an option on the ZOOM menu that squares the window automatically.

To graph a circle, we can select the CIRCLE feature from the DRAW menu and enter the coordinates of the center and the length of the radius. The graph of the circle $(x - 2)^2 + (y + 1)^2 = 16$ is shown here.

Circle(2,−1,4)

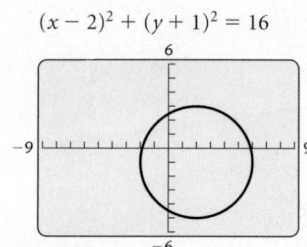

$(x - 2)^2 + (y + 1)^2 = 16$

Other methods for graphing circles will be discussed in Section 6.2.

A

B

C

D

E

Visualizing the Graph

Match the equation with its graph.

1. $y = -x^2 + 5x - 3$

2. $3x - 5y = 15$

3. $(x - 2)^2 + (y - 4)^2 = 36$

4. $y - 5x = -3$

5. $x^2 + y^2 = \dfrac{25}{4}$

6. $15y - 6x = 90$

7. $y = -\dfrac{2}{3}x - 2$

8. $(x + 3)^2 + (y - 1)^2 = 16$

9. $3x + 5y = 15$

10. $y = x^2 - x - 4$

Answers on page A-3

F

G

H

I

J

1.1 EXERCISE SET

Graph and label the given points.

1. $(4,0), (-3,-5), (-1,4), (0,2), (2,-2)$

2. $(1,4), (-4,-2), (-5,0), (2,-4), (4,0)$

3. $(-5,1), (5,1), (2,3), (2,-1), (0,1)$

4. $(4,0), (4,-3), (-5,2), (-5,0), (-1,-5)$

Express the data pictured in the graph as ordered pairs, letting the first coordinate represent the year and the second coordinate the amount.

5. **National Collegiate Athletic Association (NCAA): Total Advertisement Spending for Basketball Tournament**

Source: NCAA

6. **Daily Use of Cigarettes by 12th Graders (Percent Who Smoked Daily in Last 30 Days)**

Source: Monitoring the Future, University of Michigan Institute for Social Research and National Institute on Drug Abuse

Use substitution to determine whether the given ordered pairs are solutions of the given equation.

7. $(1,-1), (0,3); \ y = 2x - 3$

8. $(2,5), (-2,-5); \ y = 3x - 1$

9. $\left(\frac{2}{3},\frac{3}{4}\right), \left(1,\frac{3}{2}\right); \ 6x - 4y = 1$

10. $(1.5,2.6), (-3,0); \ x^2 + y^2 = 9$

11. $\left(-\frac{1}{2},-\frac{4}{5}\right), \left(0,\frac{3}{5}\right); \ 2a + 5b = 3$

12. $\left(0,\frac{3}{2}\right), \left(\frac{2}{3},1\right); \ 3m + 4n = 6$

13. $(-0.75,2.75), (2,-1); \ x^2 - y^2 = 3$

14. $(2,-4), (4,-5); \ 5x + 2y^2 = 70$

Find the intercepts and then graph the line.

15. $5x - 3y = -15$ **16.** $2x - 4y = 8$

17. $2x + y = 4$ **18.** $3x + y = 6$

19. $4y - 3x = 12$ **20.** $3y + 2x = -6$

Graph the equation.

21. $y = 3x + 5$ **22.** $y = -2x - 1$

23. $x - y = 3$ **24.** $x + y = 4$

25. $y = -\frac{3}{4}x + 3$ **26.** $3y - 2x = 3$

27. $5x - 2y = 8$ **28.** $y = 2 - \frac{4}{3}x$

29. $x - 4y = 5$ **30.** $6x - y = 4$

31. $2x + 5y = -10$ **32.** $4x - 3y = 12$

33. $y = -x^2$ **34.** $y = x^2$

35. $y = x^2 - 3$ **36.** $y = 4 - x^2$

37. $y = -x^2 + 2x + 3$ **38.** $y = x^2 + 2x - 1$

Find the distance between the pair of points. Give an exact answer and, where appropriate, an approximation to three decimal places.

39. $(4,6)$ and $(5,9)$ **40.** $(-3,7)$ and $(2,11)$

41. $(6,-1)$ and $(9,5)$ **42.** $(-4,-7)$ and $(-1,3)$

43. $(-4.2,3)$ and $(2.1,-6.4)$

44. $\left(-\frac{3}{5},-4\right)$ and $\left(-\frac{3}{5},\frac{2}{3}\right)$

45. $\left(-\frac{1}{2},4\right)$ and $\left(\frac{5}{2},4\right)$

46. $(0.6,-1.5)$ and $(-8.1,-1.5)$

47. $\left(\sqrt{3},-\sqrt{5}\right)$ and $\left(-\sqrt{6},0\right)$

48. $\left(-\sqrt{2},1\right)$ and $\left(0,\sqrt{7}\right)$

49. $(0, 0)$ and (a, b)

50. (r, s) and $(-r, -s)$

51. The points $(-3, -1)$ and $(9, 4)$ are the endpoints of the diameter of a circle. Find the length of the radius of the circle.

52. The point $(0, 1)$ is on a circle that has center $(-3, 5)$. Find the length of the diameter of the circle.

The converse of the Pythagorean theorem is also a true statement: If the sum of the squares of the lengths of two sides of a triangle is equal to the square of the length of the third side, then the triangle is a right triangle. Use the distance formula and the Pythagorean theorem to determine whether the set of points could be vertices of a right triangle.

53. $(-4, 5)$, $(6, 1)$, and $(-8, -5)$

54. $(-3, 1)$, $(2, -1)$, and $(6, 9)$

55. $(-4, 3)$, $(0, 5)$, and $(3, -4)$

56. The points $(-3, 4)$, $(2, -1)$, $(5, 2)$, and $(0, 7)$ are vertices of a quadrilateral. Show that the quadrilateral is a rectangle. (*Hint:* Show that the quadrilateral's opposite sides are the same length and that the two diagonals are the same length.)

Find the midpoint of the segment having the given endpoints.

57. $(4, -9)$ and $(-12, -3)$

58. $(7, -2)$ and $(9, 5)$

59. $(6.1, -3.8)$ and $(3.8, -6.1)$

60. $(-0.5, -2.7)$ and $(4.8, -0.3)$

61. $(-6, 5)$ and $(-6, 8)$

62. $(1, -2)$ and $(-1, 2)$

63. $\left(-\frac{1}{6}, -\frac{3}{5}\right)$ and $\left(-\frac{2}{3}, \frac{5}{4}\right)$

64. $\left(\frac{2}{9}, \frac{1}{3}\right)$ and $\left(-\frac{2}{5}, \frac{4}{5}\right)$

65. $\left(\sqrt{3}, -1\right)$ and $\left(3\sqrt{3}, 4\right)$

66. $\left(-\sqrt{5}, 2\right)$ and $\left(\sqrt{5}, \sqrt{7}\right)$

67. Graph the rectangle described in Exercise 56. Then determine the coordinates of the midpoint of each of the four sides. Are the midpoints vertices of a rectangle?

68. Graph the square with vertices $(-5, -1)$, $(7, -6)$, $(12, 6)$, and $(0, 11)$. Then determine the midpoint of each of the four sides. Are the midpoints vertices of a square?

69. The points $\left(\sqrt{7}, -4\right)$ and $\left(\sqrt{2}, 3\right)$ are endpoints of the diameter of a circle. Determine the center of the circle.

70. The points $\left(-3, \sqrt{5}\right)$ and $\left(1, \sqrt{2}\right)$ are endpoints of the diagonal of a square. Determine the center of the square.

Find an equation for a circle satisfying the given conditions.

71. Center $(2, 3)$, radius of length $\frac{5}{3}$

72. Center $(4, 5)$, diameter of length 8.2

73. Center $(-1, 4)$, passes through $(3, 7)$

74. Center $(6, -5)$, passes through $(1, 7)$

75. The points $(7, 13)$ and $(-3, -11)$ are at the ends of a diameter.

76. The points $(-9, 4)$, $(-2, 5)$, $(-8, -3)$, and $(-1, -2)$ are vertices of an inscribed square.

77. Center $(-2, 3)$, tangent (touching at one point) to the y-axis

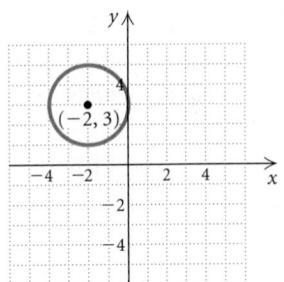

78. Center $(4, -5)$, tangent to the x-axis

Find the center and the radius of the circle. Then graph the circle.

79. $x^2 + y^2 = 4$

80. $x^2 + y^2 = 81$

81. $x^2 + (y - 3)^2 = 16$

82. $(x + 2)^2 + y^2 = 100$

83. $(x - 1)^2 + (y - 5)^2 = 36$

84. $(x - 7)^2 + (y + 2)^2 = 25$

85. $(x + 4)^2 + (y + 5)^2 = 9$

86. $(x + 1)^2 + (y - 2)^2 = 64$

Find the equation of the circle. Express the equation in standard form.

87.

88.

89.

90.

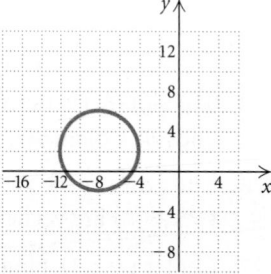

Technology Connection

In Exercises 91–94, use a graphing calculator to match the equation with one of the graphs (a)–(d), which follow.

a)

b)

c)

d)

91. $y = 3 - x$

92. $2x - y = 6$

93. $y = x^2 + 2x + 1$

94. $y = 8 - x^2$

Use a graphing calculator to graph the equation in the standard window.

95. $4x + y = 7$

96. $5x + y = -8$

97. $y = \frac{1}{3}x + 2$

98. $y = \frac{3}{2}x - 4$

99. $y = x^2 + 6$

100. $y = 5 - x^2$

101. $y = 2 - x^2$

102. $y = x^2 - 5x + 3$

Graph the equation in the standard window and in the given window. Determine which window better shows the shape of the graph and the x- and y-intercepts.

103. $y = 3x^2 - 6$
$[-4, 4, -4, 4]$

104. $y = -2x + 24$
$[-15, 15, -10, 30]$, with Xscl $= 3$ and Yscl $= 5$

105. $y = -\frac{1}{6}x^2 + \frac{1}{12}$
$[-1, 1, -0.3, 0.3]$, with Xscl $= 0.1$ and Yscl $= 0.1$

106. $y = 6 - x^2$
$[-3, 3, -3, 3]$

In Exercises 107 and 108, how would you change the window so that the circle is not distorted? Answers may vary.

107.   108.
$(x + 3)^2 + (y - 2)^2 = 36$ $(x - 4)^2 + (y + 5)^2 = 49$

109.–112. Using a graphing calculator, graph each of the circles given in Exercises 79, 82, 83, and 86, respectively.

Collaborative Discussion and Writing

To the student and the instructor: The Collaborative Discussion and Writing exercises are meant to be answered with one or more sentences. They can be discussed and answered collaboratively by the entire class or by small groups. Because of their open-ended nature, the answers to these exercises do not appear at the back of the book. They are denoted by the words "Discussion and Writing."

113. Explain how the Pythagorean theorem is used to develop the equation of a circle in standard form.

114. Explain how you could find the coordinates of a point $\frac{7}{8}$ of the way from point A to point B.

Synthesis

To the student and the instructor: The Synthesis exercises found at the end of every exercise set challenge students to combine concepts or skills studied in that section or in preceding parts of the text.

115. If the point (p, q) is in the fourth quadrant, in which quadrant is the point $(q, -p)$?

Find the distance between the pair of points and find the midpoint of the segment having the given points as endpoints.

116. $\left(a, \dfrac{1}{a}\right)$ and $\left(a + h, \dfrac{1}{a + h}\right)$

117. $\left(a, \sqrt{a}\right)$ and $\left(a + h, \sqrt{a + h}\right)$

Find an equation of a circle satisfying the given conditions.

118. Center $(-5, 8)$ with a circumference of 10π units

119. Center $(2, -7)$ with an area of 36π square units

120. Find the point on the x-axis that is equidistant from the points $(-4, -3)$ and $(-1, 5)$.

121. Find the point on the y-axis that is equidistant from the points $(-2, 0)$ and $(4, 6)$.

122. Determine whether $(-1, -3), (-4, -9)$, and $(2, 3)$ are collinear.

123. *Swimming Pool.* A swimming pool is being constructed in the corner of a yard, as shown. Before installation, the contractor needs to know measurements a_1 and a_2. Find them.

124. *An Arch of a Circle in Carpentry.* Ace Carpentry needs to cut an arch for the top of an entranceway. The arch needs to be 8 ft wide and 2 ft high. To draw the arch, the carpenters will use a stretched string with chalk attached at an end as a compass.

a) Using a coordinate system, locate the center of the circle.

b) What radius should the carpenters use to draw the arch?

*Determine whether each of the following points lies on the **unit circle**, $x^2 + y^2 = 1$.*

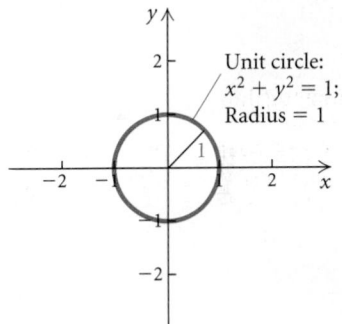

125. $\left(\dfrac{\sqrt{3}}{2}, -\dfrac{1}{2}\right)$ **126.** $(0, -1)$

127. $\left(-\dfrac{\sqrt{2}}{2}, \dfrac{\sqrt{2}}{2}\right)$ **128.** $\left(\dfrac{1}{2}, -\dfrac{\sqrt{3}}{2}\right)$

129. Prove the midpoint formula by showing that:

a) $\left(\dfrac{x_1 + x_2}{2}, \dfrac{y_1 + y_2}{2}\right)$ is equidistant from the points (x_1, y_1) and (x_2, y_2); and

b) the distance from (x_1, y_1) to the midpoint plus the distance from (x_2, y_2) to the midpoint equals the distance from (x_1, y_1) to (x_2, y_2).

130. Consider any right triangle with base b and height h, situated as shown. Show that the midpoint of the hypotenuse P is equidistant from the three vertices of the triangle.

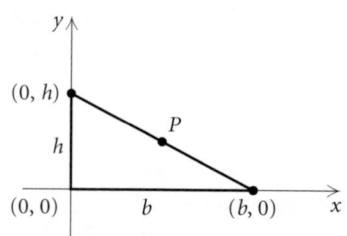

1.2

Functions and Graphs

◆ Determine whether a correspondence or a relation is a function.
◆ Find function values, or outputs, using a formula or a graph.
◆ Graph functions.
◆ Determine whether a graph is that of a function.
◆ Find the domain and the range of a function.
◆ Solve applied problems using functions.

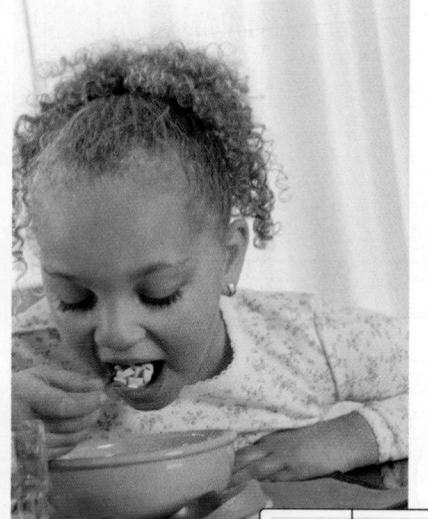

We now focus our attention on a concept that is fundamental to many areas of mathematics—the idea of a *function*.

◆ Functions

We first consider an application.

Child's Age Related to Recommended Daily Amount of Fiber. The recommended minimum amount of dietary fiber needed each day for children age 3 and older is the child's age, in years, plus 5 grams of fiber. If a child is 7 years old, the minimum recommendation per day is $7 + 5$, or 12, grams of fiber. Similarly, a 3-year-old needs $3 + 5$, or 8, grams of fiber. (*Sources: American Family Physician,* April 1996; American Health Foundation) We can express this relationship with a set of ordered pairs, a graph, and an equation.

x	y	Ordered Pairs: (x, y)	Correspondence
3	8	$(3, 8)$	$3 \longrightarrow 8$
$4\frac{1}{2}$	$9\frac{1}{2}$	$\left(4\frac{1}{2}, 9\frac{1}{2}\right)$	$4\frac{1}{2} \longrightarrow 9\frac{1}{2}$
7	12	$(7, 12)$	$7 \longrightarrow 12$
$10\frac{2}{3}$	$15\frac{2}{3}$	$\left(10\frac{2}{3}, 15\frac{2}{3}\right)$	$10\frac{2}{3} \longrightarrow 15\frac{2}{3}$
14	19	$(14, 19)$	$14 \longrightarrow 19$

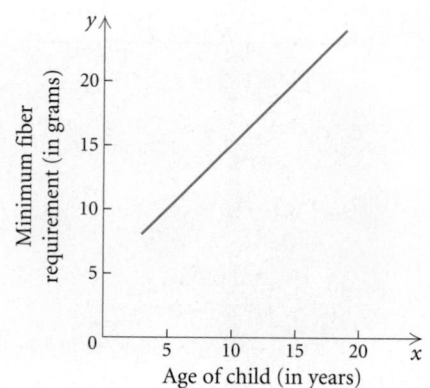

The ordered pairs express a relationship, or correspondence, between the first and second coordinates. We can see this relationship in the graph as well. The equation that describes the correspondence is

$$y = x + 5.$$

This is an example of a *function*. In this case, grams of fiber y is a function of age x; that is, y is a function of x, where x is the independent variable and y is the dependent variable.

Let's consider some other correspondences before giving the definition of a function.

Domain		Range
To each registered student	there corresponds	an I. D. number.
To each mountain bike sold	there corresponds	its price.
To each number between −3 and 3	there corresponds	the square of that number.

In each correspondence, the first set is called the **domain** and the second set is called the **range.** For each member, or **element,** in the domain, there is *exactly one* member in the range to which it corresponds. Thus each registered student has exactly *one* I. D. number, each mountain bike has exactly *one* price, and each number between −3 and 3 has exactly *one* square. Each correspondence is a *function*.

> **Function**
>
> A **function** is a correspondence between a first set, called the **domain,** and a second set, called the **range,** such that each member of the domain corresponds to *exactly one* member of the range.

It is important to note that not every correspondence between two sets is a function.

EXAMPLE 1 Determine whether each of the following correspondences is a function.

a)
$$\begin{matrix} -6 \\ 6 \end{matrix} \searrow\!\!\!\nearrow\; 36$$
$$\begin{matrix} -3 \\ 3 \end{matrix} \searrow\!\!\!\nearrow\; 9$$
$$0 \longrightarrow 0$$

b)
Jamie Foxx ⟶ *Ray*
Joaquin Phoenix ⟶ *Cinderella Man*
Samuel L. Jackson ⟶ *Walk the Line*
Paul Giamatti ⟶ *Coach Carter*
Reese Witherspoon ⟶ *Star Wars: Episode III— Revenge of the Sith*

Solution

a) This correspondence *is* a function because each member of the domain corresponds to exactly one member of the range. Note that the definition of a function allows more than one member of the domain to correspond to the same member of the range.

b) This correspondence *is not* a function because there is a member of the domain (Samuel L. Jackson) that is paired with more than one member of the range (*Coach Carter* and *Star Wars: Episode III—Revenge of the Sith*).

▷ Now Try Exercise 7.

EXAMPLE 2   Determine whether each of the following correspondences is a function.

DOMAIN	CORRESPONDENCE	RANGE
a) Years in which a presidential election occurs	The person elected	A set of presidents
b) The integers	Each integer's cube root	A subset of the real numbers
c) All states in the United States	A senator from that state	The set of all U.S. senators
d) The set of all U.S. senators	The state a senator represents	All states in the United States

Solution

a) This correspondence *is* a function, because in each presidential election *exactly one* president is elected.

b) This correspondence *is* a function, because each integer has *exactly one* cube root.

c) This correspondence *is not* a function, because each state can be paired with *two* different senators.

Wayne Allard

Ken Salazar

d) This correspondence *is* a function, because each senator represents only one state.

▷ Now Try Exercise 11.

Although a correspondence between two sets may not be a function, it is still an example of a **relation.**

> ### Relation
> A **relation** is a correspondence between a first set, called the **domain,** and a second set, called the **range,** such that each member of the domain corresponds to *at least one* member of the range.

All the correspondences in Examples 1 and 2 are relations, but, as we have seen, not all are functions. Relations are sometimes written as sets of ordered pairs (as we saw earlier in the example on dietary fiber) in which elements of the domain are the first coordinates of the ordered pairs and elements of the range are the second coordinates. For example, instead of writing $-3 \longrightarrow 9$, as we did in Example 1(a), we could write the ordered pair $(-3, 9)$.

EXAMPLE 3   Determine whether each of the following relations is a function. Identify the domain and the range.

a) $\{(9, -5), (9, 5), (2, 4)\}$
b) $\{(-2, 5), (5, 7), (0, 1), (4, -2)\}$
c) $\{(-5, 3), (0, 3), (6, 3)\}$

Solution

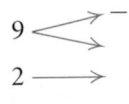

Figure 1

a) The relation *is not* a function because the ordered pairs $(9, -5)$ and $(9, 5)$ have the same first coordinate and different second coordinates (see Fig. 1).

The domain is the set of all first coordinates: $\{9, 2\}$.

The range is the set of all second coordinates: $\{-5, 5, 4\}$.

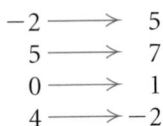

Figure 2

b) The relation *is* a function because *no* two ordered pairs have the same first coordinate and different second coordinates (see Fig. 2).

The domain is the set of all first coordinates: $\{-2, 5, 0, 4\}$.

The range is the set of all second coordinates: $\{5, 7, 1, -2\}$.

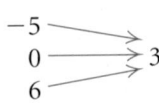

Figure 3

c) The relation *is* a function because *no* two ordered pairs have the same first coordinate and different second coordinates (see Fig. 3).

The domain is $\{-5, 0, 6\}$.

The range is $\{3\}$.

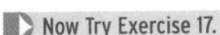
Now Try Exercise 17.

✦ Notation for Functions

Functions used in mathematics are often given by equations. They generally require that certain calculations be performed in order to determine which member of the range is paired with each member of the domain.

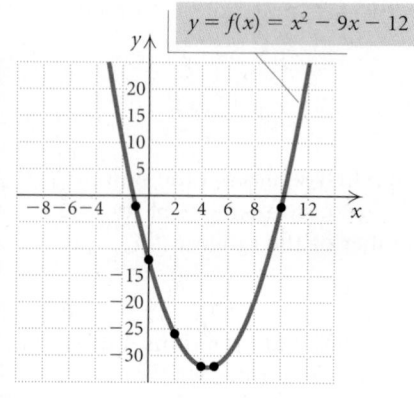

$y = f(x) = x^2 - 9x - 12$

For example, in Section 1.1 we graphed the function $y = x^2 - 9x - 12$ by doing calculations like the following:

$$\text{for } x = -2, \; y = (-2)^2 - 9(-2) - 12 = 10,$$
$$\text{for } x = 0, \; y = 0^2 - 9 \cdot 0 - 12 = -12, \quad \text{and}$$
$$\text{for } x = 1, \; y = 1^2 - 9 \cdot 1 - 12 = -20.$$

A more concise notation is often used. For $y = x^2 - 9x - 12$, the **inputs** (members of the domain) are values of x substituted into the equation. The **outputs** (members of the range) are the resulting values of y. If we call the function f, we can use x to represent an arbitrary *input* and $f(x)$—read "f of x," or "f at x," or "the value of f at x"—to represent the corresponding *output*. In this notation, the function given by $y = x^2 - 9x - 12$ is written as $f(x) = x^2 - 9x - 12$ and the above calculations would be

$$f(-2) = (-2)^2 - 9(-2) - 12 = 10,$$
$$f(0) = 0^2 - 9 \cdot 0 - 12 = -12,$$
$$f(1) = 1^2 - 9 \cdot 1 - 12 = -20.$$

Keep in mind that $f(x)$ does *not* mean $f \cdot x$.

Thus, instead of writing "when $x = -2$, the value of y is 10," we can simply write "$f(-2) = 10$," which can be read as "f of -2 is 10" or "for the input -2, the output of f is 10." The letters g and h are also often used to name functions.

EXAMPLE 4 A function f is given by $f(x) = 2x^2 - x + 3$. Find each of the following.

a) $f(0)$ **b)** $f(-7)$
c) $f(5a)$ **d)** $f(a - 4)$

Solution   We can think of this formula as follows:

$$f(\;\blacksquare\;) = 2(\;\blacksquare\;)^2 - (\;\blacksquare\;) + 3.$$

Then to find an output for a given input we think: "Whatever goes in the blank on the left goes in the blanks on the right." This gives us a "recipe" for finding outputs.

a) $f(0) = 2(0)^2 - 0 + 3 = 0 - 0 + 3 = 3$
b) $f(-7) = 2(-7)^2 - (-7) + 3 = 2 \cdot 49 + 7 + 3 = 108$
c) $f(5a) = 2(5a)^2 - 5a + 3 = 2 \cdot 25a^2 - 5a + 3 = 50a^2 - 5a + 3$
d) $f(a - 4) = 2(a - 4)^2 - (a - 4) + 3$
$$= 2(a^2 - 8a + 16) - (a - 4) + 3$$
$$= 2a^2 - 16a + 32 - a + 4 + 3$$
$$= 2a^2 - 17a + 39$$

▶ Now Try Exercise 27.

TECHNOLOGY ·················
          CONNECTION

We can find function values with a graphing calculator. Below, we illustrate finding $f(-7)$ from Example 4(b), first with the TABLE feature set in ASK mode and then with the VALUE feature from the CALC menu. In both screens, we see that $f(-7) = 108$.

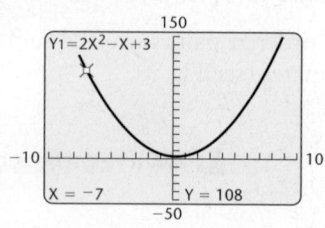

✦ Graphs of Functions

We graph functions the same way we graph equations. We find ordered pairs (x, y), or $(x, f(x))$, plot points, and complete the graph.

EXAMPLE 5 Graph each of the following functions.

a) $f(x) = x^2 - 5$
b) $f(x) = x^3 - x$
c) $f(x) = \sqrt{x + 4}$

Solution We select values for x and find the corresponding values of $f(x)$. Then we plot the points and connect them with a smooth curve.

a) $f(x) = x^2 - 5$

x	$f(x)$	$(x, f(x))$
-3	4	$(-3, 4)$
-2	-1	$(-2, -1)$
-1	-4	$(-1, -4)$
0	-5	$(0, -5)$
1	-4	$(1, -4)$
2	-1	$(2, -1)$
3	4	$(3, 4)$

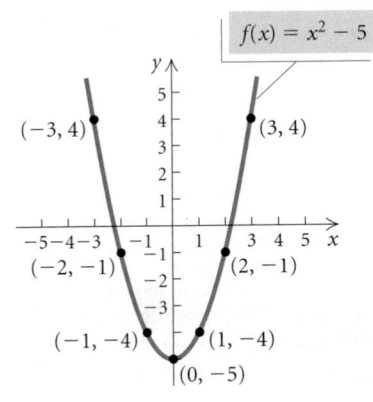

b) $f(x) = x^3 - x$

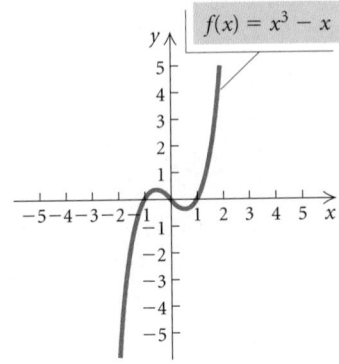

c) $f(x) = \sqrt{x + 4}$

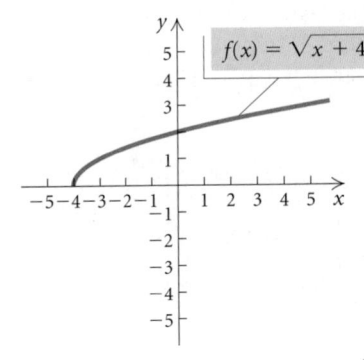

Function values can be also determined from a graph.

EXAMPLE 6 For the function $f(x) = x^2 - 5$, use the graph to find each of the following function values.

a) $f(3)$ **b)** $f(-2)$

Solution

a) To find the function value $f(3)$ from the graph at left, we locate the input 3 on the horizontal axis, move vertically to the graph of the function, and then move horizontally to find the output on the vertical axis. We see that $f(3) = 4$.

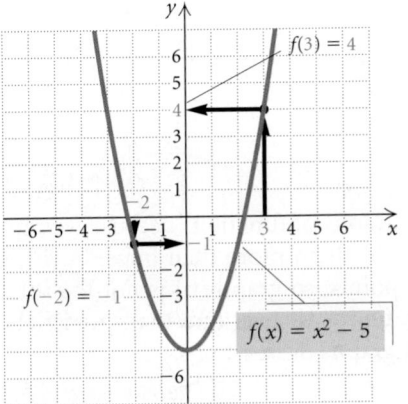

b) To find the function value $f(-2)$, we locate the input -2 on the horizontal axis, move vertically to the graph, and then move horizontally to find the output on the vertical axis. We see that $f(-2) = -1$.

 Now Try Exercise 21.

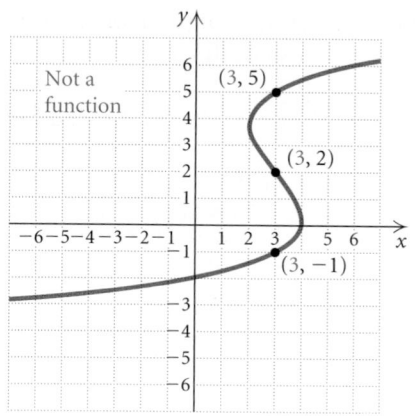

Since 3 is paired with more than one member of the range, the graph does not represent a function.

We know that when one member of the domain is paired with two or more different members of the range, the correspondence *is not* a function. Thus, when a graph contains two or more different points with the same first coordinate, the graph cannot represent a function (see the graph at left; note that 3 is paired with -1, 2, and 5). Points sharing a common first coordinate are vertically above or below each other. This leads us to the *vertical-line test.*

The Vertical-Line Test

If it is possible for a vertical line to cross a graph more than once, then the graph is *not* the graph of a function.

To apply the vertical-line test, we try to find a vertical line that crosses the graph more than once. If we succeed, then the graph is not that of a function. If we do not, then the graph is that of a function.

EXAMPLE 7   Which of the following graphs (a)–(f) (in red) are graphs of functions? In graph (f), the solid dot shows that $(-1, 1)$ belongs to the graph. The open circle shows that $(-1, -2)$ does *not* belong to the graph.

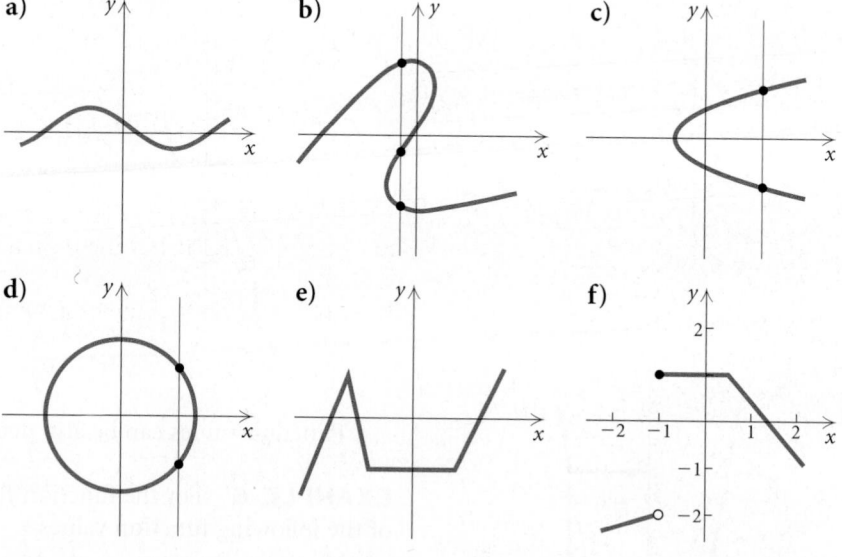

Solution   Graphs (a), (e), and (f) are graphs of functions because we cannot find a vertical line that crosses any of them more than once. In (b), a vertical line crosses the graph at three points, so graph (b) is not that of a function. Also, in (c) and (d), we can find a vertical line that crosses the graph more than once, so these are not graphs of functions.

 Now Try Exercise 41.

✦ Finding Domains of Functions

When a function f, whose inputs and outputs are real numbers, is given by a formula, the *domain* is understood to be the set of all inputs for which the expression is defined as a real number. When a substitution results in an expression that is not defined as a real number, we say that the function value *does not exist* and that the number being substituted *is not* in the domain of the function.

EXAMPLE 8   Find the indicated function values and determine whether the given values are in the domain of the function.

a) $f(1)$ and $f(3)$, for $f(x) = \dfrac{1}{x - 3}$

b) $g(16)$ and $g(-7)$, for $g(x) = \sqrt{x} + 5$

Solution

a) $f(1) = \dfrac{1}{1 - 3} = \dfrac{1}{-2} = -\dfrac{1}{2};$

Since $f(1)$ is defined, 1 is in the domain of f.

$f(3) = \dfrac{1}{3 - 3} = \dfrac{1}{0}$

Since division by 0 is not defined, the number 3 is not in the domain of f.

b) $g(16) = \sqrt{16} + 5 = 4 + 5 = 9;$

Since $g(16)$ is defined, 16 is in the domain of g.

$g(-7) = \sqrt{-7} + 5$

Since $\sqrt{-7}$ is not defined as a real number, the number -7 is not in the domain of g. ◀

Inputs that make a denominator 0 or that yield a negative radicand in an even root are not in the domain of a function.

EXAMPLE 9   Find the domain of each of the following functions.

a) $f(x) = \dfrac{1}{x - 3}$

b) $g(x) = \sqrt{3 - x} + 5$

c) $h(x) = \dfrac{3x^2 - x + 7}{x^2 + 2x - 3}$

d) $f(x) = x^3 + |x|$

Solution

a) The only input that results in a denominator of 0 is 3. The domain is $\{x \mid x \neq 3\}$. We can also write the solution using interval notation and the symbol $\cup$ for the **union,** or inclusion, of both sets: $(-\infty, 3) \cup (3, \infty)$.

b) We can substitute any number for which the radicand is nonnegative, that is, for which $3 - x \geq 0$, or $x \leq 3$. Thus the domain is $\{x \mid x \leq 3\}$, or $(-\infty, 3]$.

TECHNOLOGY
CONNECTION

When we use a graphing calculator to find function values and a function value does not exist, the calculator indicates this with an ERROR message.

In the tables below, we see in Example 8 that $f(3)$ for $f(x) = 1/(x - 3)$ and $g(-7)$ for $g(x) = \sqrt{x} + 5$ do not exist. Thus, 3 and -7 are *not* in the domains of the corresponding functions.

$y = 1/(x - 3)$

X	Y1
1	−.5
3	ERROR

X =

$y = \sqrt{x} + 5$

X	Y1
16	9
−7	ERROR

X =

INTERVAL NOTATION

REVIEW SECTION **R.1.**

c) We can substitute any real number in the numerator, but we must avoid inputs that make the denominator 0. To find those inputs, we solve $x^2 + 2x - 3 = 0$, or $(x + 3)(x - 1) = 0$. Since $x^2 + 2x - 3$ is 0 for -3 and 1, the domain consists of the set of all real numbers except -3 and 1, or $\{x \mid x \neq -3 \text{ and } x \neq 1\}$, or $(-\infty, -3) \cup (-3, 1) \cup (1, \infty)$.

d) We can substitute any real number for x. The domain is the set of all real numbers, $\mathbb{R}$, or $(-\infty, \infty)$.

▶ Now Try Exercise 47.

✦ Visualizing Domain and Range

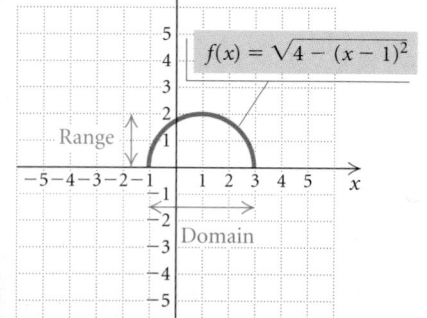

Keep the following in mind regarding the *graph* of a function:

Domain = the set of a function's inputs, found on the horizontal axis;

Range = the set of a function's outputs, found on the vertical axis.

By carefully examining the graph of a function, we may be able to determine the function's domain as well as its range. Consider the graph of $f(x) = \sqrt{4 - (x - 1)^2}$, shown at left. We look for the inputs on the x-axis that correspond to a point on the graph. We see that they extend from -1 to 3, inclusive. Thus the domain is $\{x \mid -1 \leq x \leq 3\}$, or $[-1, 3]$.

To find the range, we look for the outputs on the y-axis. We see that they extend from 0 to 2, inclusive. Thus the range of this function is $\{y \mid 0 \leq y \leq 2\}$, or $[0, 2]$.

EXAMPLE 10 Graph each of the following functions. Then estimate the domain and the range of each.

a) $f(x) = \sqrt{x + 4}$

b) $f(x) = x^3 - x$

c) $f(x) = \dfrac{1}{x - 2}$

d) $f(x) = x^4 - 2x^2 - 3$

Solution

a)

Domain $= [-4, \infty)$;
range $= [0, \infty)$

b)

Domain $=$ all real numbers, $(-\infty, \infty)$; range $=$ all real numbers, $(-\infty, \infty)$

c)

$$f(x) = \frac{1}{x - 2}$$

d)

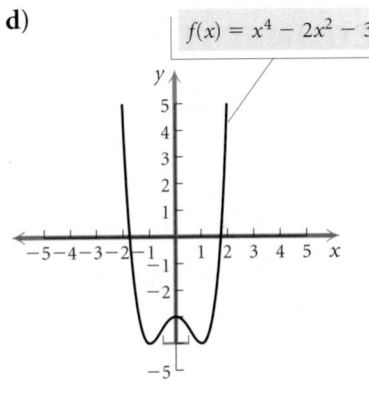

$$f(x) = x^4 - 2x^2 - 3$$

Since the graph does not touch or cross either the vertical line $x = 2$ or the x-axis ($y = 0$), 2 is excluded from the domain and 0 is excluded from the range. Domain $= (-\infty, 2) \cup (2, \infty)$; range $= (-\infty, 0) \cup (0, \infty)$

Domain $=$ all real numbers, $(-\infty, \infty)$; range $= [-4, \infty)$

▶ Now Try Exercise 71.

Always consider adding the reasoning of Example 9 to a graphical analysis. Think, "What can I substitute?" to find the domain. Think, "What do I get out?" to find the range. Thus, in Examples 10(b) and 10(d), it might not appear as though the domain is all real numbers because the graph rises steeply, but by examining the equation we see that we can indeed substitute any real number for x.

◆ Applications of Functions

EXAMPLE 11 *Speed of Sound in Air.* The speed S of sound in air is a function of the temperature t, in degrees Fahrenheit, and is given by

$$S(t) = 1087.7 \sqrt{\frac{5t + 2457}{2457}},$$

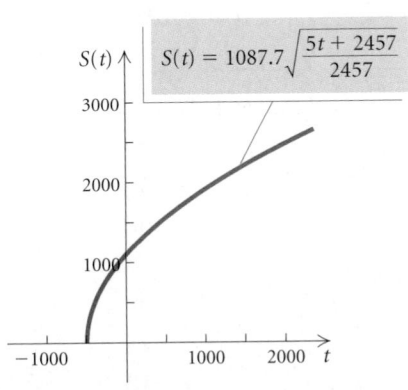

$$S(t) = 1087.7 \sqrt{\frac{5t + 2457}{2457}}$$

where S is in feet per second. Find the speed of sound in air when the temperature is $0°$, $32°$, $70°$, and $-10°$ Fahrenheit.

Solution   Using a calculator, we compute the function values. We find that

$$S(0) = 1087.7 \text{ ft/sec},$$
$$S(32) \approx 1122.6 \text{ ft/sec},$$
$$S(70) \approx 1162.6 \text{ ft/sec}, \quad \text{and}$$
$$S(-10) \approx 1076.6 \text{ ft/sec}.$$

We can visualize these values using the graph at left.

▶ Now Try Exercise 73.

CONNECTING THE CONCEPTS

FUNCTION CONCEPTS	GRAPH

FUNCTION CONCEPTS

Formula for f: $f(x) = 5 + 2x^2 - x^4$.

For every input, there is exactly one output.

$(1, 6)$ is on the graph.

For the input 1, the output is 6.

$f(1) = 6$

Domain: set of all inputs = $(-\infty, \infty)$

Range: set of all outputs = $(-\infty, 6]$

GRAPH

•••

 1.2   EXERCISE SET

In Exercises 1–14, determine whether the correspondence is a function.

1. $a \longrightarrow w$
$b \longrightarrow y$
$c \longrightarrow z$

2. $m \longrightarrow q$
$n \longrightarrow r$
$o \longrightarrow s$

3. $-6 \longrightarrow 36$
$-2 \longrightarrow 4$
2

4. $-3 \longrightarrow 2$
$1 \longrightarrow 4$
$5 \longrightarrow 6$
$9 \longrightarrow 8$

5. $m \longrightarrow A$
$n \quad B$
$r \quad C$
$s \quad D$

6. $a \longrightarrow r$
$b \quad s$
$c \quad t$
d

7.

ANIMAL	MAXIMUM SPEED ON THE GROUND (IN MILES PER HOUR)
Cheetah	70
Lion	50
Zebra	40
Reindeer	32
Giraffe	
Grizzly bear	30
Elephant	25
Squirrel	12
Giant tortoise	0.17

(*Source: The World Almanac*, 2006, p. 307)

8. WORLD'S TEN LARGEST EARTHQUAKES (1900–2005)

LOCATION AND DATE	MAGNITUDE
Chile (May 22, 1960)	→ 9.5
Prince William Sound, Alaska (March 28, 1964)	→ 9.2
Andreanof Islands, Aleutian Islands (March 9, 1957)	→ 9.1
Kamchatka (November 4, 1952)	→ 9.0
Off the coast of Sumatra, Indonesia (December 26, 2004)	
Off the coast of Ecuador (January 31, 1906)	→ 8.8
Rat Islands, Aleutian Islands (February 4, 1965)	→ 8.7
Northern Sumatra, Indonesia (March 28, 2005)	
India–China border (August 15, 1950)	→ 8.6
Kamchatka (February 3, 1923)	→ 8.5

(*Source*: National Earthquake Information Center, U.S. Geological Survey)

	DOMAIN	CORRESPONDENCE	RANGE
9.	A set of cars in a parking lot	Each car's license number	A set of letters and numbers
10.	A set of people in a town	A doctor a person uses	A set of doctors
11.	A set of members of a family	Each person's eye color	A set of colors
12.	A set of members of a rock band	An instrument each person plays	A set of instruments
13.	A set of students in a class	A student sitting in a neighboring seat	A set of students
14.	A set of bags of chips on a shelf	Each bag's weight	A set of weights

Determine whether the relation is a function. Identify the domain and the range.

15. $\{(2, 10), (3, 15), (4, 20)\}$

16. $\{(3, 1), (5, 1), (7, 1)\}$

17. $\{(-7, 3), (-2, 1), (-2, 4), (0, 7)\}$

18. $\{(1, 3), (1, 5), (1, 7), (1, 9)\}$

19. $\{(-2, 1), (0, 1), (2, 1), (4, 1), (-3, 1)\}$

20. $\{(5, 0), (3, -1), (0, 0), (5, -1), (3, -2)\}$

A graph of a function is shown. Using the graph, find the indicated function values; that is, given the input, find the output.

21. $h(1)$, $h(3)$, and $h(4)$

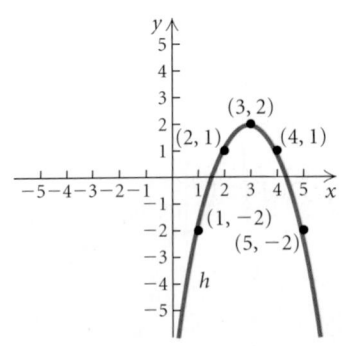

22. $t(-4)$, $t(0)$, and $t(3)$

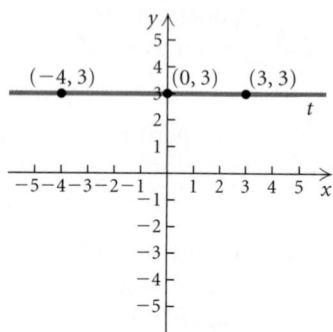

23. $s(-4)$, $s(-2)$, and $s(0)$

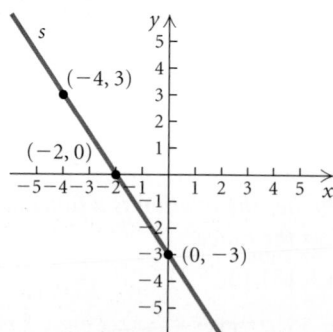

24. $g(-4)$, $g(-1)$, and $g(0)$

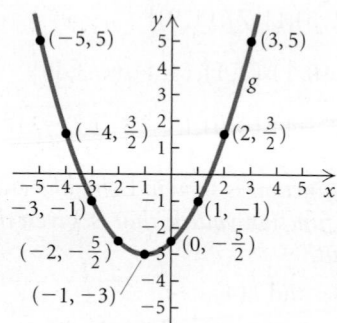

25. $f(-1)$, $f(0)$, and $f(1)$

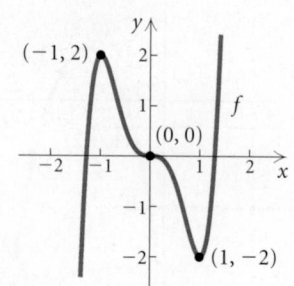

26. $g(-2)$, $g(0)$, and $g(2.4)$

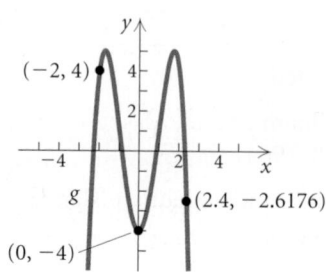

27. Given that $g(x) = 3x^2 - 2x + 1$, find each of the following.
  a) $g(0)$ **b)** $g(-1)$
  c) $g(3)$ **d)** $g(-x)$
  e) $g(1 - t)$

28. Given that $f(x) = 5x^2 + 4x$, find each of the following.
  a) $f(0)$ **b)** $f(-1)$
  c) $f(3)$ **d)** $f(t)$
  e) $f(t - 1)$

29. Given that $g(x) = x^3$, find each of the following.
  a) $g(2)$ **b)** $g(-2)$
  c) $g(-x)$ **d)** $g(3y)$
  e) $g(2 + h)$

30. Given that $f(x) = 2|x| + 3x$, find each of the following.
  a) $f(1)$ **b)** $f(-2)$
  c) $f(-x)$ **d)** $f(2y)$
  e) $f(2 - h)$

31. Given that $g(x) = \dfrac{x - 4}{x + 3}$, find each of the following.
  a) $g(5)$ **b)** $g(4)$
  c) $g(-3)$ **d)** $g(-16.25)$
  e) $g(x + h)$

32. Given that $f(x) = \dfrac{x}{2 - x}$, find each of the following.
  a) $f(2)$ **b)** $f(1)$
  c) $f(-16)$ **d)** $f(-x)$
  e) $f\left(-\dfrac{2}{3}\right)$

33. Find $g(0)$, $g(-1)$, $g(5)$, and $g\left(\frac{1}{2}\right)$ for

$$g(x) = \frac{x}{\sqrt{1 - x^2}}.$$

34. Find $h(0)$, $h(2)$, and $h(-x)$ for

$$h(x) = x + \sqrt{x^2 - 1}.$$

In Exercises 35–42, determine whether the graph is that of a function. An open dot indicates that the point does not belong to the graph.

35.

36.

37.

38.

39.

40.

41.

42.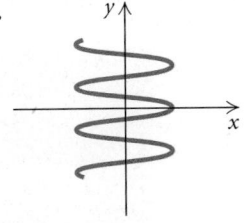

Find the domain of the function.

43. $f(x) = 7x + 4$

44. $f(x) = |3x - 2|$

45. $f(x) = 4 - \dfrac{2}{x}$

46. $f(x) = \dfrac{1}{x^4}$

47. $f(x) = \dfrac{x + 5}{2 - x}$

48. $f(x) = \dfrac{8}{x + 4}$

49. $f(x) = \dfrac{1}{x^2 - 4x - 5}$

50. $f(x) = \dfrac{x^4 - 2x^3 + 7}{3x^2 - 10x - 8}$

51. $f(x) = \sqrt{8 - x}$

52. $f(x) = x^2 - 2x$

53. $f(x) = \frac{1}{10}|x|$

54. $f(x) = \dfrac{\sqrt{x + 1}}{x}$

In Exercises 55–62, determine the domain and the range of the function.

55.

56.

57.

58.

59.

60.

61.

62.

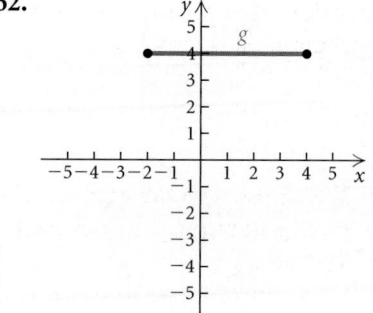

Graph the function. Then visually estimate the domain and the range.

63. $f(x) = |x|$

64. $f(x) = |x| - 2$

65. $f(x) = \sqrt{9 - x^2}$

66. $f(x) = -\sqrt{25 - x^2}$

67. $f(x) = (x - 1)^3 + 2$

68. $f(x) = (x - 2)^4 + 1$

69. $f(x) = \sqrt{7 - x}$

70. $f(x) = \sqrt{x + 8}$

71. $f(x) = -x^2 + 4x - 1$

72. $f(x) = 2x^2 - x^4 + 5$

73. *Boiling Point and Elevation.* The elevation E, in meters, above sea level at which the boiling point of water is t degrees Celsius is given by the function
$$E(t) = 1000(100 - t) + 580(100 - t)^2.$$
At what elevation is the boiling point 99.5°? 100°?

74. *Decreasing Value of the Dollar.* In 2005, it took $19.37 to equal the value of $1 in 1913. In 1990, it took only $13.20 to equal the value of $1 in 1913. The amount it takes to equal the value of $1 in 1913 can be estimated by the linear function V given by
$$V(x) = 0.4123x + 13.2617,$$
where x is the number of years since 1990. Thus, $V(11)$ gives the amount it took in 2001 to equal the value of $1 in 1913.

Source: U.S. Bureau of Labor Statistics

a) Use this function to predict the amount it will take in 2008 and in 2015 to equal the value of $1 in 1913.

b) When will it take approximately $30 to equal the value of $1 in 1913?

75. *Territorial Area of an Animal.* The territorial area of an animal is defined to be its defended, or exclusive, region. For example, a lion has a certain region over which it is considered ruler. It has been shown that the territorial area T, in acres, of predatory animals is a function of body weight w, in pounds, and is given by the function
$$T(w) = w^{1.31}.$$
Find the territorial area of animals whose body weights are 0.5 lb, 10 lb, 20 lb, 100 lb, and 200 lb.

Technology Connection

In Exercises 76–78, use a graphing calculator and the TABLE *feature set in* ASK *mode.*

76. Given that
$$h(x) = 3x^4 - 10x^3 + 5x^2 - x + 6,$$
find $h(-11)$, $h(7)$, and $h(15)$.

77. Given that
$$g(x) = 0.06x^3 - 5.2x^2 - 0.8x,$$
find $g(-2.1)$, $g(5.08)$, and $g(10.003)$. Round answers to the nearest tenth.

78. Find the indicated function values if they exist.

a) $f(-4)$ and $f(-6)$, for $f(x) = \dfrac{4}{(x-4)(x+6)}$

b) $g(-5)$ and $g(1)$, for $g(x) = \sqrt{x-1} + 3$

Collaborative Discussion and Writing

79. Explain in your own words what a function is.

80. Explain in your own words the difference between the domain of a function and the range of a function.

Skill Maintenance

To the student and the instructor: The Skill Maintenance exercises review skills covered previously in the text. You can expect such exercises in every exercise set. They provide excellent review for a final examination. Answers to all skill maintenance exercises, along with section references, appear in the answer section at the back of the book.

Use substitution to determine whether the given ordered pairs are solutions of the given equation.

81. $(0, -7)$, $(8, 11)$; $y = 0.5x + 7$

82. $\left(\frac{4}{5}, -2\right)$, $\left(\frac{11}{5}, \frac{1}{10}\right)$; $15x - 10y = 32$

Graph the equation.

83. $y = (x-1)^2$

84. $y = \frac{1}{3}x - 6$

85. $-2x - 5y = 10$

86. $(x-3)^2 + y^2 = 4$

Synthesis

87. Give an example of two different functions that have the same domain and the same range, but have no pairs in common. Answers may vary.

88. Draw a graph of a function for which the domain is $[-4, 4]$ and the range is $[1, 2] \cup [3, 5]$. Answers may vary.

89. Draw a graph of a function for which the domain is $[-3, -1] \cup [1, 5]$ and the range is $\{1, 2, 3, 4\}$. Answers may vary.

90. Suppose that for some function f, $f(x-1) = 5x$. Find $f(6)$.

91. Suppose that for some function g, $g(x+3) = 2x + 1$. Find $g(-1)$.

92. Suppose $f(x) = |x+3| - |x-4|$. Write $f(x)$ without using absolute-value notation if x is in each of the following intervals.

a) $(-\infty, -3)$
b) $[-3, 4)$
c) $[4, \infty)$

93. Suppose $g(x) = |x| + |x-1|$. Write $g(x)$ without using absolute-value notation if x is in each of the following intervals.

a) $(-\infty, 0)$
b) $[0, 1)$
c) $[1, \infty)$

1.3 Linear Functions, Slope, and Applications

◆ Determine the slope of a line given two points on the line.
◆ Solve applied problems involving slope and linear functions.

In real-life situations, we often need to make decisions on the basis of limited information. When the given information is used to formulate an equation or inequality that at least approximates the situation mathematically, we have created a **model**. One of the most frequently used mathematical models is *linear*—the graph of a linear model is a straight line.

◆ Linear Functions

Let's begin to examine the connections among equations, functions, and graphs that are straight lines. Compare the graphs of linear and nonlinear functions shown here.

Linear Functions

Nonlinear Functions

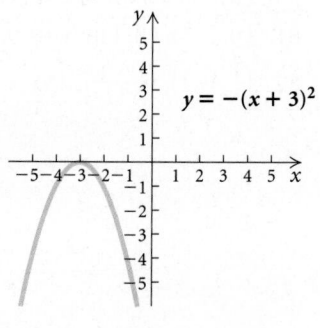

We have the following results and related terminology.

> ## Linear Functions
>
> A function f is a **linear function** if it can be written as
>
> $$f(x) = mx + b,$$
>
> where m and b are constants.
>
> (If $m = 0$, the function is a **constant function** $f(x) = b$. If $m = 1$ and $b = 0$, the function is the **identity function** $f(x) = x$.)

Linear function:
$y = mx + b$

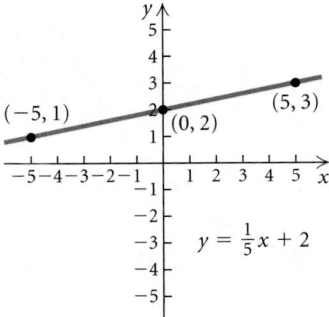

Identity function:
$y = 1 \cdot x + 0$, or $y = x$

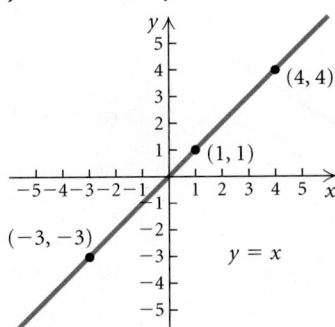

Constant function:
$y = 0 \cdot x + b$, or $y = b$ (Horizontal line)

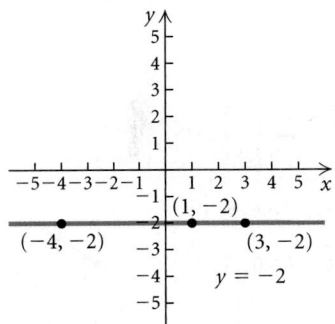

Vertical line: $x = a$
(*not* a function)

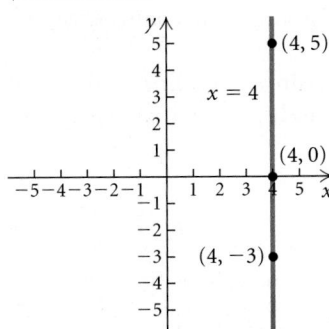

> ## Horizontal and Vertical Lines
>
> **Horizontal lines** are given by equations of the type $y = b$ or $f(x) = b$. (They are functions.)
>
> **Vertical lines** are given by equations of the type $x = a$. (They are *not* functions.)

✦ The Linear Function $f(x) = mx + b$ and Slope

To attach meaning to the constant m in the equation $f(x) = mx + b$, we first consider an application. Suppose TechMax is an office machine business that currently has two stores in locations A and B in the same city. Their total costs for the same time period are given by two functions shown in the tables and graphs that follow. The variable x represents time, in months. The variable y represents total costs, in thousands of dollars, over that amount of time. Look for a pattern.

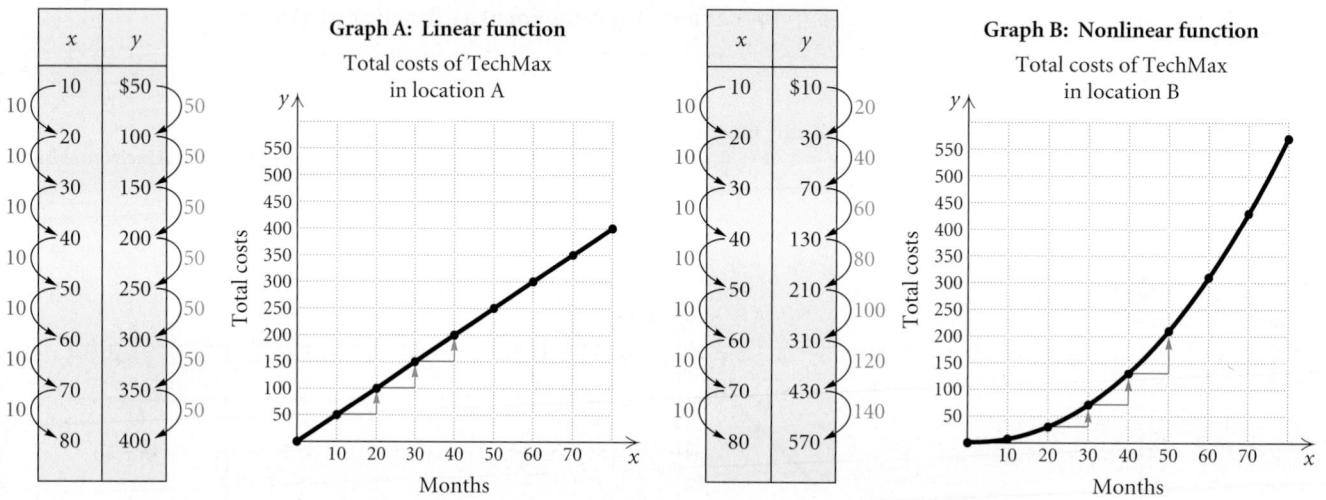

Graph A: Linear function — Total costs of TechMax in location A

x	y
10	$50
20	100
30	150
40	200
50	250
60	300
70	350
80	400

Graph B: Nonlinear function — Total costs of TechMax in location B

x	y
10	$10
20	30
30	70
40	130
50	210
60	310
70	430
80	570

We see in graph A that *every* change of 10 months results in a $50 thousand change in total costs. But in graph B, changes of 10 months do *not* result in constant changes in total costs. This is a way to distinguish linear from nonlinear functions. The rate at which a linear function changes, or the steepness of its graph, is constant.

Mathematically, we define the steepness, or **slope**, of a line as the ratio of its vertical change (rise) to the corresponding horizontal change (run). Slope represents the **rate of change** of y with respect to x.

Slope

The **slope** m of a line containing points (x_1, y_1) and (x_2, y_2) is given by

$$m = \frac{\text{rise}}{\text{run}}$$

$$= \frac{\text{the change in } y}{\text{the change in } x}$$

$$= \frac{y_2 - y_1}{x_2 - x_1} = \frac{y_1 - y_2}{x_1 - x_2}.$$

We can animate the effect of the slope m in linear functions of the type $f(x) = mx$ with a graphing calculator. Graph the equations

$$y_1 = x, \qquad y_2 = 2x,$$
$$y_3 = 5x, \quad \text{and} \quad y_4 = 10x$$

by entering them as $y_1 = \{1, 2, 5, 10\}x$. What do you think the graph of $y = 128x$ will look like?

Clear the screen and graph the following equations:

$$y_1 = x, \qquad y_2 = 0.75x,$$
$$y_3 = 0.48x, \quad \text{and} \quad y_4 = 0.12x.$$

What do you think the graph of $y = 0.000029x$ will look like?

Again clear the screen and graph each set of equations:

$$y_1 = -x, \qquad y_2 = -2x,$$
$$y_3 = -4x, \quad \text{and} \quad y_4 = -10x$$

and

$$y_1 = -x, \qquad y_2 = -\tfrac{2}{3}x,$$
$$y_3 = -\tfrac{7}{20}x, \quad \text{and} \quad y_4 = -\tfrac{1}{10}x.$$

From your observations, what do you think the graphs of $y = -200x$ and $y = -\tfrac{17}{100{,}000}x$ will look like?

How does the value of m affect the graph of a function of the form $f(x) = mx$?

EXAMPLE 1   Graph the function $f(x) = -\tfrac{2}{3}x + 1$ and determine its slope.

Solution   Since the equation for f is in the form $f(x) = mx + b$, we know it is a linear function. We can graph it by connecting two points on the graph with a straight line. We calculate two ordered pairs, plot the points, graph the function, and determine the slope:

$$f(3) = -\frac{2}{3} \cdot 3 + 1 = -2 + 1 = -1;$$

$$f(9) = -\frac{2}{3} \cdot 9 + 1 = -6 + 1 = -5;$$

Pairs: $(3, -1), (9, -5)$;

$$\text{Slope} = m = \frac{y_2 - y_1}{x_2 - x_1}$$

$$= \frac{-5 - (-1)}{9 - 3} = \frac{-4}{6} = -\frac{2}{3}.$$

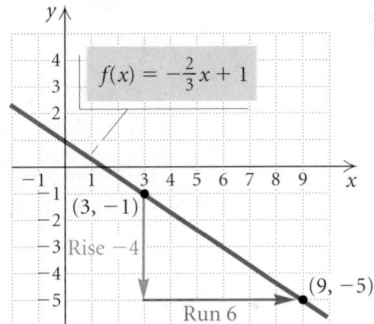

The slope is the same for any two points on a line. Thus, to check our work, note that $f(6) = -\tfrac{2}{3} \cdot 6 + 1 = -4 + 1 = -3$. Using the points $(6, -3)$ and $(3, -1)$, we have

$$m = \frac{-1 - (-3)}{3 - 6} = \frac{2}{-3} = -\frac{2}{3}.$$

We can also use the points in the opposite order when computing slope, so long as we are consistent:

$$m = \frac{-3 - (-1)}{6 - 3} = \frac{-2}{3} = -\frac{2}{3}.$$

Note also that the slope of the line is the number m in the equation for the function $f(x) = -\tfrac{2}{3}x + 1$.

▶ **Now Try Exercise 27.**

The *slope* of the line given by $f(x) = mx + b$ is m.

If a line slants up from left to right, the change in x and the change in y have the same sign, so the line has a positive slope. The larger the slope, the steeper the line, as shown in Fig. 1. If a line slants down from left to right, the change in x and the change in y are of opposite signs, so the line has a negative slope. The larger the absolute value of the slope, the steeper the line, as shown in Fig. 2. When $m = 0$, $y = 0x$, or $y = 0$. Note that this horizontal line is the x-axis, as shown in Fig. 3.

Figure 1

Figure 2

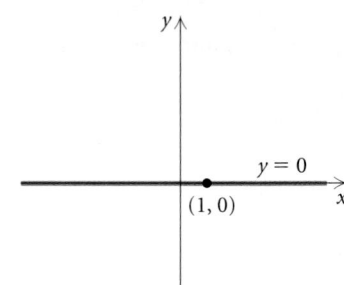

Figure 3

Horizontal and Vertical Lines

If a line is horizontal, the change in y for any two points is 0 and the change in x is nonzero. Thus a horizontal line has slope 0. (See Fig. 4.)

If a line is vertical, the change in y for any two points is nonzero and the change in x is 0. Thus the slope is *not defined* because we cannot divide by 0. (See Fig. 5.)

Horizontal lines

Figure 4

Vertical lines

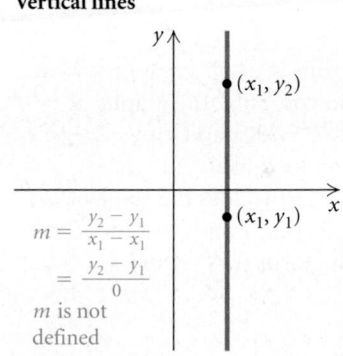

Figure 5

Note that zero slope and a slope that is not defined are two very different concepts.

EXAMPLE 2   Graph each linear equation and determine its slope.

a) $x = -2$ **b)** $y = \dfrac{5}{2}$

Solution

a) Since y is missing in $x = -2$, any value for y will do.

Figure 6

x	y
-2	0
-2	3
-2	-4

Choose any number for y; x must be -2.

The graph (see Fig. 6) is a *vertical line* 2 units to the left of the y-axis. The slope is not defined. The graph is *not* the graph of a function.

b) Since x is missing in $y = \frac{5}{2}$, any value for x will do.

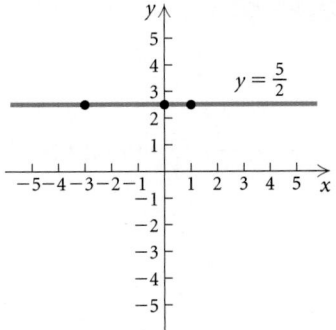

Figure 7

x	y
0	$\frac{5}{2}$
-3	$\frac{5}{2}$
1	$\frac{5}{2}$

Choose any number for x; y must be $\frac{5}{2}$.

The graph (see Fig. 7) is a *horizontal line* $\frac{5}{2}$, or $2\frac{1}{2}$, units above the x-axis. The slope is 0. The graph is the graph of a constant function.

▶ Now Try Exercises 33 and 37.

✦ Applications of Slope

Slope has many real-world applications. Numbers like 2%, 4%, and 7% are often used to represent the **grade** of a road. Such a number is meant to tell how steep a road is on a hill or mountain. For example, a 4% grade means that the road rises 4 ft for every horizontal distance of 100 ft.

Road grade $= \dfrac{a}{b}$
(expressed as a percent)

The concept of grade is also used with a treadmill. During a treadmill test, a cardiologist might change the slope, or grade, of the treadmill to measure its effect on a patient's heart rate. Another example occurs in hydrology. The strength or force of a river depends on how far the river falls vertically compared to how far it flows horizontally.

EXAMPLE 3   *Ramp for the Disabled.*   Construction laws regarding access ramps for the disabled state that every vertical rise of 1 ft requires a horizontal run of 12 ft. What is the grade, or slope, of such a ramp?

Solution   The grade, or slope, is given by $m = \frac{1}{12} \approx 0.083 \approx 8.3\%$.

Slope can also be considered as an **average rate of change.** To find the average rate of change between any two data points on a graph, we determine the slope of the line that passes through the two points.

EXAMPLE 4 *Travel Bookings Online.* The percent of travel bookings online has increased from 6% in 1999 to 55% in 2007. The graph below illustrates this trend. Find the average rate of change in the percent of travel bookings online from 1999 to 2007.

Source: PhoCusWright

Solution We determine the coordinates of two points on the graph. In this case, we use (1999, 6%) and (2007, 55%). Then we compute the slope, or average rate of change, as follows:

$$\text{Slope} = \text{Average rate of change} = \frac{\text{Change in } y}{\text{Change in } x}$$

$$= \frac{55 - 6}{2007 - 1999} = \frac{49}{8}, \text{ or } 6\frac{1}{8}.$$

The result tells us that each year from 1999 to 2007, online travel bookings increased on average by $6\frac{1}{8}$%. The average rate of change over the 8-yr period was an increase of $6\frac{1}{8}$% per year.

▶ Now Try Exercise 41.

EXAMPLE 5 *Drinking Less Soda.* In 2002, 57% of beverages sold in high schools were carbonated soft drinks. That percent decreased to 44.9% in 2005. The decline in sales of soft drinks is illustrated in the graph below. Find the average rate of change from 2002 to 2005 in the percent of beverage sales that are carbonated soft drinks.

Source: American Beverage Association

Solution   We use the coordinates of two points, $(2002, 57\%)$ and $(2005, 44.9\%)$, on the graph to compute the slope, or average rate of change:

$$\text{Slope} = \text{Average rate of change} = \frac{\text{Change in } y}{\text{Change in } x}$$

$$= \frac{44.9 - 57}{2005 - 2002} = \frac{-12.1}{3} \approx -4\%.$$

The result tells us that each year from 2002 to 2005, the percent of sales of soft drinks in high schools has decreased on average about 4%. The average rate of change over the 3-yr period was a decrease of about 4% per year.

▷ **Now Try Exercise 45.**

✦ Applications of Linear Functions

We now consider an application of linear functions.

EXAMPLE 6   *Height Estimates.*   An anthropologist can use linear functions to estimate the height of a male or a female, given the length of the humerus, the bone from the elbow to the shoulder. The height, in centimeters, of an adult male with a humerus of length x, in centimeters, is given by the function

$$M(x) = 2.89x + 70.64.$$

The height, in centimeters, of an adult female with a humerus of length x is given by the function

$$F(x) = 2.75x + 71.48.$$

A 26-cm humerus was uncovered in a ruins. Assuming it was from a female, how tall was she? What is the domain of this function?

Solution   We substitute into the function:

$$F(26) = 2.75(26) + 71.48 = 142.98.$$

Thus the female was 142.98 cm tall.

Theoretically, the domain of the function is the set of all real numbers. However, the context of the problem dictates a different domain. One could not find a bone with a length of 0 or less. Thus the domain consists of positive real numbers, that is, the interval $(0, \infty)$. A more realistic domain might be 20 cm to 60 cm, the interval $[20, 60]$.

▷ **Now Try Exercise 51.**

1.3 EXERCISE SET

In Exercises 1–4, the table of data contains input–output values for a function. Answer the following questions for each table.

a) *Is the change in the inputs x the same?*
b) *Is the change in the outputs y the same?*
c) *Is the function linear?*

1.

x	y
−3	7
−2	10
−1	13
0	16
1	19
2	22
3	25

2.

x	y
20	12.4
30	24.8
40	49.6
50	99.2
60	198.4
70	396.8
80	793.6

3.

x	y
11	3.2
26	5.7
41	8.2
56	9.3
71	11.3
86	13.7
101	19.1

4.

x	y
2	−8
4	−12
6	−16
8	−20
10	−24
12	−28
14	−32

Find the slope of the line containing the given points.

5.

6.

7.

8.

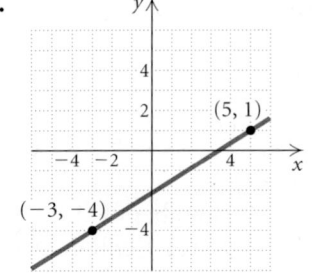

9. $(9, 4)$ and $(-1, 2)$

10. $(-3, 7)$ and $(5, -1)$

11. $(4, -9)$ and $(-5, 6)$

12. $(-6, -1)$ and $(2, -13)$

13. $(0.7, -0.1)$ and $(-0.3, -0.4)$

14. $\left(-\frac{3}{4}, -\frac{1}{4}\right)$ and $\left(\frac{2}{7}, -\frac{5}{7}\right)$

15. $(2, -2)$ and $(4, -2)$

16. $(-9, 8)$ and $(7, -6)$

17. $\left(\frac{1}{2}, -\frac{3}{5}\right)$ and $\left(-\frac{1}{2}, \frac{3}{5}\right)$

18. $(-8.26, 4.04)$ and $(3.14, -2.16)$

19. $(16, -13)$ and $(-8, -5)$

20. $(-10, -7)$ and $(-10, 7)$

21. $(\pi, -3)$ and $(\pi, 2)$

22. $(\sqrt{2}, -4)$ and $(0.56, -4)$

23. $f(4) = 3$ and $f(-2) = 15$

24. $f(-4) = -5$ and $f(4) = 1$

25. $f\left(\frac{1}{5}\right) = \frac{1}{2}$ and $f(-1) = -\frac{11}{2}$

26. $f(8) = -1$ and $f\left(-\frac{2}{3}\right) = \frac{10}{3}$

Graph the linear equation and determine its slope, if it exists.

27. $f(x) = -\frac{1}{2}x + 3$ **28.** $f(x) = \frac{3}{2}x - 4$

29. $2y - 3x = -6$ **30.** $x + 2y = 1$

31. $5x + 2y = 10$ **32.** $2y - x = 8$

33. $y = -\frac{2}{3}$ **34.** $x = 3$

Determine the slope, if it exists, of the graph of the given linear equation.

35. $y = 1.3x - 5$

36. $y = -\frac{2}{5}x + 7$

37. $x = -2$

38. $3x - 4y = -11$

39. $10y + x = 9$

40. $y = \frac{3}{4}$

41. *Public Library Visits.* The number of visits to public libraries increased from 1.1 billion in 1998 to 1.3 billion in 2003 (*Source*: American Library Association). Find the average rate of change in the number of public library visits from 1998 to 2003.

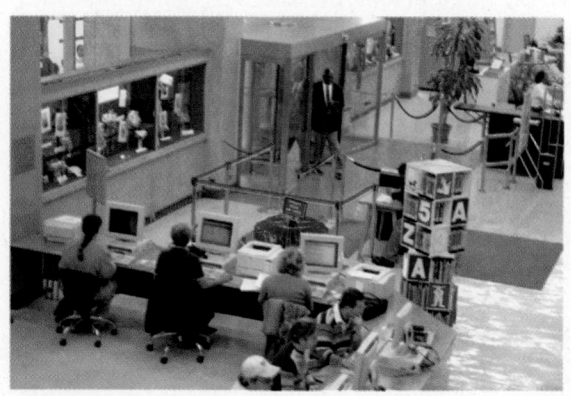

42. *HIV Cases.* HIV, human immunodeficiency virus, spreads to 10 people every minute. It is estimated that there were about 40.3 million cases of HIV worldwide in 2005. The estimated number of cases in 1985 was about 2 million. (*Source*: UNAIDS) Find the average rate of change from 1985 to 2005 in the number of adults and children worldwide with HIV.

43. *Richmond International Raceway.* The 29 NASCAR races from March 1992 to May 2006 at Richmond International Raceway, Richmond, Virginia, were sellouts. Ticket sales increased over 80%. Use the data in the graph below to find the average rate of change in attendance for the 29 consecutive races.

NASCAR Races at Richmond International Raceway

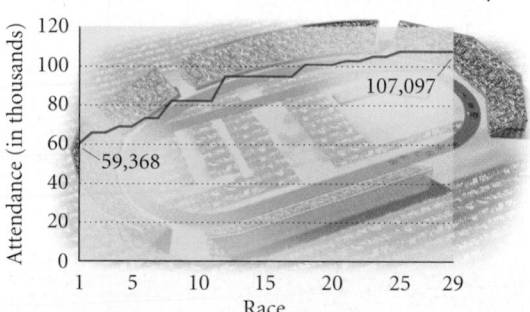

Source: NASCAR, Richmond International Raceway

44. *Decline in Teen Smoking.* The percent of 10th-grade students who have smoked daily in the last 30 days has greatly decreased, from 16.3% in 1995 to 8.3% in 2004 (*Source*: *Monitoring the Future*, University of Michigan Institute for Social Research and National Institute on Drug Abuse). Find the average rate of change over the 9-yr period in the percent of 10th-grade students who have smoked daily in the last 30 days.

45. *Victims of Violent Crime.* The number of women who have been victimized by violent crime per 1000 women, age 12 or older, has decreased from 43 in 1994 to 18.1 in 2004 (*Source*: U.S. Bureau of Justice Statistics). Find the average rate of change in the number of women who have been victimized per 1000 women, age 12 or older, from 1994 to 2004.

46. *Credit-Card Debt.* From 1992 to 2006, the average household credit-card balance has risen 172%. Use the data in the graph below to find the average rate of change in the average credit-card balance from 1992 to 2006.

Credit Card Debt

Source: CardWeb.com, Paul Bannister, Bankrate.com, and "High Credit Card Debt Shouldn't Be Taken Lightly," Jeff Reish, *Canon Daily Record*, 4/22/2006

47. *Running Rate.* Lucie Mays-Sulewski, from Westfield, Indiana, won the women's division of the 2006 Indianapolis 500 Mini-Marathon race. The first American woman to win this race since 1993, she reached the 5-mi point after 31 min 10 sec and arrived at the 10-mi point after 1 hr 1 min 38 sec. (*Source*: www.500festival.com) Find Lucie's speed in miles per minute (average rate of change) from the 5-mi point to the 10-mi point.

48. *Work Rate.* As a typist resumes work on a project, $\frac{1}{6}$ of the paper has already been typed. Six hours

later, the paper is $\frac{3}{4}$ done. Calculate the worker's typing rate.

49. *Ideal Minimum Weight.* One way to estimate the ideal minimum weight of a woman, in pounds, is to multiply her height, in inches, by 4 and subtract 130. Let W = the ideal minimum weight and h = height.
   a) Express W as a linear function of h.
   b) Find the ideal minimum weight of a woman whose height is 62 in.
   c) Find the domain of the function.

50. *Pressure at Sea Depth.* The function P, given by
$$P(d) = \tfrac{1}{33}d + 1,$$
gives the pressure, in atmospheres (atm), at a depth d, in feet, under the sea.
   a) Find $P(0)$, $P(5)$, $P(10)$, $P(33)$, and $P(200)$.
   b) Find the domain of the function.

51. *Stopping Distance on Glare Ice.* The stopping distance (at some fixed speed) of regular tires on glare ice is a function of the air temperature F, in degrees Fahrenheit. This function is estimated by
$$D(F) = 2F + 115,$$
where $D(F)$ is the stopping distance, in feet, when the air temperature is F, in degrees Fahrenheit.
   a) Find $D(0°)$, $D(-20°)$, $D(10°)$, and $D(32°)$.
   b) Explain why the domain should be restricted to $[-57.5°, 32°]$.

52. *Anthropology Estimates.* Consider Example 6 and the function
$$M(x) = 2.89x + 70.64$$
for estimating the height of a male.
   a) If a 26-cm humerus from a male is found in an archeological dig, estimate the height of the male.
   b) What is the domain of M?

53. *Reaction Time.* Suppose that while driving a car, you suddenly see a school crossing guard standing in the road. Your brain registers the information and sends a signal to your foot to hit the brake. The car travels a distance D, in feet, during this time, where D is a function of the speed r, in miles per hour, of the car when you see the crossing guard. That reaction distance is a linear function given by

$$D(r) = \frac{11}{10}r + \frac{1}{2}.$$

a) Find the slope of this line and interpret its meaning in this application.
b) Find $D(5)$, $D(10)$, $D(20)$, $D(50)$, and $D(65)$.
c) What is the domain of this function? Explain.

54. *Straight-Line Depreciation.* A marketing firm buys a new color printer for $5200 to print banners for a sales campaign. The printer is purchased on January 1 and is expected to last 8 yr, at the end of which time its *trade-in,* or *salvage value,* will be $1100. If the company figures the decline or depreciation in value to be the same each year, then the salvage value V, after t years, is given by the linear function

$V(t) = \$5200 - \$512.50t$, for $0 \le t \le 8$.

a) Find $V(0)$, $V(1)$, $V(2)$, $V(3)$, and $V(8)$.
b) Find the domain and the range of this function.

55. *Total Cost.* The Cellular Connection charges $60 for a phone and $29 per month under its economy plan. Write an equation that can be used to determine the total cost, $C(t)$, of operating a Cellular Connection phone for t months. Then find the total cost for 6 months.

56. *Total Cost.* Superior Cable Television charges a $65 installation fee and $80 per month for "deluxe" service. Write an equation that can be used to determine the total cost, $C(t)$, for t months of deluxe cable television service. Then find the total cost for 8 months of service.

In Exercises 57 and 58, the term **fixed costs** *refers to the start-up costs of operating a business. This includes machinery and building costs. The term* **variable costs**

refers to what it costs a business to produce or service one item.

57. Kara's Custom Tees experienced fixed costs of $800 and variable costs of $3 per shirt. Write an equation that can be used to determine the total costs encountered by Kara's Custom Tees when x shirts are produced. Then determine the total cost of producing 75 shirts.

58. It's My Racquet experienced fixed costs of $950 and variable costs of $18 for each tennis racquet that is restrung. Write an equation that can be used to determine the total costs encountered by It's My Racquet when x racquets are restrung. Then determine the total cost of restringing 150 tennis racquets.

Technology Connection

59. Use the VALUE feature in the CALC menu to find the function values in Exercises 50(a), 51(a), 53(b), and 54(a).

Collaborative Discussion and Writing

60. Explain as you would to a fellow student how the numerical value of slope can be used to describe the slant and the steepness of a line.

61. Discuss why the graph of a vertical line $x = a$ cannot represent a function.

Skill Maintenance

If $f(x) = x^2 - 3x$, find each of the following.

62. $f(5)$ 63. $f(-5)$

64. $f(-a)$ 65. $f(a + h)$

Synthesis

66. *Grade of a Treadmill.* A treadmill is 5 ft long and is set at an 8% grade. How high is the end of the treadmill?

Find the slope of the line containing the given points.

67. $(-c, -d)$ and $(9c, -2d)$

68. $(r, s + t)$ and (r, s)

69. $(z + q, z)$ and $(z - q, z)$

70. $(-a - b, p + q)$ and $(a + b, p - q)$

71. (a, a^2) and $(a + h, (a + h)^2)$

72. $(a, 3a + 1)$ and $(a + h, 3(a + h) + 1)$

Suppose that f is a linear function. Determine whether the statement is true or false.

73. $f(cd) = f(c)f(d)$

74. $f(c + d) = f(c) + f(d)$

75. $f(c - d) = f(c) - f(d)$

76. $f(kx) = kf(x)$

Let $f(x) = mx + b$. Find a formula for $f(x)$ given each of the following.

77. $f(x + 2) = f(x) + 2$

78. $f(3x) = 3f(x)$

1.4

Equations of Lines and Modeling

◆ Find the slope and the *y*-intercept of a line given the equation $y = mx + b$, or $f(x) = mx + b$.

◆ Graph a linear equation using the slope and the *y*-intercept.

◆ Determine equations of lines.

◆ Given the equations of two lines, determine whether their graphs are parallel or whether they are perpendicular.

◆ Model a set of data with a linear function.

y-INTERCEPT
REVIEW SECTION **1.1.**

TECHNOLOGY CONNECTION

We can explore the effect of the constant b in linear equations of the type $f(x) = mx + b$ with a graphing calculator. Begin with the graph of $y = x$. Now graph the lines $y = x + 3$ and $y = x - 4$ in the same viewing window. Try entering these equations as $y = x + \{0, 3, -4\}$ and compare the graphs. How do the last two lines differ from $y = x$? What do you think the line $y = x - 6$ will look like?

    Try graphing $y = -0.5x$, $y = -0.5x - 4$, and $y = -0.5x + 3$ in the same viewing window. Describe what happens to the graph of $y = -0.5x$ when a number b is added.

◆ Slope–Intercept Equations of Lines

Let's explore the effect of the constant b in linear equations of the type $f(x) = mx + b$. Compare the graphs of the equations

$$y = 3x$$

and

$$y = 3x - 2.$$

Note that the graph of $y = 3x - 2$ is a shift down of the graph of $y = 3x$, and that $y = 3x - 2$ has *y*-intercept $(0, -2)$. That is, the graph is parallel to $y = 3x$ and it crosses the *y*-axis at $(0, -2)$. The point $(0, -2)$ is the **y-intercept** of the graph.

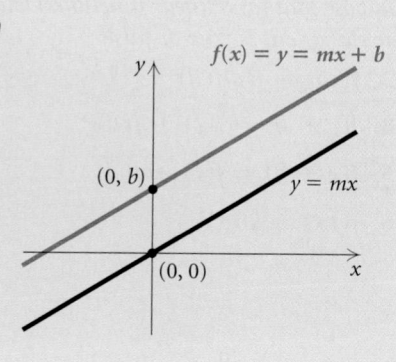

The Slope–Intercept Equation

The linear function f given by

$$f(x) = mx + b$$

is written in **slope–intercept** form. The graph of an equation in this form is a straight line parallel to $y = mx$. The constant m is called the slope, and the y-intercept is $(0, b)$.

We can read the slope m and the y-intercept $(0, b)$ directly from the equation of a line written in slope–intercept form, $y = mx + b$.

EXAMPLE 1   Find the slope and the y-intercept of the line with equation $y = -0.25x - 3.8$.

Solution

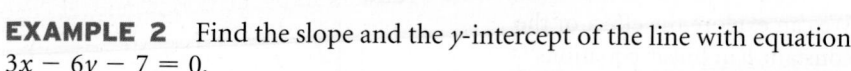

Slope $= -0.25$; y-intercept $= (0, -3.8)$ ▶ **Now Try Exercise 1.**

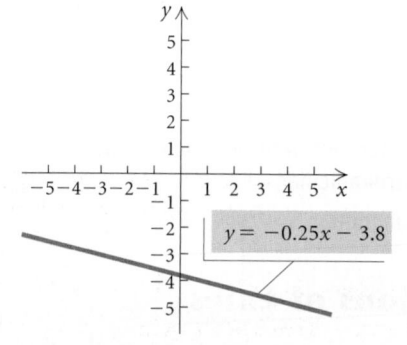

Any equation whose graph is a straight line is a **linear equation.** To find the slope and the y-intercept of the graph of a linear equation, we can solve for y, and then read the information from the equation.

EXAMPLE 2   Find the slope and the y-intercept of the line with equation $3x - 6y - 7 = 0$.

Solution   We solve for y:

$$3x - 6y - 7 = 0$$
$$-6y = -3x + 7 \qquad \text{Adding } -3x \text{ and } 7 \text{ on both sides}$$
$$-\tfrac{1}{6}(-6y) = -\tfrac{1}{6}(-3x + 7) \qquad \text{Multiplying by } -\tfrac{1}{6}$$
$$y = \tfrac{1}{2}x - \tfrac{7}{6}.$$

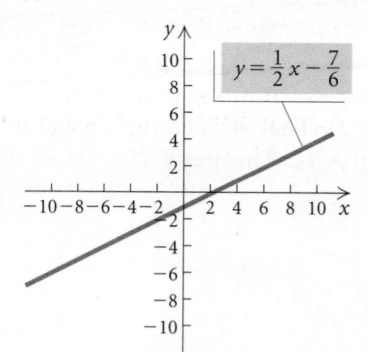

Thus the slope is $\tfrac{1}{2}$, and the y-intercept is $\left(0, -\tfrac{7}{6}\right)$.   ▶ **Now Try Exercise 11.**

EXAMPLE 3   A line has slope $-\tfrac{7}{9}$ and y-intercept $(0, 16)$. Find an equation of the line.

Solution   We use the slope–intercept equation and substitute $-\tfrac{7}{9}$ for m and 16 for b:

$$y = mx + b$$
$$y = -\tfrac{7}{9}x + 16.$$

▶ **Now Try Exercise 21.**

EXAMPLE 4 A line has slope $-\frac{2}{3}$ and contains the point $(-3, 6)$. Find an equation of the line.

Solution We use the slope–intercept equation and substitute $-\frac{2}{3}$ for m: $y = -\frac{2}{3}x + b$. Using the point $(-3, 6)$, we substitute -3 for x and 6 for y in $y = -\frac{2}{3}x + b$. Then we solve for b:

$y = mx + b$

$y = -\frac{2}{3}x + b$ Substituting $-\frac{2}{3}$ for m

$6 = -\frac{2}{3}(-3) + b$ Substituting -3 for x and 6 for y

$6 = 2 + b$

$4 = b.$ Solving for b, the y-intercept

Finally, we substitute $-\frac{2}{3}$ for m and 4 for b in $y = mx + b$ to get

$y = -\frac{2}{3}x + 4.$ ▷ **Now Try Exercise 25.**

We can graph a linear equation using its slope and y-intercept.

EXAMPLE 5 Graph: $y = -\frac{2}{3}x + 4$.

Solution This equation is in slope–intercept form, $y = mx + b$. The y-intercept is $(0, 4)$. Thus we plot $(0, 4)$. We can think of the slope $\left(m = -\frac{2}{3}\right)$ as $\frac{-2}{3}$.

$$m = \frac{\text{rise}}{\text{run}} = \frac{\text{change in } y}{\text{change in } x} = \frac{-2}{3} \begin{matrix} \leftarrow \text{Move 2 units down.} \\ \leftarrow \text{Move 3 units to the right.} \end{matrix}$$

Starting at the y-intercept and using the slope, we find another point by moving 2 units down and 3 units to the right. We get a new point $(3, 2)$. In a similar manner, we can move from $(3, 2)$ to find another point $(6, 0)$.

We could also think of the slope $\left(m = -\frac{2}{3}\right)$ as $\frac{2}{-3}$. Then we can start at $(0, 4)$ and move 2 units up and 3 units to the left. We get to another point on the graph, $(-3, 6)$. We now plot the points and draw the line. Note that we need only the y-intercept and one other point in order to graph the line, but it's a good idea to find a third point as a check that the first two points are correct.

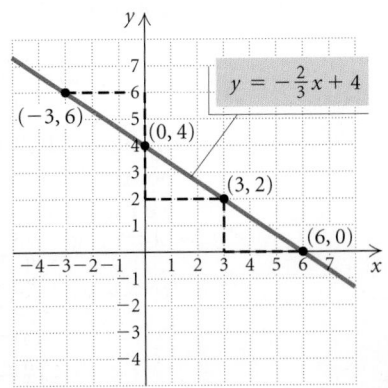

▷ **Now Try Exercise 37.**

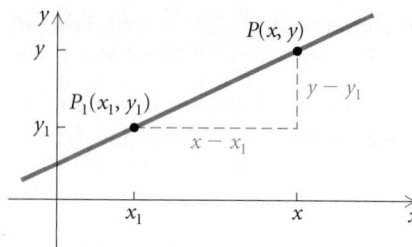

✦ Point–Slope Equations of Lines

Another formula that can be used to determine an equation of a line is the *point–slope equation*. Suppose that we have a nonvertical line and that the coordinates of point P_1 on the line are (x_1, y_1). We can think of P_1 as fixed and imagine another point P on the line with coordinates (x, y). Thus the slope is given by

$$\frac{y - y_1}{x - x_1} = m.$$

Multiplying by $x - x_1$, on both sides, we get the *point–slope equation* of the line:

$$(x - x_1) \cdot \frac{y - y_1}{x - x_1} = m \cdot (x - x_1)$$

$$y - y_1 = m(x - x_1).$$

> ### Point-Slope Equation
> The **point–slope equation** of the line with slope m passing through (x_1, y_1) is
> $$y - y_1 = m(x - x_1).$$

If we know the slope of a line and the coordinates of one point on the line, we can find an equation of the line using either the point–slope equation,

$$y - y_1 = m(x - x_1),$$

or the slope–intercept equation,

$$y = mx + b.$$

EXAMPLE 6   Find an equation of the line containing the points $(2, 3)$ and $(1, -4)$.

Solution   We first determine the slope:

$$m = \frac{-4 - 3}{1 - 2} = \frac{-7}{-1} = 7.$$

Using the Point–Slope Equation: We substitute 7 for m and either of the points $(2, 3)$ or $(1, -4)$ for (x_1, y_1) in the point–slope equation. In this case, we use $(2, 3)$.

$$\begin{aligned} y - y_1 &= m(x - x_1) && \text{Point–slope equation} \\ y - 3 &= 7(x - 2) && \text{Substituting} \\ y - 3 &= 7x - 14 \\ y &= 7x - 11, \text{ or } f(x) = 7x - 11 \end{aligned}$$

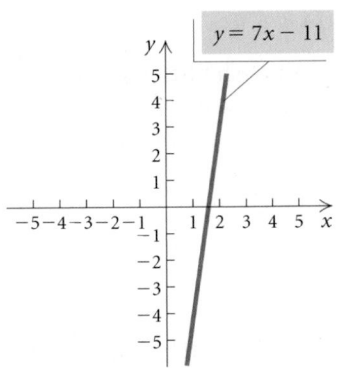

Using the Slope–Intercept Equation: We substitute 7 for m and either of the points $(2,3)$ or $(1,-4)$ for (x,y) in the slope–intercept equation and solve for b. Here we use $(1,-4)$.

$$y = mx + b \qquad \text{Slope–intercept equation}$$
$$-4 = 7 \cdot 1 + b \qquad \text{Substituting}$$
$$-4 = 7 + b$$
$$-11 = b \qquad \text{Solving for } b$$

We substitute 7 for m and -11 for b in $y = mx + b$ to get

$$y = 7x - 11, \text{ or } f(x) = 7x - 11.$$

▶ Now Try Exercise 31.

◆ Parallel Lines

Can we determine whether the graphs of two linear equations are parallel without graphing them? Let's look at three pairs of equations and their graphs.

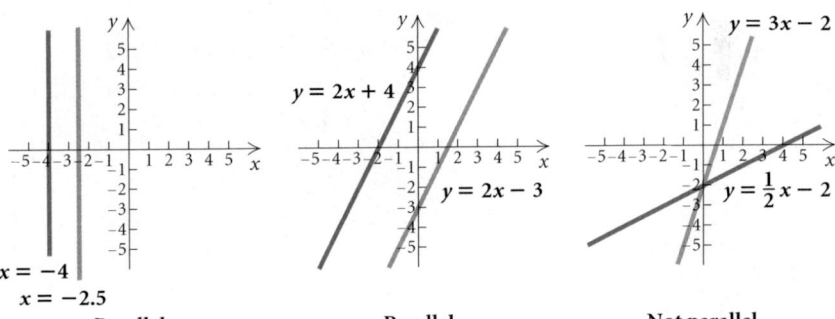

| Parallel | Parallel | Not parallel |

If two different lines, such as $x = -4$ and $x = -2.5$, are vertical, then they are parallel. Thus two equations such as $x = a_1$, $x = a_2$, where $a_1 \neq a_2$, have graphs that are *parallel lines*. Two nonvertical lines, such as $y = 2x + 4$ and $y = 2x - 3$, or, in general, $y = mx + b_1$, $y = mx + b_2$, where the slopes are the *same* and $b_1 \neq b_2$, also have graphs that are *parallel lines*.

Parallel Lines

Vertical lines are **parallel.** Nonvertical lines are **parallel** if and only if they have the same slope and different y-intercepts.

✦ Perpendicular Lines

Can we examine a pair of equations to determine whether their graphs are perpendicular without graphing the equations? Let's look at the following pairs of equations and their graphs.

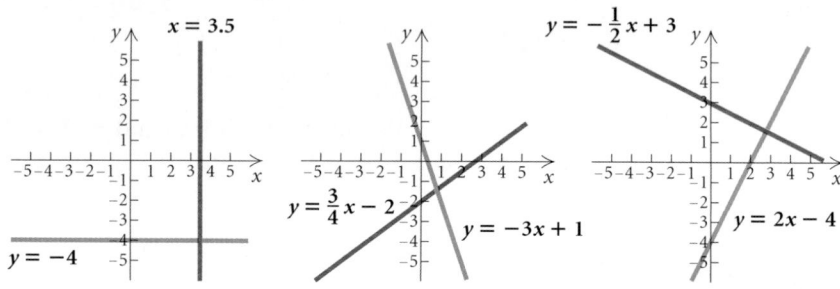

Perpendicular   Not perpendicular   Perpendicular

Perpendicular Lines

Two lines with slopes m_1 and m_2 are **perpendicular** if and only if the product of their slopes is -1:

$$m_1 m_2 = -1.$$

Lines are also **perpendicular** if one is vertical ($x = a$) and the other is horizontal ($y = b$).

If a line has slope m_1, the slope m_2 of a line perpendicular to it is $-1/m_1$ (the slope of one line is the *opposite of the reciprocal* of the other).

EXAMPLE 7   Determine whether each of the following pairs of lines is parallel, perpendicular, or neither.

a) $y + 2 = 5x$, $5y + x = -15$
b) $2y + 4x = 8$, $5 + 2x = -y$
c) $2x + 1 = y$, $y + 3x = 4$

Solution   We use the slopes of the lines to determine whether the lines are parallel or perpendicular.

a) We solve each equation for y:

$$y = 5x - 2, \qquad y = -\frac{1}{5}x - 3.$$

The slopes are 5 and $-\frac{1}{5}$. Their product is -1, so the lines are perpendicular. (See Fig. 1.)

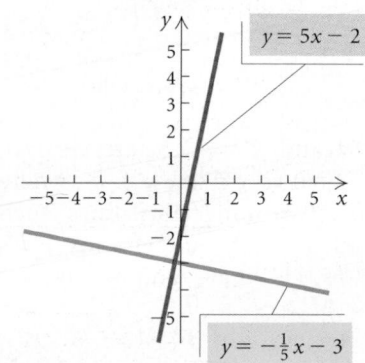

Figure 1

b) Solving each equation for y, we get

$$y = -2x + 4, \qquad y = -2x - 5.$$

We see that $m_1 = -2$ and $m_2 = -2$. Since the slopes are the same and the y-intercepts, $(0, 4)$ and $(0, -5)$, are different, the lines are parallel. (See Fig. 2.)

Figure 2

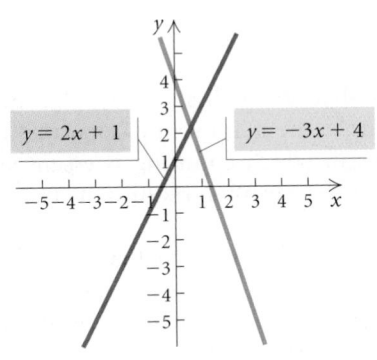

$y = 2x + 1$ $y = -3x + 4$

Figure 3

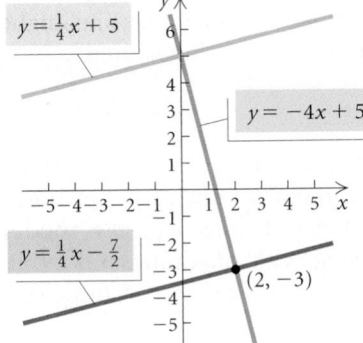

$y = \frac{1}{4}x + 5$ $y = -4x + 5$

$y = \frac{1}{4}x - \frac{7}{2}$ $(2, -3)$

c) Solving the second equation for y, we get

$$y = 2x + 1, \qquad y = -3x + 4.$$

Since $m_1 = 2$ and $m_2 = -3$, we know that $m_1 \neq m_2$ and that $m_1 m_2 = 2(-3) = -6 \neq -1$. It follows that the lines are neither parallel nor perpendicular. (See Fig. 3.) ▷ Now Try Exercises 53 and 57.

EXAMPLE 8 Write equations of the lines **(a)** parallel and **(b)** perpendicular to the graph of the line $4y - x = 20$ and containing the point $(2, -3)$.

Solution We first solve $4y - x = 20$ for y to get $y = \frac{1}{4}x + 5$. Thus the slope of the given line is $\frac{1}{4}$.

a) The line parallel to the given line will have slope $\frac{1}{4}$. We use either the slope–intercept equation or the point–slope equation for a line with slope $\frac{1}{4}$ and containing the point $(2, -3)$. Here we use the point–slope equation:

$$y - y_1 = m(x - x_1)$$
$$y - (-3) = \frac{1}{4}(x - 2)$$
$$y + 3 = \frac{1}{4}x - \frac{1}{2}$$
$$y = \frac{1}{4}x - \frac{7}{2}.$$

b) The slope of the perpendicular line is the opposite of the reciprocal of $\frac{1}{4}$, or -4. Again we use the point–slope equation to write an equation for a line with slope -4 and containing the point $(2, -3)$:

$$y - y_1 = m(x - x_1)$$
$$y - (-3) = -4(x - 2)$$
$$y + 3 = -4x + 8$$
$$y = -4x + 5.$$

▷ Now Try Exercise 61.

Summary of Terminology About Lines

TERMINOLOGY	MATHEMATICAL INTERPRETATION
Slope	$m = \dfrac{y_2 - y_1}{x_2 - x_1}$, or $\dfrac{y_1 - y_2}{x_1 - x_2}$
Slope–intercept equation	$y = mx + b$
Point–slope equation	$y - y_1 = m(x - x_1)$
Horizontal line	$y = b$
Vertical line	$x = a$
Parallel lines	$m_1 = m_2,\ b_1 \neq b_2$
Perpendicular lines	$m_1 m_2 = -1$

Creating a Mathematical Model

1. Recognize real-world problem.

2. Collect data.

3. Plot data.

4. Construct model.

5. Explain and predict.

◆ Mathematical Models

When a real-world problem can be described in mathematical language, we have a **mathematical model.** For example, the natural numbers constitute a mathematical model for situations in which counting is essential. Situations in which algebra can be brought to bear often require the use of functions as models.

Mathematical models are abstracted from real-world situations. The mathematical model gives results that allow one to predict what will happen in that real-world situation. If the predictions are inaccurate or the results of experimentation do not conform to the model, the model must be changed or discarded.

Mathematical modeling can be an ongoing process. For example, finding a mathematical model that will enable an accurate prediction of population growth is not a simple problem. Any population model that one might devise would need to be reshaped as further information is acquired.

◆ Curve Fitting

We will develop and use many kinds of mathematical models in this text. In this chapter, we have used *linear* functions as models. Other types of functions, such as quadratic, cubic, or exponential functions, can also model data. These functions are *nonlinear*. Modeling with quadratic and cubic functions is discussed in Chapter 3. Modeling with exponential functions is discussed in Chapter 4.

Quadratic function:
$y = ax^2 + bx + c, a > 0$

Cubic function:
$y = ax^3 + bx^2 + cx + d, a > 0$

Exponential function:
$y = ab^x, a, b > 0$

In general, we try to find a function that fits, as well as possible, observations (data), theoretical reasoning, and common sense. We call this **curve fitting;** it is one aspect of mathematical modeling.

Let's look at some data and related graphs or **scatterplots** and determine whether a linear function seems to fit the set of data.

Truck Sales

Year, x	Number of Trucks Sold (in millions)	Scatterplot
2000, 0	2.15	
2001, 1	2.32	
2002, 2	2.27	
2003, 3	2.36	
2004, 4	2.51	
2005, 5	2.50	

It appears that the data points can be represented or modeled by a linear function.

The graph is **linear.**

Source: Power Information Network

Fuel Ethanol Production in the United States

Year, x	Number of Gallons of Fuel Ethanol Produced (in billions)	Scatterplot
1996, 0	1.1	
1997, 1	1.3	
1998, 2	1.4	
1999, 3	1.5	
2000, 4	1.6	
2001, 5	1.7	
2002, 6	2.2	
2003, 7	2.7	
2004, 8	3.4	

It appears that the data points cannot be modeled by a linear function.

The graph is **nonlinear.**

Source: Renewable Fuels Association

Looking at the scatterplots, we see that the data on truck sales seem to be rising in a manner to suggest that a *linear function* might fit, although a "perfect" straight line cannot be drawn through the data points. A linear function does not seem to fit the data on fuel ethanol production.

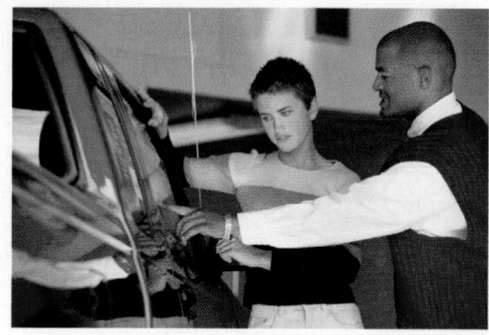

EXAMPLE 9 *Truck Sales.* Model the data in the table on truck sales on the preceding page with a linear function. Then predict the number of trucks that will be sold in 2010.

Solution   We can choose any two of the data points to determine an equation. Let's use $(0, 2.15)$ and $(5, 2.50)$.

We first determine the slope of the line:

$$m = \frac{2.50 - 2.15}{5 - 0} = \frac{0.35}{5} = 0.07.$$

Then we substitute 0.07 for m and either of the points $(0, 2.15)$ or $(5, 2.50)$ for (x_1, y_1) in the point–slope equation. In this case, we use $(0, 2.15)$. We get

$$y - 2.15 = 0.07(x - 0),$$

which simplifies to

$$y = 0.07x + 2.15,$$

where x is the number of years after 2000 and y is in millions.

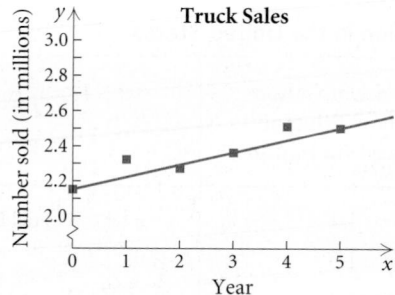

Now we can predict the number of trucks that will be sold in 2010 by substituting 10 for x in the model $(2010 - 2000 = 10)$:

$$y = 0.07x + 2.15 \qquad \text{Model}$$
$$y = 0.07(10) + 2.15 \qquad \text{Substituting}$$
$$y = 2.85.$$

We predict that there will be about 2.85 million trucks sold in 2010.

▶ **Now Try Exercise 75.**

In Example 9, if we had used the data points $(2, 2.27)$ and $(5, 2.50)$, our model would be

$$y = 0.0767x + 2.1166$$

and our prediction for the number of trucks sold would be about 2.88 million. The model that best fits the data can be found with a graphing calculator and a procedure called linear regression. This procedure is explained in the Technology Connection on the next page.

TECHNOLOGY CONNECTION

Figure 1

Figure 2

Figure 3

Figure 4

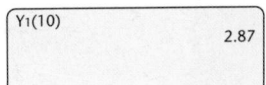

Figure 5

The Regression Line

We now consider **linear regression,** a procedure that can be used to model a set of data using a linear function. Although discussion leading to a complete understanding of this method belongs in a statistics course, we present the procedure here because we can carry it out easily using technology. The graphing calculator gives us the powerful capability to find linear models and to make predictions using them.

Consider the data presented before Example 9 on the number of trucks sold. We can fit a regression line of the form $y = mx + b$ to the data using the LINEAR REGRESSION feature on a graphing calculator.

First, we enter the data in lists on the calculator. We enter the values of the independent variable x in list L1 and the corresponding values of the dependent variable y in L2. (See Fig. 1.) The graphing calculator can then create a scatterplot of the data, as shown in Fig. 2.

When we select the LINEAR REGRESSION feature from the STAT CALC menu, we find the linear equation that best models the data. It is

$$y = 0.0688571429x + 2.17952381. \qquad \text{Regression line}$$

(See Figs. 3 and 4.) We can then graph the regression line on the same graph as the scatterplot, as shown in Fig. 5.

To predict the number of trucks that will be sold in 2010, we substitute 10 for x in the regression equation.

Using this model, we see that the number of trucks sold in 2010 is predicted to be about 2.87 million. Note that 2.87 is closer to the value 2.88 found with the data points $(2, 2.27)$ and $(5, 2.50)$ than to the value 2.85 found with the data points $(0, 2.15)$ and $(5, 2.50)$ in Example 9.

The Correlation Coefficient

On some graphing calculators with the DIAGNOSTIC feature turned on, a constant r between -1 and 1, called the **coefficient of linear correlation,** appears with the equation of the regression line. Though we cannot develop a formula for calculating r in this text, keep in mind that it is used to describe the strength of the linear relationship between x and y. The closer $|r|$ is to 1, the better the correlation. A positive value of r also indicates that the regression line has a positive slope, and a negative value of r indicates that the regression line has a negative slope. For the truck sales data just discussed,

$$r = 0.932189564,$$

which indicates a good linear correlation.

A

B

C

D

E

Visualizing the Graph

Match the equation with its graph.

1. $y = 20$

2. $5y = 2x + 15$

3. $y = -\dfrac{1}{3}x - 4$

4. $x = \dfrac{5}{3}$

5. $y = -x - 2$

6. $y = 2x$

7. $y = -3$

8. $3y = -4x$

9. $x = -10$

10. $y = x + \dfrac{7}{2}$

Answers on page A-6

F

G

H

I

J

1.4   EXERCISE SET

Find the slope and the y-intercept of the equation.

1. $y = \frac{3}{5}x - 7$

2. $f(x) = -2x + 3$

3. $x = -\frac{2}{5}$

4. $y = \frac{4}{7}$

5. $f(x) = 5 - \frac{1}{2}x$

6. $y = 2 + \frac{3}{7}x$

7. $3x + 2y = 10$

8. $2x - 3y = 12$

9. $y = -6$

10. $x = 10$

11. $5y - 4x = 8$

12. $5x - 2y + 9 = 0$

Find the slope and the y-intercept of the graph of the linear equation. Then write the equation of the line in slope–intercept form.

13.

14.

15.

16.

17.

18.

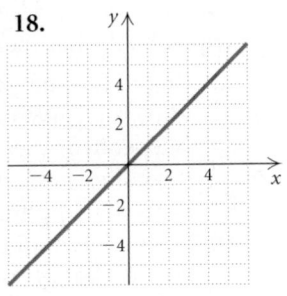

Write a slope–intercept equation for a line with the given characteristics.

19. $m = \frac{2}{9}$, y-intercept $(0, 4)$

20. $m = -\frac{3}{8}$, y-intercept $(0, 5)$

21. $m = -4$, y-intercept $(0, -7)$

22. $m = \frac{2}{7}$, y-intercept $(0, -6)$

23. $m = -4.2$, y-intercept $\left(0, \frac{3}{4}\right)$

24. $m = -4$, y-intercept $\left(0, -\frac{3}{2}\right)$

25. $m = \frac{2}{9}$, passes through $(3, 7)$

26. $m = -\frac{3}{8}$, passes through $(5, 6)$

27. $m = 3$, passes through $(1, -2)$

28. $m = -2$, passes through $(-5, 1)$

29. $m = -\frac{3}{5}$, passes through $(-4, -1)$

30. $m = \frac{2}{3}$, passes through $(-4, -5)$

31. Passes through $(-1, 5)$ and $(2, -4)$

32. Passes through $(2, -1)$ and $(7, -11)$

33. Passes through $(7, 0)$ and $(-1, 4)$

34. Passes through $(-3, 7)$ and $(-1, -5)$

35. Passes through $(0, -6)$ and $(3, -4)$

36. Passes through $(-5, 0)$ and $\left(0, \frac{4}{5}\right)$

Graph the equation using the slope and the y-intercept.

37. $y = -\frac{1}{2}x - 3$

38. $y = \frac{3}{2}x + 1$

39. $f(x) = 3x - 1$

40. $f(x) = -2x + 5$

41. $3x - 4y = 20$

42. $2x + 3y = 15$

43. $x + 3y = 18$

44. $5y - 2x = -20$

45. Find a linear function h given $h(1) = 4$ and $h(-2) = 13$.

46. Find a linear function g given $g\left(-\frac{1}{4}\right) = -6$ and $g(2) = 3$.

47. Find a linear function f given $f(5) = 1$ and $f(-5) = -3$.

48. Find a linear function h given $h(-3) = 3$ and $h(0) = 2$.

Write equations of the horizontal and the vertical lines that pass through the given point.

49. $(0, -3)$

50. $\left(-\frac{1}{4}, 7\right)$

51. $\left(\frac{2}{11}, -1\right)$

52. $(0.03, 0)$

Determine whether the pair of lines is parallel, perpendicular, or neither.

53. $y = \frac{26}{3}x - 11,$
$y = -\frac{3}{26}x - 11$

54. $y = -3x + 1,$
$y = -\frac{1}{3}x + 1$

55. $y = \frac{2}{5}x - 4,$
$y = -\frac{2}{5}x + 4$

56. $y = \frac{3}{2}x - 8,$
$y = 8 + 1.5x$

57. $x + 2y = 5,$
$2x + 4y = 8$

58. $2x - 5y = -3,$
$2x + 5y = 4$

59. $y = 4x - 5,$
$4y = 8 - x$

60. $y = 7 - x,$
$y = x + 3$

Write a slope–intercept equation for a line passing through the given point that is parallel to the given line. Then write a second equation for a line passing through the given point that is perpendicular to the given line.

61. $(3, 5),\ y = \frac{2}{7}x + 1$

62. $(-1, 6),\ f(x) = 2x + 9$

63. $(-7, 0),\ y = -0.3x + 4.3$

64. $(-4, -5),\ 2x + y = -4$

65. $(3, -2),\ 3x + 4y = 5$

66. $(8, -2),\ y = 4.2(x - 3) + 1$

67. $(3, -3),\ x = -1$

68. $(4, -5),\ y = -1$

In Exercises 69–74, determine whether the statement is true or false.

69. The lines $x = -3$ and $y = 5$ are perpendicular.

70. The lines $y = 2x - 3$ and $y = -2x - 3$ are perpendicular.

71. The lines $y = \frac{2}{5}x + 4$ and $y = \frac{2}{5}x - 4$ are parallel.

72. The intersection of the lines $y = 2$ and $x = -\frac{3}{4}$ is $\left(-\frac{3}{4}, 2\right)$.

73. The lines $x = -1$ and $x = 1$ are perpendicular.

74. The lines $2x + 3y = 4$ and $3x - 2y = 4$ are perpendicular.

75. *Twin Births.*   The graph below illustrates the upward trend in twin births.

   a) Model the data with a linear function. Let the independent variable represent the number of years after 1995; that is, the data points are $(0, 96.7)$, $(2, 104.1)$, and so on. Answers will vary depending on the data points used.

   b) With the function found in part (a), estimate the number of twin births in 2007 and in 2010.

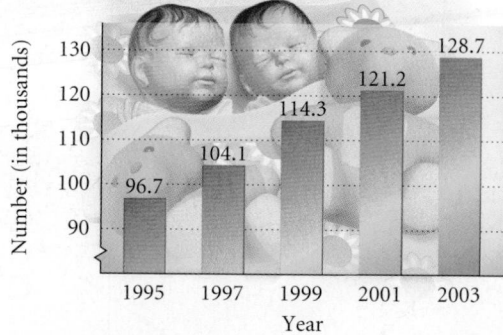

Twin Births in the United States

Source: National Center for Health Statistics, U.S. Department of Health and Human Services

76. *Triplet Births.* In recent years, the number of triplet births has increased.

   a) Model the data given in the table on the following page with a linear function. Let the independent variable represent the number of years after 1993. Answers will vary depending on the data points used.

   b) With the function found in part (a), estimate the number of triplet births in 2008 and in 2012.

Year, x	Number of Triplet Births, y
1993, 0	3834
1995, 2	4551
1997, 4	6148
1999, 6	6742
2001, 8	6885
2003, 10	7110

Sources: National Center for Health Statistics;
U.S. Department of Health and Human Services

77. *Cell-Phone Bill.*   Model the data given in the table below with a linear function and estimate the average monthly cell-phone bill in 2007 and in 2009. Answers may vary depending on the data points used.

Year, x	Average Monthly Cell-phone Bill, y
2000, 0	$45.27
2001, 1	47.37
2002, 2	48.40
2003, 3	49.91
2004, 4	50.64

Source: U.S. Bureau of the Census

78. *Prescription Drug Sales.*   The following graph illustrates the retail sales of prescription drugs for certain years. Model the data with a linear function, estimate the total sales for 2006, and predict the total sales for 2011. Answers may vary depending on the data points used.

Prescription Drug Sales

Source: U.S. Bureau of the Census

79. *Social-Security Benefits.* Model the data given in the table below with a linear function, estimate the average monthly social-security benefits for retired workers in 2005, and predict the average benefits in 2010 and in 2020. Answers may vary depending on the data points used.

Year, x	Average Monthly Social-Security Benefits for Retired Workers, y
1970, 0	$123.82
1980, 10	321.10
1990, 20	550.50
2000, 30	844.60
2003, 33	922.10

Source: Social Security Administration, *Social Security Bulletin: Annual Statistical Supplement*, 2003

80. *Sheep and Lambs.* The number of sheep and lambs on farms in the United States has declined in recent years. Model the data given in the table below with a linear function and estimate the number of sheep and lambs on farms in 2008 and in 2013.

Year, x	Sheep and Lambs on Farms in the United States, y (in thousands)
1970, 0	20,423
1975, 5	14,515
1980, 10	12,699
1985, 15	10,716
1990, 20	11,358
1995, 25	8,886
2000, 30	7,032
2005, 35	6,135

Source: National Agricultural Statistics Service, U.S. Department of Agriculture

Technology Connection

81. *Maximum Heart Rate.*   A person who is exercising should not exceed his or her maximum heart rate, which is determined on the basis of that person's sex, age, and resting heart rate. The following table relates resting heart rate and maximum heart rate for a 20-year-old man.

Resting Heart Rate, *H* (in beats per minute)	Maximum Heart Rate, *M* (in beats per minute)
50	166
60	168
70	170
80	172

Source: American Heart Association

a) Use a graphing calculator to model the data with a linear function.

b) Estimate the maximum heart rate if the resting heart rate is 40, 65, 76, and 84.

c) What is the correlation coefficient? How confident are you about using the regression line to estimate function values?

82. *Study Time versus Grades.*   A math instructor asked her students to record how much time each spent studying a chapter on functions in her algebra–trigonometry course. She collected the information together with test scores from that chapter's test. The data are listed in the following table.

Study Time, *x* (in hours)	Test Grade, *y* (in percent)
23	81%
15	85
17	80
9	75
21	86
13	80
16	85
11	93

a) Use a graphing calculator to model the data with a linear function.

b) Predict a student's score if he or she studies 24 hr, 6 hr, and 18 hr.

c) What is the correlation coefficient? How confident are you about using the regression line to predict function values?

83. *Easter Candy Sales.*   From 1999 to 2002, sales of Easter candy remained relatively constant, as shown in the following figure.

Easter Candy Sales (in billions)

1999 $1.7
2000 $1.9
2001 $1.8
2002 $1.8

Source: National Confectioners Association

a) Use a graphing calculator to model the data with a linear function.

b) Estimate the sales of Easter candy in 2005 and in 2010.

c) Find the correlation coefficient for the regression line and determine whether the line fits the data closely.

84. a) Use a graphing calculator to fit a regression line to the data in Exercise 76.

b) Estimate the number of triplet births in 2008 and compare the value with the result found in Exercise 76.

c) Find the correlation coefficient for the regression line and determine whether the line fits the data closely.

85. a) Use a graphing calculator to fit a regression line to the data in Exercise 75.

b) Estimate the number of twin births in 2010 and compare the result with the estimate found with the model in Exercise 75.

c) Find the correlation coefficient for the regression line and determine whether the line fits the data closely.

Collaborative Discussion and Writing

86. A company offers its new employees a starting salary with a guaranteed 5% increase each year. Can a linear function be used to express the yearly salary as a function of the number of years an employee has worked? Why or why not?

87. If one line has a slope of $-\frac{3}{4}$ and another has a slope of $\frac{2}{5}$, which line is steeper? Why?

Skill Maintenance

Find the slope of the line containing the given points.

88. $(5, 7)$ and $(5, -7)$

89. $(2, -8)$ and $(-5, -1)$

Find an equation for a circle satisfying the given conditions.

90. Center $(0, 3)$, diameter of length 5

91. Center $(-7, -1)$, radius of length $\frac{9}{5}$

Synthesis

92. *Road Grade.* Using the following figure, find the road grade and an equation giving the height y as a function of the horizontal distance x.

93. Find k such that the line containing the points $(-3, k)$ and $(4, 8)$ is parallel to the line containing the points $(5, 3)$ and $(1, -6)$.

94. Find an equation of the line passing through the point $(4, 5)$ and perpendicular to the line passing through the points $(-1, 3)$ and $(2, 9)$.

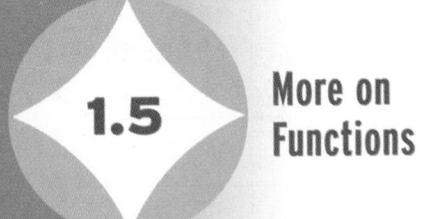

1.5

More on Functions

◆ Graph functions, looking for intervals on which the function is increasing, decreasing, or constant, and estimate relative maxima and minima.

◆ Given an application, find a function that models the application, find the domain of the function and function values, and then graph the function.

◆ Graph functions defined piecewise.

Because functions occur in so many real-world situations, it is important to be able to analyze them carefully.

◆ Increasing, Decreasing, and Constant Functions

On a given interval, if the graph of a function rises from left to right, it is said to be **increasing** on that interval. If the graph drops from left to right, it is said to be **decreasing**. If the function values stay the same from left to right, the function is said to be **constant**.

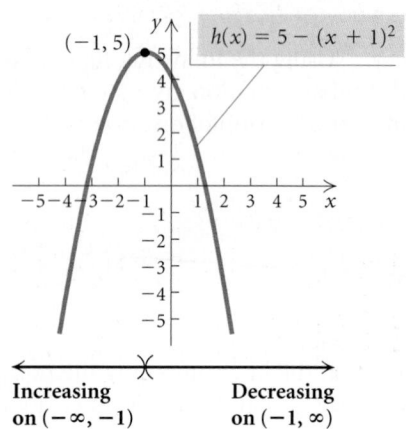

Increasing
on $(-\infty, -1)$ Decreasing
on $(-1, \infty)$

Constant

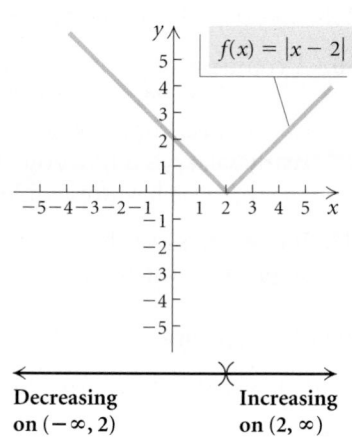

Decreasing
on $(-\infty, 2)$ Increasing
on $(2, \infty)$

We are led to the following definitions.

> ### Increasing, Decreasing, and Constant Functions
>
> A function f is said to be **increasing** on an *open* interval I, if for all a and b in that interval, $a < b$ implies $f(a) < f(b)$. (See Fig. 1.)
>
> A function f is said to be **decreasing** on an *open* interval I, if for all a and b in that interval, $a < b$ implies $f(a) > f(b)$. (See Fig. 2.)
>
> A function f is said to be **constant** on an *open* interval I, if for all a and b in that interval, $f(a) = f(b)$. (See Fig. 3.)

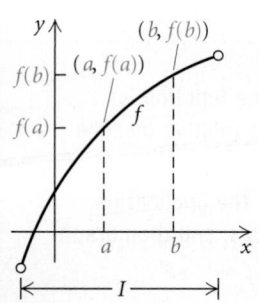

For $a < b$ in I, $f(a) < f(b)$;
f is **increasing** on I.

Figure 1

For $a < b$ in I, $f(a) > f(b)$;
f is **decreasing** on I.

Figure 2

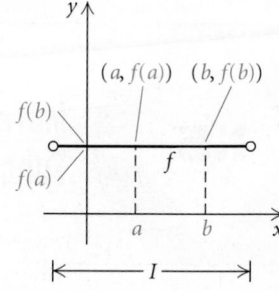

For all a and b in I, $f(a) = f(b)$;
f is **constant** on I.

Figure 3

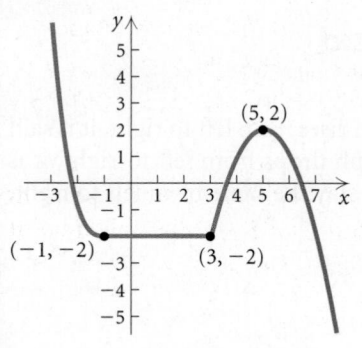

EXAMPLE 1 Determine the intervals on which the function in the figure at left is **(a)** increasing; **(b)** decreasing; **(c)** constant.

Solution When expressing interval(s) on which a function is increasing, decreasing, or constant, we consider only values in the domain of the function.

a) For x-values (that is, values in the domain) from $x = 3$ to $x = 5$, the y-values (that is, values in the range) increase from -2 to 2. Thus the function is increasing on the interval $(3, 5)$.

b) For all x-values from $-\infty$ to -1, y-values decrease; y-values also decrease for x-values from 5 to ∞. Thus the function is decreasing on the intervals $(-\infty, -1)$ and $(5, \infty)$.

c) For x-values from -1 to 3, y is -2. The function is constant on the interval $(-1, 3)$.

▶ Now Try Exercise 5.

In calculus, the slope of a line tangent to the graph of a function at a particular point is used to determine whether the function is increasing, decreasing, or constant at that point. If the slope is positive, the function is increasing; if the slope is negative, the function is decreasing. Since slope cannot be both positive and negative at the same point, a function cannot be both increasing and decreasing at a specific point. For this reason, increasing, decreasing, and constant intervals are expressed in *open interval* notation. In Example 1, if $[3, 5]$ had been used for the increasing interval and $[5, \infty)$ for a decreasing interval, the function would be both increasing and decreasing at $x = 5$. This is not possible.

✦ Relative Maximum and Minimum Values

Consider the graph shown below. Note the "peaks" and "valleys" at the x-values c_1, c_2, and c_3. The function value $f(c_2)$ is called a **relative maximum** (plural, **maxima**). Each of the function values $f(c_1)$ and $f(c_3)$ is called a **relative minimum** (plural, **minima**).

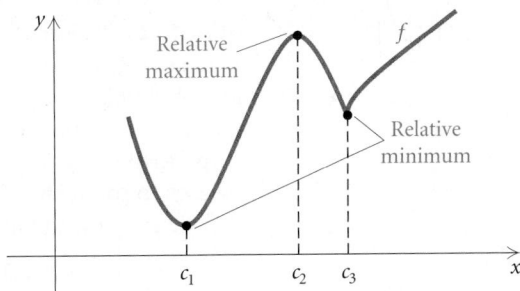

Relative Maxima and Minima

Suppose that f is a function for which $f(c)$ exists for some c in the domain of f. Then:

$f(c)$ is a **relative maximum** if there exists an *open* interval I containing c such that $f(c) > f(x)$, for all x in I where $x \neq c$; and

$f(c)$ is a **relative minimum** if there exists an *open* interval I containing c such that $f(c) < f(x)$, for all x in I where $x \neq c$.

Simply stated, $f(c)$ is a *relative* maximum if $f(c)$ is the highest point in some *open* interval, and $f(c)$ is a *relative* minimum if $f(c)$ is the lowest point in some *open* interval.

TECHNOLOGY ⋯⋯⋯⋯⋯
CONNECTION

We can approximate relative maximum and minimum values with the MAXIMUM and MINIMUM features from the CALC menu on a graphing calculator. See the *Graphing Calculator Manual* for more information on this procedure.

If you take a calculus course, you will learn a method for determining exact values of relative maxima and minima. In Section 2.4, we will find exact maximum and minimum values of quadratic functions algebraically. MAXIMUM and MINIMUM features on a graphing calculator can be used to approximate relative maxima and minima. In this section, we will read the values shown on a graph.

EXAMPLE 2 Using the graph shown below, determine any relative maxima or minima of the function $f(x) = 0.1x^3 - 0.6x^2 - 0.1x + 2$ and the intervals on which the function is increasing or decreasing.

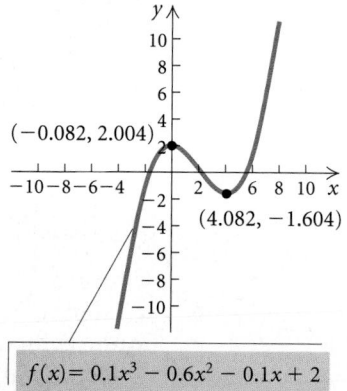

Solution We see that the *relative maximum* value of the function is 2.004. It occurs when $x = -0.082$. We also see the *relative minimum*: -1.604 at $x = 4.082$.

We note that the graph starts rising, or increasing, from the left and stops increasing at the relative maximum. From this point, the graph decreases to the relative minimum and then begins to rise again. The function is *increasing* on the intervals

$$(-\infty, -0.082) \quad \text{and} \quad (4.082, \infty)$$

and *decreasing* on the interval

$$(-0.082, 4.082).$$

▶ Now Try Exercise 15.

✦ Applications of Functions

Many real-world situations can be modeled by functions.

EXAMPLE 3 *Car Distance.* Tracy and Graham drive away from a campground at right angles to each other. Tracy's speed is 65 mph and Graham's is 55 mph.

a) Express the distance between the cars as a function of time.

b) Find the domain of the function.

Solution

a) Suppose 1 hr goes by. At that time, Tracy has traveled 65 mi and Graham has traveled 55 mi. We can use the Pythagorean theorem then to find the distance between them. This distance would be the length of the hypotenuse of a triangle with legs measuring 65 mi and 55 mi. After 2 hr, the triangle's legs would measure 130 mi and 110 mi. Noting that the distances will always be changing, we make a drawing and let $t =$ the time, in hours, that Tracy and Graham have been driving since leaving the campground.

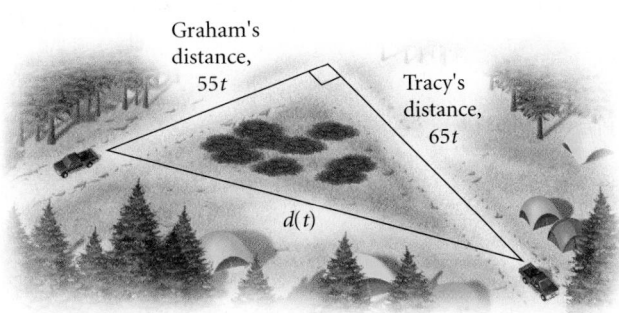

Graham's distance, $55t$

Tracy's distance, $65t$

$d(t)$

After t hours, Tracy has traveled $65t$ miles and Graham $55t$ miles. We can use the Pythagorean theorem:

$$[d(t)]^2 = (65t)^2 + (55t)^2.$$

Because distance must be nonnegative, we need consider only the positive square root when solving for $d(t)$:

$$d(t) = \sqrt{(65t)^2 + (55t)^2}$$
$$= \sqrt{4225t^2 + 3025t^2}$$
$$= \sqrt{7250t^2}$$
$$= \sqrt{7250}\,\sqrt{t^2}$$
$$\approx 85.15|t| \qquad \text{Approximating the root to two decimal places}$$
$$\approx 85.15t. \qquad \text{Since } t \geq 0, |t| = t.$$

Thus, $d(t) = 85.15t,\ t \geq 0$.

b) Since the time traveled, t, must be nonnegative, the domain is the set of nonnegative real numbers $[0, \infty)$. ▶ **Now Try Exercise 25.**

EXAMPLE 4 *Storage Area.* The Sound Shop has 20 ft of dividers with which to set off a rectangular area for the storage of overstock. If a corner of the store is used for the storage area, the partition need only form two sides of a rectangle.

a) Express the floor area of the storage space as a function of the length of the partition.

b) Find the domain of the function.

c) Using the graph shown at left, determine the dimensions that maximize the area of the floor.

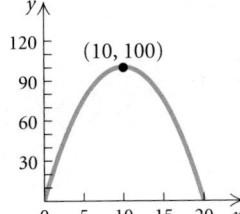

(10, 100)

Solution

a) Note that the dividers will form two sides of a rectangle. If, for example, 14 ft of dividers are used for the length of the rectangle, that would leave $20 - 14$, or 6 ft of dividers for the width. Thus if $x =$ the length, in feet, of the rectangle, then $20 - x =$ the width. We represent this information in a sketch, as shown below.

The area, $A(x)$, is given by

$$A(x) = x(20 - x) \quad \text{Area = length · width}$$
$$= 20x - x^2.$$

The function $A(x) = 20x - x^2$ can be used to express the rectangle's area as a function of the length.

b) Because the rectangle's length must be positive and only 20 ft of dividers is available, we restrict the domain of A to $\{x \mid 0 < x < 20\}$, that is, the interval $(0, 20)$.

c) On the graph of the function on the preceding page, the maximum value of the area function on the interval $(0, 20)$ appears to be 100 when $x = 10$. Thus the dimensions that maximize the area are

Length $= x = 10$ ft   and

Width $= 20 - x = 20 - 10 = 10$ ft.   ▶ **Now Try Exercise 31.**

◆ Functions Defined Piecewise

Sometimes functions are defined **piecewise** using different output formulas for different parts of the domain.

TABLE 1

x $(x < 3)$	$g(x) = \frac{1}{3}x + 3$
-3	2
0	3
2	$3\frac{2}{3}$

TABLE 2

x $(x \geq 3)$	$g(x) = -x$
3	-3
4	-4
6	-6

TABLE 3

x $(x \leq 0)$	$f(x) = 4$
-5	4
-2	4
0	4

TABLE 4

x $(0 < x \leq 2)$	$f(x) = 4 - x^2$
$\frac{1}{2}$	$3\frac{3}{4}$
1	3
2	0

TABLE 5

x $(x > 2)$	$f(x) = 2x - 6$
$2\frac{1}{2}$	-1
3	0
5	4

EXAMPLE 5 Graph the function defined as

$$g(x) = \begin{cases} \dfrac{1}{3}x + 3, & \text{for } x < 3, \\ -x, & \text{for } x \geq 3, \end{cases}$$

Solution We create the graph in two parts. We list some ordered pairs in tables, as shown at left.

a) We graph $g(x) = \frac{1}{3}x + 3$ *only* for inputs x less than 3, that is, on the interval $(-\infty, 3)$. (See Table 1.)

b) We graph $g(x) = -x$ *only* for inputs x greater than or equal to 3, that is, on the interval $[3, \infty)$. (See Table 2.)

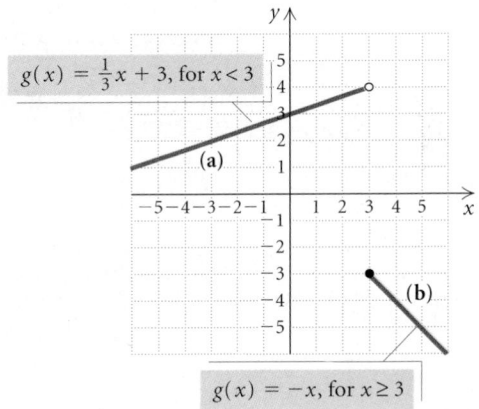

$g(x) = \frac{1}{3}x + 3$, for $x < 3$

(a)

(b)

$g(x) = -x$, for $x \geq 3$

▶ Now Try Exercise 39.

EXAMPLE 6 Graph the function defined as

$$f(x) = \begin{cases} 4, & \text{for } x \leq 0, \\ 4 - x^2, & \text{for } 0 < x \leq 2, \\ 2x - 6, & \text{for } x > 2. \end{cases}$$

Solution We create the graph in three parts, as shown and described below. We list some ordered pairs in tables, as shown at left.

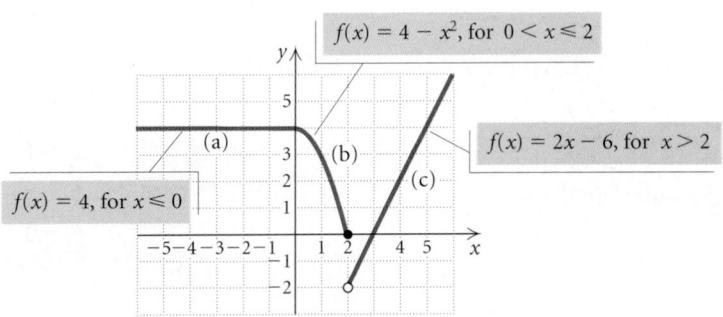

$f(x) = 4 - x^2$, for $0 < x \leq 2$

(a)

(b)

(c)

$f(x) = 2x - 6$, for $x > 2$

$f(x) = 4$, for $x \leq 0$

a) We graph $f(x) = 4$ *only* for inputs x less than or equal to 0, that is, on the interval $(-\infty, 0]$. (See Table 3.)

b) We graph $f(x) = 4 - x^2$ *only* for inputs x greater than 0 and less than or equal to 2, that is, on the interval $(0, 2]$. (See Table 4.)

c) We graph $f(x) = 2x - 6$ *only* for inputs x greater than 2, that is, on the interval $(2, \infty)$. (See Table 5.)

▶ Now Try Exercise 43.

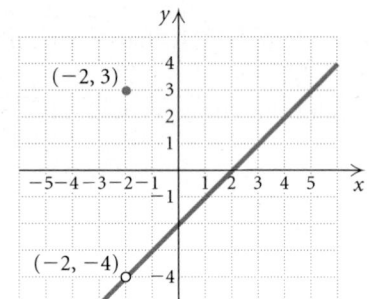

EXAMPLE 7 Graph the function defined as

$$f(x) = \begin{cases} \dfrac{x^2 - 4}{x + 2}, & \text{for } x \neq -2, \\ 3, & \text{for } x = -2. \end{cases}$$

Solution When $x \neq -2$, the denominator of $(x^2 - 4)/(x + 2)$ is nonzero, so we can simplify:

$$\frac{x^2 - 4}{x + 2} = \frac{(x + 2)(x - 2)}{x + 2} = x - 2.$$

Thus

$$f(x) = x - 2, \quad \text{for } x \neq -2.$$

The graph of this part of the piecewise function consists of a line with a "hole" at the point $(-2, -4)$, indicated by the open dot. The hole is necessary since this part is not defined for -2. At $x = -2$, we have $f(-2) = 3$ (by the definition of the function), so the point $(-2, 3)$ is plotted above the open dot.

▶ Now Try Exercise 47.

A piecewise function with importance in calculus and computer programming is the **greatest integer function,** f, denoted as $f(x) = [\![x]\!]$, or $\text{int}(x)$.

> ### Greatest Integer Function
> $f(x) = [\![x]\!] = $ the greatest integer *less than or equal to x.*

The greatest integer function pairs each input with the greatest integer *less than or equal to* that input. Thus, x-values 1, $1\frac{1}{2}$, and 1.8 are all paired with the y-value 1. Other pairings are shown below.

TECHNOLOGY
CONNECTION

When we are graphing the greatest integer function

$$f(x) = [\![x]\!]$$

on a graphing calculator, DOT mode is preferable, although it does not show the open dots at the endpoints of segments.

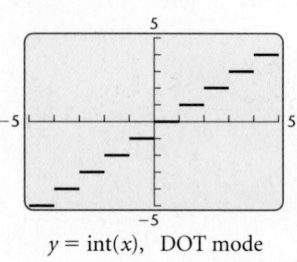

$y = \text{int}(x)$, DOT mode

$$
\begin{array}{llll}
-4 & -1 & 0 & 2 \\
-3.6 \rightarrow -4 & -\frac{7}{8} \longrightarrow -1 & \frac{1}{10} \longrightarrow 0 & 2.1 \rightarrow 2 \\
-3\frac{1}{4} & -0.25 & 0.99 & 2\frac{3}{4}
\end{array}
$$

EXAMPLE 8 Graph $f(x) = [\![x]\!]$ and determine its domain and range.

Solution The greatest integer function can also be defined as a piecewise function with an infinite number of statements.

$$f(x) = [\![x]\!] = \begin{cases} \vdots \\ -3, & \text{for } -3 \le x < -2, \\ -2, & \text{for } -2 \le x < -1, \\ -1, & \text{for } -1 \le x < 0, \\ 0, & \text{for } 0 \le x < 1, \\ 1, & \text{for } 1 \le x < 2, \\ 2, & \text{for } 2 \le x < 3, \\ 3, & \text{for } 3 \le x < 4, \\ \vdots \end{cases}$$

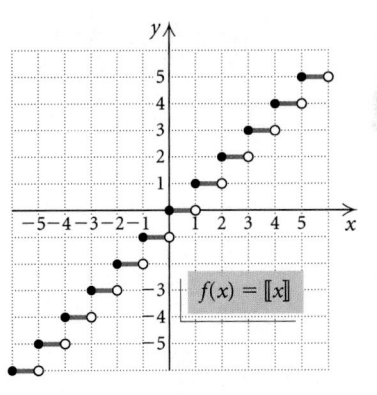

We see that the domain of $f(x)$ is the set of all real numbers, $(-\infty, \infty)$, and the range is the set of all integers, $\{\ldots, -3, -2, -1, 0, 1, 2, 3, \ldots\}$.

▶ Now Try Exercise 51.

1.5 EXERCISE SET

Determine intervals on which the function is (**a**) *increasing,* (**b**) *decreasing, and* (**c**) *constant.*

1.

2.

3.

4.

5.

6.

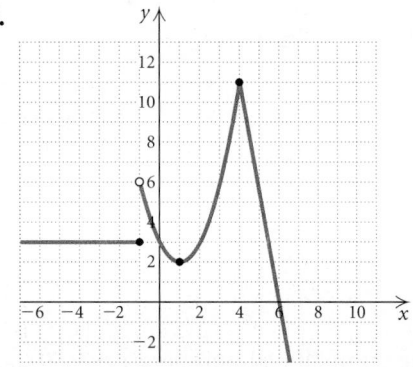

7.–12. Determine the domain and the range of each of the functions graphed in Exercises 1–6.

Using the graph, determine any relative maxima or minima of the function and the intervals on which the function is increasing or decreasing.

13. $f(x) = -x^2 + 5x - 3$

14. $f(x) = x^2 - 2x + 3$

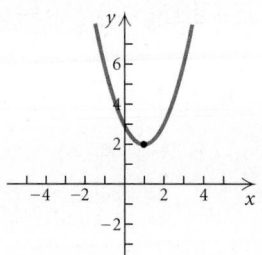

15.
$f(x) = \frac{1}{4}x^3 - \frac{1}{2}x^2 - x + 2$

$(-0.667, 2.370)$

$(2, 0)$

16.
$f(x) = -0.09x^3 + 0.5x^2 - 0.1x + 1$

$(3.601, 2.921)$

$(0.103, 0.955)$

Graph the function. Estimate the intervals on which the function is increasing or decreasing and any relative maxima or minima.

17. $f(x) = x^2$

18. $f(x) = 4 - x^2$

19. $f(x) = 5 - |x|$

20. $f(x) = |x + 3| - 5$

21. $f(x) = x^2 - 6x + 10$

22. $f(x) = -x^2 - 8x - 9$

23. *Garden Area.* Creative Landscaping has 60 yd of fencing with which to enclose a rectangular flower garden. If the garden is x yards long, express the garden's area as a function of the length.

24. *Triangular Scarf.* A seamstress is designing a triangular scarf so that the length of the base of the triangle, in inches, is 7 less than twice the height, h. Express the area of the scarf as a function of the height.

25. *Rising Balloon.* A hot-air balloon rises straight up from the ground at a rate of 120 ft/min. The balloon is tracked from a rangefinder on the ground at point P, which is 400 ft from the release point Q of the balloon. Let $d =$ the distance from the balloon to the rangefinder and $t =$ the time, in minutes, since the balloon was released. Express d as a function of t.

26. *Airplane Distance.* An airplane is flying at an altitude of 3700 ft. The slanted distance directly to the airport is d feet. Express the horizontal distance h as a function of d.

3700 ft

27. *Inscribed Rhombus.* A rhombus is inscribed in a rectangle that is w meters wide with a perimeter of 40 m. Each vertex of the rhombus is a midpoint of a side of the rectangle. Express the area of the rhombus as a function of the rectangle's width.

w

28. *Carpet Area.* A carpet installer uses 46 ft of linen tape to bind the edges of a rectangular hall runner. If the runner is w feet wide, express its area as a function of the width.

29. *Golf Distance Finder.* A device used in golf to estimate the distance d, in yards, to a hole measures the size s, in inches, that the 7-ft pin appears to be in a viewfinder. Express the distance d as a function of s.

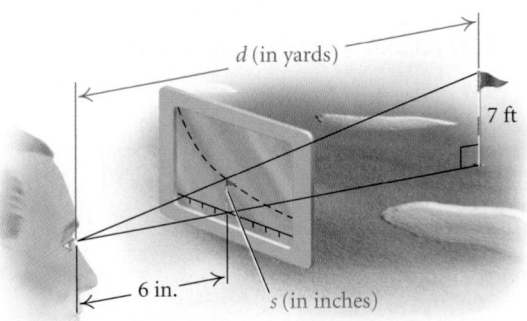

d (in yards)

7 ft

6 in.

s (in inches)

30. *Gas Tank Volume.* A gas tank has ends that are hemispheres of radius r feet. The cylindrical

midsection is 6 ft long. Express the volume of the tank as a function of r.

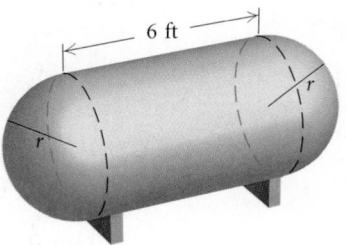

6 ft

r

r

31. *Play Space.* A daycare center has 30 ft of dividers with which to enclose a rectangular play space in a corner of a large room. The sides against the wall require no partition. Suppose the play space is x feet long.

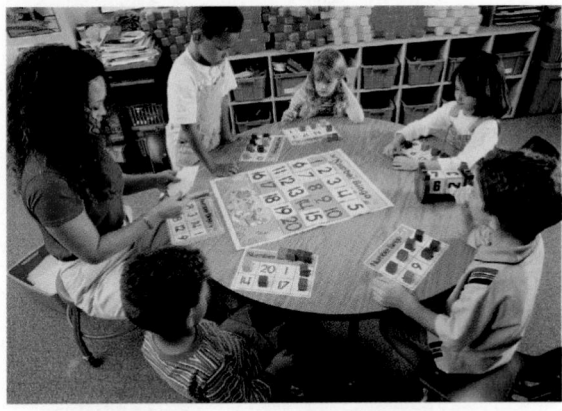

a) Express the area of the play space as a function of x.
b) Find the domain of the function.
c) Using the graph of the function shown below, determine the dimensions that yield the maximum area.

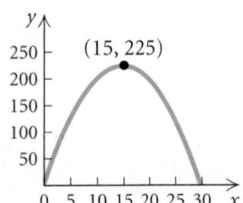

(15, 225)

32. *Corral Design.* A rancher has 360 yd of fencing with which to enclose two adjacent rectangular corrals, one for sheep and one for cattle. A river forms one side of the corrals. Suppose the width of each corral is *x* yards.

a) Express the total area of the two corrals as a function of *x*.
b) Find the domain of the function.
c) Using the graph of the function shown below, determine the dimensions that yield the maximum area.

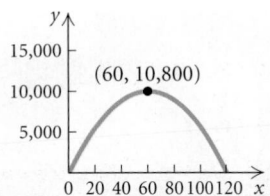

33. *Volume of a Box.* From a 12-cm by 12-cm piece of cardboard, square corners are cut out so that the sides can be folded up to make a box.

a) Express the volume of the box as a function of the length *x*, in centimeters, of a cut-out square.
b) Find the domain of the function.
c) Using the graph of the function shown below, determine the dimensions that yield the maximum volume.

34. *Molding Plastics.* Plastics Unlimited plans to produce a one-component vertical file by bending

the long side of an 8-in. by 14-in. sheet of plastic along two lines to form a U shape.

a) Express the volume of the file as a function of the height *x*, in inches, of the file.
b) Find the domain of the function.
c) Using the graph of the function shown below, determine how tall the file should be in order to maximize the volume the file can hold.

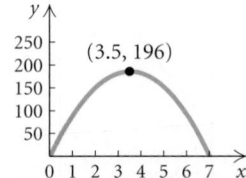

For each piecewise function, find the specified function values.

35. $g(x) = \begin{cases} x + 4, & \text{for } x \le 1, \\ 8 - x, & \text{for } x > 1 \end{cases}$
$g(-4), g(0), g(1),$ and $g(3)$

36. $f(x) = \begin{cases} 3, & \text{for } x \le -2, \\ \frac{1}{2}x + 6, & \text{for } x > -2 \end{cases}$
$f(-5), f(-2), f(0),$ and $f(2)$

37. $h(x) = \begin{cases} -3x - 18, & \text{for } x < -5, \\ 1, & \text{for } -5 \le x < 1, \\ x + 2, & \text{for } x \ge 1 \end{cases}$
$h(-8), h(-5), h(0), h(1),$ and $h(4)$

38. $f(x) = \begin{cases} -5x - 8, & \text{for } x < -2, \\ \frac{1}{2}x + 5, & \text{for } -2 \le x \le 4, \\ 10 - 2x, & \text{for } x > 4 \end{cases}$
$f(-4), f(-2), f(4),$ and $f(6)$

Graph each of the following.

39. $f(x) = \begin{cases} \frac{1}{2}x, & \text{for } x < 0, \\ x + 3, & \text{for } x \ge 0 \end{cases}$

40. $f(x) = \begin{cases} -\frac{1}{3}x + 2, & \text{for } x \le 0, \\ x - 5, & \text{for } x > 0 \end{cases}$

41. $f(x) = \begin{cases} -\frac{3}{4}x + 2, & \text{for } x < 4, \\ -1 + x, & \text{for } x \geq 4 \end{cases}$

42. $h(x) = \begin{cases} 2x - 1, & \text{for } x < 2, \\ 2 - x, & \text{for } x \geq 2 \end{cases}$

43. $f(x) = \begin{cases} x + 1, & \text{for } x \leq -3, \\ -1, & \text{for } -3 < x < 4, \\ \frac{1}{2}x, & \text{for } x \geq 4 \end{cases}$

44. $f(x) = \begin{cases} 4, & \text{for } x \leq -2, \\ x + 1, & \text{for } -2 < x < 3, \\ -x, & \text{for } x \geq 3 \end{cases}$

45. $g(x) = \begin{cases} \frac{1}{2}x - 1, & \text{for } x < 0, \\ 3, & \text{for } 0 \leq x \leq 1, \\ -2x, & \text{for } x > 1 \end{cases}$

46. $f(x) = \begin{cases} \dfrac{x^2 - 9}{x + 3}, & \text{for } x \neq -3, \\ 5, & \text{for } x = -3 \end{cases}$

47. $f(x) = \begin{cases} 2, & \text{for } x = 5, \\ \dfrac{x^2 - 25}{x - 5}, & \text{for } x \neq 5 \end{cases}$

48. $f(x) = \begin{cases} \dfrac{x^2 + 3x + 2}{x + 1}, & \text{for } x \neq -1, \\ 7, & \text{for } x = -1 \end{cases}$

49. $f(x) = [\![x]\!]$

50. $f(x) = 2[\![x]\!]$

51. $g(x) = 1 + [\![x]\!]$

52. $h(x) = \frac{1}{2}[\![x]\!] - 2$

53.–58. Find the domain and the range of each of the functions defined in Exercises 39–44.

Determine the domain and the range of the piecewise function. Then write an equation for the function.

59.

60.

61.

62.

63.

64.
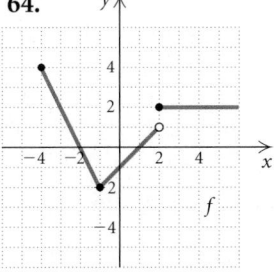

Technology Connection

Graph the function using the given viewing window. Find the intervals on which the function is increasing or decreasing and find any relative maxima or minima. Change the viewing window if it seems appropriate for further analysis.

65. $f(x) = -x^3 + 6x^2 - 9x - 4,$
$[-3, 7, -20, 15]$

66. $f(x) = 0.2x^3 - 0.2x^2 - 5x - 4,$
$[-10, 10, -30, 20]$

67. $f(x) = 1.1x^4 - 5.3x^2 + 4.07,$
$[-4, 4, -4, 8]$

68. $f(x) = 1.2(x + 3)^4 + 10.3(x + 3)^2 + 9.78,$
$[-9, 3, -40, 100]$

69. *Temperature During an Illness.* The temperature of a patient during an illness is given by the function

$$T(t) = -0.1t^2 + 1.2t + 98.6, \quad 0 \leq t \leq 12,$$

where T is the temperature, in degrees Fahrenheit, at time t, in days, after the onset of the illness.

a) Graph the function using a graphing calculator.
b) Use the MAXIMUM feature to determine at what time the patient's temperature was the highest. What was the highest temperature?

70. *Advertising Effect.* A software firm estimates that it will sell N units of a new DVD video game after spending a dollars on advertising, where

$$N(a) = -a^2 + 300a + 6, \quad 0 \le a \le 300,$$

and a is measured in thousands of dollars.

a) Graph the function using a graphing calculator.
b) Use the MAXIMUM feature to find the relative maximum.
c) For what advertising expenditure will the greatest number of games be sold? How many games will be sold for that amount?

Use a graphing calculator to find the intervals on which the function is increasing or decreasing. Consider the entire set of real numbers if no domain is given.

71. $f(x) = \dfrac{8x}{x^2 + 1}$

72. $f(x) = \dfrac{-4}{x^2 + 1}$

73. $f(x) = x\sqrt{4 - x^2}, \quad \text{for } -2 \le x \le 2$

74. $f(x) = -0.8x\sqrt{9 - x^2}, \quad \text{for } -3 \le x \le 3$

75. *Area of an Inscribed Rectangle.* A rectangle that is x feet wide is inscribed in a circle of radius 8 ft.

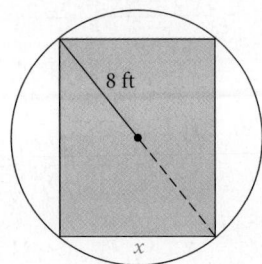

a) Express the area of the rectangle as a function of x.
b) Find the domain of the function.
c) Graph the function with a graphing calculator.
d) What dimensions maximize the area of the rectangle?

76. *Cost of Material.* A rectangular box with volume 320 ft^3 is built with a square base and top. The cost is \$1.50/ft^2 for the bottom, \$2.50/ft^2 for the sides, and \$1/ft^2 for the top. Let $x =$ the length of the base, in feet.

a) Express the cost of the box as a function of x.
b) Find the domain of the function.
c) Graph the function with a graphing calculator.
d) What dimensions minimize the cost of the box?

Collaborative Discussion and Writing

77. Describe a real-world situation that could be modeled by a function that is, in turn, increasing, then constant, and finally decreasing.

78. Simply stated, a *continuous function* is a function whose graph can be drawn without lifting the pencil from the paper. Examine several functions in this exercise set to see if they are continuous. Then explore the continuous functions to estimate the relative maxima and minima. For continuous functions, how can you connect the ideas of increasing and decreasing on an interval to relative maxima and minima?

Skill Maintenance

In each of Exercises 79–82, fill in the blank(s) with the correct term(s). Some of the given choices will not be used; others will be used more than once.

> constant
> function
> any
> midpoint formula
> y-intercept
> range
> domain
> distance formula
> exactly one
> identity
> x-intercept

79. A _____ is a correspondence between a first set, called the _____ , and a second set called the _____ , such that each member of the _____ corresponds to _____ member of the _____ .

80. The _____ is $\left(\dfrac{x_1 + x_2}{2}, \dfrac{y_1 + y_2}{2}\right)$.

81. A(n) _____ is a point $(a, 0)$.

82. A function f is a linear function if it can be written as $f(x) = mx + b$, where m and b are constants. If $m = 0$, the function is a _____ function $f(x) = b$. If $m = 1$ and $b = 0$, the function is the _____ function $f(x) = x$.

Synthesis

83. If $([\![x]\!])^2 = 25$, what are the possible inputs for x?

84. If $[\![x + 2]\!] = -3$, what are the possible inputs for x?

85. *Volume of an Inscribed Cylinder.* A right circular cylinder of height h and radius r is inscribed in a right circular cone with a height of 10 ft and a base with radius 6 ft.

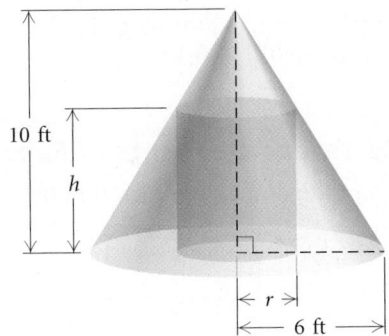

a) Express the height h of the cylinder as a function of r.
b) Express the volume V of the cylinder as a function of r.
c) Express the volume V of the cylinder as a function of h.

86. *Minimizing Power Line Costs.* A power line is constructed from a power station at point A to an island at point C, which is 1 mi opposite point B on the shore. Point B is 4 mi downshore from the power station at A. It costs \$5000 per mile to lay the power line under water and \$3000 per mile to lay the power line under land. The line comes to the shore at point S downshore from A. Let $x =$ the distance from B to S.

a) Express the cost C of laying the line as a function of x.
b) At what distance x from point B should the line come to shore in order to minimize cost?

1.6 ◆ The Algebra of Functions

◆ Find the sum, the difference, the product, and the quotient of two functions, and determine the domains of the resulting functions.

◆ Construct and simplify the difference quotient for a function.

◆ Find the composition of two functions and the domain of the composition; decompose a function as a composition of two functions.

◆ The Algebra of Functions: Sums, Differences, Products, and Quotients

We now use addition, subtraction, multiplication, and division to combine functions and obtain new functions.

Consider the following two functions f and g:

$$f(x) = x + 2 \quad \text{and} \quad g(x) = x^2 + 1.$$

Since $f(3) = 3 + 2 = 5$ and $g(3) = 3^2 + 1 = 10$, we have

$$f(3) + g(3) = 5 + 10 = 15,$$
$$f(3) - g(3) = 5 - 10 = -5,$$
$$f(3) \cdot g(3) = 5 \cdot 10 = 50, \quad \text{and}$$
$$\frac{f(3)}{g(3)} = \frac{5}{10} = \frac{1}{2}.$$

In fact, so long as x is in the domain of *both* f and g, we can easily compute $f(x) + g(x)$, $f(x) - g(x)$, $f(x) \cdot g(x)$, and, assuming $g(x) \neq 0$, $f(x)/g(x)$. Notation has been developed to facilitate this work.

Sums, Differences, Products, and Quotients of Functions

If f and g are functions and x is in the domain of each function, then

$$(f + g)(x) = f(x) + g(x),$$
$$(f - g)(x) = f(x) - g(x),$$
$$(fg)(x) = f(x) \cdot g(x),$$
$$(f/g)(x) = f(x)/g(x), \text{ provided } g(x) \neq 0.$$

EXAMPLE 1   Given that $f(x) = x + 1$ and $g(x) = \sqrt{x + 3}$, find each of the following.

a) $(f + g)(x)$ b) $(f + g)(6)$ c) $(f + g)(-4)$

Solution

a) $(f + g)(x) = f(x) + g(x)$
$\qquad\qquad\quad = x + 1 + \sqrt{x + 3}$ This cannot be simplified.

b) We can find $(f + g)(6)$ provided 6 is in the domain of *each* function. The *domain* of f is all real numbers. The *domain* of g is all real numbers x for which $x + 3 \geq 0$, or $x \geq -3$. This is the interval $[-3, \infty)$. Thus, 6 is in both domains, so we have

$$f(6) = 6 + 1 = 7, \qquad g(6) = \sqrt{6 + 3} = \sqrt{9} = 3,$$
$$(f + g)(6) = f(6) + g(6) = 7 + 3 = 10.$$

Another method is to use the formula found in part (a):

$$(f + g)(6) = 6 + 1 + \sqrt{6 + 3} = 7 + \sqrt{9} = 7 + 3 = 10.$$

c) To find $(f + g)(-4)$, we must first determine whether -4 is in the domain of each function. We note that -4 is not in the domain of g, $[-3, \infty)$; that is, $\sqrt{-4 + 3}$ is not a real number. Thus, $(f + g)(-4)$ does not exist.

▶ **Now Try Exercise 15.**

It is useful to view the concept of the sum of two functions graphically. In the graph below, we see the graphs of two functions f and g and their sum, $f + g$. Consider finding $(f + g)(4) = f(4) + g(4)$. We can locate $g(4)$ on the graph of g and measure it. Then we add that length on top of $f(4)$ on the graph of f. The sum gives us $(f + g)(4)$.

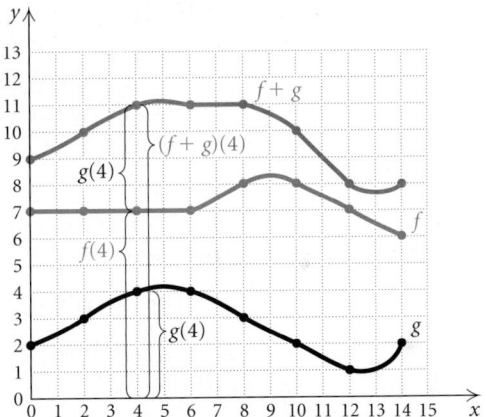

With this in mind, let's view Example 1 from a graphical perspective. Let's look at the graphs of

$$f(x) = x + 1, \qquad g(x) = \sqrt{x + 3}, \quad \text{and}$$
$$(f + g)(x) = x + 1 + \sqrt{x + 3}.$$

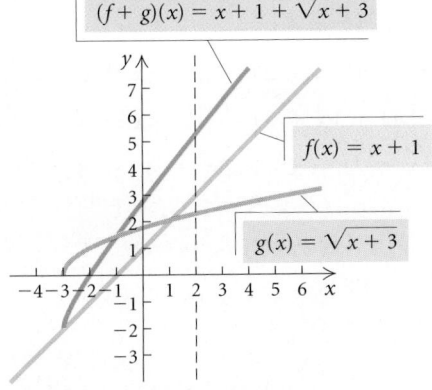

See the graph at left. Note that the domain of f is the set of all real numbers. The domain of g is $[-3, \infty)$. The domain of $f + g$ is the set of numbers in the *intersection* of the domains, that is, the set of numbers in both domains.

Domain of f		$(-\infty, \infty)$
Domain of g		$[-3, \infty)$
Domain of $f + g$		$[-3, \infty)$

Thus the domain of $f + g$ is $[-3, \infty)$.

We can confirm that the y-coordinates of the graph of $(f + g)(x)$ are the sums of the corresponding y-coordinates of the graphs of $f(x)$ and $g(x)$. Here we confirm it for $x = 2$.

$$f(x) = x + 1 \qquad\qquad g(x) = \sqrt{x + 3}$$
$$f(2) = 2 + 1 = 3; \qquad g(2) = \sqrt{2 + 3} = \sqrt{5};$$
$$(f + g)(x) = x + 1 + \sqrt{x + 3}$$
$$(f + g)(2) = 2 + 1 + \sqrt{2 + 3}$$
$$= 3 + \sqrt{5} = f(2) + g(2).$$

Let's also examine the domains of $f - g$, fg, and f/g for the functions $f(x) = x + 1$ and $g(x) = \sqrt{x + 3}$ of Example 1. The domains of $f - g$ and fg are the same as the domain of $f + g$, $[-3, \infty)$, because numbers in this interval are in the domains of *both* functions. For f/g, $g(x)$ cannot be 0. Since $\sqrt{x + 3} = 0$ when $x = -3$, we must exclude -3 and the domain of f/g is $(-3, \infty)$.

> ### Domains of f + g, f − g, fg, and f/g
>
> If f and g are functions, then the domain of the functions $f + g$, $f - g$, and fg are each the intersection of the domain of f and the domain of g. The domain of f/g is also the intersection of the domains of f and g with the exclusion of any x-values for which $g(x) = 0$.

EXAMPLE 2 Given that $f(x) = x^2 - 4$ and $g(x) = x + 2$, find each of the following.

a) The domain of $f + g$, $f - g$, fg, and f/g

b) $(f + g)(x)$ c) $(f - g)(x)$

d) $(fg)(x)$ e) $(f/g)(x)$

f) $(gg)(x)$

Solution

a) The domain of f is the set of all real numbers. The domain of g is also the set of all real numbers. The domains of $f + g$, $f - g$, and fg are the set of numbers in the intersection of the domains—that is, the set of numbers in both domains, which is again the set of real numbers. For f/g, we must exclude -2, since $g(-2) = 0$. Thus the domain of f/g is the set of real numbers excluding -2, or $(-\infty, -2) \cup (-2, \infty)$.

b) $(f + g)(x) = f(x) + g(x) = (x^2 - 4) + (x + 2) = x^2 + x - 2$

c) $(f - g)(x) = f(x) - g(x) = (x^2 - 4) - (x + 2) = x^2 - x - 6$

d) $(fg)(x) = f(x) \cdot g(x) = (x^2 - 4)(x + 2) = x^3 + 2x^2 - 4x - 8$

e) $(f/g)(x) = \dfrac{f(x)}{g(x)}$

$\qquad = \dfrac{x^2 - 4}{x + 2}$ Note that $g(x) = 0$ when $x = -2$, so $(f/g)(x)$ is not defined when $x = -2$.

$\qquad = \dfrac{(x + 2)(x - 2)}{x + 2}$ Factoring

$\qquad = x - 2$ Removing a factor of 1: $\dfrac{x + 2}{x + 2} = 1$

Thus, $(f/g)(x) = x - 2$ with the added stipulation that $x \neq -2$ since -2 is not in the domain of $(f/g)(x)$.

f) $(gg)(x) = g(x) \cdot g(x) = [g(x)]^2 = (x + 2)^2 = x^2 + 4x + 4$

▷ Now Try Exercise 21.

◆ Difference Quotients

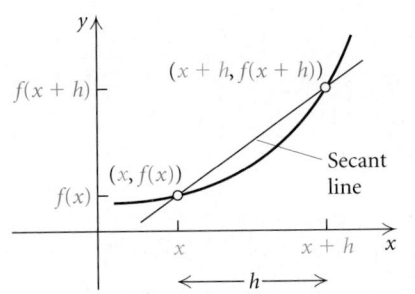

In Section 1.3, we learned that the slope of a line can be considered as an average *rate of change*. Here let's consider a nonlinear function f and draw a line through two points $(x, f(x))$ and $(x + h, f(x + h))$ as shown at left.

The slope of the line, called a **secant line**, is

$$\frac{f(x + h) - f(x)}{(x + h) - x},$$

which simplifies to

$$\frac{f(x + h) - f(x)}{h}.$$ Difference quotient

This ratio is called the **difference quotient**, or the **average rate of change**. In calculus, it is important to be able to find and simplify difference quotients.

EXAMPLE 3 For the function f given by $f(x) = 9x + 5$, find the difference quotient

$$\frac{f(x + h) - f(x)}{h}.$$

Solution We first find $f(x + h)$:

$$f(x + h) = 9(x + h) + 5 \qquad \text{Substituting } x + h \text{ for } x \text{ in } f(x) = 9x + 5$$
$$= 9x + 9h + 5.$$

Then

$$\frac{f(x + h) - f(x)}{h} = \frac{(9x + 9h + 5) - (9x + 5)}{h}$$

$$= \frac{9x + 9h + 5 - 9x - 5}{h}$$

$$= \frac{9h}{h} = \frac{h}{h} \cdot 9 = 1 \cdot 9 = 9.$$

▷ Now Try Exercise 51.

EXAMPLE 4 For the function f given by $f(x) = 2x^2 - x - 3$, find the difference quotient

$$\frac{f(x + h) - f(x)}{h}.$$

Solution We first find $f(x + h)$:

$$f(x + h) = 2(x + h)^2 - (x + h) - 3 \quad \text{Substituting } x + h \text{ for } x \text{ in } f(x) = 2x^2 - x - 3$$

$$= 2[x^2 + 2xh + h^2] - (x + h) - 3$$

$$= 2x^2 + 4xh + 2h^2 - x - h - 3.$$

Then

$$\frac{f(x + h) - f(x)}{h}$$

$$= \frac{[2x^2 + 4xh + 2h^2 - x - h - 3] - [2x^2 - x - 3]}{h}$$

$$= \frac{2x^2 + 4xh + 2h^2 - x - h - 3 - 2x^2 + x + 3}{h}$$

$$= \frac{4xh + 2h^2 - h}{h}$$

$$= \frac{h(4x + 2h - 1)}{h \cdot 1} = \frac{h}{h} \cdot \frac{4x + 2h - 1}{1} = 4x + 2h - 1.$$

▶ Now Try Exercise 53.

◆ The Composition of Functions

In real-world situations, it is not uncommon for the output of a function to depend on some input that is itself an output of another function. For instance, the amount a person pays as state income tax usually depends on the amount of adjusted gross income on the person's federal tax return, which, in turn, depends on his or her annual earnings. Such functions are called **composite functions**.

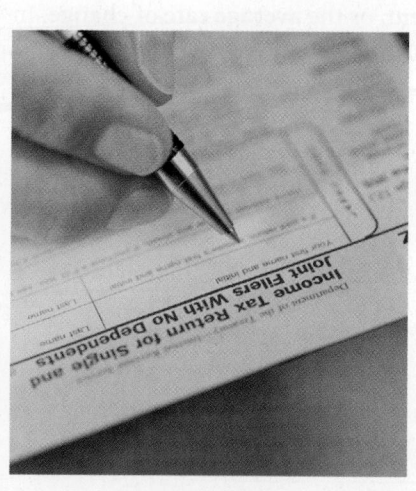

To illustrate how composite functions work, suppose a chemistry student needs a formula to convert Fahrenheit temperatures to Kelvin units. The formula

$$c(t) = \tfrac{5}{9}(t - 32)$$

gives the Celsius temperature $c(t)$ that corresponds to the Fahrenheit temperature t. The formula

$$k(c) = c + 273$$

gives the Kelvin temperature $k(c)$ that corresponds to the Celsius temperature c. Thus, 50° Fahrenheit corresponds to

$$c(50) = \tfrac{5}{9}(50 - 32) = \tfrac{5}{9}(18) = 10° \text{ Celsius}$$

and 10° Celsius corresponds to

$$k(10) = 10 + 273 = 283° \text{ Kelvin}.$$

With the TABLE feature, we can convert Fahrenheit temperatures, x, to Celsius temperatures, y_1, using

$$y_1 = \frac{5}{9}(x - 32).$$

We can also convert Celsius temperatures y_1 to Kelvin units, y_2, using

$$y_2 = y_1 + 273.$$

$$y_1 = \frac{5}{9}(x - 32), \quad y_2 = y_1 + 273$$

X	Y₁	Y₂
50	10	283
59	15	288
68	20	293
77	25	298
86	30	303
95	35	308
104	40	313

X = 50

We see that 50° Fahrenheit is the same as 283° Kelvin. This two-step procedure can be used to convert any Fahrenheit temperature to Kelvin units.

	°F Fahrenheit	°C Celsius	°K Kelvin
Boiling point of water	212°	100°	373°
	50° ➡	10° ➡	283°
Freezing point of water	32°	0°	273°
Absolute zero	−460°	−273°	0°

A student making numerous conversions might look for a formula that converts directly from Fahrenheit to Kelvin. Such a formula can be found by substitution:

$$
\begin{aligned}
k(c(t)) &= c(t) + 273 \\
&= \frac{5}{9}(t - 32) + 273 \qquad \text{Substituting} \\
&= \frac{5}{9}t - \frac{160}{9} + 273 \\
&= \frac{5}{9}t - \frac{160}{9} + \frac{2457}{9} \\
&= \frac{5t + 2297}{9}. \qquad \text{Simplifying}
\end{aligned}
$$

Since the last equation expresses the Kelvin temperature as a new function, K, of the Fahrenheit temperature, t, we can write

$$K(t) = \frac{5t + 2297}{9},$$

where $K(t)$ is the Kelvin temperature corresponding to the Fahrenheit temperature, t. Here we have $K(t) = k(c(t))$. The new function K is called the **composition** of k and c and can be denoted $k \circ c$ (read "k composed with c," "the composition of k and c," or "k circle c").

Composition of Functions

The **composite function** $f \circ g$, the **composition** of f and g, is defined as

$$(f \circ g)(x) = f(g(x)),$$

where x is in the domain of g and $g(x)$ is in the domain of f.

EXAMPLE 5   Given that $f(x) = 2x - 5$ and $g(x) = x^2 - 3x + 8$, find each of the following.

a) $(f \circ g)(x)$ and $(g \circ f)(x)$ **b)** $(f \circ g)(7)$ and $(g \circ f)(7)$

Solution   Consider each function separately:

$f(x) = 2x - 5$ This function multiplies each input by 2 and subtracts 5.

and

$g(x) = x^2 - 3x + 8.$ This function squares an input, subtracts 3 times the input from the result, and then adds 8.

a) To find $(f \circ g)(x)$, we substitute $g(x)$ for x in the equation for $f(x)$:

$$(f \circ g)(x) = f(g(x)) = f(x^2 - 3x + 8) \qquad \text{$x^2 - 3x + 8$ is the input for f.}$$

$$= 2(x^2 - 3x + 8) - 5 \qquad \text{f multiplies the input by 2 and subtracts 5.}$$

$$= 2x^2 - 6x + 16 - 5$$

$$= 2x^2 - 6x + 11.$$

To find $(g \circ f)(x)$, we substitute $f(x)$ for x in the equation for $g(x)$:

$$(g \circ f)(x) = g(f(x)) = g(2x - 5) \qquad \text{$2x - 5$ is the input for g.}$$

$$= (2x - 5)^2 - 3(2x - 5) + 8 \qquad \text{g squares the input, subtracts three times the input, and adds 8.}$$

$$= 4x^2 - 20x + 25 - 6x + 15 + 8$$

$$= 4x^2 - 26x + 48.$$

b) To find $(f \circ g)(7)$, we first find $g(7)$. Then we use $g(7)$ as an input for f:

$$(f \circ g)(7) = f(g(7)) = f(7^2 - 3 \cdot 7 + 8)$$

$$= f(36) = 2 \cdot 36 - 5$$

$$= 67.$$

To find $(g \circ f)(7)$, we first find $f(7)$. Then we use $f(7)$ as an input for g:

$$(g \circ f)(7) = g(f(7)) = g(2 \cdot 7 - 5)$$

$$= g(9) = 9^2 - 3 \cdot 9 + 8$$

$$= 62.$$

We could also find $(f \circ g)(7)$ and $(g \circ f)(7)$ by substituting 7 for x in the equations that we found in part (a):

$$(f \circ g)(x) = 2x^2 - 6x + 11$$

$$(f \circ g)(7) = 2 \cdot 7^2 - 6 \cdot 7 + 11 = 67;$$

$$(g \circ f)(x) = 4x^2 - 26x + 48$$

$$(g \circ f)(7) = 4 \cdot 7^2 - 26 \cdot 7 + 48 = 62.$$ ▶ **Now Try Exercise 67.**

Note in Example 5 that, as a rule, $(f \circ g)(x) \neq (g \circ f)(x)$. We can see this graphically, as shown in the graphs at left.

TECHNOLOGY · · · · · · · · · · · · ·
    CONNECTION

We can check our work in Example 5(b) using a graphing calculator. We enter the following on the equation-editor screen:

$$y_1 = 2x - 5$$

and

$$y_2 = x^2 - 3x + 8.$$

Then, on the home screen, we find $(f \circ g)(7)$ and $(g \circ f)(7)$ using the function notations Y1(Y2(7)) and Y2(Y1(7)), respectively.

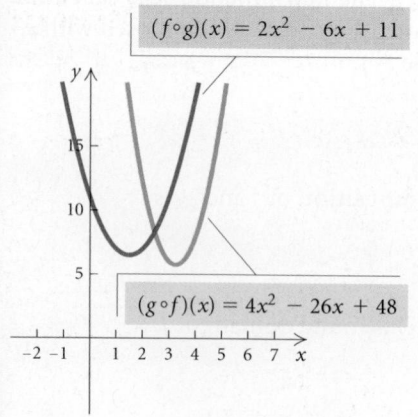

$y_1 = 2x - 5, \ y_2 = x^2 - 3x + 8$

Y1(Y2(7))	
	67
Y2(Y1(7))	
	62

EXAMPLE 6   Given that $f(x) = \sqrt{x}$ and $g(x) = x - 3$:

a) Find $f \circ g$ and $g \circ f$.

b) Find the domains of $f \circ g$ and $g \circ f$.

Solution

a) $(f \circ g)(x) = f(g(x)) = f(x - 3) = \sqrt{x - 3}$

$(g \circ f)(x) = g(f(x)) = g(\sqrt{x}) = \sqrt{x} - 3$

b) The domain of f is $\{x \mid x \geq 0\}$, or the interval $[0, \infty)$. The domain of g is $(-\infty, \infty)$.

To find the domain of $f \circ g$, we first consider the domain of g, $(-\infty, \infty)$. Next, we must consider that the outputs for g will serve as inputs for f. Since the inputs for f cannot be negative, we must have

$$g(x) \geq 0, \quad \text{or} \quad x - 3 \geq 0, \quad \text{or} \quad x \geq 3.$$

Thus the domain of $f \circ g = \{x \mid x \geq 3\}$, or the interval $[3, \infty)$, as the graph in Fig. 1 below confirms.

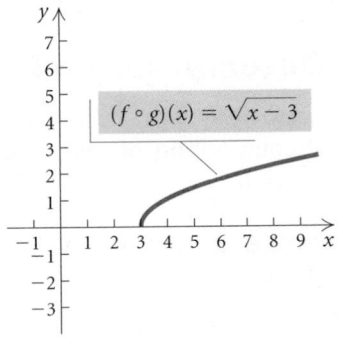

Figure 1   Figure 2

To find the domain of $g \circ f$, we first consider the domain of f, $\{x \mid x \geq 0\}$. Next, we must consider that the outputs for f will serve as inputs for g. Since g can accept *any* real number as an input, any output from f is acceptable so the entire domain of f is the domain of $g \circ f$; that is, the domain of $g \circ f = \{x \mid x \geq 0\}$ or the interval $[0, \infty)$, as the graph in Fig. 2 above confirms.

▶ **Now Try Exercise 79.**

EXAMPLE 7   Given that $f(x) = \dfrac{1}{x - 2}$ and $g(x) = \dfrac{5}{x}$, find $f \circ g$ and $g \circ f$ and the domain of each.

Solution   We have

$$(f \circ g)(x) = f(g(x)) = f\left(\frac{5}{x}\right) = \frac{1}{\dfrac{5}{x} - 2} = \frac{1}{\dfrac{5 - 2x}{x}} = \frac{x}{5 - 2x};$$

$$(g \circ f)(x) = g(f(x)) = g\left(\frac{1}{x - 2}\right) = \frac{5}{\dfrac{1}{x - 2}} = 5(x - 2).$$

The domain of $f = \{x \mid x \neq 2\}$, and the domain of $g = \{x \mid x \neq 0\}$. To find the domain of $f \circ g$, we note that since the domain of g is $\{x \mid x \neq 0\}$, 0 is *not* in the domain of $f \circ g$. Since the domain of f is $\{x \mid x \neq 2\}$, no output of $g(x)$ can be 2. We solve $5/x = 2$ for x:

$$\frac{5}{x} = 2$$

$$5 = 2x$$

$$\frac{5}{2} = x.$$

We find that $\frac{5}{2}$ is also *not* in the domain of $f \circ g$. Then the domain of $f \circ g = \left\{ x \mid x \neq 0 \text{ and } x \neq \frac{5}{2} \right\}$, or $(-\infty, 0) \cup \left(0, \frac{5}{2} \right) \cup \left(\frac{5}{2}, \infty \right)$.

To find the domain of $g \circ f$, we recall the domain of f is $\{x \mid x \neq 2\}$. Thus, 2 is *not* in the domain of $g \circ f$. Since the domain of g is $\{x \mid x \neq 0\}$ and $f(x) = 1/(x - 2)$ is never 0, there are no additional restrictions on the domain of $g \circ f$. Thus the domain of $g \circ f = \{x \mid x \neq 2\}$, or $(-\infty, 2) \cup (2, \infty)$.

▶ Now Try Exercise 75.

✦ Decomposing a Function as a Composition

In calculus, we often need to recognize how a function can be expressed as the composition of two functions. In this way, we are "decomposing" the function.

EXAMPLE 8 If $h(x) = (2x - 3)^5$, find $f(x)$ and $g(x)$ such that $h(x) = (f \circ g)(x)$.

Solution The function $h(x)$ raises $(2x - 3)$ to the 5th power. Two functions that can be used for the composition are

$$f(x) = x^5 \quad \text{and} \quad g(x) = 2x - 3.$$

We can check by forming the composition:

$$h(x) = (f \circ g)(x) = f(g(x)) = f(2x - 3) = (2x - 3)^5.$$

This is the most "obvious" solution. There can be other less obvious answers. For example, if

$$f(x) = (x + 7)^5 \quad \text{and} \quad g(x) = 2x - 10,$$

then

$$h(x) = (f \circ g)(x) = f(g(x))$$
$$= f(2x - 10)$$
$$= [(2x - 10) + 7]^5 = (2x - 3)^5. \qquad \text{▶ Now Try Exercise 91.}$$

1.6 EXERCISE SET

ven that $f(x) = x^2 - 3$ and $g(x) = 2x + 1$, find ch of the following, if it exists.

1. $(f + g)(5)$

2. $(fg)(0)$

3. $(f - g)(-1)$

4. $(fg)(2)$

5. $(f/g)\left(-\frac{1}{2}\right)$

6. $(f - g)(0)$

7. $(fg)\left(-\frac{1}{2}\right)$

8. $(f/g)\left(-\sqrt{3}\right)$

9. $(g - f)(-1)$

10. $(g/f)\left(-\frac{1}{2}\right)$

ven that $h(x) = x + 4$ and $g(x) = \sqrt{x - 1}$, find ch of the following, if it exists.

1. $(h - g)(-4)$

12. $(gh)(10)$

3. $(g/h)(1)$

14. $(h/g)(1)$

5. $(g + h)(1)$

16. $(hg)(3)$

r each pair of functions in Exercises 17–32:

Find the domain of f, g, $f + g$, $f - g$, fg, ff, f/g, and g/f.

Find $(f + g)(x)$, $(f - g)(x)$, $(fg)(x)$, $(ff)(x)$, $(f/g)(x)$, and $(g/f)(x)$.

7. $f(x) = 2x + 3$, $g(x) = 3 - 5x$

8. $f(x) = -x + 1$, $g(x) = 4x - 2$

9. $f(x) = x - 3$, $g(x) = \sqrt{x + 4}$

0. $f(x) = x + 2$, $g(x) = \sqrt{x - 1}$

1. $f(x) = 2x - 1$, $g(x) = -2x^2$

2. $f(x) = x^2 - 1$, $g(x) = 2x + 5$

3. $f(x) = \sqrt{x - 3}$, $g(x) = \sqrt{x + 3}$

4. $f(x) = \sqrt{x}$, $g(x) = \sqrt{2 - x}$

5. $f(x) = x + 1$, $g(x) = |x|$

26. $f(x) = 4|x|$, $g(x) = 1 - x$

27. $f(x) = x^3$, $g(x) = 2x^2 + 5x - 3$

28. $f(x) = x^2 - 4$, $g(x) = x^3$

29. $f(x) = \dfrac{4}{x + 1}$, $g(x) = \dfrac{1}{6 - x}$

30. $f(x) = 2x^2$, $g(x) = \dfrac{2}{x - 5}$

31. $f(x) = \dfrac{1}{x}$, $g(x) = x - 3$

32. $f(x) = \sqrt{x + 6}$, $g(x) = \dfrac{1}{x}$

In Exercises 33–38, consider the functions F and G as shown in the following graph.

33. Find the domain of F, the domain of G, and the domain of $F + G$.

34. Find the domain of $F - G$, FG, and F/G.

35. Find the domain of G/F.

36. Graph $F + G$.

37. Graph $G - F$.

38. Graph $F - G$.

In Exercises 39–44, consider the functions F and G as shown in the following graph.

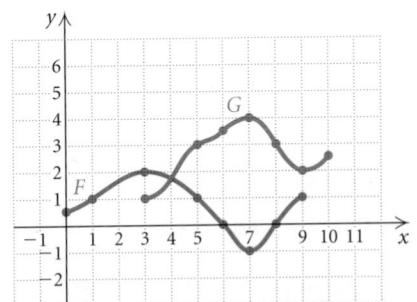

39. Find the domain of F, the domain of G, and the domain of $F + G$.

40. Find the domain of $F - G$, FG, and F/G.

41. Find the domain of G/F.

42. Graph $F + G$.

43. Graph $G - F$.

44. Graph $F - G$.

45. *Total Cost, Revenue, and Profit.* In economics, functions that involve revenue, cost, and profit are used. For example, suppose that $R(x)$ and $C(x)$ denote the total revenue and the total cost, respectively, of producing x units of a new kind of tool for King Hardware Wholesalers. Then the difference

$$P(x) = R(x) - C(x)$$

represents the total profit for producing x tools. Given

$$R(x) = 60x - 0.4x^2 \quad \text{and} \quad C(x) = 3x + 13,$$

find each of the following.

a) $P(x)$
b) $R(100)$, $C(100)$, and $P(100)$

46. *Total Cost, Revenue, and Profit.* Given that

$$R(x) = 200x - x^2 \quad \text{and} \quad C(x) = 5000 + 8x,$$

for a new radio produced by Clear Communication, find each of the following. (See Exercise 45.)

a) $P(x)$
b) $R(175)$, $C(175)$, and $P(175)$

For each function f, construct and simplify the difference quotient

$$\frac{f(x + h) - f(x)}{h}.$$

47. $f(x) = -\frac{3}{5}x + 10$ **48.** $f(x) = x - 4$

49. $f(x) = x^2 + 1$ **50.** $f(x) = 2 - x^2$

51. $f(x) = 3x - 5$ **52.** $f(x) = -\frac{1}{2}x + 7$

53. $f(x) = 3x^2 - 2x + 1$ **54.** $f(x) = 5x^2 + 4x$

55. $f(x) = 4 + 5|x|$ **56.** $f(x) = 2|x| + 3x$

57. $f(x) = x^3$ **58.** $f(x) = x^3 - 2x$

59. $f(x) = \dfrac{x - 4}{x + 3}$ **60.** $f(x) = \dfrac{x}{2 - x}$

Given that $f(x) = 3x + 1$, $g(x) = x^2 - 2x - 6$, and $h(x) = x^3$, find each of the following.

61. $(f \circ g)(-1)$ **62.** $(g \circ f)(-2)$

63. $(h \circ f)(1)$ **64.** $(g \circ h)\left(\frac{1}{2}\right)$

65. $(g \circ f)(5)$ **66.** $(f \circ g)\left(\frac{1}{3}\right)$

67. $(f \circ h)(-3)$ **68.** $(h \circ g)(3)$

Find $(f \circ g)(x)$ and $(g \circ f)(x)$ and the domain of each.

69. $f(x) = x + 3$, $g(x) = x - 3$

70. $f(x) = \frac{4}{5}x$, $g(x) = \frac{5}{4}x$

71. $f(x) = x + 1$, $g(x) = 3x^2 - 2x - 1$

72. $f(x) = 3x - 2$, $g(x) = x^2 + 5$

73. $f(x) = x^2 - 3$, $g(x) = 4x - 3$

74. $f(x) = 4x^2 - x + 10$, $g(x) = 2x - 7$

75. $f(x) = \dfrac{4}{1 - 5x}$, $g(x) = \dfrac{1}{x}$

76. $f(x) = \dfrac{6}{x}$, $g(x) = \dfrac{1}{2x + 1}$

77. $f(x) = 3x - 7$, $g(x) = \dfrac{x + 7}{3}$

78. $f(x) = \frac{2}{3}x - \frac{4}{5}$, $g(x) = 1.5x + 1.2$

79. $f(x) = 2x + 1$, $g(x) = \sqrt{x}$

80. $f(x) = \sqrt{x}$, $g(x) = 2 - 3x$

81. $f(x) = 20$, $g(x) = 0.05$

82. $f(x) = x^4$, $g(x) = \sqrt[4]{x}$

83. $f(x) = \sqrt{x + 5}$, $g(x) = x^2 - 5$

84. $f(x) = x^5 - 2$, $g(x) = \sqrt[5]{x + 2}$

85. $f(x) = x^2 + 2$, $g(x) = \sqrt{3 - x}$

86. $f(x) = 1 - x^2$, $g(x) = \sqrt{x^2 - 25}$

87. $f(x) = \dfrac{1 - x}{x}$, $g(x) = \dfrac{1}{1 + x}$

88. $f(x) = \dfrac{1}{x - 2}$, $g(x) = \dfrac{x + 2}{x}$

89. $f(x) = x^3 - 5x^2 + 3x + 7$, $g(x) = x + 1$

90. $f(x) = x - 1$, $g(x) = x^3 + 2x^2 - 3x - 9$

Find $f(x)$ and $g(x)$ such that $h(x) = (f \circ g)(x)$. Answers may vary.

91. $h(x) = (4 + 3x)^5$

92. $h(x) = \sqrt[3]{x^2 - 8}$

93. $h(x) = \dfrac{1}{(x - 2)^4}$

94. $h(x) = \dfrac{1}{\sqrt{3x + 7}}$

95. $h(x) = \dfrac{x^3 - 1}{x^3 + 1}$

96. $h(x) = |9x^2 - 4|$

97. $h(x) = \left(\dfrac{2 + x^3}{2 - x^3}\right)^6$

98. $h(x) = (\sqrt{x} - 3)^4$

99. $h(x) = \sqrt{\dfrac{x - 5}{x + 2}}$

100. $h(x) = \sqrt{1 + \sqrt{1 + x}}$

101. $h(x) = (x + 2)^3 - 5(x + 2)^2 + 3(x + 2) - 1$

102. $h(x) = 2(x - 1)^{5/3} + 5(x - 1)^{2/3}$

103. *Blouse Sizes.* A blouse that is size x in Japan is size $s(x)$ in the United States, where $s(x) = x - 3$. A blouse that is size x in the United States is size $t(x)$ in Australia, where $t(x) = x + 4$. (*Source*: www.onlineconversion.com) Find a function that will convert Japanese blouse sizes to Australian blouse sizes.

Japan   USA

Australia

SIZE ?

104. *Ripple Spread.* A stone is thrown into a pond, and a circular ripple spreads over the pond in such a way that the radius is increasing at the rate of 3 ft/sec.

$r(t)$

a) Find a function $r(t)$ for the radius in terms of t.

b) Find a function $A(r)$ for the area of the ripple in terms of the radius r.

c) Find $(A \circ r)(t)$. Explain the meaning of this function.

Technology Connection

105. Using a graphing calculator, graph the three functions in Exercise 45 in the viewing window $[0, 160, 0, 3000]$.

106. Using a graphing calculator, graph the three functions in Exercise 46 in the viewing window $[0, 200, 0, 10{,}000]$.

Collaborative Discussion and Writing

107. If $g(x) = b$, where b is a positive constant, describe how the graphs of $y = h(x)$ and $y = (h - g)(x)$ will differ.

108. Explain which values of x must be excluded from the domain of $(f \circ g)(x)$ and the domain of $(g \circ f)(x)$.

Skill Maintenance

Consider the following linear equations. Without graphing them, answer the questions below.

a) $y = x$
b) $y = -5x + 4$
c) $y = \frac{2}{3}x + 1$
d) $y = -0.1x + 6$
e) $y = 3x - 5$
f) $y = -x - 1$
g) $2x - 3y = 6$
h) $6x + 3y = 9$

109. Which, if any, have y-intercept $(0, 1)$?

110. Which, if any, have the same y-intercept?

111. Which slope down from left to right?

112. Which has the steepest slope?

113. Which pass(es) through the origin?

114. Which, if any, have the same slope?

115. Which, if any, are parallel?

116. Which, if any, are perpendicular?

Synthesis

117. Write equations of two functions f and g such that $f \circ g = g \circ f = x$. (In Section 4.1, we will study inverse functions. If $f \circ g = g \circ f = x$, functions f and g are *inverses* of each other.)

118. Write equations for two functions f and g such that the domain of $f - g$ is

$$\{x \mid x \neq -7 \text{ and } x \neq 3\}.$$

119. Find the domain of $(h/g)(x)$ given that

$$h(x) = \frac{5x}{3x - 7} \quad \text{and} \quad g(x) = \frac{x^4 - 1}{5x - 15}.$$

120. For functions h and f, find the domain of $h + f$, $h - f$, hf, and h/f if

$$h = \left\{(-4, 13), (-1, 7), (0, 5), \left(\tfrac{5}{2}, 0\right), (3, -5)\right\} \quad \text{and}$$

$$f = \{(-4, -7), (-2, -5), (0, -3), (3, 0), (5, 2), (9, 6)\}.$$

1.7 Symmetry and Transformations

◆ Determine whether a graph is symmetric with respect to the x-axis, the y-axis, and the origin.

◆ Determine whether a function is even, odd, or neither even nor odd.

◆ Given the graph of a function, graph its transformation under translations, reflections, stretchings, and shrinkings.

◆ Symmetry

Symmetry occurs often in nature and in art. For example, when viewed from the front, the bodies of most animals are at least approximately symmetric. This means that each eye is the same distance from the center of the bridge of the nose, each shoulder is the same distance from the center of the chest, and so on. Architects have used symmetry for thousands of years to enhance the beauty of buildings.

A knowledge of symmetry in mathematics helps us graph and analyze equations and functions.

Consider the points $(4, 2)$ and $(4, -2)$ that appear in the graph of $x = y^2$. (See Fig. 1.) Points like these have the same x-value but opposite y-values and are **reflections** of each other across the x-axis. If, for any point (x, y) on a graph, the point $(x, -y)$ is also on the graph, then the graph is said to be **symmetric with respect to the x-axis**. If we fold the graph on the x-axis, the parts above and below the x-axis will coincide.

Consider the points $(3, 4)$ and $(-3, 4)$ that appear in the graph of $y = x^2 - 5$. (See Fig. 2.) Points like these have the same y-value but opposite x-values and are **reflections** of each other across the y-axis. If, for any point (x, y) on a graph, the point $(-x, y)$ is also on the graph, then the graph is said to be **symmetric with respect to the y-axis**. If we fold the graph on the y-axis, the parts to the left and right of the y-axis will coincide.

Figure 3

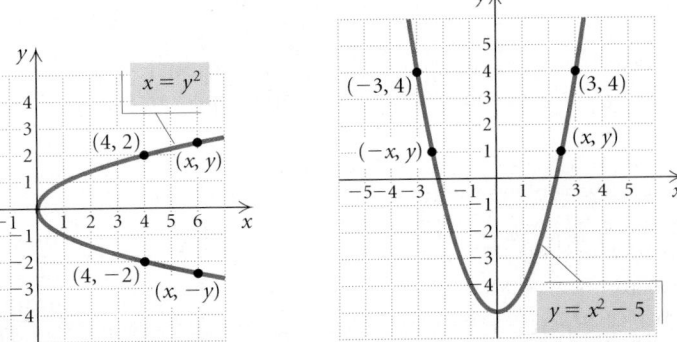

Figure 1   Figure 2

Consider the points $\left(3, \sqrt{7}\right)$ and $\left(-3, -\sqrt{7}\right)$ that appear in the graph of $x^2 = y^2 + 2$. (See Fig. 3.) Note that if we take the opposites of the coordinates of one pair, we get the other pair. If for any point (x, y) on a graph the point $(-x, -y)$ is also on the graph, then the graph is said to be **symmetric with respect to the origin**. Visually, if we rotate the graph $180°$ about the origin, the resulting figure coincides with the original.

Algebraic Tests of Symmetry

x-axis: If replacing y with $-y$ produces an equivalent equation, then the graph is *symmetric with respect to the x-axis.*

y-axis: If replacing x with $-x$ produces an equivalent equation, then the graph is *symmetric with respect to the y-axis.*

Origin: If replacing x with $-x$ and y with $-y$ produces an equivalent equation, then the graph is *symmetric with respect to the origin.*

EXAMPLE 1   Test $y = x^2 + 2$ for symmetry with respect to the x-axis, the y-axis, and the origin.

ALGEBRAIC SOLUTION

x-Axis   We replace y with $-y$:

$$y = x^2 + 2$$
$$\downarrow$$
$$-y = x^2 + 2$$
$$y = -x^2 - 2. \qquad \text{Multiplying by } -1 \\ \text{on both sides}$$

The resulting equation *is not* equivalent to the original equation, so the graph *is not* symmetric with respect to the x-axis.

y-Axis   We replace x with $-x$:

$$y = x^2 + 2$$
$$\downarrow$$
$$y = (-x)^2 + 2$$
$$y = x^2 + 2. \qquad \text{Simplifying}$$

The resulting equation *is* equivalent to the original equation, so the graph *is* symmetric with respect to the y-axis.

Origin   We replace x with $-x$ and y with $-y$:

$$y = x^2 + 2$$
$$\downarrow \qquad \downarrow$$
$$-y = (-x)^2 + 2$$
$$-y = x^2 + 2 \qquad \text{Simplifying}$$
$$y = -x^2 - 2.$$

The resulting equation *is not* equivalent to the original equation, so the graph *is not* symmetric with respect to the origin.

VISUALIZING THE SOLUTION

Let's look at the graph of $y = x^2 + 2$.

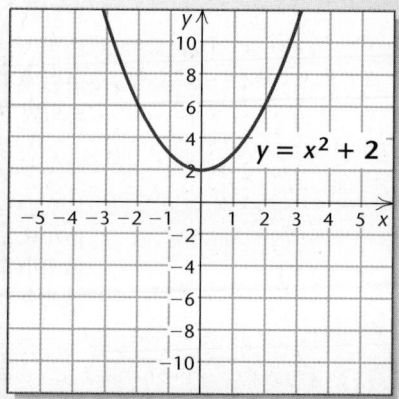

Note that if the graph were folded on the x-axis, the parts above and below the x-axis would not coincide. If it were folded on the y-axis, the parts to the left and right of the y-axis would coincide. If we rotated it 180° about the origin, the resulting graph would not coincide with the original graph.

Thus we see that the graph *is not* symmetric with respect to the x-axis or the origin. The graph *is* symmetric with respect to the y-axis.

▶ Now Try Exercise 11.

EXAMPLE 2 Test $x^2 + y^4 = 5$ for symmetry with respect to the x-axis, the y-axis, and the origin.

ALGEBRAIC SOLUTION

x-Axis We replace y with $-y$:

$$x^2 + y^4 = 5$$

$$x^2 + (-y)^4 = 5$$

$$x^2 + y^4 = 5.$$

The resulting equation *is* equivalent to the original equation. Thus the graph *is* symmetric with respect to the x-axis.

y-Axis We replace x with $-x$:

$$x^2 + y^4 = 5$$

$$(-x)^2 + y^4 = 5$$

$$x^2 + y^4 = 5.$$

The resulting equation *is* equivalent to the original equation, so the graph *is* symmetric with respect to the y-axis.

Origin We replace x with $-x$ and y with $-y$:

$$x^2 + y^4 = 5$$

$$(-x)^2 + (-y)^4 = 5$$

$$x^2 + y^4 = 5.$$

The resulting equation *is* equivalent to the original equation, so the graph *is* symmetric with respect to the origin.

VISUALIZING THE SOLUTION

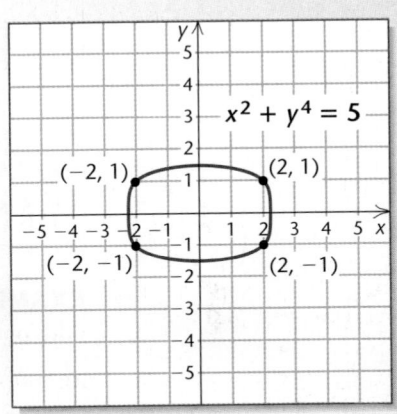

From the graph of the equation, we see symmetry with respect to both axes and with respect to the origin.

▶ Now Try Exercise 21.

✦ Even and Odd Functions

Now we relate symmetry to graphs of functions.

> **Even and Odd Functions**
>
> If the graph of a function f is symmetric with respect to the y-axis, we say that it is an **even function.** That is, for each x in the domain of f, $f(x) = f(-x)$.
>
> If the graph of a function f is symmetric with respect to the origin, we say that it is an **odd function.** That is, for each x in the domain of f, $f(-x) = -f(x)$.

An algebraic procedure for determining even and odd functions is shown below. Here we include examples of both even and odd functions. Many functions are neither even nor odd.

Algebraic Procedure for Determining Even and Odd Functions

Given the function $f(x)$:

1. Find $f(-x)$ and simplify. If $f(x) = f(-x)$, then f is even.
2. Find $-f(x)$, simplify, and compare with $f(-x)$ from step (1). If $f(-x) = -f(x)$, then f is odd.

Except for the function $f(x) = 0$, a function cannot be *both* even and odd. Thus if $f(x) \neq 0$ and we see in step (1) that $f(x) = f(-x)$ (that is, f is even), we need not continue.

EXAMPLE 3   Determine whether each of the following functions is even, odd, or neither.

a) $f(x) = 5x^7 - 6x^3 - 2x$

b) $h(x) = 5x^6 - 3x^2 - 7$

---

a) ALGEBRAIC SOLUTION

$f(x) = 5x^7 - 6x^3 - 2x$

1. $f(-x) = 5(-x)^7 - 6(-x)^3 - 2(-x)$

   $\qquad = 5(-x^7) - 6(-x^3) + 2x$

   $\qquad\qquad (-x)^7 = (-1 \cdot x)^7 = (-1)^7 x^7 = -x^7$

   $\qquad = -5x^7 + 6x^3 + 2x$

   We see that $f(x) \neq f(-x)$. Thus, f is *not* even.

2. $-f(x) = -(5x^7 - 6x^3 - 2x)$

   $\qquad = -5x^7 + 6x^3 + 2x$

   We see that $f(-x) = -f(x)$. Thus, f is odd.

VISUALIZING THE SOLUTION

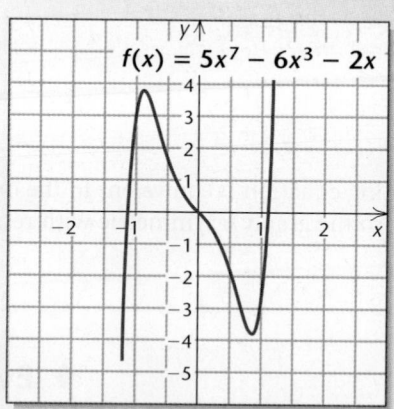

We see that the graph appears to be symmetric with respect to the origin. The function is odd.

b) ALGEBRAIC SOLUTION

$h(x) = 5x^6 - 3x^2 - 7$

1. $h(-x) = 5(-x)^6 - 3(-x)^2 - 7$

$= 5x^6 - 3x^2 - 7$

We see that $h(x) = h(-x)$. Thus the function is even.

VISUALIZING THE SOLUTION

$h(x) = 5x^6 - 3x^2 - 7$

We see that the graph appears to be symmetric with respect to the y-axis. The function is even.

▷ Now Try Exercises 39 and 41.

◆ Transformations of Functions

The graphs of some basic functions are shown below and on the following page. Others can be seen on the inside back cover of the text.

Identity function:
$y = x$

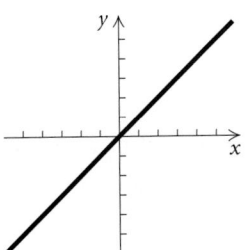

Squaring function:
$y = x^2$

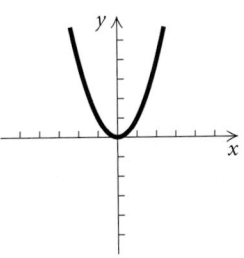

Square root function:
$y = \sqrt{x}$

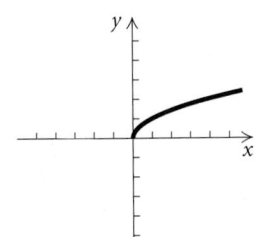

Cubing function:
$y = x^3$

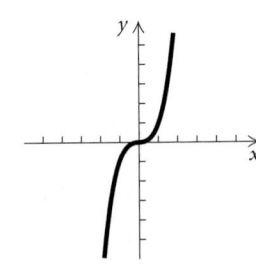

Cube root function:
$y = \sqrt[3]{x}$

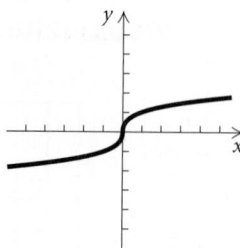

Reciprocal function:
$y = \dfrac{1}{x}$

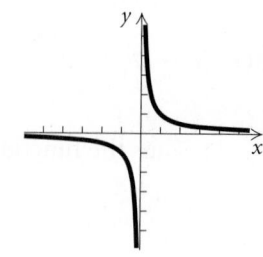

Absolute-value function:
$y = |x|$

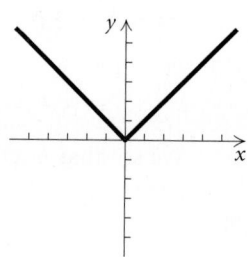

These functions can be considered building blocks for many other functions. We can create graphs of new functions by shifting them horizontally or vertically, stretching or shrinking them, and reflecting them across an axis. We now consider these **transformations.**

◆ Vertical and Horizontal Translations

Suppose that we have a function given by $y = f(x)$. Let's explore the graphs of the new functions $y = f(x) + b$ and $y = f(x) - b$, for $b > 0$.

Consider the functions $y = \frac{1}{5}x^4$, $y = \frac{1}{5}x^4 + 5$, and $y = \frac{1}{5}x^4 - 3$ and compare their graphs. What pattern do you see? Test it with some other graphs.

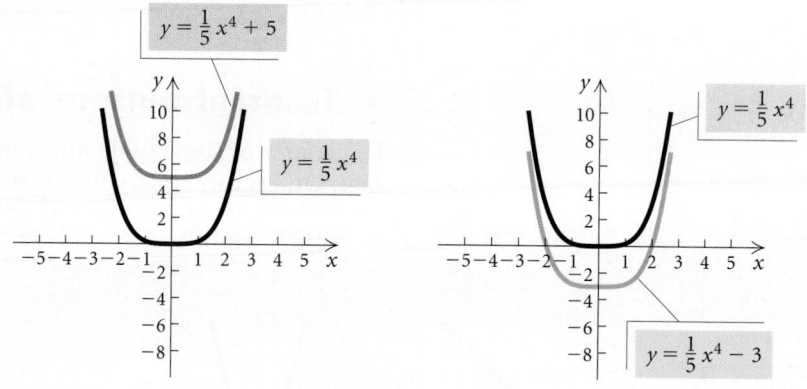

The effect of adding a constant to or subtracting a constant from $f(x)$ in $y = f(x)$ is a shift of the graph of $f(x)$ up or down. Such a shift is called a **vertical translation.**

Vertical Translation

For $b > 0$,

the graph of $y = f(x) + b$ is the graph of $y = f(x)$ shifted *up* b units;

the graph of $y = f(x) - b$ is the graph of $y = f(x)$ shifted *down* b units.

Suppose that we have a function given by $y = f(x)$. Let's explore the graphs of the new functions $y = f(x - d)$ and $y = f(x + d)$, for $d > 0$.

Consider the functions $y = \frac{1}{5}x^4$, $y = \frac{1}{5}(x - 3)^4$, and $y = \frac{1}{5}(x + 7)^4$ and compare their graphs. What pattern do you observe? Test it with some other graphs.

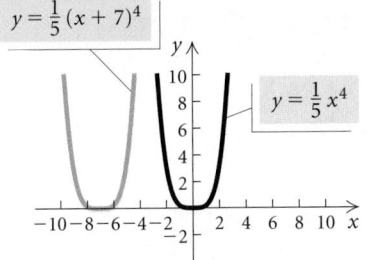

The effect of subtracting a constant from the x-value or adding a constant to the x-value in $y = f(x)$ is a shift of the graph of $f(x)$ to the right or left. Such a shift is called a **horizontal translation.**

Horizontal Translation

For $d > 0$:

the graph of $y = f(x - d)$ is the graph of $y = f(x)$ shifted *right* d units;

the graph of $y = f(x + d)$ is the graph of $y = f(x)$ shifted *left* d units.

EXAMPLE 4   Graph each of the following. Before doing so, describe how each graph can be obtained from one of the basic graphs shown on the preceding pages.

a) $g(x) = x^2 - 6$ **b)** $g(x) = |x - 4|$

c) $g(x) = \sqrt{x + 2}$ **d)** $h(x) = \sqrt{x + 2} - 3$

Solution

a) To graph $g(x) = x^2 - 6$, think of the graph of $f(x) = x^2$. Since $g(x) = f(x) - 6$, the graph of $g(x) = x^2 - 6$ is the graph of $f(x) = x^2$, shifted, or translated, *down* 6 units. (See Fig. 1.)

Let's compare some points on the graphs of f and g.

Points on f: $(-3, 9)$, $(0, 0)$, $(2, 4)$

Corresponding
points on g: $(-3, 3)$, $(0, -6)$, $(2, -2)$

We note that the y-coordinate of a point on the graph of g is 6 less than the corresponding y-coordinate on the graph of f.

Figure 1

Figure 2

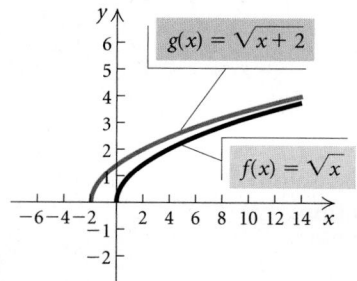

Figure 3

b) To graph $g(x) = |x - 4|$, think of the graph of $f(x) = |x|$. Since $g(x) = f(x - 4)$, the graph of $g(x) = |x - 4|$ is the graph of $f(x) = |x|$ shifted *right* 4 units. (See Fig. 2.)

Let's again compare points on the two graphs.

Point on f Corresponding point on g

$(-4, 4) \longrightarrow (0, 4)$

$(0, 0) \longrightarrow (4, 0)$

$(6, 6) \longrightarrow (10, 6)$

Observing points on f and g, we see that the x-coordinate of a point on the graph of g is 4 more than the x-coordinate of the corresponding point on f.

c) To graph $g(x) = \sqrt{x + 2}$, think of the graph of $f(x) = \sqrt{x}$. Since $g(x) = f(x + 2)$, the graph of $g(x) = \sqrt{x + 2}$ is the graph of $f(x) = \sqrt{x}$, shifted *left* 2 units. (See Fig. 3.)

d) To graph $h(x) = \sqrt{x + 2} - 3$, think of the graph of $f(x) = \sqrt{x}$. In part (c), we found that the graph of $g(x) = \sqrt{x + 2}$ is the graph of $f(x) = \sqrt{x}$ shifted left 2 units. Since $h(x) = g(x) - 3$, we shift the graph of $g(x) = \sqrt{x + 2}$ *down* 3 units. Together, the graph of $f(x) = \sqrt{x}$ is shifted *left* 2 units and *down* 3 units. (See Fig. 4.)

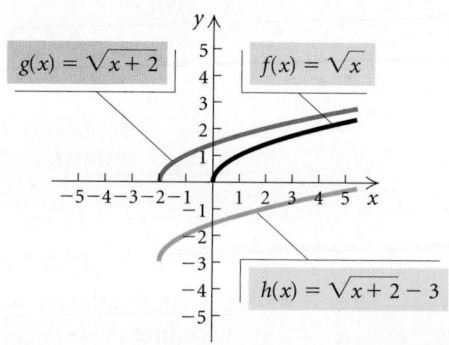

Figure 4

▷ Now Try Exercises 49 and 59.

◆ Reflections

Suppose that we have a function given by $y = f(x)$. Let's explore the graphs of the new functions $y = -f(x)$ and $y = f(-x)$.

Compare the functions $y = f(x)$ and $y = -f(x)$ by looking at the graphs of $y = \frac{1}{5}x^4$ and $y = -\frac{1}{5}x^4$ shown at left. What do you see? Test your observation with some other functions y_1 and y_2 where $y_2 = -y_1$.

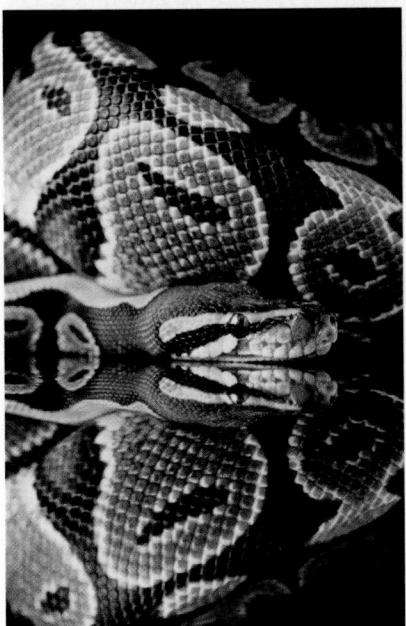

Compare the functions $y = f(x)$ and $y = f(-x)$ by looking at the graphs of $y = 2x^3 - x^4 + 5$ and $y = 2(-x)^3 - (-x)^4 + 5$ shown below. What do you see? Test your observation with some other functions in which x is replaced with $-x$.

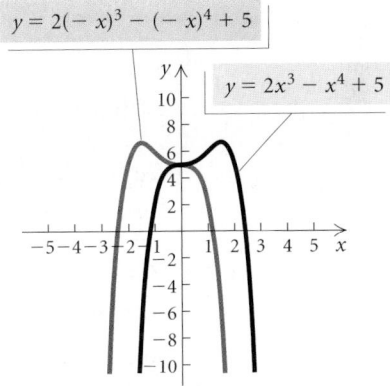

$y = 2(-x)^3 - (-x)^4 + 5$

$y = 2x^3 - x^4 + 5$

Given the graph of $y = f(x)$, we can reflect each point *across the x-axis* to obtain the graph of $y = -f(x)$. We can reflect each point of y *across the y-axis* to obtain the graph of $y = f(-x)$. The new graphs are called **reflections** of $y = f(x)$.

Reflections

The graph of $y = -f(x)$ is the **reflection** of the graph of $y = f(x)$ across the x-axis.

The graph of $y = f(-x)$ is the **reflection** of the graph of $y = f(x)$ across the y-axis.

If a point (x, y) is on the graph of $y = f(x)$, then $(x, -y)$ is on the graph of $y = -f(x)$, and $(-x, y)$ is on the graph of $y = f(-x)$.

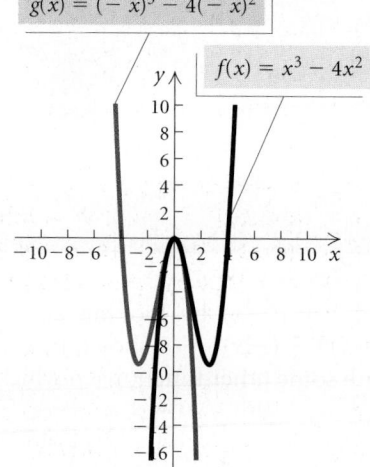

Figure 1

EXAMPLE 5   Graph each of the following. Before doing so, describe how each graph can be obtained from the graph of $f(x) = x^3 - 4x^2$.

a) $g(x) = (-x)^3 - 4(-x)^2$ **b)** $h(x) = 4x^2 - x^3$

Solution

a) We first note that

$$f(-x) = (-x)^3 - 4(-x)^2 = g(x).$$

Thus the graph of g is a *reflection* of the graph of f across the y-*axis*. (See Fig. 1.) If (x, y) is on the graph of f, then $(-x, y)$ is on the graph of g. For example, $(2, -8)$ is on f and $(-2, -8)$ is on g.

b) We first note that

$$\begin{aligned} -f(x) &= -(x^3 - 4x^2) \\ &= -x^3 + 4x^2 \\ &= 4x^2 - x^3 \\ &= h(x). \end{aligned}$$

Thus the graph of h is a *reflection* of the graph of f across the x-*axis*. (See Fig. 2.) If (x, y) is on the graph of f, then $(x, -y)$ is on the graph of h. For example, $(2, -8)$ is on f and $(2, 8)$ is on h.

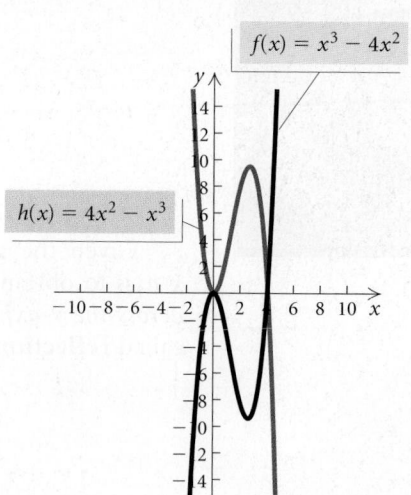

Figure 2

✦ Vertical and Horizontal Stretchings and Shrinkings

Suppose that we have a function given by $y = f(x)$. Let's explore the graphs of the new functions $y = af(x)$ and $y = f(cx)$.

Consider the functions $y = x^3 - x$, $y = \frac{1}{10}(x^3 - x)$, $y = 2(x^3 - x)$, and $y = -2(x^3 - x)$ and compare their graphs. What pattern do you observe? Test it with some other graphs.

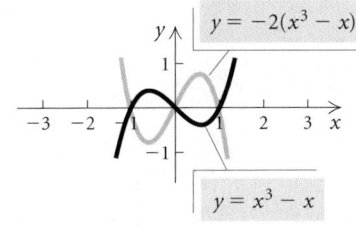

Consider any function f given by $y = f(x)$. Multiplying $f(x)$ by any constant a, where $|a| > 1$, to obtain $g(x) = af(x)$ will *stretch* the graph vertically away from the x-axis. If $0 < |a| < 1$, then the graph will be flattened or *shrunk* vertically toward the x-axis. If $a < 0$, the graph is also reflected across the x-axis.

Vertical Stretching and Shrinking

The graph of $y = af(x)$ can be obtained from the graph of $y = f(x)$ by

  stretching vertically for $|a| > 1$, or
  shrinking vertically for $0 < |a| < 1$.

For $a < 0$, the graph is also reflected across the x-axis.
(The y-coordinates of the graph of $y = af(x)$ can be obtained by multiplying the y-coordinates of $y = f(x)$ by a.)

Consider the functions $y = x^3 - x$, $y = (2x)^3 - (2x)$, $y = \left(\frac{1}{2}x\right)^3 - \left(\frac{1}{2}x\right)$, and $y = \left(-\frac{1}{2}x\right)^3 - \left(-\frac{1}{2}x\right)$ and compare their graphs. What pattern do you observe? Test it with some other graphs.

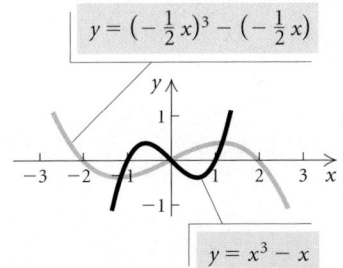

The constant c in the equation $g(x) = f(cx)$ will *stretch* the graph of $y = f(x)$ horizontally away from the y-axis if $0 < |c| < 1$. If $|c| > 1$, the graph will be *shrunk* horizontally toward the y-axis. If $c < 0$, the graph is also reflected across the y-axis.

Horizontal Stretching and Shrinking

The graph of $y = f(cx)$ can be obtained from the graph of $y = f(x)$ by

shrinking horizontally for $|c| > 1$, or

stretching horizontally for $0 < |c| < 1$.

For $c < 0$, the graph is also reflected across the y-axis.
(The x-coordinates of the graph of $y = f(cx)$ can be obtained by dividing the x-coordinates of the graph of $y = f(x)$ by c.)

It is instructive to use these concepts to create transformations of a given graph.

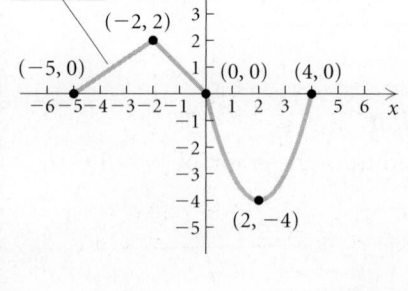

EXAMPLE 6   Shown at left is a graph of $y = f(x)$ for some function f. No formula for f is given. Graph each of the following.

a) $g(x) = 2f(x)$ **b)** $h(x) = \frac{1}{2}f(x)$

c) $r(x) = f(2x)$ **d)** $s(x) = f\left(\frac{1}{2}x\right)$

e) $t(x) = f\left(-\frac{1}{2}x\right)$

Solution

a) Since $|2| > 1$, the graph of $g(x) = 2f(x)$ is a vertical stretching of the graph of $y = f(x)$ by a factor of 2. We can consider the key points $(-5,0)$, $(-2,2)$, $(0,0)$, $(2,-4)$, and $(4,0)$ on the graph of $y = f(x)$. The transformation multiplies each y-coordinate by 2 to obtain the key points $(-5,0)$, $(-2,4)$, $(0,0)$, $(2,-8)$, and $(4,0)$ on the graph of $g(x) = 2f(x)$. The graph is shown below.

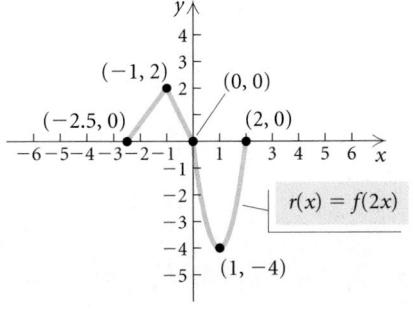

b) Since $\left|\frac{1}{2}\right| < 1$, the graph of $h(x) = \frac{1}{2}f(x)$ is a vertical shrinking of the graph of $y = f(x)$ by a factor of $\frac{1}{2}$. We again consider the key points $(-5,0)$, $(-2,2)$, $(0,0)$, $(2,-4)$, and $(4,0)$ on the graph of $y = f(x)$. The transformation multiplies each y-coordinate by $\frac{1}{2}$ to obtain the key points $(-5,0)$, $(-2,1)$, $(0,0)$, $(2,-2)$, and $(4,0)$ on the graph of $h(x) = \frac{1}{2}f(x)$. The graph is shown at left.

c) Since $|2| > 1$, the graph of $r(x) = f(2x)$ is a horizontal shrinking of the graph of $y = f(x)$. We consider the key points $(-5,0)$, $(-2,2)$, $(0,0)$, $(2,-4)$, and $(4,0)$ on the graph of $y = f(x)$. The transformation divides each x-coordinate by 2 to obtain the key points $(-2.5,0)$, $(-1,2)$, $(0,0)$, $(1,-4)$, and $(2,0)$ on the graph of $r(x) = f(2x)$. The graph is shown at left.

d) Since $\left|\frac{1}{2}\right| < 1$, the graph of $s(x) = f\left(\frac{1}{2}x\right)$ is a horizontal stretching of the graph of $y = f(x)$. We consider the key points $(-5,0)$, $(-2,2)$, $(0,0)$, $(2,-4)$, and $(4,0)$ on the graph of $y = f(x)$. The transformation divides each x-coordinate by $\frac{1}{2}$ (which is the same as multiplying by 2) to obtain the key points $(-10,0)$, $(-4,2)$, $(0,0)$, $(4,-4)$, and $(8,0)$ on the graph of $s(x) = f\left(\frac{1}{2}x\right)$. The graph is shown below.

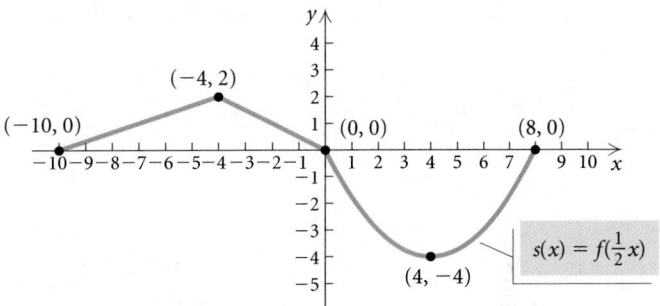

e) The graph of $t(x) = f\left(-\frac{1}{2}x\right)$ can be obtained by reflecting the graph in part (d) across the y-axis.

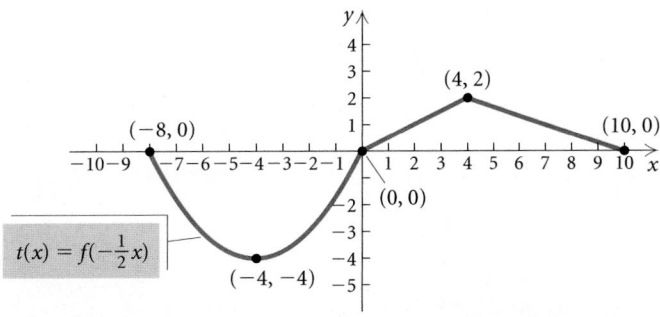

▶ Now Try Exercises 107 and 109.

EXAMPLE 7 Use the graph of $y = f(x)$ shown at left to graph
$y = -2f(x - 3) + 1.$

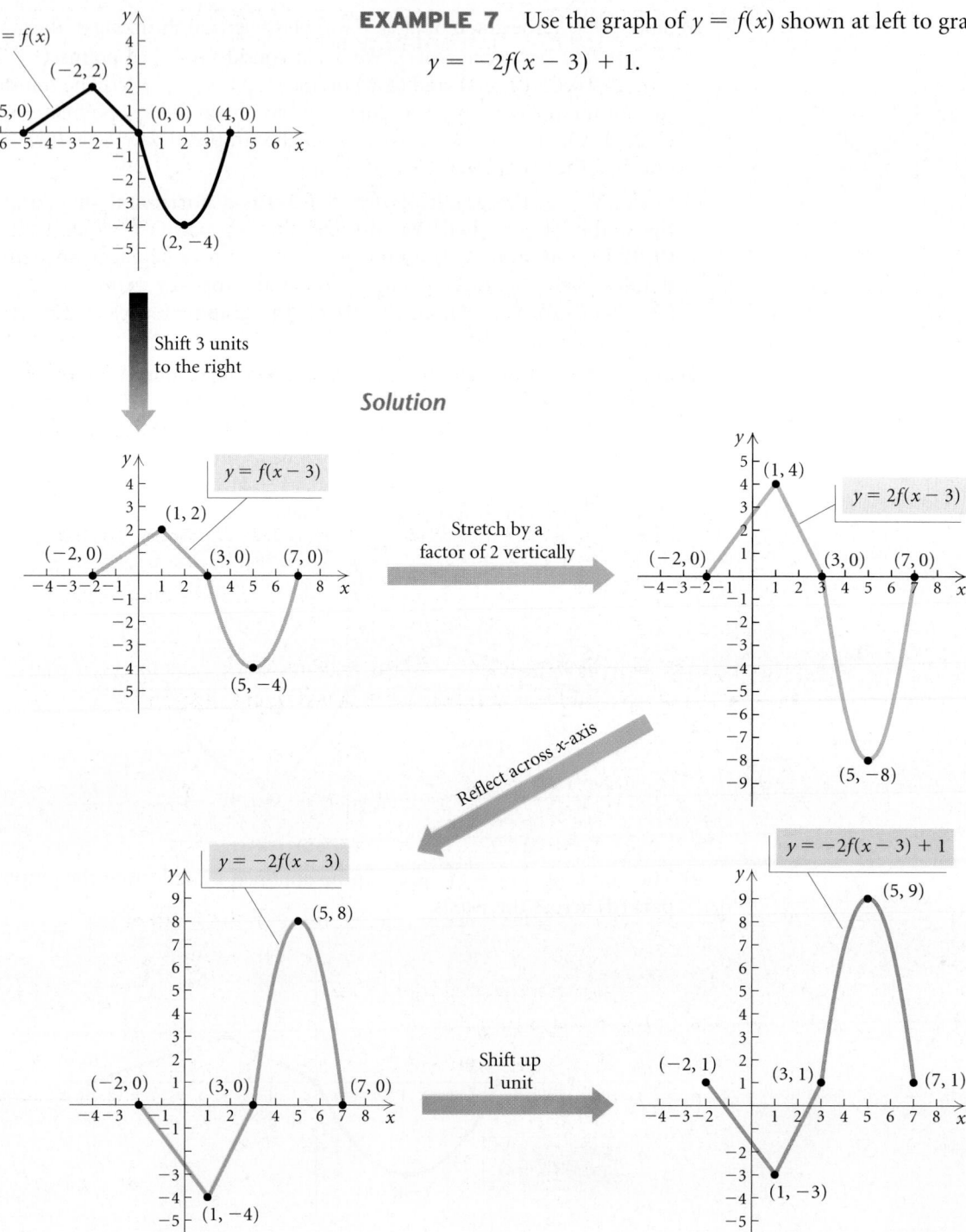

Solution

▷ **Now Try Exercise 111.**

Summary of Transformations of $y = f(x)$

Vertical Translation: $y = f(x) \pm b$

For $b > 0$,

the graph of $y = f(x) + b$ is the graph of $y = f(x)$ shifted *up* b units;

the graph of $y = f(x) - b$ is the graph of $y = f(x)$ shifted *down* b units.

Horizontal Translation: $y = f(x \mp d)$

For $d > 0$,

the graph of $y = f(x - d)$ is the graph of $y = f(x)$ shifted *right* d units;

the graph of $y = f(x + d)$ is the graph of $y = f(x)$ shifted *left* d units.

Reflections

Across the x-axis: The graph of $y = -f(x)$ is the reflection of the graph of $y = f(x)$ across the x-axis.

Across the y-axis: The graph of $y = f(-x)$ is the reflection of the graph of $y = f(x)$ across the y-axis.

Vertical Stretching or Shrinking: $y = af(x)$

The graph of $y = af(x)$ can be obtained from the graph of $y = f(x)$ by

stretching vertically for $|a| > 1$, or

shrinking vertically for $0 < |a| < 1$.

For $a < 0$, the graph is also reflected across the x-axis.

Horizontal Stretching or Shrinking: $y = f(cx)$

The graph of $y = f(cx)$ can be obtained from the graph of $y = f(x)$ by

shrinking horizontally for $|c| > 1$, or

stretching horizontally for $0 < |c| < 1$.

For $c < 0$, the graph is also reflected across the y-axis.

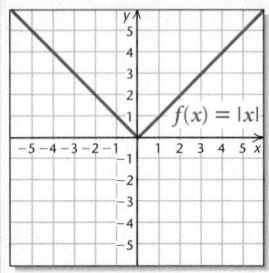

Visualizing the Graph

Match the function with its graph. Use transformation graphing techniques to obtain the graph of g from the basic function $f(x) = |x|$ shown at top left.

1. $g(x) = -2|x|$

2. $g(x) = |x - 1| + 1$

3. $g(x) = -\left|\dfrac{1}{3}x\right|$

4. $g(x) = |2x|$

5. $g(x) = |x + 2|$

6. $g(x) = |x| + 3$

7. $g(x) = -\dfrac{1}{2}|x - 4|$

8. $g(x) = \dfrac{1}{2}|x| - 3$

9. $g(x) = -|x| - 2$

Answers on page A-9

1.7 EXERCISE SET

Determine visually whether the graph is symmetric with respect to the x-axis, the y-axis, and/or the origin.

1.

2.

3.

4.

5.

6.

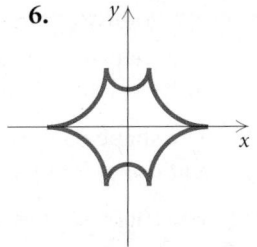

First, graph the equation and determine visually whether it is symmetric with respect to the x-axis, the y-axis, and/or the origin. Then verify your assertion algebraically.

7. $y = |x| - 2$

8. $y = |x + 5|$

9. $5y = 4x + 5$

10. $2x - 5 = 3y$

11. $5y = 2x^2 - 3$

12. $x^2 + 4 = 3y$

13. $y = \dfrac{1}{x}$

14. $y = -\dfrac{4}{x}$

Determine whether the graph is symmetric with respect to the x-axis, the y-axis, and/or the origin.

15. $5x - 5y = 0$

16. $6x + 7y = 0$

17. $3x^2 - 2y^2 = 3$

18. $5y = 7x^2 - 2x$

19. $y = |2x|$

20. $y^3 = 2x^2$

21. $2x^4 + 3 = y^2$

22. $2y^2 = 5x^2 + 12$

23. $3y^3 = 4x^3 + 2$

24. $3x = |y|$

25. $xy = 12$

26. $xy - x^2 = 3$

Find the point that is symmetric to the given point with respect to the x-axis, the y-axis, and the origin.

27. $(-5, 6)$

28. $\left(\frac{7}{2}, 0\right)$

29. $(-10, -7)$

30. $\left(1, \frac{3}{8}\right)$

31. $(0, -4)$

32. $(8, -3)$

Determine visually whether the function is even, odd, or neither even nor odd.

33.

34.

35.

36.

37.

38.

Determine whether the function is even, odd, or neither even nor odd.

39. $f(x) = -3x^3 + 2x$

40. $f(x) = 7x^3 + 4x - 2$

41. $f(x) = 5x^2 + 2x^4 - 1$

42. $f(x) = x + \dfrac{1}{x}$

43. $f(x) = x^{17}$

44. $f(x) = \sqrt[3]{x}$

45. $f(x) = \dfrac{1}{x^2}$

46. $f(x) = x - |x|$

47. $f(x) = 8$

48. $f(x) = \sqrt{x^2 + 1}$

Describe how the graph of the function can be obtained from one of the basic graphs on pages 151 and 152. Then graph the function.

49. $f(x) = (x - 3)^2$

50. $g(x) = x^2 + \frac{1}{2}$

51. $g(x) = x - 3$

52. $g(x) = -x - 2$

53. $h(x) = -\sqrt{x}$

54. $g(x) = \sqrt{x - 1}$

55. $h(x) = \dfrac{1}{x} + 4$

56. $g(x) = \dfrac{1}{x - 2}$

57. $h(x) = -3x + 3$

58. $f(x) = 2x + 1$

59. $h(x) = \frac{1}{2}|x| - 2$

60. $g(x) = -|x| + 2$

61. $g(x) = -(x - 2)^3$

62. $f(x) = (x + 1)^3$

63. $g(x) = (x + 1)^2 - 1$

64. $h(x) = -x^2 - 4$

65. $g(x) = \frac{1}{3}x^3 + 2$

66. $h(x) = (-x)^3$

67. $f(x) = \sqrt{x + 2}$

68. $f(x) = -\frac{1}{2}\sqrt{x - 1}$

69. $f(x) = \sqrt[3]{x} - 2$

70. $h(x) = \sqrt[3]{x + 1}$

Describe how the graph of the function can be obtained from one of the basic graphs on pages 151 and 152.

71. $g(x) = |3x|$

72. $f(x) = \frac{1}{2}\sqrt[3]{x}$

73. $h(x) = \dfrac{2}{x}$

74. $f(x) = |x - 3| - 4$

75. $f(x) = 3\sqrt{x} - 5$

76. $f(x) = 5 - \dfrac{1}{x}$

77. $g(x) = \left|\frac{1}{3}x\right| - 4$

78. $f(x) = \frac{2}{3}x^3 - 4$

79. $f(x) = -\frac{1}{4}(x - 5)^2$

80. $f(x) = (-x)^3 - 5$

81. $f(x) = \dfrac{1}{x + 3} + 2$

82. $g(x) = \sqrt{-x} + 5$

83. $h(x) = -(x - 3)^2 + 5$

84. $f(x) = 3(x + 4)^2 - 3$

The point $(-12, 4)$ is on the graph of $y = f(x)$. Find a point on the graph of $y = g(x)$.

85. $g(x) = \frac{1}{2}f(x)$

86. $g(x) = f(x - 2)$

87. $g(x) = f(-x)$

88. $g(x) = f(4x)$

89. $g(x) = f(x) - 2$

90. $g(x) = f(\frac{1}{2}x)$

91. $g(x) = 4f(x)$

92. $g(x) = -f(x)$

Given that $f(x) = x^2 + 3$, match the function g with a transformation of f from A–D.

93. $g(x) = x^2 + 4$ **A.** $f(x - 2)$

94. $g(x) = 9x^2 + 3$ **B.** $f(x) + 1$

95. $g(x) = (x - 2)^2 + 3$ **C.** $2f(x)$

96. $g(x) = 2x^2 + 6$ **D.** $f(3x)$

Write an equation for a function that has a graph with the given characteristics.

97. The shape of $y = x^2$, but upside-down and shifted right 8 units

98. The shape of $y = \sqrt{x}$, but shifted left 6 units and down 5 units

99. The shape of $y = |x|$, but shifted left 7 units and up 2 units

100. The shape of $y = x^3$, but upside-down and shifted right 5 units

101. The shape of $y = 1/x$, but shrunk horizontally by a factor of 2 and shifted down 3 units

102. The shape of $y = x^2$, but shifted right 6 units and up 2 units

103. The shape of $y = x^2$, but upside-down and shifted right 3 units and up 4 units

104. The shape of $y = |x|$, but stretched horizontally by a factor of 2 and shifted down 5 units

105. The shape of $y = \sqrt{x}$, but reflected across the y-axis and shifted left 2 units and down 1 unit

106. The shape of $y = 1/x$, but reflected across the x-axis and shifted up 1 unit

A graph of y = f(x) follows. No formula for f is given. In Exercises 107–114, graph the given equation.

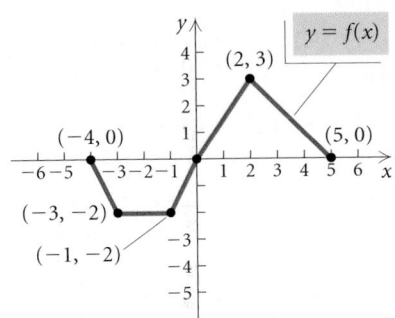

107. $g(x) = -2f(x)$ **108.** $g(x) = \frac{1}{2}f(x)$

109. $g(x) = f\left(-\frac{1}{2}x\right)$ **110.** $g(x) = f(2x)$

111. $g(x) = -\frac{1}{2}f(x-1) + 3$

112. $g(x) = -3f(x+1) - 4$

113. $g(x) = f(-x)$

114. $g(x) = -f(x)$

A graph of y = g(x) follows. No formula for g is given. In Exercises 115–118, graph the given equation.

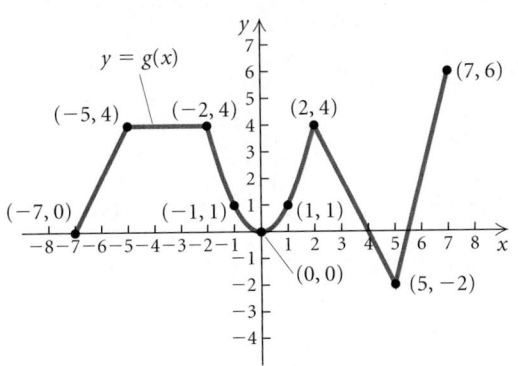

115. $h(x) = -g(x+2) + 1$

116. $h(x) = \frac{1}{2}g(-x)$

117. $h(x) = g(2x)$

118. $h(x) = 2g(x-1) - 3$

The graph of the function f is shown in figure (a). In Exercises 119–126, match the function g with one of the graphs (a)–(h), which follow. Some graphs may be used more than once.

a)

b)

c)

d)

e)

f)

g)

h)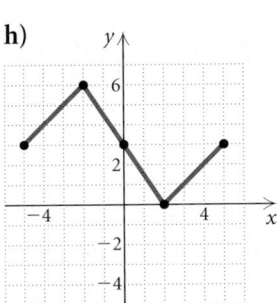

119. $g(x) = f(-x) + 3$ **120.** $g(x) = f(x) + 3$

121. $g(x) = -f(x) + 3$ **122.** $g(x) = -f(-x)$

123. $g(x) = \frac{1}{3}f(x-2)$ **124.** $g(x) = \frac{1}{3}f(x) - 3$

125. $g(x) = \frac{1}{3}f(x+2)$ **126.** $g(x) = -f(x+2)$

For each pair of functions, determine if $g(x) = f(-x)$.

127. $f(x) = 2x^4 - 35x^3 + 3x - 5$,
$g(x) = 2x^4 + 35x^3 - 3x - 5$

128. $f(x) = \frac{1}{4}x^4 + \frac{1}{5}x^3 - 81x^2 - 17$,
$g(x) = \frac{1}{4}x^4 + \frac{1}{5}x^3 + 81x^2 - 17$

A graph of the function $f(x) = x^3 - 3x^2$ *is shown below. Exercises 129–132 show graphs of functions transformed from this one. Find a formula for each function.*

129.

130.

131.

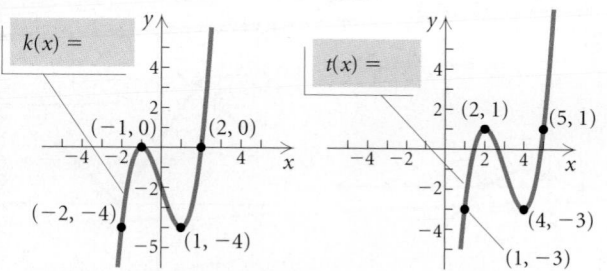

132.

Collaborative Discussion and Writing

133. Consider the constant function $f(x) = 0$. Determine whether the graph of this function is symmetric with respect to the x-axis, the y-axis, and/or the origin. Determine whether this function is even or odd.

134. Explain in your own words why the graph of $y = f(-x)$ is a reflection of the graph of $y = f(x)$ across the y-axis.

Skill Maintenance

135. Given $f(x) = 5x^2 - 7$, find each of the following.
a) $f(-3)$ b) $f(3)$
c) $f(a)$ d) $f(-a)$

136. Given $f(x) = 4x^3 - 5x$, find each of the following.
a) $f(2)$ b) $f(-2)$
c) $f(a)$ d) $f(-a)$

137. Write an equation of the line perpendicular to the graph of the line $8x - y = 10$ and containing the point $(-1, 1)$.

138. Find the slope and the y-intercept of the line with equation $2x - 9y + 1 = 0$.

Synthesis

Use the graph of the function f shown below in Exercises 139 and 140.

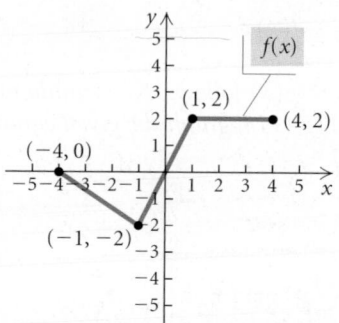

139. Graph: $y = |f(x)|$.   **140.** Graph: $y = f(|x|)$.

Use the graph of the function g shown below in Exercises 141 and 142.

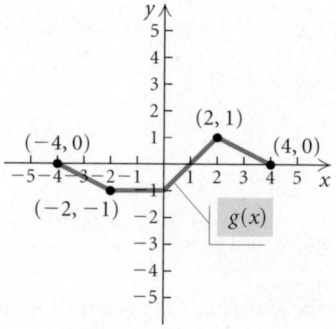

141. Graph: $y = g(|x|)$.   **142.** Graph: $y = |g(x)|$.

Determine whether the function is even, odd, or neither even nor odd.

143. $f(x) = x\sqrt{10 - x^2}$ **144.** $f(x) = \dfrac{x^2 + 1}{x^3 - 1}$

Determine whether the graph is symmetric with respect to the x-axis, the y-axis, and/or the origin.

145.
$$x^3 = y^2(2 - x)$$

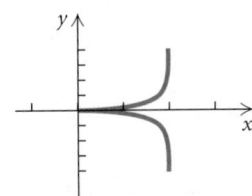

146.
$$(x^2 + y^2)^2 = 2xy$$

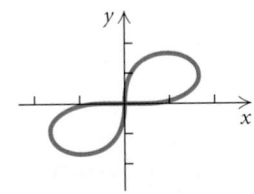

147.
$$y^2 + 4xy^2 - y^4 = x^4 - 4x^3 + 3x^2 + 2x^2y^2$$

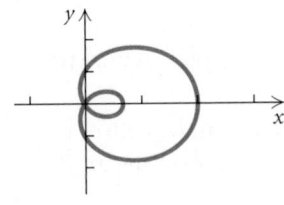

148. The graph of $f(x) = |x|$ passes through the points $(-3, 3)$, $(0, 0)$, and $(3, 3)$. Transform this function to one whose graph passes through the points $(5, 1)$, $(8, 4)$, and $(11, 1)$.

149. If $(-1, 5)$ is a point on the graph of $y = f(x)$, find b such that $(2, b)$ is on the graph of $y = f(x - 3)$.

Determine whether the statement is true or false.

150. The product of two odd functions is odd.

151. The sum of two even functions is even.

152. The product of an even function and an odd function is odd.

153. Show that if f is *any* function, then the function E defined by
$$E(x) = \frac{f(x) + f(-x)}{2}$$
is even.

154. Show that if f is *any* function, then the function O defined by
$$O(x) = \frac{f(x) - f(-x)}{2}$$
is odd.

155. Consider the functions E and O of Exercises 153 and 154.

a) Show that $f(x) = E(x) + O(x)$. This means that every function can be expressed as the sum of an even function and an odd function.
b) Let $f(x) = 4x^3 - 11x^2 + \sqrt{x} - 10$. Express f as a sum of an even function and an odd function.

CHAPTER 1 SUMMARY AND REVIEW

Important Properties and Formulas

The Distance Formula

$$d = \sqrt{(x_2 - x_1)^2 + (y_2 - y_1)^2}$$

The Midpoint Formula

$$\left(\frac{x_1 + x_2}{2}, \frac{y_1 + y_2}{2} \right)$$

Equation of a Circle

$$(x - h)^2 + (y - k)^2 = r^2$$

Terminology about Lines

Slope: $m = \dfrac{y_2 - y_1}{x_2 - x_1}$

The Slope–Intercept Equation: $y = mx + b$

The Point–Slope Equation: $y - y_1 = m(x - x_1)$

Horizontal Lines: $y = b$

Vertical Lines: $x = a$

Parallel Lines: $m_1 = m_2, \ b_1 \neq b_2$

Perpendicular Lines: $m_1 m_2 = -1,$ or $x = a, y = b$

The Algebra of Functions

The Sum of Two Functions:
$(f + g)(x) = f(x) + g(x)$

The Difference of Two Functions:
$(f - g)(x) = f(x) - g(x)$

The Product of Two Functions:
$(fg)(x) = f(x) \cdot g(x)$

The Quotient of Two Functions:
$(f/g)(x) = f(x)/g(x), \ g(x) \neq 0$

The Composition of Two Functions:
$(f \circ g)(x) = f(g(x))$

Tests for Symmetry

x-axis: If replacing y with $-y$ produces an equivalent equation, then the graph is symmetric with respect to the x-axis.

y-axis: If replacing x with $-x$ produces an equivalent equation, then the graph is symmetric with respect to the y-axis.

Origin: If replacing x with $-x$ and y with $-y$ produces an equivalent equation, then the graph is symmetric with respect to the origin.

Even Function: $f(-x) = f(x)$

Odd Function: $f(-x) = -f(x)$

Transformations

Vertical Translation: $y = f(x) \pm b$

Horizontal Translation: $y = f(x \mp d)$

Reflection across the x-axis: $y = -f(x)$

Reflection across the y-axis: $y = f(-x)$

Vertical Stretching or Shrinking: $y = af(x)$

Horizontal Stretching or Shrinking: $y = f(cx)$

REVIEW EXERCISES

Answers for all of the review exercises appear in the answer section at the back of the book. If you get an incorrect answer, restudy the objective indicated in red next to the exercise or the direction line that precedes it.

Determine whether the statement is true or false.

1. The x-intercept of the line that passes through $\left(-\frac{2}{3}, \frac{3}{2}\right)$ and the origin is $\left(-\frac{2}{3}, 0\right)$.   [1.1]

2. All functions are relations, but not all relations are functions.   [1.2]

3. If the line $ax + y = c$ is perpendicular to the line $x - by = d$, then $\dfrac{a}{b} = 1$.   [1.4]

4. The line parallel to the y-axis that passes through $(-5, 25)$ is $y = -5$.   [1.3]

5. The intersection of the lines $y = \frac{1}{2}$ and $x = -5$ is $\left(-5, \frac{1}{2}\right)$.   [1.3]

6. The domain of the function $f(x) = \dfrac{\sqrt{3 - x}}{x}$ does not contain -3 and 0.   [1.2]

Use substitution to determine whether the given ordered pairs are solutions of the given equation.   [1.1]

7. $\left(3, \frac{24}{9}\right), (0, -9); \; 2x - 9y = -18$

8. $(0, 7), (7, 1); \; y = 7$

Graph the equation.   [1.1]

9. $y = -\frac{2}{3}x + 1$

10. $2x - 4y = 8$

11. $y = 2 - x^2$

12. Find the distance between $(3, 7)$ and $(-2, 4)$.   [1.1]

13. Find the midpoint of the segment with endpoints $(3, 7)$ and $(-2, 4)$.   [1.1]

14. Find an equation of the circle with center $(-2, 6)$ and radius $\sqrt{13}$.   [1.1]

Find the center and the radius of the circle.

15. $(x + 1)^2 + (y - 3)^2 = 16$

16. $(x - 3)^2 + (y + 5)^2 = 1$

17. Find an equation of the circle having a diameter with endpoints $(-3, 5)$ and $(7, 3)$.   [1.1]

Determine whether the relation is a function. Identify the domain and the range.   [1.2]

18. $\{(3, 1), (5, 3), (7, 7), (3, 5)\}$

19. $\{(2, 7), (-2, -7), (7, -2), (0, 2), (1, -4)\}$

Determine whether the graph is that of a function.   [1.2]

20.

21.

22.

23.

24. A graph of a function is shown. Find $f(2)$, $f(-4)$, and $f(0)$.   [1.2]

Find the domain of the function.   [1.2]

25. $f(x) = 4 - 5x + x^2$

26. $f(x) = \dfrac{3}{x} + 2$

27. $f(x) = \dfrac{1}{x^2 - 6x + 5}$

28. $f(x) = \dfrac{-5x}{|16 - x^2|}$

Graph the function. Then visually estimate the domain and the range.   [1.2]

29. $f(x) = \sqrt{16 - x^2}$

30. $g(x) = |x - 5|$

31. $f(x) = x^3 - 7$

32. $h(x) = x^4 + x^2$

33. Given that $f(x) = x^2 - x - 3$, find each of the following. [1.2]

a) $f(0)$ b) $f(-3)$

c) $f(a - 1)$ d) $\dfrac{f(x + h) - f(x)}{h}$

In Exercises 34 and 35, the table of data contains input–output values for a function. Answer the following questions. [1.3]

a) *Is the change in the inputs, x, the same?*
b) *Is the change in the outputs, y, the same?*
c) *Is the function linear?*

34.

x	y
-3	8
-2	11
-1	14
0	17
1	20
2	22
3	26

35.

x	y
20	11.8
30	24.2
40	36.6
50	49.0
60	61.4
70	73.8
80	86.2

Find the slope of the line containing the given points. [1.3]

36. $(2, -11), (5, -6)$

37. $(5, 4), (-3, 4)$

38. $\left(\frac{1}{2}, 3\right), \left(\frac{1}{2}, 0\right)$

39. Find the slope and the y-intercept of the graph of
$$-2x - y = 7. \quad [1.3]$$

40. *Travel to India.* The number of American travelers to India for at least one night's stay has increased from 254,000 in 1994 to 629,000 in 2004 (*Source*: U.S. Department of Commerce, ITA, Office of Travel and Tourism Industries, July 2005). Find the average rate of change in the number of travelers from 1994 to 2004. [1.3]

41. Graph $y = -\frac{1}{4}x + 3$ using the slope and the y-intercept. [1.3]

Write a slope–intercept equation for a line with the following characteristics. [1.4]

42. $m = -\frac{2}{3}$, y-intercept $(0, -4)$

43. $m = 3$, passes through $(-2, -1)$

44. Passes through $(4, 1)$ and $(-2, -1)$

Determine whether the lines are parallel, perpendicular, or neither. [1.4]

45. $3x - 2y = 8,$
$\quad 6x - 4y = 2$

46. $y - 2x = 4,$
$\quad 2y - 3x = -7$

47. $y = \frac{3}{2}x + 7,$
$\quad y = -\frac{2}{3}x - 4$

Given the point $(1, -1)$ and the line $2x + 3y = 4$:

48. Find an equation of the line containing the given point and parallel to the given line. [1.4]

49. Find an equation of the line containing the given point and perpendicular to the given line. [1.4]

50. *Total Cost.* Clear County Cable Television charges a $25 installation fee and $20 per month for basic service. Write an equation that can be used to determine the total cost, $C(t)$, of t months of basic cable television service. Find the total cost of 6 months of service. [1.3]

51. *Temperature and Depth of the Earth.* The function T given by $T(d) = 10d + 20$ can be used to determine the temperature T, in degrees Celsius, at a depth d, in kilometers, inside the earth.

a) Find $T(5)$, $T(20)$, and $T(1000)$. [1.3]
b) The radius of the earth is about 5600 km. Use this fact to determine the domain of the function. [1.3]

52. *Drive-in Movie Sites.* Model the data given in the table on the following page with a linear function and then predict the number of drive-in sites in the United States in 2009. Answer will vary depending on the data points used. [1.4]

Year, x	Drive-in Movie Sites in the United States, y
1995, 0	593
1998, 3	524
2001, 6	440
2004, 9	402

Source: National Association of Theater Owners

Graph each of the following. [1.5]

53. $f(x) = \begin{cases} -x, & \text{for } x \leq -4, \\ \frac{1}{2}x + 1, & \text{for } x > -4 \end{cases}$

54. $f(x) = \begin{cases} x^3, & \text{for } x < -2, \\ |x|, & \text{for } -2 \leq x \leq 2, \\ \sqrt{x-1}, & \text{for } x > 2 \end{cases}$

55. $f(x) = \begin{cases} \dfrac{x^2 - 1}{x + 1}, & \text{for } x \neq -1, \\ 3, & \text{for } x = -1 \end{cases}$

56. $f(x) = [\![x]\!]$ **57.** $f(x) = [\![x - 3]\!]$

58. For the function in Exercise 54, find $f(-1)$, $f(5)$, $f(-2)$, and $f(-3)$. [1.5]

59. *Inscribed Rectangle.* A rectangle is inscribed in a semicircle of radius 2, as shown. The variable x = half the length of the rectangle. Express the area of the rectangle as a function of x. [1.5]

60. *Minimizing Surface Area.* A container firm is designing an open-top rectangular box, with a square base, that will hold 108 in³. Let x = the length of a side of the base.

a) Express the surface area as a function of x. [1.5]

b) Find the domain of the function. [1.5]

c) Using the graph shown below, determine the dimensions that will minimize the surface area of the box. [1.5]

Given that $f(x) = \sqrt{x - 2}$ and $g(x) = x^2 - 1$, find each of the following if it exists. [1.6]

61. $(f - g)(6)$ **62.** $(fg)(2)$

63. $(f + g)(-1)$

For each pair of functions in Exercises 64 and 65:

a) Find the domain of f, g, $f + g$, $f - g$, fg, and f/g. [1.6]

b) Find $(f + g)(x)$, $(f - g)(x)$, $fg(x)$, and $(f/g)(x)$. [1.6]

64. $f(x) = \dfrac{4}{x^2}$; $g(x) = 3 - 2x$

65. $f(x) = 3x^2 + 4x$; $g(x) = 2x - 1$

66. Given the total-revenue and total-cost functions $R(x) = 120x - 0.5x^2$ and $C(x) = 15x + 6$, find the total-profit function $P(x)$. [1.6]

67. For the function
$$f(x) = 3 - x^2,$$
construct and simplify the difference quotient. [1.6]

In Exercises 68 and 69, for the pair of functions:

a) Find the domain of $f \circ g$ and $g \circ f$. [1.6]

b) Find $(f \circ g)(x)$ and $(g \circ f)(x)$. [1.6]

68. $f(x) = \dfrac{4}{x^2}$; $g(x) = 3 - 2x$

69. $f(x) = 3x^2 + 4x$; $g(x) = 2x - 1$

Find $f(x)$ and $g(x)$ such that $h(x) = (f \circ g)x$. [1.6]

70. $h(x) = \sqrt{5x + 2}$

71. $h(x) = 4(5x - 1)^2 + 9$

Graph the given equation and determine visually whether it is symmetric with respect to the x-axis, the y-axis, and/or the origin. Then verify your assertion algebraically. [1.7]

72. $x^2 + y^2 = 4$

73. $y^2 = x^2 + 3$

74. $x + y = 3$

75. $y = x^2$

76. $y = x^3$

77. $y = x^4 - x^2$

Determine visually whether the function is even, odd, or neither even nor odd. [1.7]

78.

79.

80.

81.

Test whether the function is even, odd, or neither even nor odd. [1.7]

82. $f(x) = 9 - x^2$

83. $f(x) = x^3 - 2x + 4$

84. $f(x) = x^7 - x^5$

85. $f(x) = |x|$

86. $f(x) = \sqrt{16 - x^2}$

87. $f(x) = \dfrac{10x}{x^2 + 1}$

Write an equation for a function that has a graph with the given characteristics. [1.7]

88. The shape of $y = x^2$, but shifted left 3 units

89. The shape of $y = \sqrt{x}$, but upside-down and shifted right 3 units and up 4 units

90. The shape of $y = |x|$, but stretched vertically by a factor of 2 and shifted right 3 units

A graph of $y = f(x)$ is shown at the top of the next column. No formula for f is given. Graph each of the following. [1.7]

91. $y = f(x - 1)$

92. $y = f(2x)$

93. $y = -2f(x)$

94. $y = 3 + f(x)$

95. The domain of the function

$$f(x) = \frac{x + 3}{8 - 4x}$$

is which of the following? [1.2]

A. $(-3, 2)$

B. $(-\infty, 2) \cup (2, \infty)$

C. $(-\infty, -3) \cup (-3, 2) \cup (2, \infty)$

D. $(-\infty, -3) \cup (-3, \infty)$

96. The center of the circle described by the equation $(x - 1)^2 + y^2 = 9$ is which of the following? [1.1]

A. $(-1, 0)$ **B.** $(1, 0)$

C. $(0, -3)$ **D.** $(-1, 3)$

Technology Connection

97. a) Fit a regression line to the data in Exercise 52 and use it to estimate the number of drive-in sites in 2009. [1.4]

   b) What is the correlation coefficient for the regression line? How close a fit is the regression line? [1.4]

Collaborative Discussion and Writing

98. Given that $f(x) = 4x^3 - 2x + 7$, find each of the following. Then discuss how each expression differs from the other. [1.2], [1.7]

   a) $f(x) + 2$ b) $f(x + 2)$ c) $f(x) + f(2)$

99. Given the graph of $y = f(x)$, explain and contrast the effect of the constant c on the graphs of $y = f(cx)$ and $y = cf(x)$. [1.7]

100. a) Graph several functions of the type $y_1 = f(x)$ and $y_2 = |f(x)|$. Describe a procedure, involving transformations, for creating the graph of y_2 from y_1. [1.7]

b) Describe a procedure, involving transformations, for creating the graph of $y_2 = f(|x|)$ from $y_1 = f(x)$.   [1.7]

Synthesis

Find the domain.   [1.2]

101. $f(x) = \dfrac{\sqrt{1-x}}{x - |x|}$

102. $f(x) = (x - 9x^{-1})^{-1}$

103. Prove that the sum of two odd functions is odd. [1.7]

104. Describe how the graph of $y = -f(-x)$ is obtained from the graph of $y = f(x)$.   [1.7]

CHAPTER 1 TEST

1. Graph: $5x - 2y = -10$.

2. Find the distance between $(5, 8)$ and $(-1, 5)$.

3. Find the midpoint of the segment with endpoints $(-2, 6)$ and $(-4, 3)$.

4. Find an equation of the circle with center $(-1, 2)$ and radius $\sqrt{5}$.

5. Find the center and the radius of the circle
$$(x + 4)^2 + (y - 5)^2 = 36.$$

6. a) Determine whether the relation
$$\{(-4, 7), (3, 0), (1, 5), (0, 7)\}$$
is a function. Answer yes or no.
b) Find the domain of the relation.
c) Find the range of the relation.

7. Given that $f(x) = 2x^2 - x + 5$, find each of the following.
a) $f(-1)$
b) $f(a + 2)$

8. a) Graph: $f(x) = |x - 2| + 3$.
b) Visually estimate the domain of $f(x)$.
c) Visually estimate the range of $f(x)$.

Find the domain of the function.

9. $f(x) = \dfrac{1}{x - 4}$

10. $g(x) = x^3 + 2$

11. $h(x) = \sqrt{25 - x^2}$

12. Determine whether each graph is that of a function. Answer yes or no.

a)

b)

Find the slope of the line containing the given points.

13. $\left(-2, \frac{2}{3}\right), (-2, 5)$

14. $(4, -10), (-8, 12)$

15. $(-5, 6), \left(\frac{3}{4}, 6\right)$

16. *NASCAR Attendance.*   The weekend attendance at NASCAR events has increased from 5.3 million in 1995 to 6.8 million in 2004 (*Sources*: Goodyear Tire & Rubber Co. (1995–1999); NASCAR). Find the average rate of change in weekend attendance from 1995 to 2004.

17. Find the slope and the y-intercept of the graph of $-3x + 2y = 5$.

18. Write an equation for the line with $m = -\frac{5}{8}$ and y-intercept $(0, -5)$.

19. Write an equation for the line that passes through $(-5, 4)$ and $(3, -2)$.

20. Find an equation of the line containing the point $(-1, 3)$ and parallel to the line $x + 2y = -6$.

21. Determine whether the lines are parallel, perpendicular, or neither.
$$2x + 3y = -12,$$
$$2y - 3x = 8$$

22. *Hourly Earnings.* The data given in the following table show the increase in average hourly earnings of U.S. production workers since 1972. Model the data with a linear function and, using this function, predict the average hourly earnings in 2010. Answers will vary depending on the data points used.

Year, x	Average Hourly Earnings of U.S. Production Workers, y
1972, 0	3.90
1976, 4	5.06
1980, 8	6.84
1984, 12	8.48
1988, 16	9.43
1992, 20	10.76
1996, 24	12.03
2000, 28	14.00
2004, 32	15.67

Sources: U.S. Bureau of Labor Statistics; U.S. Department of Labor

23. Graph $f(x)$:
$$f(x) = \begin{cases} x^2, & \text{for } x < -1, \\ |x|, & \text{for } -1 \leq x \leq 1, \\ \sqrt{x - 1}, & \text{for } x > 1. \end{cases}$$

24. For the function in Exercise 23, find $f\left(-\frac{7}{8}\right)$, $f(5)$, and $f(-4)$.

25. Given that $f(x) = x^2 - 4x + 3$ and $g(x) = \sqrt{3 - x}$, find $(f - g)(-1)$.

26. For $f(x) = x^2$ and $g(x) = \sqrt{x - 3}$, find each of the following.
   a) The domain of f
   b) The domain of g

   c) $(f - g)(x)$
   d) $(fg)(x)$
   e) The domain of $(f/g)(x)$

27. Find $f(x)$ and $g(x)$ such that $h(x) = (f \circ g)(x) = (2x - 7)^4$.

28. Construct and simplify the difference quotient for
$$f(x) = x^2 + 4.$$

For $f(x) = \sqrt{x - 5}$ and $g(x) = x^2 + 1$:

29. Find $(f \circ g)(x)$ and $(g \circ f)(x)$.

30. Find the domain of $(f \circ g)(x)$ and of $(g \circ f)(x)$.

31. Determine whether the graph of $y = x^4 - 2x^2$ is symmetric with respect to the x-axis, the y-axis, and/or the origin.

32. Test whether the function
$$f(x) = \frac{2x}{x^2 + 1}$$
is even, odd, or neither even nor odd. Show your work.

33. Write an equation for a function that has the shape of $y = x^2$, but is shifted right 2 units and down 1 unit.

34. Write an equation for a function that has the shape of $y = x^2$, but is shifted left 2 units and down 3 units.

35. The graph of a function $y = f(x)$ is shown below. No formula for f is given. Graph $y = -\frac{1}{2}f(x)$.

Synthesis

36. If $(-3, 1)$ is a point on the graph of $y = f(x)$, what point do you know is on the graph of $y = f(3x)$?

Functions, Equations, and Inequalities

APPLICATION

Together, a dog owner and a cat owner spend an average of $376 annually for veterinary-related expenses. A dog owner spends $150 more per year than a cat owner. (*Source*: The Humane Society of the United States) Find the average annual veterinary-related expenses of a dog owner and of a cat owner.

This problem appears as Example 4 in Section 2.1.

2.1   Linear Equations, Functions, and Models

◆ Solve linear equations.
◆ Solve applied problems using linear models.
◆ Find zeros of linear functions.
◆ Solve a formula for a given variable.

> *Note to the student and the instructor*: We assume that students come to a College Algebra course with some equation-solving skills from their study of Intermediate Algebra. Thus a portion of the material in this section might be considered by some to be review in nature. We present this material here in order to use linear functions, with which students are familiar, to lay the groundwork for zeros of higher-order polynomial functions and their connection to solutions of equations and *x*-intercepts of graphs.

An **equation** is a statement that two expressions are equal. To **solve** an equation in one variable is to find all the values of the variable that make the equation true. Each of these numbers is a **solution** of the equation. The set of all solutions of an equation is its **solution set.** Some examples of **equations in one variable** are

$$2x + 3 = 5, \quad 3(x - 1) = 4x + 5, \quad x^2 - 3x + 2 = 0, \quad \text{and} \quad \frac{x - 3}{x + 4} = 1.$$

◆ Linear Equations

The first two equations above are *linear equations* in one variable. We define such equations as follows.

> A **linear equation in one variable** is an equation that is equivalent to one of the form $mx + b = 0$, where m and b are real numbers and $m \neq 0$.

Equations that have the same solution set are **equivalent equations.** For example, $2x + 3 = 5$ and $x = 1$ are equivalent equations because 1 is the solution of each equation. On the other hand, $x^2 - 3x + 2 = 0$ and $x = 1$ are not equivalent equations because 1 and 2 are both solutions of $x^2 - 3x + 2 = 0$ but 2 is not a solution of $x = 1$.

To solve an equation, we find an equivalent equation in which the variable is isolated. The following principles allow us to solve linear equations.

> ### Equation-Solving Principles
>
> For any real numbers a, b, and c:
>
> *The Addition Principle*: If $a = b$ is true, then $a + c = b + c$ is true.
>
> *The Multiplication Principle*: If $a = b$ is true, then $ac = bc$ is true.

EXAMPLE 1 Solve: $6x - 4 = 1$.

ALGEBRAIC SOLUTION

We have

$$6x - 4 = 1$$

$$6x - 4 + 4 = 1 + 4 \qquad \text{Using the addition principle to add 4 on both sides}$$

$$6x = 5 \qquad \text{Using the multiplication principle to multiply by } \tfrac{1}{6}, \text{ or divide by 6, on both sides}$$

$$\frac{6x}{6} = \frac{5}{6}$$

$$x = \frac{5}{6}. \qquad \text{Note that } 6x - 4 = 1 \text{ and } x = \tfrac{5}{6} \text{ are equivalent equations.}$$

Check:

$$6x - 4 = 1$$

$$6 \cdot \tfrac{5}{6} - 4 \; ? \; 1 \qquad \text{Substituting } \tfrac{5}{6} \text{ for } x$$

$$5 - 4 \;\Big|$$

$$1 \;\Big|\; 1 \qquad \text{TRUE}$$

The solution is $\frac{5}{6}$.

VISUALIZING THE SOLUTION

We graph $y = 6x - 4$ and $y = 1$. The first coordinate of the point of intersection of the graphs is the value of x for which $6x - 4 = 1$ and is thus the solution of the equation.

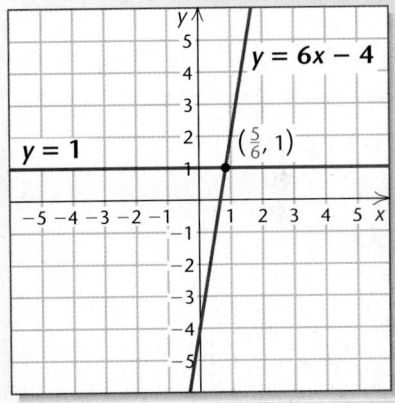

The solution is $\frac{5}{6}$.

▶ Now Try Exercise 1.

TECHNOLOGY ·
    CONNECTION

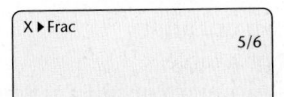

$y_1 = 6x - 4, \quad y_2 = 1$

Intersection
X = .83333333 Y = 1

X ▶ Frac
                5/6

We can use the INTERSECT feature on a graphing calculator to solve equations. We call this the **Intersect method.** To use the Intersect method to solve the equation in Example 1, for instance, we graph $y_1 = 6x - 4$ and $y_2 = 1$. The value of x for which $y_1 = y_2$ is the solution of the equation $6x - 4 = 1$. This value of x is the first coordinate of the point of intersection of the graphs of y_1 and y_2. Using the INTERSECT feature, we find that the first coordinate of this point is approximately 0.83333333.

If the solution is a rational number, we can find fraction notation for the exact solution by using the ▶FRAC feature. The solution is $\frac{5}{6}$.

EXAMPLE 2 Solve: $2(5 - 3x) = 8 - 3(x + 2)$.

Solution   We have

$$2(5 - 3x) = 8 - 3(x + 2)$$

$$10 - 6x = 8 - 3x - 6 \qquad \text{Using the distributive property}$$

$$10 - 6x = 2 - 3x \qquad \text{Collecting like terms}$$

$$10 - 6x + 6x = 2 - 3x + 6x \qquad \text{Using the addition principle to add } 6x \text{ on both sides}$$

$$10 = 2 + 3x$$

$$10 - 2 = 2 + 3x - 2 \qquad \text{Using the addition principle to add } -2, \text{ or subtract 2, on both sides}$$

$$8 = 3x$$

$$\frac{8}{3} = \frac{3x}{3} \qquad \text{Using the multiplication principle to multiply by } \frac{1}{3}, \text{ or divide by 3, on both sides}$$

$$\frac{8}{3} = x.$$

Check:

$$\begin{array}{c|c} \multicolumn{2}{c}{2(5 - 3x) = 8 - 3(x + 2)} \\ \hline 2\left(5 - 3 \cdot \frac{8}{3}\right) \; ? \; 8 - 3\left(\frac{8}{3} + 2\right) & \text{Substituting } \frac{8}{3} \text{ for } x \\ 2(5 - 8) & 8 - 3\left(\frac{14}{3}\right) \\ 2(-3) & 8 - 14 \\ -6 & -6 \qquad \text{TRUE} \end{array}$$

The solution is $\frac{8}{3}$.

▶ Now Try Exercise 19.

✦ Applications Using Linear Models

Mathematical techniques are used to answer questions arising from real-world situations. Linear equations and functions *model* many of these situations.

The following strategy is of great assistance in problem solving.

Five Steps for Problem Solving

1. **Familiarize** yourself with the problem situation. If the problem is presented in words, this means to read carefully. Some or all of the following can also be helpful.

   a) Make a drawing, if it makes sense to do so.
   b) Make a written list of the known facts and a list of what you wish to find out.
   c) Assign variables to represent unknown quantities.
   d) Organize the information in a chart or a table.
   e) Find further information. Look up a formula, consult a reference book or an expert in the field, or do research on the Internet.
   f) Guess or estimate the answer and check your guess or estimate.

(continued)

2. **Translate** the problem situation to mathematical language or symbolism. For most of the problems you will encounter in algebra, this means to write one or more equations, but sometimes an inequality or some other mathematical symbolism may be appropriate.
3. **Carry out** some type of mathematical manipulation. Use your mathematical skills to find a possible solution. In algebra, this usually means to solve an equation, an inequality, or a system of equations or inequalities.
4. **Check** to see whether your possible solution actually fits the problem situation and is thus really a solution of the problem. Although you may have solved an equation, the solution(s) of the equation might not be solution(s) of the original problem.
5. **State** the answer clearly using a complete sentence.

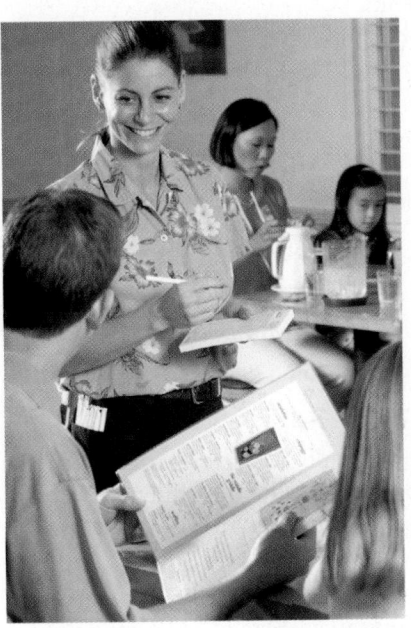

EXAMPLE 3 *Dining Out.* Americans spent about $511 billion dining out in 2006. This was a 5.1% increase over the amount spent in 2005. (*Source*: National Restaurant Association) How much was spent dining out in 2005?

Solution

1. **Familiarize.** Let's estimate that $500 billion was spent dining out in 2005. Then the amount spent in 2006, in billions of dollars, would be

$$500 + 5.1\% \cdot 500 = 1(500) + 0.051(500)$$
$$= 1.051(500)$$
$$= 525.5.$$

Since we know that $511 billion was actually spent dining out in 2006, the estimate is too high. Nevertheless, the calculations performed in checking the estimate indicate how we can translate the problem to an equation. We let x = the amount spent dining out in 2005, in billions of dollars. Then $x + 5.1\%x$, or $1 \cdot x + 0.051 \cdot x$, or $1.051x$, is the amount spent dining out in 2006.

2. **Translate.** We translate to an equation:

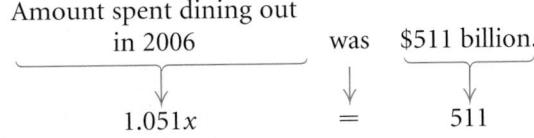

Amount spent dining out in 2006   was $511 billion.

$$1.051x \qquad = \qquad 511$$

3. **Carry out.** We solve the equation, as follows:

$$1.051x = 511$$
$$x = \frac{511}{1.051} \qquad \text{Dividing by 1.051 on both sides}$$
$$x \approx 486.$$

4. Check. Since 5.1% of $486 billion is about $25 billion and $486 billion + $25 billion = $511 billion, the answer checks.

5. State. Americans spent about $486 billion dining out in 2005.

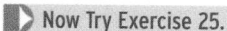

EXAMPLE 4   *Veterinary Expenses.*   Together, a dog owner and a cat owner spend an average of $376 annually for veterinary-related expenses. A dog owner spends $150 more per year than a cat owner. (*Source*: The Humane Society of the United States) Find the average annual veterinary-related expenses of a dog owner and of a cat owner.

Solution

1. Familiarize. A dog owner's spending is described in terms of a cat owner's spending, so we will let $x =$ the amount spent annually for veterinary-related expenses by a cat owner. Then $x + 150 =$ the amount spent annually by a dog owner.

2. Translate. We translate to an equation:

$$
\underbrace{\text{Dog owner's}}_{\text{expenses}} \quad \text{plus} \quad \underbrace{\text{cat owner's}}_{\text{expenses}} \quad \text{is} \quad \$376.
$$

$$
x + 150 \quad + \quad x \quad = \quad 376
$$

3. Solve. We solve the equation, as follows:

$$x + 150 + x = 376$$
$$2x + 150 = 376 \qquad \text{Collecting like terms}$$
$$2x = 226 \qquad \text{Subtracting 150 on both sides}$$
$$x = 113. \qquad \text{Dividing by 2 on both sides}$$

If $x = 113$, then $x + 150 = 113 + 150 = 263$.

4. Check. If a dog owner spends $263 annually for veterinary-related expenses and a cat owner spends $113 annually, then together they spend $263 + $113, or $376. Also, $263 is $150 more than $113. The answer checks.

5. State. A dog owner spends an average of $263 annually for veterinary-related expenses and a cat owner spends an average of $113 annually.

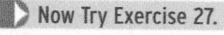

In some applications, we need to use a formula that describes the relationships among variables. When a situation involves distance, rate (also called speed or velocity), and time, for example, we use the following formula.

> **The Motion Formula**
>
> The distance d traveled by an object moving at rate r in time t is given by
>
> $$d = r \cdot t.$$

EXAMPLE 5 *Airplane Speed.* America West Airlines' fleet includes Boeing 737-200's, each with a cruising speed of 500 mph, and Bombardier deHavilland Dash 8-200's, each with a cruising speed of 302 mph (*Source*: America West Airlines). Suppose that a Dash 8-200 takes off and travels at its cruising speed. One hour later, a 737-200 takes off and follows the same route, traveling at its cruising speed. How long will it take the 737-200 to overtake the Dash 8-200?

Solution

1. **Familiarize.** We make a drawing showing both the known and the unknown information. We let t = the time, in hours, that the 737-200 travels before it overtakes the Dash 8-200. Since the Dash 8-200 takes off 1 hr before the 737, it will travel for $t + 1$ hr before being overtaken. The planes will have traveled the same distance, d, when one overtakes the other.

We can also organize the information in a table, as follows.

<table>
<tr><td></td><td align="center">d</td><td align="center">$= r \cdot t$</td><td></td></tr>
</table>

	Distance	Rate	Time	
737-200	d	500	t	$\longrightarrow d = 500t$
Dash 8-200	d	302	$t + 1$	$\longrightarrow d = 302(t + 1)$

2. **Translate.** Using the formula $d = rt$ in each row of the table, we get two expressions for d:

$$d = 500t \quad \text{and} \quad d = 302(t + 1).$$

Since the distances are the same, we have the following equation:

$$500t = 302(t + 1).$$

3. **Carry out.** We solve the equation, as follows:

$$500t = 302(t + 1)$$

$500t = 302t + 302$ Using the distributive property

$198t = 302$ Subtracting $302t$ on both sides

$t \approx 1.53.$ Dividing by 198 on both sides and rounding to the nearest hundredth

4. **Check.** If the 737-200 travels for about 1.53 hr, then the Dash 8-200 travels for about 1.53 + 1, or 2.53 hr. In 2.53 hr, the Dash 8-200 travels 302(2.53), or 764.06 mi, and in 1.53 hr, the 737-200 travels 500(1.53), or 765 mi. Since 764.06 mi ≈ 765 mi, the answer checks. (Remember that we rounded the value of t.)

5. **State.** About 1.53 hr after the 737-200 has taken off, it will overtake the Dash 8-200.

▶ **Now Try Exercise 49.**

For some applications, we need to use a formula to find the amount of interest earned by an investment or the amount of interest due on a loan.

> **The Simple-Interest Formula**
>
> The **simple interest** I on a principal of P dollars at interest rate r for t years is given by
>
> $$I = Prt.$$

EXAMPLE 6 *Student Loans.* Jared's two student loans total $12,000. One loan is at 5% simple interest and the other is at 8% simple interest. After 1 yr, Jared owes $750 in interest. What is the amount of each loan?

Solution

1. **Familiarize.** We let x = the amount borrowed at 5% interest. Then the remainder of the $12,000, or $12,000 - x$, is borrowed at 8%. We organize the information in a table, keeping in mind the formula $I = Prt$.

	Amount Borrowed	Interest Rate	Time	Amount of Interest
5% Loan	x	5%, or 0.05	1 yr	$x(0.05)(1)$, or $0.05x$
8% Loan	$12,000 - x$	8%, or 0.08	1 yr	$(12,000 - x)(0.08)(1)$, or $0.08(12,000 - x)$
Total	12,000			750

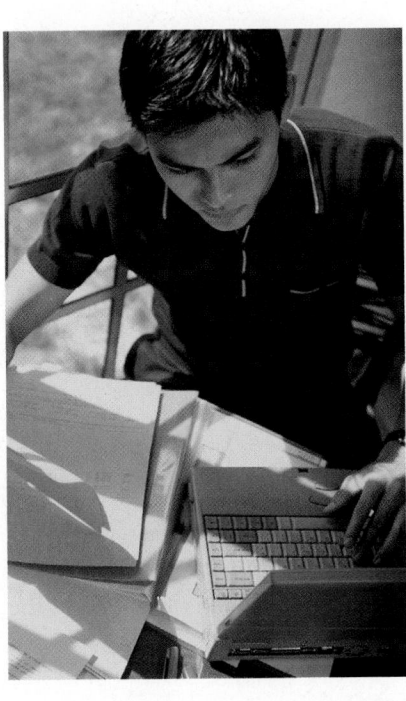

2. **Translate.** The total amount of interest on the two loans is $750. Thus we write the following equation:

Interest on 5% loan plus interest on 8% loan is $750.

$$0.05x + 0.08(12{,}000 - x) = 750$$

3. **Carry out.** We solve the equation, as follows:

$$0.05x + 0.08(12{,}000 - x) = 750$$

$$0.05x + 960 - 0.08x = 750 \qquad \text{Using the distributive property}$$

$$-0.03x + 960 = 750 \qquad \text{Collecting like terms}$$

$$-0.03x = -210 \qquad \text{Subtracting 960 on both sides}$$

$$x = 7000. \qquad \text{Dividing by } -0.03 \text{ on both sides}$$

If $x = 7000$, then $12{,}000 - x = 12{,}000 - 7000 = 5000$.

4. **Check.** The interest on $7000 at 5% for 1 yr is $7000(0.05)(1)$, or $350. The interest on $5000 at 8% for 1 yr is $5000(0.08)(1)$, or $400. Since $350 + $400 = $750, the answer checks.

5. **State.** Jared borrowed $7000 at 5% interest and $5000 at 8% interest.

▶ Now Try Exercise 35.

Sometimes we use formulas from geometry in solving applied problems. In the following example, we use the formula for the perimeter P of a rectangle with length l and width w: $P = 2l + 2w$. There is a summary of geometric formulas at the back of the book.

EXAMPLE 7 *Soccer Fields.* The length of the largest regulation soccer field is 30 yd greater than the width and the perimeter is 460 yd. Find the length and the width.

Solution

1. **Familiarize.** We first make a drawing. Since the length of the field is described in terms of the width, we let $w =$ the width, in yards. Then $w + 30 =$ the length, in yards.

2. **Translate.** We use the formula for the perimeter of a rectangle:

$$P = 2l + 2w$$
$$460 = 2(w + 30) + 2w. \quad \text{Substituting 460 for } P \text{ and } w + 30 \text{ for } l$$

3. **Carry out.** We solve the equation:

$$460 = 2(w + 30) + 2w$$
$$460 = 2w + 60 + 2w \quad \text{Using the distributive property}$$
$$460 = 4w + 60 \quad \text{Collecting like terms}$$
$$400 = 4w \quad \text{Subtracting 60 on both sides}$$
$$100 = w. \quad \text{Dividing by 4 on both sides}$$

If $w = 100$, then $w + 30 = 100 + 30 = 130$.

4. **Check.** The length, 130 yd, is 30 yd more than the width, 100 yd. Also,

$$2 \cdot 130 \text{ yd} + 2 \cdot 100 \text{ yd} = 260 \text{ yd} + 200 \text{ yd} = 460 \text{ yd}.$$

The answer checks.

5. **State.** The length of the largest regulation soccer field is 130 yd and the width is 100 yd.

▶ Now Try Exercise 43.

✦ Zeros of Linear Functions

An input for which a function's output is 0 is called a **zero** of the function. We will restrict our attention in this section to zeros of linear functions. This allows us to become familiar with the concept of a zero and it lays the groundwork for working with zeros of other types of functions later in this chapter and in succeeding chapters.

> ### Zeros of Functions
>
> An input c of a function f is called a **zero** of the function, if the output for c is 0. That is, c is a zero of f if $f(c) = 0$.

LINEAR FUNCTIONS

REVIEW SECTION 1.3.

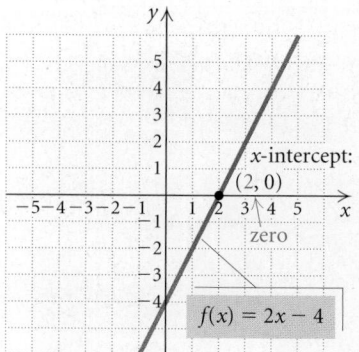

$f(x) = 2x - 4$

Recall that a linear function is given by $f(x) = mx + b$, where m and b are constants. For the linear function $f(x) = 2x - 4$, we have $f(2) = 2 \cdot 2 - 4 = 0$, so 2 is a **zero** of the function. In fact, 2 is the *only* zero of this function. In general, a **linear function $f(x) = mx + b$, with $m \neq 0$, has exactly one zero.**

Consider the graph of $f(x) = 2x - 4$, shown at left. We see from the graph that the zero, 2, is the first coordinate of the point at which the graph crosses the x-axis. This point, $(2, 0)$, is the **x-intercept** of the graph. Thus when we find the zero of a linear function, we are also finding the first coordinate of the x-intercept of the graph of the function.

For every linear function $f(x) = mx + b$, there is an associated linear equation $mx + b = 0$. When we find the zero of a function $f(x) = mx + b$, we are also finding the solution of the equation $mx + b = 0$.

EXAMPLE 8 Find the zero of $f(x) = 5x - 9$.

ALGEBRAIC SOLUTION

We find the value of x for which $f(x) = 0$:

$$5x - 9 = 0 \qquad \text{Setting } f(x) = 0$$

$$5x = 9 \qquad \text{Adding 9 on both sides}$$

$$x = \frac{9}{5}, \text{ or } 1.8. \qquad \text{Dividing by 5 on both sides}$$

The zero is $\frac{9}{5}$, or 1.8. This means that $f\left(\frac{9}{5}\right) = 0$, or $f(1.8) = 0$. Note that the *zero* of the function $f(x) = 5x - 9$ is the *solution* of the equation $5x - 9 = 0$.

VISUALIZING THE SOLUTION

We graph $f(x) = 5x - 9$.

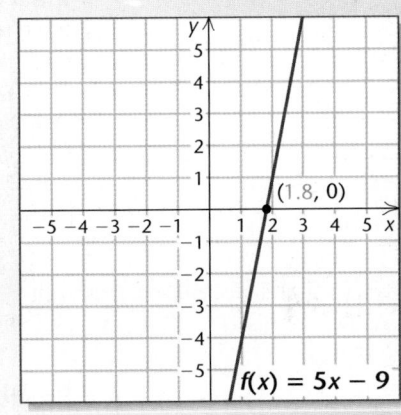

The x-intercept of the graph is $\left(\frac{9}{5}, 0\right)$, or $(1.8, 0)$. Thus, $\frac{9}{5}$, or 1.8, is the zero of the function.

▶ Now Try Exercise 63.

TECHNOLOGY · · · · · · · · · · · · · ·
   CONNECTION

$y = 5x - 9$

We can use the ZERO feature on a graphing calculator to find the zeros of a function $f(x)$ and to solve the corresponding equation $f(x) = 0$. We call this the **Zero method.** To use the Zero method in Example 8, for instance, we graph $y = 5x - 9$ and use the ZERO feature to find the coordinates of the x-intercept of the graph. Note that the x-intercept must appear in the window when the ZERO feature is used. We see that the zero of the function is 1.8.

CONNECTING THE CONCEPTS

Zeros, Solutions, and Intercepts

The zero of a linear function $f(x) = mx + b$, with $m \neq 0$, is the solution of the linear equation $mx + b = 0$ and is the first coordinate of the x-intercept of the graph of $f(x) = mx + b$. To find the zero of $f(x) = mx + b$, we solve $f(x) = 0$, or $mx + b = 0$.

FUNCTION	ZERO OF THE FUNCTION; SOLUTION OF THE EQUATION	ZERO OF THE FUNCTION; X-INTERCEPT OF THE GRAPH
Linear Function $f(x) = 2x - 4$, or $y = 2x - 4$	To find the **zero** of $f(x)$, we solve $f(x) = 0$: $$2x - 4 = 0$$ $$2x = 4$$ $$x = 2.$$ The **solution** of $2x - 4 = 0$ is 2. This is the zero of the function $f(x) = 2x - 4$. That is, $f(2) = 0$.	The zero of $f(x)$ is the first coordinate of the **x-intercept** of the graph of $y = f(x)$. 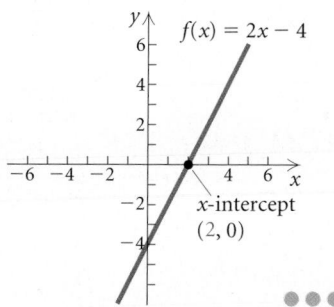

● ● ●

✦ Formulas

A **formula** is an equation that can be used to *model* a situation. For example, the formula $P = 2l + 2w$ in Example 7 gives the perimeter of a rectangle with length l and width w. We also used the motion formula, $d = r \cdot t$, in Example 5 and the simple-interest formula, $I = Prt$, in Example 6.

The equation-solving principles presented earlier can be used to solve a formula for a given letter.

EXAMPLE 9 Solve $P = 2l + 2w$ for l.

Solution We have

$$P = 2l + 2w \qquad \text{We want to isolate } l.$$
$$P - 2w = 2l \qquad \text{Subtracting } 2w \text{ on both sides}$$
$$\frac{P - 2w}{2} = l. \qquad \text{Dividing by 2 on both sides}$$

▶ Now Try Exercise 85.

The formula $l = \dfrac{P - 2w}{2}$ can be used to determine a rectangle's length if we are given its perimeter and its width.

EXAMPLE 10 The formula $A = P + Prt$ gives the amount A to which a principal of P dollars will grow when invested at simple interest rate r for t years. Solve the formula for P.

Solution We have

$$A = P + Prt \qquad \text{We want to isolate } P.$$

$$A = P(1 + rt) \qquad \text{Factoring}$$

$$\frac{A}{1 + rt} = \frac{P(1 + rt)}{1 + rt} \qquad \text{Dividing by } 1 + rt \text{ on both sides}$$

$$\frac{A}{1 + rt} = P.$$

▶ Now Try Exercise 88.

The formula $P = \dfrac{A}{1 + rt}$ can be used to determine how much should be invested at simple interest rate r in order to have A dollars t years later.

TECHNOLOGY ·····
    CONNECTION

CONNECTING THE CONCEPTS

The Intersect and Zero Methods

An equation $f(x) = g(x)$ can be solved using the Intersect method by graphing $y_1 = f(x)$ and $y_2 = g(x)$ and using the INTERSECT feature to find the first coordinate of the point of intersection of the graphs. The equation can also be solved using the Zero method by writing it with 0 on one side of the equals sign and then using the ZERO feature.

Solve: $x - 1 = 2x - 6$.

The Intersect Method
Graph

$$f(x) = y_1 = x - 1$$

and

$$g(x) = y_2 = 2x - 6.$$

Point of intersection: $(5, 4)$
Solution: 5

The Zero Method

First add $-2x$ and 6 on both sides of the equation to get 0 on one side.

$$x - 1 = 2x - 6$$
$$x - 1 - 2x + 6 = 0$$

Graph

$$y = x - 1 - 2x + 6.$$

Zero: 5
Solution: 5

●●●

2.1   EXERCISE SET

Solve.

1. $4x + 5 = 21$

2. $2y - 1 = 3$

3. $4x + 3 = 0$

4. $3x - 16 = 0$

5. $3 - x = 12$

6. $4 - x = -5$

7. $8 = 5x - 3$

8. $9 = 4x - 8$

9. $y + 1 = 2y - 7$

10. $5 - 4x = x - 13$

11. $2x + 7 = x + 3$

12. $5x - 4 = 2x + 5$

13. $3x - 5 = 2x + 1$

14. $4x + 3 = 2x - 7$

15. $4x - 5 = 7x - 2$

16. $5x + 1 = 9x - 7$

17. $5x - 2 + 3x = 2x + 6 - 4x$

18. $5x - 17 - 2x = 6x - 1 - x$

19. $7(3x + 6) = 11 - (x + 2)$

20. $4(5y + 3) = 3(2y - 5)$

21. $3(x + 1) = 5 - 2(3x + 4)$

22. $4(3x + 2) - 7 = 3(x - 2)$

23. $2(x - 4) = 3 - 5(2x + 1)$

24. $3(2x - 5) + 4 = 2(4x + 3)$

25. *Bottled-Water Sales.*   Wholesale sales of bottled water in the United States in 2005 were $10 billion. This was an increase of about 45% over sales in 2001. (*Source*: Beverage Marketing Corporation) Find the wholesale sales of bottled water in the United States in 2001.

26. *Oil Consumption.*   Projections indicate that the global demand for oil will be 103 million barrels per day in 2015. This is about a 23% increase over the daily demand in 2005. (*Source*: U.S. Energy Information Administration) What was the daily global demand for oil in 2005?

27. *Credit-Card Debt.*   For households with at least one credit card, the average U.S. credit-card debt per household was $9312 in 2004. This was $6346 more than the average credit-card debt in 1990. (*Source*: CardWeb.com) What was the average credit-card debt per household in 1990?

28. *Bald-Eagle Population.*   There are 7066 known nesting pairs of bald eagles in the lower 48 states today. This is 6649 more pairs than in 1963. (*Source*: U.S. Fish and Wildlife Service) How many nesting pairs of bald eagles were there in the lower 48 states in 1963?

29. *Data Storage.*   As consumers fill electronic devices with digital photos and music, storage needs for digital data are soaring. It is estimated that the amount of digital data stored on various devices in a typical U.S. household in 2010 will be 4430 gigabytes (GB). This is 4024 GB more than the amount of data stored in 2004. (*Source*: Coughlin Associates) Find the amount of digital data stored on various devices in a typical household in 2004.

30. *Where the Textbook Dollar Goes.*   Of each dollar spent on textbooks at college bookstores, 23.2 cents goes to the college store for profit, store operations, and personnel. On average, a college student spends $501 per year for textbooks. (*Source*: National Association of College Stores) How much of this expenditure goes to the college store?

31. *Nutrition.* A slice of carrot cake from the popular restaurant The Cheesecake Factory contains 1560 calories. This is three-fourths of the average daily calorie requirement for many adults. (*Source*: The Center for Science in the Public Interest) Find the average daily calorie requirement for these adults.

32. *Fast-Food Nutrition Information.* Together, a Big Mac and an order of Super-Size fries at McDonald's contain 1200 calories. The fries contain 20 calories more than the Big Mac. (*Source*: *American Journal of Public Health*, February 2002) How many calories are in each?

33. *Television Viewers.* In a recent week, the television networks CBS, ABC, and NBC together averaged a total of 29.1 million viewers. CBS had 1.7 million more viewers than ABC and NBC had 1.7 million fewer viewers than ABC. (*Source*: Nielsen Media Research) How many viewers did each network have?

34. *Nielsen Ratings.* Nielsen Media Research surveys TV-watching habits and provides a list of the 20 most-watched TV programs each week. Each rating point in the survey represents 1,102,000 households. One week "60 Minutes" had a rating of 11.0. How many households did this represent?

35. *Amount Borrowed.* Tamisha borrowed money from her father at 5% simple interest to help pay her tuition at Wellington Community College. At the end of 1 yr, she owed a total of $1365 in principal and interest. How much did she borrow?

36. *Amount of an Investment.* Khalid makes an investment at 4% simple interest. At the end of 1 yr, the total value of the investment is $1560. How much was originally invested?

37. *Sales Commission.* Ryan, a consumer electronics salesperson, earns a base salary of $1500 per month and a commission of 8% on the amount of sales he makes. One month Ryan received a paycheck for $2284. Find the amount of his sales for the month.

38. *Commission vs. Salary.* Juliet has a choice between receiving an $1800 monthly salary from Pearson's Furniture or a base salary of $1600 and a 4% commission on the amount of furniture she sells during the month. For what amount of sales will the two choices be equal?

39. *Cab Fare.* City Cabs charges a $1.75 pickup fee and $1.50 per mile traveled. Diego's fare for a cross-town cab ride is $19.75. How far did he travel in the cab?

40. *Hourly Wage.* Soledad worked 48 hr one week and earned a $442 paycheck. She earns time and a half (1.5 times her regular hourly wage) for the hours she works in excess of 40. What is Soledad's regular hourly wage?

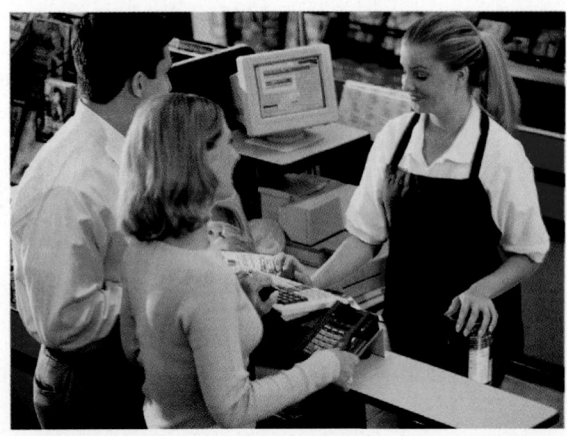

41. *Angle Measure.* In triangle *ABC*, angle *B* is five times as large as angle *A*. The measure of angle *C*

is 2° less than that of angle *A*. Find the measures of the angles. (*Hint*: The sum of the angle measures is 180°.)

42. *Angle Measure.*   In triangle *ABC*, angle *B* is twice as large as angle *A*. Angle *C* measures 20° more than angle *A*. Find the measures of the angles.

43. *Test-Plot Dimensions.*   Morgan's Seeds has a rectangular test plot with a perimeter of 322 m. The length is 25 m more than the width. Find the dimensions of the plot.

44. *Garden Dimensions.*   The children at Tiny Tots Day Care plant a rectangular vegetable garden with a perimeter of 39 m. The length is twice the width. Find the dimensions of the garden.

45. *Soccer-Field Dimensions.*   The width of the soccer field recommended for players under the age of 12 is 35 yd less than the length. The perimeter of the field is 330 yd. (*Source*: U.S. Youth Soccer) Find the dimensions of the field.

46. *Poster Dimensions.*   Marissa is designing a poster to promote the Talbot Street Art Fair. The width of the poster will be two-thirds of its height and its perimeter will be 100 in. Find the dimensions of the poster.

47. *Water Weight.*   Water accounts for 50% of a woman's weight (*Source*: National Institute for Fitness and Sport). Kimiko weighs 135 lb. How much of her body weight is water?

48. *Water Weight.*   Water accounts for 60% of a man's weight (*Source*: National Institute for Fitness and Sport). Emilio weighs 186 lb. How much of his body weight is water?

49. *Train Speeds.*   A Central Railway freight train leaves a station and travels due north at a speed of 60 mph. One hour later, an Amtrak passenger train leaves the same station and travels due north on a parallel track at a speed of 80 mph. How long will it take the passenger train to overtake the freight train?

50. *Distance Traveled.*   A private airplane leaves Midway Airport and flies due east at a speed of 180 km/h. Two hours later, a jet leaves Midway and flies due east at a speed of 900 km/h. How far from the airport will the jet overtake the private plane?

51. *Traveling Upstream.*   A kayak moves at a rate of 12 mph in still water. If the river's current flows at a rate of 4 mph, how long does it take the boat to travel 36 mi upstream?

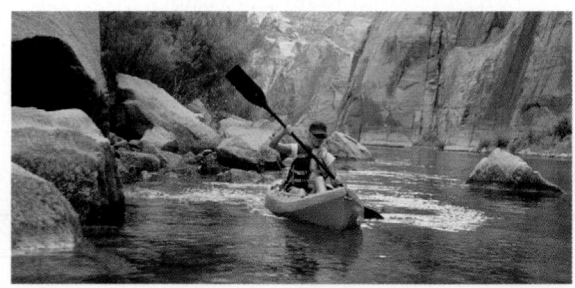

52. *Traveling Downstream.*   Angelo's kayak travels 14 km/h in still water. If the river's current flows at a rate of 2 km/h, how long will it take him to travel 20 km downstream?

53. *Flying into a Headwind.*   An airplane that travels 450 mph in still air encounters a 30-mph headwind. How long will it take the plane to travel 1050 mi into the wind?

54. *Flying with a Tailwind.*   An airplane that can travel 375 mph in still air is flying with a 25-mph tailwind. How long will it take the plane to travel 700 mi with the wind?

55. *Investment Income.*   Erica invested a total of $5000, part at 3% simple interest and part at 4% simple interest. At the end of 1 yr, the investments had earned $176 interest. How much was invested at each rate?

56. *Student Loans.*   Dimitri's two student loans total $9000. One loan is at 5% simple interest and the other is at 6% simple interest. At the end of 1 yr, Dimitri owes $492 in interest. What is the amount of each loan?

57. *Calcium Content of Foods.* Together, one 8-oz serving of plain nonfat yogurt and one 1-oz serving of Swiss cheese contain 676 mg of calcium. The yogurt contains 4 mg more than twice the calcium in the cheese. (*Source*: U.S. Department of Agriculture) Find the calcium content of each food.

58. *Working Pharmacists.* It is estimated that there will be 224,500 working pharmacists in the United States in 2010. This is about 1.84 times the number of working pharmacists in 1975. (*Source*: U.S. Department of Health and Human Services) Find the number of working pharmacists in the United States in 1975.

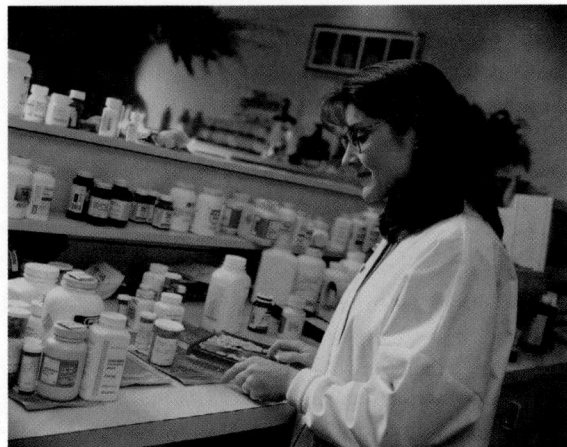

59. *Shopping Online.* Holiday shoppers spent $29.4 billion online in 2004. This was about 7% of the total holiday spending that year. (*Source*: National Retail Federation) What was the total holiday spending?

60. *Broadband Boom.* There were 37.9 million high-speed Internet customers in 2004. This was 2.4 million more than five times the number of customers in 2000. (*Source*: Federal Communications Commission) How many high-speed Internet customers were there in 2000?

61. *Volcanic Activity.* A volcano that is currently about one-half mile below the surface of the Pacific Ocean near the Big Island of Hawaii will eventually become a new Hawaiian island, Loihi. The volcano will break the surface of the ocean in about 50,000 yr. (*Source*: U.S. Geological Survey) On average, how many inches does the volcano rise in a year?

62. *Erosion.* Because of erosion, Horseshoe Falls, one of the two falls that make up Niagara Falls, is migrating upstream at a rate of 2 ft per year (*Source*: *Indianapolis Star*, February 14, 1999). At this rate, how long will it take the falls to move one-fourth mile?

Find the zero of the linear function.

63. $f(x) = x + 5$ **64.** $f(x) = 5x + 20$

65. $f(x) = -x + 18$ **66.** $f(x) = 8 + x$

67. $f(x) = 16 - x$ **68.** $f(x) = -2x + 7$

69. $f(x) = x + 12$ **70.** $f(x) = 8x + 2$

71. $f(x) = -x + 6$ **72.** $f(x) = 4 + x$

73. $f(x) = 20 - x$ **74.** $f(x) = -3x + 13$

75. $f(x) = x - 6$ **76.** $f(x) = 3x - 9$

77. $f(x) = -x + 15$ **78.** $f(x) = 4 - x$

In Exercises 79–84, use the given graph to find each of the following: (**a**) *the x-intercept and* (**b**) *the zero of the function.*

79.

80.

81.

82.

83.

84.

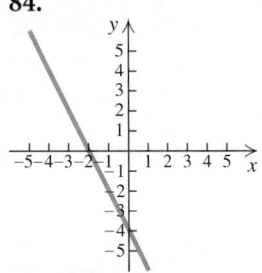

Solve.

85. $A = \frac{1}{2}bh$, for b
(Area of a triangle)

86. $A = \pi r^2$, for π
(Area of a circle)

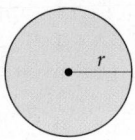

87. $P = 2l + 2w$, for w
(Perimeter of a rectangle)

88. $A = P + Prt$, for r
(Simple interest)

89. $A = \frac{1}{2}h(b_1 + b_2)$, for h
(Area of a trapezoid)

90. $A = \frac{1}{2}h(b_1 + b_2)$, for b_2

91. $V = \frac{4}{3}\pi r^3$, for π
(Volume of a sphere)

92. $V = \frac{4}{3}\pi r^3$, for r^3

93. $F = \frac{9}{5}C + 32$, for C
(Temperature conversion)

94. $Ax + By = C$, for y
(Standard linear equation)

95. $Ax + By = C$, for A

96. $2w + 2h + l = p$, for w

97. $2w + 2h + l = p$, for h

98. $3x + 4y = 12$, for y

99. $2x - 3y = 6$, for y

100. $T = \frac{3}{10}(I - 12{,}000)$, for I

101. $a = b + bcd$, for b

102. $q = p - np$, for p

103. $z = xy - xy^2$, for x

104. $st = t - 4$, for t

Technology Connection

105. Use a graphing calculator to solve the equations in Exercises 1–8.

106. Use a graphing calculator to find the zeros of the functions in Exercises 63–70.

Collaborative Discussion and Writing

107. Explain in your own words why a linear function $f(x) = mx + b$, with $m \neq 0$, has exactly one zero.

108. The formula in Exercise 93, $F = \frac{9}{5}C + 32$, can be used to convert Celsius temperature to Fahrenheit temperature. Under what circumstances would it be useful to solve this formula for C?

Skill Maintenance

109. Write a slope–intercept equation for the line containing the point $(-1, 4)$ and parallel to the line $3x + 4y = 7$.

110. Write an equation of the line containing the points $(-5, 4)$ and $(3, -2)$.

Given that $f(x) = 2x - 1$ and $g(x) = 3x + 6$, find each of the following.

111. The domain of $f + g$

112. The domain of f/g

113. $(f - g)(x)$

114. $(fg)(-1)$

Synthesis

State whether each of the following is a linear function.

115. $f(x) = 7 - \dfrac{3}{2}x$

116. $f(x) = \dfrac{3}{2x} + 5$

117. $f(x) = x^2 + 1$

118. $f(x) = \dfrac{3}{4}x - (2.4)^2$

Solve.

119. $2x - \{x - [3x - (6x + 5)]\} = 4x - 1$

120. $14 - 2[3 + 5(x - 1)] = 3\{x - 4[1 + 6(2 - x)]\}$

121. *Packaging and Price.* Dannon replaced its 8-oz cup of yogurt with a 6-oz cup and reduced the suggested retail price from 89 cents to 71 cents (*Source*: IRI). Was the price per ounce reduced by the same percent as the size of the cup? If not, find the price difference per ounce in terms of a percent.

122. *Packaging and Price.* Wisk laundry detergent replaced its 100-oz container with an 80-oz container and reduced the suggested retail price from $6.99 to $5.75 (*Source*: IRI). Was the price per ounce reduced by the same percent as the size of the container? If not, find the price difference per ounce in terms of a percent.

123. *Running vs. Walking.* A 150-lb person who runs at 6 mph for 1 hr burns about 720 calories. The same person, walking at 4 mph for 90 min, burns about 480 calories. (*Source*: FitSmart, *USA Weekend*, July 19–21, 2002) Suppose a 150-lb person runs at 6 mph for 75 min. How far would the person have to walk at 4 mph in order to burn the same number of calories used running?

124. *Bestsellers.* One week 10 copies of the novel *The DaVinci Code* by Dan Brown were sold for every 1.9 copies of John Grogan's *Marley and Me* that were sold (*Source*: USA Today Best-Selling Books). If a total of 3570 copies of the two books were sold, how many copies of each were sold?

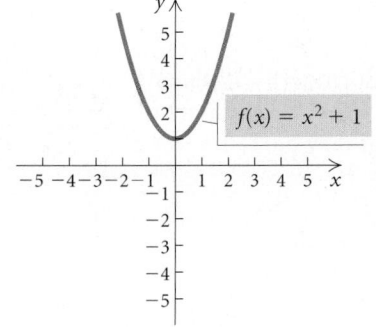

2.2 The Complex Numbers

◆ Perform computations involving complex numbers.

Some functions have zeros that are not real numbers. In order to find the zeros of such functions, we must consider the **complex-number system.**

◆ The Complex-Number System

$f(x) = x^2 + 1$

We know that the square root of a negative number is not a real number. For example, $\sqrt{-1}$ is not a real number because there is no real number x such that $x^2 = -1$. This means that certain equations, like $x^2 = -1$ or $x^2 + 1 = 0$, do not have real-number solutions and certain functions, like $f(x) = x^2 + 1$, do not have real-number zeros. Consider the graph of $f(x) = x^2 + 1$.

We see that the graph does not cross the x-axis and thus has no x-intercepts. This illustrates that the function $f(x) = x^2 + 1$ has no real-number zeros. Thus there are no real-number solutions of the corresponding equation $x^2 + 1 = 0$.

RADICAL EXPRESSIONS

REVIEW SECTION **R.6.**

We can define a number that is a solution of the equation $x^2 + 1 = 0$.

The Number i

The number i is defined such that

$$i = \sqrt{-1} \quad \text{and} \quad i^2 = -1.$$

To express roots of negative numbers in terms of i, we can use the fact that

$$\sqrt{-p} = \sqrt{-1 \cdot p} = \sqrt{-1} \cdot \sqrt{p} = i\sqrt{p}$$

when p is a positive real number.

STUDY TIP

Don't hesitate to ask questions in class at appropriate times. Most instructors welcome questions and encourage students to ask them. Other students in your class probably have the same questions you do.

EXAMPLE 1   Express each number in terms of i.

a) $\sqrt{-7}$ b) $\sqrt{-16}$ c) $-\sqrt{-13}$

d) $-\sqrt{-64}$ e) $\sqrt{-48}$

Solution

a) $\sqrt{-7} = \sqrt{-1 \cdot 7} = \sqrt{-1} \cdot \sqrt{7}$
$= i\sqrt{7}$, or $\sqrt{7}i$ ← i is *not* under the radical.

b) $\sqrt{-16} = \sqrt{-1 \cdot 16} = \sqrt{-1} \cdot \sqrt{16}$
$= i \cdot 4 = 4i$

c) $-\sqrt{-13} = -\sqrt{-1 \cdot 13} = -\sqrt{-1} \cdot \sqrt{13}$
$= -i\sqrt{13}$, or $-\sqrt{13}i$ ←

d) $-\sqrt{-64} = -\sqrt{-1 \cdot 64} = -\sqrt{-1} \cdot \sqrt{64}$
$= -i \cdot 8 = -8i$

e) $\sqrt{-48} = \sqrt{-1 \cdot 48} = \sqrt{-1} \cdot \sqrt{48}$
$= i\sqrt{16 \cdot 3} = i \cdot 4\sqrt{3}$
$= 4i\sqrt{3}$, or $4\sqrt{3}i$ ←

▶ Now Try Exercise 1.

The complex numbers are formed by adding real numbers and multiples of i.

Complex Numbers

A **complex number** is a number of the form $a + bi$, where a and b are real numbers. The number a is said to be the **real part** of $a + bi$ and the number b is said to be the **imaginary part** of $a + bi$.*

---

*Sometimes bi is considered to be the imaginary part.

Note that either a or b or both can be 0. When $b = 0$, $a + bi = a + 0i = a$, so every real number is a complex number. A complex number like $3 + 4i$ or $17i$, in which $b \neq 0$, is called an **imaginary number.** A complex number like $17i$ or $-4i$, in which $a = 0$ and $b \neq 0$, is sometimes called a **pure imaginary number.** The relationships among various types of complex numbers are shown in the figure below.

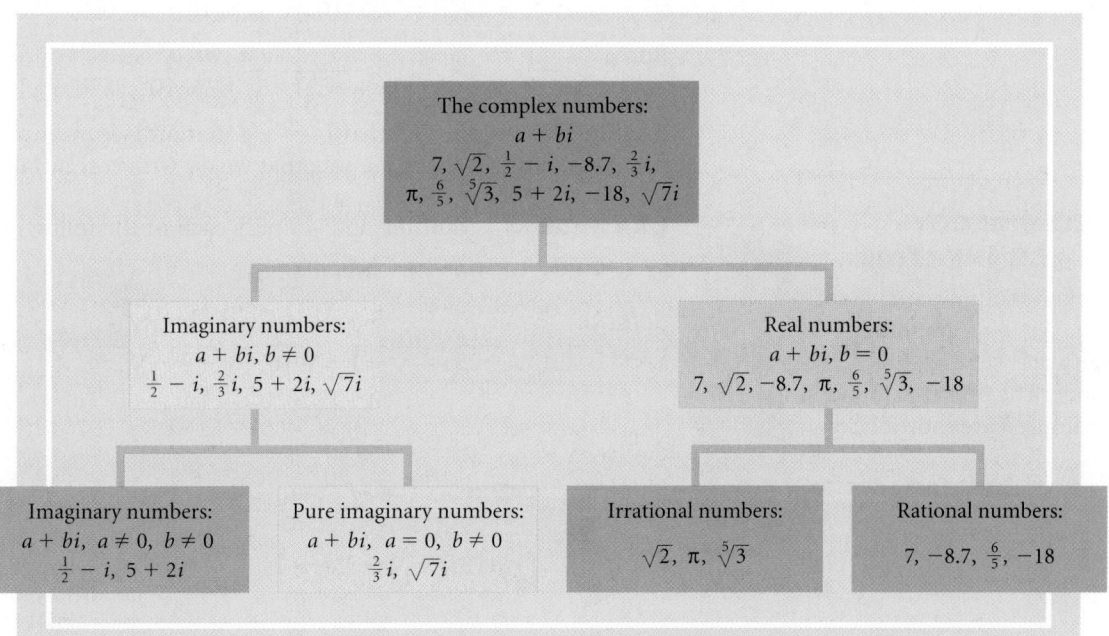

◆ Addition and Subtraction

TECHNOLOGY · · · · · · · · · · · · · · ·
CONNECTION

When set in $a + bi$ mode, most graphing calculators can perform operations on complex numbers. The operations in Example 2 are shown in the window below. Some calculators will express a complex number in the form (a, b) rather than $a + bi$.

The complex numbers obey the commutative, associative, and distributive laws. Thus we can add and subtract them as we do binomials. We collect the real parts and the imaginary parts of complex numbers just as we collect like terms in binomials.

EXAMPLE 2 Add or subtract and simplify each of the following.

a) $(8 + 6i) + (3 + 2i)$ **b)** $(4 + 5i) - (6 - 3i)$

Solution

a) $(8 + 6i) + (3 + 2i) = (8 + 3) + (6i + 2i)$

Collecting the real parts and the imaginary parts

$$= 11 + (6 + 2)i = 11 + 8i$$

b) $(4 + 5i) - (6 - 3i) = (4 - 6) + [5i - (-3i)]$

Note that 6 and $-3i$ are both being subtracted.

$$= -2 + 8i$$

▶ **Now Try Exercise 11.**

```
(8+6i)+(3+2i)
                  11+8i
(4+5i)−(6−3i)
                  −2+8i
```

✦ Multiplication

When $\sqrt{a}$ and $\sqrt{b}$ are real numbers, $\sqrt{a} \cdot \sqrt{b} = \sqrt{ab}$, but this is not true when $\sqrt{a}$ and $\sqrt{b}$ are not real numbers. Thus,

$$\sqrt{-2} \cdot \sqrt{-5} = \sqrt{-1} \cdot \sqrt{2} \cdot \sqrt{-1} \cdot \sqrt{5}$$
$$= i\sqrt{2} \cdot i\sqrt{5}$$
$$= i^2\sqrt{10} = -1\sqrt{10} = -\sqrt{10} \quad \text{is correct!}$$

But

$$\sqrt{-2} \cdot \sqrt{-5} = \sqrt{(-2)(-5)} = \sqrt{10} \quad \text{is wrong!}$$

Keeping this and the fact that $i^2 = -1$ in mind, we multiply with imaginary numbers in much the same way that we do with real numbers.

TECHNOLOGY ·············
CONNECTION

We can multiply complex numbers on a graphing calculator set in $a + bi$ mode. The products found in Example 3 are shown below.

```
√(-16)√(-25)
                    -20
(1+2i)(1+3i)
                  -5+5i
(3-7i)²
                -40-42i
```

EXAMPLE 3 Multiply and simplify each of the following.

a) $\sqrt{-16} \cdot \sqrt{-25}$ **b)** $(1 + 2i)(1 + 3i)$ **c)** $(3 - 7i)^2$

Solution

a) $\sqrt{-16} \cdot \sqrt{-25} = \sqrt{-1} \cdot \sqrt{16} \cdot \sqrt{-1} \cdot \sqrt{25}$
$$= i \cdot 4 \cdot i \cdot 5$$
$$= i^2 \cdot 20$$
$$= -1 \cdot 20 \qquad i^2 = -1$$
$$= -20$$

b) $(1 + 2i)(1 + 3i) = 1 + 3i + 2i + 6i^2$ Multiplying each term of one number by every term of the other (FOIL)
$$= 1 + 3i + 2i - 6 \qquad i^2 = -1$$
$$= -5 + 5i \qquad \text{Collecting like terms}$$

c) $(3 - 7i)^2 = 3^2 - 2 \cdot 3 \cdot 7i + (7i)^2$ Recall that $(A - B)^2 = A^2 - 2AB + B^2$.
$$= 9 - 42i + 49i^2$$
$$= 9 - 42i - 49 \qquad i^2 = -1$$
$$= -40 - 42i \qquad \qquad \text{▶ Now Try Exercise 35.}$$

Recall that -1 raised to an *even* power is 1, and -1 raised to an *odd* power is -1. Simplifying powers of i can then be done by using the fact that $i^2 = -1$ and expressing the given power of i in terms of i^2. Consider the following:

$$i = \sqrt{-1},$$
$$i^2 = -1,$$
$$i^3 = i^2 \cdot i = (-1)i = -i,$$
$$i^4 = (i^2)^2 = (-1)^2 = 1,$$
$$i^5 = i^4 \cdot i = (i^2)^2 \cdot i = (-1)^2 \cdot i = 1 \cdot i = i,$$
$$i^6 = (i^2)^3 = (-1)^3 = -1,$$
$$i^7 = i^6 \cdot i = (i^2)^3 \cdot i = (-1)^3 \cdot i = -i,$$
$$i^8 = (i^2)^4 = (-1)^4 = 1.$$

Note that the powers of i cycle through the values $i, -1, -i,$ and 1.

EXAMPLE 4 Simplify each of the following.

a) i^{37} b) i^{58}

c) i^{75} d) i^{80}

Solution

a) $i^{37} = i^{36} \cdot i = (i^2)^{18} \cdot i = (-1)^{18} \cdot i = 1 \cdot i = i$

b) $i^{58} = (i^2)^{29} = (-1)^{29} = -1$

c) $i^{75} = i^{74} \cdot i = (i^2)^{37} \cdot i = (-1)^{37} \cdot i = -1 \cdot i = -i$

d) $i^{80} = (i^2)^{40} = (-1)^{40} = 1$ ▶ Now Try Exercise 75.

These powers of i can also be simplified in terms of i^4 rather than i^2. Consider i^{37} in Example 4(a), for instance. When we divide 37 by 4, we get 9 with a remainder of 1. Then $37 = 4 \cdot 9 + 1$, so

$$i^{37} = (i^4)^9 \cdot i = 1^9 \cdot i = 1 \cdot i = i.$$

The other examples shown above can be done in a similar manner.

✦ Conjugates and Division

Conjugates of complex numbers are defined as follows.

> ### Conjugate of a Complex Number
> The **conjugate** of a complex number $a + bi$ is $a - bi$. The numbers $a + bi$ and $a - bi$ are **complex conjugates.**

Each of the following pairs of numbers are complex conjugates:

$$-3 + 7i \text{ and } -3 - 7i; \quad 14 - 5i \text{ and } 14 + 5i; \quad \text{and} \quad 8i \text{ and } -8i.$$

The product of a complex number and its conjugate is a real number.

EXAMPLE 5 Multiply each of the following.

a) $(5 + 7i)(5 - 7i)$ b) $(8i)(-8i)$

Solution

a) $(5 + 7i)(5 - 7i) = 5^2 - (7i)^2$ Using $(A + B)(A - B) = A^2 - B^2$

$\qquad\qquad\qquad\quad = 25 - 49i^2$

$\qquad\qquad\qquad\quad = 25 - 49(-1)$

$\qquad\qquad\qquad\quad = 25 + 49$

$\qquad\qquad\qquad\quad = 74$

b) $(8i)(-8i) = -64i^2$

$\qquad\qquad\quad = -64(-1)$

$\qquad\qquad\quad = 64$ ▶ Now Try Exercise 45.

With a graphing calculator set in $a + bi$ mode, we can divide complex numbers and express the real and imaginary parts in fraction form, just as we did in Example 6.

> (2−5i)/(1−6i) ▶Frac
>   32/37+7/37i

Conjugates are used when we divide complex numbers.

EXAMPLE 6   Divide $2 - 5i$ by $1 - 6i$.

Solution   We write fraction notation and then multiply by 1, using the conjugate of the denominator to form the symbol for 1.

$$\frac{2 - 5i}{1 - 6i} = \frac{2 - 5i}{1 - 6i} \cdot \frac{1 + 6i}{1 + 6i}$$ Note that $1 + 6i$ is the conjugate of the divisor, $1 - 6i$.

$$= \frac{(2 - 5i)(1 + 6i)}{(1 - 6i)(1 + 6i)}$$

$$= \frac{2 + 7i - 30i^2}{1 - 36i^2}$$

$$= \frac{2 + 7i + 30}{1 + 36}$$ $i^2 = -1$

$$= \frac{32 + 7i}{37}$$

$$= \frac{32}{37} + \frac{7}{37}i.$$ Writing the quotient in the form $a + bi$

▶ Now Try Exercise 65.

2.2   EXERCISE SET

Express the number in terms of i.

1. $\sqrt{-3}$

2. $\sqrt{-21}$

3. $\sqrt{-25}$

4. $\sqrt{-100}$

5. $-\sqrt{-33}$

6. $-\sqrt{-59}$

7. $-\sqrt{-81}$

8. $-\sqrt{-9}$

9. $\sqrt{-98}$

10. $\sqrt{-28}$

Simplify. Write answers in the form $a + bi$, where a and b are real numbers.

11. $(-5 + 3i) + (7 + 8i)$

12. $(-6 - 5i) + (9 + 2i)$

13. $(4 - 9i) + (1 - 3i)$

14. $(7 - 2i) + (4 - 5i)$

15. $(12 + 3i) + (-8 + 5i)$

16. $(-11 + 4i) + (6 + 8i)$

17. $(-1 - i) + (-3 - i)$

18. $(-5 - i) + (6 + 2i)$

19. $\left(3 + \sqrt{-16}\right) + \left(2 + \sqrt{-25}\right)$

20. $\left(7 - \sqrt{-36}\right) + \left(2 + \sqrt{-9}\right)$

21. $(10 + 7i) - (5 + 3i)$

22. $(-3 - 4i) - (8 - i)$

23. $(13 + 9i) - (8 + 2i)$

24. $(-7 + 12i) - (3 - 6i)$

25. $(6 - 4i) - (-5 + i)$

26. $(8 - 3i) - (9 - i)$

27. $(-5 + 2i) - (-4 - 3i)$

28. $(-6 + 7i) - (-5 - 2i)$

29. $(4 - 9i) - (2 + 3i)$

30. $(10 - 4i) - (8 + 2i)$

31. $7i(2 - 5i)$

32. $3i(6 + 4i)$

33. $-2i(-8 + 3i)$

34. $-6i(-5 + i)$

35. $(1 + 3i)(1 - 4i)$

36. $(1 - 2i)(1 + 3i)$

37. $(2 + 3i)(2 + 5i)$

38. $(3 - 5i)(8 - 2i)$

39. $(-4 + i)(3 - 2i)$

40. $(5 - 2i)(-1 + i)$

41. $(8 - 3i)(-2 - 5i)$

42. $(7 - 4i)(-3 - 3i)$

43. $\left(3 + \sqrt{-16}\right)\left(2 + \sqrt{-25}\right)$

44. $\left(7 - \sqrt{-16}\right)\left(2 + \sqrt{-9}\right)$

45. $(5 - 4i)(5 + 4i)$

46. $(5 + 9i)(5 - 9i)$

47. $(3 + 2i)(3 - 2i)$

48. $(8 + i)(8 - i)$

49. $(7 - 5i)(7 + 5i)$

50. $(6 - 8i)(6 + 8i)$

51. $(4 + 2i)^2$

52. $(5 - 4i)^2$

53. $(-2 + 7i)^2$

54. $(-3 + 2i)^2$

55. $(1 - 3i)^2$

56. $(2 - 5i)^2$

57. $(-1 - i)^2$

58. $(-4 - 2i)^2$

59. $(3 + 4i)^2$

60. $(6 + 5i)^2$

61. $\dfrac{3}{5 - 11i}$

62. $\dfrac{i}{2 + i}$

63. $\dfrac{5}{2 + 3i}$

64. $\dfrac{-3}{4 - 5i}$

65. $\dfrac{4 + i}{-3 - 2i}$

66. $\dfrac{5 - i}{-7 + 2i}$

67. $\dfrac{5 - 3i}{4 + 3i}$

68. $\dfrac{6 + 5i}{3 - 4i}$

69. $\dfrac{2 + \sqrt{3}i}{5 - 4i}$

70. $\dfrac{\sqrt{5} + 3i}{1 - i}$

71. $\dfrac{1 + i}{(1 - i)^2}$

72. $\dfrac{1 - i}{(1 + i)^2}$

73. $\dfrac{4 - 2i}{1 + i} + \dfrac{2 - 5i}{1 + i}$

74. $\dfrac{3 + 2i}{1 - i} + \dfrac{6 + 2i}{1 - i}$

Simplify.

75. i^{11}

76. i^7

77. i^{35}

78. i^{24}

79. i^{64}

80. i^{42}

81. $(-i)^{71}$

82. $(-i)^6$

83. $(5i)^4$

84. $(2i)^5$

Technology Connection

85. Use a graphing calculator to perform the operations in Exercises 11, 19, 21, 31, 35, 51, and 65.

86. Use a graphing calculator to perform the operations in Exercises 12, 20, 22, 24, 32, 36, and 66.

Collaborative Discussion and Writing

87. Is the sum of two imaginary numbers always an imaginary number? Explain your answer.

88. Is the product of two imaginary numbers always an imaginary number? Explain your answer.

Skill Maintenance

89. Write a slope–intercept equation for the line containing the point $(3, -5)$ and perpendicular to the line $3x - 6y = 7$.

Given that $f(x) = x^2 + 4$ and $g(x) = 3x + 5$, find each of the following.

90. The domain of $f - g$

91. The domain of f/g

92. $(f - g)(x)$

93. $(f/g)(2)$

94. For the function $f(x) = x^2 - 3x + 4$, construct and simplify the difference quotient

$$\frac{f(x + h) - f(x)}{h}.$$

Synthesis

Determine whether the statement is true or false.

95. The sum of two numbers that are conjugates of each other is always a real number.

96. The conjugate of a sum is the sum of the conjugates of the individual complex numbers.

97. The conjugate of a product is the product of the conjugates of the individual complex numbers.

Let $z = a + bi$ and $\bar{z} = a - bi$.

98. Find a general expression for $1/z$.

99. Find a general expression for $z\bar{z}$.

100. Solve $z + 6\bar{z} = 7$ for z.

2.3 Quadratic Equations, Functions, and Models

◆ Find zeros of quadratic functions and solve quadratic equations by using the principle of zero products, by using the principle of square roots, by completing the square, and by using the quadratic formula.

◆ Solve equations that are reducible to quadratic.

◆ Solve applied problems using quadratic equations.

◆ Quadratic Equations and Quadratic Functions

In this section, we will explore the relationship between the solutions of quadratic equations and the zeros of quadratic functions. We define quadratic equations and functions as follows.

> **Quadratic Equations**
>
> A **quadratic equation** is an equation equivalent to
>
> $$ax^2 + bx + c = 0, \quad a \neq 0,$$
>
> where a, b, and c are real numbers.
>
> **Quadratic Functions**
>
> A **quadratic function** f is a function that can be written in the form
>
> $$f(x) = ax^2 + bx + c, \quad a \neq 0,$$
>
> where a, b, and c are real numbers.

A quadratic equation written in the form $ax^2 + bx + c = 0$ is said to be in **standard** form.

The *zeros* of a quadratic function $f(x) = ax^2 + bx + c$ are the *solutions* of the associated quadratic equation $ax^2 + bx + c = 0$. (These so-

ZEROS OF A FUNCTION

REVIEW SECTION **2.1.**

lutions are sometimes called *roots* of the equation.) Quadratic functions can have real-number or imaginary-number zeros and quadratic equations can have real-number or imaginary-number solutions. If the zeros or solutions are real numbers, they are also the first coordinates of the x-intercepts of the graph of the quadratic function.

The following principles allow us to solve many quadratic equations.

> ### Equation-Solving Principles
>
> **The Principle of Zero Products**: If $ab = 0$ is true, then $a = 0$ or $b = 0$, and if $a = 0$ or $b = 0$, then $ab = 0$.
>
> **The Principle of Square Roots**: If $x^2 = k$, then $x = \sqrt{k}$ or $x = -\sqrt{k}$.

> FACTORING TRINOMIALS
>
> REVIEW SECTION R.4.

EXAMPLE 1 Solve: $2x^2 - x = 3$.

ALGEBRAIC SOLUTION

We have

$$2x^2 - x = 3$$
$$2x^2 - x - 3 = 0 \qquad \text{Subtracting 3 on both sides}$$
$$(x + 1)(2x - 3) = 0 \qquad \text{Factoring}$$
$$x + 1 = 0 \quad or \quad 2x - 3 = 0 \qquad \text{Using the principle of zero products}$$
$$x = -1 \quad or \quad 2x = 3$$
$$x = -1 \quad or \quad x = \frac{3}{2}.$$

Check: For $x = -1$:

$$\frac{2x^2 - x = 3}{2(-1)^2 - (-1) \;?\; 3}$$
$$2 \cdot 1 + 1$$
$$2 + 1$$
$$3 \;\bigg|\; 3 \quad \text{TRUE}$$

For $x = \frac{3}{2}$:

$$\frac{2x^2 - x = 3}{2\left(\frac{3}{2}\right)^2 - \frac{3}{2} \;?\; 3}$$
$$2 \cdot \frac{9}{4} - \frac{3}{2}$$
$$\frac{9}{2} - \frac{3}{2}$$
$$\frac{6}{2}$$
$$3 \;\bigg|\; 3 \quad \text{TRUE}$$

The solutions are -1 and $\frac{3}{2}$.

VISUALIZING THE SOLUTION

The solutions of the equation $2x^2 - x = 3$, or the equivalent equation $2x^2 - x - 3 = 0$, are the zeros of the function $f(x) = 2x^2 - x - 3$. They are also the first coordinates of the x-intercepts of the graph of $f(x) = 2x^2 - x - 3$.

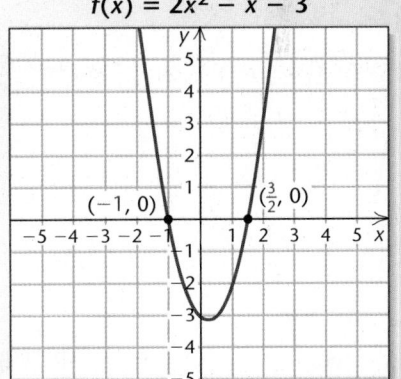

$$f(x) = 2x^2 - x - 3$$

The solutions are -1 and $\frac{3}{2}$.

▶ Now Try Exercise 3.

EXAMPLE 2 Solve: $2x^2 - 10 = 0$.

ALGEBRAIC SOLUTION

We have

$$2x^2 - 10 = 0$$

$$2x^2 = 10 \qquad \text{Adding 10 on both sides}$$

$$x^2 = 5 \qquad \text{Dividing by 2 on both sides}$$

$$x = \sqrt{5} \quad \text{or} \quad x = -\sqrt{5}. \qquad \text{Using the principle of square roots}$$

Check:

$$\begin{array}{c|c} 2x^2 - 10 = 0 \\ \hline 2\left(\pm\sqrt{5}\right)^2 - 10 \;?\; 0 & \text{We can check} \\ 2 \cdot 5 - 10 & \text{both solutions} \\ 10 - 10 & \text{at once.} \\ 0 \;\big|\; 0 \quad \text{TRUE} \end{array}$$

The solutions are $\sqrt{5}$ and $-\sqrt{5}$, or $\pm\sqrt{5}$.

VISUALIZING THE SOLUTION

The solutions of the equation $2x^2 - 10 = 0$ are the zeros of the function $f(x) = 2x^2 - 10$. Note that they are also the first coordinates of the x-intercepts of the graph of $f(x) = 2x^2 - 10$.

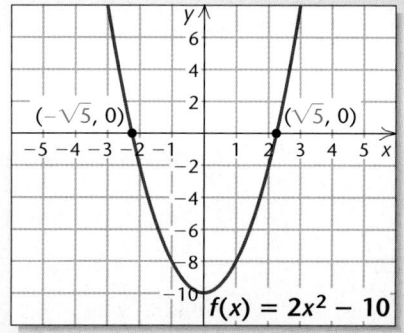

The solutions are $-\sqrt{5}$ and $\sqrt{5}$.

▶ Now Try Exercise 7.

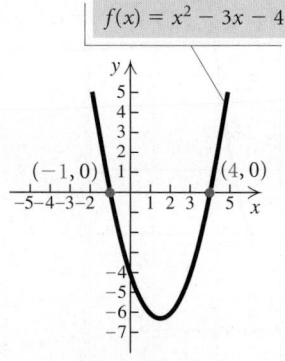

Two real-number zeros
Two x-intercepts

Figure 1

We have seen that some quadratic equations can be solved by factoring and using the principle of zero products. For example, consider the equation $x^2 - 3x - 4 = 0$:

$$x^2 - 3x - 4 = 0$$

$$(x + 1)(x - 4) = 0 \qquad \text{Factoring}$$

$$x + 1 = 0 \quad \text{or} \quad x - 4 = 0 \qquad \text{Using the principle of zero products}$$

$$x = -1 \quad \text{or} \qquad x = 4.$$

The equation $x^2 - 3x - 4 = 0$ has *two real-number* solutions, -1 and 4. These are the zeros of the associated quadratic function $f(x) = x^2 - 3x - 4$ and the first coordinates of the x-intercepts of the graph of this function. (See Fig. 1.)

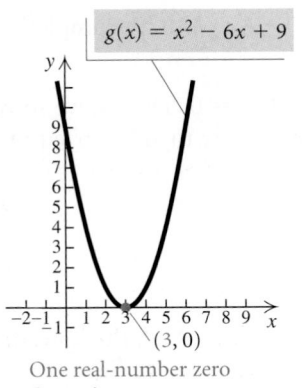

$g(x) = x^2 - 6x + 9$

(3, 0)

One real-number zero
One x-intercept

Figure 2

Next, consider the equation $x^2 - 6x + 9 = 0$. Again, we factor and use the principle of zero products:

$$x^2 - 6x + 9 = 0$$
$$(x - 3)(x - 3) = 0 \qquad \text{Factoring}$$
$$x - 3 = 0 \quad or \quad x - 3 = 0 \qquad \text{Using the principle of}$$
$$\qquad\qquad\qquad\qquad\qquad\qquad \text{zero products}$$
$$x = 3 \quad or \qquad x = 3.$$

The equation $x^2 - 6x + 9 = 0$ has *one real-number* solution, 3. It is the zero of the quadratic function $g(x) = x^2 - 6x + 9$ and the first coordinate of the x-intercept of the graph of this function. (See Fig. 2.)

The principle of square roots can be used to solve quadratic equations like $x^2 + 13 = 0$:

$$x^2 + 13 = 0$$
$$x^2 = -13$$
$$x = \pm\sqrt{-13} \qquad \text{Using the principle of square roots}$$
$$x = \pm\sqrt{13}i.$$

The equation has *two imaginary-number* solutions, $-\sqrt{13}i$ and $\sqrt{13}i$. These are the zeros of the associated quadratic function $h(x) = x^2 + 13$. Since the zeros are not real numbers, the graph of the function has no x-intercepts. (See Fig. 3.)

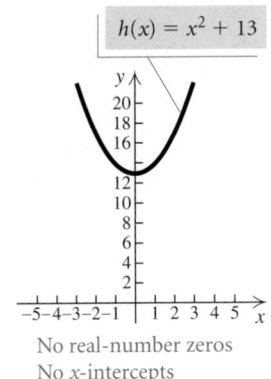

$h(x) = x^2 + 13$

No real-number zeros
No x-intercepts

Figure 3

✦ Completing the Square

Neither the principle of zero products nor the principle of square roots would yield the *exact* zeros of a function like $f(x) = x^2 - 6x - 10$ or the *exact* solutions of the associated equation $x^2 - 6x - 10 = 0$. If we wish to find exact zeros or solutions, we can use a procedure called **completing the square** and then use the principle of square roots.

TECHNOLOGY · · · · · · · · · · · ·
CONNECTION

Approximations for the zeros
of the quadratic function
$f(x) = x^2 - 6x - 10$ in
Example 3 can be found using
the Zero method.

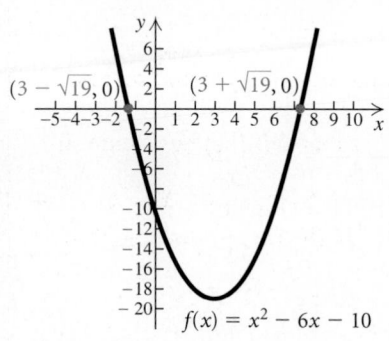

EXAMPLE 3   Find the zeros of $f(x) = x^2 - 6x - 10$ by completing the square.

Solution   We find the values of x for which $f(x) = 0$. That is, we solve the associated equation $x^2 - 6x - 10 = 0$. Our goal is to find an equivalent equation of the form $x^2 + bx + c = d$ in which $x^2 + bx + c$ is a perfect square. Since

$$x^2 + bx + \left(\frac{b}{2}\right)^2 = \left(x + \frac{b}{2}\right)^2,$$

the number c is found by taking half the coefficient of the x-term and squaring it. Thus, for the equation $x^2 - 6x - 10 = 0$, we have

$$x^2 - 6x - 10 = 0$$
$$x^2 - 6x \quad\quad = 10 \qquad\qquad \text{Adding 10}$$
$$x^2 - 6x + 9 = 10 + 9 \qquad \text{Adding 9 to complete the square:}$$
$$\left(\frac{b}{2}\right)^2 = \left(\frac{-6}{2}\right)^2 = (-3)^2 = 9$$
$$x^2 - 6x + 9 = 19.$$

Because $x^2 - 6x + 9$ is a perfect square, we are able to write it as $(x - 3)^2$, the square of a binomial. We can then use the principle of square roots to finish the solution:

$$(x - 3)^2 = 19 \qquad\qquad \text{Factoring}$$
$$x - 3 = \pm\sqrt{19} \qquad \text{Using the principle of square roots}$$
$$x = 3 \pm \sqrt{19}. \qquad \text{Adding 3}$$

Therefore, the solutions of the equation are $3 + \sqrt{19}$ and $3 - \sqrt{19}$, or simply $3 \pm \sqrt{19}$. The zeros of $f(x) = x^2 - 6x - 10$ are also $3 + \sqrt{19}$ and $3 - \sqrt{19}$, or $3 \pm \sqrt{19}$.

Decimal approximations for $3 \pm \sqrt{19}$ can be found using a calculator:

$$3 + \sqrt{19} \approx 7.359 \quad \text{and} \quad 3 - \sqrt{19} \approx -1.359.$$

The zeros are approximately 7.359 and -1.359.   ▶ **Now Try Exercise 29.**

Before we can complete the square, the coefficient of the x^2-term must be 1. When it is not, we divide by the x^2-coefficient on both sides of the equation.

EXAMPLE 4 Solve: $2x^2 - 1 = 3x$.

Solution We have

$$2x^2 - 1 = 3x$$

$$2x^2 - 3x - 1 = 0 \qquad \text{Subtracting } 3x. \text{ We are unable to factor the result.}$$

$$2x^2 - 3x = 1 \qquad \text{Adding 1}$$

$$x^2 - \frac{3}{2}x = \frac{1}{2} \qquad \text{Dividing by 2 to make the } x^2\text{-coefficient 1}$$

$$x^2 - \frac{3}{2}x + \frac{9}{16} = \frac{1}{2} + \frac{9}{16} \qquad \text{Completing the square: } \frac{1}{2}\left(-\frac{3}{2}\right) = -\frac{3}{4} \text{ and } \left(-\frac{3}{4}\right)^2 = \frac{9}{16}; \text{ adding } \frac{9}{16}$$

$$\left(x - \frac{3}{4}\right)^2 = \frac{17}{16} \qquad \text{Factoring and simplifying}$$

$$x - \frac{3}{4} = \pm\frac{\sqrt{17}}{4} \qquad \text{Using the principle of square roots and the quotient rule for radicals}$$

$$x = \frac{3}{4} \pm \frac{\sqrt{17}}{4} \qquad \text{Adding } \frac{3}{4}$$

$$x = \frac{3 \pm \sqrt{17}}{4}.$$

The solutions are

$$\frac{3 + \sqrt{17}}{4} \quad \text{and} \quad \frac{3 - \sqrt{17}}{4}, \quad \text{or} \quad \frac{3 \pm \sqrt{17}}{4}.$$

▶ **Now Try Exercise 33.**

To solve a quadratic equation by completing the square:

1. Isolate the terms with variables on one side of the equation and arrange them in descending order.
2. Divide by the coefficient of the squared term if that coefficient is not 1.
3. Complete the square by taking half the coefficient of the first-degree term and adding its square on both sides of the equation.
4. Express one side of the equation as the square of a binomial.
5. Use the principle of square roots.
6. Solve for the variable.

◆ **Using the Quadratic Formula**

Because completing the square works for *any* quadratic equation, it can be used to solve the general quadratic equation $ax^2 + bx + c = 0$ for x. The result will be a formula that can be used to solve any quadratic equation quickly.

Consider any quadratic equation in standard form:

$$ax^2 + bx + c = 0, \quad a \neq 0.$$

For now, we assume that $a > 0$ and solve by completing the square. As the steps are carried out, compare them with those of Example 4.

$$
\begin{aligned}
ax^2 + bx + c &= 0 &&\text{Standard form} \\
ax^2 + bx &= -c &&\text{Adding } -c \\
x^2 + \frac{b}{a}x &= -\frac{c}{a} &&\text{Dividing by } a
\end{aligned}
$$

Half of $\dfrac{b}{a}$ is $\dfrac{b}{2a}$ and $\left(\dfrac{b}{2a}\right)^2 = \dfrac{b^2}{4a^2}$. Thus we add $\dfrac{b^2}{4a^2}$:

$$x^2 + \frac{b}{a}x + \frac{b^2}{4a^2} = -\frac{c}{a} + \frac{b^2}{4a^2} \qquad \text{Adding } \frac{b^2}{4a^2} \text{ to complete the square}$$

$$\left(x + \frac{b}{2a}\right)^2 = -\frac{4ac}{4a^2} + \frac{b^2}{4a^2} \qquad
\begin{array}{l}\text{Factoring and finding a common}\\ \text{denominator:}\\ -\dfrac{c}{a} = -\dfrac{c}{a}\cdot\dfrac{4a}{4a} = -\dfrac{4ac}{4a^2}\end{array}$$

$$\left(x + \frac{b}{2a}\right)^2 = \frac{b^2 - 4ac}{4a^2}$$

$$x + \frac{b}{2a} = \pm\frac{\sqrt{b^2 - 4ac}}{2a} \qquad
\begin{array}{l}\text{Using the principle of square roots}\\ \text{and the quotient rule for radicals.}\\ \text{Since } a > 0,\ \sqrt{4a^2} = 2a.\end{array}$$

$$x = -\frac{b}{2a} \pm \frac{\sqrt{b^2 - 4ac}}{2a} \qquad \text{Adding } -\frac{b}{2a}$$

$$x = \frac{-b \pm \sqrt{b^2 - 4ac}}{2a}.$$

It can also be shown that this result holds if $a < 0$.

TECHNOLOGY CONNECTION

We can solve the equation $3x^2 + 2x = 7$ in Example 5 using the Intersect method. We graph $y_1 = 3x^2 + 2x$ and $y_2 = 7$ and use the INTERSECT feature to find the coordinates of the points of intersection. The first coordinates of these points are the solutions of the equation $y_1 = y_2$, or $3x^2 + 2x = 7$.

$y_1 = 3x^2 + 2x, \ y_2 = 7$

Intersection
X = −1.896805   Y = 7

$y_1 = 3x^2 + 2x, \ y_2 = 7$

Intersection
X = 1.2301386   Y = 7

The solutions are approximately -1.897 and 1.230. We could also write the equation in standard form, $3x^2 + 2x - 7 = 0$, and use the Zero method.

The Quadratic Formula

The solutions of $ax^2 + bx + c = 0,\ a \neq 0$, are given by

$$x = \frac{-b \pm \sqrt{b^2 - 4ac}}{2a}.$$

EXAMPLE 5   Solve $3x^2 + 2x = 7$. Find exact solutions and approximate solutions rounded to the nearest thousandth.

Solution   After finding standard form, we are unable to factor, so we identify a, b, and c in order to use the quadratic formula:

$$3x^2 + 2x = 7$$
$$3x^2 + 2x - 7 = 0;$$
$$a = 3, \quad b = 2, \quad c = -7.$$

We then use the quadratic formula:

$$x = \frac{-b \pm \sqrt{b^2 - 4ac}}{2a}$$

$$= \frac{-2 \pm \sqrt{2^2 - 4(3)(-7)}}{2(3)} \quad \text{Substituting}$$

$$= \frac{-2 \pm \sqrt{4 + 84}}{6} = \frac{-2 \pm \sqrt{88}}{6}$$

$$= \frac{-2 \pm \sqrt{4 \cdot 22}}{6} = \frac{-2 \pm 2\sqrt{22}}{6} = \frac{2(-1 \pm \sqrt{22})}{2 \cdot 3}$$

$$= \frac{2}{2} \cdot \frac{-1 \pm \sqrt{22}}{3} = \frac{-1 \pm \sqrt{22}}{3}.$$

The exact solutions are

$$\frac{-1 - \sqrt{22}}{3} \quad \text{and} \quad \frac{-1 + \sqrt{22}}{3}.$$

Using a calculator, we approximate the solutions as -1.897 and 1.230.

▶ Now Try Exercise 39.

EXAMPLE 6 Solve: $x^2 + 5x + 8 = 0$.

ALGEBRAIC SOLUTION

To find the solutions, we use the quadratic formula. For $x^2 + 5x + 8 = 0$, we have

$$a = 1, \quad b = 5, \quad c = 8;$$

$$x = \frac{-b \pm \sqrt{b^2 - 4ac}}{2a}$$

$$= \frac{-5 \pm \sqrt{5^2 - 4(1)(8)}}{2 \cdot 1} \quad \text{Substituting}$$

$$= \frac{-5 \pm \sqrt{-7}}{2} \quad \text{Simplifying}$$

$$= \frac{-5 \pm \sqrt{7}i}{2}.$$

The solutions are $-\frac{5}{2} - \frac{\sqrt{7}}{2}i$ and $-\frac{5}{2} + \frac{\sqrt{7}}{2}i$.

VISUALIZING THE SOLUTION

The graph of the function $f(x) = x^2 + 5x + 8$ has no x-intercepts.

$$f(x) = x^2 + 5x + 8$$

Thus the function has no real-number zeros and there are no real-number solutions of the associated equation $x^2 + 5x + 8 = 0$.

▶ Now Try Exercise 45.

◆ The Discriminant

From the quadratic formula, we know that the solutions x_1 and x_2 of a quadratic equation are given by

$$x_1 = \frac{-b + \sqrt{b^2 - 4ac}}{2a} \quad \text{and} \quad x_2 = \frac{-b - \sqrt{b^2 - 4ac}}{2a}.$$

The expression $b^2 - 4ac$ shows the nature of the solutions. This expression is called the **discriminant.** If it is 0, then it makes no difference whether we choose the plus or the minus sign in the formula. That is, $x_1 = -\dfrac{b}{2a} = x_2$, so there is just one solution. In this case, we sometimes say that there is one repeated real solution. If the discriminant is positive, there will be two real solutions. If it is negative, we will be taking the square root of a negative number; hence there will be two imaginary-number solutions, and they will be complex conjugates.

Discriminant

For $ax^2 + bx + c = 0$:

$b^2 - 4ac = 0 \longrightarrow$ One real-number solution;

$b^2 - 4ac > 0 \longrightarrow$ Two different real-number solutions;

$b^2 - 4ac < 0 \longrightarrow$ Two different imaginary-number solutions, complex conjugates.

In Example 5, the discriminant, 88, is positive, indicating that there are two different real-number solutions. If the discriminant is negative, as it is in Example 6, we know that there are two different imaginary-number solutions.

◆ Equations Reducible to Quadratic

Some equations can be treated as quadratic, provided that we make a suitable substitution. For example, consider the following:

$$x^4 - 5x^2 + 4 = 0$$
$$(x^2)^2 - 5x^2 + 4 = 0 \qquad x^4 = (x^2)^2$$

$$u^2 - 5u + 4 = 0. \qquad \text{Substituting } u \text{ for } x^2$$

The equation $u^2 - 5u + 4 = 0$ can be solved for u by factoring or using the quadratic formula. Then we can reverse the substitution, replacing u with x^2, and solve for x. Equations like the one above are said to be **reducible to quadratic,** or **quadratic in form.**

EXAMPLE 7 Solve: $x^4 - 5x^2 + 4 = 0$.

ALGEBRAIC SOLUTION

We let $u = x^2$ and substitute:

$u^2 - 5u + 4 = 0$ Substituting u for x^2

$(u - 1)(u - 4) = 0$ Factoring

$u - 1 = 0$ *or* $u - 4 = 0$ Using the principle of zero products

$u = 1$ *or* $u = 4$.

Don't stop here! We must solve for the original variable. We substitute x^2 for u and solve for x:

$x^2 = 1$ *or* $x^2 = 4$

$x = \pm 1$ *or* $x = \pm 2$.   Using the principle of square roots

The solutions are -1, 1, -2, and 2.

VISUALIZING THE SOLUTION

The solutions of the given equation are the zeros of $f(x) = x^4 - 5x^2 + 4$. Note that the zeros occur at the x-values -2, -1, 1, and 2.

$f(x) = x^4 - 5x^2 + 4$

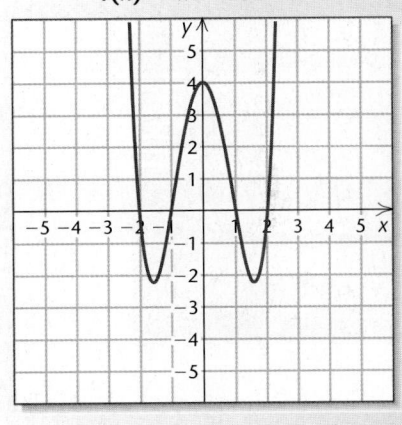

▶ Now Try Exercise 77.

TECHNOLOGY ·
CONNECTION

We can use the Zero method to solve the equation in Example 7, $x^4 - 5x^2 + 4 = 0$. We graph the function $y = x^4 - 5x^2 + 4$ and use the ZERO feature to find the zeros.

$y = x^4 - 5x^2 + 4$

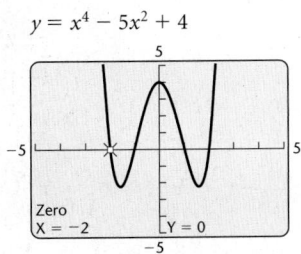

The leftmost zero is -2. Using the ZERO feature three more times, we find that the other zeros are -1, 1, and 2.

◆ Applications

Some applied problems can be translated to quadratic equations.

EXAMPLE 8   *Time of a Free Fall.*   The Petronas Towers in Kuala Lumpur, Malaysia, are 1482 ft tall. How long would it take an object dropped from the top to reach the ground?

Solution

1. **Familiarize.** The formula $s = 16t^2$ is used to approximate the distance s, in feet, that an object falls freely from rest in t seconds. In this case, the distance is 1482 ft.

2. **Translate.** We substitute 1482 for s in the formula:

$$1482 = 16t^2.$$

3. **Carry out.** We use the principle of square roots:

$$1482 = 16t^2$$

$$\frac{1482}{16} = t^2 \qquad \text{Dividing by 16}$$

$$\sqrt{\frac{1482}{16}} = t \qquad \begin{array}{l}\text{Taking the positive square root. Time} \\ \text{cannot be negative in this application.}\end{array}$$

$$9.624 \approx t.$$

4. **Check.** In 9.624 sec, a dropped object would travel a distance of $16(9.624)^2$, or about 1482 ft. The answer checks.

5. **State.** It would take about 9.624 sec for an object dropped from the top of the Petronas Towers to reach the ground.   ▶ Now Try Exercise 93.

EXAMPLE 9   *Bicycling Speed.*   Logan and Cassidy leave a campsite, Logan biking due north and Cassidy biking due east. Logan bikes 7 km/h slower than Cassidy. After 4 hr, they are 68 km apart. Find the speed of each bicyclist.

Solution

1. **Familiarize.** We let r = Cassidy's speed, in kilometers per hour. Then $r - 7$ = Logan's speed, in kilometers per hour. We will use the motion formula $d = rt$, where d is the distance, r is the rate (or speed), and t is the time. Then, after 4 hr, Cassidy has traveled $4r$ km and Logan has traveled $4(r - 7)$ km. We add these distances to the drawing, as shown below.

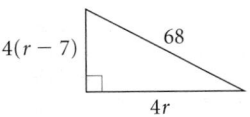

THE PYTHAGOREAN THEOREM

REVIEW SECTION **R.6.**

2. **Translate.** We use the Pythagorean theorem, $a^2 + b^2 = c^2$, where a and b are the lengths of the legs of a right triangle and c is the length of the hypotenuse:

$$(4r)^2 + [4(r - 7)]^2 = 68^2.$$

3. **Carry out.** We solve the equation:

$$(4r)^2 + [4(r - 7)]^2 = 68^2$$
$$16r^2 + 16(r^2 - 14r + 49) = 4624$$
$$16r^2 + 16r^2 - 224r + 784 = 4624$$
$$32r^2 - 224r - 3840 = 0 \qquad \text{Subtracting 4624}$$
$$r^2 - 7r - 120 = 0 \qquad \text{Dividing by 32}$$
$$(r + 8)(r - 15) = 0 \qquad \text{Factoring}$$
$$r + 8 = 0 \quad or \quad r - 15 = 0 \qquad \text{Principle of}$$
$$\text{zero products}$$
$$r = -8 \quad or \qquad r = 15.$$

4. **Check.** Since speed cannot be negative, we need to check only 15. If Cassidy's speed is 15 km/h, then Logan's speed is $15 - 7$, or 8 km/h. In 4 hr, Cassidy travels $4 \cdot 15$, or 60 km, and Logan travels $4 \cdot 8$, or 32 km. Then they are $\sqrt{60^2 + 32^2}$, or 68 km apart. The answer checks.

5. **State.** Cassidy's speed is 15 km/h, and Logan's speed is 8 km/h.

▶ **Now Try Exercise 97.**

CONNECTING THE CONCEPTS

Zeros, Solutions, and Intercepts

The zeros of a function $y = f(x)$ are also the solutions of the equation $f(x) = 0$, and the real-number zeros are the first coordinates of the x-intercepts of the graph of the function.

FUNCTION	ZEROS OF THE FUNCTION; SOLUTIONS OF THE EQUATION	ZEROS OF THE FUNCTION; X-INTERCEPTS OF THE GRAPH

Linear Function

$f(x) = 2x - 4$, or

$y = 2x - 4$

To find the **zero** of $f(x)$, we solve $f(x) = 0$:

$$2x - 4 = 0$$
$$2x = 4$$
$$x = 2.$$

The **solution** of $2x - 4 = 0$ is 2. This is the zero of the function $f(x) = 2x - 4$. That is, $f(2) = 0$.

The zero of $f(x)$ is the first coordinate of the **x-intercept** of the graph of $y = f(x)$.

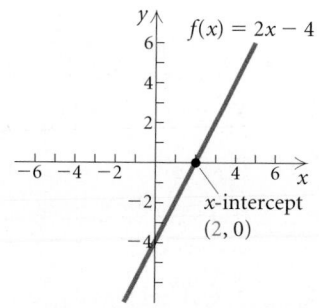

Quadratic Function

$g(x) = x^2 - 3x - 4$, or

$y = x^2 - 3x - 4$

To find the **zeros** of $g(x)$, we solve $g(x) = 0$:

$$x^2 - 3x - 4 = 0$$
$$(x + 1)(x - 4) = 0$$
$$x + 1 = 0 \quad or \quad x - 4 = 0$$
$$x = -1 \quad or \quad x = 4.$$

The **solutions** of $x^2 - 3x - 4 = 0$ are -1 and 4. They are the zeros of the function $g(x)$. That is, $g(-1) = 0$ and $g(4) = 0$.

The real-number zeros of $g(x)$ are the first coordinates of the **x-intercepts** of the graph of $y = g(x)$.

● ● ●

2.3 EXERCISE SET

Solve.

1. $(2x - 3)(3x - 2) = 0$

2. $(5x - 2)(2x + 3) = 0$

3. $x^2 - 8x - 20 = 0$

4. $x^2 + 6x + 8 = 0$

5. $3x^2 + x - 2 = 0$

6. $10x^2 - 16x + 6 = 0$

7. $4x^2 - 12 = 0$ 8. $6x^2 = 36$

9. $3x^2 = 21$ 10. $2x^2 - 20 = 0$

11. $5x^2 + 10 = 0$ 12. $4x^2 + 12 = 0$

13. $2x^2 - 34 = 0$ 14. $3x^2 = 33$

15. $2x^2 = 6x$ 16. $18x + 9x^2 = 0$

17. $3y^3 - 5y^2 - 2y = 0$ 18. $3t^3 + 2t = 5t^2$

19. $7x^3 + x^2 - 7x - 1 = 0$
    (*Hint*: Factor by grouping.)

20. $3x^3 + x^2 - 12x - 4 = 0$
    (*Hint*: Factor by grouping.)

*In Exercises 21–26, use the given graph to find each of the following: (**a**) the x-intercepts and (**b**) the zeros of the function.*

21.

22.

23.

24.

25.

26.

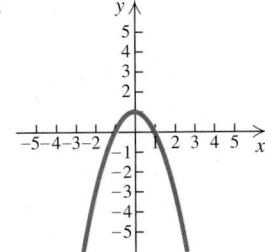

Solve by completing the square to obtain exact solutions.

27. $x^2 + 6x = 7$ 28. $x^2 + 8x = -15$

29. $x^2 = 8x - 9$ 30. $x^2 = 22 + 10x$

31. $x^2 + 8x + 25 = 0$ 32. $x^2 + 6x + 13 = 0$

33. $3x^2 + 5x - 2 = 0$ 34. $2x^2 - 5x - 3 = 0$

Use the quadratic formula to find exact solutions.

35. $x^2 - 2x = 15$ 36. $x^2 + 4x = 5$

37. $5m^2 + 3m = 2$

38. $2y^2 - 3y - 2 = 0$

39. $3x^2 + 6 = 10x$

40. $3t^2 + 8t + 3 = 0$

41. $x^2 + x + 2 = 0$

42. $x^2 + 1 = x$

43. $5t^2 - 8t = 3$

44. $5x^2 + 2 = x$

45. $3x^2 + 4 = 5x$

46. $2t^2 - 5t = 1$

47. $x^2 - 8x + 5 = 0$

48. $x^2 - 6x + 3 = 0$

49. $3x^2 + x = 5$

50. $5x^2 + 3x = 1$

51. $2x^2 + 1 = 5x$

52. $4x^2 + 3 = x$

53. $5x^2 + 2x = -2$

54. $3x^2 + 3x = -4$

For each of the following, find the discriminant,
$b^2 - 4ac$, *and then determine whether one real-number solution, two different real-number solutions, or two different imaginary-number solutions exist.*

55. $4x^2 = 8x + 5$

56. $4x^2 - 12x + 9 = 0$

57. $x^2 + 3x + 4 = 0$

58. $x^2 - 2x + 4 = 0$

59. $5t^2 - 7t = 0$

60. $5t^2 - 4t = 11$

Find the zeros of the function.

61. $f(x) = x^2 + 6x + 5$

62. $f(x) = x^2 - x - 2$

63. $f(x) = x^2 - 3x - 3$

64. $f(x) = 3x^2 + 8x + 2$

65. $f(x) = x^2 - 5x + 1$

66. $f(x) = x^2 - 3x - 7$

67. $f(x) = x^2 + 2x - 5$

68. $f(x) = x^2 - x - 4$

69. $f(x) = 2x^2 - x + 4$

70. $f(x) = 2x^2 + 3x + 2$

71. $f(x) = 3x^2 - x - 1$

72. $f(x) = 3x^2 + 5x + 1$

73. $f(x) = 5x^2 - 2x - 1$

74. $f(x) = 4x^2 - 4x - 5$

75. $f(x) = 4x^2 + 3x - 3$

76. $f(x) = x^2 + 6x - 3$

Solve.

77. $x^4 - 3x^2 + 2 = 0$

78. $x^4 + 3 = 4x^2$

79. $x^4 + 3x^2 = 10$

80. $x^4 - 8x^2 = 9$

81. $y^4 + 4y^2 - 5 = 0$

82. $y^4 - 15y^2 - 16 = 0$

83. $x - 3\sqrt{x} - 4 = 0$
(*Hint*: Let $u = \sqrt{x}$.)

84. $2x - 9\sqrt{x} + 4 = 0$

85. $m^{2/3} - 2m^{1/3} - 8 = 0$
(*Hint*: Let $u = m^{1/3}$.)

86. $t^{2/3} + t^{1/3} - 6 = 0$

87. $x^{1/2} - 3x^{1/4} + 2 = 0$

88. $x^{1/2} - 4x^{1/4} = -3$

89. $(2x - 3)^2 - 5(2x - 3) + 6 = 0$
(*Hint*: Let $u = 2x - 3$.)

90. $(3x + 2)^2 + 7(3x + 2) - 8 = 0$

91. $(2t^2 + t)^2 - 4(2t^2 + t) + 3 = 0$

92. $12 = (m^2 - 5m)^2 + (m^2 - 5m)$

Time of a Free Fall. *The formula* $s = 16t^2$ *is used to approximate the distance s, in feet, that an object falls freely from rest in t seconds. Use this formula for Exercises 93 and 94.*

93. The Warszawa Radio Mast in Poland, at 2120 ft, is the world's tallest structure (*Source: The Cambridge Fact Finder*). How long would it take an object falling freely from the top to reach the ground?

94. The tallest structure in the United States, at 2063 ft, is the KTHI-TV tower in North Dakota (*Source: The Cambridge Fact Finder*). How long would it take an object falling freely from the top to reach the ground?

Self-Employed Workers. *The function* $w(x) = -0.01x^2 + 0.27x + 8.60$ *can be used to estimate the number of self-employed workers in the United States, in millions, x years after 1980 (Source: U.S. Bureau of Labor Statistics). Use this function for Exercises 95 and 96.*

95. For what years were there (or will there be) 9.7 million self-employed workers in the United States?

96. For what years were there (or will there be) 9.1 million self-employed workers in the United States?

97. The length of a rectangular poster is 1 ft more than the width and a diagonal of the poster is 5 ft. Find the length and the width.

98. One leg of a right triangle is 7 cm less than the length of the other leg. The length of the hypotenuse is 13 cm. Find the lengths of the legs.

99. One number is 5 greater than another. The product of the numbers is 36. Find the numbers.

100. One number is 6 less than another. The product of the numbers is 72. Find the numbers.

101. *Box Construction.* An open box is made from a 10-cm by 20-cm piece of tin by cutting a square from each corner and folding up the edges. The area of the resulting base is 96 cm². What is the length of the sides of the squares?

102. *Picture-Frame Dimensions.* A picture frame measures 28 cm by 32 cm and is of uniform width. What is the width of the frame if 192 cm² of the picture shows?

103. *Dimensions of a Rug.* Find the dimensions of a Persian rug whose perimeter is 28 ft and whose area is 48 ft².

104. *Petting-Zoo Dimensions.* The director of the Glen Island Zoo wants to use 170 m of fencing to enclose a petting area of 1750 m². Find the dimensions of the petting area.

State whether the function is linear or quadratic.

105. $f(x) = 4 - 5x$

106. $f(x) = 4 - 5x^2$

107. $f(x) = 7x^2$

108. $f(x) = 23x + 6$

109. $f(x) = 1.2x - (3.6)^2$

110. $f(x) = 2 - x - x^2$

Technology Connection

Solve graphically. Round solutions to three decimal places, where appropriate.

111. $x^2 - 8x + 12 = 0$

112. $5x^2 + 42x + 16 = 0$

113. $7x^2 - 43x + 6 = 0$

114. $10x^2 - 23x + 12 = 0$

115. $6x + 1 = 4x^2$

116. $3x^2 + 5x = 3$

Use a graphing calculator to find the zeros of the function. Round to three decimal places.

117. $f(x) = 2x^2 - 5x - 4$

118. $f(x) = 4x^2 - 3x - 2$

119. $f(x) = 3x^2 + 2x - 4$

120. $f(x) = 9x^2 - 8x - 7$

121. $f(x) = 5.02x^2 - 4.19x - 2.057$

122. $f(x) = 1.21x^2 - 2.34x - 5.63$

Collaborative Discussion and Writing

123. Is it possible for a quadratic function to have one real zero and one imaginary zero? Why or why not?

124. The graph of a quadratic function can have 0, 1, or 2 *x*-intercepts. How can you predict the number of *x*-intercepts without drawing the graph or (completely) solving an equation?

Skill Maintenance

Associate's Degrees Conferred. The function $a(x) = 9096x + 387,725$ can be used to estimate the number of associate's degrees conferred x years after 1980 (Source: U.S. National Center for Education Statistics). Use this function for Exercises 125 and 126.

125. Estimate the number of associate's degrees conferred in 1998.

126. Estimate the number of associate's degrees conferred in 2010.

Determine whether the graph is symmetric with respect to the x-axis, the y-axis, and the origin.

127. $3x^2 + 4y^2 = 5$

128. $y^3 = 6x^2$

Determine whether the function is even, odd, or neither even nor odd.

129. $f(x) = 2x^3 - x$

130. $f(x) = 4x^2 + 2x - 3$

Synthesis

For each equation in Exercises 131–134, under the given condition: **(a)** *Find k and* **(b)** *find a second solution.*

131. $kx^2 - 17x + 33 = 0$; one solution is 3

132. $kx^2 - 2x + k = 0$; one solution is -3

133. $x^2 - kx + 2 = 0$; one solution is $1 + i$

134. $x^2 - (6 + 3i)x + k = 0$; one solution is 3

Solve.

135. $(x - 2)^3 = x^3 - 2$

136. $(x + 1)^3 = (x - 1)^3 + 26$

137. $(6x^3 + 7x^2 - 3x)(x^2 - 7) = 0$

138. $\left(x - \frac{1}{5}\right)\left(x^2 - \frac{1}{4}\right) + \left(x - \frac{1}{5}\right)\left(x^2 + \frac{1}{8}\right) = 0$

139. $x^2 + x - \sqrt{2} = 0$

140. $x^2 + \sqrt{5}x - \sqrt{3} = 0$

141. $2t^2 + (t - 4)^2 = 5t(t - 4) + 24$

142. $9t(t + 2) - 3t(t - 2) = 2(t + 4)(t + 6)$

143. $\sqrt{x - 3} - \sqrt[4]{x - 3} = 2$

144. $x^6 - 28x^3 + 27 = 0$

145. $\left(y + \frac{2}{y}\right)^2 + 3y + \frac{6}{y} = 4$

146. $x^2 + 3x + 1 - \sqrt{x^2 + 3x + 1} = 8$

147. Solve $\frac{1}{2}at^2 + v_0t + x_0 = 0$ for t.

Analyzing Graphs of Quadratic Functions

2.4

◆ Find the vertex, the axis of symmetry, and the maximum or minimum value of a quadratic function using the method of completing the square.

◆ Graph quadratic functions.

◆ Solve applied problems involving maximum and minimum function values.

TRANSFORMATIONS

REVIEW SECTION **1.7.**

◆ Graphing Quadratic Functions of the Type $f(x) = a(x - h)^2 + k$

The graph of a quadratic function is called a **parabola.** The graph of every parabola evolves from the graph of the squaring function $f(x) = x^2$ using transformations.

We get the graph of $f(x) = a(x - h)^2 + k$ from the graph of $f(x) = x^2$ as follows:

$$f(x) = x^2$$
$$\downarrow$$
$$f(x) = ax^2 \qquad \text{Vertical stretching or shrinking with a reflection across the x-axis if } a < 0$$
$$\downarrow$$
$$f(x) = a(x - h)^2 \qquad \text{Horizontal translation}$$
$$\downarrow$$
$$f(x) = a(x - h)^2 + k. \qquad \text{Vertical translation}$$

Consider the following graphs of the form $f(x) = a(x - h)^2 + k$. The point (h, k) at which the graph turns is called the **vertex**. The maximum or minimum value of $f(x)$ occurs at the vertex. Each graph has a line $x = h$ that is called the **axis of symmetry**.

CONNECTING THE CONCEPTS

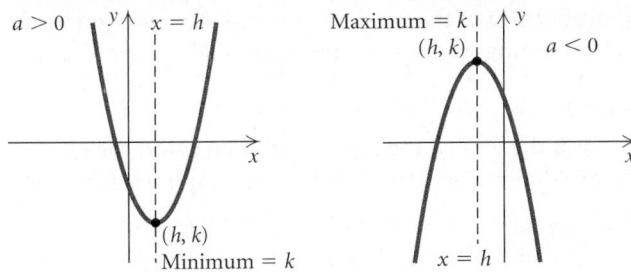

Graphing Quadratic Functions

The graph of the function $f(x) = a(x - h)^2 + k$ is a parabola that:

- opens up if $a > 0$ and down if $a < 0$;
- has (h, k) as the vertex;
- has $x = h$ as the axis of symmetry;
- has k as a minimum value (output) if $a > 0$;
- has k as a maximum value if $a < 0$. ● ● ●

As we saw in Section 1.7, the constant a serves to stretch or shrink the graph vertically. As a parabola is stretched vertically, it becomes narrower, and as it is shrunk vertically, it becomes wider. That is, as $|a|$ increases, the graph becomes narrower, and as $|a|$ gets close to 0, the graph becomes wider.

If the equation is in the form $f(x) = a(x - h)^2 + k$, we can learn a great deal about the graph without graphing.

Function	$f(x) = 3\left(x - \frac{1}{4}\right)^2 - 2$ $= 3\left(x - \frac{1}{4}\right)^2 + (-2)$	$g(x) = -3(x + 5)^2 + 7$ $= -3[x - (-5)]^2 + 7$
Vertex	$\left(\frac{1}{4}, -2\right)$	$(-5, 7)$
Axis of Symmetry	$x = \frac{1}{4}$	$x = -5$
Maximum	None (3 > 0, so graph opens up.)	7 (−3 < 0, so graph opens down.)
Minimum	−2 (3 > 0, so graph opens up.)	None (−3 < 0, so graph opens down.)

Note that the vertex (h, k) is used to find the maximum or the minimum value of the function. The maximum or minimum value is the number k, *not* the ordered pair (h, k).

◆ Graphing Quadratic Functions of the Type $f(x) = ax^2 + bx + c,\ a \neq 0$

We now use a modification of the method of completing the square as an aid in graphing and analyzing quadratic functions of the form $f(x) = ax^2 + bx + c, a \neq 0$.

EXAMPLE 1 Find the vertex, the axis of symmetry, and the maximum or minimum value of $f(x) = x^2 + 10x + 23$. Then graph the function.

Solution To express $f(x) = x^2 + 10x + 23$ in the form $f(x) = a(x - h)^2 + k$, we complete the square on the terms involving x. To do so, we take half the coefficient of x and square it, obtaining $(10/2)^2$, or 25. We now add and subtract that number on the right side:

$$f(x) = x^2 + 10x + 23 = x^2 + 10x + 25 - 25 + 23.$$

Since $25 - 25 = 0$, the new expression for the function is equivalent to the original expression. Note that this process differs from the one we used to complete the square in order to solve a quadratic equation, where we added the same number on both sides of the equation to obtain an equivalent equation. Instead, when we complete the square to write a function in the form $f(x) = a(x - h)^2 + k$, we add and subtract the same number on the right side. The entire process is shown below:

$$f(x) = x^2 + 10x + 23$$

Note that 25 completes the square for $x^2 + 10x$.

$$= x^2 + 10x + 25 - 25 + 23$$

Adding 25 − 25, or 0, to the right side

$$= (x^2 + 10x + 25) - 25 + 23$$

Regrouping

$$= (x + 5)^2 - 2$$

Factoring and simplifying

$$= [x - (-5)]^2 + (-2).$$

Writing in the form $f(x) = a(x - h)^2 + k$

Keeping in mind that this function will have a minimum value since $a > 0$ ($a = 1$), from this form of the function we know the following:

Vertex: $(-5, -2)$;

Axis of symmetry: $x = -5$;

Minimum value of the function: -2.

To graph the function, we first plot the vertex and find several points on either side of it. Then we plot these points and connect them with a smooth curve.

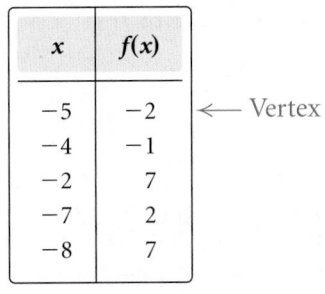

x	$f(x)$
-5	-2 ← Vertex
-4	-1
-2	7
-7	2
-8	7

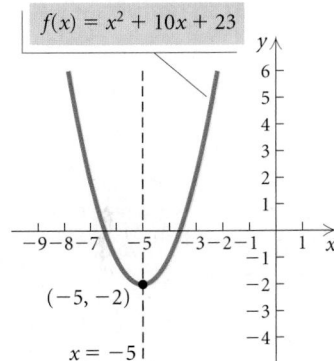

$f(x) = x^2 + 10x + 23$

The graph of $f(x) = x^2 + 10x + 23$, or $[x - (-5)]^2 + (-2)$, shown above, is a shift of the graph of $y = x^2$ left 5 units and down 2 units.

▶ **Now Try Exercise 5.**

Keep in mind that the axis of symmetry is not part of the graph; it is a characteristic of the graph. If you fold the graph on its axis of symmetry, the two halves of the graph will coincide.

EXAMPLE 2   Find the vertex, the axis of symmetry, and the maximum or minimum value of $g(x) = x^2/2 - 4x + 8$. Then graph the function.

Solution   We complete the square in order to write the function in the form $g(x) = a(x - h)^2 + k$. First, we factor $\frac{1}{2}$ out of the first two terms. This makes the coefficient of x^2 within the parentheses 1:

$$g(x) = \frac{x^2}{2} - 4x + 8$$

$$= \frac{1}{2}(x^2 - 8x) + 8. \qquad \text{Factoring } \tfrac{1}{2} \text{ out of the first two terms:}$$
$$\frac{x^2}{2} - 4x = \frac{1}{2} \cdot x^2 - \frac{1}{2} \cdot 8x$$

Next, we complete the square inside the parentheses: Half of -8 is -4, and $(-4)^2 = 16$. We add and subtract 16 inside the parentheses:

$$g(x) = \tfrac{1}{2}(x^2 - 8x + 16 - 16) + 8$$
$$= \tfrac{1}{2}(x^2 - 8x + 16) - \tfrac{1}{2} \cdot 16 + 8 \qquad \text{Using the distributive law to remove } -16 \text{ from within the parentheses}$$
$$= \tfrac{1}{2}(x - 4)^2 + 0, \text{ or } \tfrac{1}{2}(x - 4)^2. \qquad \text{Factoring and simplifying}$$

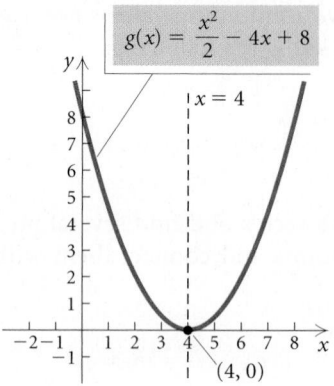

$$g(x) = \frac{x^2}{2} - 4x + 8$$

We know the following:

Vertex: $(4, 0)$;

Axis of symmetry: $x = 4$;

Minimum value of the function: 0.

Finally, we plot the vertex and several points on either side of it and draw the graph of the function. The graph of g is a vertical shrinking of the graph of $y = x^2$ along with a shift 4 units to the right. ▶ **Now Try Exercise 9.**

EXAMPLE 3 Find the vertex, the axis of symmetry, and the maximum or minimum value of $f(x) = -2x^2 + 10x - \frac{23}{2}$. Then graph the function.

Solution We have

$$
\begin{aligned}
f(x) &= -2x^2 + 10x - \frac{23}{2} \\
&= -2(x^2 - 5x) - \frac{23}{2} && \text{Factoring } -2 \text{ out of the first two terms} \\
&= -2\left(x^2 - 5x + \frac{25}{4} - \frac{25}{4}\right) - \frac{23}{2} && \text{Completing the square inside the parentheses} \\
&= -2\left(x^2 - 5x + \frac{25}{4}\right) - 2\left(-\frac{25}{4}\right) - \frac{23}{2} && \text{Using the distributive law to remove } -\frac{25}{4} \text{ from within the parentheses} \\
&= -2\left(x - \frac{5}{2}\right)^2 + \frac{25}{2} - \frac{23}{2} \\
&= -2\left(x - \frac{5}{2}\right)^2 + 1.
\end{aligned}
$$

This form of the function yields the following:

Vertex: $\left(\frac{5}{2}, 1\right)$;

Axis of symmetry: $x = \frac{5}{2}$;

Maximum value of the function: 1.

The graph is found by shifting the graph of $f(x) = x^2$ to the right $\frac{5}{2}$ units, reflecting it across the x-axis, stretching it vertically, and shifting it up 1 unit.

▶ **Now Try Exercise 13.**

In many situations, we want to find the coordinates of the vertex directly from the equation $f(x) = ax^2 + bx + c$ using a formula. One way to develop such a formula is to observe that the x-coordinate of the vertex is centered between the x-intercepts, or zeros, of the function. By averaging the two solutions of $ax^2 + bx + c = 0$, we find a formula for the x-coordinate of the vertex:

$$
\begin{aligned}
x\text{-coordinate of vertex} &= \frac{\dfrac{-b - \sqrt{b^2 - 4ac}}{2a} + \dfrac{-b + \sqrt{b^2 - 4ac}}{2a}}{2} \\
&= \frac{\dfrac{-2b}{2a}}{2} = \frac{-\dfrac{b}{a}}{2} \\
&= -\frac{b}{a} \cdot \frac{1}{2} = -\frac{b}{2a}.
\end{aligned}
$$

$$f(x) = -2x^2 + 10x - \frac{23}{2}$$

$$f(x) = ax^2 + bx + c$$

We use this value of x to find the y-coordinate of the vertex, $f\left(-\dfrac{b}{2a}\right)$.

The Vertex of a Parabola

The **vertex** of the graph of $f(x) = ax^2 + bx + c$ is

$$\left(-\frac{b}{2a}, f\left(-\frac{b}{2a}\right)\right).$$

↑   ↑

We calculate the   We substitute to
x-coordinate.   find the y-coordinate.

TECHNOLOGY CONNECTION

We can use a graphing calculator to do Example 4. Once we have graphed $y = -x^2 + 14x - 47$, we see that the graph opens down and thus has a maximum value. We can use the MAXIMUM feature to find the coordinates of the vertex. Using these coordinates, we can then find the maximum value and the range of the function along with the intervals on which the function is increasing or decreasing.

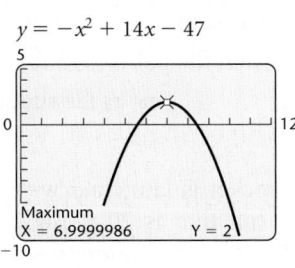

$y = -x^2 + 14x - 47$

Maximum
X = 6.9999986   Y = 2

EXAMPLE 4 For the function $f(x) = -x^2 + 14x - 47$:

a) Find the vertex.

b) Determine whether there is a maximum or minimum value and find that value.

c) Find the range.

d) On what intervals is the function increasing? decreasing?

Solution There is no need to graph the function.

a) The x-coordinate of the vertex is

$$-\frac{b}{2a} = -\frac{14}{2(-1)}, \text{ or } 7.$$

Since

$$f(7) = -7^2 + 14 \cdot 7 - 47 = 2,$$

the vertex is $(7, 2)$.

b) Since a is negative ($a = -1$), the graph opens down so the second coordinate of the vertex, 2, is the maximum value of the function.

c) The range is $(-\infty, 2]$.

d) Since the graph opens down, function values increase as we approach the vertex from the left and decrease as we move to the right from the vertex. Thus the function is increasing on the interval $(-\infty, 7)$ and decreasing on $(7, \infty)$.

▶ Now Try Exercise 25.

✦ Applications

Many real-world situations involve finding the maximum or minimum value of a quadratic function.

EXAMPLE 5 *Maximizing Area.* A stone mason has enough stones to enclose a rectangular patio with 60 ft of stone wall. If the house forms one side of the rectangle, what is the maximum area that the mason can enclose? What should the dimensions of the patio be in order to yield this area?

PROBLEM-SOLVING STRATEGY

REVIEW SECTION 2.1.

TECHNOLOGY CONNECTION

As a more complete check in Example 5, assuming that the function $A(w)$ is correct, we could examine a table of values for

$$A(w) = (60 - 2w)w$$

and/or examine its graph.

X	Y₁
14.7	449.82
14.8	449.92
14.9	449.98
15	**450**
15.1	449.98
15.2	449.92
15.3	449.82

X = 15

$y = (60 - 2x)x$

500

Maximum
-10 X = 15 Y = 450 40
0

Solution   We will use the five-step problem-solving strategy.

1. **Familiarize.** We make a drawing of the situation, using w to represent the width of the patio, in feet. Then $(60 - 2w)$ feet of stone is available for the length. Suppose the patio were 10 ft wide. It would then be $60 - 2 \cdot 10 = 40$ ft long. The area would be $(10 \text{ ft})(40 \text{ ft}) = 400 \text{ ft}^2$. If the patio were 12 ft wide, it would be $60 - 2 \cdot 12 = 36$ ft long. The area would be $(12 \text{ ft})(36 \text{ ft}) = 432 \text{ ft}^2$. If it were 16 ft wide, it would be $60 - 2 \cdot 16 = 28$ ft long and the area would be $(16 \text{ ft})(28 \text{ ft}) = 448 \text{ ft}^2$. There are more combinations of length and width than we could possibly try. Instead we will find a function that represents the area and then determine the maximum value of the function.

2. **Translate.** Since the area of a rectangle is given by length times width, we have

$$A(w) = (60 - 2w)w \qquad A = lw;\, l = 60 - 2w$$
$$= -2w^2 + 60w,$$

   where $A(w)$ is the area of the patio, in square feet, as a function of the width, w.

3. **Carry out.** To solve this problem, we need to determine the maximum value of $A(w)$ and find the dimensions for which that maximum occurs. Since A is a quadratic function and w^2 has a negative coefficient, we know that the function has a maximum value that occurs at the vertex of the graph of the function. The first coordinate of the vertex, $(w, A(w))$, is

$$w = -\frac{b}{2a} = -\frac{60}{2(-2)} = 15 \text{ ft.}$$

   Thus, if $w = 15$ ft, then the length $l = 60 - 2 \cdot 15 = 30$ ft; and the area is $15 \cdot 30$, or 450 ft^2.

4. **Check.** As a partial check, we note that $450 \text{ ft}^2 > 448 \text{ ft}^2$, which is the largest area we found in a guess in the *Familiarize* step.

5. **State.** The maximum possible area is 450 ft^2 when the patio is 15 ft wide and 30 ft long.

▶ **Now Try Exercise 39.**

EXAMPLE 6   *Height of a Rocket.*   A model rocket is launched with an initial velocity of 100 ft/sec from the top of a hill that is 20 ft high. Its height t seconds after it has been launched is given by the function $s(t) = -16t^2 + 100t + 20$. Determine the time at which the rocket reaches its maximum height and find the maximum height.

Solution

1., 2. **Familiarize** and **Translate.** We are given the function in the statement of the problem.

3. **Carry out.** We need to find the maximum value of the function and the value of t for which it occurs. Since $s(t)$ is a quadratic function and t^2 has a negative coefficient, we know that the maximum value of the func-

$s(t) = -16t^2 + 100t + 20$

tion occurs at the vertex of the graph of the function. The first coordinate of the vertex gives the time t at which the rocket reaches its maximum height. It is

$$t = -\frac{b}{2a} = -\frac{100}{2(-16)} = 3.125.$$

The second coordinate of the vertex gives the maximum height of the rocket. We substitute in the function to find it:

$$s(3.125) = -16(3.125)^2 + 100(3.125) + 20 = 176.25.$$

4. **Check.** As a check, we can complete the square to write the function in the form $s(t) = a(t - h)^2 + k$ and determine the coordinates of the vertex from this form of the function. We get

$$s(t) = -16(t - 3.125)^2 + 176.25.$$

This confirms that the vertex is $(3.125, 176.25)$, so the answer checks.

5. **State.** The rocket reaches a maximum height of 176.25 ft 3.125 sec after it has been launched.

▶ Now Try Exercise 35.

EXAMPLE 7 *Finding the Depth of a Well.* Two seconds after a chlorine tablet has been dropped into a well, a splash is heard. The speed of sound is 1100 ft/sec. How far is the top of the well from the water?

Solution

1. **Familiarize.** We first make a drawing and label it with known and unknown information. We let $s =$ the depth of the well, in feet, $t_1 =$ the time, in seconds, that it takes for the tablet to hit the water, and $t_2 =$ the time, in seconds, that it takes for the sound to reach the top of the well. This gives us the equation

$$t_1 + t_2 = 2. \tag{1}$$

2. **Translate.** Can we find any relationship between the two times and the distance s? Often in problem solving you may need to look up related formulas in a physics book, in another mathematics book, or on the Internet. We find that the formula

$$s = 16t^2$$

gives the distance, in feet, that a dropped object falls in t seconds. The time t_1 that it takes the tablet to hit the water can be found as follows:

$$s = 16t_1^2, \quad \text{or} \quad \frac{s}{16} = t_1^2, \text{ so } t_1 = \frac{\sqrt{s}}{4}. \qquad \text{Taking the positive square root} \tag{2}$$

To find an expression for t_2, the time it takes the sound to travel to the top of the well, recall that *Distance = Rate · Time.* Thus,

$$s = 1100t_2, \quad \text{or} \quad t_2 = \frac{s}{1100}. \tag{3}$$

We now have expressions for t_1 and t_2, both in terms of s. Substituting into equation (1), we obtain

$$t_1 + t_2 = 2, \quad \text{or} \quad \frac{\sqrt{s}}{4} + \frac{s}{1100} = 2. \tag{4}$$

TECHNOLOGY·············
CONNECTION

We can solve the equation in Example 7 graphically using the Intersect method. It will probably require some trial and error to determine an appropriate window.

$$y_1 = \frac{\sqrt{x}}{4} + \frac{x}{1100}, \quad y_2 = 2$$

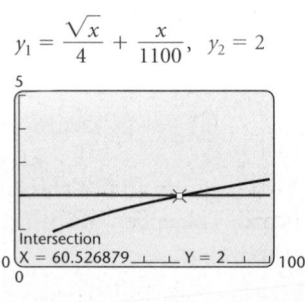

3. **Carry out.** We solve equation (4) for s. Multiplying by 1100, we get

$$275\sqrt{s} + s = 2200, \quad \text{or} \quad s + 275\sqrt{s} - 2200 = 0.$$

This equation is reducible to quadratic with $u = \sqrt{s}$. Substituting, we get

$$u^2 + 275u - 2200 = 0.$$

Using the quadratic formula, we can solve for u:

$$u = \frac{-b \pm \sqrt{b^2 - 4ac}}{2a}$$

$$= \frac{-275 + \sqrt{275^2 - 4 \cdot 1 \cdot (-2200)}}{2 \cdot 1} \qquad \text{We want only the positive solution.}$$

$$= \frac{-275 + \sqrt{84{,}425}}{2}$$

$$\approx 7.78.$$

Since $u \approx 7.78$, we have

$$\sqrt{s} = 7.78$$

$$s \approx 60.5. \qquad \text{Squaring both sides}$$

4. **Check.** To check, we can substitute 60.5 for s in equation (4) and see that $t_1 + t_2 \approx 2$. We leave the mathematics for the student.

5. **State.** The top of the well is about 60.5 ft above the water.

▶ **Now Try Exercise 47.**

Visualizing the Graph

Match the equation with its graph.

1. $y = 3x$

2. $y = -(x - 1)^2 + 3$

3. $(x + 2)^2 + (y - 2)^2 = 9$

4. $y = 3$

5. $2x - 3y = 6$

6. $(x - 1)^2 + (y + 3)^2 = 4$

7. $y = -2x + 1$

8. $y = 2x^2 - x - 4$

9. $x = -2$

10. $y = -3x^2 + 6x - 2$

Answers on page A-15

2.4 EXERCISE SET

In Exercises 1 and 2, use the given graph to find each of the following: (a) the vertex; (b) the axis of symmetry; and (c) the maximum or minimum value of the function.

1.

$\left(-\dfrac{1}{2}, -\dfrac{9}{4}\right)$

2.

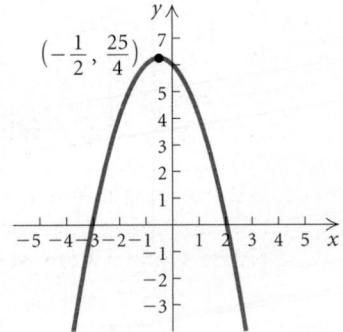

$\left(-\dfrac{1}{2}, \dfrac{25}{4}\right)$

In Exercises 3–16, (a) find the vertex; (b) find the axis of symmetry; (c) determine whether there is a maximum or minimum value and find that value; and (d) graph the function.

3. $f(x) = x^2 - 8x + 12$ **4.** $g(x) = x^2 + 7x - 8$

5. $f(x) = x^2 - 7x + 12$ **6.** $g(x) = x^2 - 5x + 6$

7. $f(x) = x^2 + 4x + 5$ **8.** $f(x) = x^2 + 2x + 6$

9. $g(x) = \dfrac{x^2}{2} + 4x + 6$ **10.** $g(x) = \dfrac{x^2}{3} - 2x + 1$

11. $g(x) = 2x^2 + 6x + 8$

12. $f(x) = 2x^2 - 10x + 14$

13. $f(x) = -x^2 - 6x + 3$

14. $f(x) = -x^2 - 8x + 5$

15. $g(x) = -2x^2 + 2x + 1$

16. $f(x) = -3x^2 - 3x + 1$

In Exercises 17–24, match the equation with one of the figures (a)–(h), which follow.

a)

b)

c)

d)

e)

f)

g)

h)

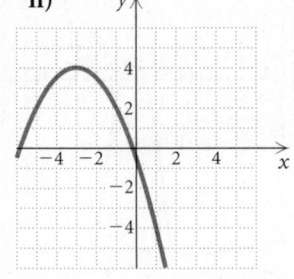

17. $y = (x + 3)^2$

18. $y = -(x - 4)^2 + 3$

19. $y = 2(x - 4)^2 - 1$

20. $y = x^2 - 3$

21. $y = -\frac{1}{2}(x + 3)^2 + 4$

22. $y = (x - 3)^2$

23. $y = -(x + 3)^2 + 4$

24. $y = 2(x - 1)^2 - 4$

In Exercises 25–34:

a) *Find the vertex.*

b) *Determine whether there is a maximum or minimum value and find that value.*

c) *Find the range.*

d) *Find the intervals on which the function is increasing and the intervals on which the function is decreasing.*

25. $f(x) = x^2 - 6x + 5$

26. $f(x) = x^2 + 4x - 5$

27. $f(x) = 2x^2 + 4x - 16$

28. $f(x) = \frac{1}{2}x^2 - 3x + \frac{5}{2}$

29. $f(x) = -\frac{1}{2}x^2 + 5x - 8$

30. $f(x) = -2x^2 - 24x - 64$

31. $f(x) = 3x^2 + 6x + 5$

32. $f(x) = -3x^2 + 24x - 49$

33. $g(x) = -4x^2 - 12x + 9$

34. $g(x) = 2x^2 - 6x + 5$

35. *Height of a Ball.* A ball is thrown directly upward from a height of 6 ft with an initial velocity of 20 ft/sec. The function $s(t) = -16t^2 + 20t + 6$ gives the height of the ball t seconds after it has been thrown. Determine the time at which the ball reaches its maximum height and find the maximum height.

36. *Height of a Projectile.* A stone is thrown directly upward from a height of 30 ft with an initial velocity of 60 ft/sec. The height of the stone t seconds after it has been thrown is given by the function $s(t) = -16t^2 + 60t + 30$. Determine the time at which the stone reaches its maximum height and find the maximum height.

37. *Height of a Rocket.* A model rocket is launched with an initial velocity of 120 ft/sec from a height of 80 ft. The height of the rocket t seconds after it has been launched is given by the function $s(t) = -16t^2 + 120t + 80$. Determine the time

at which the rocket reaches its maximum height and find the maximum height.

38. *Height of a Rocket.* A model rocket is launched with an initial velocity of 150 ft/sec from a height of 40 ft. The height of the rocket t seconds after it has been launched is given by the function $s(t) = -16t^2 + 150t + 40$. Determine the time at which the rocket reaches its maximum height and find the maximum height.

39. *Maximizing Volume.* Mendoza Manufacturing plans to produce a one-compartment vertical file by bending the long side of a 10-in. by 18-in. sheet of plastic along two lines to form a U-shape. How tall should the file be in order to maximize the volume that the file can hold?

40. *Maximizing Area.* A fourth-grade class decides to enclose a rectangular garden, using the side of the school as one side of the rectangle. What is the maximum area that the class can enclose with 32 ft of fence? What should the dimensions of the garden be in order to yield this area?

41. *Maximizing Area.* The sum of the base and the height of a triangle is 20 cm. Find the dimensions for which the area is a maximum.

42. *Maximizing Area.* The sum of the base and the height of a parallelogram is 69 cm. Find the dimensions for which the area is a maximum.

43. *Minimizing Cost.* Aki's Bicycle Designs has determined that when *x* hundred bicycles are built, the average cost per bicycle is given by

$$C(x) = 0.1x^2 - 0.7x + 2.425,$$

where $C(x)$ is in hundreds of dollars. How many bicycles should be built in order to minimize the average cost per bicycle?

Maximizing Profit. *In business, profit is the difference between revenue and cost, that is,*

$$Total\ profit = Total\ revenue - Total\ cost,$$
$$P(x) = R(x) - C(x),$$

where x is the number of units sold. Find the maximum profit and the number of units that must be sold in order to yield the maximum profit for each of the following.

44. $R(x) = 5x$, $C(x) = 0.001x^2 + 1.2x + 60$

45. $R(x) = 50x - 0.5x^2$, $C(x) = 10x + 3$

46. $R(x) = 20x - 0.1x^2$, $C(x) = 4x + 2$

47. *Finding the Height of an Elevator Shaft.* Jenelle dropped a screwdriver from the top of an elevator shaft. Exactly 5 sec later, she heard the sound of the screwdriver hitting the bottom of the shaft. How tall is the elevator shaft? (*Hint*: See Example 7.)

48. *Finding the Height of a Cliff.* A water balloon is dropped from a cliff. Exactly 3 sec later, the sound of the balloon hitting the ground reaches the top of the cliff. How high is the cliff? (*Hint*: See Example 7.)

49. *Maximizing Area.* A rancher needs to enclose two adjacent rectangular corrals, one for cattle and one for sheep. If a river forms one side of the corrals

and 240 yd of fencing is available, what is the largest total area that can be enclosed?

50. *Norman Window.* A Norman window is a rectangle with a semicircle on top. Sky Blue Windows is designing a Norman window that will require 24 ft of trim on the outer edges. What dimensions will allow the maximum amount of light to enter a house?

A Norman window

Technology Connection

Use a graphing calculator to check the answers for each of the following.

51. Exercises 3 and 15

52. Exercises 4 and 16

53. Exercises 25 and 29

54. Exercises 26 and 30

Collaborative Discussion and Writing

55. Write a problem for a classmate to solve. Design it so that it is a maximum or minimum problem using a quadratic function.

56. Discuss two ways in which we used completing the square in this chapter.

57. Suppose that the graph of $f(x) = ax^2 + bx + c$ has x-intercepts $(x_1, 0)$ and $(x_2, 0)$. What are the x-intercepts of $g(x) = -ax^2 - bx - c$? Explain.

Skill Maintenance

For each function f, construct and simplify the difference quotient

$$\frac{f(x + h) - f(x)}{h}.$$

58. $f(x) = 3x - 7$

59. $f(x) = 2x^2 - x + 4$

A graph of $y = f(x)$ follows. No formula is given for f. Make a hand-drawn graph of each of the following.

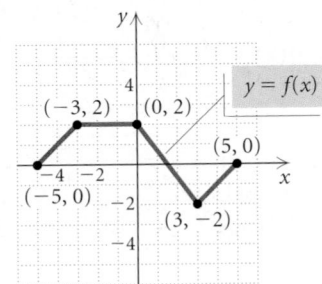

60. $g(x) = f(2x)$ **61.** $g(x) = -2f(x)$

Synthesis

62. Find b such that
$$f(x) = -4x^2 + bx + 3$$
has a maximum value of 50.

63. Find c such that
$$f(x) = -0.2x^2 - 3x + c$$
has a maximum value of -225.

64. Find a quadratic function with vertex $(4, -5)$ and containing the point $(-3, 1)$.

65. Graph: $f(x) = (|x| - 5)^2 - 3$.

66. *Minimizing Area.* A 24-in. piece of string is cut into two pieces. One piece is used to form a circle while the other is used to form a square. How should the string be cut so that the sum of the areas is a minimum?

2.5 More Equation Solving

◆ Solve rational equations.
◆ Solve radical equations.
◆ Solve equations with absolute value.

✦ Rational Equations

Equations containing rational expressions are called **rational equations.** Solving such equations involves multiplying both sides by the least common denominator (LCD) to *clear the equation of fractions.*

EXAMPLE 1 Solve: $\dfrac{x-8}{3} + \dfrac{x-3}{2} = 0$.

ALGEBRAIC SOLUTION

We have

$$\dfrac{x-8}{3} + \dfrac{x-3}{2} = 0$$ The LCD is $3 \cdot 2$, or 6.

$$6\left(\dfrac{x-8}{3} + \dfrac{x-3}{2}\right) = 6 \cdot 0$$ Multiplying by the LCD on both sides to clear fractions

$$6 \cdot \dfrac{x-8}{3} + 6 \cdot \dfrac{x-3}{2} = 0$$

$$2(x-8) + 3(x-3) = 0$$

$$2x - 16 + 3x - 9 = 0$$

$$5x - 25 = 0$$

$$5x = 25$$

$$x = 5.$$

The possible solution is 5.

Check: $\qquad \dfrac{x-8}{3} + \dfrac{x-3}{2} = 0$

$$\dfrac{5-8}{3} + \dfrac{5-3}{2} \ ?\ 0$$

$$\dfrac{-3}{3} + \dfrac{2}{2}$$

$$-1 + 1$$

$$0 \ \Big|\ 0 \quad \text{TRUE}$$

The solution is 5.

VISUALIZING THE SOLUTION

The solution of the given equation is the zero of the function

$$f(x) = \dfrac{x-8}{3} + \dfrac{x-3}{2}.$$

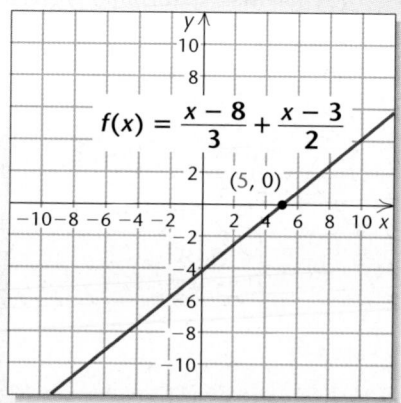

The zero of the function is 5. Thus the solution of the equation is 5.

▶ **Now Try Exercise 3.**

Caution! Clearing fractions is a valid procedure when solving rational equations but not when adding, subtracting, multiplying, or dividing rational expressions. A rational expression may have operation signs but no equals sign. A rational equation always has an equals sign. For example, $\dfrac{x-8}{3}+\dfrac{x-3}{2}$ is a rational expression but $\dfrac{x-8}{3}+\dfrac{x-3}{2}=0$ is a rational equation. To *simplify* the rational *expression* $\dfrac{x-8}{3}+\dfrac{x-3}{2}$, we first find the LCD and write each fraction with that denominator. The final result is generally a rational expression. To *solve* the rational *equation* $\dfrac{x-8}{3}+\dfrac{x-3}{2}=0$, we first multiply both sides by the LCD to clear fractions. The final result is one or more numbers. As we will see in Example 2, these numbers must be checked in the original equation.

TECHNOLOGY
   CONNECTION

We can use the Zero method to solve the equation in Example 1. We find the zero of the function

$$f(x)=\frac{x-8}{3}+\frac{x-3}{2}.$$

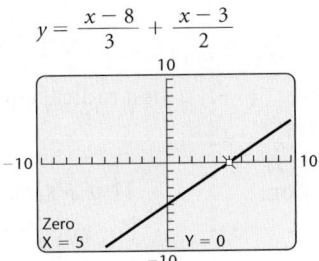

The zero of the function is 5. Thus the solution of the equation is 5.

When we use the multiplication principle to multiply (or divide) on both sides of an equation by an expression with a variable, we might not obtain an equivalent equation. We must check the possible solutions obtained in this manner by substituting them in the original equation. The next example illustrates this.

EXAMPLE 2 Solve: $\dfrac{x^2}{x-3} = \dfrac{9}{x-3}$.

Solution The LCD is $x - 3$.

$$(x-3) \cdot \dfrac{x^2}{x-3} = (x-3) \cdot \dfrac{9}{x-3}$$

$$x^2 = 9$$

$$x = -3 \quad or \quad x = 3 \qquad \text{Using the principle of square roots}$$

The possible solutions are -3 and 3. We check.

Check: For -3:   For 3:

$$\dfrac{x^2}{x-3} = \dfrac{9}{x-3} \qquad\qquad \dfrac{x^2}{x-3} = \dfrac{9}{x-3}$$

$$\dfrac{(-3)^2}{-3-3} \stackrel{?}{=} \dfrac{9}{-3-3} \qquad\qquad \dfrac{3^2}{3-3} \stackrel{?}{=} \dfrac{9}{3-3}$$

$$\left.\dfrac{9}{-6}\ \right|\ \dfrac{9}{-6} \quad \textbf{TRUE} \qquad\qquad \left.\dfrac{9}{0}\ \right|\ \dfrac{9}{0} \quad \textbf{NOT DEFINED}$$

The number -3 checks, so it is a solution. Since division by 0 is not defined, 3 is not a solution. Note that 3 is not in the domain of either $x^2/(x-3)$ or $9/(x-3)$.

▶ **Now Try Exercise 23.**

TECHNOLOGY CONNECTION

We can use a table on a graphing calculator to check the possible solutions in Example 2. We enter $y_1 = \dfrac{x^2}{x-3}$ and $y_2 = \dfrac{9}{x-3}$.

$$y_1 = \dfrac{x^2}{x-3}, \quad y_2 = \dfrac{9}{x-3}$$

X	Y1	Y2
-3	-1.5	-1.5
3	ERROR	ERROR

X =

When $x = -3$, we see that $y_1 = -1.5 = y_2$, so -3 is a solution. When $x = 3$, we get ERROR messages. This indicates that 3 is not in the domain of y_1 or y_2 and, thus, is not a solution.

◆ Radical Equations

A **radical equation** is an equation in which variables appear in one or more radicands. For example,

$$\sqrt{2x-5} - \sqrt{x-3} = 1$$

is a radical equation. The following principle is used to solve such equations.

The Principle of Powers

For any positive integer n:

If $a = b$ is true, then $a^n = b^n$ is true.

EXAMPLE 3   Solve: $5 + \sqrt{x + 7} = x$.

ALGEBRAIC SOLUTION

We first isolate the radical and then use the principle of powers.

$$5 + \sqrt{x + 7} = x$$

$$\sqrt{x + 7} = x - 5 \qquad \text{Subtracting 5 on both sides}$$

$$\left(\sqrt{x + 7}\right)^2 = (x - 5)^2 \qquad \text{Using the principle of powers; squaring both sides}$$

$$x + 7 = x^2 - 10x + 25$$

$$0 = x^2 - 11x + 18 \qquad \text{Subtracting } x \text{ and } 7$$

$$0 = (x - 9)(x - 2) \qquad \text{Factoring}$$

$$x - 9 = 0 \quad or \quad x - 2 = 0$$

$$x = 9 \quad or \quad x = 2$$

The possible solutions are 9 and 2.

Check: For 9:

$$5 + \sqrt{x + 7} = x$$

$$\begin{array}{c|c} 5 + \sqrt{9 + 7} \;?\; 9 & \\ 5 + \sqrt{16} & \\ 5 + 4 & \\ 9 & 9 \quad \textbf{TRUE} \end{array}$$

For 2:

$$5 + \sqrt{x + 7} = x$$

$$\begin{array}{c|c} 5 + \sqrt{2 + 7} \;?\; 2 & \\ 5 + \sqrt{9} & \\ 5 + 3 & \\ 8 & 2 \quad \textbf{FALSE} \end{array}$$

Since 9 checks but 2 does not, the only solution is 9.

VISUALIZING THE SOLUTION

When we graph $y = 5 + \sqrt{x + 7}$ and $y = x$, we find that the first coordinate of the point of intersection of the graphs is 9. Thus the solution of $5 + \sqrt{x + 7} = x$ is 9.

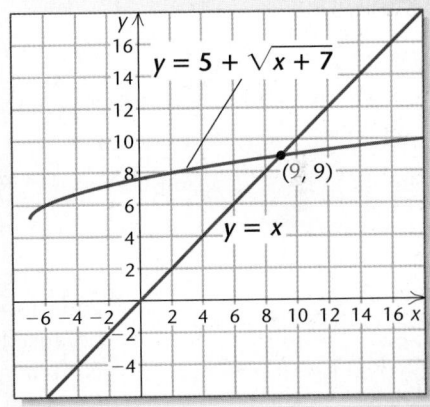

Note that the graphs show that the equation has only one solution.

▶ Now Try Exercise 53.

TECHNOLOGY ···
CONNECTION

We can use a graphing calculator to solve the equation in Example 3. We can graph $y_1 = 5 + \sqrt{x + 7}$ and $y_2 = x$. Using the INTERSECT feature, we see in the window on the left below that the solution is 9.

We can also use the ZERO feature to get this result, as shown in the window on the right. To do so, we first write the equivalent equation $5 + \sqrt{x + 7} - x = 0$. The zero of the function $f(x) = 5 + \sqrt{x + 7} - x$ is 9, so the solution of the original equation is 9.

When we raise both sides of an equation to an even power, the resulting equation can have solutions that the original equation does not. This is because the converse of the principle of powers is not necessarily true. That is, if $a^n = b^n$ is true, we do not know that $a = b$ is true. For example, $(-2)^2 = 2^2$, but $-2 \neq 2$. Thus, as we see in Example 3, it is necessary to check the possible solutions in the original equation when the principle of powers is used to raise both sides of an equation to an even power.

When a radical equation has two radical terms on one side, we isolate one of them and then use the principle of powers. If, after doing so, a radical term remains, we repeat these steps.

STUDY TIP

EXAMPLE 4 Solve: $\sqrt{x - 3} + \sqrt{x + 5} = 4$.

Solution We have

$$\sqrt{x - 3} = 4 - \sqrt{x + 5} \qquad \text{Isolating one radical}$$

$$\left(\sqrt{x - 3}\right)^2 = \left(4 - \sqrt{x + 5}\right)^2 \qquad \begin{array}{l}\text{Using the principle of powers;}\\\text{squaring both sides}\end{array}$$

$$x - 3 = 16 - 8\sqrt{x + 5} + (x + 5)$$

$$x - 3 = 21 - 8\sqrt{x + 5} + x \qquad \text{Collecting like terms}$$

$$-24 = -8\sqrt{x + 5} \qquad \begin{array}{l}\text{Isolating the remaining}\\\text{radical; subtracting } x \text{ and } 21\\\text{on both sides}\end{array}$$

$$3 = \sqrt{x + 5} \qquad \text{Dividing by } -8 \text{ on both sides}$$

$$3^2 = \left(\sqrt{x + 5}\right)^2 \qquad \begin{array}{l}\text{Using the principle of powers;}\\\text{squaring both sides}\end{array}$$

$$9 = x + 5$$

$$4 = x.$$

The number 4 checks and is the solution.

▶ **Now Try Exercise 63.**

ABSOLUTE VALUE

REVIEW SECTION **R.1.**

◆ Equations with Absolute Value

Recall that the absolute value of a number is its distance from 0 on the number line. We use this concept to solve equations with absolute value.

> For $a > 0$ and an algebraic expression X:
>
> $|X| = a$ is equivalent to $X = -a$ or $X = a$.

EXAMPLE 5   Solve each of the following.

a) $|x| = 5$

b) $|x - 3| = 2$

a) ALGEBRAIC SOLUTION

We have

$$|x| = 5$$

$x = -5$ *or* $x = 5$.   Writing an equivalent statement

The solutions are -5 and 5.

VISUALIZING THE SOLUTION

The first coordinates of the points of intersection of the graphs of $y = |x|$ and $y = 5$ are -5 and 5. These are the solutions of the equation $|x| = 5$.

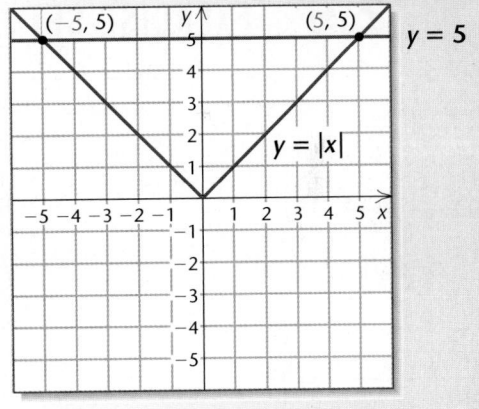

b) $|x - 3| = 2$

$x - 3 = -2$ *or* $x - 3 = 2$ Writing an equivalent statement

$x = 1$ *or* $x = 5$ Adding 3

The solutions are 1 and 5.

▶ Now Try Exercise 89.

When $a = 0$, $|X| = a$ is equivalent to $X = 0$. Note that for $a < 0$, $|X| = a$ has no solution, because the absolute value of an expression is never negative. We can use a graph to illustrate the last statement for a specific value of a. For example, if we let $a = -3$ and graph $y = |x|$ and $y = -3$, we see that the graphs do not intersect, as shown below. Thus the equation $|x| = -3$ has no solution. The solution set is the **empty set,** denoted $\varnothing$.

2.5 EXERCISE SET

Solve.

1. $\dfrac{1}{4} + \dfrac{1}{5} = \dfrac{1}{t}$

2. $\dfrac{1}{3} - \dfrac{5}{6} = \dfrac{1}{x}$

3. $\dfrac{x + 2}{4} - \dfrac{x - 1}{5} = 15$

4. $\dfrac{t + 1}{3} - \dfrac{t - 1}{2} = 1$

5. $\dfrac{1}{2} + \dfrac{2}{x} = \dfrac{1}{3} + \dfrac{3}{x}$

6. $\dfrac{1}{t} + \dfrac{1}{2t} + \dfrac{1}{3t} = 5$

7. $\dfrac{5}{3x + 2} = \dfrac{3}{2x}$

8. $\dfrac{2}{x - 1} = \dfrac{3}{x + 2}$

9. $x + \dfrac{6}{x} = 5$

10. $x - \dfrac{12}{x} = 1$

11. $\dfrac{6}{y + 3} + \dfrac{2}{y} = \dfrac{5y - 3}{y^2 - 9}$

12. $\dfrac{3}{m + 2} + \dfrac{2}{m} = \dfrac{4m - 4}{m^2 - 4}$

13. $\dfrac{2x}{x - 1} = \dfrac{5}{x - 3}$

14. $\dfrac{2x}{x + 7} = \dfrac{5}{x + 1}$

15. $\dfrac{2}{x + 5} + \dfrac{1}{x - 5} = \dfrac{16}{x^2 - 25}$

16. $\dfrac{2}{x^2 - 9} + \dfrac{5}{x - 3} = \dfrac{3}{x + 3}$

17. $\dfrac{3x}{x+2} + \dfrac{6}{x} = \dfrac{12}{x^2 + 2x}$

18. $\dfrac{3y+5}{y^2+5y} + \dfrac{y+4}{y+5} = \dfrac{y+1}{y}$

19. $\dfrac{1}{5x+20} - \dfrac{1}{x^2-16} = \dfrac{3}{x-4}$

20. $\dfrac{1}{4x+12} - \dfrac{1}{x^2-9} = \dfrac{5}{x-3}$

21. $\dfrac{2}{5x+5} - \dfrac{3}{x^2-1} = \dfrac{4}{x-1}$

22. $\dfrac{1}{3x+6} - \dfrac{1}{x^2-4} = \dfrac{3}{x-2}$

23. $\dfrac{8}{x^2-2x+4} = \dfrac{x}{x+2} + \dfrac{24}{x^3+8}$

24. $\dfrac{18}{x^2-3x+9} - \dfrac{x}{x+3} = \dfrac{81}{x^3+27}$

25. $\dfrac{x}{x-4} - \dfrac{4}{x+4} = \dfrac{32}{x^2-16}$

26. $\dfrac{x}{x-1} - \dfrac{1}{x+1} = \dfrac{2}{x^2-1}$

27. $\dfrac{1}{x-6} - \dfrac{1}{x} = \dfrac{6}{x^2-6x}$

28. $\dfrac{1}{x-15} - \dfrac{1}{x} = \dfrac{15}{x^2-15x}$

29. $\sqrt{3x-4} = 1$

30. $\sqrt{4x+1} = 3$

31. $\sqrt{2x-5} = 2$

32. $\sqrt{3x+2} = 6$

33. $\sqrt{7-x} = 2$

34. $\sqrt{5-x} = 1$

35. $\sqrt{1-2x} = 3$

36. $\sqrt{2-7x} = 2$

37. $\sqrt[3]{5x-2} = -3$

38. $\sqrt[3]{2x+1} = -5$

39. $\sqrt[4]{x^2-1} = 1$

40. $\sqrt[5]{3x+4} = 2$

41. $\sqrt{y-1} + 4 = 0$

42. $\sqrt{m+1} - 5 = 8$

43. $\sqrt{b+3} - 2 = 1$

44. $\sqrt{x-4} + 1 = 5$

45. $\sqrt{z+2} + 3 = 4$

46. $\sqrt{y-5} - 2 = 3$

47. $\sqrt{2x+1} - 3 = 3$

48. $\sqrt{3x-1} + 2 = 7$

49. $\sqrt{2-x} - 4 = 6$

50. $\sqrt{5-x} + 2 = 8$

51. $\sqrt[3]{6x+9} + 8 = 5$

52. $\sqrt[5]{2x-3} - 1 = 1$

53. $\sqrt{x+4} + 2 = x$

54. $\sqrt{x+1} + 1 = x$

55. $\sqrt{x-3} + 5 = x$

56. $\sqrt{x+3} - 1 = x$

57. $\sqrt{x+7} = x+1$

58. $\sqrt{6x+7} = x+2$

59. $\sqrt{3x+3} = x+1$

60. $\sqrt{2x+5} = x-5$

61. $\sqrt{5x+1} = x-1$

62. $\sqrt{7x+4} = x+2$

63. $\sqrt{x-3} + \sqrt{x+2} = 5$

64. $\sqrt{x} - \sqrt{x-5} = 1$

65. $\sqrt{3x-5} + \sqrt{2x+3} + 1 = 0$

66. $\sqrt{2m-3} = \sqrt{m+7} - 2$

67. $\sqrt{x} - \sqrt{3x-3} = 1$

68. $\sqrt{2x+1} - \sqrt{x} = 1$

69. $\sqrt{2y-5} - \sqrt{y-3} = 1$

70. $\sqrt{4p+5} + \sqrt{p+5} = 3$

71. $\sqrt{y+4} - \sqrt{y-1} = 1$

72. $\sqrt{y+7} + \sqrt{y+16} = 9$

73. $\sqrt{x + 5} + \sqrt{x + 2} = 3$

74. $\sqrt{6x + 6} = 5 + \sqrt{21 - 4x}$

75. $x^{1/3} = -2$

76. $t^{1/5} = 2$

77. $t^{1/4} = 3$

78. $m^{1/2} = -7$

79. $|x| = 7$

80. $|x| = 4.5$

81. $|x| = -10.7$

82. $|x| = -\frac{3}{5}$

83. $|x - 1| = 4$

84. $|x - 7| = 5$

85. $|3x| = 1$

86. $|5x| = 4$

87. $|x| = 0$

88. $|6x| = 0$

89. $|3x + 2| = 1$

90. $|7x - 4| = 8$

91. $|\frac{1}{2}x - 5| = 17$

92. $|\frac{1}{3}x - 4| = 13$

93. $|x - 1| + 3 = 6$

94. $|x + 2| - 5 = 9$

95. $|x + 3| - 2 = 8$

96. $|x - 4| + 3 = 9$

97. $|3x + 1| - 4 = -1$

98. $|2x - 1| - 5 = -3$

99. $|4x - 3| + 1 = 7$

100. $|5x + 4| + 2 = 5$

101. $12 - |x + 6| = 5$

102. $9 - |x - 2| = 7$

Solve.

103. $\dfrac{P_1 V_1}{T_1} = \dfrac{P_2 V_2}{T_2}$, for T_1
(A chemistry formula for gases)

104. $\dfrac{1}{F} = \dfrac{1}{m} + \dfrac{1}{p}$, for F
(A formula from optics)

105. $\dfrac{1}{R} = \dfrac{1}{R_1} + \dfrac{1}{R_2}$, for R_2
(Resistance)

106. $A = P(1 + i)^2$, for i
(Compound interest)

107. $\dfrac{1}{F} = \dfrac{1}{m} + \dfrac{1}{p}$, for p
(A formula from optics)

Technology Connection

108. Use a graphing calculator to do Exercises 4, 24, 58, 70, and 94.

109. Use a graphing calculator to do Exercises 5, 23, 67, 69, and 93.

Collaborative Discussion and Writing

110. Explain why it is necessary to check the possible solutions of a rational equation.

111. Explain in your own words why it is necessary to check the possible solutions when the principle of powers is used to solve an equation.

Skill Maintenance

Find the zero of the function.

112. $f(x) = -3x + 9$

113. $f(x) = 15 - 2x$

114. *Big Sites.* Together, the Mall of America in Minnesota and the Disneyland theme park in California occupy 181 acres of land. The Mall of America occupies 11 acres more than Disneyland. (*Sources:* Mall of America; Disneyland) How much land does each occupy?

115. *Sleep-Starved Americans.* Nearly half of Americans say they do not get enough sleep. Many turn to sleeping pills, filling 42 million prescriptions for these medications in 2005. This amount was 60% more than the number of prescriptions filled for sleeping pills in 2000. (*Sources:* "NBC Today Show"/Zogby International poll; IMS Health) How many prescriptions for sleeping pills were filled in 2000?

Synthesis

Solve.

116. $\dfrac{x + 3}{x + 2} - \dfrac{x + 4}{x + 3} = \dfrac{x + 5}{x + 4} - \dfrac{x + 6}{x + 5}$

117. $(x - 3)^{2/3} = 2$

118. $\sqrt{15 + \sqrt{2x + 80}} = 5$

119. $\sqrt{x + 5} + 1 = \dfrac{6}{\sqrt{x + 5}}$

120. $x^{2/3} = x$

2.6

Solving Linear Inequalities

- ◆ Solve linear inequalities.
- ◆ Solve compound inequalities.
- ◆ Solve inequalities with absolute value.
- ◆ Solve applied problems using inequalities.

An **inequality** is a sentence with $<$, $>$, $\leq$, or $\geq$ as its verb. An example is $3x - 5 < 6 - 2x$. To **solve** an inequality is to find all values of the variable that make the inequality true. Each of these numbers is a **solution** of the inequality, and the set of all such solutions is its **solution set**. Inequalities that have the same solution set are called **equivalent inequalities.**

◆ Linear Inequalities

The principles for solving inequalities are similar to those for solving equations.

> #### *Principles for Solving Inequalities*
> For any real numbers a, b, and c:
> ***The Addition Principle for Inequalities:*** If $a < b$ is true, then $a + c < b + c$ is true.
> ***The Multiplication Principle for Inequalities:*** If $a < b$ and $c > 0$ are true, then $ac < bc$ is true. If $a < b$ and $c < 0$ are true, then $ac > bc$ is true.
> Similar statements hold for $a \leq b$.

> When both sides of an inequality are multiplied by a negative number, we must reverse the inequality sign.

First-degree inequalities with one variable, like those in Example 1 below, are **linear inequalities.**

EXAMPLE 1   Solve each of the following. Then graph the solution set.

a) $3x - 5 < 6 - 2x$ **b)** $13 - 7x \geq 10x - 4$

Solution

a) $3x - 5 < 6 - 2x$

$5x - 5 < 6$	Using the addition principle for inequalities; adding $2x$
$5x < 11$	Using the addition principle for inequalities; adding 5
$x < \frac{11}{5}$	Using the multiplication principle for inequalities; multiplying by $\frac{1}{5}$ or dividing by 5

To check Example 1(a) graphically, we graph $y_1 = 3x - 5$ and $y_2 = 6 - 2x$. The graph shows that for $x < 2.2$, or $x < \frac{11}{5}$, the graph of y_1 lies below the graph of y_2, or $y_1 < y_2$.

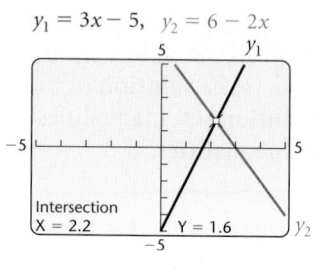

$y_1 = 3x - 5, \quad y_2 = 6 - 2x$

Any number less than $\frac{11}{5}$ is a solution. The solution set is $\left\{x \mid x < \frac{11}{5}\right\}$, or $\left(-\infty, \frac{11}{5}\right)$. The graph of the solution set is shown below.

b) $13 - 7x \geq 10x - 4$

$\quad 13 - 17x \geq -4$ Subtracting $10x$

$\quad\quad -17x \geq -17$ Subtracting 13

$\quad\quad\quad\quad x \leq 1$ Dividing by -17 and reversing the inequality sign

The solution set is $\{x \mid x \leq 1\}$, or $(-\infty, 1]$. The graph of the solution set is shown below.

> Now Try Exercise 1.

✦ Compound Inequalities

When two inequalities are joined by the word *and* or the word *or*, a **compound inequality** is formed. A compound inequality like

$$-3 < 2x + 5 \quad and \quad 2x + 5 \leq 7$$

is called a **conjunction,** because it uses the word *and*. The sentence $-3 < 2x + 5 \leq 7$ is an abbreviation for the preceding conjunction.

Compound inequalities can be solved using the addition and multiplication principles for inequalities.

EXAMPLE 2   Solve $-3 < 2x + 5 \leq 7$. Then graph the solution set.

Solution   We have

$$-3 < 2x + 5 \leq 7$$

$$-8 < 2x \leq 2 \quad \text{Subtracting 5}$$

$$-4 < x \leq 1. \quad \text{Dividing by 2}$$

The solution set is $\{x \mid -4 < x \leq 1\}$, or $(-4, 1]$. The graph of the solution set is shown below.

> Now Try Exercise 11.

TECHNOLOGY CONNECTION

We can perform a partial check of the solution of Example 2 graphically using operations from the TEST menu of a graphing calculator. We graph $y_1 = (-3 < 2x + 5)$ *and* $(2x + 5 \le 7)$ in DOT mode. The calculator graphs a segment 1 unit above the x-axis for the values of x for which this expression for y is true. Here the number 1 corresponds to "true."

$y = (-3 < 2x + 5) \text{ and } (2x + 5 \le 7)$

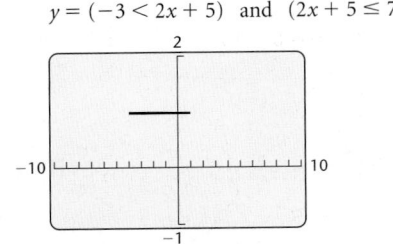

The segment extends from -4 to 1, confirming that all x-values from -4 to 1 are in the solution set. The algebraic solution indicates that the endpoint 1 is also in the solution set.

A compound inequality like $2x - 5 \le -7$ *or* $2x - 5 > 1$ is called a **disjunction,** because it contains the word *or.* Unlike some conjunctions, it cannot be abbreviated; that is, it cannot be written without the word *or.*

EXAMPLE 3 Solve $2x - 5 \le -7$ *or* $2x - 5 > 1$. Then graph the solution set.

Solution We have

$$2x - 5 \le -7 \quad or \quad 2x - 5 > 1$$
$$2x \le -2 \quad or \quad 2x > 6 \qquad \text{Adding 5}$$
$$x \le -1 \quad or \quad x > 3. \qquad \text{Dividing by 2}$$

The solution set is $\{x \mid x \le -1 \text{ or } x > 3\}$. We can also write the solution using interval notation and the symbol $\cup$ for the **union** or inclusion of both sets: $(-\infty, -1] \cup (3, \infty)$. The graph of the solution set is shown below.

> **Now Try Exercise 23.**

TECHNOLOGY CONNECTION

To check Example 3 graphically, we graph $y_1 = 2x - 5$, $y_2 = -7$, and $y_3 = 1$. Note that for $\{x \mid x \le -1 \text{ or } x > 3\}$, $y_1 \le y_2$ *or* $y_1 > y_3$.

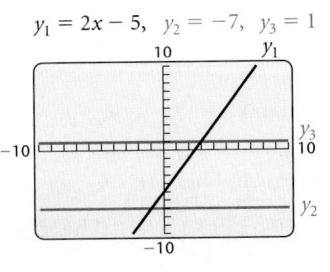

$y_1 = 2x - 5, \ y_2 = -7, \ y_3 = 1$

✦ Inequalities with Absolute Value

Inequalities sometimes contain absolute-value notation. The following properties are used to solve them.

> For $a > 0$ and an algebraic expression X:
>
> $|X| < a$ is equivalent to $-a < X < a$.
>
> $|X| > a$ is equivalent to $X < -a$ or $X > a$.
>
> Similar statements hold for $|X| \leq a$ and $|X| \geq a$.

For example,

$$|x| < 3 \text{ is equivalent to } -3 < x < 3;$$
$$|y| \geq 1 \text{ is equivalent to } y \leq -1 \text{ or } y \geq 1; \text{ and}$$
$$|2x + 3| \leq 4 \text{ is equivalent to } -4 \leq 2x + 3 \leq 4.$$

EXAMPLE 4   Solve each of the following. Then graph the solution set.

a) $|3x + 2| < 5$ **b)** $|5 - 2x| \geq 1$

Solution

a) $|3x + 2| < 5$

$$\begin{array}{ll} -5 < 3x + 2 < 5 & \text{Writing an equivalent inequality} \\ -7 < 3x < 3 & \text{Subtracting 2} \\ -\frac{7}{3} < x < 1 & \text{Dividing by 3} \end{array}$$

The solution set is $\left\{x \mid -\frac{7}{3} < x < 1\right\}$, or $\left(-\frac{7}{3}, 1\right)$. The graph of the solution set is shown below.

$$-\frac{7}{3}$$

```
       (————————)
 -5 -4 -3 -2 -1  0  1  2  3  4  5
```

b) $|5 - 2x| \geq 1$

$$\begin{array}{lll} 5 - 2x \leq -1 & or & 5 - 2x \geq 1 \\ -2x \leq -6 & or & -2x \geq -4 \\ x \geq 3 & or & x \leq 2 \end{array}$$

Writing an equivalent inequality

Subtracting 5

Dividing by -2 and reversing the inequality signs

The solution set is $\{x \mid x \leq 2 \text{ or } x \geq 3\}$, or $(-\infty, 2] \cup [3, \infty)$. The graph of the solution set is shown below.

```
                  ]  [
 -5 -4 -3 -2 -1  0  1  2  3  4  5
```

▶ Now Try Exercise 43.

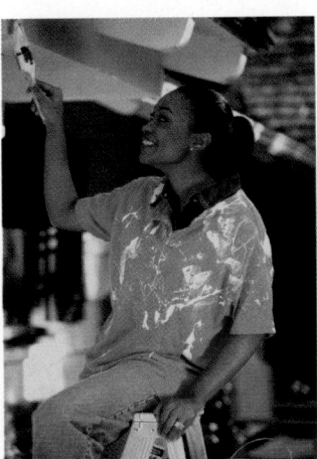

◆ An Application

EXAMPLE 5 *Income Plans.* For her house-painting job, Erica can be paid in one of two ways:

    Plan A: $250 plus $10 per hour;

    Plan B: $20 per hour.

Suppose that a job takes n hours. For what values of n is plan B better for Erica?

Solution

1. **Familiarize.** Suppose that a job takes 20 hr. Then $n = 20$, and under plan A, Erica would earn $250 + $10 \cdot 20$, or $250 + $200, or $450. Her earnings under plan B would be $20 \cdot 20$, or $400. This shows that plan A is better for Erica if a job takes 20 hr. Similarly, if a job takes 30 hr, then $n = 30$, and under plan A, Erica would earn $250 + $10 \cdot 30$, or $250 + $300, or $550. Under plan B, she would earn $20 \cdot 30$, or $600, so plan B is better in this case. To determine *all* values of n for which plan B is better for Erica, we solve an inequality. Our work in this step helps us write the inequality.

2. **Translate.** We translate to an inequality:

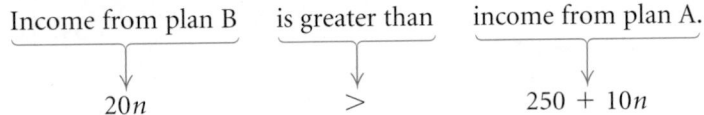

$$20n \qquad > \qquad 250 + 10n$$

3. **Carry out.** We solve the inequality:

    $20n > 250 + 10n$

    $10n > 250$ Subtracting $10n$ on both sides

      $n > 25.$ Dividing by 10 on both sides

4. **Check.** For $n = 25$, the income from plan A is $250 + $10 \cdot 25$, or $250 + $250, or $500, and the income from plan B is $20 \cdot 25$, or $500. This shows that for a job that takes 25 hr to complete, the income is the same under either plan. In the *Familiarize* step, we saw that plan B pays more for a 30-hr job. Since $30 > 25$, this provides a partial check of the result. We cannot check all values of n.

5. **State.** For values of n greater than 25 hr, plan B is better for Erica.

▶ Now Try Exercise 61.

2.6 EXERCISE SET

Solve and graph the solution set.

1. $x + 6 < 5x - 6$

2. $3 - x < 4x + 7$

3. $3x - 3 + 2x \geq 1 - 7x - 9$

4. $5y - 5 + y \leq 2 - 6y - 8$

5. $14 - 5y \leq 8y - 8$

6. $8x - 7 < 6x + 3$

7. $-\frac{3}{4}x \geq -\frac{5}{8} + \frac{2}{3}x$

8. $-\frac{5}{6}x \leq \frac{3}{4} + \frac{8}{3}x$

9. $4x(x - 2) < 2(2x - 1)(x - 3)$

10. $(x + 1)(x + 2) > x(x + 1)$

Solve and write interval notation for the solution set. Then graph the solution set.

11. $-2 \leq x + 1 < 4$

12. $-3 < x + 2 \leq 5$

13. $5 \leq x - 3 \leq 7$

14. $-1 < x - 4 < 7$

15. $-3 \leq x + 4 \leq 3$

16. $-5 < x + 2 < 15$

17. $-2 < 2x + 1 < 5$

18. $-3 \leq 5x + 1 \leq 3$

19. $-4 \leq 6 - 2x < 4$

20. $-3 < 1 - 2x \leq 3$

21. $-5 < \frac{1}{2}(3x + 1) < 7$

22. $\frac{2}{3} \leq -\frac{4}{5}(x - 3) < 1$

23. $3x \leq -6 \text{ or } x - 1 > 0$

24. $2x < 8 \text{ or } x + 3 \geq 10$

25. $2x + 3 \leq -4 \text{ or } 2x + 3 \geq 4$

26. $3x - 1 < -5 \text{ or } 3x - 1 > 5$

27. $2x - 20 < -0.8 \text{ or } 2x - 20 > 0.8$

28. $5x + 11 \leq -4 \text{ or } 5x + 11 \geq 4$

29. $x + 14 \leq -\frac{1}{4} \text{ or } x + 14 \geq \frac{1}{4}$

30. $x - 9 < -\frac{1}{2} \text{ or } x - 9 > \frac{1}{2}$

31. $|x| < 7$

32. $|x| \leq 4.5$

33. $|x| \geq 4.5$

34. $|x| > 7$

35. $|x + 8| < 9$

36. $|x + 6| \leq 10$

37. $|x + 8| \geq 9$

38. $|x + 6| > 10$

39. $\left|x - \frac{1}{4}\right| < \frac{1}{2}$

40. $|x - 0.5| \leq 0.2$

41. $|3x| < 1$

42. $|5x| \leq 4$

43. $|2x + 3| \leq 9$

44. $|3x + 4| < 13$

45. $|x - 5| > 0.1$

46. $|x - 7| \geq 0.4$

47. $|6 - 4x| \leq 8$

48. $|5 - 2x| > 10$

49. $\left|x + \frac{2}{3}\right| \leq \frac{5}{3}$

50. $\left|x + \frac{3}{4}\right| < \frac{1}{4}$

51. $\left|\dfrac{2x + 1}{3}\right| > 5$

52. $\left|\dfrac{2x - 1}{3}\right| \geq \dfrac{5}{6}$

53. $|2x - 4| < -5$

54. $|3x + 5| < 0$

55. *Cost of Business on the Internet.* The equation $y = 12.7x + 15.2$ estimates the amount that businesses will spend, in billions of dollars, on Internet software to conduct transactions via the Web, where x is the number of years after 2002 (*Source*: IDC). For what years will the spending be more than $66 billion?

56. *Digital Hubs.* The equation $y = 5x + 5$ estimates the number of U.S. households, in millions, expected to install devices that receive and manage broadband TV and Internet content to the home, where x is the number of years after 2002 (*Source*: Forrester Research). For what years are there at least 20 million homes with these devices?

57. *Moving Costs.* Acme Movers charges $100 plus $30 per hour to move a household across town. Hank's Movers charges $55 per hour. For what lengths of time does it cost less to hire Hank's Movers?

58. *Investment Income.* Gina plans to invest $12,000, part at 4% simple interest and the rest at 6% simple interest. What is the most she can invest at 4% and still be guaranteed at least $650 in interest per year?

59. *Investment Income.* Kyle plans to invest $7500, part at 4% simple interest and the rest at 5% simple interest. What is the most that he can invest at 4% and still be guaranteed at least $325 in interest per year?

60. *Checking-Account Plans.* The Addison Bank offers two checking-account plans. The Smart Checking plan charges 20¢ per check whereas the Consumer Checking plan costs $6 per month plus 5¢ per check. For what number of checks per month will the Smart Checking plan cost less?

61. *Checking-Account Plans.* Parson's Bank offers two checking-account plans. The No Frills plan charges 35¢ per check whereas the Simple Checking plan costs $5 per month plus 10¢ per check. For what number of checks per month will the Simple Checking plan cost less?

62. *Income Plans.* Karen can be paid in one of two ways for selling insurance policies:

Plan A: A salary of $750 per month, plus a commission of 10% of sales;

Plan B: A salary of $1000 per month, plus a commission of 8% of sales in excess of $2000.

For what amount of monthly sales is plan A better than plan B if we can assume that sales are always more than $2000?

63. *Income Plans.* Curt can be paid in one of two ways for the furniture he sells:

Plan A: A salary of $900 per month, plus a commission of 10% of sales;

Plan B: A salary of $1200 per month, plus a commission of 15% of sales in excess of $8000.

For what amount of monthly sales is plan B better than plan A if we can assume that Curt's sales are always more than $8000?

64. *Income Plans.* Lorenzo can be paid in one of two ways for refinishing a hardwood floor:

Plan A: $200 plus $12 per hour;
Plan B: $20 per hour.

Suppose a job takes n hours to complete. For what values of n is plan A better for Lorenzo?

Technology Connection

65. Use a graphing calculator to check your answers to Exercises 9, 21, and 41.

66. Use a graphing calculator to check your answers to Exercises 10, 22, and 42.

Collaborative Discussion and Writing

67. Explain why $|x| < p$ has no solution for $p \leq 0$.

68. Explain why all real numbers are solutions of $|x| > p$, for $p < 0$.

Skill Maintenance

In each of Exercises 69–76, fill in the blank with the correct term. Some of the given choices will not be used.

distance formula
midpoint formula
function
relation
x-intercept
y-intercept
perpendicular
parallel
horizontal lines
vertical lines
symmetric with respect to the x-axis
symmetric with respect to the y-axis
symmetric with respect to the origin
increasing
decreasing
constant

69. A(n) _____ is a point $(0, b)$.

70. The _____ is
$d = \sqrt{(x_2 - x_1)^2 + (y_2 - y_1)^2}$.

71. A(n) _____ is a correspondence such that each member of the domain corresponds to at least one member of the range.

72. A(n) _____ is a correspondence such that each member of the domain corresponds to exactly one member of the range.

73. _____ are given by equations of the type $y = b$, or $f(x) = b$.

74. Nonvertical lines are _____ if and only if they have the same slope and different y-intercepts.

75. A function f is said to be _____ on an open interval I if, for all a and b in that interval, $a < b$ implies $f(a) > f(b)$.

76. For an equation $y = f(x)$, if replacing x with $-x$ produces an equivalent equation, then the graph is _____ .

Synthesis

Solve.

77. $2x \leq 5 - 7x < 7 + x$

78. $x \leq 3x - 2 \leq 2 - x$

79. $|3x - 1| > 5x - 2$

80. $|x + 2| \leq |x - 5|$

81. $|p - 4| + |p + 4| < 8$

82. $|x| + |x + 1| < 10$

83. $|x - 3| + |2x + 5| > 6$

CHAPTER 2 SUMMARY AND REVIEW

Important Properties and Formulas

Equation-Solving Principles

The Addition Principle:

If $a = b$ is true, then $a + c = b + c$ is true.

The Multiplication Principle:

If $a = b$ is true, then $ac = bc$ is true.

The Principle of Zero Products:

If $ab = 0$ is true, then $a = 0$ or $b = 0$,

and

if $a = 0$ or $b = 0$, then $ab = 0$.

The Principle of Square Roots:

If $x^2 = k$, then $x = \sqrt{k}$ or $x = -\sqrt{k}$.

The Principle of Powers:

For any positive integer n, if $a = b$ is true, then $a^n = b^n$ is true.

Five Steps for Problem Solving

1. Familiarize.
2. Translate.
3. Carry out.
4. Check.
5. State.

Zero of a Function:

An input c of a function f is a zero of f if $f(c) = 0$.

Complex Number:	$a + bi$, a, b real, $i^2 = -1$
Imaginary Number:	$a + bi$, $b \neq 0$
Complex Conjugates:	$a + bi$, $a - bi$

Quadratic Equation:

$$ax^2 + bx + c = 0, \quad a \neq 0, \quad a, b, c \text{ real}$$

Quadratic Function:

$$f(x) = ax^2 + bx + c, \quad a \neq 0, \quad a, b, c \text{ real}$$

Quadratic Formula:

For $ax^2 + bx + c = 0$, $a \neq 0$,

$$x = \frac{-b \pm \sqrt{b^2 - 4ac}}{2a}.$$

Principles for Solving Inequalities

The Addition Principle for Inequalities:

If $a < b$ is true, then $a + c < b + c$ is true.

The Multiplication Principle for Inequalities:

If $a < b$ and $c > 0$ are true, then $ac < bc$ is true.

If $a < b$ and $c < 0$ are true, then $ac > bc$ is true.

Similar statements hold for $\leq$.

Equations and Inequalities with Absolute Value

For $a > 0$,

$$|X| = a \longrightarrow X = -a \text{ or } X = a$$
$$|X| < a \longrightarrow -a < X < a$$
$$|X| > a \longrightarrow X < -a \text{ or } X > a$$

REVIEW EXERCISES

Determine whether the statement is true or false.

1. We find the zeros of a function f by evaluating $f(0)$.   [2.1]

2. The zeros of a function f are the first coordinates of the x-intercepts of the graph of $y = f(x)$. [2.1]

3. We can use the quadratic formula to solve any quadratic equation.   [2.3]

4. The function $f(x) = -3(x + 4)^2 - 1$ has a maximum value.   [2.4]

5. For any positive integer n, if $a^n = b^n$ is true, then $a = b$ is true.   [2.5]

6. If $a < b$ is true and $c \neq 0$, then $ac < bc$ is true. [2.6]

Solve.

7. $4y - 5 = 1$ [2.1]

8. $3x - 4 = 5x + 8$ [2.1]

9. $5(3x + 1) = 2(x - 4)$ [2.1]

10. $2(n - 3) = 3(n + 5)$ [2.1]

11. $(2y + 5)(3y - 1) = 0$ [2.3]

12. $x^2 + 4x - 5 = 0$ [2.3]

13. $3x^2 + 2x = 8$ [2.3]

14. $5x^2 = 15$ [2.3]

15. $x^2 - 10 = 0$ [2.3]

Find the zero(s) of the function.

16. $f(x) = 6x - 18$ [2.1]   **17.** $f(x) = x - 4$ [2.1]

18. $f(x) = 2 - 10x$ [2.1]   **19.** $f(x) = 8 - 2x$ [2.1]

20. $f(x) = x^2 - 2x + 1$ [2.3]

21. $f(x) = x^2 + 2x - 15$ [2.3]

22. $f(x) = 2x^2 - x - 5$ [2.3]

23. $f(x) = 3x^2 + 2x - 3$ [2.3]

Solve.   [2.5]

24. $\dfrac{5}{2x + 3} + \dfrac{1}{x - 6} = 0$

25. $\dfrac{3}{8x + 1} + \dfrac{8}{2x + 5} = 1$

26. $\sqrt{5x + 1} - 1 = \sqrt{3x}$

27. $\sqrt{x - 1} - \sqrt{x - 4} = 1$

28. $|x - 4| = 3$ **29.** $|2y + 7| = 9$

Solve and write interval notation for the solution set. Then graph the solution set.   [2.6]

30. $-3 \leq 3x + 1 \leq 5$

31. $-2 < 5x - 4 \leq 6$

32. $2x < -1$ or $x + 3 > 0$

33. $3x + 7 \leq 2$ or $2x + 3 \geq 5$

34. $|6x - 1| < 5$ **35.** $|x + 4| \geq 2$

36. Solve $V = lwh$ for h.   [2.1]

37. Solve $M = n + 0.3s$ for s.   [2.1]

38. Solve $v = \sqrt{2gh}$ for h.   [2.5]

39. Solve $\dfrac{1}{a} + \dfrac{1}{b} = \dfrac{1}{t}$ for t.   [2.5]

Express in terms of i.   [2.2]

40. $-\sqrt{-40}$ **41.** $\sqrt{-12} \cdot \sqrt{-20}$

42. $\dfrac{\sqrt{-49}}{-\sqrt{-64}}$

Simplify each of the following. Write the answer in the form $a + bi$, where a and b are real numbers.   [2.2]

43. $(6 + 2i)(-4 - 3i)$ **44.** $\dfrac{2 - 3i}{1 - 3i}$

45. $(3 - 5i) - (2 - i)$

46. $(6 + 2i) + (-4 - 3i)$

47. i^{23} **48.** $(-3i)^{28}$

Solve by completing the square to obtain exact solutions. Show your work.   [2.3]

49. $x^2 - 3x = 18$ **50.** $3x^2 - 12x - 6 = 0$

Solve. Give exact solutions.   [2.3]

51. $3x^2 + 10x = 8$ **52.** $r^2 - 2r + 10 = 0$

53. $x^2 = 10 + 3x$ **54.** $x = 2\sqrt{x} - 1$

55. $y^4 - 3y^2 + 1 = 0$

56. $(x^2 - 1)^2 - (x^2 - 1) - 2 = 0$

57. $(p - 3)(3p + 2)(p + 2) = 0$

58. $x^3 + 5x^2 - 4x - 20 = 0$

In Exercises 59 and 60, complete the square to:

a) *find the vertex;*

b) *find the axis of symmetry;*

c) *determine whether there is a maximum or minimum value and find that value;*

d) *find the range;*

e) *find the intervals on which the function is increasing and find the intervals on which the function is decreasing; and*

f) *graph the function.*

59. $f(x) = -4x^2 + 3x - 1$ [2.4]

60. $f(x) = 5x^2 - 10x + 3$ [2.4]

In Exercises 61–64, match the equation with one of the figures (a)–(d), which follow.   [2.4]

a)

b)

c)

d)

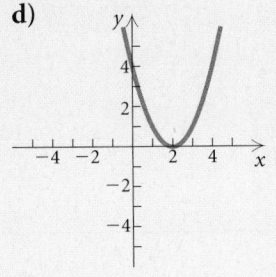

61. $y = (x - 2)^2$

62. $y = (x + 3)^2 - 4$

63. $y = -2(x + 3)^2 + 4$

64. $y = -\frac{1}{2}(x - 2)^2 + 5$

65. *Legs of a Right Triangle.*   The hypotenuse of a right triangle is 50 ft. One leg is 10 ft longer than the other. What are the lengths of the legs?   [2.3]

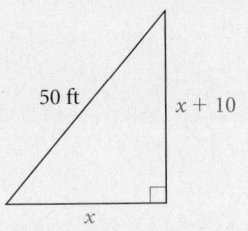

66. *Motion.*   A Riverboat Cruise Line boat travels 8 mi upstream and 8 mi downstream. The total time for both parts of the trip is 3 hr. The speed of the stream is 2 mph. What is the speed of the boat in still water?   [2.1], [2.3], [2.5]

67. *Motion.*   Two freight trains leave the same city at right angles. The first train travels at a speed of 60 km/h. In 1 hr, the trains are 100 km apart. How fast is the second train traveling?   [2.3]

68. *Sidewalk Width.*   A 60-ft by 80-ft parking lot is torn up to install a sidewalk of uniform width around its perimeter. The new area of the parking lot is two-thirds of the old area. How wide is the sidewalk?   [2.3]

69. *Maximizing Volume.*   The Berniers have 24 ft of flexible fencing with which to build a rectangular "toy corral." If the fencing is 2 ft high, what dimensions should the corral have in order to maximize its volume?   [2.4]

70. *Dimensions of a Box.*   An open box is made from a 10-cm by 20-cm piece of aluminum by cutting a square from each corner and folding up the edges. The area of the resulting base is 90 cm^2. What is the length of the sides of the squares?   [2.3]

71. *Faculty at Two-Year Colleges.*   The equation $y = 6x + 121$ estimates the number of faculty members at two-year colleges, in thousands, where x is the number of years after 1970 (*Source*: U.S. National Center for Education Statistics). For what years are there more than 325 thousand faculty members?   [2.6]

72. *Temperature Conversion.* The formula $C = \frac{5}{9}(F - 32)$ can be used to convert Fahrenheit temperatures F to Celsius temperatures C. For what Fahrenheit temperatures is the Celsius temperature lower than 45°C? [2.6]

73. Find the zeros of $f(x) = 2x^2 - 5x + 1$. [2.1]

A. $\dfrac{5 \pm \sqrt{17}}{2}$ B. $\dfrac{5 \pm \sqrt{17}}{4}$

C. $\dfrac{5 \pm \sqrt{33}}{4}$ D. $\dfrac{-5 \pm \sqrt{17}}{4}$

74. Solve: $\sqrt{4x + 1} + \sqrt{2x} = 1$. [2.5]

   A. There are two solutions.
   B. There is only one solution. It is less than 1.
   C. There is only one solution. It is greater than 1.
   D. There is no solution.

Technology Connection

Use a graphing calculator to do each of the following.

75. Exercises 8, 12, 24, 26, and 28

76. Exercises 7, 13, 25, 27, and 29

77. Exercises 16 and 20

78. Exercises 19 and 21

Collaborative Discussion and Writing

79. As the first step in solving

$$3x - 1 = 8,$$

Stella multiplies by $\frac{1}{3}$ on both sides. What advice would you give her about the procedure for solving equations?

80. If the graphs of

$$f(x) = a_1(x - h_1)^2 + k_1$$

and

$$g(x) = a_2(x - h_2)^2 + k_2$$

have the same shape, what, if anything, can you conclude about the a's, the h's, and the k's? Explain your answer.

Synthesis

Solve.

81. $\sqrt{\sqrt{\sqrt{\sqrt{x}}}} = 2$ [2.5]

82. $(x - 1)^{2/3} = 4$ [2.5]

83. $(t - 4)^{4/5} = 3$ [2.5]

84. $\sqrt{x + 2} + \sqrt[4]{x + 2} - 2 = 0$ [2.3]

85. $(2y - 2)^2 + y - 1 = 5$ [2.3]

86. Find b such that $f(x) = -3x^2 + bx - 1$ has a maximum value of 2. [2.4]

87. At the beginning of the year, $3500 was deposited in a savings account. One year later, $4000 was deposited in another account. The interest rate was the same for both accounts. At the end of the second year, there was a total of $8518.35 in the accounts. What was the annual interest rate? [2.3]

CHAPTER 2 TEST

Solve. Find exact solutions.

1. $6x + 7 = 1$

2. $3y - 4 = 5y + 6$

3. $2(4x + 1) = 8 - 3(x - 5)$

4. $(2x - 1)(x + 5) = 0$

5. $6x^2 - 36 = 0$

6. $x^2 + 4 = 0$

7. $x^2 - 2x - 3 = 0$

8. $x^2 - 5x + 3 = 0$

9. $2t^2 - 3t + 4 = 0$

10. $x + 5\sqrt{x} - 36 = 0$

11. $\dfrac{3}{3x + 4} + \dfrac{2}{x - 1} = 2$

12. $\sqrt{x + 4} - 2 = 1$

13. $\sqrt{x + 4} - \sqrt{x - 4} = 2$

14. $|4y - 3| = 5$

Solve and write interval notation for the solution set. Then graph the solution set.

15. $-7 < 2x + 3 < 9$

16. $2x - 1 \le 3 \text{ or } 5x + 6 \ge 26$

17. $|x + 3| \le 4$

18. $|x + 5| > 2$

19. Solve $V = \frac{2}{3}\pi r^2 h$ for h.

20. Solve $R = \sqrt{3np}$ for n.

21. Solve $x^2 + 4x = 1$ by completing the square. Find the exact solutions. Show your work.

22. *Parking-Lot Dimensions.* The parking lot behind Kai's Kafé has a perimeter of 210 m. The width is three-fourths of the length. What are the dimensions of the parking lot?

23. *River Current.* Deke's boat travels 12 km/h in still water. Deke travels 45 km downstream and then returns 45 km upstream in a total time of 8 hr. Find the speed of the current.

24. *Pricing.* Jessie's Juice Bar prices its bottled juices by raising the wholesale price 50% and then adding 25¢. What is the wholesale price of a bottle of juice that sells for $2.95?

Express in terms of i.

25. $\sqrt{-43}$

26. $-\sqrt{-25}$

Simplify.

27. $(5 - 2i) - (2 + 3i)$

28. $(3 + 4i)(2 - i)$

29. $\dfrac{1 - i}{6 + 2i}$

30. i^{33}

Find the zero(s) of the function.

31. $f(x) = 3x + 9$

32. $f(x) = 4x^2 - 11x - 3$

33. $f(x) = 2x^2 - x - 7$

34. For the graph of the function
$$f(x) = -x^2 + 2x + 8:$$
a) Find the vertex.
b) Find the axis of symmetry.
c) State whether there is a maximum or minimum value and find that value.
d) Find the range.
e) Find the intervals on which the function is increasing and find the intervals on which the function is decreasing.
f) Graph the function.

35. *Maximizing Area.* A homeowner wants to fence a rectangular play yard using 80 ft of fencing. The side of the house will be used as one side of the rectangle. Find the dimensions for which the area is a maximum.

36. *Moving Costs.* Morgan Movers charges $90 plus $25 per hour to move households across town. McKinley Movers charges $40 per hour for crosstown moves. For what lengths of time does it cost less to hire Morgan Movers?

Synthesis

37. Find a such that $f(x) = ax^2 - 4x + 3$ has a maximum value of 12.

Polynomial and Rational Functions

APPLICATION

The combined length of all U.S.-owned operating railroad tracks, excluding yard track, sidings, and parallel tracks, has decreased since World War I (*Source*: Association of American Railroads). The data, in miles, over years 1830 to 2003 are modeled by the quartic function

$$f(x) = 0.0045529413x^4 - 1.717853698x^3 + 185.5854163x^2 - 3481.580759x + 8715.877925,$$

where x is the number of years since 1830. Find the number of miles of operating railroad track in the United States in 1925, in 1959, and in 1992.

This problem appears as Exercise 50 in Section 3.1.

3.1   Polynomial Functions and Models

◆ Determine the behavior of the graph of a polynomial function using the leading-term test.

◆ Factor polynomial functions and find the zeros and their multiplicities.

◆ Solve applied problems using polynomial models.

There are many different kinds of functions. The constant, linear, and quadratic functions that we studied in Chapters 1 and 2 are part of a larger group of functions called *polynomial functions.*

> ### Polynomial Function
>
> A **polynomial function** P is given by
>
> $$P(x) = a_n x^n + a_{n-1} x^{n-1} + a_{n-2} x^{n-2} + \cdots + a_1 x + a_0,$$
>
> where the coefficients $a_n, a_{n-1}, \ldots, a_1, a_0$ are real numbers and the exponents are whole numbers.

The first nonzero coefficient, a_n, is called the **leading coefficient.** The term $a_n x^n$ is called the **leading term.** The **degree** of the polynomial function is n. Some examples of polynomial functions are as follows.

POLYNOMIAL FUNCTION	EXAMPLE	DEGREE	LEADING TERM	LEADING COEFFICIENT
Constant	$f(x) = 3 \quad (f(x) = 3 = 3x^0)$	0	3	3
Linear	$f(x) = \frac{2}{3}x + 5 \quad \left(f(x) = \frac{2}{3}x + 5 = \frac{2}{3}x^1 + 5\right)$	1	$\frac{2}{3}x$	$\frac{2}{3}$
Quadratic	$f(x) = 4x^2 - x + 3$	2	$4x^2$	4
Cubic	$f(x) = x^3 + 2x^2 + x - 5$	3	x^3	1
Quartic	$f(x) = -x^4 - 1.1x^3 + 0.3x^2 - 2.8x - 1.7$	4	$-x^4$	-1

The function $f(x) = 0$ can be described in many ways:

$$f(x) = 0 = 0x^2 = 0x^{15} = 0x^{48},$$

and so on. For this reason, we say that the constant function $f(x) = 0$ has no degree.

From our study of functions in Chapters 1 and 2, we know how to find or at least estimate many characteristics of a polynomial function. Let's consider two examples for review.

Quadratic Function

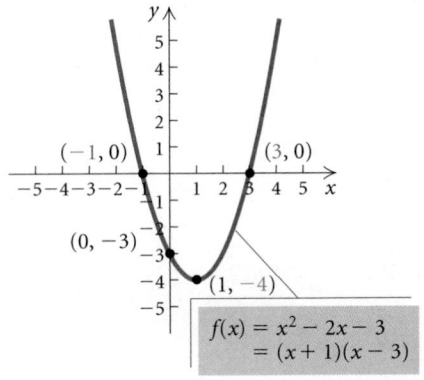

Function: $f(x) = x^2 - 2x - 3$
$\qquad = (x + 1)(x - 3)$

Zeros: $-1, 3$

x-intercepts: $(-1, 0), (3, 0)$

y-intercept: $(0, -3)$

Minimum: -4 at $x = 1$

Maximum: None

Domain: All real numbers, $(-\infty, \infty)$

Range: $[-4, \infty)$

Cubic Function

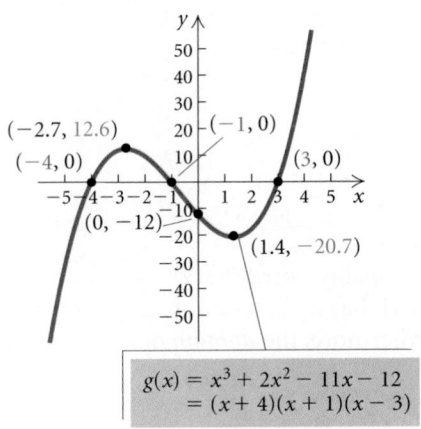

Function: $g(x) = x^3 + 2x^2 - 11x - 12$
$\qquad = (x + 4)(x + 1)(x - 3)$

Zeros: $-4, -1, 3$

x-intercepts: $(-4, 0), (-1, 0), (3, 0)$

y-intercept: $(0, -12)$

Relative minimum: -20.7 at $x = 1.4$

Relative maximum: 12.6 at $x = -2.7$

Domain: All real numbers, $(-\infty, \infty)$

Range: All real numbers, $(-\infty, \infty)$

All graphs of polynomial functions have some characteristics in common. Compare the following graphs. How do the graphs of polynomial functions differ from the graphs of nonpolynomial functions? Describe some characteristics of the graphs of polynomial functions that you observe.

Polynomial Functions

$f(x) = x^2 + 3x + 1$

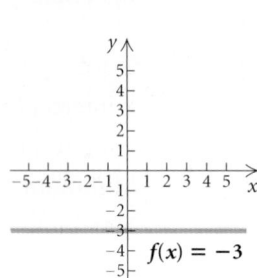

$f(x) = -3$

$f(x) = 2x^3 + x^2 + x - 1$

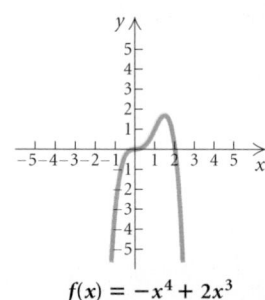

$f(x) = -x^4 + 2x^3$

Nonpolynomial Functions

$h(x) = |x + 2|$

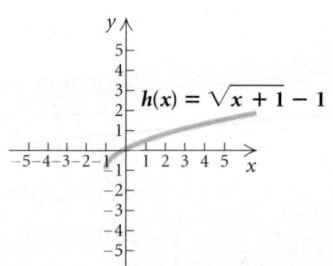

$h(x) = \sqrt{x + 1} - 1$

$h(x) = x^{4/5}$

$h(x) = \dfrac{x + 3}{x - 1}$

You probably noted that the graph of a polynomial function is *continuous,* that is, it has no holes or breaks. It is also smooth; there are no sharp corners. Furthermore, the *domain* of a polynomial function is the set of all real numbers, $(-\infty, \infty)$.

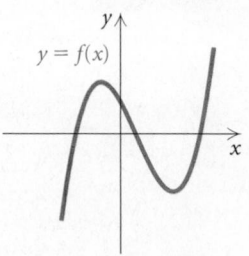

$y = f(x)$

A continuous function

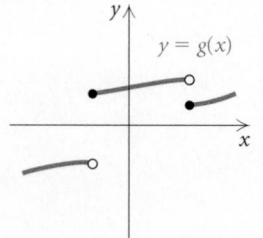

$y = g(x)$

A discontinuous function

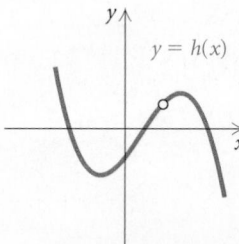

$y = h(x)$

A discontinuous function

✦ The Leading-Term Test

The behavior of the graph of a polynomial function as x becomes very large ($x \to \infty$) or very small ($x \to -\infty$) is referred to as the end behavior of the graph. The leading term of a polynomial function determines its end behavior.

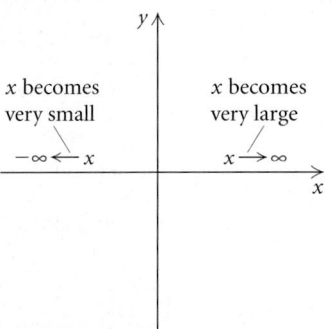

Using the graphs shown below, let's see if we can discover some general patterns by comparing the end behavior of even- and odd-degree functions. We also observe the effect of positive and negative leading coefficients.

Even Degree

$g(x) = x^2$

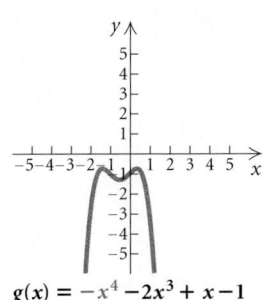
$g(x) = -x^4 - 2x^3 + x - 1$

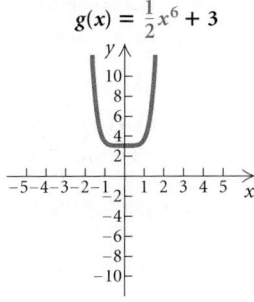
$g(x) = \frac{1}{2}x^6 + 3$

$g(x) = 1 - x - x^{10}$

Odd Degree

$f(x) = x^3$

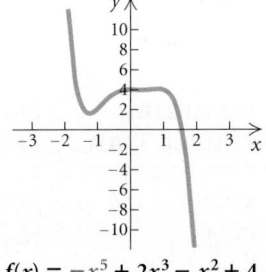
$f(x) = -x^5 + 2x^3 - x^2 + 4$

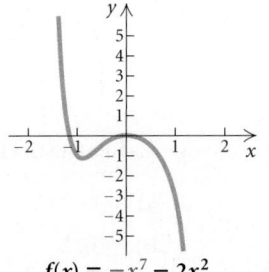
$f(x) = -x^7 - 2x^2$

$f(x) = \frac{1}{2}x^9 - 20x + 1$

We can summarize our observations as follows.

> ### The Leading-Term Test
> If a_nx^n is the leading term of a polynomial function, then the behavior of the graph as $x \to \infty$ or as $x \to -\infty$ can be described in one of the four following ways.
>
> If n is even, and $a_n > 0$:   If n is even, and $a_n < 0$:
>
>
>
> If n is odd, and $a_n > 0$:   If n is odd, and $a_n < 0$:
>
> The ⌇⌇⌇ portion of the graph is not determined by this test.

EXAMPLE 1 Using the leading-term test, match each of the following functions with one of the graphs A–D, which follow.

a) $f(x) = 3x^4 - 2x^3 + 3$ **b)** $f(x) = -5x^3 - x^2 + 4x + 2$
c) $f(x) = x^5 + \frac{1}{4}x + 1$ **d)** $f(x) = -x^6 + x^5 - 4x^3$

A.   **B.**   **C.**   **D.**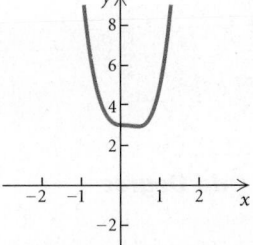

Solution

LEADING TERM	DEGREE OF LEADING TERM	SIGN OF LEADING COEFFICIENT	GRAPH
a) $3x^4$	Even	Positive	D
b) $-5x^3$	Odd	Negative	B
c) x^5	Odd	Positive	A
d) $-x^6$	Even	Negative	C

▶ Now Try Exercise 19.

✦ Finding Zeros of Factored Polynomial Functions

Let's review the meaning of the real zeros of a function and their connection to the x-intercepts of the function's graph.

CONNECTING THE CONCEPTS

Zeros, Solutions, and Intercepts

FUNCTION	ZEROS OF THE FUNCTION; SOLUTIONS OF THE EQUATION	X-INTERCEPTS OF THE GRAPH

Quadratic Polynomial

$g(x) = x^2 - 2x - 8$
$\quad = (x + 2)(x - 4),$

or

$\quad y = (x + 2)(x - 4)$

To find the **zeros** of $g(x)$, we solve $g(x) = 0$:

$x^2 - 2x - 8 = 0$
$(x + 2)(x - 4) = 0$
$x + 2 = 0 \quad or \ x - 4 = 0$
$x = -2 \ or \qquad x = 4.$

The **solutions** of $x^2 - 2x - 8 = 0$ are -2 and 4. They are the zeros of the function $g(x)$. That is,

$g(-2) = 0 \quad and \quad g(4) = 0.$

The real-number zeros of $g(x)$ are the x-coordinates of the **x-intercepts** of the graph of $y = g(x)$.

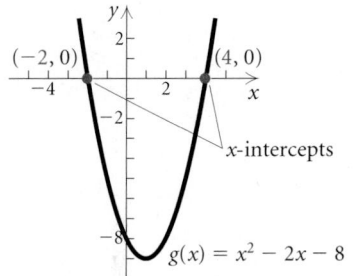

Cubic Polynomial

$h(x)$
$\quad = x^3 + 2x^2 - 5x - 6$
$\quad = (x + 3)(x + 1)(x - 2),$

or

$\quad y = (x + 3)(x + 1)(x - 2)$

To find the **zeros** of $h(x)$, we solve $h(x) = 0$:

$x^3 + 2x^2 - 5x - 6 = 0$
$(x + 3)(x + 1)(x - 2) = 0$
$x + 3 = 0 \quad or \ x + 1 = 0 \quad or \ x - 2 = 0$
$x = -3 \ or \qquad x = -1 \ or \qquad x = 2.$

The **solutions** of $x^3 + 2x^2 - 5x - 6 = 0$ are -3, -1, and 2. They are the zeros of the function $h(x)$. That is,

$h(-3) = 0,$
$h(-1) = 0, \quad and$
$h(2) = 0.$

The real-number zeros of $h(x)$ are the x-coordinates of the **x-intercepts** of the graph of $y = h(x)$.

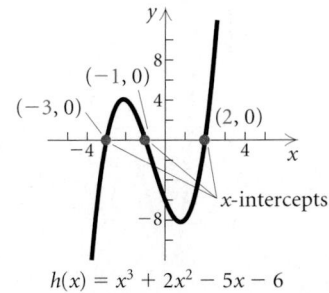

● ● ●

The connection between the real-number zeros of a function and the x-intercepts of the graph of the function is easily seen in the preceding examples. If c is a real zero of a function (that is, $f(c) = 0$), then $(c, 0)$ is an x-intercept of the graph of the function.

EXAMPLE 2 Consider $P(x) = x^3 + x^2 - 17x + 15$. Determine whether each of the numbers 2 and -5 is a zero of $P(x)$.

Solution We have

$$P(2) = (2)^3 + (2)^2 - 17(2) + 15 = -7. \qquad \text{Substituting 2 into the function}$$

Since $P(2) \neq 0$, we know that 2 is *not* a zero of the polynomial function. We also have

$$P(-5) = (-5)^3 + (-5)^2 - 17(-5) + 15 = 0. \qquad \text{Substituting } -5 \text{ into the function}$$

Since $P(-5) = 0$, we know that -5 *is* a zero of $P(x)$.

▶ Now Try Exercise 23.

$P(x) = x^3 + x^2 - 17x + 15$

Let's take a closer look at the polynomial function

$$h(x) = x^3 + 2x^2 - 5x - 6.$$

(See Connecting the Concepts on page 259.) Is there a connection between the factors of the polynomial and the zeros of the function? The factors of $h(x)$ are

$$x + 3, \qquad x + 1, \quad \text{and} \quad x - 2,$$

and the zeros are

$$-3, \qquad -1, \quad \text{and} \quad 2.$$

We note that when the polynomial is expressed as a product of linear factors, each factor determines a zero of the function. Thus if we know the linear factors of a polynomial function $f(x)$, we can easily find the zeros of $f(x)$ by solving the equation $f(x) = 0$ using the principle of zero products.

PRINCIPLE OF ZERO PRODUCTS

REVIEW SECTION **2.3**.

EXAMPLE 3 Find the zeros of

$$f(x) = 5(x - 2)(x - 2)(x - 2)(x + 1)$$
$$= 5(x - 2)^3(x + 1).$$

Solution To solve the equation $f(x) = 0$, we use the principle of zero products, solving $x - 2 = 0$ and $x + 1 = 0$. The zeros of $f(x)$ are 2 and -1. (See Fig. 1.)

$f(x) = 5(x - 2)^3(x + 1)$

Figure 1

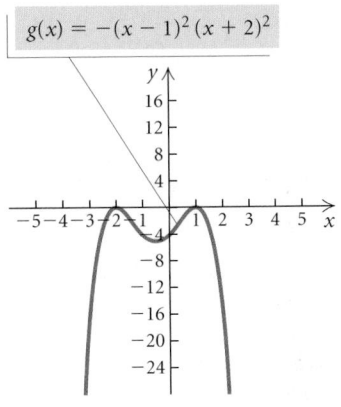

Figure 2

EXAMPLE 4   Find the zeros of

$$g(x) = -(x - 1)(x - 1)(x + 2)(x + 2)$$
$$= -(x - 1)^2(x + 2)^2.$$

Solution   To solve the equation $g(x) = 0$, we use the principle of zero products, solving $x - 1 = 0$ and $x + 2 = 0$. The zeros of $g(x)$ are 1 and -2. (See Fig. 2.)

Let's consider the occurrences of the zeros in the functions in Examples 3 and 4 and their relationship to the graphs of those functions. In Example 3, the factor $x - 2$ occurs three times. In a case like this, we say that the zero we obtain from this factor, 2, has a **multiplicity** of 3. The factor $x + 1$ occurs one time. The zero we obtain from this factor, -1, has a *multiplicity* of 1.

In Example 4, the factors $x - 1$ and $x + 2$ each occur two times. Thus both zeros, 1 and -2, have a *multiplicity* of 2.

Note, in Example 3, that the zeros have odd multiplicities and the graph crosses the x-axis at both -1 and 2. But in Example 4, the zeros have even multiplicities and the graph is tangent to (touches but does not cross) the x-axis at -2 and 1. This leads us to the following generalization.

Even and Odd Multiplicity

If $(x - c)^k$, $k \geq 1$, is a factor of a polynomial function $P(x)$ and $(x - c)^{k+1}$ is not a factor of $P(x)$ and:

- k is odd, then the graph crosses the x-axis at $(c, 0)$;
- k is even, then the graph is tangent to the x-axis at $(c, 0)$.

TECHNOLOGY ·················
CONNECTION

Using the Zero method, we can determine the zeros of the function in Example 5.

The window below shows the calculator display when we find the leftmost zero. The other zeros, 2 and 3, can be found in the same manner.

$y = x^3 - 2x^2 - 9x + 18$

Zero
X = -3   Y = 0

Some polynomials can be factored by grouping. Then we use the principle of zero products to find their zeros.

EXAMPLE 5   Find the zeros of

$$f(x) = x^3 - 2x^2 - 9x + 18.$$

Solution   We factor by grouping, as follows:

$$f(x) = x^3 - 2x^2 - 9x + 18$$
$$= x^2(x - 2) - 9(x - 2) \qquad \text{Grouping } x^3 \text{ with } -2x^2 \text{ and } -9x \text{ with 18 and factoring each group}$$
$$= (x - 2)(x^2 - 9) \qquad \text{Factoring out } x - 2$$
$$= (x - 2)(x + 3)(x - 3). \qquad \text{Factoring } x^2 - 9$$

Then, by the principle of zero products, the solutions of the equation $f(x) = 0$ are 2, -3, and 3. These are the zeros of $f(x)$.

▶ Now Try Exercise 39.

Other factoring techniques can also be used.

EXAMPLE 6   Find the zeros of
$$f(x) = x^4 + 4x^2 - 45.$$

Solution   We factor as follows:
$$f(x) = x^4 + 4x^2 - 45 = (x^2 - 5)(x^2 + 9).$$

We now solve the equation $f(x) = 0$ to determine the zeros. We use the principle of zero products:

$$(x^2 - 5)(x^2 + 9) = 0$$
$$x^2 - 5 = 0 \quad \text{or} \quad x^2 + 9 = 0$$
$$x^2 = 5 \quad \text{or} \quad x^2 = -9$$
$$x = \pm\sqrt{5} \quad \text{or} \quad x = \pm\sqrt{-9} = \pm 3i.$$

The solutions are $\pm\sqrt{5}$ and $\pm 3i$. These are the zeros of $f(x)$.

▶ **Now Try Exercise 31.**

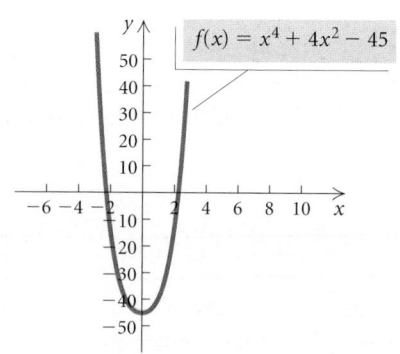

Only the real-number zeros of a function correspond to the x-intercepts of its graph. For instance, the real-number zeros of the function in Example 6, $-\sqrt{5}$ and $\sqrt{5}$, can be seen on the graph of the function at left, but the nonreal zeros, $-3i$ and $3i$, cannot.

> Every polynomial function of degree n, with $n \geq 1$, has at least one zero and at most n zeros.

This is often stated as follows: "Every polynomial function of degree n, with $n \geq 1$, has *exactly n* zeros." This statement is compatible with the preceding statement, if one takes multiplicities into account.

✦ Polynomial Models

Polynomial functions have many uses as models in science, engineering, and business. The simplest use of polynomial functions in applied problems occurs when we merely evaluate a polynomial function. In such cases, a model has already been developed.

EXAMPLE 7   *Ibuprofen in the Bloodstream.*   The polynomial function
$$M(t) = 0.5t^4 + 3.45t^3 - 96.65t^2 + 347.7t$$

can be used to estimate the number of milligrams of the pain relief medication ibuprofen in the bloodstream t hours after 400 mg of the medication has been taken. Find the number of milligrams in the bloodstream at $t = 0, 0.5, 1, 1.5,$ and so on, up to 6 hr. Round the function values to the nearest tenth.

Solution   Using a calculator, we compute the function values.

$$M(t) = 0.5t^4 + 3.45t^3 - 96.65t^2 + 347.7t;$$
$$0 \leq t \leq 6$$

$M(0) = 0,$	$M(3.5) = 255.9,$
$M(0.5) = 150.2,$	$M(4) = 193.2,$
$M(1) = 255,$	$M(4.5) = 126.9,$
$M(1.5) = 318.3,$	$M(5) = 66,$
$M(2) = 344.4,$	$M(5.5) = 20.2,$
$M(2.5) = 338.6,$	$M(6) = 0.$
$M(3) = 306.9,$	

▶ **Now Try Exercise 47.**

Recall that the domain of a polynomial function, unless restricted by a statement of the function, is $(-\infty, \infty)$. The implications of the application in Example 7 restrict the domain of the function. If we assume that a patient had not taken any of the medication before, it seems reasonable that $M(0) = 0$; that is, at time 0, there is 0 mg of the medication in the bloodstream. After the medication has been taken, $M(t)$ will be positive for a period of time and eventually decrease back to 0 when $t = 6$ and not increase again (unless another dose is taken). Thus the restricted domain is $[0, 6]$.

TECHNOLOGY CONNECTION

X	Y₁
0	0
.5	150.15
1	255
1.5	318.26
2	344.4
2.5	338.63
3	306.9

X = 0

500

Maximum
X = 2.1485504   Y = 345.76165
−200

We can evaluate the function in Example 7 with the TABLE feature of a graphing calculator set in AUTO mode. We start at 0 and use a step-value of 0.5.

As discussed above, the domain of $M(t)$ is $[0, 6]$. To determine the range, we find the relative maximum value of the function using the MAXIMUM feature.

The maximum is about 345.76 mg. It occurs approximately 2.15 hr, or 2 hr 9 min, after the initial dose has been taken. The range is about $[0, 345.76]$.

TECHNOLOGY ·····
CONNECTION

Previously, we used regression to model data with linear functions. We now expand that procedure to include quadratic, cubic, and quartic models.

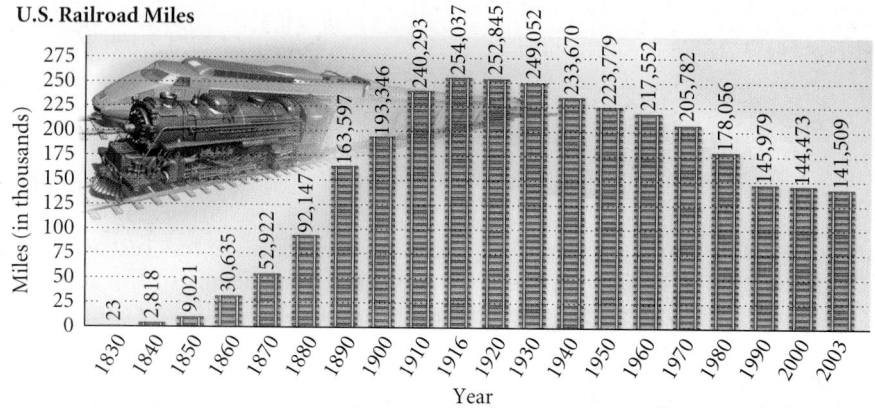

U.S. Railroad Miles

Note: The lengths exclude yard tracks, sidings, and parallel tracks.
Source: Association of American Railroads

Declining Number of Railroad Miles in the United States. The greatest combined length of U.S.-owned operating railroad track existed in 1916, when industrial activity increased during World War I. The total length has decreased ever since.

Looking at the graph at left, we note that the data, in miles, could be modeled with a cubic or a quartic function. Here we use the quartic model, where x is the number of years since 1830.

Using the REGRESSION feature with DIAGNOSTIC turned on, we get the following.

```
QuarticReg
y = ax⁴ + bx³ + ... + e
a = .0045529413
b = −1.717853698
c = 185.5854163
d = −3481.580759
↓e = 8715.877925
```

```
QuarticReg
y = ax⁴ + bx³ + ... + e
↑b = −1.717853698
c = 185.5854163
d = −3481.580759
e = 8715.877925
R² = .9846167608
```

The resulting quartic function is

$$f(x) = 0.0045529413x^4 - 1.717853698x^3 + 185.5854163x^2 - 3481.580759x + 8715.877925.$$

The scatterplot and graph are shown at left. With this function, we can estimate that there were 210,854 mi of railroad track in 1905 and 206,695 mi in 1965. Looking at the bar graph shown above, we see that these estimates appear to be fairly accurate.

If we use the function to estimate the number of miles of track in 2010 and in 2015, we get about 155,972 mi and 172,570 mi, respectively. These estimates are probably not realistic. The quartic model has a high value for R^2, approximately 0.985, over the domain of the data, but this number does not reflect the degree of accuracy for extended values. It is always important when using regression to evaluate predictions with common sense and knowledge of current trends.

3.1 EXERCISE SET

Determine the leading term, the leading coefficient, and the degree of the polynomial. Then classify the polynomial as constant, linear, quadratic, cubic, or quartic.

1. $g(x) = \frac{1}{2}x^3 - 10x + 8$

2. $f(x) = 15x^2 - 10 + 0.11x^4 - 7x^3$

3. $h(x) = 0.9x - 0.13$

4. $f(x) = -6$

5. $g(x) = 305x^4 + 4021$

6. $h(x) = 2.4x^3 + 5x^2 - x + \frac{7}{8}$

7. $h(x) = -5x^2 + 7x^3 + x^4$

8. $f(x) = 2 - x^2$

9. $g(x) = 4x^3 - \frac{1}{2}x^2 + 8$

10. $f(x) = 12 + x$

In Exercises 11–18, select one of the following four sketches to describe the end behavior of the graph of the function.

a)   b)

c)   d)

11. $f(x) = -3x^3 - x + 4$

12. $f(x) = \frac{1}{4}x^4 + \frac{1}{2}x^3 - 6x^2 + x - 5$

13. $f(x) = -x^6 + \frac{3}{4}x^4$

14. $f(x) = \frac{2}{5}x^5 - 2x^4 + x^3 - \frac{1}{2}x + 3$

15. $f(x) = -3.5x^4 + x^6 + 0.1x^7$

16. $f(x) = -x^3 + x^5 - 0.5x^6$

17. $f(x) = 10 + \frac{1}{10}x^4 - \frac{2}{5}x^3$

18. $f(x) = 2x + x^3 - x^5$

In Exercises 19–22, use the leading-term test to match the function with one of the graphs (a)–(d), which follow.

a)   b)

c)   d)

19. $f(x) = -x^6 + 2x^5 - 7x^2$

20. $f(x) = 2x^4 - x^2 + 1$

21. $f(x) = x^5 + \frac{1}{10}x - 3$

22. $f(x) = -x^3 + x^2 - 2x + 4$

23. Use substitution to determine whether 4, 5, and -2 are zeros of
$$f(x) = x^3 - 9x^2 + 14x + 24.$$

24. Use substitution to determine whether 2, 3, and -1 are zeros of
$$f(x) = 2x^3 - 3x^2 + x + 6.$$

25. Use substitution to determine whether 2, 3, and -1 are zeros of
$$g(x) = x^4 - 6x^3 + 8x^2 + 6x - 9.$$

26. Use substitution to determine whether 1, -2, and 3 are zeros of
$$g(x) = x^4 - x^3 - 3x^2 + 5x - 2.$$

Find the zeros of the polynomial function and state the multiplicity of each.

27. $f(x) = (x + 3)^2(x - 1)$

28. $f(x) = (x + 5)^3(x - 4)(x + 1)^2$

29. $f(x) = -2(x - 4)(x - 4)(x - 4)(x + 6)$

30. $f(x) = \left(x + \frac{1}{2}\right)(x + 7)(x + 7)(x + 5)$

31. $f(x) = (x^2 + 9)^3$

32. $f(x) = (x^2 - 4)^2$

33. $f(x) = x^3(x - 1)^2(x + 4)$

34. $f(x) = x^2(x + 3)^2(x - 4)(x + 1)^4$

35. $f(x) = -8(x - 3)^2(x + 4)^3 x^4$

36. $f(x) = (x^2 - 5x + 6)^2$

37. $f(x) = x^4 - 4x^2 + 3$

38. $f(x) = x^4 - 10x^2 + 9$

39. $f(x) = x^3 + 3x^2 - x - 3$

40. $f(x) = x^3 - x^2 - 2x + 2$

41. $f(x) = 2x^3 - x^2 - 8x + 4$

42. $f(x) = 3x^3 + x^2 - 48x - 16$

In Exercises 43–46, determine whether the statement is true or false.

43. If $P(x) = (x - 3)^4(x + 1)^3$, then the graph of the polynomial function $y = P(x)$ crosses the x-axis at $(3, 0)$.

44. If $P(x) = (x + 2)^2\left(x - \frac{1}{4}\right)^5$, then the graph of the polynomial function $y = P(x)$ crosses the x-axis at $\left(\frac{1}{4}, 0\right)$.

45. If $P(x) = (x - 2)^3(x + 5)^6$, then the graph of $y = P(x)$ is tangent to the x-axis at $(-5, 0)$.

46. If $P(x) = (x + 4)^2(x - 1)^2$, then the graph of $y = P(x)$ is tangent to the x-axis at $(4, 0)$.

47. *Milk Cows.* The number of milk cows on farms in the United States peaked at 24,940,000 in 1940 and decreased to 9,005,000 in 2005 (*Sources:* National Agricultural Statistics Service; U.S. Department of Agriculture).

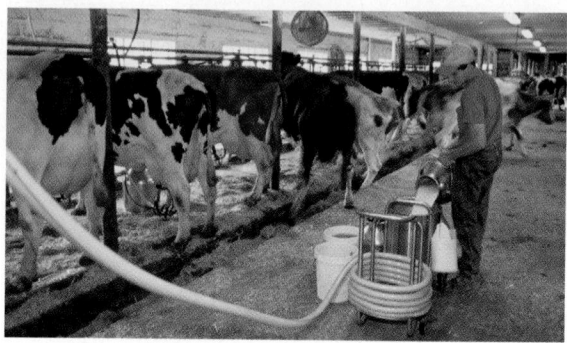

The quartic function

$$f(x) = 0.0013924589x^4 - 0.2121392316x^3$$
$$+ 3.414011377x^2 + 310.7243489x$$
$$+ 16,209.42591,$$

where x is the number of years since 1900, can be used to estimate the number of milk cows, in thousands, from 1900 to 2005. Find the number of milk cows in 1960 and in 1980.

48. *Projectile Motion.* A stone thrown downward with an initial velocity of 34.3 m/sec will travel a distance of s meters, where

$$s(t) = 4.9t^2 + 34.3t$$

and t is in seconds. If a stone is thrown downward at 34.3 m/sec from a height of 294 m, how long will it take the stone to hit the ground?

49. *Live Christmas Trees.* In 2000, about 40% of all Christmas trees in the United States were live (*Source:* National Christmas Tree Association). The quadratic function

$$f(x) = 2.375x^2 - 7.395x + 28.205,$$

where x is the number of years after 2001, can be used to estimate the number of live Christmas trees, in millions, from 2001 to 2004. Find the number of live Christmas trees in 2002 and in 2004.

50. *Railroad Miles.* The combined length of all U.S.-owned operating railroad tracks, excluding yard track, sidings, and parallel tracks, has decreased since World War I (*Source*: Association of American Railroads).

The data over the years 1830 to 2003 are modeled by the quartic function

$$f(x) = 0.0045529413x^4 - 1.717853698x^3 + 185.5854163x^2 - 3481.580759x + 8715.877925,$$

where x is the number of years since 1830 and $f(x)$ is in miles. Find the number of miles of operating railroad track in the United States in 1925, in 1959, and in 1992.

51. *Games in a Sports League.* If there are x teams in a sports league and all the teams play each other twice, a total of $N(x)$ games are played, where

$$N(x) = x^2 - x.$$

A softball league has 9 teams, each of which plays the others twice. If the league pays $45 per game for the field and umpires, how much will it cost to play the entire schedule?

52. *Windmill Power.* Under certain conditions, the power P, in watts per hour, generated by a windmill with winds blowing v miles per hour is given by

$$P(v) = 0.015v^3.$$

a) Find the power generated by 15-mph winds.

b) How fast must the wind blow in order to generate 120 watts of power in 1 hr?

53. *Auto Insurance.* The average cost of auto insurance rose only 1.5% from 2004 to 2005 after increasing almost 6% per year in the three

years prior to 2004. The average cost from 1995 to 2005 can be modeled by the quartic function

$$f(x) = -0.2607808858x^4 + 5.281857032x^3 - 30.77185315x^2 + 60.89063714x + 663.8111888,$$

where x is the number of years since 1995 (*Source*: Insurance Information Institute). Find the average cost of auto insurance in 1996, in 1999, and in 2004.

54. *Debt Held by Foreigners.* The percentage of the United States' public debt that is held by foreigners has greatly increased in recent years (*Source*: White House Office of Management and Budget). The data can be modeled by the quadratic function

$$f(x) = 0.0742857143x^2 - 0.76x + 17.14285714,$$

where x is the number of years since 1980. Find the percentage of the public debt held by foreigners in 1987, in 1996, and in 2004.

55. *Interest Compounded Annually.* When P dollars is invested at interest rate i, compounded annually, for t years, the investment grows to A dollars, where

$$A = P(1 + i)^t.$$

a) Find the interest rate i if $4000 grows to $4368.10 in 2 yr.

b) Find the interest rate i if $10,000 grows to $13,310 in 3 yr.

56. *Threshold Weight.* In a study performed by Alvin Shemesh, it was found that the **threshold weight W,** defined as the weight above which the risk of death rises dramatically, is given by

$$W(h) = \left(\frac{h}{12.3}\right)^3,$$

where W is in pounds and h is a person's height, in inches. Find the threshold weight of a person who is 5 ft 7 in. tall.

Technology Connection

Using a graphing calculator, find the real zeros of the function.

57. $f(x) = x^3 - 3x - 1$

58. $f(x) = x^3 + 3x^2 - 9x - 13$

59. $f(x) = x^4 - 2x^2$

60. $f(x) = x^4 - 2x^3 - 5.6$

61. $f(x) = x^3 - x$

62. $f(x) = 2x^3 - x^2 - 14x - 10$

63. $f(x) = x^8 + 8x^7 - 28x^6 - 56x^5 + 70x^4$
$\qquad + 56x^3 - 28x^2 - 8x + 1$

64. $f(x) = x^6 - 10x^5 + 13x^3 - 4x^2 - 5$

Using a graphing calculator, estimate the relative maxima and minima and the range of the polynomial function.

65. $g(x) = x^3 - 1.2x + 1$

66. $h(x) = -\frac{1}{2}x^4 + 3x^3 - 5x^2 + 3x + 6$

67. $f(x) = x^6 - 3.8$

68. $h(x) = 2x^3 - x^4 + 20$

69. $f(x) = x^2 + 10x - x^5$

70. $f(x) = 2x^4 - 5.6x^2 + 10$

For the scatterplots and graphs in Exercises 71–76, determine which, if any, of the following functions might be used as a model for the data.

a) *Linear,* $f(x) = mx + b$
b) *Quadratic,* $f(x) = ax^2 + bx + c, a > 0$
c) *Quadratic,* $f(x) = ax^2 + bx + c, a < 0$
d) *Polynomial, not quadratic or linear*

71.

72.

73.

74.

75.

76.
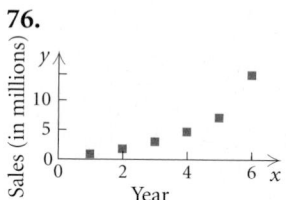

77. *Foreign-Born Population.* The percentage of the U.S. population that is foreign-born has increased in recent years, as shown in the table below.

Year	Percentage That Is Foreign-Born
1900	13.6%
1910	14.7
1920	13.2
1930	11.6
1940	8.8
1950	6.9
1960	5.4
1970	4.7
1980	6.2
1990	8.0
2000	10.4
2004	11.7

Sources: U.S. Bureau of the Census; U.S. Department of Commerce

a) Use a graphing calculator to fit cubic and quartic functions to the data. Let x represent the number of years since 1900.
b) Use the functions found in part (a) to estimate what percentage of the U.S. population will be foreign-born in 2010. Compare the estimates and determine which model gives the more realistic estimate.

78. *U.S. Farm Acreage.* As the number of farms has decreased in the United States, the average size of the remaining farms has grown larger, as shown in the following table.

Year	Average Acreage per Farm
1900	147
1910	139
1920	149
1930	157
1940	175
1950	213
1960	297
1970	374
1980	426
1990	460
1995	438
2000	436
2003	441
2004	443

Sources: Statistical History of the United States (1970); National Agricultural Statistics Service

a) Use a graphing calculator to fit quadratic, cubic, and quartic functions to the data. Let x represent the number of years since 1900.

b) With each function found in part (a), estimate the average acreage in 2010 and in 2015. Compare the estimates and determine which function gives the most realistic estimates.

79. *Unemployed.* The table below shows the number of unemployed in the United States from 1996 through 2006.

Year	Number of Unemployed (in thousands)
1996	397
1997	350
1998	340
1999	275
2000	269
2001	310
2002	360
2003	457
2004	460
2005	435
2006	411

Source: U.S. Department of Labor

a) Use a graphing calculator to fit cubic and quartic functions to the data. Let x represent the number of years since 1996.

b) Use the functions found in part (a) to estimate the number of unemployed in 2008. Compare the estimates and determine which model gives the more realistic estimate.

80. *Dog Years.* A dog's life span is typically much shorter than that of a human. Age equivalents for dogs and humans are listed in the table below.

Age of Dog, x (in years)	Human Age, $h(x)$ (in years)
0.25	5
0.5	10
1	15
2	24
4	32
6	40
8	48
10	56
14	72
18	91
21	106

Source: Country, December 1992, p. 60

a) Use a graphing calculator to fit linear and cubic functions to the data. Which function has the better fit?

b) Use the function from part (a) with the better fit to estimate the equivalent human age for dogs that are 5, 10, and 15 years old.

Collaborative Discussion and Writing

81. How is the range of a polynomial function related to the degree of the polynomial?

82. Polynomial functions are continuous. Discuss what "continuous" means in terms of the domains of these functions and the characteristics of their graphs.

Skill Maintenance

Find the distance between the pair of points.

83. $(3, -5)$ and $(0, -1)$

84. $(4, 2)$ and $(-2, -4)$

85. Find the center and the radius of the circle
$$(x - 3)^2 + (y + 5)^2 = 49.$$

86. The diameter of a circle connects the points $(-6, 5)$ and $(-2, 1)$ on the circle. Find the coordinates of the center of the circle and the length of the radius.

Solve.

87. $2y - 3 \geq 1 - y + 5$

88. $(x - 2)(x + 5) > x(x - 3)$

89. $|x + 6| \geq 7$

90. $\left|x + \frac{1}{4}\right| \leq \frac{2}{3}$

Synthesis

91. In early 1995, $2000 was deposited at a certain interest rate compounded annually. One year later, $1200 was deposited in another account at the same rate. At the end of that year, there was a total of $3573.80 in both accounts. What is the annual interest rate?

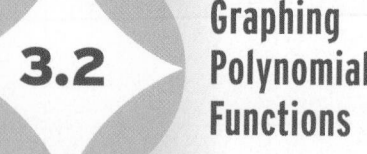

3.2   Graphing Polynomial Functions

⬥ Graph polynomial functions.

⬥ Use the intermediate value theorem to determine whether a function has a real zero between two given real numbers.

✦ Graphing Polynomial Functions

In addition to using the leading-term test and finding the zeros of the function, it is helpful to consider the following facts when graphing a polynomial function.

If $P(x)$ is a polynomial function of degree n, the graph of the function has:

- at most n real zeros, and thus at most n x-intercepts;
- at most $n - 1$ turning points.

(Turning points on a graph, also called relative maxima and minima, occur when the function changes from decreasing to increasing or from increasing to decreasing.)

EXAMPLE 1 Graph the polynomial function $h(x) = -2x^4 + 3x^3$.

Solution

1. First, we use the leading-term test to determine the end behavior of the graph. The leading term is $-2x^4$. The degree, 4, is even, and the coefficient, -2, is negative. Thus the end behavior of the graph as $x \to \infty$ and as $x \to -\infty$ can be sketched as follows.

2. The zeros of the function are the first coordinates of the x-intercepts of the graph. To find the zeros, we solve $h(x) = 0$ by factoring and using the principle of zero products.

$$-2x^4 + 3x^3 = 0$$
$$-x^3(2x - 3) = 0 \qquad \text{Factoring}$$
$$-x^3 = 0 \quad \text{or} \quad 2x - 3 = 0 \qquad \text{Using the principle of zero products}$$
$$x = 0 \quad \text{or} \quad x = \frac{3}{2}.$$

The zeros of the function are 0 and $\frac{3}{2}$. Note that the multiplicity of 0 is 3 and the multiplicity of $\frac{3}{2}$ is 1. The x-intercepts are $(0,0)$ and $\left(\frac{3}{2}, 0\right)$.

3. The zeros divide the x-axis into three intervals:

$$(-\infty, 0), \qquad \left(0, \frac{3}{2}\right), \quad \text{and} \quad \left(\frac{3}{2}, \infty\right).$$

The sign of $h(x)$ is the same for all values of x in each of the three intervals. That is, $h(x)$ is positive for all x-values in an interval or $h(x)$ is negative for all x-values in an interval. To determine which, we choose a test value for x from each interval and find $h(x)$.

Interval	$(-\infty, 0)$	$\left(0, \frac{3}{2}\right)$	$\left(\frac{3}{2}, \infty\right)$
Test Value, x	-1	1	2
Function Value, $h(x)$	-5	1	-8
Sign of $h(x)$	$-$	$+$	$-$
Location of Points on Graph	Below x-axis	Above x-axis	Below x-axis

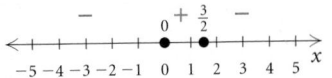

This test-point procedure also gives us three points to plot. In this case, we have $(-1, -5), (1, 1)$, and $(2, -8)$.

4. To determine the y-intercept, we find $h(0)$:

$$h(x) = -2x^4 + 3x^3$$
$$h(0) = -2 \cdot 0^4 + 3 \cdot 0^3 = 0.$$

The y-intercept is $(0, 0)$.

5. A few additional points are helpful when completing the graph.

x	$h(x)$
-1.5	-20.25
-0.5	-0.5
0.5	0.25
2.5	-31.25

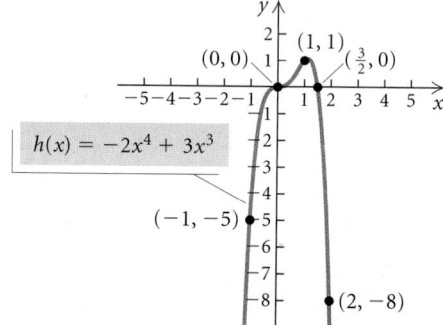

6. The degree of h is 4. The graph of h can have at most 4 x-intercepts and at most 3 turning points. In fact, it has 2 x-intercepts and 1 turning point. The zeros, 0 and $\frac{3}{2}$, each have odd multiplicities, 3 for 0 and 1 for $\frac{3}{2}$. Since the multiplicities are odd, the graph crosses the x-axis at 0 and $\frac{3}{2}$. The end behavior of the graph is what we described in step (1). As $x \to \infty$ and also as $x \to -\infty$, $h(x) \to -\infty$. The graph appears to be correct.

▶ Now Try Exercise 19.

The following is a procedure for graphing polynomial functions.

To graph a polynomial function:

1. Use the leading-term test to determine the end behavior.
2. Find the zeros of the function by solving $f(x) = 0$. Any real zeros are the first coordinates of the x-intercepts.
3. Use the x-intercepts (zeros) to divide the x-axis into intervals and choose a test point in each interval to determine the sign of all function values in that interval.
4. Find $f(0)$. This gives the y-intercept of the function.
5. If necessary, find additional function values to determine the general shape of the graph and then draw the graph.
6. As a partial check, use the facts that the graph has at most n x-intercepts and at most $n - 1$ turning points. Multiplicity of zeros can also be considered in order to check where the graph crosses or is tangent to the x-axis.

EXAMPLE 2 Graph the polynomial function

$$f(x) = 2x^3 + x^2 - 8x - 4.$$

Solution

1. The leading term is $2x^3$. The degree, 3, is odd, and the coefficient, 2, is positive. Thus the end behavior of the graph will appear as follows.

2. To find the zeros, we solve $f(x) = 0$. Here we can use factoring by grouping.

$$2x^3 + x^2 - 8x - 4 = 0$$
$$x^2(2x + 1) - 4(2x + 1) = 0 \qquad \text{Factoring by grouping}$$
$$(2x + 1)(x^2 - 4) = 0$$
$$(2x + 1)(x + 2)(x - 2) = 0 \qquad \text{Factoring a difference of squares}$$

The zeros are $-\frac{1}{2}$, -2, and 2. Each is of multiplicity 1. The x-intercepts are $(-2, 0)$, $\left(-\frac{1}{2}, 0\right)$, and $(2, 0)$.

3. The zeros divide the x-axis into four intervals:

$$(-\infty, -2), \qquad \left(-2, -\frac{1}{2}\right), \qquad \left(-\frac{1}{2}, 2\right), \quad \text{and} \quad (2, \infty).$$

We choose a test value for x from each interval and find $f(x)$.

Interval	$(-\infty, -2)$	$\left(-2, -\frac{1}{2}\right)$	$\left(-\frac{1}{2}, 2\right)$	$(2, \infty)$
Test Value, x	-3	-1	1	3
Function Value, $f(x)$	-25	3	-9	35
Sign of $f(x)$	$-$	$+$	$-$	$+$
Location of Points on Graph	Below x-axis	Above x-axis	Below x-axis	Above x-axis

The test values and corresponding function values also give us four points on the graph: $(-3, -25)$, $(-1, 3)$, $(1, -9)$, and $(3, 35)$.

4. To determine the *y*-intercept, we find $f(0)$:

$$f(x) = 2x^3 + x^2 - 8x - 4$$
$$f(0) = 2 \cdot 0^3 + 0^2 - 8 \cdot 0 - 4 = -4.$$

The *y*-intercept is $(0, -4)$.

5. We find a few additional points and complete the graph.

x	f(x)
-2.5	-9
-1.5	3.5
0.5	-7.5
1.5	-7

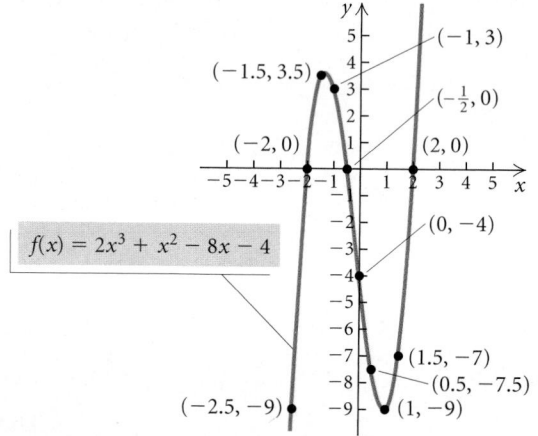

6. The degree of *f* is 3. The graph of *f* can have at most 3 *x*-intercepts and at most 2 turning points. It has 3 *x*-intercepts and 2 turning points. Each zero has a multiplicity of 1; thus the graph crosses the *x*-axis at -2, $-\frac{1}{2}$, and 2. The graph has the end behavior described in step (1). As $x \to -\infty$, $h(x) \to -\infty$, and as $x \to \infty$, $h(x) \to \infty$. The graph appears to be correct.

▶ **Now Try Exercise 29.**

Some polynomials are difficult to factor. In the next example, the polynomial is given in factored form. In Sections 3.3 and 3.4, we will learn methods that facilitate determining factors of such polynomials.

EXAMPLE 3 Graph the polynomial function

$$g(x) = x^4 - 7x^3 + 12x^2 + 4x - 16$$
$$= (x + 1)(x - 2)^2(x - 4).$$

Solution

1. The leading term is x^4. The degree, 4, is even, and the coefficient, 1, is positive. The sketch below shows the end behavior.

2. To find the zeros, we solve $g(x) = 0$:

$$(x + 1)(x - 2)^2(x - 4) = 0.$$

The zeros are -1, 2, and 4: 2 is of multiplicity 2; the others are of multiplicity 1. The *x*-intercepts are $(-1, 0)$, $(2, 0)$, and $(4, 0)$.

3. The zeros divide the x-axis into four intervals:

$$(-\infty, -1), \qquad (-1, 2), \qquad (2, 4), \quad \text{and} \quad (4, \infty).$$

We choose a test value for x from each interval and find $g(x)$.

Interval	$(-\infty, -1)$	$(-1, 2)$	$(2, 4)$	$(4, \infty)$
Test Value, x	-1.25	1	3	4.25
Function Value, $g(x)$	≈ 13.9	-6	-4	≈ 6.6
Sign of $g(x)$	$+$	$-$	$-$	$+$
Location of Points on Graph	Above x-axis	Below x-axis	Below x-axis	Above x-axis

The test values and corresponding function values also give us four points on the graph: $(-1.25, 13.9)$, $(1, -6)$, $(3, -4)$, and $(4.25, 6.6)$.

4. To determine the y-intercept, we find $g(0)$:

$$g(x) = x^4 - 7x^3 + 12x^2 + 4x - 16$$
$$g(0) = 0^4 - 7 \cdot 0^3 + 12 \cdot 0^2 + 4 \cdot 0 - 16 = -16.$$

The y-intercept is $(0, -16)$.

5. We find a few additional points and draw the graph.

x	$g(x)$
-0.5	-14.1
0.5	-11.8
1.5	-1.6
2.5	-1.3
3.5	-5.1

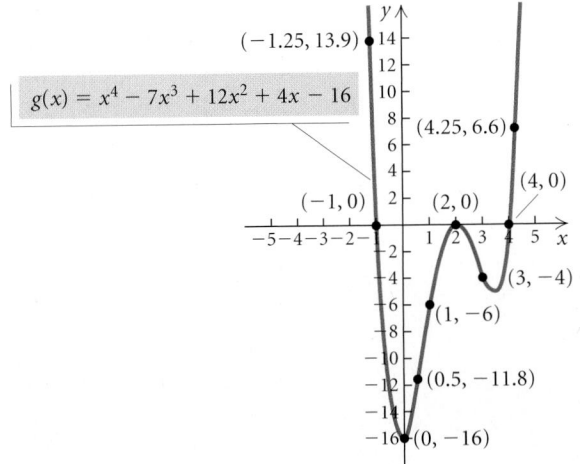

$g(x) = x^4 - 7x^3 + 12x^2 + 4x - 16$

6. The degree of g is 4. The graph of g can have at most 4 x-intercepts and at most 3 turning points. It has 3 x-intercepts and 3 turning points. One of the zeros, 2, has a multiplicity of 2, so the graph is tangent to the x-axis at 2. The other zeros, -1 and 4, each have a multiplicity of 1 so the graph crosses the x-axis at -1 and 4. The graph has the end behavior described in step (1). As $x \to \infty$ and also as $x \to -\infty$, $g(x) \to \infty$. The graph appears to be correct.

▶ Now Try Exercise 17.

STUDY TIP

Visualization is the key to understanding and retaining new concepts. This text has an exceptional art package with precise color-coding to streamline the learning process. Take time to study each art piece and observe the concept that is illustrated.

✦ The Intermediate Value Theorem

Polynomial functions P are continuous, hence their graphs are unbroken. The domain of a polynomial function, unless restricted by the statement of the function, is $(-\infty, \infty)$. Suppose two function values $P(a)$ and $P(b)$ have opposite signs. Since P is continuous, its graph must be a curve from $(a, P(a))$ to $(b, P(b))$ without a break. Then it follows that the curve must cross the x-axis at some point c between a and b—that is, the function has a zero at c between a and b.

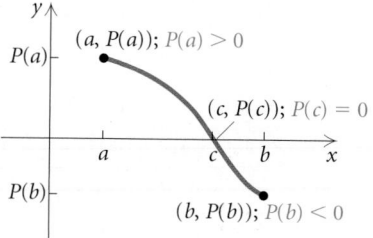

The Intermediate Value Theorem

For any polynomial function $P(x)$ with real coefficients, suppose that for $a \neq b$, $P(a)$ and $P(b)$ are of opposite signs. Then the function has a real zero between a and b.

EXAMPLE 4   Using the intermediate value theorem, determine, if possible, whether the function has a real zero between a and b.

a) $f(x) = x^3 + x^2 - 6x$; $a = -4, b = -2$

b) $f(x) = x^3 + x^2 - 6x$; $a = -1, b = 3$

c) $g(x) = \frac{1}{3}x^4 - x^3$; $a = -\frac{1}{2}, b = \frac{1}{2}$

d) $g(x) = \frac{1}{3}x^4 - x^3$; $a = 1, b = 2$

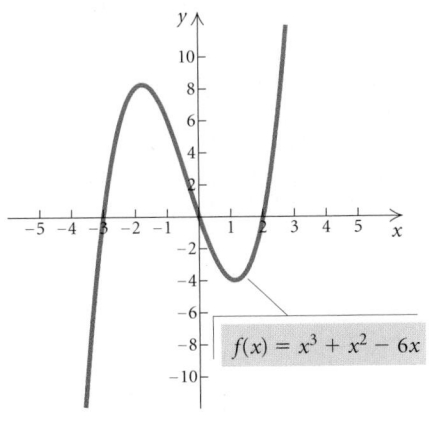

$f(x) = x^3 + x^2 - 6x$

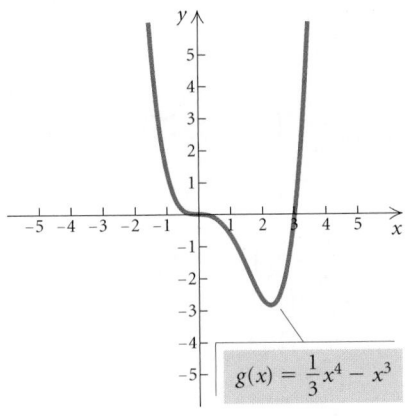

$g(x) = \frac{1}{3}x^4 - x^3$

Solution   We find $f(a)$ and $f(b)$ or $g(a)$ and $g(b)$ and determine whether they differ in sign. The graphs of $f(x)$ and $g(x)$ at left provide a visual check of the solutions.

a) $f(-4) = (-4)^3 + (-4)^2 - 6(-4) = -24,$
   $f(-2) = (-2)^3 + (-2)^2 - 6(-2) = 8$

Note that $f(-4)$ is negative and $f(-2)$ is positive. By the intermediate value theorem, since $f(-4)$ and $f(-2)$ have opposite signs, then $f(x)$ has a zero between -4 and -2. The graph confirms this.

b) $f(-1) = (-1)^3 + (-1)^2 - 6(-1) = 6,$
   $f(3) = 3^3 + 3^2 - 6(3) = 18$

Both $f(-1)$ and $f(3)$ are positive. Thus the intermediate value theorem does not allow us to determine whether there is a real zero between -1 and 3. Note that the graph of $f(x)$ shows that there are two zeros between -1 and 3.

c) $g\left(-\frac{1}{2}\right) = \frac{1}{3}\left(-\frac{1}{2}\right)^4 - \left(-\frac{1}{2}\right)^3 = \frac{7}{48},$
   $g\left(\frac{1}{2}\right) = \frac{1}{3}\left(\frac{1}{2}\right)^4 - \left(\frac{1}{2}\right)^3 = -\frac{5}{48}$

Since $g\left(-\frac{1}{2}\right)$ and $g\left(\frac{1}{2}\right)$ have opposite signs, $g(x)$ has a zero between $-\frac{1}{2}$ and $\frac{1}{2}$. The graph confirms this.

d) $g(1) = \frac{1}{3}(1)^4 - 1^3 = -\frac{2}{3},$
   $g(2) = \frac{1}{3}(2)^4 - 2^3 = -\frac{8}{3}$

Both $g(1)$ and $g(2)$ are negative. This does not necessarily mean that there is not a zero between 1 and 2. The graph of $g(x)$ does show that there are no zeros between 1 and 2, but the function values $-\frac{2}{3}$ and $-\frac{8}{3}$ do not allow us to use the intermediate value theorem to determine this.

▶ Now Try Exercises 33 and 37.

A

B

C

D

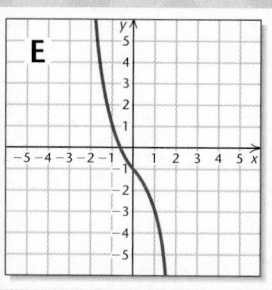

E

Visualizing the Graph

Match the function with its graph.

1. $f(x) = -x^4 - x + 5$

2. $f(x) = -3x^2 + 6x - 3$

3. $f(x) = x^4 - 4x^3 + 3x^2 + 4x - 4$

4. $f(x) = -\dfrac{2}{5}x + 4$

5. $f(x) = x^3 - 4x^2$

6. $f(x) = x^6 - 9x^4$

7. $f(x) = x^5 - 3x^3 + 2$

8. $f(x) = -x^3 - x - 1$

9. $f(x) = x^2 + 7x + 6$

10. $f(x) = \dfrac{7}{2}$

Answers on page A-19

F

G

H

I

J

3.2 EXERCISE SET

For each function in Exercises 1–6, state:

a) *the maximum number of real zeros that the function can have,*

b) *the maximum number of x-intercepts that the graph of the function can have, and*

c) *the maximum number of turning points that the graph of the function can have.*

1. $f(x) = x^5 - x^2 + 6$

2. $f(x) = -x^2 + x^4 - x^6 + 3$

3. $f(x) = x^{10} - 2x^5 + 4x - 2$

4. $f(x) = \frac{1}{4}x^3 + 2x^2$

5. $f(x) = -x - x^3$

6. $f(x) = -3x^4 + 2x^3 - x - 4$

In Exercises 7–12, use the leading-term test and your knowledge of y-intercepts to match the function with one of the graphs (a)–(f), which follow.

a)

b)

c)

d)

e)

f)

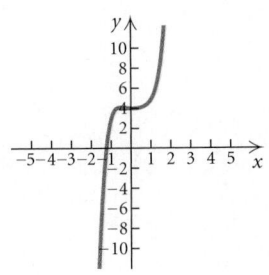

7. $f(x) = \frac{1}{4}x^2 - 5$

8. $f(x) = -0.5x^6 - x^5 + 4x^4 - 5x^3 - 7x^2 + x - 3$

9. $f(x) = x^5 - x^4 + x^2 + 4$

10. $f(x) = -\frac{1}{3}x^3 - 4x^2 + 6x + 42$

11. $f(x) = x^4 - 2x^3 + 12x^2 + x - 20$

12. $f(x) = -0.3x^7 + 0.11x^6 - 0.25x^5 + x^4 + x^3 - 6x - 5$

Graph the polynomial function. Follow the steps outlined in the procedure on page 272.

13. $f(x) = -x^3 - 2x^2$

14. $g(x) = x^4 - 4x^3 + 3x^2$

15. $h(x) = x^5 - 4x^3$

16. $f(x) = x^3 - x$

17. $h(x) = x(x - 4)(x + 1)(x - 2)$

18. $f(x) = \frac{1}{2}x^3 + \frac{5}{2}x^2$

19. $g(x) = -x^4 - 2x^3$

20. $h(x) = x^3 - 3x^2$

21. $f(x) = -\frac{1}{2}(x - 2)(x + 1)^2(x - 1)$

22. $g(x) = (x - 2)^3(x + 3)$

23. $g(x) = -x(x - 1)^2(x + 4)^2$

24. $h(x) = -x(x - 3)(x - 3)(x + 2)$

25. $f(x) = (x - 2)^2(x + 1)^4$

26. $g(x) = x^4 - 9x^2$

27. $g(x) = -(x - 1)^4$

28. $h(x) = (x + 2)^3$

29. $h(x) = x^3 + 3x^2 - x - 3$

30. $g(x) = -x^3 + 2x^2 + 4x - 8$

31. $f(x) = 6x^3 - 8x^2 - 54x + 72$

32. $h(x) = x^5 - 5x^3 + 4x$

Using the intermediate value theorem, determine, if possible, whether the function f has a real zero between a and b.

33. $f(x) = x^3 + 3x^2 - 9x - 13; a = -5, b = -4$

34. $f(x) = x^3 + 3x^2 - 9x - 13; a = 1, b = 2$

35. $f(x) = 3x^2 - 2x - 11; a = -3, b = -2$

36. $f(x) = 3x^2 - 2x - 11; a = 2, b = 3$

37. $f(x) = x^4 - 2x^2 - 6; a = 2, b = 3$

38. $f(x) = 2x^5 - 7x + 1; a = 1, b = 2$

39. $f(x) = x^3 - 5x^2 + 4; a = 4, b = 5$

40. $f(x) = x^4 - 3x^2 + x - 1; a = -3, b = -2$

Collaborative Discussion and Writing

41. Explain how to find the zeros of a polynomial function from its graph.

42. Is it possible for the graph of a polynomial function to have no y-intercept? no x-intercepts? Explain your answer.

Skill Maintenance

Match the equation with one of the graphs (a)–(f), which follow.

a)

b)

c)

d)

e)

f)
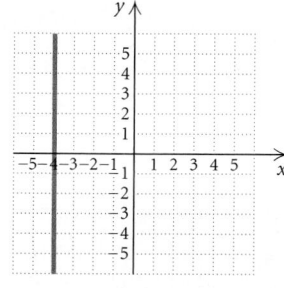

43. $y = x$

44. $x = -4$

45. $y - 2x = 6$

46. $3x + 2y = -6$

47. $y = 1 - x$

48. $y = 2$

Solve.

49. $2x - \frac{1}{2} = 4 - 3x$

50. $x^3 - x^2 - 12x = 0$

51. $6x^2 - 23x - 55 = 0$

52. $\frac{3}{4}x + 10 = \frac{1}{5} + 2x$

3.3

Polynomial Division; The Remainder and Factor Theorems

◆ Perform long division with polynomials and determine whether one polynomial is a factor of another.

◆ Use synthetic division to divide a polynomial by $x - c$.

◆ Use the remainder theorem to find a function value $f(c)$.

◆ Use the factor theorem to determine whether $x - c$ is a factor of $f(x)$.

In general, finding exact zeros of many polynomial functions is neither easy nor straightforward. In this section and the one that follows, we develop concepts that help us find exact zeros of certain polynomial functions with degree 3 or greater.

Consider the polynomial

$$h(x) = x^3 + 2x^2 - 5x - 6 = (x + 3)(x + 1)(x - 2).$$

The factors are

$$x + 3, \quad x + 1, \quad \text{and} \quad x - 2,$$

and the zeros are

$$-3, \quad -1, \quad \text{and} \quad 2.$$

When a polynomial is expressed in factored form, each factor determines a zero of the function. Thus if we know the factors of a polynomial, we can easily find the zeros. We now show how this idea can be "reversed" so that if we know the zeros of a polynomial function, we can find the factors of the polynomial.

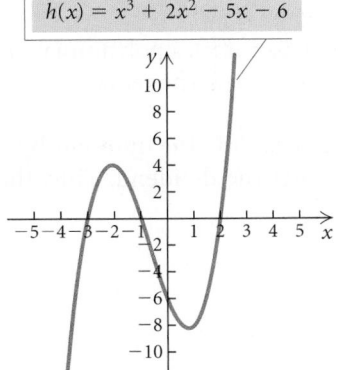

$h(x) = x^3 + 2x^2 - 5x - 6$

◆ Division and Factors

When we divide one polynomial by another, we obtain a quotient and a remainder. If the remainder is 0, then the divisor is a factor of the dividend.

EXAMPLE 1 Divide to determine whether $x + 1$ and $x - 3$ are factors of

$$x^3 + 2x^2 - 5x - 6.$$

Solution We have

$$
\begin{array}{r}
\overbrace{x^2 + x - 6}^{\text{Quotient}} \\
x + 1\overline{)x^3 + 2x^2 - 5x - 6} \\
\underline{x^3 + x^2} \\
x^2 - 5x \\
\underline{x^2 + x} \\
-6x - 6 \\
\underline{-6x - 6} \\
0
\end{array}
$$

← Dividend

Divisor ———

← Remainder

Since the remainder is 0, we know that $x + 1$ is a factor of $x^3 + 2x^2 - 5x - 6$. In fact, we know that

$$x^3 + 2x^2 - 5x - 6 = (x + 1)(x^2 + x - 6).$$

We also have

$$
\begin{array}{r}
x^2 + 5x + 10 \\
x - 3 \overline{)x^3 + 2x^2 - 5x - 6} \\
\underline{x^3 - 3x^2} \\
5x^2 - 5x \\
\underline{5x^2 - 15x} \\
10x - 6 \\
\underline{10x - 30} \\
24 \leftarrow \text{Remainder}
\end{array}
$$

Since the remainder is not 0, we know that $x - 3$ is *not* a factor of $x^3 + 2x^2 - 5x - 6$.

▶ **Now Try Exercise 3.**

When we divide a polynomial $P(x)$ by a divisor $d(x)$, a polynomial $Q(x)$ is the quotient and a polynomial $R(x)$ is the remainder. The remainder must either be 0 or have degree less than that of $d(x)$.

As in arithmetic, to check a division, we multiply the quotient by the divisor and add the remainder, to see if we get the dividend. Thus these polynomials are related as follows:

$$P(x) = d(x) \cdot Q(x) + R(x)$$

Dividend   Divisor   Quotient   Remainder

For example, if $P(x) = x^3 + 2x^2 - 5x - 6$ and $d(x) = x + 1$, as in Example 1, then $Q(x) = x^2 + x - 6$ and $R(x) = 0$, and

$$\underbrace{x^3 + 2x^2 - 5x - 6}_{P(x)} = \underbrace{(x + 1)}_{d(x)} \cdot \underbrace{(x^2 + x - 6)}_{Q(x)} + \underbrace{0}_{R(x)}.$$

◆ **The Remainder Theorem and Synthetic Division**

Consider the function

$$h(x) = x^3 + 2x^2 - 5x - 6.$$

When we divided $h(x)$ by $x + 1$ and $x - 3$ in Example 1, the remainders were 0 and 24, respectively. Let's now find the function values $h(-1)$ and $h(3)$:

$$h(-1) = (-1)^3 + 2(-1)^2 - 5(-1) - 6 = 0;$$
$$h(3) = (3)^3 + 2(3)^2 - 5(3) - 6 = 24.$$

Note that the function values are the same as the remainders. This suggests the following theorem.

> ### The Remainder Theorem
> If a number c is substituted for x in the polynomial $f(x)$, then the result $f(c)$ is the remainder that would be obtained by dividing $f(x)$ by $x - c$. That is, if $f(x) = (x - c) \cdot Q(x) + R$, then $f(c) = R$.

Proof (Optional). The equation $f(x) = d(x) \cdot Q(x) + R(x)$, where $d(x) = x - c$, is the basis of this proof. If we divide $f(x)$ by $x - c$, we obtain a quotient $Q(x)$ and a remainder $R(x)$ related as follows:

$$f(x) = (x - c) \cdot Q(x) + R(x).$$

The remainder $R(x)$ must either be 0 or have degree less than $x - c$. Thus, $R(x)$ must be a constant. Let's call this constant R. The equation above is true for any replacement of x, so we replace x with c. We get

$$\begin{aligned} f(c) &= (c - c) \cdot Q(c) + R \\ &= 0 \cdot Q(c) + R \\ &= R. \end{aligned}$$

Thus the function value $f(c)$ is the remainder obtained when we divide $f(x)$ by $x - c$.

The remainder theorem motivates us to find a rapid way of dividing by $x - c$ in order to find function values. To streamline division, we can arrange the work so that duplicate and unnecessary writing is avoided. Consider the following:

$$(4x^3 - 3x^2 + x + 7) \div (x - 2).$$

A.
$$
\begin{array}{r}
4x^2 + 5x + 11 \\
x - 2\overline{)4x^3 - 3x^2 + x + 7} \\
\underline{4x^3 - 8x^2} \\
5x^2 + x \\
\underline{5x^2 - 10x} \\
11x + 7 \\
\underline{11x - 22} \\
29
\end{array}
$$

B.
$$
\begin{array}{r}
4 \quad 5 \quad 11 \\
1 - 2\overline{)4 - 3 + 1 + 7} \\
\underline{4 - 8} \\
5 + 1 \\
\underline{5 - 10} \\
11 + 7 \\
\underline{11 - 22} \\
29
\end{array}
$$

The division in (B) is the same as that in (A), but we wrote only the coefficients. The red numerals are duplicated, so we look for an arrangement in which they are not duplicated. In place of the divisor in the form $x - c$, we can simply use c and then add rather than subtract. When the procedure is "collapsed," we have the algorithm known as **synthetic division.**

C. *Synthetic Division*

$$\underline{2|}\ \ 4 \quad\quad -3 \quad\quad 1 \quad\quad\quad 7$$

The divisor is $x - 2$; thus we use 2 in synthetic division.

$$4 \quad\quad 5 \quad\quad 11 \quad\quad 29$$

We "bring down" the 4. Then we multiply it by the 2 to get 8 and add to get 5. We then multiply 5 by 2 to get 10, add, and so on. The last number, 29, is the remainder. The others, 4, 5, and 11, are the coefficients of the quotient, $4x^2 + 5x + 11$. (Note that the degree of the quotient is 1 less than the degree of the dividend when the degree of the divisor is 1.)

When using synthetic division, we write a 0 for a missing term in the dividend.

EXAMPLE 2 Use synthetic division to find the quotient and the remainder:

$$(2x^3 + 7x^2 - 5) \div (x + 3).$$

Solution First, we note that $x + 3 = x - (-3)$.

$$\underline{-3|}\ \ 2 \quad\quad 7 \quad\quad\ 0 \quad\quad -5$$
$$-6 \quad -3 \quad\quad 9$$
$$2 \quad\quad 1 \quad -3\ |\ \ 4$$

Note: We must write a 0 for the missing x-term.

The quotient is $2x^2 + x - 3$. The remainder is 4.   ▶ **Now Try Exercise 11.**

We can now use synthetic division to find polynomial function values.

EXAMPLE 3 Given that $f(x) = 2x^5 - 3x^4 + x^3 - 2x^2 + x - 8$, find $f(10)$.

Solution By the remainder theorem, $f(10)$ is the remainder when $f(x)$ is divided by $x - 10$. We use synthetic division to find that remainder.

$$\underline{10|}\ \ 2 \quad -3 \quad\quad 1 \quad\quad -2 \quad\quad\quad 1 \quad\quad\quad\quad -8$$
$$20 \quad 170 \quad 1710 \quad 17{,}080 \quad 170{,}810$$
$$2 \quad\quad 17 \quad 171 \quad 1708 \quad 17{,}081\ |\ \ 170{,}802$$

Thus, $f(10) = 170{,}802$.   ▶ **Now Try Exercise 25.**

Compare the computations in Example 3 with those in a direct substitution:

$$f(10) = 2(10)^5 - 3(10)^4 + (10)^3 - 2(10)^2 + 10 - 8$$
$$= 2 \cdot 100{,}000 - 3 \cdot 10{,}000 + 1000 - 2 \cdot 100 + 10 - 8$$
$$= 200{,}000 - 30{,}000 + 1000 - 200 + 10 - 8$$
$$= 170{,}802.$$

EXAMPLE 4 Determine whether -4 is a zero of $f(x)$, where

$$f(x) = x^3 + 8x^2 + 8x - 32.$$

Solution   We use synthetic division and the remainder theorem to find $f(-4)$.

$$
\begin{array}{r|rrrr}
-4 & 1 & 8 & 8 & -32 \\
   &   & -4 & -16 & 32 \\
\hline
   & 1 & 4 & -8 & \;0
\end{array}
$$

Since $f(-4) = 0$, the number -4 is a zero of $f(x)$.   ▶ Now Try Exercise 31.

EXAMPLE 5   Determine whether i is a zero of $f(x)$, where

$$f(x) = x^3 - 3x^2 + x - 3.$$

Solution   We use synthetic division and the remainder theorem to find $f(i)$.

$$
\begin{array}{r|cccc}
i & 1 & -3 & 1 & -3 \\
  &   & i & -3i-1 & 3 \\
\hline
  & 1 & -3+i & -3i & \;0
\end{array}
$$

$i(-3+i) = -3i + i^2 = -3i - 1$
$i(-3i) = -3i^2 = 3$

Since $f(i) = 0$, the number i is a zero of $f(x)$.   ▶ Now Try Exercise 35.

◆ Finding Factors of Polynomials

We now consider a useful result that follows from the remainder theorem.

> **The Factor Theorem**
> For a polynomial $f(x)$, if $f(c) = 0$, then $x - c$ is a factor of $f(x)$.

Proof (Optional).   If we divide $f(x)$ by $x - c$, we obtain a quotient and a remainder, related as follows:

$$f(x) = (x - c) \cdot Q(x) + f(c).$$

Then if $f(c) = 0$, we have

$$f(x) = (x - c) \cdot Q(x),$$

so $x - c$ is a factor of $f(x)$.

The factor theorem is very useful in factoring polynomials, and hence in solving polynomial equations and finding zeros of polynomial functions. If we know a zero of a polynomial function, we know a factor.

EXAMPLE 6   Let $f(x) = x^3 + 2x^2 - 5x - 6$. Factor $f(x)$ and solve the equation $f(x) = 0$.

Solution   We look for linear factors of the form $x - c$. Let's try $x - 1$. (In the next section, we will learn a method for choosing the numbers to try for c.) We use synthetic division to determine whether $f(1) = 0$.

$$
\begin{array}{r|rrrr}
1 & 1 & 2 & -5 & -6 \\
  &   & 1 & 3 & -2 \\
\hline
  & 1 & 3 & -2 & -8
\end{array}
$$

Since $f(1) \neq 0$, we know that $x - 1$ *is not a factor* of $f(x)$. We try $x + 1$ or $x - (-1)$.

$$\begin{array}{r|rrrr} -1 & 1 & 2 & -5 & -6 \\ & & -1 & -1 & 6 \\ \hline & 1 & 1 & -6 & \,|\quad 0 \end{array}$$

Since $f(-1) = 0$, we know that $x + 1$ *is one factor* of $f(x)$ and the quotient, $x^2 + x - 6$, is another. Thus,

$$f(x) = (x + 1)(x^2 + x - 6).$$

The trinomial $x^2 + x - 6$ is easily factored in this case, so we have

$$f(x) = (x + 1)(x + 3)(x - 2).$$

Our goal is to solve the equation $f(x) = 0$. To do so, we use the principle of zero products:

$$(x + 1)(x + 3)(x - 2) = 0$$

$$x + 1 = 0 \quad \text{or} \quad x + 3 = 0 \quad \text{or} \quad x - 2 = 0$$

$$x = -1 \quad \text{or} \quad\quad x = -3 \quad \text{or} \quad\quad x = 2.$$

The solutions of the equation $x^3 + 2x^2 - 5x - 6 = 0$ are -1, -3, and 2. They are also the zeros of the function $f(x) = x^3 + 2x^2 - 5x - 6$.

▶ **Now Try Exercise 41.**

TECHNOLOGY ············
CONNECTION

In Example 6, we can use a table set in ASK mode to check the solutions of the equation

$$x^3 + 2x^2 - 5x - 6 = 0.$$

We check the solutions, -1, -3, and 2, of $f(x) = 0$ by evaluating $f(-1)$, $f(-3)$, and $f(2)$.

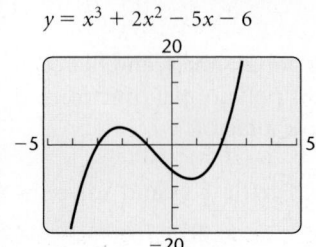

X	Y₁	
-1	0	
-3	0	
2	0	

X = 2

CONNECTING THE CONCEPTS

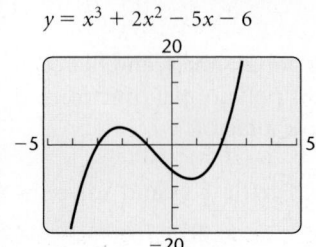

$y = x^3 + 2x^2 - 5x - 6$

Consider the function

$$f(x) = (x - 2)(x + 3)(x + 1), \quad \text{or} \quad f(x) = x^3 + 2x^2 - 5x - 6,$$

and its graph.

The following statements are equivalent:

- -3 is a zero of f.
- $f(-3) = 0$.
- -3 is a solution of $f(x) = 0$.
- $(-3, 0)$ is an x-intercept of the graph of f.
- 0 is the remainder when $f(x)$ is divided by $x - (-3)$.
- $x - (-3)$ is a factor of f.

These statements are also true for -1 and 2.

● ● ●

3.3 EXERCISE SET

1. For the function
$$f(x) = x^4 - 6x^3 + x^2 + 24x - 20,$$
use long division to determine which of the following are factors of $f(x)$.
   a) $x + 1$ b) $x - 2$ c) $x + 5$

2. For the function
$$h(x) = x^3 - x^2 - 17x - 15,$$
use long division to determine which of the following are factors of $h(x)$.
   a) $x + 5$ b) $x + 1$ c) $x + 3$

3. For the function
$$g(x) = x^3 - 2x^2 - 11x + 12,$$
use long division to determine which of the following are factors of $g(x)$.
   a) $x - 4$ b) $x - 3$ c) $x - 1$

4. For the function
$$f(x) = x^4 + 8x^3 + 5x^2 - 38x + 24,$$
use long division to determine which of the following are factors of $f(x)$.
   a) $x + 6$ b) $x + 1$ c) $x - 4$

In each of the following, a polynomial P(x) and a divisor d(x) are given. Use long division to find the quotient Q(x) and the remainder R(x) when P(x) is divided by d(x), and express P(x) in the form d(x) · Q(x) + R(x).

5. $P(x) = x^3 - 8,$
   $d(x) = x + 2$

6. $P(x) = 2x^3 - 3x^2 + x - 1,$
   $d(x) = x - 3$

7. $P(x) = x^3 + 6x^2 - 25x + 18,$
   $d(x) = x + 9$

8. $P(x) = x^3 - 9x^2 + 15x + 25,$
   $d(x) = x - 5$

9. $P(x) = x^4 - 2x^2 + 3,$
   $d(x) = x + 2$

10. $P(x) = x^4 + 6x^3,$
    $d(x) = x - 1$

Use synthetic division to find the quotient and the remainder.

11. $(2x^4 + 7x^3 + x - 12) \div (x + 3)$

12. $(x^3 - 7x^2 + 13x + 3) \div (x - 2)$

13. $(x^3 - 2x^2 - 8) \div (x + 2)$

14. $(x^3 - 3x + 10) \div (x - 2)$

15. $(3x^3 - x^2 + 4x - 10) \div (x + 1)$

16. $(4x^4 - 2x + 5) \div (x + 3)$

17. $(x^5 + x^3 - x) \div (x - 3)$

18. $(x^7 - x^6 + x^5 - x^4 + 2) \div (x + 1)$

19. $(x^4 - 1) \div (x - 1)$

20. $(x^5 + 32) \div (x + 2)$

21. $(2x^4 + 3x^2 - 1) \div \left(x - \frac{1}{2}\right)$

22. $(3x^4 - 2x^2 + 2) \div \left(x - \frac{1}{4}\right)$

Use synthetic division to find the function values.

23. $f(x) = x^3 - 6x^2 + 11x - 6$; find $f(1)$, $f(-2)$, and $f(3)$.

24. $f(x) = x^3 + 7x^2 - 12x - 3$; find $f(-3)$, $f(-2)$, and $f(1)$.

25. $f(x) = x^4 - 3x^3 + 2x + 8$; find $f(-1)$, $f(4)$, and $f(-5)$.

26. $f(x) = 2x^4 + x^2 - 10x + 1$; find $f(-10)$, $f(2)$, and $f(3)$.

27. $f(x) = 2x^5 - 3x^4 + 2x^3 - x + 8$; find $f(20)$ and $f(-3)$.

28. $f(x) = x^5 - 10x^4 + 20x^3 - 5x - 100$; find $f(-10)$ and $f(5)$.

29. $f(x) = x^4 - 16$; find $f(2)$, $f(-2)$, $f(3)$, and $f(1 - \sqrt{2})$.

30. $f(x) = x^5 + 32$; find $f(2)$, $f(-2)$, $f(3)$, and $f(2 + 3i)$.

Using synthetic division, determine whether the numbers are zeros of the polynomial function.

31. $-3, 2$; $f(x) = 3x^3 + 5x^2 - 6x + 18$

32. $-4, 2$; $f(x) = 3x^3 + 11x^2 - 2x + 8$

33. $-3, 1$; $h(x) = x^4 + 4x^3 + 2x^2 - 4x - 3$

34. $2, -1$; $g(x) = x^4 - 6x^3 + x^2 + 24x - 20$

35. $i, -2i$; $g(x) = x^3 - 4x^2 + 4x - 16$

36. $\frac{1}{3}, 2$; $h(x) = x^3 - x^2 - \frac{1}{9}x + \frac{1}{9}$

37. $-3, \frac{1}{2}$; $f(x) = x^3 - \frac{7}{2}x^2 + x - \frac{3}{2}$

38. $i, -i, -2$; $f(x) = x^3 + 2x^2 + x + 2$

Factor the polynomial $f(x)$. Then solve the equation $f(x) = 0$.

39. $f(x) = x^3 + 4x^2 + x - 6$

40. $f(x) = x^3 + 5x^2 - 2x - 24$

41. $f(x) = x^3 - 6x^2 + 3x + 10$

42. $f(x) = x^3 + 2x^2 - 13x + 10$

43. $f(x) = x^3 - x^2 - 14x + 24$

44. $f(x) = x^3 - 3x^2 - 10x + 24$

45. $f(x) = x^4 - 7x^3 + 9x^2 + 27x - 54$

46. $f(x) = x^4 - 4x^3 - 7x^2 + 34x - 24$

47. $f(x) = x^4 - x^3 - 19x^2 + 49x - 30$

48. $f(x) = x^4 + 11x^3 + 41x^2 + 61x + 30$

Sketch the graph of the polynomial function. Follow the procedure outlined on page 272. Use synthetic division and the remainder theorem to find the zeros.

49. $f(x) = x^4 - x^3 - 7x^2 + x + 6$

50. $f(x) = x^4 + x^3 - 3x^2 - 5x - 2$

51. $f(x) = x^3 - 7x + 6$

52. $f(x) = x^3 - 12x + 16$

53. $f(x) = -x^3 + 3x^2 + 6x - 8$

54. $f(x) = -x^4 + 2x^3 + 3x^2 - 4x - 4$

Technology Connection

55. Use a graphing calculator to find the function values in Exercises 23–30.

Collaborative Discussion and Writing

56. Can an nth-degree polynomial function have more than n zeros? Why or why not?

57. Suppose a polynomial function $P(x)$ has a factor $p(x)$. If $p(2) = 0$, does it follow that $P(2) = 0$? Why or why not? If $P(2) = 0$, does it follow that $p(2) = 0$? Why or why not?

Skill Maintenance

Solve. Find exact solutions.

58. $2x - 7 = 5x + 8$

59. $2x^2 + 12 = 5x$

60. $7x^2 + 4x = 3$

Consider the function
$$g(x) = x^2 + 5x - 14$$
in Exercises 61–63.

61. What are the inputs if the output is -14?

62. What is the output if the input is 3?

63. Given an output of -20, find the corresponding inputs.

64. *Catalog Sales.* Catalog retailers have witnessed a continual linear gain in sales for over a decade. Catalog sales have risen from \$27.2 billion in 1989 to \$72 billion in 2001 (*Source*: The Direct Marketing Association). Using these two data points, find a linear function, $f(x) = mx + b$, that models the data. Let x represent the number of years since 1989. Then use this function to estimate catalog sales for 2000, 2005, and 2010.

65. The sum of the base and the height of a triangle is 30 in. Find the dimensions for which the area is a maximum.

Synthesis

In Exercises 66 and 67, a graph of a polynomial function is given. On the basis of the graph:

a) *Find as many factors of the polynomial as you can.*
b) *Construct a polynomial function with the zeros shown in the graph.*
c) *Can you find any other polynomial functions with the given zeros?*
d) *Can you find any other polynomial functions with the given zeros and the same graph?*

66.

67.

68. For what values of k will the remainder be the same when $x^2 + kx + 4$ is divided by $x - 1$ and $x + 1$?

69. Find k such that $x + 2$ is a factor of
$x^3 - kx^2 + 3x + 7k$.

70. *Beam Deflection.* A beam rests at two points A and B and has a concentrated load applied to its center. Let $y =$ the deflection, in feet, of the beam at a distance of x feet from A. Under certain conditions, this deflection is given by

$$y = \frac{1}{13}x^3 - \frac{1}{14}x.$$

Find the zeros of the polynomial in the interval $[0, 2]$.

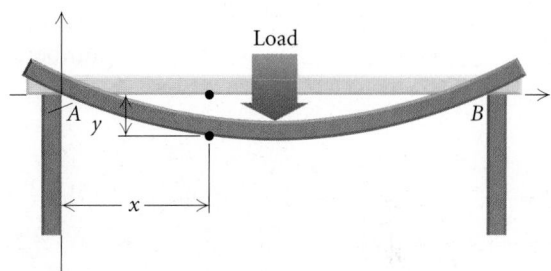

Solve.

71. $\dfrac{2x^2}{x^2 - 1} + \dfrac{4}{x + 3} = \dfrac{32}{x^3 + 3x^2 - x - 3}$

72. $\dfrac{6x^2}{x^2 + 11} + \dfrac{60}{x^3 - 7x^2 + 11x - 77} = \dfrac{1}{x - 7}$

73. Find a 15th-degree polynomial for which $x - 1$ is a factor. Answers may vary.

Use synthetic division to divide.

74. $(x^2 - 4x - 2) \div [x - (3 + 2i)]$

75. $(x^2 - 3x + 7) \div (x - i)$

3.4 Theorems about Zeros of Polynomial Functions

◆ Find a polynomial with specified zeros.

◆ For a polynomial function with integer coefficients, find the rational zeros and the other zeros, if possible.

◆ Use Descartes' rule of signs to find information about the number of real zeros of a polynomial function with real coefficients.

We will now allow the coefficients of a polynomial to be complex numbers. In certain cases, we will restrict the coefficients to be real numbers, rational numbers, or integers, as shown in the following examples.

Polynomial	Type of Coefficient
$5x^3 - 3x^2 + (2 + 4i)x + i$	Complex
$5x^3 - 3x^2 + \sqrt{2}x - \pi$	Real
$5x^3 - 3x^2 + \frac{2}{3}x - \frac{7}{4}$	Rational
$5x^3 - 3x^2 + 8x - 11$	Integer

◆ The Fundamental Theorem of Algebra

A linear, or first-degree, polynomial function $f(x) = mx + b$ (where $m \neq 0$) has just one zero, $-b/m$. It can be shown that any quadratic polynomial function with complex numbers for coefficients has at least one, and at most two, complex zeros. The following theorem is a generalization. No proof is given in this text.

> **The Fundamental Theorem of Algebra**
>
> Every polynomial function of degree n, with $n \geq 1$, has at least one zero in the system of complex numbers.

Note that although the fundamental theorem of algebra guarantees that a zero exists, it does not tell how to find it. Recall that the zeros of a polynomial function $f(x)$ are the solutions of the polynomial equation $f(x) = 0$. We now develop some concepts that can help in finding zeros. First, we consider one of the results of the fundamental theorem of algebra.

> Every polynomial function f of degree n, with $n \geq 1$, can be factored into n linear factors (not necessarily unique); that is,
> $$f(x) = a_n(x - c_1)(x - c_2) \cdots (x - c_n).$$

✦ Finding Polynomials with Given Zeros

Given several numbers, we can find a polynomial function with those numbers as its zeros.

EXAMPLE 1 Find a polynomial function of degree 3, having the zeros 1, $3i$, and $-3i$.

Solution Such a polynomial has factors $x - 1$, $x - 3i$, and $x + 3i$, so we have

$$f(x) = a_n(x - 1)(x - 3i)(x + 3i).$$

The number a_n can be any nonzero number. The simplest polynomial will be obtained if we let it be 1. If we then multiply the factors, we obtain

$$f(x) = (x - 1)(x^2 + 9) \qquad \text{Multiplying } (x - 3i)(x + 3i)$$
$$= x^3 - x^2 + 9x - 9.$$

▶ Now Try Exercise 3.

EXAMPLE 2 Find a polynomial function of degree 5 with -1 as a zero of multiplicity 3, 4 as a zero of multiplicity 1, and 0 as a zero of multiplicity 1.

Solution Proceeding as in Example 1, letting $a_n = 1$, we obtain

$$f(x) = (x + 1)^3(x - 4)(x - 0)$$
$$= x^5 - x^4 - 9x^3 - 11x^2 - 4x.$$

▶ Now Try Exercise 13.

✦ Zeros of Polynomial Functions with Real Coefficients

Consider the quadratic equation $x^2 - 2x + 2 = 0$, with real coefficients. Its solutions are $1 + i$ and $1 - i$. Note that the solutions are complex conjugates. This generalizes to any polynomial with real coefficients.

> **Nonreal Zeros: $a + bi$ and $a - bi$, $b \neq 0$**
>
> If a complex number $a + bi$, $b \neq 0$, is a zero of a polynomial function $f(x)$ with *real* coefficients, then its conjugate, $a - bi$, is also a zero. For example, if $2 + 7i$ is a zero of a polynomial function $f(x)$, with real coefficients, then its conjugate, $2 - 7i$, is also a zero. (Nonreal zeros occur in conjugate pairs.)

In order for the preceding to be true, it is essential that the coefficients be real numbers.

✦ Rational Coefficients

When a polynomial has rational numbers for coefficients, certain irrational zeros also occur in pairs, as described in the following theorem.

> ### Irrational Zeros: $a + c\sqrt{b}$ and $a - c\sqrt{b}$, b is not a perfect square
>
> If $a + c\sqrt{b}$, where a, b, and c are rational and b is not a perfect square, is a zero of a polynomial function $f(x)$ with *rational* coefficients, then its conjugate, $a - c\sqrt{b}$, is also a zero. For example, if $-3 + 5\sqrt{2}$ is a zero of a polynomial function $f(x)$, with rational coefficients, then its conjugate, $-3 - 5\sqrt{2}$, is also a zero.

EXAMPLE 3   Suppose that a polynomial function of degree 6 with rational coefficients has

$$-2 + 5i, \qquad -2i, \quad \text{and} \quad 1 - \sqrt{3}$$

as three of its zeros. Find the other zeros.

Solution   Since the coefficients are rational, and thus real, the other zeros are the conjugates of the given zeros,

$$-2 - 5i, \qquad 2i, \quad \text{and} \quad 1 + \sqrt{3}.$$

There are no other zeros because a polynomial of degree 6 can have at most 6 zeros.   ▷ Now Try Exercise 17.

EXAMPLE 4   Find a polynomial function of lowest degree with rational coefficients that has $1 - \sqrt{2}$ and $1 + 2i$ as two of its zeros.

Solution   The function must also have the zeros $1 + \sqrt{2}$ and $1 - 2i$. Because we want to find the polynomial function of lowest degree with the given zeros, we will not include additional zeros. That is, we will write a polynomial function of degree 4. Thus, if we let $a_n = 1$, the polynomial function is

$$\begin{aligned}
f(x) &= \left[x - \left(1 - \sqrt{2}\right)\right]\left[x - \left(1 + \sqrt{2}\right)\right]\left[x - (1 + 2i)\right]\left[x - (1 - 2i)\right] \\
&= (x^2 - 2x - 1)(x^2 - 2x + 5) \\
&= x^4 - 4x^3 + 8x^2 - 8x - 5.
\end{aligned}$$

▷ Now Try Exercise 39.

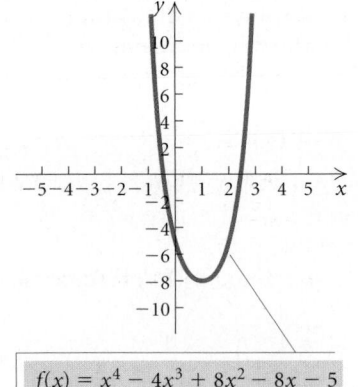

$f(x) = x^4 - 4x^3 + 8x^2 - 8x - 5$

✦ Integer Coefficients and the Rational Zeros Theorem

It is not always easy to find the zeros of a polynomial function. However, if a polynomial function has integer coefficients, there is a procedure that will yield all the rational zeros.

> **The Rational Zeros Theorem**
>
> Let
> $$P(x) = a_n x^n + a_{n-1} x^{n-1} + \cdots + a_1 x + a_0,$$
> where all the coefficients are integers. Consider a rational number denoted by p/q, where p and q are relatively prime (having no common factor besides -1 and 1). If p/q is a zero of $P(x)$, then p is a factor of a_0 and q is a factor of a_n.

EXAMPLE 5   Given $f(x) = 3x^4 - 11x^3 + 10x - 4$:

a) Find the rational zeros and then the other zeros; that is, solve $f(x) = 0$.

b) Factor $f(x)$ into linear factors.

Solution

a) Because the degree of $f(x)$ is 4, there are at most 4 distinct zeros. The rational zeros theorem says that if a rational number p/q is a zero of $f(x)$, then p must be a factor of -4 and q must be a factor of 3. Thus the possibilities for p/q are

$$\frac{Possibilities\ for\ p}{Possibilities\ for\ q}: \quad \frac{\pm 1, \pm 2, \pm 4}{\pm 1, \pm 3};$$

$Possibilities\ for\ p/q: \quad 1, -1, 2, -2, 4, -4, \frac{1}{3}, -\frac{1}{3}, \frac{2}{3}, -\frac{2}{3}, \frac{4}{3}, -\frac{4}{3}.$

To find which are zeros, we could use substitution, but synthetic division is usually more efficient. It is easier to consider the integers first. Then we consider the fractions, if the integers do not produce all the zeros.

We try 1:

$$\begin{array}{r|rrrrr} 1 & 3 & -11 & 0 & 10 & -4 \\ & & 3 & -8 & -8 & 2 \\ \hline & 3 & -8 & -8 & 2 & -2. \end{array}$$

Since $f(1) = -2$, 1 is not a zero.

We try -1:

$$\begin{array}{r|rrrrr} -1 & 3 & -11 & 0 & 10 & -4 \\ & & -3 & 14 & -14 & 4 \\ \hline & 3 & -14 & 14 & -4 & 0. \end{array}$$

We have $f(-1) = 0$, so -1 is a zero. Thus, $x + 1$ is a factor of $f(x)$. Using the results of the second division above, we can express $f(x)$ as

$$f(x) = (x + 1)(3x^3 - 14x^2 + 14x - 4).$$

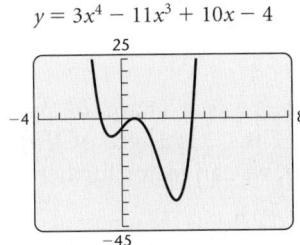

We now consider the factor $3x^3 - 14x^2 + 14x - 4$ and check the other possible zeros. We use synthetic division again, to determine whether -1 is a zero of multiplicity 2 of $f(x)$:

$$
\begin{array}{r|rrrr}
-1 & 3 & -14 & 14 & -4 \\
   &   & -3 & 17 & -31 \\
\hline
   & 3 & -17 & 31 & -35.
\end{array}
$$

We see that -1 is not a double zero. We leave it to the student to verify that $2, -2, 4,$ and -4 are not zeros. There are no other possible zeros that are integers, so we start checking the fractions.

Let's now try $\frac{2}{3}$.

$$
\begin{array}{r|rrrr}
2/3 & 3 & -14 & 14 & -4 \\
    &   & 2   & -8 & 4 \\
\hline
    & 3 & -12 & 6 & 0
\end{array}
$$

Since the remainder is 0, we know that $x - \frac{2}{3}$ is a factor of $3x^3 - 14x^2 + 14x - 4$ and is also a factor of $f(x)$. Thus, $\frac{2}{3}$ is a zero of $f(x)$.

Using the results of the synthetic division, we can factor further:

$$f(x) = (x + 1)\left(x - \tfrac{2}{3}\right)(3x^2 - 12x + 6) \qquad \text{Using the results of the last synthetic division}$$

$$= (x + 1)\left(x - \tfrac{2}{3}\right) \cdot 3 \cdot (x^2 - 4x + 2). \qquad \text{Removing a factor of 3}$$

The quadratic formula can be used to find the values of x for which $x^2 - 4x + 2 = 0$. Those values are also zeros of $f(x)$:

$$x = \frac{-b \pm \sqrt{b^2 - 4ac}}{2a}$$

$$= \frac{-(-4) \pm \sqrt{(-4)^2 - 4 \cdot 1 \cdot 2}}{2 \cdot 1}$$

$$= \frac{4 \pm \sqrt{8}}{2} = \frac{4 \pm 2\sqrt{2}}{2} = \frac{2\left(2 \pm \sqrt{2}\right)}{2}$$

$$= 2 \pm \sqrt{2}.$$

The rational zeros are -1 and $\frac{2}{3}$. The other zeros are $2 \pm \sqrt{2}$.

b) The complete factorization of $f(x)$ is

$$f(x) = 3(x + 1)\left(x - \tfrac{2}{3}\right)\left[x - \left(2 - \sqrt{2}\right)\right]\left[x - \left(2 + \sqrt{2}\right)\right].$$

▶ Now Try Exercise 55.

EXAMPLE 6   Given $f(x) = 2x^5 - x^4 - 4x^3 + 2x^2 - 30x + 15$:

a) Find the rational zeros and then the other zeros; that is, solve $f(x) = 0$.

b) Factor $f(x)$ into linear factors.

We can inspect the graph of
the function in Example 6
for zeros that appear to be
near any of the possible
rational zeros.

$y = 2x^5 - x^4 - 4x^3 + 2x^2$
$\quad - 30x + 15$

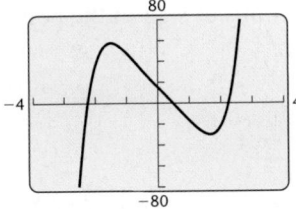

We see that, of the
possibilities in the list, only
the numbers

$$-\tfrac{5}{2}, \quad \tfrac{1}{2}, \quad \text{and} \quad \tfrac{5}{2}$$

might be rational zeros. With
the TABLE feature, we can
determine that only $\frac{1}{2}$ is actually
a rational zero.

Solution

a) Because the degree of $f(x)$ is 5, there are at most 5 distinct zeros.
   According to the rational zeros theorem, any rational zero of f must be of
   the form p/q, where p is a factor of 15 and q is a factor of 2. The possibilities are

$$\frac{\text{Possibilities for } p}{\text{Possibilities for } q}: \quad \frac{\pm 1, \pm 3, \pm 5, \pm 15}{\pm 1, \pm 2};$$

Possibilities for p/q: $\quad 1, -1, 3, -3, 5, -5, 15, -15, \tfrac{1}{2}, -\tfrac{1}{2}, \tfrac{3}{2}, -\tfrac{3}{2},$
$\qquad\qquad\qquad\qquad \tfrac{5}{2}, -\tfrac{5}{2}, \tfrac{15}{2}, -\tfrac{15}{2}.$

We use synthetic division to check each of the possibilities. Let's try
1 and -1.

$$
\begin{array}{r|rrrrrr}
1 & 2 & -1 & -4 & 2 & -30 & 15 \\
  &   & 2 & 1 & -3 & -1 & -31 \\
\hline
  & 2 & 1 & -3 & -1 & -31 & -16
\end{array}
$$

$$
\begin{array}{r|rrrrrr}
-1 & 2 & -1 & -4 & 2 & -30 & 15 \\
   &   & -2 & 3 & 1 & -3 & 33 \\
\hline
   & 2 & -3 & -1 & 3 & -33 & 48
\end{array}
$$

Since $f(1) = -16$ and $f(-1) = 48$, neither 1 nor -1 is a zero of the
function. We leave it to the student to verify that the other integer possibilities are not zeros. We now check $\frac{1}{2}$.

$$
\begin{array}{r|rrrrrr}
\tfrac{1}{2} & 2 & -1 & -4 & 2 & -30 & 15 \\
             &   & 1 & 0 & -2 & 0 & -15 \\
\hline
             & 2 & 0 & -4 & 0 & -30 & 0
\end{array}
$$

This means that $x - \frac{1}{2}$ is a factor of $f(x)$. We write the factorization and
try to factor further:

$$
\begin{aligned}
f(x) &= \left(x - \tfrac{1}{2}\right)(2x^4 - 4x^2 - 30) \\
     &= \left(x - \tfrac{1}{2}\right) \cdot 2 \cdot (x^4 - 2x^2 - 15) \qquad \text{Factoring out the 2} \\
     &= \left(x - \tfrac{1}{2}\right) \cdot 2 \cdot (x^2 - 5)(x^2 + 3). \qquad \text{Factoring the trinomial}
\end{aligned}
$$

We now solve the equation $f(x) = 0$ to determine the zeros. We use the
principle of zero products:

$$\left(x - \tfrac{1}{2}\right) \cdot 2 \cdot (x^2 - 5)(x^2 + 3) = 0$$

$x - \tfrac{1}{2} = 0 \quad$ or $\quad x^2 - 5 = 0 \qquad$ or $\quad x^2 + 3 = 0$

$\qquad x = \tfrac{1}{2} \quad$ or $\qquad x^2 = 5 \qquad$ or $\qquad x^2 = -3$

$\qquad x = \tfrac{1}{2} \quad$ or $\qquad x = \pm\sqrt{5} \quad$ or $\qquad x = \pm\sqrt{3}i.$

There is only one rational zero, $\frac{1}{2}$. The other zeros are $\pm\sqrt{5}$ and $\pm\sqrt{3}i$.

b) The factorization into linear factors is

$$f(x) = 2\left(x - \tfrac{1}{2}\right)\left(x + \sqrt{5}\right)\left(x - \sqrt{5}\right)\left(x + \sqrt{3}i\right)\left(x - \sqrt{3}i\right).$$

▶ Now Try Exercise 61.

✦ Descartes' Rule of Signs

The development of a rule that helps determine the number of positive real zeros and the number of negative real zeros of a polynomial function is credited to the French mathematician René Descartes. To use the rule, we must have the polynomial arranged in descending or ascending order, with no zero terms written in, and the *constant term* not 0. Then we determine the number of *variations of sign*, that is, the number of times, in reading through the polynomial, that successive coefficients are of different signs.

EXAMPLE 7   Determine the number of variations of sign in the polynomial function $P(x) = 2x^5 - 3x^2 + x + 4$.

Solution   We have

$$P(x) = 2x^5 - 3x^2 + x + 4$$

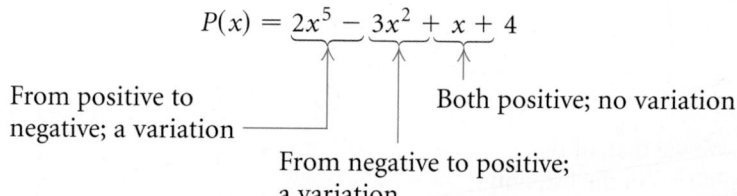

From positive to negative; a variation

Both positive; no variation

From negative to positive; a variation

The number of variations of sign is 2.

Note the following:

$$P(-x) = 2(-x)^5 - 3(-x)^2 + (-x) + 4$$
$$= -2x^5 - 3x^2 - x + 4.$$

We see that the number of variations of sign in $P(-x)$ is 1. It occurs as we go from $-x$ to 4.

We now state Descartes' rule, without proof.

Descartes' Rule of Signs

Let $P(x)$, written in descending or ascending order, be a polynomial function with real coefficients and a nonzero constant term. The number of positive real zeros of $P(x)$ is either:

1. The same as the number of variations of sign in $P(x)$, or
2. Less than the number of variations of sign in $P(x)$ by a positive even integer.

The number of negative real zeros of $P(x)$ is either:

3. The same as the number of variations of sign in $P(-x)$, or
4. Less than the number of variations of sign in $P(-x)$ by a positive even integer.

A zero of multiplicity m must be counted m times.

In each of Examples 8–10, what does Descartes' rule of signs tell you about the number of positive real zeros and the number of negative real zeros?

EXAMPLE 8 $P(x) = 2x^5 - 5x^2 - 3x + 6$

Solution The number of variations of sign in $P(x)$ is 2. Therefore, the number of positive real zeros is either 2 or less than 2 by 2, 4, 6, and so on. Thus the number of positive real zeros is either 2 or 0, since a negative number of zeros has no meaning.

$$P(-x) = -2x^5 - 5x^2 + 3x + 6$$

The number of variations of sign in $P(-x)$ is 1. Thus there is exactly 1 negative real zero. Since nonreal, complex conjugates occur in pairs, we also know the possible ways in which nonreal zeros might occur. The table at left summarizes all the possibilities for real and nonreal zeros of $P(x)$.

▶ Now Try Exercise 85.

Total Number of Zeros	5	
Positive Real	2	0
Negative Real	1	1
Nonreal	2	4

EXAMPLE 9 $P(x) = 5x^4 - 3x^3 + 7x^2 - 12x + 4$

Solution There are 4 variations of sign. Thus the number of positive real zeros is either

$$4 \quad \text{or} \quad 4 - 2 \quad \text{or} \quad 4 - 4.$$

That is, the number of positive real zeros is 4, 2, or 0.

$$P(-x) = 5x^4 + 3x^3 + 7x^2 + 12x + 4$$

There are 0 changes in sign, so there are no negative real zeros.

▶ Now Try Exercise 79.

EXAMPLE 10 $P(x) = 6x^6 - 2x^2 - 5x$

Solution As written, the polynomial does not satisfy the conditions of Descartes' rule of signs because the constant term is 0. But because x is a factor of every term, we know that the polynomial has 0 as a zero. We can then factor as follows:

$$P(x) = x(6x^5 - 2x - 5).$$

Now we analyze $Q(x) = 6x^5 - 2x - 5$ and $Q(-x) = -6x^5 + 2x - 5$. The number of variations of sign in $Q(x)$ is 1. Therefore, there is exactly 1 positive real zero. The number of variations of sign in $Q(-x)$ is 2. Thus the number of negative real zeros is 2 or 0. The same results apply to $P(x)$.

▶ Now Try Exercise 93.

STUDY TIP

It is never too soon to begin reviewing for the final examination. The Skill Maintenance exercises found in each exercise set review and reinforce skills taught in earlier sections. Be sure to do these exercises as you do the homework assignment in each section. Answers to both even-numbered and odd-numbered skill maintenance exercises, along with section references, appear at the back of the book.

3.4 EXERCISE SET

Find a polynomial function of degree 3 with the given numbers as zeros.

1. $-2, 3, 5$

2. $-1, 0, 4$

3. $-3, 2i, -2i$

4. $2, i, -i$

5. $\sqrt{2}, -\sqrt{2}, 3$

6. $-5, \sqrt{3}, -\sqrt{3}$

7. $1 - \sqrt{3}, 1 + \sqrt{3}, -2$

8. $-4, 1 - \sqrt{5}, 1 + \sqrt{5}$

9. $1 + 6i, 1 - 6i, -4$

10. $1 + 4i, 1 - 4i, -1$

11. $-\frac{1}{3}, 0, 2$

12. $-3, 0, \frac{1}{2}$

13. Find a polynomial function of degree 5 with -1 as a zero of multiplicity 3, 0 as a zero of multiplicity 1, and 1 as a zero of multiplicity 1.

14. Find a polynomial function of degree 4 with -2 as a zero of multiplicity 1, 3 as a zero of multiplicity 2, and -1 as a zero of multiplicity 1.

15. Find a polynomial function of degree 4 with -1 as a zero of multiplicity 3 and 0 as a zero of multiplicity 1.

16. Find a polynomial function of degree 5 with $-\frac{1}{2}$ as a zero of multiplicity 2, 0 as a zero of multiplicity 1, and 1 as a zero of multiplicity 2.

Suppose that a polynomial function of degree 4 with rational coefficients has the given numbers as zeros. Find the other zero(s).

17. $-1, \sqrt{3}, \frac{11}{3}$

18. $-\sqrt{2}, -1, \frac{4}{5}$

19. $-i, 2 - \sqrt{5}$

20. $i, -3 + \sqrt{3}$

21. $3i, 0, -5$

22. $3, 0, -2i$

23. $-4 - 3i, 2 - \sqrt{3}$

24. $6 - 5i, -1 + \sqrt{7}$

Suppose that a polynomial function of degree 5 with rational coefficients has the given numbers as zeros. Find the other zero(s).

25. $-\frac{1}{2}, \sqrt{5}, -4i$

26. $\frac{3}{4}, -\sqrt{3}, 2i$

27. $-5, 0, 2 - i, 4$

28. $-2, 3, 4, 1 - i$

29. $6, -3 + 4i, 4 - \sqrt{5}$

30. $-3 - 3i, 2 + \sqrt{13}, 6$

31. $-\frac{3}{4}, \frac{3}{4}, 0, 4 - i$

32. $-0.6, 0, 0.6, -3 + \sqrt{2}$

Find a polynomial function of lowest degree with rational coefficients that has the given numbers as some of its zeros.

33. $1 + i, 2$

34. $2 - i, -1$

35. $4i$

36. $-5i$

37. $-4i, 5$

38. $3, -i$

39. $1 - i, -\sqrt{5}$

40. $2 - \sqrt{3}, 1 + i$

41. $\sqrt{5}, -3i$

42. $-\sqrt{2}, 4i$

Suppose the polynomial function has the given zero. Find the other zeros.

43. $f(x) = x^3 + 5x^2 - 2x - 10; \ -5$

44. $f(x) = x^3 - x^2 + x - 1; \ 1$

45. $f(x) = x^4 - 5x^3 + 7x^2 - 5x + 6; \ -i$

46. $f(x) = x^4 - 16; \ 2i$

47. $f(x) = x^3 - 6x^2 + 13x - 20; \ 4$

48. $f(x) = x^3 - 8; \ 2$

List all possible rational zeros of the function.

49. $f(x) = x^5 - 3x^2 + 1$

50. $f(x) = x^7 + 37x^5 - 6x^2 + 12$

51. $f(x) = 2x^4 - 3x^3 - x + 8$

52. $f(x) = 3x^3 - x^2 + 6x - 9$

53. $f(x) = 15x^6 + 47x^2 + 2$

54. $f(x) = 10x^{25} + 3x^{17} - 35x + 6$

For each polynomial function:

a) *Find the rational zeros and then the other zeros; that is, solve $f(x) = 0$.*
b) *Factor $f(x)$ into linear factors.*

55. $f(x) = x^3 + 3x^2 - 2x - 6$

56. $f(x) = x^3 - x^2 - 3x + 3$

57. $f(x) = x^3 - 3x + 2$

58. $f(x) = x^3 - 2x + 4$

59. $f(x) = x^3 - 5x^2 + 11x + 17$

60. $f(x) = 2x^3 + 7x^2 + 2x - 8$

61. $f(x) = 5x^4 - 4x^3 + 19x^2 - 16x - 4$

62. $f(x) = 3x^4 - 4x^3 + x^2 + 6x - 2$

63. $f(x) = x^4 - 3x^3 - 20x^2 - 24x - 8$

64. $f(x) = x^4 + 5x^3 - 27x^2 + 31x - 10$

65. $f(x) = x^3 - 4x^2 + 2x + 4$

66. $f(x) = x^3 - 8x^2 + 17x - 4$

67. $f(x) = x^3 + 8$ **68.** $f(x) = x^3 - 8$

69. $f(x) = \frac{1}{3}x^3 - \frac{1}{2}x^2 - \frac{1}{6}x + \frac{1}{6}$

70. $f(x) = \frac{2}{3}x^3 - \frac{1}{2}x^2 + \frac{2}{3}x - \frac{1}{2}$

Find only the rational zeros of the function.

71. $f(x) = x^4 + 2x^3 - 5x^2 - 4x + 6$

72. $f(x) = x^4 - 3x^3 - 9x^2 - 3x - 10$

73. $f(x) = x^3 - x^2 - 4x + 3$

74. $f(x) = 2x^3 + 3x^2 + 2x + 3$

75. $f(x) = x^4 + 2x^3 + 2x^2 - 4x - 8$

76. $f(x) = x^4 + 6x^3 + 17x^2 + 36x + 66$

77. $f(x) = x^5 - 5x^4 + 5x^3 + 15x^2 - 36x + 20$

78. $f(x) = x^5 - 3x^4 - 3x^3 + 9x^2 - 4x + 12$

What does Descartes' rule of signs tell you about the number of positive real zeros and the number of negative real zeros of the function?

79. $f(x) = 3x^5 - 2x^2 + x - 1$

80. $g(x) = 5x^6 - 3x^3 + x^2 - x$

81. $h(x) = 6x^7 + 2x^2 + 5x + 4$

82. $P(x) = -3x^5 - 7x^3 - 4x - 5$

83. $F(p) = 3p^{18} + 2p^4 - 5p^2 + p + 3$

84. $H(t) = 5t^{12} - 7t^4 + 3t^2 + t + 1$

85. $C(x) = 7x^6 + 3x^4 - x - 10$

86. $g(z) = -z^{10} + 8z^7 + z^3 + 6z - 1$

87. $h(t) = -4t^5 - t^3 + 2t^2 + 1$

88. $P(x) = x^6 + 2x^4 - 9x^3 - 4$

89. $f(y) = y^4 + 13y^3 - y + 5$

90. $Q(x) = x^4 - 2x^2 + 12x - 8$

91. $r(x) = x^4 - 6x^2 + 20x - 24$

92. $f(x) = x^5 - 2x^3 - 8x$

93. $R(x) = 3x^5 - 5x^3 - 4x$

94. $f(x) = x^4 - 9x^2 - 6x + 4$

Sketch the graph of the polynomial function. Follow the procedure outlined on page 272. Use the rational zeros theorem when finding the zeros.

95. $f(x) = 4x^3 + x^2 - 8x - 2$

96. $f(x) = 3x^3 - 4x^2 - 5x + 2$

97. $f(x) = 2x^4 - 3x^3 - 2x^2 + 3x$

98. $f(x) = 4x^4 - 37x^2 + 9$

Technology Connection

99. Use a graphing calculator to narrow the list of possible rational zeros in Exercises 60–63. Then determine the rational zeros by evaluating the function using the TABLE feature.

Collaborative Discussion and Writing

100. If $Q(x) = -P(x)$, do $P(x)$ and $Q(x)$ have the same zeros? Why or why not?

101. Is it possible for a third-degree polynomial with rational coefficients to have no real zeros? Why or why not?

Skill Maintenance

For Exercises 102 and 103, complete the square to:

a) *find the vertex;*
b) *find the axis of symmetry; and*
c) *determine whether there is a maximum or minimum value and find that value.*

102. $f(x) = 3x^2 - 6x - 1$

103. $f(x) = x^2 - 8x + 10$

Find the zeros of the function.

104. $g(x) = x^2 - 8x - 33$

105. $f(x) = -\frac{4}{5}x + 8$

Classify the polynomial function as constant, linear, quadratic, cubic, or quartic and determine the leading term, the leading coefficient, and the degree of the polynomial. Then describe the end behavior of the function's graph.

106. $f(x) = -x^2 - 3x + 6$

107. $g(x) = -x^3 - 2x^2$

108. $h(x) = x - 2$

109. $f(x) = -\frac{4}{9}$

110. $h(x) = x^3 + \frac{1}{2}x^2 - 4x - 3$

111. $g(x) = x^4 - 2x^3 + x^2 - x + 2$

Synthesis

Use synthetic division to find the quotient and the remainder.

112. $(x^3 + 3ix^2 - 4ix - 2) \div (x + i)$

113. $(x^4 - y^4) \div (x - y)$

114. Use the rational zeros theorem and the equation $x^4 - 12 = 0$ to show that $\sqrt[4]{12}$ is irrational.

115. Consider $f(x) = 2x^3 - 5x^2 - 4x + 3$. Find the solutions of each equation.

a) $f(x) = 0$ **b)** $f(x - 1) = 0$
c) $f(x + 2) = 0$ **d)** $f(2x) = 0$

Find the rational zeros.

116. $P(x) = x^6 - 6x^5 - 72x^4 - 81x^2 + 486x + 5832$

117. $P(x) = 2x^5 - 33x^4 - 84x^3 + 2203x^2 - 3348x - 10,080$

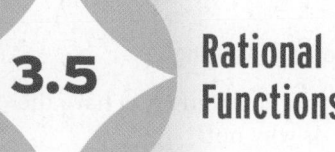

3.5 **Rational Functions**

◆ For a rational function, find the domain and graph the function, identifying all asymptotes.
◆ Solve applied problems involving rational functions.

Now we turn our attention to functions that represent the quotient of two polynomials. Whereas the sum, difference, or product of two polynomials is a polynomial, in general the quotient of two polynomials is *not* itself a polynomial.

A *rational number* can be expressed as the quotient of two integers, p/q, where $q \neq 0$. A *rational function* is formed by the quotient of two polynomials, $p(x)/q(x)$, where $q(x) \neq 0$. Here are some examples of rational functions and their graphs.

$$f(x) = \frac{1}{x}$$

$$f(x) = \frac{1}{x^2}$$

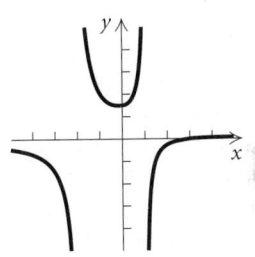

$$f(x) = \frac{x - 3}{x^2 + x - 2}$$

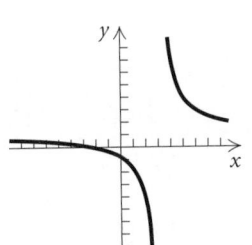

$$f(x) = \frac{2x + 5}{2x - 6}$$

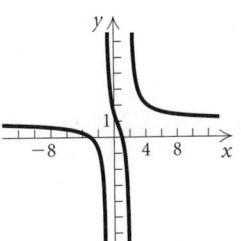

$$f(x) = \frac{x^2 + 2x - 3}{x^2 - x - 2}$$

$$f(x) = \frac{-x^2}{x + 1}$$

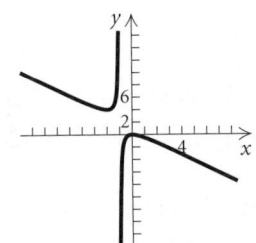

Rational Function

A **rational function** is a function f that is a quotient of two polynomials, that is,

$$f(x) = \frac{p(x)}{q(x)},$$

where $p(x)$ and $q(x)$ are polynomials and where $q(x)$ is not the zero polynomial. The domain of f consists of all inputs x for which $q(x) \neq 0$.

◆ The Domain of a Rational Function

DOMAINS OF FUNCTIONS

REVIEW SECTION **1.2.**

EXAMPLE 1 Consider

$$f(x) = \frac{1}{x - 3}.$$

Find the domain and graph f.

Solution When the denominator $x - 3$ is 0, we have $x = 3$, so the only input that results in a denominator of 0 is 3. Thus the domain is

$$\{x \mid x \neq 3\}, \text{ or } (-\infty, 3) \cup (3, \infty).$$

The graph of this function is the graph of $y = 1/x$ translated 3 units to the right.

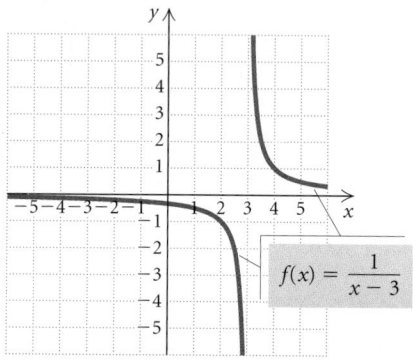

$$f(x) = \frac{1}{x - 3}$$

TECHNOLOGY CONNECTION

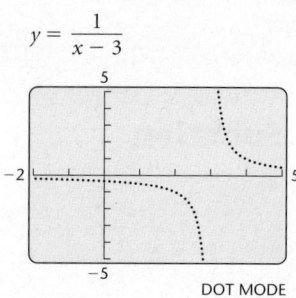

$y = \dfrac{1}{x - 3}$

CONNECTED MODE

$y = \dfrac{1}{x - 3}$

DOT MODE

The graphs at left show the function $f(x) = 1/(x - 3)$ graphed in CONNECTED mode and in DOT mode. Using CONNECTED mode can lead to an incorrect graph. In CONNECTED mode, a graphing calculator connects plotted points with line segments. In DOT mode, it simply plots unconnected points. In the first graph, the graphing calculator has connected the points plotted on either side of the x-value 3 with a line that appears to be the vertical line $x = 3$. (It is not actually vertical since it connects the last point to the left of $x = 3$ with the first point to the right of $x = 3$.) Since 3 is not in the domain of the function, the vertical line $x = 3$ cannot be part of the graph. We will see later in this section that vertical lines like $x = 3$, although not part of the graph, are important in the construction of graphs. If you have a choice when graphing rational functions, use DOT mode.

EXAMPLE 2 Determine the domain of each of the functions illustrated at the beginning of this section.

Solution The domain of each rational function will be the set of all real numbers except those values that make the denominator 0. To determine those exceptions, we set the denominator equal to 0 and solve for x.

FUNCTION	DOMAIN
$f(x) = \dfrac{1}{x}$	$\{x \mid x \neq 0\}$, or $(-\infty, 0) \cup (0, \infty)$
$f(x) = \dfrac{1}{x^2}$	$\{x \mid x \neq 0\}$, or $(-\infty, 0) \cup (0, \infty)$
$f(x) = \dfrac{x-3}{x^2+x-2} = \dfrac{x-3}{(x+2)(x-1)}$	$\{x \mid x \neq -2 \text{ and } x \neq 1\}$, or $(-\infty, -2) \cup (-2, 1) \cup (1, \infty)$
$f(x) = \dfrac{2x+5}{2x-6} = \dfrac{2x+5}{2(x-3)}$	$\{x \mid x \neq 3\}$, or $(-\infty, 3) \cup (3, \infty)$
$f(x) = \dfrac{x^2+2x-3}{x^2-x-2} = \dfrac{x^2+2x-3}{(x+1)(x-2)}$	$\{x \mid x \neq -1 \text{ and } x \neq 2\}$, or $(-\infty, -1) \cup (-1, 2) \cup (2, \infty)$
$f(x) = \dfrac{-x^2}{x+1}$	$\{x \mid x \neq -1\}$, or $(-\infty, -1) \cup (-1, \infty)$

As a partial check of the domains, we can observe the discontinuities (breaks) in the graphs of these functions (see page 301).

◆ Asymptotes

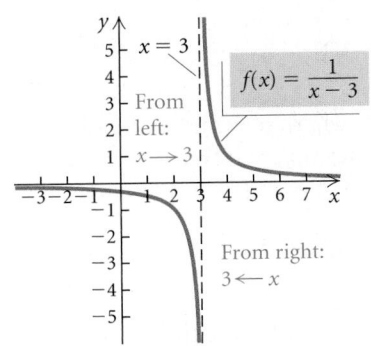

Vertical asymptote: $x = 3$

Look at the graph of $f(x) = 1/(x-3)$, shown at left. (Also see Example 1.) Let's explore what happens as x-values get closer and closer to 3 from the left. We then explore what happens as x-values get closer and closer to 3 from the right.

From the left:

x	2	$2\frac{1}{2}$	$2\frac{99}{100}$	$2\frac{9999}{10,000}$	$2\frac{999,999}{1,000,000}$	$\longrightarrow 3$
$f(x)$	-1	-2	-100	$-10,000$	$-1,000,000$	$\longrightarrow -\infty$

From the right:

x	4	$3\frac{1}{2}$	$3\frac{1}{100}$	$3\frac{1}{10,000}$	$3\frac{1}{1,000,000}$	$\longrightarrow 3$
$f(x)$	1	2	100	10,000	1,000,000	$\longrightarrow \infty$

We see that as x-values get closer and closer to 3 from the left, the function values (y-values) decrease without bound. That is, they approach negative infinity, $-\infty$. Similarly, as the x-values approach 3 from the right, the function values increase without bound. That is, they approach positive infinity, ∞. We write this as

$$f(x) \to -\infty \text{ as } x \to 3^- \quad \text{and} \quad f(x) \to \infty \text{ as } x \to 3^+.$$

We read "$f(x) \to -\infty$ as $x \to 3^-$" as "$f(x)$ decreases without bound as x approaches 3 from the left." We read "$f(x) \to \infty$ as $x \to 3^+$" as "$f(x)$ increases without bound as x approaches 3 from the right." The notation $x \to 3$ means that x gets as close to 3 as possible without being equal to 3. The vertical line $x = 3$ is said to be a *vertical asymptote* for this curve.

In general, the line $x = a$ is a **vertical asymptote** for the graph of f if any of the following is true:

$$f(x) \to \infty \text{ as } x \to a^- \quad \text{or} \quad f(x) \to -\infty \text{ as } x \to a^-, \quad \text{or}$$
$$f(x) \to \infty \text{ as } x \to a^+ \quad \text{or} \quad f(x) \to -\infty \text{ as } x \to a^+.$$

The following figures show the four ways in which a vertical asymptote can occur.

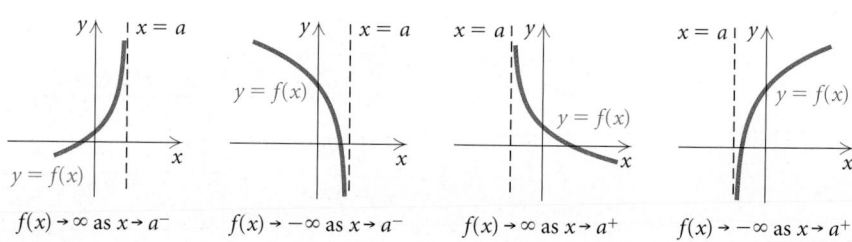

$f(x) \to \infty$ as $x \to a^-$ $f(x) \to -\infty$ as $x \to a^-$ $f(x) \to \infty$ as $x \to a^+$ $f(x) \to -\infty$ as $x \to a^+$

The vertical asymptotes of a rational function $f(x) = p(x)/q(x)$ are found by determining the zeros of $q(x)$ that are not also zeros of $p(x)$. If $p(x)$ and $q(x)$ are polynomials with no common factors other than constants, we need determine only the zeros of the denominator $q(x)$.

Determining Vertical Asymptotes

For a rational function $f(x) = p(x)/q(x)$, where $p(x)$ and $q(x)$ are polynomials with no common factors other than constants, if a is a zero of the denominator, then the line $x = a$ is a vertical asymptote for the graph of the function.

EXAMPLE 3   Determine the vertical asymptotes for the graph of each of the following functions.

a) $f(x) = \dfrac{2x - 11}{x^2 + 2x - 8}$ **b)** $g(x) = \dfrac{x - 2}{x^3 - 5x}$

Solution

a) We factor to find the zeros of the denominator:

$$x^2 + 2x - 8 = (x + 4)(x - 2).$$

The zeros of the denominator are −4 and 2. Thus the vertical asymptotes are the lines $x = -4$ and $x = 2$. (See Fig. 1.)

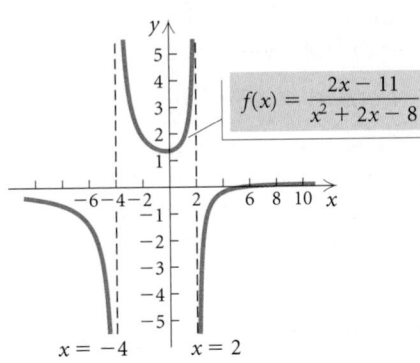

$$f(x) = \frac{2x - 11}{x^2 + 2x - 8}$$

Figure 1

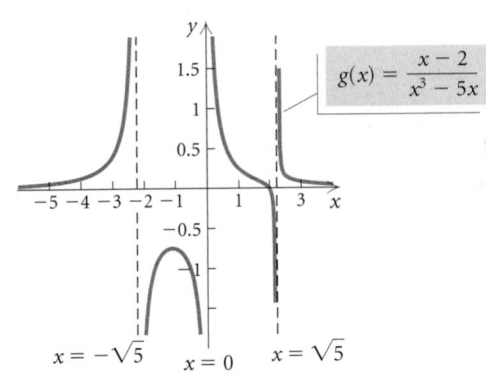

$$g(x) = \frac{x - 2}{x^3 - 5x}$$

Figure 2

b) We factor to find the zeros of the denominator:

$$x^3 - 5x = x(x^2 - 5).$$

Solving $x(x^2 - 5) = 0$, we get

$$
\begin{array}{lll}
x = 0 & or & x^2 - 5 = 0 \\
x = 0 & or & x^2 = 5 \\
x = 0 & or & x = \pm\sqrt{5}.
\end{array}
$$

The zeros of the denominator are 0, $\sqrt{5}$, and $-\sqrt{5}$. Thus the vertical asymptotes are the lines $x = 0$, $x = \sqrt{5}$, and $x = -\sqrt{5}$. (See Fig. 2.)

▶ Now Try Exercise 11.

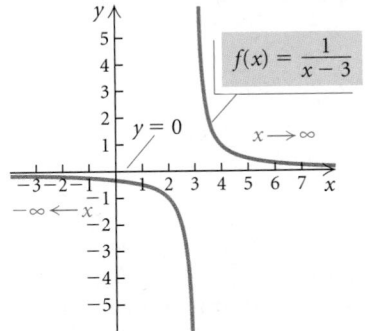

$$f(x) = \frac{1}{x - 3}$$

Horizontal asymptote: y = 0

Looking again at the graph of $f(x) = 1/(x - 3)$, shown at left (also see Example 1), let's explore what happens to $f(x) = 1/(x - 3)$ as x increases without bound (approaches positive infinity, ∞) and as x decreases without bound (approaches negative infinity, $-\infty$).

x increases without bound:

x	100	5000	1,000,000	→ ∞
$f(x)$	≈ 0.0103	≈ 0.0002	≈ 0.000001	→ 0

x decreases without bound:

x	−300	−8000	−1,000,000	→ $-\infty$
$f(x)$	≈ −0.0033	≈ −0.0001	≈ −0.000001	→ 0

We see that

$$\frac{1}{x - 3} \to 0 \text{ as } x \to \infty \quad \text{and} \quad \frac{1}{x - 3} \to 0 \text{ as } x \to -\infty.$$

Since $y = 0$ is the equation of the x-axis, we say that the curve approaches the x-axis asymptotically and that the x-axis is a *horizontal asymptote* for the curve.

In general, the line $y = b$ is a **horizontal asymptote** for the graph of f if either or both of the following are true:

$$f(x) \rightarrow b \text{ as } x \rightarrow \infty \quad \text{or} \quad f(x) \rightarrow b \text{ as } x \rightarrow -\infty.$$

The following figures illustrate four ways in which horizontal asymptotes can occur. In each case, the curve gets close to the line $y = b$ either as $x \rightarrow \infty$ or as $x \rightarrow -\infty$. Keep in mind that the symbols ∞ and $-\infty$ convey the idea of increasing without bound and decreasing without bound, respectively.

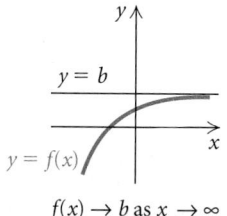

$f(x) \rightarrow b$ as $x \rightarrow \infty$

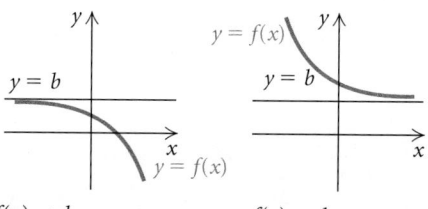

$f(x) \rightarrow b$ as $x \rightarrow -\infty$ $f(x) \rightarrow b$ as $x \rightarrow \infty$

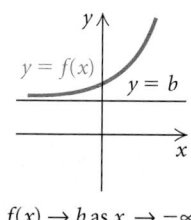

$f(x) \rightarrow b$ as $x \rightarrow -\infty$

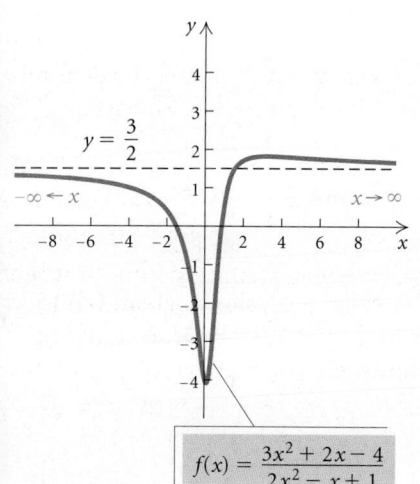

$$f(x) = \frac{3x^2 + 2x - 4}{2x^2 - x + 1}$$

How can we determine a horizontal asymptote? As x gets very large or very small, the value of the polynomial function $p(x)$ is dominated by the function's leading term. Because of this, if $p(x)$ and $q(x)$ have the *same* degree, the value of $p(x)/q(x)$ as $x \rightarrow \infty$ or as $x \rightarrow -\infty$ is dominated by the ratio of the numerator's leading coefficient to the denominator's leading coefficient.

For $f(x) = (3x^2 + 2x - 4)/(2x^2 - x + 1)$, we see that the numerator, $3x^2 + 2x - 4$, is dominated by $3x^2$ and the denominator, $2x^2 - x + 1$, is dominated by $2x^2$, so $f(x)$ approaches $3x^2/2x^2$, or $\frac{3}{2}$, as x gets very large or very small:

$$\frac{3x^2 + 2x - 4}{2x^2 - x + 1} \rightarrow \frac{3}{2}, \text{ or } 1.5, \text{ as } x \rightarrow \infty, \quad \text{and}$$

$$\frac{3x^2 + 2x - 4}{2x^2 - x + 1} \rightarrow \frac{3}{2}, \text{ or } 1.5, \text{ as } x \rightarrow -\infty.$$

We say that the curve approaches the horizontal line $y = \frac{3}{2}$ asymptotically and that $y = \frac{3}{2}$ is a *horizontal asymptote* for the curve.

It follows that when the numerator and the denominator of a rational function have the same degree, the line $y = a/b$ is the horizontal asymptote, where a and b are the leading coefficients of the numerator and the denominator, respectively.

EXAMPLE 4 Find the horizontal asymptote:

$$f(x) = \frac{-7x^4 - 10x^2 + 1}{11x^4 + x - 2}.$$

Solution The numerator and the denominator have the same degree. The ratio of the leading coefficients is $-\frac{7}{11}$, so the line $y = -\frac{7}{11}$, or $-0.\overline{63}$, is the horizontal asymptote.

▶ Now Try Exercise 15.

To check Example 4, we could evaluate the function for a very large and a very small value of *x*. Another check, one that is useful in calculus, is to multiply by 1, using $(1/x^4)/(1/x^4)$:

$$f(x) = \frac{-7x^4 - 10x^2 + 1}{11x^4 + x - 2} \cdot \frac{\dfrac{1}{x^4}}{\dfrac{1}{x^4}} = \frac{\dfrac{-7x^4}{x^4} - \dfrac{10x^2}{x^4} + \dfrac{1}{x^4}}{\dfrac{11x^4}{x^4} + \dfrac{x}{x^4} - \dfrac{2}{x^4}}$$

$$= \frac{-7 - \dfrac{10}{x^2} + \dfrac{1}{x^4}}{11 + \dfrac{1}{x^3} - \dfrac{2}{x^4}}.$$

As $|x|$ becomes very large, each expression with a power of *x* in the denominator tends toward 0. Specifically, as $x \to \infty$ or as $x \to -\infty$, we have

$$f(x) \to \frac{-7 - 0 + 0}{11 + 0 - 0}, \quad \text{or} \quad f(x) \to -\frac{7}{11}.$$

The horizontal asymptote is $y = -\frac{7}{11}$, or $-0.\overline{63}$.

We now investigate the occurrence of a horizontal asymptote when the degree of the numerator is less than the degree of the denominator.

EXAMPLE 5 Find the horizontal asymptote:

$$f(x) = \frac{2x + 3}{x^3 - 2x^2 + 4}.$$

Solution We let $p(x) = 2x + 3$, $q(x) = x^3 - 2x^2 + 4$, and $f(x) = p(x)/q(x)$. Note that as $x \to \infty$, the value of $q(x)$ grows much faster than the value of $p(x)$. Because of this, the ratio $p(x)/q(x)$ shrinks toward 0. As $x \to -\infty$, the ratio $p(x)/q(x)$ behaves in a similar manner. The horizontal asymptote is $y = 0$, the *x*-axis. This is the case for all rational functions for which the degree of the numerator is less than the degree of the denominator. Note in Example 1 that $y = 0$, the *x*-axis, is the horizontal asymptote of $f(x) = 1/(x - 3)$.

▶ Now Try Exercise 17.

The following statements describe the two ways in which a horizontal asymptote occurs.

Determining a Horizontal Asymptote

- When the numerator and the denominator of a rational function have the same degree, the line $y = a/b$ is the horizontal asymptote, where a and b are the leading coefficients of the numerator and the denominator, respectively.
- When the degree of the numerator of a rational function is less than the degree of the denominator, the x-axis, or $y = 0$, is the horizontal asymptote.
- When the degree of the numerator of a rational function is greater than the degree of the denominator, there is no horizontal asymptote.

The following statements are also true.

Crossing an Asymptote

- The graph of a rational function *never crosses* a vertical asymptote.
- The graph of a rational function *might cross* a horizontal asymptote but does not necessarily do so.

EXAMPLE 6   Graph

$$g(x) = \frac{2x^2 + 1}{x^2}.$$

Include and label all asymptotes.

Solution   Since 0 is the zero of the denominator, the y-axis, $x = 0$, is the vertical asymptote. Note also that the degree of the numerator is the same as the degree of the denominator. Thus, $y = 2/1$, or 2, is the horizontal asymptote.

To draw the graph, we first draw the asymptotes with dashed lines. Then we compute and plot some ordered pairs and draw the two branches of the curve.

x	$g(x)$
-2	$2\frac{1}{4}$
$-1\frac{1}{2}$	$2\frac{4}{9}$
-1	3
$-\frac{1}{2}$	6
$\frac{1}{2}$	6
1	3
$1\frac{1}{2}$	$2\frac{4}{9}$
2	$2\frac{1}{4}$

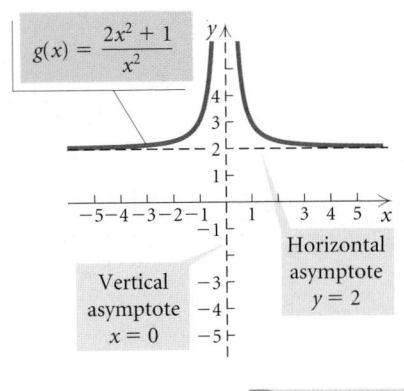

$$g(x) = \frac{2x^2 + 1}{x^2}$$

Vertical asymptote $x = 0$

Horizontal asymptote $y = 2$

▶ Now Try Exercise 37.

Sometimes a line that is neither horizontal nor vertical is an asymptote. Such a line is called an **oblique asymptote,** or a **slant asymptote.**

EXAMPLE 7 Find all the asymptotes of

$$f(x) = \frac{2x^2 - 3x - 1}{x - 2}.$$

Solution The line $x = 2$ is the vertical asymptote because 2 is the zero of the denominator. There is no horizontal asymptote because the degree of the numerator is greater than the degree of the denominator. When the degree of the numerator is 1 greater than the degree of the denominator, we divide to find an equivalent expression:

$$\frac{2x^2 - 3x - 1}{x - 2} = (2x + 1) + \frac{1}{x - 2}.$$

$$\begin{array}{r} 2x + 1 \\ x - 2 \overline{\smash{)}2x^2 - 3x - 1} \\ \underline{2x^2 - 4x} \\ x - 1 \\ \underline{x - 2} \\ 1 \end{array}$$

Now we see that when $x \to \infty$ or $x \to -\infty$, $1/(x - 2) \to 0$ and the value of $f(x) \to 2x + 1$. This means that as $|x|$ becomes very large, the graph of $f(x)$ gets very close to the graph of $y = 2x + 1$. Thus the line $y = 2x + 1$ is the oblique asymptote.

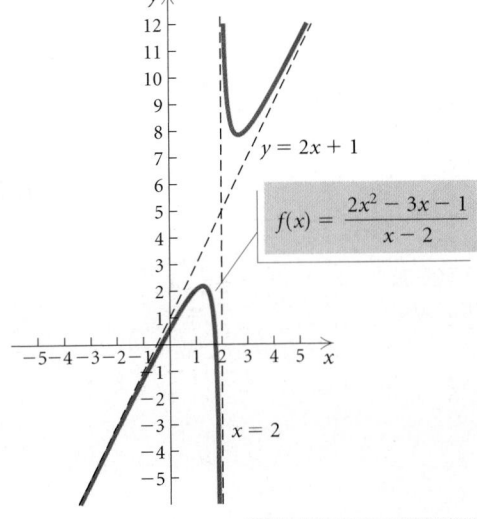

$y = 2x + 1$

$$f(x) = \frac{2x^2 - 3x - 1}{x - 2}$$

$x = 2$

▶ Now Try Exercise 51.

> **Occurrence of Lines as Asymptotes of Rational Functions**
> For a rational function $f(x) = p(x)/q(x)$, where $p(x)$ and $q(x)$ have no common factors other than constants:
>
> **Vertical asymptotes** occur at any x-values that make the denominator 0.
>
> **The x-axis is the horizontal asymptote** when the degree of the numerator is less than the degree of the denominator.
>
> **A horizontal asymptote other than the x-axis** occurs when the numerator and the denominator have the same degree.
>
> **An oblique asymptote** occurs when the degree of the numerator is 1 greater than the degree of the denominator.
>
> There can be only one horizontal asymptote or one oblique asymptote and never both.
>
> An asymptote is *not* part of the graph of the function.

The following is an outline of a procedure that we can follow to create accurate graphs of rational functions.

> To graph a rational function $f(x) = p(x)/q(x)$, where $p(x)$ and $q(x)$ have no common factor other than constants:
>
> 1. Find the real zeros of the denominator. Determine the domain of the function and sketch any vertical asymptotes.
> 2. Find the horizontal or the oblique asymptote, if there is one, and sketch it.
> 3. Find the zeros of the function. The zeros are found by determining the zeros of the numerator. These are the first coordinates of the x-intercepts of the graph.
> 4. Find $f(0)$. This gives the y-intercept $(0, f(0))$, of the function.
> 5. Find other function values to determine the general shape. Then draw the graph.

EXAMPLE 8 Graph: $f(x) = \dfrac{2x + 3}{3x^2 + 7x - 6}$.

Solution

1. We find the zeros of the denominator by solving $3x^2 + 7x - 6 = 0$. Since

$$3x^2 + 7x - 6 = (3x - 2)(x + 3),$$

the zeros are $\frac{2}{3}$ and -3. Thus the domain excludes $\frac{2}{3}$ and -3 and is

$$(-\infty, -3) \cup \left(-3, \tfrac{2}{3}\right) \cup \left(\tfrac{2}{3}, \infty\right).$$

The graph has vertical asymptotes $x = -3$ and $x = \frac{2}{3}$. We sketch these as dashed lines.

2. Because the degree of the numerator is less than the degree of the denominator, the x-axis, $y = 0$, is the horizontal asymptote.

3. To find the zeros of the numerator, we solve $2x + 3 = 0$ and get $x = -\frac{3}{2}$. Thus, $-\frac{3}{2}$ is the zero of the function, and the point $\left(-\frac{3}{2}, 0\right)$ is the x-intercept.

4. We find $f(0)$:

$$f(0) = \frac{2 \cdot 0 + 3}{3 \cdot 0^2 + 7 \cdot 0 - 6}$$

$$= \frac{3}{-6} = -\frac{1}{2}.$$

Thus, $\left(0, -\frac{1}{2}\right)$ is the y-intercept.

5. We find other function values to determine the general shape and then draw the graph. Note that the graph of this function crosses its horizontal asymptote at $x = -\frac{3}{2}$.

▶ Now Try Exercise 57.

EXAMPLE 9 Graph: $g(x) = \dfrac{x^2 - 1}{x^2 + x - 6}$.

Solution

1. We find the zeros of the denominator by solving $x^2 + x - 6 = 0$. Since

$$x^2 + x - 6 = (x + 3)(x - 2),$$

the zeros are -3 and 2. Thus the domain excludes the x-values -3 and 2 and is

$$(-\infty, -3) \cup (-3, 2) \cup (2, \infty).$$

The graph has vertical asymptotes $x = -3$ and $x = 2$. We sketch these as dashed lines.

2. The numerator and the denominator have the same degree, so the horizontal asymptote is determined by the ratio of the leading coefficients: $1/1$, or 1. Thus, $y = 1$ is the horizontal asymptote. We sketch it with a dashed line.

3. To find the zeros of the numerator, we solve $x^2 - 1 = 0$. The solutions are -1 and 1. Thus, -1 and 1 are the zeros of the function and the points $(-1, 0)$ and $(1, 0)$ are the x-intercepts.

4. We find $g(0)$:

$$g(0) = \frac{0^2 - 1}{0^2 + 0 - 6} = \frac{-1}{-6} = \frac{1}{6}.$$

Thus, $\left(0, \frac{1}{6}\right)$ is the y-intercept.

5. We find other function values to determine the general shape and then draw the graph.

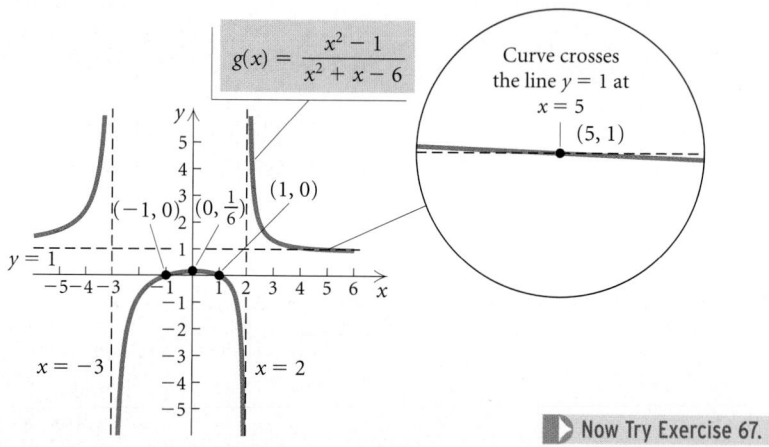

> Now Try Exercise 67.

The magnified portion of the graph in Example 9 at left shows another situation in which a graph can cross its horizontal asymptote. The point where $g(x)$ crosses $y = 1$ can be found by setting $g(x) = 1$ and solving for x:

$$\frac{x^2 - 1}{x^2 + x - 6} = 1$$

$$x^2 - 1 = x^2 + x - 6$$

$$-1 = x - 6 \qquad \text{Subtracting } x^2$$

$$5 = x. \qquad \text{Adding } 6$$

The point of intersection is $(5, 1)$. Let's observe the behavior of the curve after it crosses the horizontal asymptote at $x = 5$. (See the graph at left.) It continues to decrease for a short interval and then begins to increase, getting closer and closer to $y = 1$ as $x \to \infty$.

Graphs of rational functions can also cross an oblique asymptote. The graph of

$$f(x) = \frac{2x^3}{x^2 + 1}$$

shown below crosses its oblique asymptote $y = 2x$. **Remember, graphs can cross horizontal or oblique asymptotes, but they cannot cross vertical asymptotes.**

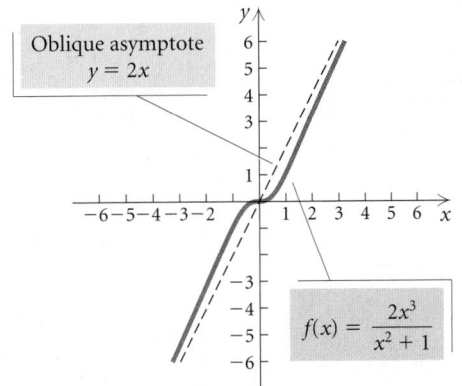

Let's now graph a rational function $f(x) = p(x)/q(x)$, where $p(x)$ and $q(x)$ have a common factor.

EXAMPLE 10 Graph: $g(x) = \dfrac{x - 2}{x^2 - x - 2}$.

Solution We first express the denominator in factored form:

$$g(x) = \frac{x - 2}{x^2 - x - 2} = \frac{x - 2}{(x + 1)(x - 2)}.$$

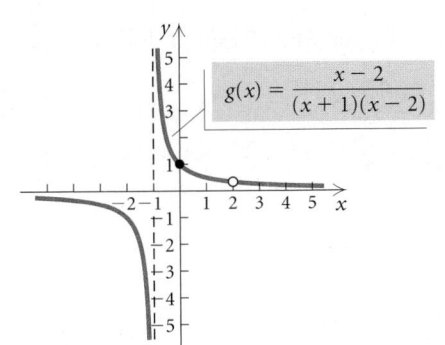

The domain of the function is $\{x \mid x \neq -1 \text{ and } x \neq 2\}$, or $(-\infty, -1) \cup (-1, 2) \cup (2, \infty)$. The zeros of the denominator are -1 and 2, and the zero of the numerator is 2. Since -1 is the only zero of the denominator that is *not* a zero of the numerator, the graph of the function has $x = -1$ as its only vertical asymptote. The degree of the numerator is less than the degree of the denominator, so $y = 0$ is the horizontal asymptote. There are no zeros of the function and thus no x-intercepts, because 2 is the only zero of the numerator and 2 is not in the domain of the function. Since $g(0) = 1$, $(0, 1)$ is the y-intercept. We draw the graph indicating the "hole" when $x = 2$ with an open circle.

The rational expression $(x - 2)/((x + 1)(x - 2))$ can be simplified. Thus,

$$g(x) = \frac{x - 2}{(x + 1)(x - 2)} = \frac{1}{x + 1}, \quad \text{where } x \neq -1 \text{ and } x \neq 2.$$

The graph of $g(x)$ is the graph of $y = 1/(x + 1)$ with the point where $x = 2$ missing. To determine the coordinates of the "hole," we substitute 2 for x in $g(x) = 1/(x + 1)$:

$$g(2) = \frac{1}{2 + 1} = \frac{1}{3}.$$

Thus the "hole" is located at $\left(2, \frac{1}{3}\right)$.

▶ Now Try Exercise 45.

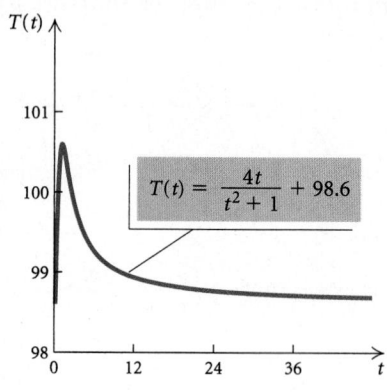

◆ Applications

EXAMPLE 11 *Temperature During an Illness.* The temperature T, in degrees Fahrenheit, of a person during an illness is given by the function

$$T(t) = \frac{4t}{t^2 + 1} + 98.6,$$

where time t is given in hours since the onset of the illness. The graph of this function is shown at left.

a) Find the temperature at $t = 0, 1, 2, 5, 12$, and 24.

b) Find the horizontal asymptote of the graph of $T(t)$. Complete:

$$T(t) \to \boxed{} \text{ as } t \to \infty.$$

c) Give the meaning of the answer to part (b) in terms of the application.

Solution

a) We have

$$T(0) = 98.6, \qquad T(1) = 100.6, \qquad T(2) = 100.2,$$
$$T(5) \approx 99.369, \qquad T(12) \approx 98.931, \quad \text{and} \quad T(24) \approx 98.766.$$

b) Since

$$T(t) = \frac{4t}{t^2 + 1} + 98.6$$
$$= \frac{98.6t^2 + 4t + 98.6}{t^2 + 1},$$

the horizontal asymptote is $y = 98.6/1$, or 98.6. Then it follows that $T(t) \to 98.6$ as $t \to \infty$.

c) As time goes on, the temperature returns to "normal," which is $98.6°$.

▶ **Now Try Exercise 73.**

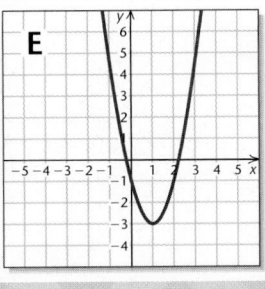

Visualizing the Graph

Match the function with its graph.

1. $f(x) = -\dfrac{1}{x^2}$

2. $f(x) = x^3 - 3x^2 + 2x + 3$

3. $f(x) = \dfrac{x^2 - 4}{x^2 - x - 6}$

4. $f(x) = -x^2 + 4x - 1$

5. $f(x) = \dfrac{x - 3}{x^2 + x - 6}$

6. $f(x) = \dfrac{3}{4}x + 2$

7. $f(x) = x^2 - 1$

8. $f(x) = x^4 - 2x^2 - 5$

9. $f(x) = \dfrac{8x - 4}{3x + 6}$

10. $f(x) = 2x^2 - 4x - 1$

Answers on page A-21

3.5 EXERCISE SET

In Exercises 1–6, use your knowledge of asymptotes and intercepts to match the equation with one of the graphs (a)–(f), which follow. List all asymptotes.

a)

b)

c)

d)

e)

f)

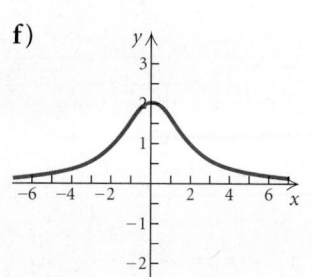

1. $f(x) = \dfrac{8}{x^2 - 4}$

2. $f(x) = \dfrac{8}{x^2 + 4}$

3. $f(x) = \dfrac{8x}{x^2 - 4}$

4. $f(x) = \dfrac{8x^2}{x^2 - 4}$

5. $f(x) = \dfrac{8x^3}{x^2 - 4}$

6. $f(x) = \dfrac{8x^3}{x^2 + 4}$

Determine the vertical asymptotes for the graph of the function.

7. $g(x) = \dfrac{1}{x^2}$

8. $f(x) = \dfrac{4}{x + 10}$

9. $h(x) = \dfrac{x + 7}{2 - x}$

10. $g(x) = \dfrac{x^4 + 2}{x}$

11. $f(x) = \dfrac{3 - x}{(x - 4)(x + 6)}$

12. $h(x) = \dfrac{x^2 + 4}{x(x + 5)(x - 2)}$

13. $g(x) = \dfrac{x^2}{2x^2 - x - 3}$

14. $f(x) = \dfrac{x + 5}{x^2 + 4x - 32}$

Determine the horizontal asymptote of the graph of the function.

15. $f(x) = \dfrac{3x^2 + 5}{4x^2 - 3}$

16. $g(x) = \dfrac{x + 6}{x^3 + 2x^2}$

17. $h(x) = \dfrac{x^2 - 4}{2x^4 + 3}$

18. $f(x) = \dfrac{x^5}{x^5 + x}$

19. $g(x) = \dfrac{x^3 - 2x^2 + x - 1}{x^2 - 16}$

20. $h(x) = \dfrac{8x^4 + x - 2}{2x^4 - 10}$

Determine the oblique asymptote of the graph of the function.

21. $g(x) = \dfrac{x^2 + 4x - 1}{x + 3}$

22. $f(x) = \dfrac{x^2 - 6x}{x - 5}$

23. $h(x) = \dfrac{x^4 - 2}{x^3 + 1}$

24. $g(x) = \dfrac{12x^3 - x}{6x^2 + 4}$

25. $f(x) = \dfrac{x^3 - x^2 + x - 4}{x^2 + 2x - 1}$

26. $h(x) = \dfrac{5x^3 - x^2 + x - 1}{x^2 - x + 2}$

Graph the function. Be sure to label all the asymptotes. List the domain and the x- and y-intercepts.

27. $f(x) = \dfrac{1}{x}$

28. $g(x) = \dfrac{1}{x^2}$

29. $h(x) = -\dfrac{4}{x^2}$

30. $f(x) = -\dfrac{6}{x}$

31. $g(x) = \dfrac{x^2 - 4x + 3}{x + 1}$

32. $h(x) = \dfrac{2x^2 - x - 3}{x - 1}$

33. $f(x) = \dfrac{1}{x + 3}$

34. $f(x) = \dfrac{1}{x - 5}$

35. $f(x) = \dfrac{-2}{x - 5}$

36. $f(x) = \dfrac{3}{3 - x}$

37. $f(x) = \dfrac{2x + 1}{x}$

38. $f(x) = \dfrac{3x - 1}{x}$

39. $f(x) = \dfrac{1}{(x - 2)^2}$

40. $f(x) = \dfrac{-2}{(x - 3)^2}$

41. $f(x) = -\dfrac{1}{x^2}$

42. $f(x) = \dfrac{1}{3x^2}$

43. $f(x) = \dfrac{1}{x^2 + 3}$

44. $f(x) = \dfrac{-1}{x^2 + 2}$

45. $f(x) = \dfrac{x^2 - 4}{x - 2}$

46. $f(x) = \dfrac{x^2 - 9}{x + 3}$

47. $f(x) = \dfrac{x - 1}{x + 2}$

48. $f(x) = \dfrac{x - 2}{x + 1}$

49. $f(x) = \dfrac{x + 3}{2x^2 - 5x - 3}$

50. $f(x) = \dfrac{3x}{x^2 + 5x + 4}$

51. $f(x) = \dfrac{x^2 - 9}{x + 1}$

52. $f(x) = \dfrac{x^2 - 4}{x - 1}$

53. $f(x) = \dfrac{x^2 + x - 2}{2x^2 + 1}$

54. $f(x) = \dfrac{x^2 - 2x - 3}{3x^2 + 2}$

55. $g(x) = \dfrac{3x^2 - x - 2}{x - 1}$

56. $f(x) = \dfrac{2x + 1}{2x^2 - 5x - 3}$

57. $f(x) = \dfrac{x - 1}{x^2 - 2x - 3}$

58. $f(x) = \dfrac{x + 2}{x^2 + 2x - 15}$

59. $f(x) = \dfrac{x - 3}{(x + 1)^3}$

60. $f(x) = \dfrac{x + 2}{(x - 1)^3}$

61. $f(x) = \dfrac{x^3 + 1}{x}$

62. $f(x) = \dfrac{x^3 - 1}{x}$

63. $f(x) = \dfrac{x^3 + 2x^2 - 15x}{x^2 - 5x - 14}$

64. $f(x) = \dfrac{x^3 + 2x^2 - 3x}{x^2 - 25}$

65. $f(x) = \dfrac{5x^4}{x^4 + 1}$

66. $f(x) = \dfrac{x + 1}{x^2 + x - 6}$

67. $f(x) = \dfrac{x^2}{x^2 - x - 2}$

68. $f(x) = \dfrac{x^2 - x - 2}{x + 2}$

Find a rational function that satisfies the given conditions. Answers may vary, but try to give the simplest answer possible.

69. Vertical asymptotes $x = -4$, $x = 5$

70. Vertical asymptotes $x = -4$, $x = 5$;
x-intercept $(-2, 0)$

71. Vertical asymptotes $x = -4$, $x = 5$; horizontal asymptote $y = \frac{3}{2}$; x-intercept $(-2, 0)$

72. Oblique asymptote $y = x - 1$

73. *Medical Dosage.* The function

$$N(t) = \frac{0.8t + 1000}{5t + 4}, \quad t \geq 15$$

gives the body concentration $N(t)$, in parts per million, of a certain dosage of medication after time t, in hours.

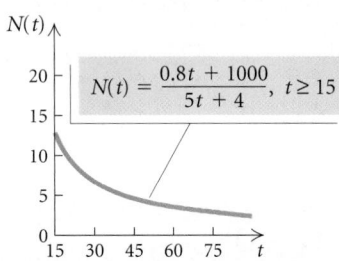

a) Find the horizontal asymptote of the graph and complete the following:

$$N(t) \to \boxed{} \text{ as } t \to \infty.$$

b) Explain the meaning of the answer to part (a) in terms of the application.

74. *Average Cost.* The average cost per disc, in dollars, for a company to produce x DVDs on exercising is given by the function

$$A(x) = \frac{2x + 100}{x}, \quad x > 0.$$

a) Find the horizontal asymptote of the graph and complete the following:

$$A(x) \to \boxed{} \text{ as } x \to \infty.$$

b) Explain the meaning of the answer to part (a) in terms of the application.

75. *Population Growth.* The population P, in thousands, of Lordsburg is given by

$$P(t) = \frac{500t}{2t^2 + 9},$$

where t is the time, in months.

a) Find the population at $t = 0, 1, 3$, and 8 months.

b) Find the horizontal asymptote of the graph and complete the following:

$$P(t) \to \boxed{} \text{ as } t \to \infty.$$

c) Explain the meaning of the answer to part (b) in terms of the application.

Technology Connection

76. *Minimizing Surface Area.* The Hold-It Container Co. is designing an open-top rectangular box, with a square base, that will hold 108 cubic centimeters.

a) Express the surface area S as a function of the length x of a side of the base.

b) Graph the function on the interval $(0, \infty)$.

c) Estimate the minimum surface area and the value of x that will yield it.

77. For Exercise 75, find the maximum population and the value of t that will yield it.

78. Graph

$$y_1 = \frac{x^3 + 4}{x} \quad \text{and} \quad y_2 = x^2$$

using the same viewing window. Explain how the parabola $y_2 = x^2$ can be thought of as a nonlinear asymptote for y_1.

Collaborative Discussion and Writing

79. Under what circumstances will a rational function have a domain consisting of all real numbers?

80. Explain why the graph of a rational function cannot have both a horizontal asymptote and an oblique asymptote.

Skill Maintenance

In each of Exercises 81–88, fill in the blank with the correct term. Some of the given choices will not be used. Others will be used more than once.

    x-intercept
    y-intercept
    odd function
    even function
    domain
    range
    slope
    distance formula
    midpoint formula
    horizontal lines
    vertical lines
    point–slope equation
    slope–intercept equation
    difference quotient
    $f(x) = f(-x)$
    $f(-x) = -f(x)$

81. The _____ of a line containing (x_1, y_1) and (x_2, y_2) is given by $(y_2 - y_1)/(x_2 - x_1)$.

82. The _____ of the line with slope m and y-intercept $(0, b)$ is $y = mx + b$.

83. The _____ of the line with slope m passing through (x_1, y_1) is $y - y_1 = m(x - x_1)$.

84. A function is a correspondence between a first set, called the _____, and a second set, called the _____, such that each member of the _____ corresponds to exactly one member of the _____.

85. For each x in the domain of an odd function f, _____.

86. A(n) _____ is a point $(a, 0)$.

87. The _____ is $\left(\dfrac{x_1 + x_2}{2}, \dfrac{y_1 + y_2}{2} \right)$.

88. _____ are given by equations of the type $x = a$.

Synthesis

Find the nonlinear asymptotes of the function.

89. $f(x) = \dfrac{x^5 + 2x^3 + 4x^2}{x^2 + 2}$

90. $f(x) = \dfrac{x^4 + 3x^2}{x^2 + 1}$

Graph the function.

91. $f(x) = \dfrac{2x^3 + x^2 - 8x - 4}{x^3 + x^2 - 9x - 9}$

92. $f(x) = \dfrac{x^3 + 4x^2 + x - 6}{x^2 - x - 2}$

Find the domain.

93. $f(x) = \sqrt{\dfrac{72}{x^2 - 4x - 21}}$

94. $f(x) = \sqrt{x^2 - 4x - 21}$

3.6 Polynomial and Rational Inequalities

◆ Solve polynomial and rational inequalities.

We will use a combination of algebraic and graphical methods to solve polynomial and rational inequalities.

◆ Polynomial Inequalities

Just as a quadratic equation can be written in the form $ax^2 + bx + c = 0$, a **quadratic inequality** can be written in the form $ax^2 + bx + c \ \ 0$, where is $<$, $>$, $\leq$, or $\geq$. Here are some examples of quadratic inequalities:

$$x^2 - 4x - 5 < 0 \quad \text{and} \quad -\tfrac{1}{2}x^2 + 4x - 7 \geq 0.$$

EXAMPLE 1   Solve: $x^2 - 4x - 5 < 0$.

Solution   We are asked to find all x-values for which $x^2 - 4x - 5 < 0$. To locate these values, we graph $f(x) = x^2 - 4x - 5$. Then we note that whenever the function changes sign, its graph passes through an x-intercept. Thus to solve $x^2 - 4x - 5 < 0$, we first solve the related equation $x^2 - 4x - 5 = 0$ to find all zeros of the function:

$$x^2 - 4x - 5 = 0$$
$$(x + 1)(x - 5) = 0.$$

The zeros are -1 and 5. Thus the x-intercepts of the graph are $(-1, 0)$ and $(5, 0)$, as shown below.

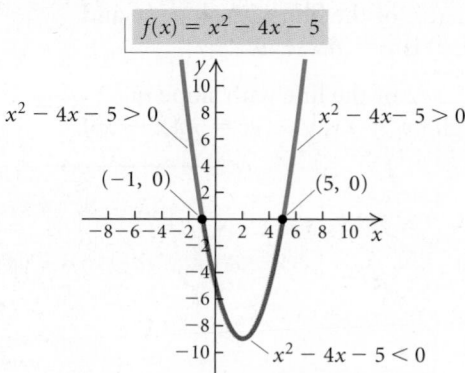

The zeros divide the x-axis into three intervals:

$$(-\infty, -1), \qquad (-1, 5), \quad \text{and} \quad (5, \infty).$$

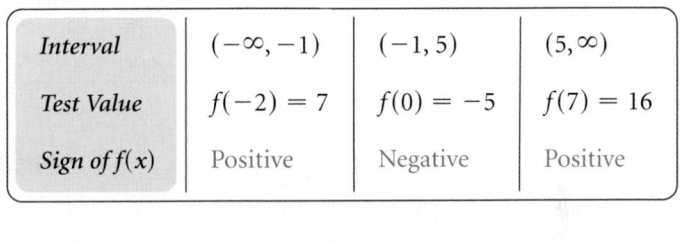

The sign of $x^2 - 4x - 5$ is the same for all values of x in a given interval. Thus we choose a test value for x from each interval and find $f(x)$. We can also determine the sign of $f(x)$ in each interval by simply looking at the graph of the function.

Interval	$(-\infty, -1)$	$(-1, 5)$	$(5, \infty)$
Test Value	$f(-2) = 7$	$f(0) = -5$	$f(7) = 16$
Sign of $f(x)$	Positive	Negative	Positive

Since we are solving $x^2 - 4x - 5 < 0$, the solution set consists of only one of the three intervals, that in which the sign of $f(x)$ is negative. We see that the solution set is $(-1, 5)$, or $\{x \mid -1 < x < 5\}$. ▶ Now Try Exercise 15.

Quadratic inequalities are one type of **polynomial inequality.** Other examples of polynomial inequalities are

$$-2x^4 + x^2 - 3 < 7, \qquad \tfrac{2}{3}x + 4 \geq 0, \quad \text{and} \quad 4x^3 - 2x^2 > 5x + 7.$$

When the inequality symbol in a polynomial inequality is replaced with an equals sign, a **related equation** is formed. Polynomial inequalities can be easily solved once the related equation has been solved.

EXAMPLE 2 Solve: $x^3 - x > 0$.

Solution We are asked to find all x-values for which $x^3 - x > 0$. To locate these values, we graph $f(x) = x^3 - x$. Then we note that whenever the function changes sign, its graph passes through an x-intercept. Thus to solve $x^3 - x > 0$, we first solve the related equation $x^3 - x = 0$ to find all zeros of the function:

$$x^3 - x = 0$$
$$x(x^2 - 1) = 0$$
$$x(x + 1)(x - 1) = 0.$$

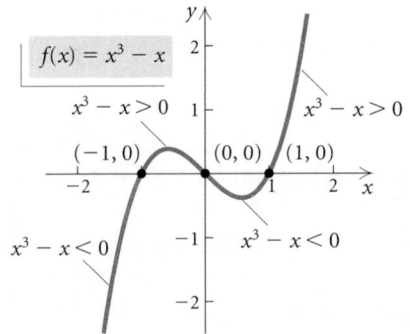

The zeros are -1, 0, and 1. Thus the x-intercepts of the graph are $(-1, 0)$, $(0, 0)$, and $(1, 0)$, as shown in the figure on the preceding page. The zeros divide the x-axis into four intervals:

$$(-\infty, -1), \quad (-1, 0), \quad (0, 1), \quad \text{and} \quad (1, \infty).$$

The sign of $x^3 - x$ is the same for all values of x in a given interval. Thus we choose a test value for x from each interval and find $f(x)$. We can also determine the sign of $f(x)$ in each interval by simply looking at the graph of the function.

Interval	$(-\infty, -1)$	$(-1, 0)$	$(0, 1)$	$(1, \infty)$
Test Value	$f(-2) = -6$	$f(-0.5) = 0.375$	$f(0.5) = -0.375$	$f(2) = 6$
Sign of $f(x)$	Negative	Positive	Negative	Positive

Since we are solving $x^3 - x > 0$, the solution set consists of only two of the four intervals, those in which the sign of $f(x)$ is *positive*. We see that the solution set is $(-1, 0) \cup (1, \infty)$, or $\{x | -1 < x < 0 \text{ or } x > 1\}$.

▶ Now Try Exercise 33.

To solve a polynomial inequality:

1. Find an equivalent inequality with 0 on one side.
2. Solve the related polynomial equation; that is, solve $f(x) = 0$.
3. Use the solutions to divide the x-axis into intervals. Then select a test value from each interval and determine the polynomial's sign on the interval.
4. Determine the intervals for which the inequality is satisfied and write interval notation or set-builder notation for the solution set. Include the endpoints of the intervals in the solution set if the inequality symbol is $\leq$ or $\geq$.

EXAMPLE 3 Solve: $3x^4 + 10x \leq 11x^3 + 4$.

Solution By subtracting $11x^3 + 4$, we form the equivalent inequality

$$3x^4 - 11x^3 + 10x - 4 \leq 0.$$

ALGEBRAIC SOLUTION

To solve the related equation

$$3x^4 - 11x^3 + 10x - 4 = 0,$$

we need to use the theorems of Section 3.4. We solved this equation in Example 5 in Section 3.4. The solutions are

$$-1, \quad 2 - \sqrt{2}, \quad \tfrac{2}{3}, \quad \text{and} \quad 2 + \sqrt{2},$$

or approximately

$$-1, \quad 0.586, \quad 0.667, \quad \text{and} \quad 3.414.$$

These numbers divide the x-axis into five intervals: $(-\infty, -1), \left(-1, 2 - \sqrt{2}\right),$ $\left(2 - \sqrt{2}, \tfrac{2}{3}\right), \left(\tfrac{2}{3}, 2 + \sqrt{2}\right),$ and $\left(2 + \sqrt{2}, \infty\right).$

We then let $f(x) = 3x^4 - 11x^3 + 10x - 4$ and, using test values for $f(x)$, determine the sign of $f(x)$ in each interval.

INTERVAL	TEST VALUE	SIGN OF $f(x)$
$(-\infty, -1)$	$f(-2) = 112$	$+$
$\left(-1, 2 - \sqrt{2}\right)$	$f(0) = -4$	$-$
$\left(2 - \sqrt{2}, 2/3\right)$	$f(0.6) = 0.0128$	$+$
$\left(2/3, 2 + \sqrt{2}\right)$	$f(1) = -2$	$-$
$\left(2 + \sqrt{2}, \infty\right)$	$f(4) = 100$	$+$

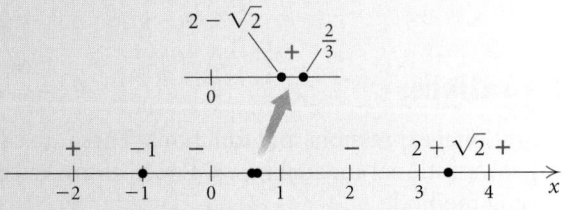

Function values are negative in the intervals $\left(-1, 2 - \sqrt{2}\right)$ and $\left(\tfrac{2}{3}, 2 + \sqrt{2}\right)$. Since the inequality sign is $\leq$, we include the endpoints of the intervals in the solution set. The solution set is

$$\left[-1, 2 - \sqrt{2}\right] \cup \left[\tfrac{2}{3}, 2 + \sqrt{2}\right], \quad \text{or}$$
$$\left\{x \mid -1 \leq x \leq 2 - \sqrt{2} \text{ or } \tfrac{2}{3} \leq x \leq 2 + \sqrt{2}\right\}.$$

VISUALIZING THE SOLUTION

Observing the graph of the function

$$f(x) = 3x^4 - 11x^3 + 10x - 4$$

and a closeup view of the graph on the interval $(0, 1)$, we see the intervals on which $f(x) \leq 0$. The values of $f(x)$ are less than or equal to 0 in two intervals.

$$f(x) = 3x^4 - 11x^3 + 10x - 4$$

$$f(x) = 3x^4 - 11x^3 + 10x - 4$$

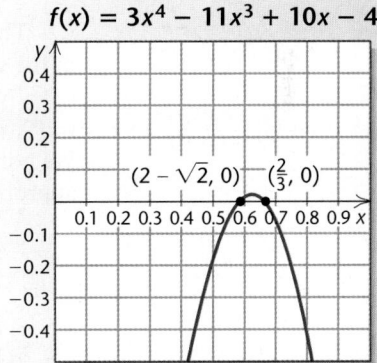

The solution set of the inequality

$$3x^4 - 11x^3 + 10x - 4 \leq 0$$

is

$$\left[-1, 2 - \sqrt{2}\right] \cup \left[\tfrac{2}{3}, 2 + \sqrt{2}\right].$$

▶ Now Try Exercise 35.

TECHNOLOGY
   CONNECTION

Polynomial inequalities can be solved quickly with a graphing calculator. Consider the inequality in Example 3:

$$3x^4 + 10x \leq 11x^3 + 4, \quad \text{or}$$
$$3x^4 - 11x^3 + 10x - 4 \leq 0.$$

We graph the related equation

$$y = 3x^4 - 11x^3 + 10x - 4$$

and use the ZERO feature. We see in the window on the left below that two of the zeros are -1 and approximately 3.414 $\left(2 + \sqrt{2} \approx 3.414\right)$. However, this window leaves us uncertain about the number of zeros of the function in the interval $[0, 1]$.

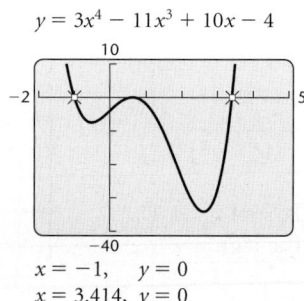

$y = 3x^4 - 11x^3 + 10x - 4$

$x = -1, \quad y = 0$
$x = 3.414, \quad y = 0$

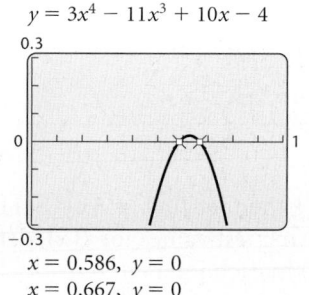

$y = 3x^4 - 11x^3 + 10x - 4$

$x = 0.586, \quad y = 0$
$x = 0.667, \quad y = 0$

The window on the right above shows another view of the zeros in the interval $[0, 1]$. Those zeros are about 0.586 and 0.667 $\left(2 - \sqrt{2} \approx 0.586; \frac{2}{3} \approx 0.667\right)$. The intervals to be considered are $(-\infty, -1)$, $(-1, 0.586)$, $(0.586, 0.667)$, $(0.667, 3.414)$, and $(3.414, \infty)$. We note on the graph where the function is negative. Then, including appropriate endpoints, we find that the solution set is approximately

$$[-1, 0.586] \cup [0.667, 3.414].$$

✦ Rational Inequalities

Some inequalities involve rational expressions and functions. These are called **rational inequalities.** To solve rational inequalities, we need to make some adjustments to the preceding method.

EXAMPLE 4   Solve: $\dfrac{x - 3}{x + 4} \geq \dfrac{x + 2}{x - 5}$.

Solution   We first subtract $(x + 2)/(x - 5)$ on both sides in order to find an equivalent inequality with 0 on one side:

$$\frac{x - 3}{x + 4} - \frac{x + 2}{x - 5} \geq 0.$$

ALGEBRAIC SOLUTION

We look for all values of x for which the related function

$$f(x) = \frac{x-3}{x+4} - \frac{x+2}{x-5}$$

is not defined or is 0. These are called **critical values.**
   A look at the denominators shows that $f(x)$ is not defined for $x = -4$ and $x = 5$. Next, we solve $f(x) = 0$:

$$\frac{x-3}{x+4} - \frac{x+2}{x-5} = 0$$

$$(x+4)(x-5)\left(\frac{x-3}{x+4} - \frac{x+2}{x-5}\right) = (x+4)(x-5) \cdot 0$$

$$(x-5)(x-3) - (x+4)(x+2) = 0$$

$$(x^2 - 8x + 15) - (x^2 + 6x + 8) = 0$$

$$-14x + 7 = 0$$

$$x = \tfrac{1}{2}.$$

The critical values are -4, $\tfrac{1}{2}$, and 5. These values divide the x-axis into four intervals:

$$(-\infty, -4), \qquad \left(-4, \tfrac{1}{2}\right), \qquad \left(\tfrac{1}{2}, 5\right), \quad \text{and} \quad (5, \infty).$$

   We then use a test value to determine the sign of $f(x)$ in each interval.

INTERVAL	TEST VALUE	SIGN OF $f(x)$
$(-\infty, -4)$	$f(-5) = 7.7$	$+$
$\left(-4, \tfrac{1}{2}\right)$	$f(-2) = -2.5$	$-$
$\left(\tfrac{1}{2}, 5\right)$	$f(3) = 2.5$	$+$
$(5, \infty)$	$f(6) = -7.7$	$-$

   Function values are positive in the intervals $(-\infty, -4)$ and $\left(\tfrac{1}{2}, 5\right)$. Since $f\left(\tfrac{1}{2}\right) = 0$ and the inequality symbol is $\geq$, we know that $\tfrac{1}{2}$ must be in the solution set. Note that since neither -4 nor 5 is in the domain of f, they cannot be part of the solution set.
   The solution set is $(-\infty, -4) \cup \left[\tfrac{1}{2}, 5\right)$.

VISUALIZING THE SOLUTION

The graph of the related function

$$f(x) = \frac{x-3}{x+4} - \frac{x+2}{x-5}$$

confirms the three critical values found algebraically: -4 and 5 where $f(x)$ is not defined and $\tfrac{1}{2}$ where $f(x) = 0$.

$$f(x) = \frac{x-3}{x+4} - \frac{x+2}{x-5}$$

   The graph shows where $f(x)$ is positive and where it is negative. Note that -4 and 5 cannot be in the solution set since y is not defined for these values. We do include $\tfrac{1}{2}$, however, since the inequality symbol is $\geq$ and $f\left(\tfrac{1}{2}\right) = 0$. The solution set is

$$(-\infty, -4) \cup \left[\tfrac{1}{2}, 5\right).$$

▶ Now Try Exercise 45.

The following is a method for solving rational inequalities.

> **To solve a rational inequality:**
>
> 1. Find an equivalent inequality with 0 on one side.
> 2. Change the inequality symbol to an equals sign and solve the related equation; that is, solve $f(x) = 0$.
> 3. Find values of the variable for which the related rational function is not defined.
> 4. The numbers found in steps (2) and (3) are called *critical values*. Use the critical values to divide the *x*-axis into intervals. Then test an *x*-value from each interval to determine the function's sign in that interval.
> 5. Select the intervals for which the inequality is satisfied and write interval notation or set-builder notation for the solution set. If the inequality symbol is ≤ or ≥, then the solutions to step (2) should be included in the solution set. The *x*-values found in step (3) are never included in the solution set.

3.6 EXERCISE SET

For the function
$$f(x) = x^2 + 2x - 15,$$
solve each of the following.

1. $f(x) = 0$
2. $f(x) < 0$
3. $f(x) \leq 0$
4. $f(x) > 0$
5. $f(x) \geq 0$

For the function
$$g(x) = x^5 - 9x^3,$$
solve each of the following.

6. $g(x) = 0$
7. $g(x) < 0$
8. $g(x) \leq 0$
9. $g(x) > 0$
10. $g(x) \geq 0$

In Exercises 11–14, a related function is graphed. Solve the given inequality.

11. $x^3 + 6x^2 < x + 30$

12. $x^4 - 27x^2 - 14x + 120 \geq 0$

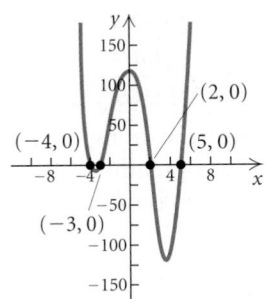

13. $\dfrac{8x}{x^2 - 4} \geq 0$

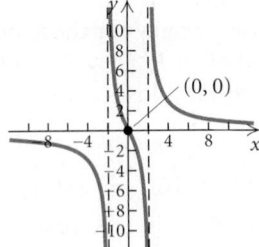

14. $\dfrac{8}{x^2 - 4} < 0$

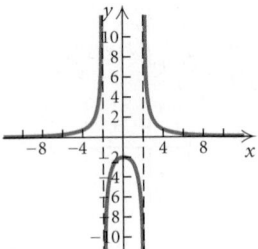

Solve.

15. $(x - 1)(x + 4) < 0$

16. $(x + 3)(x - 5) < 0$

17. $(x - 4)(x + 2) \geq 0$

18. $(x - 2)(x + 1) \geq 0$

19. $x^2 + x - 2 > 0$

20. $x^2 - x - 6 > 0$

21. $x^2 > 25$

22. $x^2 \leq 1$

23. $4 - x^2 \leq 0$

24. $11 - x^2 \geq 0$

25. $6x - 9 - x^2 < 0$

26. $x^2 + 2x + 1 \leq 0$

27. $x^2 + 12 < 4x$

28. $x^2 - 8 > 6x$

29. $4x^3 - 7x^2 \leq 15x$

30. $2x^3 - x^2 < 5x$

31. $x^3 + 3x^2 - x - 3 \geq 0$

32. $x^3 + x^2 - 4x - 4 \geq 0$

33. $x^3 - 2x^2 < 5x - 6$

34. $x^3 + x \leq 6 - 4x^2$

35. $x^5 + x^2 \geq 2x^3 + 2$

36. $x^5 + 24 > 3x^3 + 8x^2$

37. $2x^3 + 6 \leq 5x^2 + x$

38. $2x^3 + x^2 < 10 + 11x$

39. $x^3 + 5x^2 - 25x \leq 125$

40. $x^3 - 9x + 27 \geq 3x^2$

41. $\dfrac{1}{x + 4} > 0$

42. $\dfrac{1}{x - 3} \leq 0$

43. $\dfrac{-4}{2x + 5} < 0$

44. $\dfrac{-2}{5 - x} \geq 0$

45. $\dfrac{x - 4}{x + 3} - \dfrac{x + 2}{x - 1} \leq 0$

46. $\dfrac{x + 1}{x - 2} + \dfrac{x - 3}{x - 1} < 0$

47. $\dfrac{2x - 1}{x + 3} \geq \dfrac{x + 1}{3x + 1}$

48. $\dfrac{x + 5}{x - 4} > \dfrac{3x + 2}{2x + 1}$

49. $\dfrac{x + 1}{x - 2} \geq 3$

50. $\dfrac{x}{x - 5} < 2$

51. $x - 2 > \dfrac{1}{x}$

52. $4 \geq \dfrac{4}{x} + x$

53. $\dfrac{2}{x^2 - 4x + 3} \leq \dfrac{5}{x^2 - 9}$

54. $\dfrac{3}{x^2 - 4} \leq \dfrac{5}{x^2 + 7x + 10}$

55. $\dfrac{3}{x^2 + 1} \geq \dfrac{6}{5x^2 + 2}$

56. $\dfrac{4}{x^2 - 9} < \dfrac{3}{x^2 - 25}$

57. $\dfrac{5}{x^2 + 3x} < \dfrac{3}{2x + 1}$

58. $\dfrac{2}{x^2 + 3} > \dfrac{3}{5 + 4x^2}$

59. $\dfrac{5x}{7x - 2} > \dfrac{x}{x + 1}$

60. $\dfrac{x^2 - x - 2}{x^2 + 5x + 6} < 0$

61. $\dfrac{x}{x^2 + 4x - 5} + \dfrac{3}{x^2 - 25} \leq \dfrac{2x}{x^2 - 6x + 5}$

62. $\dfrac{2x}{x^2 - 9} + \dfrac{x}{x^2 + x - 12} \geq \dfrac{3x}{x^2 + 7x + 12}$

63. *Temperature During an Illness.* The temperature T, in degrees Fahrenheit, of a person during an illness is given by the function

$$T(t) = \dfrac{4t}{t^2 + 1} + 98.6,$$

where t is the time, in hours. Find the interval on which the temperature was over $100°$. (See Example 11 in Section 3.5.)

64. *Population Growth.* The population P, in thousands, of Lordsburg is given by

$$P(t) = \dfrac{500t}{2t^2 + 9},$$

where t is the time, in months. Find the interval on which the population was 40 thousand or greater. (See Exercise 75 in Exercise Set 3.5.)

65. *Total Profit.* Flexl, Inc., determines that its total profit is given by the function

$$P(x) = -3x^2 + 630x - 6000.$$

a) Flexl makes a profit for those nonnegative values of x for which $P(x) > 0$. Find the values of x for which Flexl makes a profit.
b) Flexl loses money for those nonnegative values of x for which $P(x) < 0$. Find the values of x for which Flexl loses money.

66. *Height of a Thrown Object.* The function

$$s(t) = -16t^2 + 32t + 1920$$

gives the height s, in feet, of an object thrown from a cliff that is 1920 ft high. Here t is the time, in seconds, that the object is in the air.

a) For what times is the height greater than 1920 ft?
b) For what times is the height less than 640 ft?

67. *Number of Diagonals.* A polygon with n sides has D diagonals, where D is given by the function

$$D(n) = \dfrac{n(n - 3)}{2}.$$

Find the number of sides n if

$$27 \leq D \leq 230.$$

68. *Number of Handshakes.* If there are n people in a room, the number N of possible handshakes by all the people in the room is given by the function

$$N(n) = \frac{n(n-1)}{2}.$$

For what number n of people is

$$66 \le N \le 300?$$

Technology Connection

69. Use a graphing calculator and the ZERO feature to check your answers to Exercises 15, 21, 29, 37, and 49.

Collaborative Discussion and Writing

70. Why, when solving rational inequalities, do we need to find values for which the function is undefined as well as zeros of the function?

71. Under what circumstances would a quadratic inequality have a solution set that is a closed interval? Under what circumstances would a quadratic inequality have an empty solution set?

Skill Maintenance

Find an equation for a circle satisfying the given conditions.

72. Center: $(0, -3)$; diameter of length $\frac{7}{2}$

73. Center: $(-2, 4)$; radius of length 3

In Exercises 74 and 75:

a) *Find the vertex.*
b) *Determine whether there is a maximum or minimum value and find that value.*
c) *Find the range.*

74. $g(x) = x^2 - 10x + 2$

75. $h(x) = -2x^2 + 3x - 8$

Synthesis

Solve.

76. $x^4 - 6x^2 + 5 > 0$

77. $x^4 + 3x^2 > 4x - 15$

78. $\left| \dfrac{x+3}{x-4} \right| < 2$

79. $|x^2 - 5| = 5 - x^2$

80. $(7 - x)^{-2} < 0$

81. $2|x|^2 - |x| + 2 \le 5$

82. $\left| 2 - \dfrac{1}{x} \right| \le 2 + \left| \dfrac{1}{x} \right|$

83. $\left| 1 + \dfrac{1}{x} \right| < 3$

84. $|1 + 5x - x^2| \ge 5$

85. $|x^2 + 3x - 1| < 3$

86. Write a polynomial inequality for which the solution set is $[-4, 3] \cup [7, \infty)$.

87. Write a quadratic inequality for which the solution set is $(-4, 3)$.

3.7 ◆ **Variation and Applications**

◆ Find equations of direct, inverse, and combined variation given values of the variables.

◆ Solve applied problems involving variation.

We now extend our study of formulas and functions by considering applications involving variation.

◆ Direct Variation

Suppose an executive chef earns $23 per hour. In 1 hr, $23 is earned; in 2 hr, $46 is earned; in 3 hr, $69 is earned; and so on. This gives rise to a set of ordered pairs of numbers:

$$(1, 23), \qquad (2, 46), \qquad (3, 69), \qquad (4, 92),$$

and so on. Note that the ratio of the second coordinate to the first is the same number for each pair:

$$\frac{23}{1} = 23, \qquad \frac{46}{2} = 23, \qquad \frac{69}{3} = 23, \qquad \frac{92}{4} = 23, \quad \text{and so on.}$$

Whenever a situation produces pairs of numbers in which the *ratio is constant*, we say that there is **direct variation.** Here the amount earned E varies directly as the time worked t:

$$\frac{E}{t} = 23 \text{ (a constant),} \quad \text{or} \quad E = 23t,$$

or, using function notation, $E(t) = 23t$. This equation is an equation of **direct variation.** The coefficient, 23 in the situation above, is called the **variation constant.** In this case, it is the rate of change of earnings with respect to time.

Chef's Earnings

Points plotted: (1, 23), (2, 46), (3, 69), (4, 92). Vertical axis E in dollars (Earnings) from 0 to $100; horizontal axis t Time (in hours) from 0 to 10.

The graph of $y = kx$, $k > 0$, always goes through the origin and rises from left to right. Note that as x increases, y increases; that is, the function is increasing on the interval $(0, \infty)$. The constant k is also the slope of the line.

$y = kx,$
$k > 0$

Direct Variation

If a situation gives rise to a linear function $f(x) = kx$, or $y = kx$, where k is a positive constant, we say that we have **direct variation,** or that **y varies directly as x,** or that **y is directly proportional to x.** The number k is called the **variation constant,** or **constant of proportionality.**

EXAMPLE 1 Find the variation constant and an equation of variation in which y varies directly as x, and $y = 32$ when $x = 2$.

Solution We know that $(2, 32)$ is a solution of $y = kx$. Thus,

$$y = kx$$
$$32 = k \cdot 2 \qquad \text{Substituting}$$
$$\frac{32}{2} = k, \text{ or } k = 16. \qquad \text{Solving for } k$$

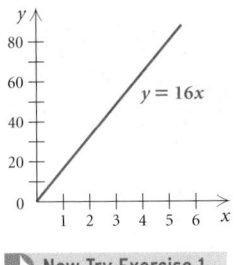

The variation constant, 16, is the rate of change of y with respect to x. The equation of variation is $y = 16x$.

▶ Now Try Exercise 1.

EXAMPLE 2 *Water from Melting Snow.* The number of centimeters W of water produced from melting snow varies directly as S, the number of centimeters of snow. Meteorologists have found that 150 cm of snow will melt to 16.8 cm of water. To how many centimeters of water will 200 cm of snow melt?

Solution We can express the amount of water as a function of the amount of snow. Thus, $W(S) = kS$, where k is the variation constant. We first find k using the given data and then find an equation of variation:

$$W(S) = kS \qquad \text{W varies directly as S.}$$
$$W(150) = k \cdot 150 \qquad \text{Substituting 150 for S}$$
$$16.8 = k \cdot 150 \qquad \text{Replacing $W(150)$ with 16.8}$$
$$\frac{16.8}{150} = k \qquad \text{Solving for k}$$
$$0.112 = k. \qquad \text{This is the variation constant.}$$

The equation of variation is $W(S) = 0.112S$.

Next, we use the equation to find how many centimeters of water will result from melting 200 cm of snow:

$$W(S) = 0.112S$$
$$W(200) = 0.112(200) \qquad \text{Substituting}$$
$$= 22.4.$$

Thus, 200 cm of snow will melt to 22.4 cm of water.

▶ Now Try Exercise 15.

◆ Inverse Variation

Speed (in miles per hour)

Suppose a bus is traveling a distance of 20 mi. At a speed of 5 mph, the trip will take 4 hr; at 10 mph, it will take 2 hr; at 20 mph, it will take 1 hr; at 40 mph, it will take $\frac{1}{2}$ hr; and so on. We plot this information on a graph, using speed as the first coordinate and time as the second coordinate to determine a set of ordered pairs:

$$(5, 4), \qquad (10, 2), \qquad (20, 1), \qquad \left(40, \tfrac{1}{2}\right), \quad \text{and so on.}$$

Note that the products of the coordinates are all the same number:

$$5 \cdot 4 = 20, \qquad 10 \cdot 2 = 20, \qquad 20 \cdot 1 = 20, \qquad 40 \cdot \tfrac{1}{2} = 20, \quad \text{and so on.}$$

Whenever a situation produces pairs of numbers in which the *product is constant*, we say that there is **inverse variation**. Here the time varies inversely as the speed:

$$rt = 20 \ (\text{a constant}), \quad \text{or} \quad t = \frac{20}{r},$$

or, using function notation, $t(r) = 20/r$. This equation is an equation of **inverse variation**. The coefficient, 20 in the situation above, is called the **variation constant**. Note that as the first number increases, the second number decreases.

It is helpful to look at the graph of $y = k/x$, $k > 0$. The graph is like the one shown below for positive values of x. Note that as x increases, y decreases; that is, the function is decreasing on the interval $(0, \infty)$.

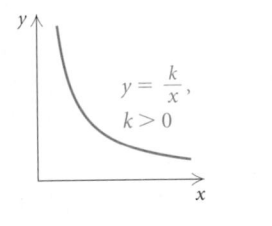

Inverse Variation

If a situation gives rise to a function $f(x) = k/x$, or $y = k/x$, where k is a positive constant, we say that we have **inverse variation,** or that **y varies inversely as x,** or that **y is inversely proportional to x.** The number k is called the **variation constant,** or **constant of proportionality.**

EXAMPLE 3   Find the variation constant and an equation of variation in which y varies inversely as x, and $y = 16$ when $x = 0.3$.

Solution   We know that $(0.3, 16)$ is a solution of $y = k/x$. We substitute:

$$y = \frac{k}{x}$$

$$16 = \frac{k}{0.3} \qquad \text{Substituting}$$

$$(0.3)16 = k \qquad \text{Solving for } k$$

$$4.8 = k.$$

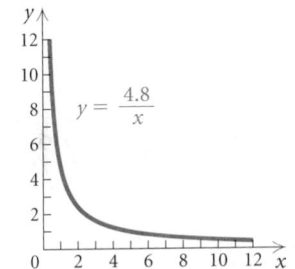

The variation constant is 4.8. The equation of variation is $y = 4.8/x$.

▶ Now Try Exercise 3.

There are many problems that translate to an equation of inverse variation.

EXAMPLE 4   *Framing a House.*   The time t required to do a job varies inversely as the number of people P who work on the job (assuming that all work at the same rate). If it takes 72 hr for 9 people to frame a house, how long will it take 12 people to complete the same job?

Solution   We can express the amount of time required, in hours, as a function of the number of people working. Thus we have $t(P) = k/P$. We first find k using the given information and then find an equation of variation:

$$t(P) = \frac{k}{P} \qquad t \text{ varies inversely as } P.$$

$$t(9) = \frac{k}{9} \qquad \text{Substituting 9 for } P$$

$$72 = \frac{k}{9} \qquad \text{Replacing } t(9) \text{ with 72}$$

$$9 \cdot 72 = k \qquad \text{Solving for } k$$

$$648 = k. \qquad \text{This is the variation constant.}$$

The equation of variation is $t(P) = 648/P$.

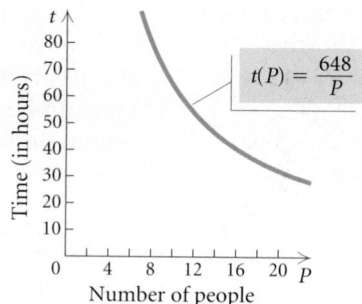

Next, we use the equation to find the time that it would take 12 people to do the job. We compute $t(12)$:

$$t(P) = \frac{648}{P}$$

$$t(12) = \frac{648}{12} \qquad \text{Substituting}$$

$$t = 54.$$

Thus it would take 54 hr for 12 people to complete the job.

▶ **Now Try Exercise 17.**

✦ Combined Variation

We now look at other kinds of variation.

---

y varies **directly as the nth power of x** if there is some positive constant k such that

$$y = kx^n.$$

y varies **inversely as the nth power of x** if there is some positive constant k such that

$$y = \frac{k}{x^n}.$$

y varies **jointly as x and z** if there is some positive constant k such that

$$y = kxz.$$

There are other types of combined variation as well. Consider the formula for the volume of a right circular cylinder, $V = \pi r^2 h$, in which V, r, and h are variables and π is a constant. We say that V varies jointly as h and the square of r.

EXAMPLE 5 Find an equation of variation in which y varies directly as the square of x, and $y = 12$ when $x = 2$.

Solution We write an equation of variation and find k:

$$y = kx^2$$
$$12 = k \cdot 2^2 \qquad \text{Substituting}$$
$$12 = k \cdot 4$$
$$3 = k.$$

Thus, $y = 3x^2$.

▶ Now Try Exercise 27.

EXAMPLE 6 Find an equation of variation in which y varies jointly as x and z, and $y = 42$ when $x = 2$ and $z = 3$.

Solution We have

$$y = kxz$$
$$42 = k \cdot 2 \cdot 3 \qquad \text{Substituting}$$
$$42 = k \cdot 6$$
$$7 = k.$$

Thus, $y = 7xz$.

▶ Now Try Exercise 29.

EXAMPLE 7 Find an equation of variation in which y varies jointly as x and z and inversely as the square of w, and $y = 105$ when $x = 3$, $z = 20$, and $w = 2$.

Solution We have

$$y = k \cdot \frac{xz}{w^2}$$
$$105 = k \cdot \frac{3 \cdot 20}{2^2} \qquad \text{Substituting}$$
$$105 = k \cdot 15$$
$$7 = k.$$

Thus, $y = 7\dfrac{xz}{w^2}$.

▶ Now Try Exercise 33.

Many applied problems can be modeled using equations of combined variation.

EXAMPLE 8 *Volume of a Tree.*   The volume of wood *V* in a tree varies jointly as the height *h* and the square of the girth *g*. (Girth is distance around.) If the volume of a redwood tree is 216 m³ when the height is 30 m and the girth is 1.5 m, what is the height of a tree whose volume is 960 m³ and girth is 2 m?

Solution   We first find *k* using the first set of data. Then we solve for *h* using the second set of data.

$$V = khg^2$$
$$216 = k \cdot 30 \cdot 1.5^2$$
$$216 = k \cdot 30 \cdot 2.25$$
$$216 = k \cdot 67.5$$
$$3.2 = k$$

Then the equation of variation is $V = 3.2hg^2$. We substitute the second set of data into the equation:

$$960 = 3.2 \cdot h \cdot 2^2$$
$$960 = 12.8 \cdot h$$
$$75 = h.$$

Thus the height of the tree is 75 m.

▶ Now Try Exercise 35.

3.7   EXERCISE SET

Find the variation constant and an equation of variation for the given situation.

1. *y* varies directly as *x*, and *y* = 54 when *x* = 12

2. *y* varies directly as *x*, and *y* = 0.1 when *x* = 0.2

3. *y* varies inversely as *x*, and *y* = 3 when *x* = 12

4. *y* varies inversely as *x*, and *y* = 12 when *x* = 5

5. *y* varies directly as *x*, and *y* = 1 when $x = \frac{1}{4}$

6. *y* varies inversely as *x*, and *y* = 0.1 when *x* = 0.5

7. *y* varies inversely as *x*, and *y* = 32 when $x = \frac{1}{8}$

8. y varies directly as x, and $y = 3$ when $x = 33$

9. y varies directly as x, and $y = \frac{3}{4}$ when $x = 2$

10. y varies inversely as x, and $y = \frac{1}{5}$ when $x = 35$

11. y varies inversely as x, and $y = 1.8$ when $x = 0.3$

12. y varies directly as x, and $y = 0.9$ when $x = 0.4$

13. *Work Rate.* The time T required to do a job varies inversely as the number of people P working. It takes 5 hr for 7 bricklayers to build a park wall. (See the graph below.) How long will it take 10 bricklayers to complete the job?

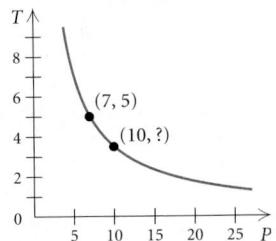

14. *Weekly Allowance.* According to Fidelity Investments *Investment Vision Magazine*, the average weekly allowance A of children varies directly as their grade level G. It is known that the average allowance of a 9th-grade student is $9.66 per week. What then is the average allowance of a 4th-grade student?

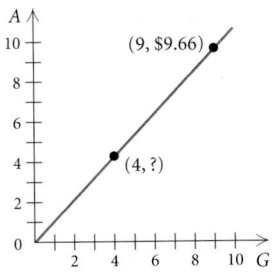

15. *Fat Intake.* The maximum number of grams of fat that should be in a diet varies directly as a person's weight. A person weighing 120 lb should have no more than 60 g of fat per day. What is the maximum daily fat intake for a person weighing 180 lb?

16. *Rate of Travel.* The time t required to drive a fixed distance varies inversely as the speed r. It takes 5 hr at a speed of 80 km/h to drive a fixed distance. How long will it take to drive the same distance at a speed of 70 km/h?

17. *Beam Weight.* The weight W that a horizontal beam can support varies inversely as the length L of the beam. Suppose an 8-m beam can support 1200 kg. How many kilograms can a 14-m beam support?

18. *House of Representatives.* The number of representatives N that each state has varies directly as the number of people P living in the state. If New York, with 19,227,088 residents, has 29 representatives, how many representatives does North Carolina, with a population of 8,541,221, have?

19. *Weight on Mars.* The weight M of an object on Mars varies directly as its weight E on Earth. A person who weighs 95 lb on Earth weighs 38 lb on Mars. How much would a 100-lb person weigh on Mars?

20. *Pumping Rate.* The time t required to empty a tank varies inversely as the rate r of pumping. If a pump can empty a tank in 45 min at the rate of 600 kL/min, how long will it take the pump to empty the same tank at the rate of 1000 kL/min?

21. *Hooke's Law.* Hooke's law states that the distance d that a spring will stretch varies directly as the mass m of an object hanging from the spring. If a 3-kg mass stretches a spring 40 cm, how far will a 5-kg mass stretch the spring?

22. *Relative Aperture.* The relative aperture, or f-stop, of a 23.5-mm diameter lens is directly proportional to the focal length F of the lens. If a 150-mm focal length has an f-stop of 6.3, find the f-stop of a 23.5-mm diameter lens with a focal length of 80 mm.

23. *Musical Pitch.* The pitch P of a musical tone varies inversely as its wavelength W. One tone has a pitch of 330 vibrations per second and a wavelength of 3.2 ft. Find the wavelength of another tone that has a pitch of 550 vibrations per second.

24. *Recycling Rechargeable Batteries.* The Indiana Household Hazardous Waste Task Force was awarded the 2002 National Community Recycling Leadership Award, with special recognition given to Monroe County Solid Waste Management District. Monroe County, Indiana, with a population of 9880, collected 4445 lb of rechargeable batteries in a recent recycling effort. (*Source*: Rechargeable Battery Recycling Corporation) If the number of pounds collected varies directly as the population, how many pounds of rechargeable batteries could a county with a population of 74,650 collect for recycling?

Find an equation of variation for the given situation.

25. y varies inversely as the square of x, and $y = 0.15$ when $x = 0.1$

26. y varies inversely as the square of x, and $y = 6$ when $x = 3$

27. y varies directly as the square of x, and $y = 0.15$ when $x = 0.1$

28. y varies directly as the square of x, and $y = 6$ when $x = 3$

29. y varies jointly as x and z, and $y = 56$ when $x = 7$ and $z = 8$

30. y varies directly as x and inversely as z, and $y = 4$ when $x = 12$ and $z = 15$

31. y varies jointly as x and the square of z, and $y = 105$ when $x = 14$ and $z = 5$

32. y varies jointly as x and z and inversely as w, and $y = \frac{3}{2}$ when $x = 2$, $z = 3$, and $w = 4$

33. y varies jointly as x and z and inversely as the product of w and p, and $y = \frac{3}{28}$ when $x = 3$, $z = 10$, $w = 7$, and $p = 8$

34. y varies jointly as x and z and inversely as the square of w, and $y = \frac{12}{5}$ when $x = 16$, $z = 3$, and $w = 5$

35. *Intensity of Light.* The intensity I of light from a light bulb varies inversely as the square of the distance d from the bulb. Suppose that I is 90 W/m^2 (watts per square meter) when the distance is 5 m. How much *farther* would it be to a point where the intensity is 40 W/m^2?

36. *Atmospheric Drag.* Wind resistance, or atmospheric drag, tends to slow down moving objects. Atmospheric drag varies jointly as an object's surface area A and velocity v. If a car traveling at a speed of 40 mph with a surface area of 37.8 ft^2 experiences a drag of 222 N (Newtons), how fast must a car with 51 ft^2 of surface area travel in order to experience a drag force of 430 N?

37. *Stopping Distance of a Car.* The stopping distance d of a car after the brakes have been applied varies directly as the square of the speed r. If a car traveling 60 mph can stop in 200 ft, how fast can a car travel and still stop in 72 ft?

38. *Weight of an Astronaut.*   The weight W of an object varies inversely as the square of the distance d from the center of the earth. At sea level (3978 mi from the center of the earth), an astronaut weighs 220 lb. Find his weight when he is 200 mi above the surface of the earth and the spacecraft is not in motion.

39. *Earned-Run Average.*   A pitcher's earned-run average E varies directly as the number R of earned runs allowed and inversely as the number I of innings pitched. In 2005, Curt Schilling of the Boston Red Sox had an earned-run average of 5.69. He gave up 59 earned runs in 93.3 innings. How many earned runs would he have given up had he pitched 200 innings with the same average? Round to the nearest whole number.

40. *Boyle's Law.*   The volume V of a given mass of a gas varies directly as the temperature T and inversely as the pressure P. If $V = 231\ \text{cm}^3$ when $T = 42°$ and $P = 20\ \text{kg/cm}^2$, what is the volume when $T = 30°$ and $P = 15\ \text{kg/cm}^2$?

Collaborative Discussion and Writing

41. If y varies directly as x^2, explain why doubling x would not cause y to be doubled as well.

42. If y varies directly as x and x varies inversely as z, how does y vary with regard to z? Why?

Skill Maintenance

43. Graph: $f(x) = \begin{cases} x - 2, & \text{for } x \le -1, \\ 3, & \text{for } -1 < x \le 2, \\ x, & \text{for } x > 2. \end{cases}$

Determine algebraically whether the graph is symmetric with respect to the x-axis, the y-axis, and/or the origin.

44. $y = 3x^4 - 3$

45. $y^2 = x$

46. $2x - 5y = 0$

Synthesis

47. *Volume and Cost.*   An 18-oz jar of peanut butter in the shape of a right circular cylinder is 5 in. high and 3 in. in diameter and sells for $1.80. For the same brand in the same store, a 28-oz jar that is $5\frac{1}{2}$ in. high and $3\frac{1}{4}$ in. in diameter sells for $3.20. If we assume that cost is directly proportional to volume, what should the price of the larger jar be? If we assume that cost is directly proportional to weight, what should the price of the larger jar be?

48. In each of the following equations, state whether y varies directly as x, inversely as x, or neither directly nor inversely as x.

   a) $7xy = 14$
   b) $x - 2y = 12$
   c) $-2x + 3y = 0$
   d) $x = \dfrac{3}{4}\, y$
   e) $\dfrac{x}{y} = 2$

49. *Area of a Circle.*   The area of a circle varies directly as the square of the length of a diameter. What is the variation constant?

50. Describe in words the variation given by the equation

$$Q = \frac{kp^2}{q^3}.$$

CHAPTER 3 SUMMARY AND REVIEW

Important Properties and Formulas

Polynomial Function:

$$P(x) = a_n x^n + a_{n-1} x^{n-1} + a_{n-2} x^{n-2} + \cdots$$
$$+ a_1 x + a_0,$$

where the coefficients $a_n, a_{n-1}, \ldots, a_1, a_0$ are real numbers and the exponents are whole numbers.

The Leading-Term Test: If $a_n x^n$ is the leading term of a polynomial function, then the behavior of the graph as $x \to \infty$ and as $x \to -\infty$ can be described in one of the four following ways.

If n is even, and $a_n > 0$:

If n is even, and $a_n < 0$:

If n is odd, and $a_n > 0$:

If n is odd, and $a_n < 0$:

The Intermediate Value Theorem: For any polynomial function $P(x)$ with real coefficients, suppose that for $a \neq b$, $P(a)$ and $P(b)$ are of opposite signs. Then the function has a real zero between a and b.

Polynomial Division:

$$P(x) = d(x) \cdot Q(x) + R(x)$$

Dividend   Divisor   Quotient   Remainder

The Remainder Theorem: If a number c is substituted for x in the polynomial $f(x)$, then the result $f(c)$ is the remainder that would be obtained by dividing $f(x)$ by $x - c$. That is, if $f(x) = (x - c) \cdot Q(x) + R$, then $f(c) = R$.

The Factor Theorem: For a polynomial $f(x)$, if $f(c) = 0$, then $x - c$ is a factor of $f(x)$.

The Fundamental Theorem of Algebra: Every polynomial function of degree n, $n \geq 1$, with complex coefficients has at least one zero in the system of complex numbers.

The Rational Zeros Theorem: Consider the polynomial function

$$P(x) = a_n x^n + a_{n-1} x^{n-1} + a_{n-2} x^{n-2} + \cdots + a_1 x$$
$$+ a_0,$$

where all the coefficients are integers and $n \geq 1$. Also, consider a rational number p/q, where p and q have no common factor other than -1 and 1. If p/q is a zero of $P(x)$, then p is a factor of a_0 and q is a factor of a_n.

Descartes' Rule of Signs

Let $P(x)$, written in descending or ascending order, be a polynomial function with real coefficients and a nonzero constant term. The number of positive real zeros of $P(x)$ is either:

1. The same as the number of variations of sign in $P(x)$, or
2. Less than the number of variations of sign in $P(x)$ by a positive even integer.

The number of negative real zeros of $P(x)$ is either:

3. The same as the number of variations of sign in $P(-x)$, or
4. Less than the number of variations of sign in $P(-x)$ by a positive even integer.

A zero of multiplicity m must be counted m times.

Rational Function:

$$f(x) = \frac{p(x)}{q(x)},$$

where $p(x)$ and $q(x)$ are polynomials and where $q(x)$ is not the zero polynomial. The domain of $f(x)$ consists of all x for which $q(x) \neq 0$.

Occurrence of Lines as Asymptotes

For a rational function $f(x) = p(x)/q(x)$, where $p(x)$ and $q(x)$ have no common factors other than constants:

Vertical asymptotes occur at any x-values that make the denominator 0.

The x-axis is the horizontal asymptote when the degree of the numerator is less than the degree of the denominator.

A horizontal asymptote other than the x-axis occurs when the numerator and the denominator have the same degree.

An oblique asymptote occurs when the degree of the numerator is 1 greater than the degree of the denominator.

Variation

Direct: $\quad y = kx$

Inverse: $\quad y = \dfrac{k}{x}$

Joint: $\quad y = kxz$

REVIEW EXERCISES

Determine whether the statement is true or false.

1. If $f(x) = (x + a)(x + b)(x - c)$, then $f(-b) = 0$.   [3.3]

2. The graph of a rational function never crosses a vertical asymptote.   [3.5]

3. For the function $g(x) = x^4 - 8x^2 - 9$, the only possible rational zeros are 1, -1, 3, and -3.   [3.4]

4. The graph of $P(x) = x^6 - x^8$ has at most 6 x-intercepts.   [3.2]

5. The domain of the function
$$f(x) = \frac{x - 4}{(x + 2)(x - 3)}$$
   is $(-\infty, -2) \cup (3, \infty)$.   [3.5]

Determine the leading term, the leading coefficient, and the degree of the polynomial. Then classify the polynomial as constant, linear, quadratic, cubic, or quartic.   [3.1]

6. $f(x) = 7x^2 - 5 + 0.45x^4 - 3x^3$

7. $h(x) = -25$

8. $g(x) = 6 - 0.5x$

9. $f(x) = \frac{1}{3}x^3 - 2x + 3$

Use the leading-term test to describe the end behavior of the graph of the function.   [3.1]

10. $f(x) = -\frac{1}{2}x^4 + 3x^2 + x - 6$

11. $f(x) = x^5 + 2x^3 - x^2 + 5x + 4$

Find the zeros of the polynomial function and state the multiplicity of each.   [3.1]

12. $g(x) = \left(x - \frac{2}{3}\right)(x + 2)^3(x - 5)^2$

13. $f(x) = x^4 - 26x^2 + 25$

14. $h(x) = x^3 + 4x^2 - 9x - 36$

15. *Interest Compounded Annually.* When P dollars is invested at interest rate i, compounded annually, for t years, the investment grows to A dollars, where

$$A = P(1 + i)^t.$$

a) Find the interest rate i if $6250 grows to $6760 in 2 yr. [3.1]

b) Find the interest rate i if $1,000,000 grows to $1,215,506.25 in 4 yr. [3.1]

Sketch the graph of the polynomial function.

16. $f(x) = -x^4 + 2x^3$ [3.2]

17. $g(x) = (x - 1)^3(x + 2)^2$ [3.2]

18. $h(x) = x^3 + 3x^2 - x - 3$ [3.2]

19. $f(x) = x^4 - 5x^3 + 6x^2 + 4x - 8$ [3.2], [3.3]

20. $g(x) = 2x^3 + 7x^2 - 14x + 5$ [3.2], [3.4]

Using the intermediate value theorem, determine, if possible, whether the function f has a zero between a and b. [3.2]

21. $f(x) = 4x^2 - 5x - 3$; $a = 1, b = 2$

22. $f(x) = x^3 - 4x^2 + \frac{1}{2}x + 2$; $a = -1, b = 1$

In each of the following, a polynomial $P(x)$ and a divisor $d(x)$ are given. Use long division to find the quotient $Q(x)$ and the remainder $R(x)$ when $P(x)$ is divided by $d(x)$, and express $P(x)$ in the form $d(x) \cdot Q(x) + R(x)$. [3.3]

23. $P(x) = 6x^3 - 2x^2 + 4x - 1$,
$d(x) = x - 3$

24. $P(x) = x^4 - 2x^3 + x + 5$,
$d(x) = x + 1$

Use synthetic division to find the quotient and the remainder. [3.3]

25. $(x^3 + 2x^2 - 13x + 10) \div (x - 5)$

26. $(x^4 + 3x^3 + 3x^2 + 3x + 2) \div (x + 2)$

27. $(x^5 - 2x) \div (x + 1)$

Use synthetic division to find the indicated function value. [3.3]

28. $f(x) = x^3 + 2x^2 - 13x + 10$; $f(-2)$

29. $f(x) = x^4 - 16$; $f(-2)$

30. $f(x) = x^5 - 4x^4 + x^3 - x^2 + 2x - 100$;
$f(-10)$

Using synthetic division, determine whether the numbers are zeros of the polynomial function. [3.3]

31. $-i, -5$; $f(x) = x^3 - 5x^2 + x - 5$

32. $-1, -2$; $f(x) = x^4 - 4x^3 - 3x^2 + 14x - 8$

33. $\frac{1}{3}, 1$; $f(x) = x^3 - \frac{4}{3}x^2 - \frac{5}{3}x + \frac{2}{3}$

34. $2, -\sqrt{3}$; $f(x) = x^4 - 5x^2 + 6$

Factor the polynomial $f(x)$. Then solve the equation $f(x) = 0$. [3.3]

35. $f(x) = x^3 + 2x^2 - 7x + 4$

36. $f(x) = x^3 + 4x^2 - 3x - 18$

37. $f(x) = x^4 - 4x^3 - 21x^2 + 100x - 100$

38. $f(x) = x^4 - 3x^2 + 2$

Find a polynomial function of degree 3 with the given numbers as zeros. [3.4]

39. $-4, -1, 2$

40. $-3, 1 - i, 1 + i$

41. $\frac{1}{2}, 1 - \sqrt{2}, 1 + \sqrt{2}$

42. Find a polynomial function of degree 4 with -5 as a zero of multiplicity 3 and $\frac{1}{2}$ as a zero of multiplicity 1. [3.4]

43. Find a polynomial function of degree 5 with -3 as a zero of multiplicity 2, 2 as a zero of multiplicity 1, and 0 as a zero of multiplicity 2. [3.4]

Suppose that a polynomial function of degree 5 with rational coefficients has the given zeros. Find the other zero(s). [3.4]

44. $-\frac{2}{3}, \sqrt{5}, i$

45. $0, 1 + \sqrt{3}, -\sqrt{3}$

46. $-\sqrt{2}, \frac{1}{2}, 1, 2$

Find a polynomial function of lowest degree with rational coefficients and the following as some of its zeros. [3.4]

47. $\sqrt{11}$

48. $-i, 6$

49. $-1, 4, 1 + i$

50. $\sqrt{5}, -2i$

51. $\frac{1}{3}, 0, -3$

List all possible rational zeros.   [3.4]

52. $h(x) = 4x^5 - 2x^3 + 6x - 12$

53. $g(x) = 3x^4 - x^3 + 5x^2 - x + 1$

54. $f(x) = x^3 - 2x^2 + x - 24$

For each polynomial function:

a) *Find the rational zeros and then the other zeros; that is, solve* $f(x) = 0$.   [3.4]

b) *Factor* $f(x)$ *into linear factors.*   [3.4]

55. $f(x) = 3x^5 + 2x^4 - 25x^3 - 28x^2 + 12x$

56. $f(x) = x^3 - 2x^2 - 3x + 6$

57. $f(x) = x^4 - 6x^3 + 9x^2 + 6x - 10$

58. $f(x) = x^3 + 3x^2 - 11x - 5$

59. $f(x) = 3x^3 - 8x^2 + 7x - 2$

60. $f(x) = x^5 - 8x^4 + 20x^3 - 8x^2 - 32x + 32$

61. $f(x) = x^6 + x^5 - 28x^4 - 16x^3 + 192x^2$

62. $f(x) = 2x^5 - 13x^4 + 32x^3 - 38x^2 + 22x - 5$

What does Descartes' rule of signs tell you about the number of positive real zeros and the number of negative real zeros of each of the following polynomial functions?   [3.4]

63. $f(x) = 2x^6 - 7x^3 + x^2 - x$

64. $h(x) = -x^8 + 6x^5 - x^3 + 2x - 2$

65. $g(x) = 5x^5 - 4x^2 + x - 1$

Graph the function. Be sure to label all the asymptotes. List the domain and the x- and y-intercepts.   [3.5]

66. $f(x) = \dfrac{x^2 - 5}{x + 2}$

67. $f(x) = \dfrac{5}{(x - 2)^2}$

68. $f(x) = \dfrac{x^2 + x - 6}{x^2 - x - 20}$

69. $f(x) = \dfrac{x - 2}{x^2 - 2x - 15}$

In Exercises 70 and 71, find a rational function that satisfies the given conditions. Answers may vary, but try to give the simplest answer possible.   [3.5]

70. Vertical asymptotes $x = -2, x = 3$

71. Vertical asymptotes $x = -2, x = 3$; horizontal asymptote $y = 4$; x-intercept $(-3, 0)$

72. *Medical Dosage.*   The function

$$N(t) = \frac{0.7t + 2000}{8t + 9}, \quad t \geq 5$$

gives the body concentration $N(t)$, in parts per million, of a certain dosage of medication after time t, in hours.

a) Find the horizontal asymptote of the graph and complete the following: [3.5]

$$N(t) \rightarrow \boxed{} \text{ as } t \rightarrow \infty.$$

b) Explain the meaning of the answer to part (a) in terms of the application.   [3.5]

Solve.   [3.6]

73. $x^2 - 9 < 0$

74. $2x^2 > 3x + 2$

75. $(1 - x)(x + 4)(x - 2) \leq 0$

76. $\dfrac{x - 2}{x + 3} < 4$

77. *Height of a Rocket.*   The function

$$S(t) = -16t^2 + 80t + 224$$

gives the height S, in feet, of a model rocket launched with a velocity of 80 ft/sec from a hill that is 224 ft high, where t is the time, in seconds.

a) Determine when the rocket reaches the ground.   [3.1]

b) On what interval is the height greater than 320 ft?   [3.1], [3.6]

78. *Population Growth.* The population P, in thousands, of Novi is given by

$$P(t) = \frac{8000t}{4t^2 + 10},$$

where t is the time, in months. Find the interval on which the population was 400,000 or greater. [3.6]

79. Find an equation of variation in which y varies directly as x, and $y = 100$ when $x = 25$. [3.7]

80. Find an equation of variation in which y varies inversely as x, and $y = 100$ when $x = 25$. [3.7]

81. *Pumping Time.* The time t required to empty a tank varies inversely as the rate r of pumping. If a pump can empty a tank in 35 min at the rate of 800 kL per minute, how long will it take the pump to empty the same tank at the rate of 1400 kL per minute? [3.7]

82. *Power of Electric Current.* The power P expended by heat in an electric circuit of fixed resistance varies directly as the square of the current C in the circuit. A circuit expends 180 watts when a current of 6 amperes is flowing. What is the amount of heat expended when the current is 10 amperes? [3.7]

83. *Test Score.* The score N on a test varies directly as the number of correct responses a. Ellen answers 28 questions correctly and earns a score of 87. What would Ellen's score have been if she had answered 25 questions correctly? [3.7]

Find an equation of variation for the given situation.

84. y varies inversely as the square of x, and $y = 12$ when $x = 2$ [3.7]

85. y varies jointly as x and the square of z and inversely as w, and $y = 2$ when $x = 16$, $w = 0.2$, and $z = \frac{1}{2}$ [3.7]

86. Determine the vertical asymptotes of the function

$$f(x) = \frac{x - 4}{(x + 1)(x - 2)(x + 4)}. \quad [3.5]$$

A. $x = 1, x = -2$, and $x = 4$
B. $x = -1, x = 2, x = -4$, and $x = 4$
C. $x = -1, x = 2$, and $x = -4$
D. $x = 4$

87. Determine the domain of the function

$$g(x) = \frac{x^2 + 2x - 3}{x^2 - 5x + 6}. \quad [3.5]$$

A. $(-\infty, 2) \cup (2, 3) \cup (3, \infty)$
B. $(-\infty, -3) \cup (-3, 1) \cup (1, \infty)$
C. $(-\infty, 2) \cup (3, \infty)$
D. $(-\infty, -3) \cup (1, \infty)$

Technology Connection

Use a graphing calculator to graph the polynomial function. Then estimate the function's **(a)** *zeros,* **(b)** *relative maxima,* **(c)** *relative minima, and* **(d)** *domain and range.* [3.1]

88. $f(x) = -2x^2 - 3x + 6$

89. $f(x) = x^3 + 3x^2 - 2x - 6$

90. $f(x) = x^4 - 3x^3 + 2x^2$

91. *Cholesterol Level and the Risk of Heart Attack.* The table below lists data concerning the relationship of cholesterol level in men to the risk of a heart attack.

Cholesterol Level	Number of Men per 100,000 Who Suffer a Heart Attack
100	30
200	65
250	100
275	130

Source: Nutrition Action Healthletter

a) Use regression on a graphing calculator to fit linear, quadratic, and cubic functions to the data. [3.1]
b) It is also known that 180 of 100,000 men with a cholesterol level of 300 have a heart attack. Which function in part (a) would best make this prediction? [3.1]
c) Use the answer to part (b) to predict the heart attack rate for men with cholesterol levels of 350 and of 400. [3.1]

Collaborative Discussion and Writing

92. Explain the difference between a polynomial function and a rational function. [3.1], [3.5]

93. Explain and contrast the three types of asymptotes considered for rational functions. [3.5]

Synthesis

Solve.

94. $x^2 \geq 5 - 2x$ [3.6]

95. $\left| 1 - \dfrac{1}{x^2} \right| < 3$ [3.6]

96. $x^4 - 2x^3 + 3x^2 - 2x + 2 = 0$ [3.5]

97. $(x - 2)^{-3} < 0$ [3.6]

98. Express $x^3 - 1$ as a product of linear factors. [3.4]

99. Find k such that $x + 3$ is a factor of $x^3 + kx^2 + kx - 15$. [3.3]

100. When $x^2 - 4x + 3k$ is divided by $x + 5$, the remainder is 33. Find the value of k. [3.3]

Find the domain of the function. [3.6]

101. $f(x) = \sqrt{x^2 + 3x - 10}$

102. $f(x) = \sqrt{x^2 - 3.1x + 2.2} + 1.75$

103. $f(x) = \dfrac{1}{\sqrt{5 - |7x + 2|}}$

CHAPTER 3 TEST

Determine the leading term, the leading coefficient, and the degree of the polynomial. Then classify the polynomial as constant, linear, quadratic, cubic, or quartic.

1. $f(x) = 2x^3 + 6x^2 - x^4 + 11$

2. $h(x) = -4.7x + 29$

3. Find the zeros of the polynomial function and state the multiplicity of each:
$$f(x) = x(3x - 5)(x - 3)^2(x + 1)^3.$$

4. From 1980 to 2000, nearly 90,000 young people under age 20 were killed by gunfire in the United States. The quartic function
$$f(x) = 0.152x^4 - 9.786x^3 + 173.317x^2$$
$$-831.220x + 4053.134$$
can be used to estimate the number of people $f(x)$ under age 20 who were killed x years after 1980. Find the number who were killed in 1986, in 1993, and in 1999.

Sketch the graph of the polynomial function.

5. $f(x) = x^3 - 5x^2 + 2x + 8$

6. $f(x) = -2x^4 + x^3 + 11x^2 - 4x + 12$

Using the intermediate value theorem, determine, if possible, whether the function has a zero between a and b.

7. $f(x) = -5x^2 + 3; \ a = 0, b = 2$

8. $g(x) = 2x^3 + 6x^2 - 3; \ a = -2, b = -1$

9. Use long division to find the quotient $Q(x)$ and the remainder $R(x)$ when $P(x)$ is divided by $d(x)$, and express $P(x)$ in the form $d(x) \cdot Q(x) + R(x)$. Show your work.
$$P(x) = x^4 + 3x^3 + 2x - 5,$$
$$d(x) = x - 1$$

10. Use synthetic division to find the quotient and remainder. Show your work.
$$(3x^3 - 12x + 7) \div (x - 5)$$

11. Use synthetic division to find $P(-3)$ for $P(x) = 2x^3 - 6x^2 + x - 4$. Show your work.

12. Use synthetic division to determine whether -2 is a zero of $f(x) = x^3 + 4x^2 + x - 6$. Answer yes or no. Show your work.

13. Find a polynomial of degree 4 with -3 as a zero of multiplicity 2 and 0 and 6 as zeros of multiplicity 1.

14. Suppose that a polynomial function of degree 5 with rational coefficients has 1, $\sqrt{3}$, and $2 - i$ as zeros. Find the other zeros.

Find a polynomial function of lowest degree with rational coefficients and the following as some of its zeros.

15. $-10, 3i$

16. $0, -\sqrt{3}, 1 - i$

List all possible rational zeros.

17. $f(x) = 2x^3 + x^2 - 2x + 12$

18. $h(x) = 10x^4 - x^3 + 2x - 5$

For each polynomial function:

a) *Find the rational zeros and then the other zeros; that is, solve $f(x) = 0$.*
b) *Factor $f(x)$ into linear factors.*

19. $f(x) = x^3 + x^2 - 5x - 5$

20. $f(x) = 2x^4 - 11x^3 + 16x^2 - x - 6$

21. $f(x) = x^3 + 4x^2 + 4x + 16$

22. $f(x) = 3x^4 - 11x^3 + 15x^2 - 9x + 2$

23. What does Descartes' rule of signs tell you about the number of positive real zeros and the number of negative real zeros of the following function?

$$g(x) = -x^8 + 2x^6 - 4x^3 - 1$$

Graph the function. Be sure to label all the asymptotes. List the domain and the x- and y-intercepts.

24. $f(x) = \dfrac{2}{(x - 3)^2}$

25. $f(x) = \dfrac{x + 3}{x^2 - 3x - 4}$

26. Find a rational function that has vertical asymptotes $x = -1$ and $x = 2$ and x-intercept $(-4, 0)$.

Solve.

27. $2x^2 > 5x + 3$

28. $\dfrac{x + 1}{x - 4} \le 3$

29. The function $S(t) = -16t^2 + 64t + 192$ gives the height S, in feet, of a model rocket launched with a velocity of 64 ft/sec from a hill that is 192 ft high.

a) Determine how long it will take the rocket to reach the ground.
b) Find the interval on which the height of the rocket is greater than 240 ft.

30. Find an equation of variation in which y varies inversely as x, and $y = 5$ when $x = 6$.

31. The stopping distance d of a car after the brakes have been applied varies directly as the square of the speed r. If a car traveling 60 mph can stop in 200 ft, how long will it take a car traveling 30 mph to stop?

32. Find an equation of variation where y varies jointly as x and the square of z and inversely as w, and $y = 100$ when $x = 0.1$, $z = 10$, and $w = 5$.

Synthesis

33. Find the domain of $f(x) = \sqrt{x^2 + x - 12}$.

Exponential and Logarithmic Functions

APPLICATION

The United States produced 3.9 billion gal of fuel ethanol in 2005. The production of corn-based ethanol has increased exponentially since 1996. (*Sources*: Energy Information Administration, Renewable Fuels Association) The following function can be used to model this growth:

$$C(t) = 1.0283(1.1483)^t,$$

where t is the number of years since 1996. Estimate the number of gallons that will be produced in 2008 and in 2010.

This problem appears as Exercise 55 in Section 4.2.

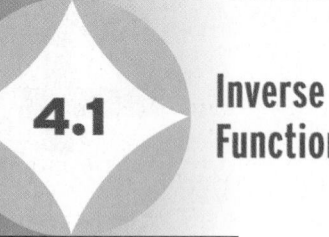

Inverse Functions

◆ Determine whether a function is one-to-one, and if it is, find a formula for its inverse.

◆ Simplify expressions of the type $(f \circ f^{-1})(x)$ and $(f^{-1} \circ f)(x)$.

◆ Inverses

When we go from an output of a function back to its input or inputs, we get an inverse relation. When that relation is a function, we have an inverse function.

Consider the relation h given as follows:

$$h = \{(-8, 5), (4, -2), (-7, 1), (3.8, 6.2)\}.$$

RELATIONS

REVIEW SECTION **1.2.**

Suppose we *interchange* the first and second coordinates. The relation we obtain is called the **inverse** of the relation h and is given as follows:

$$\text{Inverse of } h = \{(5, -8), (-2, 4), (1, -7), (6.2, 3.8)\}.$$

> ### Inverse Relation
> Interchanging the first and second coordinates of each ordered pair in a relation produces the **inverse relation.**

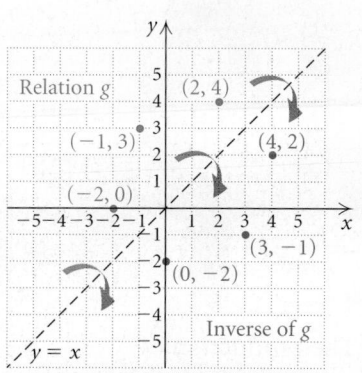

EXAMPLE 1 Consider the relation g given by

$$g = \{(2, 4), (-1, 3), (-2, 0)\}.$$

Graph the relation in blue. Find the inverse and graph it in red.

Solution The relation g is shown in blue in the figure at left. The inverse of the relation is

$$\{(4, 2), (3, -1), (0, -2)\}$$

and is shown in red. The pairs in the inverse are reflections of the pairs in g across the line $y = x$. ▷ Now Try Exercise 1.

> ### Inverse Relation
> If a relation is defined by an equation, interchanging the variables produces an equation of the **inverse relation.**

EXAMPLE 2 Find an equation for the inverse of the relation

$$y = x^2 - 5x.$$

Solution We interchange x and y and obtain an equation of the inverse:

$$x = y^2 - 5y.$$

▶ Now Try Exercise 9.

If a relation is given by an equation, then the solutions of the inverse can be found from those of the original equation by interchanging the first and second coordinates of each ordered pair. Thus the graphs of a relation and its inverse are always reflections of each other across the line $y = x$. This is illustrated with the equations of Example 2 in the tables and graph below. We will explore inverses and their graphs later in this section.

$x = y^2 - 5y$	y
6	-1
0	0
-6	2
-4	4

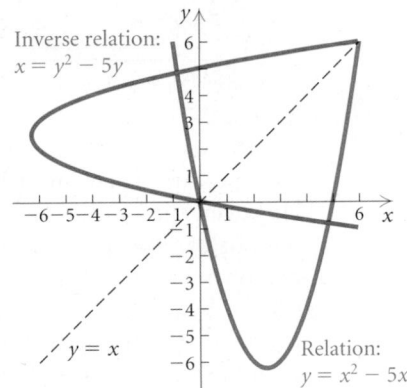

x	$y = x^2 - 5x$
-1	6
0	0
2	-6
4	-4

◆ Inverses and One-to-One Functions

Let's consider the following two functions.

Year (domain)	First-Class Postage Cost, in cents (range)
1992	
1994	29
1996	
1998	32
2000	33
2002	
2004	37
2006	39

Number (domain)	Cube (range)
-3	-27
-2	-8
-1	-1
0	0
1	1
2	8
3	27

Source: U.S. Postal Service

Suppose we reverse the arrows. Are these inverse relations functions?

Year (range)	First-Class Postage Cost, in cents (domain)
1992	
1994	29
1996	
1998	32
2000	33
2002	
2004	37
2006	39

Number (range)	Cube (domain)
−3	−27
−2	−8
−1	−1
0	0
1	1
2	8
3	27

Source: U.S. Postal Service

We see that the inverse of the postage function is not a function. Like all functions, each input in the postage function has exactly one output. However, the output for both 1996 and 1998 is 32. Thus in the inverse of the postage function, the input 32 has *two* outputs, 1996 and 1998. When two or more inputs of a function have the same output, the inverse relation cannot be a function. In the cubing function, each output corresponds to exactly one input, so its inverse is also a function. The cubing function is an example of a **one-to-one function.**

If the inverse of a function f is also a function, it is named f^{-1} (read "f-inverse").

The −1 in f^{-1} is *not* an exponent!

Do *not* misinterpret the −1 in f^{-1} as a negative exponent: f^{-1} does *not* mean the reciprocal of f and $f^{-1}(x)$ is *not* equal to $\dfrac{1}{f(x)}$.

One-to-One Functions

A function f is **one-to-one** if different inputs have different outputs—that is,

$$\text{if} \quad a \neq b, \quad \text{then} \quad f(a) \neq f(b).$$

Or a function f is **one-to-one** if when the outputs are the same, the inputs are the same—that is,

$$\text{if} \quad f(a) = f(b), \quad \text{then} \quad a = b.$$

Properties of One-to-One Functions and Inverses

- If a function f is one-to-one, then its inverse f^{-1} is a function.
- The domain of a one-to-one function f is the range of the inverse f^{-1}.
- The range of a one-to-one function f is the domain of the inverse f^{-1}.

$$D_f \qquad D_{f^{-1}}$$
$$R_f \qquad R_{f^{-1}}$$

- A function that is increasing over its domain or is decreasing over its domain is a one-to-one function.

EXAMPLE 3   Given the function f described by $f(x) = 2x - 3$, prove that f is one-to-one (that is, it has an inverse that is a function).

Solution   To show that f is one-to-one, we show that if $f(a) = f(b)$, then $a = b$. Assume that $f(a) = f(b)$ for a and b in the domain of f. Since $f(a) = 2a - 3$ and $f(b) = 2b - 3$, we have

$$2a - 3 = 2b - 3$$
$$2a = 2b \qquad \text{Adding 3}$$
$$a = b. \qquad \text{Dividing by 2}$$

Thus, if $f(a) = f(b)$, then $a = b$. This shows that f is one-to-one.

▶ **Now Try Exercise 17.**

EXAMPLE 4   Given the function g described by $g(x) = x^2$, prove that g is not one-to-one.

Solution   We can prove that g is not one-to-one by finding two numbers a and b for which $a \neq b$ and $g(a) = g(b)$. Two such numbers are -3 and 3, because $-3 \neq 3$ and $g(-3) = g(3) = 9$. Thus g is not one-to-one.

▶ **Now Try Exercise 21.**

The following graph shows a function, in blue, and its inverse, in red. To determine whether the inverse is a function, we can apply the vertical-line test to its graph. By reflecting each such vertical line back across the line $y = x$, we obtain an equivalent **horizontal-line test** for the original function.

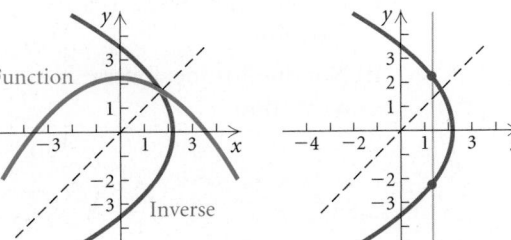

The vertical-line test shows that the inverse is not a function.

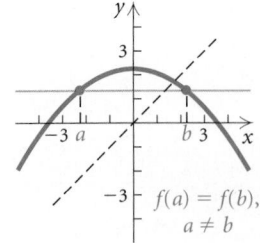

The horizontal-line test shows that the function is not one-to-one.

> ### Horizontal-Line Test
>
> If it is possible for a horizontal line to intersect the graph of a function more than once, then the function is *not* one-to-one and its inverse is *not* a function.

EXAMPLE 5 From the graph shown, determine whether each function is one-to-one and thus has an inverse that is a function.

a)

b)

c)

d)
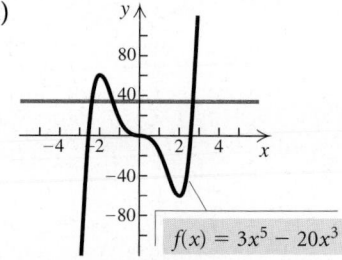

Solution For each function, we apply the horizontal-line test.

RESULT	REASON
a) One-to-one; inverse is a function	No horizontal line intersects the graph more than once.
b) Not one-to-one; inverse is not a function	There are many horizontal lines that intersect the graph more than once. Note that where the line $y = 4$ intersects the graph, the first coordinates are -2 and 2. Although these are different inputs, they have the same output, 4.
c) One-to-one; inverse is a function	No horizontal line intersects the graph more than once.
d) Not one-to-one; inverse is not a function	There are many horizontal lines that intersect the graph more than once.

▷ Now Try Exercises 25 and 27.

✦ Finding Formulas for Inverses

Suppose that a function is described by a formula. If it has an inverse that is a function, we proceed as follows to find a formula for f^{-1}.

> ### Obtaining a Formula for an Inverse
>
> If a function f is one-to-one, a formula for its inverse can generally be found as follows:
>
> 1. Replace $f(x)$ with y.
> 2. Interchange x and y.
> 3. Solve for y.
> 4. Replace y with $f^{-1}(x)$.

EXAMPLE 6 Determine whether the function $f(x) = 2x - 3$ is one-to-one, and if it is, find a formula for $f^{-1}(x)$.

Solution The graph of f is shown at left. It passes the horizontal-line test. Thus it is one-to-one and its inverse is a function. We also proved that f is one-to-one in Example 3. We find a formula for $f^{-1}(x)$.

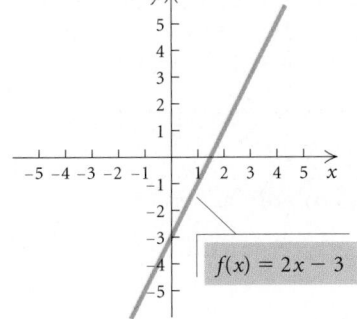

$f(x) = 2x - 3$

1. Replace $f(x)$ with y: $\qquad y = 2x - 3$
2. Interchange x and y: $\qquad x = 2y - 3$
3. Solve for y: $\qquad x + 3 = 2y$

$$\frac{x + 3}{2} = y$$

4. Replace y with $f^{-1}(x)$: $\qquad f^{-1}(x) = \dfrac{x + 3}{2}.$

▶ Now Try Exercise 47.

Consider

$$f(x) = 2x - 3 \quad \text{and} \quad f^{-1}(x) = \frac{x + 3}{2}$$

from Example 6. For the input 5, we have

$$f(5) = 2 \cdot 5 - 3 = 10 - 3 = 7.$$

The output is 7. Now we use 7 for the input in the inverse:

$$f^{-1}(7) = \frac{7 + 3}{2} = \frac{10}{2} = 5.$$

The function f takes the number 5 to 7. The inverse function f^{-1} takes the number 7 back to 5.

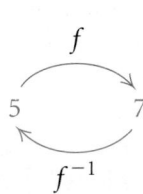

EXAMPLE 7 Graph

$$f(x) = 2x - 3 \quad \text{and} \quad f^{-1}(x) = \frac{x + 3}{2}$$

using the same set of axes. Then compare the two graphs.

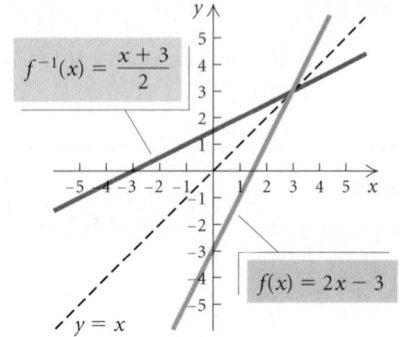

$f^{-1}(x) = \dfrac{x+3}{2}$

$f(x) = 2x - 3$

$y = x$

Solution   The graphs of f and f^{-1} are shown at left. The solutions of the inverse function can be found from those of the original function by interchanging the first and second coordinates of each ordered pair.

x	$f(x) = 2x - 3$	
-1	-5	
0	-3	← *y*-intercept
2	1	
3	3	

x	$f^{-1}(x) = \dfrac{x+3}{2}$	
-5	-1	
-3	0	← *x*-intercept
1	2	
3	3	

TECHNOLOGY CONNECTION

On some graphing calculators, we can graph the inverse of a function after graphing the function itself by accessing a drawing feature. Consult your user's manual or the *Graphing Calculator Manual* that accompanies this text for the procedure.

When we interchange x and y in finding a formula for the inverse of $f(x) = 2x - 3$, we are in effect reflecting the graph of that function across the line $y = x$. For example, when the coordinates of the *y*-intercept, $(0, -3)$, of the graph of f are reversed, we get the *x*-intercept, $(-3, 0)$, of the graph of f^{-1}. If we were to graph $f(x) = 2x - 3$ in wet ink and fold along the line $y = x$, the graph of $f^{-1}(x) = (x + 3)/2$ would be formed by the ink transferred from f.

> The graph of f^{-1} is a reflection of the graph of f across the line $y = x$.

EXAMPLE 8   Consider $g(x) = x^3 + 2$.

a) Determine whether the function is one-to-one.

b) If it is one-to-one, find a formula for its inverse.

c) Graph the function and its inverse.

Solution

$g(x) = x^3 + 2$

$(2, 10)$

$(0, 2)$

$(-2, -6)$

a) The graph of $g(x) = x^3 + 2$ is shown at left. It passes the horizontal-line test and thus has an inverse that is a function. We also know that $g(x)$ is one-to-one because it is an increasing function over its entire domain.

b) We follow the procedure for finding an inverse.

1. Replace $g(x)$ with y: $y = x^3 + 2$
2. Interchange x and y: $x = y^3 + 2$
3. Solve for y: $x - 2 = y^3$
        $\sqrt[3]{x - 2} = y$
4. Replace y with $g^{-1}(x)$: $g^{-1}(x) = \sqrt[3]{x - 2}.$

We can test a point as a partial check:

$$g(x) = x^3 + 2$$
$$g(3) = 3^3 + 2 = 27 + 2 = 29.$$

Will $g^{-1}(29) = 3$? We have

$$g^{-1}(x) = \sqrt[3]{x - 2}$$
$$g^{-1}(29) = \sqrt[3]{29 - 2} = \sqrt[3]{27} = 3.$$

Since $g(3) = 29$ and $g^{-1}(29) = 3$, we can be reasonably certain that the formula for $g^{-1}(x)$ is correct.

c) To find the graph, we reflect the graph of $g(x) = x^3 + 2$ across the line $y = x$. This can be done by plotting points.

x	$g(x)$
-2	-6
-1	1
0	2
1	3
2	10

x	$g^{-1}(x)$
-6	-2
1	-1
2	0
3	1
10	2

▶ Now Try Exercise 69.

✦ Inverse Functions and Composition

Suppose that we were to use some input a for a one-to-one function f and find its output, $f(a)$. The function f^{-1} would then take that output back to a. Similarly, if we began with an input b for the function f^{-1} and found its output, $f^{-1}(b)$, the original function f would then take that output back to b. This is summarized as follows.

If a function f is one-to-one, then f^{-1} is the unique function such that each of the following holds:

$$(f^{-1} \circ f)(x) = f^{-1}(f(x)) = x, \quad \text{for each } x \text{ in the domain of } f, \text{ and}$$
$$(f \circ f^{-1})(x) = f(f^{-1}(x)) = x, \quad \text{for each } x \text{ in the domain of } f^{-1}.$$

EXAMPLE 9 Given that $f(x) = 5x + 8$, use composition of functions to show that $f^{-1}(x) = (x - 8)/5$.

Solution We find $(f^{-1} \circ f)(x)$ and $(f \circ f^{-1})(x)$ and check to see that each is x:

$$(f^{-1} \circ f)(x) = f^{-1}(f(x))$$
$$= f^{-1}(5x + 8) = \frac{(5x + 8) - 8}{5} = \frac{5x}{5} = x;$$

$$(f \circ f^{-1})(x) = f(f^{-1}(x))$$
$$= f\left(\frac{x - 8}{5}\right) = 5\left(\frac{x - 8}{5}\right) + 8 = x - 8 + 8 = x.$$

▶ Now Try Exercise 77.

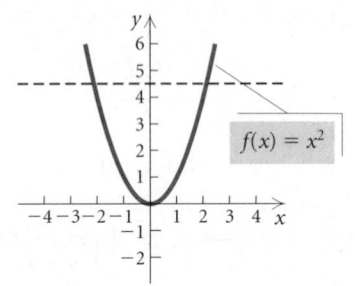

✦ Restricting a Domain

In the case in which the inverse of a function is not a function, the domain of the function can be restricted to allow the inverse to be a function. We saw in Examples 4 and 5(b) that $f(x) = x^2$ is not one-to-one. The graph is shown at left.

Suppose that we had tried to find a formula for the inverse as follows:

$$y = x^2 \qquad \text{Replacing } f(x) \text{ with } y$$
$$x = y^2 \qquad \text{Interchanging } x \text{ and } y$$
$$\pm\sqrt{x} = y. \qquad \text{Solving for } y$$

This is not the equation of a function. An input of, say, 4 would yield two outputs, -2 and 2. In such cases, it is convenient to consider "part" of the function by restricting the domain of $f(x)$. For example, if we restrict the domain of $f(x) = x^2$ to nonnegative numbers, then its inverse is a function, as shown with the graphs of $f(x) = x^2$, $x \geq 0$, and $f^{-1}(x) = \sqrt{x}$ below.

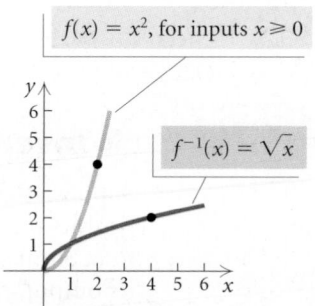

4.1 EXERCISE SET

Find the inverse of the relation.

1. $\{(7,8),(-2,8),(3,-4),(8,-8)\}$

2. $\{(0,1),(5,6),(-2,-4)\}$

3. $\{(-1,-1),(-3,4)\}$

4. $\{(-1,3),(2,5),(-3,5),(2,0)\}$

Find an equation of the inverse relation.

5. $y = 4x - 5$

6. $2x^2 + 5y^2 = 4$

7. $x^3y = -5$

8. $y = 3x^2 - 5x + 9$

9. $x = y^2 - 2y$

10. $x = \frac{1}{2}y + 4$

Graph the equation by substituting and plotting points. Then reflect the graph across the line $y = x$ to obtain the graph of its inverse.

11. $x = y^2 - 3$

12. $y = x^2 + 1$

13. $y = 3x - 2$

14. $x = -y + 4$

15. $y = |x|$

16. $x + 2 = |y|$

Given the function f, prove that f is one-to-one using the definition of a one-to-one function on page 350.

17. $f(x) = \frac{1}{3}x - 6$

18. $f(x) = 4 - 2x$

19. $f(x) = x^3 + \frac{1}{2}$

20. $f(x) = \sqrt[3]{x}$

Given the function g, prove that g is not one-to-one using the definition of a one-to-one function on page 350.

21. $g(x) = 1 - x^2$

22. $g(x) = 3x^2 + 1$

23. $g(x) = x^4 - x^2$

24. $g(x) = \dfrac{1}{x^6}$

Using the horizontal-line test, determine whether the function is one-to-one.

25. $f(x) = 2.7^x$

26. $f(x) = 2^{-x}$

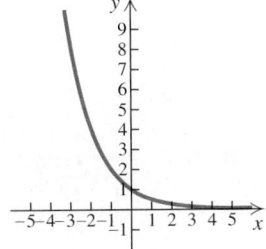

27. $f(x) = 4 - x^2$

28. $f(x) = x^3 - 3x + 1$

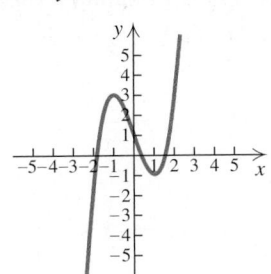

29. $f(x) = \dfrac{8}{x^2 - 4}$

30. $f(x) = \sqrt{\dfrac{10}{4 + x}}$

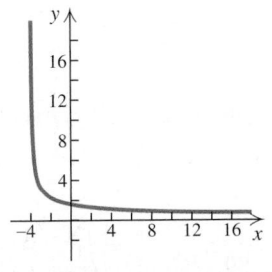

31. $f(x) = \sqrt[3]{x + 2} - 2$

32. $f(x) = \dfrac{8}{x}$

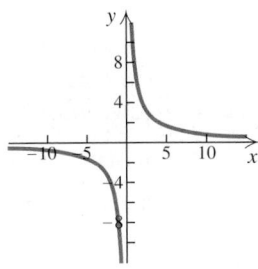

Graph the function and determine whether the function is one-to-one using the horizontal-line test.

33. $f(x) = 5x - 8$

34. $f(x) = 3 + 4x$

35. $f(x) = 1 - x^2$

36. $f(x) = |x| - 2$

37. $f(x) = |x + 2|$

38. $f(x) = -0.8$

39. $f(x) = -\dfrac{4}{x}$

40. $f(x) = \dfrac{2}{x + 3}$

41. $f(x) = \frac{2}{3}$

42. $f(x) = \frac{1}{2}x^2 + 3$

43. $f(x) = \sqrt{25 - x^2}$

44. $f(x) = -x^3 + 2$

In Exercises 45–60, for each function:

a) *Sketch the graph and use the graph to determine whether the function is one-to-one.*

b) *If the function is one-to-one, find a formula for the inverse.*

45. $f(x) = x + 4$

46. $f(x) = 7 - x$

47. $f(x) = 2x - 1$

48. $f(x) = 5x + 8$

49. $f(x) = \dfrac{4}{x + 7}$

50. $f(x) = -\dfrac{3}{x}$

51. $f(x) = \dfrac{x + 4}{x - 3}$

52. $f(x) = \dfrac{5x - 3}{2x + 1}$

53. $f(x) = x^3 - 1$

54. $f(x) = (x + 5)^3$

55. $f(x) = x\sqrt{4 - x^2}$

56. $f(x) = 2x^2 - x - 1$

57. $f(x) = 5x^2 - 2,\ x \geq 0$

58. $f(x) = 4x^2 + 3,\ x \geq 0$

59. $f(x) = \sqrt{x+1}$

60. $f(x) = \sqrt[3]{x-8}$

Find the inverse by thinking about the operations of the function and then reversing, or undoing, them. Check your work algebraically.

FUNCTION	INVERSE
61. $f(x) = 3x$	$f^{-1}(x) =$
62. $f(x) = \frac{1}{4}x + 7$	$f^{-1}(x) =$
63. $f(x) = -x$	$f^{-1}(x) =$
64. $f(x) = \sqrt[3]{x} - 5$	$f^{-1}(x) =$
65. $f(x) = \sqrt[3]{x-5}$	$f^{-1}(x) =$
66. $f(x) = x^{-1}$	$f^{-1}(x) =$

Each graph in Exercises 67–72 is the graph of a one-to-one function f. Sketch the graph of the inverse function f^{-1}.

67.

68.

69.

70.

71.

72.

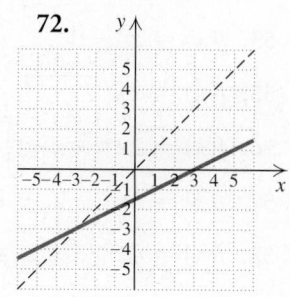

For the function f, use composition of functions to show that f^{-1} is as given.

73. $f(x) = \frac{7}{8}x,\ f^{-1}(x) = \frac{8}{7}x$

74. $f(x) = \dfrac{x+5}{4},\ f^{-1}(x) = 4x - 5$

75. $f(x) = \dfrac{1-x}{x},\ f^{-1}(x) = \dfrac{1}{x+1}$

76. $f(x) = \sqrt[3]{x+4},\ f^{-1}(x) = x^3 - 4$

77. $f(x) = \dfrac{2}{5}x + 1,\ f^{-1}(x) = \dfrac{5x-5}{2}$

78. $f(x) = \dfrac{x+6}{3x-4},\ f^{-1}(x) = \dfrac{4x+6}{3x-1}$

Find the inverse of the given one-to-one function f. Give the domain and the range of f and f^{-1}, and then graph both f and f^{-1} on the same set of axes.

79. $f(x) = 5x - 3$ **80.** $f(x) = 2 - x$

81. $f(x) = \dfrac{2}{x}$ **82.** $f(x) = -\dfrac{3}{x+1}$

83. $f(x) = \dfrac{1}{3}x^3 - 2$ **84.** $f(x) = \sqrt[3]{x} - 1$

85. $f(x) = \dfrac{x+1}{x-3}$ **86.** $f(x) = \dfrac{x-1}{x+2}$

87. Find $f(f^{-1}(5))$ and $f^{-1}(f(a))$:
$$f(x) = x^3 - 4.$$

88. Find $f^{-1}(f(p))$ and $f(f^{-1}(1253))$:
$$f(x) = \sqrt[5]{\dfrac{2x-7}{3x+4}}.$$

89. *Women's Shoe Sizes.* A function that will convert women's shoe sizes in the United States to those in Australia is
$$s(x) = \dfrac{2x-3}{2}$$

(*Source:* OnlineConversion.com).

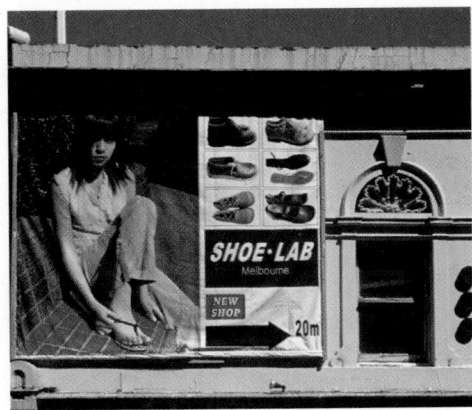

a) Determine the women's shoe sizes in Australia that correspond to sizes 5, $7\frac{1}{2}$, and 8 in the United States.
b) Find a formula for the inverse of the function.
c) Use the inverse function to determine the women's shoe sizes in the United States that correspond to sizes 3, $5\frac{1}{2}$, and 7 in Australia.

90. *Bus Chartering.* An organization determines that the cost per person of chartering a bus is given by the formula

$$C(x) = \frac{100 + 5x}{x},$$

where x is the number of people in the group and $C(x)$ is in dollars. Determine $C^{-1}(x)$ and explain what it represents.

Technology Connection

Graph the function and its inverse using a graphing calculator. Use an inverse drawing feature, if available. Find the domain and the range of f. Find the domain and the range of the inverse f^{-1}.

91. $f(x) = 0.8x + 1.7$

92. $f(x) = 2.7 - 1.08x$

93. $f(x) = \frac{1}{2}x - 4$

94. $f(x) = x^3 - 1$

95. $f(x) = \sqrt{x - 3}$

96. $f(x) = -\frac{2}{x}$

97. $f(x) = x^2 - 4, \; x \geq 0$

98. $f(x) = 3 - x^2, \; x \geq 0$

99. $f(x) = (3x - 9)^3$

100. $f(x) = \sqrt[3]{\dfrac{x - 3.2}{1.4}}$

101. *Reaction Distance.* You are driving a car when a deer suddenly darts across the road in front of you. Your brain registers the emergency and sends a signal to your foot to hit the brake. The car travels a distance D, in feet, during this time, where D is a function of the speed r, in miles per hour, that the car is traveling when you see the deer. That reaction distance D is a linear function given by

$$D(r) = \frac{11r + 5}{10}.$$

a) Find $D(0)$, $D(10)$, $D(20)$, $D(50)$, and $D(65)$.
b) Find $D^{-1}(r)$ and explain what it represents.
c) Graph the function and its inverse.

102. *Cheese Consumption.* The number of pounds of cheese consumed in the United States per person per year x years after 1990 is given by the function

$$N(x) = 0.4737x + 24.7702$$

(*Source*: U.S. Department of Agriculture).

a) Determine the cheese consumption per person in 2007 and in 2010.
b) Graph the function and its inverse.
c) Explain what the inverse represents.

Collaborative Discussion and Writing

103. Explain why an even function f does not have an inverse f^{-1}.

104. The following formulas for the conversion between Fahrenheit and Celsius temperatures have been considered several times in this text:

$$C = \frac{5}{9}(F - 32)$$

and

$$F = \frac{9}{5}C + 32.$$

Discuss these formulas from the standpoint of inverses.

Skill Maintenance

Consider the following quadratic functions. Without graphing them, answer the questions below.

a) $f(x) = 2x^2$
b) $f(x) = -x^2$
c) $f(x) = \frac{1}{4}x^2$
d) $f(x) = -5x^2 + 3$
e) $f(x) = \frac{2}{3}(x - 1)^2 - 3$
f) $f(x) = -2(x + 3)^2 + 1$
g) $f(x) = (x - 3)^2 + 1$
h) $f(x) = -4(x + 1)^2 - 3$

105. Which functions have a maximum value?

106. Which graphs open up?

107. Consider (a) and (c). Which graph is narrower?

108. Consider (d) and (e). Which graph is narrower?

109. Which graph has vertex $(-3, 1)$?

110. For which is the line of symmetry $x = 0$?

Synthesis

111. The function $f(x) = x^2 - 3$ is not one-to-one. Restrict the domain of f so that its inverse is a function. Find the inverse and state the restriction on the domain of the inverse.

112. Consider the function f given by

$$f(x) = \begin{cases} x^3 + 2, & x \le -1, \\ x^2, & -1 < x < 1, \\ x + 1, & x \ge 1. \end{cases}$$

Does f have an inverse that is a function? Why or why not?

113. Find three examples of functions that are their own inverses, that is, $f = f^{-1}$.

114. Given the function $f(x) = ax + b, a \ne 0$, find the values of a and b for which $f^{-1}(x) = f(x)$.

115. Given the graph of a function $f(x)$, how can you determine graphically if $f^{-1}(x) = f(x)$?

4.2 Exponential Functions and Graphs

◆ Graph exponential equations and functions.
◆ Solve applied problems involving exponential functions and their graphs.

We now turn our attention to the study of a set of functions that are very rich in application. Consider the following graphs. Each one illustrates an *exponential function*. In this section, we consider such functions and some important applications.

International NBA Players

Source: National Basketball Association

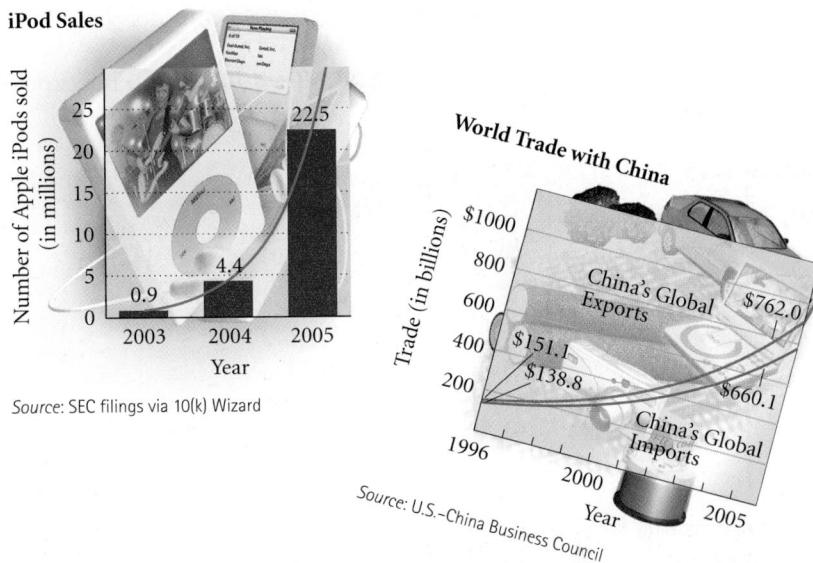

iPod Sales

Source: SEC filings via 10(k) Wizard

World Trade with China

Source: U.S.–China Business Council

EXPONENTS

REVIEW SECTIONS **R.2** AND **R.6.**

✦ Graphing Exponential Functions

We now define exponential functions. We assume that a^x has meaning for any real number x and any positive real number a and that the laws of exponents still hold, though we will not prove them here.

Exponential Function

The function $f(x) = a^x$, where x is a real number, $a > 0$ and $a \neq 1$, is called the **exponential function,** base a.

We require the base to be positive in order to avoid the complex numbers that would occur by taking even roots of negative numbers— an example is $(-1)^{1/2}$, the square root of -1, which is not a real number. The restriction $a \neq 1$ is made to exclude the constant function $f(x) = 1^x = 1$, which does not have an inverse because it is not one-to-one.

The following are examples of exponential functions:

$$f(x) = 2^x, \qquad f(x) = \left(\frac{1}{2}\right)^x, \qquad f(x) = (3.57)^x.$$

Note that, in contrast to functions like $f(x) = x^5$ and $f(x) = x^{1/2}$ in which the variable is the base of an exponential expression, the variable in an exponential function is *in the exponent.*

Let's now consider graphs of exponential functions.

EXAMPLE 1   Graph the exponential function

$$y = f(x) = 2^x.$$

Solution   We compute some function values and list the results in a table (at left).

$$f(0) = 2^0 = 1;$$
$$f(1) = 2^1 = 2;$$
$$f(2) = 2^2 = 4;$$
$$f(3) = 2^3 = 8;$$

$$f(-1) = 2^{-1} = \frac{1}{2^1} = \frac{1}{2};$$

$$f(-2) = 2^{-2} = \frac{1}{2^2} = \frac{1}{4};$$

$$f(-3) = 2^{-3} = \frac{1}{2^3} = \frac{1}{8}.$$

	y	
x	$y = f(x) = 2^x$	(x, y)
0	1	$(0, 1)$
1	2	$(1, 2)$
2	4	$(2, 4)$
3	8	$(3, 8)$
-1	$\frac{1}{2}$	$\left(-1, \frac{1}{2}\right)$
-2	$\frac{1}{4}$	$\left(-2, \frac{1}{4}\right)$
-3	$\frac{1}{8}$	$\left(-3, \frac{1}{8}\right)$

Next, we plot these points and connect them with a smooth curve. Be sure to plot enough points to determine how steeply the curve rises.

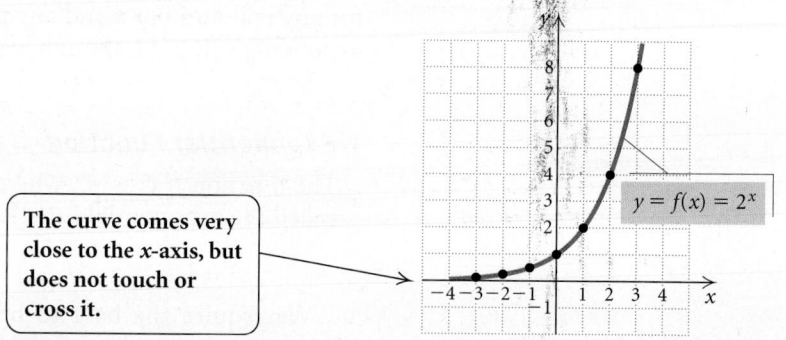

The curve comes very close to the x-axis, but does not touch or cross it.

$y = f(x) = 2^x$

HORIZONTAL ASYMPTOTES

REVIEW SECTION 3.5.

Note that as x increases, the function values increase without bound. As x decreases, the function values decrease, getting close to 0. That is, as $x \to -\infty$, $y \to 0$. Thus the x-axis, or the line $y = 0$, is a horizontal asymptote. As the x-inputs decrease, the curve gets closer and closer to this line, but does not cross it.

▶ Now Try Exercise 11.

EXAMPLE 2   Graph the exponential function $y = f(x) = \left(\frac{1}{2}\right)^x$.

Solution   We compute some function values and list the results in a table, as shown below. Before we plot these points and draw the curve, note that

$$y = f(x) = \left(\frac{1}{2}\right)^x = (2^{-1})^x = 2^{-x}.$$

x	y = f(x) = 2^{-x}	(x, y)
0	1	$(0, 1)$
1	$\frac{1}{2}$	$\left(1, \frac{1}{2}\right)$
2	$\frac{1}{4}$	$\left(2, \frac{1}{4}\right)$
3	$\frac{1}{8}$	$\left(3, \frac{1}{8}\right)$
−1	2	$(-1, 2)$
−2	4	$(-2, 4)$
−3	8	$(-3, 8)$

This tells us, before we begin graphing, that this graph is a reflection of the graph of $y = 2^x$ across the y-axis.

$$f(0) = 2^{-0} = 1; \qquad\qquad f(-1) = 2^{-(-1)} = 2^1 = 2;$$
$$f(1) = 2^{-1} = \frac{1}{2^1} = \frac{1}{2}; \qquad f(-2) = 2^{-(-2)} = 2^2 = 4;$$
$$\qquad\qquad\qquad\qquad\qquad f(-3) = 2^{-(-3)} = 2^3 = 8.$$
$$f(2) = 2^{-2} = \frac{1}{2^2} = \frac{1}{4};$$
$$f(3) = 2^{-3} = \frac{1}{2^3} = \frac{1}{8};$$

Next, we plot these points and connect them with a smooth curve.

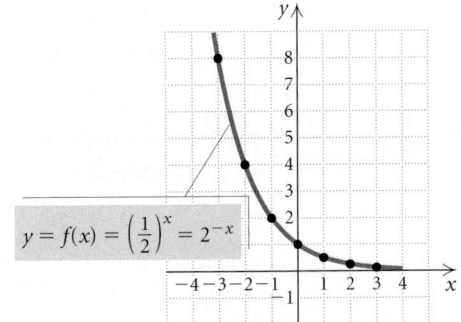

$$y = f(x) = \left(\frac{1}{2}\right)^x = 2^{-x}$$

Note that as x increases, the function values decrease, getting close to 0. The x-axis, $y = 0$, is the horizontal asymptote. As x decreases, the function values increase without bound.

▶ **Now Try Exercise 15.**

Observe the following graphs of exponential functions and look for patterns in the graphs.

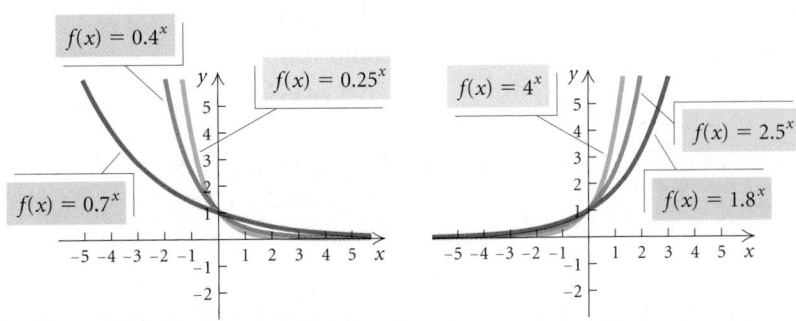

$f(x) = 0.4^x$

$f(x) = 0.25^x$

$f(x) = 4^x$

$f(x) = 2.5^x$

$f(x) = 0.7^x$

$f(x) = 1.8^x$

What relationship do you see between the base a and the shape of the resulting graph of $f(x) = a^x$? What do all the graphs have in common? How do they differ?

CONNECTING THE CONCEPTS

Properties of Exponential Functions

Let's list and compare some characteristics of exponential functions, keeping in mind that the definition of an exponential function, $f(x) = a^x$, requires that a be positive and different from 1.

$f(x) = a^x, \ a > 0, a \neq 1$

Continuous

One-to-one

Domain: $(-\infty, \infty)$

Range: $(0, \infty)$

Increasing if $a > 1$

Decreasing if $0 < a < 1$

Horizontal asymptote is x-axis

y-intercept: $(0, 1)$

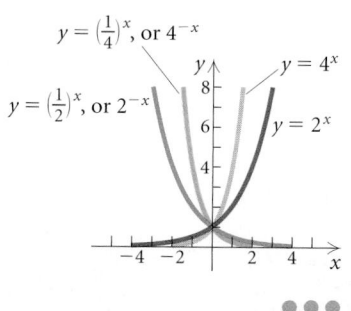

● ● ●

TRANSFORMATIONS OF
FUNCTIONS

REVIEW SECTION **1.6.**

To graph other types of exponential functions, keep in mind the ideas of translation, stretching, and reflection. All these concepts allow us to visualize the graph before drawing it.

EXAMPLE 3 Graph each of the following. Before doing so, describe how each graph can be obtained from the graph of $f(x) = 2^x$.

a) $f(x) = 2^{x-2}$ **b)** $f(x) = 2^x - 4$

c) $f(x) = 5 - 2^{-x}$ **d)** $f(x) = -0.5^x + 1$

Solution

a) The graph of $f(x) = 2^{x-2}$ is the graph of $y = 2^x$ shifted *right* 2 units.

x	$f(x)$
-2	0.0625
-1	0.125
0	0.25
1	0.5
2	1
3	2
4	4
5	8

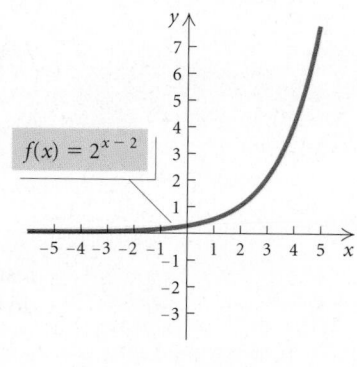

b) The graph of $f(x) = 2^x - 4$ is the graph of $y = 2^x$ shifted *down* 4 units.

x	$f(x)$
-2	-3.75
-1	-3.5
0	-3
1	-2
2	0
3	4

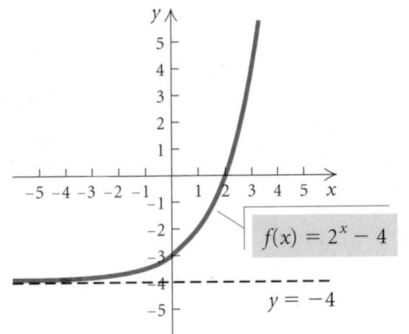

c) The graph of $f(x) = 5 - 2^{-x}$ is a reflection of the graph of $y = 2^x$ across the *y*-axis, followed by a reflection across the *x*-axis and then a shift *up* 5 units.

x	$f(x)$
-3	-3
-2	1
-1	3
0	4
1	4.5
2	4.75

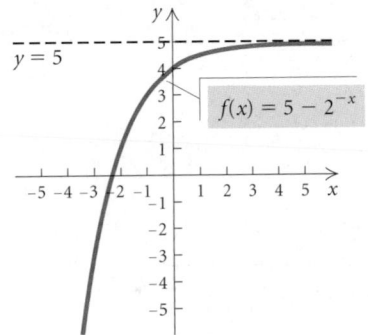

d) The graph of $f(x) = -0.5^x + 1$ or $f(x) = -\left(\frac{1}{2}\right)^x + 1 = -2^{-x} + 1$ is a reflection of the graph of $y = 2^x$ across the *y*-axis, followed by a reflection across the *x*-axis and then a shift *up* 1 unit.

x	$f(x)$
-2	-3
-1	-1
0	0
1	0.5
2	0.75
3	0.875

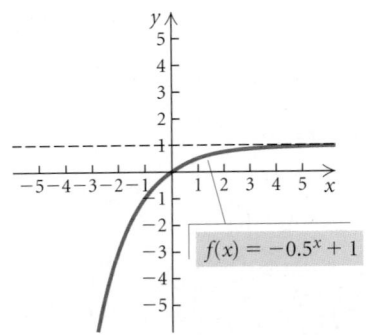

▶ Now Try Exercises 27 and 31.

✦ Applications

One of the most frequent applications of exponential functions occurs with compound interest.

EXAMPLE 4 *Compound Interest.* The amount of money A that a principal P will grow to after t years at interest rate r (in decimal form), compounded n times per year, is given by the formula

$$A = P\left(1 + \frac{r}{n}\right)^{nt}.$$

Suppose that $100,000 is invested at 6.5% interest, compounded semiannually.

a) Find a function for the amount to which the investment grows after t years.

b) Find the amount of money in the account at $t = 0, 4, 8,$ and 10 yr.

c) Graph the function.

Solution

a) Since $P = \$100,000$, $r = 6.5\% = 0.065$, and $n = 2$, we can substitute these values and write the following function:

$$A(t) = 100{,}000\left(1 + \frac{0.065}{2}\right)^{2 \cdot t} = \$100{,}000(1.0325)^{2t}.$$

b) We can compute function values with a calculator:

$$A(0) = 100{,}000(1.0325)^{2 \cdot 0} = \$100{,}000;$$
$$A(4) = 100{,}000(1.0325)^{2 \cdot 4} \approx \$129{,}157.75;$$
$$A(8) = 100{,}000(1.0325)^{2 \cdot 8} \approx \$166{,}817.25;$$
$$A(10) = 100{,}000(1.0325)^{2 \cdot 10} \approx \$189{,}583.79.$$

c) We use the function values computed in part (b) and others if we wish, and draw the graph as follows. Note that the axes are scaled differently because of the large values of A and that t is restricted to nonnegative values, because negative time values have no meaning here.

$A(t) = 100{,}000(1.0325)^{2t}$

▷ Now Try Exercise 43.

◆ The Number *e*

We now consider a very special number in mathematics. In 1741, Leonhard Euler named this number *e*. Though you may not have encountered it before, you will see here and in future mathematics courses that it has many important applications. To explain this number, we use the compound interest formula $A = P(1 + r/n)^{nt}$ discussed in Example 4. Suppose that \$1 is invested at 100% interest for 1 yr. The formula above becomes a function A defined in terms of the number of compounding periods n. Since $P = 1$, $r = 100\% = 1$, and $t = 1$,

$$A = P\left(1 + \frac{r}{n}\right)^{nt} = 1\left(1 + \frac{1}{n}\right)^{n\cdot 1} = \left(1 + \frac{1}{n}\right)^{n}.$$

Let's visualize this function with its graph shown below and explore the values of $A(n)$ as $n \to \infty$. Consider the graph for larger and larger values of n. Does this function have a horizontal asymptote?

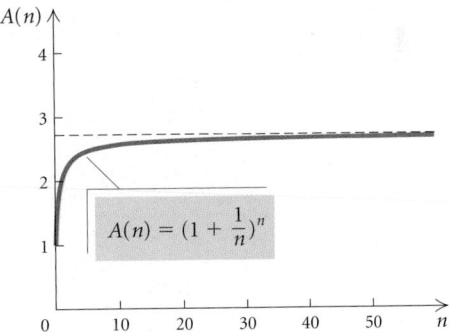

Let's find some function values using a calculator.

n, Number of Compounding Periods	$A(n) = \left(1 + \dfrac{1}{n}\right)^{n}$
1 (compounded annually)	\$2.00
2 (compounded semiannually)	2.25
3	2.3704
4 (compounded quarterly)	2.4414
5	2.4883
100	2.7048
365 (compounded daily)	2.7146
8760 (compounded hourly)	2.7181

It appears from these values that the graph does have a horizontal asymptote, $y \approx 2.7$. As the values of n get larger and larger, the function values get closer and closer to the number Euler named *e*. Its decimal representation does not terminate or repeat; it is irrational.

$$e = 2.7182818284\ldots$$

EXAMPLE 5 Find each value of e^x, to four decimal places, using the ⟨ex⟩ key on a calculator.

a) e^3 **b)** $e^{-0.23}$

c) e^0 **d)** e^1

Solution

FUNCTION VALUE	READOUT	ROUNDED
a) e^3	e^(3) 20.08553692	20.0855
b) $e^{-0.23}$	e^(−.23) .7945336025	0.7945
c) e^0	e^(0) 1	1
d) e^1	e^(1) 2.718281828	2.7183

▷ Now Try Exercises 1 and 3.

✦ Graphs of Exponential Functions, Base e

We demonstrate ways in which to graph exponential functions.

EXAMPLE 6 Graph $f(x) = e^x$ and $g(x) = e^{-x}$.

Solution We can compute points for each equation using the ⟨ex⟩ key on a calculator. (See the table at left.) Then we plot these points and draw the graphs of the functions.

x	$f(x) = e^x$	$g(x) = e^{-x}$
-2	0.135	7.389
-1	0.368	2.718
0	1	1
1	2.718	0.368
2	7.389	0.135

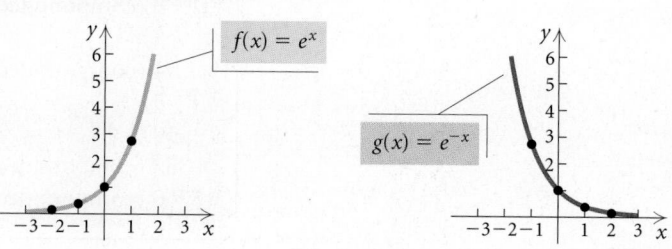

Note that the graph of *g* is a reflection of the graph of *f* across the *y*-axis.

▷ Now Try Exercise 23.

EXAMPLE 7 Graph each of the following. Before doing so, describe how each graph can be obtained from the graph of $y = e^x$.

a) $f(x) = e^{-0.5x}$ **b)** $f(x) = 1 - e^{-2x}$ **c)** $f(x) = e^{x+3}$

Solution

a) We note that the graph of $f(x) = e^{-0.5x}$ is a horizontal stretching of the graph of $y = e^x$ followed by a reflection across the y-axis.

x	$f(x)$
-2	2.718
-1	1.649
0	1
1	0.607
2	0.368

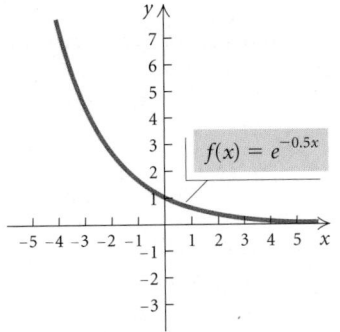

b) The graph of $f(x) = 1 - e^{-2x}$ is a horizontal shrinking of the graph of $y = e^x$, followed by a reflection across the y-axis, then across the x-axis, followed by a translation up 1 unit.

x	$f(x)$
-1	-6.389
0	0
1	0.865
2	0.982
3	0.998

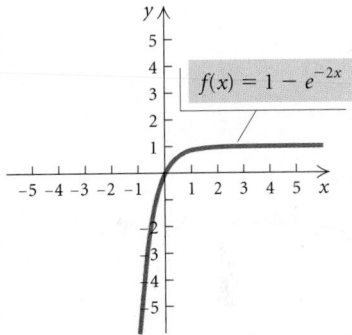

c) The graph of $f(x) = e^{x+3}$ is a translation of the graph of $y = e^x$ left 3 units.

x	$f(x)$
-7	0.018
-5	0.135
-3	1
-1	7.389
0	20.086

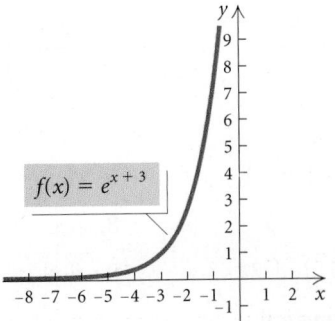

▶ **Now Try Exercises 37 and 41.**

4.2 EXERCISE SET

Find each of the following, to four decimal places, using a calculator.

1. e^4

2. e^{10}

3. $e^{-2.458}$

4. $\left(\dfrac{1}{e^3}\right)^2$

In Exercises 5–10, match the function with one of the graphs (a)–(f), which follow.

a)

b)

c)

d)

e)

f)

5. $f(x) = -2^x - 1$

6. $f(x) = -\left(\dfrac{1}{2}\right)^x$

7. $f(x) = e^x + 3$

8. $f(x) = e^{x+1}$

9. $f(x) = 3^{-x} - 2$

10. $f(x) = 1 - e^x$

Graph the function.

11. $f(x) = 3^x$

12. $f(x) = 5^x$

13. $f(x) = 6^x$

14. $f(x) = 3^{-x}$

15. $f(x) = \left(\dfrac{1}{4}\right)^x$

16. $f(x) = \left(\dfrac{2}{3}\right)^x$

17. $y = -2^x$

18. $y = 3 - 3^x$

19. $f(x) = -0.25^x + 4$

20. $f(x) = 0.6^x - 3$

21. $f(x) = 1 + e^{-x}$

22. $f(x) = 2 - e^{-x}$

23. $y = \dfrac{1}{4}e^x$

24. $y = 2e^{-x}$

25. $f(x) = 1 - e^{-x}$

26. $f(x) = e^x - 2$

Sketch the graph of the function. Describe how each graph can be obtained from the graph of a basic exponential function.

27. $f(x) = 2^{x+1}$

28. $f(x) = 2^{x-1}$

29. $f(x) = 2^x - 3$

30. $f(x) = 2^x + 1$

31. $f(x) = 4 - 3^{-x}$

32. $f(x) = 2^{x-1} - 3$

33. $f(x) = \left(\dfrac{3}{2}\right)^{x-1}$

34. $f(x) = 3^{4-x}$

35. $f(x) = 2^{x+3} - 5$

36. $f(x) = -3^{x-2}$

37. $f(x) = e^{2x}$

38. $f(x) = e^{-0.2x}$

39. $y = e^{-x+1}$

40. $y = e^{2x} + 1$

41. $f(x) = 2(1 - e^{-x})$

42. $f(x) = 1 - e^{-0.01x}$

43. *Compound Interest.* Suppose that $82{,}000$ is invested at $4\frac{1}{2}\%$ interest, compounded quarterly.

a) Find the function for the amount of money after t years.

b) Find the amount of money in the account at $t = 0, 2, 5$, and 10 yr.

44. *Compound Interest.* Suppose that $750 is invested at 7% interest, compounded semiannually.

   a) Find the function for the amount to which the investment grows after t years.

   b) Find the amount of money in the account at $t = 1, 6, 10, 15,$ and 25 yr.

45. *Interest on a CD.* On Jacob's sixth birthday, his grandparents present him with a $3000 certificate of deposit (CD) that earns 5% interest, compounded quarterly. If the CD matures on his sixteenth birthday, what amount will be available then?

46. *Interest in a College Trust Fund.* Following the birth of a child, Juan deposits $10,000 in a college trust fund where interest is 6.4%, compounded semiannually.

   a) Find a function for the amount in the account after t years.

   b) Find the amount of money in the account at $t = 0, 4, 8, 10,$ and 18 yr.

In Exercises 47–54, use the compound-interest formula to find the account balance with the given conditions.

P = principal,
r = interest rate,
n = number of compounding periods per year,
t = time, in years,
A = account balance.

	P	r	Compounded	n	t	A
47.	$3,000	4%	Semiannually		2	
48.	$12,500	3%	Quarterly		3	
49.	$120,000	2.5%	Annually		10	
50.	$120,000	2.5%	Quarterly		10	
51.	$53,500	$5\frac{1}{2}$%	Quarterly		$6\frac{1}{2}$	
52.	$6,250	$6\frac{3}{4}$%	Semiannually		$4\frac{1}{2}$	
53.	$17,400	8.1%	Daily		5	
54.	$900	7.3%	Daily		$7\frac{1}{4}$	

55. *Corn-Based Ethanol.* The United States produced 3.9 billion gal of fuel ethanol in 2005. The production of corn-based ethanol has increased exponentially from only 1.1 billion gal in 1996. (*Sources*: Energy Information Administration, Renewable Fuels Association)

The following function can be used to model this growth:

$$C(t) = 1.0283(1.1483)^t,$$

where t is the number of years since 1996. Estimate the number of gallons that will be produced in 2008 and in 2010.

56. *Growth of Bacteria* Escherichia coli. The bacteria *Escherichia coli* are commonly found in the human intestines. Suppose that 3000 of the bacteria are present at time $t = 0$. Then under certain conditions, t minutes later, the number of bacteria present is

$$N(t) = 3000(2)^{t/20}.$$

How many bacteria will be present after 10 min? 20 min? 30 min? 40 min? 60 min?

57. *Storage of Data.* The amount of data storage in gigabytes (GB) needed by a typical family in the United States has increased dramatically since 2004 (*Source*: Coughlin Associates). The function

$$G(x) = 433.6(1.5)^x,$$

where x is the number of years since 2004, models the amount of storage for recent years. Estimate the number of gigabytes needed by a typical family in 2009 and in 2014.

58. *Bachelor's Degrees Earned by Women.* The function

$$D(t) = 73,630.7487(1.0415)^t,$$

where *t* is the number of years since 1940, gives the number of bachelor's degrees conferred on women in the United States (*Sources*: National Center for Educational Statistics, U.S. Department of Education). Find the number of bachelor's degrees earned by women in 1960, in 1985, and in 2000. Then estimate the number of bachelor's degrees earned by women in 2010.

59. *World Trade with China.* China has recently taken some major steps in expanding its trade with the world. Both exports and imports have increased exponentially since 1996 (*Source*: U.S.–China Business Council).

The following functions model these trends:

Exports from China: $E(x) = 139.76(1.194)^x,$
Imports to China: $I(x) = 130.67(1.187)^x,$

where *t* is the number of years since 1996 and *E*(*x*) and *I*(*x*) are in billions of dollars. Find the exports and the imports, in billions of dollars, for 2007, 2012, and 2020.

60. *Children as a Percentage of the Population.* Children under 18 accounted for 26% of the U.S. population in 1999. This percentage was down from 36% in 1964 and is expected to continue to decrease. (*Source*: www.childstats.gov) The following function can be used to project the percentage of children in the United States:

$$K(t) = 35.37(0.99)^t,$$

where *t* is the number of years since 1964. Project the percentage of the U.S. population under age 18 in 2010 and in 2015.

61. *Salvage Value.* A top-quality phone–fax–copying machine is purchased for $1800. Its value each year is about 80% of the value of the preceding year. After *t* years, its value, in dollars, is given by the exponential function

$$V(t) = 1800(0.8)^t.$$

Find the value of the machine after 0 yr, 1 yr, 2 yr, 5 yr, and 10 yr.

62. *Fiancé(e) Visas.* The number of foreign nationals who came to the United States to marry an American using a "fiancé(e) visa" has grown exponentially in recent years. The total number of fiancé(e) visas is given by the function

$$f(x) = 5728.98(1.1214)^x,$$

where *x* is the number of years since 1990 (*Source*: U.S. Department of Homeland Security). Find the total number of visas in 2006 and in 2009.

63. *Online Sales.* As consumers become more comfortable shopping using the Internet, online retail sales will continue to increase. Online sales increased 20% from 2005 to 2006. (*Source*: National Retail Federation) Online retail sales, in billions of dollars, are given by the function

$$S(t) = 29.0626(1.3438)^t,$$

where *t* is the number of years since 1999. Find the amount of online sales in 2000 and in 2005. Then use the function to estimate the total online sales in 2007.

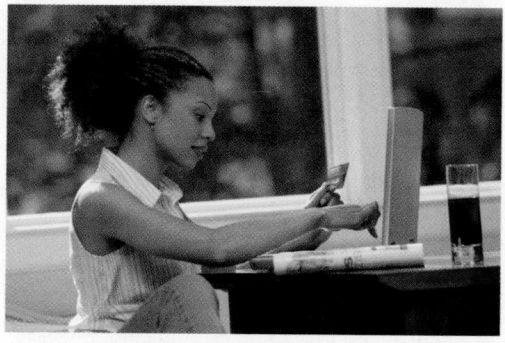

64. *Typing Speed.* Sarah is taking keyboarding at a community college. After she practices for *t* hours, her speed, in words per minute, is given by the function

$$S(t) = 200[1 - (0.86)^t].$$

What is Sarah's speed after practicing for 10 hr? 20 hr? 40 hr? 100 hr?

65. *Advertising.* A company begins a radio advertising campaign in New York City to market a new DVD video game. The percentage of the target market that buys a game is generally a function of the length of the advertising campaign. The estimated percentage is given by the function

$$f(t) = 100(1 - e^{-0.04t}),$$

where *t* is the number of days of the campaign. Find $f(25)$, the percentage of the target market that has bought the product after a 25-day advertising campaign.

66. *Growth of a Stock.* The value of a stock is given by the function

$$V(t) = 58(1 - e^{-1.1t}) + 20,$$

where *V* is the value of the stock after time *t*, in months. Find $V(1)$, $V(2)$, $V(4)$, $V(6)$, and $V(12)$.

Technology Connection

In Exercises 67–80, use a graphing calculator to match the equation with one of the figures (a)–(n), which follow.

a)

b)

c)

d)

e)

f)

g)

h)

i)

j)

k)

l)

m)

n)
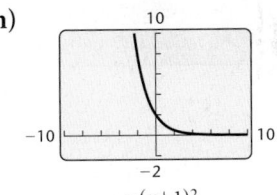

67. $y = 3^x - 3^{-x}$

68. $y = 3^{-(x+1)^2}$

69. $f(x) = -2.3^x$

70. $f(x) = 30,000(1.4)^x$

71. $y = 2^{-|x|}$

72. $y = 2^{-(x-1)}$

73. $f(x) = (0.58)^x - 1$

74. $y = 2^x + 2^{-x}$

75. $g(x) = e^{|x|}$

76. $f(x) = |2^x - 1|$

77. $y = 2^{-x^2}$

78. $y = |2^{x^2} - 8|$

79. $g(x) = \dfrac{e^x - e^{-x}}{2}$

80. $f(x) = \dfrac{e^x + e^{-x}}{2}$

Collaborative Discussion and Writing

81. Describe the differences between the graphs of $f(x) = x^3$ and $g(x) = 3^x$.

82. Suppose that $10,000 is invested for 8 yr at 6.4% interest, compounded annually. In what year will the most interest be earned? Why?

Graph the pair of equations using the same set of axes. Then compare the results.

83. $y = 3^x, \ x = 3^y$

84. $y = 1^x, \ x = 1^y$

Skill Maintenance

Simplify.

85. $(1 - 4i)(7 + 6i)$

86. $\dfrac{2 - i}{3 + i}$

Find the x-intercepts and the zeros of the function.

87. $f(x) = 2x^2 - 13x - 7$

88. $h(x) = x^3 - 3x^2 + 3x - 1$

89. $h(x) = x^4 - x^2$

90. $g(x) = x^3 + x^2 - 12x$

Solve.

91. $x^3 + 6x^2 - 16x = 0$

92. $3x^2 - 6 = 5x$

Synthesis

93. Which is larger, 7^π or π^7? 70^{80} or 80^{70}?

4.3 Logarithmic Functions and Graphs

◆ Find common and natural logarithms with and without a calculator.
◆ Convert between exponential equations and logarithmic equations.
◆ Change logarithmic bases.
◆ Graph logarithmic functions.
◆ Solve applied problems involving logarithmic functions.

We now consider *logarithmic*, or *logarithm*, *functions*. These functions are inverses of exponential functions and have many applications.

◆ Logarithmic Functions

We have noted that every exponential function (with $a > 0$ and $a \neq 1$) is one-to-one. Thus such a function has an inverse that is a function. In this section, we will name these inverse functions logarithmic functions and use them in applications. For now, we draw their graphs by interchanging x and y.

EXAMPLE 1 Graph: $x = 2^y$.

Solution Note that x is alone on one side of the equation. We can find ordered pairs that are solutions by choosing values for y and then computing the corresponding x-values.

For $y = 0, x = 2^0 = 1.$
For $y = 1, x = 2^1 = 2.$
For $y = 2, x = 2^2 = 4.$
For $y = 3, x = 2^3 = 8.$
For $y = -1, x = 2^{-1} = \dfrac{1}{2^1} = \dfrac{1}{2}.$
For $y = -2, x = 2^{-2} = \dfrac{1}{2^2} = \dfrac{1}{4}.$
For $y = -3, x = 2^{-3} = \dfrac{1}{2^3} = \dfrac{1}{8}.$

x $x = 2^y$	y	(x, y)
1	0	$(1, 0)$
2	1	$(2, 1)$
4	2	$(4, 2)$
8	3	$(8, 3)$
$\frac{1}{2}$	−1	$\left(\frac{1}{2}, -1\right)$
$\frac{1}{4}$	−2	$\left(\frac{1}{4}, -2\right)$
$\frac{1}{8}$	−3	$\left(\frac{1}{8}, -3\right)$

(1) Choose values for y.
(2) Compute values for x.

We plot the points and connect them with a smooth curve. Note that the curve does not touch or cross the y-axis. The y-axis is a vertical asymptote.

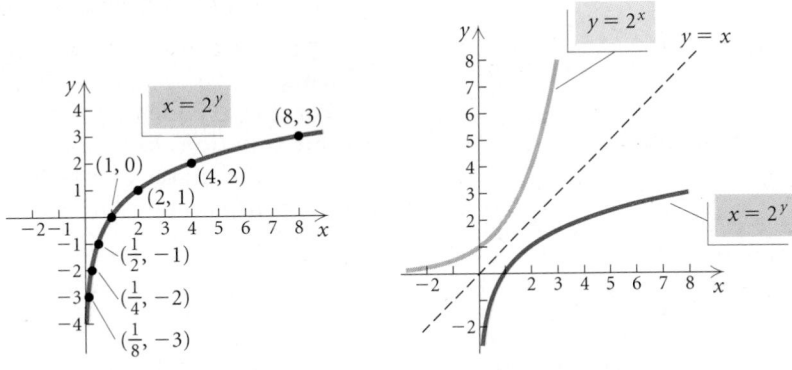

Note too that this curve looks just like the graph of $y = 2^x$, except that it is reflected across the line $y = x$, as we would expect for an inverse. The inverse of $y = 2^x$ is $x = 2^y$.

▶ Now Try Exercise 1.

To find a formula for f^{-1} when $f(x) = 2^x$, we try to use the method of Section 4.1:

1. Replace $f(x)$ with y:
$$f(x) = 2^x$$
$$y = 2^x$$

2. Interchange x and y:
$$x = 2^y$$

3. Solve for y:
$$y = \text{the power to which we raise 2 to get } x$$

4. Replace y with $f^{-1}(x)$: $\quad f^{-1}(x) = $ the power to which we raise 2 to get x.

Mathematicians have defined a new symbol to replace the words "the power to which we raise 2 to get x." That symbol is "$\log_2 x$," read "the logarithm, base 2, of x."

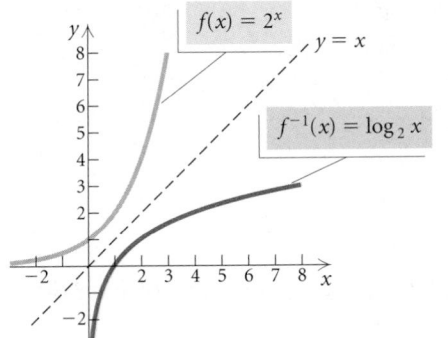

Logarithmic Function, Base 2

"$\log_2 x$," read "the logarithm, base 2, of x," means "the power to which we raise 2 to get x."

Thus if $f(x) = 2^x$, then $f^{-1}(x) = \log_2 x$. For example,

$$f^{-1}(8) = \log_2 8 = 3,$$

because

3 is the power to which we raise 2 to get 8.

Similarly, $\log_2 13$ is the power to which we raise 2 to get 13. As yet, we have no simpler way to say this other than

"$\log_2 13$ is the power to which we raise 2 to get 13."

Later, however, we will learn how to approximate this expression using a calculator.

For any exponential function $f(x) = a^x$, its inverse is called a **logarithmic function, base *a*.** The graph of the inverse can be obtained by reflecting the graph of $y = a^x$ across the line $y = x$, to obtain $x = a^y$. Then $x = a^y$ is equivalent to $y = \log_a x$. We read $\log_a x$ as "the logarithm, base *a*, of *x*."

The inverse of $f(x) = a^x$ is given by $f^{-1}(x) = \log_a x$.

> ### Logarithmic Function, Base a
>
> We define $y = \log_a x$ as that number y such that $x = a^y$, where $x > 0$ and a is a positive constant other than 1.

Let's look at the graphs of $f(x) = a^x$ and $f^{-1}(x) = \log_a x$ for $a > 1$ and $0 < a < 1$.

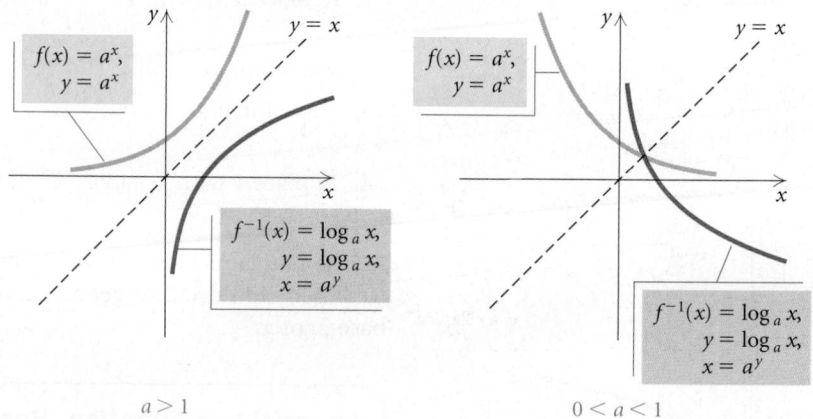

$$a > 1 \qquad\qquad 0 < a < 1$$

Note that the graphs of $f(x)$ and $f^{-1}(x)$ are reflections of each other across the line $y = x$.

CONNECTING THE CONCEPTS

Comparing Exponential Functions and Logarithmic Functions

Generally, we use a number that is greater than 1 for a logarithmic base. In the following table, we compare exponential functions and logarithmic functions with bases a greater than 1. Similar statements could be made for a, where $0 < a < 1$. It is helpful to visualize the differences by carefully observing the graphs.

EXPONENTIAL FUNCTION

$y = a^x$
$f(x) = a^x$
$a > 1$
Continuous
One-to-one
Domain: All real
   numbers, $(-\infty, \infty)$
Range: All positive
   real numbers, $(0, \infty)$
Increasing
Horizontal asymptote is x-axis:
   $(a^x \to 0$ as $x \to -\infty)$
y-intercept: $(0, 1)$
There is no x-intercept.

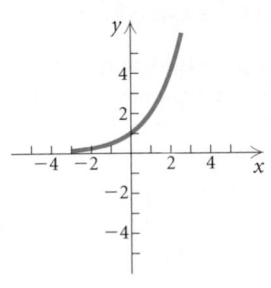

LOGARITHMIC FUNCTION

$x = a^y$
$f^{-1}(x) = \log_a x$
$a > 1$
Continuous
One-to-one
Domain: All positive
   real numbers, $(0, \infty)$
Range: All real
   numbers, $(-\infty, \infty)$
Increasing
Vertical asymptote is y-axis:
   $(\log_a x \to -\infty$ as $x \to 0^+)$
x-intercept: $(1, 0)$
There is no y-intercept.

●●●

✦ Finding Certain Logarithms

Let's use the definition of logarithms to find some logarithmic values.

EXAMPLE 2 Find each of the following logarithms.

a) $\log_{10} 10,000$ b) $\log_{10} 0.01$ c) $\log_2 8$

d) $\log_9 3$ e) $\log_6 1$ f) $\log_8 8$

Solution

a) The exponent to which we raise 10 to obtain 10,000 is 4; thus $\log_{10} 10,000 = 4$.

b) We have $0.01 = \dfrac{1}{100} = \dfrac{1}{10^2} = 10^{-2}$. The exponent to which we raise 10 to get 0.01 is -2, so $\log_{10} 0.01 = -2$.

c) $8 = 2^3$. The exponent to which we raise 2 to get 8 is 3, so $\log_2 8 = 3$.

d) $3 = \sqrt{9} = 9^{1/2}$. The exponent to which we raise 9 to get 3 is $\frac{1}{2}$, so $\log_9 3 = \frac{1}{2}$.

e) $1 = 6^0$. The exponent to which we raise 6 to get 1 is 0, so $\log_6 1 = 0$.

f) $8 = 8^1$. The exponent to which we raise 8 to get 8 is 1, so $\log_8 8 = 1$.

▶ Now Try Exercises 9 and 13.

Examples 2(e) and 2(f) illustrate two important properties of logarithms. The property $\log_a 1 = 0$ follows from the fact that $a^0 = 1$. Thus, $\log_5 1 = 0, \log_{10} 1 = 0$, and so on. The property $\log_a a = 1$ follows from the fact that $a^1 = a$. Thus, $\log_5 5 = 1, \log_{10} 10 = 1$, and so on.

$\log_a 1 = 0$ and $\log_a a = 1$,   for any logarithmic base a.

◆ Converting Between Exponential and Logarithmic Equations

It is helpful in dealing with logarithmic functions to remember that a logarithm of a number is an *exponent*. It is the exponent y in $x = a^y$. You might think to yourself, "the logarithm, base a, of a number x is the power to which a must be raised to get x."

We are led to the following. (The symbol $\longleftrightarrow$ means that the two statements are equivalent; that is, when one is true, the other is true. The words "if and only if" can be used in place of $\longleftrightarrow$.)

$\log_a x = y \longleftrightarrow x = a^y$ A logarithm is an exponent!

EXAMPLE 3   Convert each of the following to a logarithmic equation.

a) $16 = 2^x$ **b)** $10^{-3} = 0.001$ **c)** $e^t = 70$

Solution

The exponent is the logarithm.

a) $16 = 2^x$ $\log_2 16 = x$

The base remains the same.

b) $10^{-3} = 0.001 \rightarrow \log_{10} 0.001 = -3$

c) $e^t = 70 \rightarrow \log_e 70 = t$

▶ Now Try Exercise 37.

EXAMPLE 4   Convert each of the following to an exponential equation.

a) $\log_2 32 = 5$ **b)** $\log_a Q = 8$ **c)** $x = \log_t M$

Solution

The logarithm is the exponent.

a) $\log_2 32 = 5$ $2^5 = 32$

The base remains the same.

b) $\log_a Q = 8 \rightarrow a^8 = Q$

c) $x = \log_t M \rightarrow t^x = M$

▶ Now Try Exercise 47.

✦ Finding Logarithms on a Calculator

Before calculators became so widely available, base-10 logarithms, or **common logarithms,** were used extensively to simplify complicated calculations. In fact, that is why logarithms were invented. The abbreviation **log,** with no base written, is used to represent common logarithms, or base-10 logarithms. Thus,

log x **means** **log$_{10}$** x.

For example, $\log 29$ means $\log_{10} 29$. Let's compare $\log 29$ with $\log 10$ and $\log 100$:

$\left.\begin{array}{l} \log 10 = \log_{10} 10 = 1 \\ \log 29 = ? \\ \log 100 = \log_{10} 100 = 2 \end{array}\right\}$ Since 29 is between 10 and 100, it seems reasonable that $\log 29$ is between 1 and 2.

On a calculator, the key for common logarithms is generally marked **LOG**. Using that key, we find that

$\log 29 \approx 1.462397998 \approx 1.4624$

rounded to four decimal places. Since $1 < 1.4624 < 2$, our answer seems reasonable. This also tells us that $10^{1.4624} \approx 29$.

EXAMPLE 5 Find each of the following common logarithms on a calculator. If you are using a graphing calculator, set the calculator in REAL mode. Round to four decimal places.

a) $\log 645{,}778$ b) $\log 0.0000239$ c) $\log(-3)$

Solution

FUNCTION VALUE	READOUT	ROUNDED
a) $\log 645{,}778$	log(645778) 5.810083246	5.8101
b) $\log 0.0000239$	log(0.0000239) -4.621602099	-4.6216
c) $\log(-3)$	ERR:NONREAL ANS 1:Quit 2:Goto	Does not exist

Since 5.810083246 is the power to which we raise 10 to get 645,778, we can check part (a) by finding $10^{5.810083246}$. We can check part (b) in a similar manner. In part (c), $\log(-3)$ does not exist as a real number because

*If the graphing calculator is set in $a + bi$ mode, the readout is $.4771212547 + 1.364376354i$.

there is no real-number power to which we can raise 10 to get -3. The number 10 raised to any real-number power is positive. The common logarithm of a negative number does not exist as a real number. Recall that logarithmic functions are inverses of exponential functions, and since the range of an exponential function is $(0, \infty)$, the domain of $f(x) = \log_a x$ is $(0, \infty)$.

▶ Now Try Exercises 57 and 61.

◆ Natural Logarithms

Logarithms, base e, are called **natural logarithms.** The abbreviation "ln" is generally used for natural logarithms. Thus,

ln x means $\log_e x$.

For example, ln 53 means $\log_e 53$. On a calculator, the key for natural logarithms is generally marked **LN**. Using that key, we find that

$$\ln 53 \approx 3.970291914$$
$$\approx 3.9703$$

rounded to four decimal places. This also tells us that $e^{3.9703} \approx 53$.

EXAMPLE 6   Find each of the following natural logarithms on a calculator. If you are using a graphing calculator, set the calculator in REAL mode. Round to four decimal places.

a) ln 645,778   **b)** ln 0.0000239   **c)** ln (-5)
d) ln e **e)** ln 1

Solution

FUNCTION VALUE	READOUT	ROUNDED
a) ln 645,778	ln(645778) 13.37821107	13.3782
b) ln 0.0000239	ln(0.0000239) -10.6416321	-10.6416
c) ln (-5)	ERR:NONREAL ANS 1:Quit 2:Goto *	Does not exist
d) ln e	ln(e) 1	1
e) ln 1	ln(1) 0	0

*If the graphing calculator is set in $a + bi$ mode, the readout is $1.609437912 + 3.141592654i$.

Since 13.37821107 is the power to which we raise e to get 645,778, we can check part (a) by finding $e^{13.37821107}$. We can check parts (b), (d), and (e) in a similar manner. In parts (d) and (e), note that $\ln e = \log_e e = 1$ and $\ln 1 = \log_e 1 = 0$.

▶ Now Try Exercises 65 and 67.

> $\ln 1 = 0$ and $\ln e = 1$, for the logarithmic base e.

✦ Changing Logarithmic Bases

Most calculators give the values of both common logarithms and natural logarithms. To find a logarithm with a base other than 10 or e, we can use the following conversion formula.

> **The Change-of-Base Formula**
>
> For any logarithmic bases a and b, and any positive number M,
>
> $$\log_b M = \frac{\log_a M}{\log_a b}.$$

We will prove this result in the next section.

EXAMPLE 7 Find $\log_5 8$ using common logarithms.

Solution First, we let $a = 10$, $b = 5$, and $M = 8$. Then we substitute into the change-of-base formula:

$$\log_5 8 = \frac{\log_{10} 8}{\log_{10} 5} \qquad \text{Substituting}$$

$$\approx 1.2920. \qquad \text{Using a calculator}$$

Since $\log_5 8$ is the power to which we raise 5 to get 8, we would expect this power to be greater than 1 ($5^1 = 5$) and less than 2 ($5^2 = 25$), so the result is reasonable.

▶ Now Try Exercise 69.

We can also use base e for a conversion.

EXAMPLE 8 Find $\log_5 8$ using natural logarithms.

Solution Substituting e for a, 5 for b, and 8 for M, we have

$$\log_5 8 = \frac{\log_e 8}{\log_e 5}$$

$$= \frac{\ln 8}{\ln 5} \approx 1.2920.$$

▶ Now Try Exercise 75.

✦ Graphs of Logarithmic Functions

Let's now consider graphs of logarithmic functions.

EXAMPLE 9   Graph: $y = f(x) = \log_5 x$.

Solution   The equation $y = \log_5 x$ is equivalent to $x = 5^y$. We can find ordered pairs that are solutions by choosing values for y and computing the x-values. We then plot points, remembering that x is still the first coordinate.

For $y = 0, x = 5^0 = 1$.
For $y = 1, x = 5^1 = 5$.
For $y = 2, x = 5^2 = 25$.
For $y = 3, x = 5^3 = 125$.

For $y = -1, x = 5^{-1} = \dfrac{1}{5}$.

For $y = -2, x = 5^{-2} = \dfrac{1}{25}$.

x, or 5^y	y
1	0
5	1
25	2
125	3
$\dfrac{1}{5}$	-1
$\dfrac{1}{25}$	-2

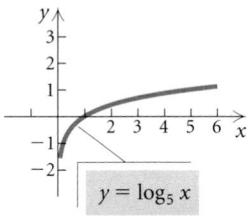

(1) Select y.
(2) Compute x.

▶ Now Try Exercise 5.

EXAMPLE 10   Graph: $g(x) = \ln x$.

Solution   To graph $y = g(x) = \ln x$, we select values for x and use a calculator to find the corresponding values of $\ln x$. We then plot points and draw the curve.

x	$g(x) = \ln x$
0.5	-0.7
1	0
2	0.7
3	1.1
4	1.4
5	1.6

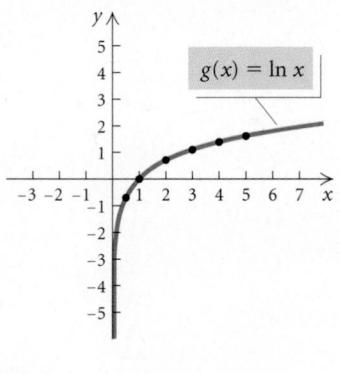

We could also write $g(x) = \ln x$, or $y = \ln x$, as $x = e^y$, select values for y, and use a calculator to find the corresponding values of x.

▶ Now Try Exercise 7.

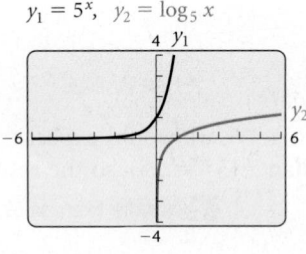

Recall that the graph of $f(x) = \log_a x$, for any base a, has the x-intercept $(1, 0)$. The domain is the set of positive real numbers, and the range is the set of all real numbers. The y-axis is the vertical asymptote.

EXAMPLE 11 Graph each of the following. Describe how each graph can be obtained from the graph of $y = \ln x$. Give the domain and the vertical asymptote of each function.

a) $f(x) = \ln(x + 3)$
b) $f(x) = 3 - \frac{1}{2}\ln x$
c) $f(x) = |\ln(x - 1)|$

Solution

a) The graph of $f(x) = \ln(x + 3)$ is a shift of the graph of $y = \ln x$ left 3 units. The domain is the set of all real numbers greater than -3, $(-3, \infty)$. The line $x = -3$ is the vertical asymptote.

x	$f(x)$
-2.9	-2.303
-2	0
0	1.099
2	1.609
4	1.946

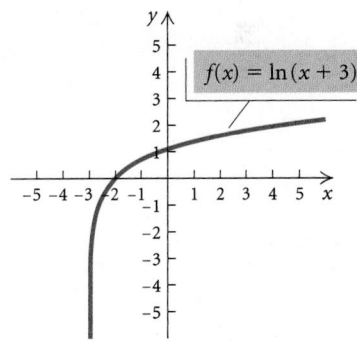

b) The graph of $f(x) = 3 - \frac{1}{2}\ln x$ is a vertical shrinking of the graph of $y = \ln x$, followed by a reflection across the x-axis, and then a translation up 3 units. The domain is the set of all positive real numbers, $(0, \infty)$. The y-axis is the vertical asymptote.

x	$f(x)$
0.1	4.151
1	3
3	2.451
6	2.104
9	1.901

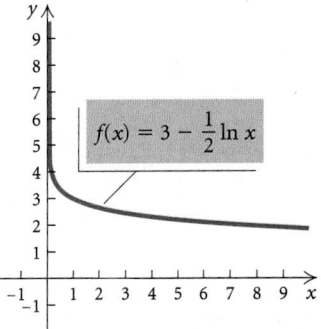

c) The graph of $f(x) = |\ln (x - 1)|$ is a translation of the graph of $y = \ln x$ right 1 unit. Then the absolute value has the effect of reflecting negative outputs across the *x*-axis. The domain is the set of all real numbers greater than 1, $(1, \infty)$. The line $x = 1$ is the vertical asymptote.

x	*f(x)*
1.1	2.303
2	0
4	1.099
6	1.609
8	1.946

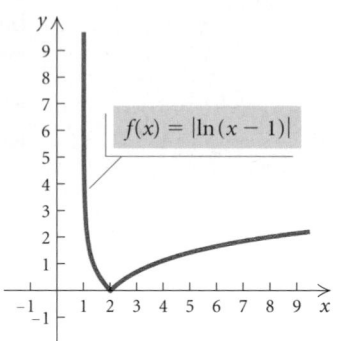

▶ Now Try Exercise 89.

✦ Applications

EXAMPLE 12   *Walking Speed.*   In a study by psychologists Bornstein and Bornstein, it was found that the average walking speed *w*, in feet per second, of a person living in a city of population *P*, in thousands, is given by the function

$$w(P) = 0.37 \ln P + 0.05$$

(*Source: International Journal of Psychology*).

a) The population of Hartford, Connecticut, is 124,848. Find the average walking speed of people living in Hartford.

b) The population of San Antonio, Texas, is 1,236,249. Find the average walking speed of people living in San Antonio.

Solution

a) Since *P* is in thousands and 124,848 = 124.848 thousand, we substitute 124.848 for *P*:

$$w(124.848) = 0.37 \ln 124.848 + 0.05 \qquad \text{Substituting}$$
$$\approx 1.8. \qquad\qquad\qquad \text{Finding the natural logarithm and simplifying}$$

The average walking speed of people living in Hartford is about 1.8 ft/sec.

b) We substitute 1236.249 for *P*:

$$w(1236.249) = 0.37 \ln 1236.249 + 0.05 \qquad \text{Substituting}$$
$$\approx 2.7.$$

The average walking speed of people living in San Antonio is about 2.7 ft/sec.

▶ Now Try Exercise 91(d).

EXAMPLE 13 *Earthquake Magnitude.* The magnitude R, measured on the Richter scale, of an earthquake of intensity I is defined as

$$R = \log \frac{I}{I_0},$$

where I_0 is a minimum intensity used for comparison. We can think of I_0 as a threshold intensity that is the weakest earthquake that can be recorded on a seismograph. If one earthquake is 10 times as intense as another, its magnitude on the Richter scale is 1 greater than that of the other. If one earthquake is 100 times as intense as another, its magnitude on the Richter scale is 2 higher, and so on. Thus an earthquake whose magnitude is 7 on the Richter scale is 10 times as intense as an earthquake whose magnitude is 6. Earthquake intensities can be interpreted as multiples of the minimum intensity I_0.

The undersea earthquake off the west coast of northern Sumatra on December 26, 2004, had an intensity of $10^{9.3} \cdot I_0$ (*Sources*: U.S. Geological Survey; National Earthquake Information Center). It caused devastating tsunamis that hit twelve Indian Ocean countries. What was its magnitude on the Richter scale?

Solution We substitute into the formula:

$$R = \log \frac{I}{I_0} = \log \frac{10^{9.3} \cdot I_0}{I_0} = \log 10^{9.3} = 9.3.$$

The magnitude of the earthquake was 9.3 on the Richter scale.

▷ Now Try Exercise 93(a).

A

B

C

D

E

Visualizing the Graph

Match the equation or function with its graph.

1. $f(x) = 4^x$

2. $f(x) = \ln x - 3$

3. $(x + 3)^2 + y^2 = 9$

4. $f(x) = 2^{-x} + 1$

5. $f(x) = \log_2 x$

6. $f(x) = x^3 - 2x^2 - x + 2$

7. $x = -3$

8. $f(x) = e^x - 4$

9. $f(x) = (x - 3)^2 + 2$

10. $3x = 6 + y$

Answers on page A-30

F

G

H

I

J

4.3 EXERCISE SET

Graph.

1. $x = 3^y$ **2.** $x = 4^y$

3. $x = \left(\frac{1}{2}\right)^y$ **4.** $x = \left(\frac{4}{3}\right)^y$

5. $y = \log_3 x$ **6.** $y = \log_4 x$

7. $f(x) = 2 \ln x$ **8.** $f(x) = \ln x$

Find each of the following. Do not use a calculator.

9. $\log_2 16$ **10.** $\log_3 9$

11. $\log_5 125$ **12.** $\log_2 64$

13. $\log 0.001$ **14.** $\log 100$

15. $\log_2 \frac{1}{4}$ **16.** $\log_8 2$

17. $\ln 1$ **18.** $\ln e$

19. $\log 10$ **20.** $\log 1$

21. $\log_5 5^4$ **22.** $\log \sqrt{10}$

23. $\log_3 \sqrt[4]{3}$ **24.** $\log 10^{8/5}$

25. $\log 10^{-7}$ **26.** $\log_5 1$

27. $\log_{49} 7$ **28.** $\log_3 3^{-2}$

29. $\ln e^{3/4}$ **30.** $\log_2 \sqrt{2}$

31. $\log_4 1$ **32.** $\ln e^{-5}$

33. $\ln \sqrt{e}$ **34.** $\log_{64} 4$

Convert to a logarithmic equation.

35. $10^3 = 1000$ **36.** $5^{-3} = \frac{1}{125}$

37. $8^{1/3} = 2$ **38.** $10^{0.3010} = 2$

39. $e^3 = t$ **40.** $Q^t = x$

41. $e^2 = 7.3891$ **42.** $e^{-1} = 0.3679$

43. $p^k = 3$ **44.** $e^{-t} = 4000$

Convert to an exponential equation.

45. $\log_5 5 = 1$ **46.** $t = \log_4 7$

47. $\log 0.01 = -2$ **48.** $\log 7 = 0.845$

49. $\ln 30 = 3.4012$

50. $\ln 0.38 = -0.9676$

51. $\log_a M = -x$

52. $\log_t Q = k$

53. $\log_a T^3 = x$

54. $\ln W^5 = t$

Find each of the following using a calculator. Round to four decimal places.

55. $\log 3$ **56.** $\log 8$

57. $\log 532$ **58.** $\log 93{,}100$

59. $\log 0.57$ **60.** $\log 0.082$

61. $\log(-2)$ **62.** $\ln 50$

63. $\ln 2$ **64.** $\ln(-4)$

65. $\ln 809.3$ **66.** $\ln 0.00037$

67. $\ln(-1.32)$ **68.** $\ln 0$

Find the logarithm using common logarithms and the change-of-base formula.

69. $\log_4 100$ **70.** $\log_3 20$

71. $\log_{100} 0.3$ **72.** $\log_\pi 100$

73. $\log_{200} 50$ **74.** $\log_{5.3} 1700$

Find the logarithm using natural logarithms and the change-of-base formula.

75. $\log_3 12$ **76.** $\log_4 25$

77. $\log_{100} 15$ **78.** $\log_9 100$

Graph the function and its inverse using the same set of axes.

79. $f(x) = 3^x$, $f^{-1}(x) = \log_3 x$

80. $f(x) = \log_4 x$, $f^{-1}(x) = 4^x$

81. $f(x) = \log x$, $f^{-1}(x) = 10^x$

82. $f(x) = e^x$, $f^{-1}(x) = \ln x$

For each of the following functions, briefly describe how the graph can be obtained from the graph of a basic logarithmic function. Then graph the function. Give the domain and the vertical asymptote of each function.

83. $f(x) = \log_2(x + 3)$

84. $f(x) = \log_3(x - 2)$

85. $y = \log_3 x - 1$ **86.** $y = 3 + \log_2 x$

87. $f(x) = 4 \ln x$ **88.** $f(x) = \frac{1}{2} \ln x$

89. $y = 2 - \ln x$ **90.** $y = \ln(x + 1)$

91. *Walking Speed.*   Refer to Example 12. Various cities and their populations are given below. Find the average walking speed in each city.

a) Indianapolis, Indiana: 784,242
b) Albuquerque, New Mexico: 484,246
c) St. Paul, Minnesota: 276,963
d) Chicago, Illinois: 2,862,244
e) Portland, Oregon: 533,492
f) Toledo, Ohio: 304,973
g) New York, New York: 8,104,079
h) Cedar Rapids, Iowa: 122,206

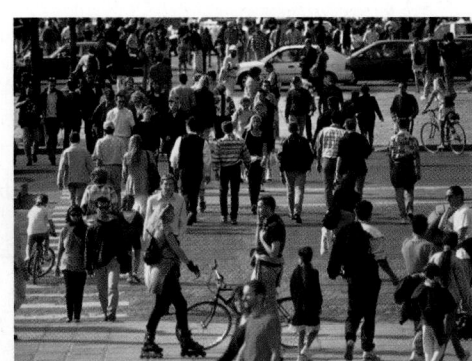

92. *Forgetting.*   Students in an accounting class took a final exam and then took equivalent forms of the exam at monthly intervals thereafter. The average score $S(t)$, as a percent, after t months was found to be given by the function

$$S(t) = 78 - 15 \log(t + 1), \quad t \geq 0.$$

a) What was the average score when the students initially took the test, $t = 0$?
b) What was the average score after 4 months? 24 months?

93. *Earthquake Magnitude.*   Refer to Example 13. Various locations of earthquakes and their intensities are given below. What was the magnitude on the Richter scale?

a) Mexico City, 1978: $10^{7.85} \cdot I_0$
b) San Francisco, 1906: $10^{8.25} \cdot I_0$
c) Chile, 1960: $10^{9.6} \cdot I_0$
d) Gujarat, India, 2001: $10^{7.9} \cdot I_0$
e) San Francisco, 1989: $10^{6.9} \cdot I_0$

94. *pH of Substances in Chemistry.*   In chemistry, the pH of a substance is defined as

$$pH = -\log[H^+],$$

where H^+ is the hydrogen ion concentration, in moles per liter. Find the pH of each substance.

Litmus paper is used to test pH.

SUBSTANCE	HYDROGEN ION CONCENTRATION
a) Pineapple juice	1.6×10^{-4}
b) Hair rinse	0.0013
c) Mouthwash	6.3×10^{-7}
d) Eggs	1.6×10^{-8}
e) Tomatoes	6.3×10^{-5}

95. Find the hydrogen ion concentration of each substance, given the pH (see Exercise 94). Express the answer in scientific notation.

SUBSTANCE	PH
a) Tap water	7
b) Rainwater	5.4
c) Orange juice	3.2
d) Wine	4.8

96. *Advertising.*   A model for advertising response is given by the function

$$N(a) = 1000 + 200 \ln a, \quad a \geq 1,$$

where $N(a)$ is the number of units sold when a is the amount spent on advertising, in thousands of dollars.

a) How many units were sold after spending $1000 ($a = 1$) on advertising?
b) How many units were sold after spending $5000?

97. *Loudness of Sound.*   The **loudness L,** in bels (after Alexander Graham Bell), of a sound of intensity I is defined to be

$$L = \log \frac{I}{I_0},$$

where I_0 is the minimum intensity detectable by the human ear (such as the tick of a watch at 20 ft under quiet conditions). If a sound is 10 times as intense as another, its loudness is 1 bel greater than that of the other. If a sound is 100 times as intense as another, its loudness is 2 bels greater, and so on. The bel is a large unit, so a subunit, the **decibel,** is generally used. For L, in decibels, the formula is

$$L = 10 \log \frac{I}{I_0}.$$

Find the loudness, in decibels, of each sound with the given intensity.

SOUND	INTENSITY
a) Library	$2510 \cdot I_0$
b) Dishwasher	$2,500,000 \cdot I_0$
c) Conversational speech	$10^6 \cdot I_0$
d) Heavy truck	$10^9 \cdot I_0$

Technology Connection

98. Use a graphing calculator that can graph inverses without the need to first find an equation of the inverse to graph the functions in Exercises 79–82.

Collaborative Discussion and Writing

99. If $\log b < 0$, what can you say about b?

100. Explain how the graph of $f(x) = \ln x$ can be used to obtain the graph of $g(x) = e^{x-2}$.

Skill Maintenance

Find the slope and the y-intercept of the line.

101. $y = 6$

102. $3x - 10y = 14$

103. $y = 2x - \frac{3}{13}$

104. $x = -4$

Use synthetic division to find the function values.

105. $g(x) = x^3 - 6x^2 + 3x + 10$; find $g(-5)$

106. $f(x) = x^4 - 2x^3 + x - 6$; find $f(-1)$

Find a polynomial function of degree 3 with the given numbers as zeros. Answers may vary.

107. $\sqrt{7}, -\sqrt{7}, 0$

108. $4i, -4i, 1$

Synthesis

Simplify.

109. $\dfrac{\log_5 8}{\log_5 2}$

110. $\dfrac{\log_3 64}{\log_3 16}$

Find the domain of the function.

111. $f(x) = \log_5 x^3$

112. $f(x) = \log_4 x^2$

113. $f(x) = \ln |x|$

114. $f(x) = \log(3x - 4)$

Solve.

115. $\log_2 (2x + 5) < 0$

116. $\log_2 (x - 3) \geq 4$

In Exercises 117–120, match the equation with one of figures (a)–(d), which follow.

a)

b)

c)

d)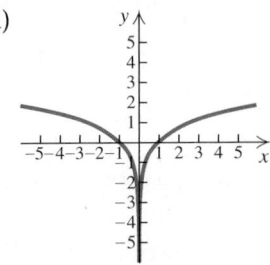

117. $f(x) = \ln |x|$

118. $f(x) = |\ln x|$

119. $f(x) = \ln x^2$

120. $g(x) = |\ln (x - 1)|$

4.4 Properties of Logarithmic Functions

◆ Convert from logarithms of products, powers, and quotients to expressions in terms of individual logarithms, and conversely.

◆ Simplify expressions of the type $\log_a a^x$ and $a^{\log_a x}$.

We now establish some properties of logarithmic functions. These properties are based on the corresponding rules for exponents.

◆ Logarithms of Products

The first property of logarithms corresponds to the product rule for exponents: $a^m \cdot a^n = a^{m+n}$.

The Product Rule

For any positive numbers M and N and any logarithmic base a,

$$\log_a MN = \log_a M + \log_a N.$$

(The logarithm of a product is the sum of the logarithms of the factors.)

EXAMPLE 1   Express as a sum of logarithms: $\log_3 (9 \cdot 27)$.

Solution   We have

$$\log_3 (9 \cdot 27) = \log_3 9 + \log_3 27. \qquad \text{Using the product rule}$$

As a check, note that

$$\log_3 (9 \cdot 27) = \log_3 243 = 5 \qquad 3^5 = 243$$

and $\log_3 9 + \log_3 27 = 2 + 3 = 5.$ $3^2 = 9; 3^3 = 27$

▶ Now Try Exercise 1.

EXAMPLE 2   Express as a single logarithm: $\log_2 p^3 + \log_2 q$.

Solution   We have

$$\log_2 p^3 + \log_2 q = \log_2 (p^3 q).$$

▶ Now Try Exercise 35.

A Proof of the Product Rule.   Let $\log_a M = x$ and $\log_a N = y$. Converting to exponential equations, we have $a^x = M$ and $a^y = N$. Then

$$MN = a^x \cdot a^y = a^{x+y}.$$

Converting back to a logarithmic equation, we get

$$\log_a MN = x + y.$$

Remembering what x and y represent, we know it follows that

$$\log_a MN = \log_a M + \log_a N.$$

✦ Logarithms of Powers

The second property of logarithms corresponds to the power rule for exponents: $(a^m)^n = a^{mn}$.

> ### The Power Rule
>
> For any positive number M, any logarithmic base a, and any real number p,
>
> $$\log_a M^p = p \log_a M.$$
>
> (The logarithm of a power of M is the exponent times the logarithm of M.)

EXAMPLE 3   Express each of the following as a product.

a) $\log_a 11^{-3}$ **b)** $\log_a \sqrt[4]{7}$ **c)** $\ln x^6$

Solution

RATIONAL EXPONENTS

REVIEW SECTION R.6.

a) $\log_a 11^{-3} = -3 \log_a 11$ Using the power rule

b) $\log_a \sqrt[4]{7} = \log_a 7^{1/4}$ Writing exponential notation

$= \frac{1}{4} \log_a 7$ Using the power rule

c) $\ln x^6 = 6 \ln x$ Using the power rule   ▶ Now Try Exercises 13 and 15.

A Proof of the Power Rule.   Let $x = \log_a M$. The equivalent exponential equation is $a^x = M$. Raising both sides to the power p, we obtain

$$(a^x)^p = M^p, \quad \text{or} \quad a^{xp} = M^p.$$

Converting back to a logarithmic equation, we get

$$\log_a M^p = xp.$$

But $x = \log_a M$, so substituting gives us

$$\log_a M^p = (\log_a M)p = p \log_a M.$$

✦ Logarithms of Quotients

The third property of logarithms corresponds to the quotient rule for exponents: $a^m/a^n = a^{m-n}$.

> ### The Quotient Rule
>
> For any positive numbers M and N, and any logarithmic base a,
>
> $$\log_a \frac{M}{N} = \log_a M - \log_a N.$$
>
> (The logarithm of a quotient is the logarithm of the numerator minus the logarithm of the denominator.

EXAMPLE 4   Express as a difference of logarithms: $\log_t \dfrac{8}{w}$.

Solution

$$\log_t \frac{8}{w} = \log_t 8 - \log_t w \qquad \text{Using the quotient rule}$$

▶ Now Try Exercise 17.

EXAMPLE 5   Express as a single logarithm: $\log_b 64 - \log_b 16$.

Solution

$$\log_b 64 - \log_b 16 = \log_b \frac{64}{16} = \log_b 4$$

▶ Now Try Exercise 37.

A Proof of the Quotient Rule.   The proof follows from both the product rule and the power rule:

$$\log_a \frac{M}{N} = \log_a MN^{-1}$$

$$= \log_a M + \log_a N^{-1} \qquad \text{Using the product rule}$$

$$= \log_a M + (-1)\log_a N \qquad \text{Using the power rule}$$

$$= \log_a M - \log_a N.$$

Common Errors

$\log_a MN \neq (\log_a M)(\log_a N)$	The logarithm of a product is *not* the product of the logarithms.
$\log_a (M + N) \neq \log_a M + \log_a N$	The logarithm of a sum is *not* the sum of the logarithms.
$\log_a \dfrac{M}{N} \neq \dfrac{\log_a M}{\log_a N}$	The logarithm of a quotient is *not* the quotient of the logarithms.
$(\log_a M)^P \neq P \log_a M$	The power of a logarithm is *not* the exponent times the logarithm.

◆ **Applying the Properties**

EXAMPLE 6   Express each of the following in terms of sums and differences of logarithms.

a) $\log_a \dfrac{x^2 y^5}{z^4}$ **b)** $\log_a \sqrt[3]{\dfrac{a^2 b}{c^5}}$ **c)** $\log_b \dfrac{a y^5}{m^3 n^4}$

Solution

a) $\log_a \dfrac{x^2 y^5}{z^4} = \log_a (x^2 y^5) - \log_a z^4 \qquad \text{Using the quotient rule}$

$$= \log_a x^2 + \log_a y^5 - \log_a z^4 \qquad \text{Using the product rule}$$

$$= 2\log_a x + 5\log_a y - 4\log_a z \qquad \text{Using the power rule}$$

b) $\log_a \sqrt[3]{\dfrac{a^2 b}{c^5}} = \log_a \left(\dfrac{a^2 b}{c^5} \right)^{1/3}$ Writing exponential notation

$$= \frac{1}{3} \log_a \frac{a^2 b}{c^5}$$ Using the power rule

$$= \frac{1}{3} (\log_a a^2 b - \log_a c^5)$$ Using the quotient rule. The parentheses must be included.

$$= \frac{1}{3} (2 \log_a a + \log_a b - 5 \log_a c)$$ Using the product rule and the power rule

$$= \frac{1}{3} (2 + \log_a b - 5 \log_a c)$$ $\log_a a = 1$

$$= \frac{2}{3} + \frac{1}{3} \log_a b - \frac{5}{3} \log_a c$$ Multiplying to remove parentheses

c) $\log_b \dfrac{a y^5}{m^3 n^4} = \log_b a y^5 - \log_b m^3 n^4$ Using the quotient rule

$$= (\log_b a + \log_b y^5) - (\log_b m^3 + \log_b n^4)$$ Using the product rule

$$= \log_b a + \log_b y^5 - \log_b m^3 - \log_b n^4$$ Removing parentheses

$$= \log_b a + 5 \log_b y - 3 \log_b m - 4 \log_b n$$ Using the power rule

▶ Now Try Exercises 25 and 31.

EXAMPLE 7 Express as a single logarithm:

$$5 \log_b x - \log_b y + \frac{1}{4} \log_b z.$$

Solution

$$5 \log_b x - \log_b y + \frac{1}{4} \log_b z = \log_b x^5 - \log_b y + \log_b z^{1/4}$$

Using the power rule

$$= \log_b \frac{x^5}{y} + \log_b z^{1/4}$$ Using the quotient rule

$$= \log_b \frac{x^5 z^{1/4}}{y}, \text{ or } \log_b \frac{x^5 \sqrt[4]{z}}{y}$$

Using the product rule

▶ Now Try Exercise 41.

EXAMPLE 8   Given that $\log_a 2 \approx 0.301$ and $\log_a 3 \approx 0.477$, find each of the following.

a) $\log_a 6$ **b)** $\log_a \dfrac{2}{3}$ **c)** $\log_a 81$

d) $\log_a \dfrac{1}{4}$ **e)** $\log_a 5$ **f)** $\dfrac{\log_a 3}{\log_a 2}$

Solution

a) $\log_a 6 = \log_a(2 \cdot 3) = \log_a 2 + \log_a 3$ Using the product rule
$$\approx 0.301 + 0.477$$
$$\approx 0.778$$

b) $\log_a \frac{2}{3} = \log_a 2 - \log_a 3$ Using the quotient rule
$$\approx 0.301 - 0.477 \approx -0.176$$

c) $\log_a 81 = \log_a 3^4 = 4 \log_a 3$ Using the power rule
$$\approx 4(0.477) \approx 1.908$$

d) $\log_a \frac{1}{4} = \log_a 1 - \log_a 4$ Using the quotient rule
$$= 0 - \log_a 2^2 \qquad \log_a 1 = 0$$
$$= -2 \log_a 2 \qquad \text{Using the power rule}$$
$$\approx -2(0.301) \approx -0.602$$

e) $\log_a 5$ *cannot* be found using these properties and the given information.
$$(\log_a 5 \neq \log_a 2 + \log_a 3) \qquad \log_a 2 + \log_a 3 = \log_a 2 \cdot 3 = \log_a 6$$

f) $\dfrac{\log_a 3}{\log_a 2} \approx \dfrac{0.477}{0.301} \approx 1.585$ We simply divide, not using any of the properties.

▶ Now Try Exercises 53 and 55.

⬥ Simplifying Expressions of the Type $\log_a a^x$ and $a^{\log_a x}$

We have two final properties of logarithms to consider. The first follows from the product rule: Since $\log_a a^x = x \log_a a = x \cdot 1 = x$, we have $\log_a a^x = x$. This property also follows from the definition of a logarithm: x is the power to which we raise a in order to get a^x.

The Logarithm of a Base to a Power

For any base a and any real number x,
$$\log_a a^x = x.$$

(The logarithm, base a, of a to a power is the power.)

EXAMPLE 9   Simplify each of the following.

a) $\log_a a^8$ **b)** $\ln e^{-t}$ **c)** $\log 10^{3k}$

Solution

a) $\log_a a^8 = 8$ 8 is the power to which we raise a in order to get a^8.

b) $\ln e^{-t} = \log_e e^{-t} = -t$ $\ln e^x = x$

c) $\log 10^{3k} = \log_{10} 10^{3k} = 3k$ ▶ Now Try Exercises 65 and 73.

Let $M = \log_a x$. Then $a^M = x$. Substituting $\log_a x$ for M, we obtain $a^{\log_a x} = x$. This also follows from the definition of a logarithm: $\log_a x$ is the power to which a is raised in order to get x.

A Base to a Logarithmic Power

For any base a and any positive real number x,

$$a^{\log_a x} = x.$$

(The number a raised to the power $\log_a x$ is x.)

EXAMPLE 10   Simplify each of the following.

a) $4^{\log_4 k}$ **b)** $e^{\ln 5}$ **c)** $10^{\log 7t}$

Solution

a) $4^{\log_4 k} = k$

b) $e^{\ln 5} = e^{\log_e 5} = 5$

c) $10^{\log 7t} = 10^{\log_{10} 7t} = 7t$ ▶ Now Try Exercises 69 and 71.

A Proof of the Change-of-Base Formula.   We close this section by proving the change-of-base formula and summarizing the properties of logarithms considered thus far in this chapter. In Section 4.3, we used the change-of-base formula,

$$\log_b M = \frac{\log_a M}{\log_a b},$$

to make base conversions in order to find logarithmic values using a calculator. Let $x = \log_b M$. Then

$b^x = M$	Definition of logarithm
$\log_a b^x = \log_a M$	Taking the logarithm on both sides
$x \log_a b = \log_a M$	Using the power rule
$x = \dfrac{\log_a M}{\log_a b},$	Dividing by $\log_a b$

so

$$x = \log_b M = \frac{\log_a M}{\log_a b}.$$

CHANGE-OF-BASE

REVIEW SECTION **4.3**.

Following is a summary of the properties of logarithms.

Summary of the Properties of Logarithms

The Product Rule: $\qquad\qquad\qquad \log_a MN = \log_a M + \log_a N$

The Power Rule: $\qquad\qquad\qquad \log_a M^p = p \log_a M$

The Quotient Rule: $\qquad\qquad \log_a \dfrac{M}{N} = \log_a M - \log_a N$

The Change-of-Base Formula: $\quad \log_b M = \dfrac{\log_a M}{\log_a b}$

Other Properties: $\qquad\qquad\quad \log_a a = 1, \qquad \log_a 1 = 0,$

$\qquad\qquad\qquad\qquad\qquad\quad \log_a a^x = x, \qquad a^{\log_a x} = x$

4.4 EXERCISE SET

Express as a sum of logarithms.

1. $\log_3 (81 \cdot 27)$

2. $\log_2 (8 \cdot 64)$

3. $\log_5 (5 \cdot 125)$

4. $\log_4 (64 \cdot 4)$

5. $\log_t 8Y$

6. $\log 0.2x$

7. $\ln xy$

8. $\ln ab$

Express as a product.

9. $\log_b t^3$

10. $\log_a x^4$

11. $\log y^8$

12. $\ln y^5$

13. $\log_c K^{-6}$

14. $\log_b Q^{-8}$

15. $\ln \sqrt[3]{4}$

16. $\ln \sqrt{a}$

Express as a difference of logarithms.

17. $\log_t \dfrac{M}{8}$

18. $\log_a \dfrac{76}{13}$

19. $\log \dfrac{x}{y}$

20. $\ln \dfrac{a}{b}$

21. $\ln \dfrac{r}{s}$

22. $\log_b \dfrac{3}{w}$

Express in terms of sums and differences of logarithms.

23. $\log_a 6xy^5 z^4$

24. $\log_a x^3 y^2 z$

25. $\log_b \dfrac{p^2 q^5}{m^4 b^9}$

26. $\log_b \dfrac{x^2 y}{b^3}$

27. $\ln \dfrac{2}{3x^3 y}$

28. $\log \dfrac{5a}{4b^2}$

29. $\log \sqrt{r^3 t}$

30. $\ln \sqrt[3]{5x^5}$

31. $\log_a \sqrt{\dfrac{x^6}{p^5 q^8}}$

32. $\log_c \sqrt[3]{\dfrac{y^3 z^2}{x^4}}$

33. $\log_a \sqrt[4]{\dfrac{m^8 n^{12}}{a^3 b^5}}$

34. $\log_a \sqrt{\dfrac{a^6 b^8}{a^2 b^5}}$

Express as a single logarithm and, if possible, simplify.

35. $\log_a 75 + \log_a 2$

36. $\log 0.01 + \log 1000$

37. $\log 10,000 - \log 100$

38. $\ln 54 - \ln 6$

39. $\frac{1}{2} \log n + 3 \log m$

40. $\frac{1}{2} \log a - \log 2$

41. $\frac{1}{2} \log_a x + 4 \log_a y - 3 \log_a x$

42. $\frac{2}{5} \log_a x - \frac{1}{3} \log_a y$

43. $\ln x^2 - 2 \ln \sqrt{x}$

44. $\ln 2x + 3(\ln x - \ln y)$

45. $\ln(x^2 - 4) - \ln(x + 2)$

46. $\log(x^3 - 8) - \log(x - 2)$

47. $\log(x^2 - 5x - 14) - \log(x^2 - 4)$

48. $\log_a \dfrac{a}{\sqrt{x}} - \log_a \sqrt{ax}$

49. $\ln x - 3[\ln(x - 5) + \ln(x + 5)]$

50. $\frac{2}{3}[\ln(x^2 - 9) - \ln(x + 3)] + \ln(x + y)$

51. $\frac{3}{2} \ln 4x^6 - \frac{4}{5} \ln 2y^{10}$

52. $120\left(\ln \sqrt[5]{x^3} + \ln \sqrt[3]{y^2} - \ln \sqrt[4]{16z^5}\right)$

Given that $\log_a 2 \approx 0.301$, $\log_a 7 \approx 0.845$, and $\log_a 11 \approx 1.041$, find each of the following, if possible. Round the answer to the nearest thousandth.

53. $\log_a \frac{2}{11}$ **54.** $\log_a 14$

55. $\log_a 98$ **56.** $\log_a \frac{1}{7}$

57. $\dfrac{\log_a 2}{\log_a 7}$ **58.** $\log_a 9$

Given that $\log_b 2 \approx 0.693$, $\log_b 3 \approx 1.099$, and $\log_b 5 \approx 1.609$, find each of the following, if possible. Round the answer to the nearest thousandth.

59. $\log_b 125$ **60.** $\log_b \frac{5}{3}$

61. $\log_b \frac{1}{6}$ **62.** $\log_b 30$

63. $\log_b \dfrac{3}{b}$ **64.** $\log_b 15b$

Simplify.

65. $\log_p p^3$ **66.** $\log_t t^{2713}$

67. $\log_e e^{|x-4|}$ **68.** $\log_q q^{\sqrt{3}}$

69. $3^{\log_3 4x}$ **70.** $5^{\log_5 (4x-3)}$

71. $10^{\log w}$ **72.** $e^{\ln x^3}$

73. $\ln e^{8t}$ **74.** $\log 10^{-k}$

75. $\log_b \sqrt{b}$ **76.** $\log_b \sqrt{b^3}$

Collaborative Discussion and Writing

77. Given that $f(x) = a^x$ and $g(x) = \log_a x$, find $(f \circ g)(x)$ and $(g \circ f)(x)$. These results are alternative proofs of what properties of logarithms already proven in this section? Explain.

78. Explain the errors, if any, in the following:
$$\log_a ab^3 = (\log_a a)(\log_a b^3) = 3 \log_a b.$$

Skill Maintenance

In each of Exercises 79–88, classify the function as linear, quadratic, cubic, quartic, rational, exponential, or logarithmic.

79. $f(x) = 5 - x^2 + x^4$ **80.** $f(x) = 2^x$

81. $f(x) = -\frac{3}{4}$ **82.** $f(x) = 4^x - 8$

83. $f(x) = -\dfrac{3}{x}$ **84.** $f(x) = \log x + 6$

85. $f(x) = -\frac{1}{3}x^3 - 4x^2 + 6x + 42$

86. $f(x) = \dfrac{x^2 - 1}{x^2 + x - 6}$

87. $f(x) = \frac{1}{2}x + 3$

88. $f(x) = 2x^2 - 6x + 3$

Synthesis

Solve for x.

89. $5^{\log_5 8} = 2x$ **90.** $\ln e^{3x-5} = -8$

Express as a single logarithm and, if possible, simplify.

91. $\log_a(x^2 + xy + y^2) + \log_a(x - y)$

92. $\log_a(a^{10} - b^{10}) - \log_a(a + b)$

Express as a sum or a difference of logarithms.

93. $\log_a \dfrac{x - y}{\sqrt{x^2 - y^2}}$ **94.** $\log_a \sqrt{9 - x^2}$

95. Given that $\log_a x = 2$, $\log_a y = 3$, and $\log_a z = 4$, find
$$\log_a \dfrac{\sqrt[4]{y^2 z^5}}{\sqrt[4]{x^3 z^{-2}}}.$$

Determine whether each of the following is true. Assume that a, x, M, and N are positive.

96. $\log_a M + \log_a N = \log_a(M + N)$

97. $\log_a M - \log_a N = \log_a \dfrac{M}{N}$

98. $\dfrac{\log_a M}{\log_a N} = \log_a M - \log_a N$

99. $\dfrac{\log_a M}{x} = \log_a M^{1/x}$

100. $\log_a x^3 = 3 \log_a x$

101. $\log_a 8x = \log_a x + \log_a 8$

102. $\log_N (MN)^x = x \log_N M + x$

Suppose that $\log_a x = 2$. Find each of the following.

103. $\log_a \left(\dfrac{1}{x} \right)$

104. $\log_{1/a} x$

105. Simplify:

$$\log_{10} 11 \cdot \log_{11} 12 \cdot \log_{12} 13 \cdots$$
$$\log_{12} 13 \cdots \log_{998} 999 \cdot \log_{999} 1000.$$

Write each of the following without using logarithms.

106. $\log_a x + \log_a y - mz = 0$

107. $\ln a - \ln b + xy = 0$

Prove each of the following for any base a and any positive number x.

108. $\log_a \left(\dfrac{1}{x} \right) = -\log_a x = \log_{1/a} x$

109. $\log_a \left(\dfrac{x + \sqrt{x^2 - 5}}{5} \right)$
$$= -\log_a \left(x - \sqrt{x^2 - 5} \right)$$

4.5 Solving Exponential and Logarithmic Equations

◆ Solve exponential equations.
◆ Solve logarithmic equations.

◆ Solving Exponential Equations

Equations with variables in the exponents, such as

$$3^x = 20 \quad \text{and} \quad 2^{5x} = 64,$$

are called **exponential equations.**

Sometimes, as is the case with the equation $2^{5x} = 64$, we can write each side as a power of the same number:

$$2^{5x} = 2^6.$$

We can then set the exponents equal and solve:

$$5x = 6$$
$$x = \tfrac{6}{5}, \text{ or } 1.2.$$

We use the following property.

Base-Exponent Property

For any $a > 0$, $a \neq 1$,

$$a^x = a^y \longleftrightarrow x = y.$$

ONE-TO-ONE FUNCTIONS

REVIEW SECTION **4.1**.

This property follows from the fact that for any $a > 0$, $a \neq 1$, $f(x) = a^x$ is a one-to-one function. If $a^x = a^y$, then $f(x) = f(y)$. Then since f is one-to-one, it follows that $x = y$. Conversely, if $x = y$, it follows that $a^x = a^y$, since we are raising a to the same power.

EXAMPLE 1 Solve: $2^{3x-7} = 32$.

ALGEBRAIC SOLUTION

Note that $32 = 2^5$. Thus we can write each side as a power of the same number:

$$2^{3x-7} = 2^5.$$

Since the bases are the same number, 2, we can use the base–exponent property and set the exponents equal:

$$3x - 7 = 5$$
$$3x = 12$$
$$x = 4.$$

Check:

$$2^{3x-7} = 32$$

$$\begin{array}{c|c} 2^{3(4)-7} \overset{?}{=} 32 & \\ 2^{12-7} & \\ 2^5 & \\ 32 & 32 \quad \text{TRUE} \end{array}$$

The solution is 4.

VISUALIZING THE SOLUTION

When we graph $y = 2^{3x-7}$ and $y = 32$, we find that the first coordinate of the point of intersection of the graphs is 4.

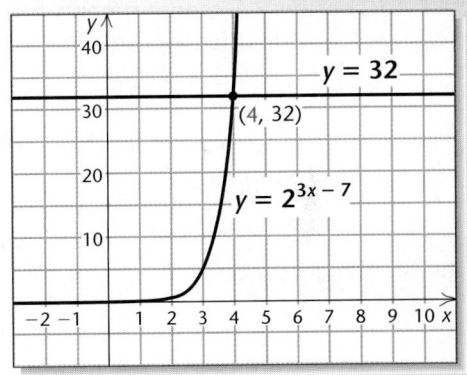

The solution of $2^{3x-7} = 32$ is 4.

▶ Now Try Exercise 7.

Another property that is necessary when solving some exponential and logarithmic equations is as follows.

Property of Logarithmic Equality

For any $M > 0$, $N > 0$, $a > 0$, and $a \neq 1$,

$$\log_a M = \log_a N \longleftrightarrow M = N.$$

This property follows from the fact that for any $a > 0$, $a \neq 1$, $f(x) = \log_a x$ is a one-to-one function. If $\log_a x = \log_a y$, then $f(x) = f(y)$. Then since f is one-to-one, it follows that $x = y$. Conversely, if $x = y$, it follows that $\log_a x = \log_a y$, since we are taking the logarithm of the same number.

When it does not seem possible to write each side as a power of the same base, we can use the property of logarithmic equality and take the logarithm with any base on each side and then use the power rule for logarithms.

EXAMPLE 2 Solve: $3^x = 20$.

ALGEBRAIC SOLUTION

We have

$$3^x = 20$$
$$\log 3^x = \log 20 \qquad \text{Taking the common logarithm on both sides}$$
$$x \log 3 = \log 20 \qquad \text{Using the power rule}$$
$$x = \frac{\log 20}{\log 3}. \qquad \text{Dividing by } \log 3$$

This is an exact answer. We cannot simplify further, but we can approximate using a calculator:

$$x = \frac{\log 20}{\log 3} \approx 2.7268.$$

We can check this by finding $3^{2.7268}$:

$$3^{2.7268} \approx 20.$$

The solution is about 2.7268.

VISUALIZING THE SOLUTION

We graph $y = 3^x$ and $y = 20$. The first coordinate of the point of intersection of the graphs is the value of x for which $3^x = 20$ and is thus the solution of the equation.

The solution is approximately 2.7268.

▶ Now Try Exercise 11.

In Example 2, we took the common logarithm on both sides of the equation. Any base will give the same result. Let's try base 3. We have

$$3^x = 20$$
$$\log_3 3^x = \log_3 20$$
$$x = \log_3 20 \qquad \log_a a^x = x$$
$$x = \frac{\log 20}{\log 3} \qquad \text{Changing from base 3 to base 10}$$
$$\approx 2.7268.$$

Note that we must change the base to do the final calculation.

EXAMPLE 3   Solve: $4^{x+3} = 3^{-x}$.

ALGEBRAIC SOLUTION

We have

$$4^{x+3} = 3^{-x}$$
$$\log 4^{x+3} = \log 3^{-x}$$

Taking the common logarithm on both sides

$$(x + 3) \log 4 = -x \log 3$$

Using the power rule

$$x \log 4 + 3 \log 4 = -x \log 3$$
$$x \log 4 + x \log 3 = -3 \log 4$$

Adding $x \log 3$ and subtracting $3 \log 4$

$$x(\log 4 + \log 3) = -3 \log 4$$
$$x = \frac{-3 \log 4}{\log 4 + \log 3}$$

Dividing by $\log 4 + \log 3$

$$x \approx -1.6737.$$

VISUALIZING THE SOLUTION

We graph $y = 4^{x+3}$ and $y = 3^{-x}$. The first coordinate of the point of intersection of the graphs is the value of x for which $4^{x+3} = 3^{-x}$ and is thus the solution of the equation.

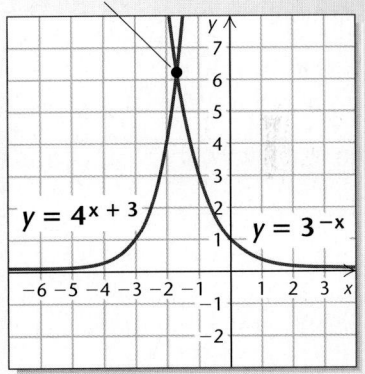

$(-1.6737, 6.2884)$

$y = 4^{x+3}$

$y = 3^{-x}$

The solution is approximately -1.6737.

▷ Now Try Exercise 19.

It will make our work easier if we take the natural logarithm when working with equations that have e as a base.

EXAMPLE 4 Solve: $e^{0.08t} = 2500$.

ALGEBRAIC SOLUTION

We have

$$e^{0.08t} = 2500$$

$$\ln e^{0.08t} = \ln 2500 \qquad \text{Taking the natural logarithm on both sides}$$

$$0.08t = \ln 2500 \qquad \begin{array}{l}\text{Finding the logarithm of a}\\ \text{base to a power: } \log_a a^x = x\end{array}$$

$$t = \frac{\ln 2500}{0.08} \qquad \text{Dividing by 0.08}$$

$$\approx 97.8.$$

The solution is about 97.8.

VISUALIZING THE SOLUTION

The first coordinate of the point of intersection of the graphs of $y = e^{0.08t}$ and $y = 2500$ is about 97.8. This is the solution of the equation.

▶ Now Try Exercise 17.

TECHNOLOGY ·······
 CONNECTION

$y_1 = e^{0.08x}, \quad y_2 = 2500$

We can solve the equations in Examples 1–4 using the Intersect method. In Example 4, for instance, we graph $y = e^{0.08x}$ and $y = 2500$ and use the INTERSECT feature to find the coordinates of the point of intersection.

The first coordinate of the point of intersection is the solution of the equation $e^{0.08x} = 2500$. The solution is about 97.8. We could also write the equation in the form $e^{0.08x} - 2500 = 0$ and use the Zero method.

EXAMPLE 5   Solve: $e^x + e^{-x} - 6 = 0$.

ALGEBRAIC SOLUTION

In this case, we have more than one term with x in the exponent:

$$e^x + e^{-x} - 6 = 0$$

$$e^x + \frac{1}{e^x} - 6 = 0 \qquad \text{Rewriting } e^{-x} \text{ with a positive exponent}$$

$$e^{2x} + 1 - 6e^x = 0. \qquad \text{Multiplying both sides by } e^x$$

This equation is reducible to quadratic with $u = e^x$:

$$u^2 - 6u + 1 = 0.$$

Using the quadratic formula, we have

$$u = \frac{-(-6) \pm \sqrt{(-6)^2 - 4 \cdot 1 \cdot 1}}{2 \cdot 1}$$

$$u = \frac{6 \pm \sqrt{32}}{2} = \frac{6 \pm 4\sqrt{2}}{2}$$

$$u = 3 \pm 2\sqrt{2}$$

$$e^x = 3 \pm 2\sqrt{2}. \qquad \text{Replacing } u \text{ with } e^x$$

We now take the natural logarithm on both sides:

$$\ln e^x = \ln\left(3 \pm 2\sqrt{2}\right)$$

$$x = \ln\left(3 \pm 2\sqrt{2}\right). \qquad \text{Using } \ln e^x = x$$

Approximating each of the solutions, we obtain 1.76 and −1.76.

VISUALIZING THE SOLUTION

The solutions of the equation

$$e^x + e^{-x} - 6 = 0$$

are the zeros of the function

$$f(x) = e^x + e^{-x} - 6.$$

Note that the solutions are also the first coordinates of the x-intercepts of the graph of the function.

$f(x) = e^x + e^{-x} - 6$

The leftmost zero is about −1.76. The zero on the right is about 1.76. The solutions of the equation are approximately −1.76 and 1.76.

▶ Now Try Exercise 23.

TECHNOLOGY ·······
   CONNECTION

$y = e^x + e^{-x} - 6$

Zero
X = −1.762747   Y = 0

We can use the Zero method in Example 5 to solve the equation $e^x + e^{-x} - 6 = 0$. We graph the function $y = e^x + e^{-x} - 6$ and use the ZERO feature to find the zeros.

   The leftmost zero is about −1.76. Using the ZERO feature one more time, we find that the other zero is about 1.76.

◆ Solving Logarithmic Equations

Equations containing variables in logarithmic expressions, such as $\log_2 x = 4$ and $\log x + \log(x + 3) = 1$, are called **logarithmic equations**. To solve logarithmic equations, we first try to obtain a single logarithmic expression on one side and then write an equivalent exponential equation.

EXAMPLE 6   Solve: $\log_3 x = -2$.

ALGEBRAIC SOLUTION

We have

$$\log_3 x = -2$$

$$3^{-2} = x \qquad \text{Converting to an exponential equation}$$

$$\frac{1}{3^2} = x$$

$$\frac{1}{9} = x.$$

Check:

$$\begin{array}{c|c} \log_3 x = -2 & \\ \hline \log_3 \dfrac{1}{9} \ ? \ -2 & \\ \log_3 3^{-2} & \\ \quad -2 & -2 \quad \text{TRUE} \end{array}$$

The solution is $\frac{1}{9}$.

VISUALIZING THE SOLUTION

When we graph $y = \log_3 x$ and $y = -2$, we find that the first coordinate of the point of intersection of the graphs is $\frac{1}{9}$.

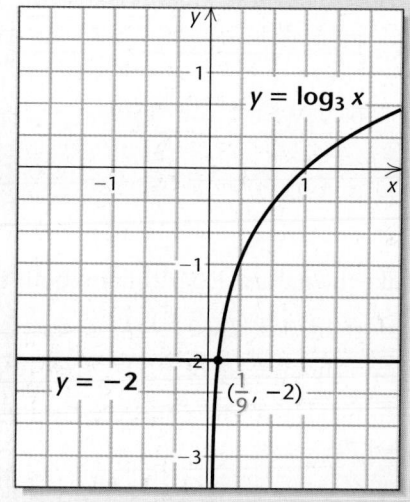

The solution of $\log_3 x = -2$ is $\frac{1}{9}$.

▶ Now Try Exercise 29.

EXAMPLE 7 Solve: $\log x + \log(x + 3) = 1$.

ALGEBRAIC SOLUTION

In this case, we have common logarithms. Writing the base of 10 will help us understand the problem:

$$\log_{10} x + \log_{10}(x + 3) = 1$$

$$\log_{10}[x(x + 3)] = 1 \qquad \text{Using the product rule to obtain a single logarithm}$$

$$x(x + 3) = 10^1 \qquad \text{Writing an equivalent exponential equation}$$

$$x^2 + 3x = 10$$

$$x^2 + 3x - 10 = 0$$

$$(x - 2)(x + 5) = 0 \qquad \text{Factoring}$$

$$x - 2 = 0 \quad or \quad x + 5 = 0$$

$$x = 2 \quad or \qquad x = -5.$$

Check: For 2:

$$\log x + \log(x + 3) = 1$$

$$\overline{\log 2 + \log(2 + 3) \;\text{?}\; 1}$$
$$\log 2 + \log 5 \;\Big|$$
$$\log(2 \cdot 5) \;\Big|$$
$$\log 10 \;\Big|$$
$$1 \;\Big|\; 1 \quad \text{TRUE}$$

For -5:

$$\log x + \log(x + 3) = 1$$

$$\overline{\log(-5) + \log(-5 + 3) \;\text{?}\; 1} \quad \text{FALSE}$$

The number -5 is not a solution because negative numbers do not have real-number logarithms. The solution is 2.

VISUALIZING THE SOLUTION

The solution of the equation

$$\log x + \log(x + 3) = 1$$

is the zero of the function

$$f(x) = \log x + \log(x + 3) - 1.$$

The solution is also the first coordinate of the x-intercept of the graph of the function.

$$f(x) = \log x + \log(x + 3) - 1$$

The solution of the equation is 2. From the graph, we can easily see that there is only one solution.

▶ Now Try Exercise 37.

TECHNOLOGY ·
CONNECTION

In Example 7, we can graph the equations

$$y_1 = \log x + \log (x + 3)$$

and

$$y_2 = 1$$

and use the Intersect method. The first coordinate of the point of intersection is the solution of the equation.

We could also graph the function

$$y = \log x + \log (x + 3) - 1$$

and use the Zero method. The zero of the function is the solution of the equation.

With either method, we see that the solution is 2. Note that the graphical solution gives only the one *true* solution.

$y_1 = \log x + \log (x + 3)$, $y_2 = 1$

$y_1 = \log x + \log (x + 3) - 1$

EXAMPLE 8   Solve: $\log_3 (2x - 1) - \log_3 (x - 4) = 2$.

ALGEBRAIC SOLUTION

We have

$$\log_3 (2x - 1) - \log_3 (x - 4) = 2$$

$$\log_3 \frac{2x - 1}{x - 4} = 2 \qquad \text{Using the quotient rule}$$

$$\frac{2x - 1}{x - 4} = 3^2 \qquad \text{Writing an equivalent exponential equation}$$

$$\frac{2x - 1}{x - 4} = 9$$

$$(x - 4) \cdot \frac{2x - 1}{x - 4} = 9(x - 4) \qquad \text{Multiplying by the LCD, } x - 4$$

$$2x - 1 = 9x - 36$$

$$35 = 7x$$

$$5 = x.$$

Check:

$$\log_3 (2x - 1) - \log_3 (x - 4) = 2$$

$$\log_3 (2 \cdot 5 - 1) - \log_3 (5 - 4) \;?\; 2$$
$$\log_3 9 - \log_3 1$$
$$2 - 0$$
$$2 \;|\; 2 \quad \text{TRUE}$$

The solution is 5.

VISUALIZING THE SOLUTION

We see that the first coordinate of the point of intersection of the graphs of

$$y = \log_3 (2x - 1) - \log_3 (x - 4)$$

and

$$y = 2$$

is 5.

$y = \log_3 (2x - 1) - \log_3 (x - 4)$

The solution is 5.

▶ Now Try Exercise 43.

EXAMPLE 9   Solve: $\ln(4x + 6) - \ln(x + 5) = \ln x$.

ALGEBRAIC SOLUTION

We have

$\ln(4x + 6) - \ln(x + 5) = \ln x$

$\quad\quad \ln \dfrac{4x + 6}{x + 5} = \ln x$ Using the quotient rule

$\quad\quad\quad \dfrac{4x + 6}{x + 5} = x$ Using the property of logarithmic equality

$(x + 5) \cdot \dfrac{4x + 6}{x + 5} = x(x + 5)$ Multiplying by $x + 5$

$\quad\quad\quad 4x + 6 = x^2 + 5x$

$\quad\quad\quad\quad\quad 0 = x^2 + x - 6$

$\quad\quad\quad\quad\quad 0 = (x + 3)(x - 2)$ Factoring

$x + 3 = 0 \quad or \quad x - 2 = 0$

$\quad x = -3 \quad or \quad\quad x = 2.$

The number -3 is not a solution because negative numbers do not have real-number logarithms. The value 2 checks and is the solution.

VISUALIZING THE SOLUTION

The solution of the equation

$\ln(4x + 6) - \ln(x + 5) = \ln x$

is the zero of the function

$f(x) = \ln(4x + 6) - \ln(x + 5)$
$\quad\quad\quad - \ln x.$

The solution is also the first coordinate of the x-intercept of the graph of the function.

$f(x) = \ln(4x + 6) - \ln(x + 5) - \ln x$

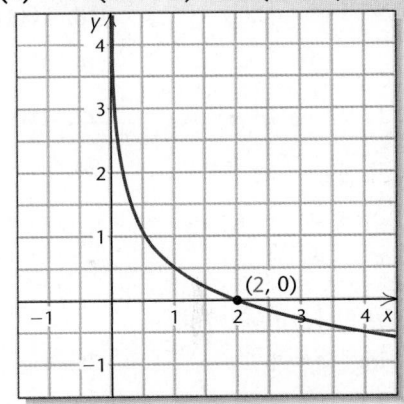

The solution of the equation is 2. From the graph, we can easily see that there is only one solution.

▶ Now Try Exercise 39.

4.5 EXERCISE SET

Solve the exponential equation.

1. $3^x = 81$

2. $2^x = 32$

3. $2^{2x} = 8$

4. $3^{7x} = 27$

5. $2^x = 33$

6. $2^x = 40$

7. $5^{4x-7} = 125$

8. $4^{3x-5} = 16$

9. $27 = 3^{5x} \cdot 9^{x^2}$

10. $3^{x^2+4x} = \frac{1}{27}$

11. $84^x = 70$

12. $28^x = 10^{-3x}$

13. $e^{-c} = 5^{2c}$

14. $15^x = 30$

15. $e^t = 1000$

16. $e^{-t} = 0.04$

17. $e^{-0.03t} = 0.08$

18. $1000e^{0.09t} = 5000$

19. $3^x = 2^{x-1}$

20. $5^{x+2} = 4^{1-x}$

21. $(3.9)^x = 48$

22. $250 - (1.87)^x = 0$

23. $e^x + e^{-x} = 5$

24. $e^x - 6e^{-x} = 1$

25. $\dfrac{e^x + e^{-x}}{e^x - e^{-x}} = 3$

26. $\dfrac{5^x - 5^{-x}}{5^x + 5^{-x}} = 8$

Solve the logarithmic equation.

27. $\log_5 x = 4$

28. $\log_2 x = -3$

29. $\log x = -4$

30. $\log x = 1$

31. $\log_{64} \frac{1}{4} = x$

32. $\log_{125} \frac{1}{25} = x$

33. $\ln x = 1$

34. $\ln x = -2$

35. $\log_2 (10 + 3x) = 5$

36. $\log_5 (8 - 7x) = 3$

37. $\log x + \log (x - 9) = 1$

38. $\log_2 (x + 1) + \log_2 (x - 1) = 3$

39. $\log_2 (x + 20) - \log_2 (x + 2) = \log_2 x$

40. $\log_3 (x + 14) - \log_3 (x + 6) = \log_3 x$

41. $\log (x + 8) - \log (x + 1) = \log 6$

42. $\log (x + 5) - \log (x - 3) = \log 2$

43. $\log_8 (x + 1) - \log_8 x = 2$

44. $\log x - \log (x + 3) = -1$

45. $\log x + \log (x + 4) = \log 12$

46. $\ln x - \ln (x - 4) = \ln 3$

47. $\log_4 (x + 3) + \log_4 (x - 3) = 2$

48. $\ln (x + 1) - \ln x = \ln 4$

49. $\log (2x + 1) - \log (x - 2) = 1$

50. $\log_5 (x + 4) + \log_5 (x - 4) = 2$

51. $\ln (x + 8) + \ln (x - 1) = 2 \ln x$

52. $\log_3 x + \log_3 (x + 1) = \log_3 2 + \log_3 (x + 3)$

Solve.

53. $\log_6 x = 1 - \log_6 (x - 5)$

54. $2^{x^2-9x} = \frac{1}{256}$

55. $9^{x-1} = 100(3^x)$

56. $2 \ln x - \ln 5 = \ln (x + 10)$

57. $e^x - 2 = -e^{-x}$

58. $2 \log 50 = 3 \log 25 + \log (x - 2)$

Technology Connection

Find approximate solution(s) of the equation.

59. $e^{7.2x} = 14.009$

60. $0.082e^{0.05x} = 0.034$

61. $xe^{3x} - 1 = 3$

62. $5e^{5x} + 10 = 3x + 40$

63. $4 \ln (x + 3.4) = 2.5$

64. $\ln x^2 = -x^2$

65. $\log_8 x + \log_8 (x + 2) = 2$

66. $\log_3 x + 7 = 4 - \log_5 x$

67. $\log_5 (x + 7) - \log_5 (2x - 3) = 1$

Approximate the point(s) of intersection of the pair of equations.

68. $y = \ln 3x, \ y = 3x - 8$

69. $2.3x + 3.8y = 12.4$, $y = 1.1 \ln(x - 2.05)$

70. $y = 2.3 \ln(x + 10.7)$, $y = 10e^{-0.07x^2}$

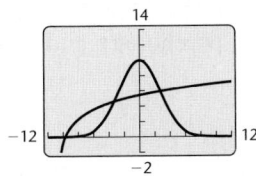

71. $y = 2.3 \ln(x + 10.7)$, $y = 10e^{-0.007x^2}$

Collaborative Discussion and Writing

72. In Example 4, we took the natural logarithm on both sides of the equation. What would have happened had we taken the common logarithm? Explain which approach seems better to you and why.

73. Explain how Exercises 33 and 34 could be solved using the graph of $f(x) = \ln x$.

Skill Maintenance

In Exercises 74–77:

a) *Find the vertex.*
b) *Find the axis of symmetry.*
c) *Determine whether there is a maximum or minimum value and find that value.*

74. $f(x) = -x^2 + 6x - 8$

75. $g(x) = x^2 - 6$

76. $H(x) = 3x^2 - 12x + 16$

77. $G(x) = -2x^2 - 4x - 7$

Synthesis

Solve using any method.

78. $\ln(\ln x) = 2$

79. $\ln(\log x) = 0$

80. $\ln \sqrt[4]{x} = \sqrt{\ln x}$

81. $\sqrt{\ln x} = \ln \sqrt{x}$

82. $\log_3(\log_4 x) = 0$

83. $(\log_3 x)^2 - \log_3 x^2 = 3$

84. $(\log x)^2 - \log x^2 = 3$

85. $\ln x^2 = (\ln x)^2$

86. $e^{2x} - 9 \cdot e^x + 14 = 0$

87. $5^{2x} - 3 \cdot 5^x + 2 = 0$

88. $x\left(\ln \frac{1}{6}\right) = \ln 6$

89. $\log_3 |x| = 2$

90. $x^{\log x} = \dfrac{x^3}{100}$

91. $\ln x^{\ln x} = 4$

92. $\dfrac{(e^{3x+1})^2}{e^4} = e^{10x}$

93. $\dfrac{\sqrt{(e^{2x} \cdot e^{-5x})^{-4}}}{e^x \div e^{-x}} = e^7$

94. $e^x < \dfrac{4}{5}$

95. $|\log_5 x| + 3 \log_5 |x| = 4$

96. $|2^{x^2} - 8| = 3$

97. Given that $a = \log_8 225$ and $b = \log_2 15$, express a as a function of b.

98. Given that $a = (\log_{125} 5)^{\log_5 125}$, find the value of $\log_3 a$.

99. Given that

$$\log_2[\log_3(\log_4 x)] = \log_3[\log_2(\log_4 y)]$$
$$= \log_4[\log_3(\log_2 z)]$$
$$= 0,$$

find $x + y + z$.

100. Given that $f(x) = e^x - e^{-x}$, find $f^{-1}(x)$ if it exists.

4.6
Applications and Models: Growth and Decay; Compound Interest

✦ Solve applied problems involving exponential growth and decay.

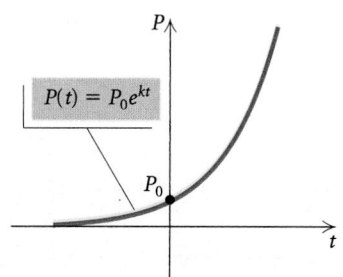

$$P(t) = P_0 e^{kt}$$

Exponential and logarithmic functions with base e are rich in applications to many fields such as business, science, psychology, and sociology.

✦ Population Growth

The function

$$P(t) = P_0 e^{kt}, \quad k > 0$$

is a model of many kinds of population growth, whether it be a population of people, bacteria, cell phones, or money. In this function, P_0 is the population at time 0, P is the population after time t, and k is called the **exponential growth rate.** The graph of such an equation is shown at left.

EXAMPLE 1   *Population Growth of China.*   In 2005, the population of China was about 1.306 billion, and the exponential growth rate was 0.6% per year (*Source: Time Almanac 2006*).

a) Find the exponential growth function.

b) Estimate the population in 2008.

c) After how long will the population be double what it was in 2005?

Solution

a) At $t = 0$ (2005), the population was 1.306 billion. We substitute 1.306 for P_0 and 0.6%, or 0.006, for k to obtain the exponential growth function

$$P(t) = 1.306 e^{0.006t},$$

where t is the number of years after 2005 and $P(t)$ is in billions.

b) In 2008, $t = 3$; that is, 3 yr have passed since 2005. To find the population in 2008, we substitute 3 for t:

$$P(3) = 1.306 e^{0.006(3)} = 1.306 e^{0.018} \approx 1.33.$$

The population will be about 1.33 billion, or 1,330,000,000, in 2008.

c) We are looking for the time T for which $P(T) = 2 \cdot 1.306$, or 2.612. The number T is called the **doubling time.** To find T, we solve the equation

$$2.612 = 1.306 e^{0.006T}.$$

**TECHNOLOGY ·················
CONNECTION**

We can find function values using a graphing calculator. Below, we find $P(3)$ from Example 1(b) with the VALUE feature from the CALC menu. We see that $P(3) \approx 1.33$.

$y = 1.306 e^{0.006x}$

X=3   Y=1.3297208

ALGEBRAIC SOLUTION

We have

$$2.612 = 1.306e^{0.006T}$$ Substituting 2.612 for $P(T)$

$$2 = e^{0.006T}$$ Dividing by 1.306

$$\ln 2 = \ln e^{0.006T}$$ Taking the natural logarithm on both sides

$$\ln 2 = 0.006T$$ $\ln e^x = x$

$$\frac{\ln 2}{0.006} = T$$ Dividing by 0.006

$$116 \approx T.$$

The population of China will be double what it was in 2005 about 116 yr after 2005.

VISUALIZING THE SOLUTION

From the graph of $y = 2.612$ and $y = 1.306e^{0.006T}$, we see that the first coordinate of the point of intersection of the graphs is about 116.

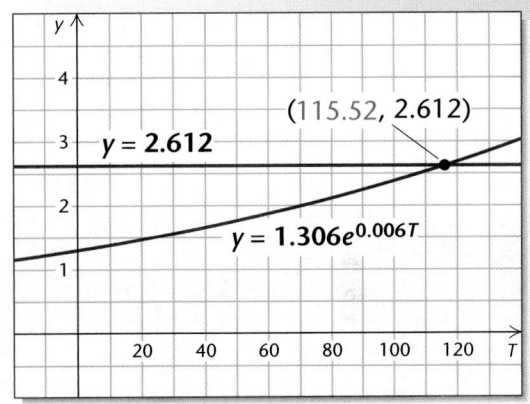

The solution of the equation is approximately 116.

▷ Now Try Exercise 1.

TECHNOLOGY ·······
CONNECTION

$y_1 = 1306e^{0.006x}$, $y_2 = 2612$

Using the Intersect method in Example 1(c), we graph the equations

$$y_1 = 1306e^{0.006x} \quad \text{and} \quad y_2 = 2612$$

and find the first coordinate of their point of intersection. It is about 116, so the population of China will be double that of 2005 about 116 yr after 2005.

◆ Interest Compounded Continuously

Now we explore the mathematics behind the concept of **interest compounded continuously.** Suppose that an amount P_0 is invested in a savings account at interest rate k *compounded continuously.* The amount $P(t)$ in the account after t years is given by the exponential function

$$P(t) = P_0 e^{kt}.$$

EXAMPLE 2   *Interest Compounded Continuously.*   Suppose that $2000 is invested at interest rate k, compounded continuously, and grows to $2983.65 in 5 yr.

a) What is the interest rate?

b) Find the exponential growth function.

c) What will the balance be after 10 yr?

d) After how long will the $2000 have doubled?

Solution

a) At $t = 0$, $P(0) = P_0 = \$2000$. Thus the exponential growth function is of the form

$$P(t) = 2000e^{kt}.$$

We know that $P(5) = \$2983.65$. We substitute and solve for k:

$$2983.65 = 2000e^{k(5)} \qquad \text{Substituting 2983.65 for } P(t) \text{ and 5 for } t$$

$$2983.65 = 2000e^{5k}$$

$$\frac{2983.65}{2000} = e^{5k} \qquad \text{Dividing by 2000}$$

$$\ln \frac{2983.65}{2000} = \ln e^{5k} \qquad \text{Taking the natural logarithm}$$

$$\ln \frac{2983.65}{2000} = 5k \qquad \text{Using } \ln e^x = x$$

$$\frac{\ln \dfrac{2983.65}{2000}}{5} = k \qquad \text{Dividing by 5}$$

$$0.08 \approx k.$$

The interest rate is about 0.08, or 8%.

b) Substituting 0.08 for k in the function $P(t) = 2000e^{kt}$, we see that the exponential growth function is

$$P(t) = 2000e^{0.08t}.$$

c) The balance after 10 yr is

$$P(10) = 2000e^{0.08(10)}$$

$$= 2000e^{0.8}$$

$$\approx \$4451.08.$$

d) To find the doubling time T, we set $P(T) = 2 \cdot P_0 = 2 \cdot \$2000 = \$4000$ and solve for T.

ALGEBRAIC SOLUTION

We have

$$4000 = 2000e^{0.08T}$$

$2 = e^{0.08T}$ Dividing by 2000

$\ln 2 = \ln e^{0.08T}$ Taking the natural logarithm

$\ln 2 = 0.08T$ $\ln e^x = x$

$\dfrac{\ln 2}{0.08} = T$ Dividing by 0.08

$8.7 \approx T.$

Thus the original investment of $2000 will double in about 8.7 yr.

VISUALIZING THE SOLUTION

The solution of the equation

$$4000 = 2000e^{0.08T},$$

or

$$2000e^{0.08T} - 4000 = 0,$$

is the zero of the function

$$y = 2000e^{0.08T} - 4000.$$

Let's observe the zero from the graph shown here.

The zero is about 8.7. Thus the solution of the equation is approximately 8.7.

▶ **Now Try Exercise 7.**

TECHNOLOGY ·
CONNECTION

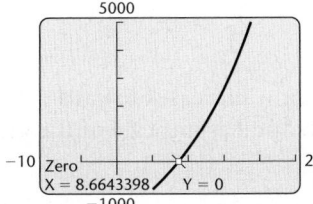

The money in Example 2 will have doubled when $P(t) = 2 \cdot P_0 = 4000$, or when $2000e^{0.08t} = 4000$. We use the Zero method. We graph the equation

$$y = 2000e^{0.08x} - 4000$$

and find the zero of the function. The zero of the function is the solution of the equation. The zero is about 8.7, so the original investment of $2000 will double in about 8.7 yr.

We can find a general expression relating the growth rate k and the doubling time T by solving the following equation:

$$2P_0 = P_0 e^{kT} \qquad \text{Substituting } 2P_0 \text{ for } P \text{ and } T \text{ for } t$$
$$2 = e^{kT} \qquad \text{Dividing by } P_0$$
$$\ln 2 = \ln e^{kT} \qquad \text{Taking the natural logarithm}$$
$$\ln 2 = kT \qquad \text{Using } \ln e^x = x$$
$$\frac{\ln 2}{k} = T.$$

Growth Rate and Doubling Time

The **growth rate k** and the **doubling time T** are related by

$$kT = \ln 2, \quad \text{or} \quad k = \frac{\ln 2}{T}, \quad \text{or} \quad T = \frac{\ln 2}{k}.$$

Note that the relationship between k and T does not depend on P_0.

EXAMPLE 3   *World Population Growth.*   The population of the world is now doubling every 57.8 yr. What is the exponential growth rate?

Solution   We have

$$k = \frac{\ln 2}{T} = \frac{\ln 2}{57.8} \approx 1.2\%.$$

The growth rate of the world population is about 1.2% per year.

 ▶ Now Try Exercise 3(e).

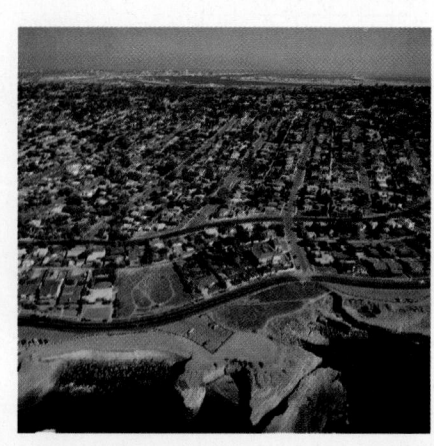

✦ Models of Limited Growth

The model $P(t) = P_0 e^{kt}$, $k > 0$, has many applications involving unlimited population growth. However, in some populations, there can be factors that prevent a population from exceeding some limiting value—perhaps a limitation on food, living space, or other natural resources. One model of such growth is

$$P(t) = \frac{a}{1 + be^{-kt}}.$$

This is called a **logistic function.** This function increases toward a *limiting value a* as $t \to \infty$. Thus, $y = a$ is the horizontal asymptote of the graph of $P(t)$.

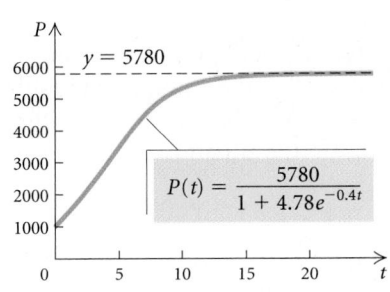

EXAMPLE 4 *Limited Population Growth.* A ship carrying 1000 passengers has the misfortune to be shipwrecked on a small island from which the passengers are never rescued. The natural resources of the island limit the population to 5780. The population gets closer and closer to this limiting value, but never reaches it. The population of the island after time t, in years, is given by the logistic function

$$P(t) = \frac{5780}{1 + 4.78e^{-0.4t}}.$$

The graph of $P(t)$ is the curve shown at left. Note that this function increases toward a limiting value of 5780. The graph has $y = 5780$ as a horizontal asymptote. Find the population after 0, 1, 2, 5, 10, and 20 yr.

Solution Using a calculator, we compute the function values. We find that

$$P(0) = 1000, \qquad P(5) \approx 3509.6,$$
$$P(1) \approx 1374.8, \qquad P(10) \approx 5314.7,$$
$$P(2) \approx 1836.2, \qquad P(20) \approx 5770.7.$$

Thus the population will be about 1000 after 0 yr, 1375 after 1 yr, 1836 after 2 yr, 3510 after 5 yr, 5315 after 10 yr, and 5771 after 20 yr.

▶ Now Try Exercise 15.

Another model of limited growth is provided by the function

$$P(t) = L(1 - e^{-kt}), \quad k > 0,$$

which is shown graphed below. This function also increases toward a limiting value L, as $x \to \infty$, so $y = L$ is the horizontal asymptote of the graph of $P(t)$.

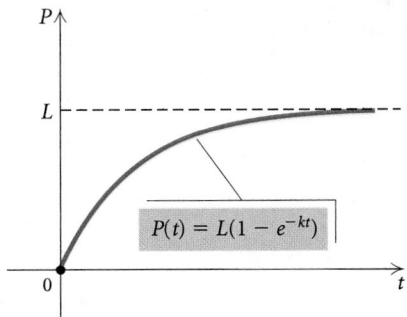

How can scientists determine that an animal bone has lost 30% of its carbon-14? The assumption is that the percentage of carbon-14 in the atmosphere is the same as that in living plants and animals. When a plant or an animal dies, the amount of carbon-14 that it contains decays exponentially. A scientist can burn an animal bone and use a Geiger counter to determine the percentage of the smoke that is carbon-14. The amount by which this varies from the percentage in the atmosphere tells how much carbon-14 has been lost.

The process of carbon-14 dating was developed by the American chemist Willard E. Libby in 1952. It is known that the radioactivity in a living plant is 16 disintegrations per gram per minute. Since the half-life of carbon-14 is 5750 years, an object with an activity of 8 disintegrations per gram per minute is 5750 years old, one with an activity of 4 disintegrations per gram per minute is 11,500 years old, and so on. Carbon-14 dating can be used to measure the age of objects up to 40,000 years old. Beyond such an age, it is too difficult to measure the radioactivity and some other method would have to be used.

Carbon-14 was used to find the age of the Dead Sea Scrolls. It was also used to refute the authenticity of the Shroud of Turin, presumed to have covered the body of Christ.

◆ Exponential Decay

The function

$$P(t) = P_0 e^{-kt}, \quad k > 0$$

is an effective model of the decline, or decay, of a population. An example is the decay of a radioactive substance. In this case, P_0 is the amount of the substance at time $t = 0$, and $P(t)$ is the amount of the substance left after time t, where k is a positive constant that depends on the situation. The constant k is called the **decay rate.**

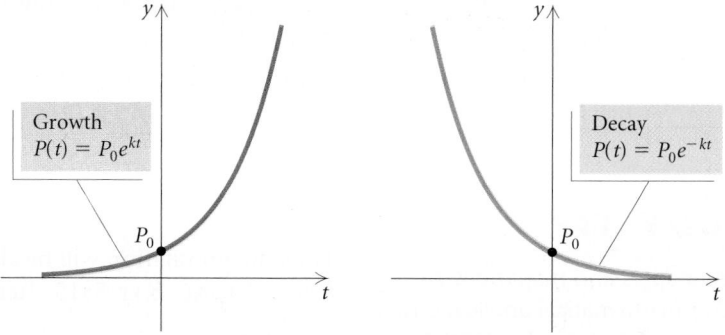

The **half-life** of bismuth is 5 days. This means that half of an amount of bismuth will cease to be radioactive in 5 days. The effect of half-life T for nonnegative inputs is shown in the graph below. The exponential function gets close to 0, but never reaches 0, as t gets very large. Thus, according to an exponential decay model, a radioactive substance never completely decays.

Radioactive decay curve

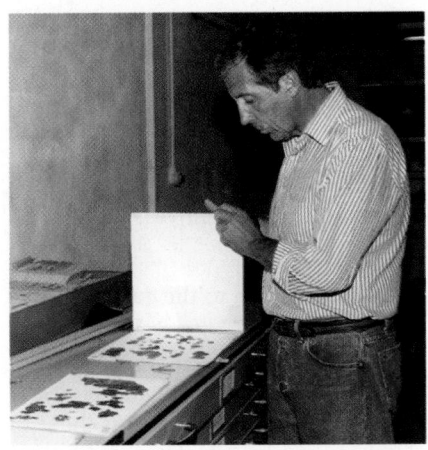

In 1947, a Bedouin youth looking for a stray goat climbed into a cave at Kirbet Qumran on the shores of the Dead Sea near Jericho and came upon earthenware jars containing an incalculable treasure of ancient manuscripts. Shown here are fragments of those so-called Dead Sea Scrolls, a portion of some 600 or so texts found so far and which concern the Jewish books of the Bible. Officials date them before 70 A.D., making them the oldest Biblical manuscripts by 1000 years.

EXAMPLE 5 *Carbon Dating.* The radioactive element carbon-14 has a half-life of 5750 yr. The percentage of carbon-14 present in the remains of organic matter can be used to determine the age of that organic matter. Archaeologists discovered that the linen wrapping from one of the Dead Sea Scrolls had lost 22.3% of its carbon-14 at the time it was found. How old was the linen wrapping?

Solution   We first find k. When $t = 5750$ (the half-life), $P(t)$ will be half of P_0. We substitute $\frac{1}{2}P_0$ for $P(t)$ and 5750 for t and solve for k. We have

$$P(t) = P_0 e^{-kt}$$
$$\tfrac{1}{2} P_0 = P_0 e^{-k(5750)}$$
$$\tfrac{1}{2} = e^{-5750k} \qquad \text{Dividing by } P_0$$
$$\ln \tfrac{1}{2} = \ln e^{-5750k} \qquad \text{Taking the natural logarithm on both sides}$$
$$\ln 0.5 = -5750k. \qquad \tfrac{1}{2} = 0.5; \ln e^x = x$$

Then

$$k = \frac{\ln 0.5}{-5750} \approx 0.00012.$$

Now we have the function

$$P(t) = P_0 e^{-0.00012t}.$$

(This function can be used for any subsequent carbon-dating problem.) If the linen wrapping has lost 22.3% of its carbon-14 from an initial amount P_0, then 77.7%P_0 is the amount present. To find the age t of the wrapping, we solve the following equation for t:

$$77.7\% P_0 = P_0 e^{-0.00012t} \qquad \text{Substituting } 77.7\% P_0 \text{ for } P$$
$$0.777 = e^{-0.00012t} \qquad \text{Dividing by } P_0 \text{ and writing } 77.7\% \text{ as } 0.777$$
$$\ln 0.777 = \ln e^{-0.00012t} \qquad \text{Taking the natural logarithm on both sides}$$
$$\ln 0.777 = -0.00012t \qquad \ln e^x = x$$
$$\frac{\ln 0.777}{-0.00012} = t \qquad \text{Dividing by } -0.00012$$
$$2103 \approx t.$$

Thus the linen wrapping on the Dead Sea Scrolls was about 2103 yr old when it was found.
▶ Now Try Exercise 9.

TECHNOLOGY
CONNECTION

Year, x	Consumer Credit (in billions)
1975, 0	$ 168.7
1980, 5	302.1
1985, 10	526.3
1990, 15	751.9
1995, 20	1122.8
1999, 24	1426.2
2000, 25	1566.5
2001, 26	1702.8
2002, 27	1762.3
2003, 28	2025.5
2004, 29	2140.4

Source: Federal Reserve Board

```
ExpReg
y=a*b^x
a=197.1583851
b=1.087040726
r2=0.990870498
r=0.9954247827
```

We now expand the regression procedure to include modeling data with an exponential function.

Consumer Credit. Total consumer short- and intermediate-term credit excluding real estate credit has increased dramatically in recent years, as shown in the table at left.

a) Use a graphing calculator to fit an exponential function to the data.

b) Estimate the total consumer credit in 2008.

Solution

a) We will fit an equation of the type $y = a \cdot b^x$ to the data, where x is the number of years since 1975. Entering the data into the calculator and carrying out the regression procedure, we find that the equation is

$$y = 197.1583851(1.087040726)^x.$$

The correlation ($r^2 = 0.990870498$) is very close to 1. This gives us an indication that the exponential function fits the data well.

b) We evaluate the function found in part (a) for $x = 33$ ($2008 - 1975 = 33$) and estimate that the total consumer credit in 2008 will be about $3097 billion, or $3,097,000,000,000.

4.6 EXERCISE SET

1. *World Population Growth.* In 2005, the world population was 6.4 billion. The exponential growth rate was 1.2% per year.

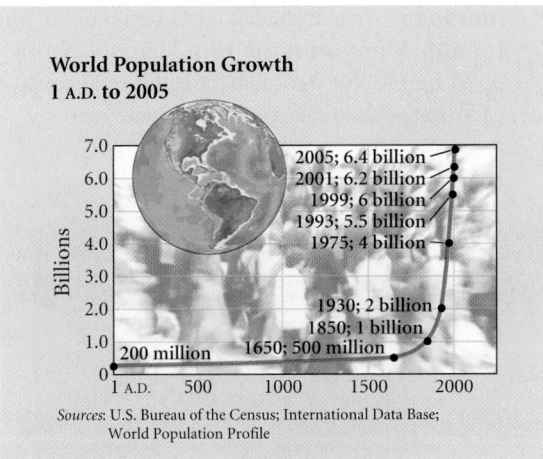

World Population Growth
1 A.D. to 2005

Sources: U.S. Bureau of the Census; International Data Base; World Population Profile

a) Find the exponential growth function.
b) Estimate the population of the world in 2008 and in 2010.
c) When will the world population be 8 billion?
d) Find the doubling time.

2. *Population Growth of Rabbits.* Under ideal conditions, a population of rabbits has an exponential growth rate of 11.7% per day. Consider an initial population of 100 rabbits.

a) Find the exponential growth function.
b) What will the population be after 7 days? after 2 weeks?
c) Find the doubling time.

3. *Population Growth.* Complete the following table.

Population	Growth Rate, k	Doubling Time, T
a) Rwanda	2.4% per year	
b) Brazil		63 yr
c) India	1.4% per year	

(continued)

Population	Growth Rate, k	Doubling Time, T
d) Finland	0.2% per year	
e) Egypt		38.5 yr
f) Philippines		36.5 yr
g) United States	0.9% per year	
h) Japan		69.3 yr
i) Ireland	1.2% per year	
j) Kenya	2.6% per year	

4. *DVD Videos.* The total number of DVD videos produced and shipped in 1998 was 0.5 million. In 2004, the total number of units reached 29.01 million.

DVD Videos

Source: Recording Industry Association of America

Assuming the exponential model applies:
a) Find the value of k and write the function.
b) Estimate the number of DVD videos produced and shipped in 2005, in 2008, and in 2011.

5. *Population Growth of Israel.* The population of Israel has a growth rate of 1.3% per year. In 2005, the population was 6,276,883. The land area of Israel is 24,839,654,400 square yards. (*Source:*

Statistical Abstract of the United States) Assuming this growth rate continues and is exponential, after how long will there be one person for every square yard of land?

6. *Value of Manhattan Island.*   In 1626, Peter Minuit of the Dutch West India Company purchased Manhattan Island from Native Americans for $24. Assuming an exponential rate of inflation of 6% per year, how much will Manhattan be worth in 2010?

7. *Interest Compounded Continuously.*   Suppose that $10,000 is invested at an interest rate of 5.4% per year, compounded continuously.

  a) Find the exponential function that describes the amount in the account after time t, in years.
  b) What is the balance after 1 yr? 2 yr? 5 yr? 10 yr?
  c) What is the doubling time?

8. *Interest Compounded Continuously.*   Complete the following table.

Initial Investment at $t = 0$, P_0	Interest Rate, k	Doubling Time, T	Amount After 5 yr
a) $35,000	6.2%		
b) $5000			$ 7,130.90
c)	8.4%		$11,414.71
d)		11 yr	$17,539.32

9. *Carbon Dating.*   A mummy discovered in the pyramid Khufu in Egypt has lost 46% of its carbon-14. Determine its age.

10. *Tomb in the Valley of the Kings.*   In February 2006, in the Valley of the Kings in Egypt, a team of archaeologists uncovered the first tomb since King Tut's tomb was found in 1922. The tomb contained five wooden sarcophagi that contained mummies. The archaeologists believe that the mummies are from the 18th Dynasty, about 3300 to 3500 yr ago. Determine the amount of carbon-14 that the mummies have lost.

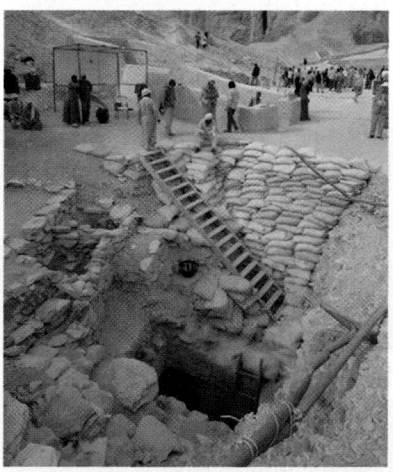

11. *Radioactive Decay.*   Complete the following table.

Radioactive Substance	Decay Rate, k	Half-life, T
a) Polonium		3 min
b) Lead		22 yr
c) Iodine-131	9.6% per day	
d) Krypton-85	6.3% per year	
e) Strontium-90		25 yr
f) Uranium-238		4560 yr
g) Plutonium		23,105 yr

12. *Number of Farms.* The number N of farms in the United States has declined continually since 1950. In 1950, there were 5,650,000 farms, and in 2004 that number had decreased to 2,110,000 (*Sources*: U.S. Department of Agriculture; National Agricultural Statistics Service).

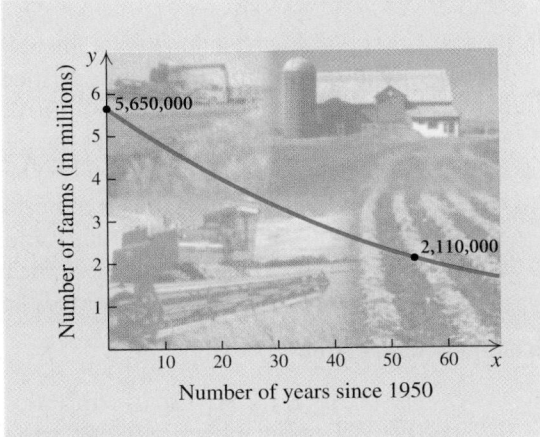

Assuming the number of farms decreased according to the exponential model:

a) Find the value of k, and write an exponential function that describes the number of farms after time t, in years, where t is the number of years since 1950.

b) Estimate the number of farms in 2006 and in 2009.

c) At this decay rate, when will only 1,000,000 farms remain?

13. *Students per Computer.* The number of students per computer in U.S. public schools has decreased continually since the 1983–1984 school year, as shown in the graph below. In the 1983–1984 school year ($t = 0$), the number of students per computer in U.S. public schools was 125.0. By the 2003–2004 school year ($t = 20$), this number had decreased to only 4.8 students per computer.

a) Find the value of k, and write an exponential function that describes the number of students per computer after time t, in years, where t is the number of years since 1983.

b) Estimate the number of students per computer in the 1995–1996 school year and in the 2007–2008 school year.

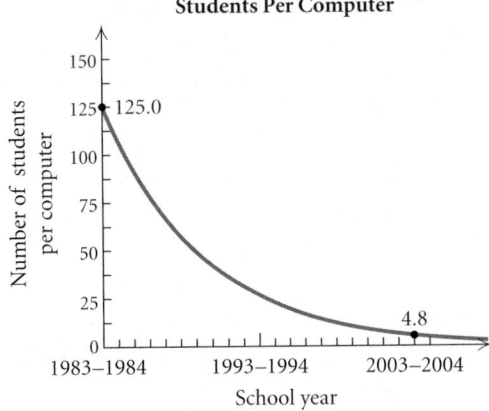

Students Per Computer

Source: Quality Education Data, Inc., Denver CO

c) At this decay rate, in what year will there be a computer for each student?

14. *1957 Studebaker Golden Hawk.* The 1957 Studebaker Golden Hawk has become a car of interest to those investing in classic cars. In 1967, a 10-year-old Golden Hawk sold for only $800, and in 2006, this car, in top condition, was worth about $27,000. (*Source*: *1957 Studebaker Golden Hawk*, George Mattar, *Hemmings Motor News*, June 2006, p. 36)

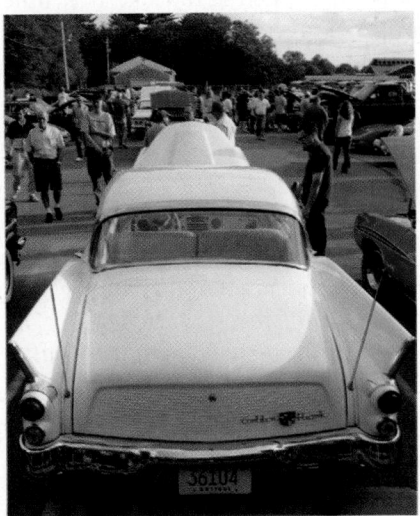

Assuming the value V_0 of the car has grown exponentially:

a) Find the value of k and determine the exponential growth function, assuming $V_0 = 800$ and t is the number of years since 1967.

b) Estimate the value of the car in 2008.
c) What is the doubling time for the value of the car?
d) After how long will the value of the car be $40,000, assuming there is no change in the growth rate?

15. *Spread of an Epidemic.* In a town whose population is 3500, a disease creates an epidemic. The number of people N infected t days after the disease has begun is given by the function

$$N(t) = \frac{3500}{1 + 19.9e^{-0.6t}}.$$

a) How many are initially infected with the disease ($t = 0$)?
b) Find the number infected after 2 days, 5 days, 8 days, 12 days, and 16 days.
c) Using this model, can you say whether all 3500 people will ever be infected? Explain.

16. *Limited Population Growth in a Lake.* A lake is stocked with 400 fish of a new variety. The size of the lake, the availability of food, and the number of other fish restrict the growth of that type of fish in the lake to a *limiting value* of 2500. The population of fish in the lake after time t, in months, is given by the function

$$P(t) = \frac{2500}{1 + 5.25e^{-0.32t}}.$$

Find the population after 0, 1, 5, 10, 15, and 20 months.

Newton's Law of Cooling. *Suppose that a body with temperature T_1 is placed in surroundings with temperature T_0 different from that of T_1. The body will either cool or warm to temperature $T(t)$ after time t, in minutes, where*

$$T(t) = T_0 + (T_1 - T_0)e^{-kt}.$$

Use this law in Exercises 17–20.

17. A cup of coffee with temperature 105°F is placed in a freezer with temperature 0°F. After 5 min, the temperature of the coffee is 70°F. What will its temperature be after 10 min?

18. A dish of lasagna baked at 375°F is taken out of the oven at 11:15 A.M. into a kitchen that is 72°F. After 3 min, the temperature of the lasagna is 365°F. What will the temperature of the lasagna be at 11:30 A.M.?

19. A chilled jello salad that has a temperature of 43°F is taken from the refrigerator and placed on the dining room table in a room that is 68°F. After 12 min, the temperature of the salad is 55°F. What will the temperature of the salad be after 20 min?

20. *When Was the Murder Committed?* The police discover the body of a murder victim. Critical to solving the crime is determining when the murder was committed. The coroner arrives at the murder scene at 12:00 P.M. She immediately takes the temperature of the body and finds it to be 94.6°F. She then takes the temperature 1 hr later and finds it to be 93.4°F. The temperature of the room is 70°F. When was the murder committed?

Technology Connection

21. *Percent of Americans 85 and Older.* In 1900, 0.2% of the U.S. population, or 122,000 people, were 85 and older. The number of people 85 and older reached 4,860,000 in 2004. The table below lists data regarding the percentage of the U.S. population 85 and older in selected years from 1900 to 2004.

Year, x	Percent of U.S. Population 85 and Older
1900, 0	0.2%
1910, 10	0.2
1920, 20	0.2
1930, 30	0.2
1940, 40	0.3
1950, 50	0.4
1960, 60	0.5
1970, 70	0.7
1980, 80	1.0
1990, 90	1.2
1995, 95	1.4
2000, 100	1.5
2001, 101	1.6
2002, 102	1.6
2003, 103	1.6
2004, 104	1.7

Source: Bureau of the Census, U.S. Department of Commerce

a) Use a graphing calculator to fit an exponential function to the data, where x is the number of years after 1900. Determine whether the function is a good fit.

b) Graph the function found in part (a) with a scatterplot of the data.

c) Estimate the percentage of the U.S. population 85 and older in 2007, in 2015, and in 2020.

22. *Forgetting.* In an art class, students were tested at the end of the course on a final exam. Then they were retested with an equivalent test at subsequent time intervals. Their scores after time x, in months, are given in the following table.

Time, x (in months)	Score, y
1	84.9%
2	84.6
3	84.4
4	84.2
5	84.1
6	83.9

a) Use a graphing calculator to fit a logarithmic function $y = a + b \ln x$ to the data.

b) Use the function to predict test scores after 8, 10, 24, and 36 months.

c) After how long will the test scores fall below 82%?

23. *College Applications.* Acceptance to the college of one's choice has become increasingly competitive. The table below lists the percent of college applicants who sent out 7 or more applications.

Year, x	Percent of College Applicants Who Sent Out 7 or More Applications, y
1967, 0	1.8%
1977, 10	4.0
1987, 20	7.9
1997, 30	10.8
2005, 38	17.4

Source: Higher Education Research Institute at UCLA

a) Create a scatterplot of the data. Let $x =$ the number of years since 1967.

b) Use a graphing calculator to fit linear, quadratic, and exponential functions to the data, where x is the number of years after 1967. Determine which function has the best fit.

c) Graph all three functions found in part (b) with the scatterplot in part (a).

d) Use the functions found in part (b) to estimate the percent of college applicants who will send out 7 or more applications in 2008. Which function provides the most realistic prediction?

24. *Cost of Political Conventions.* The total cost of the Democratic and the Republican national conventions has increased 638% over the 24-yr period between 1980 and 2004. The table below lists the total cost, in millions of dollars, for selected years.

Year, x	Total Conventions' Cost, $C(x)$ (in millions)
1980, 0	$ 23.1
1984, 4	31.8
1988, 8	44.4
1992, 12	58.8
1996, 16	90.6
2000, 20	160.8
2004*, 24	170.5

*estimate
Source: Campaign Finance Institute

a) Use a graphing calculator to fit the data with an exponential function, where x is the number of years after 1980.

b) Use the function to estimate the cost in 2008 and in 2012.

c) In what year will total cost exceed $546 million?

25. *Obesity-Related Surgeries.* The number of obesity-related surgeries in Indiana more than quadrupled from 1995 to 2002. The table below lists the number of surgeries for these years.

Year, x	Number of Obesity-Related Surgeries in Indiana, y
1995, 0	332
1996, 1	297
1997, 2	396
1998, 3	445
1999, 4	585
2000, 5	911
2001, 6	1146
2002, 7	1611

Source: Indiana State Department of Health

a) Use a graphing calculator to fit the data with an exponential function, where x is the number of years after 1995.
b) Use the function to estimate the number of obesity-related surgeries in Indiana in 2005 and in 2009.
c) In what year will the number of surgeries reach 12,000?

26. *Effect of Advertising.* A company introduced a new software product on a trial run in a city. They advertised the product on television and found the following data relating the percent P of people who bought the product after x ads were run.

Number of Ads, x	Percentage Who Bought, P
0	0.2%
10	0.7
20	2.7
30	9.2
40	27.0
50	57.6
60	83.3
70	94.8
80	98.5
90	99.6

a) Use a graphing calculator to fit a logistic function

$$P(x) = \frac{a}{1 + be^{-kx}}$$

to the data.
b) What percent of people bought the product when 55 ads were run? 100 ads?
c) Find the horizontal asymptote for the graph. Interpret the asymptote in terms of the advertising situation.

Collaborative Discussion and Writing

27. Browse through some newspapers or magazines to find some data that appear to fit an exponential model. Make a case for why such a fit is appropriate. Then fit an exponential function to the data and make some predictions.

28. *Atmospheric Pressure.* Atmospheric pressure P at an altitude a is given by

$$P = P_0 e^{-0.00005a},$$

where P_0 is the pressure at sea level, approximately 14.7 lb/in^2 (pounds per square inch). Explain how a barometer, or some device for measuring atmospheric pressure, can be used to find the height of a skyscraper.

Skill Maintenance

Fill in the blank with the correct name of the principle or rule from the given choices.

Principle of zero products
Multiplication principle for equations
Product rule
Addition principle for inequalities
Power rule
Multiplication principle for inequalities
Principle of square roots
Quotient rule

29. For any real numbers a, b, and c: If $a < b$ and $c > 0$ are true, then $ac < bc$ is true. If $a < b$ and $c < 0$ are true, then $ac > bc$ is true.

30. For any positive numbers M and N and any logarithmic base a, $\log_a MN = \log_a M + \log_a N$.

---

31. If $ab = 0$ is true, then $a = 0$ or $b = 0$, and if $a = 0$ or $b = 0$, then $ab = 0$.

---

32. If $x^2 = k$, then $x = \sqrt{k}$ or $x = -\sqrt{k}$.

---

33. For any positive number M, any logarithmic base a, and any real number p, $\log_a M^p = p \log_a M$.

---

34. For any real numbers a, b, and c: If $a = b$ is true, then $ac = bc$ is true.

Synthesis

35. *Supply and Demand.* The supply and demand for the sale of a certain type of DVD player are given by

$$S(p) = 150e^{0.004p} \quad \text{and} \quad D(p) = 480e^{-0.003p},$$

where $S(p)$ is the number of DVD players that the company is willing to sell at price p and $D(p)$ is the quantity that the public is willing to buy at price p. Find p such that $D(p) = S(p)$. This is called the **equilibrium price.**

36. *Carbon Dating.* Recently, while digging in Chaco Canyon, New Mexico, archaeologists found corn pollen that was 4000 yr old (*Source: American Anthropologist*). This was evidence that Native Americans had been cultivating crops in the Southwest centuries earlier than scientists had thought. What percent of the carbon-14 had been lost from the pollen?

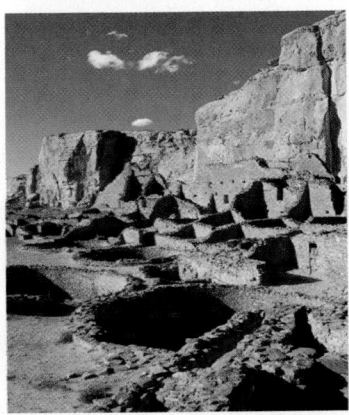

37. *Present Value.* Following the birth of a child, a parent wants to make an initial investment P_0 that will grow to $50,000 for the child's education at age 18. Interest is compounded continuously at 7%. What should the initial investment be? Such an amount is called the **present value** of $50,000 due 18 yr from now.

38. *Present Value.* Referring to Exercise 37:
  a) Solve $P = P_0 e^{kt}$ for P_0.
  b) Find the present value of $50,000 due 18 yr from now at interest rate 6.4%, compounded continuously.

39. *Electricity.* The formula

$$i = \frac{V}{R}\left[1 - e^{-(R/L)t}\right]$$

occurs in the theory of electricity. Solve for t.

40. *The Beer–Lambert Law.* A beam of light enters a medium such as water or smog with initial intensity I_0. Its intensity decreases depending on the thickness (or concentration) of the medium. The intensity I at a depth (or concentration) of x units is given by

$$I = I_0 e^{-\mu x}.$$

The constant μ (the Greek letter "mu") is called the **coefficient of absorption,** and it varies with the medium. For sea water, $\mu = 1.4$.
  a) What percentage of light intensity I_0 remains at a depth of sea water that is 1 m? 3 m? 5 m? 50 m?
  b) Plant life cannot exist below 10 m. What percentage of I_0 remains at 10 m?

41. Given that $y = ae^x$, take the natural logarithm on both sides. Let $Y = \ln y$. Consider Y as a function of x. What kind of function is Y?

42. Given that $y = ax^b$, take the natural logarithm on both sides. Let $Y = \ln y$ and $X = \ln x$. Consider Y as a function of X. What kind of function is Y?

CHAPTER 4 SUMMARY AND REVIEW

Important Properties and Formulas

One-to-One Function:	If $f(a) = f(b)$, then $a = b$.
Exponential Function:	$f(x) = a^x$, for $a > 0$ and $a \neq 1$
The Number e:	$e = 2.7182818284\ldots$
Logarithmic Function:	$f(x) = \log_a x$
A Logarithm Is an Exponent:	$\log_a x = y \longleftrightarrow x = a^y$
The Change-of-Base Formula:	$\log_b M = \dfrac{\log_a M}{\log_a b}$
The Product Rule:	$\log_a MN = \log_a M + \log_a N$
The Power Rule:	$\log_a M^p = p \log_a M$
The Quotient Rule:	$\log_a \dfrac{M}{N} = \log_a M - \log_a N$
Other Properties:	$\log_a a = 1, \qquad \log_a 1 = 0,$
	$\log_a a^x = x, \qquad a^{\log_a x} = x$
Base–Exponent Property:	$a^x = a^y \longleftrightarrow x = y$, for $a > 0$ and $a \neq 1$
Property of Logarithmic Equality:	$\log_a M = \log_a N \longleftrightarrow M = N$, for $a > 0$ and $a \neq 1$

Exponential Growth Model:	$P(t) = P_0 e^{kt}, k > 0$
Exponential Decay Model:	$P(t) = P_0 e^{-kt}, k > 0$
Interest Compounded Continuously:	$P(t) = P_0 e^{kt}, k > 0$
Limited Growth Models:	$P(t) = \dfrac{a}{1 + be^{-kt}}, k > 0$
	$P(t) = L(1 - e^{-kt}), k > 0$

REVIEW EXERCISES

Determine whether the statement is true or false.

1. The range of a one-to-one function f is the domain of the inverse f^{-1}. [4.1]

2. The y-intercept of $f(x) = e^{-x}$ is $(0, -1)$. [4.2]

3. The graph of f^{-1} is a reflection of the graph of f across $y = 0$. [4.1]

4. If it is not possible for a horizontal line to intersect the graph of a function more than once, then the function is one-to-one and its inverse is a function. [4.1]

5. The domain of all logarithmic functions is $[1, \infty)$. [4.3]

6. The horizontal asymptote of $y = 2^x$ is $y = 0$. [4.2]

7. Find the inverse of the relation [4.1]
$\{(1.3, -2.7), (8, -3), (-5, 3), (6, -3), (7, -5)\}$.

8. Find an equation of the inverse relation. [4.1]
a) $y = -2x + 3$
b) $y = 3x^2 + 2x - 1$
c) $0.8x^3 - 5.4y^2 = 3x$

Graph the function and determine whether the function is one-to-one using the horizontal-line test. [4.1]

9. $f(x) = -|x| + 3$

10. $f(x) = x^2 + 1$

11. $f(x) = 2x - \dfrac{3}{4}$

12. $f(x) = -\dfrac{6}{x + 1}$

In Exercises 13–18, given the function:
a) *Sketch the graph and determine whether the function is one-to-one.* [4.1]
b) *If it is one-to-one, find a formula for the inverse.* [4.1]

13. $f(x) = 2 - 3x$

14. $f(x) = \dfrac{x + 2}{x - 1}$

15. $f(x) = \sqrt{x - 6}$

16. $f(x) = x^3 - 8$

17. $f(x) = 3x^2 + 2x - 1$

18. $f(x) = e^x$

For the function f, use composition of functions to show that f^{-1} is as given. [4.1]

19. $f(x) = 6x - 5$, $f^{-1}(x) = \dfrac{x + 5}{6}$

20. $f(x) = \dfrac{x + 1}{x}$, $f^{-1}(x) = \dfrac{1}{x - 1}$

Find the inverse of the given one-to-one function f. Give the domain and the range of f and of f^{-1} and then graph both f and f^{-1} on the same set of axes. [4.1]

21. $f(x) = 2 - 5x$

22. $f(x) = \dfrac{x - 3}{x + 2}$

23. Find $f(f^{-1}(657))$: $f(x) = \dfrac{4x^5 - 16x^{37}}{119x}$, $x > 1$. [4.1]

24. Find $f(f^{-1}(a))$: $f(x) = \sqrt[3]{3x - 4}$. [4.1]

Graph the function.

25. $f(x) = \left(\frac{1}{3}\right)^x$ [4.2]

26. $f(x) = 1 + e^x$ [4.2]

27. $f(x) = -e^{-x}$ [4.2]

28. $f(x) = \log_2 x$ [4.3]

29. $f(x) = \frac{1}{2}\ln x$ [4.3]

30. $f(x) = \log x - 2$ [4.3]

In Exercises 31–36, match the equation with one of figures (a)–(f), which follow

a)

b)

c)

d)

e)

f)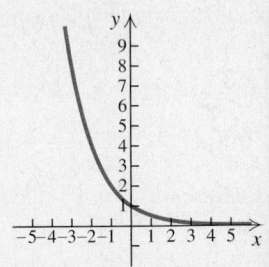

31. $f(x) = e^{x-3}$ [4.2]

32. $f(x) = \log_3 x$ [4.3]

33. $y = -\log_3(x + 1)$ [4.3]

34. $y = \left(\frac{1}{2}\right)^x$ [4.2]

35. $f(x) = 3(1 - e^{-x})$, $x \geq 0$ [4.2]

36. $f(x) = |\ln(x - 4)|$ [4.3]

Find each of the following. Do not use a calculator. [4.3]

37. $\log_5 125$ **38.** $\log 100{,}000$

39. $\ln e$ **40.** $\ln 1$

41. $\log 10^{1/4}$ **42.** $\log_3 \sqrt{3}$

43. $\log 1$ **44.** $\log 10$

45. $\log_2 \sqrt[3]{2}$ **46.** $\log 0.01$

Convert to an exponential equation. [4.3]

47. $\log_4 x = 2$

48. $\log_a Q = k$

Convert to a logarithmic equation. [4.3]

49. $4^{-3} = \frac{1}{64}$

50. $e^x = 80$

Find each of the following using a calculator. Round to four decimal places. [4.3]

51. $\log 11$ **52.** $\log 0.234$

53. $\ln 3$ **54.** $\ln 0.027$

55. $\log(-3)$ **56.** $\ln 0$

Find the logarithm using the change-of-base formula. [4.3]

57. $\log_5 24$ **58.** $\log_8 3$

Express as a single logarithm and, if possible, simplify. [4.4]

59. $3 \log_b x - 4 \log_b y + \frac{1}{2} \log_b z$

60. $\ln(x^3 - 8) - \ln(x^2 + 2x + 4) + \ln(x + 2)$

Express in terms of sums and differences of logarithms. [4.4]

61. $\ln \sqrt[4]{wr^2}$ **62.** $\log \sqrt[3]{\dfrac{M^2}{N}}$

Given that $\log_a 2 = 0.301$, $\log_a 5 = 0.699$, and $\log_a 6 = 0.778$, find each of the following. [4.4]

63. $\log_a 3$ **64.** $\log_a 50$

65. $\log_a \frac{1}{5}$ **66.** $\log_a \sqrt[3]{5}$

Simplify. [4.4]

67. $\ln e^{-5k}$ **68.** $\log_5 5^{-6t}$

Solve. [4.5]

69. $\log_4 x = 2$ **70.** $3^{1-x} = 9^{2x}$

71. $e^x = 80$ **72.** $4^{2x-1} - 3 = 61$

73. $\log_{16} 4 = x$ **74.** $\log_x 125 = 3$

75. $\log_2 x + \log_2(x - 2) = 3$

76. $\log(x^2 - 1) - \log(x - 1) = 1$

77. $\log x^2 = \log x$

78. $e^{-x} = 0.02$

79. *Saving for College.* Following the birth of twins, the grandparents deposit $16,000 in a college trust fund that earns 4.2% interest, compounded quarterly.

a) Find a function for the amount in the account after t years. [4.2]

b) Find the amount in the account at $t = 0, 6, 12,$ and 18 yr. [4.2]

80. *Whooping Cough.* In recent years, the number of new cases of whooping cough, a bacterial infection that induces a cough, has been increasing exponentially. The number of cases is estimated by the function

$$W(t) = 1665.945(1.087)^t,$$

where t is the number of years since 1980 (*Source*: Centers for Disease Control and Prevention). Find the number of new cases in 1990 and in 2000. Then use this function to estimate the number of cases in 2007. [4.2]

81. How long will it take an investment to double if it is invested at 8.6%, compounded continuously? [4.6]

82. The population of Murrayville doubled in 30 yr. What was the exponential growth rate? [4.6]

83. How old is a skeleton that has lost 27% of its carbon-14? [4.6]

84. The hydrogen ion concentration of milk is 2.3×10^{-6}. What is the pH? (See Exercise 94 in Exercise Set 4.3.) [4.3]

85. *Earthquake Magnitude.* The earthquake in
Kashgar, China, on February 25, 2003, had an
intensity of $10^{6.3} \cdot I_0$ (*Source*: U.S. Geological
Survey). What is the magnitude on the Richter
scale? [4.3]

86. What is the loudness, in decibels, of a sound
whose intensity is $1000I_0$? (See Exercise 97 in
Exercise Set 4.3.) [4.3]

87. *Walking Speed.* The average walking speed w,
in feet per second, of a person living in a city of
population P, in thousands, is given by the
function
$$w(P) = 0.37 \ln P + 0.05.$$
a) The population of Wichita, Kansas, is
353,823. Find the average walking speed.
[4.3]
b) A city's population has an average walking
speed of 3.4 ft/sec. Find the population.
[4.3]

88. *Social Security Distributions.* Cash Social
Security distributions were $35 million, or
$0.035 billion, in 1940. This amount has
increased exponentially to $492 billion in 2004.
(*Source*: Social Security Administration) Assuming the exponential growth model applies:
a) Find the exponential growth rate k. [4.6]
b) Find the exponential growth function. [4.6]
c) Estimate the total cash distributions in 1965,
in 1995, and in 2015. [4.6]
d) In what year will the cash benefits reach
$1 trillion? [4.6]

89. *The Population of Panama.* The population of
Panama was 3.039 million in 2005, and the
exponential growth rate was 1.3% per year
(*Source*: U.S. Bureau of the Census, World
Population Profile).
a) Find the exponential growth function. [4.6]
b) What will the population be in 2009? in
2015? [4.6]
c) When will the population be 10 million?
[4.6]
d) What is the doubling time? [4.6]

90. Which of the following is the horizontal
asymptote of the graph of $f(x) = e^{x-3} + 2$?
[4.2]
A. $y = -2$
B. $y = -3$
C. $y = 3$
D. $y = 2$

91. Which of the following is the domain of the
logarithmic function $f(x) = \log(2x - 3)$?
[4.3]
A. $\left(\frac{3}{2}, \infty\right)$
B. $\left(-\infty, \frac{3}{2}\right)$
C. $(3, \infty)$
D. $(-\infty, \infty)$

Technology Connection

92. *Arson Damage to Churches.* According to the federal government, 34.5% of church fires from 2001 through 2005 were caused by arson. The table below lists the dollar value (in millions) in arson damage.

Year, x	Arson Damage (in millions)
2001, 0	$2.8
2002, 1	3.3
2003, 2	3.6
2004, 3	5.0
2005, 4	8.5

Sources: U.S. Fire Administration; Bureau of Alcohol, Tobacco, Firearms, and Explosives

a) Use a graphing calculator to fit an exponential function to the data, where x is the number of years after 2001. [4.6]
b) Graph the function with a scatterplot of the data. [4.6]
c) Predict the church arson damage (in millions of dollars) in 2010. [4.6]

93. Using only a graphing calculator, determine whether the following functions are inverses of each other: [4.1]

$$f(x) = \frac{4 + 3x}{x - 2}, \quad g(x) = \frac{x + 4}{x - 3}.$$

94. a) Use a graphing calculator to graph $f(x) = 5e^{-x} \ln x$ in the viewing window $[-1, 10, -5, 5]$. [4.2], [4.3]
b) Estimate the relative maximum and minimum values of the function. [4.2], [4.3]

Collaborative Discussion and Writing

95. Suppose that you are trying to convince a fellow student that

$$\log_2 (x + 5) \neq \log_2 x + \log_2 5.$$

Give as many explanations as you can. [4.4]

96. Describe the difference between $f^{-1}(x)$ and $[f(x)]^{-1}$. [4.1]

Synthesis

Solve. [4.5]

97. $|\log_4 x| = 3$

98. $\log x = \ln x$

99. $5^{\sqrt{x}} = 625$

100. Find the domain: $f(x) = \log_3 (\ln x)$. [4.3]

CHAPTER 4 TEST

1. Find the inverse of the relation
   $$\{(-2,5),(4,3),(0,-1),(-6,-3)\}.$$

Determine whether the function is one-to-one. Answer yes or no.

2.

3.

In Exercises 4–8, given the function:

a) *Sketch the graph and determine whether the function is one-to-one.*

b) *If it is one-to-one, find a formula for the inverse.*

4. $f(x) = x^3 + 1$

5. $f(x) = 1 - x$

6. $f(x) = \dfrac{x}{2 - x}$

7. $f(x) = x^2 + x - 3$

8. Use composition of functions to show that f^{-1} is as given:
   $$f(x) = -4x + 3, \quad f^{-1}(x) = \frac{3 - x}{4}.$$

9. Find the inverse of the one-to-one function
   $$f(x) = \frac{1}{x - 4}.$$
   Give the domain and the range of f and of f^{-1} and then graph both f and f^{-1} on the same set of axes.

Graph the function.

10. $f(x) = 4^{-x}$

11. $f(x) = \log x$

12. $f(x) = e^x - 3$

13. $f(x) = \ln(x + 2)$

Find each of the following. Do not use a calculator.

14. $\log 0.00001$

15. $\ln e$

16. $\ln 1$

17. $\log_4 \sqrt[5]{4}$

18. Convert to an exponential equation: $\ln x = 4$.

19. Convert to a logarithmic equation: $3^x = 5.4$.

Find each of the following using a calculator. Round to four decimal places.

20. $\ln 16$

21. $\log 0.293$

22. Find $\log_6 10$ using the change-of-base formula.

23. Express as a single logarithm:
    $$2 \log_a x - \log_a y + \tfrac{1}{2} \log_a z.$$

24. Express $\ln \sqrt[5]{x^2 y}$ in terms of sums and differences of logarithms.

25. Given that $\log_a 2 = 0.328$ and $\log_a 8 = 0.984$, find $\log_a 4$.

26. Simplify: $\ln e^{-4t}$.

Solve.

27. $\log_{25} 5 = x$

28. $\log_3 x + \log_3 (x + 8) = 2$

29. $3^{4-x} = 27^x$

30. $e^x = 65$

31. *Earthquake Magnitude.* The earthquake in Bam, in southeast Iran, on December 26, 2003, had an intensity of $10^{6.6} \cdot I_0$ (*Source*: U.S. Geological Survey). What was its magnitude on the Richter scale?

32. *Growth Rate.* A country's population doubled in 45 yr. What was the exponential growth rate?

33. *Compound Interest.* Suppose $1000 is invested at interest rate k, compounded continuously, and grows to $1144.54 in 3 yr.
    a) Find the interest rate.
    b) Find the exponential growth function.
    c) Find the balance after 8 yr.
    d) Find the doubling time.

Synthesis

34. Solve: $4^{\sqrt[3]{x}} = 8$.

The Trigonometric Functions

APPLICATION

In Telluride, Colorado, there is a free gondola ride that provides a spectacular view of the town and the surrounding mountains. The gondolas that begin in the town at an elevation of 8725 ft travel 5750 ft to Station St. Sophia, whose altitude is 10,550 ft. They then continue 3913 ft to Mountain Village, whose elevation is 9500 ft. **(a)** What is the angle of elevation from the town to Station St. Sophia? **(b)** What is the angle of depression from Station St. Sophia to Mountain Village?

This problem appears as Example 5 in Section 5.2.

5.1

Trigonometric Functions of Acute Angles

◆ Determine the six trigonometric ratios for a given acute angle of a right triangle.

◆ Determine the trigonometric function values of 30°, 45°, and 60°.

◆ Using a calculator, find function values for any acute angle, and given a function value of an acute angle, find the angle.

◆ Given the function values of an acute angle, find the function values of its complement.

◆ The Trigonometric Ratios

We begin our study of trigonometry by considering right triangles and acute angles measured in degrees. An **acute angle** is an angle with measure greater than 0° and less than 90°. Greek letters such as α (alpha), β (beta), γ (gamma), θ (theta), and ϕ (phi) are often used to denote an angle. Consider a right triangle with one of its acute angles labeled θ. The side opposite the right angle is called the **hypotenuse.** The other sides of the triangle are referenced by their position relative to the acute angle θ. One side is opposite θ and one is adjacent to θ.

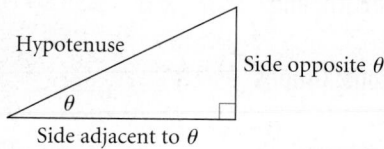

The *lengths* of the sides of the triangle are used to define the six trigonometric ratios:

sine (sin),	cosecant (csc),
cosine (cos),	secant (sec),
tangent (tan),	cotangent (cot).

The **sine of θ** is the *length* of the side opposite θ divided by the *length* of the hypotenuse (see Fig. 1):

Figure 1

$$\sin \theta = \frac{\text{length of side opposite } \theta}{\text{length of hypotenuse}}.$$

The ratio depends on the measure of angle θ and thus is a function of θ. The notation $\sin \theta$ actually means $\sin (\theta)$, where sin, or sine, is the name of the function.

The **cosine of θ** is the *length* of the side adjacent to θ divided by the *length* of the hypotenuse (see Fig. 2):

Figure 2

$$\cos \theta = \frac{\text{length of side adjacent to } \theta}{\text{length of hypotenuse}}.$$

The six trigonometric ratios, or trigonometric functions, are defined as follows.

Trigonometric Function Values of an Acute Angle θ

Let θ be an acute angle of a right triangle. Then the six trigonometric functions of θ are as follows:

$$\sin \theta = \frac{\text{side opposite } \theta}{\text{hypotenuse}}, \qquad \csc \theta = \frac{\text{hypotenuse}}{\text{side opposite } \theta},$$

$$\cos \theta = \frac{\text{side adjacent to } \theta}{\text{hypotenuse}}, \qquad \sec \theta = \frac{\text{hypotenuse}}{\text{side adjacent to } \theta},$$

$$\tan \theta = \frac{\text{side opposite } \theta}{\text{side adjacent to } \theta}, \qquad \cot \theta = \frac{\text{side adjacent to } \theta}{\text{side opposite } \theta}.$$

EXAMPLE 1 In the right triangle shown at left, find the six trigonometric function values of **(a)** θ and **(b)** α.

Solution   We use the definitions.

a) $\sin \theta = \dfrac{\text{opp}}{\text{hyp}} = \dfrac{12}{13}, \qquad \csc \theta = \dfrac{\text{hyp}}{\text{opp}} = \dfrac{13}{12},$

$\cos \theta = \dfrac{\text{adj}}{\text{hyp}} = \dfrac{5}{13}, \qquad \sec \theta = \dfrac{\text{hyp}}{\text{adj}} = \dfrac{13}{5},$ The references to opposite, adjacent, and hypotenuse are relative to θ.

$\tan \theta = \dfrac{\text{opp}}{\text{adj}} = \dfrac{12}{5}, \qquad \cot \theta = \dfrac{\text{adj}}{\text{opp}} = \dfrac{5}{12}$

b) $\sin \alpha = \dfrac{\text{opp}}{\text{hyp}} = \dfrac{5}{13}, \qquad \csc \alpha = \dfrac{\text{hyp}}{\text{opp}} = \dfrac{13}{5},$

$\cos \alpha = \dfrac{\text{adj}}{\text{hyp}} = \dfrac{12}{13}, \qquad \sec \alpha = \dfrac{\text{hyp}}{\text{adj}} = \dfrac{13}{12},$ The references to opposite, adjacent, and hypotenuse are relative to α.

$\tan \alpha = \dfrac{\text{opp}}{\text{adj}} = \dfrac{5}{12}, \qquad \cot \alpha = \dfrac{\text{adj}}{\text{opp}} = \dfrac{12}{5}$

▶ **Now Try Exercise 1.**

In Example 1(a), we note that the value of $\sin \theta$, $\frac{12}{13}$, is the reciprocal of $\frac{13}{12}$, the value of $\csc \theta$. Likewise, we see the same reciprocal relationship between the values of $\cos \theta$ and $\sec \theta$ and between the values of $\tan \theta$ and $\cot \theta$. For any angle, the cosecant, secant, and cotangent values are the reciprocals of the sine, cosine, and tangent function values, respectively.

Reciprocal Functions

$$\csc \theta = \frac{1}{\sin \theta}, \qquad \sec \theta = \frac{1}{\cos \theta}, \qquad \cot \theta = \frac{1}{\tan \theta}$$

If we know the values of the sine, cosine, and tangent functions of an angle, we can use these reciprocal relationships to find the values of the cosecant, secant, and cotangent functions of that angle.

EXAMPLE 2 Given that $\sin \phi = \frac{4}{5}$, $\cos \phi = \frac{3}{5}$, and $\tan \phi = \frac{4}{3}$, find $\csc \phi$, $\sec \phi$, and $\cot \phi$.

Solution Using the reciprocal relationships, we have

$$\csc \phi = \frac{1}{\sin \phi} = \frac{1}{\frac{4}{5}} = \frac{5}{4}, \qquad \sec \phi = \frac{1}{\cos \phi} = \frac{1}{\frac{3}{5}} = \frac{5}{3},$$

and $\quad \cot \phi = \dfrac{1}{\tan \phi} = \dfrac{1}{\frac{4}{3}} = \dfrac{3}{4}.$

▶ Now Try Exercise 7.

Triangles are said to be **similar** if their corresponding angles have the *same* measure. In similar triangles, the lengths of corresponding sides are in the same ratio. The right triangles shown below are similar. Note that the corresponding angles are equal and the length of each side of the second triangle is four times the length of the corresponding side of the first triangle.

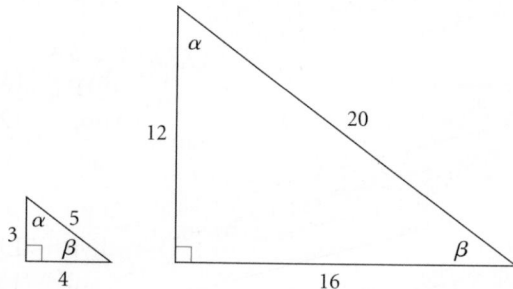

Let's observe the sine, cosine, and tangent values of β in each triangle. Can we expect corresponding function values to be the same?

First Triangle	Second Triangle
$\sin \beta = \dfrac{3}{5}$	$\sin \beta = \dfrac{12}{20} = \dfrac{3}{5}$
$\cos \beta = \dfrac{4}{5}$	$\cos \beta = \dfrac{16}{20} = \dfrac{4}{5}$
$\tan \beta = \dfrac{3}{4}$	$\tan \beta = \dfrac{12}{16} = \dfrac{3}{4}$

For the two triangles, the corresponding values of $\sin \beta$, $\cos \beta$, and $\tan \beta$ are the same. The lengths of the sides are proportional—thus the *ratios* are the same. This must be the case because in order for the sine, cosine, and tangent to be functions, there must be only one output (the ratio) for each input (the angle β).

> The trigonometric function values of θ depend only on the measure of the angle, *not* on the size of the triangle.

◆ The Six Functions Related

We can find the other five trigonometric function values of an acute angle when one of the function-value ratios is known.

EXAMPLE 3 If $\sin \beta = \frac{6}{7}$ and β is an acute angle, find the other five trigonometric function values of β.

Solution We know from the definition of the sine function that the ratio

$$\frac{6}{7} \quad \text{is} \quad \frac{\text{opp}}{\text{hyp}}.$$

PYTHAGOREAN THEOREM

REVIEW SECTION **1.1.**

Using this information, let's consider a right triangle in which the hypotenuse has length 7 and the side opposite β has length 6. To find the length of the side adjacent to β, we recall the *Pythagorean theorem*:

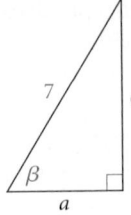

$$a^2 + b^2 = c^2$$
$$a^2 + 6^2 = 7^2$$
$$a^2 + 36 = 49$$
$$a^2 = 49 - 36 = 13$$
$$a = \sqrt{13}.$$

We now use the lengths of the three sides to find the other five ratios:

$$\sin \beta = \frac{6}{7}, \qquad\qquad \csc \beta = \frac{7}{6},$$

$$\cos \beta = \frac{\sqrt{13}}{7}, \qquad\qquad \sec \beta = \frac{7}{\sqrt{13}}, \quad \text{or} \quad \frac{7\sqrt{13}}{13},$$

$$\tan \beta = \frac{6}{\sqrt{13}}, \quad \text{or} \quad \frac{6\sqrt{13}}{13}, \qquad \cot \beta = \frac{\sqrt{13}}{6}.$$

▶ Now Try Exercise 9.

◆ Function Values of 30°, 45°, and 60°

In Examples 1 and 3, we found the trigonometric function values of an acute angle of a right triangle when the lengths of the three sides were known. In most situations, we are asked to find the function values when the measure of the acute angle is given. For certain special angles such as 30°, 45°, and 60°, which are frequently seen in applications, we can use geometry to determine the function values.

A right triangle with a 45° angle actually has two 45° angles. Thus the triangle is *isosceles*, and the legs are the same length. Let's consider such a triangle whose legs have length 1. Then we can find the length of its hypotenuse, c, using the Pythagorean theorem as follows:

$$1^2 + 1^2 = c^2, \quad \text{or} \quad c^2 = 2, \quad \text{or} \quad c = \sqrt{2}.$$

Such a triangle is shown below. From this diagram, we can easily determine the trigonometric function values of 45°.

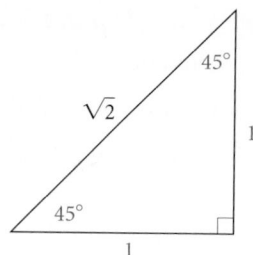

$$\sin 45° = \frac{\text{opp}}{\text{hyp}} = \frac{1}{\sqrt{2}} = \frac{\sqrt{2}}{2} \approx 0.7071,$$

$$\cos 45° = \frac{\text{adj}}{\text{hyp}} = \frac{1}{\sqrt{2}} = \frac{\sqrt{2}}{2} \approx 0.7071,$$

$$\tan 45° = \frac{\text{opp}}{\text{adj}} = \frac{1}{1} = 1$$

It is sufficient to find only the function values of the sine, cosine, and tangent, since the others are their reciprocals.

It is also possible to determine the function values of 30° and 60°. A right triangle with 30° and 60° acute angles is half of an equilateral triangle, as shown in the following figure. Thus if we choose an equilateral triangle whose sides have length 2 and take half of it, we obtain a right triangle that has a hypotenuse of length 2 and a leg of length 1. The other leg has length a, which can be found as follows:

$$a^2 + 1^2 = 2^2$$
$$a^2 + 1 = 4$$
$$a^2 = 3$$
$$a = \sqrt{3}.$$

We can now determine the function values of 30° and 60°:

$$\sin 30° = \frac{1}{2} = 0.5, \qquad\qquad \sin 60° = \frac{\sqrt{3}}{2} \approx 0.8660,$$

$$\cos 30° = \frac{\sqrt{3}}{2} \approx 0.8660, \qquad \cos 60° = \frac{1}{2} = 0.5,$$

$$\tan 30° = \frac{1}{\sqrt{3}} = \frac{\sqrt{3}}{3} \approx 0.5774, \qquad \tan 60° = \frac{\sqrt{3}}{1} = \sqrt{3} \approx 1.7321.$$

Since we will often use the function values of 30°, 45°, and 60°, either the triangles that yield them or the values themselves should be memorized.

	30°	45°	60°
sin	1/2	$\sqrt{2}/2$	$\sqrt{3}/2$
cos	$\sqrt{3}/2$	$\sqrt{2}/2$	1/2
tan	$\sqrt{3}/3$	1	$\sqrt{3}$

Let's now use what we have learned about trigonometric functions of special angles to solve problems. We will consider such applications in greater detail in Section 5.2.

EXAMPLE 4 *Height of a Hot-air Balloon.* As a hot-air balloon began to rise, the ground crew drove 1.2 mi to an observation station. The initial observation from the station estimated the angle between the ground and the line of sight to the balloon to be 30°. Approximately how high was the balloon at that point? (We are assuming that the wind velocity was low and that the balloon rose vertically for the first few minutes.)

Solution We begin with a drawing of the situation. We know the measure of an acute angle and the length of its adjacent side.

Since we want to determine the length of the opposite side, we can use the tangent ratio, or the cotangent ratio. Here we use the tangent ratio:

$$\tan 30° = \frac{\text{opp}}{\text{adj}} = \frac{h}{1.2}$$

$$1.2 \tan 30° = h$$

$$1.2\left(\frac{\sqrt{3}}{3}\right) = h \qquad \text{Substituting; } \tan 30° = \frac{\sqrt{3}}{3}$$

$$0.7 \approx h.$$

The balloon is approximately 0.7 mi, or 3696 ft, high.

▶ **Now Try Exercise 29.**

We can use a graphing calculator set in DEGREE mode to convert between D°M′S″ form and decimal degree form.

To convert D°M′S″ form to decimal degree form in Example 5, we enter 5°42′30″ using the ANGLE menu for the degree and minute symbols and (ALPHA) (+) for the third symbol. Pressing (ENTER) gives us

    5°42′30″ ≈ 5.71°.

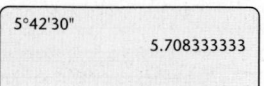

A number must always be entered for degrees even it is 0. Also, if there is a nonzero number of seconds, both degrees and minutes must be entered even if one or both is 0.

To convert decimal degree form to D°M′S″ form in Example 6, we enter 72.18 and access the ▶DMS feature in the ANGLE menu.

```
72.18 ▶DMS
                72°10′48″
```

✦ Function Values of Any Acute Angle

Historically, the measure of an angle has been expressed in degrees, minutes, and seconds. One minute, denoted $1'$, is such that $60' = 1°$, or $1' = \frac{1}{60} \cdot (1°)$. One second, denoted $1''$, is such that $60'' = 1'$, or $1'' = \frac{1}{60} \cdot (1')$. Then 61 degrees, 27 minutes, 4 seconds could be written as $61°27'4''$. This **D°M′S″ form** was common before the widespread use of scientific calculators. Now the preferred notation is to express fractional parts of degrees in **decimal degree form.** Although the D°M′S″ notation is still widely used in navigation, we will most often use the decimal form in this text.

Most scientific calculators can convert D°M′S″ notation to decimal degree notation and vice versa. Procedures among calculators vary.

EXAMPLE 5   Convert $5°42'30''$ to decimal degree notation.

Solution   We enter $5°42'30''$. The calculator gives us

$$5°42'30'' \approx 5.71°,$$

rounded to the nearest hundredth of a degree.

Without a calculator, we can convert as follows:

$$5°42'30'' = 5° + 42' + 30''$$
$$= 5° + 42' + \frac{30}{60}' \qquad 1'' = \frac{1}{60}'; 30'' = \frac{30}{60}'$$
$$= 5° + 42.5' \qquad \frac{30'}{60} = 0.5'$$
$$= 5° + \frac{42.5}{60}° \qquad 1' = \frac{1}{60}°; 42.5' = \frac{42.5}{60}°$$
$$\approx 5.71°. \qquad \frac{42.5°}{60} \approx 0.71°$$

▶ Now Try Exercise 37.

EXAMPLE 6   Convert $72.18°$ to D°M′S″ notation.

Solution   On a calculator, we enter 72.18. The result is

$$72.18° = 72°10'48''.$$

Without a calculator, we can convert as follows:

$$72.18° = 72° + 0.18 \times 1°$$
$$= 72° + 0.18 \times 60' \qquad 1° = 60'$$
$$= 72° + 10.8'$$
$$= 72° + 10' + 0.8 \times 1'$$
$$= 72° + 10' + 0.8 \times 60'' \qquad 1' = 60''$$
$$= 72° + 10' + 48''$$
$$= 72°10'48''.$$

▶ Now Try Exercise 45.

So far we have measured angles using degrees. Another useful unit for angle measure is the radian, which we will study in Section 5.4. Calculators work with either degrees or radians. Be sure to use whichever mode is appropriate. In this section, we use the degree mode.

Keep in mind the difference between an exact answer and an approximation. For example,

$$\sin 60° = \frac{\sqrt{3}}{2}. \quad \textbf{This is exact!}$$

But using a calculator, you get an answer like

$$\sin 60° \approx 0.8660254038. \quad \textbf{This is an approximation!}$$

Calculators generally provide values only of the sine, cosine, and tangent functions. You can find values of the cosecant, secant, and cotangent by taking reciprocals of the sine, cosine, and tangent functions, respectively.

EXAMPLE 7 Find the trigonometric function value, rounded to four decimal places, of each of the following.

a) $\tan 29.7°$ b) $\sec 48°$ c) $\sin 84°10'39''$

Solution

a) We check to be sure that the calculator is in DEGREE mode. The function value is

$$\tan 29.7° \approx 0.5703899297$$
$$\approx 0.5704. \quad \text{Rounded to four decimal places}$$

b) The secant function value can be found by taking the reciprocal of the cosine function value:

$$\sec 48° = \frac{1}{\cos 48°} \approx 1.49447655 \approx 1.4945.$$

c) We enter $\sin 84°10'39''$. The result is

$$\sin 84°10'39'' \approx 0.9948409474 \approx 0.9948.$$

▷ Now Try Exercises 61 and 69.

We can use a calculator to find an angle for which we know a trigonometric function value.

EXAMPLE 8 Find the acute angle, to the nearest tenth of a degree, whose sine value is approximately 0.20113.

Solution The quickest way to find the angle with a calculator is to use an inverse function key. (We first studied inverse functions in Section 4.1 and will consider inverse *trigonometric* functions in Section 6.4.) First check to be sure that your calculator is in DEGREE mode. Usually two keys must be pressed in sequence. For this example, if we press

2ND **SIN** .20113 **ENTER**,

we find that the acute angle whose sine is 0.20113 is approximately 11.60304613°, or 11.6°.

▷ Now Try Exercise 75.

25 ft

θ

6.5 ft

EXAMPLE 9 *Ladder Safety.* A paint crew has purchased new 30-ft extension ladders. The manufacturer states that the safest placement on a wall is to extend the ladder to 25 ft and to position the base 6.5 ft from the wall (*Source*: R. D. Werner Co., Inc.). What angle does the ladder make with the ground in this position?

Solution We make a drawing and then use the most convenient trigonometric function. Because we know the length of the side adjacent to θ and the length of the hypotenuse, we choose the cosine function.

From the definition of the cosine function, we have

$$\cos \theta = \frac{\text{adj}}{\text{hyp}} = \frac{6.5 \text{ ft}}{25 \text{ ft}} = 0.26.$$

Using a calculator, we find the acute angle whose cosine is 0.26:

$$\theta \approx 74.92993786°. \qquad \text{Pressing } \boxed{\text{2ND}} \; \boxed{\text{COS}} \; 0.26 \; \boxed{\text{ENTER}}$$

Thus when the ladder is in its safest position, it makes an angle of about 75° with the ground.

✦ Cofunctions and Complements

We recall that two angles are **complementary** whenever the sum of their measures is 90°. Each is the complement of the other. In a right triangle, the acute angles are complementary, since the sum of all three angle measures is 180° and the right angle accounts for 90° of this total. Thus if one acute angle of a right triangle is θ, the other is 90° − θ.

The six trigonometric function values of each of the acute angles in the triangle below are listed at the right. Note that 53° and 37° are complementary angles since 53° + 37° = 90°.

sin 37° ≈ 0.6018	csc 37° ≈ 1.6616
cos 37° ≈ 0.7986	sec 37° ≈ 1.2521
tan 37° ≈ 0.7536	cot 37° ≈ 1.3270

sin 53° ≈ 0.7986	csc 53° ≈ 1.2521
cos 53° ≈ 0.6018	sec 53° ≈ 1.6616
tan 53° ≈ 1.3270	cot 53° ≈ 0.7536

Try this with the acute, complementary angles 20.3° and 69.7° as well. What pattern do you observe? Look for this same pattern in Example 1 earlier in this section.

Note that the sine of an angle is also the cosine of the angle's complement. Similarly, the tangent of an angle is the cotangent of the angle's complement, and the secant of an angle is the cosecant of the angle's complement. These pairs of functions are called **cofunctions.** A list of cofunction identities follows.

Cofunction Identities

$\sin \theta = \cos (90° - \theta),$ $\cos \theta = \sin (90° - \theta),$

$\tan \theta = \cot (90° - \theta),$ $\cot \theta = \tan (90° - \theta),$

$\sec \theta = \csc (90° - \theta),$ $\csc \theta = \sec (90° - \theta)$

EXAMPLE 10 Given that $\sin 18° \approx 0.3090$, $\cos 18° \approx 0.9511$, and $\tan 18° \approx 0.3249$, find the six trigonometric function values of 72°.

Solution Using reciprocal relationships, we know that

$$\csc 18° = \frac{1}{\sin 18°} \approx 3.2361,$$

$$\sec 18° = \frac{1}{\cos 18°} \approx 1.0515,$$

and $$\cot 18° = \frac{1}{\tan 18°} \approx 3.0777.$$

Since 72° and 18° are complementary, we have

$$\sin 72° = \cos 18° \approx 0.9511, \qquad \cos 72° = \sin 18° \approx 0.3090,$$
$$\tan 72° = \cot 18° \approx 3.0777, \qquad \cot 72° = \tan 18° \approx 0.3249,$$
$$\sec 72° = \csc 18° \approx 3.2361, \qquad \csc 72° = \sec 18° \approx 1.0515.$$

▶ Now Try Exercise 97.

5.1 EXERCISE SET

In Exercises 1–6, find the six trigonometric function values of the specified angle.

1.

2.

3.

4.

5.

6.

7. Given that $\sin \alpha = \dfrac{\sqrt{5}}{3}$, $\cos \alpha = \dfrac{2}{3}$, and

$\tan \alpha = \dfrac{\sqrt{5}}{2}$, find csc α, sec α, and cot α.

8. Given that $\sin \beta = \dfrac{2\sqrt{2}}{3}$, $\cos \beta = \dfrac{1}{3}$, and

$\tan \beta = 2\sqrt{2}$, find csc β, sec β, and cot β.

Given a function value of an acute angle, find the other five trigonometric function values.

9. $\sin \theta = \frac{24}{25}$

10. $\cos \sigma = 0.7$

11. $\tan \phi = 2$

12. $\cot \theta = \frac{1}{3}$

13. $\csc \theta = 1.5$

14. $\sec \beta = \sqrt{17}$

15. $\cos \beta = \dfrac{\sqrt{5}}{5}$

16. $\sin \sigma = \frac{10}{11}$

Find the exact function value.

17. cos 45°

18. tan 30°

19. sec 60°

20. sin 45°

21. cot 60°

22. csc 45°

23. sin 30°

24. cos 60°

25. tan 45°

26. sec 30°

27. csc 30°

28. tan 60°

29. *Distance Across a River.*   Find the distance a across the river.

30. *Distance Between Bases.*   A baseball diamond is actually a square 90 ft on a side. If a line is drawn from third base to first base, then a right triangle *QPH* is formed, where $\angle QPH$ is 45°. Using a trigonometric function, find the distance from third base to first base.

Convert to decimal degree notation. Round to two decimal places.

31. 9°43′

32. 52°15′

33. 35°50″

34. 64°53′

35. 3°2′

36. 19°47′23″

37. 49°38′46″

38. 76°11′34″

39. 15′5″

40. 68°2″

41. 5°53″

42. 44′10″

Convert to degrees, minutes, and seconds. Round to the nearest second.

43. 17.6°

44. 20.14°

45. 83.025°

46. 67.84°

47. 11.75°

48. 29.8°

49. 47.8268°

50. 0.253°

51. 0.9°

52. 30.2505°

53. 39.45°

54. 2.4°

Find the function value. Round to four decimal places.

55. cos 51°

56. cot 17°

57. tan 4°13′

58. sin 26.1°

59. sec 38.43°

60. cos 74°10′40″

61. cos 40.35°

62. csc 45.2°

63. sin 69°

64. tan 63°48′

65. tan 85.4°

66. cos 4°

67. csc 89.5°

68. sec 35.28°

69. cot 30°25′6″

70. sin 59.2°

Find the acute angle θ, to the nearest tenth of a degree, for the given function value.

71. $\sin \theta = 0.5125$

72. $\tan \theta = 2.032$

73. $\tan \theta = 0.2226$

74. $\cos \theta = 0.3842$

75. $\sin \theta = 0.9022$

76. $\tan \theta = 3.056$

77. $\cos \theta = 0.6879$

78. $\sin \theta = 0.4005$

79. $\cot \theta = 2.127$

$$\left(Hint: \tan \theta = \frac{1}{\cot \theta}. \right)$$

80. $\csc \theta = 1.147$

81. $\sec \theta = 1.279$

82. $\cot \theta = 1.351$

Find the exact acute angle θ for the given function value.

83. $\sin \theta = \dfrac{\sqrt{2}}{2}$

84. $\cot \theta = \dfrac{\sqrt{3}}{3}$

85. $\cos \theta = \dfrac{1}{2}$

86. $\sin \theta = \dfrac{1}{2}$

87. $\tan \theta = 1$

88. $\cos \theta = \dfrac{\sqrt{3}}{2}$

89. $\csc \theta = \dfrac{2\sqrt{3}}{3}$

90. $\tan \theta = \sqrt{3}$

91. $\cot \theta = \sqrt{3}$

92. $\sec \theta = \sqrt{2}$

Use the cofunction and reciprocal identities to complete each of the following.

93. $\cos 20° = \underline{\hspace{1cm}} 70° = \dfrac{1}{\underline{\hspace{0.7cm}} 20°}$

94. $\sin 64° = \underline{\hspace{1cm}} 26° = \dfrac{1}{\underline{\hspace{0.7cm}} 64°}$

95. $\tan 52° = \cot \underline{\hspace{1cm}} = \dfrac{1}{\underline{\hspace{0.7cm}} 52°}$

96. $\sec 13° = \csc \underline{\hspace{1cm}} = \dfrac{1}{\underline{\hspace{0.7cm}} 13°}$

97. Given that

sin 65° ≈ 0.9063,	cos 65° ≈ 0.4226,
tan 65° ≈ 2.1445,	cot 65° ≈ 0.4663,
sec 65° ≈ 2.3662,	csc 65° ≈ 1.1034,

find the six function values of 25°.

98. Given that

sin 8° ≈ 0.1392,	cos 8° ≈ 0.9903,
tan 8° ≈ 0.1405,	cot 8° ≈ 7.1154,
sec 8° ≈ 1.0098,	csc 8° ≈ 7.1853,

find the six function values of 82°.

99. Given that sin 71°10′5″ ≈ 0.9465, cos 71°10′5″ ≈ 0.3228, and tan 71°10′5″ ≈ 2.9321, find the six function values of 18°49′55″.

100. Given that sin 38.7° ≈ 0.6252, cos 38.7° ≈ 0.7804, and tan 38.7° ≈ 0.8012, find the six function values of 51.3°.

101. Given that sin 82° = *p*, cos 82° = *q*, and tan 82° = *r*, find the six function values of 8° in terms of *p*, *q*, and *r*.

Technology Connection

102. Using the TABLE feature, scroll through a table of values to find the acute angle θ in each of Exercises 71–80, to the nearest tenth of a degree, for the given function value.

Collaborative Discussion and Writing

103. Explain why it is not necessary to memorize the function values for both 30° and 60°.

104. Explain the difference between reciprocal functions and cofunctions.

Skill Maintenance

Graph the function.

105. $f(x) = e^{x/2}$

106. $f(x) = 2^{-x}$

107. $h(x) = \ln x$

108. $g(x) = \log_2 x$

Solve.

109. $5^x = 625$

110. $e^t = 10,000$

111. $\log_7 x = 3$

112. $\log(3x + 1) - \log(x - 1) = 2$

Synthesis

113. Given that $\sec \beta = 1.5304$, find $\sin(90° - \beta)$.

114. Find the six trigonometric function values of α.

115. Show that the area of this right triangle is $\frac{1}{2}bc \sin A$.

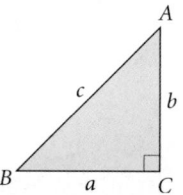

116. Show that the area of this triangle is $\frac{1}{2}ab \sin \theta$.

5.2

Applications of Right Triangles

◆ Solve right triangles.

◆ Solve applied problems involving right triangles and trigonometric functions.

◆ Solving Right Triangles

Now that we can find function values for any acute angle, it is possible to *solve* right triangles. To **solve** a triangle means to find the lengths of *all* sides and the measures of *all* angles.

EXAMPLE 1 In $\triangle ABC$ (shown on the following page), find a, b, and B, where a and b represent lengths of sides and B represents the measure of $\angle B$. Here we use standard lettering for naming the sides and angles of a right triangle: Side a is opposite angle A, side b is opposite angle B, where a and b are the legs, and side c, the hypotenuse, is opposite angle C, the right angle.

Solution In △*ABC*, we know three of the measures:

$$A = 61.7°, \qquad a = ?,$$
$$B = ?, \qquad b = ?,$$
$$C = 90°, \qquad c = 106.2.$$

Since the sum of the angle measures of any triangle is 180° and $C = 90°$, the sum of A and B is 90°. Thus,

$$B = 90° - A = 90° - 61.7° = 28.3°.$$

We are given an acute angle and the hypotenuse. This suggests that we can use the sine and cosine ratios to find a and b, respectively:

$$\sin 61.7° = \frac{\text{opp}}{\text{hyp}} = \frac{a}{106.2} \quad \text{and} \quad \cos 61.7° = \frac{\text{adj}}{\text{hyp}} = \frac{b}{106.2}.$$

Solving for a and b, we get

$$a = 106.2 \sin 61.7° \quad \text{and} \quad b = 106.2 \cos 61.7°$$
$$a \approx 93.5 \qquad\qquad\qquad b \approx 50.3.$$

Thus,

$$A = 61.7°, \qquad a \approx 93.5,$$
$$B = 28.3°, \qquad b \approx 50.3,$$
$$C = 90°, \qquad c = 106.2.$$

▶ **Now Try Exercise 1.**

EXAMPLE 2 In △*DEF* (shown at left), find D and F. Then find d.

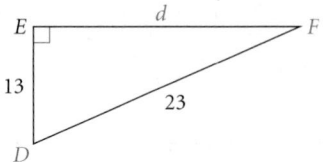

Solution In △*DEF*, we know three of the measures:

$$D = ?, \qquad d = ?,$$
$$E = 90°, \qquad e = 23,$$
$$F = ?, \qquad f = 13.$$

We know the side adjacent to D and the hypotenuse. This suggests the use of the cosine ratio:

$$\cos D = \frac{\text{adj}}{\text{hyp}} = \frac{13}{23}.$$

We now find the angle whose cosine is $\frac{13}{23}$. To the nearest hundredth of a degree,

$$D \approx 55.58°. \qquad \text{Pressing } \boxed{\text{2ND}} \ \boxed{\text{COS}} \ (13/23) \ \boxed{\text{ENTER}}$$

Since the sum of D and F is 90°, we can find F by subtracting:

$$F = 90° - D \approx 90° - 55.58° \approx 34.42°.$$

We could use the Pythagorean theorem to find d, but we will use a trigonometric function here. We could use $\cos F$, $\sin D$, or the tangent or cotangent ratios for either D or F. Let's use $\tan D$:

$$\tan D = \frac{\text{opp}}{\text{adj}} = \frac{d}{13}, \quad \text{or} \quad \tan 55.58° \approx \frac{d}{13}.$$

Then

$$d \approx 13 \tan 55.58° \approx 19.$$

The six measures are

$$D \approx 55.58°, \qquad d \approx 19,$$
$$E = 90°, \qquad e = 23,$$
$$F \approx 34.42°, \qquad f = 13.$$

▶ Now Try Exercise 5.

✦ Applications

Right triangles can be used to model and solve many applied problems in the real world.

North Rim

6.2 mi   50°

b

c

South Rim

EXAMPLE 3   *Hiking at the Grand Canyon.*   A backpacker hiking east along the North Rim of the Grand Canyon notices an unusual rock formation directly across the canyon. She decides to continue watching the landmark while hiking along the rim. In 2 hr, she has gone 6.2 mi due east and the landmark is still visible but at approximately a 50° angle to the North Rim. (See the figure at left.)

a) How many miles is she from the rock formation?

b) How far is it across the canyon from her starting point?

Solution

a) We know the side adjacent to the 50° angle and want to find the hypotenuse. We can use the cosine function:

$$\cos 50° = \frac{6.2 \text{ mi}}{c}$$

$$c = \frac{6.2 \text{ mi}}{\cos 50°} \approx 9.6 \text{ mi}.$$

After hiking 6.2 mi, she is approximately 9.6 mi from the rock formation.

b) We know the side adjacent to the 50° angle and want to find the opposite side. We can use the tangent function:

$$\tan 50° = \frac{b}{6.2 \text{ mi}}$$

$$b = 6.2 \text{ mi} \cdot \tan 50° \approx 7.4 \text{ mi}.$$

Thus it is approximately 7.4 mi across the canyon from her starting point.

▶ Now Try Exercise 19.

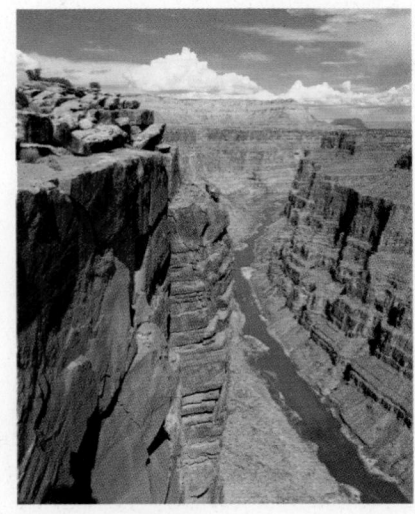

EXAMPLE 4   *Rafters for a House.*   House framers can use trigonometric functions to determine the lengths of rafters for a house. They first choose the pitch of the roof, or the ratio of the rise over the run. Then using a triangle with that ratio, they calculate the length of the rafter needed for the house. José is constructing rafters for a roof with a 10/12 pitch on a house that is 42 ft wide. Find the length x of the rafter of the house to the nearest tenth of a foot.

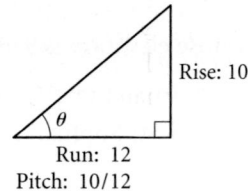

Rise: 10
Run: 12
Pitch: 10/12

Solution We first find the angle θ that the rafter makes with the side wall. We know the rise, 10, and the run, 12, so we can use the tangent function to determine the angle that corresponds to the pitch of $10/12$:

$$\tan \theta = \frac{10}{12} \approx 0.8333.$$

Thus, $\theta \approx 39.8°$. Since trigonometric function values of θ depend only on the measure of the angle and not on the size of the triangle, the angle for the rafter is also $39.8°$.

To determine the length x of the rafter, we can use the cosine function. (See the figure at left.) Note that the width of the house is 42 ft, and a leg of this triangle is half that length, 21 ft.

$$\cos 39.8° = \frac{21 \text{ ft}}{x}$$

$x \cos 39.8° = 21$ ft   Multiplying by x

$$x = \frac{21 \text{ ft}}{\cos 39.8°} \qquad \text{Dividing by } \cos 39.8°$$

$$x \approx 27.3 \text{ ft}$$

The length of the rafter for this house is approximately 27.3 ft.

▷ **Now Try Exercise 31.**

Many applications with right triangles involve an *angle of elevation* or an *angle of depression*. The angle between the horizontal and a line of sight above the horizontal is called an **angle of elevation.** The angle between the horizontal and a line of sight below the horizontal is called an **angle of depression.** For example, suppose that you are looking straight ahead and then you move your eyes up to look at an approaching airplane. The angle that your eyes pass through is an angle of elevation. If the pilot of the plane is looking forward and then looks down, the pilot's eyes pass through an angle of depression.

EXAMPLE 5 *Gondola Aerial Lift.* In Telluride, Colorado, there is a free gondola ride that provides a spectacular view of the town and the surrounding mountains. The gondolas that begin in the town at an elevation of 8725 ft travel 5750 ft to Station St. Sophia, whose altitude is 10,550 ft. They then continue 3913 ft to Mountain Village, whose elevation is 9500 ft.

a) What is the angle of elevation from the town to Station St. Sophia?

b) What is the angle of depression from Station St. Sophia to Mountain Village?

Solution We begin by labeling a drawing with the given information.

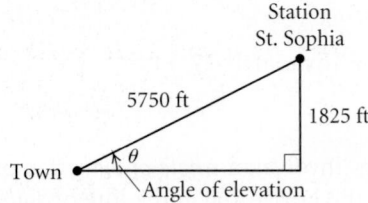

a) The difference in the elevation of Station St. Sophia and the elevation of the town is 10,550 ft − 8725 ft, or 1825 ft. This measure is the length of the side opposite the angle of elevation, θ, in the right triangle shown at left. Since we know the side opposite θ and the hypotenuse, we can find θ by using the sine function. We first find $\sin \theta$:

$$\sin \theta = \frac{1825 \text{ ft}}{5750 \text{ ft}} \approx 0.3174.$$

Using a calculator, we find that

$\theta \approx 18.5°.$ Pressing **2ND** **SIN** 0.3174 **ENTER**

Thus the angle of elevation from the town to Station St. Sophia is approximately 18.5°.

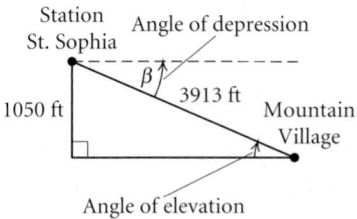

Station St. Sophia — Angle of depression

β — 3913 ft

1050 ft — Mountain Village

Angle of elevation

b) When parallel lines are cut by a transversal, alternate interior angles are equal. Thus the angle of depression, β, from Station St. Sophia to Mountain Village is equal to the angle of elevation from Mountain Village to Station St. Sophia, so we can use the right triangle shown at left.

The difference in the elevation of Station St. Sophia and the elevation of Mountain Village is 10,550 ft − 9500 ft, or 1050 ft. Since we know the side opposite the angle of elevation and the hypotenuse, we can again use the sine function:

$$\sin \beta = \frac{1050 \text{ ft}}{3913 \text{ ft}} \approx 0.2683.$$

Using a calculator, we find that

$$\beta = 15.6°.$$

The angle of depression from Station St. Sophia to Mountain Village is approximately 15.6°.

▶ Now Try Exercise 17.

EXAMPLE 6 *Cloud Height.* To measure cloud height at night, a vertical beam of light is directed on a spot on the cloud. From a point 135 ft away from the light source, the angle of elevation to the spot is found to be 67.35°. Find the height of the cloud.

h

67.35°

135 ft

Solution From the figure, we have

$$\tan 67.35° = \frac{h}{135 \text{ ft}}$$

$$h = 135 \text{ ft} \cdot \tan 67.35° \approx 324 \text{ ft}.$$

The height of the cloud is about 324 ft.

▶ Now Try Exercise 21.

Some applications of trigonometry involve the concept of direction, or bearing. In this text we present two ways of giving direction, the first below and the second in Exercise Set 5.3.

Bearing: First-Type

One method of giving direction, or bearing, involves reference to a north–south line using an acute angle. For example, N55°W means 55° west of north and S67°E means 67° east of south.

EXAMPLE 7 *Distance to a Forest Fire.* A forest ranger at point *A* sights a fire directly south. A second ranger at point *B*, 7.5 mi east, sights the same fire at a bearing of S27°23′W. How far from *A* is the fire?

Solution We first find the complement of 27°23′:

$$B = 90° - 27°23'$$ Angle *B* is opposite side *d* in the right triangle.

$$= 62°37'$$

$$\approx 62.62°.$$

From the figure shown above, we see that the desired distance *d* is part of a right triangle. We have

$$\frac{d}{7.5 \text{ mi}} \approx \tan 62.62°$$

$$d \approx 7.5 \text{ mi} \tan 62.62° \approx 14.5 \text{ mi}.$$

The forest ranger at point *A* is about 14.5 mi from the fire.

 Now Try Exercise 35.

EXAMPLE 8 *U.S. Cellular Field.* In U.S. Cellular Field, the home of the Chicago White Sox baseball team, the first row of seats in the upper deck is farther away from home plate than the last row of seats in the original Comiskey Park. Although there is no obstructed view in the U.S. Cellular Field, some of the fans still complain about the present distance from home plate to the upper deck of seats. (*Source*: *Chicago Tribune*, September 19, 1993) From a seat in the last row of the upper deck directly behind the batter, the angle of depression to home plate is 29.9°, and the angle of depression to the pitcher's mound is 24.2°. Find **(a)** the viewing distance to home plate and **(b)** the viewing distance to the pitcher's mound.

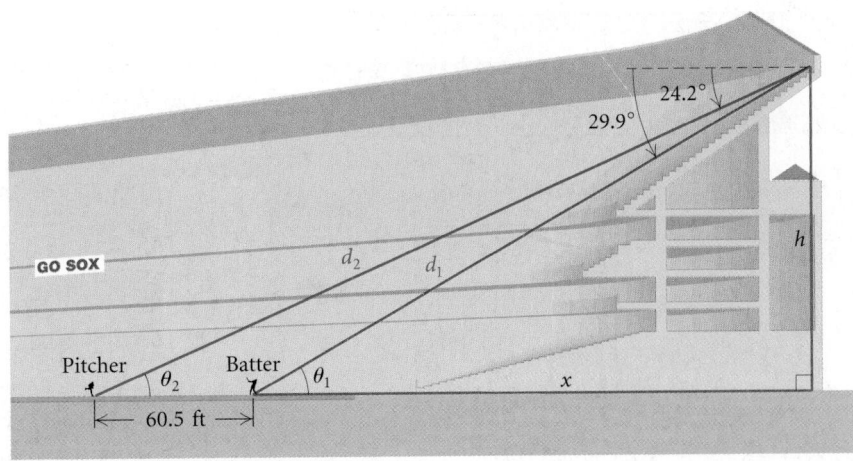

Solution From geometry we know that $\theta_1 = 29.9°$ and $\theta_2 = 24.2°$. The standard distance from home plate to the pitcher's mound is 60.5 ft. In the drawing, we let d_1 be the viewing distance to home plate, d_2 the viewing distance to the pitcher's mound, h the elevation of the last row, and x the horizontal distance from the batter to a point directly below the seat in the last row of the upper deck.

We begin by determining the distance x. We use the tangent function with $\theta_1 = 29.9°$ and $\theta_2 = 24.2°$:

$$\tan 29.9° = \frac{h}{x} \qquad \text{and} \qquad \tan 24.2° = \frac{h}{x + 60.5}$$

or $\qquad\qquad h = x \tan 29.9° \quad$ and $\qquad\qquad h = (x + 60.5) \tan 24.2°.$

Then substituting $x \tan 29.9°$ for h in the second equation, we obtain

$$x \tan 29.9° = (x + 60.5) \tan 24.2°.$$

Solving for x, we get

$$x \tan 29.9° = x \tan 24.2° + 60.5 \tan 24.2°$$
$$x \tan 29.9° - x \tan 24.2° = x \tan 24.2° + 60.5 \tan 24.2° - x \tan 24.2°$$
$$x(\tan 29.9° - \tan 24.2°) = 60.5 \tan 24.2°$$
$$x = \frac{60.5 \tan 24.2°}{\tan 29.9° - \tan 24.2°}$$
$$x \approx 216.5.$$

We can then find d_1 and d_2 using the cosine function:

$$\cos 29.9° = \frac{216.5}{d_1} \qquad \text{and} \qquad \cos 24.2° = \frac{216.5 + 60.5}{d_2}$$

or $\qquad\qquad d_1 = \frac{216.5}{\cos 29.9°} \quad$ and $\qquad\qquad d_2 = \frac{277}{\cos 24.2°}$

$$d_1 \approx 249.7 \qquad\qquad\qquad d_2 \approx 303.7.$$

The distance to home plate is about 250 ft (In the original Comiskey Park, the distance to home plate was only 150 ft.), and the distance to the pitcher's mound is about 304 ft.

5.2 EXERCISE SET

In Exercises 1–6, solve the right triangle.

1.

2.

3.

4.

5.

6.

In Exercises 7–16, solve the right triangle. (Standard lettering has been used.)

7. $A = 87°43'$, $a = 9.73$

8. $a = 12.5$, $b = 18.3$

9. $b = 100$, $c = 450$

10. $B = 56.5°$, $c = 0.0447$

11. $A = 47.58°$, $c = 48.3$

12. $B = 20.6°$, $a = 7.5$

13. $A = 35°$, $b = 40$

14. $B = 69.3°$, $b = 93.4$

15. $b = 1.86$, $c = 4.02$

16. $a = 10.2$, $c = 20.4$

17. *Aerial Photography.* An aerial photographer who photographs farm properties for a real estate company has determined from experience that the best photo is taken at a height of approximately 475 ft and a distance of 850 ft from the farmhouse. What is the angle of depression from the plane to the house?

18. *Memorial Flag Case.* A tradition in the United States is to drape an American flag over the casket of a deceased U.S. Forces veteran. At the burial, the flag is removed, folded into a triangle, and presented to the family. The folded flag will fit in an isosceles right triangle case, as shown below. The inside dimension across the bottom is $21\frac{1}{2}$ in. (*Source:* Bruce Kieffer, *Woodworker's Journal,* August 2006). Using trigonometric functions, find the length x and round the answer to the nearest tenth of an inch.

19. *Safety Line to Raft.* Each spring Bryan uses his vacation time to ready his lake property for the summer. He wants to run a new safety line from point *B* on the shore to the corner of the anchored diving raft. The current safety line, which runs perpendicular to the shore line to point *A*, is 40 ft long. He estimates the angle from *B* to the corner of the raft to be 50°. Approximately how much rope does he need for the new safety line if he allows 5 ft of rope at each end to fasten the rope?

20. *Enclosing an Area.* Alicia is enclosing a triangular area in a corner of her fenced rectangular backyard for her Labrador retriever. In order for a certain tree to be included in this pen, one side needs to be 14.5 ft and make a 53° angle with the new side. How long is the new side?

21. *Height of a Tree.* A supervisor must train a new team of loggers to estimate the heights of trees. As an example, she walks off 40 ft from the base of a tree and estimates the angle of elevation to the tree's peak to be 70°. Approximately how tall is the tree?

22. *Easel Display.* A marketing group is designing an easel to display posters advertising their

newest products. They want the easel to be 6 ft tall and the back of it to fit flush against a wall. For optimal eye contact, the best angle between the front and back legs of the easel is 23°. How far from the wall should the front legs be placed in order to obtain this angle?

23. *Golden Gate Bridge.* The Golden Gate Bridge has two main towers of equal height that support the two main cables. A visitor on a tour ship passing through San Francisco Bay views the top of one of the towers and estimates the angle of elevation to be 30°. After sailing 670 ft closer, he estimates the angle of elevation to this same tower to be 50°. Approximate the height of the tower to the nearest foot.

24. *Sand Dunes National Park.* While visiting the Sand Dunes National Park in Colorado, Cole approximated the angle of elevation to the top of a sand dune to be 20°. After walking 800 ft closer, he guessed that the angle of elevation had increased by 15°. Approximately how tall is the dune he was observing?

25. *Inscribed Pentagon.* A regular pentagon is inscribed in a circle of radius 15.8 cm. Find the perimeter of the pentagon.

26. *Height of a Weather Balloon.* A weather balloon is directly west of two observing stations that are 10 mi apart. The angles of elevation of the balloon from the two stations are 17.6° and 78.2°. How high is the balloon?

27. *Height of a Kite.* For a science fair project, a group of students tested different materials used to construct kites. Their instructor provided an instrument that accurately measures the angle of elevation. In one of the tests, the angle of elevation was 63.4° with 670 ft of string out. Assuming the string was taut, how high was the kite?

28. *Height of a Building.* A window washer on a ladder looks at a nearby building 100 ft away, noting that the angle of elevation to the top of the building is 18.7° and the angle of depression to the bottom of the building is 6.5°. How tall is the nearby building?

29. *Quilt Design.* Nancy is designing a quilt that she will enter in the quilt competition at the State Fair. The quilt consists of twelve identical squares with 4 rows of 3 squares each. Each square is to have a regular octagon inscribed in a circle, as shown in the figure. Each side of the octagon is to be 7 in. long. Find the radius of the circumscribed circle and the dimensions of the quilt. Round the answers to the nearest hundredth of an inch.

30. *Rafters for a House.* Blaise, an architect for luxury homes, is designing a house that is 46 ft wide with a roof whose pitch is 11/12. Determine the length of the rafters needed for this house. Round the answer to the nearest tenth of a foot.

31. *Rafters for a Medical Office.* The pitch of the roof for a medical office needs to be 5/12. If the building is 33 ft wide, how long must the rafters be?

32. *Angle of Elevation.* What is the angle of elevation of the sun when a 35-ft mast casts a 20-ft shadow?

33. *Distance Between Towns.* From a hot-air balloon 2 km high, the angles of depression to two towns in line with the balloon are 81.2° and 13.5°. How far apart are the towns?

34. *Distance from a Lighthouse.* From the top of a lighthouse 55 ft above sea level, the angle of depression to a small boat is 11.3°. How far from the foot of the lighthouse is the boat?

35. *Lightning Detection.* In extremely large forests, it is not cost-effective to position forest rangers in towers or to use small aircraft to continually watch for fires. Since lightning is a frequent cause of fire, lightning detectors are now commonly used instead. These devices not only give a bearing on the location but also measure the intensity of the lightning. A detector at point *Q* is situated 15 mi west of a central fire station at point *R*. The bearing from *Q* to where lightning hits due south of *R* is S37.6°E. How far is the hit from point *R*?

36. *Length of an Antenna.* A vertical antenna is mounted atop a 50-ft pole. From a point on level ground 75 ft from the base of the pole, the

antenna subtends an angle of 10.5°. Find the
length of the antenna.

75 ft

50 ft

10.5°

37. *Lobster Boat.*   A lobster boat is situated due west
of a lighthouse. A barge is 12 km south of the
lobster boat. From the barge, the bearing to the
lighthouse is N63°20′E. How far is the lobster
boat from the lighthouse?

12 km

63° 20′

North

Collaborative Discussion and Writing

38. Explain in your own words five ways in which
length c can be determined in this triangle.
Which way seems the most efficient?

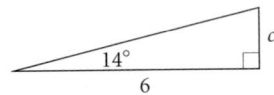

14°

6

c

39. In this section, the trigonometric functions have
been defined as functions of acute angles. Thus
the set of angles whose measures are greater than
0° and less than 90° is the domain for each
function. What appear to be the ranges for the
sine, the cosine, and the tangent functions given
this domain?

Skill Maintenance

Find the distance between the points.

40. $(-9, 3)$ and $(0, 0)$

41. $(8, -2)$ and $(-6, -4)$

42. Convert to a logarithmic equation: $e^4 = t$.

43. Convert to an exponential equation:
$\log 0.001 = -3$.

Synthesis

44. Find a, to the nearest tenth.

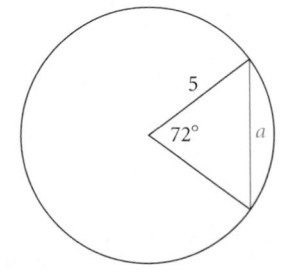

5

72°

a

45. Find h, to the nearest tenth.

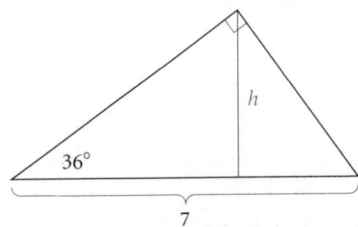

36°

7

h

46. *Diameter of a Pipe.*   A V-gauge is used to find
the diameter of a pipe. The advantage of such a
device is that it is rugged, it is accurate, and it has
no moving parts to break down. In the figure, the
measure of angle AVB is 54°. A pipe is placed in
the V-shaped slot and the distance VP is used to
estimate the diameter. The line VP is calibrated
by listing as its units the corresponding diam-
eters. This, in effect, establishes a function
between VP and d.

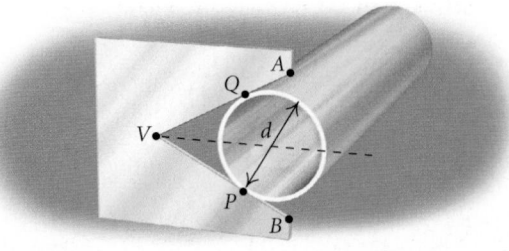

a) Suppose that the diameter of a pipe is 2 cm.
   What is the distance VP?

b) Suppose that the distance VP is 3.93 cm. What
   is the diameter of the pipe?

c) Find a formula for d in terms of VP.

d) Find a formula for VP in terms of d.

47. *Construction of Picnic Pavilions.*   A construction company is mass-producing picnic pavilions for national parks, as shown in the figure. The rafter ends are to be sawed in such a way that they will be vertical when in place. The front is 8 ft high, the back is $6\frac{1}{2}$ ft high, and the distance between the front and back is 8 ft. At what angle should the rafters be cut?

8 ft

$6\frac{1}{2}$ ft

8 ft

48. *Measuring the Radius of the Earth.*   One way to measure the radius of the earth is to climb to the top of a mountain whose height above sea level is known and measure the angle between a vertical line to the center of the earth from the top of the mountain and a line drawn from the top of the mountain to the horizon, as shown in the figure. The height of Mt. Shasta in California is 14,162 ft. From the top of Mt. Shasta, one can see the horizon on the Pacific Ocean. The angle formed between a line to the horizon and the vertical is found to be 87°53′.

Use this information to estimate the radius of the earth, in miles.

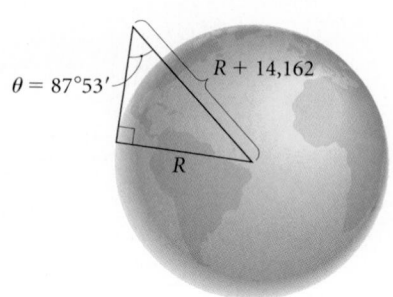

$\theta = 87°53'$

$R + 14,162$

R

49. *Sound of an Airplane.*   It is common experience to hear the sound of a low-flying airplane and look at the wrong place in the sky to see the plane. Suppose that a plane is traveling directly at you at a speed of 200 mph and an altitude of 3000 ft, and you hear the sound at what seems to be an angle of inclination of 20°. At what angle θ should you actually look in order to see the plane? Consider the speed of sound to be 1100 ft/sec.

Perceived location of plane

Actual location of plane when heard

P

A

3000 ft

θ

20°

V

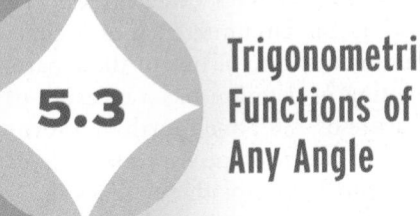

5.3 Trigonometric Functions of Any Angle

◆ Find angles that are coterminal with a given angle and find the complement and the supplement of a given angle.

◆ Determine the six trigonometric function values for any angle in standard position when the coordinates of a point on the terminal side are given.

◆ Find the function values for any angle whose terminal side lies on an axis.

◆ Find the function values for an angle whose terminal side makes an angle of 30°, 45°, or 60° with the *x*-axis.

◆ Use a calculator to find function values and angles.

◆ Angles, Rotations, and Degree Measure

An *angle* is a familiar figure in the world around us.

An **angle** is the union of two rays with a common endpoint called the **vertex.** In trigonometry, we often think of an angle as a **rotation.** To do so, think of locating a ray along the positive *x*-axis with its endpoint at the origin. This ray is called the **initial side** of the angle. Though we leave that ray fixed, think of making a copy of it and rotating it. A rotation *counterclockwise* is a **positive rotation,** and a rotation *clockwise* is a **negative rotation.** The ray at the end of the rotation is called the **terminal side** of the angle. The angle formed is said to be in **standard position.**

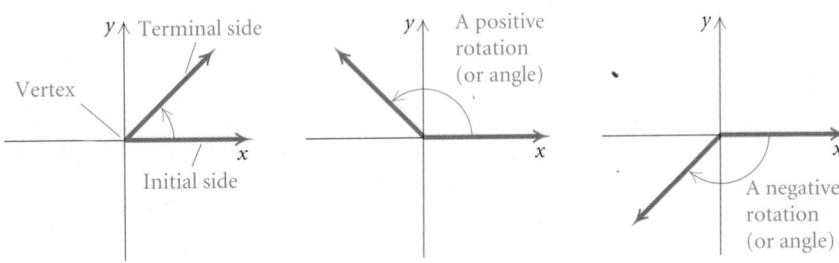

The measure of an angle or rotation may be given in degrees. The Babylonians developed the idea of dividing the circumference of a circle into 360 equal parts, or degrees. If we let the measure of one of these parts be 1°, then one complete positive revolution or rotation has a measure of 360°. One half of a revolution has a measure of 180°, one fourth of a revolution has a measure of 90°, and so on. We can also speak of an angle of measure 60°, 135°, 330°, or 420°. The terminal sides of these angles lie in quadrants I, II, IV, and I, respectively. The negative rotations −30°, −110°, and −225° represent angles with terminal sides in quadrants IV, III, and II, respectively.

If two or more angles have the same terminal side, the angles are said to be **coterminal.** To find angles coterminal with a given angle, we add or subtract multiples of 360°. For example, 420°, shown above, has the same terminal side as 60°, since 420° = 360° + 60°. Thus we say that angles of measure 60° and 420° are coterminal. The negative rotation that measures −300° is also coterminal with 60° because 60° − 360° = −300°. The set of all angles coterminal with 60° can be expressed as 60° + $n \cdot$ 360°, where n is an integer. Other examples of coterminal angles shown above are 90° and −270°, −90° and 270°, 135° and −225°, −30° and 330°, and −110° and 610°.

EXAMPLE 1 Find two positive and two negative angles that are coterminal with (a) 51° and (b) −7°.

Solution

a) We add and subtract multiples of 360°. Many answers are possible.

$$51° + 360° = 411° \qquad 51° + 3(360°) = 1131°$$

$$51° - 360° = -309° \qquad 51° - 2(360°) = -669°$$

Thus angles of measure 411°, 1131°, −309°, and −669° are coterminal with 51°.

b) We have the following:

$$-7° + 360° = 353°, \qquad -7° + 2(360°) = 713°,$$
$$-7° - 360° = -367°, \qquad -7° - 10(360°) = -3607°.$$

Thus angles of measure 353°, 713°, −367°, and −3607° are coterminal with −7°. ▶ Now Try Exercise 13.

Angles can be classified by their measures, as seen in the following figure.

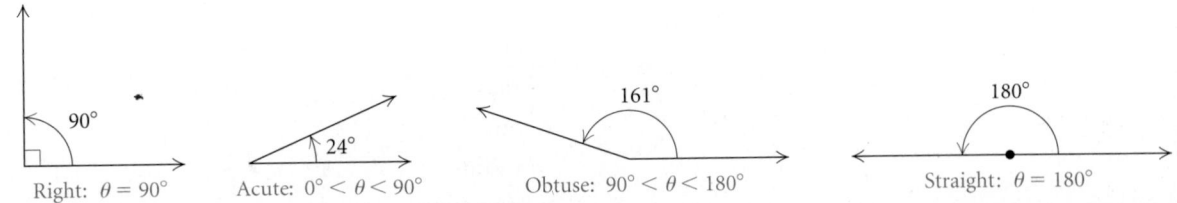

Right: $\theta = 90°$ Acute: $0° < \theta < 90°$ Obtuse: $90° < \theta < 180°$ Straight: $\theta = 180°$

Recall that two acute angles are **complementary** if their sum is 90°. For example, angles that measure 10° and 80° are complementary because 10° + 80° = 90°. Two positive angles are **supplementary** if their sum is

180°. For example, angles that measure 45° and 135° are supplementary because 45° + 135° = 180°.

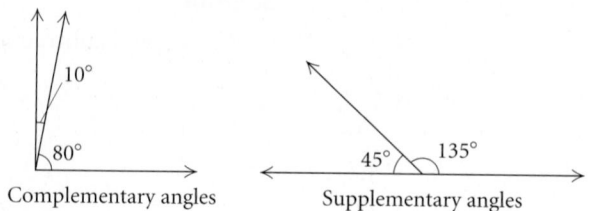

Complementary angles   Supplementary angles

EXAMPLE 2   Find the complement and the supplement of 71.46°.

Solution   We have

$$90° - 71.46° = 18.54°,$$
$$180° - 71.46° = 108.54°.$$

Thus the complement of 71.46° is 18.54° and the supplement is 108.54°.

▶ Now Try Exercise 19.

✦ Trigonometric Functions of Angles or Rotations

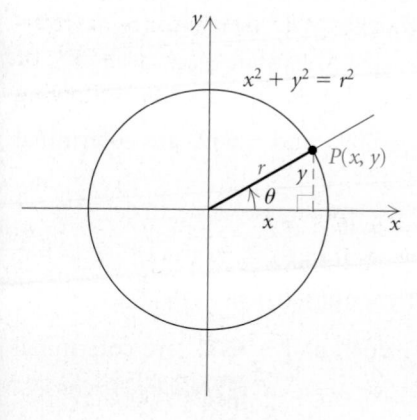

Many applied problems in trigonometry involve the use of angles that are not acute. Thus we need to extend the domains of the trigonometric functions defined in Section 5.1 to angles, or rotations, of *any* size. To do this, we first consider a right triangle with one vertex at the origin of a coordinate system and one vertex *on the positive x-axis*. (See the figure at left.) The other vertex is at P, a point on the circle whose center is at the origin and whose radius r is the length of the hypotenuse of the triangle. This triangle is a **reference triangle** for angle θ, which is in standard position. Note that y is the length of the side opposite θ and x is the length of the side adjacent to θ.

Recalling the definitions in Section 5.1, we note that three of the trigonometric functions of angle θ are defined as follows:

$$\sin \theta = \frac{\text{opp}}{\text{hyp}} = \frac{y}{r}, \qquad \cos \theta = \frac{\text{adj}}{\text{hyp}} = \frac{x}{r}, \qquad \tan \theta = \frac{\text{opp}}{\text{adj}} = \frac{y}{x}.$$

Since x and y are the coordinates of the point P and the length of the radius is the length of the hypotenuse, we can also define these functions as follows:

$$\sin \theta = \frac{y\text{-coordinate}}{\text{radius}},$$

$$\cos \theta = \frac{x\text{-coordinate}}{\text{radius}},$$

$$\tan \theta = \frac{y\text{-coordinate}}{x\text{-coordinate}}.$$

We will use these definitions for functions of angles of any measure. The following figures show angles whose terminal sides lie in quadrants II, III, and IV.

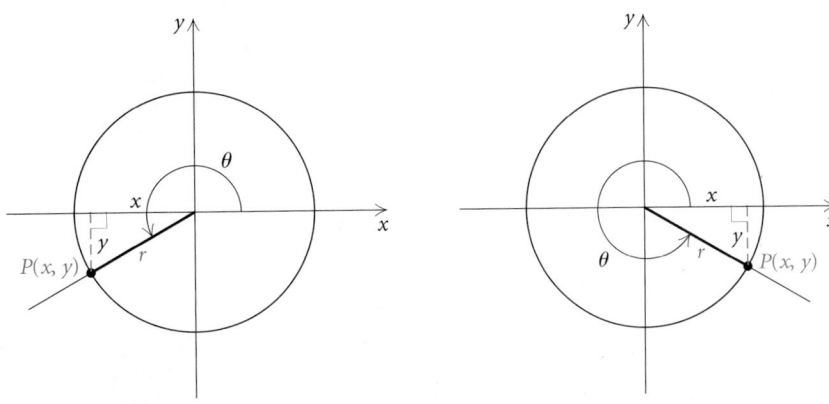

A reference triangle can be drawn for angles in any quadrant, as shown. Note that the angle is in standard position; that is, it is always measured from the positive half of the x-axis. The point $P(x, y)$ is a point, other than the vertex, on the terminal side of the angle. Each of its two coordinates may be positive, negative, or zero, depending on the location of the terminal side. *The length of the radius, which is also the length of the hypotenuse of the reference triangle, is always considered positive.* (Note that $x^2 + y^2 = r^2$, or $r = \sqrt{x^2 + y^2}$.) Regardless of the location of P, we have the following definitions.

Trigonometric Functions of Any Angle θ

Suppose that $P(x, y)$ is any point other than the vertex on the terminal side of any angle θ in standard position, and r is the radius, or distance from the origin to $P(x, y)$. Then the trigonometric functions are defined as follows:

$$\sin \theta = \frac{y\text{-coordinate}}{\text{radius}} = \frac{y}{r}, \qquad \csc \theta = \frac{\text{radius}}{y\text{-coordinate}} = \frac{r}{y},$$

$$\cos \theta = \frac{x\text{-coordinate}}{\text{radius}} = \frac{x}{r}, \qquad \sec \theta = \frac{\text{radius}}{x\text{-coordinate}} = \frac{r}{x},$$

$$\tan \theta = \frac{y\text{-coordinate}}{x\text{-coordinate}} = \frac{y}{x}, \qquad \cot \theta = \frac{x\text{-coordinate}}{y\text{-coordinate}} = \frac{x}{y}.$$

Values of the trigonometric functions can be positive, negative, or zero, depending on where the terminal side of the angle lies. The length of the radius is always positive. Thus the signs of the function values depend only on the coordinates of the point P on the terminal side of the angle. In the first quadrant, all function values are positive because both coordinates are positive. In the second quadrant, first coordinates are negative and second coordinates are positive; thus only the sine and the cosecant values are positive. Similarly, we can determine the signs of the function values in the third and fourth quadrants. *Because of the reciprocal relationships, we need learn only the signs for the sine, cosine, and tangent functions.*

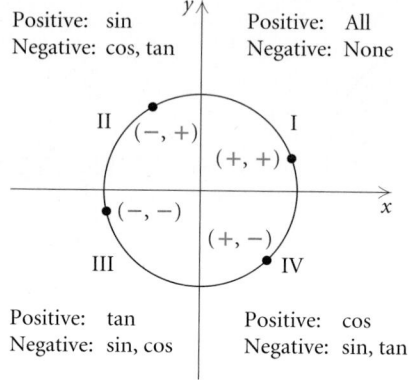

EXAMPLE 3 Find the six trigonometric function values for each angle shown.

a)

b)

c)
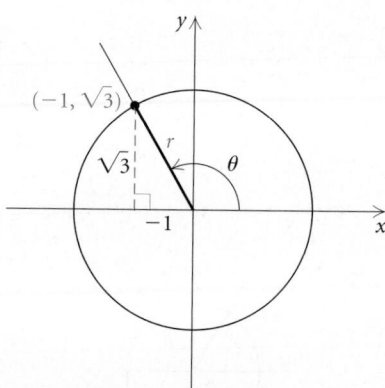

Solution

a) We first determine r, the distance from the origin $(0,0)$ to the point $(-4, -3)$. The distance between $(0,0)$ and any point (x, y) on the terminal side of the angle is

$$r = \sqrt{(x-0)^2 + (y-0)^2}$$
$$= \sqrt{x^2 + y^2}.$$

Substituting -4 for x and -3 for y, we find

$$r = \sqrt{(-4)^2 + (-3)^2}$$
$$= \sqrt{16 + 9} = \sqrt{25} = 5.$$

Using the definitions of the trigonometric functions, we can now find the function values of θ. We substitute -4 for x, -3 for y, and 5 for r:

$$\sin \theta = \frac{y}{r} = \frac{-3}{5} = -\frac{3}{5}, \qquad \csc \theta = \frac{r}{y} = \frac{5}{-3} = -\frac{5}{3},$$

$$\cos \theta = \frac{x}{r} = \frac{-4}{5} = -\frac{4}{5}, \qquad \sec \theta = \frac{r}{x} = \frac{5}{-4} = -\frac{5}{4},$$

$$\tan \theta = \frac{y}{x} = \frac{-3}{-4} = \frac{3}{4}, \qquad \cot \theta = \frac{x}{y} = \frac{-4}{-3} = \frac{4}{3}.$$

As expected, the tangent and the cotangent values are positive and the other four are negative. This is true for all angles in quadrant III.

b) We first determine r, the distance from the origin to the point $(1, -1)$:

$$r = \sqrt{1^2 + (-1)^2} = \sqrt{1 + 1} = \sqrt{2}.$$

Substituting 1 for x, -1 for y, and $\sqrt{2}$ for r, we find

$$\sin \theta = \frac{y}{r} = \frac{-1}{\sqrt{2}} = -\frac{\sqrt{2}}{2}, \qquad \csc \theta = \frac{r}{y} = \frac{\sqrt{2}}{-1} = -\sqrt{2},$$

$$\cos \theta = \frac{x}{r} = \frac{1}{\sqrt{2}} = \frac{\sqrt{2}}{2}, \qquad \sec \theta = \frac{r}{x} = \frac{\sqrt{2}}{1} = \sqrt{2},$$

$$\tan \theta = \frac{y}{x} = \frac{-1}{1} = -1, \qquad \cot \theta = \frac{x}{y} = \frac{1}{-1} = -1.$$

c) We determine r, the distance from the origin to the point $\left(-1, \sqrt{3}\right)$:

$$r = \sqrt{(-1)^2 + \left(\sqrt{3}\right)^2} = \sqrt{1 + 3} = \sqrt{4} = 2.$$

Substituting -1 for x, $\sqrt{3}$ for y, and 2 for r, we find the trigonometric function values of θ are

$$\sin \theta = \frac{\sqrt{3}}{2}, \qquad \csc \theta = \frac{2}{\sqrt{3}} = \frac{2\sqrt{3}}{3},$$

$$\cos \theta = \frac{-1}{2} = -\frac{1}{2}, \qquad \sec \theta = \frac{2}{-1} = -2,$$

$$\tan \theta = \frac{\sqrt{3}}{-1} = -\sqrt{3}, \qquad \cot \theta = \frac{-1}{\sqrt{3}} = -\frac{\sqrt{3}}{3}.$$

▶ **Now Try Exercise 27.**

Any point other than the origin on the terminal side of an angle in standard position can be used to determine the trigonometric function values of that angle. The function values are the same regardless of which point is used. To illustrate this, let's consider an angle θ in standard position whose terminal side lies on the line $y = -\frac{1}{2}x$. We can determine two second-quadrant solutions of the equation, find the length r for each point, and then compare the sine, cosine, and tangent function values using each point.

If $x = -4$, then $y = -\frac{1}{2}(-4) = 2$.

If $x = -8$, then $y = -\frac{1}{2}(-8) = 4$.

For $(-4, 2)$, $r = \sqrt{(-4)^2 + 2^2} = \sqrt{20} = 2\sqrt{5}$.

For $(-8, 4)$, $r = \sqrt{(-8)^2 + 4^2} = \sqrt{80} = 4\sqrt{5}$.

Using $(-4, 2)$ and $r = 2\sqrt{5}$, we find that

$$\sin \theta = \frac{2}{2\sqrt{5}} = \frac{1}{\sqrt{5}} = \frac{\sqrt{5}}{5}, \qquad \cos \theta = \frac{-4}{2\sqrt{5}} = \frac{-2}{\sqrt{5}} = -\frac{2\sqrt{5}}{5},$$

and $\tan \theta = \dfrac{2}{-4} = -\dfrac{1}{2}$.

Using $(-8, 4)$ and $r = 4\sqrt{5}$, we find that

$$\sin \theta = \frac{4}{4\sqrt{5}} = \frac{1}{\sqrt{5}} = \frac{\sqrt{5}}{5}, \qquad \cos \theta = \frac{-8}{4\sqrt{5}} = \frac{-2}{\sqrt{5}} = -\frac{2\sqrt{5}}{5},$$

and $\tan \theta = \dfrac{4}{-8} = -\dfrac{1}{2}$.

We see that the function values are the same using either point. Any point other than the origin on the terminal side of an angle can be used to determine the trigonometric function values.

> The trigonometric function values of θ depend only on the angle, not on the choice of the point on the terminal side that is used to compute them.

✦ The Six Functions Related

When we know one of the function values of an angle, we can find the other five if we know the quadrant in which the terminal side lies. The procedure is to sketch a reference triangle in the appropriate quadrant, use the Pythagorean theorem as needed to find the lengths of its sides, and then find the ratios of the sides.

EXAMPLE 4   Given that $\tan \theta = -\frac{2}{3}$ and θ is in the second quadrant, find the other function values.

Solution   We first sketch a second-quadrant angle. Since

$$\tan \theta = \frac{y}{x} = -\frac{2}{3} = \frac{2}{-3}, \qquad \text{Expressing } -\frac{2}{3} \text{ as } \frac{2}{-3} \text{ since } \theta \text{ is in}$$
$$\text{quadrant II}$$

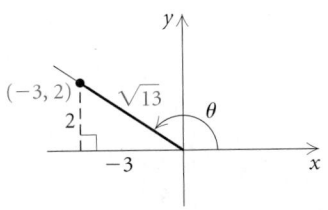

we make the legs lengths 2 and 3. The hypotenuse must then have length $\sqrt{2^2 + 3^2}$, or $\sqrt{13}$. Now we read off the appropriate ratios:

$$\sin \theta = \frac{2}{\sqrt{13}}, \quad \text{or} \quad \frac{2\sqrt{13}}{13}, \qquad \csc \theta = \frac{\sqrt{13}}{2},$$

$$\cos \theta = -\frac{3}{\sqrt{13}}, \quad \text{or} \quad -\frac{3\sqrt{13}}{13}, \qquad \sec \theta = -\frac{\sqrt{13}}{3},$$

$$\tan \theta = -\frac{2}{3}, \qquad \cot \theta = -\frac{3}{2}.$$

▶ Now Try Exercise 33.

✦ Terminal Side on an Axis

An angle whose terminal side falls on one of the axes is a **quadrantal angle.** One of the coordinates of any point on that side is 0. The definitions of the trigonometric functions still apply, but in some cases, function values will not be defined because a denominator will be 0.

EXAMPLE 5 Find the sine, cosine, and tangent values for 90°, 180°, 270°, and 360°.

Solution We first make a drawing of each angle in standard position and label a point on the terminal side. Since the function values are the same for all points on the terminal side, we choose $(0, 1)$, $(-1, 0)$, $(0, -1)$, and $(1, 0)$ for convenience. Note that $r = 1$ for each choice.

   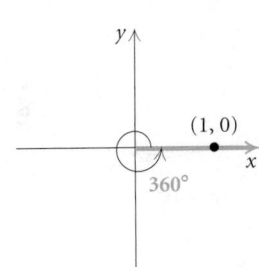

Then by the definitions we get

$$\sin 90° = \frac{1}{1} = 1, \qquad \sin 180° = \frac{0}{1} = 0, \qquad \sin 270° = \frac{-1}{1} = -1, \qquad \sin 360° = \frac{0}{1} = 0,$$

$$\cos 90° = \frac{0}{1} = 0, \qquad \cos 180° = \frac{-1}{1} = -1, \qquad \cos 270° = \frac{0}{1} = 0, \qquad \cos 360° = \frac{1}{1} = 1,$$

$$\tan 90° = \frac{1}{0}, \quad \text{Not defined} \qquad \tan 180° = \frac{0}{-1} = 0, \qquad \tan 270° = \frac{-1}{0}, \quad \text{Not defined} \qquad \tan 360° = \frac{0}{1} = 0.$$

◀

In Example 5, all the values can be found using a calculator, but you will find that it is convenient to be able to compute them mentally. It is also helpful to note that coterminal angles have the same function values. For example, 0° and 360° are coterminal; thus, $\sin 0° = 0$, $\cos 0° = 1$, and $\tan 0° = 0$.

EXAMPLE 6 Find each of the following.

a) $\sin(-90°)$ **b)** $\csc 540°$

Solution

a) We note that $-90°$ is coterminal with $270°$. Thus,

$$\sin(-90°) = \sin 270° = \frac{-1}{1} = -1.$$

b) Since $540° = 180° + 360°$, $540°$ and $180°$ are coterminal. Thus,

$$\csc 540° = \csc 180° = \frac{1}{\sin 180°} = \frac{1}{0}, \quad \text{which is not defined.}$$

▶ Now Try Exercises 43 and 53.

✦ Reference Angles: 30°, 45°, and 60°

We can also mentally determine trigonometric function values whenever the terminal side makes a 30°, 45°, or 60° angle with the *x*-axis. Consider, for example, an angle of 150°. The terminal side makes a 30° angle with the *x*-axis, since $180° - 150° = 30°$.

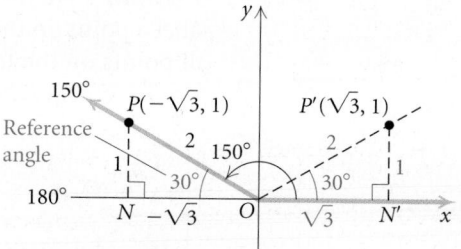

As the figure shows, $\triangle ONP$ is congruent to $\triangle ON'P'$; therefore, the ratios of the sides of the two triangles are the same. Thus the trigonometric function values are the same except perhaps for the sign. We could determine the function values directly from $\triangle ONP$, but this is not necessary. If we remember that in quadrant II, the sine is positive and the cosine and the tangent are negative, we can simply use the function values of 30° that we already know and prefix the appropriate sign. Thus,

$$\sin 150° = \sin 30° = \frac{1}{2},$$

$$\cos 150° = -\cos 30° = -\frac{\sqrt{3}}{2},$$

and $\quad \tan 150° = -\tan 30° = -\frac{1}{\sqrt{3}}, \quad \text{or} \quad -\frac{\sqrt{3}}{3}.$

Triangle ONP is the reference triangle and the acute angle $\angle NOP$ is called a *reference angle*.

Reference Angle

The **reference angle** for an angle is the acute angle formed by the terminal side of the angle and the *x*-axis.

EXAMPLE 7 Find the sine, cosine, and tangent function values for each of the following.

a) 225°   **b)** −780°

Solution

a) We draw a figure showing the terminal side of a 225° angle. The reference angle is 225° − 180°, or 45°.

Recall from Section 5.1 that $\sin 45° = \sqrt{2}/2$, $\cos 45° = \sqrt{2}/2$, and $\tan 45° = 1$. Also note that in the third quadrant, the sine and the cosine are negative and the tangent is positive. Thus we have

$$\sin 225° = -\frac{\sqrt{2}}{2}, \quad \cos 225° = -\frac{\sqrt{2}}{2}, \quad \text{and} \quad \tan 225° = 1.$$

b) We draw a figure showing the terminal side of a −780° angle. Since −780° + 2(360°) = −60°, we know that −780° and −60° are coterminal.

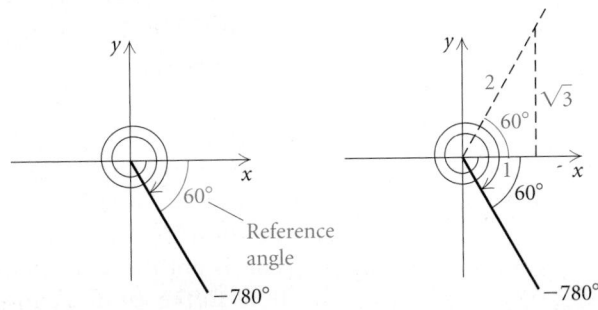

The reference angle for −60° is the acute angle formed by the terminal side of the angle and the *x*-axis. Thus the reference angle for −60° is 60°. We know that since −780° is a fourth-quadrant angle, the cosine is positive and the sine and the tangent are negative. Recalling that $\sin 60° = \sqrt{3}/2$, $\cos 60° = 1/2$, and $\tan 60° = \sqrt{3}$, we have

$$\sin(-780°) = -\frac{\sqrt{3}}{2}, \qquad \cos(-780°) = \frac{1}{2},$$

and $\tan(-780°) = -\sqrt{3}$.

▷ Now Try Exercises 45 and 49.

To find trigonometric function values of angles measured in degrees, we set the calculator in DEGREE mode. In the windows below, parts (a)–(f) of Example 8 are shown.

```
cos(112)
              -.3746065934
1/cos(500)
              -1.305407289
tan(-83.4)
              -8.64274761
```

```
1/sin(351.75)
              -6.968999424
cos(2400)
                       -.5
sin(175°40'9")
               .0755153443
```

✦ Function Values for Any Angle

When the terminal side of an angle falls on one of the axes or makes a 30°, 45°, or 60° angle with the x-axis, we can find exact function values without the use of a calculator. But this group is only a small subset of *all* angles. Using a calculator, we can approximate the trigonometric function values of *any* angle. In fact, we can approximate or find exact function values of all angles without using a reference angle.

EXAMPLE 8 Find each of the following function values using a calculator and round the answer to four decimal places, where appropriate.

a) $\cos 112°$ b) $\sec 500°$

c) $\tan(-83.4°)$ d) $\csc 351.75°$

e) $\cos 2400°$ f) $\sin 175°40'9''$

g) $\cot(-135°)$

Solution Using a calculator set in DEGREE mode, we find the values.

a) $\cos 112° \approx -0.3746$

b) $\sec 500° = \dfrac{1}{\cos 500°} \approx -1.3054$

c) $\tan(-83.4°) \approx -8.6427$

d) $\csc 351.75° = \dfrac{1}{\sin 351.75°} \approx -6.9690$

e) $\cos 2400° = -0.5$

f) $\sin 175°40'9'' \approx 0.0755$

g) $\cot(-135°) = \dfrac{1}{\tan(-135°)} = 1$

▷ Now Try Exercises 87 and 93.

In many applications, we have a trigonometric function value and want to find the measure of a corresponding angle. When only acute angles are considered, there is only one angle for each trigonometric function value. This is not the case when we extend the domain of the trigonometric functions to the set of *all* angles. For a given function value, there is an infinite number of angles that have that function value. There can be two such angles for each value in the range from 0° to 360°. To determine a unique answer in the interval (0°, 360°), the quadrant in which the terminal side lies must be specified.

The calculator gives the reference angle as an output for each function value that is entered as an input. Knowing the reference angle and the quadrant in which the terminal side lies, we can find the specified angle.

EXAMPLE 9 Given the function value and the quadrant restriction, find θ.

a) $\sin \theta = 0.2812$, $90° < \theta < 180°$

b) $\cot \theta = -0.1611$, $270° < \theta < 360°$

Solution

a) We first sketch the angle in the second quadrant. We use the calculator to find the acute angle (reference angle) whose sine is 0.2812. The reference angle is approximately 16.33°. We find the angle θ by subtracting 16.33° from 180°:

$$180° - 16.33° = 163.67°.$$

Thus, $\theta \approx 163.67°$.

b) We begin by sketching the angle in the fourth quadrant. Because the tangent and cotangent values are reciprocals, we know that

$$\tan \theta \approx \frac{1}{-0.1611} \approx -6.2073.$$

We use the calculator to find the acute angle (reference angle) whose tangent is 6.2073, ignoring the fact that $\tan \theta$ is negative. The reference angle is approximately 80.85°. We find angle θ by subtracting 80.85° from 360°:

$$360° - 80.85° = 279.15°.$$

Thus, $\theta \approx 279.15°$.

▶ Now Try Exercise 99.

5.3 EXERCISE SET

For angles of the following measures, state in which quadrant the terminal side lies. It helps to sketch the angle in standard position.

1. 187°

2. −14.3°

3. 245°15′

4. −120°

5. 800°

6. 1075°

7. −460.5°

8. 315°

9. −912°

10. 13°15′60″

11. 537°

12. −345.14°

Find two positive angles and two negative angles that are coterminal with the given angle. Answers may vary.

13. 74°

14. −81°

15. 115.3°

16. 275°10′

17. −180°

18. −310°

Find the complement and the supplement.

19. 17.11°

20. 47°38′

21. 12°3′14″

22. 9.038°

23. 45.2°

24. 67.31°

Find the six trigonometric function values for the angle shown.

25.

26.

27.

28.
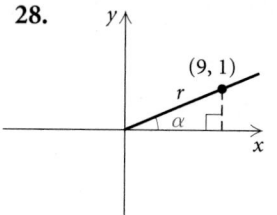

The terminal side of angle θ in standard position lies on the given line in the given quadrant. Find sin θ, cos θ, and tan θ.

29. $2x + 3y = 0$; quadrant IV

30. $4x + y = 0$; quadrant II

31. $5x - 4y = 0$; quadrant I

32. $y = 0.8x$; quadrant III

A function value and a quadrant are given. Find the other five function values. Give exact answers.

33. $\sin \theta = -\dfrac{1}{3}$, quadrant III

34. $\tan \beta = 5$, quadrant I

35. $\cot \theta = -2$, quadrant IV

36. $\cos \alpha = -\dfrac{4}{5}$, quadrant II

37. $\cos \phi = \dfrac{3}{5}$, quadrant IV

38. $\sin \theta = -\dfrac{5}{13}$, quadrant III

Find the reference angle and the exact function value if it exists.

39. $\cos 150°$

40. $\sec (-225°)$

41. $\tan (-135°)$

42. $\sin (-45°)$

43. $\sin 7560°$

44. $\tan 270°$

45. $\cos 495°$

46. $\tan 675°$

47. $\csc (-210°)$

48. $\sin 300°$

49. $\cot 570°$

50. $\cos (-120°)$

51. $\tan 330°$

52. $\cot 855°$

53. $\sec (-90°)$

54. $\sin 90°$

55. $\cos (-180°)$

56. $\csc 90°$

57. $\tan 240°$

58. $\cot (-180°)$

59. $\sin 495°$

60. $\sin 1050°$

61. $\csc 225°$

62. $\sin (-450°)$

63. $\cos 0°$

64. $\tan 480°$

65. $\cot (-90°)$

66. $\sec 315°$

67. $\cos 90°$

68. $\sin (-135°)$

69. $\cos 270°$

70. $\tan 0°$

Find the signs of the six trigonometric function values for the given angles.

71. $319°$

72. $-57°$

73. $194°$

74. $-620°$

75. $-215°$

76. $290°$

77. $-272°$

78. $91°$

Use a calculator in Exercises 79–82, but do not use the trigonometric function keys.

79. Given that

$$\sin 41° = 0.6561,$$
$$\cos 41° = 0.7547,$$
$$\tan 41° = 0.8693,$$

find the trigonometric function values for $319°$.

80. Given that

$$\sin 27° = 0.4540,$$
$$\cos 27° = 0.8910,$$
$$\tan 27° = 0.5095,$$

find the trigonometric function values for $333°$.

81. Given that

$$\sin 65° = 0.9063,$$
$$\cos 65° = 0.4226,$$
$$\tan 65° = 2.1445,$$

find the trigonometric function values for 115°.

82. Given that

$$\sin 35° = 0.5736,$$
$$\cos 35° = 0.8192,$$
$$\tan 35° = 0.7002,$$

find the trigonometric function values for 215°.

*Aerial Navigation.   In aerial navigation, directions are given in degrees clockwise from north. Thus, east is 90°, south is 180°, and west is 270°. Several aerial directions or **bearings** are given below.*

83. An airplane flies 150 km from an airport in a direction of 120°. How far east of the airport is the plane then? How far south?

84. An airplane leaves an airport and travels for 100 mi in a direction of 300°. How far north of the airport is the plane then? How far west?

85. An airplane travels at 150 km/h for 2 hr in a direction of 138° from Omaha. At the end of this time, how far south of Omaha is the plane?

86. An airplane travels at 120 km/h for 2 hr in a direction of 319° from Chicago. At the end of this time, how far north of Chicago is the plane?

Find the function value. Round to four decimal places.

87. $\tan 310.8°$ **88.** $\cos 205.5°$

89. $\cot 146.15°$ **90.** $\sin(-16.4°)$

91. $\sin 118°42'$ **92.** $\cos 273°45'$

93. $\cos(-295.8°)$ **94.** $\tan 1086.2°$

95. $\cos 5417°$ **96.** $\sec 240°55'$

97. $\csc 520°$ **98.** $\sin 3824°$

Given the function value and the quadrant restriction, find θ.

FUNCTION VALUE	INTERVAL	θ
99. $\sin \theta = -0.9956$	(270°, 360°)	
100. $\tan \theta = 0.2460$	(180°, 270°)	
101. $\cos \theta = -0.9388$	(180°, 270°)	
102. $\sec \theta = -1.0485$	(90°, 180°)	
103. $\tan \theta = -3.0545$	(270°, 360°)	
104. $\sin \theta = -0.4313$	(180°, 270°)	
105. $\csc \theta = 1.0480$	(0°, 90°)	
106. $\cos \theta = -0.0990$	(90°, 180°)	

Collaborative Discussion and Writing

107. Why do the function values of θ depend only on the angle and not on the choice of a point on the terminal side?

108. Why is the domain of the tangent function different from the domains of the sine and the cosine functions?

Skill Maintenance

Graph the function. Sketch and label any vertical asymptotes.

109. $f(x) = \dfrac{1}{x^2 - 25}$

110. $g(x) = x^3 - 2x + 1$

Determine the domain and the range of the function.

111. $f(x) = \dfrac{x - 4}{x + 2}$

112. $g(x) = \dfrac{x^2 - 9}{2x^2 - 7x - 15}$

Find the zeros of the function.

113. $f(x) = 12 - x$

114. $g(x) = x^2 - x - 6$

Find the x-intercepts of the graph of the function.

115. $f(x) = 12 - x$

116. $g(x) = x^2 - x - 6$

Synthesis

117. *Valve Cap on a Bicycle.* The valve cap on a bicycle wheel is 12.5 in. from the center of the

wheel. From the position shown, the wheel starts to roll. After the wheel has turned 390°, how far above the ground is the valve cap? Assume that the outer radius of the tire is 13.375 in.

118. *Seats of a Ferris Wheel.* The seats of a ferris wheel are 35 ft from the center of the wheel. When you board the wheel, you are 5 ft above the ground. After you have rotated through an angle of 765°, how far above the ground are you?

5.4 Radians, Arc Length, and Angular Speed

◆ Find points on the unit circle determined by real numbers.

◆ Convert between radian measure and degree measure; find coterminal, complementary, and supplementary angles.

◆ Find the length of an arc of a circle; find the measure of a central angle of a circle.

◆ Convert between linear speed and angular speed.

CIRCLES

REVIEW SECTION **1.1.**

Another useful unit of angle measure is called a *radian*. To introduce radian measure, we use a circle centered at the origin with a radius of length 1. Such a circle is called a **unit circle.** Its equation is $x^2 + y^2 = 1$.

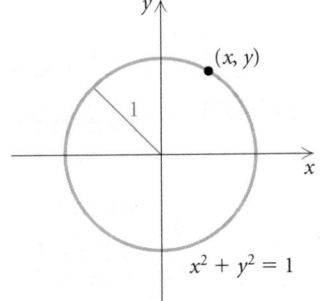

◆ Distances on the Unit Circle

The circumference of a circle of radius r is $2\pi r$. Thus for the unit circle, where $r = 1$, the circumference is 2π. If a point starts at A and travels around the circle (Fig. 1), it will travel a distance of 2π. If it travels halfway around the circle (Fig. 2), it will travel a distance of $\frac{1}{2} \cdot 2\pi$, or π.

Figure 1

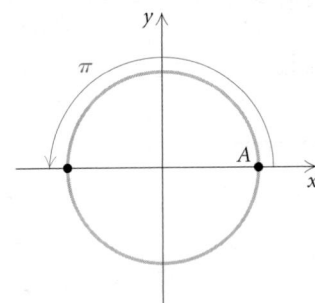

Figure 2

If a point C travels $\frac{1}{8}$ of the way around the circle (Fig. 3), it will travel a distance of $\frac{1}{8} \cdot 2\pi$, or $\pi/4$. Note that C is $\frac{1}{4}$ of the way from A to B. If a point D travels $\frac{1}{6}$ of the way around the circle (Fig. 4), it will travel a distance of $\frac{1}{6} \cdot 2\pi$, or $\pi/3$. Note that D is $\frac{1}{3}$ of the way from A to B.

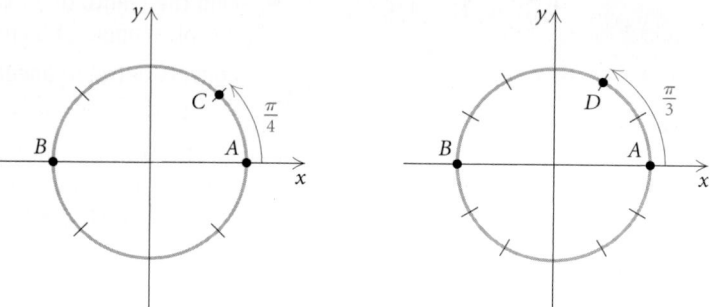

Figure 3   Figure 4

EXAMPLE 1   How far will a point travel if it goes (a) $\frac{1}{4}$, (b) $\frac{1}{12}$, (c) $\frac{3}{8}$, and (d) $\frac{5}{6}$ of the way around the unit circle?

Solution

a) $\frac{1}{4}$ of the total distance around the circle is $\frac{1}{4} \cdot 2\pi$, which is $\frac{1}{2} \cdot \pi$, or $\pi/2$.

b) The distance will be $\frac{1}{12} \cdot 2\pi$, which is $\frac{1}{6}\pi$, or $\pi/6$.

c) The distance will be $\frac{3}{8} \cdot 2\pi$, which is $\frac{3}{4}\pi$, or $3\pi/4$.

d) The distance will be $\frac{5}{6} \cdot 2\pi$, which is $\frac{5}{3}\pi$, or $5\pi/3$. Think of $5\pi/3$ as $\pi + \frac{2}{3}\pi$.

These distances are illustrated in the following figures.

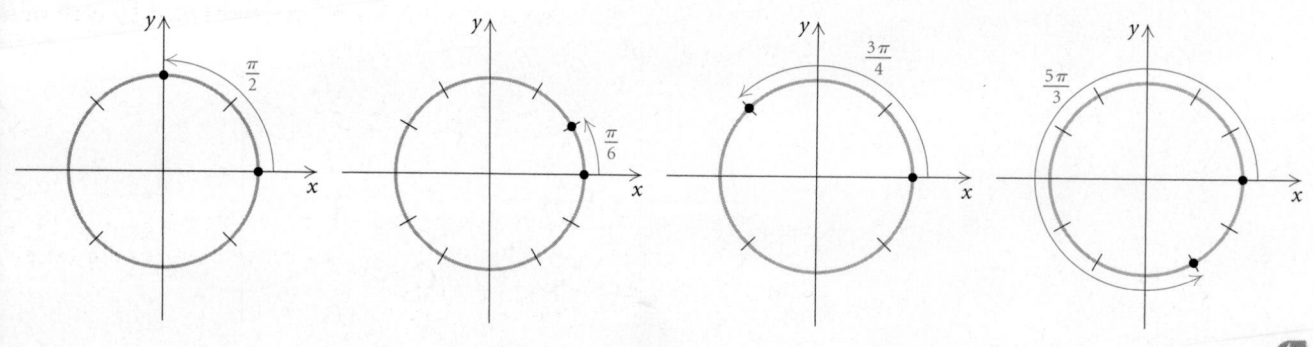

A point may travel completely around the circle and then continue. For example, if it goes around once and then continues $\frac{1}{4}$ of the way around, it will have traveled a distance of $2\pi + \frac{1}{4} \cdot 2\pi$, or $5\pi/2$ (Fig. 5). *Every* real number determines a point on the unit circle. For the positive number 10, for example, we start at A and travel counterclockwise a distance of 10. The point at which we stop is the point "determined" by the number 10. Note that $2\pi \approx 6.28$ and that $10 \approx 1.6(2\pi)$. Thus the point for 10 travels around the unit circle about $1\frac{3}{5}$ times (Fig. 6).

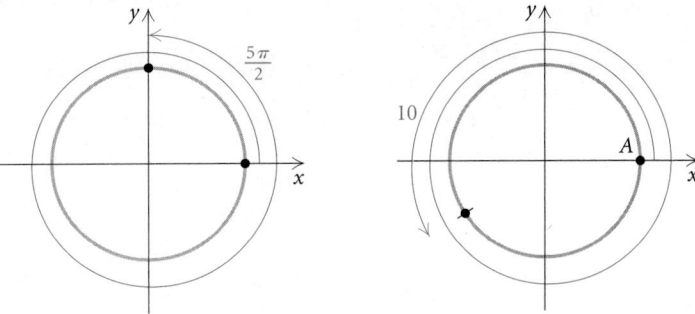

Figure 5   Figure 6

For a negative number, we move clockwise around the circle. Points for $-\pi/4$ and $-3\pi/2$ are shown in the figure below. The number 0 determines the point A.

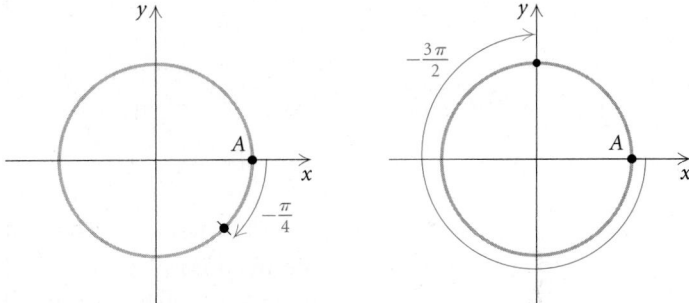

EXAMPLE 2   On the unit circle, mark the point determined by each of the following real numbers.

a) $\dfrac{9\pi}{4}$ b) $-\dfrac{7\pi}{6}$

Solution

a) Think of $9\pi/4$ as $2\pi + \frac{1}{4}\pi$. (See the figure below.) Since $9\pi/4 > 0$, the point moves counterclockwise. The point goes completely around once and then continues $\frac{1}{4}$ of the way from A to B.

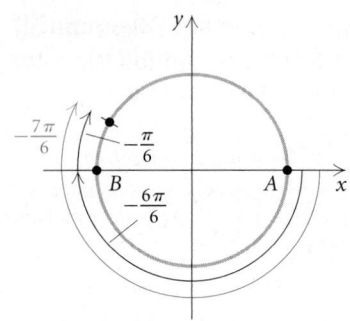

b) The number $-7\pi/6$ is negative, so the point moves clockwise. From A to B, the distance is π, or $\frac{6}{6}\pi$, so we need to go beyond B another distance of $\pi/6$, clockwise. (See the figure at left.)

▶ Now Try Exercise 1.

◆ Radian Measure

Degree measure is a common unit of angle measure in many everyday applications. But in many scientific fields and in mathematics (calculus, in particular), there is another commonly used unit of measure called the *radian*.

Consider the unit circle. Recall that this circle has radius 1. Suppose we measure, moving counterclockwise, an arc of length 1, and mark a point T on the circle.

If we draw a ray from the origin through T, we have formed an angle. The measure of that angle is 1 **radian.** The word radian comes from the word *radius*. Thus measuring 1 "radius" along the circumference of the circle determines an angle whose measure is 1 *radian*. One radian is about 57.3°. Angles that measure 2 radians, 3 radians, and 6 radians are shown below.

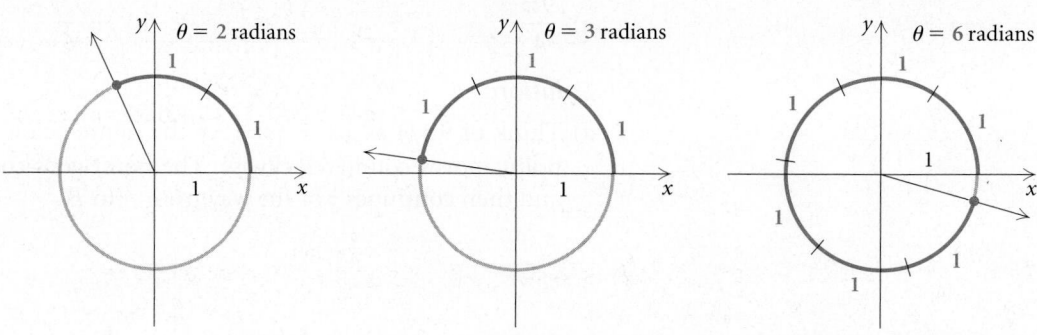

When we make a complete (counterclockwise) revolution, the terminal side coincides with the initial side on the positive x-axis. We then have an angle whose measure is 2π radians, or about 6.28 radians, which is the circumference of the circle:

$$2\pi r = 2\pi(1) = 2\pi.$$

Thus a rotation of 360° (1 revolution) has a measure of 2π radians. A half revolution is a rotation of 180°, or π radians. A quarter revolution is a rotation of 90°, or $\pi/2$ radians, and so on.

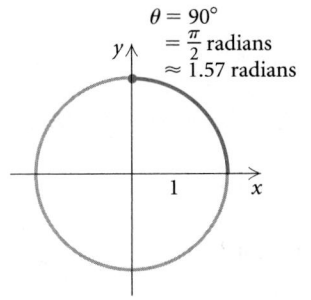

$\theta = 90°$
$= \frac{\pi}{2}$ radians
≈ 1.57 radians

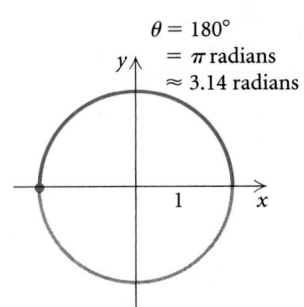

$\theta = 180°$
$= \pi$ radians
≈ 3.14 radians

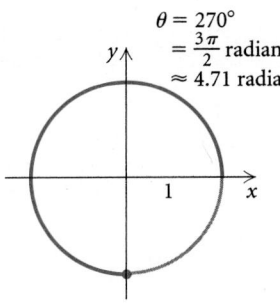

$\theta = 270°$
$= \frac{3\pi}{2}$ radians
≈ 4.71 radians

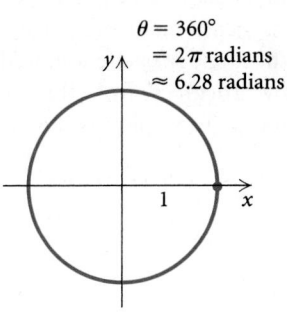

$\theta = 360°$
$= 2\pi$ radians
≈ 6.28 radians

To convert between degrees and radians, we first note that

$$360° = 2\pi \text{ radians.}$$

It follows that

$$180° = \pi \text{ radians.}$$

To make conversions, we multiply by 1, noting that:

Converting between Degree Measure and Radian Measure

$$\frac{\pi \text{ radians}}{180°} = \frac{180°}{\pi \text{ radians}} = 1.$$

To convert from degree to radian measure, multiply by $\dfrac{\pi \text{ radians}}{180°}$.

To convert from radian to degree measure, multiply by $\dfrac{180°}{\pi \text{ radians}}$.

EXAMPLE 3 Convert each of the following to radians.

a) 120°
b) $-297.25°$

Solution

a) $120° = 120° \cdot \dfrac{\pi \text{ radians}}{180°}$ Multiplying by 1

$= \dfrac{120°}{180°} \pi \text{ radians}$

$= \dfrac{2\pi}{3} \text{ radians, or about } 2.09 \text{ radians}$

To convert degrees to
radians, we set the calculator
in RADIAN mode. Then we enter
the angle measure followed
by ° (degrees) from the ANGLE
menu. Example 3 is shown here.

```
120°
              2.094395102
-297.25°
            -5.187991202
```

To convert radians to
degrees, we set the calculator in
DEGREE mode. Then we enter
the angle measure followed
by ʳ (radians) from the ANGLE
menu. Example 4 is shown here.

```
(3π/4) ʳ
                      135
8.5 ʳ
              487.0141259
```

b) $-297.25° = -297.25° \cdot \dfrac{\pi \text{ radians}}{180°}$

$$= -\dfrac{297.25°}{180°} \pi \text{ radians}$$

$$= -\dfrac{297.25\pi}{180} \text{ radians}$$

$$\approx -5.19 \text{ radians}$$

▷ Now Try Exercises 23 and 35.

EXAMPLE 4 Convert each of the following to degrees.

a) $\dfrac{3\pi}{4}$ radians　　　　　　　　**b)** 8.5 radians

Solution

a) $\dfrac{3\pi}{4}$ radians $= \dfrac{3\pi}{4}$ radians $\cdot \dfrac{180°}{\pi \text{ radians}}$　　Multiplying by 1

$$= \dfrac{3\pi}{4\pi} \cdot 180° = \dfrac{3}{4} \cdot 180° = 135°$$

b) 8.5 radians $= 8.5$ radians $\cdot \dfrac{180°}{\pi \text{ radians}}$

$$= \dfrac{8.5(180°)}{\pi} \approx 487.01°$$

▷ Now Try Exercises 47 and 55.

The radian–degree equivalents of the most commonly used angle measures are illustrated in the following figures.

When a rotation is given in radians, the word "radians" is optional and is most often omitted. **Thus if no unit is given for a rotation, the rotation is understood to be in radians.**

We can also find coterminal, complementary, and supplementary angles in radian measure just as we did for degree measure in Section 5.3.

EXAMPLE 5 Find a positive angle and a negative angle that are coterminal with $2\pi/3$. Many answers are possible.

Solution To find angles coterminal with a given angle, we add or subtract multiples of 2π:

$$\frac{2\pi}{3} + 2\pi = \frac{2\pi}{3} + \frac{6\pi}{3} = \frac{8\pi}{3},$$

$$\frac{2\pi}{3} - 3(2\pi) = \frac{2\pi}{3} - \frac{18\pi}{3} = -\frac{16\pi}{3}.$$

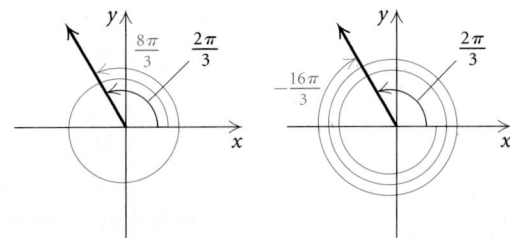

Thus, $8\pi/3$ and $-16\pi/3$ are two of the many angles coterminal with $2\pi/3$.

▶ **Now Try Exercise 11.**

EXAMPLE 6 Find the complement and the supplement of $\pi/6$.

Solution Since $90°$ equals $\pi/2$ radians, the complement of $\pi/6$ is

$$\frac{\pi}{2} - \frac{\pi}{6} = \frac{3\pi}{6} - \frac{\pi}{6} = \frac{2\pi}{6}, \quad \text{or} \quad \frac{\pi}{3}.$$

Since $180°$ equals π radians, the supplement of $\pi/6$ is

$$\pi - \frac{\pi}{6} = \frac{6\pi}{6} - \frac{\pi}{6} = \frac{5\pi}{6}.$$

Thus the complement of $\pi/6$ is $\pi/3$ and the supplement is $5\pi/6$.

▶ **Now Try Exercise 15.**

✦ Arc Length and Central Angles

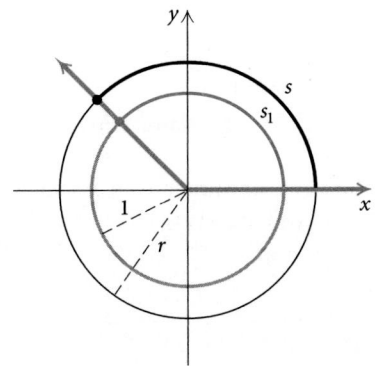

Radian measure can be determined using a circle other than a unit circle. In the figure at left, a unit circle (with radius 1) is shown along with another circle (with radius r, $r \neq 1$). The angle shown is a **central angle** of both circles.

From geometry, we know that the arcs that the angle subtends have their lengths in the same ratio as the radii of the circles. The radii of the circles are r and 1. The corresponding arc lengths are s and s_1. Thus we have the proportion

$$\frac{s}{s_1} = \frac{r}{1},$$

which also can be written as

$$\frac{s_1}{1} = \frac{s}{r}.$$

Now s_1 is the *radian measure* of the rotation in question. It is common to use a Greek letter, such as θ, for the measure of an angle or rotation and the letter s for arc length. Adopting this convention, we rewrite the proportion above as

$$\theta = \frac{s}{r}.$$

In any circle, the measure (in radians) of a central angle, the arc length the angle subtends, and the length of the radius are related in this fashion. Or, in general, the following is true.

Radian Measure

The **radian measure** θ of a rotation is the ratio of the distance s traveled by a point at a radius r from the center of rotation, to the length of the radius r:

$$\theta = \frac{s}{r}.$$

When using the formula $\theta = s/r$, be sure that θ is given in radians and s and r are expressed in the same unit.

EXAMPLE 7 Find the measure of a rotation in radians when a point 2 m from the center of rotation travels 4 m.

Solution We have

$$\theta = \frac{s}{r}$$

$$= \frac{4 \text{ m}}{2 \text{ m}} = 2. \qquad \text{The unit is understood to be radians.}$$

▶ Now Try Exercise 65.

EXAMPLE 8 Find the length of an arc of a circle of radius 5 cm associated with an angle of $\pi/3$ radians.

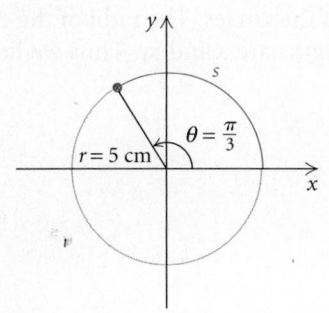

Solution We have

$$\theta = \frac{s}{r}, \quad \text{or} \quad s = r\theta.$$

Thus $s = 5 \text{ cm} \cdot \pi/3$, or about 5.24 cm.

▶ Now Try Exercise 63.

✦ Linear Speed and Angular Speed

Linear speed is defined as distance traveled per unit of time. If we use v for linear speed, s for distance, and t for time, then

$$v = \frac{s}{t}.$$

Similarly, **angular speed** is defined as amount of rotation per unit of time. For example, we might speak of the angular speed of a bicycle wheel as 150 revolutions per minute or the angular speed of the earth as 2π radians per day. The Greek letter ω (omega) is generally used for angular speed. Thus for a rotation θ and time t, angular speed is defined as

$$\omega = \frac{\theta}{t}.$$

As an example of how these definitions can be applied, let's consider the refurbished carousel at the Children's Museum in Indianapolis, Indiana. It consists of three circular rows of animals. All animals, regardless of the row, travel at the same angular speed. But the animals in the outer row travel at a greater linear speed than those in the inner rows. What is the relationship between the linear speed v and the angular speed ω?

To develop the relationship we seek, recall that, for rotations measured in radians, $\theta = s/r$. This is equivalent to

$$s = r\theta.$$

We divide by time, t, to obtain

$$\frac{s}{t} = \frac{r\theta}{t} \qquad \textbf{Dividing by } t$$

$$\underset{\displaystyle \downarrow}{\frac{s}{t}} = r \cdot \underset{\displaystyle \downarrow}{\frac{\theta}{t}}$$
$$\;\;v \qquad\qquad \omega$$

Now s/t is linear speed v and θ/t is angular speed ω. Thus we have the relationship we seek,

$$v = r\omega.$$

© 2006 The Children's Museum of Indianapolis

Linear Speed in Terms of Angular Speed

The **linear speed** v of a point a distance r from the center of rotation is given by

$$v = r\omega,$$

where ω is the **angular speed** in radians per unit of time.

For the formula $v = r\omega$, the units of distance for v and r must be the same, ω must be in radians per unit of time, and the units of time for v and ω must be the same.

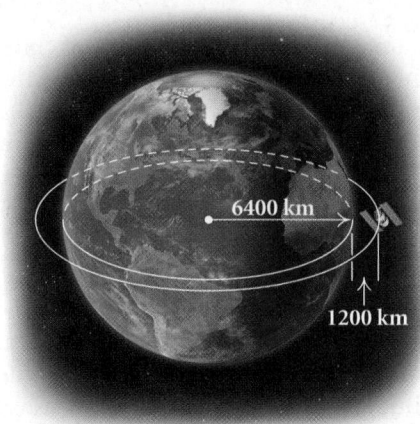

EXAMPLE 9   *Linear Speed of an Earth Satellite.*   An earth satellite in circular orbit 1200 km high makes one complete revolution every 90 min. What is its linear speed? Use 6400 km for the length of a radius of the earth.

Solution   To use the formula $v = r\omega$, we need to know r and ω:

$$r = 6400 \text{ km} + 1200 \text{ km} \qquad \text{Radius of earth plus height of satellite}$$

$$= 7600 \text{ km},$$

$$\omega = \frac{\theta}{t} = \frac{2\pi}{90 \text{ min}} = \frac{\pi}{45 \text{ min}}. \qquad \text{We have, as usual, omitted the word radians.}$$

Now, using $v = r\omega$, we have

$$v = 7600 \text{ km} \cdot \frac{\pi}{45 \text{ min}} = \frac{7600\pi}{45} \cdot \frac{\text{km}}{\text{min}} \approx 531 \frac{\text{km}}{\text{min}}.$$

Thus the linear speed of the satellite is approximately 531 km/min.

▷ Now Try Exercise 71.

EXAMPLE 10   *Angular Speed of a Capstan.*   An anchor is hoisted at a rate of 2 ft/sec as the chain is wound around a capstan with a 1.8-yd diameter. What is the angular speed of the capstan?

Solution   We will use the formula $v = r\omega$ in the form $\omega = v/r$, taking care to use the proper units. Since v is given in feet per second, we need r in feet:

$$r = \frac{d}{2} = \frac{1.8}{2} \text{ yd} \cdot \frac{3 \text{ ft}}{1 \text{ yd}} = 2.7 \text{ ft.}$$

Then ω will be in radians per second:

$$\omega = \frac{v}{r} = \frac{2 \text{ ft/sec}}{2.7 \text{ ft}} = \frac{2 \text{ ft}}{\text{sec}} \cdot \frac{1}{2.7 \text{ ft}} \approx 0.741/\text{sec}.$$

Thus the angular speed is approximately 0.741 radian/sec.

▶ Now Try Exercise 73.

The formulas $\theta = \omega t$ and $v = r\omega$ can be used in combination to find distances and angles in various situations involving rotational motion.

EXAMPLE 11   *Angle of Revolution.*   A 2006 Acura MDX is traveling at a speed of 70 mph. Its tires have an outside diameter of 28.56 in. Find the angle through which a tire turns in 10 sec.

28.56 in.

Solution   Recall that $\omega = \theta/t$, or $\theta = \omega t$. Thus we can find θ if we know ω and t. To find ω, we use the formula $v = r\omega$. The linear speed v of a point on the outside of the tire is the speed of the Acura, 70 mph. For convenience, we first convert 70 mph to feet per second:

$$v = 70 \, \frac{\text{mi}}{\text{hr}} \cdot \frac{1 \text{ hr}}{60 \text{ min}} \cdot \frac{1 \text{ min}}{60 \text{ sec}} \cdot \frac{5280 \text{ ft}}{1 \text{ mi}}$$

$$\approx 102.667 \, \frac{\text{ft}}{\text{sec}}.$$

The radius of the tire is half the diameter. Now $r = d/2 = 28.56/2 = 14.28$ in. We will convert to feet, since v is in feet per second:

$$r = 14.28 \text{ in.} \cdot \frac{1 \text{ ft}}{12 \text{ in.}}$$

$$= \frac{14.28}{12} \text{ ft}$$

$$\approx 1.19 \text{ ft}.$$

Using $v = r\omega$, we have

$$102.667 \, \frac{\text{ft}}{\text{sec}} = 1.19 \, \text{ft} \cdot \omega,$$

so

$$\omega = \frac{102.667 \, \text{ft/sec}}{1.19 \, \text{ft}} \approx \frac{86.27}{\text{sec}}.$$

Then in 10 sec,

$$\theta = \omega t = \frac{86.27}{\text{sec}} \cdot 10 \, \text{sec} \approx 863.$$

Thus the angle, in radians, through which a tire turns in 10 sec is 863.

▶ Now Try Exercise 77.

5.4   EXERCISE SET

*For each of Exercises 1–4, sketch a unit circle and mark
the points determined by the given real numbers.*

1. a) $\dfrac{\pi}{4}$ **b)** $\dfrac{3\pi}{2}$ **c)** $\dfrac{3\pi}{4}$

  d) π **e)** $\dfrac{11\pi}{4}$ **f)** $\dfrac{17\pi}{4}$

2. a) $\dfrac{\pi}{2}$ **b)** $\dfrac{5\pi}{4}$ **c)** 2π

  d) $\dfrac{9\pi}{4}$ **e)** $\dfrac{13\pi}{4}$ **f)** $\dfrac{23\pi}{4}$

3. a) $\dfrac{\pi}{6}$ **b)** $\dfrac{2\pi}{3}$ **c)** $\dfrac{7\pi}{6}$

  d) $\dfrac{10\pi}{6}$ **e)** $\dfrac{14\pi}{6}$ **f)** $\dfrac{23\pi}{4}$

4. a) $-\dfrac{\pi}{2}$ **b)** $-\dfrac{3\pi}{4}$ **c)** $-\dfrac{5\pi}{6}$

  d) $-\dfrac{5\pi}{2}$ **e)** $-\dfrac{17\pi}{6}$ **f)** $-\dfrac{9\pi}{4}$

*Find two real numbers between -2π and 2π that
determine each of the points on the unit circle.*

5.

6.

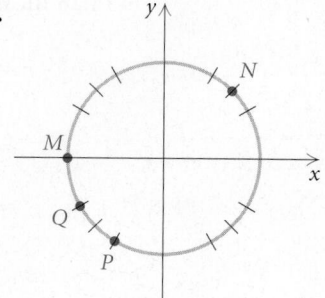

For Exercises 7 and 8, sketch a unit circle and mark the approximate location of the point determined by the given real number.

7. a) 2.4   **b)** 7.5
   c) 32   **d)** 320

8. a) 0.25   **b)** 1.8
   c) 47   **d)** 500

Find a positive angle and a negative angle that are coterminal with the given angle. Answers may vary.

9. $\dfrac{\pi}{4}$ **10.** $\dfrac{5\pi}{3}$

11. $\dfrac{7\pi}{6}$ **12.** π

13. $-\dfrac{2\pi}{3}$ **14.** $-\dfrac{3\pi}{4}$

Find the complement and the supplement.

15. $\dfrac{\pi}{3}$ **16.** $\dfrac{5\pi}{12}$

17. $\dfrac{3\pi}{8}$ **18.** $\dfrac{\pi}{4}$

19. $\dfrac{\pi}{12}$ **20.** $\dfrac{\pi}{6}$

Convert to radian measure. Leave the answer in terms of π.

21. 75°   **22.** 30°

23. 200°   **24.** −135°

25. −214.6°   **26.** 37.71°

27. −180°   **28.** 90°

29. 12.5°   **30.** 6.3°

31. −340°   **32.** −60°

Convert to radian measure. Round the answer to two decimal places.

33. 240°   **34.** 15°

35. −60°   **36.** 145°

37. 117.8°   **38.** −231.2°

39. 1.354°   **40.** 584°

41. 345°   **42.** −75°

43. 95°   **44.** 24.8°

Convert to degree measure. Round the answer to two decimal places.

45. $-\dfrac{3\pi}{4}$ **46.** $\dfrac{7\pi}{6}$

47. 8π **48.** $-\dfrac{\pi}{3}$

49. 1   **50.** −17.6

51. 2.347   **52.** 25

53. $\dfrac{5\pi}{4}$ **54.** -6π

55. −90   **56.** 37.12

57. $\dfrac{2\pi}{7}$ **58.** $\dfrac{\pi}{9}$

59. Certain positive angles are marked here in degrees. Find the corresponding radian measures.

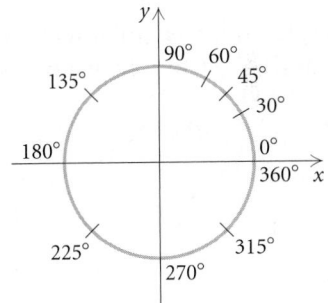

60. Certain negative angles are marked here in degrees. Find the corresponding radian measures.

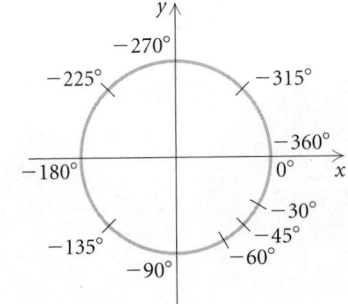

Arc Length and Central Angles.   *Complete the table.*
Round the answers to two decimal places.

	Distance, s (arc length)	Radius, r	Angle, θ
61.	8 ft	$3\frac{1}{2}$ ft	
62.	200 cm		45°
63.		4.2 in.	$\frac{5\pi}{12}$
64.	16 yd		5

65. In a circle with a 120-cm radius, an arc 132 cm long subtends an angle of how many radians? how many degrees, to the nearest degree?

66. In a circle with a 10-ft diameter, an arc 20 ft long subtends an angle of how many radians? how many degrees, to the nearest degree?

67. In a circle with a 2-yd radius, how long is an arc associated with an angle of 1.6 radians?

68. In a circle with a 5-m radius, how long is an arc associated with an angle of 2.1 radians?

69. *Angle of Revolution.*   Through how many radians does the minute hand of a clock rotate from 12:40 P.M. to 1:30 P.M.?

70. *Angle of Revolution.*   A tire on a 2006 Dodge Ram truck has an outside diameter of 31.125 in. Through what angle (in radians) does the tire turn while traveling 1 mi?

— 31.125 in.

71. *Linear Speed.*   A flywheel with a 15-cm diameter is rotating at a rate of 7 radians/sec. What is the linear speed of a point on its rim, in centimeters per minute?

72. *Linear Speed.*   A wheel with a 30-cm radius is rotating at a rate of 3 radians/sec. What is the linear speed of a point on its rim, in meters per minute?

73. *Angular Speed of a Printing Press.*   This text was printed on a four-color web heatset offset press. A cylinder on this press has a 21-in. diameter. The linear speed of a point on the cylinder's surface is 18.33 feet per second. What is the angular speed of the cylinder, in revolutions per hour? Printers often refer to the angular speed as impressions per hour (IPH). (*Source:* Bob Delano, Von Hoffmann, St. Louis, Missouri)

MEGTEC 1500

74. *Linear Speeds on a Carousel.*   When Alicia and Zoe ride the carousel described earlier in this section, Alicia always selects a horse on the outside row, whereas Zoe prefers the row closest to the center. These rows are 19 ft 3 in. and 13 ft 11 in. from the center, respectively (*Source*: The Children's Museum, Indianapolis, IN). The angular speed of the carousel is 2.4 revolutions per minute. What is the difference, in miles per hour, in the linear speeds of Alicia and Zoe?

75. *Linear Speed at the Equator.*   The earth has a 4000-mi radius and rotates one revolution every 24 hr. What is the linear speed of a point on the equator, in miles per hour?

76. *Linear Speed of the Earth.* The earth is about 93,000,000 mi from the sun and traverses its orbit, which is nearly circular, every 365.25 days. What is the linear velocity of the earth in its orbit, in miles per hour?

77. *Tour of Flanders.* Tom Boonen of Belgium won the 2005 Tour of Flanders bicycle race. The wheel of his bicycle had a 67-cm diameter. His overall average linear speed during the race was 40.423 km/h. (*Source:* Toby Holsman, Bicycle Garage Indy, Indianapolis, Indiana; www.velonews.com) What was the angular speed of the wheel, in revolutions per hour?

78. *Determining the Speed of a River.* A water wheel has a 10-ft radius. To get a good approximation of the speed of the river, you count the revolutions of the wheel and find that it makes 14 revolutions per minute (rpm). What is the speed of the river, in miles per hour?

79. *John Deere Tractor.* A rear wheel on a John Deere 8300 farm tractor has a 23-in. radius. Find the angle (in radians) through which a wheel rotates in 12 sec if the tractor is traveling at a speed of 22 mph.

Technology Connection

80. In each of Exercises 33–44, convert to radian measure using a graphing calculator.

81. In each of Exercises 45–58, convert to degree measure using a graphing calculator.

Collaborative Discussion and Writing

82. Explain in your own words why it is preferable to omit the word, or unit, *radians* in radian measures.

83. In circular motion with a fixed angular speed, the length of the radius is directly proportional to the linear speed. Explain why with an example.

84. Two new cars are each driven at an average speed of 60 mph for an extended highway test drive of 2000 mi. The diameter of the wheels of the two cars are 15 in. and 16 in., respectively. If the cars use tires of equal durability and profile, differing only by the diameter, which car will probably need new tires first? Explain your answer.

Skill Maintenance

In each of Exercises 85–92, fill in the blanks with the correct terms. Some of the given choices will not be used.

inverse
a horizontal line
a vertical line
exponential function
logarithmic function
natural
common
logarithm
one-to-one
a relation
vertical asymptote
horizontal asymptote
even function
odd function
sine of θ
cosine of θ
tangent of θ

85. The domain of a(n) _____ function f is the range of the inverse f^{-1}.

86. The _____ is the length of the side adjacent to θ divided by the length of the hypotenuse.

87. The function $f(x) = a^x$, where x is a real number, $a > 0$ and $a \neq 1$, is called the _____, base a.

88. The graph of a rational function may or may not cross a(n) _____ .

89. If the graph of a function *f* is symmetric with respect to the origin, we say that it is a(n) _____ .

90. Logarithms, base *e*, are called _____ logarithms.

91. If it is possible for a(n) _____ to intersect the graph of a function more than once, then the function is not one-to-one and its _____ is not a function.

92. A(n) _____ is an exponent.

Synthesis

93. On the earth, one degree of latitude is how many kilometers? how many miles? (Assume that the radius of the earth is 6400 km, or 4000 mi, approximately.)

94. A point on the unit circle has *y*-coordinate $-\sqrt{21}/5$. What is its *x*-coordinate? Check using a calculator.

95. A **mil** is a unit of angle measure. A right angle has a measure of 1600 mils. Convert each of the following to degrees, minutes, and seconds.

   a) 100 mils   **b)** 350 mils

96. A **grad** is a unit of angle measure similar to a degree. A right angle has a measure of 100 grads. Convert each of the following to grads.

   a) 48°   **b)** $\dfrac{5\pi}{7}$

97. *Angular Speed of a Gear Wheel.* One gear wheel turns another, the teeth being on the rims. The wheels have 40-cm and 50-cm radii, and the smaller wheel rotates at 20 rpm. Find

the angular speed of the larger wheel, in radians per second.

50 cm   40 cm

98. *Angular Speed of a Pulley.* Two pulleys, 50 cm and 30 cm in diameter, respectively, are connected by a belt. The larger pulley makes 12 revolutions per minute. Find the angular speed of the smaller pulley, in radians per second.

50 cm   30 cm

99. *Distance between Points on the Earth.* To find the distance between two points on the earth when their latitude and longitude are known, we can use a right triangle for an excellent approximation if the points are not too far apart. Point *A* is at latitude 38°27′30″ N, longitude 82°57′15″ W; and point *B* is at latitude 38°28′45″ N, longitude 82°56′30″ W. Find the distance from *A* to *B* in nautical miles. (One minute of latitude is one nautical mile.)

100. *Hands of a Clock.* At what time between noon and 1:00 P.M. are the hands of a clock perpendicular?

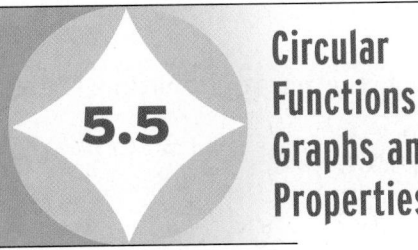

Circular Functions: Graphs and Properties

5.5

♦ Given the coordinates of a point on the unit circle, find its reflections across the x-axis, the y-axis, and the origin.

♦ Determine the six trigonometric function values for a real number when the coordinates of the point on the unit circle determined by that real number are given.

♦ Find function values for any real number using a calculator.

♦ Graph the six circular functions and state their properties.

The domains of the trigonometric functions, defined in Sections 5.1 and 5.3, have been sets of angles or rotations measured in a real number of degree units. We can also consider the domains to be sets of real numbers, or radians, introduced in Section 5.4. Many applications in calculus that use the trigonometric functions refer only to radians.

Let's again consider radian measure and the unit circle. We defined radian measure for θ as

$$\theta = \frac{s}{r}.$$

When $r = 1$,

$$\theta = \frac{s}{1}, \quad \text{or} \quad \theta = s.$$

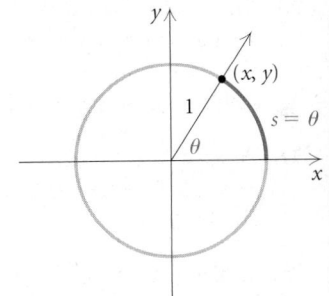

The arc length s on the unit circle is the same as the radian measure of the angle θ.

In the figure above, the point (x, y) is the point where the terminal side of the angle with radian measure s intersects the unit circle. We can now extend our definitions of the trigonometric functions using domains composed of real numbers, or radians.

In the definitions, *s can be considered the radian measure of an angle or the measure of an arc length on the unit circle. Either way, s is a real number.* To each real number s, there corresponds an arc length s on the unit circle. Trigonometric functions with domains composed of real numbers are called **circular functions.**

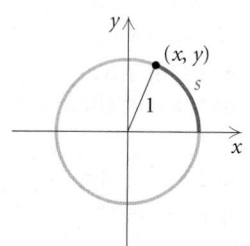

Basic Circular Functions

For a real number s that determines a point (x, y) on the unit circle:

$$\sin s = \text{second coordinate} = y,$$
$$\cos s = \text{first coordinate} = x,$$
$$\tan s = \frac{\text{second coordinate}}{\text{first coordinate}} = \frac{y}{x} \ (x \neq 0),$$
$$\csc s = \frac{1}{\text{second coordinate}} = \frac{1}{y} \ (y \neq 0),$$
$$\sec s = \frac{1}{\text{first coordinate}} = \frac{1}{x} \ (x \neq 0),$$
$$\cot s = \frac{\text{first coordinate}}{\text{second coordinate}} = \frac{x}{y} \ (y \neq 0).$$

We can consider the domains of trigonometric functions to be real numbers rather than angles. We can determine these values for a specific real number if we know the coordinates of the point on the unit circle determined by that number. As with degree measure, we can also find these function values directly using a calculator.

◆ Reflections on the Unit Circle

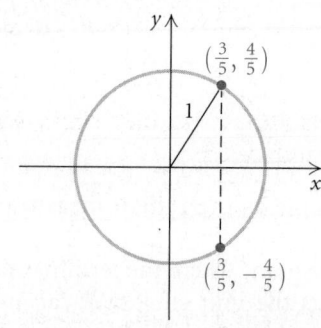

Let's consider the unit circle and a few of its points. For any point (x, y) on the unit circle, $x^2 + y^2 = 1$, we know that $-1 \leq x \leq 1$ and $-1 \leq y \leq 1$. If we know the x- or y-coordinate of a point on the unit circle, we can find the other coordinate. If $x = \frac{3}{5}$, then

$$\left(\tfrac{3}{5}\right)^2 + y^2 = 1$$
$$y^2 = 1 - \tfrac{9}{25} = \tfrac{16}{25}$$
$$y = \pm\tfrac{4}{5}.$$

Thus, $\left(\frac{3}{5}, \frac{4}{5}\right)$ and $\left(\frac{3}{5}, -\frac{4}{5}\right)$ are points on the unit circle. There are two points with an x-coordinate of $\frac{3}{5}$.

Now let's consider the radian measure $\pi/3$ and determine the coordinates of the point on the unit circle determined by $\pi/3$. We construct a right triangle by dropping a perpendicular segment from the point to the x-axis.

Since $\pi/3 = 60°$, we have a 30°–60° right triangle in which the side opposite the 30° angle is one half of the hypotenuse. The hypotenuse, or radius, is 1, so the side opposite the 30° angle is $\frac{1}{2} \cdot 1$, or $\frac{1}{2}$. Using the Pythagorean theorem, we can find the other side:

$$\left(\frac{1}{2}\right)^2 + y^2 = 1$$

$$y^2 = 1 - \frac{1}{4} = \frac{3}{4}$$

$$y = \sqrt{\frac{3}{4}} = \frac{\sqrt{3}}{2}.$$

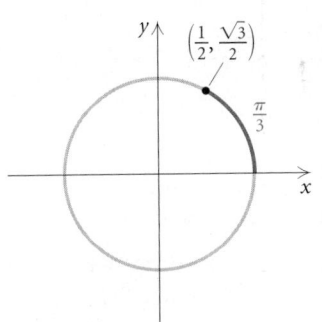

We know that y is positive since the point is in the first quadrant. Thus the coordinates of the point determined by $\pi/3$ are $x = 1/2$ and $y = \sqrt{3}/2$, or $(1/2, \sqrt{3}/2)$. We can always check to see if a point is on the unit circle by substituting into the equation $x^2 + y^2 = 1$:

$$\left(\frac{1}{2}\right)^2 + \left(\frac{\sqrt{3}}{2}\right)^2 = \frac{1}{4} + \frac{3}{4} = 1.$$

Because a unit circle is symmetric with respect to the x-axis, the y-axis, and the origin, we can use the coordinates of one point on the unit circle to find coordinates of its reflections.

EXAMPLE 1 Each of the following points lies on the unit circle. Find their reflections across the x-axis, the y-axis, and the origin.

a) $\left(\dfrac{3}{5}, \dfrac{4}{5}\right)$
b) $\left(\dfrac{\sqrt{2}}{2}, \dfrac{\sqrt{2}}{2}\right)$
c) $\left(\dfrac{1}{2}, \dfrac{\sqrt{3}}{2}\right)$

Solution

a)

b)

c)

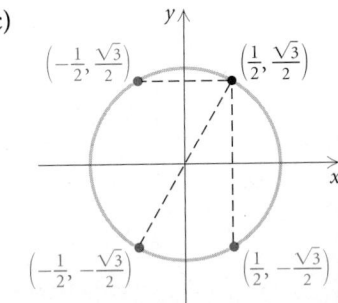

> **Now Try Exercise 1.**

✦ Finding Function Values

Knowing the coordinates of only a few points on the unit circle along with their reflections allows us to find trigonometric function values of the most frequently used real numbers, or radians.

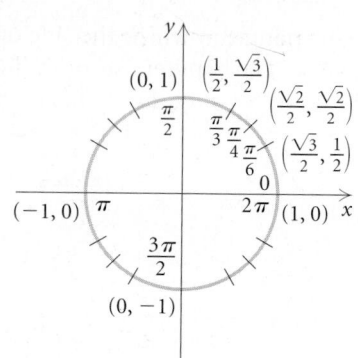

EXAMPLE 2 Find each of the following function values.

a) $\tan \dfrac{\pi}{3}$

b) $\cos \dfrac{3\pi}{4}$

c) $\sin \left(-\dfrac{\pi}{6}\right)$

d) $\cos \dfrac{4\pi}{3}$

e) $\cot \pi$

f) $\csc \left(-\dfrac{7\pi}{2}\right)$

Solution We locate the point on the unit circle determined by the rotation, and then find its coordinates using reflection if necessary.

a) The coordinates of the point determined by $\pi/3$ are $(1/2, \sqrt{3}/2)$.

b) The reflection of $(\sqrt{2}/2, \sqrt{2}/2)$ across the y-axis is $(-\sqrt{2}/2, \sqrt{2}/2)$.

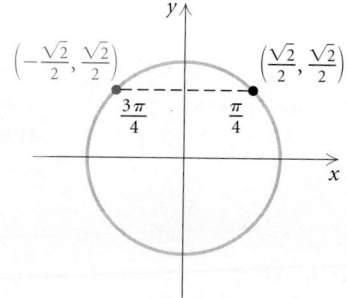

Thus, $\tan \dfrac{\pi}{3} = \dfrac{y}{x} = \dfrac{\sqrt{3}/2}{1/2} = \sqrt{3}$.

Thus, $\cos \dfrac{3\pi}{4} = x = -\dfrac{\sqrt{2}}{2}$.

c) The reflection of $(\sqrt{3}/2, 1/2)$ across the x-axis is $(\sqrt{3}/2, -1/2)$.

d) The reflection of $(1/2, \sqrt{3}/2)$ across the origin is $(-1/2, -\sqrt{3}/2)$.

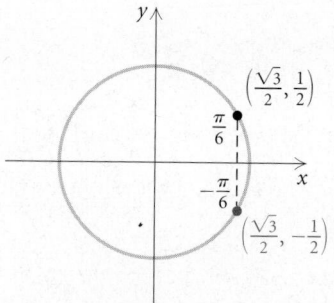

Thus, $\sin \left(-\dfrac{\pi}{6}\right) = y = -\dfrac{1}{2}$.

Thus, $\cos \dfrac{4\pi}{3} = x = -\dfrac{1}{2}$.

e) The coordinates of the point determined by π are $(-1, 0)$.

f) The coordinates of the point determined by $-7\pi/2$ are $(0, 1)$.

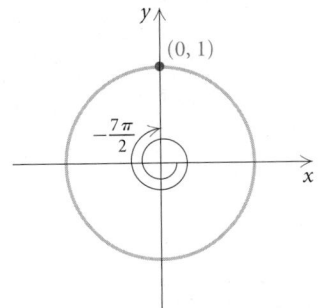

Thus, $\cot \pi = \dfrac{x}{y} = \dfrac{-1}{0}$, which is not defined.

We can also think of $\cot \pi$ as the reciprocal of $\tan \pi$. Since $\tan \pi = y/x = 0/-1 = 0$ and the reciprocal of 0 is not defined, we know that $\cot \pi$ is not defined.

Thus, $\csc\left(-\dfrac{7\pi}{2}\right) = \dfrac{1}{y} = \dfrac{1}{1} = 1.$

▶ Now Try Exercises 9 and 11.

TECHNOLOGY · · · · · · · · · · · · · · ·
CONNECTION

To find trigonometric function values of angles measured in radians, we set the calculator in RADIAN mode.

Parts (a)–(c) of Example 3 are shown in the window below.

```
cos(2π/5)
            .3090169944
tan(−3)
            .1425465431
sin(24.9)
            −.2306457059
```

Using a calculator, we can find trigonometric function values of any real number without knowing the coordinates of the point that it determines on the unit circle. Most calculators have both degree and radian modes. When finding function values of radian measures, or real numbers, we *must* set the calculator in RADIAN mode.

EXAMPLE 3 Find each of the following function values of radian measures using a calculator. Round the answers to four decimal places.

a) $\cos \dfrac{2\pi}{5}$ **b)** $\tan (-3)$

c) $\sin 24.9$ **d)** $\sec \dfrac{\pi}{7}$

Solution Using a calculator set in RADIAN mode, we find the values.

a) $\cos \dfrac{2\pi}{5} \approx 0.3090$ **b)** $\tan (-3) \approx 0.1425$

c) $\sin 24.9 \approx -0.2306$ **d)** $\sec \dfrac{\pi}{7} = \dfrac{1}{\cos \dfrac{\pi}{7}} \approx 1.1099$

Note in part (d) that the secant function value can be found by taking the reciprocal of the cosine value. Thus we can enter $\cos \pi/7$ and use the reciprocal key.

▶ Now Try Exercises 25 and 33.

TECHNOLOGY ·····································
CONNECTION

Exploration

We can graph the unit circle using a graphing calculator. We use PARAMETRIC mode with the following window and let X1T = cos T and Y1T = sin T. Here we use DEGREE mode.

WINDOW

Tmin = 0
Tmax = 360
Tstep = 15
Xmin = −1.5
Xmax = 1.5
Xscl = 1
Ymin = −1
Ymax = 1
Yscl = 1

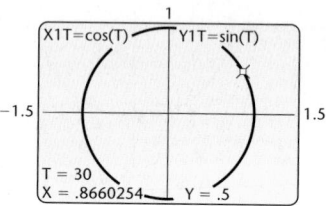

Using the trace key and an arrow key to move the cursor around the unit circle, we see the T, X, and Y values appear on the screen. What do they represent? Repeat this exercise in RADIAN mode. What do the T, X, and Y values represent? (For more on parametric equations, see Section 9.7.)

From the definitions on p. 492, we can relabel any point (x, y) on the unit circle as $(\cos s, \sin s)$, where s is any real number.

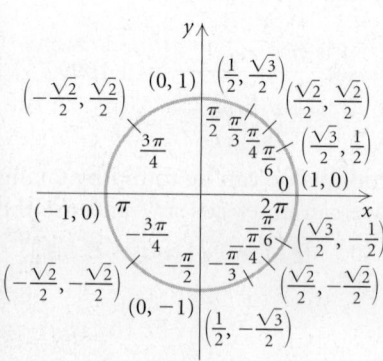

◆ Graphs of the Sine and Cosine Functions

Properties of functions can be observed from their graphs. We begin by graphing the sine and cosine functions. We make a table of values, plot the points, and then connect those points with a smooth curve. It is helpful to first draw a unit circle and label a few points with coordinates. We can either use the coordinates as the function values or find approximate sine and cosine values directly with a calculator.

s	sin s	cos s
0	0	1
$\pi/6$	0.5	0.8660
$\pi/4$	0.7071	0.7071
$\pi/3$	0.8660	0.5
$\pi/2$	1	0
$3\pi/4$	0.7071	-0.7071
π	0	-1
$5\pi/4$	-0.7071	-0.7071
$3\pi/2$	-1	0
$7\pi/4$	-0.7071	0.7071
2π	0	1

s	sin s	cos s
0	0	1
$-\pi/6$	-0.5	0.8660
$-\pi/4$	-0.7071	0.7071
$-\pi/3$	-0.8660	0.5
$-\pi/2$	-1	0
$-3\pi/4$	-0.7071	-0.7071
$-\pi$	0	-1
$-5\pi/4$	0.7071	-0.7071
$-3\pi/2$	1	0
$-7\pi/4$	0.7071	0.7071
-2π	0	1

The graphs are as follows.

The sine function

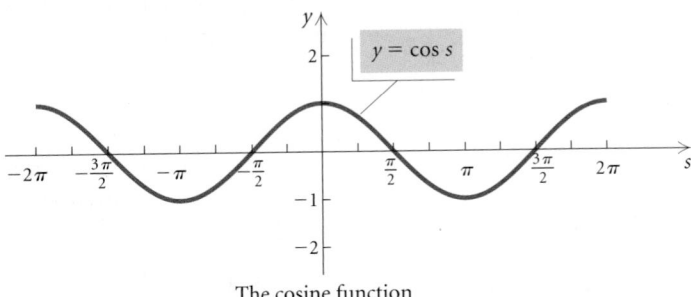

The cosine function

The sine and cosine functions are continuous functions. Note in the graph of the sine function that function values increase from 0 at $s = 0$ to 1 at $s = \pi/2$, then decrease to 0 at $s = \pi$, decrease further to -1 at $s = 3\pi/2$, and increase to 0 at 2π. The reverse pattern follows when s decreases from 0 to -2π. Note in the graph of the cosine function that function values start at 1 when $s = 0$, and decrease to 0 at $s = \pi/2$. They decrease further to -1 at $s = \pi$, then increase to 0 at $s = 3\pi/2$, and increase further to 1 at $s = 2\pi$. An identical pattern follows when s decreases from 0 to -2π.

From the unit circle and the graphs of the functions, we know that the domain of both the sine and cosine functions is the entire set of real numbers, $(-\infty, \infty)$. The range of each function is the set of all real numbers from -1 to 1, $[-1, 1]$.

> ### Domain and Range of Sine and Cosine Functions
> The *domain* of the sine and cosine functions is $(-\infty, \infty)$.
> The *range* of the sine and cosine functions is $[-1, 1]$.

TECHNOLOGY ···
   CONNECTION

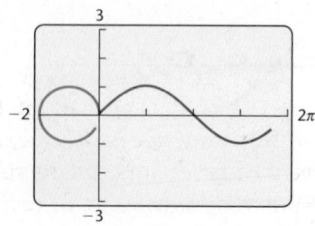

Another way to construct the sine and cosine graphs is by considering the unit circle and transferring vertical distances for the sine function and horizontal distances for the cosine function. Using a graphing calculator, we can visualize the transfer of these distances. We use the calculator set in PARAMETRIC and RADIAN modes and let $X_{1T} = \cos T - 1$ and $Y_{1T} = \sin T$ for the unit circle centered at $(-1, 0)$ and $X_{2T} = T$ and $Y_{2T} = \sin T$ for the sine curve. Use the following window settings.

Tmin = 0	Xmin = −2	Ymin = −3
Tmax = 2π	Xmax = 2π	Ymax = 3
Tstep = .1	Xscl = $\pi/2$	Yscl = 1

With the calculator set in SIMULTANEOUS mode, we can actually watch the sine function (in red) "unwind" from the unit circle (in blue). In the two screens at left, we partially illustrate this animated procedure.

Consult your calculator's instruction manual for specific keystrokes and graph both the sine curve and the cosine curve in this manner. (For more on parametric equations, see Section 9.7.)

A function with a repeating pattern is called **periodic.** The sine and cosine functions are examples of periodic functions. The values of these functions repeat themselves every 2π units. In other words, for any s, we have

$$\sin(s + 2\pi) = \sin s \quad \text{and} \quad \cos(s + 2\pi) = \cos s.$$

To see this another way, think of the part of the graph between 0 and 2π and note that the rest of the graph consists of copies of it. If we translate the graph of $y = \sin x$ or $y = \cos x$ to the left or right 2π units, we will obtain the original graph. We say that each of these functions has a period of 2π.

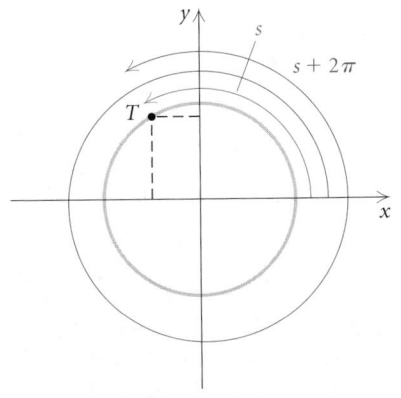

Exploration

Using the TABLE feature on a graphing calculator, compare the y-values for $y_1 = \sin x$ and $y_2 = \sin(-x)$ and for $y_3 = \cos x$ and $y_4 = \cos(-x)$. We set TblMin $= 0$ and $\triangle$Tbl $= \pi/12$.

X	Y1	Y2
0	0	0
.2618	.25882	-.2588
.5236	.5	-.5
.7854	.70711	-.7071
1.0472	.86603	-.866
1.309	.96593	-.9659
1.5708	1	-1

X = 0

X	Y3	Y4
0	1	1
.2618	.96593	.96593
.5236	.86603	.86603
.7854	.70711	.70711
1.0472	.5	.5
1.309	.25882	.25882
1.5708	0	0

X = 0

What appears to be the relationship between $\sin x$ and $\sin(-x)$ and between $\cos x$ and $\cos(-x)$?

> **Periodic Function**
>
> A function f is said to be **periodic** if there exists a positive constant p such that
>
> $$f(s + p) = f(s)$$
>
> for all s in the domain of f. The smallest such positive number p is called the period of the function.

The period p can be thought of as the length of the shortest recurring interval.

We can also use the unit circle to verify that the period of the sine and cosine functions is 2π. Consider any real number s and the point T that it determines on a unit circle, as shown at left. If we increase s by 2π, the point determined by $s + 2\pi$ is again the point T. Hence for any real number s,

$$\sin(s + 2\pi) = \sin s \quad \text{and} \quad \cos(s + 2\pi) = \cos s.$$

It is also true that $\sin(s + 4\pi) = \sin s$, $\sin(s + 6\pi) = \sin s$, and so on. In fact, for *any* integer k, the following equations are identities:

$$\sin[s + k(2\pi)] = \sin s \quad \text{and} \quad \cos[s + k(2\pi)] = \cos s,$$

or

$$\sin s = \sin(s + 2k\pi) \quad \text{and} \quad \cos s = \cos(s + 2k\pi).$$

The **amplitude** of a periodic function is defined as one half of the distance between its maximum and minimum function values. It is always positive. Both the graphs and the unit circle verify that the maximum value of the sine and cosine functions is 1, whereas the minimum value of each is -1. Thus,

$$\text{the amplitude of the sine function} = \tfrac{1}{2}\left|1 - (-1)\right| = 1$$

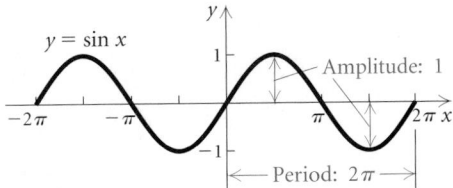

and

$$\text{the amplitude of the cosine function is } \tfrac{1}{2}\left|1 - (-1)\right| = 1.$$

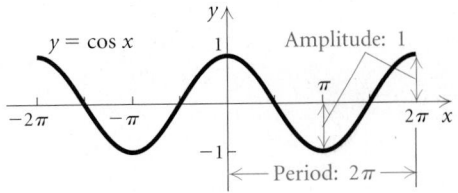

Consider any real number s and its opposite, $-s$. These numbers determine points T and T_1 on a unit circle that are symmetric with respect to the x-axis.

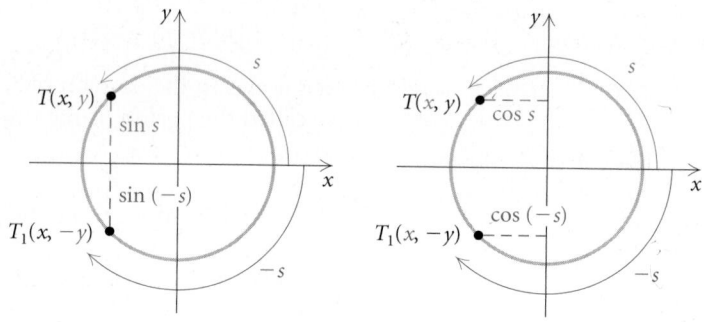

Because their second coordinates are opposites of each other, we know that for any number s,

$$\sin(-s) = -\sin s.$$

Because their first coordinates are the same, we know that for any number s,

$$\cos(-s) = \cos s.$$

Thus we have shown the following.

EVEN AND ODD FUNCTIONS

REVIEW SECTION **1.7.**

> The sine function is *odd*.
>
> The cosine function is *even*.

The following is a summary of the properties of the sine and cosine functions.

CONNECTING THE CONCEPTS

Comparing the Sine and Cosine Functions

SINE FUNCTION

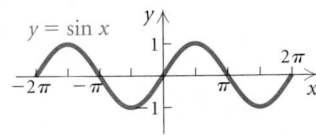

1. Continuous
2. Period: 2π
3. Domain: All real numbers
4. Range: $[-1, 1]$
5. Amplitude: 1
6. Odd: $\sin(-s) = -\sin s$

COSINE FUNCTION

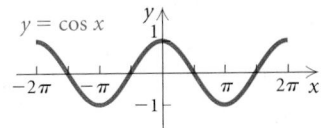

1. Continuous
2. Period: 2π
3. Domain: All real numbers
4. Range: $[-1, 1]$
5. Amplitude: 1
6. Even: $\cos(-s) = \cos s$

● ● ●

✦ Graphs of the Tangent, Cotangent, Cosecant, and Secant Functions

To graph the tangent function, we could make a table of values using a calculator, but in this case it is easier to begin with the definition of tangent and the coordinates of a few points on the unit circle. We recall that

$$\tan s = \frac{y}{x} = \frac{\sin s}{\cos s}.$$

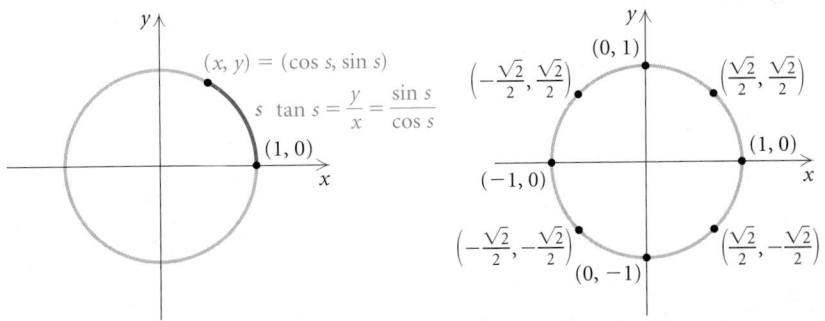

The tangent function is not defined when x, the first coordinate, is 0. That is, it is not defined for any number s whose cosine is 0:

$$s = \pm\frac{\pi}{2}, \pm\frac{3\pi}{2}, \pm\frac{5\pi}{2}, \ldots.$$

We draw vertical asymptotes at these locations (see Fig. 1 below).

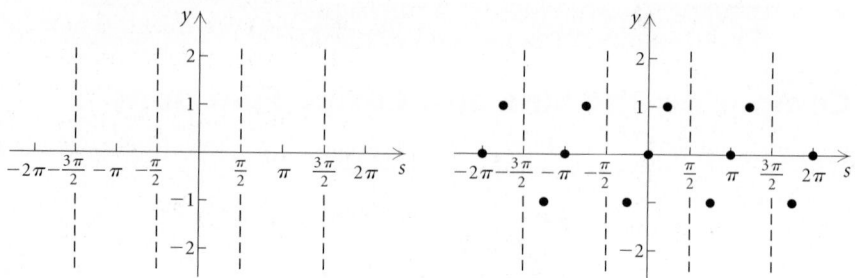

Figure 1   Figure 2

We also note that

$$\tan s = 0 \text{ at } s = 0, \pm\pi, \pm2\pi, \pm3\pi,\ldots,$$

$$\tan s = 1 \text{ at } s = \ldots -\frac{7\pi}{4}, -\frac{3\pi}{4}, \frac{\pi}{4}, \frac{5\pi}{4}, \frac{9\pi}{4},\ldots,$$

$$\tan s = -1 \text{ at } s = \ldots -\frac{9\pi}{4}, -\frac{5\pi}{4}, -\frac{\pi}{4}, \frac{3\pi}{4}, \frac{7\pi}{4},\ldots.$$

We can add these ordered pairs to the graph (see Fig. 2 above) and investigate the values in $(-\pi/2, \pi/2)$ using a calculator. Note that the function value is 0 when $s = 0$, and the values increase without bound as s increases toward $\pi/2$. The graph gets closer and closer to an asymptote as s gets closer to $\pi/2$, but it never touches the line. As s decreases from 0 to $-\pi/2$, the values decrease without bound. Again the graph gets closer and closer to an asymptote, but it never touches it. We now complete the graph.

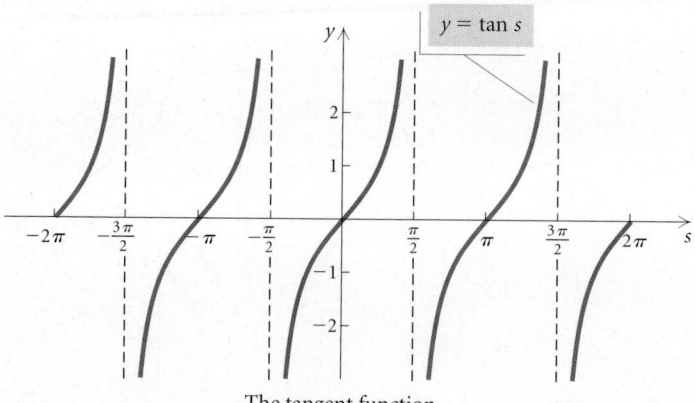

The tangent function

From the graph, we see that the tangent function is continuous except where it is not defined. The period of the tangent function is π. Note that although there is a period, there is no amplitude because there are no maximum and minimum values. When $\cos s = 0$, $\tan s$ is not defined (tan s = sin s/cos s). Thus the domain of the tangent function is the set of all real numbers except $(\pi/2) + k\pi$, where k is an integer. The range of the function is the set of all real numbers.

The cotangent function (cot s = cos s/sin s) is not defined when y, the second coordinate, is 0—that is, it is not defined for any number s whose sine is 0. Thus the cotangent is not defined for $s = 0, \pm\pi, \pm2\pi, \pm3\pi, \ldots$. The graph of the function is shown below.

The cotangent function

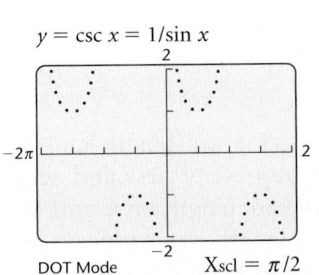
The cosecant and sine functions are reciprocal functions, as are the secant and cosine functions. The graphs of the cosecant and secant functions can be constructed by finding the reciprocals of the values of the sine and cosine functions, respectively. Thus the functions will be positive together and negative together. The cosecant function is not defined for those numbers s whose sine is 0. The secant function is not defined for those numbers s whose cosine is 0. In the graphs below, the sine and cosine functions are shown by the gray curves for reference.

The cosecant function

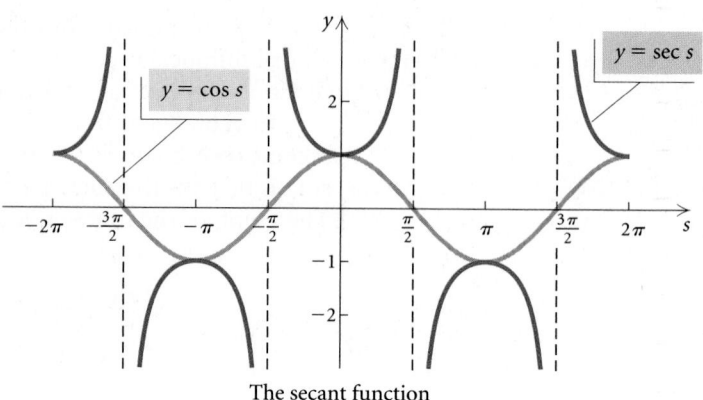

The secant function

The following is a summary of the basic properties of the tangent, cotangent, cosecant, and secant functions. These functions are continuous except where they are not defined.

CONNECTING THE CONCEPTS

Comparing the Tangent, Cotangent, Cosecant, and Secant Functions

TANGENT FUNCTION

1. Period: π
2. Domain: All real numbers except $(\pi/2) + k\pi$, where k is an integer
3. Range: All real numbers

COTANGENT FUNCTION

1. Period: π
2. Domain: All real numbers except $k\pi$, where k is an integer
3. Range: All real numbers

COSECANT FUNCTION

1. Period: 2π
2. Domain: All real numbers except $k\pi$, where k is an integer
3. Range: $(-\infty, -1] \cup [1, \infty)$

SECANT FUNCTION

1. Period: 2π
2. Domain: All real numbers except $(\pi/2) + k\pi$, where k is an integer
3. Range: $(-\infty, -1] \cup [1, \infty)$ ● ● ●

In this chapter, we have used the letter s for arc length and have avoided the letters x and y, which generally represent first and second coordinates. Nevertheless, we can represent the arc length on a unit circle by any variable, such as s, t, x, or θ. Each arc length determines a point that can be labeled with an ordered pair. The first coordinate of that ordered pair is the cosine of the arc length, and the second coordinate is the sine of the arc length. The identities we have developed hold no matter what symbols are used for variables—for example, $\cos(-s) = \cos s$, $\cos(-x) = \cos x$, $\cos(-\theta) = \cos \theta$, and $\cos(-t) = \cos t$.

5.5 EXERCISE SET

The following points are on the unit circle. Find the coordinates of their reflections across **(a)** *the x-axis,* **(b)** *the y-axis, and* **(c)** *the origin.*

1. $\left(-\dfrac{3}{4}, \dfrac{\sqrt{7}}{4}\right)$

2. $\left(\dfrac{2}{3}, \dfrac{\sqrt{5}}{3}\right)$

3. $\left(\dfrac{2}{5}, -\dfrac{\sqrt{21}}{5}\right)$

4. $\left(-\dfrac{\sqrt{3}}{2}, -\dfrac{1}{2}\right)$

5. The number $\pi/4$ determines a point on the unit circle with coordinates $\left(\sqrt{2}/2, \sqrt{2}/2\right)$. What are the coordinates of the point determined by $-\pi/4$?

6. A number β determines a point on the unit circle with coordinates $\left(-2/3, \sqrt{5}/3\right)$. What are the coordinates of the point determined by $-\beta$?

Find the function value using coordinates of points on the unit circle. Give exact answers.

7. $\sin \pi$

8. $\cos\left(-\dfrac{\pi}{3}\right)$

9. $\cot \dfrac{7\pi}{6}$

10. $\tan \dfrac{11\pi}{4}$

11. $\sin (-3\pi)$

12. $\csc \dfrac{3\pi}{4}$

13. $\cos \dfrac{5\pi}{6}$

14. $\tan\left(-\dfrac{\pi}{4}\right)$

15. $\sec \dfrac{\pi}{2}$

16. $\cos 10\pi$

17. $\cos \dfrac{\pi}{6}$

18. $\sin \dfrac{2\pi}{3}$

19. $\sin \dfrac{5\pi}{4}$

20. $\cos \dfrac{11\pi}{6}$

21. $\sin (-5\pi)$

22. $\tan \dfrac{3\pi}{2}$

23. $\cot \dfrac{5\pi}{2}$

24. $\tan \dfrac{5\pi}{3}$

Find the function value using a calculator set in RADIAN *mode. Round the answer to four decimal places, where appropriate.*

25. $\tan \dfrac{\pi}{7}$

26. $\cos\left(-\dfrac{2\pi}{5}\right)$

27. $\sec 37$

28. $\sin 11.7$

29. $\cot 342$

30. $\tan 1.3$

31. $\cos 6\pi$

32. $\sin \dfrac{\pi}{10}$

33. $\csc 4.16$

34. $\sec \dfrac{10\pi}{7}$

35. $\tan \dfrac{7\pi}{4}$

36. $\cos 2000$

37. $\sin\left(-\dfrac{\pi}{4}\right)$

38. $\cot 7\pi$

39. $\sin 0$

40. $\cos (-29)$

41. $\tan \dfrac{2\pi}{9}$

42. $\sin \dfrac{8\pi}{3}$

43. a) Sketch a graph of $y = \sin x$.
   b) By reflecting the graph in part (a), sketch a graph of $y = \sin (-x)$.
   c) By reflecting the graph in part (a), sketch a graph of $y = -\sin x$.
   d) How do the graphs in parts (b) and (c) compare?

44. a) Sketch a graph of $y = \cos x$.
   b) By reflecting the graph in part (a), sketch a graph of $y = \cos (-x)$.
   c) By reflecting the graph in part (a), sketch a graph of $y = -\cos x$.
   d) How do the graphs in parts (a) and (b) compare?

45. a) Sketch a graph of $y = \sin x$.
  b) By translating, sketch a graph of $y = \sin(x + \pi)$.
  c) By reflecting the graph of part (a), sketch a graph of $y = -\sin x$.
  d) How do the graphs of parts (b) and (c) compare?

46. a) Sketch a graph of $y = \sin x$.
  b) By translating, sketch a graph of $y = \sin(x - \pi)$.
  c) By reflecting the graph of part (a), sketch a graph of $y = -\sin x$.
  d) How do the graphs of parts (b) and (c) compare?

47. a) Sketch a graph of $y = \cos x$.
  b) By translating, sketch a graph of $y = \cos(x + \pi)$.
  c) By reflecting the graph of part (a), sketch a graph of $y = -\cos x$.
  d) How do the graphs of parts (b) and (c) compare?

48. a) Sketch a graph of $y = \cos x$.
  b) By translating, sketch a graph of $y = \cos(x - \pi)$.
  c) By reflecting the graph of part (a), sketch a graph of $y = -\cos x$.
  d) How do the graphs of parts (b) and (c) compare?

49. a) Sketch a graph of $y = \tan x$.
  b) By reflecting the graph of part (a), sketch a graph of $y = \tan(-x)$.
  c) By reflecting the graph of part (a), sketch a graph of $y = -\tan x$.
  d) How do the graphs in parts (b) and (c) compare?

50. a) Sketch a graph of $y = \sec x$.
  b) By reflecting the graph of part (a), sketch a graph of $y = \sec(-x)$.
  c) By reflecting the graph of part (a), sketch a graph of $y = -\sec x$.
  d) How do the graphs in parts (a) and (b) compare?

51. Of the six circular functions, which are even? Which are odd?

52. Of the six circular functions, which have period π? Which have period 2π?

Consider the coordinates on the unit circle for Exercises 53–56.

53. In which quadrants is the tangent function positive? negative?

54. In which quadrants is the sine function positive? negative?

55. In which quadrants is the cosine function positive? negative?

56. In which quadrants is the cosecant function positive? negative?

Technology Connection

Use a graphing calculator to determine the domain, the range, the period, and the amplitude of the function.

57. $y = (\sin x)^2$ **58.** $y = |\cos x| + 1$

59. Using a calculator, consider $(\sin x)/x$, where x is between 0 and $\pi/2$. As x approaches 0, this function approaches a limiting value. What is it?

60. Using graphs, determine all numbers x that satisfy $\sin x < \cos x$.

Collaborative Discussion and Writing

61. Describe how the graphs of the sine and cosine functions are related.

62. Explain why both the sine and cosine functions are continuous, but the tangent function, defined as sine/cosine, is not continuous.

Skill Maintenance

Graph both functions on the same set of axes, and describe how g is a transformation of f.

63. $f(x) = x^2$, $g(x) = 2x^2 - 3$

64. $f(x) = x^2$, $g(x) = (x - 2)^2$

65. $f(x) = |x|$, $g(x) = \frac{1}{2}|x - 4| + 1$

66. $f(x) = x^3$, $g(x) = -x^3$

Write an equation for a function that has a graph with the given characteristics.

67. The shape of $y = x^3$, but reflected across the x-axis, shifted right 2 units, and shifted down 1 unit

68. The shape of $y = 1/x$, but shrunk vertically by a factor of $\frac{1}{4}$ and shifted up 3 units

Synthesis

Complete. (For example, $\sin(x + 2\pi) = \sin x$.*)*

69. $\cos(-x) =$ _____

70. $\sin(-x) =$ _____

71. $\sin(x + 2k\pi), k \in \mathbb{Z} =$ _____

72. $\cos(x + 2k\pi), k \in \mathbb{Z} =$ _____

73. $\sin(\pi - x) =$ _____

74. $\cos(\pi - x) =$ _____

75. $\cos(x - \pi) =$ _____

76. $\cos(x + \pi) =$ _____

77. $\sin(x + \pi) =$ _____

78. $\sin(x - \pi) =$ _____

79. Find all numbers x that satisfy the following.

   a) $\sin x = 1$
   b) $\cos x = -1$
   c) $\sin x = 0$

80. Find $f \circ g$ and $g \circ f$, where $f(x) = x^2 + 2x$ and $g(x) = \cos x$.

Determine the domain of the function.

81. $f(x) = \sqrt{\cos x}$

82. $g(x) = \dfrac{1}{\sin x}$

83. $f(x) = \dfrac{\sin x}{\cos x}$

84. $g(x) = \log(\sin x)$

Graph.

85. $y = 3 \sin x$

86. $y = \sin|x|$

87. $y = \sin x + \cos x$

88. $y = |\cos x|$

89. One of the motivations for developing trigonometry with a unit circle is that you can actually "see" $\sin \theta$ and $\cos \theta$ on the circle. Note in the figure below that $AP = \sin \theta$ and $OA = \cos \theta$. It turns out that you can also "see" the other four trigonometric functions. Prove each of the following.

   a) $BD = \tan \theta$
   b) $OD = \sec \theta$
   c) $OE = \csc \theta$
   d) $CE = \cot \theta$

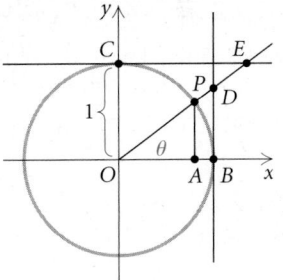

5.6 Graphs of Transformed Sine and Cosine Functions

◆ Graph transformations of $y = \sin x$ and $y = \cos x$ in the form

$$y = A \sin(Bx - C) + D$$

and

$$y = A \cos(Bx - C) + D$$

and determine the amplitude, the period, and the phase shift.

◆ Graph sums of functions.

◆ Graph functions (damped oscillations) found by multiplying trigonometric functions by other functions.

✦ Variations of Basic Graphs

In Section 5.5, we graphed all six trigonometric functions. In this section, we will consider variations of the graphs of the sine and cosine functions.

For example, we will graph equations like the following:

$$y = 5 \sin \tfrac{1}{2}x, \qquad y = \cos(2x - \pi), \quad \text{and} \quad y = \tfrac{1}{2}\sin x - 3.$$

In particular, we are interested in graphs of functions in the form

$$y = A \sin(Bx - C) + D$$

and

$$y = A \cos(Bx - C) + D,$$

where A, B, C, and D are constants. These constants have the effect of translating, reflecting, stretching, and shrinking the basic graphs. Let's first examine the effect of each constant individually. Then we will consider the combined effects of more than one constant.

> TRANSFORMATIONS OF FUNCTIONS
>
> REVIEW SECTION 1.7.

The Constant D

Let's observe the effect of the constant D in the graphs below.

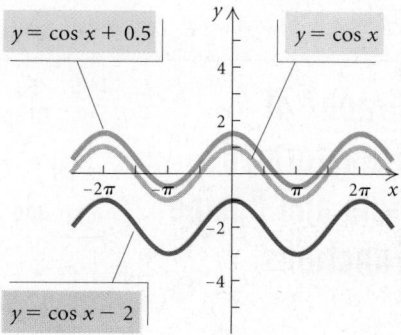

The constant D in

$$y = A \sin(Bx - C) + D \quad \text{and} \quad y = A \cos(Bx - C) + D$$

translates the graphs up D units if $D > 0$ or down $|D|$ units if $D < 0$.

EXAMPLE 1 Sketch a graph of $y = \sin x + 3$.

Solution The graph of $y = \sin x + 3$ is a *vertical* translation of the graph of $y = \sin x$ up 3 units. One way to sketch the graph is to first consider $y = \sin x$ on an interval of length 2π, say, $[0, 2\pi]$. The zeros of the function and the maximum and minimum values can be considered key points. These are

$$(0, 0), \quad \left(\frac{\pi}{2}, 1\right), \quad (\pi, 0), \quad \left(\frac{3\pi}{2}, -1\right), \quad (2\pi, 0).$$

These key points are transformed up 3 units to obtain the key points of the graph of $y = \sin x + 3$. These are

$$(0, 3), \quad \left(\frac{\pi}{2}, 4\right), \quad (\pi, 3), \quad \left(\frac{3\pi}{2}, 2\right), \quad (2\pi, 3).$$

The graph of $y = \sin x + 3$ can be sketched on the interval $[0, 2\pi]$ and extended to obtain the rest of the graph by repeating the graph on intervals of length 2π.

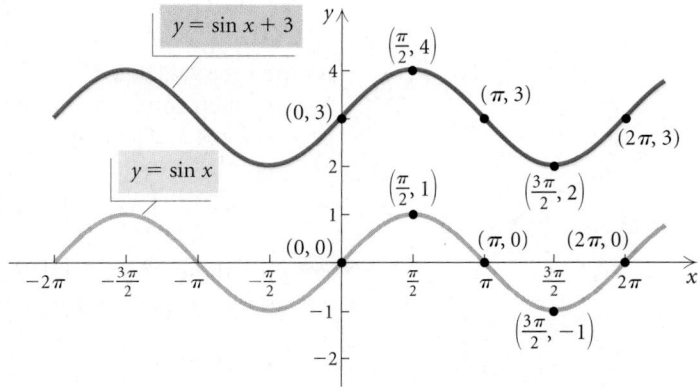

The Constant A

Next, we consider the effect of the constant A. What can we observe in the following graphs? What is the effect of the constant A on the graph of the basic function when (**a**) $0 < A < 1$? (**b**) $A > 1$? (**c**) $-1 < A < 0$? (**d**) $A < -1$?

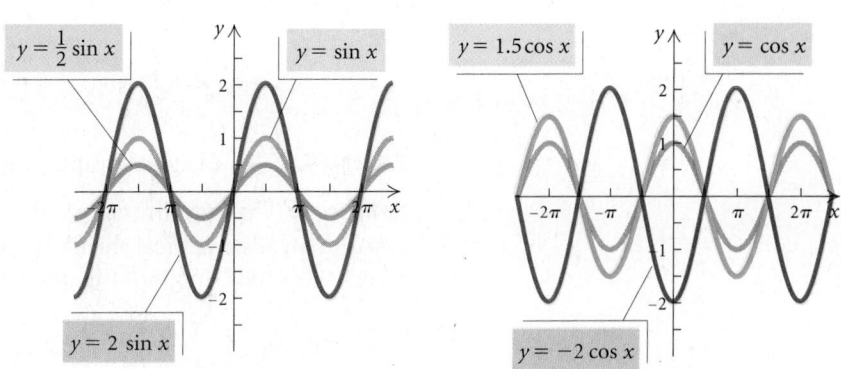

If $|A| > 1$, then there will be a vertical stretching. If $|A| < 1$, then there will be a vertical shrinking. If $A < 0$, the graph is also reflected across the x-axis.

> ### Amplitude
> The **amplitude** of the graphs of $y = A \sin(Bx - C) + D$ and $y = A \cos(Bx - C) + D$ is $|A|$.

EXAMPLE 2   Sketch a graph of $y = 2 \cos x$. What is the amplitude?

Solution   The constant 2 in $y = 2 \cos x$ has the effect of stretching the graph of $y = \cos x$ vertically by a factor of 2 units. Since the function values of $y = \cos x$ are such that $-1 \le \cos x \le 1$, the function values of $y = 2 \cos x$ are such that $-2 \le 2 \cos x \le 2$. The maximum value of $y = 2 \cos x$ is 2, and the minimum value is -2. Thus the *amplitude*, A, is $\frac{1}{2}|2 - (-2)|$, or 2.

We draw the graph of $y = \cos x$ and consider its key points,

$$(0, 1), \quad \left(\frac{\pi}{2}, 0\right), \quad (\pi, -1), \quad \left(\frac{3\pi}{2}, 0\right), \quad (2\pi, 1),$$

on the interval $[0, 2\pi]$.

We then multiply the second coordinates by 2 to obtain the key points of $y = 2 \cos x$. These are

$$(0, 2), \quad \left(\frac{\pi}{2}, 0\right), \quad (\pi, -2), \quad \left(\frac{3\pi}{2}, 0\right), \quad (2\pi, 2).$$

We plot these points and sketch the graph on the interval $[0, 2\pi]$. Then we repeat this part of the graph on adjacent intervals of length 2π.

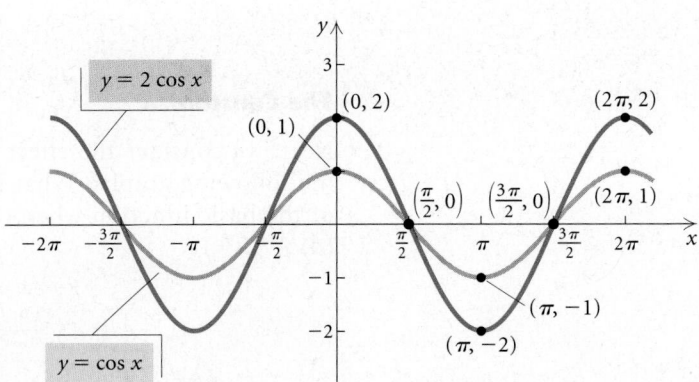

EXAMPLE 3   Sketch a graph of $y = -\frac{1}{2} \sin x$. What is the amplitude?

Solution   The amplitude of the graph is $\left|-\frac{1}{2}\right|$, or $\frac{1}{2}$. The graph of $y = -\frac{1}{2} \sin x$ is a vertical shrinking and a reflection of the graph of $y = \sin x$ across the x-axis. In graphing, the key points of $y = \sin x$,

$$(0, 0), \quad \left(\frac{\pi}{2}, 1\right), \quad (\pi, 0), \quad \left(\frac{3\pi}{2}, -1\right), \quad (2\pi, 0),$$

are transformed to

$$(0, 0), \quad \left(\frac{\pi}{2}, -\frac{1}{2}\right), \quad (\pi, 0), \quad \left(\frac{3\pi}{2}, \frac{1}{2}\right), \quad (2\pi, 0).$$

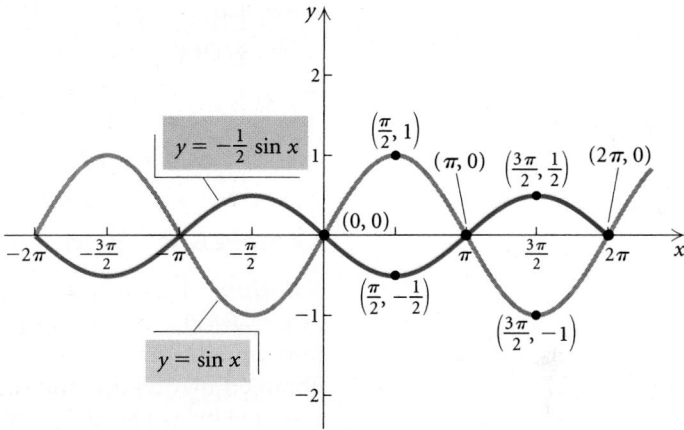

The Constant B

Now, we consider the effect of the constant B. Changes in the constants A and D *do not* change the period. But what effect, if any, does a change in B have on the period of the function? Let's observe the period of each of the following graphs.

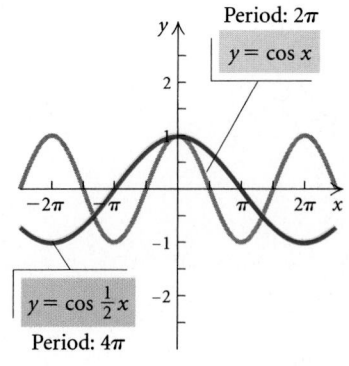

If $|B| < 1$, then there will be a horizontal stretching. If $|B| > 1$, then there will be a horizontal shrinking. If $B < 0$, the graph is also reflected across the y-axis.

Period

The **period** of the graphs of $y = A \sin (Bx - C) + D$ and $y = A \cos (Bx - C) + D$ is $\left|\dfrac{2\pi}{B}\right|$.*

EXAMPLE 4 Sketch a graph of $y = \sin 4x$. What is the period?

Solution The constant B has the effect of changing the period. The graph of $y = f(4x)$ is obtained from the graph of $y = f(x)$ by shrinking the graph horizontally. The period of $y = \sin 4x$ is $|2\pi/4|$, or $\pi/2$. The new graph is obtained by dividing the first coordinate of each ordered-pair solution of $y = f(x)$ by 4. The key points of $y = \sin x$ are

$$(0, 0), \quad \left(\frac{\pi}{2}, 1\right), \quad (\pi, 0), \quad \left(\frac{3\pi}{2}, -1\right), \quad (2\pi, 0).$$

These are transformed to the key points of $y = \sin 4x$, which are

$$(0, 0), \quad \left(\frac{\pi}{8}, 1\right), \quad \left(\frac{\pi}{4}, 0\right), \quad \left(\frac{3\pi}{8}, -1\right), \quad \left(\frac{\pi}{2}, 0\right).$$

We plot these key points and sketch in the graph on the shortened interval $[0, \pi/2]$. Then we repeat the graph on other intervals of length $\pi/2$.

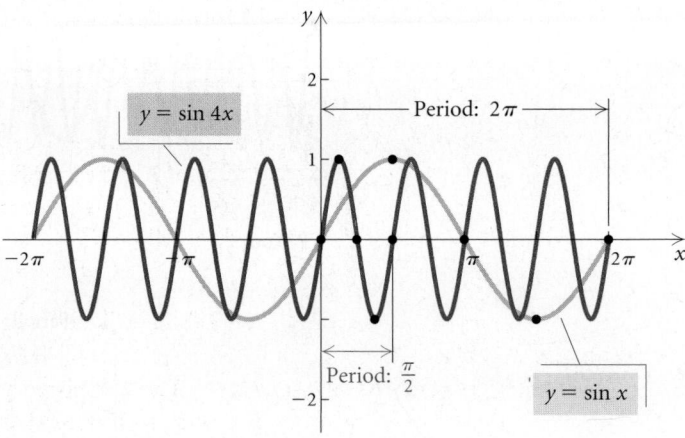

---

*The period of the graphs of $y = A \tan (Bx - C) + D$ and $y = A \cot (Bx - C) + D$ is $|\pi/B|$.
The period of the graphs of $y = A \sec (Bx - C) + D$ and $y = A \csc (Bx - C) + D$ is $|2\pi/B|$.

The Constant C

Next, we examine the effect of the constant C. The curve in each of the following graphs has an amplitude of 1 and a period of 2π, but there are six distinct graphs. What is the effect of the constant C?

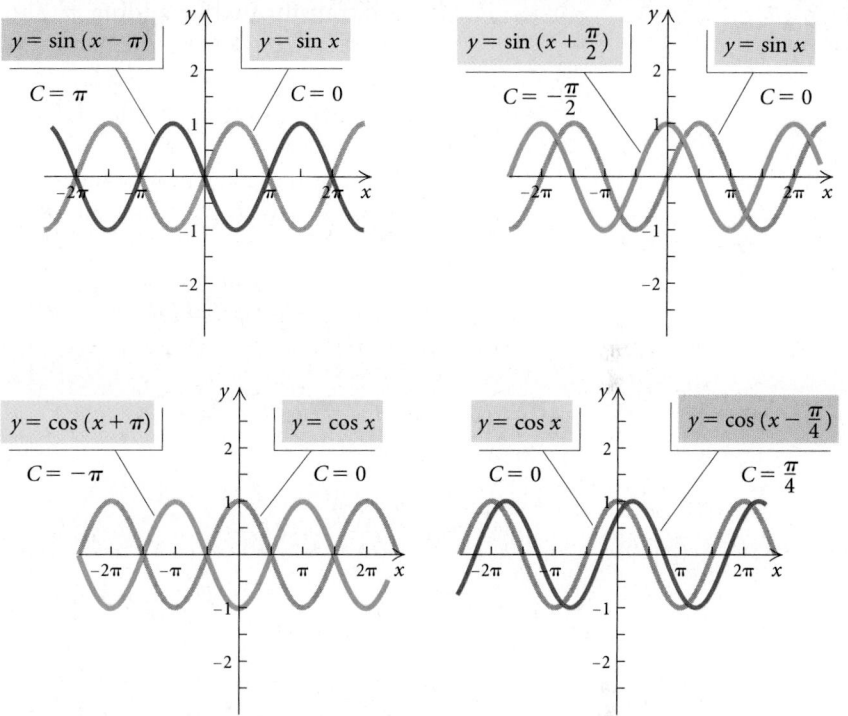

For each of the functions of the form

$$y = A \sin (Bx - C) + D \quad \text{and} \quad y = A \cos (Bx - C) + D$$

that are graphed above, the coefficient of x, which is B, is 1. In this case, the effect of the constant C on the graph of the basic function is a horizontal translation of $|C|$ units. In Example 5, which follows, $B = 1$. We will consider functions where $B \neq 1$ in Examples 6 and 7. When $B \neq 1$, the horizontal translation will be $|C/B|$.

EXAMPLE 5 Sketch a graph of $y = \sin \left(x - \dfrac{\pi}{2} \right)$.

Solution The amplitude is 1, and the period is 2π. The graph of $y = f(x - c)$ is obtained from the graph of $y = f(x)$ by translating the graph horizontally—to the right c units if $c > 0$ and to the left $|c|$ units if $c < 0$. The graph of $y = \sin (x - \pi/2)$ is a translation of the graph of

$y = \sin x$ to the right $\pi/2$ units. The value $\pi/2$ is called the **phase shift.** The key points of $y = \sin x$,

$$(0, 0), \quad \left(\frac{\pi}{2}, 1\right), \quad (\pi, 0), \quad \left(\frac{3\pi}{2}, -1\right), \quad (2\pi, 0),$$

are transformed by adding $\pi/2$ to each of the first coordinates to obtain the following key points of $y = \sin(x - \pi/2)$:

$$\left(\frac{\pi}{2}, 0\right), \quad (\pi, 1), \quad \left(\frac{3\pi}{2}, 0\right), \quad (2\pi, -1), \quad \left(\frac{5\pi}{2}, 0\right).$$

We plot these key points and sketch the curve on the interval $[\pi/2, 5\pi/2]$. Then we repeat the graph on other intervals of length 2π.

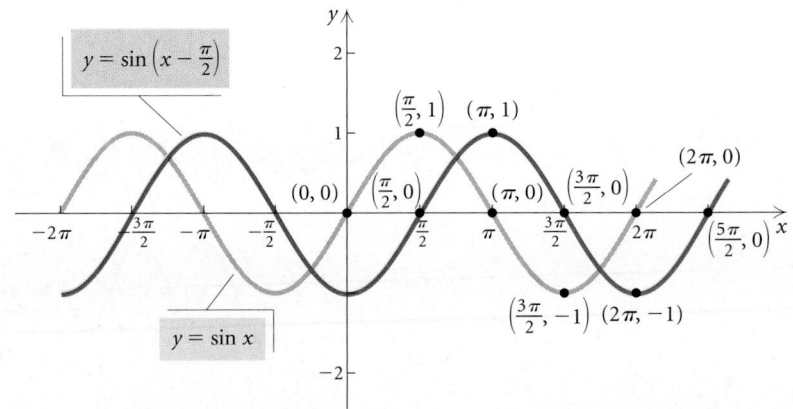

Combined Transformations

Now we consider combined transformations of graphs. It is helpful to rewrite

$$y = A \sin(Bx - C) + D \qquad \text{and} \qquad y = A \cos(Bx - C) + D$$

as

$$y = A \sin\left[B\left(x - \frac{C}{B}\right)\right] + D \quad \text{and} \quad y = A \cos\left[B\left(x - \frac{C}{B}\right)\right] + D.$$

EXAMPLE 6   Sketch a graph of $y = \cos(2x - \pi)$.

Solution   The graph of

$$y = \cos(2x - \pi)$$

is the same as the graph of

$$y = 1 \cdot \cos\left[2\left(x - \frac{\pi}{2}\right)\right] + 0.$$

The amplitude is 1. The factor 2 shrinks the period by half, making the period $|2\pi/2|$, or π. The phase shift $\pi/2$ translates the graph of $y = \cos 2x$ to the right $\pi/2$ units. Thus, to form the graph, we first graph $y = \cos x$, followed by $y = \cos 2x$ and then $y = \cos [2(x - \pi/2)]$.

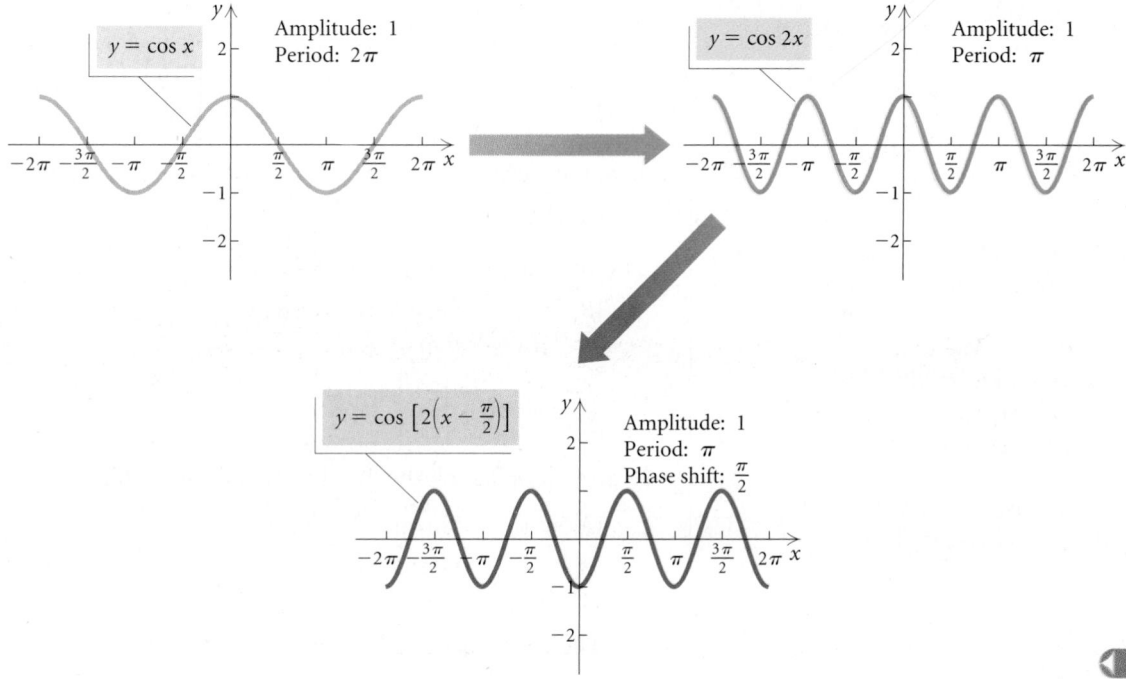

Phase Shift

The **phase shift** of the graphs

$$y = A \sin (Bx - C) + D = A \sin \left[B\left(x - \frac{C}{B} \right) \right] + D$$

and

$$y = A \cos (Bx - C) + D = A \cos \left[B\left(x - \frac{C}{B} \right) \right] + D$$

is the quantity $\dfrac{C}{B}$.

If $C/B > 0$, the graph is translated to the right C/B units. If $C/B < 0$, the graph is translated to the left $|C/B|$ units. Be sure that the horizontal stretching or shrinking based on the constant B is done before the translation based on the phase shift C/B.

Let's now summarize the effect of the constants. When graphing, we carry out the procedures in the order listed.

When graphing transformations of the tangent and cotangent functions, note that the period is $|\pi/B|$. When graphing transformations of the secant and cosecant functions, note that the period is $|2\pi/B|$.

Transformations of Sine and Cosine Functions

To graph

$$y = A \sin (Bx - C) + D = A \sin \left[B\left(x - \frac{C}{B} \right) \right] + D$$

and

$$y = A \cos (Bx - C) + D = A \cos \left[B\left(x - \frac{C}{B} \right) \right] + D,$$

follow the steps listed below in the order in which they are listed.

1. Stretch or shrink the graph horizontally according to B.

   $|B| < 1$ Stretch horizontally
   $|B| > 1$ Shrink horizontally
   $B < 0$ Reflect across the y-axis
   The *period* is $\left| \dfrac{2\pi}{B} \right|$.

2. Stretch or shrink the graph vertically according to A.

   $|A| < 1$ Shrink vertically
   $|A| > 1$ Stretch vertically
   $A < 0$ Reflect across the x-axis
   The *amplitude* is $|A|$.

3. Translate the graph horizontally according to C/B.

   $\dfrac{C}{B} < 0$ $\left| \dfrac{C}{B} \right|$ units to the left

   $\dfrac{C}{B} > 0$ $\dfrac{C}{B}$ units to the right

   The *phase shift* is $\dfrac{C}{B}$.

4. Translate the graph vertically according to D.

   $D < 0$ $|D|$ units down
   $D > 0$ D units up

EXAMPLE 7 Sketch a graph of $y = 3 \sin (2x + \pi/2) + 1$. Find the amplitude, the period, and the phase shift.

Solution We first note that

$$y = 3 \sin \left(2x + \frac{\pi}{2} \right) + 1 = 3 \sin \left[2\left(x - \left(-\frac{\pi}{4} \right) \right) \right] + 1.$$

Then we have the following:

$$\text{Amplitude} = |A| = |3| = 3,$$

$$\text{Period} = \left|\frac{2\pi}{B}\right| = \left|\frac{2\pi}{2}\right| = \pi,$$

$$\text{Phase shift} = \frac{C}{B} = \frac{-\pi/2}{2} = -\frac{\pi}{4}.$$

To create the final graph, we begin with the basic sine curve, $y = \sin x$. Then we sketch graphs of each of the following equations in sequence.

1. $y = \sin 2x$

2. $y = 3 \sin 2x$

3. $y = 3 \sin \left[2\left(x - \left(-\frac{\pi}{4}\right)\right)\right]$

4. $y = 3 \sin \left[2\left(x - \left(-\frac{\pi}{4}\right)\right)\right] + 1$

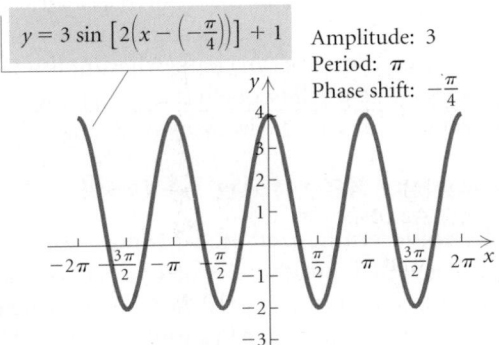

▶ Now Try Exercise 27.

All the graphs in Examples 1–7 can be checked using a graphing calculator. Even though it is faster and more accurate to graph using a calculator, graphing by hand gives us a greater understanding of the effect of changing the constants A, B, C, and D.

Graphing calculators are especially convenient when a period or a phase shift is not a multiple of $\pi/4$.

EXAMPLE 8 Graph $y = 3 \cos 2\pi x - 1$. Find the amplitude, the period, and the phase shift.

Solution First we note the following:

$$\text{Amplitude} = |A| = |3| = 3,$$

$$\text{Period} = \left|\frac{2\pi}{B}\right| = \left|\frac{2\pi}{2\pi}\right| = |1| = 1,$$

$$\text{Phase shift} = \frac{C}{B} = \frac{0}{2\pi} = 0.$$

There is no phase shift in this case because the constant $C = 0$. The graph has a vertical translation of the graph of the cosine function down 1 unit, an amplitude of 3, and a period of 1, so we can use $[-4, 4, -5, 5]$ as the viewing window.

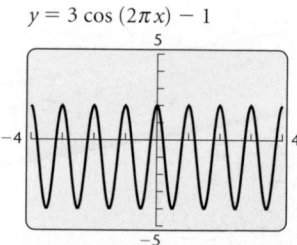

$y = 3 \cos(2\pi x) - 1$

▷ Now Try Exercise 29.

The transformation techniques that we learned in this section for graphing the sine and cosine functions can also be applied in the same manner to the other trigonometric functions. Transformations of this type appear in the synthesis exercises in Exercise Set 5.6.

An **oscilloscope** is an electronic device that converts electrical signals into graphs like those in the preceding examples. These graphs are often called sine waves. By manipulating the controls, we can change the amplitude, the period, and the phase of sine waves. The oscilloscope has many applications, and the trigonometric functions play a major role in many of them.

◆ Graphs of Sums: Addition of Ordinates

The output of an electronic synthesizer used in the recording and playing of music can be converted into sine waves by an oscilloscope. The following graphs illustrate simple tones of different frequencies. The frequency of a simple tone is the number of vibrations in the signal of the tone per second. The loudness or intensity of the tone is reflected in the height of the graph (its amplitude). The three tones in the diagrams below all have the same intensity but different frequencies.

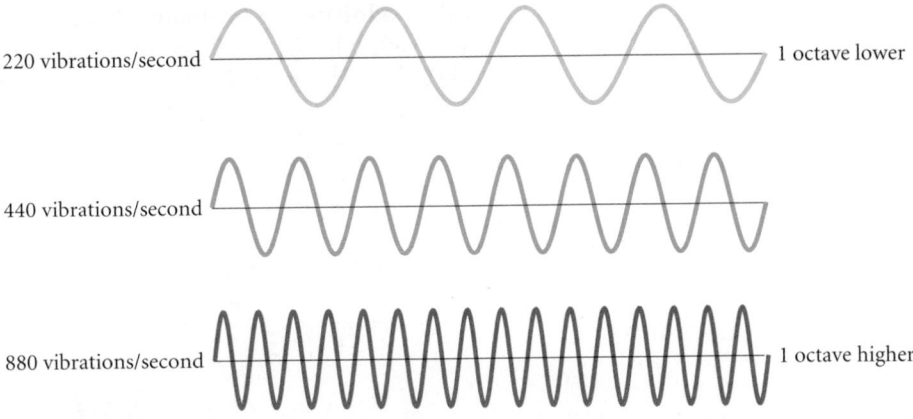

220 vibrations/second   1 octave lower

440 vibrations/second

880 vibrations/second   1 octave higher

Musical instruments can generate extremely complex sine waves. On a single instrument, overtones can become superimposed on a simple tone. When multiple notes are played simultaneously, graphs become very complicated. This can happen when multiple notes are played on a single instrument or a group of instruments, or even when the same simple note is played on different instruments.

Combinations of simple tones produce interesting curves. Consider two tones whose graphs are $y_1 = 2 \sin x$ and $y_2 = \sin 2x$. The combination of the two tones produces a new sound whose graph is $y = 2 \sin x + \sin 2x$, as shown in the following example.

EXAMPLE 9   Graph: $y = 2 \sin x + \sin 2x$.

Solution   We graph $y = 2 \sin x$ and $y = \sin 2x$ using the same set of axes.

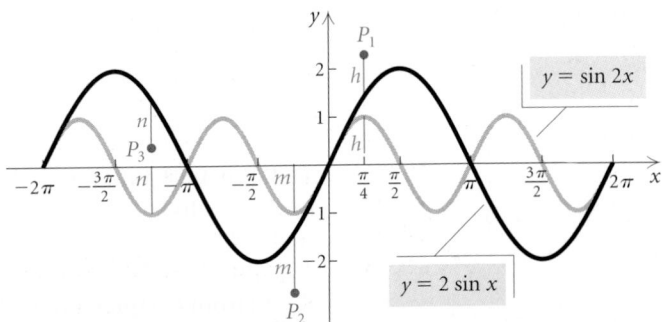

Now we graphically add some y-coordinates, or ordinates, to obtain points on the graph that we seek. At $x = \pi/4$, we transfer the distance h, which is the value of $\sin 2x$, up to add it to the value of $2 \sin x$. Point P_1 is on the graph that we seek. At $x = -\pi/4$, we use a similar procedure, but this time both ordinates are negative. Point P_2 is on the graph. At $x = -5\pi/4$, we add the negative ordinate of $\sin 2x$ to the positive ordinate of $2 \sin x$. Point P_3 is also on the graph. We continue to plot points in this fashion and then connect them to get the desired graph, shown below. This method is called **addition of ordinates,** because we add the y-values (ordinates) of $y = \sin 2x$ to the y-values (ordinates) of $y = 2 \sin x$. Note that the period of $2 \sin x$ is 2π and the period of $\sin 2x$ is π. The period of the sum $2 \sin x + \sin 2x$ is 2π, the least common multiple of 2π and π.

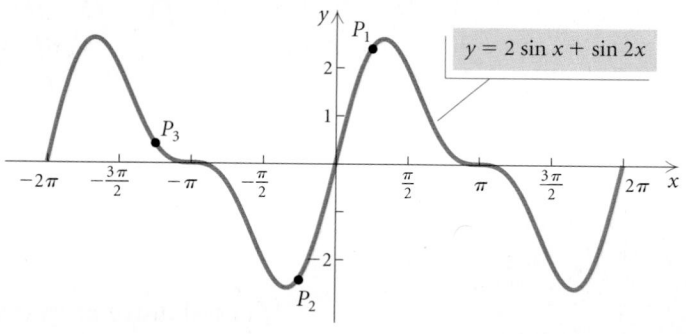

Now Try Exercise 45.

✦ Damped Oscillation: Multiplication of Ordinates

Suppose that a weight is attached to a spring and the spring is stretched and put into motion. The weight oscillates up and down. If we could assume falsely that the weight will bob up and down forever, then its height h after time t, in seconds, might be approximated by a function like

$$h(t) = 5 + 2 \sin (6\pi t).$$

Over a short time period, this might be a valid model, but experience tells us that eventually the spring will come to rest. A more appropriate model is provided by the following example, which illustrates **damped oscillation.**

EXAMPLE 10   Sketch a graph of $f(x) = e^{-x/2} \sin x$.

Solution   The function f is the product of two functions g and h, where

$$g(x) = e^{-x/2} \quad \text{and} \quad h(x) = \sin x.$$

Thus, to find function values, we can **multiply ordinates.** Let's do more analysis before graphing. Note that for any real number x,

$$-1 \leq \sin x \leq 1.$$

Recall from Chapter 4 that all values of the exponential function are positive. Thus we can multiply by $e^{-x/2}$ and obtain the inequality

$$-e^{-x/2} \leq e^{-x/2} \sin x \leq e^{-x/2}.$$

The direction of the inequality symbols does not change since $e^{-x/2} > 0$. This also tells us that the original function crosses the x-axis only at values for which $\sin x = 0$. These are the numbers $k\pi$, for any integer k.

The inequality tells us that the function f is constrained between the graphs of $y = -e^{-x/2}$ and $y = e^{-x/2}$. We start by graphing these functions using dashed lines. Since we also know that $f(x) = 0$ when $x = k\pi$, k an integer, we mark these points on the graph. Then we use a calculator and compute other function values. The graph is as follows.

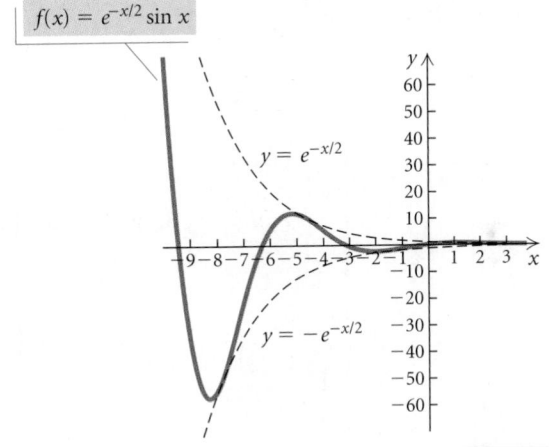

$$f(x) = e^{-x/2} \sin x$$

▶ Now Try Exercise 53.

A

B

C

D

E

Visualizing the Graph

Match the function with its graph.

1. $f(x) = -\sin x$

2. $f(x) = 2x^3 - x + 1$

3. $y = \dfrac{1}{2}\cos\left(x + \dfrac{\pi}{2}\right)$

4. $f(x) = \cos\left(\dfrac{1}{2}x\right)$

5. $y = -x^2 + x$

6. $y = \dfrac{1}{2}\log x + 4$

7. $f(x) = 2^{x-1}$

8. $f(x) = \dfrac{1}{2}\sin\left(\dfrac{1}{2}x\right) + 1$

9. $f(x) = -\cos(x - \pi)$

10. $f(x) = -\dfrac{1}{2}x^4$

Answers on page A-38

F

G

H

I

J

5.6 EXERCISE SET

Determine the amplitude, the period, and the phase shift of the function and sketch the graph of the function.

1. $y = \sin x + 1$

2. $y = \dfrac{1}{4}\cos x$

3. $y = -3\cos x$

4. $y = \sin(-2x)$

5. $y = \dfrac{1}{2}\cos x$

6. $y = \sin\left(\dfrac{1}{2}x\right)$

7. $y = \sin(2x)$

8. $y = \cos x - 1$

9. $y = 2\sin\left(\dfrac{1}{2}x\right)$

10. $y = \cos\left(x - \dfrac{\pi}{2}\right)$

11. $y = \dfrac{1}{2}\sin\left(x + \dfrac{\pi}{2}\right)$

12. $y = \cos x - \dfrac{1}{2}$

13. $y = 3\cos(x - \pi)$

14. $y = -\sin\left(\dfrac{1}{4}x\right) + 1$

15. $y = \dfrac{1}{3}\sin x - 4$

16. $y = \cos\left(\dfrac{1}{2}x + \dfrac{\pi}{2}\right)$

17. $y = -\cos(-x) + 2$

18. $y = \dfrac{1}{2}\sin\left(2x - \dfrac{\pi}{4}\right)$

Determine the amplitude, the period, and the phase shift of the function.

19. $y = 2\cos\left(\dfrac{1}{2}x - \dfrac{\pi}{2}\right)$

20. $y = 4\sin\left(\dfrac{1}{4}x + \dfrac{\pi}{8}\right)$

21. $y = -\dfrac{1}{2}\sin\left(2x + \dfrac{\pi}{2}\right)$

22. $y = -3\cos(4x - \pi) + 2$

23. $y = 2 + 3\cos(\pi x - 3)$

24. $y = 5 - 2\cos\left(\dfrac{\pi}{2}x + \dfrac{\pi}{2}\right)$

25. $y = -\dfrac{1}{2}\cos(2\pi x) + 2$

26. $y = -2\sin(-2x + \pi) - 2$

27. $y = -\sin\left(\dfrac{1}{2}x - \dfrac{\pi}{2}\right) + \dfrac{1}{2}$

28. $y = \dfrac{1}{3}\cos(-3x) + 1$

29. $y = \cos(-2\pi x) + 2$

30. $y = \dfrac{1}{2}\sin(2\pi x + \pi)$

31. $y = -\dfrac{1}{4}\cos(\pi x - 4)$

32. $y = 2\sin(2\pi x + 1)$

In Exercises 33–40, match the function with one of the graphs (a)–(h), which follow.

a)

b)

c)

d)

e)

f)

g)

h)

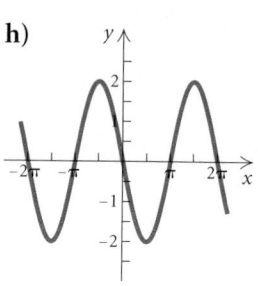

33. $y = -\cos 2x$

34. $y = \dfrac{1}{2}\sin x - 2$

35. $y = 2\cos\left(x + \dfrac{\pi}{2}\right)$

36. $y = -3\sin\dfrac{1}{2}x - 1$

37. $y = \sin(x - \pi) - 2$

38. $y = -\dfrac{1}{2}\cos\left(x - \dfrac{\pi}{4}\right)$

39. $y = \dfrac{1}{3}\sin 3x$

40. $y = \cos\left(x - \dfrac{\pi}{2}\right)$

In Exercises 41–44, determine the equation of the function that is graphed.

41.

42.

43.

44.

Graph using addition of ordinates.

45. $y = 2\cos x + \cos 2x$ **46.** $y = 3\cos x + \cos 3x$

47. $y = \sin x + \cos 2x$ **48.** $y = 2\sin x + \cos 2x$

49. $y = \sin x - \cos x$ **50.** $y = 3\cos x - \sin x$

51. $y = 3\cos x + \sin 2x$ **52.** $y = 3\sin x - \cos 2x$

Graph each of the following.

53. $f(x) = e^{-x/2}\cos x$ **54.** $f(x) = e^{-0.4x}\sin x$

55. $f(x) = 0.6x^2\cos x$ **56.** $f(x) = e^{-x/4}\sin x$

57. $f(x) = x\sin x$ **58.** $f(x) = |x|\cos x$

59. $f(x) = 2^{-x}\sin x$ **60.** $f(x) = 2^{-x}\cos x$

Technology Connection

Use a graphing calculator to graph the function.

61. $y = x + \sin x$ **62.** $y = -x - \sin x$

63. $y = \cos x - x$ **64.** $y = -(\cos x - x)$

65. $y = \cos 2x + 2x$ **66.** $y = \cos 3x + \sin 3x$

67. $y = 4\cos 2x - 2\sin x$

68. $y = 7.5\cos x + \sin 2x$

Use a graphing calculator to graph each of the following on the given interval and approximate the zeros.

69. $f(x) = \dfrac{\sin x}{x};\ [-12, 12]$

70. $f(x) = \dfrac{\cos x - 1}{x};\ [-12, 12]$

71. $f(x) = x^3\sin x;\ [-5, 5]$

72. $f(x) = \dfrac{(\sin x)^2}{x};\ [-4, 4]$

73. *Temperature During an Illness.* The temperature T of a patient during a 12-day illness is given by

$$T(t) = 101.6° + 3°\sin\left(\dfrac{\pi}{8}t\right).$$

a) Graph the function on the interval $[0, 12]$.
b) What are the maximum and the minimum temperatures during the illness?

74. *Periodic Sales.* A company in a northern climate has sales of skis as given by

$$S(t) = 10\left(1 - \cos\frac{\pi}{6}t\right),$$

where t is the time, in months ($t = 0$ corresponds to July 1), and $S(t)$ is in thousands of dollars.

a) Graph the function on a 12-month interval $[0, 12]$.
b) What is the period of the function?
c) What is the minimum amount of sales and when does it occur?
d) What is the maximum amount of sales and when does it occur?

Collaborative Discussion and Writing

75. In the equations $y = A \sin(Bx - C) + D$ and $y = A \cos(Bx - C) + D$, which constants translate the graphs and which constants stretch and shrink the graphs? Describe in your own words the effect of each constant.

76. In the transformation steps listed in this section, why must step (1) precede step (3)? Give an example that illustrates this.

Skill Maintenance

Classify the function as linear, quadratic, cubic, quartic, rational, exponential, logarithmic, or trigonometric.

77. $f(x) = \dfrac{x + 4}{x}$

78. $y = \dfrac{1}{2}\log x - 4$

79. $y = x^4 - x - 2$

80. $\dfrac{3}{4}x + \dfrac{1}{2}y = -5$

81. $f(x) = \sin x - 3$

82. $f(x) = 0.5e^{x-2}$

83. $y = \dfrac{2}{5}$

84. $y = \sin x + \cos x$

85. $y = x^2 - x^3$

86. $f(x) = \left(\dfrac{1}{2}\right)^x$

Synthesis

Find the maximum and minimum values of the function.

87. $y = 2\cos\left[3\left(x - \dfrac{\pi}{2}\right)\right] + 6$

88. $y = \dfrac{1}{2}\sin(2x - 6\pi) - 4$

The transformation techniques that we learned in this section for graphing the sine and cosine functions can also be applied to the other trigonometric functions. Sketch a graph of each of the following.

89. $y = -\tan x$

90. $y = \tan(-x)$

91. $y = -2 + \cot x$

92. $y = -\dfrac{3}{2}\csc x$

93. $y = 2\tan\dfrac{1}{2}x$

94. $y = \cot 2x$

95. $y = 2\sec(x - \pi)$

96. $y = 4\tan\left(\dfrac{1}{4}x + \dfrac{\pi}{8}\right)$

97. $y = 2\csc\left(\dfrac{1}{2}x - \dfrac{3\pi}{4}\right)$

98. $y = 4\sec(2x - \pi)$

99. *Satellite Location.* A satellite circles the earth in such a way that it is y miles from the equator (north or south, height not considered) t minutes after its launch, where

$$y(t) = 3000\left[\cos\frac{\pi}{45}(t - 10)\right].$$

$$y = 3000\left[\cos\frac{\pi}{45}(x - 10)\right]$$

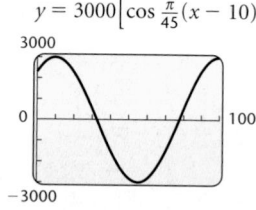

What are the amplitude, the period, and the phase shift?

100. *Water Wave.* The cross-section of a water wave is given by

$$y = 3\sin\left(\frac{\pi}{4}x + \frac{\pi}{4}\right),$$

where y is the vertical height of the water wave and x is the distance from the origin to the wave.

$$y = 3\sin\left(\frac{\pi}{4}x + \frac{\pi}{4}\right)$$

What are the amplitude, the period, and the phase shift?

101. *Damped Oscillations.* Suppose that the motion of a spring is given by

$$d(t) = 6e^{-0.8t}\cos(6\pi t) + 4,$$

where d is the distance, in inches, of a weight from the point at which the spring is attached to a ceiling, after t seconds. How far do you think the spring is from the ceiling when the spring stops bobbing?

102. *Rotating Beacon.* A police car is parked 10 ft from a wall. On top of the car is a beacon rotating in such a way that the light is at a distance $d(t)$ from point Q after t seconds, where

$$d(t) = 10\tan(2\pi t).$$

When d is positive, as shown in the figure, the light is pointing north of Q, and when d is negative, the light is pointing south of Q.

Explain the meaning of the values of t for which the function is not defined.

CHAPTER 5 SUMMARY AND REVIEW

Important Properties and Formulas

Trigonometric Function Values of an Acute Angle θ

Let θ be an acute angle of a right triangle. The six
trigonometric functions of θ are as follows:

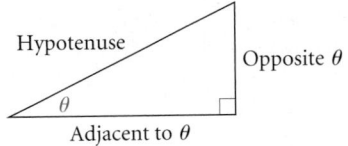

$$\sin \theta = \frac{\text{opp}}{\text{hyp}}, \quad \cos \theta = \frac{\text{adj}}{\text{hyp}}, \quad \tan \theta = \frac{\text{opp}}{\text{adj}},$$

$$\csc \theta = \frac{\text{hyp}}{\text{opp}}, \quad \sec \theta = \frac{\text{hyp}}{\text{adj}}, \quad \cot \theta = \frac{\text{adj}}{\text{opp}}.$$

Reciprocal Functions

$$\csc \theta = \frac{1}{\sin \theta}, \quad \sec \theta = \frac{1}{\cos \theta}, \quad \cot \theta = \frac{1}{\tan \theta}$$

Function Values of Special Angles

	0°	30°	45°	60°	90°
sin	0	$1/2$	$\sqrt{2}/2$	$\sqrt{3}/2$	1
cos	1	$\sqrt{3}/2$	$\sqrt{2}/2$	$1/2$	0
tan	0	$\sqrt{3}/3$	1	$\sqrt{3}$	Not defined

Cofunction Identities

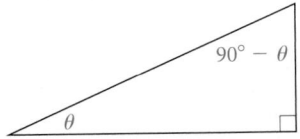

$$\sin \theta = \cos (90° - \theta), \quad \cos \theta = \sin (90° - \theta),$$
$$\tan \theta = \cot (90° - \theta), \quad \cot \theta = \tan (90° - \theta),$$
$$\sec \theta = \csc (90° - \theta), \quad \csc \theta = \sec (90° - \theta)$$

Trigonometric Functions of Any Angle θ

If $P(x, y)$ is any point on the terminal side of any angle θ in standard position,
and r is the distance from the origin to $P(x, y)$, where $r = \sqrt{x^2 + y^2}$, then

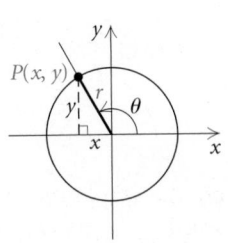

$$\sin \theta = \frac{y}{r}, \quad \cos \theta = \frac{x}{r}, \quad \tan \theta = \frac{y}{x},$$

$$\csc \theta = \frac{r}{y}, \quad \sec \theta = \frac{r}{x}, \quad \cot \theta = \frac{x}{y}.$$

Signs of Function Values

The signs of the function values depend only on the coordinates of the point P on the terminal side of an angle.

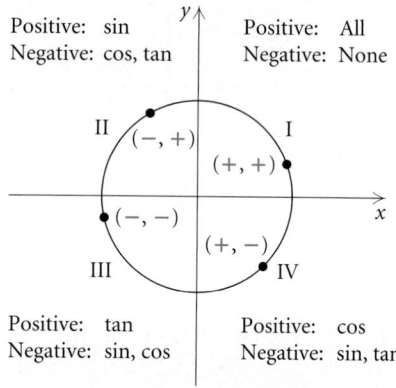

Positive: sin
Negative: cos, tan

Positive: All
Negative: None

II $(-, +)$ I $(+, +)$

$(-, -)$ $(+, -)$
III   IV

Positive: tan
Negative: sin, cos

Positive: cos
Negative: sin, tan

Radian–Degree Equivalents

Linear Speed in Terms of Angular Speed

$$v = r\omega$$

Basic Circular Functions

For a real number s that determines a point (x, y) on the unit circle:

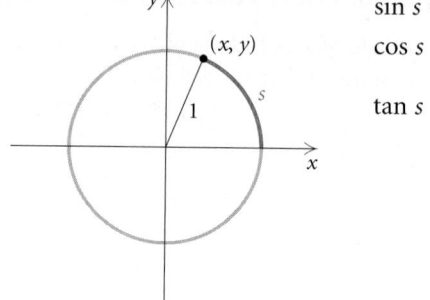

$$\sin s = y,$$
$$\cos s = x,$$
$$\tan s = \frac{y}{x}.$$

Sine is an odd function: $\sin(-s) = -\sin s$
Cosine is an even function: $\cos(-s) = \cos s$

Transformations of Sine and Cosine Functions

To graph $y = A \sin(Bx - C) + D$ and $y = A \cos(Bx - C) + D$:

1. Stretch or shrink the graph horizontally according to B. $\left(\text{Period} = \left|\dfrac{2\pi}{B}\right|\right)$

2. Stretch or shrink the graph vertically according to A. (Amplitude $= |A|$)

3. Translate the graph horizontally according to C/B. $\left(\text{Phase shift} = \dfrac{C}{B}\right)$

4. Translate the graph vertically according to D.

REVIEW EXERCISES

Determine whether the statement is true or false.

1. Given that $(-a, b)$ is a point on the unit circle and θ is in the second quadrant, then $\cos \theta$ is a. [5.3]

2. The lengths of corresponding sides in similar triangles are in the same ratio. [5.1]

3. The measure $300°$ is greater than the measure 5 radians. [5.4]

4. If $\sec \theta > 0$ and $\cot \theta < 0$, then θ is in the fourth quadrant. [5.3]

5. The amplitude of $y = \frac{1}{2} \sin x$ is twice as large as the amplitude of $y = \sin \frac{1}{2}x$. [5.6]

6. The supplement of $\frac{9}{13}\pi$ is greater than the complement of $\frac{\pi}{6}$. [5.3]

7. Find the six trigonometric function values of θ. [5.1]

8. Given that β is acute and $\sin \beta = \dfrac{\sqrt{91}}{10}$, find the other five trigonometric function values. [5.1]

Find the exact function value, if it exists.

9. $\cos 45°$ [5.1]

10. $\cot 60°$ [5.1]

11. $\cos 495°$ [5.3]

12. $\sin 150°$ [5.3]

13. $\sec (-270°)$ [5.3]

14. $\tan (-600°)$ [5.3]

15. $\csc 60°$ [5.1]

16. $\cot (-45°)$ [5.1]

17. Convert $22.27°$ to degrees, minutes, and seconds. Round to the nearest second. [5.1]

18. Convert $47°33'27''$ to decimal degree notation. Round to two decimal places. [5.1]

Find the function value. Round to four decimal places. [5.3]

19. $\tan 2184°$

20. $\sec 27.9°$

21. $\cos 18°13'42''$

22. $\sin 245°24'$

23. $\cot (-33.2°)$

24. $\sin 556.13°$

Find θ in the interval indicated. Round the answer to the nearest tenth of a degree. [5.3]

25. $\cos \theta = -0.9041$, $(180°, 270°)$

26. $\tan \theta = 1.0799$, $(0°, 90°)$

Find the exact acute angle θ, in degrees, given the function value. [5.1]

27. $\sin \theta = \dfrac{\sqrt{3}}{2}$

28. $\tan \theta = \sqrt{3}$

29. $\cos \theta = \dfrac{\sqrt{2}}{2}$

30. $\sec \theta = \dfrac{2\sqrt{3}}{3}$

31. Given that $\sin 59.1° \approx 0.8581$, $\cos 59.1° \approx 0.5135$, and $\tan 59.1° \approx 1.6709$, find the six function values for $30.9°$. [5.1]

Solve each of the following right triangles. Standard lettering has been used. [5.2]

32. $a = 7.3$, $c = 8.6$

33. $a = 30.5$, $B = 51.17°$

34. One leg of a right triangle bears east. The hypotenuse is 734 m long and bears N57°23'E. Find the perimeter of the triangle.

35. An observer's eye is 6 ft above the floor. A mural is being viewed. The bottom of the mural is at floor level. The observer looks down 13° to see the bottom and up 17° to see the top. How tall is the mural?

For angles of the following measures, state in which quadrant the terminal side lies. [5.3]

36. $142°11'5''$

37. $-635.2°$

38. $-392°$

Find a positive angle and a negative angle that are coterminal with the given angle. Answers may vary.

39. 65°   [5.3]   **40.** $\dfrac{7\pi}{3}$ [5.4]

Find the complement and the supplement.

41. 13.4°   [5.3]   **42.** $\dfrac{\pi}{6}$ [5.4]

43. Find the six trigonometric function values for the angle θ shown.   [5.3]

44. Given that $\tan\theta = 2/\sqrt{5}$ and that the terminal side is in quadrant III, find the other five function values.   [5.3]

45. An airplane travels at 530 mph for $3\frac{1}{2}$ hr in a direction of 160° from Minneapolis, Minnesota. At the end of that time, how far south of Minneapolis is the airplane?   [5.3]

46. On a unit circle, mark and label the points determined by $7\pi/6$, $-3\pi/4$, $-\pi/3$, and $9\pi/4$.   [5.4]

For angles of the following measures, convert to radian measure in terms of π, and convert to radian measure not in terms of π. Round the answer to two decimal places.   [5.4]

47. 145.2°   **48.** −30°

Convert to degree measure. Round the answer to two decimal places.   [5.4]

49. $\dfrac{3\pi}{2}$ **50.** 3

51. −4.5   **52.** 11π

53. Find the length of an arc of a circle, given a central angle of $\pi/4$ and a radius of 7 cm.   [5.4]

54. An arc 18 m long on a circle of radius 8 m subtends an angle of how many radians? how many degrees, to the nearest degree?   [5.4]

55. At one time, inside La Madeleine French Bakery and Cafe in Houston, Texas, there was one of the few remaining working watermills in the world. The 300-year-old French-built waterwheel had a radius of 7 ft and made one complete revolution in 70 sec. (*Source*: La Madeleine French Bakery and Cafe, Houston, TX) What was the linear speed, in feet per minute, of a point on the rim?   [5.4]

56. An automobile wheel has a diameter of 14 in. If the car travels at a speed of 55 mph, what is the angular velocity, in radians per hour, of a point on the edge of the wheel?   [5.4]

57. The point $\left(\frac{3}{5}, -\frac{4}{5}\right)$ is on a unit circle. Find the coordinates of its reflections across the x-axis, the y-axis, and the origin.   [5.5]

Find the exact function value, if it exists.   [5.5]

58. $\cos\pi$ **59.** $\tan\dfrac{5\pi}{4}$

60. $\sin\dfrac{5\pi}{3}$ **61.** $\sin\left(-\dfrac{7\pi}{6}\right)$

62. $\tan\dfrac{\pi}{6}$ **63.** $\cos(-13\pi)$

Find the function value. Round to four decimal places.   [5.5]

64. $\sin 24$ **65.** $\cos(-75)$

66. $\cot 16\pi$ **67.** $\tan\dfrac{3\pi}{7}$

68. $\sec 14.3$ **69.** $\cos\left(-\dfrac{\pi}{5}\right)$

70. Graph each of the six trigonometric functions from -2π to 2π.   [5.5]

71. What is the period of each of the six trigonometric functions?   [5.5]

72. Complete the following table.   [5.5]

Function	Domain	Range
sine		
cosine		
tangent		

73. Complete the following table with the sign of the specified trigonometric function value in each of the four quadrants. [5.3]

Function	I	II	III	IV
sine				
cosine				
tangent				

Determine the amplitude, the period, and the phase shift of the function, and sketch the graph of the function. [5.6]

74. $y = \sin\left(x + \dfrac{\pi}{2}\right)$

75. $y = 3 + \dfrac{1}{2}\cos\left(2x - \dfrac{\pi}{2}\right)$

In Exercises 76–79, match the function with one of the graphs (a)–(d), which follow. [5.6]

a)

b)

c)

d)

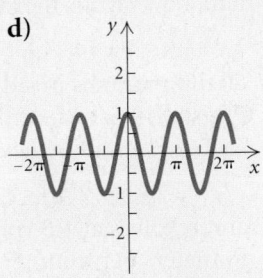

76. $y = \cos 2x$

77. $y = \dfrac{1}{2}\sin x + 1$

78. $y = -2\sin\dfrac{1}{2}x - 3$

79. $y = -\cos\left(x - \dfrac{\pi}{2}\right)$

80. Sketch a graph of $y = 3\cos x + \sin x$ for values of x between 0 and 2π. [5.6]

81. Graph: $f(x) = e^{-0.7x}\cos x$. [5.6]

82. Which of the following is the reflection of $\left(-\dfrac{1}{2}, \dfrac{\sqrt{3}}{2}\right)$ across the y-axis? [5.5]

A. $\left(\dfrac{1}{2}, -\dfrac{\sqrt{3}}{2}\right)$ **B.** $\left(\dfrac{\sqrt{3}}{2}, \dfrac{1}{2}\right)$

C. $\left(\dfrac{1}{2}, \dfrac{\sqrt{3}}{2}\right)$ **D.** $\left(\dfrac{\sqrt{3}}{2}, -\dfrac{1}{2}\right)$

83. Which of the following is the domain of the cosine function? [5.5]

A. $(-1, 1)$ **B.** $(-\infty, \infty)$

C. $[0, \infty)$ **D.** $[-1, 1]$

Collaborative Discussion and Writing

84. Compare the terms radian and degree. [5.1], [5.4]

85. Describe the shape of the graph of the cosine function. How many maximum values are there of the cosine function? Where do they occur? [5.5]

86. Does $5\sin x = 7$ have a solution for x? Why or why not? [5.5]

Synthesis

87. Graph $y = 3\sin(x/2)$, and determine the domain, the range, and the period. [5.6]

88. In the graph below, $y_1 = \sin x$ is shown and y_2 is shown in red. Express y_2 as a transformation of the graph of y_1. [5.6]

$y_1 = \sin x, \quad y_2 = ?$

89. Find the domain of $y = \log(\cos x)$. [5.6]

90. Given that $\sin x = 0.6144$ and that the terminal side is in quadrant II, find the other basic circular function values. [5.3]

CHAPTER 5 TEST

1. Find the six trigonometric function values of θ.

Find the exact function value, if it exists.

2. sin 120°

3. tan (−45°)

4. cos 3π

5. sec $\dfrac{5\pi}{4}$

6. Convert 38°27′56″ to decimal degree notation. Round to two decimal places.

Find the function values. Round to four decimal places.

7. tan 526.4°

8. sin (−12°)

9. sec $\dfrac{5\pi}{9}$

10. cos 76.07

11. Find the exact acute angle θ, in degrees, for which sin θ = $\frac{1}{2}$.

12. Given that sin 28.4° ≈ 0.4756, cos 28.4° ≈ 0.8796, and tan 28.4° ≈ 0.5407, find the six trigonometric function values for 61.6°.

13. Solve the right triangle with b = 45.1 and A = 35.9°. Standard lettering has been used.

14. Find a positive angle and a negative angle coterminal with a 112° angle.

15. Find the supplement of $\dfrac{5\pi}{6}$.

16. Given that sin θ = −4/√41 and that the terminal side is in quadrant IV, find the other five trigonometric function values.

17. Convert 210° to radian measure in terms of π.

18. Convert $\dfrac{3\pi}{4}$ to degree measure.

19. Find the length of an arc of a circle given a central angle of π/3 and a radius of 16 cm.

Consider the function y = −sin (x − π/2) + 1 for Exercises 20–23.

20. Find the amplitude.

21. Find the period.

22. Find the phase shift.

23. Which is the graph of the function?

a)

b)

c)

d)

24. *Height of a Kite.*   The angle of elevation of a kite is 65° with 490 ft of string out. Assuming the string is taut, how high is the kite?

25. *Location.*   A pickup-truck camper travels at 50 mph for 6 hr in a direction of 115° from Flagstaff, Arizona. At the end of that time, how far east of Flagstaff is the camper?

26. *Linear Speed.*   A ferris wheel has a radius of 6 m and revolves at 1.5 rpm. What is the linear speed, in meters per minute?

27. Graph: $f(x) = \frac{1}{2}x^2 \sin x$.

Synthesis

28. Determine the domain of $f(x) = \dfrac{-3}{\sqrt{\cos x}}$.

Trigonometric Identities, Inverse Functions, and Equations

APPLICATION

For a rope course and climbing wall, a guy wire is attached 47 ft high on a vertical pole. Another guy wire is attached 40 ft above the ground on the same pole. (*Source*: Experiential Resources, Inc., Todd Domeck, Owner) Find the angle between the wires if they are attached to the ground 50 ft from the pole.

This problem appears as Exercise 89 in Section 6.1.

6.1 Identities: Pythagorean and Sum and Difference

◆ State the Pythagorean identities.

◆ Simplify and manipulate expressions containing trigonometric expressions.

◆ Use the sum and difference identities to find function values.

An **identity** is an equation that is true for all *possible* replacements of the variables. The following is a list of the identities studied in Chapter 5.

> ### Basic Identities
>
> $$\sin x = \frac{1}{\csc x}, \qquad \csc x = \frac{1}{\sin x}, \qquad \sin(-x) = -\sin x,$$
> $$\cos(-x) = \cos x,$$
> $$\cos x = \frac{1}{\sec x}, \qquad \sec x = \frac{1}{\cos x}, \qquad \tan(-x) = -\tan x,$$
> $$\tan x = \frac{1}{\cot x}, \qquad \cot x = \frac{1}{\tan x}, \qquad \tan x = \frac{\sin x}{\cos x},$$
> $$\cot x = \frac{\cos x}{\sin x}$$

In this section, we will develop some other important identities.

◆ Pythagorean Identities

We now consider three other identities that are fundamental to a study of trigonometry. They are called the *Pythagorean identities*. Recall that the equation of a unit circle in the xy-plane is

$$x^2 + y^2 = 1.$$

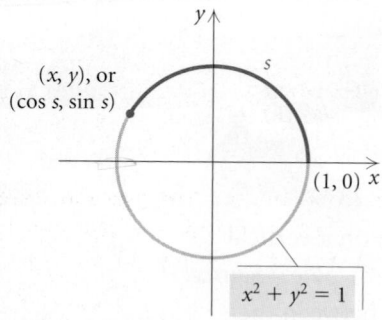

For any point on the unit circle, the coordinates x and y satisfy this equation. Suppose that a real number s determines a point on the unit circle with coordinates (x, y), or $(\cos s, \sin s)$. Then $x = \cos s$ and $y = \sin s$. Substituting $\cos s$ for x and $\sin s$ for y in the equation of the unit circle gives us the identity

$$(\cos s)^2 + (\sin s)^2 = 1, \qquad \text{Substituting } \cos s \text{ for } x \text{ and } \sin s \text{ for } y$$

which can be expressed as

$$\sin^2 s + \cos^2 s = 1.$$

It is conventional in trigonometry to use the notation $\sin^2 s$ rather than $(\sin s)^2$. Note that $\sin^2 s \neq \sin s^2$.

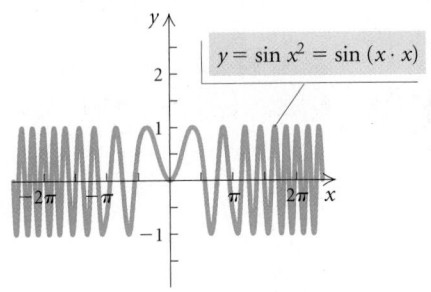

The identity $\sin^2 s + \cos^2 s = 1$ gives a relationship between the sine and the cosine of any real number s. It is an important **Pythagorean identity.**

We can divide by $\sin^2 s$ on both sides of the preceding identity:

$$\frac{\sin^2 s}{\sin^2 s} + \frac{\cos^2 s}{\sin^2 s} = \frac{1}{\sin^2 s}. \qquad \text{Dividing by } \sin^2 s$$

Simplifying gives us a second identity:

$$1 + \cot^2 s = \csc^2 s.$$

This equation is true for any replacement of s with a real number for which $\sin^2 s \neq 0$, since we divided by $\sin^2 s$. But the numbers for which $\sin^2 s = 0$ (or $\sin s = 0$) are exactly the ones for which the cotangent and cosecant functions are not defined. Hence our new equation holds for all real numbers s for which $\cot s$ and $\csc s$ are defined and is thus an identity.

The third Pythagorean identity can be obtained by dividing by $\cos^2 s$ on both sides of the first Pythagorean identity:

$$\frac{\sin^2 s}{\cos^2 s} + \frac{\cos^2 s}{\cos^2 s} = \frac{1}{\cos^2 s} \qquad \text{Dividing by } \cos^2 s$$

$$\tan^2 s + 1 = \sec^2 s. \qquad \text{Simplifying}$$

The identities we have developed hold no matter what symbols are used for the variables. For example, we could write $\sin^2 s + \cos^2 s = 1$, $\sin^2 \theta + \cos^2 \theta = 1$, or $\sin^2 x + \cos^2 x = 1$.

Pythagorean Identities

$$\sin^2 x + \cos^2 x = 1,$$
$$1 + \cot^2 x = \csc^2 x,$$
$$1 + \tan^2 x = \sec^2 x$$

It is often helpful to express the Pythagorean identities in equivalent forms.

Pythagorean Identities	Equivalent Forms
$\sin^2 x + \cos^2 x = 1$	$\sin^2 x = 1 - \cos^2 x$
	$\cos^2 x = 1 - \sin^2 x$
$1 + \cot^2 x = \csc^2 x$	$1 = \csc^2 x - \cot^2 x$
	$\cot^2 x = \csc^2 x - 1$
$1 + \tan^2 x = \sec^2 x$	$1 = \sec^2 x - \tan^2 x$
	$\tan^2 x = \sec^2 x - 1$

✦ Simplifying Trigonometric Expressions

We can factor, simplify, and manipulate trigonometric expressions in the same way that we manipulate strictly algebraic expressions.

EXAMPLE 1 Multiply and simplify: $\cos x (\tan x - \sec x)$.

Solution

$\cos x (\tan x - \sec x)$

$\quad = \cos x \tan x - \cos x \sec x$ Multiplying

$\quad = \cos x \dfrac{\sin x}{\cos x} - \cos x \dfrac{1}{\cos x}$ Recalling the identities $\tan x = \dfrac{\sin x}{\cos x}$

                           and $\sec x = \dfrac{1}{\cos x}$ and substituting

$\quad = \sin x - 1$ Simplifying   ▶ Now Try Exercise 3.

There is no general procedure for manipulating trigonometric expressions, but it is often helpful to write everything in terms of sines and cosines, as we did in Example 1. We also look for the Pythagorean identity, $\sin^2 x + \cos^2 x = 1$, within a trigonometric expression.

EXAMPLE 2 Factor and simplify: $\sin^2 x \cos^2 x + \cos^4 x$.

Solution

$\quad \sin^2 x \cos^2 x + \cos^4 x$

$\quad\quad = \cos^2 x (\sin^2 x + \cos^2 x)$ Removing a common factor

$\quad\quad = \cos^2 x \cdot (1)$ Using $\sin^2 x + \cos^2 x = 1$

$\quad\quad = \cos^2 x$ ▶ Now Try Exercise 5.

TECHNOLOGY CONNECTION

A graphing calculator can be used to perform a partial check of an identity. First, we graph the expression on the left side of the equals sign. Then we graph the expression on the right side using the same screen. If the two graphs are indistinguishable, then we have a partial verification that the equation is an identity. Of course, we can never see the entire graph, so there can always be some doubt. Also, the graphs may not overlap precisely, but you may not be able to tell because the difference between the graphs may be less than the width of a pixel. However, if the graphs are obviously different, we know that a mistake has been made.

Consider the identity in Example 1:

$$\cos x\,(\tan x - \sec x) = \sin x - 1.$$

Recalling that $\sec x = 1/\cos x$, we enter

$$y_1 = \cos x\,[\tan x - (1/\cos x)] \quad \text{and} \quad y_2 = \sin x - 1.$$

To graph, we first select SEQUENTIAL mode. Then we select the "line"-graph style for y_1 and the "path"-graph style, denoted by ─○, for y_2. The calculator will graph y_1 first. Then it will graph y_2 as the circular cursor traces the leading edge of the graph, allowing us to determine whether the graphs coincide. As you can see in the first screen on the left, the graphs appear to be identical. Thus, $\cos x\,(\tan x - \sec x) = \sin x - 1$ is most likely an identity.

The TABLE feature can also be used to check identities. Note in the table at left that the function values are the same except for those values of x for which $\cos x = 0$. The domain of y_1 excludes these values. The domain of y_2 is the set of all real numbers. Thus all real numbers except $\pm\pi/2, \pm 3\pi/2, \pm 5\pi/2, \ldots$ are possible replacements for x in the identity. Recall that an identity is an equation that is true for all *possible* replacements.

$y_1 = \cos x\,[\tan x - (1/\cos x)],$
$y_2 = \sin x - 1$

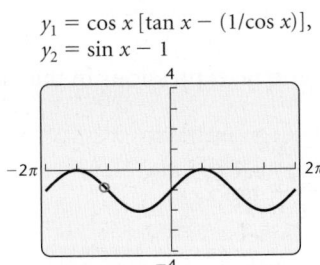

X	Y1	Y2
−6.283	−1	−1
−5.498	−.2929	−.2929
−4.712	ERROR	0
−3.927	−.2929	−.2929
−3.142	−1	−1
−2.356	−1.707	−1.707
−1.571	ERROR	−2

X = −6.28318530718

TblStart = −2π
ΔTbl = π/4

EXAMPLE 3 Simplify each of the following trigonometric expressions.

a) $\dfrac{\cot(-\theta)}{\csc(-\theta)}$

b) $\dfrac{2\sin^2 t + \sin t - 3}{1 - \cos^2 t - \sin t}$

Solution

a) $\dfrac{\cot(-\theta)}{\csc(-\theta)} = \dfrac{\dfrac{\cos(-\theta)}{\sin(-\theta)}}{\dfrac{1}{\sin(-\theta)}}$ Rewriting in terms of sines and cosines

$= \dfrac{\cos(-\theta)}{\sin(-\theta)} \cdot \sin(-\theta)$ Multiplying by the reciprocal

$= \cos(-\theta) = \cos\theta$ The cosine function is even.

b) $\dfrac{2\sin^2 t + \sin t - 3}{1 - \cos^2 t - \sin t}$

$= \dfrac{2\sin^2 t + \sin t - 3}{\sin^2 t - \sin t}$ Substituting $\sin^2 t$ for $1 - \cos^2 t$

FACTORING

REVIEW SECTION **R.4.**

$= \dfrac{(2\sin t + 3)(\sin t - 1)}{\sin t\,(\sin t - 1)}$ Factoring in both numerator and denominator

$= \dfrac{2\sin t + 3}{\sin t}$ Simplifying

$= \dfrac{2\sin t}{\sin t} + \dfrac{3}{\sin t}$

$= 2 + \dfrac{3}{\sin t},\quad$ or $\quad 2 + 3\csc t$

▶ **Now Try Exercises 17 and 19.**

We can add and subtract trigonometric rational expressions in the same way that we do algebraic expressions.

EXAMPLE 4   Add and simplify: $\dfrac{\cos x}{1 + \sin x} + \tan x.$

Solution

RATIONAL EXPRESSIONS

REVIEW SECTION **R.5.**

$\dfrac{\cos x}{1 + \sin x} + \tan x = \dfrac{\cos x}{1 + \sin x} + \dfrac{\sin x}{\cos x}$ Using $\tan x = \dfrac{\sin x}{\cos x}$

$= \dfrac{\cos x}{1 + \sin x} \cdot \dfrac{\cos x}{\cos x} + \dfrac{\sin x}{\cos x} \cdot \dfrac{1 + \sin x}{1 + \sin x}$

Multiplying by forms of 1

$= \dfrac{\cos^2 x + \sin x + \sin^2 x}{\cos x\,(1 + \sin x)}$ Adding

$= \dfrac{1 + \sin x}{\cos x\,(1 + \sin x)}$ Using $\sin^2 x + \cos^2 x = 1$

$= \dfrac{1}{\cos x},\quad$ or $\quad \sec x$ Simplifying

▶ **Now Try Exercise 27.**

When radicals occur, the use of absolute value is sometimes necessary, but it can be difficult to determine when to use it. In Examples 5 and 6, we will assume that all radicands are nonnegative. This means that the identities are meant to be confined to certain quadrants.

EXAMPLE 5   Multiply and simplify: $\sqrt{\sin^3 x \cos x} \cdot \sqrt{\cos x}.$

Solution

$\sqrt{\sin^3 x \cos x} \cdot \sqrt{\cos x} = \sqrt{\sin^3 x \cos^2 x}$

$= \sqrt{\sin^2 x \cos^2 x \sin x}$

$= \sin x \cos x \sqrt{\sin x}$

▶ **Now Try Exercise 31.**

EXAMPLE 6 Rationalize the denominator: $\sqrt{\dfrac{2}{\tan x}}$.

Solution

$$\sqrt{\frac{2}{\tan x}} = \sqrt{\frac{2}{\tan x} \cdot \frac{\tan x}{\tan x}}$$

$$= \sqrt{\frac{2 \tan x}{\tan^2 x}}$$

$$= \frac{\sqrt{2 \tan x}}{\tan x}$$

▶ Now Try Exercise 37.

Often in calculus, a substitution is a useful manipulation, as we show in the following example.

EXAMPLE 7 Express $\sqrt{9 + x^2}$ as a trigonometric function of θ without using radicals by letting $x = 3 \tan \theta$. Assume that $0 < \theta < \pi/2$. Then find $\sin \theta$ and $\cos \theta$.

Solution We have

$$\sqrt{9 + x^2} = \sqrt{9 + (3 \tan \theta)^2} \qquad \text{Substituting 3 tan } \theta \text{ for } x$$

$$= \sqrt{9 + 9 \tan^2 \theta}$$

$$= \sqrt{9(1 + \tan^2 \theta)} \qquad \text{Factoring}$$

$$= \sqrt{9 \sec^2 \theta} \qquad \text{Using } 1 + \tan^2 x = \sec^2 x$$

$$= 3|\sec \theta| = 3 \sec \theta. \qquad \text{For } 0 < \theta < \pi/2, \sec \theta > 0,$$
$$\text{so } |\sec \theta| = \sec \theta.$$

We can express $\sqrt{9 + x^2} = 3 \sec \theta$ as

$$\sec \theta = \frac{\sqrt{9 + x^2}}{3}.$$

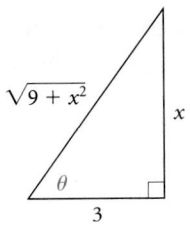

In a right triangle, we know that $\sec \theta$ is hypotenuse/adjacent, when θ is one of the acute angles. Using the Pythagorean theorem, we can determine that the side opposite θ is x. Then from the right triangle, we see that

$$\sin \theta = \frac{x}{\sqrt{9 + x^2}} \quad \text{and} \quad \cos \theta = \frac{3}{\sqrt{9 + x^2}}.$$

▶ Now Try Exercise 45.

◆ Sum and Difference Identities

We now develop some important identities involving sums or differences of two numbers (or angles), beginning with an identity for the cosine of the difference of two numbers. We use the letters u and v for these numbers.

Let's consider a real number u in the interval $[\pi/2, \pi]$ and a real number v in the interval $[0, \pi/2]$. These determine points A and B on the unit circle, as shown below. The arc length s is $u - v$, and we know that $0 \leq s \leq \pi$. Recall that the coordinates of A are $(\cos u, \sin u)$, and the coordinates of B are $(\cos v, \sin v)$.

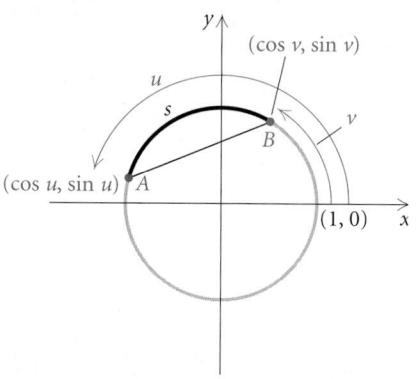

DISTANCE FORMULA
REVIEW SECTION **1.1.**

Using the distance formula, we can write an expression for the distance AB:

$$AB = \sqrt{(\cos u - \cos v)^2 + (\sin u - \sin v)^2}.$$

This can be simplified as follows:

$$AB = \sqrt{\cos^2 u - 2\cos u \cos v + \cos^2 v + \sin^2 u - 2\sin u \sin v + \sin^2 v}$$
$$= \sqrt{(\sin^2 u + \cos^2 u) + (\sin^2 v + \cos^2 v) - 2(\cos u \cos v + \sin u \sin v)}$$
$$= \sqrt{2 - 2(\cos u \cos v + \sin u \sin v)}.$$

Now let's imagine rotating the circle above so that point B is at $(1, 0)$. Although the coordinates of point A are now $(\cos s, \sin s)$, the distance AB has not changed.

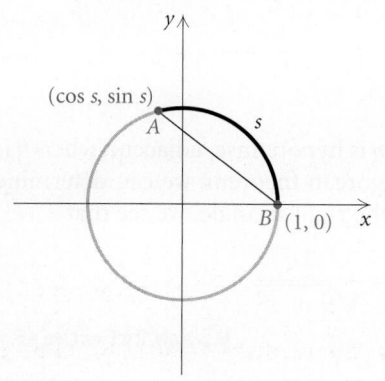

Again we use the distance formula to write an expression for the distance AB:

$$AB = \sqrt{(\cos s - 1)^2 + (\sin s - 0)^2}.$$

This can be simplified as follows:

$$AB = \sqrt{\cos^2 s - 2\cos s + 1 + \sin^2 s}$$
$$= \sqrt{(\sin^2 s + \cos^2 s) + 1 - 2\cos s}$$
$$= \sqrt{2 - 2\cos s}.$$

Equating our two expressions for AB, we obtain

$$\sqrt{2 - 2(\cos u \cos v + \sin u \sin v)} = \sqrt{2 - 2\cos s}.$$

Solving this equation for $\cos s$ gives

$$\cos s = \cos u \cos v + \sin u \sin v. \tag{1}$$

But $s = u - v$, so we have the equation

$$\cos (u - v) = \cos u \cos v + \sin u \sin v. \tag{2}$$

Formula (1) above holds when s is the length of the shortest arc from A to B. Given any real numbers u and v, the length of the shortest arc from A to B is not always $u - v$. In fact, it could be $v - u$. However, since $\cos(-x) = \cos x$, we know that $\cos(v - u) = \cos(u - v)$. Thus, $\cos s$ is always equal to $\cos(u - v)$. Formula (2) holds for all real numbers u and v. That formula is thus the identity we sought:

$$\cos(u - v) = \cos u \cos v + \sin u \sin v.$$

The cosine sum formula follows easily from the one we have just derived. Let's consider $\cos(u + v)$. This is equal to $\cos[u - (-v)]$, and by the identity above, we have

$$\cos(u + v) = \cos[u - (-v)]$$
$$= \cos u \cos(-v) + \sin u \sin(-v).$$

But $\cos(-v) = \cos v$ and $\sin(-v) = -\sin v$, so the identity we seek is the following:

$$\cos(u + v) = \cos u \cos v - \sin u \sin v.$$

EXAMPLE 8 Find $\cos(5\pi/12)$ exactly.

Solution We can express $5\pi/12$ as a difference of two numbers whose sine and cosine values are known:

$$\frac{5\pi}{12} = \frac{9\pi}{12} - \frac{4\pi}{12}, \quad \text{or} \quad \frac{3\pi}{4} - \frac{\pi}{3}.$$

Then, using $\cos(u - v) = \cos u \cos v + \sin u \sin v$, we have

$$\cos\frac{5\pi}{12} = \cos\left(\frac{3\pi}{4} - \frac{\pi}{3}\right) = \cos\frac{3\pi}{4}\cos\frac{\pi}{3} + \sin\frac{3\pi}{4}\sin\frac{\pi}{3}$$
$$= -\frac{\sqrt{2}}{2} \cdot \frac{1}{2} + \frac{\sqrt{2}}{2} \cdot \frac{\sqrt{3}}{2}$$
$$= -\frac{\sqrt{2}}{4} + \frac{\sqrt{6}}{4}$$
$$= \frac{\sqrt{6} - \sqrt{2}}{4}.$$

▶ Now Try Exercise 55.

TECHNOLOGY CONNECTION

We can check the result of Example 8 using a graphing calculator set in RADIAN mode.

```
cos(5π/12)
              .2588190451
(√(6)−√(2))/4
              .2588190451
```

Consider $\cos(\pi/2 - \theta)$. We can use the identity for the cosine of a difference to simplify as follows:

$$\cos\left(\frac{\pi}{2} - \theta\right) = \cos\frac{\pi}{2}\cos\theta + \sin\frac{\pi}{2}\sin\theta$$
$$= 0 \cdot \cos\theta + 1 \cdot \sin\theta$$
$$= \sin\theta.$$

Thus we have developed the identity

$$\sin\theta = \cos\left(\frac{\pi}{2} - \theta\right). \qquad \begin{array}{l}\text{This cofunction identity first}\\\text{appeared in Section 5.1.}\end{array} \qquad (3)$$

This identity holds for any real number θ. From it we can obtain an identity for the cosine function. We first let α be any real number. Then we replace θ in $\sin \theta = \cos(\pi/2 - \theta)$ with $\pi/2 - \alpha$. This gives us

$$\sin\left(\frac{\pi}{2} - \alpha\right) = \cos\left[\frac{\pi}{2} - \left(\frac{\pi}{2} - \alpha\right)\right] = \cos \alpha,$$

which yields the identity

$$\cos \alpha = \sin\left(\frac{\pi}{2} - \alpha\right). \qquad (4)$$

Using identities (3) and (4) and the identity for the cosine of a difference, we can obtain an identity for the sine of a sum. We start with identity (3) and substitute $u + v$ for θ:

$$\sin \theta = \cos\left(\frac{\pi}{2} - \theta\right) \qquad \text{Identity (3)}$$

$$\sin(u + v) = \cos\left[\frac{\pi}{2} - (u + v)\right] \qquad \text{Substituting } u + v \text{ for } \theta$$

$$= \cos\left[\left(\frac{\pi}{2} - u\right) - v\right]$$

$$= \cos\left(\frac{\pi}{2} - u\right)\cos v + \sin\left(\frac{\pi}{2} - u\right)\sin v$$

Using the identity for the cosine of a difference

$$= \sin u \cos v + \cos u \sin v. \qquad \text{Using identities (3) and (4)}$$

Thus the identity we seek is

$$\sin(u + v) = \sin u \cos v + \cos u \sin v.$$

To find a formula for the sine of a difference, we can use the identity just derived, substituting $-v$ for v:

$$\sin(u + (-v)) = \sin u \cos(-v) + \cos u \sin(-v).$$

Simplifying gives us

$$\sin(u - v) = \sin u \cos v - \cos u \sin v.$$

EXAMPLE 9 Find $\sin 105°$ exactly.

Solution We express $105°$ as the sum of two measures:

$$105° = 45° + 60°.$$

Then

$$\sin 105° = \sin(45° + 60°)$$

$$= \sin 45° \cos 60° + \cos 45° \sin 60°$$

Using $\sin(u + v) = \sin u \cos v + \cos u \sin v$

$$= \frac{\sqrt{2}}{2} \cdot \frac{1}{2} + \frac{\sqrt{2}}{2} \cdot \frac{\sqrt{3}}{2} = \frac{\sqrt{2} + \sqrt{6}}{4}.$$

▶ **Now Try Exercise 51.**

Formulas for the tangent of a sum or a difference can be derived using identities already established. A summary of the sum and difference identities follows.

> ### Sum and Difference Identities
>
> $\sin(u \pm v) = \sin u \cos v \pm \cos u \sin v,$
>
> $\cos(u \pm v) = \cos u \cos v \mp \sin u \sin v,$
>
> $\tan(u \pm v) = \dfrac{\tan u \pm \tan v}{1 \mp \tan u \tan v}$
>
> There are six identities here, half of them obtained by using the signs shown in color.

EXAMPLE 10 Find tan 15° exactly.

Solution We rewrite 15° as 45° − 30° and use the identity for the tangent of a difference:

$$\tan 15° = \tan(45° - 30°) = \frac{\tan 45° - \tan 30°}{1 + \tan 45° \tan 30°}$$

$$= \frac{1 - \sqrt{3}/3}{1 + 1 \cdot \sqrt{3}/3} = \frac{3 - \sqrt{3}}{3 + \sqrt{3}}.$$

▶ Now Try Exercise 53.

EXAMPLE 11 Assume that $\sin \alpha = \frac{2}{3}$ and $\sin \beta = \frac{1}{3}$ and that α and β are between 0 and $\pi/2$. Then evaluate $\sin(\alpha + \beta)$.

Solution Using the identity for the sine of a sum, we have

$$\sin(\alpha + \beta) = \sin \alpha \cos \beta + \cos \alpha \sin \beta$$

$$= \tfrac{2}{3} \cos \beta + \tfrac{1}{3} \cos \alpha.$$

To finish, we need to know the values of $\cos \beta$ and $\cos \alpha$. Using reference triangles and the Pythagorean theorem, we can determine these values from the diagrams:

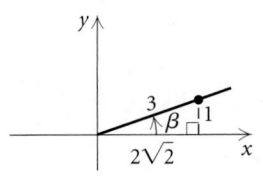

$$\cos \alpha = \frac{\sqrt{5}}{3} \quad \text{and} \quad \cos \beta = \frac{2\sqrt{2}}{3}.$$

Cosine values are positive in the first quadrant.

Substituting these values gives us

$$\sin(\alpha + \beta) = \frac{2}{3} \cdot \frac{2\sqrt{2}}{3} + \frac{1}{3} \cdot \frac{\sqrt{5}}{3}$$

$$= \frac{4}{9}\sqrt{2} + \frac{1}{9}\sqrt{5}, \quad \text{or} \quad \frac{4\sqrt{2} + \sqrt{5}}{9}.$$

▶ Now Try Exercise 65.

6.1 EXERCISE SET

Multiply and simplify.

1. $(\sin x - \cos x)(\sin x + \cos x)$

2. $\tan x (\cos x - \csc x)$

3. $\cos y \sin y (\sec y + \csc y)$

4. $(\sin x + \cos x)(\sec x + \csc x)$

5. $(\sin \phi - \cos \phi)^2$

6. $(1 + \tan x)^2$

7. $(\sin x + \csc x)(\sin^2 x + \csc^2 x - 1)$

8. $(1 - \sin t)(1 + \sin t)$

Factor and simplify.

9. $\sin x \cos x + \cos^2 x$

10. $\tan^2 \theta - \cot^2 \theta$

11. $\sin^4 x - \cos^4 x$

12. $4 \sin^2 y + 8 \sin y + 4$

13. $2 \cos^2 x + \cos x - 3$

14. $3 \cot^2 \beta + 6 \cot \beta + 3$

15. $\sin^3 x + 27$

16. $1 - 125 \tan^3 s$

Simplify.

17. $\dfrac{\sin^2 x \cos x}{\cos^2 x \sin x}$

18. $\dfrac{30 \sin^3 x \cos x}{6 \cos^2 x \sin x}$

19. $\dfrac{\sin^2 x + 2 \sin x + 1}{\sin x + 1}$

20. $\dfrac{\cos^2 \alpha - 1}{\cos \alpha + 1}$

21. $\dfrac{4 \tan t \sec t + 2 \sec t}{6 \tan t \sec t + 2 \sec t}$

22. $\dfrac{\csc(-x)}{\cot(-x)}$

23. $\dfrac{\sin^4 x - \cos^4 x}{\sin^2 x - \cos^2 x}$

24. $\dfrac{4 \cos^3 x}{\sin^2 x} \cdot \left(\dfrac{\sin x}{4 \cos x}\right)^2$

25. $\dfrac{5 \cos \phi}{\sin^2 \phi} \cdot \dfrac{\sin^2 \phi - \sin \phi \cos \phi}{\sin^2 \phi - \cos^2 \phi}$

26. $\dfrac{\tan^2 y}{\sec y} \div \dfrac{3 \tan^3 y}{\sec y}$

27. $\dfrac{1}{\sin^2 s - \cos^2 s} - \dfrac{2}{\cos s - \sin s}$

28. $\left(\dfrac{\sin x}{\cos x}\right)^2 - \dfrac{1}{\cos^2 x}$

29. $\dfrac{\sin^2 \theta - 9}{2 \cos \theta + 1} \cdot \dfrac{10 \cos \theta + 5}{3 \sin \theta + 9}$

30. $\dfrac{9 \cos^2 \alpha - 25}{2 \cos \alpha - 2} \cdot \dfrac{\cos^2 \alpha - 1}{6 \cos \alpha - 10}$

Simplify. Assume that all radicands are nonnegative.

31. $\sqrt{\sin^2 x \cos x} \cdot \sqrt{\cos x}$

32. $\sqrt{\cos^2 x \sin x} \cdot \sqrt{\sin x}$

33. $\sqrt{\cos \alpha \sin^2 \alpha} - \sqrt{\cos^3 \alpha}$

34. $\sqrt{\tan^2 x - 2 \tan x \sin x + \sin^2 x}$

35. $\left(1 - \sqrt{\sin y}\right)\left(\sqrt{\sin y} + 1\right)$

36. $\sqrt{\cos \theta}\left(\sqrt{2 \cos \theta} + \sqrt{\sin \theta \cos \theta}\right)$

Rationalize the denominator.

37. $\sqrt{\dfrac{\sin x}{\cos x}}$

38. $\sqrt{\dfrac{\cos x}{\tan x}}$

39. $\sqrt{\dfrac{\cos^2 y}{2 \sin^2 y}}$

40. $\sqrt{\dfrac{1 - \cos \beta}{1 + \cos \beta}}$

Rationalize the numerator.

41. $\sqrt{\dfrac{\cos x}{\sin x}}$

42. $\sqrt{\dfrac{\sin x}{\cot x}}$

43. $\sqrt{\dfrac{1 + \sin y}{1 - \sin y}}$

44. $\sqrt{\dfrac{\cos^2 x}{2 \sin^2 x}}$

Use the given substitution to express the given radical expression as a trigonometric function without radicals. Assume that $a > 0$ and $0 < \theta < \pi/2$. Then find expressions for the indicated trigonometric functions.

45. Let $x = a \sin \theta$ in $\sqrt{a^2 - x^2}$. Then find $\cos \theta$ and $\tan \theta$.

46. Let $x = 2 \tan \theta$ in $\sqrt{4 + x^2}$. Then find $\sin \theta$ and $\cos \theta$.

47. Let $x = 3 \sec \theta$ in $\sqrt{x^2 - 9}$. Then find $\sin \theta$ and $\cos \theta$.

48. Let $x = a \sec \theta$ in $\sqrt{x^2 - a^2}$. Then find $\sin \theta$ and $\cos \theta$.

Use the given substitution to express the given radical expression as a trigonometric function without radicals. Assume that $0 < \theta < \pi/2$.

49. Let $x = \sin \theta$ in $\dfrac{x^2}{\sqrt{1 - x^2}}$.

50. Let $x = 4 \sec \theta$ in $\dfrac{\sqrt{x^2 - 16}}{x^2}$.

Use the sum and difference identities to evaluate exactly.

51. $\sin \dfrac{\pi}{12}$

52. $\cos 75°$

53. $\tan 105°$

54. $\tan \dfrac{5\pi}{12}$

55. $\cos 15°$

56. $\sin \dfrac{7\pi}{12}$

First write each of the following as a trigonometric function of a single angle; then evaluate.

57. $\sin 37° \cos 22° + \cos 37° \sin 22°$

58. $\cos 83° \cos 53° + \sin 83° \sin 53°$

59. $\cos 19° \cos 5° - \sin 19° \sin 5°$

60. $\sin 40° \cos 15° - \cos 40° \sin 15°$

61. $\dfrac{\tan 20° + \tan 32°}{1 - \tan 20° \tan 32°}$

62. $\dfrac{\tan 35° - \tan 12°}{1 + \tan 35° \tan 12°}$

63. Derive the formula for the tangent of a sum.

64. Derive the formula for the tangent of a difference.

Assuming that $\sin u = \tfrac{3}{5}$ and $\sin v = \tfrac{4}{5}$ and that u and v are between 0 and $\pi/2$, evaluate each of the following exactly.

65. $\cos (u + v)$

66. $\tan (u - v)$

67. $\sin (u - v)$

68. $\cos (u - v)$

Assuming that $\sin \theta = 0.6249$ and $\cos \phi = 0.1102$ and that both θ and ϕ are first-quadrant angles, evaluate each of the following.

69. $\tan (\theta + \phi)$

70. $\sin (\theta - \phi)$

71. $\cos (\theta - \phi)$

72. $\cos (\theta + \phi)$

Simplify.

73. $\sin (\alpha + \beta) + \sin (\alpha - \beta)$

74. $\cos (\alpha + \beta) - \cos (\alpha - \beta)$

75. $\cos (u + v) \cos v + \sin (u + v) \sin v$

76. $\sin (u - v) \cos v + \cos (u - v) \sin v$

Technology Connection

77. Check your answers to each of Exercises 17–30 by graphing the original expression and the simplified result in the same window.

78. Check your solutions to each of Exercises 51–56 with a calculator.

Collaborative Discussion and Writing

79. What is the difference between a trigonometric equation that is an identity and a trigonometric equation that is not an identity? Give an example of each.

80. Why is it possible to use a graph to *disprove* that an equation is an identity but not to *prove* that one is?

Skill Maintenance

Solve.

81. $2x - 3 = 2\left(x - \tfrac{3}{2}\right)$

82. $x - 7 = x + 3.4$

Given that $\sin 31° = 0.5150$ and $\cos 31° = 0.8572$, find the specified function value.

83. $\sec 59°$

84. $\tan 59°$

Synthesis

Angles Between Lines. One of the identities gives an easy way to find an angle formed by two lines. Consider two lines with equations l_1: $y = m_1x + b_1$ and l_2: $y = m_2x + b_2$.

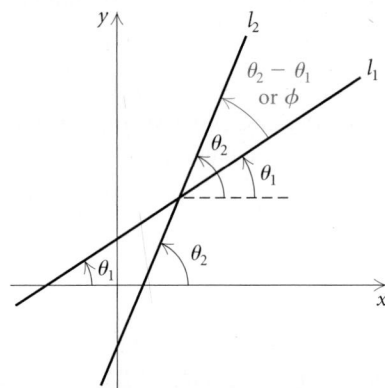

The slopes m_1 and m_2 are the tangents of the angles θ_1 and θ_2 that the lines form with the positive direction of the x-axis. Thus we have $m_1 = \tan \theta_1$ and $m_2 = \tan \theta_2$. To find the measure of $\theta_2 - \theta_1$, or ϕ, we proceed as follows:

$$\tan \phi = \tan (\theta_2 - \theta_1)$$
$$= \frac{\tan \theta_2 - \tan \theta_1}{1 + \tan \theta_2 \tan \theta_1}$$
$$= \frac{m_2 - m_1}{1 + m_2m_1}.$$

This formula also holds when the lines are taken in the reverse order. When ϕ is acute, $\tan \phi$ will be positive. When ϕ is obtuse, $\tan \phi$ will be negative.

Find the measure of the angle from l_1 to l_2.

85. l_1: $2x = 3 - 2y$,
l_2: $x + y = 5$

86. l_1: $3y = \sqrt{3}x + 3$,
l_2: $y = \sqrt{3}x + 2$

87. l_1: $y = 3$,
l_2: $x + y = 5$

88. l_1: $2x + y - 4 = 0$,
l_2: $y - 2x + 5 = 0$

89. *Rope Course and Climbing Wall.* For a rope course and climbing wall, a guy wire R is attached 47 ft high on a vertical pole. Another guy wire S is attached 40 ft above the ground on the same pole. (*Source:* Experiential Resources, Inc., Todd Domeck, Owner) Find the angle α between the wires if they are attached to the ground 50 ft from the pole.

90. *Circus Guy Wire.* In a circus, a guy wire A is attached to the top of a 30-ft pole. Wire B is used for performers to walk up to the tight wire, 10 ft above the ground. Find the angle ϕ between the wires if they are attached to the ground 40 ft from the pole.

91. Given that $f(x) = \cos x$, show that
$$\frac{f(x + h) - f(x)}{h} = \cos x \left(\frac{\cos h - 1}{h} \right) - \sin x \left(\frac{\sin h}{h} \right).$$

92. Given that $f(x) = \sin x$, show that
$$\frac{f(x + h) - f(x)}{h} = \sin x \left(\frac{\cos h - 1}{h} \right) + \cos x \left(\frac{\sin h}{h} \right).$$

Show that each of the following is not an identity by finding a replacement or replacements for which the sides of the equation do not name the same number.

93. $\dfrac{\sin 5x}{x} = \sin 5$

94. $\sqrt{\sin^2 \theta} = \sin \theta$

95. $\cos (2\alpha) = 2 \cos \alpha$

96. $\sin (-x) = \sin x$

97. $\dfrac{\cos 6x}{\cos x} = 6$

98. $\tan^2 \theta + \cot^2 \theta = 1$

Find the slope of line l_1, where m_2 is the slope of line l_2 and ϕ is the smallest positive angle from l_1 to l_2.

99. $m_2 = \frac{2}{3},\ \phi = 30°$

100. $m_2 = \frac{4}{3},\ \phi = 45°$

101. Line l_1 contains the points $(-3, 7)$ and $(-3, -2)$. Line l_2 contains $(0, -4)$ and $(2, 6)$. Find the smallest positive angle from l_1 to l_2.

102. Line l_1 contains the points $(-2, 4)$ and $(5, -1)$. Find the slope of line l_2 such that the angle from l_1 to l_2 is $45°$.

103. Find an identity for $\cos 2\theta$. (*Hint:* $2\theta = \theta + \theta$.)

104. Find an identity for $\sin 2\theta$. (*Hint:* $2\theta = \theta + \theta$.)

Derive the identity.

105. $\tan \left(x + \dfrac{\pi}{4} \right) = \dfrac{1 + \tan x}{1 - \tan x}$

106. $\sin \left(x - \dfrac{3\pi}{2} \right) = \cos x$

107. $\sin (\alpha + \beta) + \sin (\alpha - \beta) = 2 \sin \alpha \cos \beta$

108. $\dfrac{\sin (\alpha + \beta)}{\cos (\alpha - \beta)} = \dfrac{\tan \alpha + \tan \beta}{1 + \tan \alpha \tan \beta}$

6.2

Identities: Cofunction, Double-Angle, and Half-Angle

✦ Use cofunction identities to derive other identities.

✦ Use the double-angle identities to find function values of twice an angle when one function value is known for that angle.

✦ Use the half-angle identities to find function values of half an angle when one function value is known for that angle.

✦ Simplify trigonometric expressions using the double-angle and half-angle identities.

✦ Cofunction Identities

Each of the identities listed below yields a conversion to a *cofunction*. For this reason, we call them cofunction identities.

> **Cofunction Identities**
>
> $\sin \left(\dfrac{\pi}{2} - x \right) = \cos x,$ $\cos \left(\dfrac{\pi}{2} - x \right) = \sin x,$
>
> $\tan \left(\dfrac{\pi}{2} - x \right) = \cot x,$ $\cot \left(\dfrac{\pi}{2} - x \right) = \tan x,$
>
> $\sec \left(\dfrac{\pi}{2} - x \right) = \csc x,$ $\csc \left(\dfrac{\pi}{2} - x \right) = \sec x$

We verified the first two of these identities in Section 6.1. The other four can be proved using the first two and the definitions of the trigonometric functions. These identities hold for all real numbers, and thus, for all angle measures, but if we restrict θ to values such that $0° < \theta < 90°$, or $0 < \theta < \pi/2$, then we have a special application to the acute angles of a right triangle.

Comparing graphs can lead to possible identities. On the left below, we see that the graph of $y = \sin(x + \pi/2)$ is a translation of the graph of $y = \sin x$ to the left $\pi/2$ units. On the right, we see the graph of $y = \cos x$.

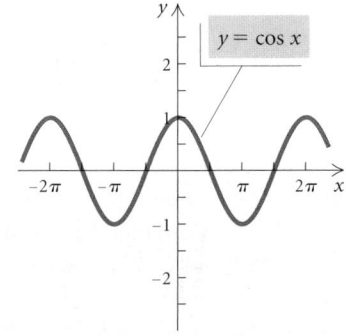

Comparing the graphs, we note a possible identity:

$$\sin\left(x + \frac{\pi}{2}\right) = \cos x.$$

The identity can be proved using the identity for the sine of a sum developed in Section 6.1.

EXAMPLE 1 Prove the identity $\sin(x + \pi/2) = \cos x$.

Solution

$$\sin\left(x + \frac{\pi}{2}\right) = \sin x \cos \frac{\pi}{2} + \cos x \sin \frac{\pi}{2} \quad \text{Using } \sin(u+v) = \sin u \cos v + \cos u \sin v$$
$$= \sin x \cdot 0 + \cos x \cdot 1$$
$$= \cos x$$

We now state four more cofunction identities. These new identities that involve the sine and cosine functions can be verified using previously established identities as seen in Example 1.

Cofunction Identities for the Sine and Cosine

$$\sin\left(x \pm \frac{\pi}{2}\right) = \pm \cos x, \qquad \cos\left(x \pm \frac{\pi}{2}\right) = \mp \sin x$$

EXAMPLE 2 Find an identity for each of the following.

a) $\tan\left(x + \dfrac{\pi}{2}\right)$ **b)** $\sec(x - 90°)$

Solution

a) We have

$$\tan\left(x + \frac{\pi}{2}\right) = \frac{\sin\left(x + \dfrac{\pi}{2}\right)}{\cos\left(x + \dfrac{\pi}{2}\right)} \qquad \text{Using } \tan x = \frac{\sin x}{\cos x}$$

$$= \frac{\cos x}{-\sin x} \qquad \text{Using cofunction identities}$$

$$= -\cot x.$$

Thus the identity we seek is

$$\tan\left(x + \frac{\pi}{2}\right) = -\cot x.$$

b) We have

$$\sec(x - 90°) = \frac{1}{\cos(x - 90°)} = \frac{1}{\sin x} = \csc x.$$

Thus, $\sec(x - 90°) = \csc x.$ ▶ Now Try Exercises 5 and 7.

◆ Double-Angle Identities

If we double an angle of measure x, the new angle will have measure $2x$. **Double-angle identities** give trigonometric function values of $2x$ in terms of function values of x. To develop these identities, we will use the sum formulas from the preceding section. We first develop a formula for $\sin 2x$. Recall that

$$\sin(u + v) = \sin u \cos v + \cos u \sin v.$$

We will consider a number x and substitute it for both u and v in this identity. Doing so gives us

$$\sin(x + x) = \sin 2x$$
$$= \sin x \cos x + \cos x \sin x$$
$$= 2 \sin x \cos x.$$

Our first double-angle identity is thus

$$\mathbf{\sin 2x = 2 \sin x \cos x.}$$

TECHNOLOGY · · · · · · · · · · · ·
    CONNECTION

Graphing calculators provide visual partial checks of identities. We can graph

$$y_1 = \sin 2x, \quad \text{and}$$
$$y_2 = 2 \sin x \cos x$$

using the "line"-graph style for y_1 and the "path"-graph style for y_2 and see that they appear to have the same graph. We can also use the TABLE feature.

$y_1 = \sin 2x, \quad y_2 = 2 \sin x \cos x$

X	Y₁	Y₂
−6.283	2E⁻¹³	0
−5.498	1	1
−4.712	0	0
−3.927	−1	−1
−3.142	0	0
−2.356	1	1
−1.571	0	0

X = −1.57079632679

ΔTbl = π/4

Double-angle identities for the cosine and tangent functions can be derived in much the same way as the identity above:

$$\cos 2x = \cos^2 x - \sin^2 x, \qquad \tan 2x = \frac{2 \tan x}{1 - \tan^2 x}.$$

EXAMPLE 3 Given that $\tan \theta = -\frac{3}{4}$ and θ is in quadrant II, find each of the following.

a) $\sin 2\theta$ **b)** $\cos 2\theta$

c) $\tan 2\theta$ **d)** The quadrant in which 2θ lies

Solution By drawing a reference triangle as shown, we find that

$$\sin \theta = \frac{3}{5}$$

and

$$\cos \theta = -\frac{4}{5}.$$

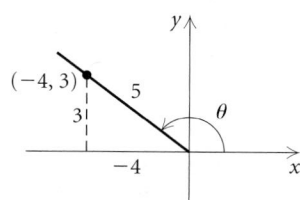

Thus we have the following.

a) $\sin 2\theta = 2 \sin \theta \cos \theta = 2 \cdot \dfrac{3}{5} \cdot \left(-\dfrac{4}{5}\right) = -\dfrac{24}{25}$

b) $\cos 2\theta = \cos^2 \theta - \sin^2 \theta = \left(-\dfrac{4}{5}\right)^2 - \left(\dfrac{3}{5}\right)^2 = \dfrac{16}{25} - \dfrac{9}{25} = \dfrac{7}{25}$

c) $\tan 2\theta = \dfrac{2 \tan \theta}{1 - \tan^2 \theta} = \dfrac{2 \cdot \left(-\frac{3}{4}\right)}{1 - \left(-\frac{3}{4}\right)^2} = \dfrac{-\frac{3}{2}}{1 - \frac{9}{16}} = -\dfrac{3}{2} \cdot \dfrac{16}{7} = -\dfrac{24}{7}$

Note that $\tan 2\theta$ could have been found more easily in this case by simply dividing:

$$\tan 2\theta = \frac{\sin 2\theta}{\cos 2\theta} = \frac{-\frac{24}{25}}{\frac{7}{25}} = -\frac{24}{7}.$$

d) Since $\sin 2\theta$ is negative and $\cos 2\theta$ is positive, we know that 2θ is in quadrant IV.

▶ **Now Try Exercise 9.**

Two other useful identities for $\cos 2x$ can be derived easily, as follows.

$$\begin{aligned} \cos 2x &= \cos^2 x - \sin^2 x \\ &= (1 - \sin^2 x) - \sin^2 x \\ &= 1 - 2 \sin^2 x \end{aligned} \qquad \begin{aligned} \cos 2x &= \cos^2 x - \sin^2 x \\ &= \cos^2 x - (1 - \cos^2 x) \\ &= 2 \cos^2 x - 1 \end{aligned}$$

Double-Angle Identities

$\sin 2x = 2 \sin x \cos x$,

$\tan 2x = \dfrac{2 \tan x}{1 - \tan^2 x}$

$\cos 2x = \cos^2 x - \sin^2 x$
$= 1 - 2 \sin^2 x$
$= 2 \cos^2 x - 1$

Solving the last two cosine double-angle identities for $\sin^2 x$ and $\cos^2 x$, respectively, we obtain two more identities:

$$\sin^2 x = \frac{1 - \cos 2x}{2} \quad \text{and} \quad \cos^2 x = \frac{1 + \cos 2x}{2}.$$

Using division and these two identities, we obtain the following useful identity:

$$\tan^2 x = \frac{1 - \cos 2x}{1 + \cos 2x}.$$

EXAMPLE 4   Find an equivalent expression for each of the following.

a) $\sin 3\theta$ in terms of function values of θ

b) $\cos^3 x$ in terms of function values of x or $2x$, raised only to the first power

Solution

a) $\sin 3\theta = \sin (2\theta + \theta)$
$= \sin 2\theta \cos \theta + \cos 2\theta \sin \theta$
$= (2 \sin \theta \cos \theta) \cos \theta + (2 \cos^2 \theta - 1) \sin \theta$
    Using $\sin 2\theta = 2 \sin \theta \cos \theta$ and $\cos 2\theta = 2 \cos^2 \theta - 1$
$= 2 \sin \theta \cos^2 \theta + 2 \sin \theta \cos^2 \theta - \sin \theta$
$= 4 \sin \theta \cos^2 \theta - \sin \theta$

We could also substitute $\cos^2 \theta - \sin^2 \theta$ or $1 - 2 \sin^2 \theta$ for $\cos 2\theta$. Each substitution leads to a different result, but all results are equivalent.

b) $\cos^3 x = \cos^2 x \cos x$
$= \dfrac{1 + \cos 2x}{2} \cos x$
$= \dfrac{\cos x + \cos x \cos 2x}{2}$

▶ Now Try Exercise 15.

◆ Half-Angle Identities

If we take half of an angle of measure x, the new angle will have measure $x/2$. **Half-angle identities** give trigonometric function values of $x/2$ in terms of function values of x. To develop these identities, we replace x with $x/2$ and take square roots. For example,

$$\sin^2 x = \frac{1 - \cos 2x}{2} \qquad \text{Solving the identity}$$
$$\cos 2x = 1 - 2\sin^2 x \text{ for } \sin^2 x$$

$$\sin^2 \frac{x}{2} = \frac{1 - \cos 2 \cdot \frac{x}{2}}{2} \qquad \text{Substituting } \frac{x}{2} \text{ for } x$$

$$\sin^2 \frac{x}{2} = \frac{1 - \cos x}{2}$$

$$\sin \frac{x}{2} = \pm\sqrt{\frac{1 - \cos x}{2}}. \qquad \text{Taking square roots}$$

The formula is called a *half-angle formula*. The use of $+$ and $-$ depends on the quadrant in which the angle $x/2$ lies. Half-angle identities for the cosine and tangent functions can be derived in a similar manner. Two additional formulas for the half-angle tangent identity are listed below.

Half-Angle Identities

$$\sin \frac{x}{2} = \pm\sqrt{\frac{1 - \cos x}{2}},$$

$$\cos \frac{x}{2} = \pm\sqrt{\frac{1 + \cos x}{2}},$$

$$\tan \frac{x}{2} = \pm\sqrt{\frac{1 - \cos x}{1 + \cos x}}$$

$$= \frac{\sin x}{1 + \cos x} = \frac{1 - \cos x}{\sin x}$$

EXAMPLE 5 Find $\tan(\pi/8)$ exactly.

Solution We have

$$\tan \frac{\pi}{8} = \tan \frac{\frac{\pi}{4}}{2} = \frac{\sin \frac{\pi}{4}}{1 + \cos \frac{\pi}{4}} = \frac{\frac{\sqrt{2}}{2}}{1 + \frac{\sqrt{2}}{2}} = \frac{\frac{\sqrt{2}}{2}}{\frac{2 + \sqrt{2}}{2}}$$

$$= \frac{\sqrt{2}}{2 + \sqrt{2}} = \frac{\sqrt{2}}{2 + \sqrt{2}} \cdot \frac{2 - \sqrt{2}}{2 - \sqrt{2}}$$

$$= \sqrt{2} - 1.$$

▶ Now Try Exercise 21.

The identities that we have developed are also useful for simplifying trigonometric expressions.

EXAMPLE 6 Simplify each of the following.

a) $\dfrac{\sin x \cos x}{\frac{1}{2} \cos 2x}$

b) $2 \sin^2 \dfrac{x}{2} + \cos x$

Solution

a) We can obtain $2 \sin x \cos x$ in the numerator by multiplying the expression by $\frac{2}{2}$:

$$\frac{\sin x \cos x}{\frac{1}{2} \cos 2x} = \frac{2}{2} \cdot \frac{\sin x \cos x}{\frac{1}{2} \cos 2x} = \frac{2 \sin x \cos x}{\cos 2x}$$

$$= \frac{\sin 2x}{\cos 2x} \qquad \text{Using } \sin 2x = 2 \sin x \cos x$$

$$= \tan 2x.$$

b) We have

$$2 \sin^2 \frac{x}{2} + \cos x = 2 \left(\frac{1 - \cos x}{2} \right) + \cos x$$

$$\text{Using } \sin \frac{x}{2} = \pm \sqrt{\frac{1 - \cos x}{2}}, \text{ or } \sin^2 \frac{x}{2} = \frac{1 - \cos x}{2}$$

$$= 1 - \cos x + \cos x$$

$$= 1. \qquad \blacktriangleright \text{ Now Try Exercise 29.}$$

6.2 EXERCISE SET

1. Given that $\sin(3\pi/10) \approx 0.8090$ and $\cos(3\pi/10) \approx 0.5878$, find each of the following.

   a) The other four function values for $3\pi/10$
   b) The six function values for $\pi/5$

2. Given that

   $$\sin \frac{\pi}{12} = \frac{\sqrt{2 - \sqrt{3}}}{2} \quad \text{and} \quad \cos \frac{\pi}{12} = \frac{\sqrt{2 + \sqrt{3}}}{2},$$

   find exact answers for each of the following.

   a) The other four function values for $\pi/12$
   b) The six function values for $5\pi/12$

3. Given that $\sin \theta = \frac{1}{3}$ and that the terminal side is in quadrant II, find exact answers for each of the following.

   a) The other function values for θ

   b) The six function values for $\pi/2 - \theta$
   c) The six function values for $\theta - \pi/2$

4. Given that $\cos \phi = \frac{4}{5}$ and that the terminal side is in quadrant IV, find exact answers for each of the following.

   a) The other function values for ϕ
   b) The six function values for $\pi/2 - \phi$
   c) The six function values for $\phi + \pi/2$

Find an equivalent expression for each of the following.

5. $\sec \left(x + \dfrac{\pi}{2} \right)$

6. $\cot \left(x - \dfrac{\pi}{2} \right)$

7. $\tan \left(x - \dfrac{\pi}{2} \right)$

8. $\csc \left(x + \dfrac{\pi}{2} \right)$

Find the exact value of sin 2θ, cos 2θ, tan 2θ, *and the quadrant in which* 2θ *lies.*

9. $\sin \theta = \dfrac{4}{5}$, θ in quadrant I

10. $\cos \theta = \dfrac{5}{13}$, θ in quadrant I

11. $\cos \theta = -\dfrac{3}{5}$, θ in quadrant III

12. $\tan \theta = -\dfrac{15}{8}$, θ in quadrant II

13. $\tan \theta = -\dfrac{5}{12}$, θ in quadrant II

14. $\sin \theta = -\dfrac{\sqrt{10}}{10}$, θ in quadrant IV

15. Find an equivalent expression for cos 4x in terms of function values of x.

16. Find an equivalent expression for $\sin^4 \theta$ in terms of function values of θ, 2θ, or 4θ, raised only to the first power.

Use the half-angle identities to evaluate exactly.

17. cos 15°   **18.** tan 67.5°

19. sin 112.5°   **20.** $\cos \dfrac{\pi}{8}$

21. tan 75°   **22.** $\sin \dfrac{5\pi}{12}$

Given that sin θ = 0.3416 *and* θ *is in quadrant I, find each of the following using identities.*

23. sin 2θ   **24.** $\cos \dfrac{\theta}{2}$

25. $\sin \dfrac{\theta}{2}$ **26.** sin 4θ

Simplify.

27. $2 \cos^2 \dfrac{x}{2} - 1$

28. $\cos^4 x - \sin^4 x$

29. $(\sin x - \cos x)^2 + \sin 2x$

30. $(\sin x + \cos x)^2$

31. $\dfrac{2 - \sec^2 x}{\sec^2 x}$

32. $\dfrac{1 + \sin 2x + \cos 2x}{1 + \sin 2x - \cos 2x}$

33. $(-4 \cos x \sin x + 2 \cos 2x)^2 + (2 \cos 2x + 4 \sin x \cos x)^2$

34. $2 \sin x \cos^3 x - 2 \sin^3 x \cos x$

Technology Connection

In Exercises 35–38, use a graphing calculator to determine which of the following expressions asserts an identity. Then derive the identity algebraically.

35. $\dfrac{\cos 2x}{\cos x - \sin x} = \cdots$

a) $1 + \cos x$ b) $\cos x - \sin x$

c) $-\cot x$ d) $\sin x (\cot x + 1)$

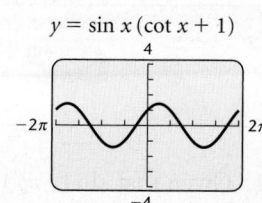

36. $2 \cos^2 \dfrac{x}{2} = \cdots$

a) $\sin x (\csc x + \tan x)$ b) $\sin x - 2 \cos x$
c) $2(\cos^2 x - \sin^2 x)$ d) $1 + \cos x$

37. $\dfrac{\sin 2x}{2 \cos x} = \cdots$

a) $\cos x$ b) $\tan x$
c) $\cos x + \sin x$ d) $\sin x$

38. $2 \sin \dfrac{\theta}{2} \cos \dfrac{\theta}{2} = \cdots$

a) $\cos^2 \theta$ b) $\sin \dfrac{\theta}{2}$

c) $\sin \theta$ d) $\sin \theta - \cos \theta$

Collaborative Discussion and Writing

39. Discuss and compare the graphs of $y = \sin x$, $y = \sin 2x$, and $y = \sin (x/2)$.

40. Find all errors in the following:

$$2 \sin^2 2x + \cos 4x$$
$$= 2(2 \sin x \cos x)^2 + 2 \cos 2x$$
$$= 8 \sin^2 x \cos^2 x + 2(\cos^2 x + \sin^2 x)$$
$$= 8 \sin^2 x \cos^2 x + 2.$$

Skill Maintenance

Complete the identity.

41. $1 - \cos^2 x =$

42. $\sec^2 x - \tan^2 x =$

43. $\sin^2 x - 1 =$

44. $1 + \cot^2 x =$

45. $\csc^2 x - \cot^2 x$

46. $1 + \tan^2 x =$

47. $1 - \sin^2 x$

48. $\sec^2 x - 1$

Consider the following functions (a)–(f). Without graphing them, answer questions 49–52 below.

a) $f(x) = 2 \sin \left(\dfrac{1}{2} x - \dfrac{\pi}{2} \right)$

b) $f(x) = \dfrac{1}{2} \cos \left(2x - \dfrac{\pi}{4} \right) + 2$

c) $f(x) = -\sin \left[2 \left(x - \dfrac{\pi}{2} \right) \right] + 2$

d) $f(x) = \sin (x + \pi) - \dfrac{1}{2}$

e) $f(x) = -2 \cos (4x - \pi)$

f) $f(x) = -\cos 2 \left(x - \dfrac{\pi}{8} \right)$

49. Which functions have a graph with an amplitude of 2?

50. Which functions have a graph with a period of π?

51. Which functions have a graph with a period of 2π?

52. Which functions have a graph with a phase shift of $\dfrac{\pi}{4}$?

Synthesis

53. Given that $\cos 51° \approx 0.6293$, find the six function values for $141°$.

Simplify.

54. $\sin \left(\dfrac{\pi}{2} - x \right) [\sec x - \cos x]$

55. $\cos (\pi - x) + \cot x \sin \left(x - \dfrac{\pi}{2} \right)$

56. $\dfrac{\cos x - \sin \left(\dfrac{\pi}{2} - x \right) \sin x}{\cos x - \cos (\pi - x) \tan x}$

57. $\dfrac{\cos^2 y \sin \left(y + \dfrac{\pi}{2} \right)}{\sin^2 y \sin \left(\dfrac{\pi}{2} - y \right)}$

Find $\sin \theta$, $\cos \theta$, and $\tan \theta$ under the given conditions.

58. $\cos 2\theta = \dfrac{7}{12}$, $\dfrac{3\pi}{2} \leq 2\theta \leq 2\pi$

59. $\tan \dfrac{\theta}{2} = -\dfrac{5}{3}$, $\pi < \theta \leq \dfrac{3\pi}{2}$

60. *Nautical Mile.* Latitude is used to measure north–south location on the earth between the equator and the poles. For example, Chicago has latitude 42°N. (See the figure.) In Great Britain, the *nautical mile* is defined as the length of a minute of arc of the earth's radius. Since the earth is flattened slightly at the poles, a British nautical mile varies with latitude. In fact, it is given, in feet, by the function

$$N(\phi) = 6066 - 31 \cos 2\phi,$$

where ϕ is the latitude in degrees.

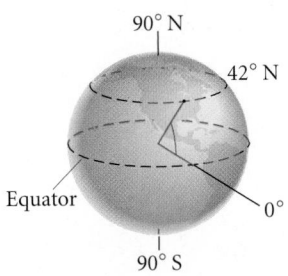

a) What is the length of a British nautical mile at Chicago?

b) What is the length of a British nautical mile at the North Pole?

c) Express $N(\phi)$ in terms of $\cos \phi$ only. That is, do not use the double angle.

61. *Acceleration Due to Gravity.* The acceleration due to gravity is often denoted by g in a formula such as $S = \frac{1}{2}gt^2$, where S is the distance that an object falls in time t. The number g relates to motion near the earth's surface and is usually considered constant. In fact, however, g is not constant, but varies slightly with latitude. If ϕ stands for latitude, in degrees, g is given with good approximation by the formula

$$g = 9.78049(1 + 0.005288 \sin^2 \phi - 0.000006 \sin^2 2\phi),$$

where g is measured in meters per second per second at sea level.

a) Chicago has latitude 42°N. Find g.
b) Philadelphia has latitude 40°N. Find g.

c) Express g in terms of $\sin \phi$ only. That is, eliminate the double angle.

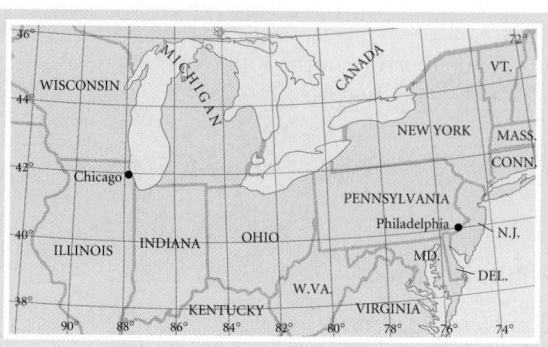

6.3

Proving Trigonometric Identities

◆ Prove identities using other identities.
◆ Use the product-to-sum identities and the sum-to-product identities to derive other identities.

◆ The Logic of Proving Identities

We outline two algebraic methods for proving identities.

Method 1. Start with either the left or the right side of the equation and obtain the other side. For example, suppose you are trying to prove that the equation $P = Q$ is an identity. You might try to produce a string of statements $(R_1, R_2,\dots$ or $T_1, T_2,\dots)$ like the following, which start with P and end with Q or start with Q and end with P:

$$
\begin{aligned}
P &= R_1 \quad \text{or} \quad Q = T_1 \\
&= R_2 \qquad\qquad\;\; = T_2 \\
&\;\;\vdots \qquad\qquad\qquad \vdots \\
&= Q \qquad\qquad\;\; = P.
\end{aligned}
$$

Method 2. Work with each side separately until you obtain the same expression. For example, suppose you are trying to prove that $P = Q$ is an identity.

You might be able to produce two strings of statements like the following, each ending with the same statement S.

$$P = R_1 \qquad Q = T_1$$
$$= R_2 \qquad\quad = T_2$$
$$\vdots \qquad\qquad \vdots$$
$$= S \qquad\quad = S.$$

The number of steps in each string might be different, but in each case the result is S.

A first step in learning to prove identities is to have at hand a list of the identities that you have already learned. Such a list is on the inside back cover of this text. Ask your instructor which ones you are expected to memorize. The more identities you prove, the easier it will be to prove new ones. A list of helpful hints follows.

Hints for Proving Identities

1. Use method 1 or 2 above.
2. Work with the more complex side first.
3. Carry out any algebraic manipulations, such as adding, subtracting, multiplying, or factoring.
4. Multiplying by 1 can be helpful when rational expressions are involved.
5. Converting all expressions to sines and cosines is often helpful.
6. Try something! Put your pencil to work and get involved. You will be amazed at how often this leads to success.

✦ Proving Identities

In what follows, method 1 is used in Examples 1–3 and method 2 is used in Examples 4 and 5.

EXAMPLE 1   Prove the identity $1 + \sin 2\theta = (\sin \theta + \cos \theta)^2$.

Solution   Let's use method 1. We begin with the right side and obtain the left side:

$$(\sin \theta + \cos \theta)^2 = \sin^2 \theta + 2 \sin \theta \cos \theta + \cos^2 \theta \qquad \text{Squaring}$$
$$= 1 + 2 \sin \theta \cos \theta \qquad \begin{array}{l}\text{Recalling the identity}\\ \sin^2 x + \cos^2 x = 1 \text{ and}\\ \text{substituting}\end{array}$$
$$= 1 + \sin 2\theta. \qquad \begin{array}{l}\text{Using } \sin 2x =\\ 2 \sin x \cos x\end{array}$$

We could also begin with the left side and obtain the right side:

$$1 + \sin 2\theta = 1 + 2 \sin \theta \cos \theta \qquad \text{Using } \sin 2x = 2 \sin x \cos x$$
$$= \sin^2 \theta + 2 \sin \theta \cos \theta + \cos^2 \theta \qquad \begin{array}{l}\text{Replacing 1 with} \\ \sin^2 \theta + \cos^2 \theta\end{array}$$
$$= (\sin \theta + \cos \theta)^2. \qquad \text{Factoring}$$

▶ **Now Try Exercise 19.**

EXAMPLE 2 Prove the identity

$$\frac{\sec t - 1}{t \sec t} = \frac{1 - \cos t}{t}.$$

Solution We use method 1, starting with the left side. Note that the left side involves sec t, whereas the right side involves cos t, so it might be wise to make use of a basic identity that involves these two expressions: $\sec t = 1/\cos t$.

$$\frac{\sec t - 1}{t \sec t} = \frac{\dfrac{1}{\cos t} - 1}{t\dfrac{1}{\cos t}} \qquad \text{Substituting } 1/\cos t \text{ for sec } t$$

$$= \left(\frac{1}{\cos t} - 1\right) \cdot \frac{\cos t}{t}$$

$$= \frac{1}{t} - \frac{\cos t}{t} \qquad \text{Multiplying}$$

$$= \frac{1 - \cos t}{t}$$

We started with the left side and obtained the right side, so the proof is complete.

▶ **Now Try Exercise 5.**

EXAMPLE 3 Prove the identity

$$\frac{\sin 2x}{\sin x} - \frac{\cos 2x}{\cos x} = \sec x.$$

Solution

$$\frac{\sin 2x}{\sin x} - \frac{\cos 2x}{\cos x} = \frac{2 \sin x \cos x}{\sin x} - \frac{\cos^2 x - \sin^2 x}{\cos x} \qquad \begin{array}{l}\text{Using double-angle} \\ \text{identities}\end{array}$$

$$= 2 \cos x - \frac{\cos^2 x - \sin^2 x}{\cos x} \qquad \text{Simplifying}$$

$$= \frac{2 \cos^2 x}{\cos x} - \frac{\cos^2 x - \sin^2 x}{\cos x} \qquad \begin{array}{l}\text{Multiplying } 2 \cos x \\ \text{by 1, or } \cos x/\cos x\end{array}$$

$$= \frac{2 \cos^2 x - \cos^2 x + \sin^2 x}{\cos x} \qquad \text{Subtracting}$$

$$= \frac{\cos^2 x + \sin^2 x}{\cos x}$$

Then $\qquad = \dfrac{1}{\cos x}$ Using a Pythagorean identity

$\qquad\qquad = \sec x$ Recalling a basic identity

▶ Now Try Exercise 15.

EXAMPLE 4   Prove the identity

$$\sin^2 x \tan^2 x = \tan^2 x - \sin^2 x.$$

Solution   For this proof, we are going to work with each side separately using method 2. We try to obtain the same expression on each side. In actual practice, you might work on one side for awhile, then work on the other side, and then go back to the first side. In other words, you work back and forth until you arrive at the same expression. Let's start with the right side:

$$\tan^2 x - \sin^2 x = \dfrac{\sin^2 x}{\cos^2 x} - \sin^2 x$$ Recalling the identity $\tan x = \dfrac{\sin x}{\cos x}$ and substituting

$$= \dfrac{\sin^2 x}{\cos^2 x} - \sin^2 x \cdot \dfrac{\cos^2 x}{\cos^2 x}$$ Multiplying by 1 in order to subtract

$$= \dfrac{\sin^2 x - \sin^2 x \cos^2 x}{\cos^2 x}$$ Carrying out the subtraction

$$= \dfrac{\sin^2 x (1 - \cos^2 x)}{\cos^2 x}$$ Factoring

$$= \dfrac{\sin^2 x \sin^2 x}{\cos^2 x}$$ Recalling the identity $1 - \cos^2 x = \sin^2 x$ and substituting

$$= \dfrac{\sin^4 x}{\cos^2 x}.$$

At this point, we stop and work with the left side, $\sin^2 x \tan^2 x$, of the original identity and try to end with the same expression that we ended with on the right side:

$$\sin^2 x \tan^2 x = \sin^2 x \dfrac{\sin^2 x}{\cos^2 x}$$ Recalling the identity $\tan x = \dfrac{\sin x}{\cos x}$ and substituting

$$= \dfrac{\sin^4 x}{\cos^2 x}.$$

We have obtained the same expression from each side, so the proof is complete.

▶ Now Try Exercise 25.

EXAMPLE 5 Prove the identity

$$\cot \phi + \csc \phi = \frac{\sin \phi}{1 - \cos \phi}.$$

Solution We are again using method 2, beginning with the left side:

$$\cot \phi + \csc \phi = \frac{\cos \phi}{\sin \phi} + \frac{1}{\sin \phi} \qquad \text{Using basic identities}$$

$$= \frac{1 + \cos \phi}{\sin \phi}. \qquad \text{Adding}$$

At this point, we stop and work with the right side of the original identity:

$$\frac{\sin \phi}{1 - \cos \phi} = \frac{\sin \phi}{1 - \cos \phi} \cdot \frac{1 + \cos \phi}{1 + \cos \phi} \qquad \text{Multiplying by 1}$$

$$= \frac{\sin \phi \, (1 + \cos \phi)}{1 - \cos^2 \phi}$$

$$= \frac{\sin \phi \, (1 + \cos \phi)}{\sin^2 \phi} \qquad \text{Using } \sin^2 x = 1 - \cos^2 x$$

$$= \frac{1 + \cos \phi}{\sin \phi}. \qquad \text{Simplifying}$$

The proof is complete since we obtained the same expression from each side.

▶ Now Try Exercise 29.

◆ Product-to-Sum and Sum-to-Product Identities

On occasion, it is convenient to convert a product of trigonometric expressions to a sum, or the reverse. The following identities are useful in this connection.

Product-to-Sum Identities

$$\sin x \cdot \sin y = \frac{1}{2}[\cos (x - y) - \cos (x + y)] \qquad (1)$$

$$\cos x \cdot \cos y = \frac{1}{2}[\cos (x - y) + \cos (x + y)] \qquad (2)$$

$$\sin x \cdot \cos y = \frac{1}{2}[\sin (x + y) + \sin (x - y)] \qquad (3)$$

$$\cos x \cdot \sin y = \frac{1}{2}[\sin (x + y) - \sin (x - y)] \qquad (4)$$

We can derive product-to-sum identities (1) and (2) using the sum and difference identities for the cosine function:

$$\cos (x + y) = \cos x \cos y - \sin x \sin y, \qquad \text{Sum identity}$$
$$\cos (x - y) = \cos x \cos y + \sin x \sin y. \qquad \text{Difference identity}$$

Subtracting the sum identity from the difference identity, we have

$$\cos (x - y) - \cos (x + y) = 2 \sin x \sin y \qquad \text{Subtracting}$$
$$\frac{1}{2} [\cos (x - y) - \cos (x + y)] = \sin x \sin y. \qquad \text{Multiplying by } \tfrac{1}{2}$$

Thus, $\sin x \sin y = \frac{1}{2}[\cos (x - y) - \cos (x + y)]$.

Adding the cosine sum and difference identities, we have

$$\cos (x - y) + \cos (x + y) = 2 \cos x \cos y \qquad \text{Adding}$$
$$\frac{1}{2} [\cos (x - y) + \cos (x + y)] = \cos x \cos y. \qquad \text{Multiplying by } \tfrac{1}{2}$$

Thus, $\cos x \cos y = \frac{1}{2}[\cos (x - y) + \cos (x + y)]$.

Identities (3) and (4) can be derived in a similar manner using the sum and difference identities for the sine function.

EXAMPLE 6 Find an identity for $2 \sin 3\theta \cos 7\theta$.

Solution We will use the identity

$$\sin x \cdot \cos y = \frac{1}{2} [\sin (x + y) + \sin (x - y)].$$

Here $x = 3\theta$ and $y = 7\theta$. Thus,

$$2 \sin 3\theta \cos 7\theta = 2 \cdot \frac{1}{2} [\sin (3\theta + 7\theta) + \sin (3\theta - 7\theta)]$$
$$= \sin 10\theta + \sin (-4\theta)$$
$$= \sin 10\theta - \sin 4\theta. \qquad \text{Using } \sin (-\theta) = -\sin \theta$$

▶ Now Try Exercise 37.

Sum-to-Product Identities

$$\sin x + \sin y = 2 \sin \frac{x + y}{2} \cos \frac{x - y}{2} \tag{5}$$

$$\sin x - \sin y = 2 \cos \frac{x + y}{2} \sin \frac{x - y}{2} \tag{6}$$

$$\cos y + \cos x = 2 \cos \frac{x + y}{2} \cos \frac{x - y}{2} \tag{7}$$

$$\cos y - \cos x = 2 \sin \frac{x + y}{2} \sin \frac{x - y}{2} \tag{8}$$

The sum-to-product identities (5)–(8) can be derived using the product-to-sum identities. Proofs are left to the exercises.

EXAMPLE 7 Find an identity for $\cos \theta + \cos 5\theta$.

Solution We will use the identity

$$\cos y + \cos x = 2 \cos \frac{x + y}{2} \cos \frac{x - y}{2}.$$

Here $x = 5\theta$ and $y = \theta$. Thus,

$$\cos \theta + \cos 5\theta = 2 \cos \frac{5\theta + \theta}{2} \cos \frac{5\theta - \theta}{2}$$

$$= 2 \cos 3\theta \cos 2\theta.$$

▶ Now Try Exercise 35.

6.3 EXERCISE SET

Prove each of the following identities.

1. $\sec x - \sin x \tan x = \cos x$

2. $\dfrac{1 + \cos \theta}{\sin \theta} + \dfrac{\sin \theta}{\cos \theta} = \dfrac{\cos \theta + 1}{\sin \theta \cos \theta}$

3. $\dfrac{1 - \cos x}{\sin x} = \dfrac{\sin x}{1 + \cos x}$

4. $\dfrac{1 + \tan y}{1 + \cot y} = \dfrac{\sec y}{\csc y}$

5. $\dfrac{1 + \tan \theta}{1 - \tan \theta} + \dfrac{1 + \cot \theta}{1 - \cot \theta} = 0$

6. $\dfrac{\sin x + \cos x}{\sec x + \csc x} = \dfrac{\sin x}{\sec x}$

7. $\dfrac{\cos^2 \alpha + \cot \alpha}{\cos^2 \alpha - \cot \alpha} = \dfrac{\cos^2 \alpha \tan \alpha + 1}{\cos^2 \alpha \tan \alpha - 1}$

8. $\sec 2\theta = \dfrac{\sec^2 \theta}{2 - \sec^2 \theta}$

9. $\dfrac{2 \tan \theta}{1 + \tan^2 \theta} = \sin 2\theta$

10. $\dfrac{\cos (u - v)}{\cos u \sin v} = \tan u + \cot v$

11. $1 - \cos 5\theta \cos 3\theta - \sin 5\theta \sin 3\theta = 2 \sin^2 \theta$

12. $\cos^4 x - \sin^4 x = \cos 2x$

13. $2 \sin \theta \cos^3 \theta + 2 \sin^3 \theta \cos \theta = \sin 2\theta$

14. $\dfrac{\tan 3t - \tan t}{1 + \tan 3t \tan t} = \dfrac{2 \tan t}{1 - \tan^2 t}$

15. $\dfrac{\tan x - \sin x}{2 \tan x} = \sin^2 \dfrac{x}{2}$

16. $\dfrac{\cos^3 \beta - \sin^3 \beta}{\cos \beta - \sin \beta} = \dfrac{2 + \sin 2\beta}{2}$

17. $\sin (\alpha + \beta) \sin (\alpha - \beta) = \sin^2 \alpha - \sin^2 \beta$

18. $\cos^2 x (1 - \sec^2 x) = -\sin^2 x$

19. $\tan \theta (\tan \theta + \cot \theta) = \sec^2 \theta$

20. $\dfrac{\cos \theta + \sin \theta}{\cos \theta} = 1 + \tan \theta$

21. $\dfrac{1 + \cos^2 x}{\sin^2 x} = 2 \csc^2 x - 1$

22. $\dfrac{\tan y + \cot y}{\csc y} = \sec y$

23. $\dfrac{1 + \sin x}{1 - \sin x} + \dfrac{\sin x - 1}{1 + \sin x} = 4 \sec x \tan x$

24. $\tan \theta - \cot \theta = (\sec \theta - \csc \theta)(\sin \theta + \cos \theta)$

25. $\cos^2 \alpha \cot^2 \alpha = \cot^2 \alpha - \cos^2 \alpha$

26. $\dfrac{\tan x + \cot x}{\sec x + \csc x} = \dfrac{1}{\cos x + \sin x}$

27. $2 \sin^2 \theta \cos^2 \theta + \cos^4 \theta = 1 - \sin^4 \theta$

28. $\dfrac{\cot \theta}{\csc \theta - 1} = \dfrac{\csc \theta + 1}{\cot \theta}$

29. $\dfrac{1 + \sin x}{1 - \sin x} = (\sec x + \tan x)^2$

30. $\sec^4 s - \tan^2 s = \tan^4 s + \sec^2 s$

31. Verify the product-to-sum identities (3) and (4) using the sine sum and difference identities.

32. Verify the sum-to-product identities (5)–(8) using the product-to-sum identities (1)–(4).

Use the product-to-sum and the sum-to-product identities to find identities for each of the following.

33. $\sin 3\theta - \sin 5\theta$

34. $\sin 7x - \sin 4x$

35. $\sin 8\theta + \sin 5\theta$

36. $\cos \theta - \cos 7\theta$

37. $\sin 7u \sin 5u$

38. $2 \sin 7\theta \cos 3\theta$

39. $7 \cos \theta \sin 7\theta$

40. $\cos 2t \sin t$

41. $\cos 55° \sin 25°$

42. $7 \cos 5\theta \cos 7\theta$

Use the product-to-sum and the sum-to-product identities to prove each of the following.

43. $\sin 4\theta + \sin 6\theta = \cot \theta (\cos 4\theta - \cos 6\theta)$

44. $\tan 2x (\cos x + \cos 3x) = \sin x + \sin 3x$

45. $\cot 4x (\sin x + \sin 4x + \sin 7x)$
$= \cos x + \cos 4x + \cos 7x$

46. $\tan \dfrac{x + y}{2} = \dfrac{\sin x + \sin y}{\cos x + \cos y}$

47. $\cot \dfrac{x + y}{2} = \dfrac{\sin y - \sin x}{\cos x - \cos y}$

48. $\tan \dfrac{\theta + \phi}{2} \tan \dfrac{\phi - \theta}{2} = \dfrac{\cos \theta - \cos \phi}{\cos \theta + \cos \phi}$

49. $\tan \dfrac{\theta + \phi}{2} (\sin \theta - \sin \phi)$
$= \tan \dfrac{\theta - \phi}{2} (\sin \theta + \sin \phi)$

50. $\sin 2\theta + \sin 4\theta + \sin 6\theta = 4 \cos \theta \cos 2\theta \sin 3\theta$

Technology Connection

In Exercises 51–56, use a graphing calculator to determine which expression (A)–(F) on the right can be used to complete the identity. Then try to prove that identity algebraically.

51. $\dfrac{\cos x + \cot x}{1 + \csc x}$

A. $\dfrac{\sin^3 x - \cos^3 x}{\sin x - \cos x}$

52. $\cot x + \csc x$

B. $\cos x$

53. $\sin x \cos x + 1$

C. $\tan x + \cot x$

54. $2 \cos^2 x - 1$

D. $\cos^3 x + \sin^3 x$

55. $\dfrac{1}{\cot x \sin^2 x}$

E. $\dfrac{\sin x}{1 - \cos x}$

56. $(\cos x + \sin x)(1 - \sin x \cos x)$

F. $\cos^4 x - \sin^4 x$

Collaborative Discussion and Writing

57. What restrictions must be placed on the variable in each of the following identities? Why?

a) $\sin 2x = \dfrac{2 \tan x}{1 + \tan^2 x}$

b) $\dfrac{1 - \cos x}{\sin x} = \dfrac{\sin x}{1 + \cos x}$

c) $2 \sin x \cos^3 x + 2 \sin^3 x \cos x = \sin 2x$

58. Explain why $\tan (x + 450°)$ cannot be simplified using the tangent sum formula, but can be simplified using the sine and cosine sum formulas.

Skill Maintenance

For each function:

a) *Graph the function.*
b) *Determine whether the function is one-to-one.*
c) *If the function is one-to-one, find an equation for its inverse.*
d) *Graph the inverse of the function.*

59. $f(x) = 3x - 2$

60. $f(x) = x^3 + 1$

61. $f(x) = x^2 - 4, \ x \ge 0$

62. $f(x) = \sqrt{x + 2}$

Solve.

63. $2x^2 = 5x$

64. $3x^2 + 5x - 10 = 18$

65. $x^4 + 5x^2 - 36 = 0$

66. $x^2 - 10x + 1 = 0$

67. $\sqrt{x - 2} = 5$

68. $x = \sqrt{x + 7} + 5$

Synthesis

Prove the identity.

69. $\ln |\tan x| = -\ln |\cot x|$

70. $\ln |\sec \theta + \tan \theta| = -\ln |\sec \theta - \tan \theta|$

71. Prove the identity
$$\log (\cos x - \sin x) + \log (\cos x + \sin x) = \log \cos 2x.$$

72. *Mechanics.* The following equation occurs in the study of mechanics:
$$\sin \theta = \dfrac{I_1 \cos \phi}{\sqrt{(I_1 \cos \phi)^2 + (I_2 \sin \phi)^2}}.$$
It can happen that $I_1 = I_2$. Assuming that this happens, simplify the equation.

73. *Alternating Current.* In the theory of alternating current, the following equation occurs:
$$R = \dfrac{1}{\omega C(\tan \theta + \tan \phi)}.$$
Show that this equation is equivalent to
$$R = \dfrac{\cos \theta \cos \phi}{\omega C \sin (\theta + \phi)}.$$

74. *Electrical Theory.* In electrical theory, the following equations occur:
$$E_1 = \sqrt{2}E_t \cos \left(\theta + \dfrac{\pi}{P} \right)$$
and
$$E_2 = \sqrt{2}E_t \cos \left(\theta - \dfrac{\pi}{P} \right).$$
Assuming that these equations hold, show that
$$\dfrac{E_1 + E_2}{2} = \sqrt{2}E_t \cos \theta \cos \dfrac{\pi}{P}$$
and
$$\dfrac{E_1 - E_2}{2} = -\sqrt{2}E_t \sin \theta \sin \dfrac{\pi}{P}.$$

6.4

Inverses of the Trigonometric Functions

✦ Find values of the inverse trigonometric functions.
✦ Simplify expressions such as $\sin(\sin^{-1}x)$ and $\sin^{-1}(\sin x)$.
✦ Simplify expressions involving compositions such as $\sin\left(\cos^{-1}\frac{1}{2}\right)$ without using a calculator.
✦ Simplify expressions such as $\sin\arctan(a/b)$ by making a drawing and reading off appropriate ratios.

In this section, we develop inverse trigonometric functions. The graphs of the sine, cosine, and tangent functions follow. Do these functions have inverses that are functions? They do have inverses if they are one-to-one, which means that they pass the horizontal-line test.

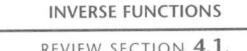

INVERSE FUNCTIONS

REVIEW SECTION **4.1.**

Note that for each function, a horizontal line (shown in red) crosses the graph more than once. Therefore, none of them has an inverse that is a function.

The graphs of an equation and its inverse are reflections of each other across the line $y = x$. Let's examine the graphs of the inverses of each of the three functions graphed above.

STUDY TIP

When you study a section of a mathematics text, read it slowly, observing all the details of the corresponding art pieces that are discussed in the paragraphs. Also note the precise color-coding in the art that enhances the learning of the concepts.

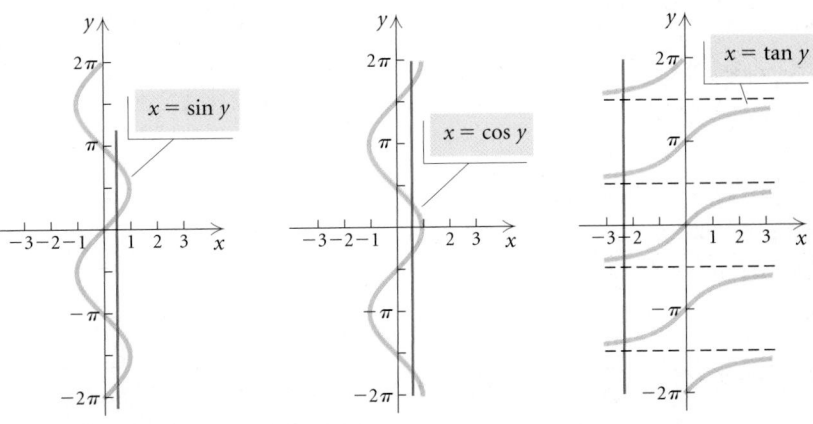

We can check again to see whether these are graphs of functions by using the vertical-line test. In each case, there is a vertical line (shown in red) that crosses the graph more than once, so each *fails* to be a function.

◆ Restricting Ranges to Define Inverse Functions

Recall that a function like $f(x) = x^2$ does not have an inverse that is a function, but by restricting the domain of f to nonnegative numbers, we have a new squaring function, $f(x) = x^2$, $x \geq 0$, that has an inverse, $f^{-1}(x) = \sqrt{x}$. This is equivalent to restricting the range of the inverse relation to exclude ordered pairs that contain negative numbers.

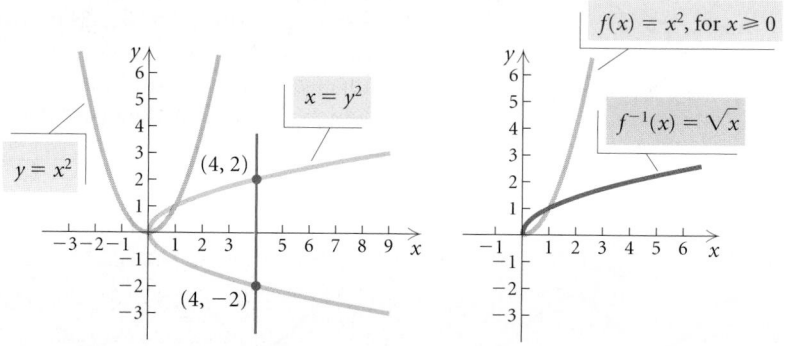

In a similar manner, we can define new trigonometric functions whose inverses are functions. We can do this by restricting either the domains of the basic trigonometric functions or the ranges of their inverse relations. This can be done in many ways, but the restrictions illustrated below with solid red curves are fairly standard in mathematics.

Figure 1

Figure 2

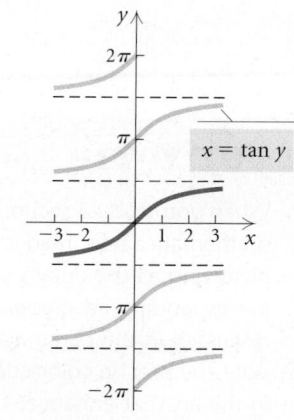

Figure 3

For the inverse sine function, we choose a range close to the origin that allows all inputs on the interval $[-1, 1]$ to have function values. Thus we choose the interval $[-\pi/2, \pi/2]$ for the range (Fig. 1). For the inverse cosine function, we choose a range close to the origin that allows all inputs on the interval $[-1, 1]$ to have function values. We choose the interval $[0, \pi]$ (Fig. 2). For the inverse tangent function, we choose a range close to the origin that allows all real numbers to have function values. The interval $(-\pi/2, \pi/2)$ satisfies this requirement (Fig. 3).

Inverse Trigonometric Functions

FUNCTION	DOMAIN	RANGE
$y = \sin^{-1} x$ $= \arcsin x$, where $x = \sin y$	$[-1, 1]$	$[-\pi/2, \pi/2]$
$y = \cos^{-1} x$ $= \arccos x$, where $x = \cos y$	$[-1, 1]$	$[0, \pi]$
$y = \tan^{-1} x$ $= \arctan x$, where $x = \tan y$	$(-\infty, \infty)$	$(-\pi/2, \pi/2)$

The notation arcsin x arises because the function value, y, is the length of an arc on the unit circle for which the sine is x. Either of the two kinds of notation above can be read "the inverse sine of x" or "the arc sine of x" or "the number (or angle) whose sine is x."

The notation $\sin^{-1} x$ is *not* exponential notation.

It does *not* mean $\dfrac{1}{\sin x}$!

TECHNOLOGY ·············
CONNECTION

Exploration
Inverse trigonometric functions can be graphed using a graphing calculator. Graph $y = \sin^{-1} x$ using the viewing window $[-3, 3, -\pi, \pi]$, with Xscl $= 1$ and Yscl $= \pi/2$. Now try graphing $y = \cos^{-1} x$ and $y = \tan^{-1} x$. Then use the graphs to confirm the domain and the range of each inverse.

The graphs of the inverse trigonometric functions are as follows.

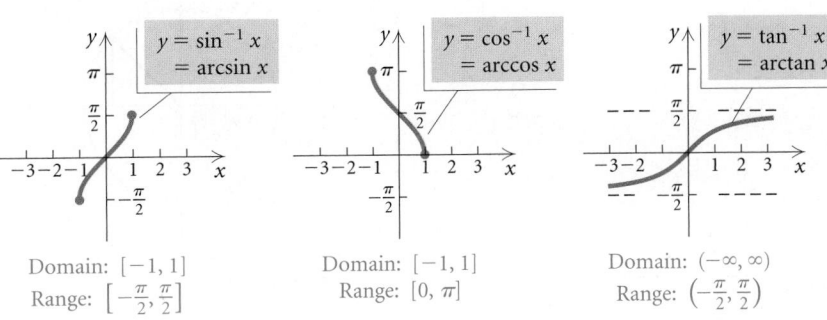

Domain: $[-1, 1]$ Domain: $[-1, 1]$ Domain: $(-\infty, \infty)$
Range: $\left[-\frac{\pi}{2}, \frac{\pi}{2}\right]$ Range: $[0, \pi]$ Range: $\left(-\frac{\pi}{2}, \frac{\pi}{2}\right)$

The following diagrams show the restricted ranges for the inverse trigonometric functions on a unit circle. Compare these graphs with the graphs above. The ranges of these functions should be memorized. The missing endpoints in the graph of the arctangent function indicate inputs that are not in the domain of the original function.

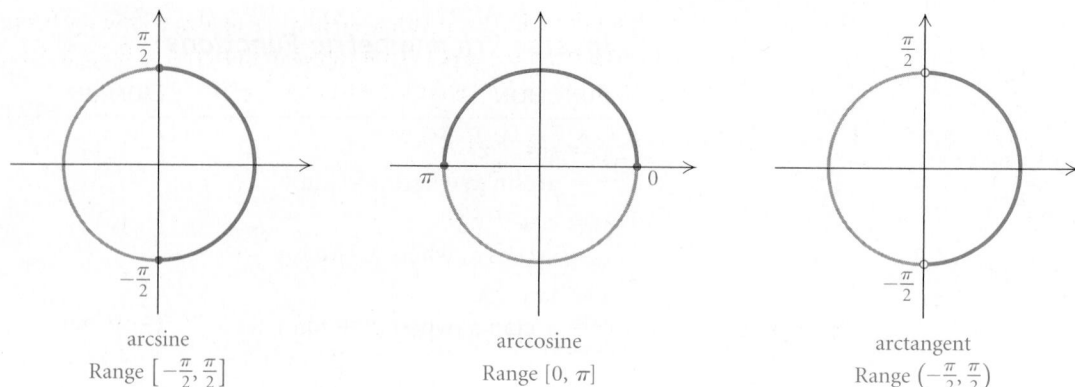

arcsine
Range $\left[-\frac{\pi}{2}, \frac{\pi}{2}\right]$

arccosine
Range $[0, \pi]$

arctangent
Range $\left(-\frac{\pi}{2}, \frac{\pi}{2}\right)$

EXAMPLE 1   Find each of the following function values.

a) $\sin^{-1} \dfrac{\sqrt{2}}{2}$ **b)** $\cos^{-1}\left(-\dfrac{1}{2}\right)$ **c)** $\tan^{-1}\left(-\dfrac{\sqrt{3}}{3}\right)$

Solution

a) Another way to state "find $\sin^{-1} \sqrt{2}/2$" is to say "find β such that $\sin \beta = \sqrt{2}/2$." In the restricted range $[-\pi/2, \pi/2]$, the only number with a sine of $\sqrt{2}/2$ is $\pi/4$. Thus, $\sin^{-1}\left(\sqrt{2}/2\right) = \pi/4$, or $45°$. (See Fig. 4 below.)

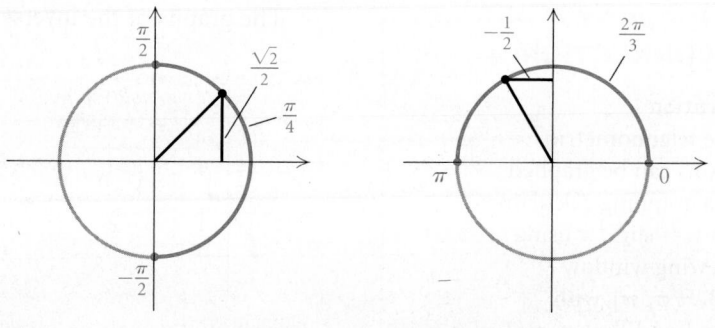

Figure 4   Figure 5

b) The only number with a cosine of $-\frac{1}{2}$ in the restricted range $[0, \pi]$ is $2\pi/3$. Thus, $\cos^{-1}\left(-\frac{1}{2}\right) = 2\pi/3$, or $120°$. (See Fig. 5 above.)

c) The only number in the restricted range $(-\pi/2, \pi/2)$ with a tangent of $-\sqrt{3}/3$ is $-\pi/6$. Thus, $\tan^{-1}\left(-\sqrt{3}/3\right)$ is $-\pi/6$, or $-30°$. (See Fig. 6 at left.)

▶ **Now Try Exercises 1 and 5.**

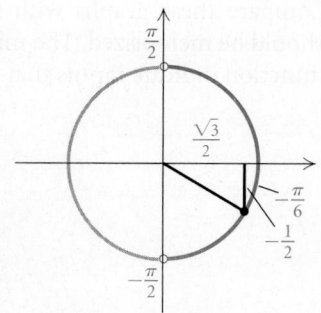

Figure 6

We can also use a calculator to find inverse trigonometric function values. On most graphing calculators, we can find inverse function values in either radians or degrees simply by selecting the appropriate mode. The key strokes involved in finding inverse function values vary with the calculator. Be sure to read the instructions for the particular calculator that you are using.

EXAMPLE 2 Approximate each of the following function values in both radians and degrees. Round radian measure to four decimal places and degree measure to the nearest tenth of a degree.

a) $\cos^{-1}(-0.2689)$

b) $\tan^{-1}(-0.2623)$

c) $\sin^{-1} 0.20345$

d) $\cos^{-1} 1.318$

e) $\csc^{-1} 8.205$

Solution

FUNCTION VALUE	MODE	READOUT	ROUNDED
a) $\cos^{-1}(-0.2689)$	Radian	1.843047111	1.8430
	Degree	105.5988209	105.6°
b) $\tan^{-1}(-0.2623)$	Radian	−.2565212141	−0.2565
	Degree	−14.69758292	−14.7°
c) $\sin^{-1} 0.20345$	Radian	.2048803359	0.2049
	Degree	11.73877855	11.7°
d) $\cos^{-1} 1.318$	Radian	ERR:DOMAIN	
	Degree	ERR:DOMAIN	

The value 1.318 is not in $[-1, 1]$, the domain of the arccosine function.

e) The cosecant function is the reciprocal of the sine function:

$\csc^{-1} 8.205 =$			
$\sin^{-1}(1/8.205)$	Radian	.1221806653	0.1222
	Degree	7.000436462	7.0°

▶ Now Try Exercises 21 and 25.

CONNECTING THE CONCEPTS

Domains and Ranges

The following is a summary of the domains and ranges of the trigonometric functions together with a summary of the domains and ranges of the inverse trigonometric functions. For completeness, we have included the arccosecant, the arcsecant, and the arccotangent, though there is a lack of uniformity in their definitions in mathematical literature.

FUNCTION	DOMAIN	RANGE
sin	All reals, $(-\infty, \infty)$	$[-1, 1]$
cos	All reals, $(-\infty, \infty)$	$[-1, 1]$
tan	All reals except $k\pi/2$, k odd	All reals, $(-\infty, \infty)$
csc	All reals except $k\pi$	$(-\infty, -1] \cup [1, \infty)$
sec	All reals except $k\pi/2$, k odd	$(-\infty, -1] \cup [1, \infty)$
cot	All reals except $k\pi$	All reals, $(-\infty, \infty)$

INVERSE FUNCTION	DOMAIN	RANGE
$\sin^{-1}$	$[-1, 1]$	$\left[-\dfrac{\pi}{2}, \dfrac{\pi}{2}\right]$
$\cos^{-1}$	$[-1, 1]$	$[0, \pi]$
$\tan^{-1}$	All reals, or $(-\infty, \infty)$	$\left(-\dfrac{\pi}{2}, \dfrac{\pi}{2}\right)$
$\csc^{-1}$	$(-\infty, -1] \cup [1, \infty)$	$\left[-\dfrac{\pi}{2}, 0\right) \cup \left(0, \dfrac{\pi}{2}\right]$
$\sec^{-1}$	$(-\infty, -1] \cup [1, \infty)$	$\left[0, \dfrac{\pi}{2}\right) \cup \left(\dfrac{\pi}{2}, \pi\right]$
$\cot^{-1}$	All reals, or $(-\infty, \infty)$	$(0, \pi)$

● ● ●

✦ Composition of Trigonometric Functions and Their Inverses

Various compositions of trigonometric functions and their inverses often occur in practice. For example, we might want to try to simplify an expression such as

$$\sin(\sin^{-1} x) \quad \text{or} \quad \sin\left(\cot^{-1}\frac{x}{2}\right).$$

COMPOSITION OF FUNCTIONS

REVIEW SECTION **1.6.**

In the expression on the left, we are finding "the sine of a number whose sine is x." Recall from Section 4.1 that if a function f has an inverse that is also a function, then

$$f(f^{-1}(x)) = x, \quad \text{for all } x \text{ in the } domain \text{ of } f^{-1},$$

and

$$f^{-1}(f(x)) = x, \quad \text{for all } x \text{ in the } domain \text{ of } f.$$

Thus, if $f(x) = \sin x$ and $f^{-1}(x) = \sin^{-1} x$, then

$$\sin(\sin^{-1} x) = x, \quad \textbf{for all } x \textbf{ in the } \textit{domain} \textbf{ of } \sin^{-1},$$

which is any number on the interval $[-1, 1]$. Similar results hold for the other trigonometric functions.

Composition of Trigonometric Functions

$\sin(\sin^{-1} x) = x, \quad$ for all x in the domain of $\sin^{-1}$.

$\cos(\cos^{-1} x) = x, \quad$ for all x in the domain of $\cos^{-1}$.

$\tan(\tan^{-1} x) = x, \quad$ for all x in the domain of $\tan^{-1}$.

EXAMPLE 3 Simplify each of the following.

a) $\cos\left(\cos^{-1}\dfrac{\sqrt{3}}{2}\right)$ 　　　　　　　　**b)** $\sin(\sin^{-1} 1.8)$

Solution

a) Since $\sqrt{3}/2$ is in $[-1, 1]$, the domain of $\cos^{-1}$, it follows that

$$\cos\left(\cos^{-1}\frac{\sqrt{3}}{2}\right) = \frac{\sqrt{3}}{2}.$$

b) Since 1.8 is not in $[-1, 1]$, the domain of $\sin^{-1}$, we cannot evaluate this expression. We know that there is no number with a sine of 1.8. Since we cannot find $\sin^{-1} 1.8$, we state that $\sin(\sin^{-1} 1.8)$ does not exist.

▶ Now Try Exercise 37.

Now let's consider an expression like $\sin^{-1}(\sin x)$. We might also suspect that this is equal to x for any x in the domain of $\sin x$, but this is not true unless x is in the range of the $\sin^{-1}$ function. Note that in order to define $\sin^{-1}$, we had to restrict the domain of the sine function. In doing so, we restricted the range of the inverse sine function. Thus,

$$\sin^{-1}(\sin x) = x, \quad \text{for all } x \text{ in the } \textit{range of } \sin^{-1}.$$

Similar results hold for the other trigonometric functions.

> **Special Cases**
>
> $\sin^{-1}(\sin x) = x$, for all x in the range of $\sin^{-1}$.
> $\cos^{-1}(\cos x) = x$, for all x in the range of $\cos^{-1}$.
> $\tan^{-1}(\tan x) = x$, for all x in the range of $\tan^{-1}$.

EXAMPLE 4 Simplify each of the following.

a) $\tan^{-1}\left(\tan \dfrac{\pi}{6}\right)$ b) $\sin^{-1}\left(\sin \dfrac{3\pi}{4}\right)$

Solution

a) Since $\pi/6$ is in $(-\pi/2, \pi/2)$, the range of the $\tan^{-1}$ function, we can use $\tan^{-1}(\tan x) = x$. Thus,

$$\tan^{-1}\left(\tan \frac{\pi}{6}\right) = \frac{\pi}{6}.$$

b) Note that $3\pi/4$ is not in $[-\pi/2, \pi/2]$, the range of the $\sin^{-1}$ function. Thus we *cannot* apply $\sin^{-1}(\sin x) = x$. Instead we first find $\sin(3\pi/4)$, which is $\sqrt{2}/2$, and substitute:

$$\sin^{-1}\left(\sin \frac{3\pi}{4}\right) = \sin^{-1}\left(\frac{\sqrt{2}}{2}\right) = \frac{\pi}{4}.$$

▶ Now Try Exercise 43.

Now we find some other function compositions.

EXAMPLE 5 Simplify each of the following.

a) $\sin[\tan^{-1}(-1)]$ b) $\cos^{-1}\left(\sin \dfrac{\pi}{2}\right)$

Solution

a) $\mathrm{Tan}^{-1}(-1)$ is the number (or angle) θ in $(-\pi/2, \pi/2)$ whose tangent is -1. That is, $\tan \theta = -1$. Thus, $\theta = -\pi/4$ and

$$\sin[\tan^{-1}(-1)] = \sin\left[-\frac{\pi}{4}\right] = -\frac{\sqrt{2}}{2}.$$

b) $\cos^{-1}\left(\sin \dfrac{\pi}{2}\right) = \cos^{-1}(1) = 0$ $\sin \dfrac{\pi}{2} = 1$

▶ Now Try Exercises 47 and 49.

Next, let's consider

$$\cos\left(\sin^{-1}\frac{3}{5}\right).$$

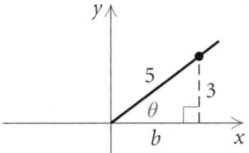

Without using a calculator, we cannot find $\sin^{-1}\frac{3}{5}$. However, we can still evaluate the entire expression by sketching a reference triangle. We are looking for angle θ such that $\sin^{-1}\frac{3}{5} = \theta$, or $\sin\theta = \frac{3}{5}$. Since $\sin^{-1}$ is defined in $[-\pi/2, \pi/2]$ and $\frac{3}{5} > 0$, we know that θ is in quadrant I. We sketch a reference right triangle, as shown at left. The angle θ in this triangle is an angle whose sine is $\frac{3}{5}$. We wish to find the cosine of this angle. Since the triangle is a right triangle, we can find the length of the base, b. It is 4. Thus we know that $\cos\theta = b/5$, or $\frac{4}{5}$. Therefore,

$$\cos\left(\sin^{-1}\frac{3}{5}\right) = \frac{4}{5}.$$

EXAMPLE 6 Find $\sin\left(\cot^{-1}\frac{x}{2}\right)$.

Solution Considering all values of x, we draw right triangles, as shown below, whose legs have lengths x and 2, so that $\cot\theta = x/2$.

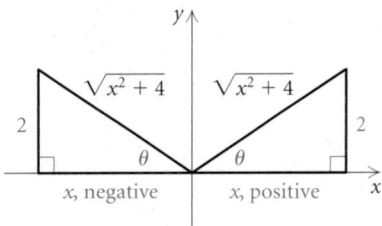

In each, we find the length of the hypotenuse and then read off the sine ratio. We get

$$\sin\left(\cot^{-1}\frac{x}{2}\right) = \frac{2}{\sqrt{x^2+4}}.$$

▶ Now Try Exercise 55.

In the following example, we use a sum identity to evaluate an expression.

EXAMPLE 7 Evaluate:

$$\sin\left(\sin^{-1}\frac{1}{2} + \cos^{-1}\frac{5}{13}\right).$$

Solution Since $\sin^{-1}\frac{1}{2}$ and $\cos^{-1}\frac{5}{13}$ are both angles, the expression is the sine of a sum of two angles, so we use the identity

$$\sin(u + v) = \sin u \cos v + \cos u \sin v.$$

Thus,

$$\sin\left(\sin^{-1}\frac{1}{2} + \cos^{-1}\frac{5}{13}\right)$$

$$= \sin\left(\sin^{-1}\frac{1}{2}\right)\cdot\cos\left(\cos^{-1}\frac{5}{13}\right) + \cos\left(\sin^{-1}\frac{1}{2}\right)\cdot\sin\left(\cos^{-1}\frac{5}{13}\right)$$

$$= \frac{1}{2}\cdot\frac{5}{13} + \cos\left(\sin^{-1}\frac{1}{2}\right)\cdot\sin\left(\cos^{-1}\frac{5}{13}\right). \qquad \text{Using composition identities}$$

Now since $\sin^{-1}\frac{1}{2} = \pi/6$, $\cos\left(\sin^{-1}\frac{1}{2}\right)$ simplifies to $\cos \pi/6$, or $\sqrt{3}/2$. We can illustrate this with a reference triangle in quadrant I.

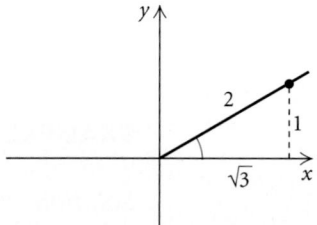

To find $\sin\left(\cos^{-1}\frac{5}{13}\right)$, we use a reference triangle in quadrant I and determine that the sine of the angle whose cosine is $\frac{5}{13}$ is $\frac{12}{13}$.

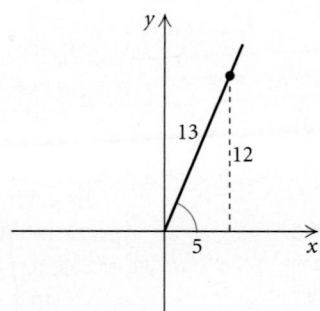

Our expression now simplifies to

$$\frac{1}{2}\cdot\frac{5}{13} + \frac{\sqrt{3}}{2}\cdot\frac{12}{13}, \quad \text{or} \quad \frac{5 + 12\sqrt{3}}{26}.$$

Thus,

$$\sin\left(\sin^{-1}\frac{1}{2} + \cos^{-1}\frac{5}{13}\right) = \frac{5 + 12\sqrt{3}}{26}.$$

▶ Now Try Exercise 63.

6.4 EXERCISE SET

Find each of the following exactly in radians and in degrees.

1. $\sin^{-1}\left(-\dfrac{\sqrt{3}}{2}\right)$ **2.** $\cos^{-1}\dfrac{1}{2}$

3. $\tan^{-1} 1$ **4.** $\sin^{-1} 0$

5. $\cos^{-1}\dfrac{\sqrt{2}}{2}$ **6.** $\sec^{-1}\sqrt{2}$

7. $\tan^{-1} 0$ **8.** $\tan^{-1}\dfrac{\sqrt{3}}{3}$

9. $\cos^{-1}\dfrac{\sqrt{3}}{2}$ **10.** $\cot^{-1}\left(-\dfrac{\sqrt{3}}{3}\right)$

11. $\csc^{-1} 2$ **12.** $\sin^{-1}\dfrac{1}{2}$

13. $\cot^{-1}\left(-\sqrt{3}\right)$ **14.** $\tan^{-1}(-1)$

15. $\sin^{-1}\left(-\dfrac{1}{2}\right)$ **16.** $\cos^{-1}\left(-\dfrac{\sqrt{2}}{2}\right)$

17. $\cos^{-1} 0$ **18.** $\sin^{-1}\dfrac{\sqrt{3}}{2}$

19. $\sec^{-1} 2$ **20.** $\csc^{-1}(-1)$

Use a calculator to find each of the following in radians, rounded to four decimal places, and in degrees, rounded to the nearest tenth of a degree.

21. $\tan^{-1} 0.3673$

22. $\cos^{-1}(-0.2935)$

23. $\sin^{-1} 0.9613$

24. $\sin^{-1}(-0.6199)$

25. $\cos^{-1}(-0.9810)$

26. $\tan^{-1} 158$

27. $\csc^{-1}(-6.2774)$

28. $\sec^{-1} 1.1677$

29. $\tan^{-1}(1.091)$

30. $\cot^{-1} 1.265$

31. $\sin^{-1}(-0.8192)$

32. $\cos^{-1}(-0.2716)$

33. State the domains of the inverse sine, inverse cosine, and inverse tangent functions.

34. State the ranges of the inverse sine, inverse cosine, and inverse tangent functions.

35. *Angle of Depression.*   An airplane is flying at an altitude of 2000 ft toward an island. The straight-line distance from the airplane to the island is d feet. Express θ, the angle of depression, as a function of d.

36. *Angle of Inclination.*   A guy wire is attached to the top of a 50-ft pole and stretched to a point that is d feet from the bottom of the pole. Express β, the angle of inclination, as a function of d.

Evaluate.

37. $\sin\left(\sin^{-1} 0.3\right)$ **38.** $\tan\left[\tan^{-1}(-4.2)\right]$

39. $\cos^{-1}\left[\cos\left(-\dfrac{\pi}{4}\right)\right]$ **40.** $\sin^{-1}\left(\sin\dfrac{2\pi}{3}\right)$

41. $\sin^{-1}\left(\sin\dfrac{\pi}{5}\right)$ **42.** $\cot^{-1}\left(\cot\dfrac{2\pi}{3}\right)$

43. $\tan^{-1}\left(\tan\dfrac{2\pi}{3}\right)$

44. $\cos^{-1}\left(\cos\dfrac{\pi}{7}\right)$

45. $\sin\left(\tan^{-1}\dfrac{\sqrt{3}}{3}\right)$

46. $\cos\left(\sin^{-1}\dfrac{\sqrt{3}}{2}\right)$

47. $\tan\left(\cos^{-1}\dfrac{\sqrt{2}}{2}\right)$

48. $\cos^{-1}(\sin\pi)$

49. $\sin^{-1}\left(\cos\dfrac{\pi}{6}\right)$

50. $\sin^{-1}\left[\tan\left(-\dfrac{\pi}{4}\right)\right]$

51. $\tan(\sin^{-1}0.1)$

52. $\cos\left(\tan^{-1}\dfrac{\sqrt{3}}{4}\right)$

53. $\sin^{-1}\left(\sin\dfrac{7\pi}{6}\right)$

54. $\tan^{-1}\left(\tan-\dfrac{3\pi}{4}\right)$

Find.

55. $\sin\left(\tan^{-1}\dfrac{a}{3}\right)$

56. $\tan\left(\cos^{-1}\dfrac{3}{x}\right)$

57. $\cot\left(\sin^{-1}\dfrac{p}{q}\right)$

58. $\sin(\cos^{-1}x)$

59. $\tan\left(\sin^{-1}\dfrac{p}{\sqrt{p^2+9}}\right)$

60. $\tan\left(\dfrac{1}{2}\sin^{-1}\dfrac{1}{2}\right)$

61. $\cos\left(\dfrac{1}{2}\sin^{-1}\dfrac{\sqrt{3}}{2}\right)$

62. $\sin\left(2\cos^{-1}\dfrac{3}{5}\right)$

Evaluate.

63. $\cos\left(\sin^{-1}\dfrac{\sqrt{2}}{2}+\cos^{-1}\dfrac{3}{5}\right)$

64. $\sin\left(\sin^{-1}\dfrac{1}{2}+\cos^{-1}\dfrac{3}{5}\right)$

65. $\sin(\sin^{-1}x+\cos^{-1}y)$

66. $\cos(\sin^{-1}x-\cos^{-1}y)$

67. $\sin(\sin^{-1}0.6032+\cos^{-1}0.4621)$

68. $\cos(\sin^{-1}0.7325-\cos^{-1}0.4838)$

Collaborative Discussion and Writing

69. Explain in your own words why the ranges of the inverse trigonometric functions are restricted.

70. How does the graph of $y=\sin^{-1}x$ differ from the graph of $y=\sin x$?

71. Why is it that

$$\sin\dfrac{5\pi}{6}=\dfrac{1}{2},$$

but

$$\sin^{-1}\left(\dfrac{1}{2}\right)\neq\dfrac{5\pi}{6}?$$

Skill Maintenance

In each of Exercises 72–80, fill in the blank with the correct term. Some of the given choices will not be used.

linear speed
angular speed
angle of elevation
angle of depression
complementary
supplementary
similar
congruent
circular
periodic
period
amplitude
acute
obtuse
quadrantal
radian measure

72. A function f is said to be _____ if there exists a positive constant p such that $f(s+p)=f(s)$ for all s in the domain of f.

73. The _____ of a rotation is the ratio of the distance s traveled by a point at a radius r from the center of rotation to the length of the radius r.

74. Triangles are _____ if their corresponding angles have the same measure.

75. The angle between the horizontal and a line of sight below the horizontal is called a(n) _____ .

76. _____ is the amount of rotation per unit of time.

77. Two positive angles are _____ if their sum is 180°.

78. The _____ of a periodic function is one half of the distance between its maximum and minimum function values.

79. A(n) _____ angle is an angle with measure greater than 0° and less than 90°.

80. Trigonometric functions with domains composed of real numbers are called _____ functions.

Synthesis

Prove the identity.

81. $\sin^{-1} x + \cos^{-1} x = \dfrac{\pi}{2}$

82. $\tan^{-1} x + \cot^{-1} x = \dfrac{\pi}{2}$

83. $\sin^{-1} x = \tan^{-1} \dfrac{x}{\sqrt{1 - x^2}}$

84. $\tan^{-1} x = \sin^{-1} \dfrac{x}{\sqrt{x^2 + 1}}$

85. $\sin^{-1} x = \cos^{-1} \sqrt{1 - x^2}$, for $x \geq 0$

86. $\cos^{-1} x = \tan^{-1} \dfrac{\sqrt{1 - x^2}}{x}$, for $x > 0$

87. *Height of a Mural.* An art student's eye is at a point A, looking at a mural of height h, with the bottom of the mural y feet above the eye. The eye is x feet from the wall. Write an expression for θ in terms of x, y, and h. Then evaluate the expression when $x = 20$ ft, $y = 7$ ft, and $h = 25$ ft.

88. Use a calculator to approximate the following expression:

$$16 \tan^{-1} \dfrac{1}{5} - 4 \tan^{-1} \dfrac{1}{239}.$$

What number does this expression seem to approximate?

6.5 Solving Trigonometric Equations

✦ Solve trigonometric equations.

When an equation contains a trigonometric expression with a variable, such as cos x, it is called a trigonometric equation. Some trigonometric equations are identities, such as $\sin^2 x + \cos^2 x = 1$. Now we consider equations, such as $2 \cos x = -1$, that are usually not identities. As we have done for other types of equations, we will solve such equations by finding all values for x that make the equation true.

EXAMPLE 1   Solve: $2 \cos x = -1$.

ALGEBRAIC SOLUTION

We first solve for $\cos x$:

$$2 \cos x = -1$$

$$\cos x = -\frac{1}{2}.$$

The solutions are numbers that have a cosine of $-\frac{1}{2}$. To find them, we use the unit circle (see Section 5.5).

There are just two points on the unit circle for which the cosine is $-\frac{1}{2}$, as shown in the following figure.

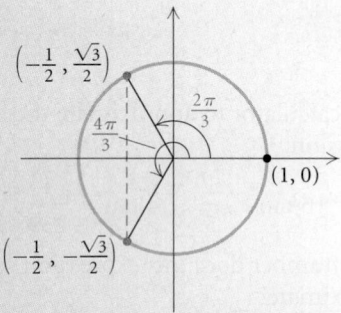

They are the points corresponding to $2\pi/3$ and $4\pi/3$. These numbers, plus any multiple of 2π, are the solutions:

$$\frac{2\pi}{3} + 2k\pi \quad \text{and} \quad \frac{4\pi}{3} + 2k\pi,$$

where k is any integer. In degrees, the solutions are

$$120° + k \cdot 360° \quad \text{and} \quad 240° + k \cdot 360°,$$

where k is any integer.

VISUALIZING THE SOLUTION

We graph $y = 2 \cos x$ and $y = -1$. The first coordinates of the points of intersection of the graphs are the values of x for which $2 \cos x = -1$.

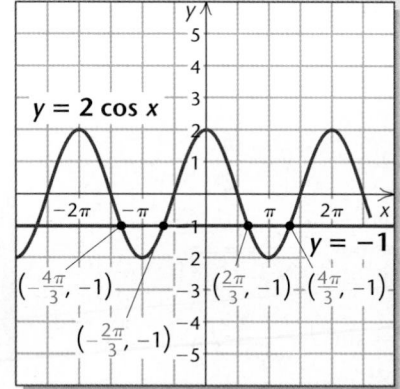

The only solutions in $[-2\pi, 2\pi]$ are

$$-\frac{4\pi}{3}, \quad -\frac{2\pi}{3}, \quad \frac{2\pi}{3}, \quad \text{and} \quad \frac{4\pi}{3}.$$

Since the cosine is periodic, there is an infinite number of solutions. Thus the entire set of solutions is

$$\frac{2\pi}{3} + 2k\pi \quad \text{and} \quad \frac{4\pi}{3} + 2k\pi,$$

where k is any integer.

▶ Now Try Exercise 1.

EXAMPLE 2 Solve: $4 \sin^2 x = 1$.

ALGEBRAIC SOLUTION

We begin by solving for $\sin x$:

$$4 \sin^2 x = 1$$

$$\sin^2 x = \frac{1}{4}$$

$$\sin x = \pm\frac{1}{2}.$$

Again, we use the unit circle to find those numbers having a sine of $\frac{1}{2}$ or $-\frac{1}{2}$.

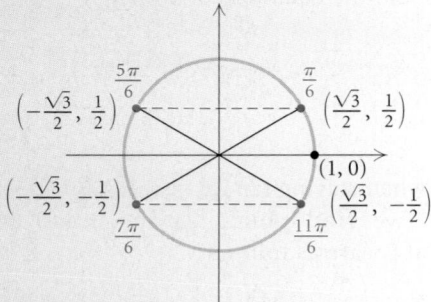

The solutions are

$$\frac{\pi}{6} + 2k\pi, \quad \frac{5\pi}{6} + 2k\pi, \quad \frac{7\pi}{6} + 2k\pi,$$

and

$$\frac{11\pi}{6} + 2k\pi,$$

where k is any integer. In degrees, the solutions are

$$30° + k \cdot 360°, \quad 150° + k \cdot 360°,$$
$$210° + k \cdot 360°, \quad \text{and} \quad 330° + k \cdot 360°,$$

where k is any integer.

The general solutions listed above could be condensed using odd as well as even multiples of π:

$$\frac{\pi}{6} + k\pi \quad \text{and} \quad \frac{5\pi}{6} + k\pi,$$

or, in degrees,

$$30° + k \cdot 180° \quad \text{and} \quad 150° + k \cdot 180°,$$

where k is any integer.

VISUALIZING THE SOLUTION

From the graph shown here, we see that the first coordinates of the points of intersection of the graphs of

$$y = 4 \sin^2 x \quad \text{and} \quad y = 1$$

in $[0, 2\pi)$ are

$$\frac{\pi}{6}, \quad \frac{5\pi}{6}, \quad \frac{7\pi}{6}, \quad \text{and} \quad \frac{11\pi}{6}.$$

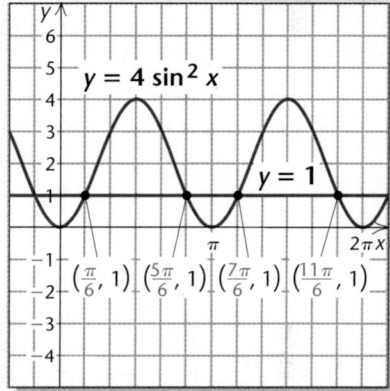

Thus, since the sine function is periodic, the general solutions are

$$\frac{\pi}{6} + k\pi \quad \text{and} \quad \frac{5\pi}{6} + k\pi,$$

or, in degrees,

$$30° + k \cdot 180° \quad \text{and} \quad 150° + k \cdot 180°,$$

where k is any integer.

▶ Now Try Exercise 13.

> In most applications, it is sufficient to find just the solutions from 0 to 2π or from 0° to 360°. We then remember that any multiple of 2π, or 360°, can be added to obtain the rest of the solutions.

We must be careful to find all solutions in $[0, 2\pi)$ when solving trigonometric equations involving double angles.

EXAMPLE 3   Solve $3 \tan 2x = -3$ in the interval $[0, 2\pi)$.

Solution   We first solve for $\tan 2x$:

$$3 \tan 2x = -3$$
$$\tan 2x = -1.$$

We are looking for solutions x to the equation for which

$$0 \le x < 2\pi.$$

Multiplying by 2, we get

$$0 \le 2x < 4\pi,$$

which is the interval we use when solving $\tan 2x = -1$.

Using the unit circle, we find points $2x$ in $[0, 4\pi)$ for which $\tan 2x = -1$. These values of $2x$ are as follows:

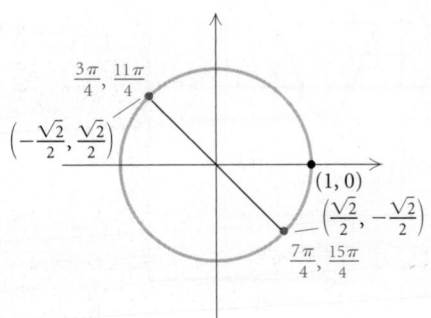

$$2x = \frac{3\pi}{4}, \quad \frac{7\pi}{4}, \quad \frac{11\pi}{4}, \quad \text{and} \quad \frac{15\pi}{4}.$$

Thus the desired values of x in $[0, 2\pi)$ are each of these values divided by 2. Therefore,

$$x = \frac{3\pi}{8}, \quad \frac{7\pi}{8}, \quad \frac{11\pi}{8}, \quad \text{and} \quad \frac{15\pi}{8}.$$

▶ **Now Try Exercise 21.**

Calculators are needed to solve some trigonometric equations. Answers can be found in radians or degrees, depending on the mode setting.

EXAMPLE 4   Solve $\dfrac{1}{2} \cos \phi + 1 = 1.2108$ in $[0, 360°)$.

Solution   We have

$$\frac{1}{2} \cos \phi + 1 = 1.2108$$

$$\frac{1}{2} \cos \phi = 0.2108$$

$$\cos \phi = 0.4216.$$

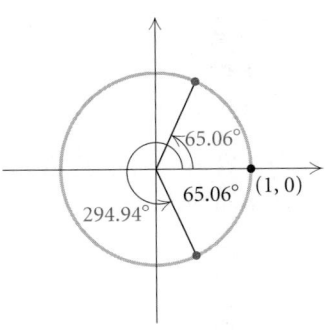

Using a calculator set in DEGREE mode, we find that the reference angle, $\cos^{-1} 0.4216$, is

$$\phi \approx 65.06°.$$

Since $\cos \phi$ is positive, the solutions are in quadrants I and IV. The solutions in $[0, 360°)$ are

$$65.06° \quad \text{and} \quad 360° - 65.06° = 294.94°. \quad \blacktriangleright \text{ Now Try Exercise 9.}$$

EXAMPLE 5 Solve $2 \cos^2 u = 1 - \cos u$ in $[0°, 360°)$.

ALGEBRAIC SOLUTION

We use the principle of zero products:

$$2 \cos^2 u = 1 - \cos u$$
$$2 \cos^2 u + \cos u - 1 = 0$$
$$(2 \cos u - 1)(\cos u + 1) = 0$$
$$2 \cos u - 1 = 0 \quad or \quad \cos u + 1 = 0$$
$$2 \cos u = 1 \quad or \quad \cos u = -1$$
$$\cos u = \frac{1}{2} \quad or \quad \cos u = -1.$$

Thus,

$$u = 60°, 300° \quad or \quad u = 180°.$$

The solutions in $[0°, 360°)$ are 60°, 180°, and 300°.

VISUALIZING THE SOLUTION

The solutions of the equation are the zeros of the function

$$y = 2 \cos^2 u + \cos u - 1.$$

Note that they are also the first coordinates of the x-intercepts of the graph.

The zeros in $[0°, 360°)$ are 60°, 180°, and 300°. Thus the solutions of the equation in $[0°, 360°)$ are 60°, 180°, and 300°.

$\blacktriangleright$ Now Try Exercise 15.

TECHNOLOGY CONNECTION

We can use either the Intersect method or the Zero method to solve trigonometric equations. Here we illustrate by solving the equation in Example 5 using both methods.

Intersect Method. We graph the equations

$$y_1 = 2 \cos^2 x \quad \text{and} \quad y_2 = 1 - \cos x$$

and use the INTERSECT feature to find the first coordinates of the points of intersection.

$y_1 = 2 \cos^2 x, \quad y_2 = 1 - \cos x$

The leftmost solution is 60°. Using the INTERSECT feature two more times, we find the other solutions, 180° and 300°.

Zero Method. We write the equation in the form

$$2 \cos^2 u + \cos u - 1 = 0.$$

Then we graph

$$y = 2 \cos^2 x + \cos x - 1$$

and use the ZERO feature to determine the zeros of the function.

$y = 2 \cos^2 x + \cos x - 1$

The leftmost zero is 60°. Using the ZERO feature two more times, we find the other zeros, 180° and 300°. The solutions in [0°, 360°) are 60°, 180°, and 300°.

EXAMPLE 6   Solve $\sin^2 \beta - \sin \beta = 0$ in $[0, 2\pi)$.

ALGEBRAIC SOLUTION

We factor and use the principle of zero products:

$$\sin^2 \beta - \sin \beta = 0$$
$$\sin \beta \, (\sin \beta - 1) = 0 \qquad \text{Factoring}$$
$$\sin \beta = 0 \quad or \quad \sin \beta - 1 = 0$$
$$\sin \beta = 0 \quad or \qquad \sin \beta = 1$$
$$\beta = 0, \pi \quad or \qquad \beta = \frac{\pi}{2}.$$

The solutions in $[0, 2\pi)$ are 0, $\pi/2$, and π.

VISUALIZING THE SOLUTION

The solutions of the equation

$$\sin^2 \beta - \sin \beta = 0$$

are the zeros of the function

$$f(\beta) = \sin^2 \beta - \sin \beta.$$

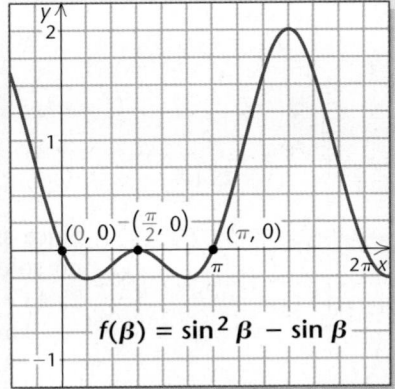

The zeros in $[0, 2\pi)$ are 0, $\pi/2$, and π. Thus the solutions of $\sin^2 \beta - \sin \beta = 0$ are 0, $\pi/2$, and π.

▷ Now Try Exercise 17.

If a trigonometric equation is quadratic but difficult or impossible to factor, we use the *quadratic formula*.

EXAMPLE 7 Solve $10 \sin^2 x - 12 \sin x - 7 = 0$ in $[0°, 360°)$.

Solution This equation is quadratic in $\sin x$ with $a = 10$, $b = -12$, and $c = -7$. Substituting into the quadratic formula, we get

$$\sin x = \frac{-b \pm \sqrt{b^2 - 4ac}}{2a} \qquad \text{Using the quadratic formula}$$

$$= \frac{-(-12) \pm \sqrt{(-12)^2 - 4(10)(-7)}}{2 \cdot 10} \qquad \text{Substituting}$$

$$= \frac{12 \pm \sqrt{144 + 280}}{20}$$

$$= \frac{12 \pm \sqrt{424}}{20}$$

$$\approx \frac{12 \pm 20.5913}{20}$$

$$\sin x \approx 1.6296 \quad or \quad \sin x \approx -0.4296.$$

Since sine values are never greater than 1, the first of the equations has no solution. Using the other equation, we find the reference angle to be 25.44°. Since $\sin x$ is negative, the solutions are in quadrants III and IV.

Thus the solutions in $[0°, 360°)$ are

$$180° + 25.44° = 205.44° \quad \text{and} \quad 360° - 25.44° = 334.56°.$$

▶ Now Try Exercise 23.

Trigonometric equations can involve more than one function.

EXAMPLE 8 Solve $2 \cos^2 x \tan x = \tan x$ in $[0, 2\pi)$.

Solution We have

$$2 \cos^2 x \tan x = \tan x$$
$$2 \cos^2 x \tan x - \tan x = 0$$
$$\tan x (2 \cos^2 x - 1) = 0$$
$$\tan x = 0 \qquad or \quad 2 \cos^2 x - 1 = 0$$
$$\cos^2 x = \frac{1}{2}$$
$$\cos x = \pm \frac{\sqrt{2}}{2}$$
$$x = 0, \pi \quad or \qquad x = \frac{\pi}{4}, \frac{3\pi}{4}, \frac{5\pi}{4}, \frac{7\pi}{4}.$$

Thus, $x = 0, \pi/4, 3\pi/4, \pi, 5\pi/4,$ and $7\pi/4$.

▶ Now Try Exercise 21.

TECHNOLOGY
CONNECTION

In Example 9, we can graph the left side and then the right side of the equation as seen in the first window below. Then we look for points of intersection. We could also rewrite the equation as $\sin x + \cos x - 1 = 0$, graph the left side, and look for the zeros of the function, as illustrated in the second window below. In each window, we see the solutions in $[0, 2\pi)$ as 0 and $\pi/2$.

This example illustrates a valuable advantage of the calculator—that is, with a graphing calculator, extraneous solutions do not appear.

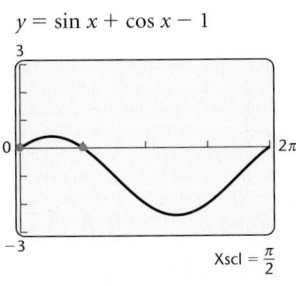

$y_1 = \sin x + \cos x, \quad y_2 = 1$

$\text{Xscl} = \frac{\pi}{2}$

$y = \sin x + \cos x - 1$

$\text{Xscl} = \frac{\pi}{2}$

When a trigonometric equation involves more than one function, it is sometimes helpful to use identities to rewrite the equation in terms of a single function.

EXAMPLE 9 Solve $\sin x + \cos x = 1$ in $[0, 2\pi)$.

Solution We have

$$\sin x + \cos x = 1$$
$$(\sin x + \cos x)^2 = 1^2 \qquad \text{Squaring both sides}$$
$$\sin^2 x + 2 \sin x \cos x + \cos^2 x = 1$$
$$2 \sin x \cos x + 1 = 1 \qquad \text{Using } \sin^2 x + \cos^2 x = 1$$
$$2 \sin x \cos x = 0$$
$$\sin 2x = 0. \qquad \text{Using } 2 \sin x \cos x = \sin 2x$$

We are looking for solutions x to the equation for which $0 \le x < 2\pi$. Multiplying by 2, we get $0 \le 2x < 4\pi$, which is the interval we consider to solve $\sin 2x = 0$. These values of $2x$ are 0, π, 2π, and 3π. Thus the desired values of x in $[0, 2\pi)$ satisfying this equation are 0, $\pi/2$, π, and $3\pi/2$. Now we check these in the original equation $\sin x + \cos x = 1$:

$$\sin 0 + \cos 0 = 0 + 1 = 1,$$
$$\sin \frac{\pi}{2} + \cos \frac{\pi}{2} = 1 + 0 = 1,$$
$$\sin \pi + \cos \pi = 0 + (-1) = -1,$$
$$\sin \frac{3\pi}{2} + \cos \frac{3\pi}{2} = (-1) + 0 = -1.$$

We find that π and $3\pi/2$ do not check, but the other values do. Thus the solutions in $[0, 2\pi)$ are

$$0 \quad \text{and} \quad \frac{\pi}{2}.$$

When the solution process involves squaring both sides, values are sometimes obtained that are not solutions of the original equation. As we saw in this example, it is important to check the possible solutions.

▶ **Now Try Exercise 39.**

EXAMPLE 10 Solve $\cos 2x + \sin x = 1$ in $[0, 2\pi)$.

ALGEBRAIC SOLUTION

We have

$$\cos 2x + \sin x = 1$$
$$1 - 2\sin^2 x + \sin x = 1 \qquad \text{Using the identity}$$
$$\qquad\qquad\qquad\qquad \cos 2x = 1 - 2\sin^2 x$$
$$-2\sin^2 x + \sin x = 0$$
$$\sin x(-2\sin x + 1) = 0 \qquad \text{Factoring}$$
$$\sin x = 0 \quad \text{ or } \quad -2\sin x + 1 = 0 \qquad \text{Principle of}$$
$$\qquad\qquad\qquad\qquad\qquad\qquad\qquad \text{zero products}$$
$$\sin x = 0 \quad \text{ or } \qquad \sin x = \frac{1}{2}$$
$$x = 0, \pi \quad \text{ or } \qquad x = \frac{\pi}{6}, \frac{5\pi}{6}.$$

All four values check. The solutions in $[0, 2\pi)$ are 0, $\pi/6$,
$5\pi/6$, and π.

VISUALIZING THE SOLUTION

We graph the function
$y = \cos 2x + \sin x - 1$ and look
for the zeros of the function.

The zeros, or solutions, in $[0, 2\pi)$
are 0, $\pi/6$, $5\pi/6$, and π.

EXAMPLE 11 Solve $\tan^2 x + \sec x - 1 = 0$ in $[0, 2\pi)$.

STUDY TIP

Check your solutions to the
odd-numbered exercises in
the exercise sets with the
step-by-step annotated
solutions in the *Student's
Solutions Manual*. If you are
still having difficulty with the
concepts of this section, make
time to view the content video
that corresponds to the section.

Solution We have

$$\tan^2 x + \sec x - 1 = 0$$
$$\sec^2 x - 1 + \sec x - 1 = 0 \qquad \text{Using the identity}$$
$$\qquad\qquad\qquad\qquad\qquad\qquad 1 + \tan^2 x = \sec^2 x, \text{ or}$$
$$\qquad\qquad\qquad\qquad\qquad\qquad \tan^2 x = \sec^2 x - 1$$
$$\sec^2 x + \sec x - 2 = 0$$
$$(\sec x + 2)(\sec x - 1) = 0 \qquad \text{Factoring}$$
$$\sec x = -2 \quad \text{ or } \quad \sec x = 1 \qquad \text{Principle of zero}$$
$$\qquad\qquad\qquad\qquad\qquad\qquad\qquad \text{products}$$
$$\cos x = -\frac{1}{2} \quad \text{ or } \quad \cos x = 1 \qquad \text{Using the identity}$$
$$\qquad\qquad\qquad\qquad\qquad\qquad\qquad \cos x = 1/\sec x$$
$$x = \frac{2\pi}{3}, \frac{4\pi}{3} \quad \text{ or } \qquad x = 0.$$

All these values check. The solutions in $[0, 2\pi)$ are 0, $2\pi/3$, and $4\pi/3$.

▶ **Now Try Exercise 27.**

A

B

C

D

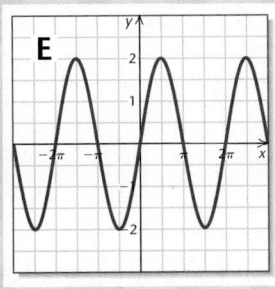

E

Visualizing the Graph

Match the equation with its graph.

1. $f(x) = \dfrac{4}{x^2 - 9}$

2. $f(x) = \dfrac{1}{2} \sin x - 1$

3. $(x - 2)^2 + (y + 3)^2 = 4$

4. $y = \sin^2 x + \cos^2 x$

5. $f(x) = 3 - \log x$

6. $f(x) = 2^{x+3} - 2$

7. $y = 2 \cos \left(x - \dfrac{\pi}{2} \right)$

8. $y = -x^3 + 3x^2$

9. $f(x) = (x - 3)^2 + 2$

10. $f(x) = -\cos x$

Answers on page A-48

F

G

H

I

J

6.5   EXERCISE SET

Solve, finding all solutions. Express the solutions in both radians and degrees.

1. $\cos x = \dfrac{\sqrt{3}}{2}$ **2.** $\sin x = -\dfrac{\sqrt{2}}{2}$

3. $\tan x = -\sqrt{3}$ **4.** $\cos x = -\dfrac{1}{2}$

5. $\sin x = \dfrac{1}{2}$ **6.** $\tan x = -1$

7. $\cos x = -\dfrac{\sqrt{2}}{2}$ **8.** $\sin x = \dfrac{\sqrt{3}}{2}$

Solve, finding all solutions in $[0, 2\pi)$ or $[0°, 360°)$.

9. $2 \cos x - 1 = -1.2814$

10. $\sin x + 3 = 2.0816$

11. $2 \sin x + \sqrt{3} = 0$

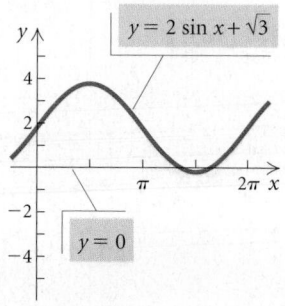

12. $2 \tan x - 4 = 1$

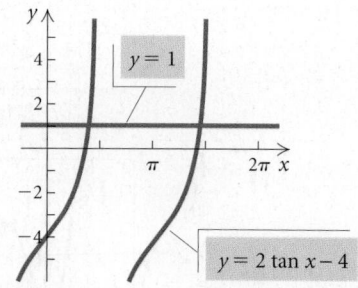

13. $2 \cos^2 x = 1$ **14.** $\csc^2 x - 4 = 0$

15. $2 \sin^2 x + \sin x = 1$ **16.** $\cos^2 x + 2 \cos x = 3$

17. $2 \cos^2 x - \sqrt{3} \cos x = 0$

18. $2 \sin^2 \theta + 7 \sin \theta = 4$

19. $6 \cos^2 \phi + 5 \cos \phi + 1 = 0$

20. $2 \sin t \cos t + 2 \sin t - \cos t - 1 = 0$

21. $\sin 2x \cos x - \sin x = 0$

22. $5 \sin^2 x - 8 \sin x = 3$

23. $\cos^2 x + 6 \cos x + 4 = 0$

24. $2 \tan^2 x = 3 \tan x + 7$

25. $7 = \cot^2 x + 4 \cot x$

26. $3 \sin^2 x = 3 \sin x + 2$

Solve, finding all solutions in $[0, 2\pi)$.

27. $\cos 2x - \sin x = 1$

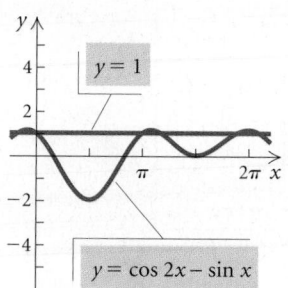

28. $2 \sin x \cos x + \sin x = 0$

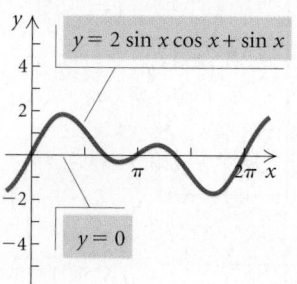

29. $\sin 4x - 2 \sin 2x = 0$

30. $\tan x \sin x - \tan x = 0$

31. $\sin 2x \cos x + \sin x = 0$

32. $\cos 2x \sin x + \sin x = 0$

33. $2 \sec x \tan x + 2 \sec x + \tan x + 1 = 0$

34. $\sin 2x \sin x - \cos 2x \cos x = -\cos x$

35. $\sin 2x + \sin x + 2 \cos x + 1 = 0$

36. $\tan^2 x + 4 = 2 \sec^2 x + \tan x$

37. $\sec^2 x - 2 \tan^2 x = 0$

38. $\cot x = \tan(2x - 3\pi)$

39. $2 \cos x + 2 \sin x = \sqrt{6}$

40. $\sqrt{3} \cos x - \sin x = 1$

41. $\sec^2 x + 2 \tan x = 6$

42. $5 \cos 2x + \sin x = 4$

43. $\cos(\pi - x) + \sin\left(x - \dfrac{\pi}{2}\right) = 1$

44. $\dfrac{\sin^2 x - 1}{\cos\left(\dfrac{\pi}{2} - x\right) + 1} = \dfrac{\sqrt{2}}{2} - 1$

Technology Connection

45. Check the solutions of Exercises 14, 19, 20, and 21 using the Zero method.

46. Check the solutions of Exercises 15, 18, 24, and 25 using the Intersect method.

Solve using a calculator, finding all solutions in $[0, 2\pi)$.

47. $x \sin x = 1$

48. $x^2 + 2 = \sin x$

49. $2 \cos^2 x = x + 1$

50. $x \cos x - 2 = 0$

51. $\cos x - 2 = x^2 - 3x$

52. $\sin x = \tan \dfrac{x}{2}$

Some graphing calculators can use regression to fit a trigonometric function to a set of data.

53. *Sales.* Sales of certain products fluctuate in cycles. The data in the following table show the total sales of skis per month for a business in a northern climate.

Month, x		Total Sales, y (in thousands)
August,	8	$ 0
November,	11	7
February,	2	14
May,	5	7
August,	8	0

a) Using the SINE REGRESSION feature on a graphing calculator, fit a sine function of the form $y = A \sin(Bx - C) + D$ to this set of data.

b) Approximate the total sales for December and for July.

54. *Daylight Hours.* The data in the following table show the number of daylight hours for certain days in Kajaani, Finland.

Day, x		Number of Daylight Hours, y
January 10,	10	5.0
February 19,	50	9.1
March 3,	62	10.4
April 28,	118	16.4
May 14,	134	18.2
June 11,	162	20.7
July 17,	198	19.5
August 22,	234	15.7
September 19,	262	12.7
October 1,	274	11.4
November 14,	318	6.7
December 28,	362	4.3

Source: The Astronomical Almanac, 1995, Washington: U.S. Government Printing Office.

a) Using the SINE REGRESSION feature on a graphing calculator, model these data with an equation of the form $y = A \sin(Bx - C) + D$.

b) Approximate the number of daylight hours in Kajaani for April 22 ($x = 112$), July 4 ($x = 185$), and December 15 ($x = 349$).

Collaborative Discussion and Writing

55. Jan lists her answer to a problem as $\pi/6 + k\pi$, for any integer k, while Jacob lists his answer as $\pi/6 + 2k\pi$ and $7\pi/6 + 2\pi k$, for any integer k. Are their answers equivalent? Why or why not?

56. An identity is an equation that is true for all possible replacements of the variables. Explain the meaning of "possible" in this definition.

Skill Maintenance

Solve the right triangle.

57.

58.

Solve.

59. $\dfrac{x}{27} = \dfrac{4}{3}$

60. $\dfrac{0.01}{0.7} = \dfrac{0.2}{h}$

Synthesis

Solve in $[0, 2\pi)$.

61. $|\sin x| = \dfrac{\sqrt{3}}{2}$

62. $|\cos x| = \dfrac{1}{2}$

63. $\sqrt{\tan x} = \sqrt[4]{3}$

64. $12 \sin x - 7\sqrt{\sin x} + 1 = 0$

65. $\ln (\cos x) = 0$

66. $e^{\sin x} = 1$

67. $\sin (\ln x) = -1$

68. $e^{\ln (\sin x)} = 1$

69. *Temperature During an Illness.* The temperature T, in degrees Fahrenheit, of a patient t days into a 12-day illness is given by

$$T(t) = 101.6° + 3° \sin \left(\dfrac{\pi}{8} t \right).$$

Find the times t during the illness at which the patient's temperature was $103°$.

70. *Satellite Location.* A satellite circles the earth in such a manner that it is y miles from the equator (north or south, height from the surface not considered) t minutes after its launch, where

$$y = 5000 \left[\cos \dfrac{\pi}{45}(t - 10) \right].$$

At what times t in the interval $[0, 240]$, the first 4 hr, is the satellite 3000 mi north of the equator?

71. *Nautical Mile.* (See Exercise 60 in Exercise Set 6.2.) In Great Britain, the *nautical mile* is defined as the length of a minute of arc of the earth's radius. Since the earth is flattened at the poles, a British nautical mile varies with latitude. In fact, it is given, in feet, by the function

$$N(\phi) = 6066 - 31 \cos 2\phi,$$

where ϕ is the latitude in degrees. At what latitude north is the length of a British nautical mile found to be 6040 ft?

72. *Acceleration Due to Gravity.* (See Exercise 61 in Exercise Set 6.2.) The acceleration due to gravity is often denoted by g in a formula such as $S = \frac{1}{2}gt^2$, where S is the distance that an object falls in t seconds. The number g is generally considered constant, but in fact it varies slightly with latitude. If ϕ stands for latitude, in degrees, an excellent approximation of g is given by the formula

$$g = 9.78049(1 + 0.005288 \sin^2 \phi - 0.000006 \sin^2 2\phi),$$

where g is measured in meters per second per second at sea level. At what latitude north does $g = 9.8$?

Solve.

73. $\cos^{-1} x = \cos^{-1} \frac{3}{5} - \sin^{-1} \frac{4}{5}$

74. $\sin^{-1} x = \tan^{-1} \frac{1}{3} + \tan^{-1} \frac{1}{2}$

75. Suppose that $\sin x = 5 \cos x$. Find $\sin x \cos x$.

CHAPTER 6 SUMMARY AND REVIEW

Important Properties and Formulas

Basic Identities

$$\sin x = \frac{1}{\csc x}, \qquad \tan x = \frac{\sin x}{\cos x},$$

$$\cos x = \frac{1}{\sec x}, \qquad \cot x = \frac{\cos x}{\sin x},$$

$$\tan x = \frac{1}{\cot x}$$

$$\sin(-x) = -\sin x,$$

$$\cos(-x) = \cos x,$$

$$\tan(-x) = -\tan x$$

Pythagorean Identities

$$\sin^2 x + \cos^2 x = 1,$$

$$1 + \cot^2 x = \csc^2 x,$$

$$1 + \tan^2 x = \sec^2 x$$

Sum and Difference Identities

$$\sin(u \pm v) = \sin u \cos v \pm \cos u \sin v,$$

$$\cos(u \pm v) = \cos u \cos v \mp \sin u \sin v,$$

$$\tan(u \pm v) = \frac{\tan u \pm \tan v}{1 \mp \tan u \tan v}$$

Double-Angle Identities

$$\sin 2x = 2 \sin x \cos x,$$

$$\cos 2x = \cos^2 x - \sin^2 x$$

$$= 1 - 2 \sin^2 x$$

$$= 2 \cos^2 x - 1,$$

$$\tan 2x = \frac{2 \tan x}{1 - \tan^2 x}$$

Half-Angle Identities

$$\sin \frac{x}{2} = \pm \sqrt{\frac{1 - \cos x}{2}},$$

$$\cos \frac{x}{2} = \pm \sqrt{\frac{1 + \cos x}{2}},$$

$$\tan \frac{x}{2} = \pm \sqrt{\frac{1 - \cos x}{1 + \cos x}}$$

$$= \frac{\sin x}{1 + \cos x}$$

$$= \frac{1 - \cos x}{\sin x}$$

Cofunction Identities

$$\sin\left(\frac{\pi}{2} - x\right) = \cos x, \qquad \cos\left(\frac{\pi}{2} - x\right) = \sin x, \qquad \sin\left(x \pm \frac{\pi}{2}\right) = \mp\cos x,$$

$$\tan\left(\frac{\pi}{2} - x\right) = \cot x, \qquad \cot\left(\frac{\pi}{2} - x\right) = \tan x, \qquad \cos\left(x \pm \frac{\pi}{2}\right) = \pm\sin x$$

$$\sec\left(\frac{\pi}{2} - x\right) = \csc x, \qquad \csc\left(\frac{\pi}{2} - x\right) = \sec x,$$

Product-to-Sum Identities

$$\sin x \cdot \sin y = \frac{1}{2}[\cos(x-y) - \cos(x+y)]$$

$$\cos x \cdot \cos y = \frac{1}{2}[\cos(x-y) + \cos(x+y)]$$

$$\sin x \cdot \cos y = \frac{1}{2}[\sin(x+y) + \sin(x-y)]$$

$$\cos x \cdot \sin y = \frac{1}{2}[\sin(x+y) - \sin(x-y)]$$

Sum-to-Product Identities

$$\sin x + \sin y = 2\sin\frac{x+y}{2}\cos\frac{x-y}{2}$$

$$\sin x - \sin y = 2\cos\frac{x+y}{2}\sin\frac{x-y}{2}$$

$$\cos y + \cos x = 2\cos\frac{x+y}{2}\cos\frac{x-y}{2}$$

$$\cos y - \cos x = 2\sin\frac{x+y}{2}\sin\frac{x-y}{2}$$

Inverse Trigonometric Functions

Function	Domain	Range
$y = \sin^{-1} x$	$[-1, 1]$	$\left[-\dfrac{\pi}{2}, \dfrac{\pi}{2}\right]$
$y = \cos^{-1} x$	$[-1, 1]$	$[0, \pi]$
$y = \tan^{-1} x$	$(-\infty, \infty)$	$\left(-\dfrac{\pi}{2}, \dfrac{\pi}{2}\right)$

Composition of Trigonometric Functions

The following are true for any x in the domain of the inverse function:

$$\sin(\sin^{-1} x) = x,$$
$$\cos(\cos^{-1} x) = x,$$
$$\tan(\tan^{-1} x) = x.$$

The following are true for any x in the range of the inverse function:

$$\sin^{-1}(\sin x) = x,$$
$$\cos^{-1}(\cos x) = x,$$
$$\tan^{-1}(\tan x) = x.$$

REVIEW EXERCISES

Determine whether the statement is true or false.

1. $\sin^2 s \neq \sin s^2$. [6.1]

2. Given $0 < \alpha < \pi/2$ and $0 < \beta < \pi/2$ and that $\sin(\alpha + \beta) = 1$ and $\sin(\alpha - \beta) = 0$, then $\alpha = \pi/4$. [6.1]

3. If the terminal side of θ is in quadrant IV, then $\tan \theta < \cos \theta$. [6.1]

4. $\cos 5\pi/12 = \cos 7\pi/12$. [6.2]

5. Given that $\sin \theta = -\dfrac{2}{5}$, $\tan \theta < \cos \theta$. [6.1]

Complete the Pythagorean identity. [6.1]

6. $1 + \cot^2 x =$

7. $\sin^2 x + \cos^2 x =$

Multiply and simplify. [6.1]

8. $(\tan y - \cot y)(\tan y + \cot y)$

9. $(\cos x + \sec x)^2$

Factor and simplify. [6.1]

10. $\sec x \csc x - \csc^2 x$

11. $3\sin^2 y - 7\sin y - 20$

12. $1000 - \cos^3 u$

Simplify. [6.1]

13. $\dfrac{\sec^4 x - \tan^4 x}{\sec^2 x + \tan^2 x}$

14. $\dfrac{2\sin^2 x}{\cos^3 x} \cdot \left(\dfrac{\cos x}{2\sin x}\right)^2$

15. $\dfrac{3\sin x}{\cos^2 x} \cdot \dfrac{\cos^2 x + \cos x \sin x}{\sin^2 x - \cos^2 x}$

16. $\dfrac{3}{\cos y - \sin y} - \dfrac{2}{\sin^2 y - \cos^2 y}$

17. $\left(\dfrac{\cot x}{\csc x}\right)^2 + \dfrac{1}{\csc^2 x}$

18. $\dfrac{4 \sin x \cos^2 x}{16 \sin^2 x \cos x}$

19. Simplify. Assume the radicand is nonnegative. [6.1]

$$\sqrt{\sin^2 x + 2 \cos x \sin x + \cos^2 x}$$

20. Rationalize the denominator: $\sqrt{\dfrac{1 + \sin x}{1 - \sin x}}$. [6.1]

21. Rationalize the numerator: $\sqrt{\dfrac{\cos x}{\tan x}}$. [6.1]

22. Given that $x = 3 \tan \theta$, express $\sqrt{9 + x^2}$ as a trigonometric function without radicals. Assume that $0 < \theta < \pi/2$. [6.1]

Use the sum and difference formulas to write equivalent expressions. You need not simplify. [6.1]

23. $\cos\left(x + \dfrac{3\pi}{2}\right)$ **24.** $\tan(45° - 30°)$

25. Simplify: $\cos 27° \cos 16° + \sin 27° \sin 16°$. [6.1]

26. Find $\cos 165°$ exactly. [6.1]

27. Given that $\tan \alpha = \sqrt{3}$ and $\sin \beta = \sqrt{2}/2$ and that α and β are between 0 and $\pi/2$, evaluate $\tan(\alpha - \beta)$ exactly. [6.1]

28. Assume that $\sin \theta = 0.5812$ and $\cos \phi = 0.2341$ and that both θ and ϕ are first-quadrant angles. Evaluate $\cos(\theta + \phi)$. [6.1]

Complete the cofunction identity. [6.2]

29. $\cos\left(x + \dfrac{\pi}{2}\right) =$ **30.** $\cos\left(\dfrac{\pi}{2} - x\right) =$

31. $\sin\left(x - \dfrac{\pi}{2}\right) =$

32. Given that $\cos \alpha = -\frac{3}{5}$ and that the terminal side is in quadrant III: [6.2]

  a) Find the other function values for α.
  b) Find the six function values for $\pi/2 - \alpha$.
  c) Find the six function values for $\alpha + \pi/2$.

33. Find an equivalent expression for $\csc\left(x - \dfrac{\pi}{2}\right)$. [6.2]

34. Find $\tan 2\theta$, $\cos 2\theta$, and $\sin 2\theta$ and the quadrant in which 2θ lies, where $\cos \theta = -\frac{4}{5}$ and θ is in quadrant III. [6.2]

35. Find $\sin \dfrac{\pi}{8}$ exactly. [6.2]

36. Given that $\sin \beta = 0.2183$ and β is in quadrant I, find $\sin 2\beta$, $\cos \dfrac{\beta}{2}$, and $\cos 4\beta$. [6.2]

Simplify. [6.2]

37. $1 - 2 \sin^2 \dfrac{x}{2}$

38. $(\sin x + \cos x)^2 - \sin 2x$

39. $2 \sin x \cos^3 x + 2 \sin^3 x \cos x$

40. $\dfrac{2 \cot x}{\cot^2 x - 1}$

Prove the identity. [6.3]

41. $\dfrac{1 - \sin x}{\cos x} = \dfrac{\cos x}{1 + \sin x}$

42. $\dfrac{1 + \cos 2\theta}{\sin 2\theta} = \cot \theta$

43. $\dfrac{\tan y + \sin y}{2 \tan y} = \cos^2 \dfrac{y}{2}$

44. $\dfrac{\sin x - \cos x}{\cos^2 x} = \dfrac{\tan^2 x - 1}{\sin x + \cos x}$

Use the product-to-sum and the sum-to-product identities to find identities for each of the following. [6.3]

45. $3 \cos 2\theta \sin\theta$

46. $\sin \theta - \sin 4\theta$

Find each of the following exactly in both radians and degrees. [6.4]

47. $\sin^{-1}\left(-\dfrac{1}{2}\right)$

48. $\cos^{-1} \dfrac{\sqrt{3}}{2}$

49. $\tan^{-1} 1$

50. $\sin^{-1} 0$

Use a calculator to find each of the following in radians, rounded to four decimal places, and in degrees, rounded to the nearest tenth of a degree.   [6.4]

51. $\cos^{-1}(-0.2194)$ 52. $\cot^{-1} 2.381$

Evaluate.   [6.4]

53. $\cos\left(\cos^{-1}\dfrac{1}{2}\right)$ 54. $\tan^{-1}\left(\tan\dfrac{\sqrt{3}}{3}\right)$

55. $\sin^{-1}\left(\sin\dfrac{\pi}{7}\right)$ 56. $\cos\left(\sin^{-1}\dfrac{\sqrt{2}}{2}\right)$

Find.   [6.4]

57. $\cos\left(\tan^{-1}\dfrac{b}{3}\right)$ 58. $\cos\left(2\sin^{-1}\dfrac{4}{5}\right)$

Solve, finding all solutions. Express the solutions in both radians and degrees.   [6.5]

59. $\cos x = -\dfrac{\sqrt{2}}{2}$ 60. $\tan x = \sqrt{3}$

Solve, finding all solutions in $[0, 2\pi)$.   [6.5]

61. $4\sin^2 x = 1$

62. $\sin 2x \sin x - \cos x = 0$

63. $2\cos^2 x + 3\cos x = -1$

64. $\sin^2 x - 7\sin x = 0$

65. $\csc^2 x - 2\cot^2 x = 0$

66. $\sin 4x + 2\sin 2x = 0$

67. $2\cos x + 2\sin x = \sqrt{2}$

68. $6\tan^2 x = 5\tan x + \sec^2 x$

69. Determine the domain of the function $\cos^{-1} x$.   [6.4]

    A. $(0, \pi)$ B. $[-1, 1]$
    C. $[-\pi/2, \pi/2]$ D. $(-\infty, \infty)$

70. Simplify $\sin^{-1}\left(\sin\dfrac{7\pi}{6}\right)$.   [6.4]

    A. $-\pi/6$ B. $7\pi/6$
    C. $-1/2$ D. $11\pi/6$

Technology Connection

In Exercises 71–74, use a graphing calculator to determine which expression (A)–(D) on the right can be used to complete the identity. Then prove the identity algebraically.   [6.3]

71. $\csc x - \cos x \cot x$ A. $\dfrac{\csc x}{\sec x}$

72. $\dfrac{1}{\sin x \cos x} - \dfrac{\cos x}{\sin x}$ B. $\sin x$

73. $\dfrac{\cot x - 1}{1 - \tan x}$ C. $\dfrac{2}{\sin x}$

74. $\dfrac{\cos x + 1}{\sin x} + \dfrac{\sin x}{\cos x + 1}$ D. $\dfrac{\sin x \cos x}{1 - \sin^2 x}$

Solve using a graphing calculator, finding all solutions in $[0, 2\pi)$.   [6.5]

75. $x \cos x = 1$

76. $2\sin^2 x = x + 1$

Collaborative Discussion and Writing

77. Prove the identity $2\cos^2 x - 1 = \cos^4 x - \sin^4 x$ in three ways:

    a) Start with the left side and deduce the right (method 1).
    b) Start with the right side and deduce the left (method 1).
    c) Work with each side separately until you deduce the same expression (method 2).

    Then determine the most efficient method and explain why you chose that method.   [6.3]

78. Why are the ranges of the inverse trigonometric functions restricted?   [6.4]

Synthesis

79. Find the measure of the angle from l_1 to l_2:   [6.1]

    l_1: $x + y = 3$ l_2: $2x - y = 5$.

80. Find an identity for $\cos(u + v)$ involving only cosines.   [6.1]

81. Simplify: $\cos\left(\dfrac{\pi}{2} - x\right)[\csc x - \sin x]$.   [6.2]

82. Find $\sin\theta$, $\cos\theta$, and $\tan\theta$ under the given conditions: [6.2]

    $$\sin 2\theta = \frac{1}{5},\ \frac{\pi}{2} \le 2\theta < \pi.$$

83. Prove the following equation to be an identity: [6.3]

    $$\ln e^{\sin t} = \sin t.$$

84. Graph: $y = \sec^{-1} x$.   [6.4]

85. Show that

    $$\tan^{-1} x = \frac{\sin^{-1} x}{\cos^{-1} x}$$

    is *not* an identity.   [6.4]

86. Solve $e^{\cos x} = 1$ in $[0, 2\pi)$.   [6.5]

CHAPTER 6 TEST

Simplify.

1. $\dfrac{2\cos^2 x - \cos x - 1}{\cos x - 1}$

2. $\left(\dfrac{\sec x}{\tan x}\right)^2 - \dfrac{1}{\tan^2 x}$

3. Rationalize the denominator:

    $$\sqrt{\frac{1 - \sin\theta}{1 + \sin\theta}}.$$

4. Given that $x = 2\sin\theta$, express $\sqrt{4 - x^2}$ as a trigonometric function without radicals. Assume $0 < \theta < \pi/2$.

Use the sum or difference identities to evaluate exactly.

5. $\sin 75°$

6. $\tan \dfrac{\pi}{12}$

7. Assuming that $\cos u = \frac{5}{13}$ and $\cos v = \frac{12}{13}$ and that u and v are between 0 and $\pi/2$, evaluate $\cos(u - v)$ exactly.

8. Given that $\cos\theta = -\frac{2}{3}$ and that the terminal side is in quadrant II, find $\cos(\pi/2 - \theta)$.

9. Given that $\sin\theta = -\frac{4}{5}$ and θ is in quadrant III, find $\sin 2\theta$ and the quadrant in which 2θ lies.

10. Use a half-angle identity to evaluate $\cos\dfrac{\pi}{12}$ exactly.

11. Given that $\sin\theta = 0.6820$ and that θ is in quadrant I, find $\cos\theta/2$.

12. Simplify: $(\sin x + \cos x)^2 - 1 + 2\sin 2x$.

Prove each of the following identities.

13. $\csc x - \cos x \cot x = \sin x$

14. $(\sin x + \cos x)^2 = 1 + \sin 2x$

15. $(\csc\beta + \cot\beta)^2 = \dfrac{1 + \cos\beta}{1 - \cos\beta}$

16. $\dfrac{1 + \sin\alpha}{1 + \csc\alpha} = \dfrac{\tan\alpha}{\sec\alpha}$

Use the product-to-sum and sum-to-product identities to find identities for each of the following.

17. $\cos 8\alpha - \cos\alpha$

18. $4\sin\beta\cos 3\beta$

19. Find $\sin^{-1}\left(-\dfrac{\sqrt{2}}{2}\right)$ exactly in degrees.

20. Find $\tan^{-1}\sqrt{3}$ exactly in radians.

21. Use a calculator to find $\cos^{-1}(-0.6716)$ in radians, rounded to four decimal places.

22. Evaluate $\cos\left(\sin^{-1}\dfrac{1}{2}\right)$.

23. Find $\tan\left(\sin^{-1}\dfrac{5}{x}\right)$.

24. Evaluate $\cos\left(\sin^{-1}\frac{1}{2}+\cos^{-1}\frac{1}{2}\right)$.

Solve, finding all solutions in $[0, 2\pi)$.

25. $4\cos^2 x = 3$

26. $2\sin^2 x = \sqrt{2}\sin x$

27. $\sqrt{3}\cos x + \sin x = 1$

Synthesis

28. Find $\cos\theta$, given that

$$\cos 2\theta = \frac{5}{6}, \quad \frac{3\pi}{2} < \theta < 2\pi.$$

Applications of Trigonometry

APPLICATION

 musician is constructing an octagonal recording studio in his home and needs to determine two distances for the electrician. The dimensions for the most acoustically perfect studio are shown in the figure on page 614 (*Source*: Tony Medeiros, Indianapolis, IN). Determine the distances from *D* to *F* and from *D* to *B* to the nearest tenth of an inch.

This problem appears as Example 2 in Section 7.2.

7.1

The Law of Sines

◆ Use the law of sines to solve triangles.

◆ Find the area of any triangle given the lengths of two sides and the measure of the included angle.

To **solve a triangle** means to find the lengths of all its sides and the measures of all its angles. We solved right triangles in Section 5.2. For review, let's solve the right triangle shown below. We begin by listing the known measures.

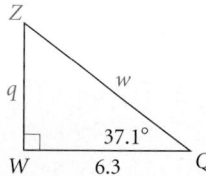

$$Q = 37.1° \qquad q = ?$$
$$W = 90° \qquad w = ?$$
$$Z = ? \qquad z = 6.3$$

Since the sum of the three angle measures of any triangle is 180°, we can immediately find the measure of the third angle:

$$Z = 180° - (90° + 37.1°)$$
$$= 52.9°.$$

Then using the tangent and cosine ratios, respectively, we can find q and w:

$$\tan 37.1° = \frac{q}{6.3}, \quad \text{or}$$
$$q = 6.3 \tan 37.1° \approx 4.8,$$

and

$$\cos 37.1° = \frac{6.3}{w}, \quad \text{or}$$
$$w = \frac{6.3}{\cos 37.1°} \approx 7.9.$$

Now all six measures are known and we have solved triangle QWZ.

$$Q = 37.1° \qquad q \approx 4.8$$
$$W = 90° \qquad w \approx 7.9$$
$$Z = 52.9° \qquad z = 6.3$$

◆ Solving Oblique Triangles

The trigonometric functions can also be used to solve triangles that are not right triangles. Such triangles are called **oblique**. Any triangle, right or oblique, can be solved *if at least one side and any other two measures are known*. The five possible situations are illustrated on the next page.

1. AAS: Two angles of a triangle and a side opposite one of them are known.

AAS

2. ASA: Two angles of a triangle and the included side are known.

ASA

3. SSA: Two sides of a triangle and an angle opposite one of them are known. (In this case, there may be no solution, one solution, or two solutions. The latter is known as the ambiguous case.)

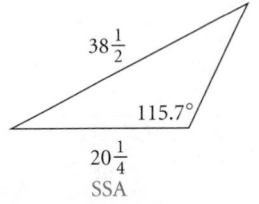

SSA

4. SAS: Two sides of a triangle and the included angle are known.

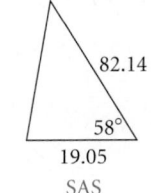

SAS

5. SSS: All three sides of the triangle are known.

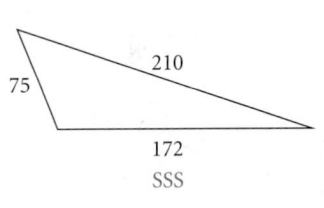

SSS

The list above does not include the situation in which only the three angle measures are given. The reason for this lies in the fact that the angle measures determine *only the shape* of the triangle and *not the size*, as shown with the following triangles. Thus we cannot solve a triangle when only the three angle measures are given.

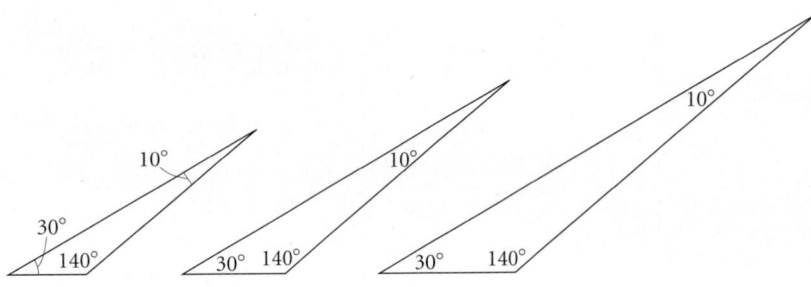

In order to solve oblique triangles, we need to derive the *law of sines* and the *law of cosines*. The law of sines applies to the first three situations listed above. The law of cosines, which we develop in Section 7.2, applies to the last two situations.

◆ The Law of Sines

We consider any oblique triangle. It may or may not have an obtuse angle. Although we look at only the acute-triangle case, the derivation of the obtuse-triangle case is essentially the same.

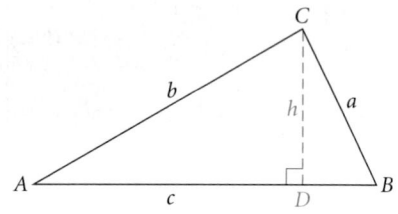

In acute $\triangle ABC$ at left, we have drawn an altitude from vertex C. It has length h. From $\triangle ADC$, we have

$$\sin A = \frac{h}{b}, \quad \text{or} \quad h = b \sin A.$$

From $\triangle BDC$, we have

$$\sin B = \frac{h}{a}, \quad \text{or} \quad h = a \sin B.$$

With $h = b \sin A$ and $h = a \sin B$, we now have

$$a \sin B = b \sin A$$

$$\frac{a \sin B}{\sin A \sin B} = \frac{b \sin A}{\sin A \sin B} \qquad \text{Dividing by } \sin A \sin B$$

$$\frac{a}{\sin A} = \frac{b}{\sin B}. \qquad \text{Simplifying}$$

There is no danger of dividing by 0 here because we are dealing with triangles whose angles are never 0° or 180°. Thus the sine value will never be 0.

If we were to consider altitudes from vertex A and vertex B in the triangle shown above, the same argument would give us

$$\frac{b}{\sin B} = \frac{c}{\sin C} \quad \text{and} \quad \frac{a}{\sin A} = \frac{c}{\sin C}.$$

We combine these results to obtain the law of sines.

The Law of Sines

In any triangle ABC,

$$\frac{a}{\sin A} = \frac{b}{\sin B} = \frac{c}{\sin C}.$$

✦ Solving Triangles (AAS and ASA)

When two angles and a side of any triangle are known, the law of sines can be used to solve the triangle.

EXAMPLE 1 In $\triangle EFG$, $e = 4.56$, $E = 43°$, and $G = 57°$. Solve the triangle.

Solution We first make a drawing. We know three of the six measures.

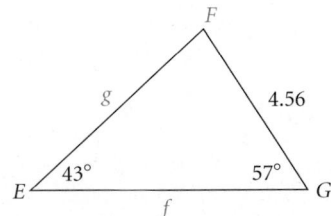

$$E = 43° \qquad e = 4.56$$
$$F = ? \qquad f = ?$$
$$G = 57° \qquad g = ?$$

From the figure, we see that we have the AAS situation. We begin by finding F:

$$F = 180° - (43° + 57°) = 80°.$$

We can now find the other two sides, using the law of sines:

$$\frac{f}{\sin F} = \frac{e}{\sin E}$$

$$\frac{f}{\sin 80°} = \frac{4.56}{\sin 43°} \qquad \text{Substituting}$$

$$f = \frac{4.56 \sin 80°}{\sin 43°} \qquad \text{Solving for } f$$

$$f \approx 6.58;$$

$$\frac{g}{\sin G} = \frac{e}{\sin E}$$

$$\frac{g}{\sin 57°} = \frac{4.56}{\sin 43°} \qquad \text{Substituting}$$

$$g = \frac{4.56 \sin 57°}{\sin 43°} \qquad \text{Solving for } g$$

$$g \approx 5.61.$$

Thus, we have solved the triangle:

$$E = 43°, \qquad e = 4.56,$$
$$F = 80°, \qquad f \approx 6.58,$$
$$G = 57°, \qquad g \approx 5.61.$$

▶ Now Try Exercise 1.

The law of sines is frequently used in determining distances.

EXAMPLE 2 *Rescue Mission.* During a rescue mission, a Marine fighter pilot receives data on an unidentified aircraft from an AWACS plane and is instructed to intercept the aircraft. The diagram shown below appears on the screen, but before the distance to the point of interception appears on the screen, communications are jammed. Fortunately, the pilot remembers the law of sines. How far must the pilot fly?

Solution   We let x represent the distance that the pilot must fly in order to intercept the aircraft and Z represent the point of interception. We first find angle Z:

$$Z = 180° - (115° + 27°)$$
$$= 38°.$$

Because this application involves the ASA situation, we use the law of sines to determine x:

$$\frac{x}{\sin X} = \frac{z}{\sin Z}$$

$$\frac{x}{\sin 115°} = \frac{500}{\sin 38°}\qquad \text{Substituting}$$

$$x = \frac{500 \sin 115°}{\sin 38°}\qquad \text{Solving for } x$$

$$x \approx 736.$$

Thus the pilot must fly approximately 736 km in order to intercept the unidentified aircraft.

▶ **Now Try Exercise 23.**

◆ Solving Triangles (SSA)

When two sides of a triangle and an angle opposite one of them are known, the law of sines can be used to solve the triangle.

Suppose for $\triangle ABC$ that b, c, and B are given. The various possibilities are as shown in the eight cases on the following page: 5 cases when B is acute and 3 cases when B is obtuse. Note that $b < c$ in cases 1, 2, 3, and 6; $b = c$ in cases 4 and 7; and $b > c$ in cases 5 and 8.

Angle B Is Acute

Case 1: No solution
$b < c$; side b is too short to reach the base. No triangle is formed.

Case 2: One solution
$b < c$; side b just reaches the base and is perpendicular to it.

Case 3: Two solutions
$b < c$; an arc of radius b meets the base at two points. (This case is called the **ambiguous case.**)

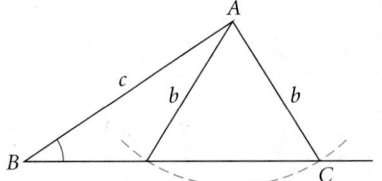

Case 4: One solution
$b = c$; an arc of radius b meets the base at just one point, other than B.

Case 5: One solution
$b > c$; an arc of radius b meets the base at just one point.

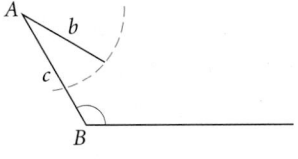

Angle B Is Obtuse

Case 6: No solution
$b < c$; side b is too short to reach the base. No triangle is formed.

Case 7: No solution
$b = c$; an arc of radius b meets the base only at point B. No triangle is formed.

Case 8: One solution
$b > c$; an arc of radius b meets the base at just one point.

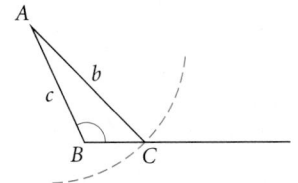

The eight cases above lead us to three possibilities in the SSA situation: *no* solution, *one* solution, or *two* solutions. Let's investigate these possibilities further, looking for ways to recognize the number of solutions.

EXAMPLE 3 *No Solution.* In △QRS, $q = 15$, $r = 28$, and $Q = 43.6°$. Solve the triangle.

Solution We make a drawing and list the known measures.

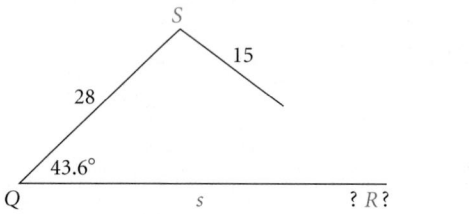

$Q = 43.6°$	$q = 15$
$R = ?$	$r = 28$
$S = ?$	$s = ?$

We observe the SSA situation and use the law of sines to find R:

$$\frac{q}{\sin Q} = \frac{r}{\sin R}$$

$$\frac{15}{\sin 43.6°} = \frac{28}{\sin R} \quad \text{Substituting}$$

$$\sin R = \frac{28 \sin 43.6°}{15} \quad \text{Solving for } \sin R$$

$$\sin R \approx 1.2873.$$

Since there is no angle with a sine greater than 1, there is *no solution*.

▶ **Now Try Exercise 13.**

EXAMPLE 4 *One Solution.* In △XYZ, $x = 23.5$, $y = 9.8$, and $X = 39.7°$. Solve the triangle.

Solution We make a drawing and organize the given information.

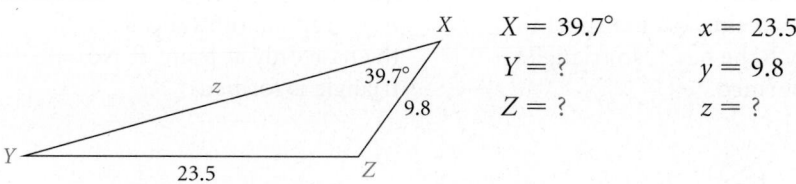

$X = 39.7°$	$x = 23.5$
$Y = ?$	$y = 9.8$
$Z = ?$	$z = ?$

We see the SSA situation and begin by finding Y with the law of sines:

$$\frac{x}{\sin X} = \frac{y}{\sin Y}$$

$$\frac{23.5}{\sin 39.7°} = \frac{9.8}{\sin Y} \quad \text{Substituting}$$

$$\sin Y = \frac{9.8 \sin 39.7°}{23.5} \quad \text{Solving for } \sin Y$$

$$\sin Y \approx 0.2664.$$

There are two angles less than 180° with a sine of 0.2664. They are 15.4° and 164.6°, to the nearest tenth of a degree. An angle of 164.6° cannot be an angle of this triangle because it already has an angle of 39.7° and these two angles would total more than 180°. Thus, 15.4° is the only possibility for Y. Therefore,

$$Z \approx 180° - (39.7° + 15.4°) \approx 124.9°.$$

We now find z:

$$\frac{z}{\sin Z} = \frac{x}{\sin X}$$

$$\frac{z}{\sin 124.9°} = \frac{23.5}{\sin 39.7°} \qquad \text{Substituting}$$

$$z = \frac{23.5 \sin 124.9°}{\sin 39.7°} \qquad \text{Solving for } z$$

$$z \approx 30.2.$$

We now have solved the triangle:

$$X = 39.7°, \qquad x = 23.5,$$
$$Y \approx 15.4°, \qquad y = 9.8,$$
$$Z \approx 124.9°, \qquad z \approx 30.2.$$

▶ Now Try Exercise 5.

The next example illustrates the ambiguous case in which there are two possible solutions.

EXAMPLE 5 *Two Solutions.* In $\triangle ABC$, $b = 15$, $c = 20$, and $B = 29°$. Solve the triangle.

Solution We make a drawing, list the known measures, and see that we again have the SSA situation.

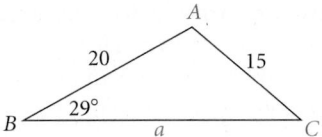

$$A = ? \qquad a = ?$$
$$B = 29° \qquad b = 15$$
$$C = ? \qquad c = 20$$

We first find C:

$$\frac{b}{\sin B} = \frac{c}{\sin C}$$

$$\frac{15}{\sin 29°} = \frac{20}{\sin C} \qquad \text{Substituting}$$

$$\sin C = \frac{20 \sin 29°}{15} \approx 0.6464. \qquad \text{Solving for } \sin C$$

There are two angles less than 180° with a sine of 0.6464. They are 40° and 140°, to the nearest degree. This gives us two possible solutions.

Possible Solution I.

If $C = 40°$, then

$$A = 180° - (29° + 40°) = 111°.$$

Then we find a:

$$\frac{a}{\sin A} = \frac{b}{\sin B}$$

$$\frac{a}{\sin 111°} = \frac{15}{\sin 29°}$$

$$a = \frac{15 \sin 111°}{\sin 29°} \approx 29.$$

These measures make a triangle as shown below; thus we have a solution.

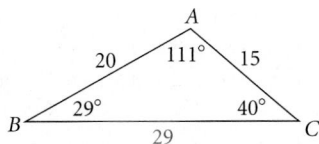

Possible Solution II.

If $C = 140°$, then

$$A = 180° - (29° + 140°) = 11°.$$

Then we find a:

$$\frac{a}{\sin A} = \frac{b}{\sin B}$$

$$\frac{a}{\sin 11°} = \frac{15}{\sin 29°}$$

$$a = \frac{15 \sin 11°}{\sin 29°} \approx 6.$$

These measures make a triangle as shown below; thus we have a second solution.

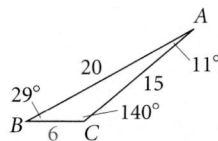

▶ **Now Try Exercise 3.**

Examples 3–5 illustrate the SSA situation. Note that we need not memorize the eight cases or the procedures in finding no solution, one solution, or two solutions. When we are using the law of sines, the sine value leads us directly to the correct solution or solutions.

✦ The Area of a Triangle

The familiar formula for the area of a triangle, $A = \frac{1}{2}bh$, can be used only when h is known. However, we can use the method used to derive the law of sines to derive an area formula that does not involve the height.

Consider a general triangle $\triangle ABC$, with area K, as shown below.

A is acute.

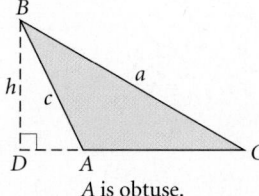

A is obtuse.

Note that in the triangle on the right, $\sin (\angle CAB) = \sin (\angle DAB)$, since $\sin \theta = \sin (180° - \theta)$. Then in each $\triangle ADB$,

$$\sin A = \frac{h}{c}, \quad \text{or} \quad h = c \sin A.$$

Substituting into the formula $K = \frac{1}{2}bh$, we get

$$K = \frac{1}{2}bc \sin A.$$

Any pair of sides and the included angle could have been used. Thus we also have

$$K = \tfrac{1}{2} ab \sin C \quad \text{and} \quad K = \tfrac{1}{2} ac \sin B.$$

> ### The Area of a Triangle
> The area K of any $\triangle ABC$ is one half the product of the lengths of two sides and the sine of the included angle:
>
> $$K = \frac{1}{2} bc \sin A = \frac{1}{2} ab \sin C = \frac{1}{2} ac \sin B.$$

EXAMPLE 6 *Area of a Triangular Garden.* A university landscaping architecture department is designing a garden for a triangular area in a dormitory complex. Two sides of the garden, formed by the sidewalks in front of buildings A and B, measure 172 ft and 186 ft, respectively, and together form a 53° angle. The third side of the garden, formed by the sidewalk along Crossroads Avenue, measures 160 ft. What is the area of the garden to the nearest square foot?

Solution Since we do not know a height of the triangle, we use the area formula:

$$K = \frac{1}{2} ab \sin C$$

$$K = \frac{1}{2} \cdot 186 \text{ ft} \cdot 172 \text{ ft} \cdot \sin 53°$$

$$K \approx 12{,}775 \text{ ft}^2.$$

The area of the garden is approximately 12,775 ft².

▶ Now Try Exercise 25.

7.1   EXERCISE SET

Solve the triangle, if possible.

1. $B = 38°, C = 21°, b = 24$

2. $A = 131°, C = 23°, b = 10$

3. $A = 36.5°, a = 24, b = 34$

4. $B = 118.3°, C = 45.6°, b = 42.1$

5. $C = 61°10', c = 30.3, b = 24.2$

6. $A = 126.5°, a = 17.2, c = 13.5$

7. $c = 3$ mi, $B = 37.48°, C = 32.16°$

8. $a = 2345$ mi, $b = 2345$ mi, $A = 124.67°$

9. $b = 56.78$ yd, $c = 56.78$ yd, $C = 83.78°$

10. $A = 129°32', C = 18°28', b = 1204$ in.

11. $a = 20.01$ cm, $b = 10.07$ cm, $A = 30.3°$

12. $b = 4.157$ km, $c = 3.446$ km, $C = 51°48'$

13. $A = 89°, a = 15.6$ in., $b = 18.4$ in.

14. $C = 46°32', a = 56.2$ m, $c = 22.1$ m

15. $a = 200$ m, $A = 32.76°, C = 21.97°$

16. $B = 115°, c = 45.6$ yd, $b = 23.8$ yd

Find the area of the triangle.

17. $B = 42°, a = 7.2$ ft, $c = 3.4$ ft

18. $A = 17°12', b = 10$ in., $c = 13$ in.

19. $C = 82°54', a = 4$ yd, $b = 6$ yd

20. $C = 75.16°, a = 1.5$ m, $b = 2.1$ m

21. $B = 135.2°, a = 46.12$ ft, $c = 36.74$ ft

22. $A = 113°, b = 18.2$ cm, $c = 23.7$ cm

Solve.

23. *Lunar Crater.*   Points A and B are on opposite sides of a lunar crater. Point C is 50 m from A. The measure of $\angle BAC$ is determined to be 112° and the measure of $\angle ACB$ is determined to be 42°. What is the width of the crater?

24. *Rock Concert.*   In preparation for an outdoor rock concert, a stage crew must determine how far apart to place the two large speaker columns on stage (see the figure below). What generally works best is to place them at 50° angles to the center of the front row. The distance from the center of the front row to each of the speakers is 10 ft. How far apart does the crew need to place the speakers on stage?

Speaker   50°   50°
Stage
10 ft   10 ft

25. *Area of Back Yard.*   A new homeowner has a triangular-shaped back yard. Two of the three sides measure 53 ft and 42 ft and form an included angle of 135°. To determine the amount of fertilizer and grass seed to be purchased, the owner has to know, or at least approximate,

the area of the yard. Find the area of the yard to the nearest square foot.

26. *Boarding Stable.* A rancher operates a boarding stable and temporarily needs to make an extra pen. He has a piece of rope 38 ft long and plans to tie the rope to one end of the barn (*S*) and run the rope around a tree (*T*) and back to the barn (*Q*). The tree is 21 ft from where the rope is first tied, and the rope from the barn to the tree makes an angle of 35° with the barn. Does the rancher have enough rope if he allows $4\frac{1}{2}$ ft at each end to fasten the rope?

27. *Length of Pole.* A pole leans away from the sun at an angle of 7° to the vertical. When the angle of elevation of the sun is 51°, the pole casts a shadow 47 ft long on level ground. How long is the pole?

In Exercises 28–31, keep in mind the two types of bearing considered in Sections 5.2 and 5.3.

28. *Reconnaissance Airplane.* A reconnaissance airplane leaves its airport on the east coast of the United States and flies in a direction of 85°. Because of bad weather, it returns to another airport 230 km to the north of its home base.

For the return trip, it flies in a direction of 283°. What is the total distance that the airplane flew?

29. *Fire Tower.* A ranger in fire tower *A* spots a fire at a direction of 295°. A ranger in fire tower *B*, located 45 mi at a direction of 45° from tower *A*, spots the same fire at a direction of 255°. How far from tower *A* is the fire? from tower *B*?

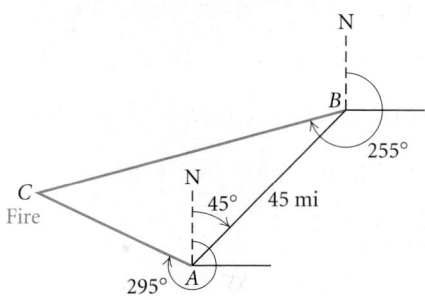

30. *Lighthouse.* A boat leaves lighthouse A and sails 5.1 km. At this time it is sighted from lighthouse B, 7.2 km west of A. The bearing of the boat from B is N65°10′E. How far is the boat from B?

31. *Mackinac Island.* Mackinac Island is located 18 mi N31°20′W of Cheboygan, Michigan, where the Coast Guard cutter Mackinaw is stationed. A freighter in distress radios the Coast Guard cutter for help. It radios its position as S78°40′E of

Mackinac Island and N64°10′E of Cheboygan. How far is the freighter from Cheboygan?

Michigan
Mackinac Island
Cheboygan

32. *Gears.*   Three gears are arranged as shown in the figure below. Find the angle ϕ.

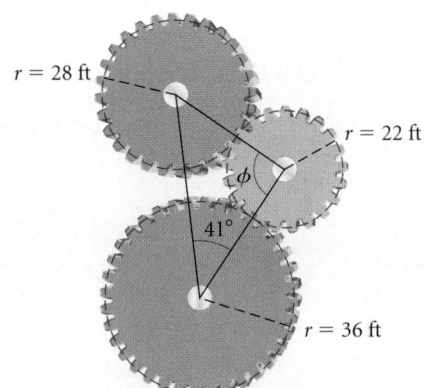

$r = 28$ ft
$r = 22$ ft
ϕ
41°
$r = 36$ ft

Collaborative Discussion and Writing

33. Explain why the law of sines cannot be used to find the first angle when solving a triangle given three sides.

34. We considered eight cases of solving triangles given two sides and an angle opposite one of them. Describe the relationship between side b and the height h in each.

Skill Maintenance

Find the acute angle A, in both radians and degrees, for the given function value.

35. $\cos A = 0.2213$

36. $\cos A = 1.5612$

Convert to decimal degree notation.

37. $18°14′20″$

38. $125°3′42″$

39. Find the absolute value: $|-5|$.

Find the values.

40. $\cos \dfrac{\pi}{6}$

41. $\sin 45°$

42. $\sin 300°$

43. $\cos \left(-\dfrac{2\pi}{3} \right)$

44. Multiply: $(1 - i)(1 + i)$.

Synthesis

45. Prove the following area formulas for a general triangle ABC with area represented by K.

$$K = \frac{a^2 \sin B \sin C}{2 \sin A}$$

$$K = \frac{c^2 \sin A \sin B}{2 \sin C}$$

$$K = \frac{b^2 \sin C \sin A}{2 \sin B}$$

46. *Area of a Parallelogram.*   Prove that the area of a parallelogram is the product of two adjacent sides and the sine of the included angle.

s_1
S
s_2

47. *Area of a Quadrilateral.*   Prove that the area of a quadrilateral is one half the product of the lengths of its diagonals and the sine of the angle between the diagonals.

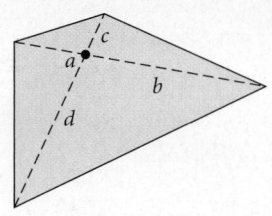

c
a
b
d

48. Find d.

11 in.
50°
15 in.
12 in.
d

49. *Recording Studio.* A musician is constructing an octagonal recording studio in his home. The studio with dimensions shown below is to be built within a rectangular 31′9″ by 29′9″ room. (*Source*: Tony Medeiros, Indianapolis, IN) Point *D* is 9″ from wall 2, and points *C* and *B* are each 9″ from wall 1. Using the law of sines and right triangles, determine to the nearest tenth of an inch how far point *A* is from wall 1 and from wall 4. (For more information on this studio, see Example 2 in Section 7.2.)

The Law of Cosines

◆ Use the law of cosines to solve triangles.

◆ Determine whether the law of sines or the law of cosines should be applied to solve a triangle.

The law of sines is used to solve triangles given a side and two angles (AAS and ASA) or given two sides and an angle opposite one of them (SSA). A second law, called the *law of cosines*, is needed to solve triangles given two sides and the included angle (SAS) or given three sides (SSS).

◆ The Law of Cosines

To derive this property, we consider any △*ABC* placed on a coordinate system. We position the origin at one of the vertices—say, *C*—and the positive half of the x-axis along one of the sides—say, *CB*. Let (x, y) be the coordinates of vertex *A*. Point *B* has coordinates $(a, 0)$ and point *C* has coordinates $(0, 0)$.

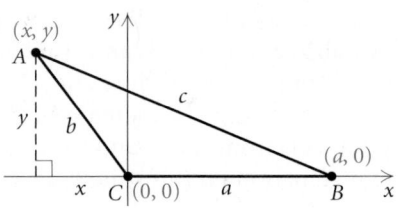

Then $\cos C = \dfrac{x}{b}$, so $x = b \cos C$

and $\sin C = \dfrac{y}{b}$, so $y = b \sin C$.

Thus point *A* has coordinates

$$(b \cos C,\ b \sin C).$$

Next, we use the distance formula to determine c^2:

$$c^2 = (x - a)^2 + (y - 0)^2,$$

or $\quad c^2 = (b \cos C - a)^2 + (b \sin C - 0)^2.$

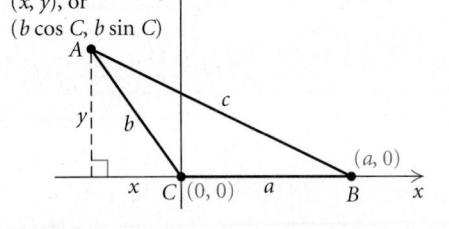

Now we multiply and simplify:

$$
\begin{aligned}
c^2 &= b^2 \cos^2 C - 2ab \cos C + a^2 + b^2 \sin^2 C \\
&= a^2 + b^2(\sin^2 C + \cos^2 C) - 2ab \cos C \\
&= a^2 + b^2 - 2ab \cos C. \qquad \text{Using the identity} \\
& \sin^2 x + \cos^2 x = 1
\end{aligned}
$$

Had we placed the origin at one of the other vertices, we would have obtained

$$a^2 = b^2 + c^2 - 2bc \cos A$$

or $\quad b^2 = a^2 + c^2 - 2ac \cos B.$

The Law of Cosines

In any triangle *ABC*,

$$a^2 = b^2 + c^2 - 2bc \cos A,$$
$$b^2 = a^2 + c^2 - 2ac \cos B,$$

or $\quad c^2 = a^2 + b^2 - 2ab \cos C.$

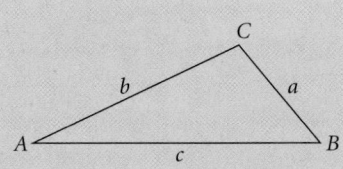

Thus, in any triangle, the square of a side is the sum of the squares of the other two sides, minus twice the product of those sides and the cosine of the included angle. When the included angle is 90°, the law of cosines reduces to the Pythagorean theorem.

✦ Solving Triangles (SAS)

When two sides of a triangle and the included angle are known, we can use the law of cosines to find the third side. The law of cosines or the law of sines can then be used to finish solving the triangle.

EXAMPLE 1 Solve $\triangle ABC$ if $a = 32$, $c = 48$, and $B = 125.2°$.

Solution We first label a triangle with the known and unknown measures.

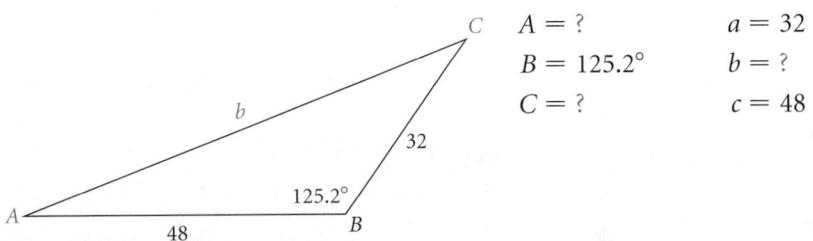

$$A = ? \qquad a = 32$$
$$B = 125.2° \qquad b = ?$$
$$C = ? \qquad c = 48$$

We can find the third side using the law of cosines, as follows:

$$b^2 = a^2 + c^2 - 2ac \cos B$$
$$b^2 = 32^2 + 48^2 - 2 \cdot 32 \cdot 48 \cos 125.2° \qquad \text{Substituting}$$
$$b^2 \approx 5098.8$$
$$b \approx 71.$$

We now have $a = 32$, $b \approx 71$, and $c = 48$, and we need to find the other two angle measures. At this point, we can find them in two ways. One way uses the law of sines. The ambiguous case may arise, however, and we would have to be alert to this possibility. The advantage of using the law of cosines again is that if we solve for the cosine and find that its value is *negative*, then we know that the angle is obtuse. If the value of the cosine is *positive*, then the angle is acute. Thus we use the law of cosines to find a second angle.

Let's find angle A. We select the formula from the law of cosines that contains $\cos A$ and substitute:

$$a^2 = b^2 + c^2 - 2bc \cos A$$
$$32^2 = 71^2 + 48^2 - 2 \cdot 71 \cdot 48 \cos A \qquad \text{Substituting}$$
$$1024 = 5041 + 2304 - 6816 \cos A$$
$$-6321 = -6816 \cos A$$
$$\cos A \approx 0.9273768$$
$$A \approx 22.0°.$$

The third angle is now easy to find:

$$C \approx 180° - (125.2° + 22.0°)$$
$$\approx 32.8°.$$

Thus,

$$A \approx 22.0°, \qquad a = 32,$$
$$B = 125.2°, \qquad b \approx 71,$$
$$C \approx 32.8°, \qquad c = 48.$$

 Now Try Exercise 1.

Due to errors created by rounding, answers may vary depending on the order in which they are found. Had we found the measure of angle C first in Example 1, the angle measures would have been $C \approx 34.1°$ and $A \approx 20.7°$. Variances in rounding also change the answers. Had we used 71.4 for b in Example 1, the angle measures would have been $A \approx 21.5°$ and $C \approx 33.3°$.

Suppose we used the law of sines at the outset in Example 1 to find b. We were given only three measures: $a = 32$, $c = 48$, and $B = 125.2°$. When substituting these measures into the proportions, we see that there is not enough information to use the law of sines:

$$\frac{a}{\sin A} = \frac{b}{\sin B} \rightarrow \frac{32}{\sin A} = \frac{b}{\sin 125.2°},$$
$$\frac{b}{\sin B} = \frac{c}{\sin C} \rightarrow \frac{b}{\sin 125.2°} = \frac{48}{\sin C},$$
$$\frac{a}{\sin A} = \frac{c}{\sin C} \rightarrow \frac{32}{\sin A} = \frac{48}{\sin C}.$$

In all three situations, the resulting equation, after the substitutions, still has two unknowns. Thus we cannot use the law of sines to find b.

EXAMPLE 2 *Recording Studio.* A musician is constructing an octagonal recording studio in his home and needs to determine two distances for the electrician. The dimensions for the most acoustically perfect studio are shown in the figure below. (*Source*: Tony Medeiros, Indianapolis IN) Determine the distances from D to F and from D to B to the nearest tenth of an inch.

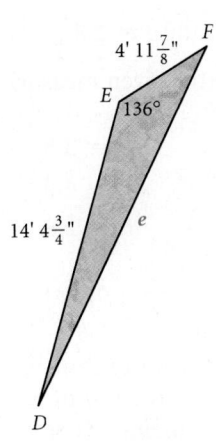

Solution   We begin by connecting points D and F and labeling the known measures of $\triangle DEF$. Converting the measures to decimal notation in inches, we have

$$d = 4'11\frac{7}{8}'' = 59.875 \text{ in.,}$$

$$f = 14'4\frac{3}{4}'' = 172.75 \text{ in.,}$$

$$E = 136°.$$

We can find the measure of the third side, e, using the law of cosines:

$$e^2 = d^2 + f^2 - 2 \cdot d \cdot f \cdot \cos E$$ Using the law of cosines

$$e^2 = (59.875 \text{ in.})^2 + (172.75 \text{ in.})^2$$

$$- 2(59.875 \text{ in.})(172.75 \text{ in.}) \cos 136°$$ Substituting

$$e^2 \approx 48{,}308.4257 \text{ in}^2$$

$$e \approx 219.8 \text{ in.}$$

Thus it is approximately 219.8 in. from D to F.

We continue by connecting points D and B and labeling the known measures of $\triangle DCB$:

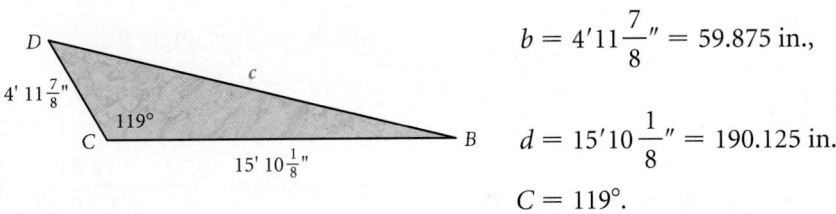

$$b = 4'11\frac{7}{8}'' = 59.875 \text{ in.,}$$

$$d = 15'10\frac{1}{8}'' = 190.125 \text{ in.,}$$

$$C = 119°.$$

Using the law of cosines, we can determine c, the length of the third side:

$$c^2 = b^2 + d^2 - 2 \cdot b \cdot d \cdot \cos C$$ Using the law of cosines

$$c^2 = (59.875 \text{ in.})^2 + (190.125 \text{ in.})^2$$

$$- 2(59.875 \text{ in.})(190.125 \text{ in.}) \cos 119°$$ Substituting

$$c^2 \approx 50{,}770.4191 \text{ in}^2$$

$$c \approx 225.3 \text{ in.}$$

The distance from D to B is approximately 225.3 in.

▶ Now Try Exercise 25.

✦ Solving Triangles (SSS)

When all three sides of a triangle are known, the law of cosines can be used to solve the triangle.

EXAMPLE 3 Solve $\triangle RST$ if $r = 3.5$, $s = 4.7$, and $t = 2.8$.

Solution We sketch a triangle and label it with the given measures.

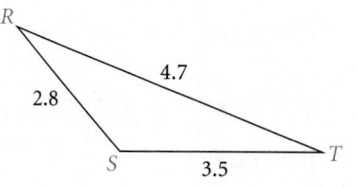

$$
\begin{array}{ll}
R = ? & r = 3.5 \\
S = ? & s = 4.7 \\
T = ? & t = 2.8
\end{array}
$$

Since we do not know any of the angle measures, we cannot use the law of sines. We begin instead by finding an angle with the law of cosines. We choose to find S first and select the formula that contains $\cos S$:

$$s^2 = r^2 + t^2 - 2rt \cos S$$
$$(4.7)^2 = (3.5)^2 + (2.8)^2 - 2(3.5)(2.8) \cos S \qquad \text{Substituting}$$
$$\cos S = \frac{(3.5)^2 + (2.8)^2 - (4.7)^2}{2(3.5)(2.8)}$$
$$\cos S \approx -0.1020408$$
$$S \approx 95.86°.$$

Similarly, we find angle R:

$$r^2 = s^2 + t^2 - 2st \cos R$$
$$(3.5)^2 = (4.7)^2 + (2.8)^2 - 2(4.7)(2.8) \cos R$$
$$\cos R = \frac{(4.7)^2 + (2.8)^2 - (3.5)^2}{2(4.7)(2.8)}$$
$$\cos R \approx 0.6717325$$
$$R \approx 47.80°.$$

Then

$$T \approx 180° - (95.86° + 47.80°) \approx 36.34°.$$

Thus,

$$
\begin{array}{ll}
R \approx 47.80°, & r = 3.5, \\
S \approx 95.86°, & s = 4.7, \\
T \approx 36.34°, & t = 2.8.
\end{array}
$$

▶ Now Try Exercise 3.

EXAMPLE 4 *Knife Bevel.* Knifemakers know that the *bevel* of the blade (the angle formed at the cutting edge of the blade) determines the cutting characteristics of the knife. A small bevel like that of a straight razor makes for a keen edge, but is impractical for heavy-duty cutting because the edge dulls quickly and is prone to chipping. A large bevel is suitable for heavy-duty work like chopping wood. Survival knives, being universal in application, are a compromise between small and large bevels. The diagram at left illustrates the blade of a hand-made Randall Model 18 survival knife. What is its bevel? (*Source:* Randall Made Knives, P.O. Box 1988, Orlando, FL 32802)

Solution We know three sides of a triangle. We can use the law of cosines to find the bevel, angle A.

$$a^2 = b^2 + c^2 - 2bc \cos A$$
$$(0.5)^2 = 2^2 + 2^2 - 2 \cdot 2 \cdot 2 \cdot \cos A$$
$$0.25 = 4 + 4 - 8 \cos A$$
$$\cos A = \frac{4 + 4 - 0.25}{8}$$
$$\cos A = 0.96875$$
$$A \approx 14.36°.$$

Thus the bevel is approximately $14.36°$.

▶ Now Try Exercise 29.

CONNECTING THE CONCEPTS

Choosing the Appropriate Law

The following summarizes the situations in which to use the law of sines and the law of cosines.

To solve an oblique triangle:

Use the *law of sines* for: Use the *law of cosines* for:

AAS   SAS
ASA   SSS
SSA

● ● ●

The law of cosines can also be used for the SSA situation, but since the process involves solving a quadratic equation, we do not include that option in the list above.

EXAMPLE 5 In $\triangle ABC$, three measures are given. Determine which law to use when solving the triangle. You need not solve the triangle.

a) $a = 14, b = 23, c = 10$
b) $a = 207, B = 43.8°, C = 57.6°$
c) $A = 112°, C = 37°, a = 84.7$
d) $B = 101°, a = 960, c = 1042$
e) $b = 17.26, a = 27.29, A = 39°$
f) $A = 61°, B = 39°, C = 80°$

Solution It is helpful to make a drawing of a triangle with the given information. The triangle need not be drawn to scale. The given parts are shown in color.

	FIGURE	SITUATION	LAW TO USE
a)		SSS	Law of Cosines
b)		ASA	Law of Sines
c)		AAS	Law of Sines
d)		SAS	Law of Cosines
e)		SSA	Law of Sines
f)		AAA	Cannot be solved

▶ Now Try Exercises 17 and 19.

STUDY TIP

The InterAct Math Tutorial software that accompanies this text provides practice exercises that correlate at the objective level to the odd-numbered exercises in the text. Each practice exercise is accompanied by an example and guided solution designed to involve students in the solution process. This software is available in your campus lab or on CD-ROM.

7.2 EXERCISE SET

Solve the triangle, if possible.

1. $A = 30°$, $b = 12$, $c = 24$

2. $B = 133°$, $a = 12$, $c = 15$

3. $a = 12$, $b = 14$, $c = 20$

4. $a = 22.3$, $b = 22.3$, $c = 36.1$

5. $B = 72°40'$, $c = 16$ m, $a = 78$ m

6. $C = 22.28°$, $a = 25.4$ cm, $b = 73.8$ cm

7. $a = 16$ m, $b = 20$ m, $c = 32$ m

8. $B = 72.66°$, $a = 23.78$ km, $c = 25.74$ km

9. $a = 2$ ft, $b = 3$ ft, $c = 8$ ft

10. $A = 96°13'$, $b = 15.8$ yd, $c = 18.4$ yd

11. $a = 26.12$ km, $b = 21.34$ km, $c = 19.25$ km

12. $C = 28°43'$, $a = 6$ mm, $b = 9$ mm

13. $a = 60.12$ mi, $b = 40.23$ mi, $C = 48.7°$

14. $a = 11.2$ cm, $b = 5.4$ cm, $c = 7$ cm

15. $b = 10.2$ in., $c = 17.3$ in., $A = 53.456°$

16. $a = 17$ yd, $b = 15.4$ yd, $c = 1.5$ yd

Determine which law applies. Then solve the triangle.

17. $A = 70°$, $B = 12°$, $b = 21.4$

18. $a = 15$, $c = 7$, $B = 62°$

19. $a = 3.3$, $b = 2.7$, $c = 2.8$

20. $a = 1.5$, $b = 2.5$, $A = 58°$

21. $A = 40.2°$, $B = 39.8°$, $C = 100°$

22. $a = 60$, $b = 40$, $C = 47°$

23. $a = 3.6$, $b = 6.2$, $c = 4.1$

24. $B = 110°30'$, $C = 8°10'$, $c = 0.912$

Solve.

25. *Poachers.* A park ranger establishes an observation post from which to watch for poachers. Despite losing her map, the ranger does have a compass and a rangefinder. She observes some poachers, and the rangefinder indicates that they are 500 ft from her position. They are headed toward big game that she knows to be 375 ft from her position. Using her compass, she finds that the poachers' azimuth (the direction measured as an angle from north) is 355° and that of the big game is 42°. What is the distance between the poachers and the game?

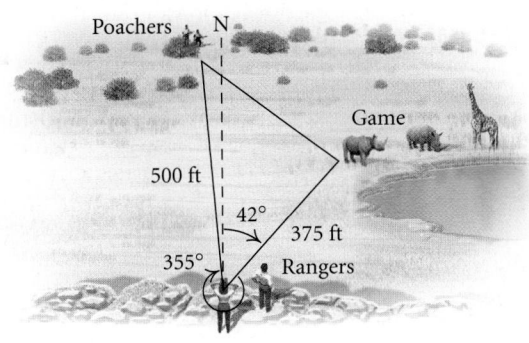

26. *Circus Highwire Act.* A circus highwire act walks up an approach wire to reach a highwire. The approach wire is 122 ft long and is currently anchored so that it forms the maximum allowable angle of 35° with the ground. A greater approach angle causes the aerialists to slip. However, the aerialists find that there is enough room to anchor the approach wire 30 ft back in order to make the approach angle less severe. When this is done, how much farther will they have to walk up the approach wire, and what will the new approach angle be?

27. *In-line Skater.* An in-line skater skates on a fitness trail along the Pacific Ocean from point A to point B. As shown below, two streets intersecting at point C also intersect the trail at A and B. In her car, the skater found the lengths of AC and BC to be approximately 0.5 mi and 1.3 mi, respectively. From a map, she estimates the included angle at C to be 110°. How far did she skate from A to B?

28. *Baseball Bunt.* A batter in a baseball game drops a bunt down the first-base line. It rolls 34 ft at an angle of 25° with the base path. The pitcher's mound is 60.5 ft from home plate. How far must the pitcher travel to pick up the ball? (*Hint*: A baseball diamond is a square.)

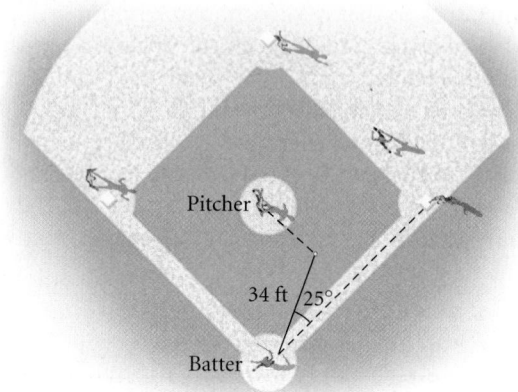

Pitcher

34 ft / 25°

Batter

29. *Survival Trip.*   A group of college students is learning to navigate for an upcoming survival trip. On a map, they have been given three points at which they are to check in. The map also shows the distances between the points. However, to navigate they need to know the angle measurements. Calculate the angles for them.

S

31.6 km   22.4 km

T   U
Start

45.2 km

30. *Ships.*   Two ships leave harbor at the same time. The first sails N15°W at 25 knots (a knot is one nautical mile per hour). The second sails N32°E at 20 knots. After 2 hr, how far apart are the ships?

N

d

N15°W

N32°E

31. *Airplanes.*   Two airplanes leave an airport at the same time. The first flies 150 km/h in a direction of 320°. The second flies 200 km/h in a direction of 200°. After 3 hr, how far apart are the planes?

32. *Slow-Pitch Softball.*   A slow-pitch softball diamond is a square 65 ft on a side. The pitcher's mound is 46 ft from home plate. How far is it from the pitcher's mound to first base?

33. *Isosceles Trapezoid.*   The longer base of an isosceles trapezoid measures 14 ft. The nonparallel sides measure 10 ft, and the base angles measure 80°.

a) Find the length of a diagonal.
b) Find the area.

34. *Area of Sail.*   A sail that is in the shape of an isosceles triangle has a vertex angle of 38°. The angle is included by two sides, each measuring 20 ft. Find the area of the sail.

35. Three circles are arranged as shown in the figure below. Find the length *PQ*.

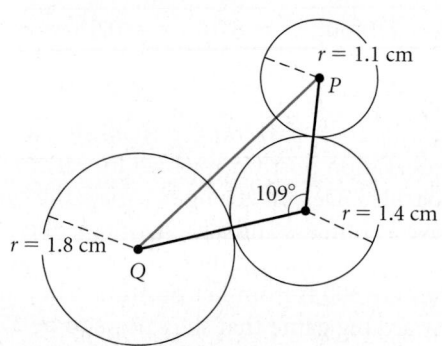

r = 1.1 cm
P

109°
r = 1.4 cm

r = 1.8 cm
Q

36. *Swimming Pool.*   A triangular swimming pool measures 44 ft on one side and 32.8 ft on another side. These sides form an angle that measures 40.8°. How long is the other side?

Collaborative Discussion and Writing

37. Try to solve this triangle using the law of cosines. Then explain why it is easier to solve it using the law of sines.

C

11.1   a

19°
A   B
28.5

38. Explain why we cannot solve a triangle given SAS with the law of sines.

Skill Maintenance

Classify the function as linear, quadratic, cubic, quartic, rational, exponential, logarithmic, or trigonometric.

39. $f(x) = -\frac{3}{4}x^4$

40. $y - 3 = 17x$

41. $y = \sin^2 x - 3 \sin x$

42. $f(x) = 2^{x-1/2}$

43. $f(x) = \dfrac{x^2 - 2x + 3}{x - 1}$

44. $f(x) = 27 - x^3$

45. $y = e^x + e^{-x} - 4$

46. $y = \log_2(x - 2) - \log_2(x + 3)$

47. $f(x) = -\cos(\pi x - 3)$

48. $y = \frac{1}{2}x^2 - 2x + 2$

Synthesis

49. *Canyon Depth.* A bridge is being built across a canyon. The length of the bridge is 5045 ft. From the deepest point in the canyon, the angles of elevation of the ends of the bridge are 78° and 72°. How deep is the canyon?

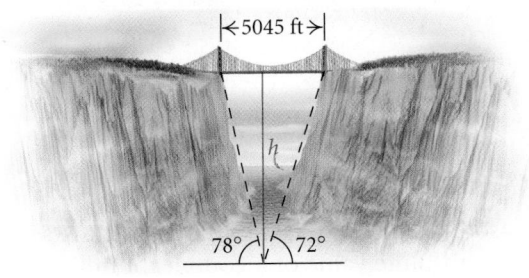

50. *Heron's Formula.* If a, b, and c are the lengths of the sides of a triangle, then the area K of the triangle is given by
$$K = \sqrt{s(s-a)(s-b)(s-c)},$$
where $s = \frac{1}{2}(a + b + c)$. The number s is called the *semiperimeter*. Prove Heron's formula. (*Hint:* Use the area formula $K = \frac{1}{2}bc \sin A$ developed in Section 7.1.) Then use Heron's formula to find the area of the triangular swimming pool described in Exercise 36.

51. *Area of Isosceles Triangle.* Find a formula for the area of an isosceles triangle in terms of the congruent sides and their included angle. Under what conditions will the area of a triangle with fixed congruent sides be maximum?

52. *Reconnaissance Plane.* A reconnaissance plane patrolling at 5000 ft sights a submarine at bearing 35° and at an angle of depression of 25°. A carrier is at bearing 105° and at an angle of depression of 60°. How far is the submarine from the carrier?

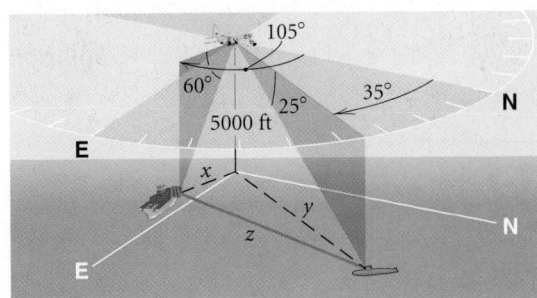

7.3

Complex Numbers: Trigonometric Form

◆ Graph complex numbers.

◆ Given a complex number in standard form, find trigonometric, or polar, notation; and given a complex number in trigonometric form, find standard notation.

◆ Use trigonometric notation to multiply and divide complex numbers.

◆ Use DeMoivre's theorem to raise complex numbers to powers.

◆ Find the nth roots of a complex number.

◆ Graphical Representation

Just as real numbers can be graphed on a line, complex numbers can be graphed on a plane. We graph a complex number $a + bi$ in the same way that we graph an ordered pair of real numbers (a, b). However, in place of an x-axis, we have a real axis, and in place of a y-axis, we have an imaginary axis. Horizontal distances correspond to the real part of a number. Vertical distances correspond to the imaginary part.

> COMPLEX NUMBERS
>
> REVIEW SECTION **2.2.**

EXAMPLE 1   Graph each of the following complex numbers.

a) $3 + 2i$ b) $-4 - 5i$ c) $-3i$

d) $-1 + 3i$ e) 2

Solution

We recall that the absolute value of a real number is its distance from 0 on the number line. The absolute value of a complex number is its distance from the origin in the complex plane. For example, if $z = a + bi$, then using the distance formula, we have

$$|z| = |a + bi| = \sqrt{(a - 0)^2 + (b - 0)^2} = \sqrt{a^2 + b^2}.$$

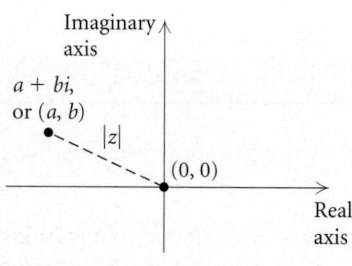

> ### Absolute Value of a Complex Number
>
> The **absolute value of a complex number** $a + bi$ is
>
> $$|a + bi| = \sqrt{a^2 + b^2}.$$

TECHNOLOGY CONNECTION

We can check our work in Example 2 with a graphing calculator. Note that $\sqrt{5} \approx 2.236067977$ and $\frac{4}{5} = 0.8$.

EXAMPLE 2 Find the absolute value of each of the following.

a) $3 + 4i$ **b)** $-2 - i$ **c)** $\frac{4}{5}i$

Solution

a) $|3 + 4i| = \sqrt{3^2 + 4^2} = \sqrt{9 + 16} = \sqrt{25} = 5$

b) $|-2 - i| = \sqrt{(-2)^2 + (-1)^2} = \sqrt{5}$

c) $\left|\frac{4}{5}i\right| = \left|0 + \frac{4}{5}i\right| = \sqrt{0^2 + \left(\frac{4}{5}\right)^2} = \frac{4}{5}$

▶ Now Try Exercises 3 and 5.

✦ Trigonometric Notation for Complex Numbers

Now let's consider a nonzero complex number $a + bi$. Suppose that its absolute value is r. If we let θ be an angle in standard position whose terminal side passes through the point (a, b), as shown in the figure, then

$$\cos \theta = \frac{a}{r}, \quad \text{or} \quad a = r \cos \theta$$

and

$$\sin \theta = \frac{b}{r}, \quad \text{or} \quad b = r \sin \theta.$$

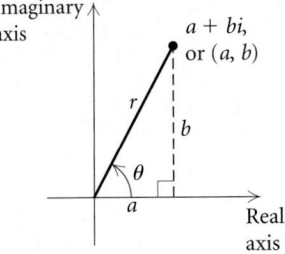

Substituting these values for a and b into the $(a + bi)$ notation, we get

$$a + bi = r \cos \theta + (r \sin \theta)i$$
$$= r(\cos \theta + i \sin \theta).$$

STUDY TIP

It is never too soon to begin reviewing for the final examination. Take a few minutes each week to read the highlighted (blue-screened boxed) formulas, theorems, and properties. There is also at least one Connecting the Concepts feature in each chapter. Spend time reviewing the organized information and art in this special feature.

This is **trigonometric notation** for a complex number $a + bi$. The number r is called the **absolute value** of $a + bi$, and θ is called the **argument** of $a + bi$. Trigonometric notation for a complex number is also called **polar notation.**

> ### Trigonometric Notation for Complex Numbers
> $a + bi = r(\cos \theta + i \sin \theta)$

To find trigonometric notation for a complex number given in **standard notation**, $a + bi$, we must find r and determine the angle θ for which $\sin \theta = b/r$ and $\cos \theta = a/r$.

EXAMPLE 3 Find trigonometric notation for each of the following complex numbers.

a) $1 + i$ **b)** $\sqrt{3} - i$

Solution

a) We note that $a = 1$ and $b = 1$. Then

$$r = \sqrt{a^2 + b^2} = \sqrt{1^2 + 1^2} = \sqrt{2},$$

$$\sin \theta = \frac{b}{r} = \frac{1}{\sqrt{2}}, \quad \text{or} \quad \frac{\sqrt{2}}{2},$$

and

$$\cos \theta = \frac{a}{r} = \frac{1}{\sqrt{2}}, \quad \text{or} \quad \frac{\sqrt{2}}{2}.$$

Since θ is in quadrant I, $\theta = \pi/4$, or $45°$, and we have

$$1 + i = \sqrt{2}\left(\cos \frac{\pi}{4} + i \sin \frac{\pi}{4} \right),$$

or

$$1 + i = \sqrt{2}(\cos 45° + i \sin 45°).$$

b) We see that $a = \sqrt{3}$ and $b = -1$. Then

$$r = \sqrt{(\sqrt{3})^2 + (-1)^2} = 2,$$

$$\sin \theta = \frac{-1}{2} = -\frac{1}{2},$$

and

$$\cos \theta = \frac{\sqrt{3}}{2}.$$

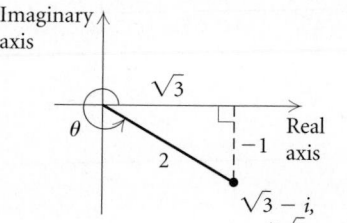

Since θ is in quadrant IV, $\theta = 11\pi/6$, or $330°$, and we have

$$\sqrt{3} - i = 2\left(\cos \frac{11\pi}{6} + i \sin \frac{11\pi}{6} \right),$$

or

$$\sqrt{3} - i = 2(\cos 330° + i \sin 330°).$$

▷ **Now Try Exercise 13.**

In changing to trigonometric notation, note that there are many angles satisfying the given conditions. We ordinarily choose the *smallest positive* angle.

To change from trigonometric notation to standard notation, $a + bi$, we recall that $a = r \cos \theta$ and $b = r \sin \theta$.

TECHNOLOGY ⋯⋯⋯⋯⋯
CONNECTION

We can perform the
computations in Example 4
on a graphing calculator.

Degree Mode

2(cos(120)+isin(120))
                    −1+1.732050808i

Radian Mode

√(8)(cos(7π/4)+isin(7π/4))
                            2−2i

EXAMPLE 4 Find standard notation, $a + bi$, for each of the following complex numbers.

a) $2(\cos 120° + i \sin 120°)$ **b)** $\sqrt{8}\left(\cos \frac{7\pi}{4} + i \sin \frac{7\pi}{4}\right)$

Solution

a) Rewriting, we have

$$2(\cos 120° + i \sin 120°) = 2 \cos 120° + (2 \sin 120°)i.$$

Thus,

$$a = 2 \cos 120° = 2 \cdot \left(-\frac{1}{2}\right) = -1$$

and

$$b = 2 \sin 120° = 2 \cdot \frac{\sqrt{3}}{2} = \sqrt{3},$$

so

$$2(\cos 120° + i \sin 120°) = -1 + \sqrt{3}i.$$

b) Rewriting, we have

$$\sqrt{8}\left(\cos \frac{7\pi}{4} + i \sin \frac{7\pi}{4}\right) = \sqrt{8} \cos \frac{7\pi}{4} + \left(\sqrt{8} \sin \frac{7\pi}{4}\right)i.$$

Thus,

$$a = \sqrt{8} \cos \frac{7\pi}{4} = \sqrt{8} \cdot \frac{\sqrt{2}}{2} = 2$$

and

$$b = \sqrt{8} \sin \frac{7\pi}{4} = \sqrt{8} \cdot \left(-\frac{\sqrt{2}}{2}\right) = -2,$$

so

$$\sqrt{8}\left(\cos \frac{7\pi}{4} + i \sin \frac{7\pi}{4}\right) = 2 - 2i.$$

▶ Now Try Exercises 23 and 27.

✦ Multiplication and Division with Trigonometric Notation

Multiplication of complex numbers is easier to manage with trigonometric notation than with standard notation. We simply multiply the absolute values and add the arguments. Let's state this in a more formal manner.

> ### Complex Numbers: Multiplication
>
> For any complex numbers $r_1(\cos \theta_1 + i \sin \theta_1)$ and $r_2(\cos \theta_2 + i \sin \theta_2)$,
>
> $$r_1(\cos \theta_1 + i \sin \theta_1) \cdot r_2(\cos \theta_2 + i \sin \theta_2)$$
> $$= r_1 r_2[\cos (\theta_1 + \theta_2) + i \sin (\theta_1 + \theta_2)].$$

Proof

$$r_1(\cos \theta_1 + i \sin \theta_1) \cdot r_2(\cos \theta_2 + i \sin \theta_2) =$$
$$r_1 r_2(\cos \theta_1 \cos \theta_2 - \sin \theta_1 \sin \theta_2) + r_1 r_2(\sin \theta_1 \cos \theta_2 + \cos \theta_1 \sin \theta_2)i$$

Now, using identities for sums of angles, we simplify, obtaining

$$r_1 r_2 \cos (\theta_1 + \theta_2) + r_1 r_2 \sin (\theta_1 + \theta_2)i,$$

or

$$r_1 r_2 [\cos (\theta_1 + \theta_2) + i \sin (\theta_1 + \theta_2)],$$

which was to be shown.

TECHNOLOGY
CONNECTION

We can multiply complex numbers on a graphing calculator. The products in Example 5 are shown below.

Degree Mode

```
3(cos(40)+isin(40))*4(cos(20)+
isin(20))

            6+10.39230485i
```

Radian Mode

```
2(cos(π)+isin(π))*3(cos(-π/2)+
isin(-π/2))

                         6i
```

EXAMPLE 5 Multiply and express the answer to each of the following in standard notation.

a) $3(\cos 40° + i \sin 40°)$ and $4(\cos 20° + i \sin 20°)$

b) $2(\cos \pi + i \sin \pi)$ and $3\left[\cos \left(-\dfrac{\pi}{2}\right) + i \sin \left(-\dfrac{\pi}{2}\right)\right]$

Solution

a) $3(\cos 40° + i \sin 40°) \cdot 4(\cos 20° + i \sin 20°)$
$$= 3 \cdot 4 \cdot [\cos (40° + 20°) + i \sin (40° + 20°)]$$
$$= 12(\cos 60° + i \sin 60°)$$
$$= 12\left(\frac{1}{2} + \frac{\sqrt{3}}{2}i\right)$$
$$= 6 + 6\sqrt{3}i$$

b) $2(\cos \pi + i \sin \pi) \cdot 3\left[\cos \left(-\dfrac{\pi}{2}\right) + i \sin \left(-\dfrac{\pi}{2}\right)\right]$
$$= 2 \cdot 3 \cdot \left[\cos \left(\pi + \left(-\frac{\pi}{2}\right)\right) + i \sin \left(\pi + \left(-\frac{\pi}{2}\right)\right)\right]$$
$$= 6\left(\cos \frac{\pi}{2} + i \sin \frac{\pi}{2}\right)$$
$$= 6(0 + i \cdot 1)$$
$$= 6i$$

EXAMPLE 6   Convert to trigonometric notation and multiply:

$$(1 + i)(\sqrt{3} - i).$$

Solution   We first find trigonometric notation:

$$1 + i = \sqrt{2}(\cos 45° + i \sin 45°),$$ See Example 3(a).
$$\sqrt{3} - i = 2(\cos 330° + i \sin 330°).$$ See Example 3(b).

Then we multiply:

$$\sqrt{2}(\cos 45° + i \sin 45°) \cdot 2(\cos 330° + i \sin 330°)$$
$$= 2\sqrt{2}[\cos (45° + 330°) + i \sin (45° + 330°)]$$
$$= 2\sqrt{2}(\cos 375° + i \sin 375°)$$
$$= 2\sqrt{2}(\cos 15° + i \sin 15°).$$ 375° has the same terminal side as 15°.

▶ Now Try Exercise 35.

To divide complex numbers, we divide the absolute values and subtract the arguments. We state this fact below, but omit the proof.

> **Complex Numbers: Division**
>
> For any complex numbers $r_1(\cos \theta_1 + i \sin \theta_1)$ and $r_2(\cos \theta_2 + i \sin \theta_2)$, $r_2 \neq 0$,
>
> $$\frac{r_1(\cos \theta_1 + i \sin \theta_1)}{r_2(\cos \theta_2 + i \sin \theta_2)} = \frac{r_1}{r_2}[\cos (\theta_1 - \theta_2) + i \sin (\theta_1 - \theta_2)].$$

EXAMPLE 7   Divide

$$2\left(\cos \frac{3\pi}{2} + i \sin \frac{3\pi}{2}\right) \quad \text{by} \quad 4\left(\cos \frac{\pi}{2} + i \sin \frac{\pi}{2}\right)$$

and express the solution in standard notation.

Solution   We have

$$\frac{2\left(\cos \dfrac{3\pi}{2} + i \sin \dfrac{3\pi}{2}\right)}{4\left(\cos \dfrac{\pi}{2} + i \sin \dfrac{\pi}{2}\right)} = \frac{2}{4}\left[\cos \left(\frac{3\pi}{2} - \frac{\pi}{2}\right) + i \sin \left(\frac{3\pi}{2} - \frac{\pi}{2}\right)\right]$$

$$= \frac{1}{2}(\cos \pi + i \sin \pi)$$

$$= \frac{1}{2}(-1 + i \cdot 0)$$

$$= -\frac{1}{2}.$$

**TECHNOLOGY ·············
CONNECTION**

We can find quotients, like the one in Example 8, on a graphing calculator.

```
(1 + i)/(1 − i)

                       i
```

EXAMPLE 8   Convert to trigonometric notation and divide:

$$\frac{1 + i}{1 - i}.$$

Solution   We first convert to trigonometric notation:

$$1 + i = \sqrt{2}(\cos 45° + i \sin 45°),$$ See Example 3(a).
$$1 - i = \sqrt{2}(\cos 315° + i \sin 315°).$$

We now divide:

$$\frac{\sqrt{2}(\cos 45° + i \sin 45°)}{\sqrt{2}(\cos 315° + i \sin 315°)}$$

$$= 1[\cos(45° - 315°) + i \sin(45° - 315°)]$$
$$= \cos(-270°) + i \sin(-270°)$$
$$= 0 + i \cdot 1$$
$$= i.$$ ▶ **Now Try Exercise 39.**

✦ Powers of Complex Numbers

An important theorem about powers and roots of complex numbers is named for the French mathematician Abraham DeMoivre (1667–1754). Let's consider the square of a complex number $r(\cos \theta + i \sin \theta)$:

$$[r(\cos \theta + i \sin \theta)]^2 = [r(\cos \theta + i \sin \theta)] \cdot [r(\cos \theta + i \sin \theta)]$$
$$= r \cdot r \cdot [\cos(\theta + \theta) + i \sin(\theta + \theta)]$$
$$= r^2(\cos 2\theta + i \sin 2\theta).$$

Similarly, we see that

$$[r(\cos \theta + i \sin \theta)]^3$$
$$= r \cdot r \cdot r \cdot [\cos(\theta + \theta + \theta) + i \sin(\theta + \theta + \theta)]$$
$$= r^3(\cos 3\theta + i \sin 3\theta).$$

DeMoivre's theorem is the generalization of these results.

> ### DeMoivre's Theorem
>
> For any complex number $r(\cos \theta + i \sin \theta)$ and any natural number n,
>
> $$[r(\cos \theta + i \sin \theta)]^n = r^n(\cos n\theta + i \sin n\theta).$$

EXAMPLE 9 Find each of the following.

a) $(1 + i)^9$ 　　　　　　　　　　　**b)** $(\sqrt{3} - i)^{10}$

Solution

a) We first find trigonometric notation:

$$1 + i = \sqrt{2}(\cos 45° + i \sin 45°). \qquad \text{See Example 3(a).}$$

Then

$$
\begin{aligned}
(1 + i)^9 &= \left[\sqrt{2}(\cos 45° + i \sin 45°)\right]^9 \\
&= \left(\sqrt{2}\right)^9\left[\cos (9 \cdot 45°) + i \sin (9 \cdot 45°)\right] \qquad \text{DeMoivre's theorem} \\
&= 2^{9/2}(\cos 405° + i \sin 405°) \\
&= 16\sqrt{2}(\cos 45° + i \sin 45°) \qquad \text{405° has the same terminal side as 45°.} \\
&= 16\sqrt{2}\left(\frac{\sqrt{2}}{2} + i\frac{\sqrt{2}}{2}\right) \\
&= 16 + 16i.
\end{aligned}
$$

b) We first convert to trigonometric notation:

$$\sqrt{3} - i = 2(\cos 330° + i \sin 330°). \qquad \text{See Example 3(b).}$$

Then

$$
\begin{aligned}
(\sqrt{3} - i)^{10} &= [2(\cos 330° + i \sin 330°)]^{10} \\
&= 2^{10}(\cos 3300° + i \sin 3300°) \\
&= 1024(\cos 60° + i \sin 60°) \qquad \text{3300° has the same terminal side as 60°.} \\
&= 1024\left(\frac{1}{2} + i\frac{\sqrt{3}}{2}\right) \\
&= 512 + 512\sqrt{3}i.
\end{aligned}
$$

▶ **Now Try Exercise 47.**

✦ Roots of Complex Numbers

As we will see, every nonzero complex number has two square roots. A nonzero complex number has three cube roots, four fourth roots, and so on. In general, a nonzero complex number has n different nth roots. They can be found using the formula that we now state but do not prove.

> **Roots of Complex Numbers**
>
> The nth roots of a complex number $r(\cos \theta + i \sin \theta)$, $r \neq 0$, are given by
>
> $$r^{1/n}\left[\cos\left(\frac{\theta}{n} + k \cdot \frac{360°}{n}\right) + i \sin\left(\frac{\theta}{n} + k \cdot \frac{360°}{n}\right)\right],$$
>
> where $k = 0, 1, 2, \ldots, n - 1$.

EXAMPLE 10   Find the square roots of $2 + 2\sqrt{3}i$.

Solution   We first find trigonometric notation:

$$2 + 2\sqrt{3}i = 4(\cos 60° + i \sin 60°).$$

Then $n = 2, 1/n = 1/2$, and $k = 0, 1$; and

$$[4(\cos 60° + i \sin 60°)]^{1/2}$$

$$= 4^{1/2}\left[\cos\left(\frac{60°}{2} + k \cdot \frac{360°}{2}\right) + i \sin\left(\frac{60°}{2} + k \cdot \frac{360°}{2}\right)\right], \quad k = 0, 1$$

$$= 2[\cos(30° + k \cdot 180°) + i \sin(30° + k \cdot 180°), \quad k = 0, 1.$$

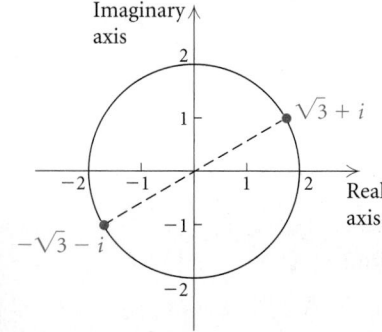

Thus the roots are

$$2(\cos 30° + i \sin 30°) \text{ for } k = 0$$

and $2(\cos 210° + i \sin 210°) \text{ for } k = 1,$

or $\sqrt{3} + i$ and $-\sqrt{3} - i.$ ▶ Now Try Exercise 57.

In Example 10, we see that the two square roots of the number are opposites of each other. We can illustrate this graphically. We also note that the roots are equally spaced about a circle of radius r—in this case, $r = 2$. The roots are $360°/2$, or $180°$ apart.

EXAMPLE 11   Find the cube roots of 1. Then locate them on a graph.

Solution   We begin by finding trigonometric notation:

$$1 = 1(\cos 0° + i \sin 0°).$$

Then $n = 3, 1/n = 1/3$, and $k = 0, 1, 2$; and

$$[1(\cos 0° + i \sin 0°)]^{1/3}$$

$$= 1^{1/3}\left[\cos\left(\frac{0°}{3} + k \cdot \frac{360°}{3}\right) + i \sin\left(\frac{0°}{3} + k \cdot \frac{360°}{3}\right)\right], \quad k = 0, 1, 2.$$

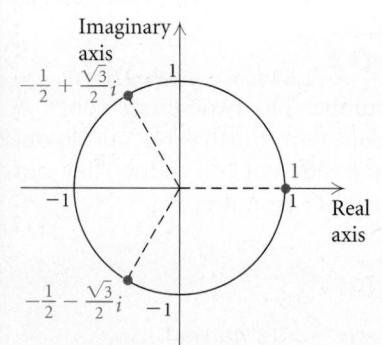

The roots are

$$1(\cos 0° + i \sin 0°), \quad 1(\cos 120° + i \sin 120°),$$

and $1(\cos 240° + i \sin 240°),$

or $1, \quad -\frac{1}{2} + \frac{\sqrt{3}}{2}i, \quad \text{and} \quad -\frac{1}{2} - \frac{\sqrt{3}}{2}i.$

The graphs of the cube roots lie equally spaced about a circle of radius 1. The roots are $360°/3$, or $120°$ apart.   ▶ Now Try Exercise 59.

The nth roots of 1 are often referred to as the **nth roots of unity.** In Example 11, we found the cube roots of unity.

TECHNOLOGY
CONNECTION

Using a graphing calculator set in PARAMETRIC mode, we can approximate the nth roots of a number p. We use the following window and let

$$X_{1T} = (p^{\wedge}(1/n)) \cos T \quad \text{and} \quad Y_{1T} = (p^{\wedge}(1/n)) \sin T.$$

WINDOW

Tmin $= 0$

Tmax $= 360$, if in degree mode, or
$= 2\pi$, if in radian mode

Tstep $= 360/n$, or $2\pi/n$

Xmin $= -3$, Xmax $= 3$, Xscl $= 1$

Ymin $= -2$, Ymax $= 2$, Yscl $= 1$

To find the fifth roots of 8, enter $X_{1T} = (8^{\wedge}(1/5)) \cos T$ and $Y_{1T} = (8^{\wedge}(1/5)) \sin T$. In this case, use DEGREE mode. After the graph has been generated, use the TRACE feature to locate the fifth roots. The T, X, and Y values appear on the screen. What do they represent?

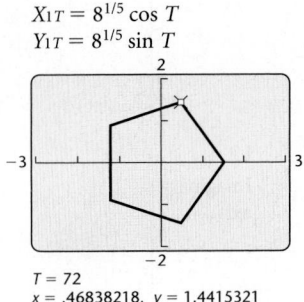

$X_{1T} = 8^{1/5} \cos T$
$Y_{1T} = 8^{1/5} \sin T$

$T = 72$
$x = .46838218,\ y = 1.4415321$

Three of the fifth roots of 8 are approximately

$$1.5157, \qquad 0.46838 + 1.44153i, \quad \text{and} \quad -1.22624 + 0.89092i.$$

Find the other two. Then use a calculator to approximate the cube roots of unity that were found in Example 11. Also approximate the fourth roots of 5 and the tenth roots of unity.

7.3 EXERCISE SET

Graph the complex number and find its absolute value.

1. $4 + 3i$

2. $-2 - 3i$

3. i

4. $-5 - 2i$

5. $4 - i$

6. $6 + 3i$

7. 3

8. $-2i$

Express the indicated number in both standard notation and trigonometric notation.

9.

10.

11.

12.

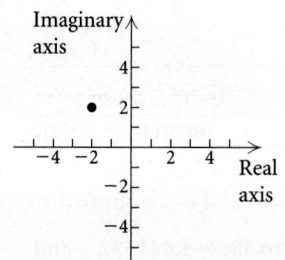

Find trigonometric notation.

13. $1 - i$

14. $-10\sqrt{3} + 10i$

15. $-3i$

16. $-5 + 5i$

17. $\sqrt{3} + i$

18. 4

19. $\dfrac{2}{5}$

20. $7.5i$

21. $-3\sqrt{2} - 3\sqrt{2}i$

22. $-\dfrac{9}{2} - \dfrac{9\sqrt{3}}{2}i$

Find standard notation, $a + bi$.

23. $3(\cos 30° + i \sin 30°)$

24. $6(\cos 120° + i \sin 120°)$

25. $10(\cos 270° + i \sin 270°)$

26. $3(\cos 0° + i \sin 0°)$

27. $\sqrt{8}\left(\cos \dfrac{\pi}{4} + i \sin \dfrac{\pi}{4}\right)$

28. $5\left(\cos \dfrac{\pi}{3} + i \sin \dfrac{\pi}{3}\right)$

29. $2\left(\cos \dfrac{\pi}{2} + i \sin \dfrac{\pi}{2}\right)$

30. $3\left[\cos \left(-\dfrac{3\pi}{4}\right) + i \sin \left(-\dfrac{3\pi}{4}\right)\right]$

31. $\sqrt{2}[\cos(-60°) + i \sin(-60°)]$

32. $4(\cos 135° + i \sin 135°)$

Multiply or divide and leave the answer in trigonometric notation.

33. $\dfrac{12(\cos 48° + i \sin 48°)}{3(\cos 6° + i \sin 6°)}$

34. $5\left(\cos \dfrac{\pi}{3} + i \sin \dfrac{\pi}{3}\right) \cdot 2\left(\cos \dfrac{\pi}{4} + i \sin \dfrac{\pi}{4}\right)$

35. $2.5(\cos 35° + i \sin 35°) \cdot 4.5(\cos 21° + i \sin 21°)$

36. $\dfrac{\dfrac{1}{2}\left(\cos \dfrac{2\pi}{3} + i \sin \dfrac{2\pi}{3}\right)}{\dfrac{3}{8}\left(\cos \dfrac{\pi}{6} + i \sin \dfrac{\pi}{6}\right)}$

Convert to trigonometric notation and then multiply or divide.

37. $(1 - i)(2 + 2i)$

38. $\left(1 + i\sqrt{3}\right)(1 + i)$

39. $\dfrac{1 - i}{1 + i}$

40. $\dfrac{1 - i}{\sqrt{3} - i}$

41. $\left(3\sqrt{3} - 3i\right)(2i)$

42. $\left(2\sqrt{3} + 2i\right)(2i)$

43. $\dfrac{2\sqrt{3} - 2i}{1 + \sqrt{3}i}$

44. $\dfrac{3 - 3\sqrt{3}i}{\sqrt{3} - i}$

Raise the number to the given power and write trigonometric notation for the answer.

45. $\left[2\left(\cos\dfrac{\pi}{3} + i\sin\dfrac{\pi}{3}\right)\right]^3$

46. $[2(\cos 120° + i\sin 120°)]^4$

47. $(1 + i)^6$

48. $\left(-\sqrt{3} + i\right)^5$

Raise the number to the given power and write standard notation for the answer.

49. $[3(\cos 20° + i\sin 20°)]^3$

50. $[2(\cos 10° + i\sin 10°)]^9$

51. $(1 - i)^5$ **52.** $(2 + 2i)^4$

53. $\left(\dfrac{1}{\sqrt{2}} - \dfrac{1}{\sqrt{2}}i\right)^{12}$ **54.** $\left(\dfrac{\sqrt{3}}{2} + \dfrac{1}{2}i\right)^{10}$

Find the square roots of the number.

55. $-i$ **56.** $1 + i$

57. $2\sqrt{2} - 2\sqrt{2}i$ **58.** $-\sqrt{3} - i$

Find the cube roots of the number.

59. i **60.** $-64i$

61. $2\sqrt{3} - 2i$ **62.** $1 - \sqrt{3}i$

63. Find and graph the fourth roots of 16.

64. Find and graph the fourth roots of i.

65. Find and graph the fifth roots of -1.

66. Find and graph the sixth roots of 1.

67. Find the tenth roots of 8.

68. Find the ninth roots of -4.

69. Find the sixth roots of -1.

70. Find the fourth roots of 12.

Find all the complex solutions of the equation.

71. $x^3 = 1$ **72.** $x^5 - 1 = 0$

73. $x^4 + i = 0$ **74.** $x^4 + 81 = 0$

75. $x^6 + 64 = 0$ **76.** $x^5 + \sqrt{3} + i = 0$

Technology Connection

77. Using a graphing calculator, check your work in each of the odd-numbered Exercises 13–53.

78. Using a graphing calculator, check your work in each of the even-numbered Exercises 14–54.

Collaborative Discussion and Writing

79. Find and graph the square roots of $1 - i$. Explain geometrically why they are the opposites of each other.

80. Explain why trigonometric notation for a complex number is not unique, but rectangular, or standard, notation is unique.

Skill Maintenance

Convert to degree measure.

81. $\dfrac{\pi}{12}$ **82.** 3π

Convert to radian measure.

83. $330°$ **84.** $-225°$

85. Find r.

86. Graph these points in the rectangular coordinate system: $(2, -1), (0, 3)$, and $\left(-\dfrac{1}{2}, -4\right)$.

Find the function value using coordinates of points on the unit circle.

87. $\sin\dfrac{2\pi}{3}$ **88.** $\cos\dfrac{\pi}{6}$

89. $\cos\dfrac{\pi}{4}$ **90.** $\sin\dfrac{5\pi}{6}$

Synthesis

Solve.

91. $x^2 + (1 - i)x + i = 0$

92. $3x^2 + (1 + 2i)x + 1 - i = 0$

93. Find polar notation for $(\cos\theta + i\sin\theta)^{-1}$.

94. Show that for any complex number z,
$$|z| = |-z|.$$

95. Show that for any complex number z and its conjugate $\bar{z}$,
$$|z| = |\bar{z}|.$$
(*Hint*: Let $z = a + bi$ and $\bar{z} = a - bi$.)

96. Show that for any complex number z and its conjugate $\bar{z}$,
$$|z\bar{z}| = |z^2|.$$
(*Hint*: Let $z = a + bi$ and $\bar{z} = a - bi$.)

97. Show that for any complex number z,
$$|z^2| = |z|^2.$$

98. Show that for any complex numbers z and w,
$$|z \cdot w| = |z| \cdot |w|.$$
(*Hint*: Let $z = r_1(\cos \theta_1 + i \sin \theta_1)$ and $w = r_2(\cos \theta_2 + i \sin \theta_2)$.)

99. Show that for any complex number z and any nonzero, complex number w,
$$\left| \frac{z}{w} \right| = \frac{|z|}{|w|}. \quad \text{(Use the hint for Exercise 98.)}$$

100. On a complex plane, graph $|z| = 1$.

101. On a complex plane, graph $z + \bar{z} = 3$.

7.4 Polar Coordinates and Graphs

◆ Graph points given their polar coordinates.
◆ Convert from rectangular coordinates to polar coordinates and from polar coordinates to rectangular coordinates.
◆ Convert from rectangular equations to polar equations and from polar equations to rectangular equations.
◆ Graph polar equations.

◆ Polar Coordinates

All graphing throughout this text has been done with rectangular coordinates, (x, y), in the Cartesian coordinate system. We now introduce the polar coordinate system. As shown in the diagram at left, any point P has rectangular coordinates (x, y) and polar coordinates (r, θ). On a polar graph, the origin is called the **pole** and the positive half of the x-axis is called the **polar axis**. The point P can be plotted given the directed angle θ from the polar axis to the ray OP and the directed distance r from the pole to the point. The angle θ can be expressed in degrees or radians.

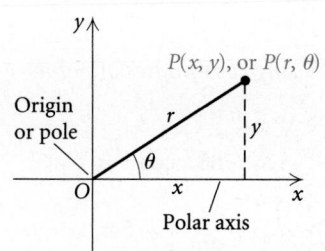

To plot points on a polar graph:
1. Locate the directed angle θ.
2. Move a directed distance r from the pole. If $r > 0$, move along ray OP. If $r < 0$, move in the opposite direction of ray OP.

Polar graph paper, shown below, facilitates plotting. Points B and G illustrate that θ may be in radians. Points E and F illustrate that the polar coordinates of a point are not unique.

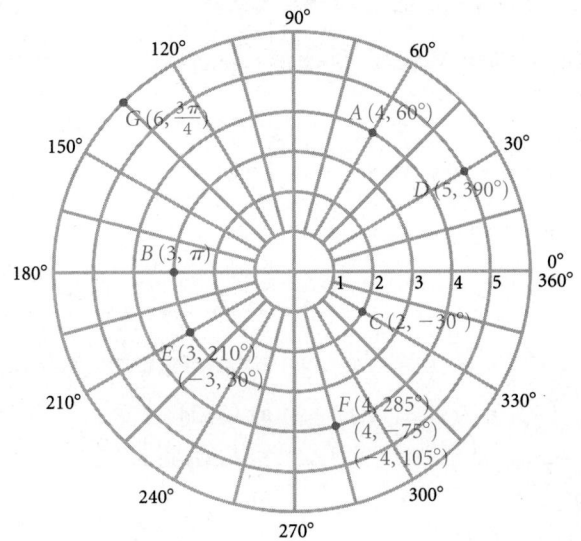

EXAMPLE 1 Graph each of the following points.

a) $A(3, 60°)$ **b)** $B(0, 10°)$

c) $C(-5, 120°)$ **d)** $D(1, -60°)$

e) $E\left(2, \dfrac{3\pi}{2}\right)$ **f)** $F\left(-4, \dfrac{\pi}{3}\right)$

Solution

▶ Now Try Exercises 3 and 7.

To convert from rectangular to polar coordinates and from polar to rectangular coordinates, we need to recall the following relationships.

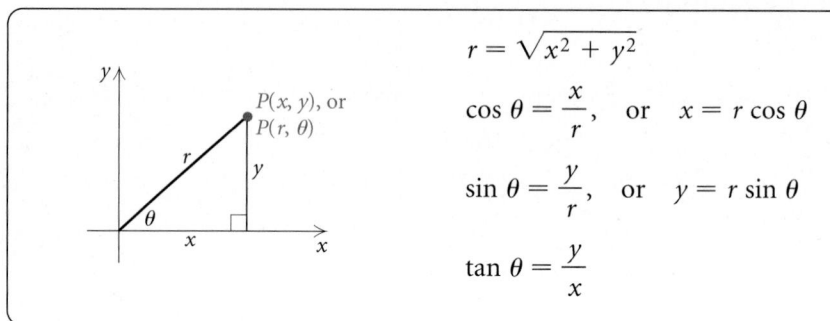

$$r = \sqrt{x^2 + y^2}$$

$$\cos \theta = \frac{x}{r}, \quad \text{or} \quad x = r \cos \theta$$

$$\sin \theta = \frac{y}{r}, \quad \text{or} \quad y = r \sin \theta$$

$$\tan \theta = \frac{y}{x}$$

EXAMPLE 2   Convert each of the following to polar coordinates.

a) $(3, 3)$ b) $\left(2\sqrt{3}, -2\right)$

Solution

a) We first find r:

$$r = \sqrt{3^2 + 3^2} = \sqrt{18} = 3\sqrt{2}.$$

Then we determine θ:

$$\tan \theta = \frac{3}{3} = 1; \quad \text{therefore,} \quad \theta = 45°, \text{or } \frac{\pi}{4}.$$

We know that $\theta = \pi/4$ and not $5\pi/4$ since $(3, 3)$ is in quadrant I. Thus, $(r, \theta) = \left(3\sqrt{2}, 45°\right)$, or $\left(3\sqrt{2}, \pi/4\right)$. Other possibilities for polar coordinates include $\left(3\sqrt{2}, -315°\right)$ and $\left(-3\sqrt{2}, 5\pi/4\right)$.

b) We first find r:

$$r = \sqrt{\left(2\sqrt{3}\right)^2 + (-2)^2} = \sqrt{12 + 4} = \sqrt{16} = 4.$$

Then we determine θ:

$$\tan \theta = \frac{-2}{2\sqrt{3}} = -\frac{1}{\sqrt{3}}; \quad \text{therefore,} \quad \theta = 330°, \text{or } \frac{11\pi}{6}.$$

Thus, $(r, \theta) = (4, 330°)$, or $(4, 11\pi/6)$. Other possibilities for polar coordinates for this point include $(4, -\pi/6)$ and $(-4, 150°)$.

▶ Now Try Exercise 19.

It is easier to convert from polar to rectangular coordinates than from rectangular to polar coordinates.

EXAMPLE 3 Convert each of the following to rectangular coordinates.

a) $\left(10, \dfrac{\pi}{3}\right)$ **b)** $(-5, 135°)$

Solution

a) The ordered pair $(10, \pi/3)$ gives us $r = 10$ and $\theta = \pi/3$. We now find x and y:

$$x = r \cos \theta = 10 \cos \frac{\pi}{3} = 10 \cdot \frac{1}{2} = 5$$

and

$$y = r \sin \theta = 10 \sin \frac{\pi}{3} = 10 \cdot \frac{\sqrt{3}}{2} = 5\sqrt{3}.$$

Thus, $(x, y) = \left(5, 5\sqrt{3}\right)$.

b) From the ordered pair $(-5, 135°)$, we know that $r = -5$ and $\theta = 135°$. We now find x and y:

$$x = -5 \cos 135° = -5 \cdot \left(-\frac{\sqrt{2}}{2}\right) = \frac{5\sqrt{2}}{2}$$

and

$$y = -5 \sin 135° = -5 \cdot \left(\frac{\sqrt{2}}{2}\right) = -\frac{5\sqrt{2}}{2}.$$

Thus, $(x, y) = \left(\dfrac{5\sqrt{2}}{2}, -\dfrac{5\sqrt{2}}{2}\right)$. ▶ Now Try Exercises 27 and 33.

◆ Polar and Rectangular Equations

Some curves have simpler equations in polar coordinates than in rectangular coordinates. For others, the reverse is true.

EXAMPLE 4 Convert each of the following to a polar equation.

a) $x^2 + y^2 = 25$ **b)** $2x - y = 5$

Solution

a) We have

$$
\begin{aligned}
x^2 + y^2 &= 25 \\
(r \cos \theta)^2 + (r \sin \theta)^2 &= 25 \quad \text{Substituting for } x \text{ and } y \\
r^2 \cos^2 \theta + r^2 \sin^2 \theta &= 25 \\
r^2(\cos^2 \theta + \sin^2 \theta) &= 25 \\
r^2 &= 25 \quad \cos^2 \theta + \sin^2 \theta = 1 \\
r &= 5.
\end{aligned}
$$

This example illustrates that the polar equation of a circle centered at the origin is much simpler than the rectangular equation.

b) We have

$$2x - y = 5$$
$$2(r \cos \theta) - (r \sin \theta) = 5$$
$$r(2 \cos \theta - \sin \theta) = 5.$$

In this example, we see that the rectangular equation is simpler than the polar equation.

▶ Now Try Exercises 39 and 43.

EXAMPLE 5 Convert each of the following to a rectangular equation.

a) $r = 4$

b) $r \cos \theta = 6$

c) $r = 2 \cos \theta + 3 \sin \theta$

Solution

a) We have

$$r = 4$$
$$\sqrt{x^2 + y^2} = 4 \qquad \text{Substituting for } r$$
$$x^2 + y^2 = 16. \qquad \text{Squaring}$$

In squaring, we must be careful not to introduce solutions of the equation that are not already present. In this case, we did not, because the graph of either equation is a circle of radius 4 centered at the origin.

b) We have

$$r \cos \theta = 6$$
$$x = 6. \qquad x = r \cos \theta$$

The graph of $r \cos \theta = 6$, or $x = 6$, is a vertical line.

c) We have

$$r = 2 \cos \theta + 3 \sin \theta$$
$$r^2 = 2r \cos \theta + 3r \sin \theta \qquad \text{Multiplying both sides by } r$$
$$x^2 + y^2 = 2x + 3y. \qquad \begin{array}{l}\text{Substituting } x^2 + y^2 \text{ for } r^2, \\ x \text{ for } r \cos \theta, \text{ and } y \text{ for } r \sin \theta\end{array}$$

▶ Now Try Exercises 51 and 55.

✦ Graphing Polar Equations

To graph a polar equation, we can make a table of values, choosing values of θ and calculating corresponding values of r. We plot the points and complete the graph, as we do when graphing a rectangular equation. A difference occurs in the case of a polar equation, however, because as θ increases sufficiently, points may begin to repeat and the curve will be traced again and again. When this happens, the curve is complete.

EXAMPLE 6   Graph: $r = 1 - \sin\theta$.

Solution   We first make a table of values. Note that the points begin to repeat at $\theta = 360°$. We plot these points and draw the curve, as shown below.

θ	r
0°	1
15°	0.7412
30°	0.5
45°	0.2929
60°	0.1340
75°	0.0341
90°	0
105°	0.0341
120°	0.1340
135°	0.2929
150°	0.5
165°	0.7412
180°	1

θ	r
195°	1.2588
210°	1.5
225°	1.7071
240°	1.8660
255°	1.9659
270°	2
285°	1.9659
300°	1.8660
315°	1.7071
330°	1.5
345°	1.2588
360°	1
375°	0.7412
390°	0.5

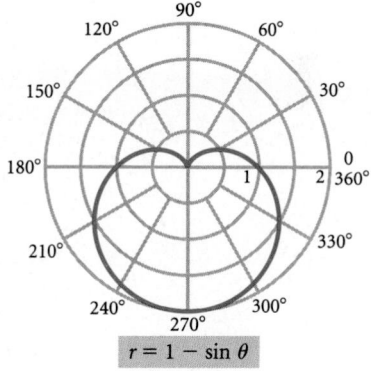

$r = 1 - \sin\theta$

Because of its heart shape, this curve is called a *cardioid*.

▶ Now Try Exercise 69.

TECHNOLOGY CONNECTION

We can graph polar equations using a graphing calculator. The equation usually must be written first in the form $r = f(\theta)$. It is necessary to decide on not only the best window dimensions but also the range of values for θ. Typically, we begin with a range of 0 to 2π for θ in radians and 0° to 360° for θ in degrees. Because most polar graphs are curved, it is important to square the window to minimize distortion.

Graph $r = 4 \sin 3\theta$. Begin by setting the calculator in POLAR mode, and use either of the following windows:

WINDOW (Radians)	WINDOW (Degrees)
θmin = 0	θmin = 0
θmax = 2π	θmax = 360
θstep = $\pi/24$	θstep = 1
Xmin = −9	Xmin = −9
Xmax = 9	Xmax = 9
Xscl = 1	Xscl = 1
Ymin = −6	Ymin = −6
Ymax = 6	Ymax = 6
Yscl = 1	Yscl = 1

$r = 4 \sin 3\theta$

We observe the same graph in both windows. The calculator allows us to view the curve as it is formed.

Now graph each of the following equations and observe the effect of changing the coefficient of $\sin 3\theta$ and the coefficient of θ:

$$r = 2 \sin 3\theta, \quad r = 6 \sin 3\theta, \quad r = 4 \sin \theta,$$
$$r = 4 \sin 5\theta, \quad r = 4 \sin 2\theta, \quad r = 4 \sin 4\theta.$$

Polar equations of the form $r = a \cos n\theta$ and $r = a \sin n\theta$ have rose-shaped curves. The number a determines the length of the petals, and the number n determines the number of petals. If n is odd, there are n petals. If n is even, there are $2n$ petals.

EXAMPLE 7 Graph each of the following polar equations. Try to visualize the shape of the curve before graphing it.

a) $r = 3$
b) $r = 5 \sin \theta$
c) $r = 2 \csc \theta$

Solution

For each graph, we can begin with a table of values. Then we plot points and complete the graph.

a) $r = 3$

For all values of θ, r is 3. Thus the graph of $r = 3$ is a circle of radius 3 centered at the origin.

θ	r
0°	3
60°	3
135°	3
210°	3
300°	3
360°	3

$r = 3$

We can verify our graph by converting to the equivalent rectangular equation. For $r = 3$, we substitute $\sqrt{x^2 + y^2}$ for r and square. The resulting equation,

$$x^2 + y^2 = 3^2,$$

is the equation of a circle with radius 3 centered at the origin.

b) $r = 5 \sin \theta$

θ	r
0°	0
15°	1.2941
30°	2.5
45°	3.5355
60°	4.3301
75°	4.8296
90°	5
105°	4.8296
120°	4.3301
135°	3.5355
150°	2.5
165°	1.2941
180°	0

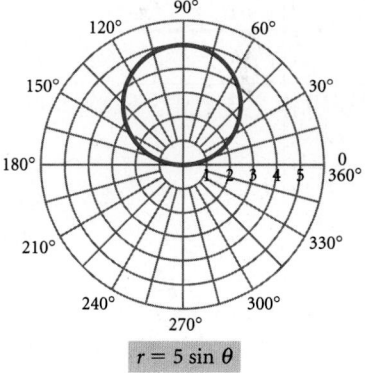

$r = 5 \sin \theta$

c) $r = 2 \csc \theta$

We can rewrite $r = 2 \csc \theta$ as $r = 2/\sin \theta$.

θ	r
0°	Not defined
15°	7.7274
30°	4
45°	2.8284
60°	2.3094
75°	2.0706
90°	2
105°	2.0706
120°	2.3094
135°	2.8284
150°	4
165°	7.7274
180°	Not defined

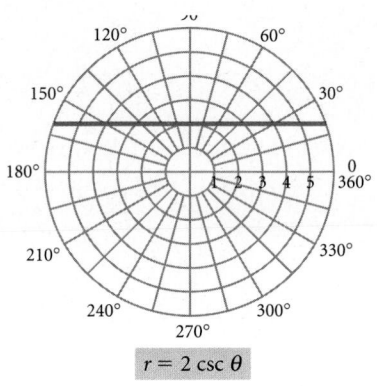

$r = 2 \csc \theta$

▶ Now Try Exercise 63.

$y = 2$

We can check our graph in Example 7(c) by converting the polar equation to the equivalent rectangular equation:

$$r = 2 \csc \theta$$

$$r = \frac{2}{\sin \theta}$$

$$r \sin \theta = 2$$

$$y = 2. \quad \text{Substituting } y \text{ for } r \sin \theta$$

The graph of $y = 2$ is a horizontal line passing through $(0, 2)$ on a rectangular grid.

A

B

C

D

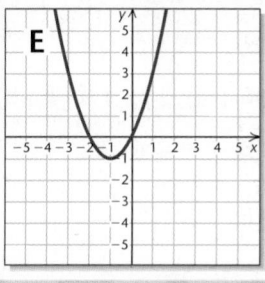

E

Visualizing the Graph

Match the equation with its graph.

1. $f(x) = 2^{(1/2)x}$

2. $y = -2 \sin x$

3. $y = (x + 1)^2 - 1$

4. $f(x) = \dfrac{x - 3}{x^2 + x - 6}$

5. $r = 1 + \sin \theta$

6. $f(x) = 2 \log x + 3$

7. $(x - 3)^2 + y^2 = \dfrac{25}{4}$

8. $y = -\cos\left(x - \dfrac{\pi}{2}\right)$

9. $r = 3 \cos 2\theta$

10. $f(x) = x^4 - x^3 + x^2 - x$

Answers on page A-53

F

G

H

I

J

7.4 EXERCISE SET

Graph the point on a polar grid.

1. $(2, 45°)$ **2.** $(4, \pi)$ **3.** $(3.5, 210°)$

4. $(-3, 135°)$ **5.** $\left(1, \dfrac{\pi}{6}\right)$ **6.** $(2.75, 150°)$

7. $\left(-5, \dfrac{\pi}{2}\right)$ **8.** $(0, 15°)$ **9.** $(3, -315°)$

10. $\left(1.2, -\dfrac{2\pi}{3}\right)$ **11.** $(4.3, -60°)$ **12.** $(3, 405°)$

Find polar coordinates of points A, B, C, and D. Give three answers for each point.

13.

14.

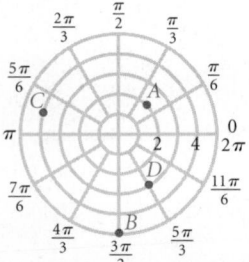

Find the polar coordinates of the point. Express the angle in degrees and then in radians, using the smallest possible positive angle.

15. $(0, -3)$ **16.** $(-4, 4)$

17. $\left(3, -3\sqrt{3}\right)$ **18.** $\left(-\sqrt{3}, 1\right)$

19. $\left(4\sqrt{3}, -4\right)$ **20.** $\left(2\sqrt{3}, 2\right)$

21. $\left(-\sqrt{2}, -\sqrt{2}\right)$ **22.** $\left(-3, 3\sqrt{3}\right)$

23. $\left(1, \sqrt{3}\right)$ **24.** $(0, -1)$

25. $\left(\dfrac{5\sqrt{2}}{2}, -\dfrac{5\sqrt{2}}{2}\right)$ **26.** $\left(-\dfrac{3}{2}, -\dfrac{3\sqrt{3}}{2}\right)$

Find the rectangular coordinates of the point.

27. $(5, 60°)$ **28.** $(0, -23°)$

29. $(-3, 45°)$ **30.** $(6, 30°)$

31. $(3, -120°)$ **32.** $\left(7, \dfrac{\pi}{6}\right)$

33. $\left(-2, \dfrac{5\pi}{3}\right)$ **34.** $(1.4, 225°)$

35. $(2, 210°)$ **36.** $\left(1, \dfrac{7\pi}{4}\right)$

37. $\left(-6, \dfrac{5\pi}{6}\right)$ **38.** $(4, 180°)$

Convert to a polar equation.

39. $3x + 4y = 5$ **40.** $5x + 3y = 4$

41. $x = 5$ **42.** $y = 4$

43. $x^2 + y^2 = 36$ **44.** $x^2 - 4y^2 = 4$

45. $x^2 = 25y$ **46.** $2x - 9y + 3 = 0$

47. $y^2 - 5x - 25 = 0$ **48.** $x^2 + y^2 = 8y$

49. $x^2 - 2x + y^2 = 0$ **50.** $3x^2 y = 81$

Convert to a rectangular equation.

51. $r = 5$ **52.** $\theta = \dfrac{3\pi}{4}$

53. $r \sin \theta = 2$ **54.** $r = -3 \sin \theta$

55. $r + r \cos \theta = 3$ **56.** $r = \dfrac{2}{1 - \sin \theta}$

57. $r - 9 \cos \theta = 7 \sin \theta$ **58.** $r + 5 \sin \theta = 7 \cos \theta$

59. $r = 5 \sec \theta$ **60.** $r = 3 \cos \theta$

61. $\theta = \dfrac{5\pi}{3}$ **62.** $r = \cos \theta - \sin \theta$

Graph the equation.

63. $r = \sin \theta$ **64.** $r = 1 - \cos \theta$

65. $r = 4 \cos 2\theta$ **66.** $r = 1 - 2 \sin \theta$

67. $r = \cos \theta$ **68.** $r = 2 \sec \theta$

69. $r = 2 - \cos 3\theta$ **70.** $r = \dfrac{1}{1 + \cos \theta}$

Technology Connection

Use a graphing calculator to convert from rectangular coordinates to polar coordinates. Express the answer in both degrees and radians, using the smallest possible positive angle.

71. $(3, 7)$

72. $\left(-2, -\sqrt{5}\right)$

73. $\left(-\sqrt{10}, 3.4\right)$

74. $(0.9, -6)$

Use a graphing calculator to convert from polar coordinates to rectangular coordinates. Round the coordinates to the nearest hundredth.

75. $(3, -43°)$

76. $\left(-5, \dfrac{\pi}{7}\right)$

77. $\left(-4.2, \dfrac{3\pi}{5}\right)$

78. $(2.8, 166°)$

In Exercises 79–90, use a graphing calculator to match the equation with one of figures (a)–(l), which follow. Try matching the graphs mentally before using a calculator.

a)

b)

c)

d)

e)

f)

g)

h)

i)

j)

k)

l)

79. $r = 3 \sin 2\theta$

80. $r = 4 \cos \theta$

81. $r = \theta$

82. $r^2 = \sin 2\theta$

83. $r = \dfrac{5}{1 + \cos \theta}$

84. $r = 1 + 2 \sin \theta$

85. $r = 3 \cos 2\theta$

86. $r = 3 \sec \theta$

87. $r = 3 \sin \theta$

88. $r = 4 \cos 5\theta$

89. $r = 2 \sin 3\theta$

90. $r \sin \theta = 6$

Graph.

91. $r = \sin \theta \tan \theta$ (Cissoid)

92. $r = 3\theta$ (Spiral of Archimedes)

93. $r = e^{\theta/10}$ (Logarithmic spiral)

94. $r = 10^{2\theta}$ (Logarithmic spiral)

95. $r = \cos 2\theta \sec \theta$ (Strophoid)

96. $r = \cos 2\theta - 2$ (Peanut)

97. $r = \frac{1}{4} \tan^2 \theta \sec \theta$ (Semicubical parabola)

98. $r = \sin 2\theta + \cos \theta$ (Twisted sister)

Collaborative Discussion and Writing

99. Explain why the rectangular coordinates of a point are unique and the polar coordinates of a point are not unique.

100. Give an example of an equation that is easier to graph in polar notation than in rectangular notation and explain why.

Skill Maintenance

Solve.

101. $2x - 4 = x + 8$ **102.** $4 - 5y = 3$

Graph.

103. $y = 2x - 5$ **104.** $4x - y = 6$

105. $x = -3$ **106.** $y = 0$

Synthesis

107. Convert to a rectangular equation:

$$r = \sec^2 \frac{\theta}{2}.$$

108. The center of a regular hexagon is at the origin, and one vertex is the point $(4, 0°)$. Find the coordinates of the other vertices.

7.5 Vectors and Applications

- ◆ Determine whether two vectors are equivalent.
- ◆ Find the sum, or resultant, of two vectors.
- ◆ Resolve a vector into its horizontal and vertical components.
- ◆ Solve applied problems involving vectors.

We measure some quantities using only their magnitudes. For example, we describe time, length, and mass using units like seconds, feet, and kilograms, respectively. However, to measure quantities like **displacement, velocity,** or **force,** we need to describe a *magnitude* and a *direction.* Together magnitude and direction describe a **vector.** The following are some examples.

Displacement

An object moves a certain distance in a certain direction.

A surveyor steps 20 yd to the northeast.

A hiker follows a trail 5 mi to the west.

A batter hits a ball 100 m along the left-field line.

Velocity

An object travels at a certain speed in a certain direction.

A breeze is blowing 15 mph from the northwest.

An airplane is traveling 450 km/h in a direction of 243°.

Force

A push or pull is exerted on an object in a certain direction.

A force of 200 lb is required to pull a cart up a 30° incline.

A 25-lb force is required to lift a box upward.

A force of 15 newtons is exerted downward on the handle of a jack. (A newton, abbreviated N, is a unit of force used in physics, and 1 N ≈ 0.22 lb.)

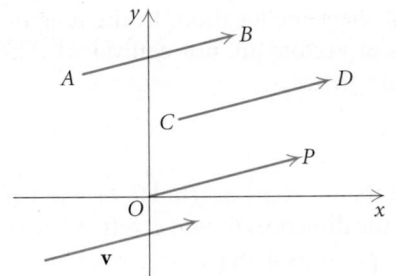

✦ Vectors

Vectors can be graphically represented by directed line segments. The length is chosen, according to some scale, to represent the **magnitude of the vector,** and the direction of the directed line segment represents the **direction of the vector.** For example, if we let 1 cm represent 5 km/h, then a 15-km/h wind from the northwest would be represented by a directed line segment 3 cm long, as shown in the figure at left.

> ### *Vector*
>
> A **vector** in the plane is a directed line segment. Two vectors are **equivalent** if they have the same *magnitude* and *direction.*

Consider a vector drawn from point A to point B. Point A is called the **initial point** of the vector, and point B is called the **terminal point.** Symbolic notation for this vector is $\overrightarrow{AB}$ (read "vector AB"). Vectors are also denoted by boldface letters such as $\mathbf{u}$, $\mathbf{v}$, and $\mathbf{w}$. The four vectors in the figure at left have the *same* length and direction. Thus they represent **equivalent** vectors; that is,

$$\overrightarrow{AB} = \overrightarrow{CD} = \overrightarrow{OP} = \mathbf{v}.$$

In the context of vectors, we use $=$ to mean equivalent.

The length, or **magnitude,** of $\overrightarrow{AB}$ is expressed as $|\overrightarrow{AB}|$. In order to determine whether vectors are equivalent, we find their magnitudes and directions.

EXAMPLE 1 The vectors $\mathbf{u}$, $\overrightarrow{OR}$, and $\mathbf{w}$ are shown in the figure below. Show that $\mathbf{u} = \overrightarrow{OR} = \mathbf{w}$.

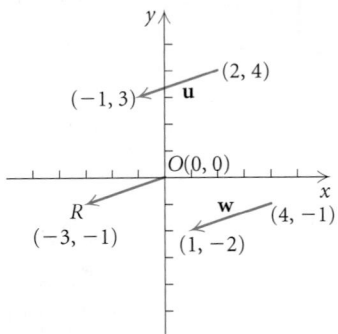

Solution We first find the length of each vector using the distance formula.

$$|\mathbf{u}| = \sqrt{[2 - (-1)]^2 + (4 - 3)^2} = \sqrt{9 + 1} = \sqrt{10},$$
$$|\overrightarrow{OR}| = \sqrt{[0 - (-3)]^2 + [0 - (-1)]^2} = \sqrt{9 + 1} = \sqrt{10},$$
$$|\mathbf{w}| = \sqrt{(4 - 1)^2 + [-1 - (-2)]^2} = \sqrt{9 + 1} = \sqrt{10}.$$

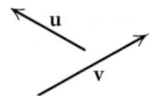

u ≠ **v** (not equivalent)
Different magnitudes;
different directions

u ≠ **v**
Same magnitude;
different directions

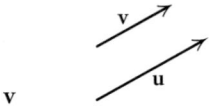

u ≠ **v**
Different magnitudes;
same direction

u = **v**
Same magnitude;
same direction

Vector sum
5
3
4

Thus

$$|\mathbf{u}| = |\overrightarrow{OR}| = |\mathbf{w}|.$$

The vectors **u**, $\overrightarrow{OR}$, and **w** appear to go in the same direction so we check their slopes. If the lines that they are on all have the same slope, the vectors have the same direction. We calculate the slopes:

$$\text{Slope} = \overset{\mathbf{u}}{\underset{}{\frac{4-3}{2-(-1)}}} = \overset{\overrightarrow{OR}}{\underset{}{\frac{0-(-1)}{0-(-3)}}} = \overset{\mathbf{w}}{\underset{}{\frac{-1-(-2)}{4-1}}} = \frac{1}{3}.$$

Since **u**, $\overrightarrow{OR}$, and **w** have the *same* magnitude and the *same* direction,

$$\mathbf{u} = \overrightarrow{OR} = \mathbf{w}.$$

▶ Now Try Exercise 1.

Keep in mind that the equivalence of vectors requires only the same magnitude and the same direction—not the same location. In the illustrations at left, each of the first three pairs of vectors are not equivalent. The fourth set of vectors is an example of equivalence.

◆ Vector Addition

Suppose a person takes 4 steps east and then 3 steps north. He or she will then be 5 steps from the starting point in the direction shown at left. A vector 4 units long and pointing to the right represents 4 steps east and a vector 3 units long and pointing up represents 3 steps north. The **sum** of the two vectors is the vector 5 steps in magnitude and in the direction shown. The sum is also called the **resultant** of the two vectors.

In general, two nonzero vectors **u** and **v** can be added geometrically by placing the initial point of **v** at the terminal point of **u** and then finding the vector that has the same initial point as **u** and the same terminal point as **v**, as shown in the following figure.

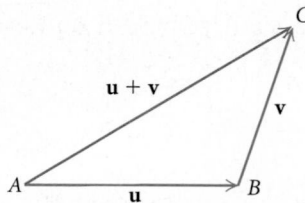

The sum **u** + **v** is the vector represented by the directed line segment from the initial point *A* of **u** to the terminal point *C* of **v**. That is, if

$$\mathbf{u} = \overrightarrow{AB} \quad \text{and} \quad \mathbf{v} = \overrightarrow{BC},$$

then

$$\mathbf{u} + \mathbf{v} = \overrightarrow{AB} + \overrightarrow{BC} = \overrightarrow{AC}.$$

We can also describe vector addition by placing the initial points of the vectors together, completing a parallelogram, and finding the diagonal of the parallelogram. (See the figure on the left on the following page.) This description of addition is sometimes called the **parallelogram law** of vector addition. Vector addition is **commutative.** As shown in the figure on the right below, both **u** + **v** and **v** + **u** are represented by the same directed line segment.

 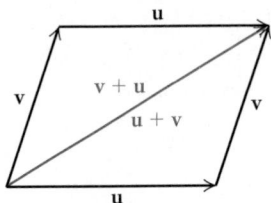

◆ Applications

If two forces F_1 and F_2 act on an object, the *combined* effect is the sum, or resultant, $F_1 + F_2$ of the separate forces.

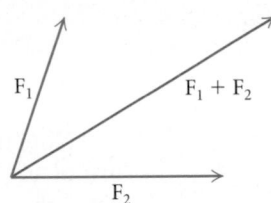

EXAMPLE 2 Forces of 15 newtons and 25 newtons act on an object at right angles to each other. Find their sum, or resultant, giving the magnitude of the resultant and the angle that it makes with the larger force.

Solution We make a drawing—this time, a rectangle—using **v** or $\overrightarrow{OB}$ to represent the resultant. To find the magnitude, we use the Pythagorean theorem:

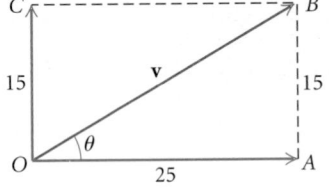

$$|\mathbf{v}|^2 = 15^2 + 25^2 \quad \text{Here } |\mathbf{v}| \text{ denotes the length, or magnitude, of v.}$$
$$|\mathbf{v}| = \sqrt{15^2 + 25^2}$$
$$|\mathbf{v}| \approx 29.2.$$

To find the direction, we note that since OAB is a right triangle,

$$\tan \theta = \tfrac{15}{25} = 0.6.$$

Using a calculator, we find θ, the angle that the resultant makes with the larger force:

$$\theta = \tan^{-1}(0.6) \approx 31°.$$

The resultant $\overrightarrow{OB}$ has a magnitude of 29.2 and makes an angle of 31° with the larger force.   ▶ Now Try Exercise 13.

AERIAL BEARINGS

REVIEW SECTION **5.3.**

Pilots must adjust the direction of their flight when there is a crosswind. Both the wind and the aircraft velocities can be described by vectors.

Airplane airspeed

Windspeed

EXAMPLE 3 *Airplane Speed and Direction.* An airplane travels on a bearing of 100° at an airspeed of 190 km/h while a wind is blowing 48 km/h from 220°. Find the ground speed of the airplane and the direction of its track, or course, over the ground.

Solution We first make a drawing. The wind is represented by $\overrightarrow{OC}$ and the velocity vector of the airplane by $\overrightarrow{OA}$. The resultant velocity vector is **v**, the sum of the two vectors. The angle θ between **v** and $\overrightarrow{OA}$ is called a **drift angle**.

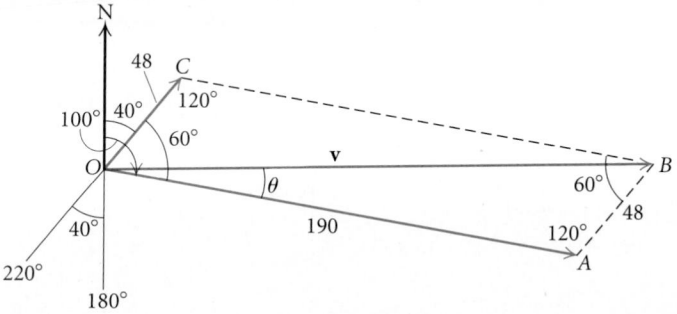

Note that the measure of $\angle COA = 100° - 40° = 60°$. Thus the measure of $\angle CBA$ is also 60° (opposite angles of a parallelogram are equal). Since the sum of all the angles of the parallelogram is 360° and $\angle OCB$ and $\angle OAB$ have the same measure, each must be 120°. By the *law of cosines* in $\triangle OAB$, we have

$$|\mathbf{v}|^2 = 48^2 + 190^2 - 2 \cdot 48 \cdot 190 \cos 120°$$
$$|\mathbf{v}|^2 = 47{,}524$$
$$|\mathbf{v}| = 218.$$

Thus, $|\mathbf{v}|$ is 218 km/h. By the *law of sines* in the same triangle,

$$\frac{48}{\sin \theta} = \frac{218}{\sin 120°},$$

or

$$\sin \theta = \frac{48 \sin 120°}{218} \approx 0.1907$$
$$\theta \approx 11°.$$

Thus, $\theta = 11°$, to the nearest degree. The ground speed of the airplane is 218 km/h, and its track is in the direction of $100° - 11°$, or 89°.

▶ **Now Try Exercise 27.**

◆ Components

Given a vector **w**, we may want to find two other vectors **u** and **v** whose sum is **w**. The vectors **u** and **v** are called **components** of **w** and the process of finding them is called **resolving**, or **representing**, a vector into its vector components.

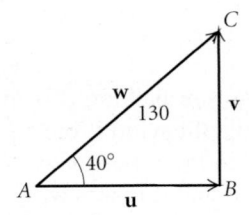

When we resolve a vector, we generally look for perpendicular components. Most often, one component will be parallel to the *x*-axis and the other will be parallel to the *y*-axis. For this reason, they are often called the **horizontal** and **vertical** components of a vector. In the figure at left, the vector $\mathbf{w} = \overrightarrow{AC}$ is resolved as the sum of $\mathbf{u} = \overrightarrow{AB}$ and $\mathbf{v} = \overrightarrow{BC}$. The horizontal component of $\mathbf{w}$ is $\mathbf{u}$ and the vertical component is $\mathbf{v}$.

EXAMPLE 4 A vector $\mathbf{w}$ has a magnitude of 130 and is inclined 40° with the horizontal. Resolve the vector into horizontal and vertical components.

Solution We first make a drawing showing horizontal and vertical vectors $\mathbf{u}$ and $\mathbf{v}$ whose sum is $\mathbf{w}$.

From $\triangle ABC$, we find $|\mathbf{u}|$ and $|\mathbf{v}|$ using the definitions of the cosine and sine functions:

$$\cos 40° = \frac{|\mathbf{u}|}{130}, \quad \text{or} \quad |\mathbf{u}| = 130 \cos 40° \approx 100,$$

$$\sin 40° = \frac{|\mathbf{v}|}{130}, \quad \text{or} \quad |\mathbf{v}| = 130 \sin 40° \approx 84.$$

Thus the horizontal component of $\mathbf{w}$ is 100 right, and the vertical component of $\mathbf{w}$ is 84 up. ▶ **Now Try Exercise 31.**

EXAMPLE 5 *Shipping Crate.* A wooden shipping crate that weighs 816 lb is placed on a loading ramp that makes an angle of 25° with the horizontal. To keep the crate from sliding, a chain is hooked to the crate and to a pole at the top of the ramp. Find the magnitude of the components of the crate's weight (disregarding friction) perpendicular and parallel to the incline.

Solution We first make a drawing illustrating the forces with a rectangle. We let

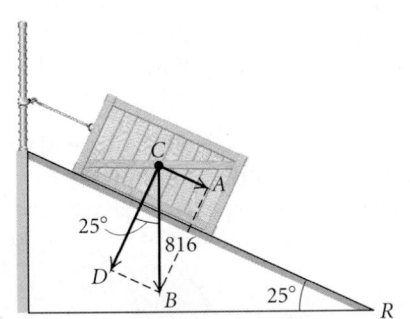

$|\overrightarrow{CB}|$ = the weight of the crate = 816 lb (force of gravity),

$|\overrightarrow{CD}|$ = the magnitude of the component of the crate's weight perpendicular to the incline (force against the ramp), and

$|\overrightarrow{CA}|$ = the magnitude of the component of the crate's weight parallel to the incline (force that pulls the crate down the ramp).

The angle at *R* is given to be 25° and $\angle BCD = \angle R = 25°$ because the sides of these angles are, respectively, perpendicular. Using the cosine and sine functions, we find that

$$\cos 25° = \frac{|\overrightarrow{CD}|}{816}, \quad \text{or} \quad |\overrightarrow{CD}| = 816 \cos 25° \approx 740 \text{ lb}, \quad \text{and}$$

$$\sin 25° = \frac{|\overrightarrow{CA}|}{816}, \quad \text{or} \quad |\overrightarrow{CA}| = 816 \sin 25° \approx 345 \text{ lb}.$$

▶ **Now Try Exercise 35.**

7.5   EXERCISE SET

Sketch the pair of vectors and determine whether they are equivalent. Use the following ordered pairs for the initial and terminal points.

$A(-2, 2)$ $E(-4, 1)$ $I(-6, -3)$
$B(3, 4)$ $F(2, 1)$ $J(3, 1)$
$C(-2, 5)$ $G(-4, 4)$ $K(-3, -3)$
$D(-1, -1)$ $H(1, 2)$ $O(0, 0)$

1. $\overrightarrow{GE}$, $\overrightarrow{BJ}$ **2.** $\overrightarrow{DJ}$, $\overrightarrow{OF}$

3. $\overrightarrow{DJ}$, $\overrightarrow{AB}$ **4.** $\overrightarrow{CG}$, $\overrightarrow{FO}$

5. $\overrightarrow{DK}$, $\overrightarrow{BH}$ **6.** $\overrightarrow{BA}$, $\overrightarrow{DI}$

7. $\overrightarrow{EG}$, $\overrightarrow{BJ}$ **8.** $\overrightarrow{GC}$, $\overrightarrow{FO}$

9. $\overrightarrow{GA}$, $\overrightarrow{BH}$ **10.** $\overrightarrow{JD}$, $\overrightarrow{CG}$

11. $\overrightarrow{AB}$, $\overrightarrow{ID}$ **12.** $\overrightarrow{OF}$, $\overrightarrow{HB}$

13. Two forces of 32 N (newtons) and 45 N act on an object at right angles. Find the magnitude of the resultant and the angle that it makes with the smaller force.

14. Two forces of 50 N and 60 N act on an object at right angles. Find the magnitude of the resultant and the angle that it makes with the larger force.

15. Two forces of 410 N and 600 N act on an object. The angle between the forces is 47°. Find the magnitude of the resultant and the angle that it makes with the larger force.

16. Two forces of 255 N and 325 N act on an object. The angle between the forces is 64°. Find the magnitude of the resultant and the angle that it makes with the smaller force.

In Exercises 17–24, magnitudes of vectors **u** *and* **v** *and the angle θ between the vectors are given. Find the sum of* **u** $+$ **v**. *Give the magnitude to the nearest tenth and give the direction by specifying to the nearest degree the angle that the resultant makes with* **u**.

17. $|\mathbf{u}| = 45$, $|\mathbf{v}| = 35$, $\theta = 90°$

18. $|\mathbf{u}| = 54$, $|\mathbf{v}| = 43$, $\theta = 150°$

19. $|\mathbf{u}| = 10$, $|\mathbf{v}| = 12$, $\theta = 67°$

20. $|\mathbf{u}| = 25$, $|\mathbf{v}| = 30$, $\theta = 75°$

21. $|\mathbf{u}| = 20$, $|\mathbf{v}| = 20$, $\theta = 117°$

22. $|\mathbf{u}| = 30$, $|\mathbf{v}| = 30$, $\theta = 123°$

23. $|\mathbf{u}| = 23$, $|\mathbf{v}| = 47$, $\theta = 27°$

24. $|\mathbf{u}| = 32$, $|\mathbf{v}| = 74$, $\theta = 72°$

25. *Hot-Air Balloon.*   A hot-air balloon is rising vertically 10 ft/sec while the wind is blowing horizontally 5 ft/sec. Find the speed **v** of the balloon and the angle θ that it makes with the horizontal.

26. *Ship.*   A ship sails first N80°E for 120 nautical mi, and then S20°W for 200 nautical mi. How far is the ship, then, from the starting point, and in what direction?

27. *Boat.*   A boat heads 35°, propelled by a force of 750 lb. A wind from 320° exerts a force of 150 lb on the boat. How large is the resultant force **F**, and in what direction is the boat moving?

28. *Airplane.* An airplane flies 32° for 210 km, and then 280° for 170 km. How far is the airplane, then, from the starting point, and in what direction?

29. *Airplane.* An airplane has an airspeed of 150 km/h. It is to make a flight in a direction of 70° while there is a 25-km/h wind from 340°. What will the airplane's actual heading be?

30. *Wind.* A wind has an easterly component (*from* the east) of 10 km/h and a southerly component (*from* the south) of 16 km/h. Find the magnitude and the direction of the wind.

31. A vector **w** has magnitude 100 and points southeast. Resolve the vector into easterly and southerly components.

32. A vector **u** with a magnitude of 150 lb is inclined to the right and upward 52° from the horizontal. Resolve the vector into components.

33. *Airplane.* An airplane takes off at a speed **S** of 225 mph at an angle of 17° with the horizontal. Resolve the vector **S** into components.

34. *Wheelbarrow.* A wheelbarrow is pushed by applying a 97-lb force **F** that makes a 38° angle with the horizontal. Resolve **F** into its horizontal and vertical components. (The horizontal component is the effective force in the direction of motion and the vertical component adds weight to the wheelbarrow.)

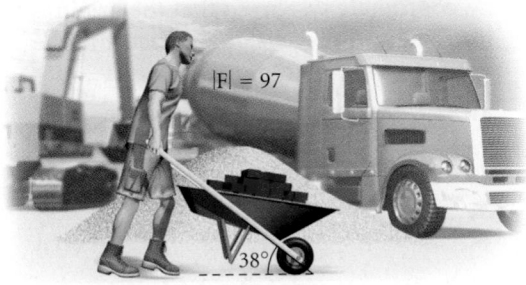

35. *Luggage Wagon.* A luggage wagon is being pulled with vector force **V**, which has a magnitude of 780 lb at an angle of elevation of 60°. Resolve the vector **V** into components.

36. *Hot-air Balloon.* A hot-air balloon exerts a 1200-lb pull on a tether line at a 45° angle with the horizontal. Resolve the vector **B** into components.

37. *Airplane.* An airplane is flying at 200 km/h in a direction of 305°. Find the westerly and northerly components of its velocity.

38. *Baseball.* A baseball player throws a baseball with a speed **S** of 72 mph at an angle of 45° with the horizontal. Resolve the vector **S** into components.

39. A block weighing 100 lb rests on a 25° incline. Find the magnitude of the components of the block's weight perpendicular and parallel to the incline.

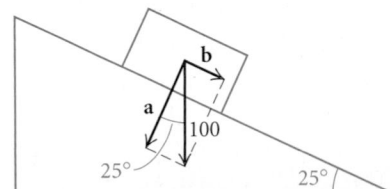

40. A shipping crate that weighs 450 kg is placed on a loading ramp that makes an angle of 30° with the horizontal. Find the magnitude of the components of the crate's weight perpendicular and parallel to the incline.

41. An 80-lb block of ice rests on a 37° incline. What force parallel to the incline is necessary in order to keep the ice from sliding down?

42. What force is necessary to pull a 3500-lb truck up a 9° incline?

Collaborative Discussion and Writing

43. Describe the concept of a vector as though you were explaining it to a classmate. Use the concept of an arrow shot from a bow in the explanation.

44. Explain why vectors $\overrightarrow{QR}$ and $\overrightarrow{RQ}$ are not equivalent.

Skill Maintenance

In each of Exercises 45–54, fill in the blank with the correct term. Some of the given choices will not be used.

> angular speed
> linear speed
> acute
> obtuse
> secant of θ
> cotangent of θ
> identity
> inverse
> absolute value
> sines
> cosine
> common
> natural
> horizontal line
> vertical line
> double-angle
> half-angle
> coterminal
> reference angle

45. Logarithms, base e, are called _____ logarithms.

46. _____ identities give trigonometric function values of $x/2$ in terms of function values of x.

47. _____ is distance traveled per unit of time.

48. The sine of an angle is also the _____ of the angle's complement.

49. A(n) _____ is an equation that is true for all possible replacements of the variables.

50. The _____ is the length of the side adjacent to θ divided by the length of the side opposite θ.

51. If two or more angles have the same terminal side, the angles are said to be _____ .

52. In any triangle, the sides are proportional to the _____ of the opposite angles.

53. If it is possible for a(n) _____ to intersect the graph of a function more than once, then the function is not one-to-one and its _____ is not a function.

54. The _____ for an angle is the _____ angle formed by the terminal side of the angle and the x-axis.

Synthesis

55. *Eagle's Flight.* An eagle flies from its nest 7 mi in the direction northeast, where it stops to rest on a cliff. It then flies 8 mi in the direction S30°W to land on top of a tree. Place an xy-coordinate system so that the origin is the bird's nest, the x-axis points east, and the y-axis points north.

a) At what point is the cliff located?
b) At what point is the tree located?

7.6 Vector Operations

- ✦ Perform calculations with vectors in component form.
- ✦ Express a vector as a linear combination of unit vectors.
- ✦ Express a vector in terms of its magnitude and its direction.
- ✦ Find the angle between two vectors using the dot product.
- ✦ Solve applied problems involving forces in equilibrium.

✦ Position Vectors

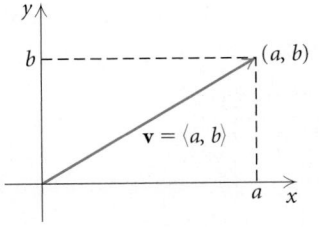

Let's consider a vector **v** whose initial point is the *origin* in an *xy*-coordinate system and whose terminal point is (a, b). We say that the vector is in **standard position** and refer to it as a position vector. Note that the ordered pair (a, b) defines the vector uniquely. Thus we can use (a, b) to denote the vector. To emphasize that we are thinking of a vector and to avoid the confusion of notation with ordered-pair and interval notation, we generally write

$$\mathbf{v} = \langle a, b \rangle.$$

The coordinate a is the *scalar* **horizontal component** of the vector, and the coordinate b is the *scalar* **vertical component** of the vector. By **scalar,** we mean a *numerical* quantity rather than a *vector* quantity. Thus, $\langle a, b \rangle$ is considered to be the *component form* of **v**. Note that a and b are *not* vectors and should not be confused with the vector component definition given in Section 7.5.

Now consider $\overrightarrow{AC}$ with $A = (x_1, y_1)$ and $C = (x_2, y_2)$. Let's see how to find the position vector equivalent to $\overrightarrow{AC}$. As you can see in the figure below, the initial point A is relocated to the origin $(0, 0)$. The coordinates of P are found by subtracting the coordinates of A from the coordinates of C. Thus, $P = (x_2 - x_1, y_2 - y_1)$ and the position vector is $\overrightarrow{OP}$.

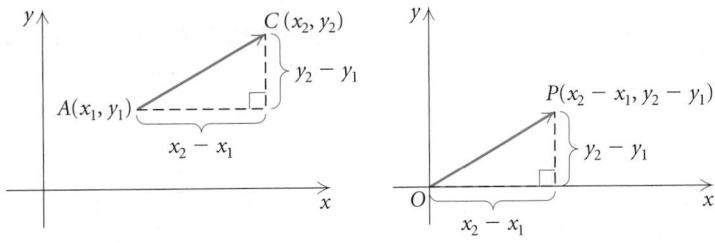

It can be shown that $\overrightarrow{OP}$ and $\overrightarrow{AC}$ have the same magnitude and direction and are therefore equivalent. Thus, $\overrightarrow{AC} = \overrightarrow{OP} = \langle x_2 - x_1, y_2 - y_1 \rangle$.

Component Form of a Vector

The **component form** of $\overrightarrow{AC}$ with $A = (x_1, y_1)$ and $C = (x_2, y_2)$ is

$$\overrightarrow{AC} = \langle x_2 - x_1, y_2 - y_1 \rangle.$$

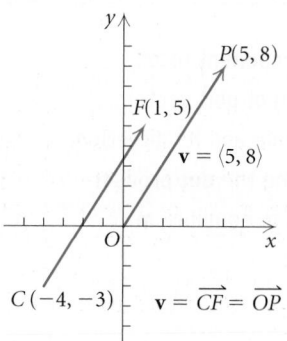

EXAMPLE 1 Find the component form of $\overrightarrow{CF}$ if $C = (-4, -3)$ and $F = (1, 5)$.

Solution We have

$$\overrightarrow{CF} = \langle 1 - (-4), 5 - (-3) \rangle = \langle 5, 8 \rangle.$$

Note that vector $\overrightarrow{CF}$ is equivalent to *position vector* $\overrightarrow{OP}$ with $P = (5, 8)$ as shown in the figure at left. ◀

Now that we know how to write vectors in component form, let's restate some definitions that we first considered in Section 7.5.

The length of a vector $\mathbf{v}$ is easy to determine when the components of the vector are known. For $\mathbf{v} = \langle v_1, v_2 \rangle$, we have

$$|\mathbf{v}|^2 = v_1^2 + v_2^2 \quad \text{Using the Pythagorean theorem}$$
$$|\mathbf{v}| = \sqrt{v_1^2 + v_2^2}.$$

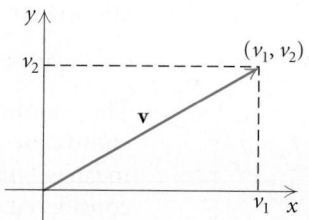

Length of a Vector
The **length,** or **magnitude,** of a vector $\mathbf{v} = \langle v_1, v_2 \rangle$ is given by
$$|\mathbf{v}| = \sqrt{v_1^2 + v_2^2}.$$

EXAMPLE 2 Find the length, or magnitude, of vector $\mathbf{v} = \langle 5, 8 \rangle$, illustrated in Example 1.

Solution

$$|\mathbf{v}| = \sqrt{v_1^2 + v_2^2} \qquad \text{Length of vector } v = \langle v_1, v_2 \rangle$$
$$|\mathbf{v}| = \sqrt{5^2 + 8^2} \qquad \text{Substituting 5 for } v_1 \text{ and 8 for } v_2$$
$$= \sqrt{25 + 64}$$
$$= \sqrt{89}$$

▶ Now Try Exercises 1 and 7.

Two vectors are **equivalent** if they have the *same* magnitude and the *same* direction.

Equivalent Vectors
Let $\mathbf{u} = \langle u_1, u_2 \rangle$ and $\mathbf{v} = \langle v_1, v_2 \rangle$. Then
$$\langle u_1, u_2 \rangle = \langle v_1, v_2 \rangle \quad \text{if and only if} \quad u_1 = v_1 \quad \text{and} \quad u_2 = v_2.$$

✦ Operations on Vectors

To multiply a vector **v** by a positive real number, we multiply its length by the number. Its direction stays the same. When a vector **v** is multiplied by 2, for instance, its length is doubled and its direction is not changed. When a vector is multiplied by 1.6, its length is increased by 60% and its direction stays the same. To multiply a vector **v** by a negative real number, we multiply its length by the number and reverse its direction. When a vector is multiplied by -2, its length is doubled and its direction is reversed. Since real numbers work like scaling factors in vector multiplication, we call them **scalars** and the products $k\mathbf{v}$ are called **scalar multiples** of **v**.

Scalar multiples of **v**

Scalar Multiplication

For a real number k and a vector $\mathbf{v} = \langle v_1, v_2 \rangle$, the **scalar product** of k and **v** is

$$k\mathbf{v} = k\langle v_1, v_2 \rangle = \langle kv_1, kv_2 \rangle.$$

The vector $k\mathbf{v}$ is a **scalar multiple** of the vector **v**.

EXAMPLE 3 Let $\mathbf{u} = \langle -5, 4 \rangle$ and $\mathbf{w} = \langle 1, -1 \rangle$. Find $-7\mathbf{w}$, $3\mathbf{u}$, and $-1\mathbf{w}$.

Solution

$$-7\mathbf{w} = -7\langle 1, -1 \rangle = \langle -7, 7 \rangle,$$
$$3\mathbf{u} = 3\langle -5, 4 \rangle = \langle -15, 12 \rangle,$$
$$-1\mathbf{w} = -1\langle 1, -1 \rangle = \langle -1, 1 \rangle$$

In Section 7.5, we used the parallelogram law to add two vectors, but now we can add two vectors using components. To add two vectors given in component form, we add the corresponding components. Let $\mathbf{u} = \langle u_1, u_2 \rangle$ and $\mathbf{v} = \langle v_1, v_2 \rangle$. Then

$$\mathbf{u} + \mathbf{v} = \langle u_1 + v_1, u_2 + v_2 \rangle.$$

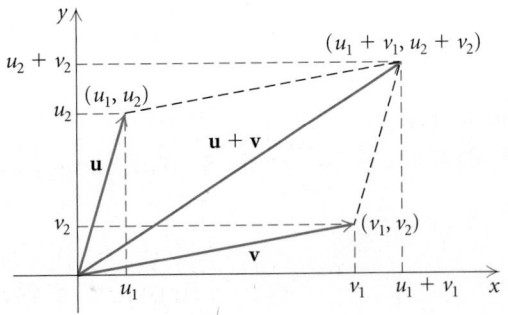

For example, if $\mathbf{v} = \langle -3, 2 \rangle$ and $\mathbf{w} = \langle 5, -9 \rangle$, then

$$\mathbf{v} + \mathbf{w} = \langle -3 + 5, 2 + (-9) \rangle = \langle 2, -7 \rangle.$$

> **Vector Addition**
>
> If $\mathbf{u} = \langle u_1, u_2 \rangle$ and $\mathbf{v} = \langle v_1, v_2 \rangle$, then
>
> $$\mathbf{u} + \mathbf{v} = \langle u_1 + v_1, u_2 + v_2 \rangle.$$

Before we define vector subtraction, we need to define $-\mathbf{v}$. The opposite of $\mathbf{v} = \langle v_1, v_2 \rangle$, shown below, is

$$-\mathbf{v} = (-1)\mathbf{v} = (-1)\langle v_1, v_2 \rangle$$
$$= \langle -v_1, -v_2 \rangle.$$

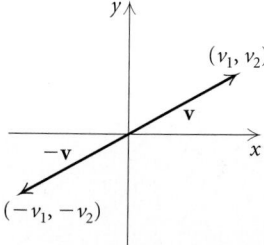

Vector subtraction such as $\mathbf{u} - \mathbf{v}$ involves subtracting corresponding components. We show this by rewriting $\mathbf{u} - \mathbf{v}$ as $\mathbf{u} + (-\mathbf{v})$. If $\mathbf{u} = \langle u_1, u_2 \rangle$ and $\mathbf{v} = \langle v_1, v_2 \rangle$, then

$$\mathbf{u} - \mathbf{v} = \mathbf{u} + (-\mathbf{v}) = \langle u_1, u_2 \rangle + \langle -v_1, -v_2 \rangle$$
$$= \langle u_1 + (-v_1), u_2 + (-v_2) \rangle$$
$$= \langle u_1 - v_1, u_2 - v_2 \rangle.$$

We can illustrate vector subtraction with parallelograms, just as we did vector addition.

Sketch $\mathbf{u}$ and $\mathbf{v}$.

Sketch $-\mathbf{v}$.

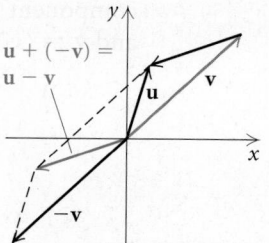

Sketch $\mathbf{u} + (-\mathbf{v})$, or $\mathbf{u} - \mathbf{v}$, using the parallelogram law.

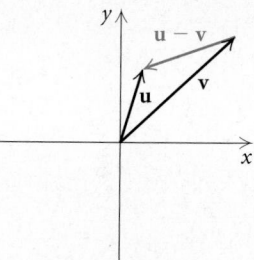

$\mathbf{u} - \mathbf{v}$ is the vector from the terminal point of $\mathbf{v}$ to the terminal point of $\mathbf{u}$.

> ### Vector Subtraction
>
> If $\mathbf{u} = \langle u_1, u_2 \rangle$ and $\mathbf{v} = \langle v_1, v_2 \rangle$, then
>
> $$\mathbf{u} - \mathbf{v} = \langle u_1 - v_1, u_2 - v_2 \rangle.$$

It is interesting to compare the sum of two vectors with the difference of the same two vectors in the same parallelogram. The vectors $\mathbf{u} + \mathbf{v}$ and $\mathbf{u} - \mathbf{v}$ are the diagonals of the parallelogram.

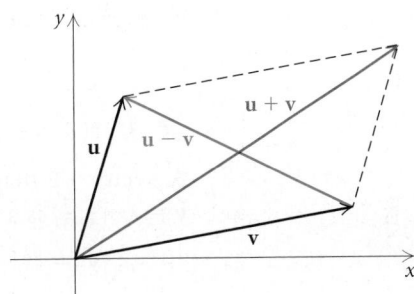

EXAMPLE 4 Do the following calculations, where $\mathbf{u} = \langle 7, 2 \rangle$ and $\mathbf{v} = \langle -3, 5 \rangle$.

a) $\mathbf{u} + \mathbf{v}$ b) $\mathbf{u} - 6\mathbf{v}$

c) $3\mathbf{u} + 4\mathbf{v}$ d) $|5\mathbf{v} - 2\mathbf{u}|$

Solution

a) $\mathbf{u} + \mathbf{v} = \langle 7, 2 \rangle + \langle -3, 5 \rangle = \langle 7 + (-3), 2 + 5 \rangle = \langle 4, 7 \rangle$

b) $\mathbf{u} - 6\mathbf{v} = \langle 7, 2 \rangle - 6\langle -3, 5 \rangle = \langle 7, 2 \rangle - \langle -18, 30 \rangle = \langle 25, -28 \rangle$

c) $3\mathbf{u} + 4\mathbf{v} = 3\langle 7, 2 \rangle + 4\langle -3, 5 \rangle = \langle 21, 6 \rangle + \langle -12, 20 \rangle = \langle 9, 26 \rangle$

d) $|5\mathbf{v} - 2\mathbf{u}| = |5\langle -3, 5 \rangle - 2\langle 7, 2 \rangle| = |\langle -15, 25 \rangle - \langle 14, 4 \rangle|$

$$= |\langle -29, 21 \rangle|$$
$$= \sqrt{(-29)^2 + 21^2}$$
$$= \sqrt{1282}$$
$$\approx 35.8$$

▶ Now Try Exercises 9 and 11.

Before we state the properties of vector addition and scalar multiplication, we need to define another special vector—the zero vector. The vector whose initial and terminal points are both $(0, 0)$ is the **zero vector,** denoted by $\mathbf{O}$, or $\langle 0, 0 \rangle$. Its magnitude is 0. In vector addition, the zero vector is the additive identity vector:

$$\mathbf{v} + \mathbf{O} = \mathbf{v}. \qquad \langle v_1, v_2 \rangle + \langle 0, 0 \rangle = \langle v_1, v_2 \rangle$$

Operations on vectors share many of the same properties as operations on real numbers.

Properties of Vector Addition and Scalar Multiplication

For all vectors $\mathbf{u}$, $\mathbf{v}$, and $\mathbf{w}$, and for all scalars b and c:

1. $\mathbf{u} + \mathbf{v} = \mathbf{v} + \mathbf{u}$.
2. $\mathbf{u} + (\mathbf{v} + \mathbf{w}) = (\mathbf{u} + \mathbf{v}) + \mathbf{w}$.
3. $\mathbf{v} + \mathbf{O} = \mathbf{v}$.
4. $1\mathbf{v} = \mathbf{v}$; $0\mathbf{v} = \mathbf{O}$.
5. $\mathbf{v} + (-\mathbf{v}) = \mathbf{O}$.
6. $b(c\mathbf{v}) = (bc)\mathbf{v}$.
7. $(b + c)\mathbf{v} = b\mathbf{v} + c\mathbf{v}$.
8. $b(\mathbf{u} + \mathbf{v}) = b\mathbf{u} + b\mathbf{v}$.

✦ Unit Vectors

A vector of magnitude, or length, 1 is called a **unit vector.** The vector $\mathbf{v} = \left\langle -\frac{3}{5}, \frac{4}{5} \right\rangle$ is a unit vector because

$$|\mathbf{v}| = \left|\left\langle -\tfrac{3}{5}, \tfrac{4}{5} \right\rangle\right| = \sqrt{\left(-\tfrac{3}{5}\right)^2 + \left(\tfrac{4}{5}\right)^2}$$

$$= \sqrt{\tfrac{9}{25} + \tfrac{16}{25}}$$

$$= \sqrt{\tfrac{25}{25}} = \sqrt{1} = 1.$$

EXAMPLE 5 Find a unit vector that has the same direction as the vector $\mathbf{w} = \langle -3, 5 \rangle$.

Solution We first find the length of $\mathbf{w}$:

$$|\mathbf{w}| = \sqrt{(-3)^2 + 5^2} = \sqrt{34}.$$

Thus we want a vector whose length is $1/\sqrt{34}$ of $\mathbf{w}$ and whose direction is the same as vector $\mathbf{w}$. That vector is

$$\mathbf{u} = \frac{1}{\sqrt{34}}\,\mathbf{w} = \frac{1}{\sqrt{34}}\langle -3, 5 \rangle = \left\langle \frac{-3}{\sqrt{34}}, \frac{5}{\sqrt{34}} \right\rangle.$$

The vector $\mathbf{u}$ is a *unit vector* because

$$|\mathbf{u}| = \left|\frac{1}{\sqrt{34}}\,\mathbf{w}\right| = \sqrt{\left(\frac{-3}{\sqrt{34}}\right)^2 + \left(\frac{5}{\sqrt{34}}\right)^2} = \sqrt{\frac{9}{34} + \frac{25}{34}}$$

$$= \sqrt{\frac{34}{34}} = \sqrt{1} = 1.$$

▷ **Now Try Exercise 33.**

Unit Vector

If $\mathbf{v}$ is a vector and $\mathbf{v} \neq \mathbf{O}$, then

$$\frac{1}{|\mathbf{v}|} \cdot \mathbf{v}, \quad \text{or} \quad \frac{\mathbf{v}}{|\mathbf{v}|},$$

is a **unit vector** in the direction of $\mathbf{v}$.

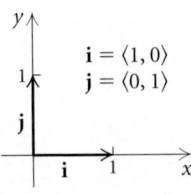

Although unit vectors can have any direction, the unit vectors parallel to the *x*- and *y*-axes are particularly useful. They are defined as

$$\mathbf{i} = \langle 1, 0 \rangle \quad \text{and} \quad \mathbf{j} = \langle 0, 1 \rangle.$$

Any vector can be expressed as a **linear combination** of unit vectors **i** and **j**. For example, let $\mathbf{v} = \langle v_1, v_2 \rangle$. Then

$$\mathbf{v} = \langle v_1, v_2 \rangle = \langle v_1, 0 \rangle + \langle 0, v_2 \rangle$$
$$= v_1 \langle 1, 0 \rangle + v_2 \langle 0, 1 \rangle = v_1 \mathbf{i} + v_2 \mathbf{j}.$$

EXAMPLE 6 Express the vector $\mathbf{r} = \langle 2, -6 \rangle$ as a linear combination of **i** and **j**.

Solution

$$\mathbf{r} = \langle 2, -6 \rangle = 2\mathbf{i} + (-6)\mathbf{j} = 2\mathbf{i} - 6\mathbf{j}$$

▶ Now Try Exercise 39.

EXAMPLE 7 Write the vector $\mathbf{q} = -\mathbf{i} + 7\mathbf{j}$ in component form.

Solution

$$\mathbf{q} = -\mathbf{i} + 7\mathbf{j} = -1\mathbf{i} + 7\mathbf{j} = \langle -1, 7 \rangle$$

Vector operations can also be performed when vectors are written as linear combinations of **i** and **j**.

EXAMPLE 8 If $\mathbf{a} = 5\mathbf{i} - 2\mathbf{j}$ and $\mathbf{b} = -\mathbf{i} + 8\mathbf{j}$, find $3\mathbf{a} - \mathbf{b}$.

Solution

$$3\mathbf{a} - \mathbf{b} = 3(5\mathbf{i} - 2\mathbf{j}) - (-\mathbf{i} + 8\mathbf{j})$$
$$= 15\mathbf{i} - 6\mathbf{j} + \mathbf{i} - 8\mathbf{j}$$
$$= 16\mathbf{i} - 14\mathbf{j}$$

▶ Now Try Exercise 45.

✦ Direction Angles

The terminal point *P* of a unit vector in standard position is a point on the unit circle denoted by $(\cos \theta, \sin \theta)$. Thus the unit vector can be expressed in component form,

$$\mathbf{u} = \langle \cos \theta, \sin \theta \rangle,$$

or as a linear combination of the unit vectors **i** and **j**,

$$\mathbf{u} = (\cos \theta)\mathbf{i} + (\sin \theta)\mathbf{j},$$

where the components of **u** are functions of the **direction angle** θ measured counterclockwise from the *x*-axis to the vector. As θ varies from 0 to 2π, the point *P* traces the circle $x^2 + y^2 = 1$. This takes in all possible directions for unit vectors so the equation $\mathbf{u} = (\cos \theta)\mathbf{i} + (\sin \theta)\mathbf{j}$ describes every possible unit vector in the plane.

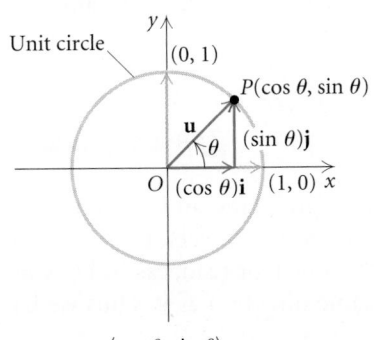

UNIT CIRCLE

REVIEW SECTION **5.5.**

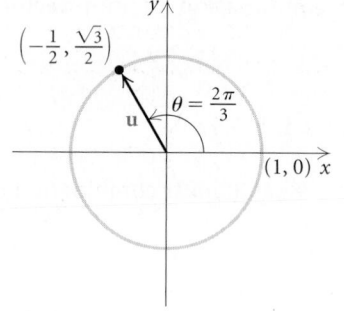

EXAMPLE 9 Calculate and sketch the unit vector $\mathbf{u} = (\cos \theta)\mathbf{i} + (\sin \theta)\mathbf{j}$ for $\theta = 2\pi/3$. Include the unit circle in your sketch.

Solution

$$\mathbf{u} = \left(\cos \frac{2\pi}{3} \right)\mathbf{i} + \left(\sin \frac{2\pi}{3} \right)\mathbf{j}$$

$$= \left(-\frac{1}{2} \right)\mathbf{i} + \left(\frac{\sqrt{3}}{2} \right)\mathbf{j}$$

▶ Now Try Exercise 49.

Let $\mathbf{v} = \langle v_1, v_2 \rangle$ with direction angle θ. Using the definition of the tangent function, we can determine the direction angle from the components of $\mathbf{v}$:

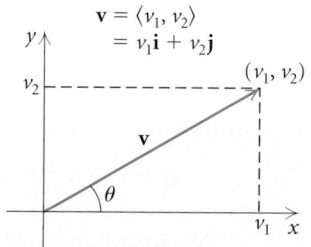

$$\tan \theta = \frac{v_2}{v_1}$$

$$\theta = \tan^{-1} \frac{v_2}{v_1}.$$

EXAMPLE 10 Determine the direction angle θ of the vector $\mathbf{w} = -4\mathbf{i} - 3\mathbf{j}$.

Solution We know that

$$\mathbf{w} = -4\mathbf{i} - 3\mathbf{j} = \langle -4, -3 \rangle.$$

Thus we have

$$\tan \theta = \frac{-3}{-4} = \frac{3}{4} \quad \text{and} \quad \theta = \tan^{-1} \frac{3}{4}.$$

Since $\mathbf{w}$ is in the third quadrant, we know that θ is a third-quadrant angle. The reference angle is

$$\tan^{-1} \frac{3}{4} \approx 37°, \quad \text{and} \quad \theta \approx 180° + 37°, \text{ or } 217°.$$

▶ Now Try Exercise 55.

It is convenient for work with applied problems and in subsequent courses, such as calculus, to have a way to express a vector so that both its magnitude and its direction can be determined, or read, easily. Let $\mathbf{v}$ be a vector. Then $\mathbf{v}/|\mathbf{v}|$ is a unit vector in the same direction as $\mathbf{v}$. Thus we have

$$\frac{\mathbf{v}}{|\mathbf{v}|} = (\cos \theta)\mathbf{i} + (\sin \theta)\mathbf{j}$$

$$\mathbf{v} = |\mathbf{v}|[(\cos \theta)\mathbf{i} + (\sin \theta)\mathbf{j}] \quad \text{Multiplying by } |\mathbf{v}|$$

$$\mathbf{v} = |\mathbf{v}|(\cos \theta)\mathbf{i} + |\mathbf{v}|(\sin \theta)\mathbf{j}.$$

Let's revisit the applied problem in Example 3 of Section 7.5 and use this new notation.

EXAMPLE 11 *Airplane Speed and Direction.* An airplane travels on a bearing of 100° at an airspeed of 190 km/h while a wind is blowing 48 km/h from 220°. Find the ground speed of the airplane and the direction of its track, or course, over the ground.

Solution We first make a drawing. The wind is represented by $\overrightarrow{OC}$ and the velocity vector of the airplane by $\overrightarrow{OA}$. The resultant velocity vector is **v**, the sum of the two vectors:

$$\mathbf{v} = \overrightarrow{OC} + \overrightarrow{OA}.$$

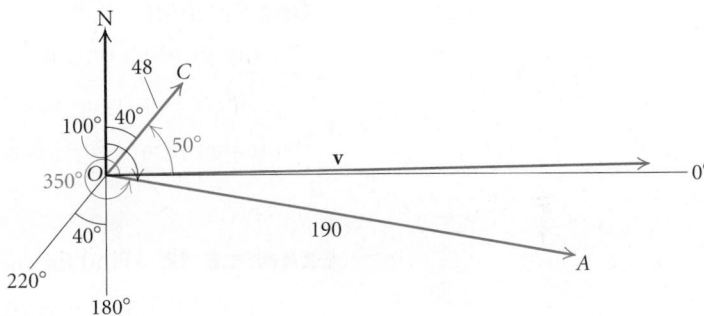

The bearing (measured from north) of the airspeed vector $\overrightarrow{OA}$ is 100°. Its *direction angle* (measured counterclockwise from the positive *x*-axis) is 350°. The bearing (measured from north) of the wind vector $\overrightarrow{OC}$ is 220°. Its direction angle (measured counterclockwise from the positive *x*-axis) is 50°. The magnitudes of $\overrightarrow{OA}$ and $\overrightarrow{OC}$ are 190 and 48, respectively. We have

$$\overrightarrow{OA} = 190(\cos 350°)\mathbf{i} + 190(\sin 350°)\mathbf{j}, \quad \text{and}$$
$$\overrightarrow{OC} = 48(\cos 50°)\mathbf{i} + 48(\sin 50°)\mathbf{j}.$$

Thus,

$$\mathbf{v} = \overrightarrow{OA} + \overrightarrow{OC}$$
$$= [190(\cos 350°)\mathbf{i} + 190(\sin 350°)\mathbf{j}] + [48(\cos 50°)\mathbf{i} + 48(\sin 50°)\mathbf{j}]$$
$$= [190(\cos 350°) + 48(\cos 50°)]\mathbf{i} + [190(\sin 350°) + 48(\sin 50°)]\mathbf{j}$$
$$\approx 217.97\mathbf{i} + 3.78\mathbf{j}.$$

From this form, we can determine the ground speed and the course:

$$\text{Ground speed} \approx \sqrt{(217.97)^2 + (3.78)^2}$$
$$\approx 218 \text{ km/h}.$$

We let α be the direction angle of **v**. Then

$$\tan \alpha = \frac{3.78}{217.97}$$

$$\alpha = \tan^{-1} \frac{3.78}{217.97} \approx 1°.$$

Thus the course of the airplane (the direction from north) is 90° − 1°, or 89°. ◀

✦ Angle Between Vectors

When a vector is multiplied by a scalar, the result is a vector. When two vectors are added, the result is also a vector. Thus we might expect the product of two vectors to be a vector as well, but it is not. The *dot product* of two vectors is a real number, or scalar. This product is useful in finding the angle between two vectors and in determining whether two vectors are perpendicular.

> ### Dot Product
>
> The **dot product** of two vectors $\mathbf{u} = \langle u_1, u_2 \rangle$ and $\mathbf{v} = \langle v_1, v_2 \rangle$ is
>
> $$\mathbf{u} \cdot \mathbf{v} = u_1 v_1 + u_2 v_2.$$
>
> (Note that $u_1 v_1 + u_2 v_2$ is a *scalar*, not a vector.)

EXAMPLE 12   Find the indicated dot product when

$$\mathbf{u} = \langle 2, -5 \rangle, \quad \mathbf{v} = \langle 0, 4 \rangle, \quad \text{and} \quad \mathbf{w} = \langle -3, 1 \rangle.$$

a) $\mathbf{u} \cdot \mathbf{w}$

b) $\mathbf{w} \cdot \mathbf{v}$

Solution

a) $\mathbf{u} \cdot \mathbf{w} = 2(-3) + (-5)1 = -6 - 5 = -11$

b) $\mathbf{w} \cdot \mathbf{v} = -3(0) + 1(4) = 0 + 4 = 4$ ◀

The dot product can be used to find the angle between two vectors. The angle *between* two vectors is the smallest positive angle formed by the two directed line segments. Thus the angle θ between $\mathbf{u}$ and $\mathbf{v}$ is the same angle as between $\mathbf{v}$ and $\mathbf{u}$, and $0 \le \theta \le \pi$.

> ### Angle Between Two Vectors
>
> If θ is the angle between two *nonzero* vectors $\mathbf{u}$ and $\mathbf{v}$, then
>
> $$\cos \theta = \frac{\mathbf{u} \cdot \mathbf{v}}{|\mathbf{u}|\,|\mathbf{v}|}.$$

EXAMPLE 13   Find the angle between $\mathbf{u} = \langle 3, 7 \rangle$ and $\mathbf{v} = \langle -4, 2 \rangle$.

Solution   We begin by finding $\mathbf{u} \cdot \mathbf{v}$, $|\mathbf{u}|$, and $|\mathbf{v}|$:

$$\mathbf{u} \cdot \mathbf{v} = 3(-4) + 7(2) = 2,$$
$$|\mathbf{u}| = \sqrt{3^2 + 7^2} = \sqrt{58}, \quad \text{and}$$
$$|\mathbf{v}| = \sqrt{(-4)^2 + 2^2} = \sqrt{20}.$$

Then

$$\cos \alpha = \frac{\mathbf{u} \cdot \mathbf{v}}{|\mathbf{u}||\mathbf{v}|} = \frac{2}{\sqrt{58}\sqrt{20}}$$

$$\alpha = \cos^{-1}\frac{2}{\sqrt{58}\sqrt{20}} \approx 86.6°.$$

▷ Now Try Exercise 63.

✦ Forces in Equilibrium

When several forces act through the same point on an object, their vector sum must be **O** in order for a balance to occur. When a balance occurs, then the object is either stationary or moving in a straight line without acceleration. The fact that the vector sum must be **O** for a balance, and vice versa, allows us to solve many applied problems involving forces.

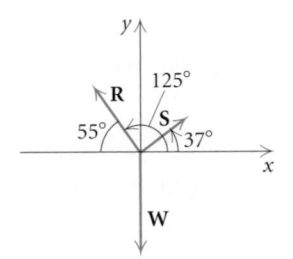

EXAMPLE 14 *Suspended Block.* A 350-lb block is suspended by two cables, as shown at left. At point A, there are three forces acting: **W**, the block pulling down, and **R** and **S**, the two cables pulling upward and outward. Find the tension in each cable.

Solution We draw a force diagram with the initial points of each vector at the origin. For there to be a balance, the vector sum must be the vector **O**: **R** + **S** + **W** = **O**. We can express each vector in terms of its magnitude and its direction angle:

$$\mathbf{R} = |\mathbf{R}|[(\cos 125°)\mathbf{i} + (\sin 125°)\mathbf{j}],$$
$$\mathbf{S} = |\mathbf{S}|[(\cos 37°)\mathbf{i} + (\sin 37°)\mathbf{j}], \quad \text{and}$$
$$\mathbf{W} = |\mathbf{W}|[(\cos 270°)\mathbf{i} + (\sin 270°)\mathbf{j}]$$
$$= 350(\cos 270°)\mathbf{i} + 350(\sin 270°)\mathbf{j} = -350\mathbf{j}.$$

Substituting for **R**, **S**, and **W** in **R** + **S** + **W** = **O**, we have

$$[|\mathbf{R}|(\cos 125°) + |\mathbf{S}|(\cos 37°)]\mathbf{i} + [|\mathbf{R}|(\sin 125°) + |\mathbf{S}|(\sin 37°) - 350]\mathbf{j}$$
$$= 0\mathbf{i} + 0\mathbf{j}.$$

This gives us two equations:

$$|\mathbf{R}|(\cos 125°) + |\mathbf{S}|(\cos 37°) = 0 \quad \text{and} \quad \textbf{(1)}$$
$$|\mathbf{R}|(\sin 125°) + |\mathbf{S}|(\sin 37°) - 350 = 0. \quad \textbf{(2)}$$

Solving equation (1) for $|R|$, we get

$$|R| = -\frac{|S|(\cos 37°)}{\cos 125°}. \quad \textbf{(3)}$$

Substituting this expression for $|R|$ in equation (2) gives us

$$-\frac{|S|(\cos 37°)}{\cos 125°}(\sin 125°) + |S|(\sin 37°) - 350 = 0.$$

Then solving this equation for $|S|$, we get $|S| \approx 201$, and substituting 201 for $|S|$ in equation (3), we get $|R| \approx 280$. The tensions in the cables are 280 lb and 201 lb.

▷ Now Try Exercise 83.

7.6 EXERCISE SET

Find the component form of the vector given the initial and terminal points. Then find the length of the vector.

1. $\overrightarrow{MN}$; $M(6, -7)$, $N(-3, -2)$

2. $\overrightarrow{CD}$; $C(1, 5)$, $D(5, 7)$

3. $\overrightarrow{FE}$; $E(8, 4)$, $F(11, -2)$

4. $\overrightarrow{BA}$; $A(9, 0)$, $B(9, 7)$

5. $\overrightarrow{KL}$; $K(4, -3)$, $L(8, -3)$

6. $\overrightarrow{GH}$; $G(-6, 10)$, $H(-3, 2)$

7. Find the magnitude of vector **u** if $\mathbf{u} = \langle -1, 6 \rangle$.

8. Find the magnitude of vector $\overrightarrow{ST}$ if $\overrightarrow{ST} = \langle -12, 5 \rangle$.

Do the indicated calculations in Exercises 9–26 for the vectors

$\mathbf{u} = \langle 5, -2 \rangle$, $\mathbf{v} = \langle -4, 7 \rangle$, and $\mathbf{w} = \langle -1, -3 \rangle$.

9. $\mathbf{u} + \mathbf{w}$
10. $\mathbf{w} + \mathbf{u}$

11. $|3\mathbf{w} - \mathbf{v}|$
12. $6\mathbf{v} + 5\mathbf{u}$

13. $\mathbf{v} - \mathbf{u}$
14. $|2\mathbf{w}|$

15. $5\mathbf{u} - 4\mathbf{v}$
16. $-5\mathbf{v}$

17. $|3\mathbf{u}| - |\mathbf{v}|$
18. $|\mathbf{v}| + |\mathbf{u}|$

19. $\mathbf{v} + \mathbf{u} + 2\mathbf{w}$
20. $\mathbf{w} - (\mathbf{u} + 4\mathbf{v})$

21. $2\mathbf{v} + \mathbf{O}$
22. $10|7\mathbf{w} - 3\mathbf{u}|$

23. $\mathbf{u} \cdot \mathbf{w}$
24. $\mathbf{w} \cdot \mathbf{u}$

25. $\mathbf{u} \cdot \mathbf{v}$
26. $\mathbf{v} \cdot \mathbf{w}$

*The vectors **u**, **v**, and **w** are drawn below. Copy them on a sheet of paper. Then sketch each of the vectors in Exercises 27–30.*

27. $\mathbf{u} + \mathbf{v}$
28. $\mathbf{u} - 2\mathbf{v}$

29. $\mathbf{u} + \mathbf{v} + \mathbf{w}$
30. $\frac{1}{2}\mathbf{u} - \mathbf{w}$

31. Vectors **u**, **v**, and **w** are determined by the sides of $\triangle ABC$ below.

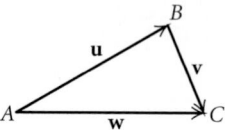

a) Find an expression for **w** in terms of **u** and **v**.
b) Find an expression for **v** in terms of **u** and **w**.

32. In $\triangle ABC$, vectors **u** and **w** are determined by the sides shown, where P is the midpoint of side BC. Find an expression for **v** in terms of **u** and **w**.

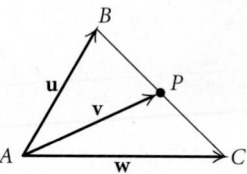

Find a unit vector that has the same direction as the given vector.

33. $\mathbf{v} = \langle -5, 12 \rangle$
34. $\mathbf{u} = \langle 3, 4 \rangle$

35. $\mathbf{w} = \langle 1, -10 \rangle$
36. $\mathbf{a} = \langle 6, -7 \rangle$

37. $\mathbf{r} = \langle -2, -8 \rangle$
38. $\mathbf{t} = \langle -3, -3 \rangle$

*Express the vector as a linear combination of the unit vectors **i** and **j**.*

39. $\mathbf{w} = \langle -4, 6 \rangle$
40. $\mathbf{r} = \langle -15, 9 \rangle$

41. $\mathbf{s} = \langle 2, 5 \rangle$
42. $\mathbf{u} = \langle 2, -1 \rangle$

*Express the vector as a linear combination of **i** and **j**.*

43.

44.

Systems of Equations and Matrices

APPLICATION

S kiers and snowboarders suffer about 288,400 injuries each winter, with skiing accounting for about 400 more injuries than snowboarding (*Source*: U.S. Consumer Product Safety Commission). How many injuries occur in each winter sport?

This problem appears as Exercise 41 in Section 8.1.

For Exercises 45–48, use the vectors

$\mathbf{u} = 2\mathbf{i} + \mathbf{j}, \quad \mathbf{v} = -3\mathbf{i} - 10\mathbf{j}, \quad \text{and} \quad \mathbf{w} = \mathbf{i} - 5\mathbf{j}.$

*Perform the indicated vector operations and state the answer in two forms: (a) as a linear combination of **i** and **j** and (b) in component form.*

45. $4\mathbf{u} - 5\mathbf{w}$　　　　　**46.** $\mathbf{v} + 3\mathbf{w}$

47. $\mathbf{u} - (\mathbf{v} + \mathbf{w})$　　　　**48.** $(\mathbf{u} - \mathbf{v}) + \mathbf{w}$

Sketch (include the unit circle) and calculate the unit vector $\mathbf{u} = (\cos \theta)\mathbf{i} + (\sin \theta)\mathbf{j}$ for the given direction angle.

49. $\theta = \dfrac{\pi}{2}$　　　　　**50.** $\theta = \dfrac{\pi}{3}$

51. $\theta = \dfrac{4\pi}{3}$　　　　　**52.** $\theta = \dfrac{3\pi}{2}$

Determine the direction angle θ of the vector, to the nearest degree.

53. $\mathbf{u} = \langle -2, -5 \rangle$　　　　**54.** $\mathbf{w} = \langle 4, -3 \rangle$

55. $\mathbf{q} = \mathbf{i} + 2\mathbf{j}$　　　　　**56.** $\mathbf{w} = 5\mathbf{i} - \mathbf{j}$

57. $\mathbf{t} = \langle 5, 6 \rangle$　　　　　**58.** $\mathbf{b} = \langle -8, -4 \rangle$

Find the magnitude and the direction angle θ of the vector.

59. $\mathbf{u} = 3[(\cos 45°)\mathbf{i} + (\sin 45°)\mathbf{j}]$

60. $\mathbf{w} = 6[(\cos 150°)\mathbf{i} + (\sin 150°)\mathbf{j}]$

61. $\mathbf{v} = \left\langle -\dfrac{1}{2}, \dfrac{\sqrt{3}}{2} \right\rangle$

62. $\mathbf{u} = -\mathbf{i} - \mathbf{j}$

Find the angle between the given vectors, to the nearest tenth of a degree.

63. $\mathbf{u} = \langle 2, -5 \rangle, \ \mathbf{v} = \langle 1, 4 \rangle$

64. $\mathbf{a} = \langle -3, -3 \rangle, \ \mathbf{b} = \langle -5, 2 \rangle$

65. $\mathbf{w} = \langle 3, 5 \rangle, \ \mathbf{r} = \langle 5, 5 \rangle$

66. $\mathbf{v} = \langle -4, 2 \rangle, \ \mathbf{t} = \langle 1, -4 \rangle$

67. $\mathbf{a} = \mathbf{i} + \mathbf{j}, \ \mathbf{b} = 2\mathbf{i} - 3\mathbf{j}$

68. $\mathbf{u} = 3\mathbf{i} + 2\mathbf{j}, \ \mathbf{v} = -\mathbf{i} + 4\mathbf{j}$

Express each vector in Exercises 69–72 in the form $a\mathbf{i} + b\mathbf{j}$ and sketch each in the coordinate plane.

69. The unit vectors $\mathbf{u} = (\cos \theta)\mathbf{i} + (\sin \theta)\mathbf{j}$ for $\theta = \pi/6$ and $\theta = 3\pi/4$. Include the unit circle $x^2 + y^2 = 1$ in your sketch.

70. The unit vectors $\mathbf{u} = (\cos \theta)\mathbf{i} + (\sin \theta)\mathbf{j}$ for $\theta = -\pi/4$ and $\theta = -3\pi/4$. Include the unit circle $x^2 + y^2 = 1$ in your sketch.

71. The unit vector obtained by rotating $\mathbf{j}$ counterclockwise $3\pi/4$ radians about the origin

72. The unit vector obtained by rotating $\mathbf{j}$ clockwise $2\pi/3$ radians about the origin

For the vectors in Exercises 73 and 74, find the unit vectors $\mathbf{u} = (\cos \theta)\mathbf{i} + (\sin \theta)\mathbf{j}$ in the same direction.

73. $-\mathbf{i} + 3\mathbf{j}$　　　　　**74.** $6\mathbf{i} - 8\mathbf{j}$

For the vectors in Exercises 75 and 76, express each vector in terms of its magnitude and its direction.

75. $2\mathbf{i} - 3\mathbf{j}$　　　　　**76.** $5\mathbf{i} + 12\mathbf{j}$

77. Use a sketch to show that

$$\mathbf{v} = 3\mathbf{i} - 6\mathbf{j} \quad \text{and} \quad \mathbf{u} = -\mathbf{i} + 2\mathbf{j}$$

have opposite directions.

78. Use a sketch to show that

$$\mathbf{v} = 3\mathbf{i} - 6\mathbf{j} \quad \text{and} \quad \mathbf{u} = \tfrac{1}{2}\mathbf{i} - \mathbf{j}$$

have the same direction.

Exercises 79–82 appeared first in Exercise Set 7.5, where we used the law of cosines and the law of sines to solve the applied problems. For this exercise set, solve the problem using the vector form

$$\mathbf{v} = |\mathbf{v}|[(\cos \theta)\mathbf{i} + (\sin \theta)\mathbf{j}].$$

79. *Ship.*　A ship sails first N80°E for 120 nautical mi, and then S20°W for 200 nautical mi. How far is the ship, then, from the starting point, and in what direction?

80. *Boat.*　A boat heads 35°, propelled by a force of 750 lb. A wind from 320° exerts a force of 150 lb on the boat. How large is the resultant force, and in what direction is the boat moving?

81. *Airplane.*　An airplane has an airspeed of 150 km/h. It is to make a flight in a direction of 70° while there is a 25-km/h wind from 340°. What will the airplane's actual heading be?

82. *Airplane.*　An airplane flies 32° for 210 mi, and then 280° for 170 mi. How far is the airplane, then, from the starting point, and in what direction?

83. Two cables support a 1000-lb weight, as shown. Find the tension in each cable.

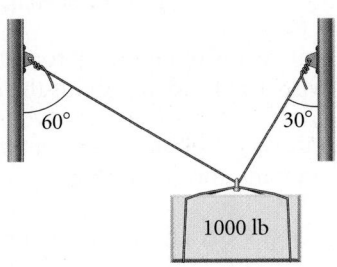

1000 lb

84. A 2500-kg block is suspended by two ropes, as shown. Find the tension in each rope.

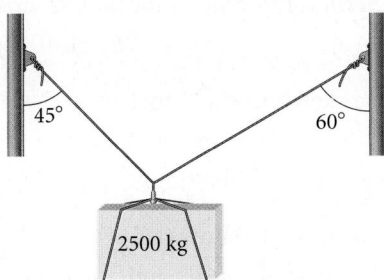

2500 kg

85. A 150-lb sign is hanging from the end of a hinged boom, supported by a cable inclined 42° with the horizontal. Find the tension in the cable and the compression in the boom.

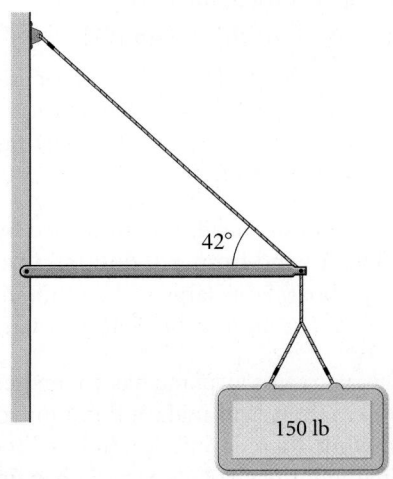

150 lb

86. A weight of 200 lb is supported by a frame made of two rods and hinged at points A, B, and C. Find the forces exerted by the two rods.

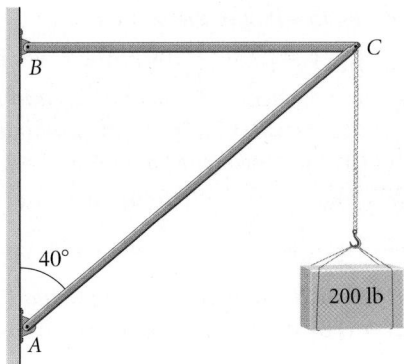

200 lb

Let $\mathbf{u} = \langle u_1, u_2 \rangle$ *and* $\mathbf{v} = \langle v_1, v_2 \rangle$. *Prove each of the following properties.*

87. $\mathbf{u} + \mathbf{v} = \mathbf{v} + \mathbf{u}$

88. $\mathbf{u} \cdot \mathbf{v} = \mathbf{v} \cdot \mathbf{u}$

Collaborative Discussion and Writing

89. Explain how unit vectors are related to the unit circle.

90. Write a vector sum problem for a classmate for which the answer is $\mathbf{v} = 5\mathbf{i} - 8\mathbf{j}$.

Skill Maintenance

Find the slope and the y-intercept of the line with the given equation.

91. $-\frac{1}{5}x - y = 15$ **92.** $y = 7$

Find the zeros of the function.

93. $x^3 - 4x^2 = 0$ **94.** $6x^2 + 7x = 55$

Synthesis

95. If the dot product of two nonzero vectors $\mathbf{u}$ and $\mathbf{v}$ is 0, then the vectors are perpendicular (**orthogonal**). Let $\mathbf{u} = \langle u_1, u_2 \rangle$ and $\mathbf{v} = \langle v_1, v_2 \rangle$.
   a) Prove that if $\mathbf{u} \cdot \mathbf{v} = 0$, then $\mathbf{u}$ and $\mathbf{v}$ are perpendicular.
   b) Give an example of two perpendicular vectors and show that their dot product is 0.

96. If $\overrightarrow{PQ}$ is any vector, what is $\overrightarrow{PQ} + \overrightarrow{QP}$?

97. Find all the unit vectors that are parallel to the vector $\langle 3, -4 \rangle$.

98. Find a vector of length 2 whose direction is the opposite of the direction of the vector $\mathbf{v} = -\mathbf{i} + 2\mathbf{j}$. How many such vectors are there?

99. Given the vector $\overrightarrow{AB} = 3\mathbf{i} - \mathbf{j}$ and A is the point $(2, 9)$, find the point B.

100. Find vector $\mathbf{v}$ from point A to the origin, where $\overrightarrow{AB} = 4\mathbf{i} - 2\mathbf{j}$ and B is the point $(-2, 5)$.

CHAPTER 7 SUMMARY AND REVIEW

Important Properties and Formulas

The Law of Sines

$$\frac{a}{\sin A} = \frac{b}{\sin B} = \frac{c}{\sin C}$$

The Law of Cosines

$$a^2 = b^2 + c^2 - 2bc \cos A,$$
$$b^2 = a^2 + c^2 - 2ac \cos B,$$
$$c^2 = a^2 + b^2 - 2ab \cos C$$

The Area of a Triangle

$$K = \frac{1}{2} bc \sin A = \frac{1}{2} ab \sin C = \frac{1}{2} ac \sin B$$

Complex Numbers

Absolute Value: $|a + bi| = \sqrt{a^2 + b^2}$

Trigonometric Notation: $a + bi = r(\cos \theta + i \sin \theta)$

Multiplication: $r_1(\cos \theta_1 + i \sin \theta_1) \cdot r_2(\cos \theta_2 + i \sin \theta_2) = r_1 r_2[\cos (\theta_1 + \theta_2) + i \sin (\theta_1 + \theta_2)]$

Division: $\dfrac{r_1(\cos \theta_1 + i \sin \theta_1)}{r_2(\cos \theta_2 + i \sin \theta_2)} = \dfrac{r_1}{r_2}[\cos (\theta_1 - \theta_2) + i \sin (\theta_1 - \theta_2)], \quad r_2 \neq 0$

DeMoivre's Theorem

$$[r(\cos \theta + i \sin \theta)]^n = r^n(\cos n\theta + i \sin n\theta)$$

_____

Roots of Complex Numbers

The nth roots of $r(\cos \theta + i \sin \theta)$ are

$$r^{1/n}\left[\cos\left(\frac{\theta}{n} + k \cdot \frac{360°}{n}\right) + i \sin\left(\frac{\theta}{n} + k \cdot \frac{360°}{n}\right)\right], \quad r \neq 0, k = 0, 1, 2, \ldots, n - 1.$$

_____

Vectors

If $\mathbf{u} = \langle u_1, u_2 \rangle$ and $\mathbf{v} = \langle v_1, v_2 \rangle$ and k is a scalar, then:

Length: $\quad |\mathbf{v}| = \sqrt{v_1^2 + v_2^2}$

Addition: $\quad \mathbf{u} + \mathbf{v} = \langle u_1 + v_1, u_2 + v_2 \rangle$

Subtraction: $\quad \mathbf{u} - \mathbf{v} = \langle u_1 - v_1, u_2 - v_2 \rangle$

Scalar Multiplication: $\quad k\mathbf{v} = \langle kv_1, kv_2 \rangle$

Dot Product: $\quad \mathbf{u} \cdot \mathbf{v} = u_1 v_1 + u_2 v_2$

Angle Between Two Vectors: $\quad \cos \theta = \dfrac{\mathbf{u} \cdot \mathbf{v}}{|\mathbf{u}|\,|\mathbf{v}|}$

REVIEW EXERCISES

Determine whether the statement is true or false.

1. For any point (x, y) on the unit circle, $\langle x, y \rangle$ is a unit vector. [7.6]

2. The law of sines can be used to solve a triangle when all three sides are known. [7.1]

3. Two vectors are equivalent if they have the same magnitude and the lines that they are on have the same slope. [7.5]

4. Vectors $\langle 8, -2 \rangle$ and $\langle -8, 2 \rangle$ are equivalent. [7.6]

5. Any triangle, right or oblique, can be solved if at least one angle and any other two measures are known. [7.1]

6. When two angles and an included side of a triangle are known, the triangle cannot be solved using the law of cosines. [7.2]

Solve $\triangle ABC$, if possible. [7.1]

7. $a = 23.4$ ft, $b = 15.7$ ft, $c = 8.3$ ft

8. $B = 27°$, $C = 35°$, $b = 19$ in.

9. $A = 133°28'$, $C = 31°42'$, $b = 890$ m

10. $B = 37°$, $b = 4$ yd, $c = 8$ yd

11. Find the area of $\triangle ABC$ if $b = 9.8$ m, $c = 7.3$ m, and $A = 67.3°$. [7.1]

12. A parallelogram has sides of lengths 3.21 ft and 7.85 ft. One of its angles measures $147°$. Find the area of the parallelogram. [7.1]

13. *Sandbox.* A child-care center has a triangular-shaped sandbox. Two of the three sides measure 15 ft and 12.5 ft and form an included angle of $42°$. To determine the amount of sand that is needed to fill the box, the director must deter-

mine the area of the floor of the box. Find the area of the floor of the box to the nearest square foot. [7.1]

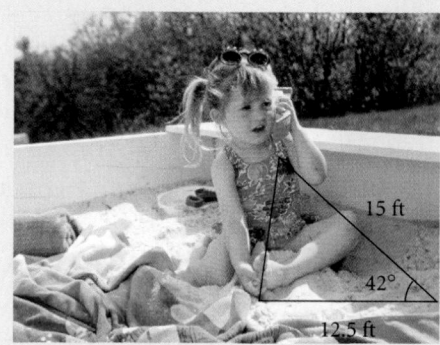

14. *Flower Garden.* A triangular flower garden has sides of lengths 11 m, 9 m, and 6 m. Find the angles of the garden to the nearest degree. [7.2]

15. In an isosceles triangle, the base angles each measure 52.3° and the base is 513 ft long. Find the lengths of the other two sides to the nearest foot. [7.1]

16. *Airplanes.* Two airplanes leave an airport at the same time. The first flies 175 km/h in a direction of 305.6°. The second flies 220 km/h in a direction of 195.5°. After 2 hr, how far apart are the planes? [7.2]

Graph the complex number and find its absolute value. [7.3]

17. $2 - 5i$

18. 4

19. $2i$

20. $-3 + i$

Find trigonometric notation. [7.3]

21. $1 + i$

22. $-4i$

23. $-5\sqrt{3} + 5i$

24. $\dfrac{3}{4}$

Find standard notation, a + bi. [7.3]

25. $4(\cos 60° + i \sin 60°)$

26. $7(\cos 0° + i \sin 0°)$

27. $5\left(\cos \dfrac{2\pi}{3} + i \sin \dfrac{2\pi}{3}\right)$

28. $2\left[\cos\left(-\dfrac{\pi}{3}\right) + i \sin\left(-\dfrac{\pi}{3}\right)\right]$

Convert to trigonometric notation and then multiply or divide, expressing the answer in standard notation. [7.3]

29. $\left(1 + i\sqrt{3}\right)(1 - i)$

30. $\dfrac{2 - 2i}{2 + 2i}$

31. $\dfrac{2 + 2\sqrt{3}i}{\sqrt{3} - i}$

32. $i\left(3 - 3\sqrt{3}i\right)$

Raise the number to the given power and write trigonometric notation for the answer. [7.3]

33. $[2(\cos 60° + i \sin 60°)]^3$

34. $(1 - i)^4$

Raise the number to the given power and write standard notation for the answer. [7.3]

35. $(1 + i)^6$

36. $\left(\dfrac{1}{2} + \dfrac{\sqrt{3}}{2}i\right)^{10}$

37. Find the square roots of $-1 + i$. [7.3]

38. Find the cube roots of $3\sqrt{3} - 3i$. [7.3]

39. Find and graph the fourth roots of 81. [7.3]

40. Find and graph the fifth roots of 1. [7.3]

Find all the complex solutions of the equation. [7.3]

41. $x^4 - i = 0$

42. $x^3 + 1 = 0$

43. Find the polar coordinates of each of these points. Give three answers for each point. [7.4]

Find the polar coordinates of the point. Express the answer in degrees and then in radians. [7.4]

44. $\left(-4\sqrt{2}, 4\sqrt{2}\right)$

45. $(0, -5)$

Find the rectangular coordinates of the point. [7.4]

46. $\left(3, \dfrac{\pi}{4}\right)$

47. $(-6, -120°)$

Convert to a polar equation. [7.4]

48. $5x - 2y = 6$

49. $y = 3$

50. $x^2 + y^2 = 9$

51. $y^2 - 4x - 16 = 0$

Convert to a rectangular equation. [7.4]

52. $r = 6$

53. $r + r \sin \theta = 1$

54. $r = \dfrac{3}{1 - \cos \theta}$

55. $r - 2 \cos \theta = 3 \sin \theta$

In Exercises 56–59, match the equation with one of figures (a)–(d), which follow. [7.4]

a)

b)

c)

d)

56. $r = 2 \sin \theta$

57. $r^2 = \cos 2\theta$

58. $r = 1 + 3 \cos \theta$

59. $r \sin \theta = 4$

Magnitudes of vectors **u** *and* **v** *and the angle* θ *between the vectors are given. Find the magnitude of the sum,* **u** + **v**, *to the nearest tenth and give the direction by specifying to the nearest degree the angle that it makes with the vector* **u**. [7.5]

60. $|\mathbf{u}| = 12$, $|\mathbf{v}| = 15$, $\theta = 120°$

61. $|\mathbf{u}| = 41$, $|\mathbf{v}| = 60$, $\theta = 25°$

The vectors **u**, **v**, *and* **w** *are drawn below. Copy them on a sheet of paper. Then sketch each of the vectors in Exercises 62 and 63.* [7.5]

62. **u** − **v**

63. $\mathbf{u} + \frac{1}{2}\mathbf{w}$

64. Forces of 230 N and 500 N act on an object. The angle between the forces is 52°. Find the resultant, giving the angle that it makes with the smaller force. [7.5]

65. *Wind.* A wind has an easterly component of 15 km/h and a southerly component of 25 km/h. Find the magnitude and the direction of the wind. [7.5]

66. *Ship.* A ship sails N75°E for 90 nautical mi, and then S10°W for 100 nautical mi. How far is the ship, then, from the starting point, and in what direction? [7.5]

Find the component form of the vector given the initial and terminal points. [7.6]

67. $\overrightarrow{AB}$; $A(2, -8)$, $B(-2, -5)$

68. $\overrightarrow{TR}$; $R(0, 7)$, $T(-2, 13)$

69. Find the magnitude of vector **u** if $\mathbf{u} = \langle 5, -6 \rangle$. [7.6]

Do the calculations in Exercises 70–73 for the vectors

$\mathbf{u} = \langle 3, -4 \rangle$, $\mathbf{v} = \langle -3, 9 \rangle$ *and* $\mathbf{w} = \langle -2, -5 \rangle$. [7.6]

70. $4\mathbf{u} + \mathbf{w}$

71. $2\mathbf{w} - 6\mathbf{v}$

72. $|\mathbf{u}| + |2\mathbf{w}|$

73. $\mathbf{u} \cdot \mathbf{w}$

74. Find a unit vector that has the same direction as $\mathbf{v} = \langle -6, -2 \rangle$. [7.6]

75. Express the vector $\mathbf{t} = \langle -9, 4 \rangle$ as a linear combination of the unit vectors **i** and **j**. [7.6]

76. Determine the direction angle θ of the vector $\mathbf{w} = \langle -4, -1 \rangle$ to the nearest degree. [7.6]

77. Find the magnitude and the direction angle θ of $\mathbf{u} = -5\mathbf{i} - 3\mathbf{j}$. [7.6]

78. Find the angle between $\mathbf{u} = \langle 3, -7 \rangle$ and $\mathbf{v} = \langle 2, 2 \rangle$ to the nearest tenth of a degree. [7.6]

79. *Airplane.* An airplane has an airspeed of 160 mph. It is to make a flight in a direction of 80° while there is a 20-mph wind from 310°. What will the airplane's actual heading be? [7.6]

Do the calculations in Exercises 80–83 for the vectors

$\mathbf{u} = 2\mathbf{i} + 5\mathbf{j}$, $\mathbf{v} = -3\mathbf{i} + 10\mathbf{j}$, *and* $\mathbf{w} = 4\mathbf{i} + 7\mathbf{j}$. [7.6]

80. $5\mathbf{u} - 8\mathbf{v}$

81. $\mathbf{u} - (\mathbf{v} + \mathbf{w})$

82. $|\mathbf{u} - \mathbf{v}|$

83. $3|\mathbf{w}| + |\mathbf{v}|$

84. Express the vector $\overrightarrow{PQ}$ in the form $a\mathbf{i} + b\mathbf{j}$, if P is the point $(1, -3)$ and Q is the point $(-4, 2)$. [7.6]

*Express each vector in Exercises 85 and 86 in the form a***i** + b**j** *and sketch each in the coordinate plane.* [7.6]

85. The unit vectors **u** = (cos θ)**i** + (sin θ)**j** for θ = π/4 and θ = 5π/4. Include the unit circle $x^2 + y^2 = 1$ in your sketch.

86. The unit vector obtained by rotating **j** counter-clockwise 2π/3 radians about the origin.

87. Express the vector 3**i** − **j** as a product of its magnitude and its direction.

88. Determine the trigonometric notation for 1 − *i*. [7.3]

A. $\sqrt{2}\left(\cos\dfrac{5\pi}{4} + i\sin\dfrac{5\pi}{4}\right)$

B. $\sqrt{2}\left(\cos\dfrac{7\pi}{4} - \sin\dfrac{7\pi}{4}\right)$

C. $\cos\dfrac{7\pi}{4} + i\sin\dfrac{7\pi}{4}$

D. $\sqrt{2}\left(\cos\dfrac{7\pi}{4} + i\sin\dfrac{7\pi}{4}\right)$

89. Convert the polar equation *r* = 100 to a rectangular equation. [7.4]

A. $x^2 + y^2 = 10{,}000$

B. $x^2 + y^2 = 100$

C. $\sqrt{x^2 + y^2} = 10$

D. $\sqrt{x^2 + y^2} = 1000$

Technology Connection

Use a graphing calculator to convert from rectangular to polar coordinates. Express the answer in degrees and then in radians. [7.4]

90. (−2, 5)

91. $(-4.2, \sqrt{7})$

Use a graphing calculator to convert from polar to rectangular coordinates. Round the coordinates to the nearest hundredth. [7.4]

92. (2, −15°)

93. $\left(-2.3, \dfrac{\pi}{5}\right)$

Collaborative Discussion and Writing

94. Explain why these statements are not contradictory:

The number 1 has one real cube root.
The number 1 has three complex cube roots.

[7.1]

95. Summarize how you can tell algebraically when solving triangles whether there is no solution, one solution, or two solutions. [7.1], [7.2]

96. *Golf: Distance versus Accuracy.* It is often argued in golf that the farther you hit the ball, the more accurate it must be to stay safe. (Safe means not in the woods, water, or some other hazard.) In his book *Golf and the Spirit* (p. 54), M. Scott Peck asserts "Deviate 5° from your aiming point on a 150-yd shot, and your ball will land approximately 20 yd to the side of where you wanted it to be. Do the same on a 300-yd shot, and it will be 40 yd off target. Twenty yards may well be in the range of safety; 40 yards probably won't. This principle not infrequently allows a mediocre, short-hitting golfer like myself to score better than the long hitter." Check the accuracy of the mathematics in this statement, and comment on Peck's assertion. [7.2]

Synthesis

97. Let **u** = 12**i** + 5**j**. Find a vector that has the same direction as **u** but has length 3. [7.6]

98. A parallelogram has sides of lengths 3.42 and 6.97. Its area is 18.4. Find the sizes of its angles. [7.1]

CHAPTER 7 TEST

Solve △ABC, if possible.

1. $a = 18$ ft, $B = 54°$, $C = 43°$

2. $b = 8$ m, $c = 5$ m, $C = 36°$

3. $a = 16.1$ in., $b = 9.8$ in., $c = 11.2$ in.

4. Find the area of △ABC if $C = 106.4°$, $a = 7$ cm, and $b = 13$ cm.

5. *Distance Across a Lake.*   Points A and B are on opposite sides of a lake. Point C is 52 m from A. The measure of ∠BAC is determined to be 108°, and the measure of ∠ACB is determined to be 44°. What is the distance from A to B?

6. *Location of Airplanes.*   Two airplanes leave an airport at the same time. The first flies 210 km/h in a direction of 290°. The second flies 180 km/h in a direction of 185°. After 3 hr, how far apart are the planes?

7. Graph: $-4 + i$.

8. Find the absolute value of $2 - 3i$.

9. Find trigonometric notation for $3 - 3i$.

10. Divide and express the result in standard notation $a + bi$:

$$\frac{2\left(\cos \dfrac{2\pi}{3} + i \sin \dfrac{2\pi}{3}\right)}{8\left(\cos \dfrac{\pi}{6} + i \sin \dfrac{\pi}{6}\right)}.$$

11. Find $(1 - i)^8$ and write standard notation for the answer.

12. Find the polar coordinates of $\left(-1, \sqrt{3}\right)$. Express the angle in degrees using the smallest possible positive angle.

13. Convert $\left(-1, \dfrac{2\pi}{3}\right)$ to rectangular coordinates.

14. Convert to a polar equation: $x^2 + y^2 = 10$.

15. Graph: $r = 1 - \cos \theta$.

16. Which of the following is the graph of $r = 3 \cos \theta$?

a)

b)

c)

d)

17. For vectors **u** and **v**, $|\mathbf{u}| = 8$, $|\mathbf{v}| = 5$, and the angle between the vectors is 63°. Find **u** + **v**. Give the magnitude to the nearest tenth, and give the direction by specifying the angle that the resultant makes with **u**, to the nearest degree.

18. For $\mathbf{u} = 2\mathbf{i} - 7\mathbf{j}$ and $\mathbf{v} = 5\mathbf{i} + \mathbf{j}$, find $2\mathbf{u} - 3\mathbf{v}$.

19. Find a unit vector in the same direction as $-4\mathbf{i} + 3\mathbf{j}$.

Synthesis

20. A parallelogram has sides of length 15.4 and 9.8. Its area is 72.9. Find the measures of the angles.

8.1 Systems of Equations in Two Variables

◆ Solve a system of two linear equations in two variables by graphing.
◆ Solve a system of two linear equations in two variables using the substitution and the elimination methods.
◆ Use systems of two linear equations to solve applied problems.

A **system of equations** is composed of two or more equations considered simultaneously. For example,

$$x - y = 5,$$
$$2x + y = 1$$

is a **system of two linear equations in two variables.** The solution set of this system consists of all ordered pairs that make *both* equations true. The ordered pair $(2, -3)$ is a solution of the system of equations above. We can verify this by substituting 2 for x and -3 for y in *each* equation.

$$\begin{array}{c|c} x - y = 5 \\ \hline 2 - (-3) \;?\; 5 \\ 2 + 3 \\ 5 \;\bigm|\; 5 \quad \text{TRUE} \end{array} \qquad \begin{array}{c|c} 2x + y = 1 \\ \hline 2 \cdot 2 + (-3) \;?\; 1 \\ 4 - 3 \\ 1 \;\bigm|\; 1 \quad \text{TRUE} \end{array}$$

◆ Solving Systems of Equations Graphically

Recall that the graph of a linear equation is a line that contains all the ordered pairs in the solution set of the equation. When we graph a system of linear equations, each point at which the graphs intersect is a solution of *both* equations and therefore a **solution of the system of equations.**

EXAMPLE 1 Solve the following system of equations graphically.

$$x - y = 5,$$
$$2x + y = 1$$

Solution   We graph the equations on the same set of axes, as shown below.

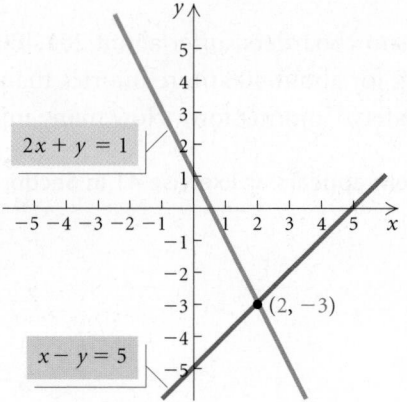

$2x + y = 1$

$x - y = 5$

$(2, -3)$

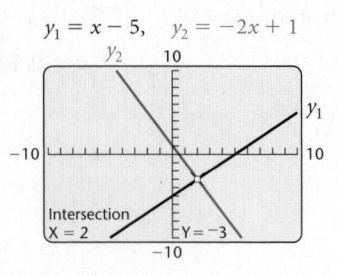

We see that the graphs intersect at a single point, $(2, -3)$, so $(2, -3)$ is the solution of the system of equations. To check this solution, we substitute 2 for x and -3 for y in both equations, as we did above.

▶ **Now Try Exercise 7.**

The graphs of most of the systems of equations that we use to model applications intersect at a single point, like the system above. However, it is possible that the graphs will have no points in common or infinitely many points in common. Each of these possibilities is illustrated below.

  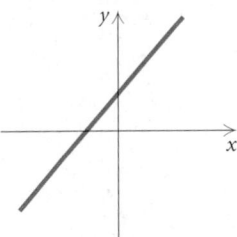

Exactly one common point
One solution

Parallel lines
No common points
No solution

Lines are identical
Infinitely many common points
Infinitely many solutions

Consistent
Independent

Inconsistent
Independent

Consistent
Dependent

If a system of equations has at least one solution, it is **consistent.** If the system has no solutions, it is **inconsistent.** In addition, if a system of two linear equations in two variables has an infinite number of solutions, the equations are **dependent.** Otherwise, they are **independent.**

◆ The Substitution Method

Solving a system of equations graphically is not always accurate when the solutions are not integers. A solution like $\left(\frac{43}{27}, -\frac{19}{27}\right)$, for instance, will be difficult to determine from a hand-drawn graph.

Algebraic methods for solving systems of equations, when used correctly, always give accurate results. One such technique is the **substitution method.** It is used most often when a variable is alone on one side of an equation or when it is easy to solve for a variable. To apply the substitution method, we begin by using one of the equations to express one variable in terms of the other; then we substitute that expression in the other equation of the system.

EXAMPLE 2 Use the substitution method to solve the system of equations

$$x - y = 5, \quad (1)$$
$$2x + y = 1. \quad (2)$$

Solution First, we solve equation (1) for x. (We could have solved for y instead.) We have

$$x - y = 5, \qquad (1)$$
$$x = y + 5. \qquad \text{Solving for } x$$

Then we substitute $y + 5$ for x in equation (2). This gives an equation in one variable, which we know how to solve:

$$2x + y = 1 \qquad (2)$$
$$2(y + 5) + y = 1 \qquad \text{The parentheses are necessary.}$$
$$2y + 10 + y = 1 \qquad \text{Removing parentheses}$$
$$3y + 10 = 1 \qquad \text{Collecting like terms on the left}$$
$$3y = -9 \qquad \text{Subtracting 10 on both sides}$$
$$y = -3. \qquad \text{Dividing by 3 on both sides}$$

Now we substitute -3 for y in either of the original equations (this is called **back-substitution**) and solve for x. We choose equation (1):

$$x - y = 5, \quad (1)$$
$$x - (-3) = 5 \qquad \text{Substituting } -3 \text{ for } y$$
$$x + 3 = 5$$
$$x = 2. \qquad \text{Subtracting 3 on both sides}$$

We have previously checked the pair $(2, -3)$ in both equations. The solution of the system of equations is $(2, -3)$.

▶ Now Try Exercise 17.

◆ **The Elimination Method**

Another algebraic technique for solving systems of equations is the **elimination method.** With this method, we eliminate a variable by adding two equations. If the coefficients of a particular variable are opposites, we can eliminate that variable simply by adding the original equations. For example, if the x-coefficient is -3 in one equation and is 3 in the other equation, then the sum of the x-terms will be 0 and thus the variable x will be eliminated when we add the equations.

EXAMPLE 3 Use the elimination method to solve the system of equations

$$2x + y = 2, \quad (1)$$
$$x - y = 7. \quad (2)$$

ALGEBRAIC SOLUTION

Since the y-coefficients, 1 and -1, are opposites, we can eliminate y by adding the equations:

$$
\begin{array}{ll}
2x + y = 2 & (1) \\
\underline{x - y = 7} & (2) \\
3x \quad\;\;\; = 9 & \text{Adding} \\
x = 3.
\end{array}
$$

We then back-substitute 3 for x in either equation and solve for y. We choose equation (1):

$$
\begin{array}{ll}
2x + y = 2 & (1) \\
2 \cdot 3 + y = 2 & \text{Substituting 3 for } x \\
6 + y = 2 & \\
y = -4.
\end{array}
$$

We check the solution by substituting the pair $(3, -4)$ in both equations.

$$
\begin{array}{c|c}
2x + y = 2 & x - y = 7 \\
\hline
2 \cdot 3 + (-4) \;?\; 2 & 3 - (-4) \;?\; 7 \\
6 - 4 \;\Big|\; & 3 + 4 \;\Big|\; \\
2 \;\Big|\; 2 \quad \text{TRUE} & 7 \;\Big|\; 7 \quad \text{TRUE}
\end{array}
$$

The solution is $(3, -4)$.

VISUALIZING THE SOLUTION

We graph $2x + y = 2$ and $x - y = 7$.

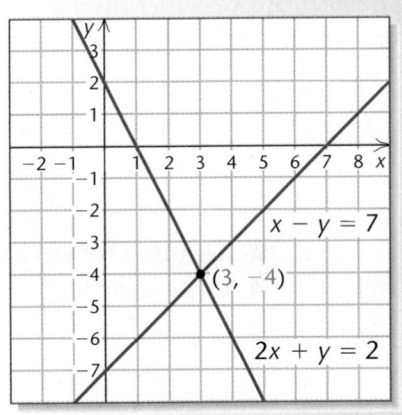

The graphs intersect at the point $(3, -4)$, so the solution of the system of equations is $(3, -4)$.

▶ Now Try Exercise 29.

Before we add, it might be necessary to multiply one or both equations by suitable constants in order to find two equations in which coefficients are opposites.

EXAMPLE 4 Use the elimination method to solve the system of equations

$$4x + 3y = 11, \quad (1)$$
$$-5x + 2y = 15. \quad (2)$$

ALGEBRAIC SOLUTION

We can obtain x-coefficients that are opposites by multiplying the first equation by 5 and the second equation by 4:

$$
\begin{array}{ll}
20x + 15y = 55 & \text{Multiplying equation (1) by 5} \\
-20x + 8y = 60 & \text{Multiplying equation (2) by 4} \\
\hline
23y = 115 & \text{Adding} \\
y = 5.
\end{array}
$$

We then back-substitute 5 for y in either equation (1) or (2) and solve for x. We choose equation (1):

$$
\begin{array}{ll}
4x + 3y = 11 & (1) \\
4x + 3 \cdot 5 = 11 & \text{Substituting 5 for } y \\
4x + 15 = 11 \\
4x = -4 \\
x = -1.
\end{array}
$$

We can check the pair $(-1, 5)$ by substituting in both equations. The solution is $(-1, 5)$.

VISUALIZING THE SOLUTION

We graph $4x + 3y = 11$ and $-5x + 2y = 15$.

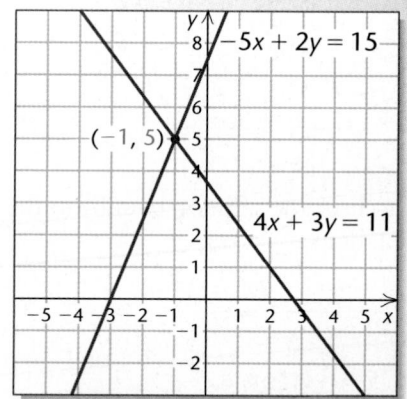

The graphs intersect at the point $(-1, 5)$, so the solution of the system of equations is $(-1, 5)$.

▷ Now Try Exercise 31.

In Example 4, the two systems

$$
\begin{array}{ccc}
4x + 3y = 11, & & 20x + 15y = 55, \\
-5x + 2y = 15 & \text{and} & -20x + 8y = 60
\end{array}
$$

are **equivalent** because they have exactly the same solutions. When we use the elimination method, we often multiply one or both equations by constants to find equivalent equations that allow us to eliminate a variable by adding.

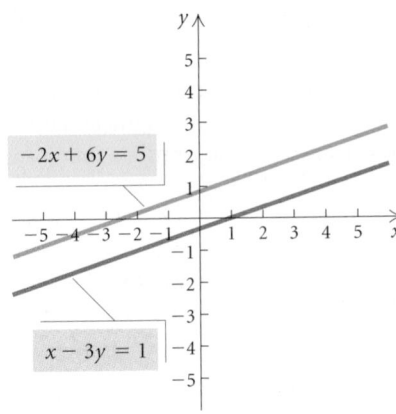

$-2x + 6y = 5$

$x - 3y = 1$

Figure 1

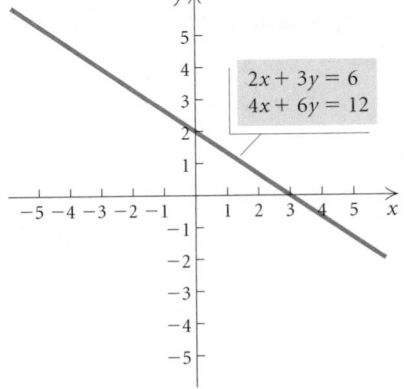

$2x + 3y = 6$
$4x + 6y = 12$

Figure 2

x	$-\frac{2}{3}x + 2$
$-\frac{3}{2}y + 3$	y
-3	4
0	2
6	-2

EXAMPLE 5 Solve each of the following systems of equations using the elimination method.

a) $x - 3y = 1,$ (1)   **b)** $2x + 3y = 6,$ (1)

    $-2x + 6y = 5$ (2) $4x + 6y = 12$ (2)

Solution

a) We multiply equation (1) by 2 and add:

$$
\begin{array}{ll}
2x - 6y = 2 & \text{Multiplying equation (1) by 2} \\
\underline{-2x + 6y = 5} & \text{(2)} \\
0 = 7. & \text{Adding}
\end{array}
$$

There are no values of x and y for which $0 = 7$ is true, so the system has *no solution*. The solution set is $\varnothing$. The system of equations is inconsistent. The graphs of the equations are parallel lines, as shown in Fig. 1.

b) We multiply equation (1) by -2 and add:

$$
\begin{array}{ll}
-4x - 6y = -12 & \text{Multiplying equation (1) by } -2 \\
\underline{4x + 6y = 12} & \text{(2)} \\
0 = 0. & \text{Adding}
\end{array}
$$

We obtain the equation $0 = 0$, which is true for all values of x and y. This tells us that the equations are dependent, so there are *infinitely many solutions*. That is, any solution of one equation of the system is also a solution of the other. The graphs of the equations are identical, as shown in Fig. 2.

Solving either equation for y, we have $y = -\frac{2}{3}x + 2$, so we can write the solutions of the system as ordered pairs (x, y), where y is expressed as $-\frac{2}{3}x + 2$. Thus the solutions can be written in the form $\left(x, -\frac{2}{3}x + 2\right)$. Any real value that we choose for x then gives us a value for y and thus an ordered pair in the solution set. For example,

$$\text{if } x = -3, \quad \text{then } -\tfrac{2}{3}x + 2 = -\tfrac{2}{3}(-3) + 2 = 4,$$
$$\text{if } x = 0, \quad \text{then } -\tfrac{2}{3}x + 2 = -\tfrac{2}{3}\cdot 0 + 2 = 2, \quad \text{and}$$
$$\text{if } x = 6, \quad \text{then } -\tfrac{2}{3}x + 2 = -\tfrac{2}{3}\cdot 6 + 2 = -2.$$

Thus some of the solutions are $(-3, 4)$, $(0, 2)$, and $(6, -2)$.

Similarly, solving either equation for x, we have $x = -\frac{3}{2}y + 3$, so the solutions (x, y) can also be written, expressing x as $-\frac{3}{2}y + 3$, in the form $\left(-\frac{3}{2}y + 3, y\right)$.

Since the two forms of the solutions are equivalent, they yield the same solution set, as illustrated in the table at left. Note, for example, that when $y = 4$, we have the solution $(-3, 4)$; when $y = 2$, we have $(0, 2)$; and when $y = -2$, we have $(6, -2)$.   ▶ **Now Try Exercise 33.**

✦ Applications

Frequently the most challenging and time-consuming step in the problem-solving process is translating a situation to mathematical language. However, in many cases, this task is made easier if we translate to more than one equation in more than one variable.

EXAMPLE 6 *Snack Mixtures.* At SnackMix.com, caramel corn worth $2.50 per pound is mixed with honey roasted mixed nuts worth $7.50 per pound in order to get 20 lb of a mixture worth $4.50 per pound. How much of each snack is used?

Solution   We use the five-step problem-solving process.

1. **Familiarize.** Let's begin by making a guess. Suppose 16 lb of caramel corn and 4 lb of nuts are used. Then the total weight of the mixture would be 16 lb + 4 lb, or 20 lb, the desired weight. The total values of these amounts of ingredients are found by multiplying the price per pound by the number of pounds used:

Caramel corn:	$2.50(16) = $40
Nuts:	$7.50(4) = $30
Total value:	$70.

   The desired value of the mixture is $4.50 per pound, so the value of 20 lb would be $4.50(20), or $90. Thus we see that our guess, which led to a total of $70, is incorrect. Nevertheless, these calculations will help us to translate.

2. **Translate.** We organize the information in a table. We let x = the number of pounds of caramel corn in the mixture and y = the number of pounds of nuts.

	Caramel Corn	Nuts	Mixture	
Price per Pound	$2.50	$7.50	$4.50	
Number of Pounds	x	y	20	→ $x + y = 20$
Value of Mixture	$2.50x$	$7.50y$	4.50(20), or 90	→ $2.50x + 7.50y = 90$

From the second row of the table, we get one equation:

$$x + y = 20.$$

The last row of the table yields a second equation:

$$2.50x + 7.50y = 90, \quad \text{or} \quad 2.5x + 7.5y = 90.$$

We can multiply by 10 on both sides of the second equation to clear the decimals. This gives us the following system of equations:

$$x + y = 20, \qquad (1)$$
$$25x + 75y = 900. \qquad (2)$$

3. Carry out. We carry out the solution as follows.

ALGEBRAIC SOLUTION

Using the elimination method, we multiply equation (1) by -25 and add it to equation (2):

$$\begin{array}{r} -25x - 25y = -500 \\ \underline{25x + 75y = 900} \\ 50y = 400 \\ y = 8. \end{array}$$

Then we back-substitute to find x:

$$\begin{array}{ll} x + y = 20 & (1) \\ x + 8 = 20 & \text{Substituting 8 for } y \\ x = 12. \end{array}$$

VISUALIZING THE SOLUTION

The solution of the system of equations is the point of intersection of the graphs of the equations.

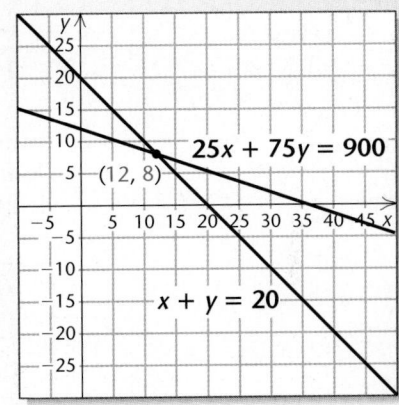

The graphs intersect at the point $(12, 8)$, so the solution of the system of equations is $(12, 8)$.

4. Check. If 12 lb of caramel corn and 8 lb of nuts are used, the mixture weighs $12 + 8$, or 20 lb. The value of the mixture is $\$2.50(12) + \$7.50(8)$, or $\$30 + \$60$, or $\$90$. Since the possible solution yields the desired weight and value of the mixture, our result checks.

5. State. The mixture should consist of 12 lb of caramel corn and 8 lb of honey roasted nuts.

▷ Now Try Exercise 61.

EXAMPLE 7 *Boating.* Kerry's motorboat takes 3 hr to make a downstream trip with a 3-mph current. The return trip against the same current takes 5 hr. Find the speed of the boat in still water.

Solution

1. **Familiarize.** We first make a drawing, letting r = the speed of the boat in still water, in miles per hour, and d = the distance traveled, in miles. When the boat is traveling downstream, the current adds to its speed, so the downstream speed is $r + 3$. On the other hand, the current slows the boat down when it travels upstream, so the upstream speed is $r - 3$.

Downstream:
Speed: $r + 3$
Time: 3 hr
Distance: d

Upstream:
Speed: $r - 3$
Time: 5 hr
Distance: d

2. **Translate.** We organize the information in a table. Using the formula *Distance* = *Rate* (or *Speed*) · *Time*, we find that each row of the table yields an equation.

	Distance	Rate	Time	
Downstream	d	$r + 3$	3	⟶ $d = (r + 3)3$
Upstream	d	$r - 3$	5	⟶ $d = (r - 3)5$

We have a system of equations:

$$d = (r + 3)3, \quad (1)$$
$$d = (r - 3)5. \quad (2)$$

3. **Carry out.** We find r using substitution:

$(r + 3)3 = (r - 3)5$	Substituting $(r + 3)3$ for d in equation (2)
$3r + 9 = 5r - 15$	Multiplying
$9 = 2r - 15$	Subtracting $3r$ on both sides
$24 = 2r$	Adding 15 on both sides
$12 = r.$	Dividing by 2 on both sides

4. **Check.** If $r = 12$, then the boat's speed downstream is $r + 3 = 12 + 3$, or 15 mph, and the speed upstream is $r - 3 = 12 - 3$, or 9 mph. At 15 mph, in 3 hr the boat travels $15 \cdot 3 = 45$ mi; at 9 mph, in 5 hr the boat travels $9 \cdot 5 = 45$ mi. Since the distances are the same, the answer checks.

5. **State.** The speed of the boat in still water is 12 mph.

▶ Now Try Exercise 57.

EXAMPLE 8 *Supply and Demand.* Suppose that the price and the supply of the Star Station satellite radio are related by the equation

$$y = 90 + 30x,$$

where y is the price, in dollars, at which the seller is willing to supply x thousand units. Also suppose that the price and the demand for the same model of satellite radio are related by the equation

$$y = 200 - 25x,$$

where y is the price, in dollars, at which the consumer is willing to buy x thousand units.

The **equilibrium point** for this product is the pair (x, y) that is a solution of both equations. The **equilibrium price** is the price at which the amount of the product that the seller is willing to supply is the same as the amount demanded by the consumer. Find the equilibrium point for this product.

Solution

1., 2. Familiarize and **Translate.** We are given a system of equations in the statement of the problem, so no further translation is necessary.

$$y = 90 + 30x, \quad (1)$$
$$y = 200 - 25x. \quad (2)$$

We substitute some values for x in each equation to get an idea of the corresponding prices. When $x = 1$,

$$y = 90 + 30 \cdot 1 = 120, \qquad \text{Substituting in equation (1)}$$
$$y = 200 - 25 \cdot 1 = 175. \qquad \text{Substituting in equation (2)}$$

This indicates that the price when 1 thousand units are supplied is lower than the price when 1 thousand units are demanded.

When $x = 4$,

$$y = 90 + 30 \cdot 4 = 210, \qquad \text{Substituting in equation (1)}$$
$$y = 200 - 25 \cdot 4 = 100. \qquad \text{Substituting in equation (2)}$$

In this case, the price related to supply is higher than the price related to demand. It would appear that the x-value we are looking for is between 1 and 4.

STUDY TIP

Make an effort to do your homework as soon as possible after each class. Make this part of your routine, choosing a time and a place where you can focus with a minimum of interruptions.

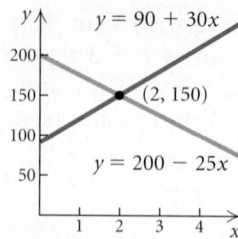

3. **Carry out.** We use the substitution method:

$$200 - 25x = 90 + 30x \qquad \text{Substituting } 200 - 25x \text{ for } y \text{ in equation (1)}$$

$$110 = 55x \qquad \text{Adding } 25x \text{ and subtracting } 90 \text{ on both sides}$$

$$2 = x. \qquad \text{Dividing by } 55 \text{ on both sides}$$

We now back-substitute 2 for x in either equation and find y:

$$y = 200 - 25x \qquad (2)$$

$$y = 200 - 25 \cdot 2 \qquad \text{Substituting 2 for } x$$

$$y = 200 - 50$$

$$y = 150.$$

4. **Check.** We can check by substituting 2 for x and 150 for y in both equations. Also note that 2 is between 1 and 4, as expected from the *Familiarize* and *Translate* steps.

5. **State.** The equilibrium point is (2, $150). That is, the equilibrium supply is 2 thousand units and the equilibrium price is $150.

▶ Now Try Exercise 49.

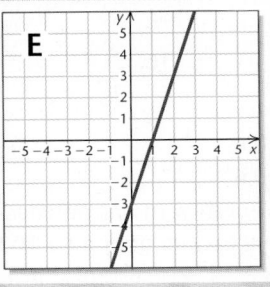

Visualizing the Graph

Match the equation or system of equations with its graph.

1. $2x - 3y = 6$

2. $f(x) = x^2 - 2x - 3$

3. $f(x) = -x^2 + 4$

4. $(x - 2)^2 + (y + 3)^2 = 9$

5. $f(x) = x^3 - 2$

6. $f(x) = -(x - 1)^2(x + 1)^2$

7. $f(x) = \dfrac{x - 1}{x^2 - 4}$

8. $f(x) = \dfrac{x^2 - x - 6}{x^2 - 1}$

9. $x - y = -1,$
   $2x - y = 2$

10. $3x - y = 3,$
    $2y = 6x - 6$

Answers on page A-56

8.1 EXERCISE SET

In Exercises 1–6, match the system of equations with one of the graphs (a)–(f), which follow.

a)

b)

c)

d)

e)

f)

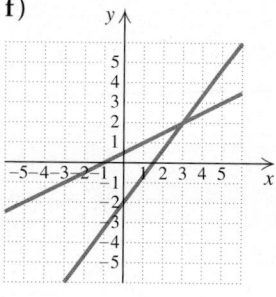

1. $x + y = -2,$
  $y = x - 8$

2. $x - y = -5,$
  $x = -4y$

3. $x - 2y = -1,$
  $4x - 3y = 6$

4. $2x - y = 1,$
  $x + 2y = -7$

5. $2x - 3y = -1,$
  $-4x + 6y = 2$

6. $4x - 2y = 5,$
  $6x - 3y = -10$

Solve graphically.

7. $x + y = 2,$
  $3x + y = 0$

8. $x + y = 1,$
  $3x + y = 7$

9. $x + 2y = 1,$
  $x + 4y = 3$

10. $3x + 4y = 5,$
  $x - 2y = 5$

11. $y + 1 = 2x,$
  $y - 1 = 2x$

12. $2x - y = 1,$
  $3y = 6x - 3$

13. $x - y = -6,$
  $y = -2x$

14. $2x + y = 5,$
  $x = -3y$

15. $2y = x - 1,$
  $3x = 6y + 3$

16. $y = 3x + 2,$
  $3x - y = -3$

Solve using the substitution method.

17. $x + y = 9,$
  $2x - 3y = -2$

18. $3x - y = 5,$
  $x + y = \frac{1}{2}$

19. $x - 2y = 7,$
  $x = y + 4$

20. $x + 4y = 6,$
  $x = -3y + 3$

21. $y = 2x - 6,$
  $5x - 3y = 16$

22. $3x + 5y = 2,$
  $2x - y = -3$

23. $x - 5y = 4,$
  $y = 7 - 2x$

24. $5x + 3y = -1,$
  $x + y = 1$

25. $2x - 3y = 5,$
  $5x + 4y = 1$

26. $3x + 4y = 6,$
  $2x + 3y = 5$

27. $x + 2y = 2,$
  $4x + 4y = 5$

28. $2x - y = 2,$
  $4x + y = 3$

Solve using the elimination method. Also determine whether each system is consistent or inconsistent and whether the equations are dependent or independent.

29. $x + 2y = 7,$
  $x - 2y = -5$

30. $3x + 4y = -2,$
  $-3x - 5y = 1$

31. $x - 3y = 2,$
  $6x + 5y = -34$

32. $x + 3y = 0,$
  $20x - 15y = 75$

33. $3x - 12y = 6,$
  $2x - 8y = 4$

34. $2x + 6y = 7,$
  $3x + 9y = 10$

35. $2x = 5 - 3y,$
  $4x = 11 - 7y$

36. $7(x - y) = 14,$
  $2x = y + 5$

37. $0.3x - 0.2y = -0.9,$
  $0.2x - 0.3y = -0.6$
  (*Hint*: Since each coefficient has one decimal place, first multiply each equation by 10 to clear the decimals.)

38. $0.2x - 0.3y = 0.3,$
$0.4x + 0.6y = -0.2$
(*Hint*: Since each coefficient has one decimal place, first multiply each equation by 10 to clear the decimals.)

39. $\frac{1}{5}x + \frac{1}{2}y = 6,$
$\frac{3}{5}x - \frac{1}{2}y = 2$
(*Hint*: First multiply by the least common denominator to clear fractions.)

40. $\frac{2}{3}x + \frac{3}{5}y = -17,$
$\frac{1}{2}x - \frac{1}{3}y = -1$
(*Hint*: First multiply by the least common denominator to clear fractions.)

41. *Winter Sports Injuries.* Skiers and snowboarders suffer about 288,400 injuries each winter, with skiing accounting for about 400 more injuries than snowboarding (*Source*: U.S. Consumer Product Safety Commission). How many injuries occur in each winter sport?

42. *Annual College Student Spending.* College students spend $183 more each year on textbooks and course materials than on computer equipment. They spend a total of $819 on textbooks and course materials and on computer equipment each year. (*Source*: National Association of College Stores) How much is spent each year on textbooks and course materials and how much is spent on computer equipment?

43. *Street Names.* The two most common names for streets in the United States are Second Street and Main Street, with 15,684 streets bearing one of these names. There are 260 more streets named Second Street than Main Street. (*Source*: 2006 Tele Atlas digital map data) How many streets bear each name?

44. *Museum Admission Prices.* Admission to the Indianapolis Children's Museum costs $5 more for an adult than for a child (*Source*: Indianapolis Children's Museum). Admission to the museum for Barbara and Jeff Johnson and their five children costs $59. Find the cost of each adult's admission and each child's admission.

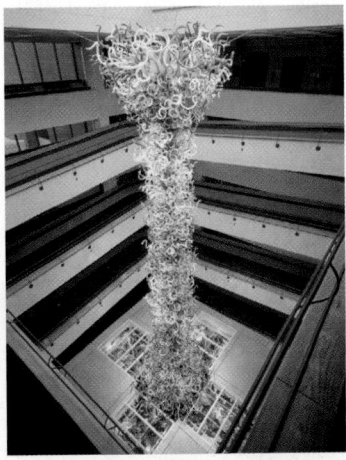

© 2006 Dale Chihuly; Photograph © 2006 The Children's Museum of Indianapolis; photograph by Garry Chilluffo

45. *Visiting the Smithsonian.* The museums of the Smithsonian Institution and the Smithsonian website hosted a total of nearly 142 million visitors in 2005. The museums had about 94 million fewer visitors than the website. (*Source*: Smithsonian Institution) Find the number of visitors to the museums and to the website.

46. *Mail-Order Business.* A mail-order lacrosse equipment business shipped 120 packages one day. Customers are charged $3.50 for each standard-delivery package and $7.50 for each express-delivery package. Total shipping charges for the day were $596. How many of each kind of package were shipped?

47. *Sales Promotions.* During a one-month promotional campaign, Fran's Flix gave either a free DVD rental or a 12-serving box of microwave popcorn to new members. It cost the store $1 for each free rental and $2 for each box of popcorn. In all, 48 new members were signed up and the store's cost for the incentives was $86. How many of each incentive were given away?

48. *Concert Ticket Prices.* One evening 1500 concert tickets were sold for the Fairmont Summer Jazz Festival. Tickets cost $25 for covered pavilion seats and $15 for lawn seats. Total receipts were $28,500. How many of each type of ticket were sold?

49. *Supply and Demand.* The supply and demand for a particular model of personal digital assistant are related to price by the equations

$$y = 70 + 2x,$$
$$y = 175 - 5x,$$

respectively, where y is the price, in dollars, and x is the number of units, in thousands. Find the equilibrium point for this product.

50. *Supply and Demand.* The supply and demand for a particular model of treadmill are related to price by the equations

$$y = 240 + 40x,$$
$$y = 500 - 25x,$$

respectively, where y is the price, in dollars, and x is the number of units, in thousands. Find the equilibrium point for this product.

The point at which a company's costs equal its revenues is the break-even point. In Exercises 51–54, C represents the production cost, in dollars, of x units of a product and R represents the revenue, in dollars, from the sale of x units. Find the number of units that must be produced and sold in order to break even. That is, find the value of x for which C = R.

51. $C = 14x + 350,$
    $R = 16.5x$

52. $C = 8.5x + 75,$
    $R = 10x$

53. $C = 15x + 12,000,$
    $R = 18x - 6000$

54. $C = 3x + 400,$
    $R = 7x - 600$

55. *Nutrition.* A one-cup serving of spaghetti with meatballs contains 260 Cal (calories) and 32 g of carbohydrates. A one-cup serving of chopped iceberg lettuce contains 5 Cal and 1 g of carbohydrates. (*Source: Home and Garden Bulletin No. 72*, U.S. Government Printing Office, Washington, D.C. 20402) How many servings of each would be required to obtain 400 Cal and 50 g of carbohydrates?

56. *Nutrition.* One serving of tomato soup contains 100 Cal and 18 g of carbohydrates. One slice of whole wheat bread contains 70 Cal and 13 g of carbohydrates. (*Source: Home and Garden Bulletin No. 72*, U.S. Government Printing Office, Washington, D.C. 20402) How many servings of each would be required to obtain 230 Cal and 42 g of carbohydrates?

57. *Motion.* A Leisure Time Cruises riverboat travels 46 km downstream in 2 hr. It travels 51 km upstream in 3 hr. Find the speed of the boat and the speed of the stream.

58. *Motion.* A DC10 travels 3000 km with a tail wind in 3 hr. It travels 3000 km with a head wind in 4 hr. Find the speed of the plane and the speed of the wind.

59. *Investment.* Bernadette inherited $15,000 and invested it in two municipal bonds, which pay 7% and 9% simple interest. The annual interest is $1230. Find the amount invested at each rate.

60. *Tee Shirt Sales.* Mack's Tee Shirt Shack sold 36 shirts one day. All short-sleeved tee shirts cost $12 each and all long-sleeved tee shirts cost $18 each. Total receipts for the day were $522. How many of each kind of shirt were sold?

61. *Coffee Mixtures.* The owner of The Daily Grind coffee shop mixes French roast coffee worth $9.00 per pound with Kenyan coffee worth $7.50 per pound in order to get 10 lb of a mixture worth $8.40 per pound. How much of each type of coffee was used?

62. *Commissions.* Jackson Manufacturing offers its sales representatives a choice between being paid a commission of 8% of sales or being paid a monthly salary of $1500 plus a commission of 1% of sales. For what monthly sales do the two plans pay the same amount?

63. *Motion.* A Boeing 747 flies the 3000-mi distance from Los Angeles to New York, with a tail wind, in 5 hr. The return trip, against the wind, takes 6 hr. Find the speed of the plane and the speed of the wind.

64. *Motion.* Two private airplanes travel toward each other from cities that are 780 km apart at speeds of 190 km/h and 200 km/h. They left at the same time. In how many hours will they meet?

Technology Connection

65. Use a graphing calculator to solve the systems of equations in Exercises 7, 17, and 29.

66. Use a graphing calculator to solve the systems of equations in Exercises 8, 18, and 30.

67. *Beef and Chicken Consumption.* The amount of beef consumed in the United States has remained fairly constant in recent years while the amount of chicken consumed has increased, as shown by the data in the following table.

Year	Per Capita Beef Consumption (in pounds)	Per Capita Chicken Consumption (in pounds)
1995	63.5	48.2
2000	64.5	54.2
2002	64.5	56.8
2003	62.0	57.5

Source: U.S. Department of Agriculture, Economic Research Service

a) Find linear regression functions $b(x)$ and $c(x)$ that represent the per capita beef consumption and the per capita chicken consumption,

respectively, in number of pounds x years after 1995.

b) Use the functions found in part (a) to estimate when chicken consumption will equal beef consumption.

68. *Prescription Drug Sales.* The table below lists the percentages of brand-name and generic drugs sold in recent years.

Year	Percentage of Brand-Name Drugs Sold	Percentage of Generic Drugs Sold
1995	59.8	40.2
2000	57.6	42.4
2002	57.9	42.1
2004	51.9	48.1

Source: National Association of Chain Drug Stores

a) Find linear functions $b(x)$ and $g(x)$ that represent the percentages of brand-name and generic drugs sold, respectively, x years after 1995.

b) Use the functions found in part (a) to estimate when the percentages of brand-name and generic drugs sold will be equal.

Collaborative Discussion and Writing

69. Explain in your own words when the elimination method for solving a system of equations is preferable to the substitution method.

70. Cassidy solves the equation $2x + 5 = 3x - 7$ by finding the point of intersection of the graphs of $y_1 = 2x + 5$ and $y_2 = 3x - 7$. She finds the same point when she solves the system of equations

$$y = 2x + 5,$$
$$y = 3x - 7.$$

Explain the difference between the solutions.

Skill Maintenance

71. *Book-Club Purchases.* Members of book clubs purchased a total of about 110 million books in 2005. Paperback sales exceeded sales of hardbacks by about 40 million books. (*Source*: Book Industry Study Group, Inc.) How many copies of each type of book were purchased?

72. *Soy-Food Sales.*   Soy consumption has been growing in recent years. Soy-food sales in the United States totaled $4.1 billion in 2005. This was a 46% increase over soy-food sales in 2000. (*Source:* "Soyafoods: The U.S. Market 2006") Find the amount of soyfood sales in 2000.

Consider the function

$$f(x) = x^2 - 4x + 3$$

in Exercises 73–76.

73. What are the inputs if the output is 15?

74. Given an output of 8, find the corresponding inputs.

75. What is the output if the input is -2?

76. Find the zeros of the function.

Synthesis

77. *Motion.*   Nancy jogs and walks to campus each day. She averages 4 km/h walking and 8 km/h jogging. The distance from home to the campus is 6 km and she makes the trip in 1 hr. How far does she jog on each trip?

78. *e-Commerce.*   shirts.com advertises a limited-time sale, offering 1 turtleneck for $15 and 2 turtlenecks for $25. A total of 1250 turtlenecks are sold and $16,750 is taken in. How many customers ordered 2 turtlenecks?

79. *Motion.*   A train leaves Union Station for Central Station, 216 km away, at 9 A.M. One hour later, a train leaves Central Station for Union Station. They meet at noon. If the second train

had started at 9 A.M. and the first train at 10:30 A.M., they would still have met at noon. Find the speed of each train.

80. *Antifreeze Mixtures.*   An automobile radiator contains 16 L of antifreeze and water. This mixture is 30% antifreeze. How much of this mixture should be drained and replaced with pure antifreeze so that the final mixture will be 50% antifreeze?

81. Two solutions of the equation $Ax + By = 1$ are $(3, -1)$ and $(-4, -2)$. Find A and B.

82. *Ticket Line.*   You are in line at a ticket window. There are 2 more people ahead of you in line than there are behind you. In the entire line, there are three times as many people as there are behind you. How many people are ahead of you?

83. *Gas Mileage.*   The Honda Civic Hybrid vehicle, powered by gasoline–electric technology, gets 49 miles per gallon (mpg) in city driving and 51 mpg in highway driving (*Source:* Honda.com). The car is driven 447 mi on 9 gal of gasoline. How many miles were driven in the city and how many were driven on the highway?

84. *Motion.*   Heather is standing on a railroad bridge, as shown in the figure below. A train is approaching from the direction shown by the yellow arrow. If Heather runs at a speed of 10 mph toward the train, she will reach point P on the bridge at the same moment that the train does. If she runs to point Q at the other end of the bridge at a speed of 10 mph, she will reach point Q also at the same moment that the train does. How fast, in miles per hour, is the train traveling?

8.2 Systems of Equations in Three Variables

◆ Solve systems of linear equations in three variables.
◆ Use systems of three equations to solve applied problems.
◆ Model a situation using a quadratic function.

A **linear equation in three variables** is an equation equivalent to one of the form $Ax + By + Cz = D$, where A, B, C, and D are real numbers and A, B, and C are not all 0. A **solution of a system of three equations in three variables** is an ordered triple that makes all three equations true. For example, the triple $(2, -1, 0)$ is a solution of the system of equations

$$4x + 2y + 5z = 6,$$
$$2x - y + z = 5,$$
$$3x + 2y - z = 4.$$

We can verify this by substituting 2 for x, -1 for y, and 0 for z in each equation.

◆ Solving Systems of Equations in Three Variables

We will solve systems of equations in three variables using an algebraic method called **Gaussian elimination**, named for the German mathematician Karl Friedrich Gauss (1777–1855). Our goal is to transform the original system to an equivalent one of the form

$$Ax + By + Cz = D,$$
$$Ey + Fz = G,$$
$$Hz = K.$$

Then we solve the third equation for z and back-substitute to find y and then x.

Each of the following operations can be used to transform the original system to an equivalent system in the desired form.

1. Interchange any two equations.
2. Multiply both sides of one of the equations by a nonzero constant.
3. Add a nonzero multiple of one equation to another equation.

EXAMPLE 1 Solve the following system of equations:

$$x - 2y + 3z = 11, \quad (1)$$
$$4x + 2y - 3z = 4, \quad (2)$$
$$3x + 3y - z = 4. \quad (3)$$

Solution First, we choose one of the variables to eliminate using two different pairs of equations. Let's eliminate x from equations (2) and (3). We multiply equation (1) by -4 and add it to equation (2). We also multiply equation (1) by -3 and add it to equation (3).

$$
\begin{array}{ll}
-4x + 8y - 12z = -44 & \text{Multiplying (1) by} -4 \\
\underline{4x + 2y - 3z = 4} & \text{(2)} \\
10y - 15z = -40; & \text{(4)}
\end{array}
$$

$$
\begin{array}{ll}
-3x + 6y - 9z = -33 & \text{Multiplying (1) by} -3 \\
\underline{3x + 3y - z = 4} & \text{(3)} \\
9y - 10z = -29. & \text{(5)}
\end{array}
$$

Now we have

$$
\begin{array}{ll}
x - 2y + 3z = 11, & \text{(1)} \\
10y - 15z = -40, & \text{(4)} \\
9y - 10z = -29. & \text{(5)}
\end{array}
$$

Next, we multiply equation (5) by 10 to make the y-coefficient a multiple of the y-coefficient in the equation above it:

$$
\begin{array}{ll}
x - 2y + 3z = 11, & \text{(1)} \\
10y - 15z = -40, & \text{(4)} \\
90y - 100z = -290. & \text{(6)}
\end{array}
$$

Now we multiply equation (4) by -9 and add it to equation (6):

$$
\begin{array}{ll}
-90y + 135z = 360 & \text{Multiplying (4) by} -9 \\
\underline{90y - 100z = -290} & \text{(6)} \\
35z = 70. & \text{(7)}
\end{array}
$$

We now have the system of equations

$$
\begin{array}{ll}
x - 2y + 3z = 11, & \text{(1)} \\
10y - 15z = -40, & \text{(4)} \\
35z = 70. & \text{(7)}
\end{array}
$$

We solve equation (7) for z:

$$
35z = 70
$$
$$
z = 2.
$$

Then we back-substitute 2 for z in equation (4) and solve for y:

$$
10y - 15 \cdot 2 = -40
$$
$$
10y - 30 = -40
$$
$$
10y = -10
$$
$$
y = -1.
$$

Finally, we back-substitute -1 for y and 2 for z in equation (1) and solve for x:

$$x - 2(-1) + 3 \cdot 2 = 11$$
$$x + 2 + 6 = 11$$
$$x = 3.$$

We can check the triple $(3, -1, 2)$ in each of the three original equations. Since it makes all three equations true, the solution is $(3, -1, 2)$.

▶ **Now Try Exercise 1.**

EXAMPLE 2   Solve the following system of equations:

$$
\begin{aligned}
x + y + z &= 7, & (1) \\
3x - 2y + z &= 3, & (2) \\
x + 6y + 3z &= 25. & (3)
\end{aligned}
$$

Solution   We multiply equation (1) by -3 and add it to equation (2). We also multiply equation (1) by -1 and add it to equation (3).

$$
\begin{aligned}
x + y + z &= 7, & (1) \\
-5y - 2z &= -18, & (4) \\
5y + 2z &= 18 & (5)
\end{aligned}
$$

Next, we add equation (4) to equation (5):

$$
\begin{aligned}
x + y + z &= 7, & (1) \\
-5y - 2z &= -18, & (4) \\
0 &= 0.
\end{aligned}
$$

The equation $0 = 0$ tells us that equation (3) of the original system is dependent on the first two equations. Thus the original system is equivalent to

$$
\begin{aligned}
x + y + z &= 7, & (1) \\
3x - 2y + z &= 3. & (2)
\end{aligned}
$$

In this particular case, the original system has infinitely many solutions. (In some cases, a system containing dependent equations could be inconsistent.) To find an expression for these solutions, we first solve equation (4) for either y or z. We choose to solve for y:

$$
\begin{aligned}
-5y - 2z &= -18 & (4) \\
-5y &= 2z - 18 \\
y &= -\tfrac{2}{5}z + \tfrac{18}{5}.
\end{aligned}
$$

Then we back-substitute in equation (1) to find an expression for x in terms of z:

$$
\begin{aligned}
x - \tfrac{2}{5}z + \tfrac{18}{5} + z &= 7 \qquad \text{Substituting } -\tfrac{2}{5}z + \tfrac{18}{5} \text{ for } y \\
x + \tfrac{3}{5}z + \tfrac{18}{5} &= 7 \\
x + \tfrac{3}{5}z &= \tfrac{17}{5} \\
x &= -\tfrac{3}{5}z + \tfrac{17}{5}.
\end{aligned}
$$

The solutions of the system of equations are ordered triples of the form $\left(-\frac{3}{5}z + \frac{17}{5}, -\frac{2}{5}z + \frac{18}{5}, z\right)$, where z can be any real number. Any real number that we use for z then gives us values for x and y and thus an ordered triple in the solution set. For example, if we choose $z = 0$, we have the solution $\left(\frac{17}{5}, \frac{18}{5}, 0\right)$. If we choose $z = -1$, we have $(4, 4, -1)$.

▷ **Now Try Exercise 9.**

If we get a false equation, such as $0 = -5$, at some stage of the elimination process, we conclude that the original system is *inconsistent*. That is, it has no solutions.

Although systems of three linear equations in three variables do not lend themselves well to graphical solutions, it is of interest to picture some possible solutions. The graph of a linear equation in three variables is a plane. Thus the solution set of such a system is the intersection of three planes. Some possibilities are shown below.

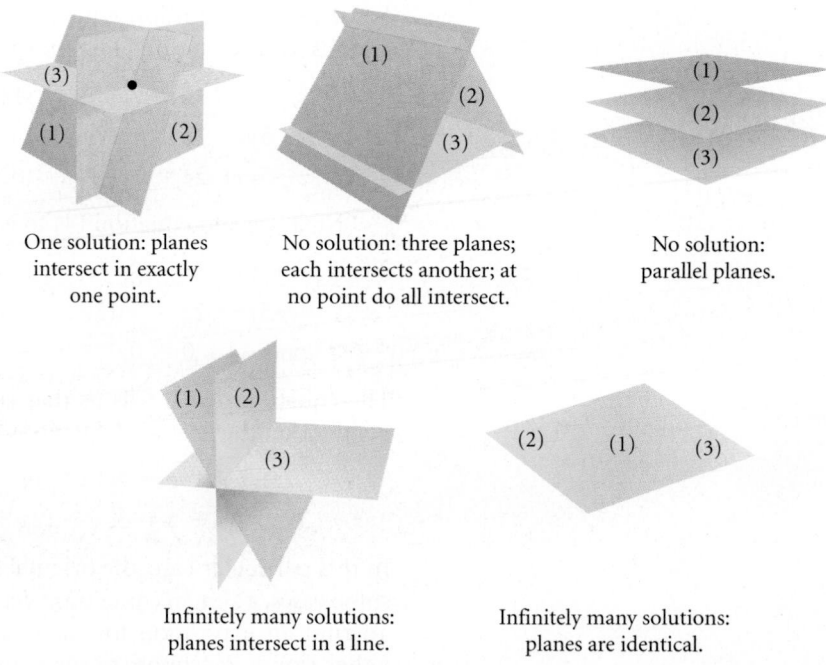

One solution: planes intersect in exactly one point.

No solution: three planes; each intersects another; at no point do all intersect.

No solution: parallel planes.

Infinitely many solutions: planes intersect in a line.

Infinitely many solutions: planes are identical.

◆ Applications

Systems of equations in three or more variables allow us to solve many problems in fields such as business, the social and natural sciences, and engineering.

EXAMPLE 3 *Investment.* Moira inherited $15,000 and invested part of it in a money market account, part in municipal bonds, and part in a mutual fund. After 1 yr, she received a total of $730 in simple interest from the three investments. The money market account paid 4% annually, the bonds paid 5% annually, and the mutual fund paid 6% annually. There was $2000 more invested in the mutual fund than in bonds. Find the amount that Moira invested in each category.

Solution

1. **Familiarize.** We let x, y, and z represent the amounts invested in the money market account, the bonds, and the mutual fund, respectively. Then the amounts of income produced annually by each investment are given by 4%x, 5%y, and 6%z, or $0.04x$, $0.05y$, and $0.06z$.

2. **Translate.** The fact that a total of $15,000 was invested gives us one equation:

   $$x + y + z = 15,000.$$

   Since the total interest was $730, we have a second equation:

   $$0.04x + 0.05y + 0.06z = 730.$$

   Another statement in the problem gives us a third equation.

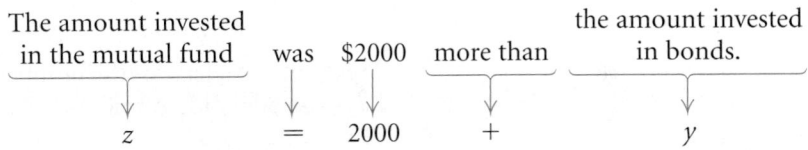

   The amount invested in the mutual fund   was $2000   more than   the amount invested in bonds.

   $$z \quad = \quad 2000 \quad + \quad y$$

   We now have a system of three equations:

   $$\begin{array}{ll} x + y + z = 15{,}000, & \qquad x + y + z = 15{,}000, \\ 0.04x + 0.05y + 0.06z = 730, \quad \text{or} & \quad 4x + 5y + 6z = 73{,}000, \\ z = 2000 + y; & \qquad\quad -y + z = 2000. \end{array}$$

3. **Carry out.** Solving the system of equations, we get

   $$(7000, 3000, 5000).$$

4. **Check.** The sum of the numbers is 15,000. The income produced is

   $$0.04(7000) + 0.05(3000) + 0.06(5000) = 280 + 150 + 300, \quad \text{or} \quad \$730.$$

   Also the amount invested in the mutual fund, $5000, is $2000 more than the amount invested in bonds, $3000. Our solution checks in the original problem.

5. **State.** Moira invested $7000 in a money market account, $3000 in municipal bonds, and $5000 in a mutual fund.

▷ Now Try Exercise 27.

✦ Mathematical Models and Applications

In a situation in which a quadratic function will serve as a mathematical model, we may wish to find an equation, or formula, for the function. For a linear model, we can find an equation if we know two data points. For a quadratic function, we need three data points.

EXAMPLE 4 *Fast-Food Alternatives.* McDonald's introduced a popular line of premium salads in 2003. The table below lists the number of salads sold at this fast-food chain in each of the first 3 years. Use the data to find a quadratic function that gives the number of salads sold as a function of the number of years after 2003. Then use the function to estimate the number of salads sold in 2006.

YEAR	NUMBER OF SALADS SOLD (in millions)
2003	133
2004	179
2005	173

Source: McDonald's

Solution   We let $x =$ the number of years after 2003 and $f(x) =$ the number of salads sold, in millions. Then $x = 0$ corresponds to 2003, $x = 1$ corresponds to 2004, and $x = 2$ corresponds to 2005. We use the three data points $(0, 133)$, $(1, 179)$, and $(2, 173)$ to find a, b, and c in the function $f(x) = ax^2 + bx + c$. First, we substitute:

$$f(x) = \quad ax^2 + \quad bx \quad + c$$

For $(0, 133)$: $133 = a \cdot 0^2 + b \cdot 0 + c$;

For $(1, 179)$: $179 = a \cdot 1^2 + b \cdot 1 + c$;

For $(2, 173)$: $173 = a \cdot 2^2 + b \cdot 2 + c$.

**TECHNOLOGY
CONNECTION**

The function in Example 4 can also be found using the QUADRATIC REGRESSION feature on a graphing calculator. Note that the method of Example 4 works when we have exactly three data points, whereas the QUADRATIC REGRESSION feature on a graphing calculator can be used for three or more points.

We now have a system of equations in the variables a, b, and c:

$$c = 133,$$
$$a + b + c = 179,$$
$$4a + 2b + c = 173.$$

Solving this system of equations, we get $(-26, 72, 133)$. Thus,

$$f(x) = -26x^2 + 72x + 133.$$

To estimate the number of salads sold in 2006, we find $f(3)$, since 2006 is 3 yr after 2003:

$$f(3) = -26 \cdot 3^2 + 72 \cdot 3 + 133$$
$$= 115 \text{ million salads.*}$$

▶ **Now Try Exercise 33.**

---

*Although a function might fit a set of data exactly, the function will not necessarily yield good projections beyond the scope of the data.

8.2 EXERCISE SET

Solve the system of equations.

1. $x + y + z = 2,$
$6x - 4y + 5z = 31,$
$5x + 2y + 2z = 13$

2. $x + 6y + 3z = 4,$
$2x + y + 2z = 3,$
$3x - 2y + z = 0$

3. $x - y + 2z = -3,$
$x + 2y + 3z = 4,$
$2x + y + z = -3$

4. $x + y + z = 6,$
$2x - y - z = -3,$
$x - 2y + 3z = 6$

5. $x + 2y - z = 5,$
$2x - 4y + z = 0,$
$3x + 2y + 2z = 3$

6. $2x + 3y - z = 1,$
$x + 2y + 5z = 4,$
$3x - y - 8z = -7$

7. $x + 2y - z = -8,$
$2x - y + z = 4,$
$8x + y + z = 2$

8. $x + 2y - z = 4,$
$4x - 3y + z = 8,$
$5x - y = 12$

9. $2x + y - 3z = 1,$
$x - 4y + z = 6,$
$4x - 7y - z = 13$

10. $x + 3y + 4z = 1,$
$3x + 4y + 5z = 3,$
$x + 8y + 11z = 2$

11. $4a + 9b = 8,$
$8a + 6c = -1,$
$6b + 6c = -1$

12. $3p + 2r = 11,$
$q - 7r = 4,$
$p - 6q = 1$

13. $2x + z = 1,$
$3y - 2z = 6,$
$x - 2y = -9$

14. $3x + 4z = -11,$
$x - 2y = 5,$
$4y - z = -10$

15. $w + x + y + z = 2,$
$w + 2x + 2y + 4z = 1,$
$-w + x - y - z = -6,$
$-w + 3x + y - z = -2$

16. $w + x - y + z = 0,$
$-w + 2x + 2y + z = 5,$
$-w + 3x + y - z = -4,$
$-2w + x + y - 3z = -7$

17. *Athletic Footwear.* Americans spent a total of about $6.7 billion on cross-training shoes, running shoes, and walking shoes in 2004. The amount spent on walking shoes was $0.3 billion more than the total amount spent on cross-training and running shoes. The amount spent on running shoes was $0.4 billion more than the amount spent on cross-training shoes. (*Source*: National Sporting Goods Association) How much was spent on each type of shoe?

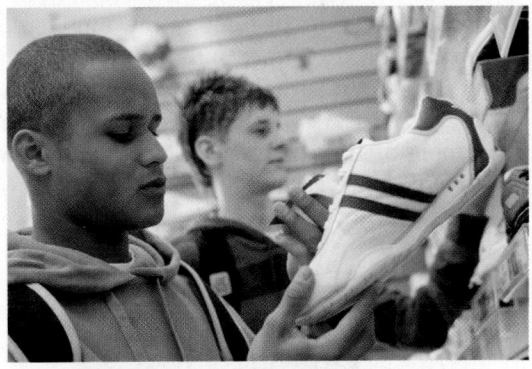

18. *Toy Sales.* Three of the highest-grossing toy categories in 2005 were infant/preschool toys, dolls, and games/puzzles. Together they had gross sales of $8.2 billion. Sales of dolls and games/puzzles together were $2 billion more than sales of infant/preschool toys, and sales of games/puzzles were $0.3 billion less than doll sales. (*Source*: Toy Industry Association) Find the amount of sales of each type of toy.

19. *Jolts of Caffeine.* Considering an 8-oz serving size, 1 serving each of brewed coffee, Red Bull energy drink, and Mountain Dew soda contains 197 mg of caffeine. One serving of brewed coffee has 6 mg more caffeine than two servings of Mountain Dew. One serving of Red Bull contains 37 mg less caffeine than one serving each of brewed coffee and Mountain Dew. (*Source*: Australian Institute of Sport) Find the amount of caffeine in one serving of each beverage.

20. *Spring Cleaning.* In a group of 100 adults, 70 say they are most likely to do spring housecleaning in March, April, or May. Of these 70, the number who clean in April is 14 more than the total number who clean in March and May. The total number who clean in April and May is 2 more than three times the number who clean in March. (*Source*: Zoomerang online survey) Find the number who clean in each month.

21. *Low-Carb Gardening.* Gardeners on a low-carbohydrate diet are interested in knowing the carbohydrate content of the vegetables they plant. Together, 1 cup of raw lettuce, 6 raw asparagus spears, and 1 cup of raw tomatoes contain 12 grams of carbohydrates. One cup of raw lettuce and 6 raw asparagus spears have one-half the carbohydrates of 1 cup of raw tomatoes. One cup each of raw lettuce and raw tomatoes have three times the carbohydrate content of 6 raw asparagus spears. (*Source*: Burpee Seeds) Find the number of grams of carbohydrates in the given portion size of each vegetable.

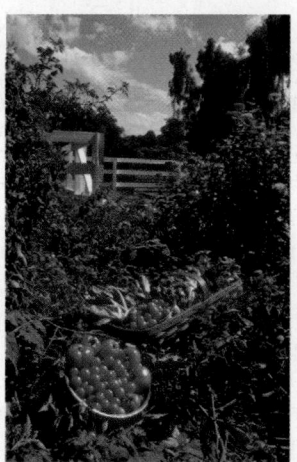

22. *Leisure Activities.* A total of about 162.2 million adult Americans spent leisure time reading books, surfing the Internet, and playing video games in 2004. Readers outnumbered video-game players by 49.9 million. Together, the number of adults who surfed the Internet and played video games exceeded the number who read by 7.2 million.

(*Source*: Mediamark Research, Inc.) How many adults participated in each activity?

23. *e-Commerce.* computerwarehouse.com charges $3 for shipping orders up to 10 lb, $5 for orders from 10 lb up to 15 lb, and $7.50 for orders of 15 lb or more. One day shipping charges for 150 orders totaled $680. The number of orders under 10 lb was three times the number of orders weighing 15 lb or more. Find the number of packages shipped at each rate.

24. *Mail-Order Business.* Natural Fibers Clothing charges $4 for shipping orders of $25 or less, $8 for orders from $25.01 to $75, and $10 for orders over $75. One week shipping charges for 600 orders totaled $4280. Eighty more orders for $25 or less were shipped than orders for more than $75. Find the number of orders shipped at each rate.

25. *Nutrition.* A hospital dietician must plan a lunch menu that provides 485 Cal, 41.5 g of carbohydrates, and 35 mg of calcium. A 3-oz serving of broiled ground beef contains 245 Cal, 0 g of carbohydrates, and 9 mg of calcium. One baked potato contains 145 Cal, 34 g of carbohydrates, and 8 mg of calcium. A one-cup serving of strawberries contains 45 Cal, 10 g of carbohydrates, and 21 mg of calcium. (*Source*: *Home and Garden Bulletin No. 72*, U.S. Government Printing Office, Washington, D.C. 20402) How many servings of each are required to provide the desired nutritional values?

26. *Nutrition.* A diabetic patient wishes to prepare a meal consisting of roasted chicken breast, mashed potatoes, and peas. A 3-oz serving of roasted skinless chicken breast contains 140 Cal, 27 g of protein, and 64 mg of sodium. A one-cup serving of mashed potatoes contains 160 Cal, 4 g of protein, and 636 mg of sodium, and a one-cup serving of peas contains 125 Cal, 8 g of protein, and 139 mg of sodium. (*Source*: *Home and Garden Bulletin No. 72*, U.S. Government Printing Office, Washington, D.C. 20402) How many

servings of each should be used if the meal is to contain 415 Cal, 50.5 g of protein, and 553 mg of sodium?

27. *Investment.* Jamal earns a year-end bonus of $5000 and puts it in 3 one-year investments that pay $243 in simple interest. Part is invested at 3%, part at 4%, and part at 6%. There is $1500 more invested at 6% than at 3%. Find the amount invested at each rate.

28. *Investment.* Casey receives $126 per year in simple interest from three investments. Part is invested at 2%, part at 3%, and part at 4%. There is $500 more invested at 3% than at 2%. The amount invested at 4% is three times the amount invested at 3%. Find the amount invested at each rate.

29. *Price Increases.* Orange juice, a raisin bagel, and a cup of coffee from Kelly's Koffee Kart cost a total of $4.10. Kelly posts a notice announcing that, effective the following week, the price of orange juice will increase 50% and the price of bagels will increase 20%. After the increase, the same purchase will cost a total of $5.10, and orange juice will cost twice as much as coffee. Find the price of each item before the increase.

30. *Cost of Snack Food.* Martin and Eva pool their loose change to buy snacks on their coffee break. One day, they spent $5 on 1 carton of milk, 2 donuts, and 1 cup of coffee. The next day, they spent $5.50 on 3 donuts and 2 cups of coffee. The third day, they bought 1 carton of milk, 1 donut, and 2 cups of coffee and spent $5.25. On the fourth day, they have a total of $5.45 left. Is this enough to buy 2 cartons of milk and 2 donuts?

31. *Golf.* On an 18-hole golf course, there are par-3 holes, par-4 holes, and par-5 holes. A golfer who shoots par on every hole has a score of 72. The sum of the number of par-3 holes and the number of par-5 holes is 8. How many of each type of hole are there on the golf course?

32. *Golf.* On an 18-hole golf course, there are par-3 holes, par-4 holes, and par-5 holes. A golfer who shoots par on every hole has a score of 70. There are twice as many par-4 holes as there are par-5 holes. How many of each type of hole are there on the golf course?

33. *Airport Security Violations.* The table below lists the number of fines levied on airline passengers for security violations by the Transportation Security Administration, represented in terms of the number of years since 2002.

YEAR, x	NUMBER OF FINES
2002, 0	279
2004, 2	9741
2005, 3	4459

Source: Transportation Security Administration

a) Fit a quadratic function $f(x) = ax^2 + bx + c$ to the data.
b) Use the function to estimate the number of fines levied in 2003.

34. *Female Smokers.* The table below lists the percentages of females age 18 to 24 who smoke, represented in terms of number of years since 1995.

Year, x	Percent of Females Age 18 to 24 Who Smoke
1995, 0	22%
2000, 5	25
2003, 8	22

Source: U.S. National Center for Health Statistics

a) Fit a quadratic function $f(x) = ax^2 + bx + c$ to the data.
b) Use the function to estimate the percent of females age 18 to 24 who smoked in 2004.

35. *Number of Marriages.*   The table below lists the number of marriages, in thousands, in Arkansas, represented as number of years since 1990.

Year, x	Number of Marriages (in thousands)
1990, 0	36
2000, 10	42
2004, 14	36

Source: U.S. National Center for Health Statistics, *Vital Statistics of the United States*, annual, Monthly Vital Statistics Reports

a) Fit a quadratic function $f(x) = ax^2 + bx + c$ to the data.

b) Use the function to estimate the number of marriages in Arkansas in 2008.

36. *Red-Meat Consumption.*   The table below lists the per capita consumption of red meat, in pounds, in the United States, represented as years since 1990.

Year, x	Red-Meat Consumption (in pounds)
1990, 0	112
2000, 10	114
2003, 13	112

Source: U.S. Department of Agriculture, Economic Research Service, *Food Consumption, Prices, and Expenditures*

a) Fit a quadratic function $f(x) = ax^2 + bx + c$ to the data.

b) Use the function to estimate the per capita consumption of red meat in 2010.

Technology Connection

37. *Morning Newspapers.*   The table below lists the number of morning newspapers in the United States in various years.

Year	Number of Morning Newspapers
1920	437
1940	380
1960	312
1980	387
2000	766
2004	813

Source: *Editor & Publisher*

a) Use a graphing calculator to fit a quadratic function $f(x)$ to the data, where x is the number of years after 1920.

b) Use the function found in part (a) to estimate the number of morning newspapers in 2008.

38. *Preprimary School Enrollment.*   The table below lists the number of children 3 to 5 years old enrolled in nursery school and kindergarten, in millions, in various years.

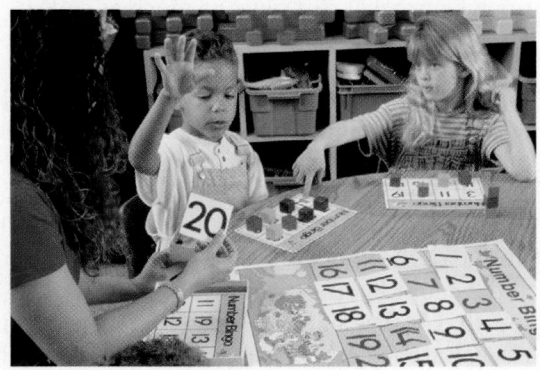

Year	Number of Children Enrolled in Preprimary School (in millions)
1995	7.739
2000	7.592
2002	7.504
2003	7.921

Source: U.S. Bureau of the Census, *Current Population Reports*

a) Use a graphing calculator to fit a quadratic function $n(x)$ to the data, where x is the number of years after 1995.

b) Use the function found in part (a) to estimate the number of children enrolled in preprimary school in 2005.

Collaborative Discussion and Writing

39. Given two linear equations in three variables, $Ax + By + Cz = D$ and $Ex + Fy + Gz = H$, explain how you could find a third equation such that the system contains dependent equations.

40. Write a problem for a classmate to solve that can be translated to a system of three equations in three variables.

Skill Maintenance

In each of Exercises 41–48, fill in the blank with the correct term. Some of the given choices will not be used.

Descartes' rule of signs
the leading-term test
the intermediate value theorem
the fundamental theorem of algebra
a polynomial function
a rational function
a one-to-one function
a constant function
a horizontal asymptote
a vertical asymptote
an oblique asymptote
direct variation
inverse variation
a horizontal line
a vertical line
parallel
perpendicular

41. Two lines with slopes m_1 and m_2 are _____ if and only if the product of their slopes is -1.

42. We can use _____ to determine the behavior of the graph of a polynomial function as $x \to \infty$ or as $x \to -\infty$.

43. If it is possible for _____ to cross a graph more than once, then the graph is not the graph of a function.

44. A function is _____ if different inputs have different outputs.

45. _____ is a function that is a quotient of two polynomials.

46. If a situation gives rise to a function $f(x) = k/x$, or $y = k/x$, where k is a positive constant, we say that we have _____.

47. _____ of a rational function $p(x)/q(x)$, where $p(x)$ and $q(x)$ have no common factors other than constants, occurs at an x-value that makes the denominator 0.

48. When the numerator and the denominator of a rational function have the same degree, the graph of the function has _____.

Synthesis

In Exercises 49 and 50, let u represent $1/x$, v represent $1/y$, and w represent $1/z$. Solve first for u, v, and w. Then solve the system of equations.

49.
$$\frac{2}{x} - \frac{1}{y} - \frac{3}{z} = -1,$$
$$\frac{2}{x} - \frac{1}{y} + \frac{1}{z} = -9,$$
$$\frac{1}{x} + \frac{2}{y} - \frac{4}{z} = 17$$

50.
$$\frac{2}{x} + \frac{2}{y} - \frac{3}{z} = 3,$$
$$\frac{1}{x} - \frac{2}{y} - \frac{3}{z} = 9,$$
$$\frac{7}{x} - \frac{2}{y} + \frac{9}{z} = -39$$

51. Find the sum of the angle measures at the tips of the star.

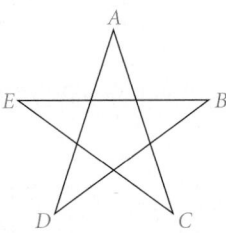

52. *Transcontinental Railroad.*   Use the following facts to find the year in which the first U.S. transcontinental railroad was completed. The sum of the digits in the year is 24. The units digit is 1 more than the hundreds digit. Both the tens and the units digits are multiples of three.

In Exercises 53 and 54, three solutions of an equation are given. Use a system of three equations in three variables to find the constants and write the equation.

53. $Ax + By + Cz = 12$;
$\left(1,\frac{3}{4},3\right), \left(\frac{4}{3},1,2\right),$ and $(2,1,1)$

54. $y = B - Mx - Nz$;
$(1,1,2), (3,2,-6),$ and $\left(\frac{3}{2},1,1\right)$

In Exercises 55 and 56, four solutions of the equation $y = ax^3 + bx^2 + cx + d$ are given. Use a system of four equations in four variables to find the constants a, b, c, and d and write the equation.

55. $(-2,59), (-1,13), (1,-1),$ and $(2,-17)$

56. $(-2,-39), (-1,-12), (1,-6),$ and $(3,16)$

57. *Theater Attendance.*   A performance at the Bingham Performing Arts Center was attended by 100 people. The audience consisted of adults, students, and children. The ticket prices were $10 for adults, $3 for students, and 50 cents for children. The total amount of money taken in was $100. How many adults, students, and children were in attendance? Does there seem to be some information missing? Do some careful reasoning.

8.3   Matrices and Systems of Equations

◆ Solve systems of equations using matrices.

◆ Matrices and Row-Equivalent Operations

In this section, we consider additional techniques for solving systems of equations. You have probably observed that when we solve a system of equations, we perform computations with the coefficients and the constants and continually rewrite the variables. We can streamline the solution process by omitting the variables until a solution is found. For example, the system

$$2x - 3y = 7,$$
$$x + 4y = -2$$

can be written more simply as

$$\begin{bmatrix} 2 & -3 & | & 7 \\ 1 & 4 & | & -2 \end{bmatrix}.$$

The vertical line replaces the equals signs.

A rectangular array of numbers like the one above is called a **matrix** (plural, **matrices**). The matrix above is called an **augmented matrix** for the given system of equations, because it contains not only the coefficients but also the constant terms. The matrix

$$\begin{bmatrix} 2 & -3 \\ 1 & 4 \end{bmatrix}$$

is called the **coefficient matrix** of the system.

The **rows** of a matrix are horizontal, and the **columns** are vertical. The augmented matrix above has 2 rows and 3 columns, and the coefficient matrix has 2 rows and 2 columns. A matrix with m rows and n columns is said to be of **order** $m \times n$. Thus the order of the augmented matrix above is 2×3, and the order of the coefficient matrix is 2×2. When $m = n$, a matrix is said to be **square.** The coefficient matrix above is a square matrix. The numbers 2 and 4 lie on the **main diagonal** of the coefficient matrix. The numbers in a matrix are called **entries.**

◆ Gaussian Elimination with Matrices

In Section 8.2, we described a series of operations that can be used to transform a system of equations to an equivalent system. Each of these operations corresponds to one that can be used to produce *row-equivalent matrices.*

Row-Equivalent Operations

1. Interchange any two rows.
2. Multiply each entry in a row by the same nonzero constant.
3. Add a nonzero multiple of one row to another row.

We can use these operations on the augmented matrix of a system of equations to solve the system.

EXAMPLE 1 Solve the following system of equations:

$$\begin{aligned} 2x - y + 4z &= -3, \\ x - 2y - 10z &= -6, \\ 3x + 4z &= 7. \end{aligned}$$

Solution First, we write the augmented matrix, writing 0 for the missing y-term in the last equation:

$$\begin{bmatrix} 2 & -1 & 4 & -3 \\ 1 & -2 & -10 & -6 \\ 3 & 0 & 4 & 7 \end{bmatrix}.$$

Our goal is to find a row-equivalent matrix of the form

$$\begin{bmatrix} 1 & a & b & c \\ 0 & 1 & d & e \\ 0 & 0 & 1 & f \end{bmatrix}.$$

The variables can then be reinserted to form equations from which we can complete the solution. This is done by working from the bottom equation to the top and using back-substitution.

The first step is to multiply and/or interchange rows so that each number in the first column below the first number is a multiple of that number. In this case, we interchange the first and second rows to obtain a 1 in the upper left-hand corner.

$$\left[\begin{array}{ccc|c} 1 & -2 & -10 & -6 \\ 2 & -1 & 4 & -3 \\ 3 & 0 & 4 & 7 \end{array}\right] \quad \begin{array}{l} \text{New row 1} = \text{row 2} \\ \text{New row 2} = \text{row 1} \end{array}$$

Next, we multiply the first row by -2 and add it to the second row. We also multiply the first row by -3 and add it to the third row.

$$\left[\begin{array}{ccc|c} 1 & -2 & -10 & -6 \\ 0 & 3 & 24 & 9 \\ 0 & 6 & 34 & 25 \end{array}\right] \quad \begin{array}{l} \text{Row 1 is unchanged.} \\ \text{New row 2} = -2(\text{row 1}) + \text{row 2} \\ \text{New row 3} = -3(\text{row 1}) + \text{row 3} \end{array}$$

Now we multiply the second row by $\frac{1}{3}$ to get a 1 in the second row, second column.

$$\left[\begin{array}{ccc|c} 1 & -2 & -10 & -6 \\ 0 & 1 & 8 & 3 \\ 0 & 6 & 34 & 25 \end{array}\right] \quad \text{New row 2} = \tfrac{1}{3}(\text{row 2})$$

Then we multiply the second row by -6 and add it to the third row.

$$\left[\begin{array}{ccc|c} 1 & -2 & -10 & -6 \\ 0 & 1 & 8 & 3 \\ 0 & 0 & -14 & 7 \end{array}\right] \quad \text{New row 3} = -6(\text{row 2}) + \text{row 3}$$

Finally, we multiply the third row by $-\frac{1}{14}$ to get a 1 in the third row, third column.

$$\left[\begin{array}{ccc|c} 1 & -2 & -10 & -6 \\ 0 & 1 & 8 & 3 \\ 0 & 0 & 1 & -\frac{1}{2} \end{array}\right] \quad \text{New row 3} = -\tfrac{1}{14}(\text{row 3})$$

Now we can write the system of equations that corresponds to the last matrix above:

$$\begin{array}{rcl} x - 2y - 10z &=& -6, \quad (1) \\ y + 8z &=& 3, \quad (2) \\ z &=& -\tfrac{1}{2}. \quad (3) \end{array}$$

We back-substitute $-\frac{1}{2}$ for z in equation (2) and solve for y:

$$y + 8\left(-\tfrac{1}{2}\right) = 3$$
$$y - 4 = 3$$
$$y = 7.$$

TECHNOLOGY CONNECTION

Row-equivalent operations can be performed on a graphing calculator. For example, to interchange the first and second rows of the augmented matrix, as we did in the first step in Example 1, we enter the matrix as matrix **A** and select "rowSwap" from the MATRIX MATH menu. Some graphing calculators will not automatically store the matrix produced using a row-equivalent operation, so when several operations are to be performed in succession, it is helpful to store the result of each operation as it is produced. In the window below, we see both the matrix produced by the rowSwap operation and the indication that this matrix is stored as matrix **B**.

```
rowSwap([A],1,2)→[B]
[[1  -2  -10  -6]
 [2  -1  4    -3]
 [3  0   4    7 ]]
```

Next, we back-substitute 7 for y and $-\frac{1}{2}$ for z in equation (1) and solve for x:

$$x - 2 \cdot 7 - 10\left(-\tfrac{1}{2}\right) = -6$$
$$x - 14 + 5 = -6$$
$$x - 9 = -6$$
$$x = 3.$$

The triple $\left(3, 7, -\frac{1}{2}\right)$ checks in the original system of equations, so it is the solution.

Now Try Exercise 15.

The procedure followed in Example 1 is called **Gaussian elimination with matrices.** The last matrix in Example 1 is in **row-echelon form.** To be in this form, a matrix must have the following properties.

> ### Row-Echelon Form
>
> 1. If a row does not consist entirely of 0's, then the first nonzero element in the row is a 1 (called a **leading 1**).
> 2. For any two successive nonzero rows, the leading 1 in the lower row is farther to the right than the leading 1 in the higher row.
> 3. All the rows consisting entirely of 0's are at the bottom of the matrix.
>
> If a fourth property is also satisfied, a matrix is said to be in **reduced row-echelon form:**
>
> 4. Each column that contains a leading 1 has 0's everywhere else.

EXAMPLE 2 Which of the following matrices are in row-echelon form? Which, if any, are in reduced row-echelon form?

a) $\begin{bmatrix} 1 & -3 & 5 & | & -2 \\ 0 & 1 & -4 & | & 3 \\ 0 & 0 & 1 & | & 10 \end{bmatrix}$ b) $\begin{bmatrix} 0 & -1 & | & 2 \\ 0 & 1 & | & 5 \end{bmatrix}$ c) $\begin{bmatrix} 1 & -2 & -6 & 4 & | & 7 \\ 0 & 3 & 5 & -8 & | & -1 \\ 0 & 0 & 1 & 9 & | & 2 \end{bmatrix}$

d) $\begin{bmatrix} 1 & 0 & 0 & | & -2.4 \\ 0 & 1 & 0 & | & 0.8 \\ 0 & 0 & 1 & | & 5.6 \end{bmatrix}$ e) $\begin{bmatrix} 1 & 0 & 0 & 0 & | & \frac{2}{3} \\ 0 & 1 & 0 & 0 & | & -\frac{1}{4} \\ 0 & 0 & 1 & 0 & | & \frac{6}{7} \\ 0 & 0 & 0 & 0 & | & 0 \end{bmatrix}$ f) $\begin{bmatrix} 1 & -4 & 2 & | & 5 \\ 0 & 0 & 0 & | & 0 \\ 0 & 1 & -3 & | & -8 \end{bmatrix}$

Solution The matrices in (a), (d), and (e) satisfy the row-echelon criteria and thus are in row-echelon form. In (b) and (c), the first nonzero elements of the first and second rows, respectively, are not 1. In (f), the row consisting entirely of 0's is not at the bottom of the matrix. Thus the matrices in (b), (c), and (f) are not in row-echelon form. In (d) and (e), not only are the row-echelon criteria met but each column that contains a leading 1 also has 0's elsewhere, so these matrices are in reduced row-echelon form.

STUDY TIP

The *Graphing Calculator Manual* that accompanies this text contains the keystrokes for performing all the row-equivalent operations in Example 1.

◆ Gauss–Jordan Elimination

We have seen that with Gaussian elimination we perform row-equivalent operations on a matrix to obtain a row-equivalent matrix in row-echelon form. When we continue to apply these operations until we have a matrix in *reduced* row-echelon form, we are using **Gauss–Jordan elimination.** This method is named for Karl Friedrich Gauss and Wilhelm Jordan (1842–1899).

EXAMPLE 3   Use Gauss–Jordan elimination to solve the system of equations in Example 1.

Solution   Using Gaussian elimination in Example 1, we obtained the matrix

$$\begin{bmatrix} 1 & -2 & -10 & \bigm| & -6 \\ 0 & 1 & 8 & \bigm| & 3 \\ 0 & 0 & 1 & \bigm| & -\frac{1}{2} \end{bmatrix}.$$

We continue to perform row-equivalent operations until we have a matrix in reduced row-echelon form. We multiply the third row by 10 and add it to the first row. We also multiply the third row by -8 and add it to the second row.

$$\begin{bmatrix} 1 & -2 & 0 & \bigm| & -11 \\ 0 & 1 & 0 & \bigm| & 7 \\ 0 & 0 & 1 & \bigm| & -\frac{1}{2} \end{bmatrix} \qquad \begin{array}{l} \text{New row 1} = 10(\text{row 3}) + \text{row 1} \\ \text{New row 2} = -8(\text{row 3}) + \text{row 2} \end{array}$$

Next, we multiply the second row by 2 and add it to the first row.

$$\begin{bmatrix} 1 & 0 & 0 & \bigm| & 3 \\ 0 & 1 & 0 & \bigm| & 7 \\ 0 & 0 & 1 & \bigm| & -\frac{1}{2} \end{bmatrix} \qquad \text{New row 1} = 2(\text{row 2}) + \text{row 1}$$

Writing the system of equations that corresponds to this matrix, we have

$$\begin{aligned} x \qquad\quad &= 3, \\ y \quad\ &= 7, \\ z &= -\tfrac{1}{2}. \end{aligned}$$

We can actually read the solution, $\left(3, 7, -\frac{1}{2}\right)$, directly from the last column of the reduced row-echelon matrix.   ▶ Now Try Exercise 27.

EXAMPLE 4   Solve the following system of equations:

$$\begin{aligned} 3x - 4y - \ \ z &= 6, \\ 2x - \ y + \ z &= -1, \\ 4x - 7y - 3z &= 13. \end{aligned}$$

Solution   We write the augmented matrix and use Gauss–Jordan elimination.

$$\begin{bmatrix} 3 & -4 & -1 & \bigm| & 6 \\ 2 & -1 & 1 & \bigm| & -1 \\ 4 & -7 & -3 & \bigm| & 13 \end{bmatrix}$$

TECHNOLOGY CONNECTION

After an augmented matrix is entered in a graphing calculator, reduced row-echelon form can be found directly using the "rref" operation from the MATRIX MATH menu.

```
rref([A])▶Frac
 [[1 0 0  3  ]
  [0 1 0  7  ]
  [0 0 1 -1/2]]
```

The application PolySmlt from the APPS menu can also be used to solve a system of equations.

We begin by multiplying the second and third rows by 3 so that each number in the first column below the first number, 3, is a multiple of that number.

$$\left[\begin{array}{ccc|c} 3 & -4 & -1 & 6 \\ 6 & -3 & 3 & -3 \\ 12 & -21 & -9 & 39 \end{array}\right]$$ New row 2 = 3(row 2)
New row 3 = 3(row 3)

Next, we multiply the first row by -2 and add it to the second row. We also multiply the first row by -4 and add it to the third row.

$$\left[\begin{array}{ccc|c} 3 & -4 & -1 & 6 \\ 0 & 5 & 5 & -15 \\ 0 & -5 & -5 & 15 \end{array}\right]$$ New row 2 = -2(row 1) + row 2
New row 3 = -4(row 1) + row 3

Now we add the second row to the third row.

$$\left[\begin{array}{ccc|c} 3 & -4 & -1 & 6 \\ 0 & 5 & 5 & -15 \\ 0 & 0 & 0 & 0 \end{array}\right]$$ New row 3 = row 2 + row 3

We can stop at this stage because we have a row consisting entirely of 0's. The last row of the matrix corresponds to the equation $0 = 0$, which is true for all values of x, y, and z. Consequently, the equations are dependent and the system is equivalent to

$$3x - 4y - z = 6,$$
$$5y + 5z = -15.$$

This particular system has infinitely many solutions. (A system containing dependent equations could be inconsistent.)

Solving the second equation for y gives us

$$y = -z - 3.$$

Substituting $-z - 3$ for y in the first equation and solving for x, we get

$$3x - 4(-z - 3) - z = 6$$
$$x = -z - 2.$$

Then the solutions of this system are of the form

$$(-z - 2, -z - 3, z),$$

where z can be any real number.   ▶ Now Try Exercise 33.

Similarly, if we obtain a row whose only nonzero entry occurs in the last column, we have an inconsistent system of equations. For example, in the matrix

$$\left[\begin{array}{ccc|c} 1 & 0 & 3 & -2 \\ 0 & 1 & 5 & 4 \\ 0 & 0 & 0 & 6 \end{array}\right],$$

the last row corresponds to the false equation $0 = 6$, so we know the original system of equations has no solution.

8.3 EXERCISE SET

Determine the order of the matrix.

1. $\begin{bmatrix} 1 & -6 \\ -3 & 2 \\ 0 & 5 \end{bmatrix}$ **2.** $\begin{bmatrix} 7 \\ -5 \\ -1 \\ 3 \end{bmatrix}$

3. $\begin{bmatrix} 2 & -4 & 0 & 9 \end{bmatrix}$ **4.** $\begin{bmatrix} -8 \end{bmatrix}$

5. $\begin{bmatrix} 1 & -5 & -8 \\ 6 & 4 & -2 \\ -3 & 0 & 7 \end{bmatrix}$ **6.** $\begin{bmatrix} 13 & 2 & -6 & 4 \\ -1 & 18 & 5 & -12 \end{bmatrix}$

Write the augmented matrix for the system of equations.

7. $2x - y = 7,$
$\quad x + 4y = -5$

8. $3x + 2y = 8,$
$\quad 2x - 3y = 15$

9. $x - 2y + 3z = 12,$
$\quad 2x \qquad - 4z = 8,$
$\qquad 3y + z = 7$

10. $x + y - z = 7,$
$\qquad 3y + 2z = 1,$
$\quad -2x - 5y \qquad = 6$

Write the system of equations that corresponds to the augmented matrix.

11. $\left[\begin{array}{cc|c} 3 & -5 & 1 \\ 1 & 4 & -2 \end{array}\right]$ **12.** $\left[\begin{array}{cc|c} 1 & 2 & -6 \\ 4 & 1 & -3 \end{array}\right]$

13. $\left[\begin{array}{ccc|c} 2 & 1 & -4 & 12 \\ 3 & 0 & 5 & -1 \\ 1 & -1 & 1 & 2 \end{array}\right]$ **14.** $\left[\begin{array}{ccc|c} -1 & -2 & 3 & 6 \\ 0 & 4 & 1 & 2 \\ 2 & -1 & 0 & 9 \end{array}\right]$

Solve the system of equations using Gaussian elimination or Gauss–Jordan elimination.

15. $4x + 2y = 11,$
$\quad 3x - y = 2$

16. $2x + y = 1,$
$\quad 3x + 2y = -2$

17. $5x - 2y = -3,$
$\quad 2x + 5y = -24$

18. $2x + y = 1,$
$\quad 3x - 6y = 4$

19. $3x + 4y = 7,$
$\quad -5x + 2y = 10$

20. $5x - 3y = -2,$
$\quad 4x + 2y = 5$

21. $3x + 2y = 6,$
$\quad 2x - 3y = -9$

22. $x - 4y = 9,$
$\quad 2x + 5y = 5$

23. $x - 3y = 8,$
$\quad -2x + 6y = 3$

24. $4x - 8y = 12,$
$\quad -x + 2y = -3$

25. $-2x + 6y = 4,$
$\quad 3x - 9y = -6$

26. $6x + 2y = -10,$
$\quad -3x - y = 6$

27. $x + 2y - 3z = 9,$
$\quad 2x - y + 2z = -8,$
$\quad 3x - y - 4z = 3$

28. $x - y + 2z = 0,$
$\quad x - 2y + 3z = -1,$
$\quad 2x - 2y + z = -3$

29. $4x - y - 3z = 1,$
$\quad 8x + y - z = 5,$
$\quad 2x + y + 2z = 5$

30. $3x + 2y + 2z = 3,$
$\quad x + 2y - z = 5,$
$\quad 2x - 4y + z = 0$

31. $x - 2y + 3z = -4,$
$\quad 3x + y - z = 0,$
$\quad 2x + 3y - 5z = 1$

32. $2x - 3y + 2z = 2,$
$\quad x + 4y - z = 9,$
$\quad -3x + y - 5z = 5$

33. $2x - 4y - 3z = 3,$
$\quad x + 3y + z = -1,$
$\quad 5x + y - 2z = 2$

34. $x + y - 3z = 4,$
$\quad 4x + 5y + z = 1,$
$\quad 2x + 3y + 7z = -7$

35. $p + q + r = 1,$
$\quad p + 2q + 3r = 4,$
$\quad 4p + 5q + 6r = 7$

36. $m + n + t = 9,$
$\quad m - n - t = -15,$
$\quad 3m + n + t = 2$

37. $a + b - c = 7,$
$\quad a - b + c = 5,$
$\quad 3a + b - c = -1$

38. $a - b + c = 3,$
$\quad 2a + b - 3c = 5,$
$\quad 4a + b - c = 11$

39. $-2w + 2x + 2y - 2z = -10,$
$\quad w + x + y + z = -5,$
$\quad 3w + x - y + 4z = -2,$
$\quad w + 3x - 2y + 2z = -6$

40. $-w + 2x - 3y + z = -8,$
$\quad -w + x + y - z = -4,$
$\quad w + x + y + z = 22,$
$\quad -w + x - y - z = -14$

Use Gaussian elimination or Gauss–Jordan elimination in Exercises 41–44.

41. *Time of Return.* The Houlihans pay their babysitter $5 per hour before 11 P.M. and $7.50 per hour after 11 P.M. One evening they went out for 5 hr and paid the sitter $30. What time did they come home?

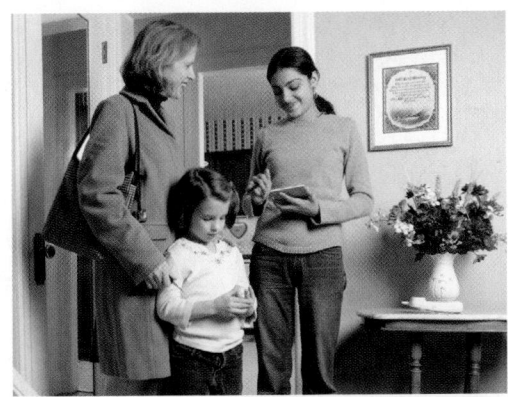

42. *Advertising Expense.* eAuction.com spent a total of $11 million on advertising in fiscal years 2004, 2005, and 2006. The amount spent in 2006 was three times the amount spent in 2004. The amount spent in 2005 was $3 million less than the amount spent in 2006. How much was spent on advertising each year?

43. *Borrowing.* Gonzalez Manufacturing borrowed $30,000 to buy a new piece of equipment. Part of the money was borrowed at 8%, part at 10%, and part at 12%. The annual interest was $3040, and the total amount borrowed at 8% and 10% was twice the amount borrowed at 12%. How much was borrowed at each rate?

44. *Stamp Purchase.* Ricardo spent $21.15 on 39¢ and 24¢ stamps. He bought a total of 60 stamps. How many of each type did he buy?

Collaborative Discussion and Writing

45. Solve the following system of equations using matrices and Gaussian elimination. Then solve it again using Gauss–Jordan elimination. Do you prefer one method over the other? Why or why not?

$$3x + 4y + 2z = 0,$$
$$x - y - z = 10,$$
$$2x + 3y + 3z = -10$$

46. Explain in your own words why the augmented matrix below represents a system of dependent equations.

$$\begin{bmatrix} 1 & -3 & 2 & | & -5 \\ 0 & 1 & -4 & | & 8 \\ 0 & 0 & 0 & | & 0 \end{bmatrix}$$

Skill Maintenance

Classify the function as linear, quadratic, cubic, quartic, rational, exponential, or logarithmic.

47. $f(x) = 3^{x-1}$

48. $f(x) = 3x - 1$

49. $f(x) = \dfrac{3x - 1}{x^2 + 4}$

50. $f(x) = -\frac{3}{4}x^4 + \frac{9}{2}x^3 + 2x^2 - 4$

51. $f(x) = \ln(3x - 1)$

52. $f(x) = \frac{3}{4}x^3 - x$

53. $f(x) = 3$

54. $f(x) = 2 - x - x^2$

Synthesis

In Exercises 55 and 56, three solutions of the equation $y = ax^2 + bx + c$ are given. Use a system of three equations in three variables and Gaussian elimination or Gauss–Jordan elimination to find the constants a, b, and c and write the equation.

55. $(-3, 12), (-1, -7),$ and $(1, -2)$

56. $(-1, 0), (1, -3),$ and $(3, -22)$

57. Find two different row-echelon forms of

$$\begin{bmatrix} 1 & 5 \\ 3 & 2 \end{bmatrix}.$$

58. Consider the system of equations

$$x - y + 3z = -8,$$
$$2x + 3y - z = 5,$$
$$3x + 2y + 2kz = -3k.$$

For what value(s) of k, if any, will the system have
a) no solution?
b) exactly one solution?
c) infinitely many solutions?

Solve using matrices.

59. $y = x + z,$
$3y + 5z = 4,$
$x + 4 = y + 3z$

60. $x + y = 2z,$
$2x - 5z = 4,$
$x - z = y + 8$

61. $x - 4y + 2z = 7,$
$3x + y + 3z = -5$

62. $x - y - 3z = 3,$
$-x + 3y + z = -7$

63. $4x + 5y = 3,$
$-2x + y = 9,$
$3x - 2y = -15$

64. $2x - 3y = -1,$
$-x + 2y = -2,$
$3x - 5y = 1$

8.4

Matrix Operations

✦ Add, subtract, and multiply matrices when possible.

✦ Write a matrix equation equivalent to a system of equations.

In Section 8.3, we used matrices to solve systems of equations. Matrices are useful in many other types of applications as well. In this section, we study matrices and some of their properties.

A capital letter is generally used to name a matrix, and lower-case letters with double subscripts generally denote its entries. For example, a_{47}, read "a sub four seven," indicates the entry in the fourth row and the seventh column. A general term is represented by a_{ij}. The notation a_{ij} indicates the entry in row i and column j. In general, we can write a matrix as

$$\mathbf{A} = [a_{ij}] = \begin{bmatrix} a_{11} & a_{12} & a_{13} & \cdots & a_{1n} \\ a_{21} & a_{22} & a_{23} & \cdots & a_{2n} \\ a_{31} & a_{32} & a_{33} & \cdots & a_{3n} \\ \vdots & \vdots & \vdots & & \vdots \\ a_{m1} & a_{m2} & a_{m3} & \cdots & a_{mn} \end{bmatrix}.$$

The matrix above has m rows and n columns. That is, its order is $m \times n$.

Two matrices are **equal** if they have the same order and corresponding entries are equal.

✦ Matrix Addition and Subtraction

To add or subtract matrices, we add or subtract their corresponding entries. The matrices must have the same order for this to be possible.

> **Addition and Subtraction of Matrices**
> Given two $m \times n$ matrices $\mathbf{A} = [a_{ij}]$ and $\mathbf{B} = [b_{ij}]$, their sum is
> $$\mathbf{A} + \mathbf{B} = [a_{ij} + b_{ij}]$$
> and their difference is
> $$\mathbf{A} - \mathbf{B} = [a_{ij} - b_{ij}].$$

Addition of matrices is both commutative and associative.

**TECHNOLOGY ·················
CONNECTION**

We can use a graphing calculator to add matrices. In Example 1(a), we enter **A** and **B** and then find **A** + **B**.

```
[A]+[B]
            [[1  -3]
             [6  3.5]]
```

We can do the same for the matrices in Example 1(b).

```
[A]+[B]
            [[0  1]
             [0  3]
             [3  1]]
```

EXAMPLE 1   Find $\mathbf{A} + \mathbf{B}$ for each of the following.

a) $\mathbf{A} = \begin{bmatrix} -5 & 0 \\ 4 & \frac{1}{2} \end{bmatrix}, \quad \mathbf{B} = \begin{bmatrix} 6 & -3 \\ 2 & 3 \end{bmatrix}$

b) $\mathbf{A} = \begin{bmatrix} 1 & 3 \\ -1 & 5 \\ 6 & 0 \end{bmatrix}, \quad \mathbf{B} = \begin{bmatrix} -1 & -2 \\ 1 & -2 \\ -3 & 1 \end{bmatrix}$

Solution   We have a pair of 2×2 matrices in part (a) and a pair of 3×2 matrices in part (b). Since each pair of matrices has the same order, we can add the corresponding entries.

a) $\mathbf{A} + \mathbf{B} = \begin{bmatrix} -5 & 0 \\ 4 & \frac{1}{2} \end{bmatrix} + \begin{bmatrix} 6 & -3 \\ 2 & 3 \end{bmatrix}$

$= \begin{bmatrix} -5 + 6 & 0 + (-3) \\ 4 + 2 & \frac{1}{2} + 3 \end{bmatrix} = \begin{bmatrix} 1 & -3 \\ 6 & 3\frac{1}{2} \end{bmatrix}$

b) $\mathbf{A} + \mathbf{B} = \begin{bmatrix} 1 & 3 \\ -1 & 5 \\ 6 & 0 \end{bmatrix} + \begin{bmatrix} -1 & -2 \\ 1 & -2 \\ -3 & 1 \end{bmatrix}$

$= \begin{bmatrix} 1 + (-1) & 3 + (-2) \\ -1 + 1 & 5 + (-2) \\ 6 + (-3) & 0 + 1 \end{bmatrix} = \begin{bmatrix} 0 & 1 \\ 0 & 3 \\ 3 & 1 \end{bmatrix}$

▷ **Now Try Exercise 5.**

EXAMPLE 2 Find **C** − **D** for each of the following.

a) $\mathbf{C} = \begin{bmatrix} 1 & 2 \\ -2 & 0 \\ -3 & -1 \end{bmatrix}$, $\mathbf{D} = \begin{bmatrix} 1 & -1 \\ 1 & 3 \\ 2 & 3 \end{bmatrix}$

b) $\mathbf{C} = \begin{bmatrix} 5 & -6 \\ -3 & 4 \end{bmatrix}$, $\mathbf{D} = \begin{bmatrix} -4 \\ 1 \end{bmatrix}$

TECHNOLOGY
CONNECTION

We can use a graphing calculator to subtract matrices. In Example 2(a), we enter **C** and **D** and then find **C** − **D**.

```
[C]−[D]
          [[0    3]
           [−3  −3]
           [−5  −4]]
```

Solution

a) Since the order of each matrix is 3 × 2, we can subtract corresponding entries:

$$\mathbf{C} - \mathbf{D} = \begin{bmatrix} 1 & 2 \\ -2 & 0 \\ -3 & -1 \end{bmatrix} - \begin{bmatrix} 1 & -1 \\ 1 & 3 \\ 2 & 3 \end{bmatrix}$$

$$= \begin{bmatrix} 1-1 & 2-(-1) \\ -2-1 & 0-3 \\ -3-2 & -1-3 \end{bmatrix} = \begin{bmatrix} 0 & 3 \\ -3 & -3 \\ -5 & -4 \end{bmatrix}.$$

b) **C** is a 2 × 2 matrix and **D** is a 2 × 1 matrix. Since the matrices do not have the same order, we cannot subtract. ▷ **Now Try Exercise 13.**

The **opposite,** or **additive inverse,** of a matrix is obtained by replacing each entry with its opposite, or additive inverse.

EXAMPLE 3 Find −**A** and **A** + (−**A**) for

$$\mathbf{A} = \begin{bmatrix} 1 & 0 & 2 \\ 3 & -1 & 5 \end{bmatrix}.$$

Solution To find −**A**, we replace each entry of **A** with its opposite.

$$-\mathbf{A} = \begin{bmatrix} -1 & 0 & -2 \\ -3 & 1 & -5 \end{bmatrix},$$

$$\mathbf{A} + (-\mathbf{A}) = \begin{bmatrix} 1 & 0 & 2 \\ 3 & -1 & 5 \end{bmatrix} + \begin{bmatrix} -1 & 0 & -2 \\ -3 & 1 & -5 \end{bmatrix} = \begin{bmatrix} 0 & 0 & 0 \\ 0 & 0 & 0 \end{bmatrix} \triangleleft$$

A matrix having 0's for all its entries is called a **zero matrix.** When a zero matrix is added to a second matrix of the same order, the second matrix is unchanged. Thus a zero matrix is an **additive identity.** For example,

$$\begin{bmatrix} 2 & 3 & -4 \\ 0 & 6 & 5 \end{bmatrix} + \begin{bmatrix} 0 & 0 & 0 \\ 0 & 0 & 0 \end{bmatrix} = \begin{bmatrix} 2 & 3 & -4 \\ 0 & 6 & 5 \end{bmatrix}.$$

The matrix

$$\begin{bmatrix} 0 & 0 & 0 \\ 0 & 0 & 0 \end{bmatrix}$$

is the additive identity for any 2 × 3 matrix.

✦ Scalar Multiplication

When we find the product of a number and a matrix, we obtain a **scalar product**.

> ### Scalar Product
> The **scalar product** of a number k and a matrix **A** is the matrix denoted $k\mathbf{A}$, obtained by multiplying each entry of **A** by the number k. The number k is called a **scalar**.

TECHNOLOGY CONNECTION

Scalar products, like those in Example 4, can be found using a graphing calculator.

```
3[A]
              [[-9   0]
               [ 12  15]]
(-1)[A]
              [[3    0 ]
               [-4  -5]]
```

EXAMPLE 4 Find $3\mathbf{A}$ and $(-1)\mathbf{A}$ for

$$\mathbf{A} = \begin{bmatrix} -3 & 0 \\ 4 & 5 \end{bmatrix}.$$

Solution   We have

$$3\mathbf{A} = 3\begin{bmatrix} -3 & 0 \\ 4 & 5 \end{bmatrix} = \begin{bmatrix} 3(-3) & 3 \cdot 0 \\ 3 \cdot 4 & 3 \cdot 5 \end{bmatrix} = \begin{bmatrix} -9 & 0 \\ 12 & 15 \end{bmatrix},$$

$$(-1)\mathbf{A} = -1\begin{bmatrix} -3 & 0 \\ 4 & 5 \end{bmatrix} = \begin{bmatrix} -1(-3) & -1 \cdot 0 \\ -1 \cdot 4 & -1 \cdot 5 \end{bmatrix} = \begin{bmatrix} 3 & 0 \\ -4 & -5 \end{bmatrix}.$$

▶ Now Try Exercise 9.

The properties of matrix addition and scalar multiplication are similar to the properties of addition and multiplication of real numbers.

> ### Properties of Matrix Addition and Scalar Multiplication
> For any $m \times n$ matrices **A**, **B**, and **C** and any scalars k and l:
>
> | | |
> |---|---|
> | $\mathbf{A} + \mathbf{B} = \mathbf{B} + \mathbf{A}.$ | *Commutative Property of Addition* |
> | $\mathbf{A} + (\mathbf{B} + \mathbf{C}) = (\mathbf{A} + \mathbf{B}) + \mathbf{C}.$ | *Associative Property of Addition* |
> | $(kl)\mathbf{A} = k(l\mathbf{A}).$ | *Associative Property of Scalar Multiplication* |
> | $k(\mathbf{A} + \mathbf{B}) = k\mathbf{A} + k\mathbf{B}.$ | *Distributive Property* |
> | $(k + l)\mathbf{A} = k\mathbf{A} + l\mathbf{A}.$ | *Distributive Property* |
>
> There exists a unique matrix **0** such that:
>
> | | |
> |---|---|
> | $\mathbf{A} + \mathbf{0} = \mathbf{0} + \mathbf{A} = \mathbf{A}.$ | *Additive Identity Property* |
>
> There exists a unique matrix $-\mathbf{A}$ such that:
>
> | | |
> |---|---|
> | $\mathbf{A} + (-\mathbf{A}) = -\mathbf{A} + \mathbf{A} = \mathbf{0}.$ | *Additive Inverse Property* |

EXAMPLE 5 *Production.* Mitchell Fabricators, Inc., manufactures three styles of bicycle frames in its two plants. The following table shows the number of each style produced at each plant in April.

	Mountain Bike	Racing Bike	Touring Bike
North Plant	150	120	100
South Plant	180	90	130

a) Write a 2 × 3 matrix **A** that represents the information in the table.

b) The manufacturer increased production of each style by 20% in May. Find a matrix **M** that represents the increased production figures.

c) Find the matrix **A** + **M** and tell what it represents.

Solution

a) Write the entries in the table in a 2 × 3 matrix **A**.

$$\mathbf{A} = \begin{bmatrix} 150 & 120 & 100 \\ 180 & 90 & 130 \end{bmatrix}$$

b) The production in May will be represented by **A** + 20%**A**, or **A** + 0.2**A**, or 1.2**A**. Thus,

$$\mathbf{M} = (1.2)\begin{bmatrix} 150 & 120 & 100 \\ 180 & 90 & 130 \end{bmatrix} = \begin{bmatrix} 180 & 144 & 120 \\ 216 & 108 & 156 \end{bmatrix}.$$

c) $\mathbf{A} + \mathbf{M} = \begin{bmatrix} 150 & 120 & 100 \\ 180 & 90 & 130 \end{bmatrix} + \begin{bmatrix} 180 & 144 & 120 \\ 216 & 108 & 156 \end{bmatrix}$

$$= \begin{bmatrix} 330 & 264 & 220 \\ 396 & 198 & 286 \end{bmatrix}$$

The matrix **A** + **M** represents the total production of each of the three styles of frames at each plant in April and May.   ▶ Now Try Exercise 29.

◆ Products of Matrices

Matrix multiplication is defined in such a way that it can be used in solving systems of equations and in many applications.

> ### Matrix Multiplication
>
> For an $m \times n$ matrix $\mathbf{A} = [a_{ij}]$ and an $n \times p$ matrix $\mathbf{B} = [b_{ij}]$, the **product AB** = $[c_{ij}]$ is an $m \times p$ matrix, where
>
> $$c_{ij} = a_{i1} \cdot b_{1j} + a_{i2} \cdot b_{2j} + a_{i3} \cdot b_{3j} + \cdots + a_{in} \cdot b_{nj}.$$

In other words, the entry c_{ij} in **AB** is obtained by multiplying the entries in row i of **A** by the corresponding entries in column j of **B** and adding the results.

> Note that we can multiply two matrices only when the number of columns in the first matrix is equal to the number of rows in the second matrix.

EXAMPLE 6 For

$$A = \begin{bmatrix} 3 & 1 & -1 \\ 2 & 0 & 3 \end{bmatrix}, \quad B = \begin{bmatrix} 1 & 6 \\ 3 & -5 \\ -2 & 4 \end{bmatrix}, \quad \text{and} \quad C = \begin{bmatrix} 4 & -6 \\ 1 & 2 \end{bmatrix},$$

find each of the following.

a) **AB**   b) **BA**

c) **BC**   d) **AC**

Solution

a) **A** is a 2×3 matrix and **B** is a 3×2 matrix, so **AB** will be a 2×2 matrix.

$$AB = \begin{bmatrix} 3 & 1 & -1 \\ 2 & 0 & 3 \end{bmatrix} \begin{bmatrix} 1 & 6 \\ 3 & -5 \\ -2 & 4 \end{bmatrix}$$

$$= \begin{bmatrix} 3 \cdot 1 + 1 \cdot 3 + (-1)(-2) & 3 \cdot 6 + 1(-5) + (-1)(4) \\ 2 \cdot 1 + 0 \cdot 3 + 3(-2) & 2 \cdot 6 + 0(-5) + 3 \cdot 4 \end{bmatrix} = \begin{bmatrix} 8 & 9 \\ -4 & 24 \end{bmatrix}$$

b) **B** is a 3×2 matrix and **A** is a 2×3 matrix, so **BA** will be a 3×3 matrix.

$$BA = \begin{bmatrix} 1 & 6 \\ 3 & -5 \\ -2 & 4 \end{bmatrix} \begin{bmatrix} 3 & 1 & -1 \\ 2 & 0 & 3 \end{bmatrix}$$

$$= \begin{bmatrix} 1 \cdot 3 + 6 \cdot 2 & 1 \cdot 1 + 6 \cdot 0 & 1(-1) + 6 \cdot 3 \\ 3 \cdot 3 + (-5)(2) & 3 \cdot 1 + (-5)(0) & 3(-1) + (-5)(3) \\ -2 \cdot 3 + 4 \cdot 2 & -2 \cdot 1 + 4 \cdot 0 & -2(-1) + 4 \cdot 3 \end{bmatrix} = \begin{bmatrix} 15 & 1 & 17 \\ -1 & 3 & -18 \\ 2 & -2 & 14 \end{bmatrix}$$

> Note in parts (a) and (b) that $\mathbf{AB} \neq \mathbf{BA}$. Multiplication of matrices is generally not commutative.

TECHNOLOGY ···············
CONNECTION

When the product **AC** in Example 6(d) is entered on a graphing calculator, an ERROR message is returned, indicating that the dimensions of the matrices are mismatched.

[A] [C]

ERR:DIM MISMATCH
1: Quit
2: Goto

c) **B** is a 3×2 matrix and **C** is a 2×2 matrix, so **BC** will be a 3×2 matrix.

$$\mathbf{BC} = \begin{bmatrix} 1 & 6 \\ 3 & -5 \\ -2 & 4 \end{bmatrix} \begin{bmatrix} 4 & -6 \\ 1 & 2 \end{bmatrix}$$

$$= \begin{bmatrix} 1 \cdot 4 + 6 \cdot 1 & 1(-6) + 6 \cdot 2 \\ 3 \cdot 4 + (-5)(1) & 3(-6) + (-5)(2) \\ -2 \cdot 4 + 4 \cdot 1 & -2(-6) + 4 \cdot 2 \end{bmatrix} = \begin{bmatrix} 10 & 6 \\ 7 & -28 \\ -4 & 20 \end{bmatrix}$$

d) The product **AC** is not defined because the number of columns of **A**, 3, is not equal to the number of rows of **C**, 2. ▶ **Now Try Exercise 23.**

EXAMPLE 7 *Dairy Profit.* Dalton's Dairy produces no-fat ice cream and frozen yogurt. The following table shows the number of gallons of each product that are sold at the dairy's three retail outlets one week.

	Store 1	Store 2	Store 3
No-Fat Ice Cream (in gallons)	100	80	120
Frozen Yogurt (in gallons)	160	120	100

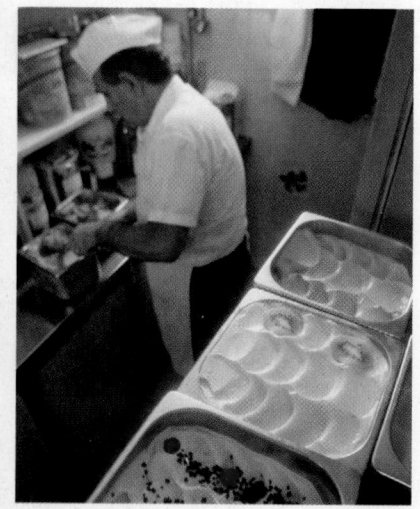

On each gallon of no-fat ice cream, the dairy's profit is $4, and on each gallon of frozen yogurt, it is $3. Use matrices to find the total profit on these items at each store for the given week.

Solution We can write the table showing the distribution of the products as a 2×3 matrix:

$$\mathbf{D} = \begin{bmatrix} 100 & 80 & 120 \\ 160 & 120 & 100 \end{bmatrix}.$$

The profit per gallon for each product can also be written as a matrix:

$$\mathbf{P} = \begin{bmatrix} 4 & 3 \end{bmatrix}.$$

Then the total profit at each store is given by the matrix product **PD**:

$$\mathbf{PD} = \begin{bmatrix} 4 & 3 \end{bmatrix} \begin{bmatrix} 100 & 80 & 120 \\ 160 & 120 & 100 \end{bmatrix}$$

$$= \begin{bmatrix} 4 \cdot 100 + 3 \cdot 160 & 4 \cdot 80 + 3 \cdot 120 & 4 \cdot 120 + 3 \cdot 100 \end{bmatrix}$$

$$= \begin{bmatrix} 880 & 680 & 780 \end{bmatrix}.$$

The total profit on no-fat ice cream and frozen yogurt for the given week was $880 at store 1, $680 at store 2, and $780 at store 3.

▶ **Now Try Exercise 33.**

A matrix that consists of a single row, like **P** in Example 7, is called a **row matrix.** Similarly, a matrix that consists of a single column, like

$$\begin{bmatrix} 8 \\ -3 \\ 5 \end{bmatrix},$$

is called a **column matrix.**

We have already seen that matrix multiplication is generally not commutative. Nevertheless, matrix multiplication does have some properties that are similar to those for multiplication of real numbers.

Properties of Matrix Multiplication

For matrices **A**, **B**, and **C**, assuming that the indicated operations are possible:

$\mathbf{A(BC)} = \mathbf{(AB)C}.$ *Associative Property of Multiplication*

$\mathbf{A(B + C)} = \mathbf{AB} + \mathbf{AC}.$ *Distributive Property*

$\mathbf{(B + C)A} = \mathbf{BA} + \mathbf{CA}.$ *Distributive Property*

✦ Matrix Equations

We can write a matrix equation equivalent to a system of equations.

EXAMPLE 8   Write a matrix equation equivalent to the following system of equations:

$$\begin{aligned} 4x + 2y - z &= 3, \\ 9x + z &= 5, \\ 4x + 5y - 2z &= 1. \end{aligned}$$

Solution   We write the coefficients on the left in a matrix. We then write the product of that matrix and the column matrix containing the variables, and set the result equal to the column matrix containing the constants on the right:

$$\begin{bmatrix} 4 & 2 & -1 \\ 9 & 0 & 1 \\ 4 & 5 & -2 \end{bmatrix} \begin{bmatrix} x \\ y \\ z \end{bmatrix} = \begin{bmatrix} 3 \\ 5 \\ 1 \end{bmatrix}.$$

If we let

$$\mathbf{A} = \begin{bmatrix} 4 & 2 & -1 \\ 9 & 0 & 1 \\ 4 & 5 & -2 \end{bmatrix}, \quad \mathbf{X} = \begin{bmatrix} x \\ y \\ z \end{bmatrix}, \quad \text{and} \quad \mathbf{B} = \begin{bmatrix} 3 \\ 5 \\ 1 \end{bmatrix},$$

we can write this matrix equation as $\mathbf{AX} = \mathbf{B}$.   ▶ Now Try Exercise 39.

In the next section, we will solve systems of equations using a matrix equation like the one in Example 8.

8.4 EXERCISE SET

Find x and y.

1. $[5 \quad x] = [y \quad -3]$

2. $\begin{bmatrix} 6x \\ 25 \end{bmatrix} = \begin{bmatrix} -9 \\ 5y \end{bmatrix}$

3. $\begin{bmatrix} 3 & 2x \\ y & -8 \end{bmatrix} = \begin{bmatrix} 3 & -2 \\ 1 & -8 \end{bmatrix}$

4. $\begin{bmatrix} x-1 & 4 \\ y+3 & -7 \end{bmatrix} = \begin{bmatrix} 0 & 4 \\ -2 & -7 \end{bmatrix}$

For Exercises 5–20, let

$$A = \begin{bmatrix} 1 & 2 \\ 4 & 3 \end{bmatrix}, \qquad B = \begin{bmatrix} -3 & 5 \\ 2 & -1 \end{bmatrix},$$

$$C = \begin{bmatrix} 1 & -1 \\ -1 & 1 \end{bmatrix}, \qquad D = \begin{bmatrix} 1 & 1 \\ 1 & 1 \end{bmatrix},$$

$$E = \begin{bmatrix} 1 & 3 \\ 2 & 6 \end{bmatrix}, \qquad F = \begin{bmatrix} 3 & 3 \\ -1 & -1 \end{bmatrix},$$

$$0 = \begin{bmatrix} 0 & 0 \\ 0 & 0 \end{bmatrix}, \qquad I = \begin{bmatrix} 1 & 0 \\ 0 & 1 \end{bmatrix}.$$

Find each of the following.

5. A + B

6. B + A

7. E + 0

8. 2A

9. 3F

10. (−1)D

11. 3F + 2A

12. A − B

13. B − A

14. AB

15. BA

16. 0F

17. CD

18. EF

19. AI

20. IA

Find the product, if possible.

21. $\begin{bmatrix} -1 & 0 & 7 \\ 3 & -5 & 2 \end{bmatrix} \begin{bmatrix} 6 \\ -4 \\ 1 \end{bmatrix}$

22. $[6 \quad -1 \quad 2] \begin{bmatrix} 1 & 4 \\ -2 & 0 \\ 5 & -3 \end{bmatrix}$

23. $\begin{bmatrix} -2 & 4 \\ 5 & 1 \\ -1 & -3 \end{bmatrix} \begin{bmatrix} 3 & -6 \\ -1 & 4 \end{bmatrix}$

24. $\begin{bmatrix} 2 & -1 & 0 \\ 0 & 5 & 4 \end{bmatrix} \begin{bmatrix} -3 & 1 & 0 \\ 0 & 2 & -1 \\ 5 & 0 & 4 \end{bmatrix}$

25. $\begin{bmatrix} 1 \\ -5 \\ 3 \end{bmatrix} \begin{bmatrix} -6 & 5 & 8 \\ 0 & 4 & -1 \end{bmatrix}$

26. $\begin{bmatrix} 2 & 0 & 0 \\ 0 & -1 & 0 \\ 0 & 0 & 3 \end{bmatrix} \begin{bmatrix} 0 & -4 & 3 \\ 2 & 1 & 0 \\ -1 & 0 & 6 \end{bmatrix}$

27. $\begin{bmatrix} 1 & -4 & 3 \\ 0 & 8 & 0 \\ -2 & -1 & 5 \end{bmatrix} \begin{bmatrix} 3 & 0 & 0 \\ 0 & -4 & 0 \\ 0 & 0 & 1 \end{bmatrix}$

28. $\begin{bmatrix} 4 \\ -5 \end{bmatrix} \begin{bmatrix} 2 & 0 \\ 6 & -7 \\ 0 & -3 \end{bmatrix}$

29. *Budget.* For the month of June, Nelia budgets $150 for food, $80 for clothes, and $40 for entertainment.

   a) Write a 1 × 3 matrix **B** that represents the amounts budgeted for these items.

   b) After receiving a raise, Nelia increases the amount budgeted for each item in July by 5%. Find a matrix **R** that represents the new amounts.

   c) Find **B** + **R** and tell what the entries represent.

30. *Produce.* The produce manager at Dugan's Market orders 40 lb of tomatoes, 20 lb of zucchini, and 30 lb of onions from a local farmer one week.

a) Write a 1 × 3 matrix **A** that represents the amount of each item ordered.

b) The following week the produce manager increases her order by 10%. Find a matrix **B** that represents this order.

c) Find **A** + **B** and tell what the entries represent.

31. *Nutrition.* A 3-oz serving of roasted, skinless chicken breast contains 140 Cal, 27 g of protein, 3 g of fat, 13 mg of calcium, and 64 mg of sodium. One-half cup of potato salad contains 180 Cal, 4 g of protein, 11 g of fat, 24 mg of calcium, and 662 mg of sodium. One broccoli spear contains 50 Cal, 5 g of protein, 1 g of fat, 82 mg of calcium, and 20 mg of sodium. (*Source*: *Home and Garden Bulletin No. 72*, U.S. Government Printing Office, Washington, D.C. 20402)

a) Write 1 × 5 matrices **C**, **P**, and **B** that represent the nutritional values of each food.

b) Find **C** + 2**P** + 3**B** and tell what the entries represent.

32. *Nutrition.* One slice of cheese pizza contains 290 Cal, 15 g of protein, 9 g of fat, and 39 g of carbohydrates. One-half cup of gelatin dessert contains 70 Cal, 2 g of protein, 0 g of fat, and 17 g of carbohydrates. One cup of whole milk contains 150 Cal, 8 g of protein, 8 g of fat, and 11 g of carbohydrates. (*Source*: *Home and Garden Bulletin No. 72*, U.S. Government Printing Office, Washington, D.C. 20402)

a) Write 1 × 4 matrices **P**, **G**, and **M** that represent the nutritional values of each food.

b) Find 3**P** + 2**G** + 2**M** and tell what the entries represent.

33. *Food Service Management.* The food service manager at a large hospital is concerned about maintaining reasonable food costs. The table below lists the cost per serving, in cents, for items on four menus.

Menu	Meat	Potato	Vegetable	Salad	Dessert
1	45.29	6.63	10.94	7.42	8.01
2	53.78	4.95	9.83	6.16	12.56
3	47.13	8.47	12.66	8.29	9.43
4	51.64	7.12	11.57	9.35	10.72

On a particular day, a dietician orders 65 meals from menu 1, 48 from menu 2, 93 from menu 3, and 57 from menu 4.

a) Write the information in the table as a 4 × 5 matrix **M**.

b) Write a row matrix **N** that represents the number of each menu ordered.

c) Find the product **NM**.

d) State what the entries of **NM** represent.

34. *Food Service Management.* A college food service manager uses a table like the one below to show the number of units of ingredients, by weight, required for various menu items.

	White Cake	Bread	Coffee Cake	Sugar Cookies
Flour	1	2.5	0.75	0.5
Milk	0	0.5	0.25	0
Eggs	0.75	0.25	0.5	0.5
Butter	0.5	0	0.5	1

The cost per unit of each ingredient is 15 cents for flour, 28 cents for milk, 54 cents for eggs, and 83 cents for butter.

a) Write the information in the table as a 4 × 4 matrix **M**.

b) Write a row matrix **C** that represents the cost per unit of each ingredient.

c) Find the product **CM**.

d) State what the entries of **CM** represent.

35. *Production Cost.* Karin supplies two small campus coffee shops with homemade chocolate chip cookies, oatmeal cookies, and peanut butter cookies. The table below lists the number of each type of cookie, in dozens, that Karin sold in one week.

	Mugsy's Coffee Shop	The Coffee Club
Chocolate Chip	8	15
Oatmeal	6	10
Peanut Butter	4	3

Karin spends $3 for the ingredients for one dozen chocolate chip cookies, $1.50 for the ingredients for one dozen oatmeal cookies, and $2 for the ingredients for one dozen peanut butter cookies.

a) Write the information in the table as a 3 × 2 matrix **S**.
b) Write a row matrix **C** that represents the cost, per dozen, of the ingredients for each type of cookie.
c) Find the product **CS**.
d) State what the entries of **CS** represent.

36. *Profit.* A manufacturer produces exterior plywood, interior plywood, and fiberboard, which are shipped to two distributors. The table below lists the number of units of each type of product that are shipped to each warehouse.

	Distributor 1	Distributor 2
Exterior Plywood	900	500
Interior Plywood	450	1000
Fiberboard	600	700

The profits from each unit of exterior plywood, interior plywood, and fiberboard are $5, $8, and $4, respectively.

a) Write the information in the table as a 3 × 2 matrix **M**.
b) Write a row matrix **P** that represents the profit, per unit, of each type of product.
c) Find the product **PM**.
d) State what the entries of **PM** represent.

37. *Profit.* In Exercise 35, suppose that Karin's profits on one dozen chocolate chip, oatmeal, and peanut butter cookies are $6, $4.50, and $5.20, respectively.

a) Write a row matrix **P** that represents this information.
b) Use the matrices **S** and **P** to find Karin's total profit from each coffee shop.

38. *Production Cost.* In Exercise 36, suppose that the manufacturer's production costs for each unit of exterior plywood, interior plywood, and fiberboard are $20, $25, and $15, respectively.

a) Write a row matrix **C** that represents this information.
b) Use the matrices **M** and **C** to find the total production cost for the products shipped to each distributor.

Write a matrix equation equivalent to the system of equations.

39. $2x - 3y = 7,$
$x + 5y = -6$

40. $-x + y = 3,$
$5x - 4y = 16$

41. $x + y - 2z = 6,$
$3x - y + z = 7,$
$2x + 5y - 3z = 8$

42. $3x - y + z = 1,$
$x + 2y - z = 3,$
$4x + 3y - 2z = 11$

43. $3x - 2y + 4z = 17,$
$2x + y - 5z = 13$

44. $3x + 2y + 5z = 9,$
$4x - 3y + 2z = 10$

45.
$$
\begin{aligned}
-4w + x - y + 2z &= 12, \\
w + 2x - y - z &= 0, \\
-w + x + 4y - 3z &= 1, \\
2w + 3x + 5y - 7z &= 9
\end{aligned}
$$

46.
$$
\begin{aligned}
12w + 2x + 4y - 5z &= 2, \\
-w + 4x - y + 12z &= 5, \\
2w - x + 4y &= 13, \\
2x + 10y + z &= 5
\end{aligned}
$$

Technology Connection

47. Use a graphing calculator to perform the operations in Exercises 5, 9, 13, and 15.

48. Use a graphing calculator to perform the operations in Exercises 6, 8, 12, and 18.

Collaborative Discussion and Writing

49. Is it true that if $\mathbf{AB} = \mathbf{0}$, for matrices $\mathbf{A}$ and $\mathbf{B}$, then $\mathbf{A} = \mathbf{0}$ or $\mathbf{B} = \mathbf{0}$? Why or why not?

50. Explain how Karin could use the matrix products found in Exercises 35 and 37 in making business decisions.

Skill Maintenance

In Exercises 51–54:

a) *Find the vertex.*
b) *Find the axis of symmetry.*
c) *Determine whether there is a maximum or minimum value and find that value.*
d) *Graph the function.*

51. $f(x) = x^2 - x - 6$

52. $f(x) = 2x^2 - 5x - 3$

53. $f(x) = -x^2 - 3x + 2$

54. $f(x) = -3x^2 + 4x + 4$

Synthesis

For Exercises 55–58, let
$$
\mathbf{A} = \begin{bmatrix} -1 & 0 \\ 2 & 1 \end{bmatrix} \quad and \quad \mathbf{B} = \begin{bmatrix} 1 & -1 \\ 0 & 2 \end{bmatrix}.
$$

55. Show that
$$
(\mathbf{A} + \mathbf{B})(\mathbf{A} - \mathbf{B}) \neq \mathbf{A}^2 - \mathbf{B}^2,
$$
where
$$
\mathbf{A}^2 = \mathbf{AA} \quad and \quad \mathbf{B}^2 = \mathbf{BB}.
$$

56. Show that
$$
(\mathbf{A} + \mathbf{B})(\mathbf{A} + \mathbf{B}) \neq \mathbf{A}^2 + 2\mathbf{AB} + \mathbf{B}^2.
$$

57. Show that
$$
(\mathbf{A} + \mathbf{B})(\mathbf{A} - \mathbf{B}) = \mathbf{A}^2 + \mathbf{BA} - \mathbf{AB} - \mathbf{B}^2.
$$

58. Show that
$$
(\mathbf{A} + \mathbf{B})(\mathbf{A} + \mathbf{B}) = \mathbf{A}^2 + \mathbf{BA} + \mathbf{AB} + \mathbf{B}^2.
$$

In Exercises 59–63, let
$$
\mathbf{A} = \begin{bmatrix}
a_{11} & a_{12} & a_{13} & \cdots & a_{1n} \\
a_{21} & a_{22} & a_{23} & \cdots & a_{2n} \\
a_{31} & a_{32} & a_{33} & \cdots & a_{3n} \\
\vdots & \vdots & \vdots & & \vdots \\
a_{m1} & a_{m2} & a_{m3} & \cdots & a_{mn}
\end{bmatrix},
$$

$$
\mathbf{B} = \begin{bmatrix}
b_{11} & b_{12} & b_{13} & \cdots & b_{1n} \\
b_{21} & b_{22} & b_{23} & \cdots & b_{2n} \\
b_{31} & b_{32} & b_{33} & \cdots & b_{3n} \\
\vdots & \vdots & \vdots & & \vdots \\
b_{m1} & b_{m2} & b_{m3} & \cdots & b_{mn}
\end{bmatrix},
$$

$$
and \quad \mathbf{C} = \begin{bmatrix}
c_{11} & c_{12} & c_{13} & \cdots & c_{1n} \\
c_{21} & c_{22} & c_{23} & \cdots & c_{2n} \\
c_{31} & c_{32} & c_{33} & \cdots & c_{3n} \\
\vdots & \vdots & \vdots & & \vdots \\
c_{m1} & c_{m2} & c_{m3} & \cdots & c_{mn}
\end{bmatrix},
$$

and let k and l be any scalars.

59. Prove that $\mathbf{A} + \mathbf{B} = \mathbf{B} + \mathbf{A}$.

60. Prove that $\mathbf{A} + (\mathbf{B} + \mathbf{C}) = (\mathbf{A} + \mathbf{B}) + \mathbf{C}$.

61. Prove that $(kl)\mathbf{A} = k(l\mathbf{A})$.

62. Prove that $k(\mathbf{A} + \mathbf{B}) = k\mathbf{A} + k\mathbf{B}$.

63. Prove that $(k + l)\mathbf{A} = k\mathbf{A} + l\mathbf{A}$.

8.5   Inverses of Matrices

◆ Find the inverse of a square matrix, if it exists.

◆ Use inverses of matrices to solve systems of equations.

In this section, we continue our study of matrix algebra, finding the **multiplicative inverse,** or simply **inverse,** of a square matrix, if it exists. Then we use such inverses to solve systems of equations.

◆ The Identity Matrix

Recall that, for real numbers, $a \cdot 1 = 1 \cdot a = a$; 1 is the multiplicative identity. A multiplicative identity matrix is very similar to the number 1.

> **Identity Matrix**
>
> For any positive integer n, the $n \times n$ **identity matrix** is an $n \times n$ matrix with 1's on the main diagonal and 0's elsewhere and is denoted by
>
> $$\mathbf{I} = \begin{bmatrix} 1 & 0 & 0 & \cdots & 0 \\ 0 & 1 & 0 & \cdots & 0 \\ 0 & 0 & 1 & \cdots & 0 \\ \vdots & \vdots & \vdots & & \vdots \\ 0 & 0 & 0 & \cdots & 1 \end{bmatrix}.$$
>
> Then $\mathbf{AI} = \mathbf{IA} = \mathbf{A}$, for any $n \times n$ matrix $\mathbf{A}$.

EXAMPLE 1   For

$$\mathbf{A} = \begin{bmatrix} 4 & -7 \\ -3 & 2 \end{bmatrix} \quad \text{and} \quad \mathbf{I} = \begin{bmatrix} 1 & 0 \\ 0 & 1 \end{bmatrix},$$

find each of the following.

a) **AI**   b) **IA**

Solution

a) $\mathbf{AI} = \begin{bmatrix} 4 & -7 \\ -3 & 2 \end{bmatrix}\begin{bmatrix} 1 & 0 \\ 0 & 1 \end{bmatrix}$

$= \begin{bmatrix} 4 \cdot 1 - 7 \cdot 0 & 4 \cdot 0 - 7 \cdot 1 \\ -3 \cdot 1 + 2 \cdot 0 & -3 \cdot 0 + 2 \cdot 1 \end{bmatrix} = \begin{bmatrix} 4 & -7 \\ -3 & 2 \end{bmatrix} = \mathbf{A}$

b) $\mathbf{IA} = \begin{bmatrix} 1 & 0 \\ 0 & 1 \end{bmatrix} \begin{bmatrix} 4 & -7 \\ -3 & 2 \end{bmatrix}$

$= \begin{bmatrix} 1 \cdot 4 + 0(-3) & 1(-7) + 0 \cdot 2 \\ 0 \cdot 4 + 1(-3) & 0(-7) + 1 \cdot 2 \end{bmatrix}$

$= \begin{bmatrix} 4 & -7 \\ -3 & 2 \end{bmatrix} = \mathbf{A}$

✦ The Inverse of a Matrix

Recall that for every nonzero real number a, there is a multiplicative inverse $1/a$, or a^{-1}, such that $a \cdot a^{-1} = a^{-1} \cdot a = 1$. The multiplicative inverse of a matrix behaves in a similar manner.

> **Inverse of a Matrix**
>
> For an $n \times n$ matrix $\mathbf{A}$, if there is a matrix $\mathbf{A}^{-1}$ for which $\mathbf{A}^{-1} \cdot \mathbf{A} = \mathbf{I} = \mathbf{A} \cdot \mathbf{A}^{-1}$, then $\mathbf{A}^{-1}$ is the **inverse** of $\mathbf{A}$.

We read $\mathbf{A}^{-1}$ as "$\mathbf{A}$ inverse." Note that not every matrix has an inverse.

EXAMPLE 2   Verify that

$$\mathbf{B} = \begin{bmatrix} 4 & -3 \\ 3 & -2 \end{bmatrix} \quad \text{is the inverse of} \quad \mathbf{A} = \begin{bmatrix} -2 & 3 \\ -3 & 4 \end{bmatrix}.$$

Solution   We show that $\mathbf{BA} = \mathbf{I} = \mathbf{AB}$.

$$\mathbf{BA} = \begin{bmatrix} 4 & -3 \\ 3 & -2 \end{bmatrix} \begin{bmatrix} -2 & 3 \\ -3 & 4 \end{bmatrix} = \begin{bmatrix} 1 & 0 \\ 0 & 1 \end{bmatrix}$$

$$\mathbf{AB} = \begin{bmatrix} -2 & 3 \\ -3 & 4 \end{bmatrix} \begin{bmatrix} 4 & -3 \\ 3 & -2 \end{bmatrix} = \begin{bmatrix} 1 & 0 \\ 0 & 1 \end{bmatrix}$$

Since $\mathbf{BA} = \mathbf{I} = \mathbf{AB}$, we know that $\mathbf{B}$ is the inverse of $\mathbf{A}$.

▶ Now Try Exercise 1.

We can find the inverse of a square matrix, if it exists, by using row-equivalent operations as in the Gauss–Jordan elimination method. For example, consider the matrix

$$\mathbf{A} = \begin{bmatrix} -2 & 3 \\ -3 & 4 \end{bmatrix}.$$

To find its inverse, we first form an **augmented matrix** consisting of **A** on the left side and the 2×2 identity matrix on the right side:

$$\left[\begin{array}{cc|cc} -2 & 3 & 1 & 0 \\ -3 & 4 & 0 & 1 \end{array}\right].$$

$\underbrace{}$ $\underbrace{}$
↑   ↑
The 2×2 The 2×2
matrix A   identity matrix

Then we attempt to transform the augmented matrix to one of the form

$$\left[\begin{array}{cc|cc} 1 & 0 & a & b \\ 0 & 1 & c & d \end{array}\right].$$

$\underbrace{}$ $\underbrace{}$
↑   ↑
The 2×2 The matrix A^{-1}
identity matrix

If we can do this, the matrix on the right, $\begin{bmatrix} a & b \\ c & d \end{bmatrix}$, is $\mathbf{A}^{-1}$.

EXAMPLE 3   Find $\mathbf{A}^{-1}$, where

$$\mathbf{A} = \begin{bmatrix} -2 & 3 \\ -3 & 4 \end{bmatrix}.$$

Solution   First, we write the augmented matrix. Then we transform it to the desired form.

$$\left[\begin{array}{cc|cc} -2 & 3 & 1 & 0 \\ -3 & 4 & 0 & 1 \end{array}\right]$$

$$\left[\begin{array}{cc|cc} 1 & -\frac{3}{2} & -\frac{1}{2} & 0 \\ -3 & 4 & 0 & 1 \end{array}\right] \qquad \text{New row 1} = -\tfrac{1}{2}(\text{row 1})$$

$$\left[\begin{array}{cc|cc} 1 & -\frac{3}{2} & -\frac{1}{2} & 0 \\ 0 & -\frac{1}{2} & -\frac{3}{2} & 1 \end{array}\right] \qquad \text{New row 2} = 3(\text{row 1}) + \text{row 2}$$

$$\left[\begin{array}{cc|cc} 1 & -\frac{3}{2} & -\frac{1}{2} & 0 \\ 0 & 1 & 3 & -2 \end{array}\right] \qquad \text{New row 2} = -2(\text{row 2})$$

$$\left[\begin{array}{cc|cc} 1 & 0 & 4 & -3 \\ 0 & 1 & 3 & -2 \end{array}\right] \qquad \text{New row 1} = \tfrac{3}{2}(\text{row 2}) + \text{row 1}$$

Thus,

$$\mathbf{A}^{-1} = \begin{bmatrix} 4 & -3 \\ 3 & -2 \end{bmatrix},$$

which we verified in Example 2.

▶ **Now Try Exercise 5.**

TECHNOLOGY ·············
CONNECTION

The ⬛**x⁻¹** key on a graphing calculator can be used to find the inverse of a matrix like the one in Example 3.

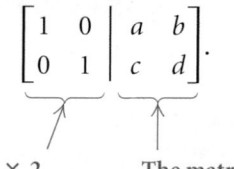

[A]⁻¹
        [[4 −3]
         [3 −2]]

EXAMPLE 4 Find $\mathbf{A}^{-1}$, where

$$\mathbf{A} = \begin{bmatrix} 1 & 2 & -1 \\ 3 & 5 & 3 \\ 2 & 4 & 3 \end{bmatrix}.$$

Solution First, we write the augmented matrix. Then we transform it to the desired form.

$$\begin{bmatrix} 1 & 2 & -1 & | & 1 & 0 & 0 \\ 3 & 5 & 3 & | & 0 & 1 & 0 \\ 2 & 4 & 3 & | & 0 & 0 & 1 \end{bmatrix}$$

$$\begin{bmatrix} 1 & 2 & -1 & | & 1 & 0 & 0 \\ 0 & -1 & 6 & | & -3 & 1 & 0 \\ 0 & 0 & 5 & | & -2 & 0 & 1 \end{bmatrix}$$
New row 2 = −3(row 1) + row 2
New row 3 = −2(row 1) + row 3

$$\begin{bmatrix} 1 & 2 & -1 & | & 1 & 0 & 0 \\ 0 & -1 & 6 & | & -3 & 1 & 0 \\ 0 & 0 & 1 & | & -\frac{2}{5} & 0 & \frac{1}{5} \end{bmatrix}$$
New row 3 = $\frac{1}{5}$(row 3)

$$\begin{bmatrix} 1 & 2 & 0 & | & \frac{3}{5} & 0 & \frac{1}{5} \\ 0 & -1 & 0 & | & -\frac{3}{5} & 1 & -\frac{6}{5} \\ 0 & 0 & 1 & | & -\frac{2}{5} & 0 & \frac{1}{5} \end{bmatrix}$$
New row 1 = row 3 + row 1
New row 2 = −6(row 3) + row 2

$$\begin{bmatrix} 1 & 0 & 0 & | & -\frac{3}{5} & 2 & -\frac{11}{5} \\ 0 & -1 & 0 & | & -\frac{3}{5} & 1 & -\frac{6}{5} \\ 0 & 0 & 1 & | & -\frac{2}{5} & 0 & \frac{1}{5} \end{bmatrix}$$
New row 1 = 2(row 2) + row 1

$$\begin{bmatrix} 1 & 0 & 0 & | & -\frac{3}{5} & 2 & -\frac{11}{5} \\ 0 & 1 & 0 & | & \frac{3}{5} & -1 & \frac{6}{5} \\ 0 & 0 & 1 & | & -\frac{2}{5} & 0 & \frac{1}{5} \end{bmatrix}$$
New row 2 = −1(row 2)

Thus,

$$\mathbf{A}^{-1} = \begin{bmatrix} -\frac{3}{5} & 2 & -\frac{11}{5} \\ \frac{3}{5} & -1 & \frac{6}{5} \\ -\frac{2}{5} & 0 & \frac{1}{5} \end{bmatrix}.$$

▶ Now Try Exercise 11.

If a matrix has an inverse, we say that it is **invertible,** or **nonsingular.** When we cannot obtain the identity matrix on the left using the Gauss–Jordan method, then no inverse exists. This occurs when we obtain a row consisting entirely of 0's in either of the two matrices in the augmented matrix. In this case, we say that **A** is a **singular matrix.**

✦ Solving Systems of Equations

MATRIX EQUATIONS

REVIEW SECTION 8.4.

We can write a system of n linear equations in n variables as a matrix equation $\mathbf{AX} = \mathbf{B}$. If $\mathbf{A}$ has an inverse, then the system of equations has a unique solution that can be found by solving for $\mathbf{X}$, as follows:

$$\mathbf{AX} = \mathbf{B}$$
$$\mathbf{A}^{-1}(\mathbf{AX}) = \mathbf{A}^{-1}\mathbf{B} \qquad \text{Multiplying by } A^{-1} \text{ on the left on both sides}$$
$$(\mathbf{A}^{-1}\mathbf{A})\mathbf{X} = \mathbf{A}^{-1}\mathbf{B} \qquad \text{Using the associative property of matrix multiplication}$$
$$\mathbf{IX} = \mathbf{A}^{-1}\mathbf{B} \qquad A^{-1}A = I$$
$$\mathbf{X} = \mathbf{A}^{-1}\mathbf{B}. \qquad IX = X$$

Matrix Solutions of Systems of Equations

For a system of n linear equations in n variables, $\mathbf{AX} = \mathbf{B}$, if $\mathbf{A}$ is an invertible matrix, then the unique solution of the system is given by

$$\mathbf{X} = \mathbf{A}^{-1}\mathbf{B}.$$

Since matrix multiplication is not commutative in general, care must be taken to multiply *on the left* by $\mathbf{A}^{-1}$.

EXAMPLE 5 Use an inverse matrix to solve the following system of equations:

$$-2x + 3y = 4,$$
$$-3x + 4y = 5.$$

Solution We write an equivalent matrix equation, $\mathbf{AX} = \mathbf{B}$:

$$\underset{A}{\begin{bmatrix} -2 & 3 \\ -3 & 4 \end{bmatrix}} \cdot \underset{X}{\begin{bmatrix} x \\ y \end{bmatrix}} = \underset{B}{\begin{bmatrix} 4 \\ 5 \end{bmatrix}}$$

In Example 3, we found that

$$\mathbf{A}^{-1} = \begin{bmatrix} 4 & -3 \\ 3 & -2 \end{bmatrix}.$$

We also verified this in Example 2. Now we have

$$\mathbf{X} = \mathbf{A}^{-1}\mathbf{B}$$
$$\begin{bmatrix} x \\ y \end{bmatrix} = \begin{bmatrix} 4 & -3 \\ 3 & -2 \end{bmatrix}\begin{bmatrix} 4 \\ 5 \end{bmatrix} = \begin{bmatrix} 1 \\ 2 \end{bmatrix}.$$

The solution of the system of equations is $(1, 2)$. ▶ Now Try Exercise 25.

TECHNOLOGY CONNECTION

To use a graphing calculator to solve the system of equations in Example 5, we enter $\mathbf{A}$ and $\mathbf{B}$ and then enter the notation $\mathbf{A}^{-1}\mathbf{B}$ on the home screen.

```
[A]⁻¹[B]
                    [[1]
                     [2]]
```

8.5 EXERCISE SET

Determine whether **B** *is the inverse of* **A**.

1. $\mathbf{A} = \begin{bmatrix} 1 & -3 \\ -2 & 7 \end{bmatrix}$, $\mathbf{B} = \begin{bmatrix} 7 & 3 \\ 2 & 1 \end{bmatrix}$

2. $\mathbf{A} = \begin{bmatrix} 3 & 2 \\ 4 & 3 \end{bmatrix}$, $\mathbf{B} = \begin{bmatrix} 3 & -2 \\ -4 & 3 \end{bmatrix}$

3. $\mathbf{A} = \begin{bmatrix} -1 & -1 & 6 \\ 1 & 0 & -2 \\ 1 & 0 & -3 \end{bmatrix}$, $\mathbf{B} = \begin{bmatrix} 2 & 3 & 2 \\ 3 & 3 & 4 \\ 1 & 1 & 1 \end{bmatrix}$

4. $\mathbf{A} = \begin{bmatrix} -2 & 0 & -3 \\ 5 & 1 & 7 \\ -3 & 0 & 4 \end{bmatrix}$, $\mathbf{B} = \begin{bmatrix} 4 & 0 & -3 \\ 1 & 1 & 1 \\ -3 & 0 & 2 \end{bmatrix}$

Use the Gauss–Jordan method to find $\mathbf{A}^{-1}$, *if it exists. Check your answers by finding* $\mathbf{A}^{-1}\mathbf{A}$ *and* $\mathbf{A}\mathbf{A}^{-1}$.

5. $\mathbf{A} = \begin{bmatrix} 3 & 2 \\ 5 & 3 \end{bmatrix}$

6. $\mathbf{A} = \begin{bmatrix} 3 & 5 \\ 1 & 2 \end{bmatrix}$

7. $\mathbf{A} = \begin{bmatrix} 6 & 9 \\ 4 & 6 \end{bmatrix}$

8. $\mathbf{A} = \begin{bmatrix} -4 & -6 \\ 2 & 3 \end{bmatrix}$

9. $\mathbf{A} = \begin{bmatrix} 4 & -3 \\ 1 & -2 \end{bmatrix}$

10. $\mathbf{A} = \begin{bmatrix} 0 & -1 \\ 1 & 0 \end{bmatrix}$

11. $\mathbf{A} = \begin{bmatrix} 3 & 1 & 0 \\ 1 & 1 & 1 \\ 1 & -1 & 2 \end{bmatrix}$

12. $\mathbf{A} = \begin{bmatrix} 1 & 0 & 1 \\ 2 & 1 & 0 \\ 1 & -1 & 1 \end{bmatrix}$

13. $\mathbf{A} = \begin{bmatrix} 1 & -4 & 8 \\ 1 & -3 & 2 \\ 2 & -7 & 10 \end{bmatrix}$

14. $\mathbf{A} = \begin{bmatrix} -2 & 5 & 3 \\ 4 & -1 & 3 \\ 7 & -2 & 5 \end{bmatrix}$

15. $\mathbf{A} = \begin{bmatrix} 2 & 3 & 2 \\ 3 & 3 & 4 \\ -1 & -1 & -1 \end{bmatrix}$

16. $\mathbf{A} = \begin{bmatrix} 1 & 2 & 3 \\ 2 & -1 & -2 \\ -1 & 3 & 3 \end{bmatrix}$

17. $\mathbf{A} = \begin{bmatrix} 1 & 2 & -1 \\ -2 & 0 & 1 \\ 1 & -1 & 0 \end{bmatrix}$

18. $\mathbf{A} = \begin{bmatrix} 7 & -1 & -9 \\ 2 & 0 & -4 \\ -4 & 0 & 6 \end{bmatrix}$

19. $\mathbf{A} = \begin{bmatrix} 1 & 3 & -1 \\ 0 & 2 & -1 \\ 1 & 1 & 0 \end{bmatrix}$

20. $\mathbf{A} = \begin{bmatrix} -1 & 0 & -1 \\ -1 & 1 & 0 \\ 0 & 1 & 1 \end{bmatrix}$

21. $\mathbf{A} = \begin{bmatrix} 1 & 2 & 3 & 4 \\ 0 & 1 & 3 & -5 \\ 0 & 0 & 1 & -2 \\ 0 & 0 & 0 & -1 \end{bmatrix}$

22. $\mathbf{A} = \begin{bmatrix} -2 & -3 & 4 & 1 \\ 0 & 1 & 1 & 0 \\ 0 & 4 & -6 & 1 \\ -2 & -2 & 5 & 1 \end{bmatrix}$

23. $\mathbf{A} = \begin{bmatrix} 1 & -14 & 7 & 38 \\ -1 & 2 & 1 & -2 \\ 1 & 2 & -1 & -6 \\ 1 & -2 & 3 & 6 \end{bmatrix}$

24. $\mathbf{A} = \begin{bmatrix} 10 & 20 & -30 & 15 \\ 3 & -7 & 14 & -8 \\ -7 & -2 & -1 & 2 \\ 4 & 4 & -3 & 1 \end{bmatrix}$

In Exercises 25–28, a system of equations is given, together with the inverse of the coefficient matrix. Use the inverse of the coefficient matrix to solve the system of equations.

25. $\begin{aligned} 11x + 3y &= -4, \\ 7x + 2y &= 5; \end{aligned}$ $\mathbf{A}^{-1} = \begin{bmatrix} 2 & -3 \\ -7 & 11 \end{bmatrix}$

26. $\begin{aligned} 8x + 5y &= -6, \\ 5x + 3y &= 2; \end{aligned}$ $\mathbf{A}^{-1} = \begin{bmatrix} -3 & 5 \\ 5 & -8 \end{bmatrix}$

27. $\begin{aligned} 3x + y \quad &= 2, \\ 2x - y + 2z &= -5, \\ x + y + z &= 5; \end{aligned}$ $\mathbf{A}^{-1} = \dfrac{1}{9}\begin{bmatrix} 3 & 1 & -2 \\ 0 & -3 & 6 \\ -3 & 2 & 5 \end{bmatrix}$

28. $\begin{aligned} y - z &= -4, \\ 4x + y \quad &= -3, \\ 3x - y + 3z &= 1; \end{aligned}$ $\mathbf{A}^{-1} = \dfrac{1}{5}\begin{bmatrix} -3 & 2 & -1 \\ 12 & -3 & 4 \\ 7 & -3 & 4 \end{bmatrix}$

Solve the system of equations using the inverse of the coefficient matrix of the equivalent matrix equation.

29. $4x + 3y = 2,$
$\quad x - 2y = 6$

30. $2x - 3y = 7,$
$\quad 4x + y = -7$

31. $5x + y = 2,$
$\quad 3x - 2y = -4$

32. $\quad x - 6y = 5,$
$\quad -x + 4y = -5$

33. $x \quad + z = 1,$
$\quad 2x + y \quad = 3,$
$\quad x - y + z = 4$

34. $\quad x + 2y + 3z = -1,$
$\quad 2x - 3y + 4z = 2,$
$\quad -3x + 5y - 6z = 4$

35. $2x + 3y + 4z = 2,$
$\quad x - 4y + 3z = 2,$
$\quad 5x + y + z = -4$

36. $x + y \quad = 2,$
$\quad 3x \quad + 2z = 5,$
$\quad 2x + 3y - 3z = 9$

37. $2w - 3x + 4y - 5z = 0,$
$\quad 3w - 2x + 7y - 3z = 2,$
$\quad w + x - y + z = 1,$
$\quad -w - 3x - 6y + 4z = 6$

38. $5w - 4x + 3y - 2z = -6,$
$\quad w + 4x - 2y + 3z = -5,$
$\quad 2w - 3x + 6y - 9z = 14,$
$\quad 3w - 5x + 2y - 4z = -3$

39. *Sales.* Stefan sold a total of 145 Italian sausages and hot dogs from his curbside pushcart and collected $242.05. He sold 45 more hot dogs than sausages. How many of each did he sell?

40. *Price of School Supplies.* Miranda bought 4 lab record books and 3 highlighters for $13.93. Victor bought 3 lab record books and 2 highlighters for $10.25. Find the price of each item.

41. *Cost.* Evergreen Landscaping bought 4 tons of topsoil, 3 tons of mulch, and 6 tons of pea gravel for $2825. The next week the firm bought 5 tons of topsoil, 2 tons of mulch, and 5 tons of pea gravel for $2663. Pea gravel costs $17 less per ton than topsoil. Find the price per ton for each item.

42. *Investment.* Selena receives $230 per year in simple interest from three investments totaling $8500. Part is invested at 2.2%, part at 2.65%, and the rest at 3.05%. There is $1500 more

invested at 3.05% than at 2.2%. Find the amount invested at each rate.

Technology Connection

Use a graphing calculator to do the following.

43. Exercises 5, 13, and 21

44. Exercises 6, 14, and 24

45. Exercises 29, 35, and 37

46. Exercises 30, 34, and 38

Collaborative Discussion and Writing

47. For square matrices $\mathbf{A}$ and $\mathbf{B}$, is it true, in general, that $(\mathbf{A} + \mathbf{B})^{-1} = \mathbf{A}^{-1} + \mathbf{B}^{-1}$? Explain.

48. For square matrices $\mathbf{A}$ and $\mathbf{B}$, is it true, in general, that $(\mathbf{AB})^{-1} = \mathbf{A}^{-1}\mathbf{B}^{-1}$? Explain.

Skill Maintenance

Use synthetic division to find the function values.

49. $f(x) = x^3 - 6x^2 + 4x - 8$; find $f(-2)$

50. $f(x) = 2x^4 - x^3 + 5x^2 + 6x - 4$; find $f(3)$

Solve.

51. $2x^2 + x = 7$

52. $\dfrac{1}{x+1} - \dfrac{6}{x-1} = 1$

53. $\sqrt{2x + 1} - 1 = \sqrt{2x - 4}$

54. $x - \sqrt{x} - 6 = 0$

Factor the polynomial $f(x)$.

55. $f(x) = x^3 - 3x^2 - 6x + 8$

56. $f(x) = x^4 + 2x^3 - 16x^2 - 2x + 15$

Synthesis

State the conditions under which $\mathbf{A}^{-1}$ exists. Then find a formula for $\mathbf{A}^{-1}$.

57. $\mathbf{A} = [x]$

58. $\mathbf{A} = \begin{bmatrix} x & 0 \\ 0 & y \end{bmatrix}$

59. $\mathbf{A} = \begin{bmatrix} 0 & 0 & x \\ 0 & y & 0 \\ z & 0 & 0 \end{bmatrix}$

60. $\mathbf{A} = \begin{bmatrix} x & 1 & 1 & 1 \\ 0 & y & 0 & 0 \\ 0 & 0 & z & 0 \\ 0 & 0 & 0 & w \end{bmatrix}$

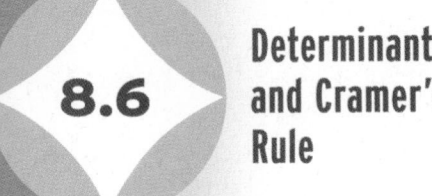

8.6 Determinants and Cramer's Rule

◆ Evaluate determinants of square matrices.
◆ Use Cramer's rule to solve systems of equations.

◆ Determinants of Square Matrices

With every square matrix, we associate a number called its *determinant*.

Determinant of a 2 × 2 Matrix

The **determinant** of the matrix $\begin{bmatrix} a & c \\ b & d \end{bmatrix}$ is denoted $\begin{vmatrix} a & c \\ b & d \end{vmatrix}$ and is defined as

$$\begin{vmatrix} a & c \\ b & d \end{vmatrix} = ad - bc.$$

EXAMPLE 1 Evaluate: $\begin{vmatrix} 2 & -3 \\ -4 & 1 \end{vmatrix}$.

Solution

$\begin{vmatrix} 2 & -3 \\ -4 & 1 \end{vmatrix}$ The arrows indicate the products involved.

$= 2 \cdot 1 - (-4)(-3)$

$= 2 - 12$

$= -10$ ▶ Now Try Exercise 1.

We now consider a way to evaluate determinants of square matrices of order 3 × 3 or higher.

◆ Evaluating Determinants Using Cofactors

Often we first find minors and cofactors of matrices in order to evaluate determinants.

Minor

For a square matrix $\mathbf{A} = [a_{ij}]$, the **minor** M_{ij} of an element a_{ij} is the determinant of the matrix formed by deleting the ith row and the jth column of $\mathbf{A}$.

EXAMPLE 2   For the matrix

$$\mathbf{A} = [a_{ij}] = \begin{bmatrix} -8 & 0 & 6 \\ 4 & -6 & 7 \\ -1 & -3 & 5 \end{bmatrix},$$

find each of the following.

a) M_{11} 　　　　　　　　　　　　　　　**b)** M_{23}

Solution

a) For M_{11}, we delete the first row and the first column and find the determinant of the 2×2 matrix formed by the remaining elements.

$$\begin{bmatrix} -8 & 0 & 6 \\ 4 & -6 & 7 \\ -1 & -3 & 5 \end{bmatrix} \qquad \begin{aligned} M_{11} &= \begin{vmatrix} -6 & 7 \\ -3 & 5 \end{vmatrix} \\ &= (-6) \cdot 5 - (-3) \cdot 7 \\ &= -30 - (-21) \\ &= -30 + 21 \\ &= -9 \end{aligned}$$

b) For M_{23}, we delete the second row and the third column and find the determinant of the 2×2 matrix formed by the remaining elements.

$$\begin{bmatrix} -8 & 0 & 6 \\ 4 & -6 & 7 \\ -1 & -3 & 5 \end{bmatrix} \qquad \begin{aligned} M_{23} &= \begin{vmatrix} -8 & 0 \\ -1 & -3 \end{vmatrix} \\ &= -8(-3) - (-1)0 \\ &= 24 \end{aligned}$$

▶ **Now Try Exercise 9.**

Cofactor

For a square matrix $\mathbf{A} = [a_{ij}]$, the **cofactor** A_{ij} of an element a_{ij} is given by

$$A_{ij} = (-1)^{i+j} M_{ij},$$

where M_{ij} is the minor of a_{ij}.

EXAMPLE 3   For the matrix given in Example 2, find each of the following.

a) A_{11} 　　　　　　　　　　　　　　　**b)** A_{23}

Solution

a) In Example 2, we found that $M_{11} = -9$. Then

$$A_{11} = (-1)^{1+1}(-9) = (1)(-9) = -9.$$

b) In Example 2, we found that $M_{23} = 24$. Then

$$A_{23} = (-1)^{2+3}(24) = (-1)(24) = -24.$$ ▶ **Now Try Exercise 11.**

Consider the matrix **A** given by

$$\mathbf{A} = \begin{bmatrix} a_{11} & a_{12} & a_{13} \\ a_{21} & a_{22} & a_{23} \\ a_{31} & a_{32} & a_{33} \end{bmatrix}.$$

The determinant of the matrix, denoted $|\mathbf{A}|$, can be found by multiplying each element of the first column by its cofactor and adding:

$$|\mathbf{A}| = a_{11}A_{11} + a_{21}A_{21} + a_{31}A_{31}.$$

Because

$$A_{11} = (-1)^{1+1}M_{11} = M_{11},$$
$$A_{21} = (-1)^{2+1}M_{21} = -M_{21},$$

and $\quad A_{31} = (-1)^{3+1}M_{31} = M_{31},$

we can write

$$|\mathbf{A}| = a_{11} \cdot \begin{vmatrix} a_{22} & a_{23} \\ a_{32} & a_{33} \end{vmatrix} - a_{21} \cdot \begin{vmatrix} a_{12} & a_{13} \\ a_{32} & a_{33} \end{vmatrix} + a_{31} \cdot \begin{vmatrix} a_{12} & a_{13} \\ a_{22} & a_{23} \end{vmatrix}.$$

It can be shown that we can determine $|\mathbf{A}|$ by choosing *any* row or column, multiplying each element in that row or column by its cofactor, and adding. This is called *expanding* across a row or down a column. We just expanded down the first column. We now define the determinant of a square matrix of any order.

Determinant of Any Square Matrix

For any square matrix **A** of order $n \times n$ ($n > 1$), we define the **determinant** of **A**, denoted $|\mathbf{A}|$, as follows. Choose any row or column. Multiply each element in that row or column by its cofactor and add the results. The determinant of a 1×1 matrix is simply the element of the matrix. The value of a determinant will be the same no matter which row or column is chosen.

EXAMPLE 4 Evaluate $|\mathbf{A}|$ by expanding across the third row.

$$\mathbf{A} = \begin{bmatrix} -8 & 0 & 6 \\ 4 & -6 & 7 \\ -1 & -3 & 5 \end{bmatrix}$$

Solution   We have

$$|\mathbf{A}| = (-1)A_{31} + (-3)A_{32} + 5A_{33}$$

$$= (-1)(-1)^{3+1} \cdot \begin{vmatrix} 0 & 6 \\ -6 & 7 \end{vmatrix} + (-3)(-1)^{3+2} \cdot \begin{vmatrix} -8 & 6 \\ 4 & 7 \end{vmatrix}$$

$$+ 5(-1)^{3+3} \cdot \begin{vmatrix} -8 & 0 \\ 4 & -6 \end{vmatrix}$$

$$= (-1) \cdot 1 \cdot [0 \cdot 7 - (-6)6] + (-3)(-1)[-8 \cdot 7 - 4 \cdot 6]$$

$$+ 5 \cdot 1 \cdot [-8(-6) - 4 \cdot 0]$$

$$= -[36] + 3[-80] + 5[48]$$

$$= -36 - 240 + 240 = -36.$$

The value of this determinant is -36 no matter which row or column we expand upon.

▶ **Now Try Exercise 13.**

✦ Cramer's Rule

Determinants can be used to solve systems of linear equations. Consider a system of two linear equations:

$$a_1 x + b_1 y = c_1,$$
$$a_2 x + b_2 y = c_2.$$

Solving this system using the elimination method, we obtain

$$x = \frac{c_1 b_2 - c_2 b_1}{a_1 b_2 - a_2 b_1}$$

and

$$y = \frac{a_1 c_2 - a_2 c_1}{a_1 b_2 - a_2 b_1}.$$

The numerators and denominators of these expressions can be written as determinants:

$$x = \frac{\begin{vmatrix} c_1 & b_1 \\ c_2 & b_2 \end{vmatrix}}{\begin{vmatrix} a_1 & b_1 \\ a_2 & b_2 \end{vmatrix}} \quad \text{and} \quad y = \frac{\begin{vmatrix} a_1 & c_1 \\ a_2 & c_2 \end{vmatrix}}{\begin{vmatrix} a_1 & b_1 \\ a_2 & b_2 \end{vmatrix}}.$$

If we let

$$D = \begin{vmatrix} a_1 & b_1 \\ a_2 & b_2 \end{vmatrix}, \quad D_x = \begin{vmatrix} c_1 & b_1 \\ c_2 & b_2 \end{vmatrix}, \quad \text{and} \quad D_y = \begin{vmatrix} a_1 & c_1 \\ a_2 & c_2 \end{vmatrix},$$

we have

$$x = \frac{D_x}{D} \quad \text{and} \quad y = \frac{D_y}{D}.$$

This procedure for solving systems of equations is known as *Cramer's rule*.

> ### Cramer's Rule for 2 × 2 Systems
> The solution of the system of equations
>
> $$a_1 x + b_1 y = c_1,$$
> $$a_2 x + b_2 y = c_2$$
>
> is given by
>
> $$x = \frac{D_x}{D}, \qquad y = \frac{D_y}{D},$$
>
> where
>
> $$D = \begin{vmatrix} a_1 & b_1 \\ a_2 & b_2 \end{vmatrix}, \qquad D_x = \begin{vmatrix} c_1 & b_1 \\ c_2 & b_2 \end{vmatrix},$$
>
> $$D_y = \begin{vmatrix} a_1 & c_1 \\ a_2 & c_2 \end{vmatrix}, \quad \text{and} \quad D \neq 0.$$

TECHNOLOGY CONNECTION

To use Cramer's rule to solve the system of equations in Example 5 on a graphing calculator, we first enter the matrices corresponding to D, D_x, and D_y, respectively, as follows:

$$\mathbf{A} = \begin{bmatrix} 2 & 5 \\ 5 & -2 \end{bmatrix},$$

$$\mathbf{B} = \begin{bmatrix} 7 & 5 \\ -3 & -2 \end{bmatrix}, \quad \text{and}$$

$$\mathbf{C} = \begin{bmatrix} 2 & 7 \\ 5 & -3 \end{bmatrix}.$$

Then

$$x = \frac{\det(\mathbf{B})}{\det(\mathbf{A})} \quad \text{and}$$

$$y = \frac{\det(\mathbf{C})}{\det(\mathbf{A})}.$$

```
det ([B])/det([A])
  ▶Frac
                    -1/29
det ([C])/det([A])
  ▶Frac
                    41/29
```

Note that the denominator D contains the coefficients of x and y, in the same position as in the original equations. For x, the numerator is obtained by replacing the x-coefficients in D (the a's) with the c's. For y, the numerator is obtained by replacing the y-coefficients in D (the b's) with the c's.

EXAMPLE 5 Solve using Cramer's rule:

$$2x + 5y = 7,$$
$$5x - 2y = -3.$$

Solution We have

$$x = \frac{\begin{vmatrix} 7 & 5 \\ -3 & -2 \end{vmatrix}}{\begin{vmatrix} 2 & 5 \\ 5 & -2 \end{vmatrix}} = \frac{7(-2) - (-3)5}{2(-2) - 5 \cdot 5} = \frac{1}{-29} = -\frac{1}{29},$$

$$y = \frac{\begin{vmatrix} 2 & 7 \\ 5 & -3 \end{vmatrix}}{\begin{vmatrix} 2 & 5 \\ 5 & -2 \end{vmatrix}} = \frac{2(-3) - 5 \cdot 7}{-29} = \frac{-41}{-29} = \frac{41}{29}.$$

The solution is $\left(-\frac{1}{29}, \frac{41}{29}\right)$.

▷ **Now Try Exercise 27.**

Cramer's rule works only when a system of equations has a unique solution. This occurs when $D \neq 0$. If $D = 0$ and D_x and D_y are also 0, then the equations are dependent. If $D = 0$ and D_x and/or D_y is not 0, then the system is inconsistent.

Cramer's rule can be extended to a system of n linear equations in n variables. We consider a 3×3 system.

Cramer's Rule for 3 × 3 Systems

The solution of the system of equations

$$a_1x + b_1y + c_1z = d_1,$$
$$a_2x + b_2y + c_2z = d_2,$$
$$a_3x + b_3y + c_3z = d_3$$

is given by

$$x = \frac{D_x}{D}, \qquad y = \frac{D_y}{D}, \qquad z = \frac{D_z}{D},$$

where

$$D = \begin{vmatrix} a_1 & b_1 & c_1 \\ a_2 & b_2 & c_2 \\ a_3 & b_3 & c_3 \end{vmatrix}, \qquad D_x = \begin{vmatrix} d_1 & b_1 & c_1 \\ d_2 & b_2 & c_2 \\ d_3 & b_3 & c_3 \end{vmatrix},$$

$$D_y = \begin{vmatrix} a_1 & d_1 & c_1 \\ a_2 & d_2 & c_2 \\ a_3 & d_3 & c_3 \end{vmatrix}, \qquad D_z = \begin{vmatrix} a_1 & b_1 & d_1 \\ a_2 & b_2 & d_2 \\ a_3 & b_3 & d_3 \end{vmatrix}, \quad \text{and } D \neq 0.$$

Note that the determinant D_x is obtained from D by replacing the x-coefficients with d_1, d_2, and d_3. D_y and D_z are obtained in a similar manner. As with a system of two equations, Cramer's rule cannot be used if $D = 0$. If $D = 0$ and D_x, D_y, and D_z are 0, the equations are dependent. If $D = 0$ and one of D_x, D_y, or D_z is not 0, then the system is inconsistent.

EXAMPLE 6   Solve using Cramer's rule:

$$x - 3y + 7z = 13,$$
$$x + y + z = 1,$$
$$x - 2y + 3z = 4.$$

Solution We have

$$D = \begin{vmatrix} 1 & -3 & 7 \\ 1 & 1 & 1 \\ 1 & -2 & 3 \end{vmatrix} = -10, \qquad D_x = \begin{vmatrix} 13 & -3 & 7 \\ 1 & 1 & 1 \\ 4 & -2 & 3 \end{vmatrix} = 20,$$

$$D_y = \begin{vmatrix} 1 & 13 & 7 \\ 1 & 1 & 1 \\ 1 & 4 & 3 \end{vmatrix} = -6, \qquad D_z = \begin{vmatrix} 1 & -3 & 13 \\ 1 & 1 & 1 \\ 1 & -2 & 4 \end{vmatrix} = -24.$$

Then

$$x = \frac{D_x}{D} = \frac{20}{-10} = -2,$$

$$y = \frac{D_y}{D} = \frac{-6}{-10} = \frac{3}{5},$$

$$z = \frac{D_z}{D} = \frac{-24}{-10} = \frac{12}{5}.$$

The solution is $\left(-2, \frac{3}{5}, \frac{12}{5}\right)$. In practice, it is not necessary to evaluate D_z. When we have found values for x and y, we can substitute them into one of the equations to find z.

▶ Now Try Exercise 35.

8.6 EXERCISE SET

Evaluate the determinant.

1. $\begin{vmatrix} 5 & 3 \\ -2 & -4 \end{vmatrix}$

2. $\begin{vmatrix} -8 & 6 \\ -1 & 2 \end{vmatrix}$

3. $\begin{vmatrix} 4 & -7 \\ -2 & 3 \end{vmatrix}$

4. $\begin{vmatrix} -9 & -6 \\ 5 & 4 \end{vmatrix}$

5. $\begin{vmatrix} -2 & -\sqrt{5} \\ -\sqrt{5} & 3 \end{vmatrix}$

6. $\begin{vmatrix} \sqrt{5} & -3 \\ 4 & 2 \end{vmatrix}$

7. $\begin{vmatrix} x & 4 \\ x & x^2 \end{vmatrix}$

8. $\begin{vmatrix} y^2 & -2 \\ y & 3 \end{vmatrix}$

Use the following matrix for Exercises 9–16:

$$A = \begin{bmatrix} 7 & -4 & -6 \\ 2 & 0 & -3 \\ 1 & 2 & -5 \end{bmatrix}.$$

9. Find M_{11}, M_{32}, and M_{22}.

10. Find M_{13}, M_{31}, and M_{23}.

11. Find A_{11}, A_{32}, and A_{22}.

12. Find A_{13}, A_{31}, and A_{23}.

13. Evaluate $|A|$ by expanding across the second row.

14. Evaluate $|A|$ by expanding down the second column.

15. Evaluate $|A|$ by expanding down the third column.

16. Evaluate $|A|$ by expanding across the first row.

Use the following matrix for Exercises 17–22:

$$\mathbf{A} = \begin{bmatrix} 1 & 0 & 0 & -2 \\ 4 & 1 & 0 & 0 \\ 5 & 6 & 7 & 8 \\ -2 & -3 & -1 & 0 \end{bmatrix}.$$

17. Find M_{41} and M_{33}.

18. Find M_{12} and M_{44}.

19. Find A_{24} and A_{43}.

20. Find A_{22} and A_{34}.

21. Evaluate $|\mathbf{A}|$ by expanding across the first row.

22. Evaluate $|\mathbf{A}|$ by expanding down the third column.

Evaluate the determinant.

23. $\begin{vmatrix} 3 & 1 & 2 \\ -2 & 3 & 1 \\ 3 & 4 & -6 \end{vmatrix}$

24. $\begin{vmatrix} 3 & -2 & 1 \\ 2 & 4 & 3 \\ -1 & 5 & 1 \end{vmatrix}$

25. $\begin{vmatrix} x & 0 & -1 \\ 2 & x & x^2 \\ -3 & x & 1 \end{vmatrix}$

26. $\begin{vmatrix} x & 1 & -1 \\ x^2 & x & x \\ 0 & x & 1 \end{vmatrix}$

Solve using Cramer's rule.

27. $-2x + 4y = 3,$
$\quad 3x - 7y = 1$

28. $5x - 4y = -3,$
$\quad 7x + 2y = 6$

29. $2x - y = 5,$
$\quad x - 2y = 1$

30. $3x + 4y = -2,$
$\quad 5x - 7y = 1$

31. $2x + 9y = -2,$
$\quad 4x - 3y = 3$

32. $2x + 3y = -1,$
$\quad 3x + 6y = -0.5$

33. $2x + 5y = 7,$
$\quad 3x - 2y = 1$

34. $3x + 2y = 7,$
$\quad 2x + 3y = -2$

35. $3x + 2y - z = 4,$
$\quad 3x - 2y + z = 5,$
$\quad 4x - 5y - z = -1$

36. $\quad 3x - y + 2z = 1,$
$\quad\quad x - y + 2z = 3,$
$\quad -2x + 3y + z = 1$

37. $3x + 5y - z = -2,$
$\quad x - 4y + 2z = 13,$
$\quad 2x + 4y + 3z = 1$

38. $3x + 2y + 2z = 1,$
$\quad 5x - y - 6z = 3,$
$\quad 2x + 3y + 3z = 4$

39. $x - 3y - 7z = 6,$
$\quad 2x + 3y + z = 9,$
$\quad 4x + y = 7$

40. $x - 2y - 3z = 4,$
$\quad 3x - 2z = 8,$
$\quad 2x + y + 4z = 13$

41. $\quad 6y + 6z = -1,$
$\quad 8x + 6z = -1,$
$\quad 4x + 9y = 8$

42. $3x + 5y = 2,$
$\quad 2x - 3z = 7,$
$\quad 4y + 2z = -1$

Technology Connection

Use a graphing calculator to do the following.

43. Exercises 1 and 23

44. Exercises 2 and 24

For each matrix $\mathbf{A}$, evaluate $|\mathbf{A}|$ on a graphing calculator.

45. $\mathbf{A} = \begin{bmatrix} 1 & 0 & 0 & -2 \\ 4 & 1 & 0 & 0 \\ 5 & 6 & 7 & 8 \\ -2 & -3 & -1 & 0 \end{bmatrix}$

46. $\mathbf{A} = \begin{bmatrix} 5 & -4 & 2 & -2 \\ 3 & -3 & -4 & 7 \\ -2 & 3 & 2 & 4 \\ -8 & 9 & 5 & -5 \end{bmatrix}$

Use a graphing calculator to do the following.

47. Exercises 29 and 37

48. Exercises 30 and 38

Collaborative Discussion and Writing

49. Explain why the system of equations
$$a_1x + b_1y = c_1,$$
$$a_2x + b_2y = c_2$$
is either dependent or inconsistent when
$$\begin{vmatrix} a_1 & b_1 \\ a_2 & b_2 \end{vmatrix} = 0.$$

50. If the lines $a_1x + b_1y = c_1$ and $a_2x + b_2y = c_2$ are parallel, what can you say about the values of

$$\begin{vmatrix} a_1 & b_1 \\ a_2 & b_2 \end{vmatrix}, \quad \begin{vmatrix} c_1 & b_1 \\ c_2 & b_2 \end{vmatrix}, \quad \text{and} \quad \begin{vmatrix} a_1 & c_1 \\ a_2 & c_2 \end{vmatrix}?$$

Skill Maintenance

Determine whether the function is one-to-one, and if it is, find a formula for $f^{-1}(x)$.

51. $f(x) = 3x + 2$

52. $f(x) = x^2 - 4$

53. $f(x) = |x| + 3$

54. $f(x) = \sqrt[3]{x} + 1$

Simplify. Write answers in the form $a + bi$, where a and b are real numbers.

55. $(3 - 4i) - (-2 - i)$

56. $(5 + 2i) + (1 - 4i)$

57. $(1 - 2i)(6 + 2i)$

58. $\dfrac{3 + i}{4 - 3i}$

Synthesis

Solve.

59. $\begin{vmatrix} x & 5 \\ -4 & x \end{vmatrix} = 24$

60. $\begin{vmatrix} y & 2 \\ 3 & y \end{vmatrix} = y$

61. $\begin{vmatrix} x & -3 \\ -1 & x \end{vmatrix} \geq 0$

62. $\begin{vmatrix} y & -5 \\ -2 & y \end{vmatrix} < 0$

63. $\begin{vmatrix} x + 3 & 4 \\ x - 3 & 5 \end{vmatrix} = -7$

64. $\begin{vmatrix} m + 2 & -3 \\ m + 5 & -4 \end{vmatrix} = 3m - 5$

65. $\begin{vmatrix} 2 & x & 1 \\ 1 & 2 & -1 \\ 3 & 4 & -2 \end{vmatrix} = -6$

66. $\begin{vmatrix} x & 2 & x \\ 3 & -1 & 1 \\ 1 & -2 & 2 \end{vmatrix} = -10$

Rewrite the expression using a determinant. Answers may vary.

67. $2L + 2W$

68. $\pi r + \pi h$

69. $a^2 + b^2$

70. $\frac{1}{2}h(a + b)$

71. $2\pi r^2 + 2\pi rh$

72. $x^2y^2 - Q^2$

8.7 Systems of Inequalities and Linear Programming

- ✦ Graph linear inequalities.
- ✦ Graph systems of linear inequalities.
- ✦ Solve linear programming problems.

A graph of an inequality is a drawing that represents its solutions. We have already seen that an inequality in one variable can be graphed on a number line. An inequality in two variables can be graphed on a coordinate plane.

✦ Graphs of Linear Inequalities

A statement like $5x - 4y < 20$ is a linear inequality in two variables.

> ### Linear Inequality in Two Variables
>
> A **linear inequality in two variables** is an inequality that can be written in the form
>
> $$Ax + By < C,$$
>
> where A, B, and C are real numbers and A and B are not both zero. The symbol $<$ may be replaced with $\leq$, $>$, or $\geq$.

A solution of a linear inequality in two variables is an ordered pair (x, y) for which the inequality is true. For example, $(1, 3)$ is a solution of $5x - 4y < 20$ because $5 \cdot 1 - 4 \cdot 3 < 20$, or $-7 < 20$, is true. On the other hand, $(2, -6)$ is not a solution of $5x - 4y < 20$ because $5 \cdot 2 - 4 \cdot (-6) \not< 20$, or $34 \not< 20$.

The **solution set** of an inequality is the set of all ordered pairs that make it true. The **graph of an inequality** represents its solution set.

EXAMPLE 1 Graph: $y < x + 3$.

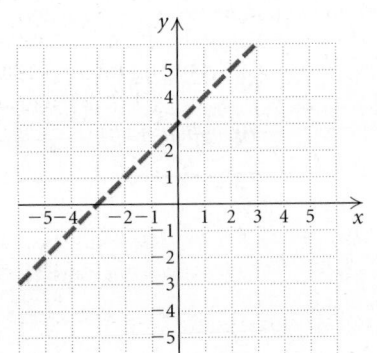

Solution   We begin by graphing the **related equation** $y = x + 3$. We use a dashed line because the inequality symbol is $<$. This indicates that the line itself is not in the solution set of the inequality.

Note that the line divides the coordinate plane into two regions called **half-planes.** One of these half-planes satisfies the inequality. Either *all* points in a half-plane are in the solution set of the inequality or *none* is.

To determine which half-plane satisfies the inequality, we try a test point in either region. The point $(0, 0)$ is usually a convenient choice so long as it does not lie on the line.

$$
\begin{array}{c|c}
\multicolumn{2}{l}{y < x + 3} \\
\hline
0 \;?\; 0 + 3 \\
0 \;|\; 3 & \text{TRUE}
\end{array}
$$

Since $(0, 0)$ satisfies the inequality, so do all points in the half-plane that contains $(0, 0)$. We shade this region to show the solution set of the inequality.

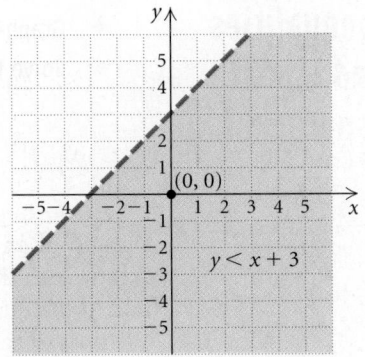

▶ Now Try Exercise 13.

In general, we use the following procedure to graph linear inequalities in two variables.

> **To graph a linear inequality in two variables:**
>
> 1. Replace the inequality symbol with an equals sign and graph this related equation. If the inequality symbol is $<$ or $>$, draw the line dashed. If the inequality symbol is $\leq$ or $\geq$, draw the line solid.
> 2. The graph consists of a half-plane on one side of the line and, if the line is solid, the line as well. To determine which half-plane to shade, test a point not on the line in the original inequality. If that point is a solution, shade the half-plane containing that point. If not, shade the opposite half-plane.

EXAMPLE 2   Graph: $3x + 4y \geq 12$.

Solution

1. First, we graph the related equation $3x + 4y = 12$. We use a solid line because the inequality symbol is $\geq$. This indicates that the line is included in the solution set.

2. To determine which half-plane to shade, we test a point in either region. We choose $(0, 0)$.

$$3x + 4y \geq 12$$

$$3 \cdot 0 + 4 \cdot 0 \ ? \ 12$$
$$0 \ | \ 12 \quad \text{FALSE}$$

Because $(0, 0)$ is *not* a solution, all the points in the half-plane that does *not* contain $(0, 0)$ are solutions. We shade that region, as shown in the figure below.

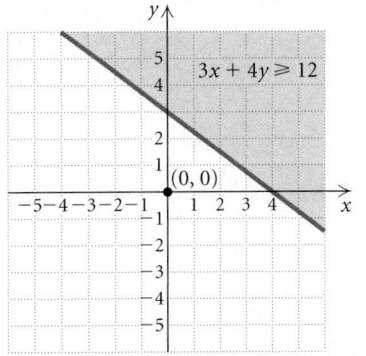

TECHNOLOGY CONNECTION

To graph the inequality in Example 2 on a graphing calculator, we first enter the related equation in the form $y = \dfrac{-3x + 12}{4}$. Then we select the "shade above" graph style.

$y = \dfrac{-3x + 12}{4}$

Some calculators have an application called Inequalz on the APPS menu that can be used to graph this inequality.

▷ Now Try Exercise 17.

EXAMPLE 3   Graph $x > -3$ on a plane.

Solution

1. First, we graph the related equation $x = -3$. We use a dashed line because the inequality symbol is $>$. This indicates that the line is not included in the solution set.

2. The inequality tells us that all points (x, y) for which $x > -3$ are solutions. These are the points to the right of the line. We can also use a test point to determine the solutions. We choose $(5, 1)$.

$$\frac{x > -3}{5 \; ? \; -3} \quad \text{TRUE}$$

Because $(5, 1)$ is a solution, we shade the region containing that point—that is, the region to the right of the dashed line.

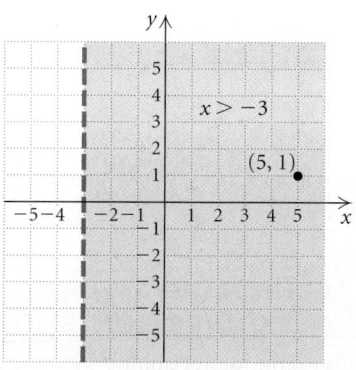

▶ Now Try Exercise 23.

EXAMPLE 4   Graph $y \leq 4$ on a plane.

Solution

1. First, we graph the related equation $y = 4$. We use a solid line because the inequality symbol is $\leq$.

2. The inequality tells us that all points (x, y) for which $y \leq 4$ are solutions of the inequality. These are the points on or below the line. We can also use a test point to determine the solutions. We choose $(-2, 5)$.

$$\frac{y \leq 4}{5 \; ? \; 4} \quad \text{FALSE}$$

Because $(-2, 5)$ is not a solution, we shade the half-plane that does not contain that point.

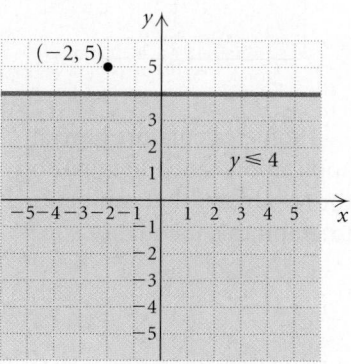

▶ Now Try Exercise 25.

We can graph inequalities, such as the one in Example 3, on a calculator that has the Inequalz application on the APPS menu.

We can graph the inequality $y \leq 4$ in Example 4 using Inequalz or by first graphing $y = 4$ and then using the "shade below" graph style.

$y = 4$

◆ Systems of Linear Inequalities

A system of inequalities in two variables consists of two or more inequalities in two variables considered simultaneously. For example,

$$x + y \leq 4,$$
$$x - y \geq 2$$

is a system of two *linear* inequalities in two variables.

A solution of a system of inequalities is an ordered pair that is a solution of each inequality in the system. To graph a system of linear inequalities, we graph each inequality and determine the region that is common to *all* the solution sets.

EXAMPLE 5   Graph the solution set of the system

$$x + y \le 4,$$
$$x - y \ge 2.$$

Solution   We graph $x + y \le 4$ by first graphing the equation $x + y = 4$ using a solid line. Next, we choose $(0, 0)$ as a test point and find that it is a solution of $x + y \le 4$, so we shade the half-plane containing $(0, 0)$ using red. Next, we graph $x - y = 2$ using a solid line. We find that $(0, 0)$ is not a solution of $x - y \ge 2$, so we shade the half-plane that does not contain $(0, 0)$ using green. The arrows at the ends of each line help to indicate the half-plane that contains each solution set.

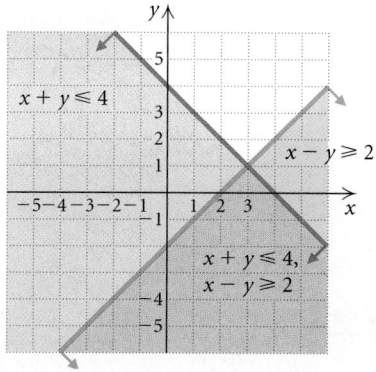

The solution set of the system of equations is the region shaded both red and green, or brown, including parts of the lines $x + y = 4$ and $x - y = 2$.

▷ Now Try Exercise 43.

A system of inequalities may have a graph that consists of a polygon and its interior. As we will see later in this section, it is important in many applications to be able to find the vertices of such a polygon.

EXAMPLE 6   Graph the following system of inequalities and find the coordinates of any vertices formed:

$$3x - y \le 6, \quad (1)$$
$$y - 3 \le 0, \quad (2)$$
$$x + y \ge 0. \quad (3)$$

Solution We graph the related equations $3x - y = 6$, $y - 3 = 0$, and $x + y = 0$ using solid lines. The half-plane containing the solution set for each inequality is indicated by the arrows at the ends of each line. We shade the region common to all three solution sets.

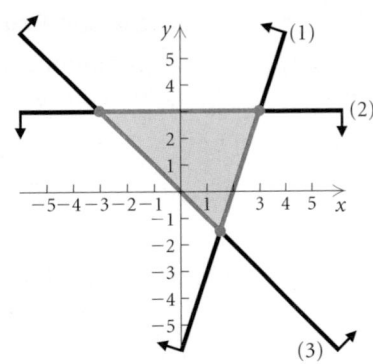

To find the vertices, we solve three systems of equations. The system of equations from inequalities (1) and (2) is

$$3x - y = 6,$$
$$y - 3 = 0.$$

Solving, we obtain the vertex $(3, 3)$.

The system of equations from inequalities (1) and (3) is

$$3x - y = 6,$$
$$x + y = 0.$$

Solving, we obtain the vertex $\left(\frac{3}{2}, -\frac{3}{2}\right)$.

The system of equations from inequalities (2) and (3) is

$$y - 3 = 0,$$
$$x + y = 0.$$

Solving, we obtain the vertex $(-3, 3)$.   ▷ **Now Try Exercise 55.**

TECHNOLOGY ⋯⋯⋯⋯
CONNECTION

If a system of inequalities is graphed using the Inequalz application from the APPS menu, the PoI-Trace feature can be used to find the coordinates of the vertices. Refer to the Graphing Calculator Manual that accompanies the text for the procedure to follow.

✦ Applications: Linear Programming

In many applications, we want to find a maximum or minimum value. In business, for example, we might want to maximize profit and minimize cost. **Linear programming** can tell us how to do this.

In our study of linear programming, we will consider linear functions of two variables that are to be maximized or minimized subject to several conditions, or **constraints.** These constraints are expressed as inequalities. The solution set of the system of inequalities made up of the constraints contains all the **feasible solutions** of a linear programming problem. The function that we want to maximize or minimize is called the **objective function.**

It can be shown that the maximum and minimum values of the objective function occur at a vertex of the region of feasible solutions. Thus we have the following procedure.

Linear Programming Procedure

To find the maximum or minimum value of a linear objective function subject to a set of constraints:

1. Graph the region of feasible solutions.
2. Determine the coordinates of the vertices of the region.
3. Evaluate the objective function at each vertex. The largest and smallest of those values are the maximum and minimum values of the function, respectively.

EXAMPLE 7 *Maximizing Profit.* Dovetail Carpentry Shop makes bookcases and desks. Each bookcase requires 5 hr of woodworking and 4 hr of finishing. Each desk requires 10 hr of woodworking and 3 hr of finishing. Each month the shop has 600 hr of labor available for woodworking and 240 hr for finishing. The profit on each bookcase is $40 and on each desk is $75. How many of each product should be made each month in order to maximize profit?

Solution We let $x =$ the number of bookcases to be produced and $y =$ the number of desks. Then the profit P is given by the function

$$P = 40x + 75y.$$ To emphasize that P is a function of two variables, we sometimes write $P(x, y) = 40x + 75y.$

We know that x bookcases require $5x$ hr of woodworking and y desks require $10y$ hr of woodworking. Since there is no more than 600 hr of labor available for woodworking, we have one constraint:

$$5x + 10y \leq 600.$$

Similarly, the bookcases and desks require $4x$ hr and $3y$ hr of finishing, respectively. There is no more than 240 hr of labor available for finishing, so we have a second constraint:

$$4x + 3y \leq 240.$$

We also know that $x \geq 0$ and $y \geq 0$ because the carpentry shop cannot make a negative number of either product.

Thus we want to maximize the objective function

$$P = 40x + 75y$$

subject to the constraints

$$5x + 10y \leq 600,$$
$$4x + 3y \leq 240,$$
$$x \geq 0,$$
$$y \geq 0.$$

We graph the system of inequalities and determine the vertices. Next, we evaluate the objective function P at each vertex.

Vertices (x, y)	Profit $P = 40x + 75y$	
$(0,0)$	$P = 40 \cdot 0 + 75 \cdot 0 = 0$	
$(60,0)$	$P = 40 \cdot 60 + 75 \cdot 0 = 2400$	
$(24,48)$	$P = 40 \cdot 24 + 75 \cdot 48 = 4560$	← Maximum
$(0,60)$	$P = 40 \cdot 0 + 75 \cdot 60 = 4500$	

The carpentry shop will make a maximum profit of $4560 when 24 bookcases and 48 desks are produced.   ▶ Now Try Exercise 65.

TECHNOLOGY ·······················
CONNECTION

We can create a table in which an objective function is evaluated at each vertex of a system of inequalities if the system has been graphed using the Inequalz application in the APPS menu. Refer to the Graphing Calculator Manual that accompanies the text for details.

8.7   EXERCISE SET

In Exercises 1–8, match the inequality with one of the graphs (a)–(h), which follow.

a)   b)

c)   d)

e)   f)

g)   h)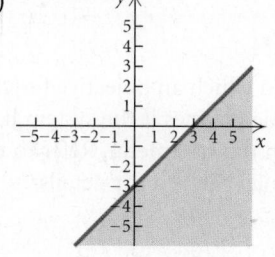

1. $y > x$

2. $y < -2x$

3. $y \leq x - 3$

4. $y \geq x + 5$

5. $2x + y < 4$

6. $3x + y < -6$

7. $2x - 5y > 10$

8. $3x - 9y < 9$

Graph.

9. $y > 2x$

10. $2y < x$

11. $y + x \geq 0$

12. $y - x < 0$

13. $y > x - 3$

14. $y \leq x + 4$

15. $x + y < 4$

16. $x - y \geq 5$

17. $3x - 2y \leq 6$

18. $2x - 5y < 10$

19. $3y + 2x \geq 6$

20. $2y + x \leq 4$

21. $3x - 2 \leq 5x + y$

22. $2x - 6y \geq 8 + 2y$

23. $x < -4$

24. $y \geq 5$

25. $y > -3$

26. $x \leq 5$

27. $-4 < y < -1$
   (*Hint:* Think of this as $-4 < y$ and $y < -1$.)

28. $-3 \leq x \leq 3$
   (*Hint:* Think of this as $-3 \leq x$ and $x \leq 3$.)

29. $y \geq |x|$

30. $y \leq |x + 2|$

In Exercises 31–36, match the system of inequalities with one of the graphs (a)–(f), which follow.

a)   b)

c)   d)

e)

f)
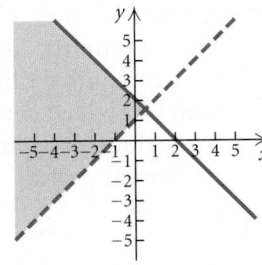

31. $y > x + 1,$
$\quad y \le 2 - x$

32. $y < x - 3,$
$\quad y \ge 4 - x$

33. $\quad 2x + y < 4,$
$\quad 4x + 2y > 12$

34. $x \le 5,$
$\quad y \ge 1$

35. $x + y \le 4,$
$\quad x - y \ge -3,$
$\quad x \ge 0,$
$\quad y \ge 0$

36. $x - y \ge -2,$
$\quad x + y \le 6,$
$\quad x \ge 0,$
$\quad y \ge 0$

Find a system of inequalities with the given graph. Answers may vary.

37.

38.

39.

40.

41.

42.
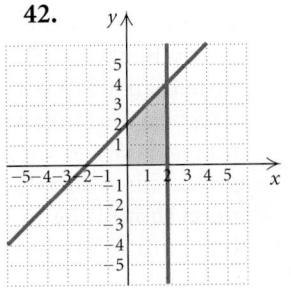

Graph the system of inequalities. Then find the coordinates of the vertices.

43. $y \le x,$
$\quad y \ge 3 - x$

44. $y \ge x,$
$\quad y \le x - 5$

45. $y \ge x,$
$\quad y \le x - 4$

46. $y \ge x,$
$\quad y \le 2 - x$

47. $y \ge -3,$
$\quad x \ge 1$

48. $y \le -2,$
$\quad x \ge 2$

49. $x \le 3,$
$\quad y \ge 2 - 3x$

50. $x \ge -2,$
$\quad y \le 3 - 2x$

51. $x + y \le 1,$
$\quad x - y \le 2$

52. $y + 3x \ge 0,$
$\quad y + 3x \le 2$

53. $2y - x \le 2,$
$\quad y + 3x \ge -1$

54. $\quad y \le 2x + 1,$
$\quad y \ge -2x + 1,$
$\quad x - 2 \le 0$

55. $\quad x - y \le 2,$
$\quad x + 2y \ge 8,$
$\quad y - 4 \le 0$

56. $x + 2y \le 12,$
$\quad 2x + y \le 12,$
$\quad x \ge 0,$
$\quad y \ge 0$

57. $4y - 3x \ge -12,$
$\quad 4y + 3x \ge -36,$
$\quad y \le 0,$
$\quad x \le 0$

58. $8x + 5y \le 40,$
$\quad x + 2y \le 8,$
$\quad x \ge 0,$
$\quad y \ge 0$

59. $3x + 4y \ge 12,$
$\quad 5x + 6y \le 30,$
$\quad 1 \le x \le 3$

60. $y - x \ge 1,$
$\quad y - x \le 3,$
$\quad 2 \le x \le 5$

Find the maximum and the minimum values of the function and the values of x and y for which they occur.

61. $P = 17x - 3y + 60,$ subject to
$$6x + 8y \le 48,$$
$$0 \le y \le 4,$$
$$0 \le x \le 7.$$

62. $Q = 28x - 4y + 72,$ subject to
$$5x + 4y \ge 20,$$
$$0 \le y \le 4,$$
$$0 \le x \le 3.$$

63. $F = 5x + 36y,$ subject to
$$5x + 3y \le 34,$$
$$3x + 5y \le 30,$$
$$x \ge 0,$$
$$y \ge 0.$$

64. $G = 16x + 14y$, subject to
$$3x + 2y \leq 12,$$
$$7x + 5y \leq 29,$$
$$x \geq 0,$$
$$y \geq 0.$$

65. *Maximizing Income.* Golden Harvest Foods makes jumbo biscuits and regular biscuits. The oven can cook at most 200 biscuits per day. Each jumbo biscuit requires 2 oz of flour, each regular biscuit requires 1 oz of flour, and there is 300 oz of flour available. The income from each jumbo biscuit is $0.10 and from each regular biscuit is $0.08. How many of each size biscuit should be made in order to maximize income? What is the maximum income?

66. *Maximizing Mileage.* Omar owns a car and a moped. He can afford 12 gal of gasoline to be split between the car and the moped. Omar's car gets 20 mpg and, with the fuel currently in the tank, can hold at most an additional 10 gal of gas. His moped gets 100 mpg and can hold at most 3 gal of gas. How many gallons of gasoline should each vehicle use if Omar wants to travel as far as possible? What is the maximum number of miles that he can travel?

20 mpg

100 mpg

67. *Maximizing Profit.* Norris Mill can convert logs into lumber and plywood. In a given week, the mill can turn out 400 units of production, of which 100 units of lumber and 150 units of plywood are required by regular customers. The profit is $20 per unit of lumber and $30 per unit of plywood. How many units of each should the mill produce in order to maximize the profit?

68. *Maximizing Profit.* Sunnydale Farm includes 240 acres of cropland. The farm owner wishes to plant this acreage in corn and oats. The profit per acre in corn production is $40 and in oats is $30.

A total of 320 hr of labor is available. Each acre of corn requires 2 hr of labor, whereas each acre of oats requires 1 hr of labor. How should the land be divided between corn and oats in order to yield the maximum profit? What is the maximum profit?

69. *Minimizing Cost.* An animal feed to be mixed from soybean meal and oats must contain at least 120 lb of protein, 24 lb of fat, and 10 lb of mineral ash. Each 100-lb sack of soybean meal costs $15 and contains 50 lb of protein, 8 lb of fat, and 5 lb of mineral ash. Each 100-lb sack of oats costs $5 and contains 15 lb of protein, 5 lb of fat, and 1 lb of mineral ash. How many sacks of each should be used to satisfy the minimum requirements at minimum cost?

70. *Minimizing Cost.* Suppose that in the preceding problem the oats were replaced by alfalfa, which costs $8 per 100 lb and contains 20 lb of protein, 6 lb of fat, and 8 lb of mineral ash. How much of each is now required in order to minimize the cost?

71. *Maximizing Income.* Clayton is planning to invest up to $40,000 in corporate and municipal bonds. The least he is allowed to invest in corporate bonds is $6000, and he does not want to invest more than $22,000 in corporate bonds. He also does not want to invest more than $30,000 in municipal bonds. The interest is 8% on corporate bonds and $7\frac{1}{2}$% on municipal bonds. This is simple interest for one year. How much should he invest in each type of bond in order to maximize his income? What is the maximum income?

72. *Maximizing Income.* Margaret is planning to invest up to $22,000 in certificates of deposit at City Bank and People's Bank. She wants to invest at least $2000 but no more than $14,000 at City Bank. People's Bank does not insure more than a $15,000 investment, so she will invest no more than that in People's Bank. The interest is 6% at City Bank and $6\frac{1}{2}$% at People's Bank. This is simple interest for one year. How much should she invest in each bank in order to maximize her income? What is the maximum income?

73. *Minimizing Transportation Cost.*   An airline with two types of airplanes, P_1 and P_2, has contracted with a tour group to provide transportation for a minimum of 2000 first-class, 1500 tourist-class, and 2400 economy-class passengers. For a certain trip, airplane P_1 costs $12 thousand to operate and can accommodate 40 first-class, 40 tourist-class, and 120 economy-class passengers, whereas airplane P_2 costs $10 thousand to operate and can accommodate 80 first-class, 30 tourist-class, and 40 economy-class passengers. How many of each type of airplane should be used in order to minimize the operating cost?

74. *Minimizing Transportation Cost.*   Suppose that in the preceding problem a new airplane P_3 becomes available, having an operating cost for the same trip of $15 thousand and accommodating 40 first-class, 40 tourist-class, and 80 economy-class passengers. If airplane P_1 were replaced by airplane P_3, how many of P_2 and P_3 should be used in order to minimize the operating cost?

75. *Maximizing Profit.*   It takes Just Sew 2 hr of cutting and 4 hr of sewing to make a knit suit. It takes 4 hr of cutting and 2 hr of sewing to make a worsted suit. At most 20 hr per day are available for cutting and at most 16 hr per day are available for sewing. The profit is $34 on a knit suit and $31 on a worsted suit. How many of each kind of suit should be made each day in order to maximize profit? What is the maximum profit?

76. *Maximizing Profit.*   Cambridge Metal Works manufactures two sizes of gears. The smaller gear requires 4 hr of machining and 1 hr of polishing and yields a profit of $25. The larger gear requires 1 hr of machining and 1 hr of polishing and yields a profit of $10. The firm has available at most 24 hr per day for machining and 9 hr per day for polishing. How many of each type of gear should be produced each day in order to maximize profit? What is the maximum profit?

77. *Minimizing Nutrition Cost.*   Suppose that it takes 12 units of carbohydrates and 6 units of protein to satisfy Jacob's minimum weekly requirements. A particular type of meat contains 2 units of carbohydrates and 2 units of protein per pound. A particular cheese contains 3 units of carbohydrates and 1 unit of protein per pound. The meat costs $3.50 per pound and the cheese costs $4.60 per pound. How many pounds of each are needed in order to minimize the cost and still meet the minimum requirements?

78. *Minimizing Salary Cost.*   The Spring Hill school board is analyzing education costs for Hill Top School. It wants to hire teachers and teacher's aides to make up a faculty that satisfies its needs at minimum cost. The average annual salary for a teacher is $35,000 and for a teacher's aide is $18,000. The school building can accommodate a faculty of no more than 50 but needs at least 20 faculty members to function properly. The school must have at least 12 aides, but the number of teachers must be at least twice the number of aides in order to accommodate the expectations of the community. How many teachers and teacher's aides should be hired in order to minimize salary costs?

79. *Maximizing Animal Support in a Forest.*   A certain area of forest is populated by two species of animals, which scientists refer to as A and B for simplicity. The forest supplies two kinds of food, referred to as F_1 and F_2. For one year, each member of species A requires 1 unit of F_1 and 0.5 unit of F_2. Each member of species B requires 0.2 unit of F_1 and 1 unit of F_2. The forest can normally supply at most 600 units of F_1 and 525 units of F_2 per year. What is the maximum total number of these animals that the forest can support?

80. *Maximizing Animal Support in a Forest.* Refer to Exercise 79. If there is a wet spring, then supplies of food increase to 1080 units of F_1 and 810 units of F_2. In this case, what is the maximum total number of these animals that the forest can support?

Technology Connection

Use a graphing calculator to do the following.

81. Exercises 9, 13, and 25

82. Exercises 10, 14, and 24

Collaborative Discussion and Writing

83. Write an applied linear programming problem for a classmate to solve. Devise your problem so that the answer is "The bakery will make a maximum profit when 5 dozen pies and 12 dozen cookies are baked."

84. Describe how the graph of a linear inequality differs from the graph of a linear equation.

Skill Maintenance

Solve.

85. $-5 \le x + 2 < 4$

86. $|x - 3| \ge 2$

87. $x^2 - 2x \le 3$

88. $\dfrac{x - 1}{x + 2} > 4$

Synthesis

Graph the system of inequalities.

89. $y \ge x^2 - 2,$
    $y \le 2 - x^2$

90. $y < x + 1,$
    $y \ge x^2$

Graph the inequality.

91. $|x + y| \le 1$

92. $|x| + |y| \le 1$

93. $|x| > |y|$

94. $|x - y| > 0$

95. *Allocation of Resources.* Significant Sounds manufactures two types of speaker assemblies. The less expensive assembly, which sells for $350, consists of one midrange speaker and one tweeter. The more expensive speaker assembly, which sells for $600, consists of one woofer, one midrange speaker, and two tweeters. The manufacturer has in stock 44 woofers, 60 midrange speakers, and 90 tweeters. How many of each type of speaker assembly should be made in order to maximize income? What is the maximum income?

96. *Allocation of Resources.* Sitting Pretty Furniture produces chairs and sofas. Each chair requires 20 ft of wood, 1 lb of foam rubber, and 2 yd^2 of fabric. Each sofa requires 100 ft of wood, 50 lb of foam rubber, and 20 yd^2 of fabric. The manufacturer has in stock 1900 ft of wood, 500 lb of foam rubber, and 240 yd^2 of fabric. The chairs can be sold for $80 each and the sofas for $300 each. How many of each should be produced in order to maximize income? What is the maximum income?

8.8 Partial Fractions

✦ Decompose rational expressions into partial fractions.

There are situations in calculus in which it is useful to write a rational expression as a sum of two or more simpler rational expressions. For example, in the equation

$$\frac{4x - 13}{2x^2 + x - 6} = \frac{3}{x + 2} + \frac{-2}{2x - 3},$$

each fraction on the right side is called a **partial fraction.** The expression on the right side is the **partial fraction decomposition** of the rational expression on the left side. In this section, we learn how such decompositions are created.

✦ Partial Fraction Decompositions

The procedure for finding the partial fraction decomposition of a rational expression involves factoring its denominator into linear and quadratic factors.

Procedure for Decomposing a Rational Expression into Partial Fractions

Consider any rational expression $P(x)/Q(x)$ such that $P(x)$ and $Q(x)$ have no common factor other than 1 or -1.

1. If the degree of $P(x)$ is greater than or equal to the degree of $Q(x)$, divide to express $P(x)/Q(x)$ as a quotient + remainder/$Q(x)$ and follow steps (2)–(5) to decompose the resulting rational expression.
2. If the degree of $P(x)$ is less than the degree of $Q(x)$, factor $Q(x)$ into linear factors of the form $(px + q)^n$ and/or quadratic factors of the form $(ax^2 + bx + c)^m$. Any quadratic factor $ax^2 + bx + c$ must be *irreducible*, meaning that it cannot be factored into linear factors with rational coefficients.
3. Assign to each linear factor $(px + q)^n$ the sum of n partial fractions:

$$\frac{A_1}{px + q} + \frac{A_2}{(px + q)^2} + \cdots + \frac{A_n}{(px + q)^n}.$$

(continued)

4. Assign to each quadratic factor $(ax^2 + bx + c)^m$ the sum of m partial fractions:

$$\frac{B_1x + C_1}{ax^2 + bx + c} + \frac{B_2x + C_2}{(ax^2 + bx + c)^2} + \cdots + \frac{B_mx + C_m}{(ax^2 + bx + c)^m}.$$

5. Apply algebraic methods, as illustrated in the following examples, to find the constants in the numerators of the partial fractions.

EXAMPLE 1 Decompose into partial fractions:

$$\frac{4x - 13}{2x^2 + x - 6}.$$

Solution The degree of the numerator is less than the degree of the denominator. We begin by factoring the denominator: $(x + 2)(2x - 3)$. We know that there are constants A and B such that

$$\frac{4x - 13}{(x + 2)(2x - 3)} = \frac{A}{x + 2} + \frac{B}{2x - 3}.$$

To determine A and B, we add the expressions on the right:

$$\frac{4x - 13}{(x + 2)(2x - 3)} = \frac{A(2x - 3) + B(x + 2)}{(x + 2)(2x - 3)}.$$

Next, we equate the numerators:

$$4x - 13 = A(2x - 3) + B(x + 2).$$

Since the last equation containing A and B is true for all x, we can substitute any value of x and still have a true equation. If we choose $x = \frac{3}{2}$, then $2x - 3 = 0$ and A will be eliminated when we make the substitution. This gives us

$$4\left(\tfrac{3}{2}\right) - 13 = A\left(2 \cdot \tfrac{3}{2} - 3\right) + B\left(\tfrac{3}{2} + 2\right)$$
$$-7 = 0 + \tfrac{7}{2}B.$$

Solving, we obtain $B = -2$.

If we choose $x = -2$, then $x + 2 = 0$ and B will be eliminated when we make the substitution. This gives us

$$4(-2) - 13 = A[2(-2) - 3] + B(-2 + 2)$$
$$-21 = -7A + 0.$$

Solving, we obtain $A = 3$.

The decomposition is as follows:

$$\frac{4x - 13}{2x^2 + x - 6} = \frac{3}{x + 2} + \frac{-2}{2x - 3}, \quad \text{or} \quad \frac{3}{x + 2} - \frac{2}{2x - 3}.$$

To check, we can add to see if we get the expression on the left.

▶ Now Try Exercise 3.

EXAMPLE 2 Decompose into partial fractions:

$$\frac{7x^2 - 29x + 24}{(2x - 1)(x - 2)^2}.$$

Solution The degree of the numerator is 2 and the degree of the denominator is 3, so the degree of the numerator is less than the degree of the denominator. The denominator is given in factored form. The decomposition has the following form:

$$\frac{7x^2 - 29x + 24}{(2x - 1)(x - 2)^2} = \frac{A}{2x - 1} + \frac{B}{x - 2} + \frac{C}{(x - 2)^2}.$$

As in Example 1, we add the expressions on the right:

$$\frac{7x^2 - 29x + 24}{(2x - 1)(x - 2)^2} = \frac{A(x - 2)^2 + B(2x - 1)(x - 2) + C(2x - 1)}{(2x - 1)(x - 2)^2}.$$

Then we equate the numerators. This gives us

$$7x^2 - 29x + 24 = A(x - 2)^2 + B(2x - 1)(x - 2) + C(2x - 1).$$

Since the equation containing A, B, and C is true for all x, we can substitute any value of x and still have a true equation. In order to have $2x - 1 = 0$, we let $x = \frac{1}{2}$. This gives us

$$7\left(\tfrac{1}{2}\right)^2 - 29 \cdot \tfrac{1}{2} + 24 = A\left(\tfrac{1}{2} - 2\right)^2 + 0 + 0$$
$$\tfrac{45}{4} = \tfrac{9}{4}A.$$

Solving, we obtain $A = 5$.

In order to have $x - 2 = 0$, we let $x = 2$. Substituting gives us

$$7(2)^2 - 29(2) + 24 = 0 + 0 + C(2 \cdot 2 - 1)$$
$$-6 = 3C.$$

Solving, we obtain $C = -2$.

To find B, we choose any value for x except $\frac{1}{2}$ or 2 and replace A with 5 and C with -2. We let $x = 1$:

$$7 \cdot 1^2 - 29 \cdot 1 + 24 = 5(1 - 2)^2 + B(2 \cdot 1 - 1)(1 - 2)$$
$$+ (-2)(2 \cdot 1 - 1)$$
$$2 = 5 - B - 2$$
$$B = 1.$$

The decomposition is as follows:

$$\frac{7x^2 - 29x + 24}{(2x - 1)(x - 2)^2} = \frac{5}{2x - 1} + \frac{1}{x - 2} - \frac{2}{(x - 2)^2}.$$

▶ Now Try Exercise 7.

EXAMPLE 3 Decompose into partial fractions:

$$\frac{6x^3 + 5x^2 - 7}{3x^2 - 2x - 1}.$$

Solution   The degree of the numerator is greater than that of the denominator. Thus we divide and find an equivalent expression:

$$
\begin{array}{r}
2x + 3 \\
3x^2 - 2x - 1{\overline{\smash{\big)}\,6x^3 + 5x^2 - 7}} \\
\underline{6x^3 - 4x^2 - 2x } \\
9x^2 + 2x - 7 \\
\underline{9x^2 - 6x - 3} \\
8x - 4
\end{array}
$$

The original expression is thus equivalent to

$$2x + 3 + \frac{8x - 4}{3x^2 - 2x - 1}.$$

We decompose the fraction to get

$$\frac{8x - 4}{(3x + 1)(x - 1)} = \frac{5}{3x + 1} + \frac{1}{x - 1}.$$

The final result is

$$2x + 3 + \frac{5}{3x + 1} + \frac{1}{x - 1}.$$

▶ Now Try Exercise 17.

Systems of equations can also be used to decompose rational expressions. Let's reconsider Example 2.

EXAMPLE 4   Decompose into partial fractions:

$$\frac{7x^2 - 29x + 24}{(2x - 1)(x - 2)^2}.$$

Solution   The decomposition has the following form:

$$\frac{A}{2x - 1} + \frac{B}{x - 2} + \frac{C}{(x - 2)^2}.$$

We first add as in Example 2:

$$
\begin{aligned}
\frac{7x^2 - 29x + 24}{(2x - 1)(x - 2)^2} &= \frac{A}{2x - 1} + \frac{B}{x - 2} + \frac{C}{(x - 2)^2} \\
&= \frac{A(x - 2)^2 + B(2x - 1)(x - 2) + C(2x - 1)}{(2x - 1)(x - 2)^2}.
\end{aligned}
$$

Then we equate numerators:

$$
\begin{aligned}
7x^2 &- 29x + 24 \\
&= A(x - 2)^2 + B(2x - 1)(x - 2) + C(2x - 1) \\
&= A(x^2 - 4x + 4) + B(2x^2 - 5x + 2) + C(2x - 1) \\
&= Ax^2 - 4Ax + 4A + 2Bx^2 - 5Bx + 2B + 2Cx - C,
\end{aligned}
$$

or

$$
\begin{aligned}
7x^2 &- 29x + 24 \\
&= (A + 2B)x^2 + (-4A - 5B + 2C)x + (4A + 2B - C).
\end{aligned}
$$

Next, we equate corresponding coefficients:

$$7 = A + 2B,$$ The coefficients of the x^2-terms must be the same.

$$-29 = -4A - 5B + 2C,$$ The coefficients of the x-terms must be the same.

$$24 = 4A + 2B - C.$$ The constant terms must be the same.

SYSTEMS OF EQUATIONS
IN THREE VARIABLES

REVIEW SECTION **8.2** OR **8.5**.

We now have a system of three equations. You should confirm that the solution of the system is

$$A = 5, \quad B = 1, \quad \text{and} \quad C = -2.$$

The decomposition is as follows:

$$\frac{7x^2 - 29x + 24}{(2x - 1)(x - 2)^2} = \frac{5}{2x - 1} + \frac{1}{x - 2} - \frac{2}{(x - 2)^2}.$$

▶ **Now Try Exercise 15.**

STUDY TIP

The review icons in the text margins provide references to earlier sections in which you can find content related to the concept at hand. Reviewing this earlier content will add to your understanding of the current concept.

EXAMPLE 5   Decompose into partial fractions:

$$\frac{11x^2 - 8x - 7}{(2x^2 - 1)(x - 3)}.$$

Solution   The decomposition has the following form:

$$\frac{11x^2 - 8x - 7}{(2x^2 - 1)(x - 3)} = \frac{Ax + B}{2x^2 - 1} + \frac{C}{x - 3}.$$

Adding and equating numerators, we get

$$11x^2 - 8x - 7 = (Ax + B)(x - 3) + C(2x^2 - 1)$$
$$= Ax^2 - 3Ax + Bx - 3B + 2Cx^2 - C,$$

or $$11x^2 - 8x - 7 = (A + 2C)x^2 + (-3A + B)x + (-3B - C).$$

We then equate corresponding coefficients:

$$11 = A + 2C,$$ The coefficients of the x^2-terms

$$-8 = -3A + B,$$ The coefficients of the x-terms

$$-7 = -3B - C.$$ The constant terms

We solve this system of three equations and obtain

$$A = 3, \quad B = 1, \quad \text{and} \quad C = 4.$$

The decomposition is as follows:

$$\frac{11x^2 - 8x - 7}{(2x^2 - 1)(x - 3)} = \frac{3x + 1}{2x^2 - 1} + \frac{4}{x - 3}.$$

▶ **Now Try Exercise 25.**

8.8 EXERCISE SET

Decompose into partial fractions.

1. $\dfrac{x + 7}{(x - 3)(x + 2)}$

2. $\dfrac{2x}{(x + 1)(x - 1)}$

3. $\dfrac{7x - 1}{6x^2 - 5x + 1}$

4. $\dfrac{13x + 46}{12x^2 - 11x - 15}$

5. $\dfrac{3x^2 - 11x - 26}{(x^2 - 4)(x + 1)}$

6. $\dfrac{5x^2 + 9x - 56}{(x - 4)(x - 2)(x + 1)}$

7. $\dfrac{9}{(x + 2)^2(x - 1)}$

8. $\dfrac{x^2 - x - 4}{(x - 2)^3}$

9. $\dfrac{2x^2 + 3x + 1}{(x^2 - 1)(2x - 1)}$

10. $\dfrac{x^2 - 10x + 13}{(x^2 - 5x + 6)(x - 1)}$

11. $\dfrac{x^4 - 3x^3 - 3x^2 + 10}{(x + 1)^2(x - 3)}$

12. $\dfrac{10x^3 - 15x^2 - 35x}{x^2 - x - 6}$

13. $\dfrac{-x^2 + 2x - 13}{(x^2 + 2)(x - 1)}$

14. $\dfrac{26x^2 + 208x}{(x^2 + 1)(x + 5)}$

15. $\dfrac{6 + 26x - x^2}{(2x - 1)(x + 2)^2}$

16. $\dfrac{5x^3 + 6x^2 + 5x}{(x^2 - 1)(x + 1)^3}$

17. $\dfrac{6x^3 + 5x^2 + 6x - 2}{2x^2 + x - 1}$

18. $\dfrac{2x^3 + 3x^2 - 11x - 10}{x^2 + 2x - 3}$

19. $\dfrac{2x^2 - 11x + 5}{(x - 3)(x^2 + 2x - 5)}$

20. $\dfrac{3x^2 - 3x - 8}{(x - 5)(x^2 + x - 4)}$

21. $\dfrac{-4x^2 - 2x + 10}{(3x + 5)(x + 1)^2}$

22. $\dfrac{26x^2 - 36x + 22}{(x - 4)(2x - 1)^2}$

23. $\dfrac{36x + 1}{12x^2 - 7x - 10}$

24. $\dfrac{-17x + 61}{6x^2 + 39x - 21}$

25. $\dfrac{-4x^2 - 9x + 8}{(3x^2 + 1)(x - 2)}$

26. $\dfrac{11x^2 - 39x + 16}{(x^2 + 4)(x - 8)}$

Collaborative Discussion and Writing

27. Describe the two methods used to find the constants in a partial fraction decomposition.

28. What would you say to a classmate who tells you that the partial fraction decomposition of

$$\frac{3x^2 - 8x + 9}{(x + 3)(x^2 - 5x + 6)}$$

is

$$\frac{2}{x + 3} + \frac{x - 1}{x^2 - 5x + 6}?$$

Explain.

29. Explain the error in the following process.

$$\frac{x^2 + 4}{(x + 2)(x + 1)} = \frac{A}{x + 2} + \frac{B}{x + 1}$$

$$= \frac{A(x + 1) + B(x + 2)}{(x + 2)(x + 1)}$$

Then

$$x^2 + 4 = A(x + 1) + B(x + 2).$$

When $x = -1$:

$$(-1)^2 + 4 = A(-1 + 1) + B(-1 + 2)$$
$$5 = B.$$

When $x = -2$:

$$(-2)^2 + 4 = A(-2 + 1) + B(-2 + 2)$$
$$8 = -A$$
$$-8 = A.$$

Thus,

$$\frac{x^2 + 4}{(x + 2)(x + 1)} = \frac{-8}{x + 2} + \frac{5}{x + 1}.$$

Skill Maintenance

Find the zeros of the polynomial function.

30. $f(x) = x^3 - 3x^2 + x - 3$

31. $f(x) = x^3 + x^2 - 3x - 2$

32. $f(x) = x^4 - x^3 - 5x^2 - x - 6$

33. $f(x) = x^3 + 5x^2 + 5x - 3$

Synthesis

Decompose into partial fractions.

34. $\dfrac{9x^3 - 24x^2 + 48x}{(x - 2)^4(x + 1)}$

[*Hint*: Let the expression equal

$$\frac{A}{x + 1} + \frac{P(x)}{(x - 2)^4}$$

and find $P(x)$].

35. $\dfrac{x}{x^4 - a^4}$

36. $\dfrac{1}{e^{-x} + 3 + 2e^x}$

37. $\dfrac{1 + \ln x^2}{(\ln x + 2)(\ln x - 3)^2}$

CHAPTER 8 SUMMARY AND REVIEW

Important Properties and Formulas

Row-Equivalent Operations

1. Interchange any two rows.
2. Multiply each entry in a row by the same nonzero constant.
3. Add a nonzero multiple of one row to another row.

Row-Echelon Form

1. If a row does not consist entirely of 0's, then the first nonzero element in the row is a 1 (called a leading 1).
2. For any two successive nonzero rows, the leading 1 in the lower row is farther to the right than the leading 1 in the higher row.
3. All the rows consisting entirely of 0's are at the bottom of the matrix.

If a fourth property is also satisfied, a matrix is said to be in reduced row-echelon form:

4. Each column that contains a leading 1 has 0's everywhere else.

Properties of Matrix Addition and Scalar Multiplication

For matrices $\mathbf{A}$, $\mathbf{B}$, and $\mathbf{C}$ and any scalars k and l, assuming that the indicated operation is possible:

Commutative Property of Addition:

$$\mathbf{A} + \mathbf{B} = \mathbf{B} + \mathbf{A}.$$

Associative Property of Addition:

$$\mathbf{A} + (\mathbf{B} + \mathbf{C}) = (\mathbf{A} + \mathbf{B}) + \mathbf{C}.$$

Associative Property of Scalar Multiplication:

$$(kl)\mathbf{A} = k(l\mathbf{A}).$$

Additive Identity Property:
There exists a unique matrix $\mathbf{0}$ such that
$\mathbf{A} + \mathbf{0} = \mathbf{0} + \mathbf{A} = \mathbf{A}.$

Additive Inverse Property:
There exists a unique matrix $-\mathbf{A}$ such that
$\mathbf{A} + (-\mathbf{A}) = -\mathbf{A} + \mathbf{A} = \mathbf{0}.$

Distributive Properties:

$$k(\mathbf{A} + \mathbf{B}) = k\mathbf{A} + k\mathbf{B},$$
$$(k + l)\mathbf{A} = k\mathbf{A} + l\mathbf{A}.$$

Properties of Matrix Multiplication

For matrices $\mathbf{A}$, $\mathbf{B}$, and $\mathbf{C}$, assuming that the indicated operation is possible:

Associative Property of Multiplication:

$$\mathbf{A}(\mathbf{BC}) = (\mathbf{AB})\mathbf{C}.$$

Distributive Properties:

$$\mathbf{A}(\mathbf{B} + \mathbf{C}) = \mathbf{AB} + \mathbf{AC},$$
$$(\mathbf{B} + \mathbf{C})\mathbf{A} = \mathbf{BA} + \mathbf{CA}.$$

Matrix Solutions of Systems of Equations

For a system of n linear equations in n variables, $\mathbf{AX} = \mathbf{B}$, if $\mathbf{A}$ is an invertible matrix, then the unique solution of the system is given by $\mathbf{X} = \mathbf{A}^{-1}\mathbf{B}$.

Determinant of a 2×2 Matrix

The **determinant** of the matrix $\begin{bmatrix} a & c \\ b & d \end{bmatrix}$ is

denoted $\begin{vmatrix} a & c \\ b & d \end{vmatrix}$ and is defined as

$$\begin{vmatrix} a & c \\ b & d \end{vmatrix} = ad - bc.$$

Determinant of Any Square Matrix

For any square matrix $\mathbf{A}$ of order $n \times n$ ($n > 1$), we define the **determinant** of $\mathbf{A}$, denoted $|\mathbf{A}|$, as follows. Choose any row or column. Multiply each element in that row or column by its cofactor and add the results. The determinant of a 1×1 matrix is simply the element of the matrix. The value of a determinant will be the same, no matter which row or column is chosen.

Cramer's Rule for 2×2 Systems

The solution of the system of equations

$$a_1 x + b_1 y = c_1,$$
$$a_2 x + b_2 y = c_2$$

is given by

$$x = \frac{D_x}{D}, \qquad y = \frac{D_y}{D},$$

where

$$D = \begin{vmatrix} a_1 & b_1 \\ a_2 & b_2 \end{vmatrix}, \qquad D_x = \begin{vmatrix} c_1 & b_1 \\ c_2 & b_2 \end{vmatrix},$$

$$D_y = \begin{vmatrix} a_1 & c_1 \\ a_2 & c_2 \end{vmatrix}, \quad \text{and} \quad D \neq 0.$$

Cramer's Rule for 3×3 Systems

The solution of the system of equations

$$a_1 x + b_1 y + c_1 z = d_1,$$
$$a_2 x + b_2 y + c_2 z = d_2,$$
$$a_3 x + b_3 y + c_3 z = d_3$$

is given by

$$x = \frac{D_x}{D}, \qquad y = \frac{D_y}{D}, \qquad z = \frac{D_z}{D},$$

where

$$D = \begin{vmatrix} a_1 & b_1 & c_1 \\ a_2 & b_2 & c_2 \\ a_3 & b_3 & c_3 \end{vmatrix}, \qquad D_x = \begin{vmatrix} d_1 & b_1 & c_1 \\ d_2 & b_2 & c_2 \\ d_3 & b_3 & c_3 \end{vmatrix},$$

$$D_y = \begin{vmatrix} a_1 & d_1 & c_1 \\ a_2 & d_2 & c_2 \\ a_3 & d_3 & c_3 \end{vmatrix}, \qquad D_z = \begin{vmatrix} a_1 & b_1 & d_1 \\ a_2 & b_2 & d_2 \\ a_3 & b_3 & d_3 \end{vmatrix},$$

and $D \neq 0$.

To Graph a Linear Inequality in Two Variables:

1. Replace the inequality symbol with an equals sign and graph this related equation. If the inequality symbol is $<$ or $>$, draw the line dashed. If the inequality symbol is $\leq$ or $\geq$, draw the line solid.
2. The graph consists of a half-plane on one side of the line and, if the line is solid, the line as well. To determine which half-plane to shade, test a point not on the line in the original inequality.

If that point is a solution, shade the half-plane containing that point. If not, shade the opposite half-plane.

Linear Programming Procedure

To find the maximum or minimum value of a linear objective function subject to a set of constraints:

1. Graph the region of feasible solutions.
2. Determine the coordinates of the vertices of the region.
3. Evaluate the objective function at each vertex. The largest and smallest of those values are the maximum and minimum values of the function, respectively.

Procedure for Decomposing a Rational Expression into Partial Fractions

Consider any rational expression $P(x)/Q(x)$ such that $P(x)$ and $Q(x)$ have no common factor other than 1 or -1.

1. If the degree of $P(x)$ is greater than or equal to the degree of $Q(x)$, divide to express $P(x)/Q(x)$ as a quotient $+$ remainder/$Q(x)$ and follow steps (2)–(5) to decompose the resulting rational expression.
2. If the degree of $P(x)$ is less than the degree of $Q(x)$, factor $Q(x)$ into linear factors of the form $(px + q)^n$ and/or quadratic factors of the form $(ax^2 + bx + c)^m$. Any quadratic factor $ax^2 + bx + c$ must be irreducible, meaning that it cannot be factored into linear factors with rational coefficients.
3. Assign to each linear factor $(px + q)^n$ the sum of n partial fractions:

$$\frac{A_1}{px + q} + \frac{A_2}{(px + q)^2} + \cdots + \frac{A_n}{(px + q)^n}.$$

4. Assign to each quadratic factor $(ax^2 + bx + c)^m$ the sum of m partial fractions:

$$\frac{B_1 x + C_1}{ax^2 + bx + c} + \frac{B_2 x + C_2}{(ax^2 + bx + c)^2} + \cdots +$$

$$\frac{B_m x + C_m}{(ax^2 + bx + c)^m}.$$

5. Apply algebraic methods to find the constants in the numerators of the partial fractions.

REVIEW EXERCISES

Determine whether the statement is true or false.

1. A system of equations with exactly one solution is consistent and has independent equations.   [8.1]

2. A system of two linear equations in two variables can have exactly two solutions.   [8.1]

3. For any $m \times n$ matrices $\mathbf{A}$ and $\mathbf{B}$, $\mathbf{A} + \mathbf{B} = \mathbf{B} + \mathbf{A}$. [8.4]

4. In general, matrix multiplication is commutative. [8.4]

In Exercises 5–12, match the equations or inequalities with one of the graphs (a)–(h), which follow.

a)

b)

c)

d)

e)

f)

g)

h)

5. $x + y = 7,$
$2x - y = 5$ [8.1]

6. $3x - 5y = -8,$
$4x + 3y = -1$ [8.1]

7. $y = 2x - 1,$
$4x - 2y = 2$ [8.1]

8. $6x - 3y = 5,$
$y = 2x + 3$ [8.1]

9. $y \le 3x - 4$ [8.7]

10. $2x - 3y \ge 6$ [8.7]

11. $x - y \le 3,$
$x + y \le 5$ [8.7]

12. $2x + \ y \ge 4,$
$3x - 5y \le 15$ [8.7]

Solve.

13. $5x - 3y = -4,$
$3x - \ y = -4$
[8.1]

14. $2x + 3y = 2,$
$5x - \ y = -29$
[8.1]

15. $x + \ 5y = 12,$
$5x + 25y = 12$
[8.1]

16. $x + \ y = -2,$
$-3x - 3y = 6$
[8.1]

17. $2x - 4y + 3z = -3,$
$-5x + 2y - \ z = 7,$
$3x + 2y - 2z = 4$ [8.2]

18. $x + 5y + 3z = 0,$
$3x - 2y + 4z = 0,$
$2x + 3y - \ z = 0$ [8.2]

19. $x - y = 5,$
$y - z = 6,$
$z - w = 7,$
$x + w = 8$ [8.2]

20. Classify each of the systems in Exercises 13–19 as consistent or inconsistent.   [8.1], [8.2]

21. Classify each of the systems in Exercises 13–19 as having dependent or independent equations. [8.1], [8.2]

Solve the system of equations using Gaussian elimination or Gauss–Jordan elimination.   [8.3]

22. $x + 2y = 5,$
$2x - 5y = -8$

23. $3x + 4y + \ 2z = 3,$
$5x - 2y - 13z = 3,$
$4x + 3y - \ 3z = 6$

24. $3x + 5y + \ z = 0,$
$2x - 4y - 3z = 0,$
$x + 3y + \ z = 0$

25. $w + \ x + \ y + \ z = -2,$
$-3w - 2x + 3y + 2z = 10,$
$2w + 3x + 2y - \ z = -12,$
$2w + 4x - \ y + \ z = 1$

26. *Coins.*   The value of 75 coins, consisting of nickels and dimes, is $5.95. How many of each kind are there?   [8.1]

27. *Investment.*   The Mendez family invested $5000, part at 3% and the remainder at 3.5%. The annual income from both investments is $167. What is the amount invested at each rate?   [8.1]

28. *Nutrition.*   A dietician must plan a breakfast menu that provides 460 Cal, 9 g of fat, and 55 mg of calcium. One plain bagel contains 200 Cal, 2 g of fat, and 29 mg of calcium. A one-tablespoon serving of cream cheese contains 100 Cal, 10 g of fat, and 24 mg of calcium. One banana contains 105 Cal, 1 g of fat, and 7 g of calcium. (*Source: Home and Garden Bulletin No. 72*, U.S. Government Printing Office, Washington D.C. 20402) How many servings of each are required to provide the desired nutritional values?   [8.2]

29. *Test Scores.*   A student has a total of 226 on three tests. The sum of the scores on the first and second tests exceeds the score on the third test by 62. The first score exceeds the second by 6. Find the three scores.   [8.2]

30. *Lowfat Ice Cream Consumption.*   The table below lists the per capita consumption of lowfat ice cream, in pounds, in the United States, represented as number of years since 2000.

Year, x	Lowfat Ice Cream Consumption (in pounds)
2000, 0	7.3
2002, 2	6.5
2003, 3	6.7

Source: U.S. Department of Agriculture, Economic Research Service, *Food Consumption, Prices, and Expenditures*

a) Use a system of equations to fit a quadratic function $f(x) = ax^2 + bx + c$ to the data. [8.2]
b) Use the function to estimate the per capita consumption of lowfat ice cream in 2005. [8.2]

For Exercises 31–38, let

$$A = \begin{bmatrix} 1 & -1 & 0 \\ 2 & 3 & -2 \\ -2 & 0 & 1 \end{bmatrix},$$

$$B = \begin{bmatrix} -1 & 0 & 6 \\ 1 & -2 & 0 \\ 0 & 1 & -3 \end{bmatrix},$$

and

$$C = \begin{bmatrix} -2 & 0 \\ 1 & 3 \end{bmatrix}.$$

Find each of the following, if possible.   [8.4]

31. $A + B$ **32.** $-3A$

33. $-A$ **34.** AB

35. $B + C$ **36.** $A - B$

37. BA **38.** $A + 3B$

39. *Food Service Management.*   The table below lists the cost per serving, in cents, for items on four menus that are served at an elder-care facility.

Menu	Meat	Potato	Vegetable	Salad	Dessert
1	46.1	5.9	10.1	8.5	11.4
2	54.6	4.6	9.6	7.6	10.6
3	48.9	5.5	12.7	9.4	9.3
4	51.3	4.8	11.3	6.9	12.7

On a particular day, a dietician orders 32 meals from menu 1, 19 from menu 2, 43 from menu 3, and 38 from menu 4.

a) Write the information in the table as a 4×5 matrix **M**. [8.4]
b) Write a row matrix **N** that represents the number of each menu ordered. [8.4]
c) Find the product **NM**. [8.4]
d) State what the entries of **NM** represent. [8.4]

Find $\mathbf{A}^{-1}$, *if it exists.*   [8.5]

40. $\mathbf{A} = \begin{bmatrix} -2 & 0 \\ 1 & 3 \end{bmatrix}$

41. $\mathbf{A} = \begin{bmatrix} 0 & 0 & 3 \\ 0 & -2 & 0 \\ 4 & 0 & 0 \end{bmatrix}$

42. $\mathbf{A} = \begin{bmatrix} 1 & 0 & 0 & 0 \\ 0 & 4 & -5 & 0 \\ 0 & 2 & 2 & 0 \\ 0 & 0 & 0 & 1 \end{bmatrix}$

43. Write a matrix equation equivalent to this system of equations: [8.4]

$$3x - 2y + 4z = 13,$$
$$x + 5y - 3z = 7,$$
$$2x - 3y + 7z = -8.$$

Solve the system of equations using the inverse of the coefficient matrix of the equivalent matrix equation.   [8.5]

44. $2x + 3y = 5,$
$3x + 5y = 11$

45. $5x - y + 2z = 17,$
$3x + 2y - 3z = -16,$
$4x - 3y - z = 5$

46. $w - x - y + z = -1,$
$2w + 3x - 2y - z = 2,$
$-w + 5x + 4y - 2z = 3,$
$3w - 2x + 5y + 3z = 4$

Evaluate the determinant.   [8.6]

47. $\begin{vmatrix} 1 & -2 \\ 3 & 4 \end{vmatrix}$

48. $\begin{vmatrix} \sqrt{3} & -5 \\ -3 & -\sqrt{3} \end{vmatrix}$

49. $\begin{vmatrix} 2 & -1 & 1 \\ 1 & 2 & -1 \\ 3 & 4 & -3 \end{vmatrix}$

50. $\begin{vmatrix} 1 & -1 & 2 \\ -1 & 2 & 0 \\ -1 & 3 & 1 \end{vmatrix}$

Solve using Cramer's rule.   [8.6]

51. $5x - 2y = 19,$
$7x + 3y = 15$

52. $x + y = 4,$
$4x + 3y = 11$

53. $3x - 2y + z = 5,$
$4x - 5y - z = -1,$
$3x + 2y - z = 4$

54. $2x - y - z = 2,$
$3x + 2y + 2z = 10,$
$x - 5y - 3z = -2$

Graph.   [8.7]

55. $y \le 3x + 6$

56. $4x - 3y \ge 12$

57. Graph this system of inequalities and find the coordinates of any vertices formed.   [8.7]

$$2x + y \ge 9,$$
$$4x + 3y \ge 23,$$
$$x + 3y \ge 8,$$
$$x \ge 0,$$
$$y \ge 0$$

58. Find the maximum and minimum values of $T = 6x + 10y$ subject to

$$x + y \le 10,$$
$$5x + 10y \ge 50,$$
$$x \ge 2,$$
$$y \ge 0.$$ [8.7]

59. *Maximizing a Test Score.* Marita is taking a test that contains questions in group A worth 7 points each and questions in group B worth 12 points each. The total number of questions answered must be at least 8. If Marita knows that group A questions take 8 min each and group B questions take 10 min each and the maximum time for the test is 80 min, how many questions from each group must she answer correctly in order to maximize her score? What is the maximum score?   [8.7]

Decompose into partial fractions.   [8.8]

60. $\dfrac{5}{(x + 2)^2(x + 1)}$

61. $\dfrac{-8x + 23}{2x^2 + 5x - 12}$

62. Solve: $2x + y = 7,$
$x - 2y = 6.$ [8.1]

A. x and y are both positive numbers.
B. x and y are both negative numbers.
C. x is positive and y is negative.
D. x is negative and y is positive.

63. Which is *not* a row-equivalent operation on a matrix?   [8.3]

   A. Interchange any two columns.
   B. Interchange any two rows.
   C. Add two rows.
   D. Multiply each entry in a row by -3.

Collaborative Discussion and Writing

64. Write a problem for a classmate to solve that can be translated to a system of equations. Devise the problem so that the solution is "The caterer sold 20 cheese trays and 35 seafood trays."   [8.1]

65. For square matrices **A** and **B**, is it true, in general, that $(\mathbf{AB})^2 = \mathbf{A}^2\mathbf{B}^2$? Explain.   [8.4]

Synthesis

66. One year, Don invested a total of $40,000, part at 4%, part at 5%, and the rest at $5\frac{1}{2}$%. The total amount of interest received on the investments was $1990. The interest received on the $5\frac{1}{2}$% investment was $590 more than the interest received on the 4% investment. How much was invested at each rate?   [8.2]

Solve.

67. $\dfrac{2}{3x} + \dfrac{4}{5y} = 8,$

$\dfrac{5}{4x} - \dfrac{3}{2y} = -6$
   [8.1]

68. $\dfrac{3}{x} - \dfrac{4}{y} + \dfrac{1}{z} = -2,$

$\dfrac{5}{x} + \dfrac{1}{y} - \dfrac{2}{z} = 1,$

$\dfrac{7}{x} + \dfrac{3}{y} + \dfrac{2}{z} = 19$
   [8.2]

Graph.   [8.7]

69. $|x| - |y| \le 1$

70. $|xy| > 1$

CHAPTER 8 TEST

Solve. Use any method. Also determine whether each system is consistent or inconsistent and whether the equations are dependent or independent.

1. $3x + 2y = 1,$
$2x - y = -11$

2. $2x - y = 3,$
$2y = 4x - 6$

3. $x - y = 4,$
$3y = 3x - 8$

4. $2x - 3y = 8,$
$5x - 2y = 9$

Solve.

5. $4x + 2y + z = 4,$
$3x - y + 5z = 4,$
$5x + 3y - 3z = -2$

6. *Ticket Sales.*   One evening 750 tickets were sold for Shortridge Community College's spring musical. Tickets cost $3 for students and $5 for nonstudents. Total receipts were $3066. How many of each type of ticket were sold?

7. Tricia, Maria, and Antonio can process 352 telephone orders per day. Tricia and Maria together can process 224 orders per day while Tricia and Antonio together can process 248 orders per day. How many orders can each of them process alone?

For Exercises 8–13, let

$$\mathbf{A} = \begin{bmatrix} 1 & -1 & 3 \\ -2 & 5 & 2 \end{bmatrix}, \quad \mathbf{B} = \begin{bmatrix} -5 & 1 \\ -2 & 4 \end{bmatrix}, \quad \text{and}$$

$$\mathbf{C} = \begin{bmatrix} 3 & -4 \\ -1 & 0 \end{bmatrix}.$$

Find each of the following, if possible.

8. $\mathbf{B} + \mathbf{C}$

9. $\mathbf{A} - \mathbf{C}$

10. $\mathbf{CB}$

11. $\mathbf{AB}$

12. $2\mathbf{A}$

13. $\mathbf{C}^{-1}$

14. *Food Service Management.* The table below lists the cost per serving, in cents, for items on three lunch menus served at a senior citizens' center.

Menu	Main Dish	Side Dish	Dessert
1	49	10	13
2	43	12	11
3	51	8	12

On a particular day, 26 Menu 1 meals, 18 Menu 2 meals, and 23 Menu 3 meals are served.

a) Write the information in the table as a 3×3 matrix $\mathbf{M}$.
b) Write a row matrix $\mathbf{N}$ that represents the number of each menu served.
c) Find the product $\mathbf{NM}$.
d) State what the entries of $\mathbf{NM}$ represent.

15. Write a matrix equation equivalent to the system of equations

$$3x - 4y + 2z = -8,$$
$$2x + 3y + z = 7,$$
$$x - 5y - 3z = 3.$$

16. Solve the system of equations using the inverse of the coefficient matrix of the equivalent matrix equation.

$$3x + 2y + 6z = 2,$$
$$x + y + 2z = 1,$$
$$2x + 2y + 5z = 3$$

Evaluate the determinant.

17. $\begin{vmatrix} 3 & -5 \\ 8 & 7 \end{vmatrix}$

18. $\begin{vmatrix} 2 & -1 & 4 \\ -3 & 1 & -2 \\ 5 & 3 & -1 \end{vmatrix}$

19. Solve using Cramer's rule. Show your work.

$$5x + 2y = -1,$$
$$7x + 6y = 1$$

20. Graph: $3x + 4y \leq -12$.

21. Find the maximum and minimum values of $Q = 2x + 3y$ subject to

$$x + y \leq 6,$$
$$2x - 3y \geq -3,$$
$$x \geq 1,$$
$$y \geq 0.$$

22. *Maximizing Profit.* Casey's Cakes prepares pound cakes and carrot cakes. In a given week, at most 100 cakes can be prepared, of which 25 pound cakes and 15 carrot cakes are required by regular customers. The profit from each pound cake is $3 and the profit from each carrot cake is $4. How many of each type of cake should be prepared in order to maximize the profit?

23. Decompose into partial fractions:

$$\frac{3x - 11}{x^2 + 2x - 3}.$$

Synthesis

24. Three solutions of the equation $Ax - By = Cz - 8$ are $(2, -2, 2)$, $(-3, -1, 1)$, and $(4, 2, 9)$. Find A, B, and C.

Analytic Geometry Topics

APPLICATION

Ted Hansen of Hansen Woodworking Designs has been commissioned to make a rectangular tabletop with an area of $\sqrt{2}$ m² and a diagonal of $\sqrt{3}$ m for the Decorators' Show House. Find the dimensions of the tabletop.

This problem appears as Exercise 60 in Section 9.4.

9.1 The Parabola

✦   Given an equation of a parabola, complete the square, if necessary, and then find the vertex, the focus, and the directrix and graph the parabola.

A **conic section** is formed when a right circular cone with two parts, called *nappes*, is intersected by a plane. One of four types of curves can be formed: a parabola, a circle, an ellipse, or a hyperbola.

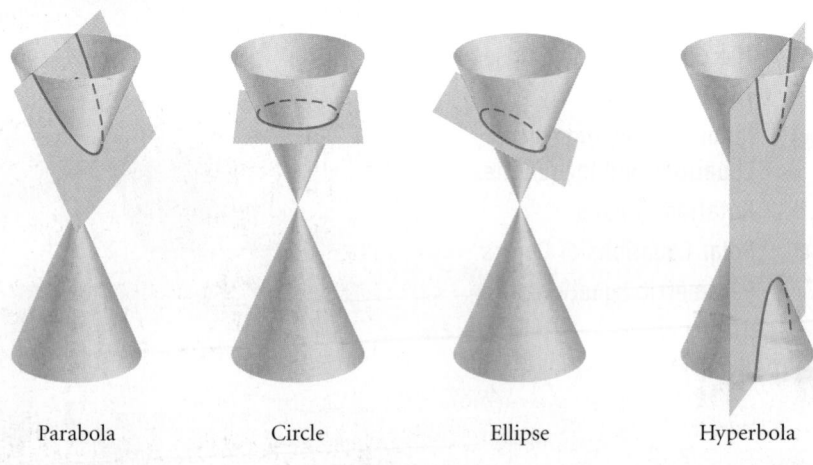

Parabola   Circle   Ellipse   Hyperbola

Conic Sections

Conic sections can be defined algebraically using second-degree equations of the form $Ax^2 + Bxy + Cy^2 + Dx + Ey + F = 0$. In addition, they can be defined geometrically as a set of points that satisfy certain conditions.

✦ Parabolas

In Section 2.4, we saw that the graph of the quadratic function $f(x) = ax^2 + bx + c$, $a \neq 0$, is a parabola. A parabola can be defined geometrically.

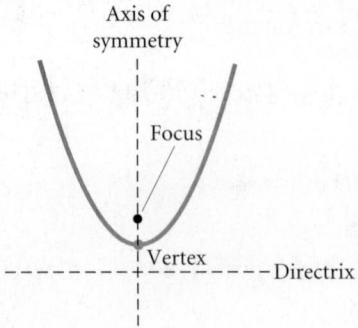

> ### Parabola
> A **parabola** is the set of all points in a plane equidistant from a fixed line (the **directrix**) and a fixed point not on the line (the **focus**).

The line that is perpendicular to the directrix and contains the focus is the **axis of symmetry.** The **vertex** is the midpoint of the segment between the focus and the directrix. (See the figure at left.)

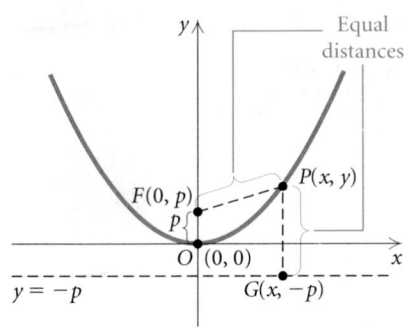

Figure 1

Let's derive the standard equation of a parabola with vertex $(0,0)$ and directrix $y = -p$, where $p > 0$. We place the coordinate axes as shown in Fig. 1. The y-axis is the axis of symmetry and contains the focus F. The distance from the focus to the vertex is the same as the distance from the vertex to the directrix. Thus the coordinates of F are $(0, p)$.

Let $P(x, y)$ be any point on the parabola and consider $\overline{PG}$ perpendicular to the line $y = -p$. The coordinates of G are $(x, -p)$. By the definition of a parabola,

$$PF = PG. \qquad \text{The distance from } P \text{ to the focus is the same as the distance from } P \text{ to the directrix.}$$

Then using the distance formula, we have

$$\sqrt{(x-0)^2 + (y-p)^2} = \sqrt{(x-x)^2 + [y-(-p)]^2}$$
$$x^2 + y^2 - 2py + p^2 = y^2 + 2py + p^2 \qquad \text{Squaring both sides and squaring the binomials}$$
$$x^2 = 4py.$$

We have shown that if $P(x, y)$ is on the parabola shown in Fig. 1, then its coordinates satisfy this equation. The converse is also true, but we will not prove it here.

Note that if $p > 0$, as above, the graph opens up. If $p < 0$, the graph opens down.

The equation of a parabola with vertex $(0,0)$ and directrix $x = -p$ is derived similarly. Such a parabola opens either to the right ($p > 0$), as shown in Fig. 2, or to the left ($p < 0$).

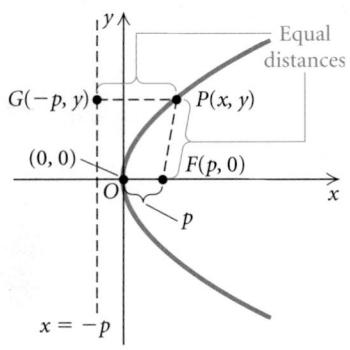

Figure 2

> ### Standard Equation of a Parabola with Vertex at the Origin
>
> The standard equation of a parabola with vertex $(0,0)$ and directrix $y = -p$ is
>
> $$x^2 = 4py.$$
>
> The focus is $(0, p)$ and the y-axis is the axis of symmetry.
>
> The standard equation of a parabola with vertex $(0,0)$ and directrix $x = -p$ is
>
> $$y^2 = 4px.$$
>
> The focus is $(p, 0)$ and the x-axis is the axis of symmetry.

EXAMPLE 1 Find the focus and the directrix of the parabola $y = -\frac{1}{12}x^2$. Then graph the parabola.

Solution We write $y = -\frac{1}{12}x^2$ in the form $x^2 = 4py$:

$$-\tfrac{1}{12}x^2 = y \qquad \text{Given equation}$$
$$x^2 = -12y \qquad \text{Multiplying by } -12 \text{ on both sides}$$
$$x^2 = 4(-3)y. \qquad \text{Standard form}$$

Thus, $p = -3$, so the focus is $(0, p)$, or $(0, -3)$. The directrix is $y = -p = -(-3) = 3$.

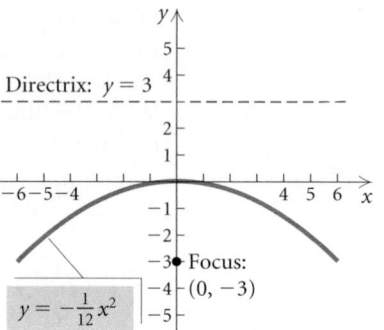

EXAMPLE 2   Find an equation of the parabola with vertex $(0,0)$ and focus $(5,0)$. Then graph the parabola.

Solution   The focus is on the x-axis so the line of symmetry is the x-axis. Thus the equation is of the type

$$y^2 = 4px.$$

Since the focus $(5,0)$ is 5 units to the right of the vertex, $p = 5$ and the equation is

$$y^2 = 4(5)x, \quad \text{or} \quad y^2 = 20x.$$

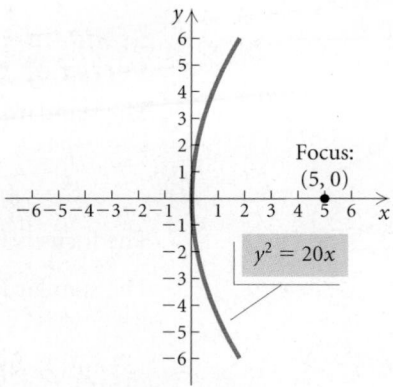

✦ Finding Standard Form by Completing the Square

If a parabola with vertex at the origin is translated horizontally $|h|$ units and vertically $|k|$ units, it has an equation as follows.

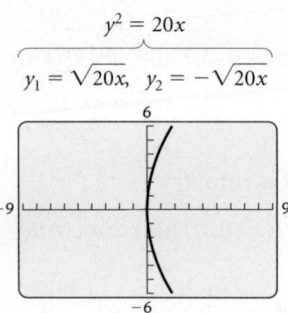

Standard Equation of a Parabola with Vertex (*h,k*) and Vertical Axis of Symmetry

The standard equation of a parabola with vertex (h, k) and vertical axis of symmetry is

$$(x - h)^2 = 4p(y - k),$$

where the vertex is (h, k), the focus is $(h, k + p)$, and the directrix is $y = k - p$.

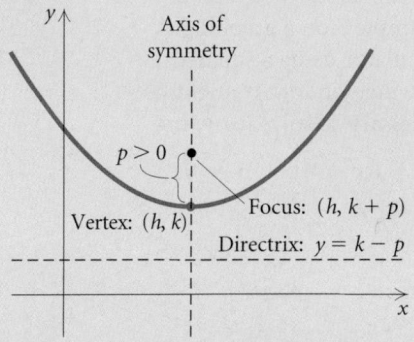

(When $p < 0$, the parabola opens down.)

Standard Equation of a Parabola with Vertex (*h,k*) and Horizontal Axis of Symmetry

The standard equation of a parabola with vertex (h, k) and horizontal axis of symmetry is

$$(y - k)^2 = 4p(x - h),$$

where the vertex is (h, k), the focus is $(h + p, k)$, and the directrix is $x = h - p.$

(When $p < 0$, the parabola opens to the left.)

COMPLETING THE SQUARE

REVIEW SECTION **2.3.**

STUDY TIP

There is a video presentation for each section of the textbook. Make time to visit your math lab or media center to view these presentations. Pause the video and take notes or work through the examples. You can proceed at your own pace, replaying all or part of a presentation as many times as you need to.

We can complete the square on equations of the form

$$y = ax^2 + bx + c \quad \text{or} \quad x = ay^2 + by + c$$

in order to write them in standard form.

EXAMPLE 3   For the parabola

$$x^2 + 6x + 4y + 5 = 0,$$

find the vertex, the focus, and the directrix. Then draw the graph.

Solution   We first complete the square:

$$x^2 + 6x + 4y + 5 = 0$$
$$x^2 + 6x \qquad = -4y - 5 \qquad \text{Subtracting } 4y \text{ and } 5 \text{ on both sides}$$
$$x^2 + 6x + 9 = -4y - 5 + 9 \qquad \text{Adding 9 on both sides to complete the square on the left side}$$

$$x^2 + 6x + 9 = -4y + 4$$
$$(x + 3)^2 = -4(y - 1) \qquad \text{Factoring}$$
$$[x - (-3)]^2 = 4(-1)(y - 1). \qquad \text{Writing standard form: } (x - h)^2 = 4p(y - k)$$

We see that $h = -3$, $k = 1$, and $p = -1$, so we have the following:

Vertex (h, k): $(-3, 1)$;
Focus $(h, k + p)$: $(-3, 1 + (-1))$, or $(-3, 0)$;
Directrix $y = k - p$: $y = 1 - (-1)$, or $y = 2$.

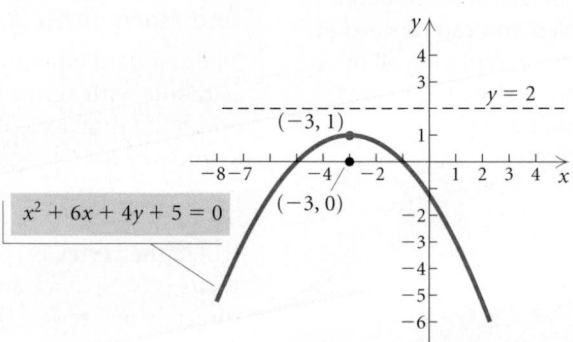

> Now Try Exercise 23.

EXAMPLE 4   For the parabola

$$y^2 - 2y - 8x - 31 = 0,$$

find the vertex, the focus, and the directrix. Then draw the graph.

Solution   We first complete the square:

$$y^2 - 2y - 8x - 31 = 0$$
$$y^2 - 2y \qquad = 8x + 31 \qquad \text{Adding } 8x \text{ and } 31 \text{ on both sides}$$
$$y^2 - 2y + 1 = 8x + 31 + 1 \qquad \text{Adding 1 on both sides to complete the square on the left side}$$

$$y^2 - 2y + 1 = 8x + 32$$
$$(y - 1)^2 = 8(x + 4) \qquad \text{Factoring}$$
$$(y - 1)^2 = 4(2)[x - (-4)]. \qquad \text{Writing standard form: } (y - k)^2 = 4p(x - h)$$

We see that $h = -4$, $k = 1$, and $p = 2$, so we have the following:

Vertex (h, k): $(-4, 1)$;
Focus $(h + p, k)$: $(-4 + 2, 1)$, or $(-2, 1)$;
Directrix $x = h - p$: $x = -4 - 2$, or $x = -6$.

> Now Try Exercise 29.

TECHNOLOGY
CONNECTION

$$y^2 - 2y - 8x - 31 = 0$$

$$y_1 = \frac{2 + \sqrt{32x + 128}}{2},$$

$$y_2 = \frac{2 - \sqrt{32x + 128}}{2}$$

We can check the graph in Example 4 on a graphing calculator using a squared viewing window. If the Conics application is available on the APPS menu, we can use the values of h, k, and p from the standard form of the equation to draw the graph. If not, we can begin by solving the original equation for y using the quadratic formula:

$$y^2 - 2y - 8x - 31 = 0$$
$$y^2 - 2y + (-8x - 31) = 0$$
$$a = 1, \quad b = -2, \quad c = -8x - 31$$
$$y = \frac{-(-2) \pm \sqrt{(-2)^2 - 4 \cdot 1(-8x - 31)}}{2 \cdot 1}$$
$$y = \frac{2 \pm \sqrt{32x + 128}}{2}.$$

We now graph

$$y_1 = \frac{2 + \sqrt{32x + 128}}{2} \quad \text{and} \quad y_2 = \frac{2 - \sqrt{32x + 128}}{2}.$$

✦ Applications

Parabolas have many applications. For example, cross sections of car headlights, flashlights, and searchlights are parabolas. The bulb is located at the focus and light from that point is reflected outward parallel to the axis of symmetry. Satellite dishes and field microphones used at sporting events often have parabolic cross sections. Incoming radio waves or sound waves parallel to the axis are reflected into the focus. Cables hung between structures in suspension bridges, such as the Golden Gate Bridge, form parabolas. When a cable supports only its own weight, however, it forms a curve called a *catenary* rather than a parabola.

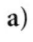

9.1 EXERCISE SET

In Exercises 1–6, match the equation with one of the graphs (a)–(f), which follow.

a)

b)

c)

d)

e)

f)

1. $x^2 = 8y$

2. $y^2 = -10x$

3. $(y - 2)^2 = -3(x + 4)$

4. $(x + 1)^2 = 5(y - 2)$

5. $13x^2 - 8y - 9 = 0$

6. $41x + 6y^2 = 12$

Find the vertex, the focus, and the directrix. Then draw the graph.

7. $x^2 = 20y$ **8.** $x^2 = 16y$

9. $y^2 = -6x$ **10.** $y^2 = -2x$

11. $x^2 - 4y = 0$ **12.** $y^2 + 4x = 0$

13. $x = 2y^2$ **14.** $y = \frac{1}{2}x^2$

Find an equation of a parabola satisfying the given conditions.

15. Focus $(4, 0)$, directrix $x = -4$

16. Focus $\left(0, \frac{1}{4}\right)$, directrix $y = -\frac{1}{4}$

17. Focus $(0, -\pi)$, directrix $y = \pi$

18. Focus $\left(-\sqrt{2}, 0\right)$, directrix $x = \sqrt{2}$

19. Focus $(3, 2)$, directrix $x = -4$

20. Focus $(-2, 3)$, directrix $y = -3$

Find the vertex, the focus, and the directrix. Then draw the graph.

21. $(x + 2)^2 = -6(y - 1)$

22. $(y - 3)^2 = -20(x + 2)$

23. $x^2 + 2x + 2y + 7 = 0$

24. $y^2 + 6y - x + 16 = 0$

25. $x^2 - y - 2 = 0$

26. $x^2 - 4x - 2y = 0$

27. $y = x^2 + 4x + 3$

28. $y = x^2 + 6x + 10$

29. $y^2 - y - x + 6 = 0$

30. $y^2 + y - x - 4 = 0$

31. *Satellite Dish.* An engineer designs a satellite dish with a parabolic cross section. The dish is 15 ft wide at the opening and the focus is placed 4 ft from the vertex.

a) Position a coordinate system with the origin at the vertex and the *x*-axis on the parabola's axis of symmetry and find an equation of the parabola.

b) Find the depth of the satellite dish at the vertex.

32. *Headlight Mirror.*   A car headlight mirror has a parabolic cross section with diameter 6 in. and depth 1 in.

6 in.   Focus

⊢1 in.

a) Position a coordinate system with the origin at the vertex and the *x*-axis on the parabola's axis of symmetry and find an equation of the parabola.

b) How far from the vertex should the bulb be positioned if it is to be placed at the focus?

33. *Spotlight.*   A spotlight has a parabolic cross section that is 4 ft wide at the opening and 1.5 ft deep at the vertex. How far from the vertex is the focus?

34. *Field Microphone.*   A field microphone used at a football game has a parabolic cross section and is 18 in. deep. The focus is 4 in. from the vertex. Find the width of the microphone at the opening.

Technology Connection

Use a graphing calculator to find the vertex, the focus, and the directrix of each of the following.

35. $4.5x^2 - 7.8x + 9.7y = 0$

36. $134.1y^2 + 43.4x - 316.6y - 122.4 = 0$

Collaborative Discussion and Writing

37. Is a parabola always the graph of a function? Why or why not?

38. Explain how the distance formula is used to find the standard equation of a parabola.

Skill Maintenance

Consider the following linear equations. Without graphing them, answer the questions below.

a) $y = 2x$
b) $y = \frac{1}{3}x + 5$
c) $y = -3x - 2$
d) $y = -0.9x + 7$
e) $y = -5x + 3$
f) $y = x + 4$
g) $8x - 4y = 7$
h) $3x + 6y = 2$

39. Which has/have *x*-intercept $\left(\frac{2}{3}, 0\right)$?

40. Which has/have *y*-intercept $(0, 7)$?

41. Which slant up from left to right?

42. Which has the least steep slant?

43. Which has/have slope $\frac{1}{3}$?

44. Which, if any, contain the point $(3, 7)$?

45. Which, if any, are parallel?

46. Which, if any, are perpendicular?

Synthesis

47. Find an equation of the parabola with a vertical axis of symmetry and vertex $(-1, 2)$ and containing the point $(-3, 1)$.

48. Find an equation of a parabola with a horizontal axis of symmetry and vertex $(-2, 1)$ and containing the point $(-3, 5)$.

49. *Suspension Bridge.*   The cables of a 200-ft portion of the roadbed of a suspension bridge are positioned as shown below. Vertical cables are to be spaced every 20 ft along this portion of the roadbed. Calculate the lengths of these vertical cables.

10 ft

50 ft

←——— 200 ft ———→

9.2 The Circle and the Ellipse

◆ Given an equation of a circle, complete the square, if necessary, and then find the center and the radius and graph the circle.

◆ Given an equation of an ellipse, complete the square, if necessary, and then find the center, the vertices, and the foci and graph the ellipse.

◆ Circles

We can define a circle geometrically.

Circle

A **circle** is the set of all points in a plane that are at a fixed distance from a fixed point (the **center**) in the plane.

CIRCLES

REVIEW SECTION **1.1.**

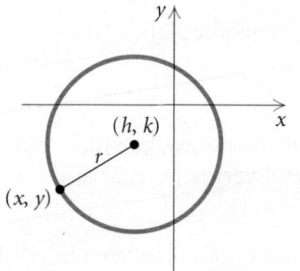

Circles were introduced in Section 1.1. Recall the standard equation of a circle with center (h, k) and radius r.

Standard Equation of a Circle

The standard equation of a circle with center (h, k) and radius r is

$$(x - h)^2 + (y - k)^2 = r^2.$$

EXAMPLE 1 For the circle

$$x^2 + y^2 - 16x + 14y + 32 = 0,$$

find the center and the radius. Then graph the circle.

Solution First, we complete the square twice:

$$x^2 + y^2 - 16x + 14y + 32 = 0$$
$$x^2 - 16x \qquad + y^2 + 14y \qquad = -32$$
$$x^2 - 16x + 64 + y^2 + 14y + 49 = -32 + 64 + 49$$

$\left[\frac{1}{2}(-16)\right]^2 = (-8)^2 = 64$ and $\left(\frac{1}{2} \cdot 14\right)^2 = 7^2 = 49$; adding 64 and 49 on both sides to complete the square twice on the left side

$$(x - 8)^2 + (y + 7)^2 = 81$$
$$(x - 8)^2 + [y - (-7)]^2 = 9^2. \qquad \text{Writing standard form}$$

The center is $(8, -7)$ and the radius is 9. We graph the circle.

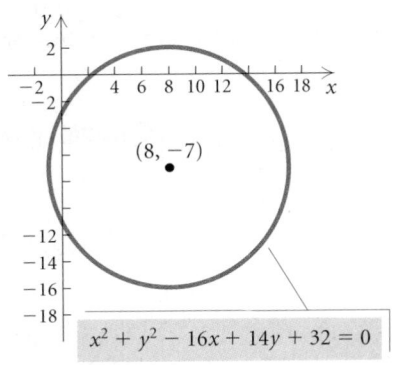

$$x^2 + y^2 - 16x + 14y + 32 = 0$$

▶ Now Try Exercise 7.

TECHNOLOGY CONNECTION

To use a graphing calculator to graph the circle in Example 1, it might be necessary to solve for y first. The original equation can be solved using the quadratic formula, or the standard form of the equation can be solved using the principle of square roots. The second alternative is illustrated here:

$$(x - 8)^2 + (y + 7)^2 = 81$$

$$(y + 7)^2 = 81 - (x - 8)^2$$

$$y + 7 = \pm\sqrt{81 - (x - 8)^2} \qquad \begin{array}{l}\text{Using the}\\\text{principle of}\\\text{square roots}\end{array}$$

$$y = -7 \pm \sqrt{81 - (x - 8)^2}.$$

Then we graph

$$y_1 = -7 + \sqrt{81 - (x - 8)^2}$$

and

$$y_2 = -7 - \sqrt{81 - (x - 8)^2}$$

in a squared viewing window.

If the Circle application is available on the APPS menu, we can use the equation in the form

$$x^2 + y^2 - 16x + 14y + 32 = 0$$

to obtain the graph.

Some graphing calculators have a DRAW feature that provides a quick way to graph a circle when the center and the radius are known. This feature is described on p. 68.

$$(x - 8)^2 + (y + 7)^2 = 81$$

$$y_1 = -7 + \sqrt{81 - (x - 8)^2},$$
$$y_2 = -7 - \sqrt{81 - (x - 8)^2}$$

✦ Ellipses

We have studied two conic sections, the parabola and the circle. Now we turn our attention to a third, the *ellipse*.

> ### *Ellipse*
>
> An **ellipse** is the set of all points in a plane, the sum of whose distances from two fixed points (the **foci**) is constant. The **center** of an ellipse is the midpoint of the segment between the foci.

We can draw an ellipse by first placing two thumbtacks in a piece of cardboard. These are the foci (singular, *focus*). We then attach a piece of string to the tacks. Its length is the constant sum of the distances $d_1 + d_2$ from the foci to any point on the ellipse. Next, we trace a curve with a pen held tight against the string. The figure traced is an ellipse.

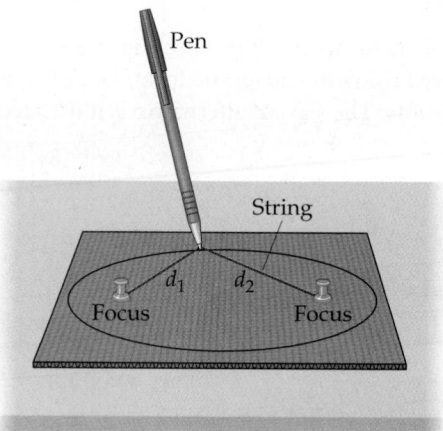

Let's first consider the ellipse shown below with center at the origin. The points F_1 and F_2 are the foci. The segment $\overline{A'A}$ is the **major axis,** and the points A' and A are the **vertices.** The segment $\overline{B'B}$ is the **minor axis,** and the points B' and B are the **y-intercepts.** Note that the major axis of an ellipse is longer than the minor axis.

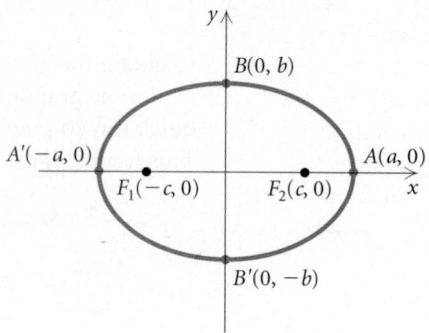

Standard Equation of an Ellipse with Center at the Origin

Major Axis Horizontal

$$\frac{x^2}{a^2} + \frac{y^2}{b^2} = 1, \quad a > b > 0$$

Vertices: $(-a, 0), (a, 0)$

y-intercepts:
$(0, -b), (0, b)$

Foci: $(-c, 0), (c, 0)$,
where $c^2 = a^2 - b^2$

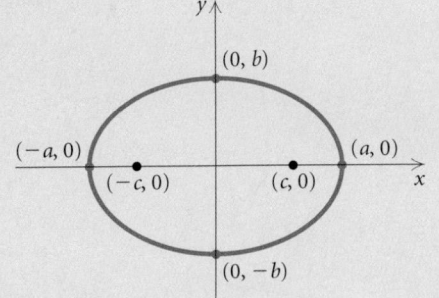

Major Axis Vertical

$$\frac{x^2}{b^2} + \frac{y^2}{a^2} = 1, \quad a > b > 0$$

Vertices: $(0, -a), (0, a)$

x-intercepts:
$(-b, 0), (b, 0)$

Foci: $(0, -c), (0, c)$,
where $c^2 = a^2 - b^2$

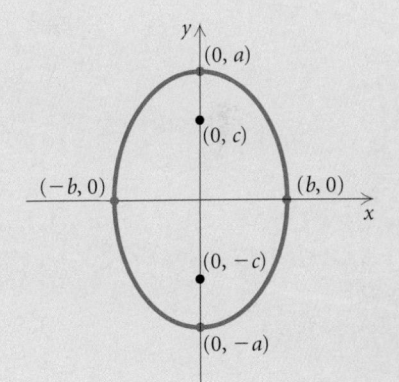

EXAMPLE 2 Find the standard equation of the ellipse with vertices $(-5, 0)$ and $(5, 0)$ and foci $(-3, 0)$ and $(3, 0)$. Then graph the ellipse.

Solution Since the foci are on the x-axis and the origin is the midpoint of the segment between them, the major axis is horizontal and $(0, 0)$ is the center of the ellipse. Thus the equation is of the form

$$\frac{x^2}{a^2} + \frac{y^2}{b^2} = 1.$$

Since the vertices are $(-5, 0)$ and $(5, 0)$ and the foci are $(-3, 0)$ and $(3, 0)$, we know that $a = 5$ and $c = 3$. These values can be used to find b^2:

$$c^2 = a^2 - b^2$$
$$3^2 = 5^2 - b^2$$
$$9 = 25 - b^2$$
$$b^2 = 16.$$

Thus the equation of the ellipse is

$$\frac{x^2}{5^2} + \frac{y^2}{4^2} = 1, \quad \text{or} \quad \frac{x^2}{25} + \frac{y^2}{16} = 1.$$

STUDY TIP

If you are finding it difficult to master a particular topic or concept, talk about it with a classmate. Verbalizing your questions about the material might help clarify it for you. If your classmate is also finding the material difficult, it is possible that the majority of the students in your class are confused, and you can ask your instructor to explain the concept again.

To graph the ellipse, we plot the vertices $(-5, 0)$ and $(5, 0)$. Since $b^2 = 16$, we know that $b = 4$ and the y-intercepts are $(0, -4)$ and $(0, 4)$. We plot these points as well and connect the four points we have plotted with a smooth curve.

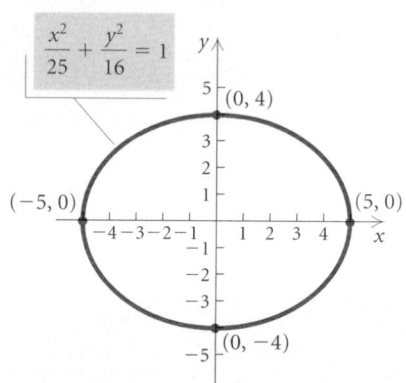

$$\frac{x^2}{25} + \frac{y^2}{16} = 1$$

▶ Now Try Exercise 31.

TECHNOLOGY CONNECTION

$$\frac{x^2}{25} + \frac{y^2}{16} = 1$$

$$y_1 = -\sqrt{\frac{400 - 16x^2}{25}},$$

$$y_2 = \sqrt{\frac{400 - 16x^2}{25}}$$

To draw the graph in Example 2 using a graphing calculator, it might be necessary to solve for y first:

$$y = \pm \sqrt{\frac{400 - 16x^2}{25}}.$$

Then we graph

$$y_1 = -\sqrt{\frac{400 - 16x^2}{25}} \quad \text{and} \quad y_2 = \sqrt{\frac{400 - 16x^2}{25}}$$

or

$$y_1 = -\sqrt{\frac{400 - 16x^2}{25}} \quad \text{and} \quad y_2 = -y_1$$

in a squared viewing window.

The Ellipse application on the APPS menu of some calculators can be used to graph this ellipse without first solving for y.

EXAMPLE 3 For the ellipse

$$9x^2 + 4y^2 = 36,$$

find the vertices and the foci. Then draw the graph.

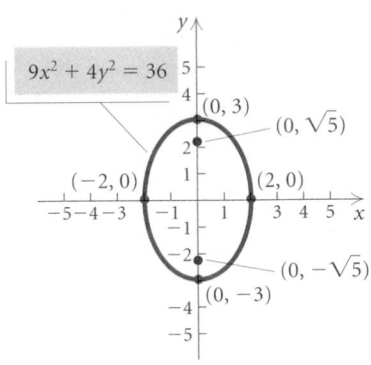

Solution We first find standard form:

$$9x^2 + 4y^2 = 36$$

$$\frac{9x^2}{36} + \frac{4y^2}{36} = \frac{36}{36} \qquad \text{Dividing by 36 on both sides to get 1 on the right side}$$

$$\frac{x^2}{4} + \frac{y^2}{9} = 1$$

$$\frac{x^2}{2^2} + \frac{y^2}{3^2} = 1. \qquad \text{Writing standard form}$$

Thus, $a = 3$ and $b = 2$. The major axis is vertical, so the vertices are $(0, -3)$ and $(0, 3)$. Since we know that $c^2 = a^2 - b^2$, we have $c^2 = 3^2 - 2^2 = 5$, so $c = \sqrt{5}$ and the foci are $\left(0, -\sqrt{5}\right)$ and $\left(0, \sqrt{5}\right)$.

To graph the ellipse, we plot the vertices. Note also that since $b = 2$, the x-intercepts are $(-2, 0)$ and $(2, 0)$. We plot these points as well and connect the four points we have plotted with a smooth curve.

▷ **Now Try Exercise 25.**

If the center of an ellipse is not at the origin but at some point (h, k), then we can think of an ellipse with center at the origin being translated horizontally $|h|$ units and vertically $|k|$ units.

Standard Equation of an Ellipse with Center at (h, k)

Major Axis Horizontal

$$\frac{(x - h)^2}{a^2} + \frac{(y - k)^2}{b^2} = 1, \ a > b > 0$$

Vertices: $(h - a, k), (h + a, k)$

Length of minor axis: $2b$

Foci: $(h - c, k), (h + c, k)$, where $c^2 = a^2 - b^2$

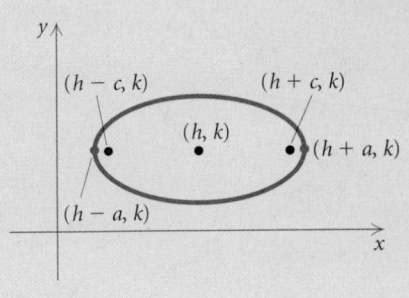

Major Axis Vertical

$$\frac{(x - h)^2}{b^2} + \frac{(y - k)^2}{a^2} = 1, \ a > b > 0$$

Vertices: $(h, k - a), (h, k + a)$

Length of minor axis: $2b$

Foci: $(h, k - c), (h, k + c)$, where $c^2 = a^2 - b^2$

EXAMPLE 4 For the ellipse

$$4x^2 + y^2 + 24x - 2y + 21 = 0,$$

find the center, the vertices, and the foci. Then draw the graph.

Solution   First, we complete the square twice to get standard form:

$$4x^2 + y^2 + 24x - 2y + 21 = 0$$

$$4x^2 + 24x + y^2 - 2y + 21 = 0 \qquad \text{Rearranging}$$

$$4(x^2 + 6x \quad\;\;) + (y^2 - 2y \quad\;\;) = -21$$

$$4(x^2 + 6x + 9) + (y^2 - 2y + 1) = -21 + 4 \cdot 9 + 1$$

> Completing the square twice by adding $4 \cdot 9$ and 1 on both sides

$$4(x + 3)^2 + (y - 1)^2 = 16$$

$$\frac{1}{16}[4(x + 3)^2 + (y - 1)^2] = \frac{1}{16} \cdot 16$$

$$\frac{(x + 3)^2}{4} + \frac{(y - 1)^2}{16} = 1$$

$$\frac{[x - (-3)]^2}{2^2} + \frac{(y - 1)^2}{4^2} = 1.$$

> Writing standard form:
> $$\frac{(x - h)^2}{b^2} + \frac{(y - k)^2}{a^2} = 1$$

The center is $(-3, 1)$. Note that $a = 4$ and $b = 2$. The major axis is vertical, so the vertices are 4 units above and below the center:

$$(-3, 1 + 4) \text{ and } (-3, 1 - 4), \quad \text{or} \quad (-3, 5) \text{ and } (-3, -3).$$

We know that $c^2 = a^2 - b^2$, so $c^2 = 4^2 - 2^2 = 12$ and $c = \sqrt{12}$, or $2\sqrt{3}$. Then the foci are $2\sqrt{3}$ units above and below the center:

$$\left(-3, 1 + 2\sqrt{3}\right) \quad \text{and} \quad \left(-3, 1 - 2\sqrt{3}\right).$$

To graph the ellipse, we plot the vertices. Note also that since $b = 2$, two other points on the graph are the endpoints of the minor axis, 2 units right and left of the center:

$$(-3 + 2, 1) \text{ and } (-3 - 2, 1), \quad \text{or} \quad (-1, 1) \text{ and } (-5, 1).$$

We plot these points as well and connect the four points with a smooth curve.

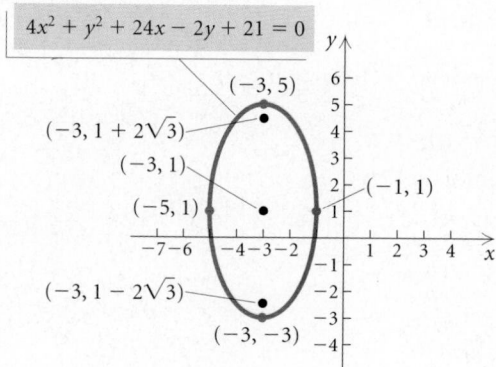

Now Try Exercise 43.

✦ Applications

An exciting medical application of an ellipse is a device called a *lithotripter*. One type of this device uses electromagnetic technology to generate a shock wave to pulverize kidney stones. The wave originates at one focus of an ellipse and is reflected to the kidney stone, which is positioned at the other focus. Recovery time following the use of this technique is much shorter than with conventional surgery and the mortality rate is far lower.

A room with an ellipsoidal ceiling is known as a *whispering gallery*. In such a room, a word whispered at one focus can be clearly heard at the other. Whispering galleries are found in the rotunda of the Capitol Building in Washington, D.C., and in the Mormon Tabernacle in Salt Lake City.

Ellipses have many other applications. Planets travel around the sun in elliptical orbits with the sun at one focus, for example, and satellites travel around the earth in elliptical orbits as well.

Lithotripter

9.2   EXERCISE SET

In Exercises 1–6, match the equation with one of the graphs (a)–(f), which follow.

a)

b)

c)

d)

e)

f)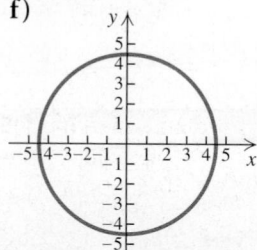

1. $x^2 + y^2 = 5$

2. $y^2 = 20 - x^2$

3. $x^2 + y^2 - 6x + 2y = 6$

4. $x^2 + y^2 + 10x - 12y = 3$

5. $x^2 + y^2 - 5x + 3y = 0$

6. $x^2 + 4x - 2 = 6y - y^2 - 6$

Find the center and the radius of the circle with the given equation. Then draw the graph.

7. $x^2 + y^2 - 14x + 4y = 11$

8. $x^2 + y^2 + 2x - 6y = -6$

9. $x^2 + y^2 + 6x - 2y = 6$

10. $x^2 + y^2 - 4x + 2y = 4$

11. $x^2 + y^2 + 4x - 6y - 12 = 0$

12. $x^2 + y^2 - 8x - 2y - 19 = 0$

13. $x^2 + y^2 - 6x - 8y + 16 = 0$

14. $x^2 + y^2 - 2x + 6y + 1 = 0$

15. $x^2 + y^2 + 6x - 10y = 0$

16. $x^2 + y^2 - 7x - 2y = 0$

17. $x^2 + y^2 - 9x = 7 - 4y$

18. $y^2 - 6y - 1 = 8x - x^2 + 3$

In Exercises 19–22, match the equation with one of the graphs (a)–(d), which follow.

a)

b)

c)

d)

19. $16x^2 + 4y^2 = 64$

20. $4x^2 + 5y^2 = 20$

21. $x^2 + 9y^2 - 6x + 90y = -225$

22. $9x^2 + 4y^2 + 18x - 16y = 11$

Find the vertices and the foci of the ellipse with the given equation. Then draw the graph.

23. $\dfrac{x^2}{4} + \dfrac{y^2}{1} = 1$

24. $\dfrac{x^2}{25} + \dfrac{y^2}{36} = 1$

25. $16x^2 + 9y^2 = 144$

26. $9x^2 + 4y^2 = 36$

27. $2x^2 + 3y^2 = 6$

28. $5x^2 + 7y^2 = 35$

29. $4x^2 + 9y^2 = 1$

30. $25x^2 + 16y^2 = 1$

Find an equation of an ellipse satisfying the given conditions.

31. Vertices: $(-7,0)$ and $(7,0)$;
   foci: $(-3,0)$ and $(3,0)$

32. Vertices: $(0,-6)$ and $(0,6)$;
   foci: $(0,-4)$ and $(0,4)$

33. Vertices: $(0,-8)$ and $(0,8)$;
   length of minor axis: 10

34. Vertices: $(-5,0)$ and $(5,0)$;
   length of minor axis: 6

35. Foci: $(-2,0)$ and $(2,0)$;
   length of major axis: 6

36. Foci: $(0,-3)$ and $(0,3)$;
   length of major axis: 10

Find the center, the vertices, and the foci of the ellipse. Then draw the graph.

37. $\dfrac{(x-1)^2}{9} + \dfrac{(y-2)^2}{4} = 1$

38. $\dfrac{(x-1)^2}{1} + \dfrac{(y-2)^2}{4} = 1$

39. $\dfrac{(x+3)^2}{25} + \dfrac{(y-5)^2}{36} = 1$

40. $\dfrac{(x-2)^2}{16} + \dfrac{(y+3)^2}{25} = 1$

41. $3(x+2)^2 + 4(y-1)^2 = 192$

42. $4(x-5)^2 + 3(y-4)^2 = 48$

43. $4x^2 + 9y^2 - 16x + 18y - 11 = 0$

44. $x^2 + 2y^2 - 10x + 8y + 29 = 0$

45. $4x^2 + y^2 - 8x - 2y + 1 = 0$

46. $9x^2 + 4y^2 + 54x - 8y + 49 = 0$

*The **eccentricity** of an ellipse is defined as $e = c/a$. For an ellipse, $0 < c < a$, so $0 < e < 1$. When e is close to 0, an ellipse appears to be nearly circular. When e is close to 1, an ellipse is very flat.*

47. Observe the shapes of the ellipses in Examples 2 and 4. Which ellipse has the smaller eccentricity? Confirm your answer by computing the eccentricity of each ellipse.

48. Which ellipse below has the smaller eccentricity? (Assume that the coordinate systems have the same scale.)

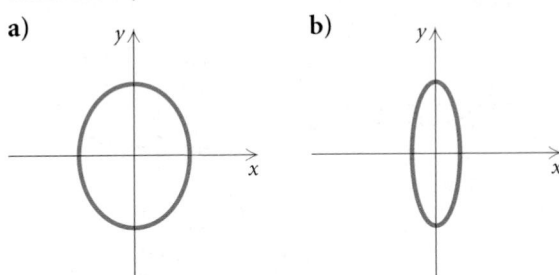

a)   **b)**

49. Find an equation of an ellipse with vertices $(0,-4)$ and $(0,4)$ and $e = \frac{1}{4}$.

50. Find an equation of an ellipse with vertices $(-3,0)$ and $(3,0)$ and $e = \frac{7}{10}$.

51. *Bridge Supports.*   The bridge support shown in the figure below is the top half of an ellipse. Assuming that a coordinate system is super-imposed on the drawing in such a way that point Q, the center of the ellipse, is at the origin, find an equation of the ellipse.

52. *The Ellipse.*   In Washington, D.C., there is a large grassy area south of the White House known as the Ellipse. It is an ellipse with major axis of length 1048 ft and minor axis of length 898 ft. Assuming that a coordinate system is superimposed on the area in such a way that the center is at the origin and the major and minor axes are on the *x*- and *y*-axes of the coordinate system, respectively, find an equation of the ellipse.

53. *The Earth's Orbit.*   The maximum distance of the earth from the sun is 9.3×10^7 mi. The minimum distance is 9.1×10^7 mi. The sun is at one focus of the elliptical orbit. Find the distance from the sun to the other focus.

54. *Carpentry.*   A carpenter is cutting a 3-ft by 4-ft elliptical sign from a 3-ft by 4-ft piece of plywood. The ellipse will be drawn using a string attached to the board at the foci of the ellipse.

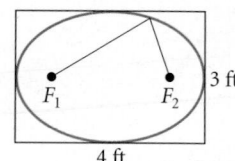

a) How far from the ends of the board should the string be attached?
b) How long should the string be?

Technology Connection

Use a graphing calculator to find the center and the vertices of each of the following.

55. $4x^2 + 9y^2 - 16.025x + 18.0927y - 11.346 = 0$

56. $9x^2 + 4y^2 + 54.063x - 8.016y + 49.872 = 0$

Collaborative Discussion and Writing

57. Explain why function notation is not used in this section.

58. Is the center of an ellipse part of the graph of the ellipse? Why or why not?

Skill Maintenance

In each of Exercises 59–66, fill in the blank with the correct term. Some of the given choices will not be used.

piecewise function
linear equation
factor
remainder
solution
zero
x-intercept
y-intercept
parabola
circle
ellipse
midpoint
distance
one real-number solution
two different real-number solutions
two different imaginary-number solutions

59. The _____ between two points (x_1, y_1) and (x_2, y_2) is given by $\left(\dfrac{x_1 + x_2}{2}, \dfrac{y_1 + y_2}{2} \right)$.

60. An input *c* of a function *f* is a(n) _____ of the function if $f(c) = 0$.

61. A(n) _____ of the graph of an equation is a point $(0, b)$.

62. For a quadratic equation $ax^2 + bx + c = 0$, if $b^2 - 4ac > 0$, the equation has _____.

63. Given a polynomial $f(x)$, then $f(c)$ is the _____ that would be obtained by dividing $f(x)$ by $x - c$.

64. A(n) _____ is the set of all points in a plane the sum of whose distances from two fixed points is constant.

65. A(n) _____ is the set of all points in a plane equidistant from a fixed line and a fixed point not on the line.

66. A(n) _____ is the set of all points in a plane that are at a fixed distance from a fixed point in the plane.

Synthesis

Find an equation of an ellipse satisfying the given conditions.

67. Vertices: $(3,-4),(3,6)$;
endpoints of minor axis: $(1,1),(5,1)$

68. Vertices: $(-1,-1),(-1,5)$;
endpoints of minor axis: $(-3,2),(1,2)$

69. Vertices: $(-3,0)$ and $(3,0)$;
passing through $\left(2,\frac{22}{3}\right)$

70. Center: $(-2,3)$; major axis vertical;
length of major axis: 4;
length of minor axis: 1

71. *Bridge Arch.* A bridge with a semielliptical arch spans a river as shown below. What is the clearance 6 ft from the riverbank?

14 ft

50 ft

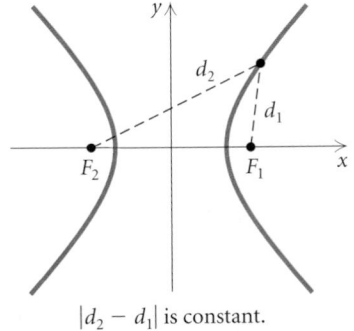

$|d_2 - d_1|$ is constant.

◆ Given an equation of a hyperbola, complete the square, if necessary, and then find the center, the vertices, and the foci and graph the hyperbola.

9.3 The Hyperbola

The last type of conic section that we study is the *hyperbola*.

Hyperbola

A **hyperbola** is the set of all points in a plane for which the absolute value of the difference of the distances from two fixed points (the **foci**) is constant. The midpoint of the segment between the foci is the **center** of the hyperbola.

◆ Standard Equations of Hyperbolas

We first consider the equation of a hyperbola with center at the origin. In the figure at right, F_1 and F_2 are the foci. The segment $\overline{V_2 V_1}$ is the **transverse axis** and the points V_2 and V_1 are the **vertices**.

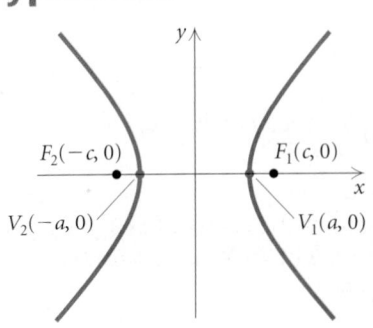

Standard Equation of a Hyperbola with Center at the Origin

Transverse Axis Horizontal

$$\frac{x^2}{a^2} - \frac{y^2}{b^2} = 1$$

Vertices: $(-a, 0), (a, 0)$

Foci: $(-c, 0), (c, 0),$
where $c^2 = a^2 + b^2$

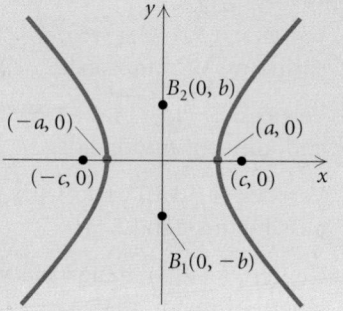

Transverse Axis Vertical

$$\frac{y^2}{a^2} - \frac{x^2}{b^2} = 1$$

Vertices: $(0, -a), (0, a)$

Foci: $(0, -c), (0, c),$
where $c^2 = a^2 + b^2$

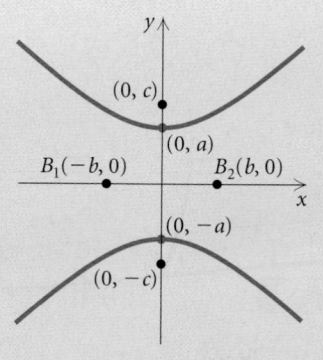

The segment $\overline{B_1 B_2}$ is the **conjugate axis** of the hyperbola.

To graph a hyperbola with a horizontal transverse axis, it is helpful to begin by graphing the lines $y = -(b/a)x$ and $y = (b/a)x$. These are the **asymptotes** of the hyperbola. For a hyperbola with a vertical transverse axis, the asymptotes are $y = -(a/b)x$ and $y = (a/b)x$. As $|x|$ gets larger and larger, the graph of the hyperbola gets closer and closer to the asymptotes.

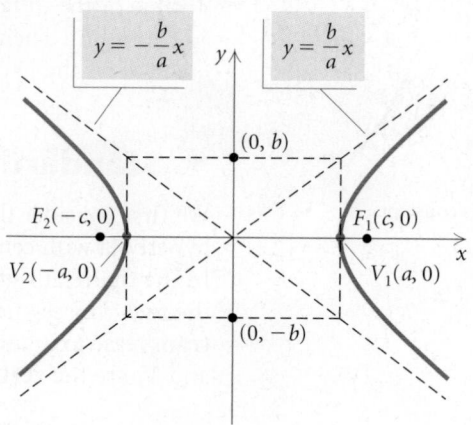

EXAMPLE 1 Find an equation of the hyperbola with vertices $(0, -4)$ and $(0, 4)$ and foci $(0, -6)$ and $(0, 6)$.

Solution We know that $a = 4$ and $c = 6$. We find b^2:

$$c^2 = a^2 + b^2$$
$$6^2 = 4^2 + b^2$$
$$36 = 16 + b^2$$
$$20 = b^2.$$

Since the vertices and the foci are on the y-axis, we know that the transverse axis is vertical. We can now write the equation of the hyperbola:

$$\frac{y^2}{a^2} - \frac{x^2}{b^2} = 1$$
$$\frac{y^2}{16} - \frac{x^2}{20} = 1.$$

▶ Now Try Exercise 7.

STUDY TIP

Take the time to include all the steps when doing your homework problems. This will help you organize your thinking and avoid computational errors. It will also give you complete, step-by-step solutions of the exercises that can be used to study for an exam.

EXAMPLE 2 For the hyperbola given by

$$9x^2 - 16y^2 = 144,$$

find the vertices, the foci, and the asymptotes. Then graph the hyperbola.

Solution First, we find standard form:

$$9x^2 - 16y^2 = 144$$
$$\frac{1}{144}(9x^2 - 16y^2) = \frac{1}{144} \cdot 144 \qquad \text{Multiplying by } \tfrac{1}{144} \text{ to get 1 on the right side}$$
$$\frac{x^2}{16} - \frac{y^2}{9} = 1$$
$$\frac{x^2}{4^2} - \frac{y^2}{3^2} = 1. \qquad \text{Writing standard form}$$

The hyperbola has a horizontal transverse axis, so the vertices are $(-a, 0)$ and $(a, 0)$, or $(-4, 0)$ and $(4, 0)$. From the standard form of the equation, we know that $a^2 = 4^2$, or 16, and $b^2 = 3^2$, or 9. We find the foci:

$$c^2 = a^2 + b^2$$
$$c^2 = 16 + 9$$
$$c^2 = 25$$
$$c = 5.$$

Thus the foci are $(-5, 0)$ and $(5, 0)$.

Next, we find the asymptotes:

$$y = -\frac{b}{a}x = -\frac{3}{4}x \quad \text{and} \quad y = \frac{b}{a}x = \frac{3}{4}x.$$

To draw the graph, we sketch the asymptotes first. This is easily done by drawing the rectangle with horizontal sides passing through $(0, 3)$ and $(0, -3)$ and vertical sides through $(4, 0)$ and $(-4, 0)$. Then we draw and extend the diagonals of this rectangle. The two extended diagonals are the asymptotes of the hyperbola. Next, we plot the vertices and draw the branches of the hyperbola outward from the vertices toward the asymptotes.

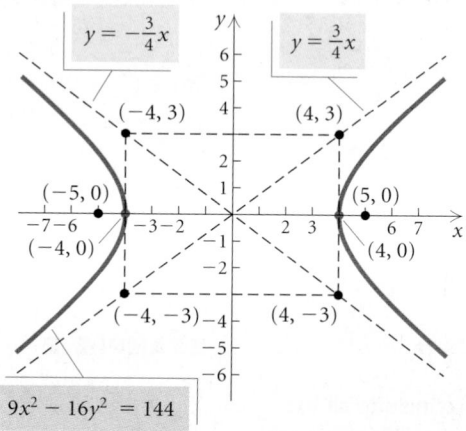

> **Now Try Exercise 17.**

TECHNOLOGY ·······
CONNECTION

To graph the hyperbola in Example 2 on a graphing calculator, it might be necessary to solve for y first and then graph the top and bottom halves of the hyperbola in the same squared viewing window.

$$9x^2 - 16y^2 = 144$$

$$y_1 = \sqrt{\frac{9x^2 - 144}{16}}, \quad y_2 = -\sqrt{\frac{9x^2 - 144}{16}}$$

The Hyperbola application on the APPS menu of some calculators uses the standard form of the equation to draw the graph.

If a hyperbola with center at the origin is translated horizontally $|h|$ units and vertically $|k|$ units, the center is at the point (h, k).

Standard Equation of a Hyperbola with Center (h, k)

Transverse Axis Horizontal

$$\frac{(x-h)^2}{a^2} - \frac{(y-k)^2}{b^2} = 1$$

Vertices: $(h-a, k), (h+a, k)$

Asymptotes: $y - k = \dfrac{b}{a}(x-h), y - k = -\dfrac{b}{a}(x-h)$

Foci: $(h-c, k), (h+c, k)$, where $c^2 = a^2 + b^2$

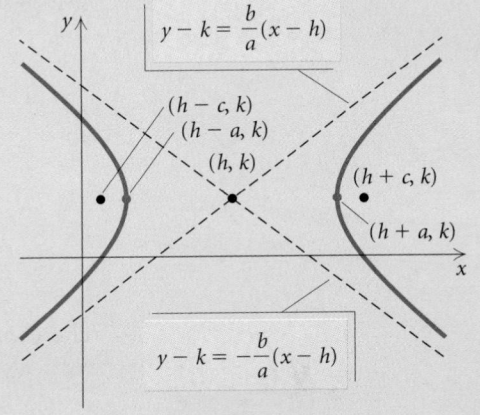

Transverse Axis Vertical

$$\frac{(y-k)^2}{a^2} - \frac{(x-h)^2}{b^2} = 1$$

Vertices: $(h, k-a), (h, k+a)$

Asymptotes: $y - k = \dfrac{a}{b}(x-h), y - k = -\dfrac{a}{b}(x-h)$

Foci: $(h, k-c), (h, k+c)$, where $c^2 = a^2 + b^2$

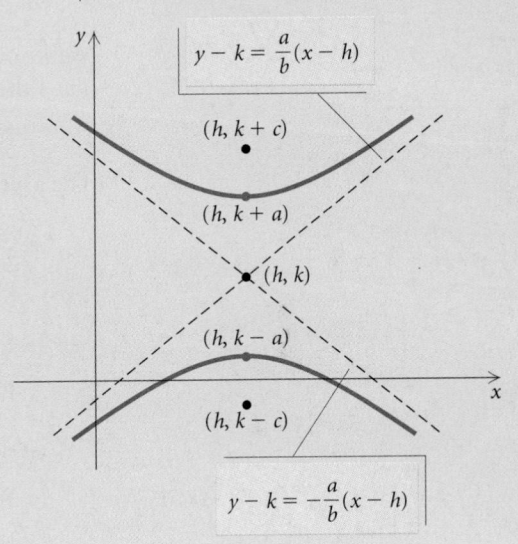

EXAMPLE 3   For the hyperbola given by

$$4y^2 - x^2 + 24y + 4x + 28 = 0,$$

find the center, the vertices, and the foci. Then draw the graph.

Solution   First, we complete the square to get standard form:

$$4y^2 - x^2 + 24y + 4x + 28 = 0$$
$$4(y^2 + 6y \qquad) - (x^2 - 4x \qquad) = -28$$
$$4(y^2 + 6y + 9 - 9) - (x^2 - 4x + 4 - 4) = -28$$
$$4(y^2 + 6y + 9) + 4(-9) - (x^2 - 4x + 4) - (-4) = -28$$
$$4(y^2 + 6y + 9) - 36 - (x^2 - 4x + 4) + 4 = -28$$
$$4(y^2 + 6y + 9) - (x^2 - 4x + 4) = -28 + 36 - 4$$
$$4(y + 3)^2 - (x - 2)^2 = 4$$
$$\frac{(y + 3)^2}{1} - \frac{(x - 2)^2}{4} = 1 \qquad \text{Dividing by 4}$$
$$\frac{[y - (-3)]^2}{1^2} - \frac{(x - 2)^2}{2^2} = 1. \qquad \text{Standard form}$$

The center is $(2, -3)$. Note that $a = 1$ and $b = 2$. The transverse axis is vertical, so the vertices are 1 unit below and above the center:

$$(2, -3 - 1) \text{ and } (2, -3 + 1), \quad \text{or} \quad (2, -4) \text{ and } (2, -2).$$

We know that $c^2 = a^2 + b^2$, so $c^2 = 1^2 + 2^2 = 1 + 4 = 5$ and $c = \sqrt{5}$. Thus the foci are $\sqrt{5}$ units below and above the center:

$$\left(2, -3 - \sqrt{5}\right) \quad \text{and} \quad \left(2, -3 + \sqrt{5}\right).$$

The asymptotes are

$$y - (-3) = \frac{1}{2}(x - 2) \quad \text{and} \quad y - (-3) = -\frac{1}{2}(x - 2),$$

or

$$y + 3 = \frac{1}{2}(x - 2) \quad \text{and} \quad y + 3 = -\frac{1}{2}(x - 2).$$

We sketch the asymptotes, plot the vertices, and draw the graph.

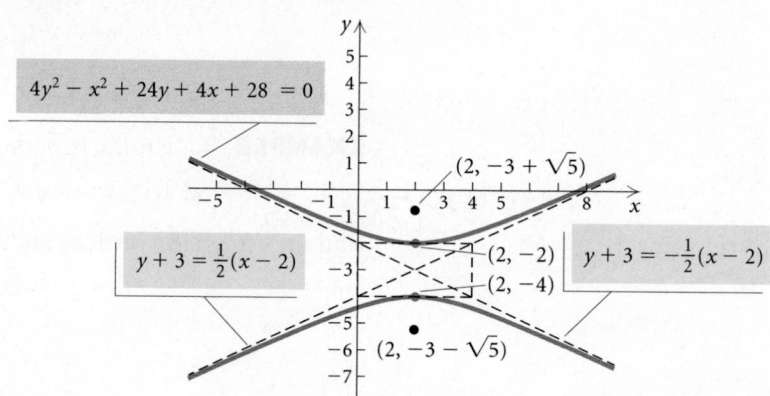

▶ Now Try Exercise 29.

CONNECTING THE CONCEPTS

Classifying Equations of Conic Sections

EQUATION	TYPE OF CONIC SECTION	GRAPH

$x - 4 + 4y = y^2$

Only one variable is squared, so this cannot be a circle, an ellipse, or a hyperbola. Find an equivalent equation:
$$x = (y - 2)^2.$$
This is an equation of a parabola.

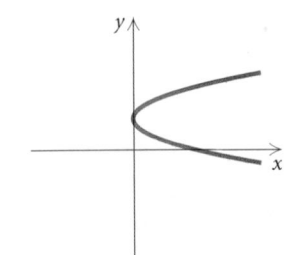

$3x^2 + 3y^2 = 75$

Both variables are squared, so this cannot be a parabola. The squared terms are added, so this cannot be a hyperbola. Divide by 3 on both sides to find an equivalent equation:
$$x^2 + y^2 = 25.$$
This is an equation of a circle.

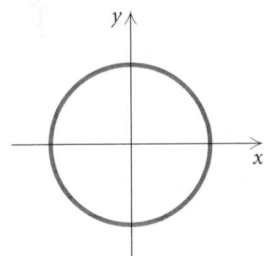

$y^2 = 16 - 4x^2$

Both variables are squared, so this cannot be a parabola. Add $4x^2$ on both sides to find an equivalent equation: $4x^2 + y^2 = 16$. The squared terms are added, so this cannot be a hyperbola. The coefficients of x^2 and y^2 are not the same, so this is not a circle. Divide by 16 on both sides to find an equivalent equation:
$$\frac{x^2}{4} + \frac{y^2}{16} = 1.$$
This is an equation of an ellipse.

$x^2 = 4y^2 + 36$

Both variables are squared, so this cannot be a parabola. Subtract $4y^2$ on both sides to find an equivalent equation: $x^2 - 4y^2 = 36$. The squared terms are not added, so this cannot be a circle or an ellipse. Divide by 36 on both sides to find an equivalent equation:
$$\frac{x^2}{36} - \frac{y^2}{9} = 1.$$
This is an equation of a hyperbola.

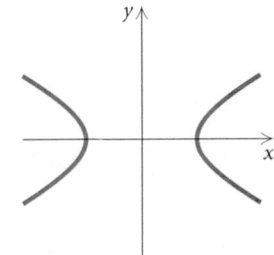

✦ Applications

Some comets travel in hyperbolic paths with the sun at one focus. Such comets pass by the sun only one time, unlike those with elliptical orbits, which reappear at intervals. A cross section of an amphitheater might be one branch of a hyperbola. A cross section of a nuclear cooling tower might also be a hyperbola.

One other application of hyperbolas is in the long-range navigation system LORAN. This system uses transmitting stations in three locations to send out simultaneous signals to a ship or aircraft. The difference in the arrival times of the signals from one pair of transmitters is recorded on the ship or aircraft. This difference is also recorded for signals from another pair of transmitters. For each pair, a computation is performed to determine the difference in the distances from each member of the pair to the ship or aircraft. If each pair of differences is kept constant, two hyperbolas can be drawn. Each has one of the pairs of transmitters as foci, and the ship or aircraft lies on the intersection of two of their branches.

LORAN

9.3 EXERCISE SET

In Exercises 1–6, match the equation with one of the graphs (a)–(f), which follow.

a)

b)

c)

d)

e)

f)

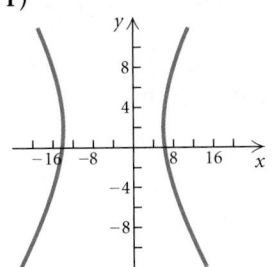

1. $\dfrac{x^2}{25} - \dfrac{y^2}{9} = 1$

2. $\dfrac{y^2}{4} - \dfrac{x^2}{36} = 1$

3. $\dfrac{(y-1)^2}{16} - \dfrac{(x+3)^2}{1} = 1$

4. $\dfrac{(x+4)^2}{100} - \dfrac{(y-2)^2}{81} = 1$

5. $25x^2 - 16y^2 = 400$

6. $y^2 - x^2 = 9$

Find an equation of a hyperbola satisfying the given conditions.

7. Vertices at $(0,3)$ and $(0,-3)$; foci at $(0,5)$ and $(0,-5)$

8. Vertices at $(1,0)$ and $(-1,0)$; foci at $(2,0)$ and $(-2,0)$

9. Asymptotes $y = \frac{3}{2}x,\ y = -\frac{3}{2}x$; one vertex $(2,0)$

10. Asymptotes $y = \frac{5}{4}x,\ y = -\frac{5}{4}x$; one vertex $(0,3)$

Find the center, the vertices, the foci, and the asymptotes. Then draw the graph.

11. $\dfrac{x^2}{4} - \dfrac{y^2}{4} = 1$

12. $\dfrac{x^2}{1} - \dfrac{y^2}{9} = 1$

13. $\dfrac{(x-2)^2}{9} - \dfrac{(y+5)^2}{1} = 1$

14. $\dfrac{(x-5)^2}{16} - \dfrac{(y+2)^2}{9} = 1$

15. $\dfrac{(y+3)^2}{4} - \dfrac{(x+1)^2}{16} = 1$

16. $\dfrac{(y+4)^2}{25} - \dfrac{(x+2)^2}{16} = 1$

17. $x^2 - 4y^2 = 4$ 18. $4x^2 - y^2 = 16$

19. $9y^2 - x^2 = 81$ 20. $y^2 - 4x^2 = 4$

21. $x^2 - y^2 = 2$ 22. $x^2 - y^2 = 3$

23. $y^2 - x^2 = \frac{1}{4}$ 24. $y^2 - x^2 = \frac{1}{9}$

Find the center, the vertices, the foci, and the asymptotes of the hyperbola. Then draw the graph.

25. $x^2 - y^2 - 2x - 4y - 4 = 0$

26. $4x^2 - y^2 + 8x - 4y - 4 = 0$

27. $36x^2 - y^2 - 24x + 6y - 41 = 0$

28. $9x^2 - 4y^2 + 54x + 8y + 41 = 0$

29. $9y^2 - 4x^2 - 18y + 24x - 63 = 0$

30. $x^2 - 25y^2 + 6x - 50y = 41$

31. $x^2 - y^2 - 2x - 4y = 4$

32. $9y^2 - 4x^2 - 54y - 8x + 41 = 0$

33. $y^2 - x^2 - 6x - 8y - 29 = 0$

34. $x^2 - y^2 = 8x - 2y - 13$

*The **eccentricity** of a hyperbola is defined as $e = c/a$. For a hyperbola, $c > a > 0$, so $e > 1$. When e is close to 1, a hyperbola appears to be very narrow. As the eccentricity increases, the hyperbola becomes "wider."*

35. Observe the shapes of the hyperbolas in Examples 2 and 3. Which hyperbola has the larger eccentricity? Confirm your answer by computing the eccentricity of each hyperbola.

36. Which hyperbola below has the larger eccentricity? (Assume that the coordinate systems have the same scale.)

a)

b)

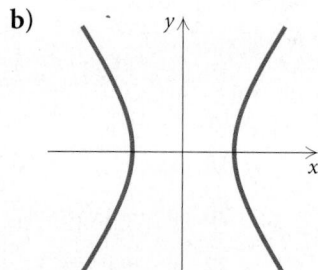

37. Find an equation of a hyperbola with vertices $(3, 7)$ and $(-3, 7)$ and $e = \frac{5}{3}$.

38. Find an equation of a hyperbola with vertices $(-1, 3)$ and $(-1, 7)$ and $e = 4$.

39. *Hyperbolic Mirror.* Certain telescopes contain both a parabolic mirror and a hyperbolic mirror. In the telescope shown in the figure below, the

parabola and the hyperbola share focus F_1, which is 14 m above the vertex of the parabola. The hyperbola's second focus F_2 is 2 m above the parabola's vertex. The vertex of the hyperbolic mirror is 1 m below F_1. Position a coordinate system with the origin at the center of the hyperbola and with the foci on the y-axis. Then find the equation of the hyperbola.

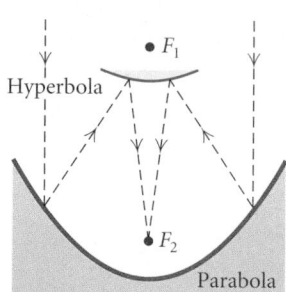

40. *Nuclear Cooling Tower.* A cross section of a nuclear cooling tower is a hyperbola with equation

$$\frac{x^2}{90^2} - \frac{y^2}{130^2} = 1.$$

The tower is 450 ft tall and the distance from the top of the tower to the center of the hyperbola is half the distance from the base of the tower to the center of the hyperbola. Find the diameter of the top and the base of the tower.

Technology Connection

Use a graphing calculator to find the center, the vertices, and the asymptotes.

41. $5x^2 - 3.5y^2 + 14.6x - 6.7y + 3.4 = 0$

42. $x^2 - y^2 - 2.046x - 4.088y - 4.228 = 0$

Collaborative Discussion and Writing

43. How does the graph of a parabola differ from the graph of one branch of a hyperbola?

44. Are the asymptotes of a hyperbola part of the graph of the hyperbola? Why or why not?

Skill Maintenance

In Exercises 45–48, given the function:
a) *Determine whether it is one-to-one.*
b) *If it is one-to-one, find a formula for the inverse.*

45. $f(x) = 2x - 3$

46. $f(x) = x^3 + 2$

47. $f(x) = \dfrac{5}{x - 1}$

48. $f(x) = \sqrt{x + 4}$

Solve.

49. $x + y = 5,$
$\quad x - y = 7$

50. $3x - 2y = 5,$
$\quad 5x + 2y = 3$

51. $2x - 3y = 7,$
$\quad 3x + 5y = 1$

52. $3x + 2y = -1,$
$\quad 2x + 3y = 6$

Synthesis

Find an equation of a hyperbola satisfying the given conditions.

53. Vertices at $(3, -8)$ and $(3, -2)$;
asymptotes $y = 3x - 14, y = -3x + 4$

54. Vertices at $(-9, 4)$ and $(-5, 4)$;
asymptotes $y = 3x + 25, y = -3x - 17$

55. *Navigation.* Two radio transmitters positioned 300 mi apart along the shore send simultaneous signals to a ship that is 200 mi offshore, sailing parallel to the shoreline. The signal from transmitter S reaches the ship 200 microseconds later than the signal from transmitter T. The signals travel at a speed of 186,000 miles per second, or 0.186 mile per microsecond. Find the equation of the hyperbola with foci S and T on which the ship is located. (*Hint*: For any point on the hyperbola, the absolute value of the difference of its distances from the foci is $2a$.)

9.4 Nonlinear Systems of Equations and Inequalities

◆ Solve a nonlinear system of equations.

◆ Use nonlinear systems of equations to solve applied problems.

◆ Graph nonlinear systems of inequalities.

The systems of equations that we have studied so far have been composed of linear equations. Now we consider systems of two equations in two variables in which at least one equation is not linear.

◆ Nonlinear Systems of Equations

The graphs of the equations in a nonlinear system of equations can have no point of intersection or one or more points of intersection. The coordinates of each point of intersection represent a solution of the system of equations.

When no point of intersection exists, the system of equations has no real-number solution.

Solutions of nonlinear systems of equations can be found using the substitution or elimination method. The substitution method is preferable for a system consisting of one linear equation and one nonlinear equation. The elimination method is preferable in most, but not all, cases when both equations are nonlinear.

EXAMPLE 1 Solve the following system of equations:

$$x^2 + y^2 = 25, \qquad (1) \qquad \text{The graph is a circle.}$$
$$3x - 4y = 0. \qquad (2) \qquad \text{The graph is a line.}$$

ALGEBRAIC SOLUTION

We use the substitution method. First, we solve equation (2) for x:

$$x = \tfrac{4}{3}y. \qquad (3) \qquad \text{We could have solved for } y \text{ instead.}$$

Next, we substitute $\tfrac{4}{3}y$ for x in equation (1) and solve for y:

$$\left(\tfrac{4}{3}y\right)^2 + y^2 = 25$$
$$\tfrac{16}{9}y^2 + y^2 = 25$$
$$\tfrac{25}{9}y^2 = 25$$
$$y^2 = 9 \qquad \text{Multiplying by } \tfrac{9}{25}$$
$$y = \pm 3.$$

Now we substitute these numbers for y in equation (3) and solve for x:

$$x = \tfrac{4}{3}(3) = 4, \qquad \text{The pair } (4, 3) \text{ appears to be a solution.}$$
$$x = \tfrac{4}{3}(-3) = -4. \qquad \text{The pair } (-4, -3) \text{ appears to be a solution.}$$

Check: For $(4, 3)$:

$$
\begin{array}{c|c}
x^2 + y^2 = 25 & 3x - 4y = 0 \\
\hline
4^2 + 3^2 \ ?\ 25 & 3(4) - 4(3) \ ?\ 0 \\
16 + 9 & 12 - 12 \\
25 \ \big|\ 25 \ \text{TRUE} & 0 \ \big|\ 0 \ \text{TRUE}
\end{array}
$$

For $(-4, -3)$:

$$
\begin{array}{c|c}
x^2 + y^2 = 25 & 3x - 4y = 0 \\
\hline
(-4)^2 + (-3)^2 \ ?\ 25 & 3(-4) - 4(-3) \ ?\ 0 \\
16 + 9 & -12 + 12 \\
25 \ \big|\ 25 \ \text{TRUE} & 0 \ \big|\ 0 \ \text{TRUE}
\end{array}
$$

The pairs $(4, 3)$ and $(-4, -3)$ check, so they are the solutions.

VISUALIZING THE SOLUTION

The ordered pairs corresponding to the points of intersection of the graphs of the equations are the solutions of the system of equations.

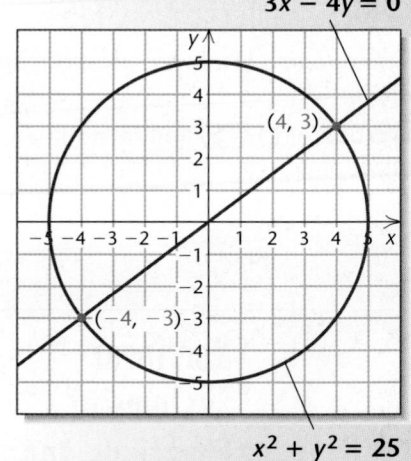

We see that the solutions are $(4, 3)$ and $(-4, -3)$.

▶ Now Try Exercise 7.

TECHNOLOGY ··
CONNECTION

To solve the system of equations in Example 1 on a graphing calculator, we graph both equations in the same viewing window. Note that there are two points of intersection. We can find their coordinates using the INTERSECT feature.

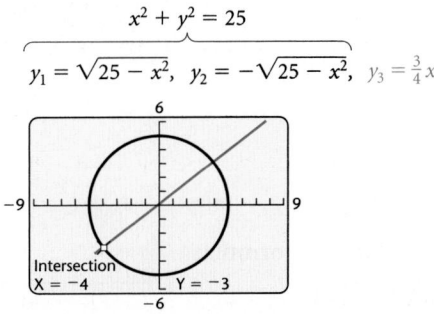

The solutions are $(4, 3)$ and $(-4, -3)$.
The graph can also be used to check the solutions that we found algebraically.

In the solution in Example 1, suppose that to find x, we had substituted 3 and -3 in equation (1) rather than equation (3). If $y = 3$, $y^2 = 9$, and if $y = -3$, $y^2 = 9$, so both substitutions can be performed at the same time:

$$x^2 + y^2 = 25 \qquad (1)$$
$$x^2 + (\pm 3)^2 = 25$$
$$x^2 + 9 = 25$$
$$x^2 = 16$$
$$x = \pm 4.$$

Thus, if $y = 3$, $x = 4$ or $x = -4$, and if $y = -3$, $x = 4$ or $x = -4$. The possible solutions are $(4, 3)$, $(-4, 3)$, $(4, -3)$, and $(-4, -3)$. A check reveals that $(4, -3)$ and $(-4, 3)$ are not solutions of equation (2). Since a circle and a line can intersect in at most two points, it is clear that there can be at most two real-number solutions.

EXAMPLE 2 Solve the following system of equations:

$$x + y = 5, \qquad (1) \qquad \text{The graph is a line.}$$
$$y = 3 - x^2. \qquad (2) \qquad \text{The graph is a parabola.}$$

ALGEBRAIC SOLUTION

We use the substitution method, substituting $3 - x^2$ for y in equation (1):

$$x + 3 - x^2 = 5$$
$$-x^2 + x - 2 = 0 \qquad \text{Subtracting 5 and rearranging}$$
$$x^2 - x + 2 = 0. \qquad \text{Multiplying by } -1$$

Next, we use the quadratic formula:

$$x = \frac{-b \pm \sqrt{b^2 - 4ac}}{2a} = \frac{-(-1) \pm \sqrt{(-1)^2 - 4(1)(2)}}{2(1)}$$

$$= \frac{1 \pm \sqrt{1 - 8}}{2} = \frac{1 \pm \sqrt{-7}}{2} = \frac{1 \pm i\sqrt{7}}{2} = \frac{1}{2} \pm \frac{\sqrt{7}}{2}i.$$

Now, we substitute these values for x in equation (1) and solve for y:

$$\frac{1}{2} + \frac{\sqrt{7}}{2}i + y = 5$$

$$y = 5 - \frac{1}{2} - \frac{\sqrt{7}}{2}i = \frac{9}{2} - \frac{\sqrt{7}}{2}i$$

and $\quad \dfrac{1}{2} - \dfrac{\sqrt{7}}{2}i + y = 5$

$$y = 5 - \frac{1}{2} + \frac{\sqrt{7}}{2}i = \frac{9}{2} + \frac{\sqrt{7}}{2}i.$$

The solutions are

$$\left(\frac{1}{2} + \frac{\sqrt{7}}{2}i, \frac{9}{2} - \frac{\sqrt{7}}{2}i \right) \quad \text{and} \quad \left(\frac{1}{2} - \frac{\sqrt{7}}{2}i, \frac{9}{2} + \frac{\sqrt{7}}{2}i \right).$$

There are no real-number solutions.

VISUALIZING THE SOLUTION

We graph the equations, as shown below.

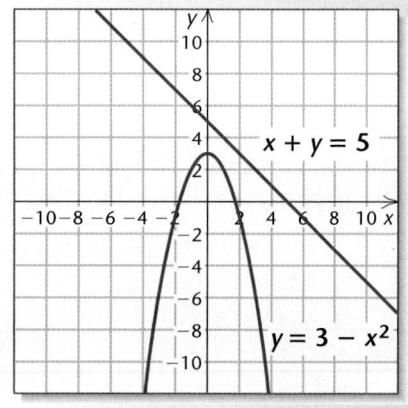

Note that there are no points of intersection. This indicates that there are no real-number solutions.

▶ Now Try Exercise 17.

EXAMPLE 3 Solve the following system of equations:

$$2x^2 + 5y^2 = 39, \quad (1) \qquad \text{The graph is an ellipse.}$$
$$3x^2 - y^2 = -1. \quad (2) \qquad \text{The graph is a hyperbola.}$$

ALGEBRAIC SOLUTION

We use the elimination method. First, we multiply equation (2) by 5 and add to eliminate the y^2-term:

$$
\begin{array}{ll}
2x^2 + 5y^2 = 39 & (1) \\
\underline{15x^2 - 5y^2 = -5} & \text{Multiplying (2) by 5} \\
17x^2 \quad\quad = 34 & \text{Adding} \\
x^2 = 2 & \\
x = \pm\sqrt{2}. &
\end{array}
$$

If $x = \sqrt{2}$, $x^2 = 2$, and if $x = -\sqrt{2}$, $x^2 = 2$. Thus substituting $\sqrt{2}$ or $-\sqrt{2}$ for x in equation (2) gives us

$$
\begin{aligned}
3\left(\pm\sqrt{2}\right)^2 - y^2 &= -1 \\
3 \cdot 2 - y^2 &= -1 \\
6 - y^2 &= -1 \\
-y^2 &= -7 \\
y^2 &= 7 \\
y &= \pm\sqrt{7}.
\end{aligned}
$$

Thus, for $x = \sqrt{2}$, we have $y = \sqrt{7}$ or $y = -\sqrt{7}$, and for $x = -\sqrt{2}$, we have $y = \sqrt{7}$ or $y = -\sqrt{7}$. The possible solutions are $\left(\sqrt{2}, \sqrt{7}\right)$, $\left(\sqrt{2}, -\sqrt{7}\right)$, $\left(-\sqrt{2}, \sqrt{7}\right)$, and $\left(-\sqrt{2}, -\sqrt{7}\right)$. All four pairs check, so they are the solutions.

VISUALIZING THE SOLUTION

We graph the equations and observe that there are four points of intersection.

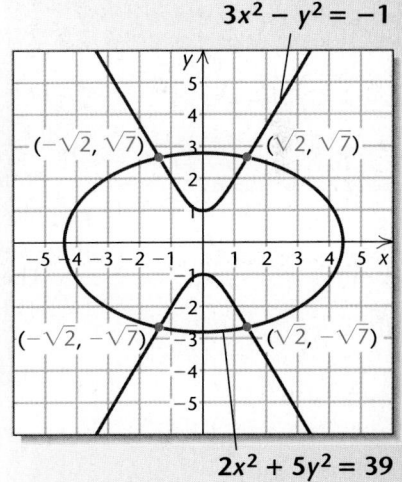

The coordinates of the points of intersection are $\left(\sqrt{2}, \sqrt{7}\right)$, $\left(\sqrt{2}, -\sqrt{7}\right)$, $\left(-\sqrt{2}, \sqrt{7}\right)$, and $\left(-\sqrt{2}, -\sqrt{7}\right)$. These are the solutions of the system of equations.

▶ Now Try Exercise 27.

TECHNOLOGY CONNECTION

To solve the system of equations in Example 3 graphically on a graphing calculator, we first graph both equations in the same viewing window. There are four points of intersection. We can use the INTERSECT feature to find their coordinates.

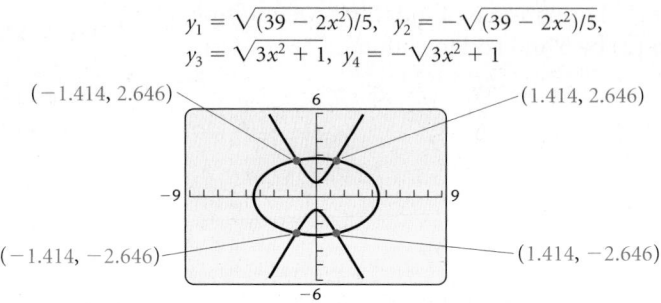

$$y_1 = \sqrt{(39 - 2x^2)/5}, \;\; y_2 = -\sqrt{(39 - 2x^2)/5},$$
$$y_3 = \sqrt{3x^2 + 1}, \;\; y_4 = -\sqrt{3x^2 + 1}$$

$(-1.414, 2.646)$ $(1.414, 2.646)$

$(-1.414, -2.646)$ $(1.414, -2.646)$

Note that the algebraic method yields exact solutions, whereas the graphical method yields decimal approximations of the solutions on most graphing calculators.

The solutions are approximately $(1.414, 2.646)$, $(1.414, -2.646)$, $(-1.414, 2.646)$, and $(-1.414, -2.646)$.

EXAMPLE 4 Solve the following system of equations:

$$x^2 - 3y^2 = 6, \qquad (1)$$
$$xy = 3. \qquad (2)$$

ALGEBRAIC SOLUTION

We use the substitution method. First, we solve equation (2) for y:

$$xy = 3 \qquad (2)$$

$$y = \frac{3}{x}. \qquad (3) \qquad \text{Dividing by } x$$

Next, we substitute $3/x$ for y in equation (1) and solve for x:

$$x^2 - 3\left(\frac{3}{x}\right)^2 = 6$$

$$x^2 - 3 \cdot \frac{9}{x^2} = 6$$

$$x^2 - \frac{27}{x^2} = 6$$

$$x^4 - 27 = 6x^2 \qquad \text{Multiplying by } x^2$$

$$x^4 - 6x^2 - 27 = 0$$

$$u^2 - 6u - 27 = 0 \qquad \text{Letting } u = x^2$$

$$(u - 9)(u + 3) = 0 \qquad \text{Factoring}$$

$$u = 9 \quad or \quad u = -3 \qquad \text{Principle of zero products}$$

$$x^2 = 9 \quad or \quad x^2 = -3 \qquad \text{Substituting } x^2 \text{ for } u$$

$$x = \pm 3 \quad or \quad x = \pm i\sqrt{3}.$$

Since $y = 3/x$,

when $x = 3$, $\qquad y = \dfrac{3}{3} = 1;$

when $x = -3$, $\qquad y = \dfrac{3}{-3} = -1;$

when $x = i\sqrt{3}$, $\qquad y = \dfrac{3}{i\sqrt{3}} = \dfrac{3}{i\sqrt{3}} \cdot \dfrac{-i\sqrt{3}}{-i\sqrt{3}} = -i\sqrt{3};$

when $x = -i\sqrt{3}$, $\quad y = \dfrac{3}{-i\sqrt{3}} = \dfrac{3}{-i\sqrt{3}} \cdot \dfrac{i\sqrt{3}}{i\sqrt{3}} = i\sqrt{3}.$

The pairs $(3, 1)$, $(-3, -1)$, $\left(i\sqrt{3}, -i\sqrt{3}\right)$, and $\left(-i\sqrt{3}, i\sqrt{3}\right)$ check, so they are the solutions.

VISUALIZING THE SOLUTION

The coordinates of the points of intersection of the graphs of the equations give us the real-number solutions of the system of equations. These graphs do not show us the imaginary-number solutions.

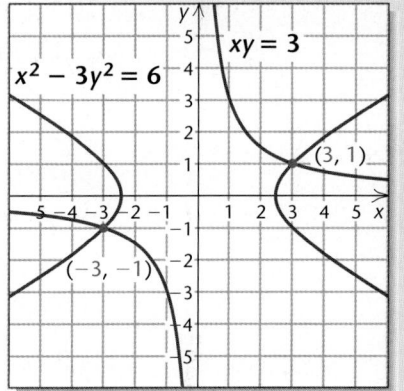

▶ Now Try Exercise 19.

✦ Modeling and Problem Solving

EXAMPLE 5 *Dimensions of a Piece of Land.* For a student recreation building at Southport Community College, an architect wants to lay out a rectangular piece of land that has a perimeter of 204 m and an area of 2565 m^2. Find the dimensions of the piece of land.

Solution

1. **Familiarize.** We make a drawing and label it, letting l = the length of the piece of land, in meters, and w = the width, in meters.

$$\text{Perimeter} = 2w + 2l$$
$$= 204 \text{ m}$$

2. **Translate.** We now have the following:

   Perimeter: $2w + 2l = 204,$ (1)

   Area: $lw = 2565.$ (2)

3. **Carry out.** We solve the system of equations:

   $$2w + 2l = 204,$$
   $$lw = 2565.$$

   Solving the second equation for l gives us $l = 2565/w$. We then substitute $2565/w$ for l in equation (1) and solve for w:

   $$2w + 2\left(\frac{2565}{w}\right) = 204$$
   $$2w^2 + 2(2565) = 204w \qquad \text{Multiplying by } w$$
   $$2w^2 - 204w + 2(2565) = 0$$
   $$w^2 - 102w + 2565 = 0 \qquad \text{Multiplying by } \tfrac{1}{2}$$
   $$(w - 57)(w - 45) = 0$$
   $$w = 57 \quad or \quad w = 45. \qquad \text{Principle of zero products}$$

   If $w = 57$, then $l = 2565/w = 2565/57 = 45$. If $w = 45$, then $l = 2565/w = 2565/45 = 57$. Since length is generally considered to be longer than width, we have the solution $l = 57$ and $w = 45$, or $(57, 45)$.

4. **Check.** If $l = 57$ and $w = 45$, the perimeter is $2 \cdot 45 + 2 \cdot 57$, or 204. The area is $57 \cdot 45$, or 2565. The numbers check.

5. **State.** The length of the piece of land is 57 m and the width is 45 m.

▶ Now Try Exercise 57.

◆ Nonlinear Systems of Inequalities

SYSTEMS OF INEQUALITIES

REVIEW SECTION **8.7.**

Recall that a solution of a system of inequalities is an ordered pair that is a solution of each inequality in the system. We graphed systems of linear inequalities in Section 8.7. Now we graph a nonlinear system of inequalities.

EXAMPLE 6 Graph the solution set of the system

$$x^2 + y^2 \le 25,$$
$$3x - 4y > 0.$$

Solution We graph $x^2 + y^2 \le 25$ by first graphing the equation of the circle $x^2 + y^2 = 25$. We use a solid line since the inequality symbol is $\le$. Next we choose $(0,0)$ as a test point and find that it is a solution of $x^2 + y^2 \le 25$, so we shade the region that contains $(0,0)$ using red. This is the region inside the circle. Now we graph the line $3x - 4y = 0$ using a dashed line since the inequality symbol is $>$. The point $(0,0)$ is on the line, so we choose another test point, say $(0, 2)$. We find that this point is not a solution of $3x - 4y > 0$, so we shade the half-plane that does not contain $(0, 2)$ using green. The solution set of the system of inequalities is the region shaded both red and green, or brown, including part of the circle $x^2 + y^2 = 25$.

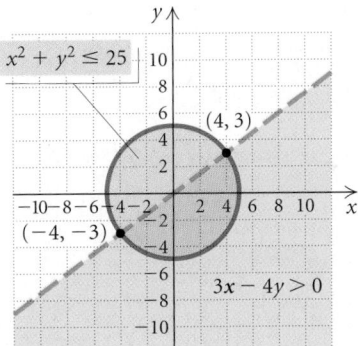

To find the points of intersection of the graphs, we solve the system of equations

$$x^2 + y^2 = 25,$$
$$3x - 4y = 0.$$

In Example 1 we found that these points are $(4, 3)$ and $(-4, -3)$.

▷ Now Try Exercise 71.

To use a graphing calculator to graph the system of inequalities in Example 7, we first graph $y_1 = 4 - x^2$ and $y_2 = 2 - x$. Using the test point $(0, 0)$ for each inequality, we find that we should shade below y_1 and above y_2. We can find the points of intersection of the graphs, $(-1, 3)$ and $(2, 0)$, using the INTERSECT feature.

$y_1 = 4 - x^2, \ y_2 = 2 - x$

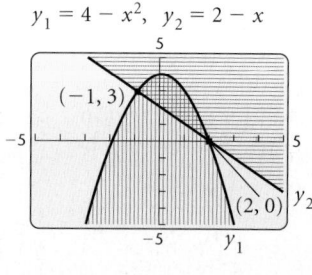

EXAMPLE 7   Graph the solution set of the system

$$y \leq 4 - x^2,$$
$$x + y \geq 2.$$

Solution   We graph $y \leq 4 - x^2$ by first graphing the equation of the parabola $y = 4 - x^2$. We use a solid line since the inequality symbol is $\leq$. Next, we choose $(0, 0)$ as a test point and find that it is a solution of $y \leq 4 - x^2$, so we shade the region that contains $(0, 0)$ using red. Now we graph the line $x + y = 2$, again using a solid line since the inequality symbol is $\geq$. We test the point $(0, 0)$ and find that it is not a solution of $x + y \geq 2$, so we shade the half-plane that does not contain $(0, 0)$ using green. The solution set of the system of inequalities is the region shaded both red and green, or brown, including part of the parabola $y = 4 - x^2$ and part of the line $x + y = 2$.

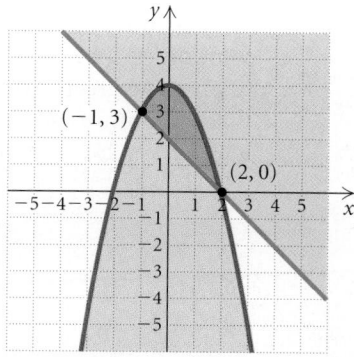

Solving the system of equations

$$y = 4 - x^2,$$
$$x + y = 2,$$

we find that the points of intersection of the graphs are $(-1, 3)$ and $(2, 0)$.

▷ **Now Try Exercise 73.**

A

B

C

D

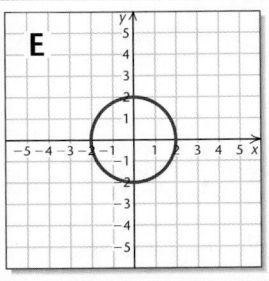

E

Visualizing the Graph

Match the equation with its graph.

1. $y = x^3 - 3x$

2. $y = x^2 + 2x - 3$

3. $y = \dfrac{x - 1}{x^2 - x - 2}$

4. $y = -3x + 2$

5. $x + y = 3,$
$2x + 5y = 3$

6. $9x^2 - 4y^2 = 36,$
$x^2 + y^2 = 9$

7. $5x^2 + 5y^2 = 20$

8. $4x^2 + 16y^2 = 64$

9. $y = \log_2 x$

10. $y = 2^x$

Answers on page A-67

F

G

H

I

J

9.4   EXERCISE SET

In Exercises 1–6, match the system of equations with one of the graphs (a)–(f), which follow.

a)

b)

c)

d)

e)

f)
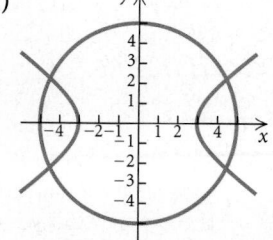

1. $x^2 + y^2 = 16,$
$x + y = 3$

2. $16x^2 + 9y^2 = 144,$
$x - y = 4$

3. $y = x^2 - 4x - 2,$
$2y - x = 1$

4. $4x^2 - 9y^2 = 36,$
$x^2 + y^2 = 25$

5. $y = x^2 - 3,$
$x^2 + 4y^2 = 16$

6. $y^2 - 2y = x + 3,$
$xy = 4$

Solve.

7. $x^2 + y^2 = 25,$
$y - x = 1$

8. $x^2 + y^2 = 100,$
$y - x = 2$

9. $4x^2 + 9y^2 = 36,$
$3y + 2x = 6$

10. $9x^2 + 4y^2 = 36,$
$3x + 2y = 6$

11. $x^2 + y^2 = 25,$
$y^2 = x + 5$

12. $y = x^2,$
$x = y^2$

13. $x^2 + y^2 = 9,$
$x^2 - y^2 = 9$

14. $y^2 - 4x^2 = 4,$
$4x^2 + y^2 = 4$

15. $y^2 - x^2 = 9,$
$2x - 3 = y$

16. $x + y = -6,$
$xy = -7$

17. $y^2 = x + 3,$
$2y = x + 4$

18. $y = x^2,$
$3x = y + 2$

19. $x^2 + y^2 = 25,$
$xy = 12$

20. $x^2 - y^2 = 16,$
$x + y^2 = 4$

21. $x^2 + y^2 = 4,$
$16x^2 + 9y^2 = 144$

22. $x^2 + y^2 = 25,$
$25x^2 + 16y^2 = 400$

23. $x^2 + 4y^2 = 25,$
$x + 2y = 7$

24. $y^2 - x^2 = 16,$
$2x - y = 1$

25. $x^2 - xy + 3y^2 = 27,$
$x - y = 2$

26. $2y^2 + xy + x^2 = 7,$
$x - 2y = 5$

27. $x^2 + y^2 = 16,$
$y^2 - 2x^2 = 10$

28. $x^2 + y^2 = 14,$
$x^2 - y^2 = 4$

29. $x^2 + y^2 = 5,$
$xy = 2$

30. $x^2 + y^2 = 20,$
$xy = 8$

31. $3x + y = 7,$
$4x^2 + 5y = 56$

32. $2y^2 + xy = 5,$
$4y + x = 7$

33. $a + b = 7,$
$ab = 4$

34. $p + q = -4,$
$pq = -5$

35. $x^2 + y^2 = 13,$
$xy = 6$

36. $x^2 + 4y^2 = 20,$
$xy = 4$

37. $x^2 + y^2 + 6y + 5 = 0,$
$x^2 + y^2 - 2x - 8 = 0$

38. $2xy + 3y^2 = 7,$
$3xy - 2y^2 = 4$

39. $2a + b = 1,$
$b = 4 - a^2$

40. $4x^2 + 9y^2 = 36,$
$x + 3y = 3$

41. $a^2 + b^2 = 89,$
$a - b = 3$

42. $xy = 4,$
$x + y = 5$

43. $xy - y^2 = 2,$
$2xy - 3y^2 = 0$

44. $4a^2 - 25b^2 = 0,$
$2a^2 - 10b^2 = 3b + 4$

45. $m^2 - 3mn + n^2 + 1 = 0,$
$3m^2 - mn + 3n^2 = 13$

46. $ab - b^2 = -4,$
$ab - 2b^2 = -6$

47. $x^2 + y^2 = 5,$
$x - y = 8$

48. $4x^2 + 9y^2 = 36,$
$y - x = 8$

49. $a^2 + b^2 = 14,$
$ab = 3\sqrt{5}$

50. $x^2 + xy = 5,$
$2x^2 + xy = 2$

51. $x^2 + y^2 = 25,$
$9x^2 + 4y^2 = 36$

52. $x^2 + y^2 = 1,$
$9x^2 - 16y^2 = 144$

53. $5y^2 - x^2 = 1,$
$xy = 2$

54. $x^2 - 7y^2 = 6,$
$xy = 1$

55. *Picture Frame Dimensions.*   Frank's Frame Shop is building a frame for a rectangular oil painting with a perimeter of 28 cm and a diagonal of 10 cm. Find the dimensions of the painting.

56. *Landscaping.*   Green Leaf Landscaping is planting a rectangular wildflower garden with a perimeter of 6 m and a diagonal of $\sqrt{5}$ m. Find the dimensions of the garden.

57. *Graphic Design.*   Marcia Graham, owner of Graham's Graphics, is designing an advertising brochure for the Art League's spring show. Each page of the brochure is rectangular with an area of 20 in^2 and a perimeter of 18 in. Find the dimensions of the brochure.

58. *Sign Dimensions.*   Peden's Advertising is building a rectangular sign with an area of 2 yd^2 and a perimeter of 6 yd. Find the dimensions of the sign.

59. *Banner Design.*   A rectangular banner with an area of $\sqrt{3}$ m^2 is being designed to advertise an exhibit at the Davis Gallery. The length of a diagonal is 2 m. Find the dimensions of the banner.

60. *Carpentry.*   Ted Hansen of Hansen Woodworking Designs has been commissioned to make a rectangular tabletop with an area of $\sqrt{2}$ m^2 and a diagonal of $\sqrt{3}$ m for the Decorators' Show House. Find the dimensions of the tabletop.

61. *Fencing.*   It will take 210 yd of fencing to enclose a rectangular dog run. The area of the run is 2250 yd^2. What are the dimensions of the run?

62. *Office Dimensions.*   The diagonal of the floor of a rectangular office cubicle is 1 ft longer than the length of the cubicle and 3 ft longer than twice the width. Find the dimensions of the cubicle.

63. *Seed Test Plots.* The Burton Seed Company has two square test plots. The sum of their areas is 832 ft^2 and the difference of their areas is 320 ft^2. Find the length of a side of each plot.

64. *Investment.* Jenna made an investment for 1 yr that earned \$7.50 simple interest. If the principal had been \$25 more and the interest rate 1% less, the interest would have been the same. Find the principal and the interest rate.

In Exercises 65–70, match the system of inequalities with one of the graphs (a)–(f), which follow.

a)

b)

c)

d)

e)

f)

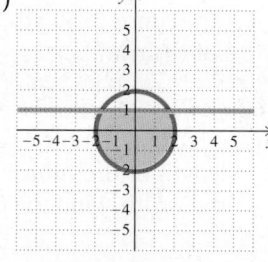

65. $x^2 + y^2 \le 5,$
$x + y > 2$

66. $y \le 2 - x^2,$
$y \ge x^2 - 2$

67. $y \ge x^2,$
$y > x$

68. $x^2 + y^2 \le 4,$
$y \le 1$

69. $y \ge x^2 + 1,$
$x + y \le 1$

70. $x^2 + y^2 \le 9,$
$y > x$

Graph the system of inequalities. Then find the coordinates of the points of intersection of the graphs.

71. $x^2 + y^2 \le 16,$
$y < x$

72. $x^2 + y^2 \le 10,$
$y > x$

73. $x^2 \le y,$
$x + y \ge 2$

74. $x \ge y^2,$
$x - y \le 2$

75. $x^2 + y^2 \le 25,$
$x - y > 5$

76. $x^2 + y^2 \ge 9,$
$x - y > 3$

77. $y \ge x^2 - 3,$
$y \le 2x$

78. $y \le 3 - x^2,$
$y \ge x + 1$

79. $y \ge x^2,$
$y < x + 2$

80. $y \le 1 - x^2,$
$y > x - 1$

Technology Connection

Solve using a graphing calculator.

81. $y - \ln x = 2,$
$y = x^2$

82. $y = \ln(x + 4),$
$x^2 + y^2 = 6$

83. $e^x - y = 1,$
$3x + y = 4$

84. $y - e^{-x} = 1,$
$y = 2x + 5$

85. $y = e^x,$
$x - y = -2$

86. $y = e^{-x},$
$x + y = 3$

87. $x^2 + y^2 = 19{,}380{,}510.36,$
$27{,}942.25x - 6.125y = 0$

88. $2x + 2y = 1660,$
$xy = 35{,}325$

89. $14.5x^2 - 13.5y^2 - 64.5 = 0,$
$5.5x - 6.3y - 12.3 = 0$

90. $13.5xy + 15.6 = 0,$
$5.6x - 6.7y - 42.3 = 0$

91. $0.319x^2 + 2688.7y^2 = 56{,}548,$
$0.306x^2 - 2688.7y^2 = 43{,}452$

92. $18.465x^2 + 788.723y^2 = 6408,$
$106.535x^2 - 788.723y^2 = 2692$

Collaborative Discussion and Writing

93. Which conic sections, if any, have equations that can be expressed using function notation? Explain why you answered as you did.

94. Write a problem that can be translated to a nonlinear system of equations, and ask a classmate to solve it. Devise the problem so that the solution is "The dimensions of the rectangle are 6 ft by 8 ft."

Skill Maintenance

Solve.

95. $2^{3x} = 64$

96. $5^x = 27$

97. $\log_3 x = 4$

98. $\log(x - 3) + \log x = 1$

Synthesis

99. Find an equation of the circle that passes through the points $(2, 4)$ and $(3, 3)$ and whose center is on the line $3x - y = 3$.

100. Find an equation of the circle that passes through the points $(-2, 3)$ and $(-4, 1)$ and whose center is on the line $5x + 8y = -2$.

101. Find an equation of an ellipse centered at the origin that passes through the points $\left(1, \sqrt{3}/2\right)$ and $\left(\sqrt{3}, 1/2\right)$.

102. Find an equation of a hyperbola of the type
$$\frac{x^2}{b^2} - \frac{y^2}{a^2} = 1$$
that passes through the points $\left(-3, -3\sqrt{5}/2\right)$ and $(-3/2, 0)$.

103. Find an equation of the circle that passes through the points $(4, 6)$, $(-6, 2)$, and $(1, -3)$.

104. Find an equation of the circle that passes through the points $(2, 3)$, $(4, 5)$, and $(0, -3)$.

105. Show that a hyperbola does not intersect its asymptotes. That is, solve the system of equations
$$\frac{x^2}{a^2} - \frac{y^2}{b^2} = 1,$$
$$y = \frac{b}{a}x \left(\text{or } y = -\frac{b}{a}x\right).$$

106. *Numerical Relationship.* Find two numbers whose product is 2 and the sum of whose reciprocals is $\frac{33}{8}$.

107. *Numerical Relationship.* The square of a number exceeds twice the square of another number by $\frac{1}{8}$. The sum of their squares is $\frac{5}{16}$. Find the numbers.

108. *Box Dimensions.* Four squares with sides 5 in. long are cut from the corners of a rectangular metal sheet that has an area of 340 in². The edges are bent up to form an open box with a volume of 350 in³. Find the dimensions of the box.

109. *Numerical Relationship.* The sum of two numbers is 1, and their product is 1. Find the sum of their cubes. There is a method to solve this problem that is easier than solving a nonlinear system of equations. Can you discover it?

110. Solve for x and y:
$$x^2 - y^2 = a^2 - b^2,$$
$$x - y = a - b.$$

Solve.

111. $x^3 + y^3 = 72,$
$x + y = 6$

112. $a + b = \dfrac{5}{6},$
$\dfrac{a}{b} + \dfrac{b}{a} = \dfrac{13}{6}$

113. $p^2 + q^2 = 13,$
$\dfrac{1}{pq} = -\dfrac{1}{6}$

114. $x^2 + y^2 = 4,$
$(x - 1)^2 + y^2 = 4$

115. $5^{x+y} = 100,$
$3^{2x-y} = 1000$

116. $e^x - e^{x+y} = 0,$
$e^y - e^{x-y} = 0$

9.5   Rotation of Axes

◆ Use rotation of axes to graph conic sections.

◆ Use the discriminant to determine the type of conic represented by a given equation.

In Section 9.1, we saw that conic sections can be defined algebraically using a second-degree equation of the form $Ax^2 + Bxy + Cy^2 + Dx + Ey + F = 0$. Up to this point, we have considered only equations of this form for which $B = 0$. Now we turn our attention to equations of conics that contain an xy-term.

CONIC SECTIONS

REVIEW SECTIONS 9.1–9.3.

◆ Rotation of Axes

When B is nonzero, the graph of $Ax^2 + Bxy + Cy^2 + Dx + Ey + F = 0$ is a conic section with an axis that is not parallel to the x- or y-axis. We use a technique called **rotation of axes** when we graph such an equation. The goal is to rotate the x- and y-axes through a positive angle θ to yield an $x'y'$-coordinate system, as shown at left. For the appropriate choice of θ, the graph of any conic section with an xy-term will have its axis parallel to the x'-axis or the y'-axis.

Algebraically we want to rewrite an equation in the xy-coordinate system

$$Ax^2 + Bxy + Cy^2 + Dx + Ey + F = 0$$

in the form

$$A'(x')^2 + C'(y')^2 + D'x' + E'y' + F' = 0$$

in the $x'y'$-coordinate system. Equations of this second type were graphed in Sections 9.1–9.3.

To achieve our goal, we find formulas relating the xy-coordinates of a point and the $x'y'$-coordinates of the same point. We begin by letting P be a point with coordinates (x, y) in the xy-coordinate system and (x', y') in the $x'y'$-coordinate system.

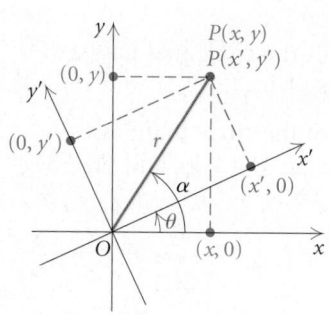

We let r represent the distance OP, and we let α represent the angle from the x-axis to OP. Then

$$\cos \alpha = \frac{x}{r} \quad \text{and} \quad \sin \alpha = \frac{y}{r},$$

so

$$x = r \cos \alpha \quad \text{and} \quad y = r \sin \alpha.$$

We also see from the figure above that

$$\cos (\alpha - \theta) = \frac{x'}{r} \quad \text{and} \quad \sin (\alpha - \theta) = \frac{y'}{r},$$

so

$$x' = r \cos (\alpha - \theta) \quad \text{and} \quad y' = r \sin (\alpha - \theta).$$

Then

$$x' = r \cos \alpha \cos \theta + r \sin \alpha \sin \theta$$

and

$$y' = r \sin \alpha \cos \theta - r \cos \alpha \sin \theta.$$

Substituting x for $r \cos \alpha$ and y for $r \sin \alpha$ gives us

$$x' = x \cos \theta + y \sin \theta \tag{1}$$

and

$$y' = y \cos \theta - x \sin \theta. \tag{2}$$

We can use these formulas to find the $x'y'$-coordinates of any point given that point's xy-coordinates and an angle of rotation θ. To express xy-coordinates in terms of $x'y'$-coordinates and an angle of rotation θ, we solve the system composed of equations (1) and (2) above for x and y. (See Exercise 45.) We get

$$x = x' \cos \theta - y' \sin \theta$$

and

$$y = x' \sin \theta + y' \cos \theta.$$

Rotation of Axes Formulas

If the x- and y-axes are rotated about the origin through a positive acute angle θ, then the coordinates (x, y) and (x', y') of a point P in the xy- and $x'y'$-coordinate systems are related by the following formulas:

$$x' = x \cos \theta + y \sin \theta, \qquad y' = -x \sin \theta + y \cos \theta;$$
$$x = x' \cos \theta - y' \sin \theta, \qquad y = x' \sin \theta + y' \cos \theta.$$

EXAMPLE 1 Suppose that the xy-axes are rotated through an angle of 45°. Write the equation $xy = 1$ in the $x'y'$-coordinate system.

Solution We substitute 45° for θ in the rotation of axes formulas for x and y:

$$x = x' \cos 45° - y' \sin 45°,$$
$$y = x' \sin 45° + y' \cos 45°.$$

Then we have

$$x = x'\left(\frac{\sqrt{2}}{2}\right) - y'\left(\frac{\sqrt{2}}{2}\right) = \frac{\sqrt{2}}{2}(x' - y')$$

and

$$y = x'\left(\frac{\sqrt{2}}{2}\right) + y'\left(\frac{\sqrt{2}}{2}\right) = \frac{\sqrt{2}}{2}(x' + y').$$

Next, we substitute these expressions for x and y in the equation $xy = 1$:

$$\frac{\sqrt{2}}{2}(x' - y') \cdot \frac{\sqrt{2}}{2}(x' + y') = 1$$

$$\frac{1}{2}[(x')^2 - (y')^2] = 1$$

$$\frac{(x')^2}{2} - \frac{(y')^2}{2} = 1, \quad \text{or} \quad \frac{(x')^2}{(\sqrt{2})^2} - \frac{(y')^2}{(\sqrt{2})^2} = 1.$$

We have the equation of a hyperbola in the $x'y'$-coordinate system with its axis on the x'-axis and with vertices $\left(-\sqrt{2}, 0\right)$ and $\left(\sqrt{2}, 0\right)$. Its asymptotes are $y' = -x'$ and $y' = x'$. These correspond to the axes of the xy-coordinate system.

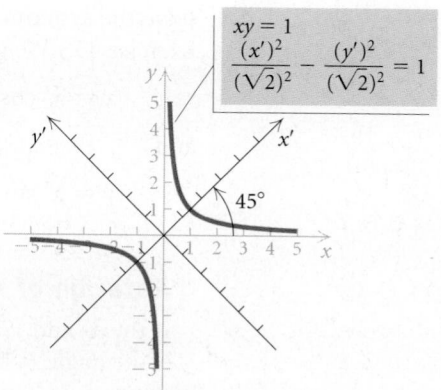

$$xy = 1$$
$$\frac{(x')^2}{(\sqrt{2})^2} - \frac{(y')^2}{(\sqrt{2})^2} = 1$$

Now let's substitute the rotation of axes formulas for x and y in the equation

$$Ax^2 + Bxy + Cy^2 + Dx + Ey + F = 0.$$

We have

$$A(x' \cos \theta - y' \sin \theta)^2 + B(x' \cos \theta - y' \sin \theta)(x' \sin \theta + y' \cos \theta)$$
$$+ C(x' \sin \theta + y' \cos \theta)^2 + D(x' \cos \theta - y' \sin \theta)$$
$$+ E(x' \sin \theta + y' \cos \theta) + F = 0.$$

Performing the operations indicated and collecting like terms yields the equation

$$A'(x')^2 + B'x'y' + C'(y')^2 + D'x' + E'y' + F' = 0, \qquad (3)$$

where

$$A' = A \cos^2 \theta + B \sin \theta \cos \theta + C \sin^2 \theta,$$
$$B' = 2(C - A) \sin \theta \cos \theta + B(\cos^2 \theta - \sin^2 \theta),$$
$$C' = A \sin^2 \theta - B \sin \theta \cos \theta + C \cos^2 \theta,$$
$$D' = D \cos \theta + E \sin \theta,$$
$$E' = -D \sin \theta + E \cos \theta, \quad \text{and}$$
$$F' = F.$$

Recall that our goal is to produce an equation without an $x'y'$-term, or with $B' = 0$. Then we must have

$$2(C - A) \sin \theta \cos \theta + B(\cos^2 \theta - \sin^2 \theta) = 0$$
$$(C - A) \sin 2\theta + B \cos 2\theta = 0 \qquad \text{Using double-angle formulas}$$
$$B \cos 2\theta = (A - C) \sin 2\theta$$
$$\frac{\cos 2\theta}{\sin 2\theta} = \frac{A - C}{B}$$
$$\cot 2\theta = \frac{A - C}{B}.$$

Thus, when θ is chosen so that

$$\cot 2\theta = \frac{A - C}{B},$$

equation (3) will have no $x'y'$-term. Although we will not do so here, it can be shown that we can always find θ such that $0° < 2\theta < 180°$, or $0° < \theta < 90°$.

Eliminating the xy-Term

To eliminate the xy-term from the equation

$$Ax^2 + Bxy + Cy^2 + Dx + Ey + F = 0, \quad B \neq 0,$$

select an angle θ such that

$$\cot 2\theta = \frac{A - C}{B}, \quad 0° < 2\theta < 180°,$$

and use the rotation of axes formulas.

EXAMPLE 2 Graph the equation

$$3x^2 - 2\sqrt{3}xy + y^2 + 2x + 2\sqrt{3}y = 0.$$

Solution We have

$$A = 3, \quad B = -2\sqrt{3}, \quad C = 1, \quad D = 2, \quad E = 2\sqrt{3}, \quad \text{and} \quad F = 0.$$

To select the angle of rotation θ, we must have

$$\cot 2\theta = \frac{A - C}{B} = \frac{3 - 1}{-2\sqrt{3}} = \frac{2}{-2\sqrt{3}} = -\frac{1}{\sqrt{3}}.$$

Thus, $2\theta = 120°$, and $\theta = 60°$. We substitute this value for θ in the rotation of axes formulas for x and y:

$$x = x' \cos 60° - y' \sin 60°,$$
$$y = x' \sin 60° + y' \cos 60°.$$

This gives us

$$x = x' \cdot \frac{1}{2} - y' \cdot \frac{\sqrt{3}}{2} = \frac{x'}{2} - \frac{y'\sqrt{3}}{2}$$

and

$$y = x' \cdot \frac{\sqrt{3}}{2} + y' \cdot \frac{1}{2} = \frac{x'\sqrt{3}}{2} + \frac{y'}{2}.$$

Now we substitute these expressions for x and y in the given equation:

$$3\left(\frac{x'}{2} - \frac{y'\sqrt{3}}{2}\right)^2 - 2\sqrt{3}\left(\frac{x'}{2} - \frac{y'\sqrt{3}}{2}\right)\left(\frac{x'\sqrt{3}}{2} + \frac{y'}{2}\right) +$$
$$\left(\frac{x'\sqrt{3}}{2} + \frac{y'}{2}\right)^2 + 2\left(\frac{x'}{2} - \frac{y'\sqrt{3}}{2}\right) + 2\sqrt{3}\left(\frac{x'\sqrt{3}}{2} + \frac{y'}{2}\right) = 0.$$

After simplifying, we get

$$4(y')^2 + 4x' = 0, \quad \text{or}$$
$$(y')^2 = -x'.$$

This is the equation of a parabola with its vertex at $(0,0)$ of the $x'y'$-coordinate system and axis of symmetry $y' = 0$. We sketch the graph.

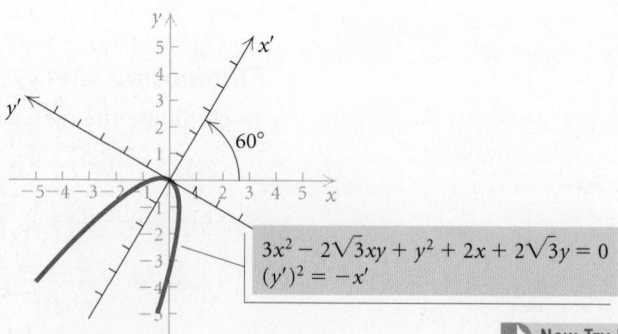

$$3x^2 - 2\sqrt{3}xy + y^2 + 2x + 2\sqrt{3}y = 0$$
$$(y')^2 = -x'$$

▶ Now Try Exercise 23.

✦ The Discriminant

It is possible to determine the type of conic represented by the equation $Ax^2 + Bxy + Cy^2 + Dx + Ey + F = 0$ before rotating the axes. Using the expressions for A', B', and C' in terms of A, B, C, and θ developed earlier, it can be shown that

$$(B')^2 - 4A'C' = B^2 - 4AC.$$

Now when θ is chosen so that

$$\cot 2\theta = \frac{A - C}{B},$$

rotation of axes gives us an equation

$$A'(x')^2 + C'(y')^2 + D'x' + E'y' + F' = 0.$$

If A' and C' have the same sign, or $A'C' > 0$, then the graph of this equation is an ellipse or a circle. If A' and C' have different signs, or $A'C' < 0$, then the graph is a hyperbola. And, if either $A' = 0$ or $C' = 0$, or $A'C' = 0$, the graph is a parabola.

Since $B' = 0$ and $(B')^2 - 4A'C' = B^2 - 4AC$, it follows that $B^2 - 4AC = -4A'C'$. Then the graph is an ellipse or a circle if $B^2 - 4AC < 0$, a hyperbola if $B^2 - 4AC > 0$, or a parabola if $B^2 - 4AC = 0$. (There are certain special cases, called *degenerate conics*, where these statements do not hold, but we will not concern ourselves with these here.) The expression $B^2 - 4AC$ is the **discriminant** of the equation $Ax^2 + Bxy + Cy^2 + Dx + Ey + F = 0$.

The graph of the equation

$$Ax^2 + Bxy + Cy^2 + Dx + Ey + F = 0$$

is, except in degenerate cases,

1. an ellipse or a circle if $B^2 - 4AC < 0$,
2. a hyperbola if $B^2 - 4AC > 0$, and
3. a parabola if $B^2 - 4AC = 0$.

EXAMPLE 3 Graph the equation $3x^2 + 2xy + 3y^2 = 16$.

Solution We have

$$A = 3, \quad B = 2, \quad \text{and} \quad C = 3, \quad \text{so}$$
$$B^2 - 4AC = 2^2 - 4 \cdot 3 \cdot 3 = 4 - 36 = -32.$$

Since the discriminant is negative, the graph is an ellipse or a circle. Now, to rotate the axes, we begin by determining θ:

$$\cot 2\theta = \frac{A - C}{B} = \frac{3 - 3}{2} = \frac{0}{2} = 0.$$

Then $2\theta = 90°$ and $\theta = 45°$, so

$$\sin\theta = \frac{\sqrt{2}}{2} \quad \text{and} \quad \cos\theta = \frac{\sqrt{2}}{2}.$$

Substituting in the rotation of axes formulas gives

$$x = x'\cos\theta - y'\sin\theta = x'\left(\frac{\sqrt{2}}{2}\right) - y'\left(\frac{\sqrt{2}}{2}\right) = \frac{\sqrt{2}}{2}(x' - y')$$

and

$$y = x'\sin\theta + y'\cos\theta = x'\left(\frac{\sqrt{2}}{2}\right) + y'\left(\frac{\sqrt{2}}{2}\right) = \frac{\sqrt{2}}{2}(x' + y').$$

Now we substitute for x and y in the given equation:

$$3\left[\frac{\sqrt{2}}{2}(x' - y')\right]^2 + 2\left[\frac{\sqrt{2}}{2}(x' - y')\right]\left[\frac{\sqrt{2}}{2}(x' + y')\right] +$$
$$3\left[\frac{\sqrt{2}}{2}(x' + y')\right]^2 = 16.$$

After simplifying, we have

$$4(x')^2 + 2(y')^2 = 16, \quad \text{or}$$
$$\frac{(x')^2}{4} + \frac{(y')^2}{8} = 1.$$

This is the equation of an ellipse with vertices $\left(0, -\sqrt{8}\right)$ and $\left(0, \sqrt{8}\right)$, or $\left(0, -2\sqrt{2}\right)$ and $\left(0, 2\sqrt{2}\right)$, on the y'-axis. The x'-intercepts are $(-2, 0)$ and $(2, 0)$. We sketch the graph.

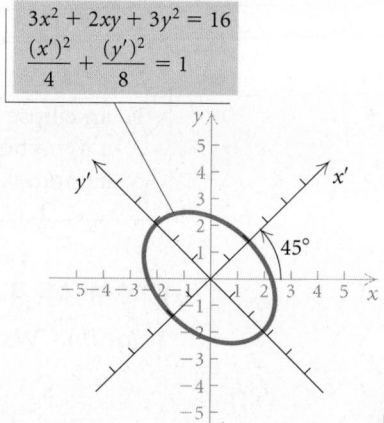

$3x^2 + 2xy + 3y^2 = 16$
$\dfrac{(x')^2}{4} + \dfrac{(y')^2}{8} = 1$

▶ Now Try Exercise 21.

EXAMPLE 4   Graph the equation $4x^2 - 24xy - 3y^2 - 156 = 0$.

Solution   We have

$$A = 4, \quad B = -24, \quad \text{and} \quad C = -3, \quad \text{so}$$
$$B^2 - 4AC = (-24)^2 - 4 \cdot 4(-3) = 576 + 48 = 624.$$

Since the discriminant is positive, the graph is a hyperbola. To rotate the axes, we begin by determining θ:

$$\cot 2\theta = \frac{A - C}{B} = \frac{4 - (-3)}{-24} = -\frac{7}{24}.$$

Since $\cot 2\theta < 0$, we have $90° < 2\theta < 180°$. From the triangle at left, we see that $\cos 2\theta = -\frac{7}{25}$.

Using half-angle formulas, we have

$$\sin \theta = \sqrt{\frac{1 - \cos 2\theta}{2}} = \sqrt{\frac{1 - \left(-\frac{7}{25}\right)}{2}} = \frac{4}{5}$$

and

$$\cos \theta = \sqrt{\frac{1 + \cos 2\theta}{2}} = \sqrt{\frac{1 + \left(-\frac{7}{25}\right)}{2}} = \frac{3}{5}.$$

Substituting in the rotation of axes formulas gives us

$$x = x' \cos \theta - y' \sin \theta = \tfrac{3}{5}x' - \tfrac{4}{5}y'$$

and

$$y = x' \sin \theta + y' \cos \theta = \tfrac{4}{5}x' + \tfrac{3}{5}y'.$$

Now we substitute for x and y in the given equation:

$$4\left(\tfrac{3}{5}x' - \tfrac{4}{5}y'\right)^2 - 24\left(\tfrac{3}{5}x' - \tfrac{4}{5}y'\right)\left(\tfrac{4}{5}x' + \tfrac{3}{5}y'\right) - 3\left(\tfrac{4}{5}x' + \tfrac{3}{5}y'\right)^2 - 156 = 0.$$

After simplifying, we have

$$13(y')^2 - 12(x')^2 - 156 = 0$$
$$13(y')^2 - 12(x')^2 = 156$$
$$\frac{(y')^2}{12} - \frac{(x')^2}{13} = 1.$$

The graph of this equation is a hyperbola with vertices $\left(0, -\sqrt{12}\right)$ and $\left(0, \sqrt{12}\right)$, or $\left(0, -2\sqrt{3}\right)$ and $\left(0, 2\sqrt{3}\right)$, on the y'-axis. Since we know that $\sin \theta = \tfrac{4}{5}$ and $0° < \theta < 90°$, we can use a calculator to find that $\theta \approx 53.1°$. Thus the xy-axes are rotated through an angle of about $53.1°$ in order to obtain the $x'y'$-axes. We sketch the graph.

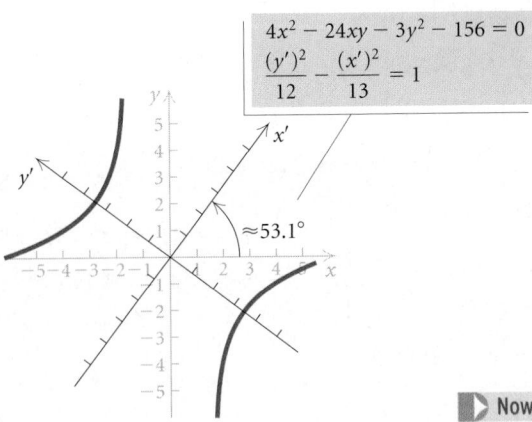

$$4x^2 - 24xy - 3y^2 - 156 = 0$$
$$\frac{(y')^2}{12} - \frac{(x')^2}{13} = 1$$

▶ Now Try Exercise 35.

9.5 EXERCISE SET

For the given angle of rotation and coordinates of a point in the xy-coordinate system, find the coordinates of the point in the x'y'-coordinate system.

1. $\theta = 45°, \left(\sqrt{2}, -\sqrt{2}\right)$ **2.** $\theta = 45°, (-1, 3)$

3. $\theta = 30°, (0, 2)$ **4.** $\theta = 60°, \left(0, \sqrt{3}\right)$

For the given angle of rotation and coordinates of a point in the x'y'-coordinate system, find the coordinates of the point in the xy-coordinate system.

5. $\theta = 45°, (1, -1)$ **6.** $\theta = 45°, \left(-3\sqrt{2}, \sqrt{2}\right)$

7. $\theta = 30°, (2, 0)$ **8.** $\theta = 60°, \left(-1, -\sqrt{3}\right)$

Use the discriminant to determine whether the graph of the equation is an ellipse (or a circle), a hyperbola, or a parabola.

9. $3x^2 - 5xy + 3y^2 - 2x + 7y = 0$

10. $5x^2 + 6xy - 4y^2 + x - 3y + 4 = 0$

11. $x^2 - 3xy - 2y^2 + 12 = 0$

12. $4x^2 + 7xy + 2y^2 - 3x + y = 0$

13. $4x^2 - 12xy + 9y^2 - 3x + y = 0$

14. $6x^2 + 5xy + 6y^2 + 15 = 0$

15. $2x^2 - 8xy + 7y^2 + x - 2y + 1 = 0$

16. $x^2 + 6xy + 9y^2 - 3x + 4y = 0$

17. $8x^2 - 7xy + 5y^2 - 17 = 0$

18. $x^2 + xy - y^2 - 4x + 3y - 2 = 0$

Graph the equation.

19. $3x^2 + 2xy + 3y^2 = 16$

20. $3x^2 + 10xy + 3y^2 + 8 = 0$

21. $x^2 - 10xy + y^2 + 36 = 0$

22. $x^2 + 2xy + y^2 + 4\sqrt{2}x - 4\sqrt{2}y = 0$

23. $x^2 - 2\sqrt{3}xy + 3y^2 - 12\sqrt{3}x - 12y = 0$

24. $13x^2 + 6\sqrt{3}xy + 7y^2 - 16 = 0$

25. $7x^2 + 6\sqrt{3}xy + 13y^2 - 32 = 0$

26. $x^2 + 4xy + y^2 - 9 = 0$

27. $11x^2 + 10\sqrt{3}xy + y^2 = 32$

28. $5x^2 - 8xy + 5y^2 = 81$

29. $\sqrt{2}x^2 + 2\sqrt{2}xy + \sqrt{2}y^2 - 8x + 8y = 0$

30. $x^2 + 2\sqrt{3}xy + 3y^2 - 8x + 8\sqrt{3}y = 0$

31. $x^2 + 6\sqrt{3}xy - 5y^2 + 8x - 8\sqrt{3}y - 48 = 0$

32. $3x^2 - 2xy + 3y^2 - 6\sqrt{2}x + 2\sqrt{2}y - 26 = 0$

33. $x^2 + xy + y^2 = 24$

34. $4x^2 + 3\sqrt{3}xy + y^2 = 55$

35. $4x^2 - 4xy + y^2 - 8\sqrt{5}x - 16\sqrt{5}y = 0$

36. $9x^2 - 24xy + 16y^2 - 400x - 300y = 0$

37. $11x^2 + 7xy - 13y^2 = 621$

38. $3x^2 + 4xy + 6y^2 = 28$

Collaborative Discussion and Writing

39. Explain how the procedure you would follow for graphing an equation of the form $Ax^2 + Bxy + Cy^2 + Dx + Ey + F = 0$ when $B \neq 0$ differs from the procedure you would follow when $B = 0$.

40. Discuss some circumstances under which you might use rotation of axes.

Skill Maintenance

Convert to radian measure.

41. $120°$ **42.** $-315°$

Convert to degree measure.

43. $\dfrac{\pi}{3}$ **44.** $\dfrac{3\pi}{4}$

Synthesis

45. Solve this system of equations for x and y:
$$x' = x\cos\theta + y\sin\theta,$$
$$y' = y\cos\theta - x\sin\theta.$$
Show your work.

46. Show that substituting $x' \cos \theta - y' \sin \theta$ for x and $x' \sin \theta + y' \cos \theta$ for y in the equation

$$Ax^2 + Bxy + Cy^2 + Dx + Ey + F = 0$$

yields the equation

$$A'(x')^2 + B'x'y' + C'(y')^2 + D'x' + E'y' + F' = 0,$$

where

$A' = A \cos^2 \theta + B \sin \theta \cos \theta + C \sin^2 \theta,$
$B' = 2(C - A) \sin \theta \cos \theta + B(\cos^2 \theta - \sin^2 \theta),$
$C' = A \sin^2 \theta - B \sin \theta \cos \theta + C \cos^2 \theta,$
$D' = D \cos \theta + E \sin \theta,$
$E' = -D \sin \theta + E \cos \theta,$ and
$F' = F.$

47. Show that $A + C = A' + C'.$

48. Show that for any angle θ, the equation $x^2 + y^2 = r^2$ becomes $(x')^2 + (y')^2 = r^2$ when the rotation of axes formulas are applied.

9.6

Polar Equations of Conics

✦ Graph polar equations of conics.
✦ Convert from polar equations of conics to rectangular equations of conics.
✦ Find polar equations of conics.

CONIC SECTIONS

REVIEW SECTIONS **9.1–9.3.**

In Sections 9.1–9.3, we saw that the parabola, the ellipse, and the hyperbola have different definitions in rectangular coordinates. When polar coordinates are used, we can give a single definition that applies to all three conics.

An Alternate Definition of Conics

Let L be a fixed line (the **directrix**); let F be a fixed point (the **focus**), not on L; and let e be a positive constant (the **eccentricity**). A **conic** is the set of all points P in the plane such that

$$\frac{PF}{PL} = e,$$

where PF is the distance from P to F and PL is the distance from P to L. The conic is a parabola if $e = 1$, an ellipse if $e < 1$, and a hyperbola if $e > 1$.

Note that if $e = 1$, then $PF = PL$ and the alternate definition of a parabola is identical to the definition presented in Section 9.1.

✦ Polar Equations of Conics

To derive equations for the conics in polar coordinates, we position the focus F at the pole and position the directrix L either perpendicular to the polar axis or parallel to it. In the figure below, we place L perpendicular to the polar axis and p units to the right of the focus, or pole.

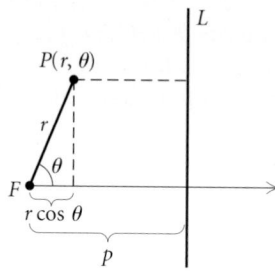

Note that $PL = p - r \cos \theta$. Then if P is any point on the conic, we have

$$\frac{PF}{PL} = e$$

$$\frac{r}{p - r \cos \theta} = e$$

$$r = ep - er \cos \theta$$

$$r + er \cos \theta = ep$$

$$r(1 + e \cos \theta) = ep$$

$$r = \frac{ep}{1 + e \cos \theta}.$$

Thus we see that the polar equation of a conic with focus at the pole and directrix perpendicular to the polar axis and p units to the right of the pole is

$$r = \frac{ep}{1 + e \cos \theta},$$

where e is the eccentricity of the conic.

For an ellipse and a hyperbola, we can make the following statement regarding eccentricity.

For an ellipse and a hyperbola, the **eccentricity** e is given by

$$e = \frac{c}{a},$$

where c is the distance from the center to a focus and a is the distance from the center to a vertex.

EXAMPLE 1 Describe and graph the conic $r = \dfrac{18}{6 + 3 \cos \theta}$.

Solution We begin by dividing the numerator and the denominator by 6 to obtain a constant term of 1 in the denominator:

$$r = \dfrac{3}{1 + 0.5 \cos \theta}.$$

This equation is in the form

$$r = \dfrac{ep}{1 + e \cos \theta}$$

with $e = 0.5$. Since $e < 1$, the graph is an ellipse. Also, since $e = 0.5$ and $ep = 0.5p = 3$, we have $p = 6$. Thus the ellipse has a vertical directrix that lies 6 units to the right of the pole.

It follows that the major axis is horizontal and lies on the polar axis. The vertices are found by letting $\theta = 0$ and $\theta = \pi$. They are $(2, 0)$ and $(6, \pi)$. The center of the ellipse is at the midpoint of the segment connecting the vertices, or at $(2, \pi)$.

The length of the major axis is 8, so we have $2a = 8$, or $a = 4$. From the equation of the conic, we know that $e = 0.5$. Using the equation $e = c/a$, we can find that $c = 2$. Finally, using $a = 4$ and $c = 2$ in $b^2 = a^2 - c^2$ gives us

$$b^2 = 4^2 - 2^2 = 16 - 4 = 12$$
$$b = \sqrt{12}, \text{ or } 2\sqrt{3},$$

so the length of the minor axis is $\sqrt{12}$, or $2\sqrt{3}$.

We sketch the graph.

TECHNOLOGY ⋯⋯⋯⋯⋯
CONNECTION

We can check the graph in Example 1 by graphing the equation in POLAR (POL) mode in a square window.

$$r = \dfrac{18}{6 + 3 \cos \theta}$$

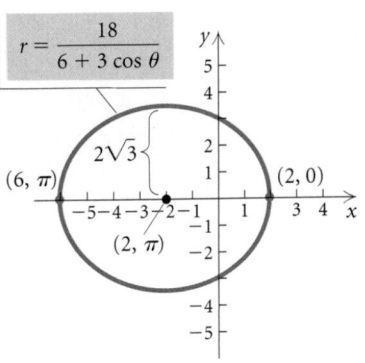

▶ **Now Try Exercise 7.**

Other derivations similar to the one on p. 822 lead to the following result.

> ### Polar Equations of Conics
> A polar equation of any of the four forms
>
> $$r = \frac{ep}{1 \pm e \cos \theta}, \qquad r = \frac{ep}{1 \pm e \sin \theta}$$
>
> is a conic section. The conic is a parabola if $e = 1$, an ellipse if $0 < e < 1$, and a hyperbola if $e > 1$.

The table below describes the polar equations of conics with a focus at the pole and the directrix either perpendicular to or parallel to the polar axis.

Equation	Description
$r = \dfrac{ep}{1 + e \cos \theta}$	Vertical directrix p units to the right of the pole (or focus)
$r = \dfrac{ep}{1 - e \cos \theta}$	Vertical directrix p units to the left of the pole (or focus)
$r = \dfrac{ep}{1 + e \sin \theta}$	Horizontal directrix p units above the pole (or focus)
$r = \dfrac{ep}{1 - e \sin \theta}$	Horizontal directrix p units below the pole (or focus)

EXAMPLE 2   Describe and graph the conic $r = \dfrac{10}{5 - 5 \sin \theta}$.

Solution   We first divide the numerator and the denominator by 5:

$$r = \frac{2}{1 - \sin \theta}.$$

This equation is in the form

$$r = \frac{ep}{1 - e \sin \theta}$$

with $e = 1$, so the graph is a parabola. Since $e = 1$ and $ep = 1 \cdot p = 2$, we have $p = 2$. Thus the parabola has a horizontal directrix 2 units below the pole.

It follows that the parabola has a vertical axis of symmetry.

Since the directrix lies below the focus, or pole, the parabola opens up. The vertex is the midpoint of the segment of the axis of symmetry from the focus to the directrix. We find it by letting $\theta = 3\pi/2$. It is $(1, 3\pi/2)$.

TECHNOLOGY ·············
CONNECTION

We can check the graph in
Example 2 by graphing the
equation in POLAR mode in a
square window.

$$r = \frac{10}{5 - 5 \sin \theta}$$

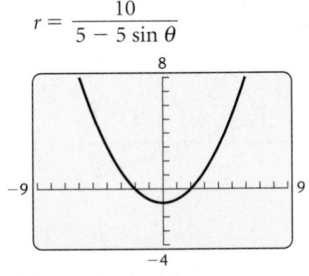

To help determine the shape of the graph, we find two additional points. When $\theta = 0$, $r = 2$, and when $\theta = \pi$, $r = 2$, so we have the points $(2, 0)$ and $(2, \pi)$. We sketch the graph.

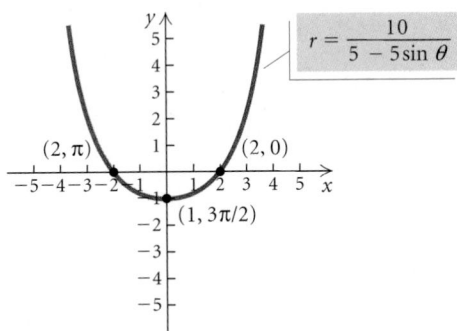

▶ Now Try Exercise 17.

EXAMPLE 3 Describe and graph the conic $r = \dfrac{4}{2 + 6 \sin \theta}$.

Solution We first divide the numerator and the denominator by 2:

$$r = \frac{2}{1 + 3 \sin \theta}.$$

This equation is in the form

$$r = \frac{ep}{1 + e \sin \theta}$$

with $e = 3$. Since $e > 1$, the graph is a hyperbola. We have $e = 3$ and $ep = 3p = 2$, so $p = \frac{2}{3}$. Thus the hyperbola has a horizontal directrix that lies $\frac{2}{3}$ unit above the pole.

It follows that the transverse axis is vertical. To find the vertices, we let $\theta = \pi/2$ and $\theta = 3\pi/2$. The vertices are $(1/2, \pi/2)$ and $(-1, 3\pi/2)$.

The center of the hyperbola is the midpoint of the segment connecting the vertices, or $(3/4, \pi/2)$. Thus the distance c from the center to a focus is $3/4$. Using $c = 3/4$, $e = 3$, and $e = c/a$, we have $a = 1/4$. Then since $c^2 = a^2 + b^2$, we have $b^2 = c^2 - a^2$, or

$$b^2 = \left(\frac{3}{4}\right)^2 - \left(\frac{1}{4}\right)^2 = \frac{9}{16} - \frac{1}{16} = \frac{1}{2}$$

$$b = \frac{1}{\sqrt{2}}, \text{ or } \frac{\sqrt{2}}{2}.$$

TECHNOLOGY ················
CONNECTION

To check the graph in Example 3, we can graph the equation in POLAR mode and in DOT mode in a square window.

$$r = \frac{4}{2 + 6\sin\theta}$$

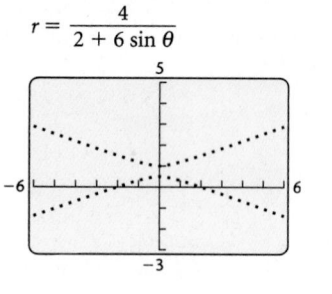

Knowing the values of a and b allows us to sketch the asymptotes. We can also easily plot the points $(2, 0)$ and $(2, \pi)$ on the polar axis.

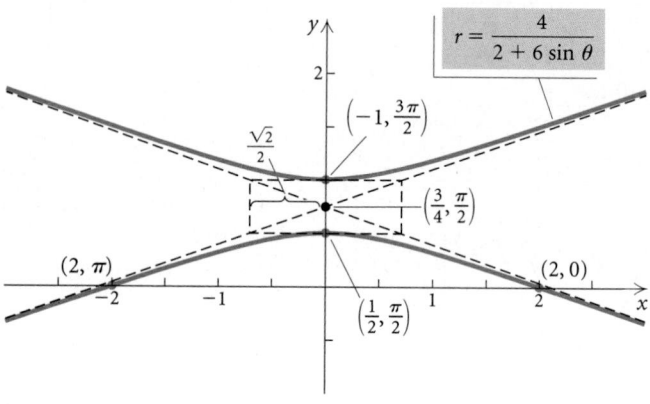

▶ Now Try Exercise 9.

✦ Converting from Polar to Rectangular Equations

We can use the relationships between polar and rectangular coordinates that were developed in Section 7.4 to convert polar equations of conics to rectangular equations.

EXAMPLE 4   Convert to a rectangular equation: $r = \dfrac{2}{1 - \sin\theta}$.

Solution   We have

$$r = \frac{2}{1 - \sin\theta}$$

$r - r\sin\theta = 2$	Multiplying by $1 - \sin\theta$
$r = r\sin\theta + 2$	
$\sqrt{x^2 + y^2} = y + 2$	Substituting $\sqrt{x^2 + y^2}$ for r and y for $r\sin\theta$
$x^2 + y^2 = y^2 + 4y + 4$	Squaring both sides
$x^2 = 4y + 4$, or	
$x^2 - 4y - 4 = 0.$	

This is the equation of a parabola, as we should have anticipated, since $e = 1$.

▶ Now Try Exercise 23.

✦ Finding Polar Equations of Conics

We can find the polar equation of a conic with a focus at the pole if we know its eccentricity and the equation of the directrix.

EXAMPLE 5   Find a polar equation of the conic with a focus at the pole, eccentricity $\frac{1}{3}$, and directrix $r = 2 \csc \theta$.

Solution   The equation of the directrix can be written

$$r = \frac{2}{\sin \theta}, \quad \text{or} \quad r \sin \theta = 2.$$

This corresponds to the equation $y = 2$ in rectangular coordinates, so the directrix is a horizontal line 2 units above the polar axis. Using the table on p. 824, we see that the equation is of the form

$$r = \frac{ep}{1 + e \sin \theta}.$$

Substituting $\frac{1}{3}$ for e and 2 for p gives us

$$r = \frac{\frac{1}{3} \cdot 2}{1 + \frac{1}{3} \sin \theta} = \frac{\frac{2}{3}}{1 + \frac{1}{3} \sin \theta} = \frac{2}{3 + \sin \theta}.$$

▶ Now Try Exercise 39.

9.6   EXERCISE SET

In Exercises 1–6, match the equation with one of the graphs (a)–(f), which follow.

a)

b)

c)

d)

e)

f)

1. $r = \dfrac{3}{1 + \cos \theta}$

2. $r = \dfrac{4}{1 + 2 \sin \theta}$

3. $r = \dfrac{8}{4 - 2 \cos \theta}$

4. $r = \dfrac{12}{4 + 6 \sin \theta}$

5. $r = \dfrac{5}{3 - 3 \sin \theta}$

6. $r = \dfrac{6}{3 + 2 \cos \theta}$

For each equation:

a) *Tell whether the equation describes a parabola, an ellipse, or a hyperbola.*

b) *State whether the directrix is vertical or horizontal and give its location in relation to the pole.*

c) *Find the vertex or vertices.*

d) *Graph the equation.*

7. $r = \dfrac{1}{1 + \cos \theta}$

8. $r = \dfrac{4}{2 + \cos \theta}$

9. $r = \dfrac{15}{5 - 10 \sin \theta}$

10. $r = \dfrac{12}{4 + 8 \sin \theta}$

11. $r = \dfrac{8}{6 - 3 \cos \theta}$

12. $r = \dfrac{6}{2 + 2 \sin \theta}$

13. $r = \dfrac{20}{10 + 15 \sin \theta}$

14. $r = \dfrac{10}{8 - 2 \cos \theta}$

15. $r = \dfrac{9}{6 + 3 \cos \theta}$

16. $r = \dfrac{4}{3 - 9 \sin \theta}$

17. $r = \dfrac{3}{2 - 2 \sin \theta}$

18. $r = \dfrac{12}{3 + 9 \cos \theta}$

19. $r = \dfrac{4}{2 - \cos \theta}$

20. $r = \dfrac{5}{1 - \sin \theta}$

21. $r = \dfrac{7}{2 + 10 \sin \theta}$

22. $r = \dfrac{3}{8 - 4 \cos \theta}$

23–38. Convert the equations in Exercises 7–22 to rectangular equations.

Find a polar equation of the conic with a focus at the pole and the given eccentricity and directrix.

39. $e = 2, r = 3 \csc \theta$

40. $e = \frac{2}{3}, r = -\sec \theta$

41. $e = 1, r = 4 \sec \theta$

42. $e = 3, r = 2 \csc \theta$

43. $e = \frac{1}{2}, r = -2 \sec \theta$

44. $e = 1, r = 4 \csc \theta$

45. $e = \frac{3}{4}, r = 5 \csc \theta$

46. $e = \frac{4}{5}, r = 2 \sec \theta$

47. $e = 4, r = -2 \csc \theta$

48. $e = 3, r = 3 \csc \theta$

Collaborative Discussion and Writing

49. Consider the graphs of

$$r = \frac{e}{1 - e \sin \theta}$$

for $e = 0.2, 0.4, 0.6,$ and 0.8. Explain the effect of the value of e on the graph.

50. Would you prefer to graph a conic in rectangular form or in polar form? Why?

Skill Maintenance

For $f(x) = (x - 3)^2 + 4$, find each of the following.

51. $f(t)$

52. $f(2t)$

53. $f(t - 1)$

54. $f(t + 2)$

Synthesis

Parabolic Orbit. Suppose that a comet travels in a parabolic orbit with the sun as its focus. Position a polar coordinate system with the pole at the sun and the axis of the orbit perpendicular to the polar axis. When the comet is the given distance from the sun, the segment from the comet to the sun makes the given angle with the polar axis. Find a polar equation of the orbit, assuming that the directrix lies above the pole.

55. 100 million miles, $\dfrac{\pi}{6}$

56. 120 million miles, $\dfrac{\pi}{4}$

9.7 Parametric Equations

♦ Graph parametric equations.

♦ Determine an equivalent rectangular equation for parametric equations.

♦ Determine parametric equations for a rectangular equation.

♦ Determine the location of a moving object at a specific time.

✦ Graphing Parametric Equations

We have graphed *plane curves* that are composed of sets of ordered pairs (x, y) in the rectangular coordinate plane. Now we discuss a way to represent plane curves in which x and y are functions of a third variable t.

EXAMPLE 1   Graph the curve represented by the equations

$$x = \tfrac{1}{2}t, \qquad y = t^2 - 3; \quad -3 \le t \le 3.$$

Solution   We can choose values for t between -3 and 3 and find the corresponding values of x and y. When $t = -3$, we have

$$x = \tfrac{1}{2}(-3) = -\tfrac{3}{2}, \qquad y = (-3)^2 - 3 = 6.$$

The table below lists other ordered pairs. We plot these points and then draw the curve.

t	x	y	(x, y)
-3	$-\frac{3}{2}$	6	$\left(-\frac{3}{2}, 6\right)$
-2	-1	1	$(-1, 1)$
-1	$-\frac{1}{2}$	-2	$\left(-\frac{1}{2}, -2\right)$
0	0	-3	$(0, -3)$
1	$\frac{1}{2}$	-2	$\left(\frac{1}{2}, -2\right)$
2	1	1	$(1, 1)$
3	$\frac{3}{2}$	6	$\left(\frac{3}{2}, 6\right)$

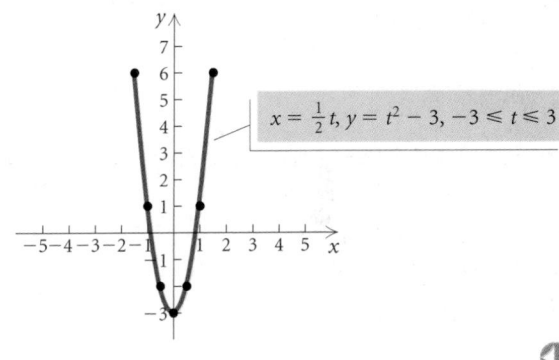

$x = \tfrac{1}{2}t, y = t^2 - 3, -3 \le t \le 3$

The curve above appears to be part of a parabola. Let's verify this by finding the equivalent rectangular equation. Solving $x = \tfrac{1}{2}t$ for t, we get $t = 2x$. Substituting $2x$ for t in $y = t^2 - 3$, we have

$$y = (2x)^2 - 3 = 4x^2 - 3.$$

This is a quadratic equation. Hence its graph is a parabola. Thus the curve is part of the parabola $y = 4x^2 - 3$. Since $-3 \le t \le 3$ and $x = \tfrac{1}{2}t$, we must include the restriction $-\tfrac{3}{2} \le x \le \tfrac{3}{2}$ when we write the equivalent rectangular equation:

$$y = 4x^2 - 3, \quad -\tfrac{3}{2} \le x \le \tfrac{3}{2}.$$

The equations $x = \frac{1}{2}t$ and $y = t^2 - 3$ are **parametric equations** for the curve. The variable t is the **parameter**.

Parametric Equations

If f and g are continuous functions of t on an interval I, then the set of ordered pairs (x, y) such that $x = f(t)$ and $y = g(t)$ is a **plane curve**. The equations $x = f(t)$ and $y = g(t)$ are **parametric equations** for the curve. The variable t is the **parameter**.

✦ Determining a Rectangular Equation for Given Parametric Equations

EXAMPLE 2 Find a rectangular equation equivalent to each pair of parametric equations.

a) $x = t^2,\ y = t - 1;\ -1 \leq t \leq 4$

b) $x = \sqrt{t},\ y = 2t + 3;\ 0 \leq t \leq 3$

Solution

a) We can first solve either equation for t. We choose the equation $y = t - 1$:

$$y = t - 1$$
$$y + 1 = t.$$

We then substitute $y + 1$ for t in $x = t^2$:

$$x = t^2$$
$$x = (y + 1)^2. \quad \text{Substituting}$$

This is an equation of a parabola that opens to the right. Given that $-1 \leq t \leq 4$, we have the corresponding restrictions on x and y: $0 \leq x \leq 16$ and $-2 \leq y \leq 3$. Thus the equivalent rectangular equation is

$$x = (y + 1)^2; \quad 0 \leq x \leq 16.$$

b) We first solve $x = \sqrt{t}$ for t:

$$x = \sqrt{t}$$
$$x^2 = t.$$

Then we substitute x^2 for t in $y = 2t + 3$:

$$y = 2t + 3$$
$$y = 2x^2 + 3. \quad \text{Substituting}$$

When $0 \leq t \leq 3$, we have $0 \leq x \leq \sqrt{3}$. The equivalent rectangular equation is

$$y = 2x^2 + 3; \quad 0 \leq x \leq \sqrt{3}.$$

▶ Now Try Exercise 5.

We can graph parametric equations on a graphing calculator set in PARAMETRIC mode. The window dimensions include minimum and maximum values for x, y, and t. For the parametric equations in Example 2(b), we can use the settings shown below.

WINDOW
  Tmin = 0
  Tmax = 3
  Tstep = .1
  Xmin = −3
  Xmax = 3
  Xscl = 1
  Ymin = −2
  Ymax = 10
  Yscl = 1

$x = \sqrt{t}, \quad y = 2t + 3;$
$0 \le t \le 3$

EXAMPLE 3 Find a rectangular equation equivalent to each pair of parametric equations.

a) $x = \cos t,\ y = \sin t;\ 0 \le t \le 2\pi$

b) $x = 5 \cos t,\ y = 3 \sin t;\ 0 \le t \le 2\pi$

Solution

a) First, we square both sides of each parametric equation:

$$x^2 = \cos^2 t \quad \text{and} \quad y^2 = \sin^2 t.$$

This allows us to use the trigonometric identity $\sin^2 \theta + \cos^2 \theta = 1$. Substituting, we get

$$x^2 + y^2 = 1.$$

This is the equation of a circle with center $(0, 0)$ and radius 1.

b) First, we solve for $\cos t$ and $\sin t$ in the parametric equations:

$$x = 5 \cos t \qquad\qquad y = 3 \sin t$$

$$\frac{x}{5} = \cos t, \qquad\qquad \frac{y}{3} = \sin t.$$

Using the identity $\sin^2 \theta + \cos^2 \theta = 1$, we can substitute to eliminate the parameter:

$$\sin^2 t + \cos^2 t = 1$$

$$\left(\frac{y}{3}\right)^2 + \left(\frac{x}{5}\right)^2 = 1 \qquad \text{Substituting}$$

$$\frac{x^2}{25} + \frac{y^2}{9} = 1.$$

This is the equation of an ellipse centered at the origin with vertices at $(5, 0)$ and $(−5, 0)$.

▶ Now Try Exercise 13.

✦ Determining Parametric Equations for a Given Rectangular Equation

Many sets of parametric equations can represent the same plane curve. In fact, there are infinitely many such equations.

EXAMPLE 4   Find three sets of parametric equations for the parabola

$$y = 4 - (x + 3)^2.$$

Solution

If $x = t$, then $y = 4 - (t + 3)^2$, or $-5 - 6t - t^2$.

If $x = t - 3$, then $y = 4 - (t - 3 + 3)^2$, or $4 - t^2$.

If $x = \dfrac{t}{3}$, then $y = 4 - \left(\dfrac{t}{3} + 3\right)^2$, or $-\dfrac{t^2}{9} - 2t - 5$.

▷ **Now Try Exercise 21.**

✦ Applications

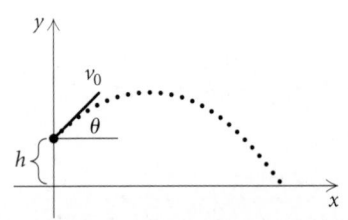

The motion of an object that is propelled upward can be described with parametric equations. Such motion is called **projectile motion.** It can be shown using more advanced mathematics that, neglecting air resistance, the following equations describe the path of a projectile propelled upward at an angle θ with the horizontal from a height h, in feet, at an initial speed v_0, in feet per second:

$$x = (v_0 \cos \theta)t, \qquad y = h + (v_0 \sin \theta)t - 16t^2.$$

We can use these equations to determine the location of the object at time t, in seconds.

EXAMPLE 5   *Projectile Motion.*   A baseball is thrown from a height of 6 ft with an initial speed of 100 ft/sec at an angle of 45° with the horizontal.

a) Find parametric equations that give the position of the ball at time t, in seconds.

b) Find the height of the ball after 1 sec, 2 sec, and 3 sec.

c) Determine how long the ball is in the air.

d) Determine the horizontal distance that the ball travels.

e) Find the maximum height of the ball.

Solution

a) We substitute 6 for h, 100 for v_0, and 45° for θ in the equations above:

$$x = (v_0 \cos \theta)t$$
$$= (100 \cos 45°)t$$
$$= \left(100 \cdot \frac{\sqrt{2}}{2}\right)t = 50\sqrt{2}t;$$
$$y = h + (v_0 \sin \theta)t - 16t^2$$
$$= 6 + (100 \sin 45°)t - 16t^2$$
$$= 6 + \left(100 \cdot \frac{\sqrt{2}}{2}\right)t - 16t^2$$
$$= 6 + 50\sqrt{2}t - 16t^2.$$

b) The height of the ball at time t is represented by y.

When $t = 1$, $y = 6 + 50\sqrt{2}(1) - 16(1)^2 \approx 60.7$ ft.
When $t = 2$, $y = 6 + 50\sqrt{2}(2) - 16(2)^2 \approx 83.4$ ft.
When $t = 3$, $y = 6 + 50\sqrt{2}(3) - 16(3)^2 \approx 74.1$ ft.

c) The ball hits the ground when $y = 0$. Thus, in order to determine how long the ball is in the air, we solve the equation $y = 0$:

$$6 + 50\sqrt{2}t - 16t^2 = 0$$
$$-16t^2 + 50\sqrt{2}t + 6 = 0 \qquad \text{Standard form}$$
$$t = \frac{-50\sqrt{2} \pm \sqrt{\left(50\sqrt{2}\right)^2 - 4(-16)(6)}}{2(-16)}$$

Using the quadratic formula

$$t \approx -0.1 \quad or \quad t \approx 4.5.$$

The negative value for t has no meaning in this application. Thus we determine that the ball is in the air for about 4.5 sec.

d) Since the ball is in the air for about 4.5 sec, the horizontal distance that it travels is given by

$$x = 50\sqrt{2}(4.5) \approx 318.2 \text{ ft.}$$

e) To find the maximum height of the ball, we find the maximum value of y. This occurs at the vertex of the quadratic function represented by y. At the vertex, we have

$$t = -\frac{b}{2a} = -\frac{50\sqrt{2}}{2(-16)} \approx 2.2.$$

When $t = 2.2$,

$$y = 6 + 50\sqrt{2}(2.2) - 16(2.2)^2 \approx 84.1 \text{ ft.}$$

▶ Now Try Exercise 25.

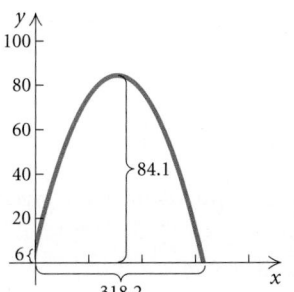

The path of a fixed point on the circumference of a circle as it rolls along a line is called a **cycloid.** For example, a point on the rim of a bicycle wheel traces a cycloid curve.

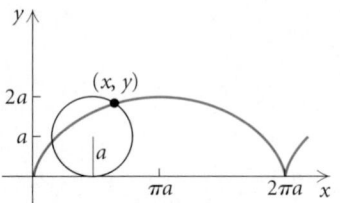

The parametric equations of a cycloid are

$$x = a(t - \sin t), \qquad y = a(1 - \cos t),$$

where a is the radius of the circle that traces the curve and t is in radian measure. The graph of the cycloid described by the parametric equations

$$x = 3(t - \sin t), \qquad y = 3(1 - \cos t); \quad 0 \le t \le 6\pi$$

is shown below.

9.7   EXERCISE SET

Graph the plane curve given by the parametric equations. Then find an equivalent rectangular equation.

1. $x = \frac{1}{2}t, \; y = 6t - 7; \; -1 \le t \le 6$

2. $x = t, \; y = 5 - t; \; -2 \le t \le 3$

3. $x = 4t^2, \; y = 2t; \; -1 \le t \le 1$

4. $x = \sqrt{t}, \; y = 2t + 3; \; 0 \le t \le 8$

Find a rectangular equation equivalent to the given pair of parametric equations.

5. $x = t^2, \; y = \sqrt{t}; \; 0 \le t \le 4$

6. $x = t^3 + 1, \; y = t; \; -3 \le t \le 3$

7. $x = t + 3, \; y = \dfrac{1}{t + 3}; \; -2 \le t \le 2$

8. $x = 2t^3 + 1, \; y = 2t^3 - 1; \; -4 \le t \le 4$

9. $x = 2t - 1$, $y = t^2$; $-3 \le t \le 3$

10. $x = \frac{1}{3}t$, $y = t$; $-5 \le t \le 5$

11. $x = e^{-t}$, $y = e^t$; $-\infty < t < \infty$

12. $x = 2 \ln t$, $y = t^2$; $0 < t < \infty$

13. $x = 3 \cos t$, $y = 3 \sin t$; $0 \le t \le 2\pi$

14. $x = 2 \cos t$, $y = 4 \sin t$; $0 \le t \le 2\pi$

15. $x = \cos t$, $y = 2 \sin t$; $0 \le t \le 2\pi$

16. $x = 2 \cos t$, $y = 2 \sin t$; $0 \le t \le 2\pi$

17. $x = \sec t$, $y = \cos t$; $-\frac{\pi}{2} < t < \frac{\pi}{2}$

18. $x = \sin t$, $y = \csc t$; $0 < t < \pi$

19. $x = 1 + 2 \cos t$, $y = 2 + 2 \sin t$; $0 \le t \le 2\pi$

20. $x = 2 + \sec t$, $y = 1 + 3 \tan t$; $0 < t < \frac{\pi}{2}$

Find two sets of parametric equations for the rectangular equation.

21. $y = 4x - 3$

22. $y = x^2 - 1$

23. $y = (x - 2)^2 - 6x$

24. $y = x^3 + 3$

25. *Projectile Motion.* A ball is thrown from a height of 7 ft with an initial speed of 80 ft/sec at an angle of 30° with the horizontal.

a) Find parametric equations that give the position of the ball at time t, in seconds.
b) Find the height of the ball after 1 sec and 2 sec.
c) Determine how long the ball is in the air.
d) Determine the horizontal distance that the ball travels.
e) Find the maximum height of the ball.

26. *Projectile Motion.* A projectile is launched from the ground with an initial speed of 200 ft/sec at an angle of 60° with the horizontal.

a) Find parametric equations that give the position of the projectile at time t, in seconds.

b) Find the height of the projectile after 4 sec and 8 sec.
c) Determine how long the projectile is in the air.
d) Determine the horizontal distance that the projectile travels.
e) Find the maximum height of the projectile.

Collaborative Discussion and Writing

27. Show that $x = a \cos t + h$ and $y = b \sin t + k$; $0 \le t \le 2\pi$, are parametric equations of an ellipse with center (h, k).

28. For the parametric equations $x = a \cos t$, $y = a \sin t$; $0 \le t \le 2\pi$, explain what a represents in terms of the graph of the equations.

Skill Maintenance

Graph.

29. $y = x^3$

30. $x = y^3$

31. $f(x) = \sqrt{x - 2}$

32. $f(x) = \frac{3}{x^2 - 1}$

Synthesis

33. Consider the curve described by
$$x = 3 \cos t, \qquad y = 3 \sin t; \quad 0 \le t \le 2\pi.$$
As t increases, the curve is traced in the counterclockwise direction. How can the equations be changed so that the curve is traced in the clockwise direction?

34. Find an equivalent rectangular equation for the curve described by
$$x = \cos^3 t, \qquad y = \sin^3 t; \quad 0 \le t \le 2\pi.$$

CHAPTER 9 SUMMARY AND REVIEW

Important Properties and Formulas

Standard Equation of a Parabola with Vertex at the Origin

The standard equation of a parabola with vertex $(0,0)$ and directrix $y = -p$ is

$$x^2 = 4py.$$

The focus is $(0,p)$ and the y-axis is the axis of symmetry.

The standard equation of a parabola with vertex $(0,0)$ and directrix $x = -p$ is

$$y^2 = 4px.$$

The focus is $(p,0)$ and the x-axis is the axis of symmetry.

Standard Equation of a Parabola with Vertex (h,k) and Vertical Axis of Symmetry

The standard equation of a parabola with vertex (h,k) and vertical axis of symmetry is

$$(x - h)^2 = 4p(y - k),$$

where the vertex is (h,k), the focus is $(h, k + p)$, and the directrix is $y = k - p$.

Standard Equation of a Parabola with Vertex (h,k) and Horizontal Axis of Symmetry

The standard equation of a parabola with vertex (h,k) and horizontal axis of symmetry is

$$(y - k)^2 = 4p(x - h),$$

where the vertex is (h,k), the focus is $(h + p, k)$, and the directrix is $x = h - p$.

Standard Equation of a Circle

The standard equation of a circle with center (h,k) and radius r is

$$(x - h)^2 + (y - k)^2 = r^2.$$

Standard Equation of an Ellipse with Center at the Origin

Major axis horizontal

$$\frac{x^2}{a^2} + \frac{y^2}{b^2} = 1, \ a > b > 0$$

Vertices: $(-a,0), (a,0)$
y-intercepts: $(0,-b), (0,b)$
Foci: $(-c,0), (c,0)$, where $c^2 = a^2 - b^2$

Major axis vertical

$$\frac{x^2}{b^2} + \frac{y^2}{a^2} = 1, \ a > b > 0$$

Vertices: $(0,-a), (0,a)$
x-intercepts: $(-b,0), (b,0)$
Foci: $(0,-c), (0,c)$, where $c^2 = a^2 - b^2$

Standard Equation of an Ellipse with Center at (h,k)

Major axis horizontal

$$\frac{(x - h)^2}{a^2} + \frac{(y - k)^2}{b^2} = 1, \ a > b > 0$$

Vertices: $(h - a, k), (h + a, k)$
Length of minor axis: $2b$
Foci: $(h - c, k), (h + c, k)$, where $c^2 = a^2 - b^2$

Major axis vertical

$$\frac{(x-h)^2}{b^2} + \frac{(y-k)^2}{a^2} = 1, \ a > b > 0$$

Vertices: $(h, k-a), (h, k+a)$

Length of minor axis: $2b$

Foci: $(h, k-c), (h, k+c)$, where $c^2 = a^2 - b^2$

Standard Equation of a Hyperbola with Center at the Origin

Transverse axis horizontal

$$\frac{x^2}{a^2} - \frac{y^2}{b^2} = 1$$

Vertices: $(-a, 0), (a, 0)$

Asymptotes: $y = -\frac{b}{a}x, \ y = \frac{b}{a}x$

Foci: $(-c, 0), (c, 0)$, where $c^2 = a^2 + b^2$

Transverse axis vertical

$$\frac{y^2}{a^2} - \frac{x^2}{b^2} = 1$$

Vertices: $(0, -a), (0, a)$

Asymptotes: $y = -\frac{a}{b}x, \ y = \frac{a}{b}x$

Foci: $(0, -c), (0, c)$, where $c^2 = a^2 + b^2$

Standard Equation of a Hyperbola with Center at (h, k)

Transverse axis horizontal

$$\frac{(x-h)^2}{a^2} - \frac{(y-k)^2}{b^2} = 1$$

Vertices: $(h-a, k), (h+a, k)$

Asymptotes: $y - k = \frac{b}{a}(x-h)$,

$$y - k = -\frac{b}{a}(x-h)$$

Foci: $(h-c, k), (h+c, k)$, where $c^2 = a^2 + b^2$

Transverse axis vertical

$$\frac{(y-k)^2}{a^2} - \frac{(x-h)^2}{b^2} = 1$$

Vertices: $(h, k-a), (h, k+a)$

Asymptotes: $y - k = \frac{a}{b}(x-h)$,

$$y - k = -\frac{a}{b}(x-h)$$

Foci: $(h, k-c), (h, k+c)$, where $c^2 = a^2 + b^2$

Rotation of Axes Formulas

$x' = x\cos\theta + y\sin\theta,$ $x = x'\cos\theta - y'\sin\theta,$

$y' = -x\sin\theta + y\cos\theta;$ $y = x'\sin\theta + y'\cos\theta$

Eliminating the xy-Term

To eliminate the xy-term from the equation

$$Ax^2 + Bxy + Cy^2 + Dx + Ey + F = 0, \quad B \neq 0,$$

select an angle θ such that

$$\cot 2\theta = \frac{A-C}{B}, \quad 0 < 2\theta < 180°,$$

and use the rotation of axes formulas.

The Discriminant

The graph of the equation $Ax^2 + Bxy + Cy^2 + Dx + Ey + F = 0$ is, except in degenerate cases,

1. an ellipse or a circle if $B^2 - 4AC < 0$,
2. a hyperbola if $B^2 - 4AC > 0$,   and
3. a parabola if $B^2 - 4AC = 0$.

Polar Equations of Conics

A polar equation of any of the four forms

$$r = \frac{ep}{1 \pm e\cos\theta}, \qquad r = \frac{ep}{1 \pm e\sin\theta}$$

is a conic section. The conic is a parabola if $e = 1$, an ellipse if $0 < e < 1$, and a hyperbola if $e > 1$.

REVIEW EXERCISES

Determine whether the statement is true or false.

1. The graph of $x + y^2 = 1$ is a parabola that opens to the left.   [9.1]

2. The graph of $\dfrac{(x-2)^2}{4} + \dfrac{(y+3)^2}{9}$ is an ellipse with center $(-2, 3)$.   [9.2]

3. The hyperbola $\dfrac{x^2}{5} - \dfrac{y^2}{10} = 1$ has a horizontal transverse axis.   [9.3]

4. Every nonlinear system of equations has at least one real-number solution.   [9.4]

5. The graph of $2x^2 + xy + 2y^2 = 10$ is a parabola.   [9.5]

In Exercises 6–13, match the equation with one of the graphs (a)–(h), which follow.

a)

b)

c)

d)

e)

f)

g)

h)

6. $y^2 = 5x$ [9.1]

7. $y^2 = 9 - x^2$ [9.2]

8. $3x^2 + 4y^2 = 12$ [9.2]

9. $9y^2 - 4x^2 = 36$ [9.3]

10. $x^2 + y^2 + 2x - 3y = 8$ [9.2]

11. $4x^2 + y^2 - 16x - 6y = 15$ [9.2]

12. $x^2 - 8x + 6y = 0$ [9.1]

13. $\dfrac{(x+3)^2}{16} - \dfrac{(y-1)^2}{25} = 1$ [9.3]

14. Find an equation of the parabola with directrix $y = \frac{3}{2}$ and focus $\left(0, -\frac{3}{2}\right)$.   [9.1]

15. Find the focus, the vertex, and the directrix of the parabola given by
$$y^2 = -12x.$$ [9.1]

16. Find the vertex, the focus, and the directrix of the parabola given by
$$x^2 + 10x + 2y + 9 = 0.$$ [9.1]

17. Find the center, the vertices, and the foci of the ellipse given by
$$16x^2 + 25y^2 - 64x + 50y - 311 = 0.$$
Then draw the graph.   [9.2]

18. Find an equation of the ellipse having vertices $(0, -4)$ and $(0, 4)$ with minor axis of length 6.   [9.2]

19. Find the center, the vertices, the foci, and the asymptotes of the hyperbola given by
$$x^2 - 2y^2 + 4x + y - \tfrac{1}{8} = 0.$$ [9.3]

20. *Spotlight.* A spotlight has a parabolic cross section that is 2 ft wide at the opening and 1.5 ft deep at the vertex. How far from the vertex is the focus? [9.1]

Solve. [9.4]

21. $x^2 - 16y = 0$,
$x^2 - y^2 = 64$

22. $4x^2 + 4y^2 = 65$,
$6x^2 - 4y^2 = 25$

23. $x^2 - y^2 = 33$,
$x + y = 11$

24. $x^2 - 2x + 2y^2 = 8$,
$2x + y = 6$

25. $x^2 - y = 3$,
$2x - y = 3$

26. $x^2 + y^2 = 25$,
$x^2 - y^2 = 7$

27. $x^2 - y^2 = 3$,
$y = x^2 - 3$

28. $x^2 + y^2 = 18$,
$2x + y = 3$

29. $x^2 + y^2 = 100$,
$2x^2 - 3y^2 = -120$

30. $x^2 + 2y^2 = 12$,
$xy = 4$

31. *Numerical Relationship.* The sum of two numbers is 11 and the sum of their squares is 65. Find the numbers. [9.4]

32. *Dimensions of a Rectangle.* A rectangle has a perimeter of 38 m and an area of 84 m². What are the dimensions of the rectangle? [9.4]

33. *Numerical Relationship.* Find two positive integers whose sum is 12 and the sum of whose reciprocals is $\frac{3}{8}$. [9.4]

34. *Perimeter.* The perimeter of a square is 12 cm more than the perimeter of another square. The area of the first square exceeds the area of the other by 39 cm². Find the perimeter of each square. [9.4]

35. *Radius of a Circle.* The sum of the areas of two circles is 130π ft². The difference of the areas is 112π ft². Find the radius of each circle. [9.4]

Graph the system of inequalities. Then find the coordinates of the points of intersection of the graphs. [9.4]

36. $y \le 4 - x^2$,
$x - y \le 2$

37. $x^2 + y^2 \le 16$,
$x + y < 4$

38. $y \ge x^2 - 1$,
$y < 1$

39. $x^2 + y^2 \le 9$,
$x \le -1$

Graph the equation. [9.5]

40. $5x^2 - 2xy + 5y^2 - 24 = 0$

41. $x^2 - 10xy + y^2 + 12 = 0$

42. $5x^2 + 6\sqrt{3}xy - y^2 = 16$

43. $x^2 + 2xy + y^2 - \sqrt{2}x + \sqrt{2}y = 0$

Graph the equation. State whether the directrix is vertical or horizontal, describe its location in relation to the pole, and find the vertex or vertices. [9.6]

44. $r = \dfrac{6}{3 - 3\sin\theta}$

45. $r = \dfrac{8}{2 + 4\cos\theta}$

46. $r = \dfrac{4}{2 - \cos\theta}$

47. $r = \dfrac{18}{9 + 6\sin\theta}$

48.–51. Convert the equations in Exercises 44–47 to rectangular equations. [9.6]

Find a polar equation of the conic with a focus at the pole and the given eccentricity and directrix. [9.6]

52. $e = \frac{1}{2}, r = 2\sec\theta$

53. $e = 3, r = -6\csc\theta$

54. $e = 1, r = -4\sec\theta$

55. $e = 2, r = 3\csc\theta$

Graph the plane curve given by the set of parametric equations and the restrictions for the parameter. Then find the equivalent rectangular equation. [9.7]

56. $x = t, y = 2 + t; \quad -3 \le t \le 3$

57. $x = \sqrt{t}, y = t - 1; \quad 0 \le t \le 9$

58. $x = 2\cos t, y = 2\sin t; \quad 0 \le t \le 2\pi$

59. $x = 3\sin t, y = \cos t; \quad 0 \le t \le 2\pi$

Find two sets of parametric equations for the given rectangular equation. [9.7]

60. $y = 2x - 3$

61. $y = x^2 + 4$

62. *Projectile Motion.* A projectile is launched from the ground with an initial speed of 150 ft/sec at an angle of 45° with the horizontal. [9.7]

   a) Find parametric equations that give the position of the projectile at time t, in seconds.

   b) Find the height of the projectile after 3 sec and 6 sec.

   c) Determine how long the projectile is in the air.

   d) Determine the horizontal distance that the projectile travels.

   e) Find the maximum height of the projectile.

63. The vertex of the parabola $y^2 - 4y - 12x - 8 = 0$ is which of the following? [9.1]

   A. $(1, -2)$
   B. $(-1, 2)$
   C. $(2, -1)$
   D. $(-2, 1)$

64. Which of the following cannot be a number of solutions possible for a system of equations representing an ellipse and a straight line? [9.4]

   A. 0
   B. 1
   C. 2
   D. 4

Collaborative Discussion and Writing

65. What would you say to a classmate who tells you that it is always possible to visualize all the solutions of a nonlinear system of equations? [9.4]

66. Is a circle a special type of ellipse? Why or why not? [9.2]

Synthesis

67. Find an equation of the ellipse containing the point $\left(-1/2, 3\sqrt{3}/2\right)$ and with vertices $(0, -3)$ and $(0, 3)$. [9.2]

68. Find two numbers whose product is 4 and the sum of whose reciprocals is $\frac{65}{56}$. [9.4]

69. Find an equation of the circle that passes through the points $(10, 7)$, $(-6, 7)$, and $(-8, 1)$. [9.2], [9.4]

70. *Navigation.* Two radio transmitters positioned 400 mi apart along the shore send simultaneous signals to a ship that is 250 mi offshore, sailing parallel to the shoreline. The signal from transmitter A reaches the ship 300 microseconds before the signal from transmitter B. The signals travel at a speed of 186,000 miles per second, or 0.186 mile per microsecond. Find the equation of the hyperbola with foci A and B on which the ship is located. (*Hint*: For any point on the hyperbola, the absolute value of the difference of its distances from the foci is $2a$.) [9.3]

CHAPTER 9 TEST

In Exercises 1–4, match the equation with one of the graphs (a)–(d), which follow.

a)

b)

c)

d)

1. $4x^2 - y^2 = 4$

2. $x^2 - 2x - 3y = 5$

3. $x^2 + 4x + y^2 - 2y - 4 = 0$

4. $9x^2 + 4y^2 = 36$

Find the vertex, the focus, and the directrix of the parabola. Then draw the graph.

5. $x^2 = 12y$

6. $y^2 + 2y - 8x - 7 = 0$

7. Find an equation of the parabola with focus $(0, 2)$ and directrix $y = -2$.

8. Find the center and the radius of the circle given by $x^2 + y^2 + 2x - 6y - 15 = 0$. Then draw the graph.

Find the center, the vertices, and the foci of the ellipse. Then draw the graph.

9. $9x^2 + 16y^2 = 144$

10. $\dfrac{(x + 1)^2}{4} + \dfrac{(y - 2)^2}{9} = 1$

11. Find an equation of the ellipse having vertices $(0, -5)$ and $(0, 5)$ and with minor axis of length 4.

Find the center, the vertices, the foci, and the asymptotes of the hyperbola. Then draw the graph.

12. $4x^2 - y^2 = 4$

13. $\dfrac{(y - 2)^2}{4} - \dfrac{(x + 1)^2}{9} = 1$

14. Find the asymptotes of the hyperbola given by $2y^2 - x^2 = 18$.

15. *Satellite Dish.* A satellite dish has a parabolic cross section that is 18 in. wide at the opening and 6 in. deep at the vertex. How far from the vertex is the focus?

Solve.

16. $2x^2 - 3y^2 = -10$,
$\quad x^2 + 2y^2 = 9$

17. $x^2 + y^2 = 13$,
$\quad x + y = 1$

18. $x + y = 5$,
$\quad xy = 6$

19. *Landscaping.* Leisurescape is planting a rectangular flower garden with a perimeter of 18 ft and a diagonal of $\sqrt{41}$ ft. Find the dimensions of the garden.

20. *Fencing.* It will take 210 ft of fencing to enclose a rectangular playground with an area of 2700 ft^2. Find the dimensions of the playground.

21. Graph the system of inequalities. Then find the coordinates of the points of intersection of the graphs.

$$y \geq x^2 - 4,$$
$$y < 2x - 1$$

22. Graph: $5x^2 - 8xy + 5y^2 = 9$.

23. Graph $r = \dfrac{2}{1 - \sin \theta}$. State whether the directrix is vertical or horizontal, describe its location in relation to the pole, and find the vertex or vertices.

24. Find a polar equation of the conic with a focus at the pole, eccentricity 2, and directrix $r = 3 \sec \theta$.

25. Graph the plane curve given by the parametric equations $x = \sqrt{t}, y = t + 2; 0 \le t \le 16$.

26. Find a rectangular equation equivalent to $x = 3 \cos \theta, y = 3 \sin \theta; 0 \le \theta \le 2\pi$.

27. Find two sets of parametric equations for the rectangular equation $y = x - 5$.

28. *Projectile Motion.* A projectile is launched from a height of 10 ft with an initial speed of 250 ft/sec at an angle of 30° with the horizontal.

  a) Find parametric equations that give the position of the projectile at time t, in seconds.

b) Find the height of the projectile after 1 sec and 3 sec.

c) Determine how long the projectile is in the air.

d) Determine the horizontal distance that the projectile travels.

e) Find the maximum height of the projectile.

Synthesis

29. Find an equation of the circle for which the endpoints of a diameter are $(1, 1)$ and $(5, -3)$.

Sequences, Series, and Combinatorics

APPLICATION

How many games can be played in a 9-team sports league if each team plays all other teams once? twice?

This problem appears as Exercise 24 in Section 10.6.

10.1 Sequences and Series

- ✦ Find terms of sequences given the nth term.
- ✦ Look for a pattern in a sequence and try to determine a general term.
- ✦ Convert between sigma notation and other notation for a series.
- ✦ Construct the terms of a recursively defined sequence.

In this section, we discuss sets or lists of numbers, considered in order, and their sums.

✦ Sequences

Suppose that $1000 is invested at 6%, compounded annually. The amounts to which the account will grow after 1 yr, 2 yr, 3 yr, 4 yr, and so on, form the following sequence of numbers:

$$
\begin{array}{cccc}
(1) & (2) & (3) & (4) \\
\downarrow & \downarrow & \downarrow & \downarrow \\
\$1060.00, & \$1123.60, & \$1191.02, & \$1262.48,\dots.
\end{array}
$$

We can think of this as a function that pairs 1 with $1060.00, 2 with $1123.60, 3 with $1191.02, and so on. A **sequence** is thus a *function*, where the domain is a set of consecutive positive integers beginning with 1.

If we continue to compute the amounts of money in the account forever, we obtain an **infinite sequence** with function values

$1060.00, \$1123.60, \$1191.02, \$1262.48, \$1338.23, \$1418.52,\dots.

The dots "..." at the end indicate that the sequence goes on without stopping. If we stop after a certain number of years, we obtain a **finite sequence:**

$1060.00, \$1123.60, \$1191.02, \$1262.48.

Sequences

An **infinite sequence** is a function having for its domain the set of positive integers, $\{1, 2, 3, 4, 5, \dots\}$.

A **finite sequence** is a function having for its domain a set of positive integers, $\{1, 2, 3, 4, 5, \dots, n\}$, for some positive integer n.

Consider the sequence given by the formula

$$a(n) = 2^n, \quad \text{or} \quad a_n = 2^n.$$

Some of the function values, also known as the **terms** of the sequence, follow:

$$a_1 = 2^1 = 2,$$
$$a_2 = 2^2 = 4,$$
$$a_3 = 2^3 = 8,$$
$$a_4 = 2^4 = 16,$$
$$a_5 = 2^5 = 32.$$

The first term of the sequence is denoted as a_1, the fifth term as a_5, and the nth term, or **general term**, as a_n. This sequence can also be denoted as

$$2, 4, 8, \ldots, \quad \text{or as} \quad 2, 4, 8, \ldots, 2^n, \ldots.$$

EXAMPLE 1 Find the first 4 terms and the 23rd term of the sequence whose general term is given by $a_n = (-1)^n n^2$.

Solution We have $a_n = (-1)^n n^2$, so

$$a_1 = (-1)^1 \cdot 1^2 = -1,$$
$$a_2 = (-1)^2 \cdot 2^2 = 4,$$
$$a_3 = (-1)^3 \cdot 3^2 = -9,$$
$$a_4 = (-1)^4 \cdot 4^2 = 16,$$
$$a_{23} = (-1)^{23} \cdot 23^2 = -529.$$

▶ Now Try Exercise 1.

Note in Example 1 that the power $(-1)^n$ causes the signs of the terms to alternate between positive and negative, depending on whether n is even or odd. This kind of sequence is called an **alternating sequence.**

TECHNOLOGY ·
CONNECTION

X	Y₁	
1	−1	
2	4	
3	−9	
4	16	
23	−529	

X =

We can use a graphing calculator to find the desired terms of the sequence in Example 1. We enter $y_1 = (-1)^x x^2$. We then set up a table in ASK mode and enter 1, 2, 3, 4, and 23 as values for x.

We can also use the SEQ feature to find the terms of a sequence. Suppose, for example, that we want to find the first 5 terms of the sequence whose general term is given by $a_n = n/(n + 1)$. We select SEQ from the LIST OPS menu and enter the general term, the variable, and the numbers of the first and last terms desired. The calculator will write the terms horizontally as a list. The list can also be written in fraction notation.

STUDY TIP

Refer to the *Graphing Calculator Manual* that accompanies this text to find the keystrokes for finding the terms of a sequence.

```
seq(X/(X+1),X,1,5)▶Frac
{1/2 2/3 3/4 4/...
```

```
seq(X/(X+1),X,1,5)▶Frac
.../3 3/4 4/5 5/6}
```

We use the ▷ key to view the two items that do not initially appear on the screen. The first 5 terms of the sequence are 1/2, 2/3, 3/4, 4/5, and 5/6.

We can graph a sequence just as we graph other functions. Consider the function given by $f(x) = x + 1$ and the sequence whose general term is given by $a_n = n + 1$. The graph of $f(x) = x + 1$ is shown on the left below. If we remove all the points from this graph except those whose first coordinates are positive integers, we have the graph of the sequence $a_n = n + 1$ as shown on the right below.

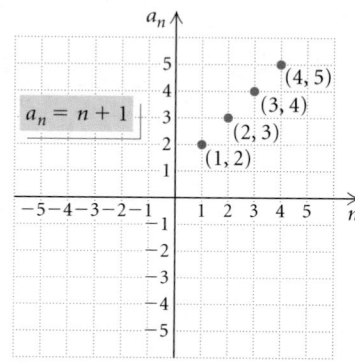

◆ Finding the General Term

When only the first few terms of a sequence are known, we do not know for sure what the general term is, but we might be able to make a prediction by looking for a pattern.

EXAMPLE 2 For each of the following sequences, predict the general term.

a) $1, \sqrt{2}, \sqrt{3}, 2, \ldots$ **b)** $-1, 3, -9, 27, -81, \ldots$

c) $2, 4, 8, \ldots$

Solution

a) These are square roots of consecutive integers, so the general term might be $\sqrt{n}$.

b) These are powers of 3 with alternating signs, so the general term might be $(-1)^n 3^{n-1}$.

c) If we see the pattern of powers of 2, we will see 16 as the next term and guess 2^n for the general term. Then the sequence could be written with more terms as

$$2, 4, 8, 16, 32, 64, 128, \ldots .$$

If we see that we can get the second term by adding 2, the third term by adding 4, and the next term by adding 6, and so on, we will see 14 as the next term. A general term for the sequence is $n^2 - n + 2$, and the sequence can be written with more terms as

$$2, 4, 8, 14, 22, 32, 44, 58, \ldots .$$

▶ Now Try Exercise 19.

Example 2(c) illustrates that, in fact, you can never be certain about the general term when only a few terms are given. The fewer the given terms, the greater the uncertainty.

◆ Sums and Series

Series

Given the infinite sequence

$$a_1, a_2, a_3, a_4, \ldots, a_n, \ldots,$$

the sum of the terms

$$a_1 + a_2 + a_3 + \cdots + a_n + \cdots$$

is called an **infinite series.** A **partial sum** is the sum of the first n terms:

$$a_1 + a_2 + a_3 + \cdots + a_n.$$

A partial sum is also called a **finite series,** or n**th partial sum,** and is denoted S_n.

EXAMPLE 3 For the sequence $-2, 4, -6, 8, -10, 12, -14, \ldots$, find each of the following.

a) S_1 b) S_4 c) S_5

Solution

a) $S_1 = -2$
b) $S_4 = -2 + 4 + (-6) + 8 = 4$
c) $S_5 = -2 + 4 + (-6) + 8 + (-10) = -6$ ▶ Now Try Exercise 29.

TECHNOLOGY ···
     CONNECTION

We can use a graphing calculator to find partial sums of a sequence when a formula for the general term is known. Suppose, for example, that we want to find S_1, S_2, S_3, and S_4 for the sequence whose general term is given by $a_n = n^2 - 3$. We can use the CUMSUM feature from the LIST OPS menu. The calculator will write the partial sums as a list. (Note that the calculator can be set in either FUNCTION mode or SEQUENCE mode. Here we show SEQUENCE mode.)

```
cumSum(seq(n2−3,
 n, 1, 4))
              {-2 -1 5 18}
```

We have $S_1 = -2$, $S_2 = -1$, $S_3 = 5$, and $S_4 = 18$.

✦ Sigma Notation

The Greek letter Σ (sigma) can be used to simplify notation when the general term of a sequence is a formula. For example, the sum of the first four terms of the sequence 3, 5, 7, 9,..., $2k + 1$,... can be named as follows, using what is called **sigma notation,** or **summation notation:**

$$\sum_{k=1}^{4} (2k + 1).$$

This is read "the sum as k goes from 1 to 4 of $2k + 1$." The letter k is called the **index of summation.** The index of summation might start at a number other than 1, and letters other than k can be used.

EXAMPLE 4 Find and evaluate each of the following sums.

a) $\displaystyle\sum_{k=1}^{5} k^3$
  b) $\displaystyle\sum_{k=0}^{4} (-1)^k 5^k$
  c) $\displaystyle\sum_{i=8}^{11} \left(2 + \frac{1}{i}\right)$

Solution

a) We replace k with 1, 2, 3, 4, and 5. Then we add the results.

$$\sum_{k=1}^{5} k^3 = 1^3 + 2^3 + 3^3 + 4^3 + 5^3$$
$$= 1 + 8 + 27 + 64 + 125$$
$$= 225$$

b) $\displaystyle\sum_{k=0}^{4} (-1)^k 5^k = (-1)^0 5^0 + (-1)^1 5^1 + (-1)^2 5^2 + (-1)^3 5^3 + (-1)^4 5^4$

$$= 1 - 5 + 25 - 125 + 625 = 521$$

c) $\displaystyle\sum_{i=8}^{11} \left(2 + \frac{1}{i}\right) = \left(2 + \frac{1}{8}\right) + \left(2 + \frac{1}{9}\right) + \left(2 + \frac{1}{10}\right) + \left(2 + \frac{1}{11}\right)$

$$= 8\frac{1691}{3960}$$

▶ **Now Try Exercise 33.**

TECHNOLOGY · · · · · · · · · · · · ·
CONNECTION

We can combine the SUM and SEQ features on a graphing calculator to add the terms of a sequence. We find the sum in Example 4(a) as shown below.

```
sum(seq(n^3, n, 1,
5))
                    225
```

EXAMPLE 5 Write sigma notation for each sum.

a) $1 + 2 + 4 + 8 + 16 + 32 + 64$

b) $-2 + 4 - 6 + 8 - 10$

c) $x + \dfrac{x^2}{2} + \dfrac{x^3}{3} + \dfrac{x^4}{4} + \cdots$

Solution

a) $1 + 2 + 4 + 8 + 16 + 32 + 64$

This is the sum of powers of 2, beginning with 2^0, or 1, and ending with 2^6, or 64. Sigma notation is $\sum_{k=0}^{6} 2^k$.

b) $-2 + 4 - 6 + 8 - 10$

Disregarding the alternating signs, we see that this is the sum of the first 5 even integers. Note that $2k$ is a formula for the kth positive even integer, and $(-1)^k = -1$ when k is odd and $(-1)^k = 1$ when k is even. Thus the general term is $(-1)^k(2k)$. The sum begins with $k = 1$ and ends with $k = 5$, so sigma notation is $\sum_{k=1}^{5}(-1)^k(2k)$.

c) $x + \dfrac{x^2}{2} + \dfrac{x^3}{3} + \dfrac{x^4}{4} + \cdots$

The general term is x^k/k, beginning with $k = 1$. This is also an infinite series. We use the symbol ∞ for infinity and write the series using sigma notation: $\sum_{k=1}^{\infty}(x^k/k)$. ▷ Now Try Exercise 51.

✦ Recursive Definitions

A sequence may be defined **recursively** or by using a **recursion formula**. Such a definition lists the first term, or the first few terms, and then describes how to determine the remaining terms from the given terms.

EXAMPLE 6 Find the first 5 terms of the sequence defined by

$$a_1 = 5, \qquad a_{n+1} = 2a_n - 3, \quad \text{for } n \geq 1.$$

Solution

$a_1 = 5,$

$a_2 = 2a_1 - 3 = 2 \cdot 5 - 3 = 7,$

$a_3 = 2a_2 - 3 = 2 \cdot 7 - 3 = 11,$

$a_4 = 2a_3 - 3 = 2 \cdot 11 - 3 = 19,$

$a_5 = 2a_4 - 3 = 2 \cdot 19 - 3 = 35.$ ▷ Now Try Exercise 61.

TECHNOLOGY ···
        CONNECTION

Many graphing calculators have the capability to work with recursively defined sequences when they are set in SEQUENCE mode. In Example 6, for instance, the function could be entered as $u(n) = 2 * u(n - 1) - 3$ with $u(n\text{Min}) = 5$. We can read the terms of the sequence from a table.

Plot1 Plot2 Plot3
nMin=1
\u(n)▤2∗u(n−1)−3
u(nMin)▤{5}
\v(n)=
v(nMin)=
\w(n)=

n	$u(n)$	
1	5	
2	7	
3	11	
4	19	
5	35	
6	67	
7	131	
$n = 1$		

10.1 EXERCISE SET

In each of the following, the nth term of a sequence is given. Find the first 4 terms, a_{10}, and a_{15}.

1. $a_n = 4n - 1$

2. $a_n = (n - 1)(n - 2)(n - 3)$

3. $a_n = \dfrac{n}{n - 1}, \ n \geq 2$

4. $a_n = n^2 - 1, \ n \geq 3$

5. $a_n = \dfrac{n^2 - 1}{n^2 + 1}$

6. $a_n = \left(-\dfrac{1}{2}\right)^{n-1}$

7. $a_n = (-1)^n n^2$

8. $a_n = (-1)^{n-1}(3n - 5)$

9. $a_n = 5 + \dfrac{(-2)^{n+1}}{2^n}$

10. $a_n = \dfrac{2n - 1}{n^2 + 2n}$

Find the indicated term of the given sequence.

11. $a_n = 5n - 6; \ a_8$

12. $a_n = (3n - 4)(2n + 5); \ a_7$

13. $a_n = (2n + 3)^2; \ a_6$

14. $a_n = (-1)^{n-1}(4.6n - 18.3); \ a_{12}$

15. $a_n = 5n^2(4n - 100); \ a_{11}$

16. $a_n = \left(1 + \dfrac{1}{n}\right)^2; \ a_{80}$

17. $a_n = \ln e^n; \ a_{67}$

18. $a_n = 2 - \dfrac{1000}{n}; \ a_{100}$

Predict the general term, or nth term, a_n, of the sequence. Answers may vary.

19. $2, 4, 6, 8, 10, \ldots$

20. $3, 9, 27, 81, 243, \ldots$

21. $-2, 6, -18, 54, \ldots$

22. $-2, 3, 8, 13, 18, \ldots$

23. $\frac{2}{3}, \frac{3}{4}, \frac{4}{5}, \frac{5}{6}, \frac{6}{7}, \ldots$

24. $\sqrt{2}, 2, \sqrt{6}, 2\sqrt{2}, \sqrt{10}, \ldots$

25. $1 \cdot 2, 2 \cdot 3, 3 \cdot 4, 4 \cdot 5, \ldots$

26. $-1, -4, -7, -10, -13, \ldots$

27. $0, \log 10, \log 100, \log 1000, \ldots$

28. $\ln e^2, \ln e^3, \ln e^4, \ln e^5, \ldots$

Find the indicated partial sums for the sequence.

29. $1, 2, 3, 4, 5, 6, 7, \ldots; \ S_3 \text{ and } S_7$

30. $1, -3, 5, -7, 9, -11, \ldots; \ S_2 \text{ and } S_5$

31. $2, 4, 6, 8, \ldots; \ S_4 \text{ and } S_5$

32. $1, \frac{1}{4}, \frac{1}{9}, \frac{1}{16}, \frac{1}{25}, \ldots; \ S_1 \text{ and } S_5$

Find and evaluate the sum.

33. $\displaystyle\sum_{k=1}^{5} \dfrac{1}{2k}$

34. $\displaystyle\sum_{i=1}^{6} \dfrac{1}{2i + 1}$

35. $\displaystyle\sum_{i=0}^{6} 2^i$

36. $\displaystyle\sum_{k=4}^{7} \sqrt{2k - 1}$

37. $\displaystyle\sum_{k=7}^{10} \ln k$

38. $\displaystyle\sum_{k=1}^{4} \pi k$

39. $\displaystyle\sum_{k=1}^{8} \dfrac{k}{k + 1}$

40. $\displaystyle\sum_{i=1}^{5} \dfrac{i - 1}{i + 3}$

41. $\displaystyle\sum_{i=1}^{5} (-1)^i$

42. $\displaystyle\sum_{k=0}^{5} (-1)^{k+1}$

43. $\displaystyle\sum_{k=1}^{8} (-1)^{k+1} 3k$

44. $\displaystyle\sum_{k=0}^{7} (-1)^k 4^{k+1}$

45. $\displaystyle\sum_{k=0}^{6} \dfrac{2}{k^2 + 1}$

46. $\displaystyle\sum_{i=1}^{10} i(i + 1)$

47. $\displaystyle\sum_{k=0}^{5} (k^2 - 2k + 3)$

48. $\displaystyle\sum_{k=1}^{10} \dfrac{1}{k(k + 1)}$

49. $\displaystyle\sum_{i=0}^{10} \dfrac{2^i}{2^i + 1}$

50. $\displaystyle\sum_{k=0}^{3} (-2)^{2k}$

Write sigma notation.

51. $5 + 10 + 15 + 20 + 25 + \cdots$

52. $7 + 14 + 21 + 28 + 35 + \cdots$

53. $2 - 4 + 8 - 16 + 32 - 64$

54. $3 + 6 + 9 + 12 + 15$

55. $-\dfrac{1}{2} + \dfrac{2}{3} - \dfrac{3}{4} + \dfrac{4}{5} - \dfrac{5}{6} + \dfrac{6}{7}$

56. $\dfrac{1}{1^2} + \dfrac{1}{2^2} + \dfrac{1}{3^2} + \dfrac{1}{4^2} + \dfrac{1}{5^2}$

57. $4 - 9 + 16 - 25 + \cdots + (-1)^n n^2$

58. $9 - 16 + 25 + \cdots + (-1)^{n+1} n^2$

59. $\dfrac{1}{1 \cdot 2} + \dfrac{1}{2 \cdot 3} + \dfrac{1}{3 \cdot 4} + \dfrac{1}{4 \cdot 5} + \cdots$

60. $\dfrac{1}{1 \cdot 2^2} + \dfrac{1}{2 \cdot 3^2} + \dfrac{1}{3 \cdot 4^2} + \dfrac{1}{4 \cdot 5^2} + \cdots$

Find the first 4 terms of the recursively defined sequence.

61. $a_1 = 4, \; a_{n+1} = 1 + \dfrac{1}{a_n}$

62. $a_1 = 256, \; a_{n+1} = \sqrt{a_n}$

63. $a_1 = 6561, \; a_{n+1} = (-1)^n \sqrt{a_n}$

64. $a_1 = e^Q, \; a_{n+1} = \ln a_n$

65. $a_1 = 2, a_2 = 3, \; a_{n+1} = a_n + a_{n-1}$

66. $a_1 = -10, a_2 = 8, \; a_{n+1} = a_n - a_{n-1}$

67. *Compound Interest.* Suppose that $1000 is invested at 6.2%, compounded annually. The value of the investment after n years is given by the sequence model
$$a_n = \$1000(1.062)^n, \; n = 1, 2, 3, \ldots .$$
a) Find the first 10 terms of the sequence.
b) Find the value of the investment after 20 yr.

68. *Salvage Value.* The value of an office machine is $5200. Its salvage value each year is 75% of its value the year before. Give a sequence that lists the salvage value of the machine for each year of a 10-yr period.

69. *Bacteria Growth.* Suppose a single cell of bacteria divides into two every 15 min. Suppose that the same rate of division is maintained for 4 hr. Give a sequence that lists the number of cells after successive 15-min periods.

70. *Salary Sequence.* Torrey is paid $8.30 per hour for working at Red Freight Limited. Each year he receives a $0.30 hourly raise. Give a sequence that lists Torrey's hourly salary over a 10-yr period.

71. *Fibonacci Sequence: Rabbit Population Growth.* One of the most famous recursively defined sequences is the **Fibonacci sequence**. In 1202, the Italian mathematician Leonardo da Pisa, also called Fibonacci, proposed the following model for rabbit population growth. Suppose that every month each mature pair of rabbits in the population produces a new pair that begins reproducing after two months, and also suppose that no rabbits die. Beginning with one pair of newborn rabbits, the population can be modeled by the following recursively defined sequence:
$$a_1 = 1, \; a_2 = 1, \; a_n = a_{n-1} + a_{n-2}, \quad \text{for } n \geq 3,$$
where a_n is the total number of pairs of rabbits in month n. Find the first 7 terms of the Fibonacci sequence.

Technology Connection

Use a graphing calculator to construct a table of values for the first 10 terms of the sequence.

72. $a_n = \sqrt{n + 1} - \sqrt{n}$

73. $a_n = \left(1 + \dfrac{1}{n}\right)^n$

74. $a_1 = 2$, $a_{n+1} = \dfrac{1}{2}\left(a_n + \dfrac{2}{a_n}\right)$

75. $a_1 = 2$, $a_{n+1} = \sqrt{1 + \sqrt{a_n}}$

76. *Prescription-Drug Sales.*   The table below lists the retail sales of prescription drugs in the United States in recent years.

Year	Retail Sales of Prescription Drugs (in billions)
2000	$146
2001	164
2002	183
2003	203
2004	221

Source: U.S. Bureau of the Census

a) Use a graphing calculator to fit a linear sequence regression function

$$a_n = an + b$$

to the data, where n is the number of years after 2000.
b) Estimate the retail sales of prescription drugs in 2005, in 2008, and in 2010. Round to the nearest billion.

77. *Declining Volkswagen Sales.*   The following table lists the sales of Volkswagen automobiles in recent years.

Year, n	Sales, a_n (in thousands)
1999	316
2001	356
2003	303
2004	225

Source: Automotive News

a) Use a graphing calculator to fit a quadratic sequence regression function

$$a_n = an^2 + bn + c$$

to the data, where n is the year.

b) Estimate the sales of Volkswagens in 1998, in 2000, in 2002, and in 2005. Round to the nearest thousand.

Collaborative Discussion and Writing

78. a) Find the first few terms of the sequence $a_n = n^2 - n + 41$ and describe the pattern you observe.
b) Does the pattern you found in part (a) hold for all choices of n? Why or why not?

79. The Fibonacci sequence has intrigued mathematicians for centuries. In fact, a journal called the *Fibonacci Quarterly* is devoted to publishing the results pertaining to such sequences. Do some research on the connection of the Fibonacci sequence to the idea of the "Golden Section."

Skill Maintenance

Solve.

80. $3x - 2y = 3$,
$2x + 3y = -11$

81. *Most Popular Web Sites.*   Yahoo and Google were the two most-visited web sites in April 2006. Together they were visited 228.1 million times. Yahoo was visited 17.7 million more times than Google. (*Source:* Nielsen/NetRatings) How many visits did each site have?

Find the center and the radius of the circle with the given equation.

82. $x^2 + y^2 - 6x + 4y = 3$

83. $x^2 + y^2 + 5x - 8y = 2$

Synthesis

Find the first 5 terms of the sequence, and then find S_5.

84. $a_n = \dfrac{1}{2^n} \log 1000^n$

85. $a_n = i^n$, $i = \sqrt{-1}$

86. $a_n = \ln(1 \cdot 2 \cdot 3 \cdots n)$

For each sequence, find a formula for S_n.

87. $a_n = \ln n$

88. $a_n = \dfrac{1}{n} - \dfrac{1}{n+1}$

10.2 Arithmetic Sequences and Series

♦ For any arithmetic sequence, find the nth term when n is given and n when the nth term is given, and given two terms, find the common difference and construct the sequence.

♦ Find the sum of the first n terms of an arithmetic sequence.

A sequence in which each term after the first is found by adding the same number to the preceding term is an **arithmetic sequence.**

♦ Arithmetic Sequences

The sequence 2, 5, 8, 11, 14, 17,... is arithmetic because adding 3 to any term produces the next term. In other words, the difference between any term and the preceding one is 3. Arithmetic sequences are also called *arithmetic progressions*.

> ### Arithmetic Sequence
>
> A sequence is **arithmetic** if there exists a number d, called the **common difference,** such that $a_{n+1} = a_n + d$ for any integer $n \geq 1$.

EXAMPLE 1 For each of the following arithmetic sequences, identify the first term, a_1, and the common difference, d.

a) 4, 9, 14, 19, 24,...
b) 34, 27, 20, 13, 6, -1, -8,...
c) 2, $2\frac{1}{2}$, 3, $3\frac{1}{2}$, 4, $4\frac{1}{2}$,...

Solution The first term, a_1, is the first term listed. To find the common difference, d, we choose any term beyond the first and subtract the preceding term from it.

SEQUENCE	FIRST TERM, a_1	COMMON DIFFERENCE, d
a) 4, 9, 14, 19, 24,...	4	5 $(9 - 4 = 5)$
b) 34, 27, 20, 13, 6, -1, -8,...	34	-7 $(27 - 34 = -7)$
c) 2, $2\frac{1}{2}$, 3, $3\frac{1}{2}$, 4, $4\frac{1}{2}$,...	2	$\frac{1}{2}$ $\left(2\frac{1}{2} - 2 = \frac{1}{2}\right)$

We obtained the common difference by subtracting a_1 from a_2. Had we subtracted a_2 from a_3 or a_3 from a_4, we would have obtained the same values for d. Thus we can check by adding d to each term in a sequence to see if we progress correctly to the next term.

Check:

a) $4 + 5 = 9$, $9 + 5 = 14$, $14 + 5 = 19$, $19 + 5 = 24$

b) $34 + (-7) = 27$, $27 + (-7) = 20$, $20 + (-7) = 13$,
   $13 + (-7) = 6$, $6 + (-7) = -1$, $-1 + (-7) = -8$

c) $2 + \frac{1}{2} = 2\frac{1}{2}$, $2\frac{1}{2} + \frac{1}{2} = 3$, $3 + \frac{1}{2} = 3\frac{1}{2}$, $3\frac{1}{2} + \frac{1}{2} = 4$,
   $4 + \frac{1}{2} = 4\frac{1}{2}$

▶ Now Try Exercise 1.

To find a formula for the general, or *n*th, term of any arithmetic sequence, we denote the common difference by d, write out the first few terms, and look for a pattern:

$a_1,$

$a_2 = a_1 + d,$

$a_3 = a_2 + d = (a_1 + d) + d = a_1 + 2d,$ Substituting for a_2

$a_4 = a_3 + d = (a_1 + 2d) + d = a_1 + 3d.$ Substituting for a_3

Note that the coefficient of d in each case is 1 less than the subscript.

Generalizing, we obtain the following formula.

---

nth Term of an Arithmetic Sequence

The **nth term** of an arithmetic sequence is given by

$$a_n = a_1 + (n - 1)d,   \text{for any integer } n \geq 1.$$

EXAMPLE 2   Find the 14th term of the arithmetic sequence 4, 7, 10, 13, ...

Solution   We first note that $a_1 = 4$, $d = 7 - 4$, or 3, and $n = 14$. Then using the formula for the *n*th term, we obtain

$$a_n = a_1 + (n - 1)d$$
$$a_{14} = 4 + (14 - 1) \cdot 3   \text{Substituting}$$
$$= 4 + 13 \cdot 3 = 4 + 39$$
$$= 43.$$

The 14th term is 43.

▶ Now Try Exercise 9.

EXAMPLE 3 In the sequence of Example 2, which term is 301? That is, find n if $a_n = 301$.

Solution We substitute 301 for a_n, 4 for a_1, and 3 for d in the formula for the nth term and solve for n:

$$a_n = a_1 + (n - 1)d$$
$$301 = 4 + (n - 1) \cdot 3 \qquad \text{Substituting}$$
$$301 = 4 + 3n - 3$$
$$301 = 3n + 1 \qquad\qquad \text{Solving for } n$$
$$300 = 3n$$
$$100 = n.$$

The term 301 is the 100th term of the sequence.

▶ Now Try Exercise 15.

Given two terms and their places in an arithmetic sequence, we can construct the sequence.

EXAMPLE 4 The 3rd term of an arithmetic sequence is 8, and the 16th term is 47. Find a_1 and d and construct the sequence.

Solution We know that $a_3 = 8$ and $a_{16} = 47$. Thus we would have to add d 13 times to get from 8 to 47. That is,

$$8 + 13d = 47. \qquad a_3 \text{ and } a_{16} \text{ are } 16 - 3, \text{ or } 13, \text{ terms apart.}$$

Solving $8 + 13d = 47$, we obtain

$$13d = 39$$
$$d = 3.$$

Since $a_3 = 8$, we subtract d twice to get a_1. Thus,

$$a_1 = 8 - 2 \cdot 3 = 2. \qquad a_1 \text{ and } a_3 \text{ are } 3 - 1, \text{ or } 2, \text{ terms apart.}$$

The sequence is 2, 5, 8, 11,.... Note that we could also subtract d 15 times from a_{16} in order to find a_1.

▶ Now Try Exercise 23.

In general, d should be subtracted $n - 1$ times from a_n in order to find a_1.

◆ Sum of the First n Terms of an Arithmetic Sequence

Consider the arithmetic sequence

$$3, 5, 7, 9, \dots .$$

When we add the first 4 terms of the sequence, we get S_4, which is

$$3 + 5 + 7 + 9, \quad \text{or} \quad 24.$$

This sum is called an **arithmetic series.** To find a formula for the sum of the first n terms, S_n, of an arithmetic sequence, we first denote an arithmetic sequence, as follows:

> **This term is two terms back from the last. If you add d to this term, the result is the next-to-last term, $a_n - d$.**

$$a_1, \quad (a_1 + d), \quad (a_1 + 2d), \quad \ldots, \quad (a_n - 2d), \quad (a_n - d), \quad a_n.$$

> **This is the next-to-last term. If you add d to this term, the result is a_n.**

Then S_n is given by

$$S_n = a_1 + (a_1 + d) + (a_1 + 2d) + \cdots + (a_n - 2d)$$
$$+ (a_n - d) + a_n. \tag{1}$$

Reversing the order of the addition gives us

$$S_n = a_n + (a_n - d) + (a_n - 2d) + \cdots + (a_1 + 2d)$$
$$+ (a_1 + d) + a_1. \tag{2}$$

If we add corresponding terms of each side of equations (1) and (2), we get

$$2S_n = [a_1 + a_n] + [(a_1 + d) + (a_n - d)] + [(a_1 + 2d) + (a_n - 2d)]$$
$$+ \cdots + [(a_n - 2d) + (a_1 + 2d)]$$
$$+ [(a_n - d) + (a_1 + d)] + [a_n + a_1].$$

In the expression for $2S_n$, there are n expressions in square brackets. Each of these expressions is equivalent to $a_1 + a_n$. Thus the expression for $2S_n$ can be written in simplified form as

$$2S_n = [a_1 + a_n] + [a_1 + a_n] + [a_1 + a_n] + \cdots + [a_n + a_1]$$
$$+ [a_n + a_1] + [a_n + a_1].$$

Since $a_1 + a_n$ is being added n times, it follows that

$$2S_n = n(a_1 + a_n),$$

from which we get the following formula.

Sum of the First n Terms

The sum of the first n terms of an arithmetic sequence is given by

$$S_n = \frac{n}{2}(a_1 + a_n).$$

EXAMPLE 5   Find the sum of the first 100 natural numbers.

Solution   The sum is

$$1 + 2 + 3 + \cdots + 99 + 100.$$

This is the sum of the first 100 terms of the arithmetic sequence for which

$$a_1 = 1, \qquad a_n = 100, \quad \text{and} \quad n = 100.$$

Thus substituting into the formula

$$S_n = \frac{n}{2}(a_1 + a_n),$$

we get

$$S_{100} = \frac{100}{2}(1 + 100) = 50(101) = 5050.$$

The sum of the first 100 natural numbers is 5050.

▷ **Now Try Exercise 27.**

EXAMPLE 6   Find the sum of the first 15 terms of the arithmetic sequence 4, 7, 10, 13,... .

Solution   Note that $a_1 = 4$, $d = 3$, and $n = 15$. Before using the formula

$$S_n = \frac{n}{2}(a_1 + a_n),$$

we find the last term, a_{15}:

$a_{15} = 4 + (15 - 1)3$ Substituting into the formula $a_n = a_1 + (n - 1)d$

$\quad\; = 4 + 14 \cdot 3 = 46.$

Thus,

$$S_{15} = \frac{15}{2}(4 + 46) = \frac{15}{2}(50) = 375.$$

The sum of the first 15 terms is 375.

▷ **Now Try Exercise 25.**

EXAMPLE 7   Find the sum: $\displaystyle\sum_{k=1}^{130} (4k + 5)$.

Solution   It is helpful to first write out a few terms:

$$9 + 13 + 17 + \cdots.$$

It appears that this is an arithmetic series coming from an arithmetic sequence with $a_1 = 9$, $d = 4$, and $n = 130$. Before using the formula

$$S_n = \frac{n}{2}(a_1 + a_n),$$

we find the last term, a_{130}:

$$a_{130} = 4 \cdot 130 + 5 \qquad \text{The } k\text{th term is } 4k + 5.$$
$$= 520 + 5$$
$$= 525.$$

Thus,

$$S_{130} = \frac{130}{2}(9 + 525) \qquad \text{Substituting into } S_n = \frac{n}{2}(a_1 + a_n)$$
$$= 34{,}710.$$

▶ **Now Try Exercise 33.**

◆ Applications

The translation of some applications and problem-solving situations may involve arithmetic sequences or series. We consider some examples.

EXAMPLE 8 *Hourly Wages.* Gloria accepts a job, starting with an hourly wage of $14.25, and is promised a raise of 15¢ per hour every 2 months for 5 yr. At the end of 5 yr, what will Gloria's hourly wage be?

Solution It helps to first write down the hourly wage for several 2-month time periods:

Beginning: $14.25,
After two months: $14.40,
After four months: $14.55,
and so on.

What appears is a sequence of numbers: 14.25, 14.40, 14.55, ... This sequence is arithmetic, because adding 0.15 each time gives us the next term.

We want to find the last term of an arithmetic sequence, so we use the formula $a_n = a_1 + (n - 1)d$. We know that $a_1 = 14.25$ and $d = 0.15$, but what is n? That is, how many terms are in the sequence? Each year there are $12/2$, or 6 raises, since Gloria gets a raise every 2 months. There are 5 yr, so the total number of raises will be $5 \cdot 6$, or 30. Thus there will be 31 terms: the original wage and 30 increased rates.

Substituting in the formula $a_n = a_1 + (n - 1)d$ gives us

$$a_{31} = 14.25 + (31 - 1) \cdot 0.15$$
$$= 18.75.$$

Thus, at the end of 5 yr, Gloria's hourly wage will be $18.75.

▶ **Now Try Exercise 43.**

The calculations in Example 8 could be done in a number of ways. There is often a variety of ways in which a problem can be solved. In this chapter, we will concentrate on the use of sequences and series and their related formulas.

EXAMPLE 9 *Total in a Stack.* A stack of telephone poles has 30 poles in the bottom row. There are 29 poles in the second row, 28 in the next row, and so on. How many poles are in the stack if there are 5 poles in the top row?

Solution A picture will help in this case. The following figure shows the ends of the poles and the way in which they stack.

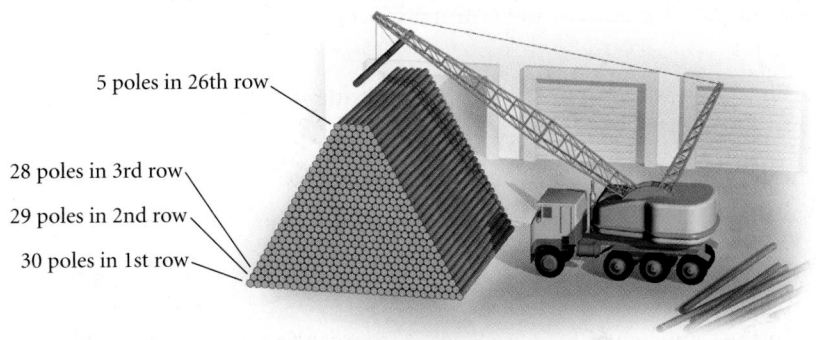

5 poles in 26th row

28 poles in 3rd row
29 poles in 2nd row
30 poles in 1st row

Since the number of poles goes from 30 in a row up to 5 in the top row, there must be 26 rows. We want the sum

$$30 + 29 + 28 + \cdots + 5.$$

Thus we have an arithmetic series. We use the formula

$$S_n = \frac{n}{2}(a_1 + a_n),$$

with $n = 26$, $a_1 = 30$, and $a_{26} = 5$.
  Substituting, we get

$$S_{26} = \frac{26}{2}(30 + 5) = 455.$$

There are 455 poles in the stack.

▶ **Now Try Exercise 39.**

10.2 EXERCISE SET

Find the first term and the common difference.

1. $3, 8, 13, 18, \ldots$

2. $\$1.08, \$1.16, \$1.24, \$1.32, \ldots$

3. $9, 5, 1, -3, \ldots$

4. $-8, -5, -2, 1, 4, \ldots$

5. $\frac{3}{2}, \frac{9}{4}, 3, \frac{15}{4}, \ldots$

6. $\frac{3}{5}, \frac{1}{10}, -\frac{2}{5}, \ldots$

7. $\$316, \$313, \$310, \$307, \ldots$

8. Find the 11th term of the arithmetic sequence $0.07, 0.12, 0.17, \ldots$.

9. Find the 12th term of the arithmetic sequence $2, 6, 10, \ldots$.

10. Find the 17th term of the arithmetic sequence $7, 4, 1, \ldots$.

11. Find the 14th term of the arithmetic sequence $3, \frac{7}{3}, \frac{5}{3}, \ldots$.

12. Find the 13th term of the arithmetic sequence $\$1200, \$964.32, \$728.64, \ldots$.

13. Find the 10th term of the arithmetic sequence $\$2345.78, \$2967.54, \$3589.30, \ldots$.

14. In the sequence of Exercise 9, what term is the number 106?

15. In the sequence of Exercise 8, what term is the number 1.67?

16. In the sequence of Exercise 10, what term is -296?

17. In the sequence of Exercise 11, what term is -27?

18. Find a_{20} when $a_1 = 14$ and $d = -3$.

19. Find a_1 when $d = 4$ and $a_8 = 33$.

20. Find d when $a_1 = 8$ and $a_{11} = 26$.

21. Find n when $a_1 = 25$, $d = -14$, and $a_n = -507$.

22. In an arithmetic sequence, $a_{17} = -40$ and $a_{28} = -73$. Find a_1 and d. Write the first 5 terms of the sequence.

23. In an arithmetic sequence, $a_{17} = \frac{25}{3}$ and $a_{32} = \frac{95}{6}$. Find a_1 and d. Write the first 5 terms of the sequence.

24. Find the sum of the first 14 terms of the series $11 + 7 + 3 + \cdots$.

25. Find the sum of the first 20 terms of the series $5 + 8 + 11 + 14 + \cdots$.

26. Find the sum of the first 300 natural numbers.

27. Find the sum of the first 400 even natural numbers.

28. Find the sum of the odd numbers 1 to 199, inclusive.

29. Find the sum of the multiples of 7 from 7 to 98, inclusive.

30. Find the sum of all multiples of 4 that are between 14 and 523.

31. If an arithmetic series has $a_1 = 2$, $d = 5$, and $n = 20$, what is S_n?

32. If an arithmetic series has $a_1 = 7$, $d = -3$, and $n = 32$, what is S_n?

Find the sum.

33. $\displaystyle\sum_{k=1}^{40} (2k + 3)$

34. $\displaystyle\sum_{k=5}^{20} 8k$

35. $\displaystyle\sum_{k=0}^{19} \frac{k - 3}{4}$

36. $\displaystyle\sum_{k=2}^{50} (2000 - 3k)$

37. $\displaystyle\sum_{k=12}^{57} \frac{7 - 4k}{13}$

38. $\displaystyle\sum_{k=101}^{200} (1.14k - 2.8) - \sum_{k=1}^{5} \left(\frac{k + 4}{10} \right)$

39. *Pole Stacking.* How many poles will be in a stack of telephone poles if there are 50 in the first layer, 49 in the second, and so on, with 6 in the top layer?

40. *Investment Return.* Max is an investment counselor. He sets up an investment situation for a client that will return $5000 the first year, $6125 the second year, $7250 the third year, and so on, for 25 yr. How much is received from the investment altogether?

41. *Garden Plantings.* A gardener is making a planting in the shape of a trapezoid. It will have 35 plants in the front row, 31 in the second row, 27 in the third row, and so on. If the pattern is consistent, how many plants will there be in the last row? How many plants are there altogether?

42. *Band Formation.* A formation of a marching band has 10 marchers in the front row, 12 in the second row, 14 in the third row, and so on, for 8 rows. How many marchers are in the last row? How many marchers are there altogether?

43. *Total Savings.* If 10¢ is saved on October 1, 20¢ is saved on October 2, 30¢ on October 3, and so on, how much is saved during the 31 days of October?

44. *Parachutist Free Fall.* When a parachutist jumps from an airplane, the distances, in feet, that the parachutist falls in each successive second before pulling the ripcord to release the parachute are as follows:

$$16, 48, 80, 112, 144, \ldots.$$

Is this sequence arithmetic? What is the common difference? What is the total distance fallen after 10 sec?

45. *Theater Seating.* Theaters are often built with more seats per row as the rows move toward the back. Suppose that the first balcony of a theater has 28 seats in the first row, 32 in the second, 36 in the third, and so on, for 20 rows. How many seats are in the first balcony altogether?

46. *Small Group Interaction.* In a social science study, Stephan found the following data regarding an interaction measurement r_n for groups of size n.

n	r_n
3	0.5908
4	0.6080
5	0.6252
6	0.6424
7	0.6596
8	0.6768
9	0.6940
10	0.7112

Source: *American Sociological Review*, 17 (1952)

Is this sequence arithmetic? What is the common difference?

47. *Raw Material Production.* In an industrial situation, it took 3 units of raw materials to produce 1 unit of a product. The raw material needs thus formed the sequence

$$3, 6, 9, \ldots, 3n, \ldots.$$

Is this sequence arithmetic? What is the common difference?

Collaborative Discussion and Writing

48. The sum of the first n terms of an arithmetic sequence can be given by

$$S_n = \frac{n}{2}[2a_1 + (n - 1)d].$$

Compare this formula to

$$S_n = \frac{n}{2}(a_1 + a_n).$$

Discuss the reasons for the use of one formula over the other.

49. It is said that as a young child, the mathematician Karl F. Gauss (1777–1855) was able to compute the sum $1 + 2 + 3 + \cdots + 100$ very quickly in his head to the amazement of a teacher. Explain how Gauss might have done this had he possessed some knowledge of arithmetic sequences and series. Then give a formula for the sum of the first n natural numbers.

Skill Maintenance

Solve.

50. $7x - 2y = 4,$
$x + 3y = 17$

51. $2x + y + 3z = 12,$
$x - 3y + 2z = 11,$
$5x + 2y - 4z = -4$

52. Find the vertices and the foci of the ellipse with the equation $9x^2 + 16y^2 = 144.$

53. Find an equation of the ellipse with vertices $(0, -5)$ and $(0, 5)$ and minor axis of length 4.

Synthesis

54. Find three numbers in an arithmetic sequence such that the sum of the first and third is 10 and the product of the first and second is 15.

55. Find a formula for the sum of the first n odd natural numbers:
$$1 + 3 + 5 + \cdots + (2n - 1).$$

56. Find the first 10 terms of the arithmetic sequence for which
$$a_1 = \$8760 \quad \text{and} \quad d = -\$798.23.$$
Then find the sum of the first 10 terms.

57. Find the first term and the common difference for the arithmetic sequence for which
$$a_2 = 40 - 3q \quad \text{and} \quad a_4 = 10p + q.$$

58. The zeros of this polynomial function form an arithmetic sequence. Find them.
$$f(x) = x^4 + 4x^3 - 84x^2 - 176x + 640$$

*If p, m, and q form an arithmetic sequence, it can be shown that $m = (p + q)/2$. (See Exercise 65.) The number m is the **arithmetic mean,** or **average,** of p and q. Given two numbers p and q, if we find k other numbers $m_1, m_2, \ldots, m_k$ such that*
$$p, m_1, m_2, \ldots, m_k, q$$
forms an arithmetic sequence, we say that we have "inserted k arithmetic means between p and q."

59. Insert three arithmetic means between 4 and 12.

60. Insert three arithmetic means between -3 and 5.

61. Insert four arithmetic means between 4 and 13.

62. Insert ten arithmetic means between 27 and 300.

63. Insert enough arithmetic means between 1 and 50 so that the sum of the resulting series will be 459.

64. *Straight-Line Depreciation.* A company buys an office machine for $5200 on January 1 of a given year. The machine is expected to last for 8 yr, at the end of which time its **trade-in value,** or **salvage value,** will be $1100. If the company's accountant figures the decline in value to be the same each year, then its **book values,** or **salvage values,** after t years, $0 \le t \le 8$, form an arithmetic sequence given by
$$a_t = C - t\left(\frac{C - S}{N}\right),$$
where C is the original cost of the item ($5200), N is the number of years of expected life (8), and S is the salvage value ($1100).

a) Find the formula for a_t for the straight-line depreciation of the office machine.

b) Find the salvage value after 0 yr, 1 yr, 2 yr, 3 yr, 4 yr, 7 yr, and 8 yr.

65. Prove that if p, m, and q form an arithmetic sequence, then
$$m = \frac{p + q}{2}.$$

Geometric Sequences and Series

- ✦ Identify the common ratio of a geometric sequence, and find a given term and the sum of the first *n* terms.
- ✦ Find the sum of an infinite geometric series, if it exists.

A sequence in which each term after the first is found by multiplying the preceding term by the same number is a **geometric sequence.**

✦ Geometric Sequences

Consider the sequence

$$2, \ 6, \ 18, \ 54, \ 162, \ldots .$$

Note that multiplying each term by 3 produces the next term. We call the number 3 the **common ratio** because it can be found by dividing any term by the preceding term. A geometric sequence is also called a *geometric progression.*

> ### Geometric Sequence
>
> A sequence is **geometric** if there is a number r, called the **common ratio,** such that
>
> $$\frac{a_{n+1}}{a_n} = r, \quad \text{or} \quad a_{n+1} = a_n r, \quad \text{for any integer } n \geq 1.$$

EXAMPLE 1 For each of the following geometric sequences, identify the common ratio.

a) 3, 6, 12, 24, 48,...

b) 1, $-\dfrac{1}{2}$, $\dfrac{1}{4}$, $-\dfrac{1}{8}$,...

c) $5200, $3900, $2925, $2193.75,...

d) $1000, $1060, $1123.60,...

Solution

SEQUENCE	COMMON RATIO
a) 3, 6, 12, 24, 48,...	2 $\left(\frac{6}{3} = 2, \frac{12}{6} = 2, \text{and so on}\right)$
b) 1, $-\frac{1}{2}$, $\frac{1}{4}$, $-\frac{1}{8}$,...	$-\frac{1}{2}$ $\left(\frac{-\frac{1}{2}}{1} = -\frac{1}{2}, \frac{\frac{1}{4}}{-\frac{1}{2}} = -\frac{1}{2}, \text{and so on}\right)$
c) \$5200, \$3900, \$2925, \$2193.75,...	0.75 $\left(\frac{\$3900}{\$5200} = 0.75, \frac{\$2925}{\$3900} = 0.75, \text{and so on}\right)$
d) \$1000, \$1060, \$1123.60,...	1.06 $\left(\frac{\$1060}{\$1000} = 1.06, \frac{\$1123.60}{\$1060} = 1.06, \text{and so on}\right)$

▷ **Now Try Exercise 1.**

We now find a formula for the general, or *n*th, term of a geometric sequence. Let a_1 be the first term and *r* the common ratio. The first few terms are as follows:

$$a_1,$$
$$a_2 = a_1 r,$$
$$a_3 = a_2 r = (a_1 r)r = a_1 r^2, \quad \text{Substituting } a_1 r \text{ for } a_2$$
$$a_4 = a_3 r = (a_1 r^2)r = a_1 r^3. \quad \text{Substituting } a_1 r^2 \text{ for } a_3$$

Note that the exponent is 1 less than the subscript.

Generalizing, we obtain the following.

*n*th Term of a Geometric Sequence

The ***n*th term** of a geometric sequence is given by

$$a_n = a_1 r^{n-1}, \quad \text{for any integer } n \geq 1.$$

EXAMPLE 2   Find the 7th term of the geometric sequence 4, 20, 100,... .

Solution   We first note that

$$a_1 = 4 \quad \text{and} \quad n = 7.$$

To find the common ratio, we can divide any term (other than the first) by the preceding term. Since the second term is 20 and the first is 4, we get

$$r = \frac{20}{4}, \quad \text{or} \quad 5.$$

Then using the formula $a_n = a_1 r^{n-1}$, we have

$$a_7 = 4 \cdot 5^{7-1} = 4 \cdot 5^6 = 4 \cdot 15{,}625 = 62{,}500.$$

Thus the 7th term is 62,500.   ▷ **Now Try Exercise 11.**

EXAMPLE 3 Find the 10th term of the geometric sequence 64, −32, 16, −8,.... .

Solution We first note that

$$a_1 = 64, \qquad n = 10, \quad \text{and} \quad r = \frac{-32}{64}, \text{or} -\frac{1}{2}.$$

Then using the formula $a_n = a_1 r^{n-1}$, we have

$$a_{10} = 64 \cdot \left(-\frac{1}{2}\right)^{10-1} = 64 \cdot \left(-\frac{1}{2}\right)^9 = 2^6 \cdot \left(-\frac{1}{2^9}\right) = -\frac{1}{2^3} = -\frac{1}{8}.$$

Thus the 10th term is $-\frac{1}{8}$. ▶ Now Try Exercise 15.

◆ Sum of the First *n* Terms of a Geometric Sequence

Next, we develop a formula for the sum S_n of the first n terms of a geometric sequence:

$$a_1, \ a_1 r, \ a_1 r^2, \ a_1 r^3, \ldots, \ a_1 r^{n-1}, \ldots .$$

The associated **geometric series** is given by

$$S_n = a_1 + a_1 r + a_1 r^2 + a_1 r^3 + \cdots + a_1 r^{n-1}. \tag{1}$$

We want to find a formula for this sum. If we multiply on both sides of equation (1) by r, we have

$$rS_n = a_1 r + a_1 r^2 + a_1 r^3 + a_1 r^4 + \cdots + a_1 r^n. \tag{2}$$

Subtracting equation (2) from equation (1), we see that the differences of the red terms are 0, leaving

$$S_n - rS_n = a_1 - a_1 r^n,$$

or

$$S_n(1 - r) = a_1(1 - r^n). \qquad \text{Factoring}$$

Dividing on both sides by $1 - r$ gives us the following formula.

Sum of the First n Terms

The sum of the first n terms of a geometric sequence is given by

$$S_n = \frac{a_1(1 - r^n)}{1 - r}, \quad \text{for any } r \neq 1.$$

EXAMPLE 4 Find the sum of the first 7 terms of the geometric sequence 3, 15, 75, 375,.... .

Solution We first note that

$$a_1 = 3, \qquad n = 7, \quad \text{and} \quad r = \frac{15}{3}, \text{or } 5.$$

Then using the formula

$$S_n = \frac{a_1(1 - r^n)}{1 - r},$$

we have

$$S_7 = \frac{3(1 - 5^7)}{1 - 5}$$

$$= \frac{3(1 - 78{,}125)}{-4}$$

$$= 58{,}593.$$

Thus the sum of the first 7 terms is 58,593. ▶ Now Try Exercise 23.

EXAMPLE 5 Find the sum: $\displaystyle\sum_{k=1}^{11} (0.3)^k$.

Solution This is a geometric series with $a_1 = 0.3$, $r = 0.3$, and $n = 11$. Thus,

$$S_{11} = \frac{0.3(1 - 0.3^{11})}{1 - 0.3}$$

$$\approx 0.42857.$$ ▶ Now Try Exercise 35.

✦ Infinite Geometric Series

The sum of the terms of an infinite geometric sequence is an **infinite geometric series.** For some geometric sequences, S_n gets close to a specific number as n gets large. For example, consider the infinite series

$$\frac{1}{2} + \frac{1}{4} + \frac{1}{8} + \frac{1}{16} + \cdots + \frac{1}{2^n} + \cdots.$$

We can visualize S_n by considering the area of a square. For S_1, we shade half the square. For S_2, we shade half the square plus half the remaining part, or $\frac{1}{4}$. For S_3, we shade the parts shaded in S_2 plus half the remaining part. We see that the values of S_n will continue to get close to 1 (shading the complete square).

$S_1 = \frac{1}{2}$

$S_2 = \frac{3}{4}$

$S_3 = \frac{7}{8}$

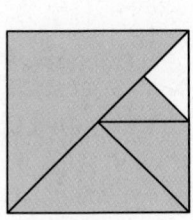

$S_4 = \frac{15}{16}$

We examine some partial sums. Note that each of the partial sums is less than 1, but S_n gets very close to 1 as n gets large.

n	S_n
1	0.5
5	0.96875
10	0.9990234375
20	0.9999990463
30	0.9999999991

We say that 1 is the **limit** of S_n and also that 1 is the **sum of the infinite geometric sequence.** The sum of an infinite geometric sequence is denoted S_∞. In this case, $S_\infty = 1$.

Some infinite sequences do not have sums. Consider the infinite geometric series

$$2 + 4 + 8 + 16 + \cdots + 2^n + \cdots.$$

We again examine some partial sums. Note that as n gets large, S_n gets large without bound. This sequence does not have a sum.

n	S_n
1	2
5	62
10	2,046
20	2,097,150
30	2,147,483,646

It can be shown (but we will not do so here) that the sum of the terms of an infinite geometric series exists if and only if $|r| < 1$ (that is, the absolute value of the common ratio is less than 1).

To find a formula for the sum of an infinite geometric series, we first consider the sum of the first n terms:

$$S_n = \frac{a_1(1 - r^n)}{1 - r} = \frac{a_1 - a_1 r^n}{1 - r}. \qquad \text{Using the distributive law}$$

For $|r| < 1$, values of r^n get close to 0 as n gets large. As r^n gets close to 0, so does $a_1 r^n$. Thus, S_n gets close to $a_1/(1 - r)$.

> **Limit or Sum of an Infinite Geometric Series**
> When $|r| < 1$, the limit or sum of an infinite geometric series is given by
> $$S_\infty = \frac{a_1}{1 - r}.$$

EXAMPLE 6 Determine whether each of the following infinite geometric series has a limit. If a limit exists, find it.

a) $1 + 3 + 9 + 27 + \cdots$
b) $-2 + 1 - \frac{1}{2} + \frac{1}{4} - \frac{1}{8} + \cdots$

Solution

a) Here $r = 3$, so $|r| = |3| = 3$. Since $|r| > 1$, the series *does not* have a limit.

b) Here $r = -\frac{1}{2}$, so $|r| = \left|-\frac{1}{2}\right| = \frac{1}{2}$. Since $|r| < 1$, the series *does* have a limit. We find the limit:

$$S_\infty = \frac{a_1}{1 - r} = \frac{-2}{1 - \left(-\frac{1}{2}\right)} = \frac{-2}{\frac{3}{2}} = -\frac{4}{3}.$$

▶ Now Try Exercises 27 and 31.

EXAMPLE 7 Find fraction notation for $0.78787878\ldots$, or $0.\overline{78}$.

Solution We can express this as

$$0.78 + 0.0078 + 0.000078 + \cdots.$$

Then we see that this is an infinite geometric series, where $a_1 = 0.78$ and $r = 0.01$. Since $|r| < 1$, this series has a limit:

$$S_\infty = \frac{a_1}{1 - r} = \frac{0.78}{1 - 0.01} = \frac{0.78}{0.99} = \frac{78}{99}, \quad \text{or} \quad \frac{26}{33}.$$

Thus fraction notation for $0.78787878\ldots$ is $\frac{26}{33}$. You can check this on your calculator.

▶ Now Try Exercise 45.

✦ Applications

The translation of some applications and problem-solving situations may involve geometric sequences or series. Examples 9 and 10 in particular show applications in business and economics.

EXAMPLE 8   *A Daily Doubling Salary.*   Suppose someone offered you a job for the month of September (30 days) under the following conditions. You will be paid $0.01 for the first day, $0.02 for the second, $0.04 for the third, and so on, doubling your previous day's salary each day. How much would you earn? (Would you take the job? Make a conjecture before reading further.)

Solution   You earn $0.01 the first day, $0.01(2) the second day, $0.01(2)(2) the third day, and so on. The amount earned is the geometric series

$$\$0.01 + \$0.01(2) + \$0.01(2^2) + \$0.01(2^3) + \cdots + \$0.01(2^{29}),$$

where $a_1 = \$0.01$, $r = 2$, and $n = 30$. Using the formula

$$S_n = \frac{a_1(1 - r^n)}{1 - r},$$

we have

$$S_{30} = \frac{\$0.01(1 - 2^{30})}{1 - 2} = \$10{,}737{,}418.23.$$

The pay exceeds $10.7 million for the month.   ▶ **Now Try Exercise 51.**

EXAMPLE 9   *The Amount of an Annuity.*   An **annuity** is a sequence of equal payments, made at equal time intervals, that earn interest. Fixed deposits in a savings account are an example of an annuity. Suppose that to save money to buy a car, Andrea deposits $1000 at the *end* of each of 5 yr in an account that pays 8% interest, compounded annually. The total amount in the account at the end of 5 yr is called the **amount of the annuity.** Find that amount.

Solution   The following time diagram can help visualize the problem. Note that no deposit is made until the end of the first year.

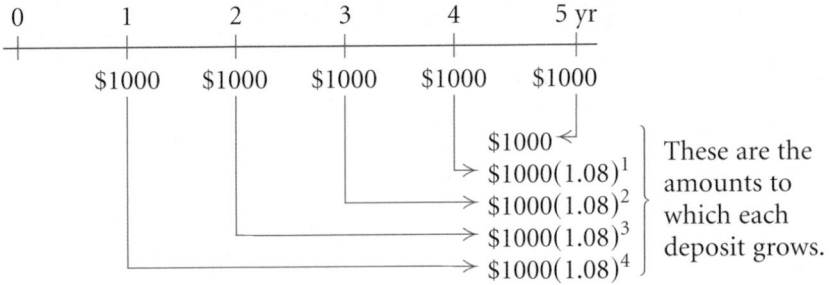

The amount of the annuity is the geometric series

$$\$1000 + \$1000(1.08)^1 + \$1000(1.08)^2 + \$1000(1.08)^3 + \$1000(1.08)^4,$$

where $a_1 = \$1000$, $n = 5$, and $r = 1.08$. Using the formula

$$S_n = \frac{a_1(1 - r^n)}{1 - r},$$

we have

$$S_5 = \frac{\$1000(1 - 1.08^5)}{1 - 1.08} \approx \$5866.60.$$

The amount of the annuity is $5866.60.

▶ Now Try Exercise 55.

EXAMPLE 10 *The Economic Multiplier.* Large sporting events have a significant impact on the economy of the host city. Those attending the 2006 NCAA men's Final Four basketball competition in Indianapolis poured $45 million into the local economy (*Source*: WISH TV). Assume that 60% of that money is spent again in the city, and then 60% of that money is spent again, and so on. This is known as the *economic multiplier effect*. Find the total effect on the economy.

Solution   The total economic effect is given by the infinite series

$$\$45,000,000 + \$45,000,000(0.6) + \$45,000,000(0.6)^2 + \cdots.$$

Since $|r| = |0.6| = 0.6 < 1$, the series has a sum. Using the formula for the sum of an infinite geometric series, we have

$$S_\infty = \frac{a_1}{1 - r} = \frac{\$45,000,000}{1 - 0.6} = \$112,500,000.$$

The total effect of the spending on the economy is $112,500,000.

▶ Now Try Exercise 59.

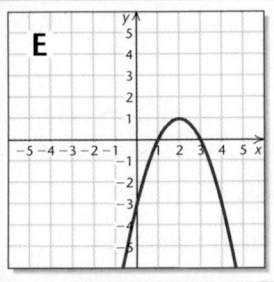

Visualizing the Graph

Match the equation with its graph.

1. $(x - 1)^2 + (y + 2)^2 = 9$

2. $y = x^3 - x^2 + x - 1$

3. $f(x) = 2^x$

4. $f(x) = x$

5. $a_n = n$

6. $y = \log(x + 3)$

7. $f(x) = -(x - 2)^2 + 1$

8. $f(x) = (x - 2)^2 - 1$

9. $y = \dfrac{1}{x - 1}$

10. $y = -3x + 4$

Answers on page A-75

10.3 EXERCISE SET

Find the common ratio.

1. 2, 4, 8, 16,...

2. 18, −6, 2, −$\frac{2}{3}$,...

3. −1, 1, −1, 1,...

4. −8, −0.8, −0.08, −0.008,...

5. $\frac{2}{3}$, −$\frac{4}{3}$, $\frac{8}{3}$, −$\frac{16}{3}$,...

6. 75, 15, 3, $\frac{3}{5}$,...

7. 6.275, 0.6275, 0.06275,...

8. $\dfrac{1}{x}$, $\dfrac{1}{x^2}$, $\dfrac{1}{x^3}$,...

9. 5, $\dfrac{5a}{2}$, $\dfrac{5a^2}{4}$, $\dfrac{5a^3}{8}$,...

10. $780, $858, $943.80, $1038.18,...

Find the indicated term.

11. 2, 4, 8, 16,...; the 7th term

12. 2, −10, 50, −250,...; the 9th term

13. 2, $2\sqrt{3}$, 6,...; the 9th term

14. 1, −1, 1, −1,...; the 57th term

15. $\frac{7}{625}$, −$\frac{7}{25}$,...; the 23rd term

16. $1000, $1060, $1123.60,...; the 5th term

Find the nth, or general, term.

17. 1, 3, 9,...   18. 25, 5, 1,...

19. 1, −1, 1, −1,...   20. −2, 4, −8,...

21. $\dfrac{1}{x}$, $\dfrac{1}{x^2}$, $\dfrac{1}{x^3}$,...   22. 5, $\dfrac{5a}{2}$, $\dfrac{5a^2}{4}$, $\dfrac{5a^3}{8}$,...

23. Find the sum of the first 7 terms of the geometric series
$$6 + 12 + 24 + \cdots.$$

24. Find the sum of the first 10 terms of the geometric series
$$16 − 8 + 4 − \cdots.$$

25. Find the sum of the first 9 terms of the geometric series
$$\tfrac{1}{18} − \tfrac{1}{6} + \tfrac{1}{2} − \cdots.$$

26. Find the sum of the geometric series
$$−8 + 4 + (−2) + \cdots + \left(−\tfrac{1}{32}\right).$$

Find the sum, if it exists.

27. $4 + 2 + 1 + \cdots$

28. $7 + 3 + \frac{9}{7} + \cdots$

29. $25 + 20 + 16 + \cdots$

30. $100 − 10 + 1 − \frac{1}{10} + \cdots$

31. $8 + 40 + 200 + \cdots$

32. $−6 + 3 − \frac{3}{2} + \frac{3}{4} − \cdots$

33. $0.6 + 0.06 + 0.006 + \cdots$

34. $\displaystyle\sum_{k=0}^{10} 3^k$ 35. $\displaystyle\sum_{k=1}^{11} 15\left(\frac{2}{3}\right)^k$

36. $\displaystyle\sum_{k=0}^{50} 200(1.08)^k$ 37. $\displaystyle\sum_{k=1}^{\infty} \left(\frac{1}{2}\right)^{k-1}$

38. $\displaystyle\sum_{k=1}^{\infty} 2^k$ 39. $\displaystyle\sum_{k=1}^{\infty} 12.5^k$

40. $\displaystyle\sum_{k=1}^{\infty} 400(1.0625)^k$ 41. $\displaystyle\sum_{k=1}^{\infty} \$500(1.11)^{-k}$

42. $\displaystyle\sum_{k=1}^{\infty} \$1000(1.06)^{-k}$ 43. $\displaystyle\sum_{k=1}^{\infty} 16(0.1)^{k-1}$

44. $\displaystyle\sum_{k=1}^{\infty} \frac{8}{3}\left(\frac{1}{2}\right)^{k-1}$

Find fraction notation.

45. 0.131313..., or 0.$\overline{13}$ 46. 0.2222..., or 0.$\overline{2}$

47. 8.999$\overline{9}$ 48. 6.1616$\overline{16}$

49. 3.4125$\overline{125}$ 50. 12.7809$\overline{809}$

51. *Daily Doubling Salary.* Suppose someone offered you a job for the month of February (28 days) under the following conditions. You will be paid $0.01 the 1st day, $0.02 the 2nd, $0.04 the 3rd, and so on, doubling your previous day's salary each day. How much would you earn altogether?

52. *Bouncing Ping-Pong Ball.* A ping-pong ball is dropped from a height of 16 ft and always rebounds $\frac{1}{4}$ of the distance fallen.

a) How high does it rebound the 6th time?
b) Find the total sum of the rebound heights of the ball.

53. *Bungee Jumping.* A bungee jumper always rebounds 60% of the distance fallen. A bungee jump is made using a cord that stretches to 200 ft.

a) After jumping and then rebounding 9 times, how far has a bungee jumper traveled upward (the total rebound distance)?
b) About how far will a jumper have traveled upward (bounced) before coming to rest?

54. *Population Growth.* Hadleytown has a present population of 100,000, and the population is increasing by 3% each year.

a) What will the population be in 15 yr?
b) How long will it take for the population to double?

55. *Amount of an Annuity.* To create a college fund, a parent makes a sequence of 18 yearly deposits of $1000 each in a savings account on which interest is compounded annually at 3.2%. Find the amount of the annuity.

56. *Amount of an Annuity.* A sequence of yearly payments of P dollars is invested at the end of each of N years at interest rate i, compounded annually. The total amount in the account, or the amount of the annuity, is V.

a) Show that

$$V = \frac{P[(1 + i)^N - 1]}{i}.$$

b) Suppose that interest is compounded n times per year and deposits are made every compounding period. Show that the formula for V is then given by

$$V = \frac{P\left[\left(1 + \dfrac{i}{n}\right)^{nN} - 1\right]}{i/n}.$$

57. *Loan Repayment.* A family borrows $120,000. The loan is to be repaid in 13 yr at 12% interest, compounded annually. How much will be repaid at the end of 13 yr?

58. *Doubling the Thickness of Paper.* A piece of paper is 0.01 in. thick. It is cut and stacked repeatedly in such a way that its thickness is doubled each time for 20 times. How thick is the result?

Start   Step 1   Step 2   Step 3

59. *The Economic Multiplier.* Suppose the government is making a $13,000,000,000 expenditure for educational improvement. If 85% of this is spent again, and so on, what is the total effect on the economy?

60. *Advertising Effect.* Great Grains Cereal Company is about to market a new low-fat cereal in a city of 5,000,000 people. They plan an advertising campaign that they think will induce 30% of the people to buy the product. They estimate that if those people like the product, they will induce 30% · 30% · 5,000,000 more to buy the product, and those will induce 30% · 30% · 30% · 5,000,000, and so on. In all, how many people will buy the product as a result of the advertising campaign? What percentage of the population is this?

Technology Connection

61. Use a graphing calculator to find the sum in Exercise 35.

62. Use a graphing calculator to find the sum in Exercise 34.

Collaborative Discussion and Writing

63. Write a problem for a classmate to solve. Devise the problem so that a geometric series is involved and the solution is "The total amount in the bank is $900(1.08)^{40}$, or about \$19,552."

64. The infinite series
$$S_\infty = 2 + \frac{1}{2} + \frac{1}{2 \cdot 3} + \frac{1}{2 \cdot 3 \cdot 4} + \frac{1}{2 \cdot 3 \cdot 4 \cdot 5} + \cdots$$
is not geometric, but it does have a sum. Consider $S_1, S_2, S_3, S_4, S_5,$ and S_6. Construct a table and a graph of the sequence. Expand the sequence of sums, if needed. Make a conjecture about the value of S_∞ and explain your reasoning.

Skill Maintenance

For each pair of functions, find $(f \circ g)(x)$ and $(g \circ f)(x)$.

65. $f(x) = x^2,\ g(x) = 4x + 5$

66. $f(x) = x - 1,\ g(x) = x^2 + x + 3$

Solve.

67. $5^x = 35$

68. $\log_2 x = -4$

Synthesis

69. Prove that
$$\sqrt{3} - \sqrt{2}, \quad 4 - \sqrt{6}, \quad \text{and} \quad 6\sqrt{3} - 2\sqrt{2}$$
form a geometric sequence.

70. Consider the sequence
$$4,\ 20.4,\ 104.04,\ 531.6444,\ldots.$$
What is the error in using $a_{277} = 4(5.1)^{276}$ to find the 277th term?

71. Consider the sequence
$$x + 3,\ x + 7,\ 4x - 2,\ldots.$$
a) If the sequence is arithmetic, find x and then determine each of the 3 terms and the 4th term.

b) If the sequence is geometric, find x and then determine each of the 3 terms and the 4th term.

72. Find the sum of the first n terms of
$$1 + x + x^2 + \cdots.$$

73. Find the sum of the first n terms of
$$x^2 - x^3 + x^4 - x^5 + \cdots.$$

In Exercises 74 and 75, assume that $a_1, a_2, a_3, \ldots$ is a geometric sequence.

74. Prove that $a_1^2, a_2^2, a_3^2, \ldots$, is a geometric sequence.

75. Prove that $\ln a_1, \ln a_2, \ln a_3, \ldots$, is an arithmetic sequence.

76. Prove that $5^{a_1}, 5^{a_2}, 5^{a_3}, \ldots$, is a geometric sequence, if $a_1, a_2, a_3, \ldots$, is an arithmetic sequence.

77. The sides of a square are 16 cm long. A second square is inscribed by joining the midpoints of the sides, successively. In the second square, we repeat the process, inscribing a third square. If this process is continued indefinitely, what is the sum of all the areas of all the squares? (*Hint:* Use an infinite geometric series.)

<table>
<tr><td>**10.4**</td><td>**Mathematical Induction**</td></tr>
</table>

⬥ List the statements of an infinite sequence that is defined by a formula.

⬥ Do proofs by mathematical induction.

In this section, we learn to prove a sequence of mathematical statements using a procedure called *mathematical induction.*

⬥ Sequences of Statements

Infinite sequences of statements occur often in mathematics. In an infinite sequence of statements, there is a statement for each natural number. For example, consider the sequence of statements represented by the following:

"For each x between 0 and 1, $0 < x^n < 1$."

Let's think of this as $S(n)$, or S_n. Substituting natural numbers for n gives a sequence of statements. We list a few of them.

Statement 1, S_1:   For x between 0 and 1, $0 < x^1 < 1$.

Statement 2, S_2:   For x between 0 and 1, $0 < x^2 < 1$.

Statement 3, S_3:   For x between 0 and 1, $0 < x^3 < 1$.

Statement 4, S_4:   For x between 0 and 1, $0 < x^4 < 1$.

In this context, the symbols S_1, S_2, S_3, and so on, do not represent sums.

EXAMPLE 1   List the first four statements in the sequence that can be obtained from each of the following.

a) $\log n < n$

b) $1 + 3 + 5 + \cdots + (2n - 1) = n^2$

Solution

a) This time, S_n is "$\log n < n$."

S_1: $\log 1 < 1$

S_2: $\log 2 < 2$

S_3: $\log 3 < 3$

S_4: $\log 4 < 4$

b) This time, S_n is "$1 + 3 + 5 + \cdots + (2n - 1) = n^2$."

S_1: $1 = 1^2$

S_2: $1 + 3 = 2^2$

S_3: $1 + 3 + 5 = 3^2$

S_4: $1 + 3 + 5 + 7 = 4^2$

▶ Now Try Exercise 1.

✦ Proving Infinite Sequences of Statements

We now develop a method of proof, called **mathematical induction**, which we can use to try to prove that all statements in an infinite sequence of statements are true. The statements usually have the form:

"For all natural numbers n, S_n",

where S_n is some mathematical sentence such as those of the preceding examples. Of course, we cannot prove each statement of an infinite sequence individually. Instead, we try to show that "whenever S_k holds, then S_{k+1} must hold." We abbreviate this as $S_k \to S_{k+1}$. (This is also read "If S_k, then S_{k+1}," or "S_k implies S_{k+1}.") Suppose that we could somehow establish that this holds for all natural numbers k. Then we would have the following:

$S_1 \to S_2$ meaning "if S_1 is true, then S_2 is true";
$S_2 \to S_3$ meaning "if S_2 is true, then S_3 is true";
$S_3 \to S_4$ meaning "if S_3 is true, then S_4 is true";

and so on, indefinitely.

Even knowing that $S_k \to S_{k+1}$, we would still not be certain whether there is *any* k for which S_k is true. All we would know is that "if S_k is true, then S_{k+1} is true." Suppose now that S_k is true for some k, say, $k = 1$. We then must have the following.

S_1 is true.   We have verified, or proved, this.

$S_1 \to S_2$ This means that whenever S_1 is true, S_2 is true.

Therefore, S_2 is true.

$S_2 \to S_3$ This means that whenever S_2 is true, S_3 is true.

Therefore, S_3 is true.

and so on.

We conclude that S_n is true for all natural numbers n.

This leads us to the principle of mathematical induction, which we use to prove the types of statements considered here.

The Principle of Mathematical Induction

We can prove an infinite sequence of statements S_n by showing the following.

(1) *Basis step.* S_1 is true.
(2) *Induction step.* For all natural numbers k, $S_k \to S_{k+1}$.

Mathematical induction is analogous to lining up a sequence of dominoes. The induction step tells us that if any one domino is knocked over, then the one next to it will be hit and knocked over. The basis step tells us that the first domino can indeed be knocked over. Note that in order for all dominoes to fall, *both* conditions must be satisfied.

S_1

$S_k \to S_{k+1}$

When you are learning to do proofs by mathematical induction, it is helpful to first write out S_n, S_1, S_k, and S_{k+1}. This helps to identify what is to be assumed and what is to be deduced.

EXAMPLE 2   Prove: For every natural number n,

$$1 + 3 + 5 + \cdots + (2n - 1) = n^2.$$

Proof   We first list S_n, S_1, S_k, and S_{k+1}.

S_n: $1 + 3 + 5 + \cdots + (2n - 1) = n^2$

S_1: $1 = 1^2$

S_k: $1 + 3 + 5 + \cdots + (2k - 1) = k^2$

S_{k+1}: $1 + 3 + 5 + \cdots + (2k - 1) + [2(k + 1) - 1] = (k + 1)^2$

(1) *Basis step.* S_1, as listed, is true since $1 = 1^2$, or $1 = 1$.

(2) *Induction step.* We let k be any natural number. We assume S_k to be true and try to show that it implies that S_{k+1} is true. Now S_k is

$$1 + 3 + 5 + \cdots + (2k - 1) = k^2.$$

Starting with the left side of S_{k+1} and substituting k^2 for $1 + 3 + 5 + \cdots + (2k - 1)$, we have

$$\underbrace{1 + 3 + \cdots + (2k - 1)} + [2(k + 1) - 1]$$

$$= k^2 + [2(k + 1) - 1]$$
$$= k^2 + 2k + 2 - 1$$
$$= k^2 + 2k + 1 = (k + 1)^2.$$

We have derived S_{k+1} from S_k. Thus we have shown that for all natural numbers k, $S_k \to S_{k+1}$. This completes the induction step. It and the basis step tell us that the proof is complete.   ▶ **Now Try Exercise 5.**

EXAMPLE 3 Prove: For every natural number n,

$$\frac{1}{2} + \frac{1}{4} + \frac{1}{8} + \cdots + \frac{1}{2^n} = \frac{2^n - 1}{2^n}.$$

Proof We first list S_n, S_1, S_k, and S_{k+1}.

S_n: $\quad \dfrac{1}{2} + \dfrac{1}{4} + \dfrac{1}{8} + \cdots + \dfrac{1}{2^n} = \dfrac{2^n - 1}{2^n}$

S_1: $\quad \dfrac{1}{2^1} = \dfrac{2^1 - 1}{2^1}$

S_k: $\quad \dfrac{1}{2} + \dfrac{1}{4} + \dfrac{1}{8} + \cdots + \dfrac{1}{2^k} = \dfrac{2^k - 1}{2^k}$

S_{k+1}: $\quad \dfrac{1}{2} + \dfrac{1}{4} + \dfrac{1}{8} + \cdots + \dfrac{1}{2^k} + \dfrac{1}{2^{k+1}} = \dfrac{2^{k+1} - 1}{2^{k+1}}$

(1) *Basis step.* We show S_1 to be true as follows:

$$\frac{2^1 - 1}{2^1} = \frac{2 - 1}{2} = \frac{1}{2}.$$

(2) *Induction step.* We let k be any natural number. We assume S_k to be true and try to show that it implies that S_{k+1} is true. Now S_k is

$$\frac{1}{2} + \frac{1}{4} + \frac{1}{8} + \cdots + \frac{1}{2^k} = \frac{2^k - 1}{2^k}.$$

Starting with the left side of S_{k+1} and substituting

$$\frac{2^k - 1}{2^k} \quad \text{for} \quad \frac{1}{2} + \frac{1}{4} + \cdots + \frac{1}{2^k},$$

we have

$$\underbrace{\frac{1}{2} + \frac{1}{4} + \frac{1}{8} + \cdots + \frac{1}{2^k}} + \frac{1}{2^{k+1}}$$
$$\downarrow$$
$$= \frac{2^k - 1}{2^k} + \frac{1}{2^{k+1}} = \frac{2^k - 1}{2^k} \cdot \frac{2}{2} + \frac{1}{2^{k+1}} = \frac{(2^k - 1) \cdot 2 + 1}{2^{k+1}}$$
$$= \frac{2^{k+1} - 2 + 1}{2^{k+1}} = \frac{2^{k+1} - 1}{2^{k+1}}.$$

We have derived S_{k+1} from S_k. Thus we have shown that for all natural numbers k, $S_k \rightarrow S_{k+1}$. This completes the induction step. It and the basis step tell us that the proof is complete. ▶ **Now Try Exercise 15.**

EXAMPLE 4 Prove: For every natural number n, $n < 2^n$.

Proof We first list S_n, S_1, S_k, and S_{k+1}.

$$S_n: \quad n < 2^n$$
$$S_1: \quad 1 < 2^1$$
$$S_k: \quad k < 2^k$$
$$S_{k+1}: \quad k + 1 < 2^{k+1}$$

(1) *Basis step.* S_1, as listed, is true since $2^1 = 2$ and $1 < 2$.

(2) *Induction step.* We let k be any natural number. We assume S_k to be true and try to show that it implies that S_{k+1} is true. Now

$$k < 2^k \qquad \text{This is } S_k.$$
$$2k < 2 \cdot 2^k \qquad \text{Multiplying by 2 on both sides}$$
$$2k < 2^{k+1} \qquad \text{Adding exponents on the right}$$
$$k + k < 2^{k+1}. \qquad \text{Rewriting } 2k \text{ as } k + k$$

Since k is any natural number, we know that $1 \leq k$. Thus,

$$k + 1 \leq k + k. \qquad \text{Adding } k \text{ on both sides of } 1 \leq k$$

Putting the results $k + 1 \leq k + k$ and $k + k < 2^{k+1}$ together gives us

$$k + 1 < 2^{k+1}. \qquad \text{This is } S_{k+1}.$$

We have derived S_{k+1} from S_k. Thus we have shown that for all natural numbers k, $S_k \rightarrow S_{k+1}$. This completes the induction step. It and the basis step tell us that the proof is complete. ▶ **Now Try Exercise 11.**

10.4 EXERCISE SET

List the first five statements in the sequence that can be obtained from each of the following. Determine whether each of the statements is true or false.

1. $n^2 < n^3$

2. $n^2 - n + 41$ is prime. Find a value for n for which the statement is false.

3. A polygon of n sides has $[n(n - 3)]/2$ diagonals.

4. The sum of the angles of a polygon of n sides is $(n - 2) \cdot 180°$.

Use mathematical induction to prove each of the following.

5. $2 + 4 + 6 + \cdots + 2n = n(n + 1)$

6. $4 + 8 + 12 + \cdots + 4n = 2n(n + 1)$

7. $1 + 5 + 9 + \cdots + (4n - 3) = n(2n - 1)$

8. $3 + 6 + 9 + \cdots + 3n = \dfrac{3n(n + 1)}{2}$

9. $2 + 4 + 8 + \cdots + 2^n = 2(2^n - 1)$

10. $2 \leq 2^n$

11. $n < n + 1$

12. $3^n < 3^{n+1}$

13. $2n \leq 2^n$

14. $\dfrac{1}{1 \cdot 2} + \dfrac{1}{2 \cdot 3} + \cdots + \dfrac{1}{n(n + 1)} = \dfrac{n}{n + 1}$

15. $\dfrac{1}{1 \cdot 2 \cdot 3} + \dfrac{1}{2 \cdot 3 \cdot 4} + \dfrac{1}{3 \cdot 4 \cdot 5} + \cdots$

$\qquad + \dfrac{1}{n(n + 1)(n + 2)} = \dfrac{n(n + 3)}{4(n + 1)(n + 2)}$

16. If x is any real number greater than 1, then for any natural number n, $x \leq x^n$.

The following formulas can be used to find sums of powers of natural numbers. Use mathematical induction to prove each formula.

17. $1 + 2 + 3 + \cdots + n = \dfrac{n(n + 1)}{2}$

18. $1^2 + 2^2 + 3^2 + \cdots + n^2 = \dfrac{n(n + 1)(2n + 1)}{6}$

19. $1^3 + 2^3 + 3^3 + \cdots + n^3 = \dfrac{n^2(n + 1)^2}{4}$

20. $1^4 + 2^4 + 3^4 + \cdots + n^4$

$\qquad = \dfrac{n(n + 1)(2n + 1)(3n^2 + 3n - 1)}{30}$

21. $1^5 + 2^5 + 3^5 + \cdots + n^5$

$\qquad = \dfrac{n^2(n + 1)^2(2n^2 + 2n - 1)}{12}$

Use mathematical induction to prove each of the following.

22. $\displaystyle\sum_{i=1}^{n} (3i - 1) = \dfrac{n(3n + 1)}{2}$

23. $\displaystyle\sum_{i=1}^{n} i(i + 1) = \dfrac{n(n + 1)(n + 2)}{3}$

24. $\left(1 + \dfrac{1}{1}\right)\left(1 + \dfrac{1}{2}\right)\left(1 + \dfrac{1}{3}\right) \cdots \left(1 + \dfrac{1}{n}\right)$

$\qquad = n + 1$

25. The sum of n terms of an arithmetic sequence:

$a_1 + (a_1 + d) + (a_1 + 2d) + \cdots + [a_1 + (n - 1)d]$

$\qquad = \dfrac{n}{2}[2a_1 + (n - 1)d]$

Collaborative Discussion and Writing

26. Write an explanation of the idea behind mathematical induction for a fellow student.

27. Find two statements not considered in this section that are not true for all natural numbers. Then try to find where a proof by mathematical induction fails.

Skill Maintenance

Solve.

28. $2x - 3y = 1,$
$3x - 4y = 3$

29. $x + y + z = 3,$
$2x - 3y - 2z = 5,$
$3x + 2y + 2z = 8$

30. *e-Commerce.* ebooks.com ran a one-day promotion offering a hardback title for $24.95 and a paperback title for $9.95. A total of 80 books were sold and $1546 was taken in. How many of each type of book were sold?

31. *Investment.* Martin received $104 in simple interest one year from three investments. Part is invested at 1.5%, part at 2%, and part at 3%. The amount invested at 2% is twice the amount invested at 1.5%. There is $400 more invested at 3% than at 2%. Find the amount invested at each rate.

Synthesis

Use mathematical induction to prove each of the following.

32. The sum of n terms of a geometric sequence:

$a_1 + a_1 r + a_1 r^2 + \cdots + a_1 r^{n-1} = \dfrac{a_1 - a_1 r^n}{1 - r}.$

33. $x + y$ is a factor of $x^{2n} - y^{2n}$.

Prove each of the following using mathematical induction. Do the basis step for $n = 2$.

34. For every natural number $n \geq 2$,

$\qquad 2n + 1 < 3^n.$

35. For every natural number $n \geq 2$,

$\log_a(b_1 b_2 \cdots b_n)$

$\qquad = \log_a b_1 + \log_a b_2 + \cdots + \log_a b_n.$

Prove each of the following for any complex numbers z_1, $z_2, \ldots, z_n$, where $i^2 = -1$ and $\bar{z}$ is the conjugate of z. (See Section 2.2.)

36. $\overline{z^n} = \bar{z}^n$

37. $\overline{z_1 + z_2 + \cdots + z_n} = \bar{z}_1 + \bar{z}_2 + \cdots + \bar{z}_n$

38. $\overline{z_1 z_2 \cdots z_n} = \bar{z}_1 \cdot \bar{z}_2 \cdots \bar{z}_n$

39. i^n is either $1, -1, i$, or $-i$.

For any integers a and b, b is a factor of a if there exists an integer c such that a = bc. Prove each of the following for any natural number n.

40. 2 is a factor of $n^2 + n$.

41. 3 is a factor of $n^3 + 2n$.

42. *The Tower of Hanoi Problem.* There are three pegs on a board. On one peg are *n* disks, each smaller than the one on which it rests. The problem is to move this pile of disks to another peg. The final order must be the same, but you can move only one disk at a time and can never place a larger disk on a smaller one.

a) What is the *smallest* number of moves needed to move 3 disks? 4 disks? 2 disks? 1 disk?
b) Conjecture a formula for the *smallest* number of moves needed to move *n* disks. Prove it by mathematical induction.

10.5

Combinatorics: Permutations

◆ Evaluate factorial and permutation notation and solve related applied problems.

In order to study probability, it is first necessary to learn about **combinatorics,** the theory of counting.

◆ Permutations

In this section, we will consider the part of combinatorics called *permutations.*

> The study of permutations involves *order* and *arrangements*.

EXAMPLE 1 How many 3-letter code symbols can be formed with the letters A, B, C *without* repetition (that is, using each letter only once)?

Solution Consider placing the letters in these boxes.

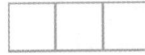

We can select any of the 3 letters for the first letter in the symbol. Once this letter has been selected, the second must be selected from the 2 remaining letters. After this, the third letter is already determined, since only 1 possibility is left. That is, we can place any of the 3 letters in the first box, either of the remaining 2 letters in the second box, and the only remaining letter in the third box. The possibilities can be arrived at using a **tree diagram,** as shown below.

TREE DIAGRAM   OUTCOMES

		OUTCOMES	
A	B — C	ABC	
	C — B	ACB	Each outcome represents one permutation of the letters A, B, C.
B	A — C	BAC	
	C — A	BCA	
C	A — B	CAB	
	B — A	CBA	

We see that there are 6 possibilities. The set of all the possibilities is

$$\{ABC, ACB, BAC, BCA, CAB, CBA\}.$$

Suppose that we perform an experiment such as selecting letters (as in the preceding example), flipping a coin, or drawing a card. The results are called **outcomes.** An **event** is a set of outcomes. The following principle pertains to the counting of actions that occur together, or are combined to form an event.

The Fundamental Counting Principle

Given a combined action, or *event,* in which the first action can be performed in n_1 ways, the second action can be performed in n_2 ways, and so on, the total number of ways in which the combined action can be performed is the product

$$n_1 \cdot n_2 \cdot n_3 \cdot \cdots \cdot n_k.$$

Thus, in Example 1, there are 3 choices for the first letter, 2 for the second letter, and 1 for the third letter, making a total of $3 \cdot 2 \cdot 1$, or 6 possibilities.

EXAMPLE 2 How many 3-letter code symbols can be formed with the letters A, B, C, D, and E *with* repetition (that is, allowing letters to be repeated)?

Solution Since repetition is allowed, there are 5 choices for the first letter, 5 choices for the second, and 5 for the third. Thus, by the fundamental counting principle, there are $5 \cdot 5 \cdot 5$, or 125 code symbols.

> **Permutation**
>
> A **permutation** of a set of n objects is an ordered arrangement of all n objects.

Consider, for example, a set of 4 objects

$$\{A, B, C, D\}.$$

To find the number of ordered arrangements of the set, we select a first letter: There are 4 choices. Then we select a second letter: There are 3 choices. Then we select a third letter: There are 2 choices. Finally, there is 1 choice for the last selection. Thus, by the fundamental counting principle, there are $4 \cdot 3 \cdot 2 \cdot 1$, or 24, permutations of a set of 4 objects.

We can find a formula for the total number of permutations of all objects in a set of n objects. We have n choices for the first selection, $n - 1$ choices for the second, $n - 2$ for the third, and so on. For the nth selection, there is only 1 choice.

> **The Total Number of Permutations of n Objects**
>
> The total number of permutations of n objects, denoted $_nP_n$, is given by
>
> $$_nP_n = n(n - 1)(n - 2) \cdots 3 \cdot 2 \cdot 1.$$

TECHNOLOGY CONNECTION

We can find the total number of permutations of n objects, as in Example 3, using the $_nP_r$ operation from the MATH PRB (probability) menu on a graphing calculator.

```
4 nPr 4
                 24
7 nPr 7
               5040
```

EXAMPLE 3 Find each of the following.

a) $_4P_4$ **b)** $_7P_7$

Solution

Start with 4.

a) $_4P_4 = 4 \cdot 3 \cdot 2 \cdot 1 = 24$

4 factors

b) $_7P_7 = 7 \cdot 6 \cdot 5 \cdot 4 \cdot 3 \cdot 2 \cdot 1 = 5040$

▶ Now Try Exercise 1.

EXAMPLE 4 In how many different ways can 9 packages be placed in 9 mailboxes, one package in a box?

Solution We have

$$_9P_9 = 9 \cdot 8 \cdot 7 \cdot 6 \cdot 5 \cdot 4 \cdot 3 \cdot 2 \cdot 1 = 362{,}880.$$

▶ Now Try Exercise 23.

✦ Factorial Notation

We will use products such as $7 \cdot 6 \cdot 5 \cdot 4 \cdot 3 \cdot 2 \cdot 1$ so often that it is convenient to adopt a notation for them. For the product

$$7 \cdot 6 \cdot 5 \cdot 4 \cdot 3 \cdot 2 \cdot 1,$$

we write 7!, read "7 factorial."

We now define factorial notation for natural numbers and for 0.

Factorial Notation

For any natural number n,

$$n! = n(n - 1)(n - 2) \cdots 3 \cdot 2 \cdot 1.$$

For the number 0,

$$0! = 1.$$

We define 0! as 1 so that certain formulas can be stated concisely and with a consistent pattern.

Here are some examples.

$$
\begin{aligned}
7! &= 7 \cdot 6 \cdot 5 \cdot 4 \cdot 3 \cdot 2 \cdot 1 = 5040 \\
6! &= 6 \cdot 5 \cdot 4 \cdot 3 \cdot 2 \cdot 1 = 720 \\
5! &= 5 \cdot 4 \cdot 3 \cdot 2 \cdot 1 = 120 \\
4! &= 4 \cdot 3 \cdot 2 \cdot 1 = 24 \\
3! &= 3 \cdot 2 \cdot 1 = 6 \\
2! &= 2 \cdot 1 = 2 \\
1! &= 1 = 1 \\
0! &= 1 = 1
\end{aligned}
$$

We now see that the following statement is true.

$$_nP_n = n!$$

We will often need to manipulate factorial notation. For example, note that

$$
\begin{aligned}
8! &= 8 \cdot 7 \cdot 6 \cdot 5 \cdot 4 \cdot 3 \cdot 2 \cdot 1 \\
&= 8 \cdot (7 \cdot 6 \cdot 5 \cdot 4 \cdot 3 \cdot 2 \cdot 1) = 8 \cdot 7!.
\end{aligned}
$$

Generalizing, we get the following.

For any natural number n, $n! = n(n - 1)!$.

By using this result repeatedly, we can further manipulate factorial notation.

EXAMPLE 5   Rewrite 7! with a factor of 5!.

Solution   We have

$$7! = 7 \cdot 6! = 7 \cdot 6 \cdot 5!.$$

In general, we have the following.

For any natural numbers k and n, with $k < n$,

$$n! = \underbrace{n(n-1)(n-2)\cdots[n-(k-1)]}_{k \text{ factors}} \cdot \underbrace{(n-k)!}_{n-k \text{ factors}}$$

✦ Permutations of *n* Objects Taken *k* at a Time

Consider a set of 5 objects

$$\{A, B, C, D, E\}.$$

How many ordered arrangements can be formed using 3 objects without repetition? Examples of such an arrangement are EBA, CAB, and BCD. There are 5 choices for the first object, 4 choices for the second, and 3 choices for the third. By the fundamental counting principle, there are

$$5 \cdot 4 \cdot 3,$$

or

60 *permutations* of a set of 5 objects taken 3 at a time.

Note that

$$5 \cdot 4 \cdot 3 = \frac{5 \cdot 4 \cdot 3 \cdot 2 \cdot 1}{2 \cdot 1}, \quad \text{or} \quad \frac{5!}{2!}.$$

Permutation of n Objects Taken k at a Time

A **permutation** of a set of *n* objects taken *k* at a time is an ordered arrangement of *k* objects taken from the set.

Consider a set of *n* objects and the selection of an ordered arrangement of *k* of them. There would be *n* choices for the first object. Then there would remain $n-1$ choices for the second, $n-2$ choices for the third, and so on. We make *k* choices in all, so there are *k* factors in the product. By the fundamental counting principle, the total number of permutations is

$$\underbrace{n(n-1)(n-2)\cdots[n-(k-1)]}_{k \text{ factors}}.$$

We can express this in another way by multiplying by 1, as follows:

$$n(n-1)(n-2)\cdots[n-(k-1)]\cdot\frac{(n-k)!}{(n-k)!}$$

$$=\frac{n(n-1)(n-2)\cdots[n-(k-1)](n-k)!}{(n-k)!}$$

$$=\frac{n!}{(n-k)!}.$$

This gives us the following.

The Number of Permutations of n Objects Taken k at a Time

The number of permutations of a set of n objects taken k at a time, denoted $_nP_k$, is given by

$$_nP_k = \underbrace{n(n-1)(n-2)\cdots[n-(k-1)]}_{k\ \text{factors}} \tag{1}$$

$$=\frac{n!}{(n-k)!}. \tag{2}$$

TECHNOLOGY CONNECTION

We can do computations like the one in Example 6 using the $_nP_r$ operation from the MATH PRB menu on a graphing calculator.

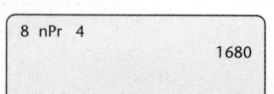

```
8 nPr  4
              1680
```

EXAMPLE 6 Compute $_8P_4$ using both forms of the formula.

Solution Using form (1), we have

The 8 tells where to start.

$$_8P_4 = 8\cdot7\cdot6\cdot5 = 1680.$$

The 4 tells how many factors.

Using form (2), we have

$$_8P_4 = \frac{8!}{(8-4)!}$$

$$=\frac{8!}{4!}$$

$$=\frac{8\cdot7\cdot6\cdot5\cdot4!}{4!} = \frac{8\cdot7\cdot6\cdot5\cdot\cancel{4!}}{\cancel{4!}}$$

$$= 8\cdot7\cdot6\cdot5 = 1680.$$

▶ Now Try Exercise 3.

EXAMPLE 7 *Flags of Nations.* The flags of many nations consist of three vertical stripes. For example, the flag of Ireland, shown on the following page, has its first stripe green, second white, and third orange.

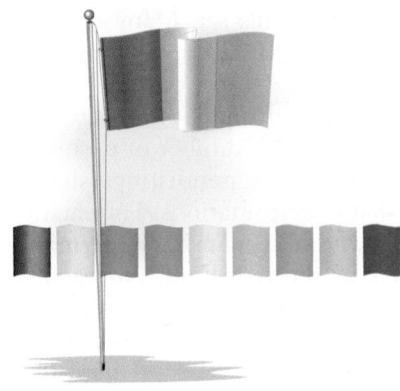

Suppose that the following 9 colors are available:

{black, yellow, red, blue, white, gold, orange, pink, purple}.

How many different flags of 3 colors can be made without repetition of colors in a flag? This assumes that the order in which the stripes appear is considered.

Solution   We are determining the number of permutations of 9 objects taken 3 at a time. There is no repetition of colors. Using form (1), we get

$$_9P_3 = \underbrace{9 \cdot 8 \cdot 7}_{\text{3 factors}} = 504.$$

▶ Now Try Exercise 37(a).

EXAMPLE 8   *Batting Orders.*   A baseball manager arranges the batting order as follows: The 4 infielders will bat first. Then the 3 outfielders, the catcher, and the pitcher will follow, not necessarily in that order. How many different batting orders are possible?

Solution   The infielders can bat in $_4P_4$ different ways, the rest in $_5P_5$ different ways. Then by the fundamental counting principle, we have

$$_4P_4 \cdot {_5P_5} = 4! \cdot 5!,\quad \text{or}\quad 2880 \text{ possible batting orders.}$$

▶ Now Try Exercise 31.

If we allow repetition, a situation like the following can occur.

EXAMPLE 9   How many 5-letter code symbols can be formed with the letters A, B, C, and D if we allow a letter to occur more than once?

Solution   We can select each of the 5 letters in 4 ways. That is, we can select the first letter in 4 ways, the second in 4 ways, and so on. Thus there are 4^5, or 1024 arrangements.

▶ Now Try Exercise 37(b).

> The number of distinct arrangements of n objects taken k at a time, allowing repetition, is n^k.

◆ Permutations of Sets with Nondistinguishable Objects

Consider a set of 7 marbles, 4 of which are blue and 3 of which are red. Although the marbles are all different, when they are lined up, one red marble will look just like any other red marble. In this sense, we say that the red marbles are nondistinguishable and, similarly, the blue marbles are nondistinguishable.

We know that there are 7! permutations of this set. Many of them will look alike, however. We develop a formula for finding the number of distinguishable permutations.

Consider a set of n objects in which n_1 are of one kind, n_2 are of a second kind, ..., and n_k are of a kth kind. The total number of permutations of the set is $n!$, but this includes many that are nondistinguishable. Let N be the total number of distinguishable permutations. For each of these N permutations, there are $n_1!$ actual, nondistinguishable permutations, obtained by permuting the objects of the first kind. For each of these $N \cdot n_1!$ permutations, there are $n_2!$ nondistinguishable permutations, obtained by permuting the objects of the second kind, and so on. By the fundamental counting principle, the total number of permutations, including those that are nondistinguishable, is

$$N \cdot n_1! \cdot n_2! \cdot \cdots \cdot n_k!.$$

Then we have $N \cdot n_1! \cdot n_2! \cdot \cdots \cdot n_k! = n!$. Solving for N, we obtain

$$N = \frac{n!}{n_1! \cdot n_2! \cdot \cdots \cdot n_k!}.$$

Now, to finish our problem with the marbles, we have

$$N = \frac{7!}{4!\,3!}$$

$$= \frac{7 \cdot 6 \cdot 5 \cdot 4!}{4! \cdot 3 \cdot 2 \cdot 1} = \frac{7 \cdot \cancel{3} \cdot \cancel{2} \cdot 5 \cdot \cancel{4!}}{\cancel{4!} \cdot \cancel{3} \cdot \cancel{2} \cdot 1}$$

$$= \frac{7 \cdot 5}{1}, \quad \text{or} \quad 35$$

distinguishable permutations of the marbles.

In general:

> For a set of n objects in which n_1 are of one kind, n_2 are of another kind, ..., and n_k are of a kth kind, the number of distinguishable permutations is
>
> $$\frac{n!}{n_1! \cdot n_2! \cdot \cdots \cdot n_k!}.$$

EXAMPLE 10   In how many distinguishable ways can the letters of the word CINCINNATI be arranged?

Solution   There are 2 C's, 3 I's, 3 N's, 1 A, and 1 T for a total of 10 letters. Thus,

$$N = \frac{10!}{2! \cdot 3! \cdot 3! \cdot 1! \cdot 1!}, \quad \text{or} \quad 50,400.$$

The letters of the word CINCINNATI can be arranged in 50,400 distinguishable ways.

▶ Now Try Exercise 31.

10.5 EXERCISE SET

Evaluate.

1. $_6P_6$

2. $_4P_3$

3. $_{10}P_7$

4. $_{10}P_3$

5. $5!$

6. $7!$

7. $0!$

8. $1!$

9. $\dfrac{9!}{5!}$

10. $\dfrac{9!}{4!}$

11. $(8-3)!$

12. $(8-5)!$

13. $\dfrac{10!}{7!\,3!}$

14. $\dfrac{7!}{(7-2)!}$

15. $_8P_0$

16. $_{13}P_1$

17. $_{52}P_4$

18. $_{52}P_5$

19. $_nP_3$

20. $_nP_2$

21. $_nP_1$

22. $_nP_0$

In each of Exercises 23–41, give your answer using permutation notation, factorial notation, or other operations. Then evaluate.

How many permutations are there of the letters in each of the following words if all the letters are used without repetition?

23. MARVIN

24. JUDY

25. UNDERMOST

26. COMBINES

27. How many permutations are there of the letters of the word UNDERMOST if the letters are taken 4 at a time?

28. How many permutations are there of the letters of the word COMBINES if the letters are taken 5 at a time?

29. How many 5-digit numbers can be formed using the digits 2, 4, 6, 8, and 9 without repetition? with repetition?

30. In how many ways can 7 athletes be arranged in a straight line?

31. *Program Planning.* A program is planned to have 5 rock numbers and 4 speeches. In how many ways can this be done if a rock number and a speech are to alternate and a rock number is to come first?

32. How many distinguishable code symbols can be formed from the letters of the word BUSINESS? BIOLOGY? MATHEMATICS?

33. *Phone Numbers.* How many 7-digit phone numbers can be formed with the digits 0, 1, 2, 3, 4, 5, 6, 7, 8, and 9, assuming that the first number cannot be 0 or 1? Accordingly, how many telephone numbers can there be within a given area code, before the area needs to be split with a new area code?

34. A professor is going to grade her 24 students on a curve. She will give 3 A's, 5 B's, 9 C's, 4 D's, and 3 F's. In how many ways can she do this?

35. Suppose the expression $a^2b^3c^4$ is rewritten without exponents. In how many ways can this be done?

36. *Coin Arrangements.* A penny, a nickel, a dime, and a quarter are arranged in a straight line.

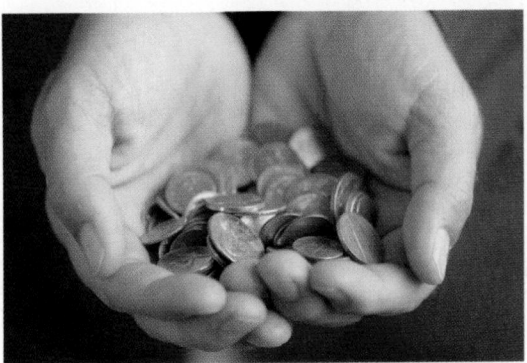

a) Considering just the coins, in how many ways can they be lined up?

b) Considering the coins and heads and tails, in how many ways can they be lined up?

37. How many code symbols can be formed using 5 out of 6 letters of A, B, C, D, E, F if the letters:

a) are not repeated?
b) can be repeated?
c) are not repeated but must begin with D?
d) are not repeated but must begin with DE?

38. *License Plates.* A state forms its license plates by first listing a number that corresponds to the county in which the owner of the car resides. (The names of the counties are alphabetized and the number is its location in that order.) Then the plate lists a letter of the alphabet, and this is followed by a number from 1 to 9999. How many such plates are possible if there are 80 counties?

39. *Zip Codes.* A U.S. postal zip code is a five-digit number.

a) How many zip codes are possible if any of the digits 0 to 9 can be used?
b) If each post office has its own zip code, how many possible post offices can there be?

40. *Zip-Plus-4 Codes.* A zip-plus-4 postal code uses a 9-digit number like 75247-5456. How many 9-digit zip-plus-4 postal codes are possible?

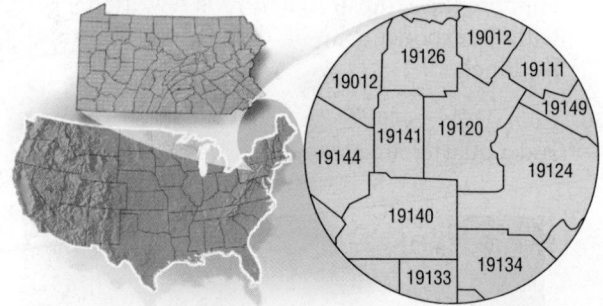

41. *Social Security Numbers.* A social security number is a 9-digit number like 243-47-0825.

a) How many different social security numbers can there be?
b) There are about 300 million people in the United States. Can each person have a unique social security number?

Collaborative Discussion and Writing

42. How "long" is 15!? Suppose you own 15 different books and decide to make up all the possible arrangements of the books on a shelf. About how long, in years, would it take you if you make one arrangement per second? Write out the reasoning you used for this problem in the form of a paragraph.

43. *Circular Arrangements.* In how many ways can the numbers on a clock face be arranged? See if you can derive a formula for the number of distinct circular arrangements of n objects. Explain your reasoning.

Skill Maintenance

Find the zero(s) of the function.

44. $f(x) = 4x - 9$

45. $f(x) = x^2 + x - 6$

46. $f(x) = 2x^2 - 3x - 1$

47. $f(x) = x^3 - 4x^2 - 7x + 10$

Synthesis

Solve for n.

48. $_nP_5 = 7 \cdot {_nP_4}$ **49.** $_nP_4 = 8 \cdot {_{n-1}P_3}$

50. $_nP_5 = 9 \cdot {_{n-1}P_4}$ **51.** $_nP_4 = 8 \cdot {_nP_3}$

52. Show that $n! = n(n - 1)(n - 2)(n - 3)!$.

53. *Single-Elimination Tournaments.* In a single-elimination sports tournament consisting of n teams, a team is eliminated when it loses one game. How many games are required to complete the tournament?

54. *Double-Elimination Tournaments.* In a double-elimination softball tournament consisting of n teams, a team is eliminated when it loses two games. At most, how many games are required to complete the tournament?

◆ Evaluate combination notation and solve related applied problems.

10.6 Combinatorics: Combinations

We now consider counting techniques in which order is not considered.

◆ Combinations

We sometimes make a selection from a set *without regard to order*. Such a selection is called a *combination*. If you play cards, for example, you know that in most situations the *order* in which you hold cards is not important. That is,

The hand   is "equivalent" to these hands.

Each hand contains the same combination of three cards.

EXAMPLE 1 Find all the combinations of 3 letters taken from the set of 5 letters {A, B, C, D, E}.

Solution The combinations are

{A, B, C},	{A, B, D},
{A, B, E},	{A, C, D},
{A, C, E},	{A, D, E},
{B, C, D},	{B, C, E},
{B, D, E},	{C, D, E}.

There are 10 combinations of the 5 letters taken 3 at a time.

When we find all the combinations from a set of 5 objects taken 3 at a time, we are finding all the 3-element subsets. When a set is named, the order of the elements is *not* considered. Thus,

{A, C, B} names the same set as {A, B, C}.

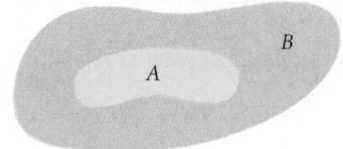

Subset

Set A is a subset of set B, denoted $A \subseteq B$, if every element of A is an element of B.

The elements of a subset are not ordered. When thinking of *combinations*, do *not* think about order!

Combination

A **combination** containing k objects is a subset containing k objects.

We want to develop a formula for computing the number of combinations of n objects taken k at a time without actually listing the combinations or subsets.

Combination Notation

The number of combinations of n objects taken k at a time is denoted $_nC_k$.

We call $_nC_k$ **combination notation.** We want to derive a general formula for $_nC_k$ for any $k \leq n$. First, it is true that $_nC_n = 1$, because a set with n objects has only 1 subset with n objects, the set itself. Second, $_nC_1 = n$, because a set with n objects has n subsets with 1 element each. Finally, $_nC_0 = 1$, because a set with n objects has only one subset with 0 elements, namely, the empty set $\varnothing$. To consider other possibilities, let's return to Example 1 and compare the number of combinations with the number of permutations.

COMBINATIONS			PERMUTATIONS			
$\{A, B, C\} \longrightarrow$	ABC	BCA	CAB	CBA	BAC	ACB
$\{A, B, D\} \longrightarrow$	ABD	BDA	DAB	DBA	BAD	ADB
$\{A, B, E\} \longrightarrow$	ABE	BEA	EAB	EBA	BAE	AEB
$\{A, C, D\} \longrightarrow$	ACD	CDA	DAC	DCA	CAD	ADC
$\{A, C, E\} \longrightarrow$	ACE	CEA	EAC	ECA	CAE	AEC
$\{A, D, E\} \longrightarrow$	ADE	DEA	EAD	EDA	DAE	AED
$\{B, C, D\} \longrightarrow$	BCD	CDB	DBC	DCB	CBD	BDC
$\{B, C, E\} \longrightarrow$	BCE	CEB	EBC	ECB	CBE	BEC
$\{B, D, E\} \longrightarrow$	BDE	DEB	EBD	EDB	DBE	BED
$\{C, D, E\} \longrightarrow$	CDE	DEC	ECD	EDC	DCE	CED

$_5C_3$ of these

$3! \cdot {_5C_3}$ of these

Note that each combination of 3 objects yields 6, or 3!, permutations.

$$3! \cdot {}_5C_3 = 60 = {}_5P_3 = 5 \cdot 4 \cdot 3,$$

so

$${}_5C_3 = \frac{{}_5P_3}{3!} = \frac{5 \cdot 4 \cdot 3}{3 \cdot 2 \cdot 1} = 10.$$

In general, the number of combinations of n objects taken k at a time, ${}_nC_k$, times the number of permutations of these objects, $k!$, must equal the number of permutations of n objects taken k at a time:

$$k! \cdot {}_nC_k = {}_nP_k$$

$${}_nC_k = \frac{{}_nP_k}{k!}$$

$$= \frac{1}{k!} \cdot {}_nP_k$$

$$= \frac{1}{k!} \cdot \frac{n!}{(n-k)!} = \frac{n!}{k!(n-k)!}.$$

Combinations of n Objects Taken k at a Time

The total number of combinations of n objects taken k at a time, denoted ${}_nC_k$, is given by

$${}_nC_k = \frac{n!}{k!(n-k)!}, \tag{1}$$

or

$${}_nC_k = \frac{{}_nP_k}{k!} = \frac{n(n-1)(n-2)\cdots[n-(k-1)]}{k!}. \tag{2}$$

Another kind of notation for ${}_nC_k$ is **binomial coefficient notation.** The reason for such terminology will be seen later.

Binomial Coefficient Notation

$$\binom{n}{k} = {}_nC_k$$

You should be able to use either notation and either form of the formula.

EXAMPLE 2 Evaluate $\binom{7}{5}$, using forms (1) and (2).

Solution

a) By form (1),

$$\binom{7}{5} = \frac{7!}{5!\,(7-5)!} = \frac{7!}{5!\,2!}$$

$$= \frac{7\cdot 6\cdot 5\cdot 4\cdot 3\cdot 2\cdot 1}{5\cdot 4\cdot 3\cdot 2\cdot 1\cdot 2\cdot 1} = \frac{7\cdot 6}{2\cdot 1} = 21.$$

b) By form (2),

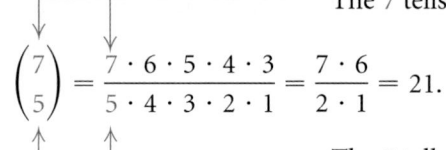

The 7 tells where to start.

$$\binom{7}{5} = \frac{7\cdot 6\cdot 5\cdot 4\cdot 3}{5\cdot 4\cdot 3\cdot 2\cdot 1} = \frac{7\cdot 6}{2\cdot 1} = 21.$$

The 5 tells how many factors there are in both the numerator and the denominator and where to start the denominator. ▶ Now Try Exercise 11.

Be sure to keep in mind that $\binom{n}{k}$ does not mean $n \div k$, or n/k.

EXAMPLE 3 Evaluate $\binom{n}{0}$ and $\binom{n}{2}$.

Solution We use form (1) for the first expression and form (2) for the second. Then

$$\binom{n}{0} = \frac{n!}{0!\,(n-0)!} = \frac{n!}{1\cdot n!} = 1,$$

using form (1), and

$$\binom{n}{2} = \frac{n(n-1)}{2!} = \frac{n(n-1)}{2}, \quad \text{or} \quad \frac{n^2 - n}{2},$$

using form (2). ▶ Now Try Exercise 19.

Note that

$$\binom{7}{2} = \frac{7\cdot 6}{2\cdot 1} = 21,$$

so that using the result of Example 2 gives us

$$\binom{7}{5} = \binom{7}{2}.$$

This says that the number of 5-element subsets of a set of 7 objects is the same as the number of 2-element subsets of a set of 7 objects. When 5 elements are chosen from a set, one also chooses *not* to include 2 elements. To see this, consider the set {A, B, C, D, E, F, G}:

$\{B, G\}$

$\{A, B, C, D, E, F, G\}$ Each time we form a subset with 5 elements, we leave behind a subset with 2 elements, and vice versa.

$\{A, C, D, E, F\}$

In general, we have the following. This result provides an alternative way to compute combinations.

Subsets of Size k and of Size n − k

$$\binom{n}{k} = \binom{n}{n-k} \quad \text{and} \quad {}_nC_k = {}_nC_{n-k}$$

The number of subsets of size k of a set with n objects is the same as the number of subsets of size $n - k$. The number of combinations of n objects taken k at a time is the same as the number of combinations of n objects taken $n - k$ at a time.

We now solve problems involving combinations.

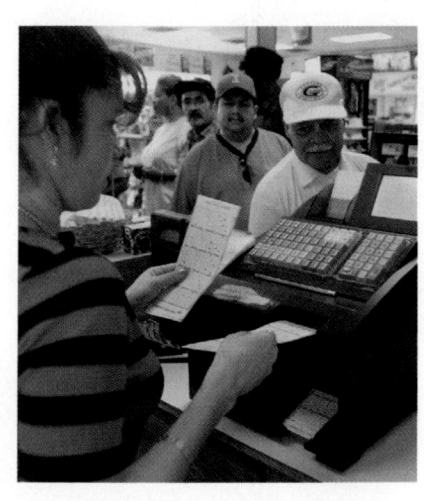

EXAMPLE 4 *Michigan Lottery.* Run by the state of Michigan, Classic Lotto 47 is a twice-weekly lottery game with jackpots starting at $1 million. For a wager of $1, a player can choose 6 numbers from 1 through 47. If the numbers match those drawn by the state, the player wins. (*Source:* www.michigan.gov/lottery)

a) How many 6-number combinations are there?

b) Suppose it takes you 10 min to pick your numbers and buy a game ticket. How many tickets can you buy in 4 days?

c) How many people would you have to hire for 4 days to buy tickets with all the possible combinations and ensure that you win?

Solution

a) No order is implied here. You pick any 6 different numbers from 1 through 47. Thus the number of combinations is

$$
{}_{47}C_6 = \binom{47}{6} = \frac{47!}{6!\,(47-6)!} = \frac{47!}{6!\,41!}
$$

$$
= \frac{47 \cdot 46 \cdot 45 \cdot 44 \cdot 43 \cdot 42}{6 \cdot 5 \cdot 4 \cdot 3 \cdot 2 \cdot 1}
$$

$$
= 10,737,573.
$$

b) First we find the number of minutes in 4 days:

$$4 \text{ days} = 4 \text{ days} \cdot \frac{24 \text{ hr}}{1 \text{ day}} \cdot \frac{60 \text{ min}}{1 \text{ hr}} = 5760 \text{ min}.$$

Thus you could buy 5760/10, or 576 tickets in 4 days.

c) You would need to hire 10,737,573/576, or about 18,642 people, to buy tickets with all the possible combinations and ensure a win. (This presumes lottery tickets can be bought 24 hours a day.)

> Now Try Exercise 23.

EXAMPLE 5   How many committees can be formed from a group of 5 governors and 7 senators if each committee consists of 3 governors and 4 senators?

Solution   The 3 governors can be selected in $_5C_3$ ways and the 4 senators can be selected in $_7C_4$ ways. If we use the fundamental counting principle, it follows that the number of possible committees is

$$
\begin{aligned}
_5C_3 \cdot {_7C_4} &= \frac{5!}{3!\,2!} \cdot \frac{7!}{4!\,3!} \\[4pt]
&= \frac{5 \cdot 4 \cdot 3!}{3! \cdot 2 \cdot 1} \cdot \frac{7 \cdot 6 \cdot 5 \cdot 4!}{4! \cdot 3 \cdot 2 \cdot 1} \\[4pt]
&= \frac{5 \cdot 2 \cdot 2 \cdot 3!}{3! \cdot 2 \cdot 1} \cdot \frac{7 \cdot 3 \cdot 2 \cdot 5 \cdot 4!}{4! \cdot 3 \cdot 2 \cdot 1} \\[4pt]
&= 10 \cdot 35 \\[4pt]
&= 350.
\end{aligned}
$$

> Now Try Exercise 27.

CONNECTING THE CONCEPTS

Permutations and Combinations

PERMUTATIONS

Permutations involve order and arrangements of objects.

Given 5 books, we can arrange 3 of them on a shelf in $_5P_3$, or 60 ways.

Placing the books in different orders produces different arrangements.

COMBINATIONS

Combinations do not involve order or arrangements of objects.

Given 5 books, we can select 3 of them in $_5C_3$, or 10 ways.

The order in which the books are chosen does not matter.

● ● ●

10.6   EXERCISE SET

Evaluate.

1. $_{13}C_2$

2. $_9C_6$

3. $\begin{pmatrix} 13 \\ 11 \end{pmatrix}$

4. $\begin{pmatrix} 9 \\ 3 \end{pmatrix}$

5. $\begin{pmatrix} 7 \\ 1 \end{pmatrix}$

6. $\begin{pmatrix} 8 \\ 8 \end{pmatrix}$

7. $\dfrac{_5P_3}{3!}$

8. $\dfrac{_{10}P_5}{5!}$

9. $\begin{pmatrix} 6 \\ 0 \end{pmatrix}$

10. $\begin{pmatrix} 6 \\ 1 \end{pmatrix}$

11. $\begin{pmatrix} 6 \\ 2 \end{pmatrix}$

12. $\begin{pmatrix} 6 \\ 3 \end{pmatrix}$

13. $\begin{pmatrix} 7 \\ 0 \end{pmatrix} + \begin{pmatrix} 7 \\ 1 \end{pmatrix} + \begin{pmatrix} 7 \\ 2 \end{pmatrix} + \begin{pmatrix} 7 \\ 3 \end{pmatrix} + \begin{pmatrix} 7 \\ 4 \end{pmatrix} + \begin{pmatrix} 7 \\ 5 \end{pmatrix}$
$+ \begin{pmatrix} 7 \\ 6 \end{pmatrix} + \begin{pmatrix} 7 \\ 7 \end{pmatrix}$

14. $\begin{pmatrix} 6 \\ 0 \end{pmatrix} + \begin{pmatrix} 6 \\ 1 \end{pmatrix} + \begin{pmatrix} 6 \\ 2 \end{pmatrix} + \begin{pmatrix} 6 \\ 3 \end{pmatrix} + \begin{pmatrix} 6 \\ 4 \end{pmatrix} + \begin{pmatrix} 6 \\ 5 \end{pmatrix} + \begin{pmatrix} 6 \\ 6 \end{pmatrix}$

15. $_{52}C_4$

16. $_{52}C_5$

17. $\begin{pmatrix} 27 \\ 11 \end{pmatrix}$

18. $\begin{pmatrix} 37 \\ 8 \end{pmatrix}$

19. $\begin{pmatrix} n \\ 1 \end{pmatrix}$

20. $\begin{pmatrix} n \\ 3 \end{pmatrix}$

21. $\begin{pmatrix} m \\ m \end{pmatrix}$

22. $\begin{pmatrix} t \\ 4 \end{pmatrix}$

In each of the following exercises, give an expression for the answer using permutation notation, combination notation, factorial notation, or other operations. Then evaluate.

23. *Fraternity Officers.* There are 23 students in a fraternity. How many sets of 4 officers can be selected?

24. *League Games.* How many games can be played in a 9-team sports league if each team plays all other teams once? twice?

25. *Test Options.* On a test, a student is to select 10 out of 13 questions. In how many ways can this be done?

26. *Senate Committees.* Suppose the Senate of the United States consists of 58 Republicans and 42 Democrats. How many committees can be formed consisting of 6 Republicans and 4 Democrats?

27. *Test Options.* Of the first 10 questions on a test, a student must answer 7. Of the second 5 questions, the student must answer 3. In how many ways can this be done?

28. *Lines and Triangles from Points.* How many lines are determined by 8 points, no 3 of which are collinear? How many triangles are determined by the same points?

29. *Poker Hands.* How many 5-card poker hands are possible with a 52-card deck?

30. *Bridge Hands.* How many 13-card bridge hands are possible with a 52-card deck?

31. *Baskin-Robbins Ice Cream.* Burt Baskin and Irv Robbins began making ice cream in 1945. Initially they developed 31 flavors—one for each day of the month. (*Source*: Baskin-Robbins)

a) How many 2-dip cones are possible using the 31 original flavors if order of flavors is to be considered and no flavor is repeated?

b) How many 2-dip cones are possible if order is to be considered and a flavor can be repeated?

c) How many 2-dip cones are possible if order is not considered and no flavor is repeated?

Collaborative Discussion and Writing

32. Explain why a "combination" lock should really be called a "permutation" lock.

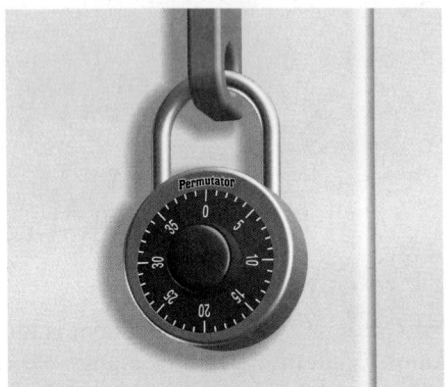

33. Give an explanation that you might use with a fellow student to explain that

$$\binom{n}{k} = \binom{n}{n-k}.$$

Skill Maintenance

Solve.

34. $3x - 7 = 5x + 10$

35. $2x^2 - x = 3$

36. $x^2 + 5x + 1 = 0$

37. $x^3 + 3x^2 - 10x = 24$

Synthesis

38. *Full House.* A full house in poker consists of a pair (two of a kind) and three of a kind. How many full houses are there that consist of 3 aces and 2 queens? (See Section 7.8 for a description of a 52-card deck.)

39. *Flush.* A flush in poker consists of a 5-card hand with all cards of the same suit. How many 5-card hands (flushes) are there that consist of all diamonds?

40. There are n points on a circle. How many quadrilaterals can be inscribed with these points as vertices?

41. *League Games.* How many games are played in a league with n teams if each team plays each other team once? twice?

Solve for n.

42. $\binom{n+1}{3} = 2 \cdot \binom{n}{2}$

43. $\binom{n}{n-2} = 6$

44. $\binom{n}{3} = 2 \cdot \binom{n-1}{2}$

45. $\binom{n+2}{4} = 6 \cdot \binom{n}{2}$

46. How many line segments are determined by the n vertices of an n-gon? Of these, how many are diagonals? Use mathematical induction to prove the result for the diagonals.

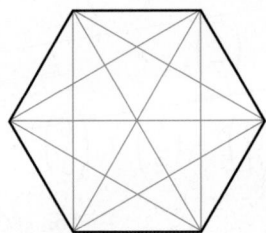

47. Prove that

$$\binom{n}{k-1} + \binom{n}{k} = \binom{n+1}{k}$$

for any natural numbers n and k, $k \le n$.

10.7 The Binomial Theorem

♦ Expand a power of a binomial using Pascal's triangle or factorial notation.

♦ Find a specific term of a binomial expansion.

♦ Find the total number of subsets of a set of n objects.

In this section, we consider ways of expanding a binomial $(a + b)^n$.

✦ Binomial Expansions Using Pascal's Triangle

Consider the following expanded powers of $(a + b)^n$, where $a + b$ is any binomial and n is a whole number. Look for patterns.

$$(a + b)^0 = 1$$
$$(a + b)^1 = a + b$$
$$(a + b)^2 = a^2 + 2ab + b^2$$
$$(a + b)^3 = a^3 + 3a^2b + 3ab^2 + b^3$$
$$(a + b)^4 = a^4 + 4a^3b + 6a^2b^2 + 4ab^3 + b^4$$
$$(a + b)^5 = a^5 + 5a^4b + 10a^3b^2 + 10a^2b^3 + 5ab^4 + b^5$$

Each expansion is a polynomial. There are some patterns to be noted.

1. There is one more term than the power of the exponent, n. That is, there are $n + 1$ terms in the expansion of $(a + b)^n$.

2. In each term, the sum of the exponents is n, the power to which the binomial is raised.

3. The exponents of a start with n, the power of the binomial, and decrease to 0. The last term has no factor of a. The first term has no factor of b, so powers of b start with 0 and increase to n.

4. The coefficients start at 1 and increase through certain values about "half"-way and then decrease through these same values back to 1.

Let's explore the coefficients further. Suppose that we want to find an expansion of $(a + b)^6$. The patterns we noted above indicate that there are 7 terms in the expansion:

$$a^6 + c_1a^5b + c_2a^4b^2 + c_3a^3b^3 + c_4a^2b^4 + c_5ab^5 + b^6.$$

How can we determine the value of each coefficient, c_i? We can do so in two different ways. The first method involves writing the coefficients in a triangular array, as follows. This is known as **Pascal's triangle:**

$$
\begin{array}{c}
(a + b)^0: \qquad\qquad\qquad 1 \\
(a + b)^1: \qquad\qquad\quad 1 \quad 1 \\
(a + b)^2: \qquad\qquad 1 \quad 2 \quad 1 \\
(a + b)^3: \qquad\quad 1 \quad 3 \quad 3 \quad 1 \\
(a + b)^4: \qquad 1 \quad 4 \quad 6 \quad 4 \quad 1 \\
(a + b)^5: \quad 1 \quad 5 \quad 10 \quad 10 \quad 5 \quad 1
\end{array}
$$

There are many patterns in the triangle. Find as many as you can.

Perhaps you discovered a way to write the next row of numbers, given the numbers in the row above it. There are always 1's on the outside. Each remaining number is the sum of the two numbers above it. Let's try to find an expansion for $(a + b)^6$ by adding another row using the patterns we have discovered:

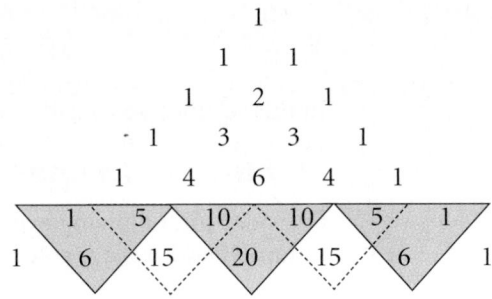

We see that in the last row

the 1st and last numbers are **1**;

the 2nd number is $1 + 5$, or **6**;

the 3rd number is $5 + 10$, or **15**;

the 4th number is $10 + 10$, or **20**;

the 5th number is $10 + 5$, or **15**; and

the 6th number is $5 + 1$, or **6**.

Thus the expansion for $(a + b)^6$ is

$$(a + b)^6 = 1a^6 + 6a^5b + 15a^4b^2 + 20a^3b^3 + 15a^2b^4 + 6ab^5 + 1b^6.$$

To find an expansion for $(a + b)^8$, we complete two more rows of Pascal's triangle:

```
                    1
                 1     1
              1     2     1
           1     3     3     1
        1     4     6     4     1
     1     5    10    10     5     1
  1     6    15    20    15     6     1
1     7    21    35    35    21     7     1
1   8   28   56   70   56   28   8   1
```

Thus the expansion of $(a + b)^8$ is

$$(a + b)^8 = a^8 + 8a^7b + 28a^6b^2 + 56a^5b^3 + 70a^4b^4 + 56a^3b^5$$
$$+ 28a^2b^6 + 8ab^7 + b^8.$$

We can generalize our results as follows.

> **The Binomial Theorem Using Pascal's Triangle**
>
> For any binomial $a + b$ and any natural number n,
>
> $$(a + b)^n = c_0 a^n b^0 + c_1 a^{n-1} b^1 + c_2 a^{n-2} b^2 + \cdots$$
> $$+ c_{n-1} a^1 b^{n-1} + c_n a^0 b^n,$$
>
> where the numbers $c_0, c_1, c_2, \ldots, c_{n-1}, c_n$ are from the $(n + 1)$st row of Pascal's triangle.

EXAMPLE 1 Expand: $(u - v)^5$.

Solution We have $(a + b)^n$, where $a = u$, $b = -v$, and $n = 5$. We use the 6th row of Pascal's triangle:

$$1 \quad 5 \quad 10 \quad 10 \quad 5 \quad 1$$

Then we have

$$(u - v)^5 = [u + (-v)]^5$$
$$= 1(u)^5 + 5(u)^4(-v)^1 + 10(u)^3(-v)^2 + 10(u)^2(-v)^3$$
$$+ 5(u)(-v)^4 + 1(-v)^5$$
$$= u^5 - 5u^4 v + 10u^3 v^2 - 10u^2 v^3 + 5uv^4 - v^5.$$

Note that the signs of the terms alternate between $+$ and $-$. When the power of $-v$ is odd, the sign is $-$. ▶ Now Try Exercise 5.

EXAMPLE 2 Expand: $\left(2t + \dfrac{3}{t}\right)^4$.

Solution We have $(a + b)^n$, where $a = 2t$, $b = 3/t$, and $n = 4$. We use the 5th row of Pascal's triangle:

$$1 \quad 4 \quad 6 \quad 4 \quad 1$$

Then we have

$$\left(2t + \frac{3}{t}\right)^4 = 1(2t)^4 + 4(2t)^3\left(\frac{3}{t}\right)^1 + 6(2t)^2\left(\frac{3}{t}\right)^2 + 4(2t)^1\left(\frac{3}{t}\right)^3 + 1\left(\frac{3}{t}\right)^4$$

$$= 1(16t^4) + 4(8t^3)\left(\frac{3}{t}\right) + 6(4t^2)\left(\frac{9}{t^2}\right) + 4(2t)\left(\frac{27}{t^3}\right) + 1\left(\frac{81}{t^4}\right)$$

$$= 16t^4 + 96t^2 + 216 + 216t^{-2} + 81t^{-4}. \qquad \text{▶ Now Try Exercise 9.}$$

✦ Binomial Expansion Using Factorial Notation

Suppose that we want to find the expansion of $(a + b)^{11}$. The disadvantage in using Pascal's triangle is that we must compute all the preceding rows of the triangle to obtain the row needed for the expansion. The following method avoids this. It also enables us to find a specific term—say, the 8th term—without computing all the other terms of the expansion. This method is useful in such courses as finite mathematics, calculus, and statistics, and it uses the *binomial coefficient notation* $\binom{n}{k}$ developed in Section 10.6.

We can restate the binomial theorem as follows.

The Binomial Theorem Using Factorial Notation

For any binomial $a + b$ and any natural number n,

$$(a + b)^n = \binom{n}{0}a^nb^0 + \binom{n}{1}a^{n-1}b^1 + \binom{n}{2}a^{n-2}b^2 + \cdots$$

$$+ \binom{n}{n-1}a^1b^{n-1} + \binom{n}{n}a^0b^n$$

$$= \sum_{k=0}^{n} \binom{n}{k}a^{n-k}b^k.$$

The binomial theorem can be proved by mathematical induction, but we will not do so here. This form shows why $\binom{n}{k}$ is called a *binomial coefficient*.

EXAMPLE 3   Expand: $(x^2 - 2y)^5$.

Solution   We have $(a + b)^n$, where $a = x^2$, $b = -2y$, and $n = 5$. Then using the binomial theorem, we have

$$(x^2 - 2y)^5 = \binom{5}{0}(x^2)^5 + \binom{5}{1}(x^2)^4(-2y) + \binom{5}{2}(x^2)^3(-2y)^2$$

$$+ \binom{5}{3}(x^2)^2(-2y)^3 + \binom{5}{4}x^2(-2y)^4 + \binom{5}{5}(-2y)^5$$

$$= \frac{5!}{0!\,5!}x^{10} + \frac{5!}{1!\,4!}x^8(-2y) + \frac{5!}{2!\,3!}x^6(4y^2) + \frac{5!}{3!\,2!}x^4(-8y^3)$$

$$+ \frac{5!}{4!\,1!}x^2(16y^4) + \frac{5!}{5!\,0!}(-32y^5)$$

$$= 1 \cdot x^{10} + 5x^8(-2y) + 10x^6(4y^2) + 10x^4(-8y^3)$$

$$+ 5x^2(16y^4) + 1 \cdot (-32y^5)$$

$$= x^{10} - 10x^8y + 40x^6y^2 - 80x^4y^3 + 80x^2y^4 - 32y^5.$$

▶ Now Try Exercise 11.

EXAMPLE 4 Expand: $\left(\dfrac{2}{x} + 3\sqrt{x}\right)^4$.

Solution   We have $(a + b)^n$, where $a = 2/x$, $b = 3\sqrt{x}$, and $n = 4$. Then using the binomial theorem, we have

$$\left(\frac{2}{x} + 3\sqrt{x}\right)^4 = \binom{4}{0}\left(\frac{2}{x}\right)^4 + \binom{4}{1}\left(\frac{2}{x}\right)^3(3\sqrt{x}) + \binom{4}{2}\left(\frac{2}{x}\right)^2(3\sqrt{x})^2$$

$$+ \binom{4}{3}\left(\frac{2}{x}\right)(3\sqrt{x})^3 + \binom{4}{4}(3\sqrt{x})^4$$

$$= \frac{4!}{0!\,4!}\left(\frac{16}{x^4}\right) + \frac{4!}{1!\,3!}\left(\frac{8}{x^3}\right)(3x^{1/2})$$

$$+ \frac{4!}{2!\,2!}\left(\frac{4}{x^2}\right)(9x) + \frac{4!}{3!\,1!}\left(\frac{2}{x}\right)(27x^{3/2})$$

$$+ \frac{4!}{4!\,0!}(81x^2)$$

$$= \frac{16}{x^4} + \frac{96}{x^{5/2}} + \frac{216}{x} + 216x^{1/2} + 81x^2.$$

▷ **Now Try Exercise 13.**

✦ Finding a Specific Term

Suppose that we want to determine only a particular term of an expansion. The method we have developed will allow us to find such a term without computing all the rows of Pascal's triangle or all the preceding coefficients.

Note that in the binomial theorem, $\binom{n}{0}a^n b^0$ gives us the 1st term, $\binom{n}{1}a^{n-1}b^1$ gives us the 2nd term, $\binom{n}{2}a^{n-2}b^2$ gives us the 3rd term, and so on. This can be generalized as follows.

Finding the (k + 1)st Term

The $(k + 1)$st term of $(a + b)^n$ is $\binom{n}{k}a^{n-k}b^k$.

EXAMPLE 5   Find the 5th term in the expansion of $(2x - 5y)^6$.

Solution   First, we note that $5 = 4 + 1$. Thus, $k = 4$, $a = 2x$, $b = -5y$, and $n = 6$. Then the 5th term of the expansion is

$$\binom{6}{4}(2x)^{6-4}(-5y)^4, \quad \text{or} \quad \frac{6!}{4!\,2!}(2x)^2(-5y)^4, \quad \text{or} \quad 37{,}500x^2y^4.$$

▷ **Now Try Exercise 21.**

EXAMPLE 6 Find the 8th term in the expansion of $(3x - 2)^{10}$.

Solution First, we note that $8 = 7 + 1$. Thus, $k = 7$, $a = 3x$, $b = -2$, and $n = 10$. Then the 8th term of the expansion is

$$\binom{10}{7}(3x)^{10-7}(-2)^7, \quad \text{or} \quad \frac{10!}{7!\,3!}(3x)^3(-2)^7, \quad \text{or} \quad -414{,}720x^3.$$

▶ Now Try Exercise 27.

✦ Total Number of Subsets

Suppose that a set has n objects. The number of subsets containing k elements is $\binom{n}{k}$ by a result of Section 10.6. The total number of subsets of a set is the number of subsets with 0 elements, plus the number of subsets with 1 element, plus the number of subsets with 2 elements, and so on. The total number of subsets of a set with n elements is

$$\binom{n}{0} + \binom{n}{1} + \binom{n}{2} + \cdots + \binom{n}{n}.$$

Now consider the expansion of $(1 + 1)^n$:

$$(1 + 1)^n = \binom{n}{0} \cdot 1^n + \binom{n}{1} \cdot 1^{n-1} \cdot 1^1 + \binom{n}{2} \cdot 1^{n-2} \cdot 1^2$$

$$+ \cdots + \binom{n}{n} \cdot 1^n$$

$$= \binom{n}{0} + \binom{n}{1} + \binom{n}{2} + \cdots + \binom{n}{n}.$$

Thus the total number of subsets is $(1 + 1)^n$, or 2^n. We have proved the following.

Total Number of Subsets

The total number of subsets of a set with n elements is 2^n.

EXAMPLE 7 The set $\{A, B, C, D, E\}$ has how many subsets?

Solution The set has 5 elements, so the number of subsets is 2^5, or 32.

▶ Now Try Exercise 31.

EXAMPLE 8 *Condiment Choices.* The fast-food chain Wendy's offers the following condiments on its single hamburger:

$$\{\text{catsup}, \text{mustard}, \text{mayonnaise}, \text{tomato}, \text{lettuce}, \text{onion}, \text{pickle}\}.$$

In how many different ways can Wendy's serve a single hamburger?

Solution   Each combination of condiments consists of the elements of a subset of the set of all possible condiments. (The empty set is a plain hamburger with no condiments.) The total number of choices possible is

$$\binom{7}{0} + \binom{7}{1} + \binom{7}{2} + \cdots + \binom{7}{7} = 2^7 = 128.$$

Thus Wendy's can serve a single hamburger in 128 different ways.

▶ Now Try Exercise 33.

10.7   EXERCISE SET

Expand.

1. $(x + 5)^4$

2. $(x - 1)^4$

3. $(x - 3)^5$

4. $(x + 2)^9$

5. $(x - y)^5$

6. $(x + y)^8$

7. $(5x + 4y)^6$

8. $(2x - 3y)^5$

9. $\left(2t + \dfrac{1}{t}\right)^7$

10. $\left(3y - \dfrac{1}{y}\right)^4$

11. $(x^2 - 1)^5$

12. $(1 + 2q^3)^8$

13. $\left(\sqrt{5} + t\right)^6$

14. $\left(x - \sqrt{2}\right)^6$

15. $\left(a - \dfrac{2}{a}\right)^9$

16. $(1 + 3)^n$

17. $\left(\sqrt{2} + 1\right)^6 - \left(\sqrt{2} - 1\right)^6$

18. $\left(1 - \sqrt{2}\right)^4 + \left(1 + \sqrt{2}\right)^4$

19. $(x^{-2} + x^2)^4$

20. $\left(\dfrac{1}{\sqrt{x}} - \sqrt{x}\right)^6$

Find the indicated term of the binomial expansion.

21. 3rd; $(a + b)^7$

22. 6th; $(x + y)^8$

23. 6th; $(x - y)^{10}$

24. 5th; $(p - 2q)^9$

25. 12th; $(a - 2)^{14}$

26. 11th; $(x - 3)^{12}$

27. 5th; $\left(2x^3 - \sqrt{y}\right)^8$

28. 4th; $\left(\dfrac{1}{b^2} + \dfrac{b}{3}\right)^7$

29. Middle; $(2u - 3v^2)^{10}$

30. Middle two; $\left(\sqrt{x} + \sqrt{3}\right)^5$

Determine the number of subsets of each of the following.

31. A set of 7 elements

32. A set of 6 members

33. The set of letters of the Greek alphabet, which contains 24 letters

34. The set of letters of the English alphabet, which contains 26 letters

35. What is the degree of $(x^5 + 3)^4$?

36. What is the degree of $(2 - 5x^3)^7$?

Expand each of the following, where $i^2 = -1$.

37. $(3 + i)^5$

38. $(1 + i)^6$

39. $\left(\sqrt{2} - i\right)^4$

40. $\left(\dfrac{\sqrt{3}}{2} - \dfrac{1}{2}i\right)^{11}$

41. Find a formula for $(a - b)^n$. Use sigma notation.

42. Expand and simplify:
$$\frac{(x + h)^{13} - x^{13}}{h}.$$

43. Expand and simplify:
$$\frac{(x + h)^n - x^n}{h}.$$
Use sigma notation.

Collaborative Discussion and Writing

44. Discuss the advantages and disadvantages of each method of finding a binomial expansion. Give examples of when you might use one method rather than the other.

45. Blaise Pascal (1623–1662) was a French scientist and philosopher who founded the modern theory of probability. Do some research on Pascal and see if you can find out how he discovered his famous "triangle of numbers."

Skill Maintenance

Given that $f(x) = x^2 + 1$ and $g(x) = 2x - 3$, find each of the following.

46. $(f + g)(x)$

47. $(fg)(x)$

48. $(f \circ g)(x)$

49. $(g \circ f)(x)$

Synthesis

Solve for x.

50. $\displaystyle\sum_{k=0}^{8} \binom{8}{k} x^{8-k} 3^k = 0$

51. $\displaystyle\sum_{k=0}^{4} \binom{4}{k} (-1)^k x^{4-k} 6^k = 81$

52. Find the term of
$$\left(\frac{3x^2}{2} - \frac{1}{3x}\right)^{12}$$
that does not contain x.

53. Find the middle term of $(x^2 - 6y^{3/2})^6$.

54. Find the ratio of the 4th term of
$$\left(p^2 - \frac{1}{2} p \sqrt[3]{q}\right)^5$$
to the 3rd term.

55. Find the term of
$$\left(\sqrt[3]{x} - \frac{1}{\sqrt{x}}\right)^7$$
containing $1/x^{1/6}$.

56. *Money Combinations.* A money clip contains one each of the following bills: \$1, \$2, \$5, \$10, \$20, \$50, and \$100. How many different sums of money can be formed using the bills?

Find the sum.

57. $_{100}C_0 + {}_{100}C_1 + \cdots + {}_{100}C_{100}$

58. $_nC_0 + {}_nC_1 + \cdots + {}_nC_n$

Simplify.

59. $\displaystyle\sum_{k=0}^{23} \binom{23}{k} (\log_a x)^{23-k} (\log_a t)^k$

60. $\displaystyle\sum_{k=0}^{15} \binom{15}{k} i^{30-2k}$

61. Use mathematical induction and the property
$$\binom{n}{r-1} + \binom{n}{r} = \binom{n+1}{r}$$
to prove the binomial theorem.

10.8 ▷ Probability

◆ Compute the probability of a simple event.

When a coin is tossed, we can reason that the chance, or likelihood, that it will fall heads is 1 out of 2, or the **probability** that it will fall heads is $\frac{1}{2}$. Of course, this does not mean that if a coin is tossed 10 times it will necessarily fall heads 5 times. If the coin is a "fair coin" and it is tossed a great many times, however, it will fall heads very nearly half of the time. Here we give an introduction to two kinds of probability, **experimental** and **theoretical.**

◆ Experimental and Theoretical Probability

If we toss a coin a great number of times—say, 1000—and count the number of times it falls heads, we can determine the probability that it will fall heads. If it falls heads 503 times, we would calculate the probability of its falling heads to be

$$\frac{503}{1000}, \quad \text{or} \quad 0.503.$$

This is an **experimental** determination of probability. Such a determination of probability is discovered by the observation and study of data and is quite common and very useful. Here, for example, are some probabilities that have been determined *experimentally*:

1. The probability that a woman will get breast cancer in her lifetime is $\frac{1}{11}$.
2. If you kiss someone who has a cold, the probability of your catching a cold is 0.07.
3. A person who has just been released from prison has an 80% probability of returning.

If we consider a coin and reason that it is just as likely to fall heads as tails, we would calculate the probability that it will fall heads to be $\frac{1}{2}$. This is a **theoretical** determination of probability. Here are some other probabilities that have been determined *theoretically*, using mathematics:

1. If there are 30 people in a room, the probability that two of them have the same birthday (excluding year) is 0.706.
2. While on a trip, you meet someone and, after a period of conversation, discover that you have a common acquaintance. The typical reaction, "It's a small world!", is actually not appropriate, because the probability of such an occurrence is quite high—just over 22%.

In summary, experimental probabilities are determined by making observations and gathering data. Theoretical probabilities are determined by reasoning mathematically. Examples of experimental and theoretical probability like those above, especially those we do not expect, lead us to see the value of a study of probability. You might ask, "What is the *true* probability?" In fact, there is none. Experimentally, we can determine probabilities within certain limits. These may or may not agree with the probabilities that we obtain theoretically. There are situations in which it is much easier to determine one of these types of probabilities than the other. For example, it would be quite difficult to arrive at the probability of catching a cold using theoretical probability.

◆ Computing Experimental Probabilities

We first consider experimental determination of probability. The basic principle we use in computing such probabilities is as follows.

Principle P (Experimental)

Given an experiment in which n observations are made, if a situation, or event, E occurs m times out of n observations, then we say that the *experimental probability* of the event, $P(E)$, is given by

$$P(E) = \frac{m}{n}.$$

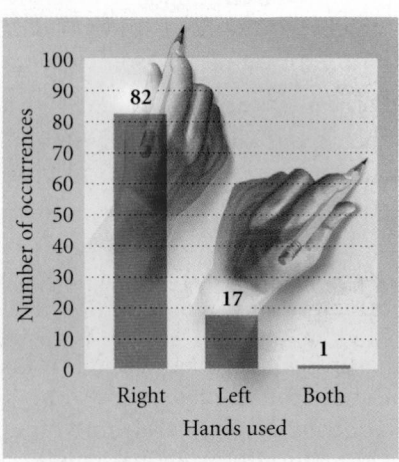

EXAMPLE 1   *Sociological Survey.*   The authors of this text conducted an experimental survey to determine the number of people who are left-handed, right-handed, or both. The results are shown in the graph at left.

a) Determine the probability that a person is right-handed.

b) Determine the probability that a person is left-handed.

c) Determine the probability that a person is ambidextrous (uses both hands with equal ability).

d) There are 120 bowlers in most tournaments held by the Professional Bowlers Association. On the basis of the data in this experiment, how many of the bowlers would you expect to be left-handed?

Solution

a) The number of people who are right-handed is 82, the number who are left-handed is 17, and the number who are ambidextrous is 1. The total number of observations is $82 + 17 + 1$, or 100. Thus the probability that a person is right-handed is P, where

$$P = \frac{82}{100}, \quad \text{or} \quad 0.82, \quad \text{or} \quad 82\%.$$

b) The probability that a person is left-handed is P, where

$$P = \frac{17}{100}, \quad \text{or} \quad 0.17, \quad \text{or} \quad 17\%.$$

c) The probability that a person is ambidextrous is P, where

$$P = \frac{1}{100}, \quad \text{or} \quad 0.01, \quad \text{or} \quad 1\%.$$

d) There are 120 bowlers, and from part (b) we can expect 17% to be left-handed. Since

$$17\% \text{ of } 120 = 0.17 \cdot 120 = 20.4,$$

we can expect that about 20 of the bowlers will be left-handed.

▷ Now Try Exercise 1.

EXAMPLE 2 *Quality Control.* It is very important for a manufacturer to maintain the quality of its products. In fact, companies hire quality control inspectors to ensure this process. The goal is to produce as few defective products as possible. But since a company is producing thousands of products every day, it cannot afford to check every product to see if it is defective. To find out what percentage of its products are defective, the company checks a smaller sample.

The U.S. Department of Agriculture requires that 80% of the seeds that a company produces must sprout. To determine the quality of the seeds it produces, a company takes 500 seeds from those it has produced and plants them. It finds that 417 of the seeds sprout.

a) What is the probability that a seed will sprout?

b) Did the seeds meet government standards?

Solution

a) We know that 500 seeds were planted and 417 sprouted. The probability of a seed sprouting is P, where

$$P = \frac{417}{500} = 0.834, \quad \text{or} \quad 83.4\%.$$

b) Since the percentage of seeds that sprouted exceeded the 80% requirement, the seeds meet government standards. ◀

EXAMPLE 3 *Television Ratings.* There are an estimated 110,200,000 households with televisions in the United States. Each week, viewing information is collected and reported. One week, 12,077,000 households tuned in to the news show "60 Minutes" on CBS and 10,672,000 households tuned in to the drama "Lost" on ABC (*Source*: Nielsen Media Research). What is the probability that a television household tuned in to "60 Minutes" during the given week? to "Lost"?

Solution The probability that a television household was tuned in to "60 Minutes" is P, where

$$P = \frac{12,077,000}{110,200,000} \approx 0.110 \approx 11.0\%.$$

The probability that a television household was tuned in to "Lost" is P, where

$$P = \frac{10,672,000}{110,200,000} \approx 0.097 \approx 9.7\%.$$

✦ Theoretical Probability

Suppose that we perform an experiment such as flipping a coin, throwing a dart, drawing a card from a deck, or checking an item off an assembly line for quality. Each possible result of such an experiment is called an **outcome.** The set of all possible outcomes is called the **sample space.** An **event** is a set of outcomes, that is, a subset of the sample space.

EXAMPLE 4 *Dart Throwing.* Consider the dartboard at left. Assume that the experiment is "throwing a dart" and that the dart hits the board. Find each of the following.

a) The outcomes

b) The sample space

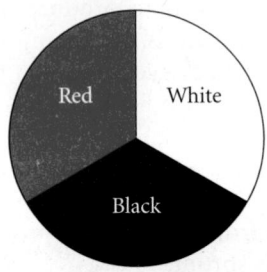

Solution

a) The outcomes are *hitting black* (B), *hitting red* (R), and *hitting white* (W).

b) The sample space is {*hitting black, hitting red, hitting white*}, which can be simply stated as {B, R, W}.

EXAMPLE 5 *Die Rolling.* A die (plural, dice) is a cube with six faces, each containing a number of dots from 1 to 6 on each side.

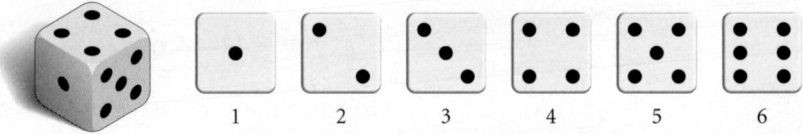

Suppose a die is rolled. Find each of the following.

a) The outcomes

b) The sample space

Solution

a) The outcomes are 1, 2, 3, 4, 5, 6.

b) The sample space is {1, 2, 3, 4, 5, 6}.

We denote the probability that an event E occurs as $P(E)$. For example, "a coin falling heads" may be denoted H. Then $P(H)$ represents the probability of the coin falling heads. When all the outcomes of an experiment have the same probability of occurring, we say that they are *equally likely*. To see the distinction between events that are equally likely and those that are not, consider the dartboards shown below.

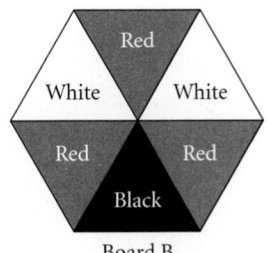

Board A   Board B

For board A, the events *hitting black*, *hitting red*, and *hitting white* are equally likely, because the black, red, and white areas are the same. However, for board B the areas are not the same so these events are not equally likely.

Principle P (Theoretical)

If an event E can occur m ways out of n possible equally likely outcomes of a sample space S, then the **theoretical probability** of the event, $P(E)$, is given by

$$P(E) = \frac{m}{n}.$$

EXAMPLE 6   What is the probability of rolling a 3 on a die?

Solution   On a fair die, there are 6 equally likely outcomes and there is 1 way to roll a 3. By Principle P, $P(3) = \frac{1}{6}$.   ▶ Now Try Exercise 7(a).

EXAMPLE 7   What is the probability of rolling an even number on a die?

Solution   The event is rolling an *even* number. It can occur 3 ways (getting 2, 4, or 6). The number of equally likely outcomes is 6. By Principle P, $P(\text{even}) = \frac{3}{6}$, or $\frac{1}{2}$.   ▶ Now Try Exercise 7(d).

We can find probabilities related to a standard bridge deck of 52 cards. Such a deck is made up as shown in the following figure.

A DECK OF
52 CARDS

EXAMPLE 8 What is the probability of drawing an ace from a well-shuffled deck of cards?

Solution There are 52 outcomes (the number of cards in the deck), they are equally likely (from a well-shuffled deck), and there are 4 ways to obtain an ace, so by Principle P, we have

$$P(\text{drawing an ace}) = \frac{4}{52}, \quad \text{or} \quad \frac{1}{13}.$$

EXAMPLE 9 Suppose that we select, without looking, one marble from a bag containing 3 red marbles and 4 green marbles. What is the probability of selecting a red marble?

Solution There are 3 + 4, or 7, equally likely ways of selecting any marble, and since the number of ways of getting a red marble is 3, we have

$$P(\text{selecting a red marble}) = \frac{3}{7}.$$

▷ Now Try Exercise 7(b).

The following are some results that follow from Principle P.

> **Probability Properties**
> **a)** If an event E cannot occur, then $P(E) = 0$.
> **b)** If an event E is certain to occur, then $P(E) = 1$.
> **c)** The probability that an event E will occur is a number from 0 to 1: $0 \le P(E) \le 1$.

For example, in coin tossing, the event that a coin will land on its edge has probability 0. The event that a coin falls either heads or tails has probability 1.

In the following examples, we use the combinatorics that we studied in Sections 10.5 and 10.6 to calculate theoretical probabilities.

We can use the $_nC_r$ operation from the MATH PRB menu and the ▶Frac operation from the MATH MATH menu to compute the probabilities in Examples 10 and 11 on a graphing calculator.

```
13 nCr 2/52 nCr 2▶Frac
                    1/17
```

```
6 nCr 1*4 nCr 2/10 nCr
3▶Frac
                    3/10
```

EXAMPLE 10   Suppose that 2 cards are drawn from a well-shuffled deck of 52 cards. What is the probability that both of them are spades?

Solution   The number of ways n of drawing 2 cards from a well-shuffled deck of 52 cards is $_{52}C_2$. Since 13 of the 52 cards are spades, the number of ways m of drawing 2 spades is $_{13}C_2$. Thus,

$$P(\text{getting 2 spades}) = \frac{m}{n} = \frac{_{13}C_2}{_{52}C_2} = \frac{78}{1326} = \frac{1}{17}.$$

▶ Now Try Exercise 13.

EXAMPLE 11   Suppose that 3 people are selected at random from a group that consists of 6 men and 4 women. What is the probability that 1 man and 2 women are selected?

Solution   The number of ways of selecting 3 people from a group of 10 is $_{10}C_3$. One man can be selected in $_6C_1$ ways, and 2 women can be selected in $_4C_2$ ways. By the fundamental counting principle, the number of ways of selecting 1 man and 2 women is $_6C_1 \cdot {}_4C_2$. Thus the probability that 1 man and 2 women are selected is

$$P = \frac{_6C_1 \cdot {}_4C_2}{_{10}C_3} = \frac{3}{10}.$$

▶ Now Try Exercise 9.

EXAMPLE 12   *Rolling Two Dice.*   What is the probability of getting a total of 8 on a roll of a pair of dice?

Solution   On each die, there are 6 possible outcomes. The outcomes are paired so there are $6 \cdot 6$, or 36, possible ways in which the two can fall. (Assuming that the dice are different—say, one red and one blue—can help in visualizing this.)

The pairs that total 8 are as shown in the figure above. There are 5 possible ways of getting a total of 8, so the probability is $\frac{5}{36}$.

▶ Now Try Exercise 15.

10.8 EXERCISE SET

1. *Select a Number.*   In a survey conducted by the authors, 100 people were polled and asked to select a number from 1 to 5. The results are shown in the following table.

Number Chosen	1	2	3	4	5
Number Who Chose That Number	18	24	23	23	12

a) What is the probability that the number chosen is 1? 2? 3? 4? 5?

b) What general conclusion might be made from the results of the experiment?

2. *Mason Dots®.*   Made by the Tootsie Industries of Chicago, Illinois, Mason Dots® is a gumdrop candy. A box was opened by the authors and was found to contain the following number of gumdrops:

Orange	9
Lemon	8
Strawberry	7
Grape	6
Lime	5
Cherry	4

If we take one gumdrop out of the box, what is the probability of getting a lemon? lime? orange? grape? strawberry? licorice?

3. *Junk Mail.*   In experimental studies, the U.S. Postal Service has found that the probability that a piece of advertising is opened and read is 78%. A business sends out 15,000 pieces of advertising. How many of these can the company expect to be opened and read?

4. *Linguistics.*   An experiment was conducted by the authors to determine the relative occurrence of various letters of the English alphabet. The front page of a newspaper was considered. In all, there were 9136 letters. The number of occur-

rences of each letter of the alphabet is listed in the following table.

Letter	Number of Occurrences	Probability
A	853	853/9136 ≈ 9.3%
B	136	
C	273	
D	286	
E	1229	
F	173	
G	190	
H	399	
I	539	
J	21	
K	57	
L	417	
M	231	
N	597	
O	705	
P	238	
Q	4	
R	609	
S	745	
T	789	
U	240	
V	113	
W	127	
X	20	
Y	124	
Z	21	21/9136 ≈ 0.2%

a) Complete the table of probabilities with the percentage, to the nearest tenth of a percent, of the occurrence of each letter.

b) What is the probability of a vowel occurring?

c) What is the probability of a consonant occurring?

5. *"Wheel of Fortune®."*   The results of the experiment in Exercise 4 can be quite useful to a person playing the popular television game show

"Wheel of Fortune." Players guess letters in order to spell out a phrase, a person, or a thing.

a) What 5 consonants have the greatest probability of occurring?

b) What vowel has the greatest probability of occurring?

c) The winner of the main part of the show plays for a grand prize and at one time was allowed to guess 5 consonants and a vowel in order to discover the secret wording. The 5 consonants R, S, T, L, N, and the vowel E seemed to be chosen most often. Do the results in parts (a) and (b) support such a choice?

6. *Card Drawing.* Suppose we draw a card from a well-shuffled deck of 52 cards.

a) How many equally likely outcomes are there?

What is the probability of drawing each of the following?

b) A queen   **c)** A heart
d) A 7   **e)** A red card
f) A 9 or a king   **g)** A black ace

7. *Marbles.* Suppose we select, without looking, one marble from a bag containing 4 red marbles and 10 green marbles. What is the probability of selecting each of the following?

a) A red marble
b) A green marble
c) A purple marble
d) A red or a green marble

8. *Production Unit.* The sales force of a business consists of 10 men and 10 women. A production unit of 4 people is set up at random. What is the probability that 2 men and 2 women are chosen?

9. *Coin Drawing.* A sack contains 7 dimes, 5 nickels, and 10 quarters. Eight coins are drawn at random. What is the probability of getting 4 dimes, 3 nickels, and 1 quarter?

10. *Michigan Lottery.* Run by the state of Michigan, Classic Lotto 47 is a twice-weekly lottery game with jackpots starting at $1 million. For a wager of $1, a player can choose 6 numbers from 1 through 47. If the numbers match those drawn by the state, the player wins. (*Source:*

www.michigan.gov/lottery) Ava buys 1 game ticket. What is her probability of winning?

Five-Card Poker Hands. Suppose that 5 cards are drawn from a deck of 52 cards. What is the probability of drawing each of the following?

11. 3 sevens and 2 kings

12. 5 aces

13. 5 spades

14. 4 aces and 1 five

15. *Tossing Three Coins.* Three coins are flipped. An outcome might be HTH.

a) Find the sample space.

What is the probability of getting each of the following?

b) Exactly one head
c) At most two tails
d) At least one head
e) Exactly two tails

Roulette. An American roulette wheel contains 38 slots numbered 00, 0, 1, 2, 3, ..., 35, 36. Eighteen of the slots numbered 1–36 are colored red and 18 are colored black. The 00 and 0 slots are considered to be uncolored. The wheel is spun, and a ball is rolled around the rim until it falls into a slot. What is the probability that the ball falls into each of the following?

16. A red slot   **17.** A black slot

18. The 00 slot   **19.** The 0 slot

20. Either the 00 or the 0 slot

21. A red or a black slot   **22.** The number 24

23. An odd-numbered slot

24. *Dartboard.* The figure below shows a dartboard. A dart is thrown and hits the board. Find the probabilities

$$P(\text{red}), \quad P(\text{green}), \quad P(\text{blue}), \quad P(\text{yellow}).$$

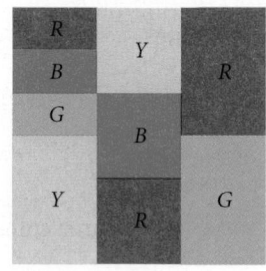

Technology Connection

25. *Random-Number Generator.* Many graphing calculators have a **random-number generator.** This feature produces a random number in the interval $[0, 1]$. (Consult your user's manual.) We can use such a feature to simulate coin flipping. A number r such that $0 \le r \le 0.5$ would indicate heads, H. A number r such that $0.5 < r \le 1.0$ would indicate tails, T. Use a random-number generator 100 times.

   a) What is the experimental probability of getting heads?
   b) What is the experimental probability of getting tails?

Collaborative Discussion and Writing

26. *Random Best-Selling Novels.* Sir Arthur Stanley Eddington, an astronomer, once wrote in a satirical essay that if a monkey were left alone long enough with a typewriter and typed randomly, any great novel could be replicated. What is the probability that the following passage could have been written by a monkey? Ignore capital letters and punctuation and consider only letters and spaces.
   "*It was the best of times, it was the worst of times,...*" (Charles Dickens, 1859). Explain your answer.

27. Find at least one use of probability in today's newspaper. Make a report.

Skill Maintenance

In each of Exercises 28–35, fill in the blank with the correct term. Some of the given choices will be used more than once. Others will not be used.

   range
   domain
   function
   an inverse function
   a composite function
   direct variation
   inverse variation
   factor
   solution
   zero
   y-intercept
   one-to-one
   rational
   permutation
   combination
   arithmetic sequence
   geometric sequence

28. A(n) _____ of a function is an input for which the output is 0.

29. A function is _____ if different inputs have different outputs.

30. A(n) _____ is a correspondence between a first set, called the _____ , and a second set, called the _____ , such that each member of the _____ corresponds to exactly one member of the _____ .

31. The first coordinate of an x-intercept of a function is a(n) _____ of the function.

32. A selection made from a set without regard to order is a(n) _____ .

33. If we have a function $f(x) = k/x$, where k is a positive constant, we have _____ .

34. For a polynomial function $f(x)$, if $f(c) = 0$, then $x - c$ is a(n) _____ of the polynomial.

35. We have $\dfrac{a_{n+1}}{a_n} = r$, for any integer $n \ge 1$, in a(n) _____ .

Synthesis

Five-Card Poker Hands.   *Suppose that 5 cards are drawn from a deck of 52 cards. For the following exercises, give both a reasoned expression and an answer.*

36. *Royal Flush.*   A *royal flush* consists of a 5-card hand with A-K-Q-J-10 of the same suit.

  a) How many royal flushes are there?
  b) What is the probability of getting a royal flush?

37. *Straight Flush.*   A *straight flush* consists of 5 cards in sequence in the same suit, but excludes royal flushes. An ace can be used low, before a two, or high, following a king.

  a) How many straight flushes are there?
  b) What is the probability of getting a straight flush?

38. *Four of a Kind.*   A *four-of-a-kind* is a 5-card hand in which 4 of the cards are of the same denomination, such as J-J-J-J-6, 7-7-7-7-A, or 2-2-2-2-5.

  a) How many four-of-a-kind hands are there?
  b) What is the probability of getting four of a kind?

39. *Full House.*   A *full house* consists of a pair and 3 of a kind, such as Q-Q-Q-4-4.

  a) How many full houses are there?
  b) What is the probability of getting a full house?

40. *Three of a Kind.*   A *three-of-a-kind* is a 5-card hand in which exactly 3 of the cards are of the same denomination and the other 2 are *not*, such as Q-Q-Q-10-7.

  a) How many three-of-a-kind hands are there?
  b) What is the probability of getting three of a kind?

41. *Flush.*   An ordinary *flush* is a 5-card hand in which all the cards are of the same suit, but not all in sequence (not a straight or royal flush).

  a) How many flushes are there?
  b) What is the probability of getting a flush?

42. *Two Pairs.*   A hand with *two pairs* is a hand like Q-Q-3-3-A.

  a) How many hands with two pairs are there?
  b) What is the probability of getting two pairs?

43. *Straight.*   An ordinary *straight* is any 5 cards in sequence, but not of the same suit—for example, 4 of spades, 5 of hearts, 6 of diamonds, 7 of hearts, and 8 of clubs.

  a) How many straights are there?
  b) What is the probability of getting a straight?

CHAPTER 10 SUMMARY AND REVIEW

Important Properties and Formulas

Arithmetic Sequences and Series

General term: $a_{n+1} = a_n + d$
$a_n = a_1 + (n-1)d$

Common difference: d

Sum of the first n terms: $S_n = \dfrac{n}{2}(a_1 + a_n)$

Geometric Sequences and Series

General term: $a_{n+1} = a_n r$
$a_n = a_1 r^{n-1}$

Common ratio: r

Sum of the first n terms: $S_n = \dfrac{a_1(1 - r^n)}{1 - r}$

Sum of an infinite geometric series:

$S_\infty = \dfrac{a_1}{1 - r}, \quad |r| < 1$

The Principle of Mathematical Induction

(1) *Basis step*: Prove S_1 is true.
(2) *Induction step*: Prove for all numbers k,
$S_k \rightarrow S_{k+1}$.

The Fundamental Counting Principle

The total number of ways in which k actions can be performed together is $n_1 \cdot n_2 \cdot n_3 \cdots n_k$, where the first action can be performed in n_1 ways, the second in n_2 ways, and so on.

Factorial Notation

For any natural number n,

$n! = n(n-1)(n-2) \cdots 3 \cdot 2 \cdot 1$

and $0! = 1$.

Permutations of n Objects Taken n at a Time

$_nP_n = n! = n(n-1)(n-2) \cdots 3 \cdot 2 \cdot 1$

Permutations of n Objects Taken k at a Time

$_nP_k = \underbrace{n(n-1)(n-2) \cdots [n-(k-1)]}_{k \text{ factors}}$

$= \dfrac{n!}{(n-k)!}$

Permutations of Sets with Some Nondistinguishable Objects

$$\dfrac{n!}{n_1! \cdot n_2! \cdots \cdots n_k!},$$

where n_1 objects are of one kind, n_2 are of another kind, and so on.

Combinations of n Objects Taken k at a Time

$_nC_k = \begin{pmatrix} n \\ k \end{pmatrix} = \dfrac{_nP_k}{k!} = \dfrac{n!}{k!\,(n-k)!}$

$= \dfrac{n(n-1)(n-2) \cdots [n-(k-1)]}{k!}$

The Binomial Theorem

$(a + b)^n = \displaystyle\sum_{k=0}^{n} \begin{pmatrix} n \\ k \end{pmatrix} a^{n-k} b^k$

The $(k + 1)$st Term of Binomial Expansion

The $(k + 1)$st term of $(a + b)^n$ is $\binom{n}{k}a^{n-k}b^k$.

Total Number of Subsets

The total number of subsets of a set with n elements is 2^n.

Probability Principle P (Experimental)

$P(E) = \dfrac{m}{n}$, where an event E occurs m times out of n observations.

Probability Principle P (Theoretical)

$P(E) = \dfrac{m}{n}$, where an event E can occur m ways out of n possible equally likely outcomes.

REVIEW EXERCISES

Determine whether the statement is true or false.

1. A sequence is a function. [10.1]

2. An infinite geometric series with $r = -1$ has a limit. [10.3]

3. Permutations involve order and arrangements of objects. [10.5]

4. The total number of subsets of a set with n elements is n^2. [10.7]

5. Find the first 4 terms, a_{11}, and a_{23}:

$$a_n = (-1)^n\left(\frac{n^2}{n^4 + 1}\right). \quad [10.1]$$

6. Predict the general, or nth, term. Answers may vary.

$$2, -5, 10, -17, 26, \ldots \quad [10.1]$$

7. Find and evaluate:

$$\sum_{k=1}^{4} \frac{(-1)^{k+1}3^k}{3^k - 1}. \quad [10.1]$$

8. Write sigma notation:

$$0 + 3 + 8 + 15 + 24 + 35 + 48. \quad [10.1]$$

9. Find the 10th term of the arithmetic sequence

$$\frac{3}{4}, \frac{13}{12}, \frac{17}{12}, \ldots . \quad [10.2]$$

10. Find the 6th term of the arithmetic sequence

$$a - b, a, a + b, \ldots . \quad [10.2]$$

11. Find the sum of the first 18 terms of the arithmetic sequence

$$4, 7, 10, \ldots . \quad [10.2]$$

12. Find the sum of the first 200 natural numbers. [10.2]

13. The 1st term in an arithmetic sequence is 5, and the 17th term is 53. Find the 3rd term. [10.2]

14. The common difference in an arithmetic sequence is 3. The 10th term is 23. Find the first term. [10.2]

15. For a geometric sequence, $a_1 = -2$, $r = 2$, and $a_n = -64$. Find n and S_n. [10.3]

16. For a geometric sequence, $r = \frac{1}{2}$, $n = 5$, and $S_n = \frac{31}{2}$. Find a_1 and a_n. [10.3]

Find the sum of each infinite geometric series, if it exists. [10.3]

17. $25 + 27.5 + 30.25 + 33.275 + \cdots$

18. $0.27 + 0.0027 + 0.000027 + \cdots$

19. $\frac{1}{2} - \frac{1}{6} + \frac{1}{18} - \cdots$

20. Find fraction notation for $2.\overline{43}$. [10.3]

21. Insert four arithmetic means between 5 and 9. [10.2]

22. *Bouncing Golfball.*   A golfball is dropped from a height of 30 ft to the pavement. It always rebounds three fourths of the distance that it drops. How far (up and down) will the ball have traveled when it hits the pavement for the 6th time?   [10.3]

23. *The Amount of an Annuity.*   To create a college fund, a parent makes a sequence of 18 yearly deposits of $2000 each in a savings account on which interest is compounded annually at 2.8%. Find the amount of the annuity.   [10.3]

24. *Total Gift.*   Suppose you receive 10¢ on the first day of the year, 12¢ on the 2nd day, 14¢ on the 3rd day, and so on.

   a) How much will you receive on the 365th day? [10.2]

   b) What is the sum of these 365 gifts?   [10.2]

25. *The Economic Multiplier.*   Suppose the government is making a $24,000,000,000 expenditure for travel to Mars. If 73% of this amount is spent again, and so on, what is the total effect on the economy?   [10.3]

Use mathematical induction to prove each of the following.   [10.4]

26. For every natural number n,

$$1 + 4 + 7 + \cdots + (3n - 2) = \frac{n(3n - 1)}{2}.$$

27. For every natural number n,

$$1 + 3 + 3^2 + \cdots + 3^{n-1} = \frac{3^n - 1}{2}.$$

28. For every natural number $n \geq 2$,

$$\left(1 - \frac{1}{2}\right)\left(1 - \frac{1}{3}\right) \cdots \left(1 - \frac{1}{n}\right) = \frac{1}{n}.$$

29. *Book Arrangements.*   In how many ways can 6 books be arranged on a shelf?   [10.5]

30. *Flag Displays.*   If 9 different signal flags are available, how many different displays are possible using 4 flags in a row?   [10.5]

31. *Prize Choices.*   The winner of a contest can choose any 8 of 15 prizes. How many different sets of prizes can be chosen?   [10.6]

32. *Fraternity–Sorority Names.*   The Greek alphabet contains 24 letters. How many fraternity or sorority names can be formed using 3 different letters?   [10.5]

33. *Letter Arrangements.*   In how many distinguishable ways can the letters of the word TENNESSEE be arranged?   [10.5]

34. *Floor Plans.*   A manufacturer of houses has 1 floor plan but achieves variety by having 3 different roofs, 4 different ways of attaching the garage, and 3 different types of entrances. Find the number of different houses that can be produced.   [10.5]

35. *Code Symbols.*   How many code symbols can be formed using 5 out of 6 of the letters of G, H, I, J, K, L if the letters:

   a) cannot be repeated?   [10.5]

   b) can be repeated?   [10.5]

   c) cannot be repeated but must begin with K? [10.5]

   d) cannot be repeated but must end with IGH? [10.5]

36. Determine the number of subsets of a set containing 8 members.   [10.7]

Expand.   [10.7]

37. $(m + n)^7$

38. $\left(x - \sqrt{2}\right)^5$

39. $(x^2 - 3y)^4$

40. $\left(a + \dfrac{1}{a}\right)^8$

41. $(1 + 5i)^6$, where $i^2 = -1$ [10.7]

42. Find the 4th term of $(a + x)^{12}$.   [10.7]

43. Find the 12th term of $(2a - b)^{18}$. Do not multiply out the factorials.   [10.7]

44. *Rolling Dice.*   What is the probability of getting a 10 on a roll of a pair of dice? on a roll of 1 die? [10.8]

45. *Drawing a Card.*   From a deck of 52 cards, 1 card is drawn at random. What is the probability that it is a club?   [10.8]

46. *Drawing Three Cards.* From a deck of 52 cards, 3 are drawn at random without replacement. What is the probability that 2 are aces and 1 is a king? [10.8]

47. *Election Poll.* Three people were running for mayor in an election campaign. A poll was conducted to see which candidate was favored. During the polling, 86 favored candidate A, 97 favored B, and 23 favored C. Assuming that the poll is a valid indicator of the election results, what is the probability that the election will be won by A? B? C? [10.8]

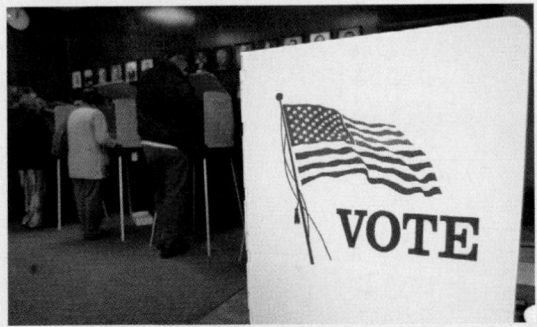

48. Which of the following is the 25th term of the arithmetic sequence 12, 10, 8, 6,...? [10.2]

A. −38
B. −36
C. 32
D. 60

49. What is the probability of getting a total of 4 on a roll of a pair of dice? [10.8]

A. $\frac{1}{12}$
B. $\frac{1}{9}$
C. $\frac{1}{6}$
D. $\frac{5}{36}$

Technology Connection

50. Use a graphing calculator to construct a table of values for the first 10 terms of this sequence.
$$a_1 = 0.3, \quad a_{k+1} = 5a_k + 1 \quad [10.1]$$

51. *Women in the Civilian Labor Force.* The table below lists the number of women in the civilian labor force in the United States in various years.

Year	Women in the Civilian Labor Force (in millions)
1980	45.487
1990	56.829
2000	66.303
2004	68.421

Source: U.S. Bureau of Labor Statistics

a) Find a linear sequence function $a_n = an + b$ that models the data. Let n represent the number of years after 1980. [10.1]
b) Use the sequence found in part (a) to estimate the number of women in the civilian labor force in 2010. [10.1]

Collaborative Discussion and Writing

52. Write an exercise for a classmate to solve. Design it so that the solution is $_9C_4$. [10.6]

53. *Chain Business Deals.* Chain letters have been outlawed by the U.S. government. Nevertheless, "chain" business deals still exist and they can be fraudulent. Suppose that a salesperson is charged with the task of hiring 4 new salespersons. Each of them gives half of his or her profits to the person who hires them. Each of these people hires 4 new salespersons. Each of these gives half of his or her profits to the person who hired them. Half of these profits then go back to the original hiring person. Explain the lure of this business to someone who has managed several sequences of hirings. Explain the fallacy of such a business as well. Keep in mind that there are about 300 million people in the United States. [10.3]

Synthesis

54. Explain why the following cannot be proved by mathematical induction: For every natural number n,

a) $3 + 5 + \cdots + (2n + 1) = (n + 1)^2$.   [10.4]

b) $1 + 3 + \cdots + (2n - 1) = n^2 + 3$.   [10.4]

55. Suppose that $a_1, a_2, \ldots, a_n$ and $b_1, b_2, \ldots, b_n$ are geometric sequences. Prove that $c_1, c_2, \ldots, c_n$ is a geometric sequence, where $c_n = a_n b_n$.   [10.3]

56. Suppose that $a_1, a_2, \ldots, a_n$ is an arithmetic sequence. Is $b_1, b_2, \ldots, b_n$ an arithmetic sequence if:

a) $b_n = |a_n|$?   [10.2]   b) $b_n = a_n + 8$?   [10.2]

c) $b_n = 7a_n$?   [10.2]   d) $b_n = \dfrac{1}{a_n}$?   [10.2]

e) $b_n = \log a_n$?   [10.2] f) $b_n = a_n^3$?   [10.2]

57. The zeros of this polynomial function form an arithmetic sequence. Find them.   [10.2]
$$f(x) = x^4 - 4x^3 - 4x^2 + 16x$$

58. Write the first 3 terms of the infinite geometric series with $r = -\frac{1}{3}$ and $S_\infty = \frac{3}{8}$.   [10.3]

59. Simplify:
$$\sum_{k=0}^{10} (-1)^k \binom{10}{k} (\log x)^{10-k} (\log y)^k. \quad [10.6]$$

Solve for n.   [10.6]

60. $\binom{n}{6} = 3 \cdot \binom{n-1}{5}$ **61.** $\binom{n}{n-1} = 36$

62. Solve for a:
$$\sum_{k=0}^{5} \binom{5}{k} 9^{5-k} a^k = 0. \quad [10.7]$$

CHAPTER 10 TEST

1. For the sequence whose nth term is $a_n = (-1)^n(2n + 1)$, find a_{21}.

2. Find the first 5 terms of the sequence with general term
$$a_n = \frac{n + 1}{n + 2}.$$

3. Find and evaluate:
$$\sum_{k=1}^{4} (k^2 + 1).$$

Write sigma notation.

4. $4 + 8 + 12 + 16 + 20 + 24$

5. $2 + 4 + 8 + 16 + 32 + \cdots$

6. Find the first 4 terms of the recursively defined sequence
$$a_1 = 3, \quad a_{n+1} = 2 + \frac{1}{a_n}.$$

7. Find the 15th term of the arithmetic sequence $2, 5, 8, \ldots$.

8. The 1st term of an arithmetic sequence is 8 and the 21st term is 108. Find the 7th term.

9. Find the sum of the first 20 terms of the series $17 + 13 + 9 + \cdots$.

10. Find the sum: $\sum_{k=1}^{25} (2k + 1)$.

11. Find the 11th term of the geometric sequence $10, -5, \frac{5}{2}, -\frac{5}{4}, \ldots$.

12. For a geometric sequence, $r = 0.2$ and $S_4 = 1248$. Find a_1.

Find the sum, if it exists.

13. $\sum_{k=1}^{8} 2^k$

14. $18 + 6 + 2 + \cdots$

15. Find fraction notation for $0.\overline{56}$.

16. *Salvage Value.*   The value of an office machine is $10,000. Its salvage value each year is 80% of its value the year before. Give a sequence that lists the salvage value of the machine for each year of a 6-yr period.

17. *Hourly Wage.*   Tamika accepts a job, starting with an hourly wage of $8.50, and is promised a raise of 25¢ per hour every three months for 4 yr. What will Tamika's hourly wage be at the end of the 4-yr period?

18. *Amount of an Annuity.*   To create a college fund, a parent makes a sequence of 18 equal yearly deposits of $2500 in a savings account on which interest is compounded annually at 5.6%. Find the amount of the annuity.

19. Use mathematical induction to prove that, for every natural number n,

$$2 + 5 + 8 + \cdots + (3n - 1) = \frac{n(3n + 1)}{2}.$$

Evaluate.

20. $_{15}P_6$ 21. $_{21}C_{10}$ 22. $\binom{n}{4}$

23. How many 4-digit numbers can be formed using the digits 1, 3, 5, 6, 7, and 9 without repetition?

24. How many code symbols can be formed using 4 of the 6 letters A, B, C, X, Y, Z if the letters:
    a) can be repeated?
    b) are not repeated but must begin with Z?

25. *Scuba Club Officers.*   The Bay Woods Scuba Club has 28 members. How many sets of 4 officers can be selected from this group?

26. *Test Options.*   On a test with 20 questions, a student must answer 8 of the first 12 questions and 4 of the last 8. In how many ways can this be done?

27. Expand: $(x + 1)^5$.

28. Find the 5th term of the binomial expansion $(x - y)^7$.

29. Determine the number of subsets of a set containing 9 members.

30. *Marbles.*   Suppose we select, without looking, one marble from a bag containing 6 red marbles and 8 blue marbles. What is the probability of selecting a blue marble?

31. *Drawing Coins.*   Ethan has 6 pennies, 5 dimes, and 4 quarters in his pocket. Six coins are drawn at random. What is the probability of getting 1 penny, 2 dimes, and 3 quarters?

Synthesis

32. Solve for n: $_{n}P_7 = 9 \cdot _{n}P_6$.

Appendix

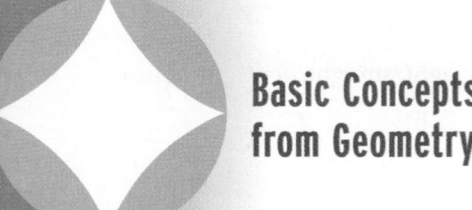

Basic Concepts from Geometry

- ✦ Classify an angle as right, straight, acute, or obtuse.
- ✦ Identify complementary and supplementary angles and find the measure of a complement or a supplement of a given angle.
- ✦ Find the lengths of sides of similar triangles.
- ✦ Given the lengths of any two sides of a right triangle, find the length of the third side.

In this appendix, we present a review of some basic concepts from geometry. A summary of formulas from geometry is found near the back of the book.

✦ Classifying Angles

The following are ways in which we classify angles.

Types of Angles

Right angle: An angle whose measure is 90°.

Straight angle: An angle whose measure is 180°.

Acute angle: An angle whose measure is greater than 0° and less than 90°.

Obtuse angle: An angle whose measure is greater than 90° and less than 180°.

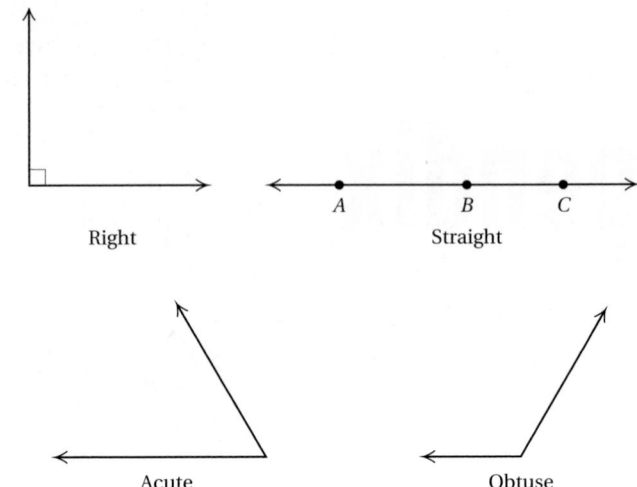

Right   Straight

Acute   Obtuse

EXAMPLE 1   Classify the angle as right, straight, acute, or obtuse.

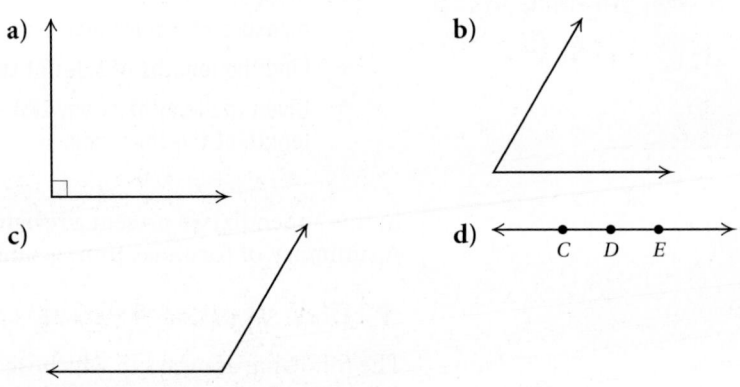

a)

b)

c)

d)

Solution

a) We note that the measure of this angle is 90°, so it is a right angle. (We could also use a protractor to measure the angle.)

b) We note that the measure of this angle is greater than 0° and less than 90°. It is an acute angle.

c) We note that the measure of this angle is greater than 90° and less than 180°. It is an obtuse angle.

d) We note that the measure of this angle is 180°, so it is a straight angle.

▶ Now Try Exercise 1.

◆ Complementary and Supplementary Angles

We can describe the relationship between certain pairs of angles on the basis of the sum of their measures.

> Two angles are **complementary** if the sum of their measures is 90°. Each angle is called a **complement** of the other.

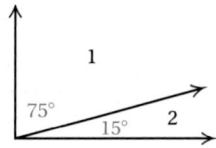

∠1 and ∠2 above are **complementary** angles.

$$m\angle 1 + m\angle 2 = 90°$$
$$75° \ + \ 15° \ = 90°$$

If two angles are complementary, each is an acute angle. When complementary angles are adjacent to each other, they form a right angle.

EXAMPLE 2 Identify each pair of complementary angles.

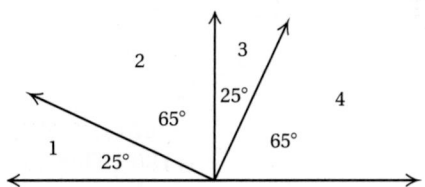

Solution We look for pairs of angles for which the sum of the measures is 90°. They are

∠1 and ∠2,

∠1 and ∠4,

∠2 and ∠3,

∠3 and ∠4.

EXAMPLE 3 Find the measure of a complement of an angle of 39°.

Solution

$$90° - 39° = 51°$$

The measure of a complement is 51°.　　　▷ Now Try Exercise 7.

Next, consider ∠1 and ∠2 as shown below. Because the sum of their measures is 180°, ∠1 and ∠2 are said to be **supplementary.** Note that when supplementary angles are adjacent, they form a straight angle.

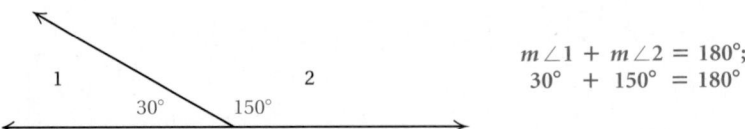

$$m\angle 1 + m\angle 2 = 180°;$$
$$30° + 150° = 180°$$

> Two angles are **supplementary** if the sum of their measures is 180°. Each angle is called a **supplement** of the other.

EXAMPLE 4   Identify each pair of supplementary angles.

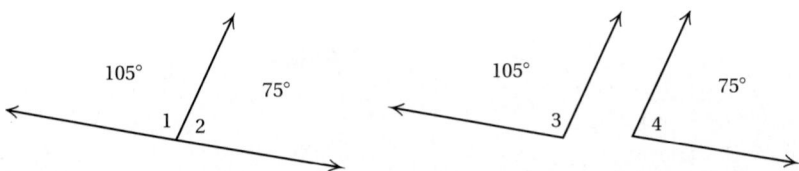

Solution   We look for pairs of angles for which the sum of the measures is 180°. They are

∠1 and ∠2,

∠1 and ∠4,

∠2 and ∠3,

∠3 and ∠4.

EXAMPLE 5   Find the measure of a supplement of an angle of 112°.

Solution

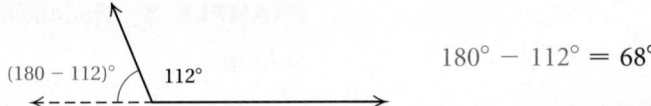

$$180° - 112° = 68°$$

The measure of a supplement is 68°.

▶ **Now Try Exercise 15.**

◆ Similar Triangles

Similar figures have the same shape but are not necessarily the same size.

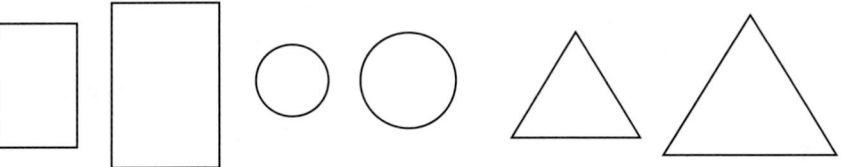

Similar figures

EXAMPLE 6   Which pairs of triangles appear to be similar?

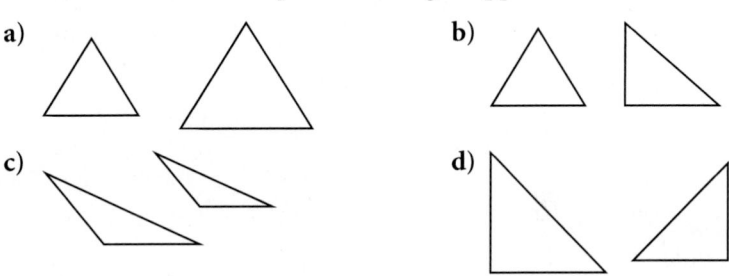

a)

b)

c)

d)

Solution   Pairs (a), (c), and (d) appear to be similar because they appear to have the same shape.

Similar triangles have corresponding sides and angles.

EXAMPLE 7 $\triangle ABC$ and $\triangle DEF$ are similar. Name their corresponding sides and angles.

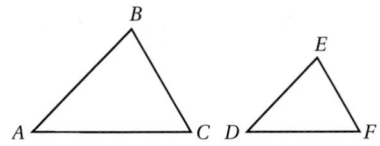

Solution

$\overline{AB} \leftrightarrow \overline{DE}$ $\angle A \leftrightarrow \angle D$ The symbol $\leftrightarrow$ means "corresponds to."

$\overline{AC} \leftrightarrow \overline{DF}$ $\angle B \leftrightarrow \angle E$

$\overline{BC} \leftrightarrow \overline{EF}$ $\angle C \leftrightarrow \angle F$

▶ **Now Try Exercise 23.**

Two triangles are **similar** if and only if their vertices can be matched so that the corresponding angles have the same measure and the lengths of corresponding sides are proportional.

To say that $\triangle ABC$ and $\triangle DEF$ are similar, we write "$\triangle ABC \sim \triangle DEF$." We will agree that this symbol also tells us the way in which the vertices are matched.

$$\triangle ABC \sim \triangle DEF$$

Thus, $\triangle ABC \sim \triangle DEF$ means that

$$\angle A \leftrightarrow \angle D$$
$$\angle B \leftrightarrow \angle E \quad \text{and} \quad \frac{AB}{DE} = \frac{AC}{DF} = \frac{BC}{EF}.$$
$$\angle C \leftrightarrow \angle F$$

EXAMPLE 8 Suppose that $\triangle PQR \sim \triangle STV$. Name the corresponding angles. Which sides are proportional?

Solution

$$\angle P \leftrightarrow \angle S$$
$$\angle Q \leftrightarrow \angle T \quad \text{and} \quad \frac{PQ}{ST} = \frac{PR}{SV} = \frac{QR}{TV}.$$
$$\angle R \leftrightarrow \angle V$$

▶ Now Try Exercise 27.

EXAMPLE 9 These triangles are similar. Which sides are proportional?

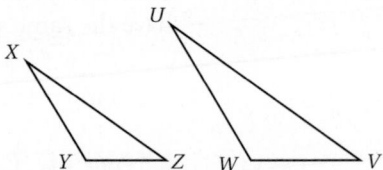

Solution It appears that if we match X with U, Y with W, and Z with V, the corresponding angles have the same measure. Thus,

$$\frac{XY}{UW} = \frac{XZ}{UV} = \frac{YZ}{WV}.$$

▶ Now Try Exercise 31.

✦ Proportions and Similar Triangles

We can find lengths of sides in similar triangles.

EXAMPLE 10 If $\triangle RAE \sim \triangle GQL$, find QL and GL.

Solution Since $\triangle RAE \sim \triangle GQL$, the corresponding sides are proportional. Thus,

$$\frac{6}{9} = \frac{4}{QL}$$

$$6(QL) = 4 \cdot 9 \qquad \text{Multiplying by } 9(QL) \text{ on both sides}$$

$$6(QL) = 36$$

$$QL = 6 \qquad \text{Dividing by 6 on both sides}$$

and

$$\frac{6}{9} = \frac{7}{GL}$$

$$6(GL) = 7 \cdot 9$$

$$6(GL) = 63$$

$$GL = 10\frac{1}{2}.$$

▶ Now Try Exercise 35.

Similar triangles and proportions can often be used to find lengths that would ordinarily be difficult to measure. For example, we could find the height of a flagpole without climbing it or the distance across a river without crossing it.

EXAMPLE 11 *Height of a Flagpole.* How high is a flagpole that casts a 56-ft shadow at the same time that a 6-ft man casts a 5-ft shadow?

Solution If we use the sun's rays to represent the third side of the triangle in our drawing of the situation, we see that we have similar triangles. Let p = the height of the flagpole. Then the ratio of 6 to p is the same as the ratio of 5 to 56. Thus we have the proportion

$$\text{Height of man} \rightarrow \frac{6}{p} = \frac{5}{56} \leftarrow \text{Length of man's shadow} \\ \text{Height of pole} \rightarrow \qquad \leftarrow \text{Length of pole's shadow}$$

$$6 \cdot 56 = 5 \cdot p \qquad \text{Multiplying by } 56p \text{ on both sides}$$

$$\frac{6 \cdot 56}{5} = p \qquad \text{Dividing by 5 on both sides}$$

$$67.2 = p \qquad \text{Simplifying}$$

The height of the flagpole is 67.2 ft.

▶ Now Try Exercise 37.

EXAMPLE 12 *F-106 Blueprint.* A blueprint for an F-106 Delta Dart fighter plane is a scale drawing. Each wing of the plane has a triangular shape. Find the length of side *a* of the wing.

Solution We let *a* = the length of the wing. Thus we have the proportion

Length on the blueprint → $\dfrac{0.447}{19.2} = \dfrac{0.875}{a}$ ← Length on the blueprint
Length of the wing →   ← Length of the wing

$$0.447 \cdot a = 0.875 \cdot 19.2 \qquad \text{Multiplying by 19.2}a$$

$$a = \frac{0.875 \cdot 19.2}{0.447} \qquad \text{Dividing by 0.447}$$

$$a \approx 37.6 \text{ ft}$$

The length of side *a* of the wing is about 37.6 ft.   ▷ **Now Try Exercise 39.**

◆ Right Triangles

A **right triangle** is a triangle with a 90° angle, as shown in the figure below. The small square in the corner indicates the 90° angle.

In a right triangle, the longest side is called the **hypotenuse.** It is the side opposite the right angle. The other two sides are called **legs.** We generally use the letters *a* and *b* for the lengths of the legs and *c* for the length of the hypotenuse. They are related as follows.

> ### The Pythagorean Theorem
> In any right triangle, if *a* and *b* are the lengths of the legs and *c* is the length of the hypotenuse, then
>
> $$a^2 + b^2 = c^2.$$
>
> The equation $a^2 + b^2 = c^2$ is called the **Pythagorean equation.**

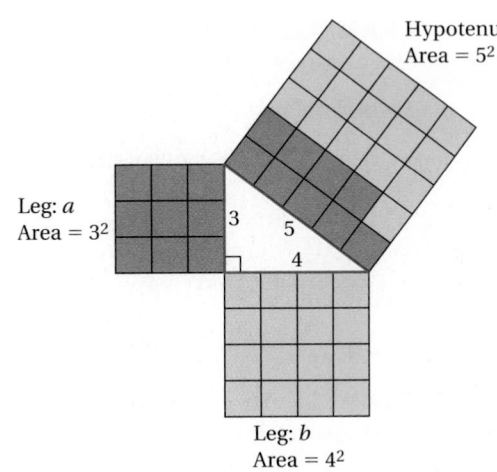

Hypotenuse: c
Area = 5^2

Leg: a
Area = 3^2

Leg: b
Area = 4^2

$a^2 + b^2 = c^2$
$3^2 + 4^2 = 5^2$
$9 + 16 = 25$

The Pythagorean theorem is named after the ancient Greek mathematician Pythagoras (569?–500? B.C.). It is uncertain who actually proved this result the first time. A proof can be found in most geometry books.

If we know the lengths of any two sides of a right triangle, we can find the length of the third side.

EXAMPLE 13 Find the length of the hypotenuse of this right triangle. Give an exact answer and an approximation to three decimal places.

Solution

$4^2 + 5^2 = c^2$ Substituting in the Pythagorean equation

$16 + 25 = c^2$

$41 = c^2$

$\sqrt{41} = c$ Exact answer

$6.403 \approx c$ Using a calculator to find an approximation

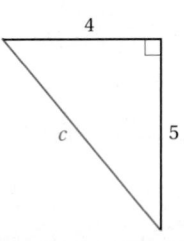

▶ Now Try Exercise 41.

EXAMPLE 14 Find the length b of the leg of this right triangle. Give an exact answer and an approximation to three decimal places.

Solution

$10^2 + b^2 = 12^2$ Substituting in the Pythagorean equation

$100 + b^2 = 144$

$b^2 = 144 - 100$

$b^2 = 44$

$b = \sqrt{44}$ Exact answer

$b \approx 6.633$ Using a calculator

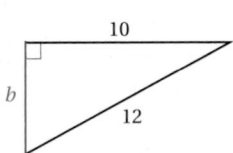

▶ Now Try Exercise 45.

EXAMPLE 15 Find the length b of the leg of this right triangle. Give an exact answer and an approximation to three decimal places.

Solution

$$1^2 + b^2 = \left(\sqrt{7}\right)^2$$ Substituting in the Pythagorean equation

$$1 + b^2 = 7$$

$$b^2 = 7 - 1 = 6$$

$$b = \sqrt{6}$$ Exact answer

$$b \approx 2.449$$ Using a calculator

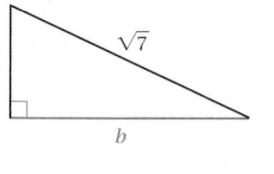

▶ **Now Try Exercise 47.**

EXAMPLE 16 Find the length a of the leg of this right triangle. Give an exact answer and an approximation to three decimal places.

Solution

$$a^2 + 10^2 = 15^2$$

$$a^2 + 100 = 225$$

$$a^2 = 225 - 100$$

$$a^2 = 125$$

$$a = \sqrt{125}$$ Exact answer

$$a \approx 11.180$$ Using a calculator

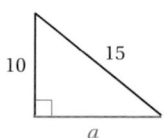

◆ An Application

EXAMPLE 17 *Dimensions of a Softball Diamond.* A slow-pitch softball diamond is actually a square 65 ft on a side. How far is it from home plate to second base? Give an exact answer and an approximation to three decimal places. (This can be helpful information when lining up the bases.)

Solution

a) We first make a drawing. We note that the first and second base lines, together with a line from home plate to second base, form a right triangle. We label the unknown distance d.

b) We know that $65^2 + 65^2 = d^2$. We solve this equation:

$$4225 + 4225 = d^2$$
$$8450 = d^2.$$

Exact answer: $\sqrt{8450} \text{ ft} = d$

Approximation: $91.924 \text{ ft} \approx d$

▶ Now Try Exercise 61.

EXERCISE SET

Classify the angle as right, straight, acute, or obtuse.

1.

2.

3.

4.

5.

6.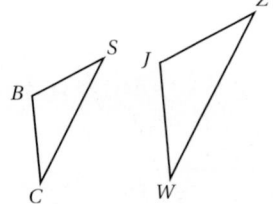

Find the measure of a complement of an angle with the given measure.

7. $11°$ **8.** $83°$ **9.** $67°$ **10.** $5°$

11. $58°$ **12.** $32°$ **13.** $29°$ **14.** $54°$

Find the measure of a supplement of an angle with the given measure.

15. $3°$ **16.** $54°$ **17.** $139°$ **18.** $13°$

19. $85°$ **20.** $129°$ **21.** $102°$ **22.** $45°$

For each pair of similar triangles, name the corresponding angles and sides.

23.

24.

25.

26.

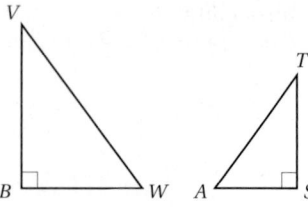

For each pair of similar triangles, name the angles with the same measure and name the proportional sides.

27. $\triangle ABC \sim \triangle RST$

28. $\triangle PQR \sim \triangle STV$

29. $\triangle MES \sim \triangle CLF$

30. $\triangle SMH \sim \triangle WLK$

Name the proportional sides in these similar triangles.

31.

32.

33.

34.

35. If $\triangle ABC \sim \triangle PQR$, find QR and PR.

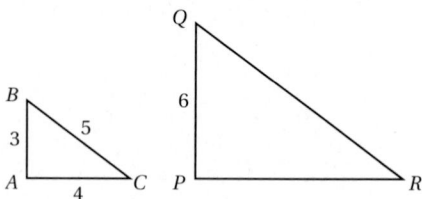

36. If $\triangle MAC \sim \triangle GET$, find AM and GT.

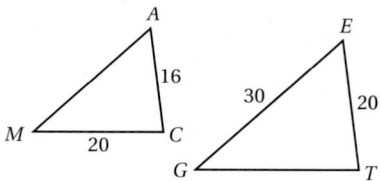

37. How high is a tree that casts a 27-ft shadow at the same time that a 4-ft fence post casts a 3-ft shadow?

38. How high is a flagpole that casts a 42-ft shadow at the same time that a $5\frac{1}{2}$-ft woman casts a 7-ft shadow?

39. Find the distance across the river. Assume that the ratio of d to 25 ft is the same as the ratio of 40 ft to 10 ft.

40. To measure the height of a hill, a string is drawn tight from level ground to the top of the hill. A 3-ft yardstick is placed under the string, touching it at point P, a distance of 5 ft from point G, where the string touches the ground. The string is then detached and found to be 120 ft long. How high is the hill?

Find the length of the third side of the right triangle. Give an exact answer and an approximation to three decimal places.

41.

42.

43.

44.

45.

46.

47.

48.

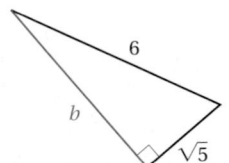

In a right triangle, find the length of the side not given. Give an exact answer and an approximation to three decimal places.

49. $a = 10, \ b = 24$ **50.** $a = 5, \ b = 12$

51. $a = 9, \ c = 15$ **52.** $a = 18, \ c = 30$

53. $b = 1, \ c = \sqrt{5}$ **54.** $b = 1, \ c = \sqrt{2}$

55. $a = 1, \ c = \sqrt{3}$ **56.** $a = \sqrt{3}, \ b = \sqrt{5}$

57. $c = 10, \ b = 5\sqrt{3}$ **58.** $a = 5, \ b = 5$

59. $a = \sqrt{2}, \ b = \sqrt{7}$ **60.** $c = \sqrt{7}, \ a = \sqrt{2}$

Solve. Give an exact answer and an approximation to three decimal places.

61. *Airport Distance.* An airplane is flying at an altitude of 4100 ft. The slanted distance directly to the airport is 15,100 ft. How far is the airplane horizontally from the airport?

62. *Surveying Distance.* A surveyor had poles located at points P, Q, and R. The distances that the surveyor was able to measure are marked on the drawing. What is the approximate distance from P to R?

63. *Cordless Telephones.* Becky's new cordless telephone has clear reception up to 300 ft from its base. Her phone is located near a window in her apartment, 180 ft above ground level. How far into her backyard can Becky use her phone?

64. *Rope Course.* An outdoor rope course consists of a cable that slopes downward from a height of 37 ft to a resting place 30 ft above the ground. The trees that the cable connects are 24 ft apart. How long is the cable?

65. *Diagonal of a Square.* Find the length of a diagonal of a square whose sides are 3 cm long.

66. *Ladder Height.* A 10-m ladder is leaning against a building. The bottom of the ladder is 5 m from the building. How high is the top of the ladder?

67. *Guy Wire.* How long is a guy wire reaching from the top of a 12-ft pole to a point on the ground 8 ft from the base of the pole?

68. *Diagonal of a Soccer Field.* The largest regulation soccer field is 100 yd wide and 130 yd long. Find the length of a diagonal of such a field.

Answers

Exercise Set R.1

1. $\sqrt[3]{8}, 0, 9, \sqrt{25}$ **3.** $\sqrt{7}, 5.242242224\ldots, -\sqrt{14}, \sqrt[5]{5},$ $\sqrt[3]{4}$ **5.** $-12, 5.\overline{3}, -\frac{7}{3}, \sqrt[3]{8}, 0, -1.96, 9, 4\frac{2}{3}, \sqrt{25}, \frac{5}{7}$
7. $5.\overline{3}, -\frac{7}{3}, -1.96, 4\frac{2}{3}, \frac{5}{7}$ **9.** $-12, 0$
11. $[-3, 3]$;
13. $[-4, -1)$;
15. $(-\infty, -2]$;
17. $(3.8, \infty)$;
19. $(7, \infty)$;   **21.** $(0, 5)$
23. $[-9, -4)$ **25.** $[x, x + h]$ **27.** (p, ∞) **29.** True
31. False   **33.** True   **35.** False   **37.** False   **39.** True
41. True   **43.** True   **45.** False
47. Commutative property of multiplication
49. Multiplicative identity property
51. Associative property of multiplication
53. Commutative property of multiplication
55. Commutative property of addition
57. Multiplicative inverse property   **59.** 7.1   **61.** 347
63. $\sqrt{97}$ **65.** 0   **67.** $\frac{5}{4}$ **69.** 11   **71.** 6   **73.** 5.4
75. $\frac{21}{8}$ **77.** 7   **79.** Discussion and Writing
81. Answers may vary; $0.124124412444\ldots$
83. Answers may vary; -0.00999 **85.**

Exercise Set R.2

1. $\dfrac{1}{3^7}$ **3.** $\dfrac{y^4}{x^5}$ **5.** $\dfrac{t^6}{mn^{12}}$ **7.** 1   **9.** x^9 **11.** 5^2, or 25
13. 1   **15.** y^{-4}, or $\dfrac{1}{y^4}$ **17.** 7^{-1}, or $\dfrac{1}{7}$ **19.** $6x^5$

21. $-15a^{-12}$, or $-\dfrac{15}{a^{12}}$ **23.** $15a^{-1}b^5$, or $\dfrac{15b^5}{a}$
25. $-42x^{-1}y^{-4}$, or $-\dfrac{42}{xy^4}$ **27.** $72x^5$ **29.** $-200n^5$
31. b^3 **33.** x^{-21}, or $\dfrac{1}{x^{21}}$ **35.** x^3y^{-3}, or $\dfrac{x^3}{y^3}$
37. $8xy^{-5}$, or $\dfrac{8x}{y^5}$ **39.** $8a^3b^6$ **41.** $-32x^{15}$ **43.** $\dfrac{c^2d^4}{25}$
45. $432m^{-8}$, or $\dfrac{432}{m^8}$ **47.** $\dfrac{8x^{-9}y^{21}}{z^{-3}}$, or $\dfrac{8y^{21}z^3}{x^9}$
49. $2^{-5}a^{-20}b^{25}c^{-10}$, or $\dfrac{b^{25}}{32a^{20}c^{10}}$ **51.** 4.05×10^5
53. 3.9×10^{-7} **55.** 2.346×10^{11} **57.** 1.04×10^{-3}
59. 1.6×10^{-5} **61.** 0.000083   **63.** 20,700,000
65. 34,960,000,000   **67.** 0.0000000541   **69.** 231,900,000
71. 1.395×10^3 **73.** 2.21×10^{-10} **75.** 8×10^{-14}
77. 2.5×10^5 **79.** 3.627×10^9 mi   **81.** 3.6×10^{-7} m
83. $\$1.19 \times 10^7$ **85.** 1.332×10^{14} disintegrations   **87.** 2
89. 2048   **91.** 5   **93.** \$2883.67   **95.** \$8763.54
97. Discussion and Writing   **99.** \$170,797.30
101. \$309.79   **103.** x^{8t} **105.** t^{8x} **107.** $9x^{2a}y^{2b}$

Exercise Set R.3

1. $-5y^4, 3y^3, 7y^2, -y, -4; 4$ **3.** $3a^4b, -7a^3b^3, 5ab, -2; 6$
5. $3x^2y - 5xy^2 + 7xy + 2$ **7.** $3x + 2y - 2z - 3$
9. $-2x^2 + 6x - 2$ **11.** $x^4 - 3x^3 - 4x^2 + 9x - 3$
13. $2a^4 - 2a^3b - a^2b + 4ab^2 - 3b^3$ **15.** $x^2 + 2x - 15$
17. $x^2 + 10x + 24$ **19.** $2a^2 + 13a + 15$
21. $4x^2 + 8xy + 3y^2$ **23.** $y^2 + 10y + 25$
25. $x^2 - 8x + 16$ **27.** $25x^2 - 30x + 9$
29. $4x^2 + 12xy + 9y^2$ **31.** $4x^4 - 12x^2y + 9y^2$
33. $a^2 - 9$ **35.** $4x^2 - 25$ **37.** $9x^2 - 4y^2$
39. $4x^2 + 12xy + 9y^2 - 16$ **41.** $x^4 - 1$
43. Discussion and Writing   **45.** $a^{2n} - b^{2n}$
47. $a^{2n} + 2a^nb^n + b^{2n}$ **49.** $x^6 - 1$ **51.** $x^{a^2 - b^2}$
53. $a^2 + b^2 + c^2 + 2ab + 2ac + 2bc$

Exercise Set R.4

1. $2(x - 5)$ 3. $3x^2(x^2 - 3)$ 5. $4(a^2 - 3a + 4)$
7. $(b - 2)(a + c)$ 9. $(x + 3)(x^2 + 6)$
11. $(y - 1)(y^2 + 3)$ 13. $12(2x - 3)(x^2 + 3)$
15. $(a - 3)(a^2 - 2)$ 17. $(x - 1)(x^2 - 5)$
19. $(p + 2)(p + 4)$ 21. $(x - 2)(x - 6)$
23. $(t + 3)(t + 5)$ 25. $(x + 3y)(x - 9y)$
27. $2(n - 12)(n + 2)$ 29. $(y^2 + 3)(y^2 - 7)$
31. $y^2(y + 2)(y + 7)$ 33. $2x(x + 3y)(x - 4y)$
35. $(2n - 7)(n + 8)$ 37. $(3x + 2)(4x + 1)$
39. $(4x + 3)(x + 3)$ 41. $(2y - 3)(y + 2)$
43. $(3a - 4b)(2a - 7b)$ 45. $4(3a - 4)(a + 1)$
47. $(m + 2)(m - 2)$ 49. $(2z + 9)(2z - 9)$
51. $6(x + y)(x - y)$ 53. $4x(y^2 + z)(y^2 - z)$
55. $7p(q^2 + y^2)(q + y)(q - y)$ 57. $(y - 3)^2$
59. $(2z + 3)^2$ 61. $(1 - 4x)^2$ 63. $a(a + 12)^2$
65. $4(p - q)^2$ 67. $(x + 2)(x^2 - 2x + 4)$
69. $(m - 1)(m^2 + m + 1)$ 71. $2(y - 4)(y^2 + 4y + 16)$
73. $3a^2(a - 2)(a^2 + 2a + 4)$ 75. $(t^2 + 1)(t^4 - t^2 + 1)$
77. $3ab(6a - 5b)$ 79. $(x - 4)(x^2 + 5)$
81. $8(x + 2)(x - 2)$ 83. Prime   85. $(m + 3n)(m - 3n)$
87. $(x + 4)(x + 5)$ 89. $(y - 5)(y - 1)$
91. $(2a + 1)(a + 4)$ 93. $(3x - 1)(2x + 3)$
95. $(y - 9)^2$ 97. $(3z - 4)^2$ 99. $(xy - 7)^2$
101. $4a(x + 7)(x - 2)$ 103. $3(z - 2)(z^2 + 2z + 4)$
105. $2ab(2a^2 + 3b^2)(4a^4 - 6a^2b^2 + 9b^4)$
107. $(y - 3)(y + 2)(y - 2)$ 109. $(x - 1)(x^2 + 1)$
111. $5(m^2 + 2)(m^2 - 2)$ 113. $2(x + 3)(x + 2)(x - 2)$
115. $(2c - d)^2$ 117. $(m^3 + 10)(m^3 - 2)$
119. $p(1 - 4p)(1 + 4p + 16p^2)$
121. Discussion and Writing   123. $(y^2 + 12)(y^2 - 7)$
125. $\left(y + \frac{4}{7}\right)\left(y - \frac{2}{7}\right)$ 127. $\left(x + \frac{3}{2}\right)^2$ 129. $\left(x - \frac{1}{2}\right)^2$
131. $h(3x^2 + 3xh + h^2)$ 133. $(y + 4)(y - 7)$
135. $(x^n + 8)(x^n - 3)$ 137. $(x + a)(x + b)$
139. $(5y^m + x^n - 1)(5y^m - x^n + 1)$
141. $y(y - 1)^2(y - 2)$

Exercise Set R.5

1. $\{x \mid x \text{ is a real number}\}$
3. $\{x \mid x \text{ is a real number } and \ x \neq 0 \ and \ x \neq 1\}$
5. $\{x \mid x \text{ is a real number } and \ x \neq -5 \ and \ x \neq 1\}$
7. $\{x \mid x \text{ is a real number } and \ x \neq -2 \ and \ x \neq 2 \ and \ x \neq -5\}$
9. $\dfrac{x + 2}{x - 2}$ 11. $\dfrac{x - 3}{x}$ 13. $\dfrac{2(y + 4)}{y - 1}$ 15. $-\dfrac{1}{x + 8}$
17. $\dfrac{1}{x - y}$ 19. $\dfrac{(x + 5)(2x + 3)}{7x}$ 21. $\dfrac{a + 2}{a - 5}$
23. $m + n$ 25. $\dfrac{3(x - 4)}{2(x + 4)}$ 27. $\dfrac{1}{x + y}$ 29. $\dfrac{x - y - z}{x + y + z}$
31. $\dfrac{3}{x}$ 33. 1 35. $\dfrac{7}{8z}$ 37. $\dfrac{3x - 4}{(x + 2)(x - 2)}$
39. $\dfrac{-y + 10}{(y + 4)(y - 5)}$ 41. $\dfrac{4x - 8y}{(x + y)(x - y)}$ 43. $\dfrac{y - 2}{y - 1}$

45. $\dfrac{x + y}{2x - 3y}$ 47. $\dfrac{3x - 4}{(x - 2)(x - 1)}$ 49. $\dfrac{5a^2 + 10ab - 4b^2}{(a + b)(a - b)}$
51. $\dfrac{11x^2 - 18x + 8}{(2 + x)(2 - x)^2}$, or $\dfrac{11x^2 - 18x + 8}{(x + 2)(x - 2)^2}$ 53. 0
55. $\dfrac{x + y}{x}$ 57. $x - y$ 59. $\dfrac{c^2 - 2c + 4}{c}$ 61. $\dfrac{xy}{x - y}$
63. $\dfrac{a^2 - 1}{a^2 + 1}$ 65. $\dfrac{3(x - 1)^2(x + 2)}{(x - 3)(x + 3)(-x + 10)}$ 67. $\dfrac{1 + a}{1 - a}$
69. $\dfrac{b + a}{b - a}$ 71. Discussion and Writing   73. $2x + h$
75. $3x^2 + 3xh + h^2$ 77. x^5
79. $\dfrac{(n + 1)(n + 2)(n + 3)}{2 \cdot 3}$ 81. $\dfrac{x^3 + 2x^2 + 11x + 20}{2(x + 1)(2 + x)}$

Exercise Set R.6

1. 11 3. $4|y|$ 5. $|b + 1|$ 7. $-3x$ 9. $3x^2$ 11. 2
13. $6\sqrt{5}$ 15. $6\sqrt{2}$ 17. $3\sqrt[3]{2}$ 19. $8\sqrt{2}|c|d^2$
21. $2|x||y|\sqrt[4]{3x^2}$ 23. $|x - 2|$ 25. $10\sqrt{3}$ 27. $6\sqrt{11}$
29. $2x^2y\sqrt{6}$ 31. $3x\sqrt[3]{4y}$ 33. $2(x + 4)\sqrt[3]{(x + 4)^2}$
35. $\dfrac{m^2n^4}{2}$ 37. 2 39. $\dfrac{1}{2x}$ 41. $\dfrac{4a\sqrt[3]{a}}{3b}$ 43. $\dfrac{x\sqrt{7x}}{6y^3}$
45. $51\sqrt{2}$ 47. $4\sqrt{5}$ 49. $-2x\sqrt{2} - 12\sqrt{5x}$ 51. 1
53. $-9 - 5\sqrt{15}$ 55. $4 + 2\sqrt{3}$ 57. $11 - 2\sqrt{30}$
59. About $13{,}709.5$ ft   61. (a) $h = \dfrac{a}{2}\sqrt{3}$; (b) $A = \dfrac{a^2}{4}\sqrt{3}$
63. 8 65. $\dfrac{\sqrt{6}}{3}$ 67. $\dfrac{\sqrt[3]{10}}{2}$ 69. $\dfrac{2\sqrt[3]{6}}{3}$ 71. $\dfrac{9 - 3\sqrt{5}}{2}$
73. $-\dfrac{\sqrt{6}}{6}$ 75. $\dfrac{6\sqrt{m} + 6\sqrt{n}}{m - n}$ 77. $\dfrac{6}{5\sqrt{3}}$ 79. $\dfrac{7}{\sqrt[3]{98}}$
81. $\dfrac{11}{\sqrt{33}}$ 83. $\dfrac{76}{27 + 3\sqrt{5} - 9\sqrt{3} - \sqrt{15}}$
85. $\dfrac{a - b}{3a\sqrt{a} - 3a\sqrt{b}}$ 87. $\sqrt[4]{x^3}$ 89. 8 91. $\dfrac{1}{5}$
93. $\dfrac{a\sqrt[4]{a}}{\sqrt[4]{b^3}}$, or $a\sqrt[4]{\dfrac{a}{b^3}}$ 95. $mn^2\sqrt[3]{m^2n}$ 97. $13^{5/4}$
99. $20^{2/3}$ 101. $11^{1/6}$ 103. $5^{5/6}$ 105. 4 107. $8a^2$
109. $\dfrac{x^3}{3b^{-2}}$, or $\dfrac{x^3b^2}{3}$ 111. $x\sqrt[3]{y}$ 113. $n\sqrt[3]{mn^2}$
115. $a\sqrt[12]{a^5} + a^2\sqrt[12]{a}$ 117. $\sqrt[6]{288}$ 119. $\sqrt[12]{x^{11}y^7}$
121. $a\sqrt[6]{a^5}$ 123. $(a + x)\sqrt[12]{(a + x)^{11}}$
125. Discussion and Writing   127. $\dfrac{(2 + x^2)\sqrt{1 + x^2}}{1 + x^2}$
129. $a^{a/2}$

Exercise Set R.7

1. 10 3. 11 5. -1 7. -12 9. 2 11. -1
13. $\frac{18}{5}$ 15. -3 17. 1 19. 0 21. $-\frac{1}{10}$ 23. 5
25. $-\frac{3}{2}$ 27. $\frac{20}{7}$ 29. $-7, 4$ 31. $0, 8$ 33. -3
35. 10 37. $-4, 8$ 39. $-2, -\frac{2}{3}$ 41. $-\frac{3}{4}, \frac{2}{3}$ 43. $-\frac{4}{3}, \frac{7}{4}$

45. $-2, 7$ **47.** $-6, 6$ **49.** $-12, 12$ **51.** $-\sqrt{10}, \sqrt{10}$
53. $-\sqrt{3}, \sqrt{3}$ **55.** Discussion and Writing   **57.** $\frac{23}{66}$
59. 8   **61.** $-\frac{6}{5}, -\frac{1}{4}, 0, \frac{2}{3}$ **63.** $-3, -2, 3$

Review Exercises: Chapter R

1. True   **2.** False   **3.** True   **4.** True
5. $12, -3, -1, -19, 31, 0$ **6.** $12, 31$
7. $-43.89, 12, -3, -\frac{1}{5}, -1, -\frac{4}{3}, 7\frac{2}{3}, -19, 31, 0$
8. All of them   **9.** $\sqrt{7}, \sqrt[3]{10}$ **10.** $12, 31, 0$ **11.** $[-3, 5)$
12. 3.5   **13.** 16   **14.** 10   **15.** 117   **16.** -10
17. 3,261,000   **18.** 0.00041   **19.** 1.432×10^{-2}
20. 4.321×10^4 **21.** 7.8125×10^{-22} **22.** 5.46×10^{-32}
23. $-14a^{-2}b^7$, or $\dfrac{-14b^7}{a^2}$ **24.** $6x^9y^{-6}z^6$, or $\dfrac{6x^9z^6}{y^6}$ **25.** 3
26. -2 **27.** $\dfrac{b}{a}$ **28.** $\dfrac{x+y}{xy}$ **29.** -4
30. $25x^4 - 10\sqrt{2}x^2 + 2$ **31.** $13\sqrt{5}$ **32.** $x^3 + t^3$
33. $10a^2 - 7ab - 12b^2$ **34.** $8xy^4 - 9xy^2 + 4x^2 + 2y - 7$
35. $(x+2)(x^2-3)$ **36.** $3a(2a+3b^2)(2a-3b^2)$
37. $(x+12)^2$ **38.** $x(9x-1)(x+4)$
39. $(2x-1)(4x^2+2x+1)$
40. $(3x^2+5y^2)(9x^4-15x^2y^2+25y^4)$
41. $6(x+2)(x^2-2x+4)$
42. $(x-1)(2x+3)(2x-3)$ **43.** $(3x-5)^2$
44. $3(6x^2-x+2)$ **45.** $(ab-3)(ab+2)$ **46.** 3
47. $\dfrac{x-5}{(x+5)(x+3)}$ **48.** $y^3\sqrt[6]{y}$ **49.** $\sqrt[3]{(a+b)^2}$
50. $b\sqrt[5]{b^2}$ **51.** $\dfrac{m^4n^2}{3}$ **52.** $\dfrac{23-9\sqrt{3}}{22}$
53. About 18.8 ft   **54.** 7   **55.** -1 **56.** 3   **57.** $-\frac{1}{13}$
58. -8 **59.** $-4, 5$ **60.** $-6, \frac{1}{2}$ **61.** $-1, 3$ **62.** $-4, 4$
63. $-\sqrt{7}, \sqrt{7}$ **64.** B   **65.** C
66. Discussion and Writing: Anya is probably not
following the rules for order of operations. She is subtracting
6 from 15 first, then dividing the difference by 3, and finally
multiplying the quotient by 4. The correct answer is 7.
67. Discussion and Writing: When the number 4 is raised to
a positive integer power, the last digit of the result is 4 or 6.
Since the calculator returns $4.398046511 \times 10^{12}$, or
4,398,046,511,000, we can conclude that this result is an
approximation.   **68.** \$553.67   **69.** \$606.92   **70.** \$942.54
71. \$857.57   **72.** $x^{2n} + 6x^n - 40$ **73.** $t^{2a} + 2 + t^{-2a}$
74. $y^{2b} - z^{2c}$ **75.** $a^{3n} - 3a^{2n}b^n + 3a^nb^{2n} - b^{3n}$
76. $(y^n + 8)^2$ **77.** $(x^t - 7)(x^t + 4)$
78. $m^{3n}(m^n - 1)(m^{2n} + m^n + 1)$

Test: Chapter R

1. [R.1] **(a)** $-8, 0, 36$; **(b)** $-8, \frac{11}{3}, 0, -5.49, 36, 10\frac{1}{6}$;
(c) $\frac{11}{3}, -5.49, 10\frac{1}{6}$; **(d)** $-8, 0$ **2.** [R.1] $\frac{14}{5}$
3. [R.1] 19.4   **4.** [R.1] $1.2|x||y|$

5. [R.1] $(-3, 6]$; 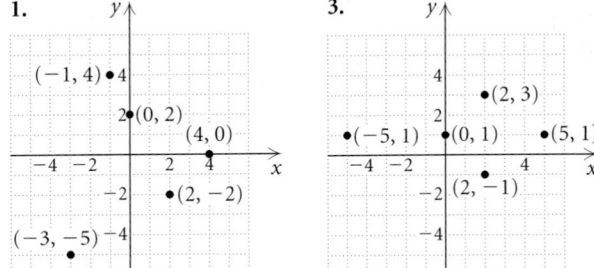   **6.** [R.1] 12
7. [R.2] -5 **8.** [R.2] 3.67×10^{-5} **9.** [R.2] 4,510,000
10. [R.2] 7.5×10^6 **11.** [R.2] x^{-3}, or $\dfrac{1}{x^3}$
12. [R.2] $72y^{14}$ **13.** [R.2] $-15a^4b^{-1}$, or $-\dfrac{15a^4}{b}$
14. [R.3] $3x^4 - 5x^3 + x^2 + 5x$ **15.** [R.3] $2x^2 + x - 15$
16. [R.3] $4y^2 - 4y + 1$ **17.** [R.5] $\dfrac{x-y}{xy}$ **18.** [R.6] $3\sqrt{6}$
19. [R.6] $2\sqrt[3]{5}$ **20.** [R.6] $21\sqrt{3}$ **21.** [R.6] $6\sqrt{5}$
22. [R.6] $4 + \sqrt{3}$ **23.** [R.4] $(y+3)(y-6)$
24. [R.4] $x(x+5)^2$ **25.** [R.4] $(2n-3)(n+4)$
26. [R.4] $2(2x+3)(2x-3)$
27. [R.4] $(m-2)(m^2+2m+4)$ **28.** [R.5] $\dfrac{x-5}{x-2}$
29. [R.5] $\dfrac{x+3}{(x+1)(x+5)}$ **30.** [R.6] $\dfrac{35+5\sqrt{3}}{46}$
31. [R.6] $\sqrt[5]{t^5}$ **32.** [R.6] $7^{3/5}$ **33.** [R.6] 13 ft
34. [R.7] 4   **35.** [R.7] $\frac{15}{4}$ **36.** [R.7] $-\frac{3}{2}, -1$
37. [R.7] $-\sqrt{11}, \sqrt{11}$
38. [R.3] $x^2 - 2xy + y^2 - 2x + 2y + 1$

CHAPTER 1

Visualizing the Graph

1. H   **2.** B   **3.** D   **4.** A   **5.** G   **6.** I
7. C   **8.** J   **9.** F   **10.** E

Exercise Set 1.1

1. (graph with points $(-1, 4)$, $(0, 2)$, $(4, 0)$, $(2, -2)$, $(-3, -5)$)
3. (graph with points $(2, 3)$, $(-5, 1)$, $(0, 1)$, $(5, 1)$, $(2, -1)$)

5. $(2000, 310.6), (2001, 311.2), (2002, 348.2), (2003, 361.6),$
$(2004, 435.8), (2005, 467.7)$ **7.** Yes; no   **9.** Yes; no
11. No; yes   **13.** No; yes

15. x-intercept: $(-3, 0)$;
y-intercept: $(0, 5)$;

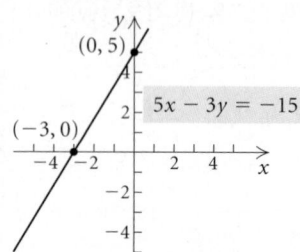

17. x-intercept: $(2, 0)$;
y-intercept: $(0, 4)$;

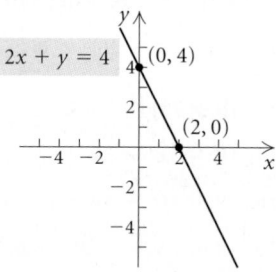

19. x-intercept: $(-4, 0)$;
y-intercept: $(0, 3)$;

21.

23.

25.

27.

29.

31.

33.

35.

37.

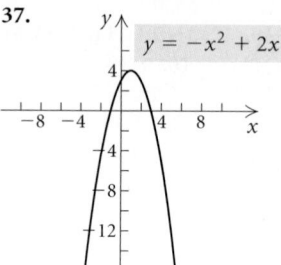

39. $\sqrt{10}$, 3.162

41. $\sqrt{45}$, 6.708   **43.** $\sqrt{128.05}$, 11.316   **45.** 3
47. $\sqrt{14 + 6\sqrt{2}}$, 4.742   **49.** $\sqrt{a^2 + b^2}$ **51.** 6.5
53. Yes   **55.** No   **57.** $(-4, -6)$ **59.** $(4.95, -4.95)$
61. $\left(-6, \frac{13}{2}\right)$ **63.** $\left(-\frac{5}{12}, \frac{13}{40}\right)$ **65.** $\left(2\sqrt{3}, \frac{3}{2}\right)$
67.

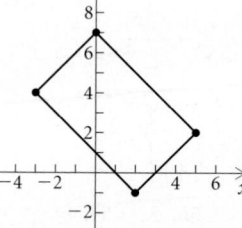

$\left(-\frac{1}{2}, \frac{3}{2}\right), \left(\frac{7}{2}, \frac{1}{2}\right), \left(\frac{5}{2}, \frac{9}{2}\right), \left(-\frac{3}{2}, \frac{11}{2}\right)$; no

69. $\left(\dfrac{\sqrt{7} + \sqrt{2}}{2}, -\dfrac{1}{2}\right)$ **71.** $(x - 2)^2 + (y - 3)^2 = \dfrac{25}{9}$

73. $(x + 1)^2 + (y - 4)^2 = 25$
75. $(x - 2)^2 + (y - 1)^2 = 169$
77. $(x + 2)^2 + (y - 3)^2 = 4$
79. $(0, 0)$; 2;   **81.** $(0, 3)$; 4;

83. (1, 5); 6;

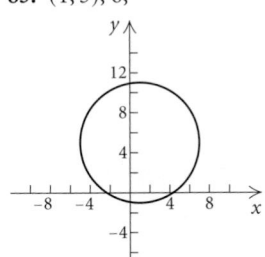

$(x - 1)^2 + (y - 5)^2 = 36$

85. $(-4, -5)$; 3;

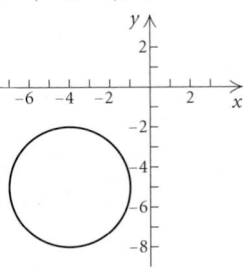

$(x + 4)^2 + (y + 5)^2 = 9$

87. $(x + 2)^2 + (y - 1)^2 = 3^2$
89. $(x - 5)^2 + (y + 5)^2 = 15^2$
91. (b)   **93.** (a)
95.

$4x + y = 7$

97. $y = \frac{1}{3}x + 2$

99.

$y = x^2 + 6$

101.

$y = 2 - x^2$

103. Standard window   **105.** $[-1, 1, -0.3, 0.3]$
107. Square the window; for example, $[-12, 9, -4, 10]$.
109.–111. Left to the student   **113.** Discussion and Writing
115. Third quadrant   **117.** $\sqrt{h^2 + h + 2a} - 2\sqrt{a^2 + ah}$,
$\left(\dfrac{2a + h}{2}, \dfrac{\sqrt{a} + \sqrt{a + h}}{2} \right)$
119. $(x - 2)^2 + (y + 7)^2 = 36$ **121.** (0, 4)
123. $a_1 \approx 2.7$ ft, $a_2 \approx 37.3$ ft   **125.** Yes   **127.** Yes
129. Let $P_1 = (x_1, y_1)$, $P_2 = (x_2, y_2)$, and
$M = \left(\dfrac{x_1 + x_2}{2}, \dfrac{y_1 + y_2}{2} \right)$. Let $d(AB)$ denote the distance
from point A to point B.

(a) $d(P_1M) = \sqrt{\left(\dfrac{x_1 + x_2}{2} - x_1 \right)^2 + \left(\dfrac{y_1 + y_2}{2} - y_1 \right)^2}$

$= \dfrac{1}{2} \sqrt{(x_2 - x_1)^2 + (y_2 - y_1)^2}$;

$d(P_2M) = \sqrt{\left(\dfrac{x_1 + x_2}{2} - x_2 \right)^2 + \left(\dfrac{y_1 + y_2}{2} - y_2 \right)^2}$

$= \dfrac{1}{2} \sqrt{(x_1 - x_2)^2 + (y_1 - y_2)^2}$

$= \dfrac{1}{2} \sqrt{(x_2 - x_1)^2 + (y_2 - y_1)^2} = d(P_1M)$

(b) $d(P_1M) + d(P_2M) = \dfrac{1}{2} \sqrt{(x_2 - x_1)^2 + (y_2 - y_1)^2}$

$+ \dfrac{1}{2} \sqrt{(x_2 - x_1)^2 + (y_2 - y_1)^2}$

$= \sqrt{(x_2 - x_1)^2 + (y_2 - y_1)^2}$

$= d(P_1P_2)$.

Exercise Set 1.2

1. Yes   **3.** Yes   **5.** No   **7.** Yes   **9.** Yes   **11.** Yes
13. No   **15.** Function; domain: {2, 3, 4}; range: {10, 15, 20}
17. Not a function; domain: {−7, −2, 0}; range: {3, 1, 4, 7}
19. Function; domain: {−2, 0, 2, 4, −3}; range: {1}
21. $h(1) = -2$; $h(3) = 2$; $h(4) = 1$
23. $s(-4) = 3$; $s(-2) = 0$; $s(0) = -3$
25. $f(-1) = 2$; $f(0) = 0$; $f(1) = -2$
27. **(a)** 1; **(b)** 6; **(c)** 22; **(d)** $3x^2 + 2x + 1$; **(e)** $3t^2 - 4t + 2$
29. **(a)** 8; **(b)** −8; **(c)** $-x^3$; **(d)** $27y^3$; **(e)** $8 + 12h + 6h^2 + h^3$
31. **(a)** $\dfrac{1}{8}$; **(b)** 0; **(c)** does not exist; **(d)** $\dfrac{81}{53}$, or approximately
1.5283; **(e)** $\dfrac{x + h - 4}{x + h + 3}$ **33.** 0; does not exist; does not exist
as a real number; $\dfrac{1}{\sqrt{3}}$, or $\dfrac{\sqrt{3}}{3}$ **35.** No   **37.** Yes
39. Yes   **41.** No   **43.** All real numbers, or $(-\infty, \infty)$
45. $\{x \mid x \neq 0\}$, or $(-\infty, 0) \cup (0, \infty)$
47. $\{x \mid x \neq 2\}$, or $(-\infty, 2) \cup (2, \infty)$
49. $\{x \mid x \neq -1 \text{ and } x \neq 5\}$, or $(-\infty, -1) \cup (-1, 5) \cup (5, \infty)$
51. $\{x \mid x \leq 8\}$, or $(-\infty, 8]$ **53.** All real numbers, or $(-\infty, \infty)$
55. Domain: $[0, 5]$; range: $[0, 3]$
57. Domain: $[-2\pi, 2\pi]$; range: $[-1, 1]$
59. Domain: $(-\infty, \infty)$; range: {−3}
61. Domain: $[-5, 3]$; range: $[-2, 2]$
63. Domain: all real numbers; range: $[0, \infty)$
65. Domain: $[-3, 3]$; range: $[0, 3]$
67. Domain: all real numbers; range: all real numbers
69. Domain: $(-\infty, 7]$; range: $[0, \infty)$
71. Domain: all real numbers; range: $(-\infty, 3]$
73. 645 m; 0 m   **75.** 0.4 acre; 20.4 acres; 50.6 acres;
416.9 acres; 1033.6 acres   **77.** $g(-2.1) \approx -21.8$;
$g(5.08) \approx -130.4$; $g(10.003) \approx -468.3$
79. Discussion and Writing
81. [1.1] $(0, -7)$, no; $(8, 11)$, yes
82. [1.1] $\left(\frac{4}{5}, -2 \right)$, yes; $\left(\frac{11}{5}, \frac{1}{10} \right)$, yes
83. [1.1]

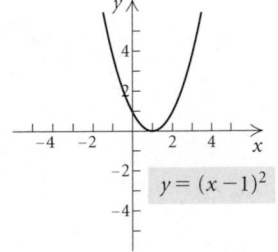

$y = (x - 1)^2$

84. [1.1]

$y = \frac{1}{3}x - 6$

85. [1.1]

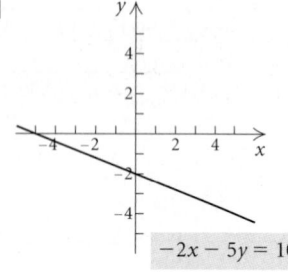

$-2x - 5y = 10$

86. [1.1]

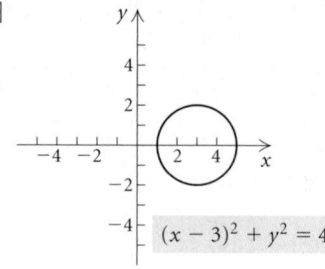

$(x - 3)^2 + y^2 = 4$

87. $f(x) = x, g(x) = x + 1$ **89.**

91. -7 **93.** (a) $f(x) = -2x + 1$; (b) $f(x) = 1$;
(c) $f(x) = 2x - 1$

Exercise Set 1.3

1. (a) Yes; (b) yes; (c) yes   **3.** (a) Yes; (b) no; (c) no
5. $-\frac{3}{5}$ **7.** 0   **9.** $\frac{1}{5}$ **11.** $-\frac{5}{3}$ **13.** 0.3   **15.** 0
17. $-\frac{6}{5}$ **19.** $-\frac{1}{3}$ **21.** Not defined   **23.** -2 **25.** 5
27. $; m = -\frac{1}{2}$

$f(x) = -\frac{1}{2}x + 3$

29. $; m = \frac{3}{2}$

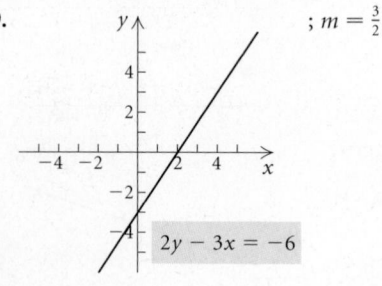

$2y - 3x = -6$

31. $; m = -\frac{5}{2}$

$5x + 2y = 10$

33. $; m = 0$

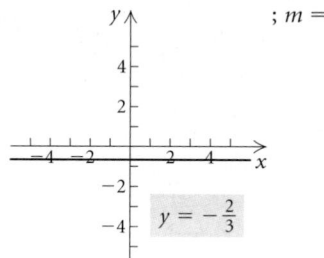

$y = -\frac{2}{3}$

35. 1.3   **37.** Not defined   **39.** $-\frac{1}{10}$ **41.** The average
rate of change over the 5-yr period was 0.04 billion, or
40 million, visits per year.   **43.** The average rate of change in
attendance for the 29 races was 1646 per race.
45. The average rate of change over the 10-yr period was
-2.49 per 1000 women per year.
47. $\frac{75}{457}$ mi per minute, or about $\frac{1}{6}$ mi per minute
49. (a) $W(h) = 4h - 130$; (b) 118 lb; (c) $\{h \mid h > 32.5\}$, or
$(32.5, \infty)$ **51.** (a) 115 ft, 75 ft, 135 ft, 179 ft; (b) Below
$-57.5°$, stopping distance is negative; above $32°$, ice doesn't
form.   **53.** (a) $\frac{11}{10}$. For each mile per hour faster that the car
travels, it takes $\frac{11}{10}$ ft longer to stop; (b) 6, 11.5, 22.5, 55.5, 72;
(c) $\{r \mid r > 0\}$, or $(0, \infty)$. If r is allowed to be 0, the function
says that a stopped car has a reaction distance of $\frac{1}{2}$ ft.
55. $C(t) = 60 + 29t$; $C(6) = \$234$
57. $C(x) = 800 + 3x$; $C(75) = \$1025$
59. Left to the student   **61.** Discussion and Writing
62. [1.2] 10   **63.** [1.2] 40   **64.** [1.2] $a^2 + 3a$
65. [1.2] $a^2 + 2ah + h^2 - 3a - 3h$ **67.** $-\dfrac{d}{10c}$ **69.** 0
71. $2a + h$ **73.** False   **75.** False   **77.** $f(x) = x + b$

Visualizing the Graph

1. E   **2.** D   **3.** A   **4.** J   **5.** C   **6.** F
7. H   **8.** G   **9.** B   **10.** I

Exercise Set 1.4

1. $\frac{3}{5}$; $(0, -7)$ **3.** Slope is not defined; there is no y-intercept.
5. $-\frac{1}{2}$; $(0, 5)$ **7.** $-\frac{3}{2}$; $(0, 5)$ **9.** 0; $(0, -6)$
11. $\frac{4}{5}$; $(0, \frac{8}{5})$ **13.** 4; $(0, -2)$; $y = 4x - 2$
15. -1, $(0, 0)$; $y = -x$ **17.** 0, $(0, -3)$; $y = -3$
19. $y = \frac{2}{9}x + 4$ **21.** $y = -4x - 7$ **23.** $y = -4.2x + \frac{3}{4}$
25. $y = \frac{2}{9}x + \frac{19}{3}$ **27.** $y = 3x - 5$ **29.** $y = -\frac{3}{5}x - \frac{17}{5}$

31. $y = -3x + 2$ **33.** $y = -\frac{1}{2}x + \frac{7}{2}$ **35.** $y = \frac{2}{3}x - 6$

37.

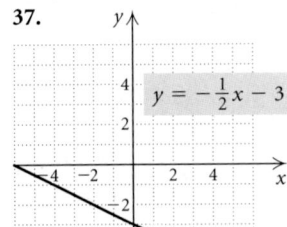

$y = -\frac{1}{2}x - 3$

39.

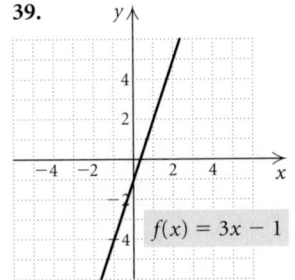

$f(x) = 3x - 1$

41.

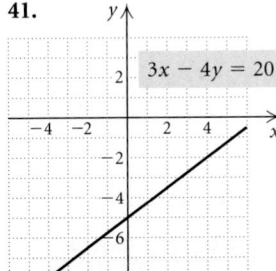

$3x - 4y = 20$

43.

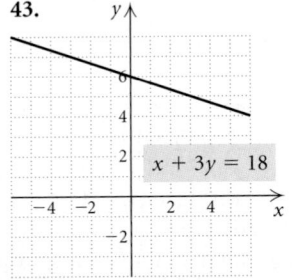

$x + 3y = 18$

45. $h(x) = -3x + 7$ **47.** $f(x) = \frac{2}{5}x - 1$

49. Horizontal: $y = -3$; vertical: $x = 0$

51. Horizontal: $y = -1$; vertical: $x = \frac{2}{11}$ **53.** Perpendicular

55. Neither parallel nor perpendicular   **57.** Parallel

59. Perpendicular   **61.** $y = \frac{2}{7}x + \frac{29}{7}$; $y = -\frac{7}{2}x + \frac{31}{2}$

63. $y = -0.3x - 2.1$; $y = \frac{10}{3}x + \frac{70}{3}$

65. $y = -\frac{3}{4}x + \frac{1}{4}$; $y = \frac{4}{3}x - 6$ **67.** $x = 3$; $y = -3$

69. True   **71.** True   **73.** False   **75.** (a) Using $(0, 96.7)$ and $(6, 121.2)$: $y = 4.08x + 96.7$ (rounding m to the nearest hundredth), or $y = \frac{49}{12}x + \frac{967}{10}$; (b) 2007: about 145,660; 2010: about 157,900   **77.** Using $(1, 47.37)$ and $(4, 50.64)$: $y = 1.09x + 46.28$; 2007: \$53.91; 2009: \$56.09   **79.** Using $(10, 321.10)$ and $(30, 844.60)$: $y = 26.175x + 59.35$; 2005: \$975.48; 2010: \$1106.35; 2020: \$1368.10

81. (a) $M = 0.2H + 156$; (b) 164, 169, 171, 173; (c) $r = 1$; the regression line fits the data perfectly and should be a good predictor.   **83.** (a) $y = 0.02x + 1.77$, where x is the number of years after 1999; (b) 2005: \$1.89 billion; 2010: \$1.99 billion; (c) $r \approx 0.3162$. The line does not fit the data well.

85. (a) $y = 4.055x + 96.78$; (b) about 157,605 twin births; this value is only 295 less than the value found in Exercise 75; (c) $r \approx 0.9980$; the line fits the data well.

87. Discussion and Writing   **88.** [1.3] Not defined

89. [1.3] -1 **90.** [1.1] $x^2 + (y - 3)^2 = 6.25$

91. [1.1] $(x + 7)^2 + (y + 1)^2 = \frac{81}{25}$ **93.** -7.75

Exercise Set 1.5

1. (a) $(-5, 1)$; (b) $(3, 5)$; (c) $(1, 3)$

3. (a) $(-3, -1)$, $(3, 5)$; (b) $(1, 3)$; (c) $(-5, -3)$

5. (a) $(-\infty, -8)$, $(-3, -2)$; (b) $(-8, -6)$;
(c) $(-6, -3)$, $(-2, \infty)$

7. Domain: $[-5, 5]$; range: $[-3, 3]$

9. Domain: $[-5, -1] \cup [1, 5]$; range: $[-4, 6]$

11. Domain: $(-\infty, \infty)$; range: $(-\infty, 3]$

13. Relative maximum: 3.25 at $x = 2.5$; increasing: $(-\infty, 2.5)$; decreasing: $(2.5, \infty)$

15. Relative maximum: 2.370 at $x = -0.667$; relative minimum: 0 at $x = 2$; increasing: $(-\infty, -0.667)$, $(2, \infty)$; decreasing: $(-0.667, 2)$

17. Increasing: $(0, \infty)$; decreasing: $(-\infty, 0)$; relative minimum: 0 at $x = 0$

19. Increasing: $(-\infty, 0)$; decreasing: $(0, \infty)$; relative maximum: 5 at $x = 0$

21. Increasing: $(3, \infty)$; decreasing: $(-\infty, 3)$; relative minimum: 1 at $x = 3$

23. $A(x) = 30x - x^2$ **25.** $d(t) = \sqrt{(120t)^2 + (400)^2}$

27. $A(w) = 10w - \frac{w^2}{2}$ **29.** $d(s) = \frac{14}{s}$

31. (a) $A(x) = x(30 - x)$, or $30x - x^2$; (b) $\{x \mid 0 < x < 30\}$; (c) 15 ft by 15 ft

33. (a) $V(x) = x(12 - 2x)(12 - 2x)$, or $4x(6 - x)^2$; (b) $\{x \mid 0 < x < 6\}$; (c) 8 cm by 8 cm by 2 cm

35. $g(-4) = 0$; $g(0) = 4$; $g(1) = 5$; $g(3) = 5$

37. $h(-8) = 6$; $h(-5) = 1$; $h(0) = 1$; $h(1) = 3$; $h(4) = 6$

39.   **41.**

47.

49.

$f(x) = [\![x]\!]$

51.

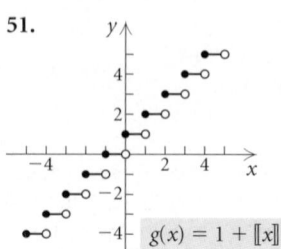

$g(x) = 1 + [\![x]\!]$

53. Domain: $(-\infty, \infty)$; range: $(-\infty, 0) \cup [3, \infty)$
55. Domain: $(-\infty, \infty)$; range: $(-1, \infty)$
57. Domain: $(-\infty, \infty)$; range: $\{y \mid y \le -2 \text{ or } y = -1 \text{ or } y > 2\}$
59. Domain: $(-\infty, \infty)$; range: $\{-5, -2, 4\}$

$$f(x) = \begin{cases} -2, & \text{for } x < 2, \\ -5, & \text{for } x = 2, \\ 4, & \text{for } x > 2 \end{cases}$$

61. Domain: $(-\infty, \infty)$; range: $(-\infty, -1] \cup [2, \infty)$;

$$g(x) = \begin{cases} x, & \text{for } x \le -1, \\ 2, & \text{for } -1 < x < 2, \\ x, & \text{for } x \ge 2 \end{cases}$$

63. Domain: $[-5, 3]$; range: $(-3, 5)$;

$$h(x) = \begin{cases} x + 8, & \text{for } -5 \le x < -3, \\ 3, & \text{for } -3 \le x \le 1, \\ 3x - 6, & \text{for } 1 < x \le 3 \end{cases}$$

65. Increasing: $(1, 3)$; decreasing: $(-\infty, 1)$, $(3, \infty)$; relative maximum: -4 at $x = 3$; relative minimum: -8 at $x = 1$
67. Increasing: $(-1.552, 0)$, $(1.552, \infty)$; decreasing: $(-\infty, -1.552)$, $(0, 1.552)$; relative maximum: 4.07 at $x = 0$;
69. (a) $y = -0.1x^2 + 1.2x + 98.6$ **(b)** 6 days after the illness began; $102.2°F$

71. Increasing: $(-1, 1)$; decreasing: $(-\infty, -1)$, $(1, \infty)$
73. Increasing: $(-1.414, 1.414)$; decreasing: $(-2, -1.414)$, $(1.414, 2)$ **75. (a)** $A(x) = x\sqrt{256 - x^2}$;
(b) $\{x \mid 0 < x < 16\}$;   **(c)** $y = x\sqrt{256 - x^2}$

(d) 11.314 ft by 11.314 ft   **77.** Discussion and Writing
79. [1.2] Function; domain; range; domain; exactly one; range
80. [1.1] Midpoint formula   **81.** [1.1] x-intercept
82. [1.3] Constant; identity
83. $\{x \mid -5 \le x < -4 \text{ or } 5 \le x < 6\}$

85. (a) $h(r) = \dfrac{30 - 5r}{3}$;   **(b)** $V(r) = \pi r^2 \left(\dfrac{30 - 5r}{3} \right)$;
(c) $V(h) = \pi h \left(\dfrac{30 - 3h}{5} \right)^2$

Exercise Set 1.6

1. 33   **3.** -1 **5.** Does not exist   **7.** 0   **9.** 1
11. Does not exist   **13.** 0   **15.** 5
17. (a) Domain of f, g, $f + g$, $f - g$, fg, and ff: $(-\infty, \infty)$;
domain of f/g: $\left(-\infty, \frac{3}{5}\right) \cup \left(\frac{3}{5}, \infty\right)$;
domain of g/f: $\left(-\infty, -\frac{3}{2}\right) \cup \left(-\frac{3}{2}, \infty\right)$;
(b) $(f + g)(x) = -3x + 6$; $(f - g)(x) = 7x$;
$(fg)(x) = -10x^2 - 9x + 9$; $(ff)(x) = 4x^2 + 12x + 9$;
$(f/g)(x) = \dfrac{2x + 3}{3 - 5x}$; $(g/f)(x) = \dfrac{3 - 5x}{2x + 3}$
19. (a) Domain of f: $(-\infty, \infty)$; domain of g: $[-4, \infty)$;
domain of $f + g$, $f - g$, and fg: $[-4, \infty)$;
domain of ff: $(-\infty, \infty)$; domain of f/g: $(-4, \infty)$;
domain of g/f: $[-4, 3) \cup (3, \infty)$;
(b) $(f + g)(x) = x - 3 + \sqrt{x + 4}$;
$(f - g)(x) = x - 3 - \sqrt{x + 4}$; $(fg)(x) = (x - 3)\sqrt{x + 4}$;
$(ff)(x) = x^2 - 6x + 9$; $(f/g)(x) = \dfrac{x - 3}{\sqrt{x + 4}}$;
$(g/f)(x) = \dfrac{\sqrt{x + 4}}{x - 3}$
21. (a) Domain of f, g, $f + g$, $f - g$, fg, and ff: $(-\infty, \infty)$;
domain of f/g: $(-\infty, 0) \cup (0, \infty)$;
domain of g/f: $\left(-\infty, \frac{1}{2}\right) \cup \left(\frac{1}{2}, \infty\right)$
(b) $(f + g)(x) = -2x^2 + 2x - 1$;
$(f - g)(x) = 2x^2 + 2x - 1$; $(fg)(x) = -4x^3 + 2x^2$;
$(ff)(x) = 4x^2 - 4x + 1$; $(f/g)(x) = \dfrac{2x - 1}{-2x^2}$;
$(g/f)(x) = \dfrac{-2x^2}{2x - 1}$
23. (a) Domain of f: $[3, \infty)$; domain of g: $[-3, \infty)$;
domain of $f + g$, $f - g$, fg, and ff: $[3, \infty)$;
domain of f/g: $[3, \infty)$; domain of g/f: $(3, \infty)$;
(b) $(f + g)(x) = \sqrt{x - 3} + \sqrt{x + 3}$;
$(f - g)(x) = \sqrt{x - 3} - \sqrt{x + 3}$; $(fg)(x) = \sqrt{x^2 - 9}$;
$(ff)(x) = |x - 3|$; $(f/g)(x) = \dfrac{\sqrt{x - 3}}{\sqrt{x + 3}}$; $(g/f)(x) = \dfrac{\sqrt{x + 3}}{\sqrt{x - 3}}$
25. (a) Domain of f, g, $f + g$, $f - g$, fg, and ff: $(-\infty, \infty)$;
domain of f/g: $(-\infty, 0) \cup (0, \infty)$;
domain of g/f: $(-\infty, -1) \cup (-1, \infty)$;
(b) $(f + g)(x) = x + 1 + |x|$; $(f - g)(x) = x + 1 - |x|$;
$(fg)(x) = (x + 1)|x|$; $(ff)(x) = x^2 + 2x + 1$;
$(f/g)(x) = \dfrac{x + 1}{|x|}$; $(g/f)(x) = \dfrac{|x|}{x + 1}$
27. (a) Domain of f, g, $f + g$, $f - g$, fg, and ff: $(-\infty, \infty)$;
domain of f/g: $(-\infty, -3) \cup \left(-3, \frac{1}{2}\right) \cup \left(\frac{1}{2}, \infty\right)$;
domain of g/f: $(-\infty, 0) \cup (0, \infty)$;

(b) $(f + g)(x) = x^3 + 2x^2 + 5x - 3$;
$(f - g)(x) = x^3 - 2x^2 - 5x + 3$;
$(fg)(x) = 2x^5 + 5x^4 - 3x^3$; $(ff)(x) = x^6$;
$(f/g)(x) = \dfrac{x^3}{2x^2 + 5x - 3}$; $(g/f)(x) = \dfrac{2x^2 + 5x - 3}{x^3}$
29. (a) Domain of f: $(-\infty, -1) \cup (-1, \infty)$;
domain of g: $(-\infty, 6) \cup (6, \infty)$; domain of $f + g, f - g$, and
fg: $(-\infty, -1) \cup (-1, 6) \cup (6, \infty)$;
domain of ff: $(-\infty, -1) \cup (-1, \infty)$;
domain of f/g and g/f: $(-\infty, -1) \cup (-1, 6) \cup (6, \infty)$;
(b) $(f + g)(x) = \dfrac{4}{x + 1} + \dfrac{1}{6 - x}$;
$(f - g)(x) = \dfrac{4}{x + 1} - \dfrac{1}{6 - x}$; $(fg)(x) = \dfrac{4}{(x + 1)(6 - x)}$;
$(ff)(x) = \dfrac{16}{(x + 1)^2}$; $(f/g)(x) = \dfrac{4(6 - x)}{x + 1}$;
$(g/f)(x) = \dfrac{x + 1}{4(6 - x)}$
31. (a) Domain of f: $(-\infty, 0) \cup (0, \infty)$;
domain of g: $(-\infty, \infty)$; domain of $f + g, f - g, fg$, and ff:
$(-\infty, 0) \cup (0, \infty)$; domain of f/g: $(-\infty, 0) \cup (0, 3) \cup (3, \infty)$;
domain of g/f: $(-\infty, 0) \cup (0, \infty)$;
(b) $(f + g)(x) = \dfrac{1}{x} + x - 3$; $(f - g)(x) = \dfrac{1}{x} - x + 3$;
$(fg)(x) = 1 - \dfrac{3}{x}$; $(ff)(x) = \dfrac{1}{x^2}$; $(f/g)(x) = \dfrac{1}{x(x - 3)}$;
$(g/f)(x) = x(x - 3)$
33. Domain of F: $[2, 11]$; domain of G: $[1, 9]$; domain of
$F + G$: $[2, 9]$ **35.** $[2, 3) \cup (3, 9]$
37.

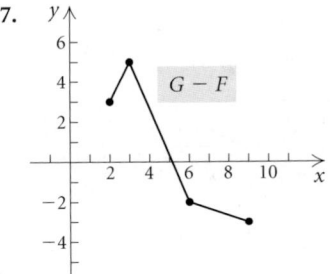

39. Domain of F: $[0, 9]$; domain of G: $[3, 10]$; domain of
$F + G$: $[3, 9]$ **41.** $[3, 6) \cup (6, 8) \cup (8, 9]$
43.

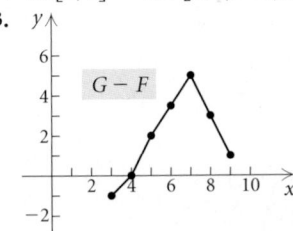

45. (a) $P(x) = -0.4x^2 + 57x - 13$; **(b)** $R(100) = 2000$;
$C(100) = 313$; $P(100) = 1687$ **47.** $-\dfrac{3}{5}$ **49.** $2x + h$
51. 3 **53.** $6x + 3h - 2$ **55.** $\dfrac{5|x + h| - 5|x|}{h}$

57. $3x^2 + 3xh + h^2$ **59.** $\dfrac{7}{(x + h + 3)(x + 3)}$ **61.** -8
63. 64 **65.** 218 **67.** -80
69. $(f \circ g)(x) = (g \circ f)(x) = x$;
domain of $f \circ g$ and $g \circ f$: $(-\infty, \infty)$
71. $(f \circ g)(x) = 3x^2 - 2x$; $(g \circ f)(x) = 3x^2 + 4x$; domain
of $f \circ g$ and $g \circ f$: $(-\infty, \infty)$
73. $(f \circ g)(x) = 16x^2 - 24x + 6$; $(g \circ f)(x) = 4x^2 - 15$;
domain of $f \circ g$ and $g \circ f$: $(-\infty, \infty)$
75. $(f \circ g)(x) = \dfrac{4x}{x - 5}$; $(g \circ f)(x) = \dfrac{1 - 5x}{4}$;
domain of $f \circ g$: $(-\infty, 0) \cup (0, 5) \cup (5, \infty)$;
domain of $g \circ f$: $\left(-\infty, \frac{1}{5}\right) \cup \left(\frac{1}{5}, \infty\right)$
77. $(f \circ g)(x) = (g \circ f)(x) = x$;
domain of $f \circ g$ and $g \circ f$: $(-\infty, \infty)$
79. $(f \circ g)(x) = 2\sqrt{x} + 1$; $(g \circ f)(x) = \sqrt{2x + 1}$;
domain of $f \circ g$: $[0, \infty)$; domain of $g \circ f$: $\left[-\frac{1}{2}, \infty\right)$
81. $(f \circ g)(x) = 20$; $(g \circ f)(x) = 0.05$; domain of $f \circ g$ and
$g \circ f$: $(-\infty, \infty)$
83. $(f \circ g)(x) = |x|$; $(g \circ f)(x) = x$;
domain of $f \circ g$: $(-\infty, \infty)$; domain of $g \circ f$: $[-5, \infty)$
85. $(f \circ g)(x) = 5 - x$; $(g \circ f)(x) = \sqrt{1 - x^2}$;
domain of $f \circ g$: $(-\infty, 3]$; domain of $g \circ f$: $[-1, 1]$
87. $(f \circ g)(x) = (g \circ f)(x) = x$;
domain of $f \circ g$: $(-\infty, -1) \cup (-1, \infty)$;
domain of $g \circ f$: $(-\infty, 0) \cup (0, \infty)$
89. $(f \circ g)(x) = x^3 - 2x^2 - 4x + 6$;
$(g \circ f)(x) = x^3 - 5x^2 + 3x + 8$;
domain of $f \circ g$ and $g \circ f$: $(-\infty, \infty)$
91. $f(x) = x^5$; $g(x) = 4 + 3x$
93. $f(x) = \dfrac{1}{x}$; $g(x) = (x - 2)^4$
95. $f(x) = \dfrac{x - 1}{x + 1}$; $g(x) = x^3$
97. $f(x) = x^6$; $g(x) = \dfrac{2 + x^3}{2 - x^3}$
99. $f(x) = \sqrt{x}$; $g(x) = \dfrac{x - 5}{x + 2}$
101. $f(x) = x^3 - 5x^2 + 3x - 1$; $g(x) = x + 2$
103. $f(x) = x + 1$ **105.** Left to the student
107. Discussion and Writing   **109.** [1.4] (c)
110. [1.4] None   **111.** [1.3] (b), (d), (f), and (h)
112. [1.3] (b)   **113.** [1.4] (a)   **114.** [1.4] (c) and (g)
115. [1.4] (c) and (g)   **116.** [1.4] (a) and (f)
117. $f(x) = 2x + 5$, $g(x) = \dfrac{x - 5}{2}$; answers may vary
119. $(-\infty, -1) \cup (-1, 1) \cup \left(1, \frac{7}{3}\right) \cup \left(\frac{7}{3}, 3\right) \cup (3, \infty)$

Visualizing the Graph

1. C   **2.** B   **3.** A   **4.** E   **5.** G   **6.** D   **7.** H
8. I   **9.** F

A-10 ANSWERS

Exercise Set 1.7

1. x-axis, no; y-axis, yes; origin, no
3. x-axis, yes; y-axis, no; origin, no
5. x-axis, no; y-axis, no; origin, yes
7. x-axis, no; y-axis, yes; origin, no
9. x-axis, no; y-axis, no; origin, no
11. x-axis, no; y-axis, yes; origin, no
13. x-axis, no; y-axis, no; origin, yes
15. x-axis, no; y-axis, no; origin, yes
17. x-axis, yes; y-axis, yes; origin, yes
19. x-axis, no; y-axis, yes; origin, no
21. x-axis, yes; y-axis, yes; origin, yes
23. x-axis, no; y-axis, no; origin, no
25. x-axis, no; y-axis, no; origin, yes
27. x-axis: $(-5, -6)$; y-axis: $(5, 6)$; origin: $(5, -6)$
29. x-axis: $(-10, 7)$; y-axis: $(10, -7)$; origin: $(10, 7)$
31. x-axis: $(0, 4)$; y-axis: $(0, -4)$; origin: $(0, 4)$
33. Even   35. Odd   37. Neither   39. Odd
41. Even   43. Odd   45. Even   47. Even
49. Start with the graph of $f(x) = x^2$. Shift it right 3 units.

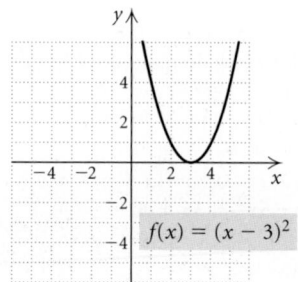

51. Start with the graph of $g(x) = x$. Shift it down 3 units.

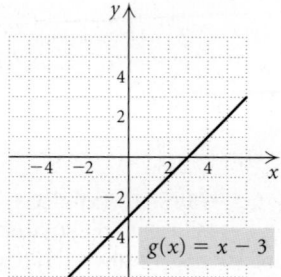

53. Start with the graph of $h(x) = \sqrt{x}$. Reflect it across the x-axis.

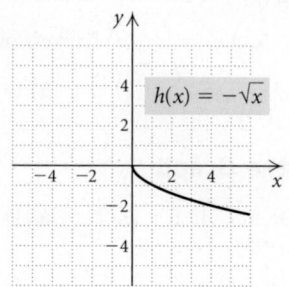

55. Start with the graph of $h(x) = \dfrac{1}{x}$. Shift it up 4 units.

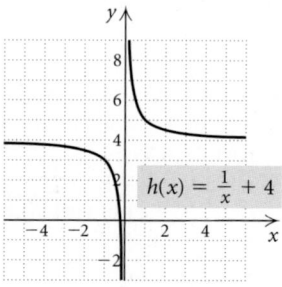

57. Start with the graph of $h(x) = x$. Stretch it vertically by multiplying each y-coordinate by 3. Then reflect it across the x-axis and shift it up 3 units.

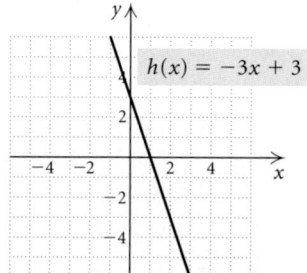

59. Start with the graph of $h(x) = |x|$. Shrink it vertically by multiplying each y-coordinate by $\frac{1}{2}$. Then shift it down 2 units.

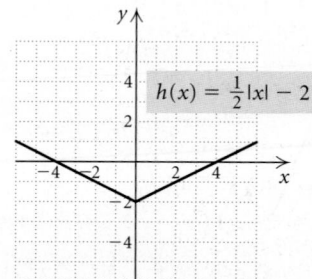

61. Start with the graph of $g(x) = x^3$. Shift it right 2 units. Then reflect it across the x-axis.

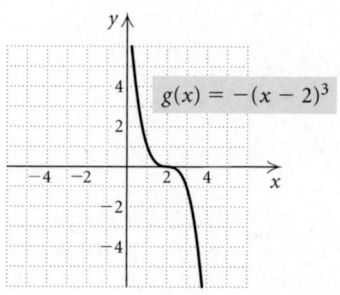

63. Start with the graph of $g(x) = x^2$. Shift it left 1 unit. Then shift it down 1 unit.

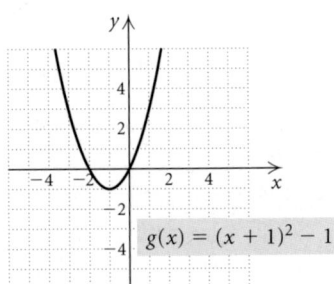

$g(x) = (x + 1)^2 - 1$

65. Start with the graph of $g(x) = x^3$. Shrink it vertically by multiplying each y-coordinate by $\frac{1}{3}$. Then shift it up 2 units.

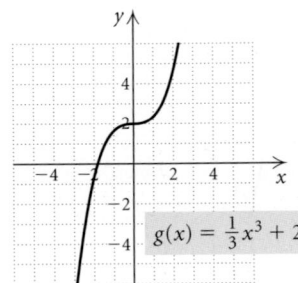

$g(x) = \frac{1}{3}x^3 + 2$

67. Start with the graph of $f(x) = \sqrt{x}$. Shift it left 2 units.

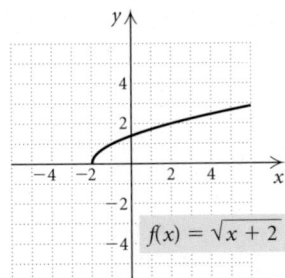

$f(x) = \sqrt{x + 2}$

69. Start with the graph of $f(x) = \sqrt[3]{x}$. Shift it down 2 units.

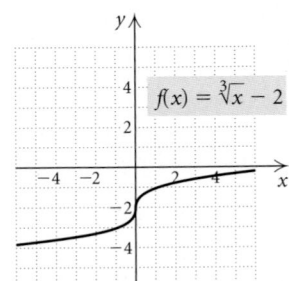

$f(x) = \sqrt[3]{x} - 2$

71. Start with the graph of $f(x) = |x|$. Shrink it horizontally by multiplying each x-coordinate by $\frac{1}{3}$ (or dividing each x-coordinate by 3).

73. Start with the graph of $h(x) = \dfrac{1}{x}$. Stretch it vertically by multiplying each y-coordinate by 2.

75. Start with the graph of $g(x) = \sqrt{x}$. Stretch it vertically by multiplying each y-coordinate by 3. Then shift it down 5 units.

77. Start with the graph of $f(x) = |x|$. Stretch it horizontally by multiplying each x-coordinate by 3. Then shift it down 4 units.

79. Start with the graph of $g(x) = x^2$. Shift it right 5 units, shrink it vertically by multiplying each y-coordinate by $\frac{1}{4}$, and reflect it across the x-axis.

81. Start with the graph of $g(x) = 1/x$. Shift it left 3 units, then up 2 units.

83. Start with the graph of $h(x) = x^2$. Shift it right 3 units. Then reflect it across the x-axis and shift it up 5 units.

85. $(-12, 2)$ **87.** $(12, 4)$ **89.** $(-12, 2)$ **91.** $(-12, 16)$

93. B   **95.** A   **97.** $f(x) = -(x - 8)^2$

99. $f(x) = |x + 7| + 2$ **101.** $f(x) = \dfrac{1}{2x} - 3$

103. $f(x) = -(x - 3)^2 + 4$ **105.** $f(x) = \sqrt{-(x + 2)} - 1$

107.

$g(x) = -2f(x)$

109.

$g(x) = f\left(-\frac{1}{2}x\right)$

111.

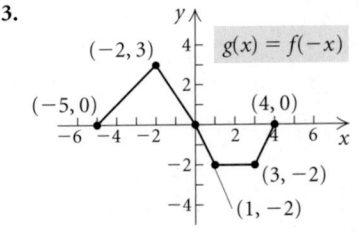

$g(x) = -\frac{1}{2}f(x - 1) + 3$

113.

$g(x) = f(-x)$

115.

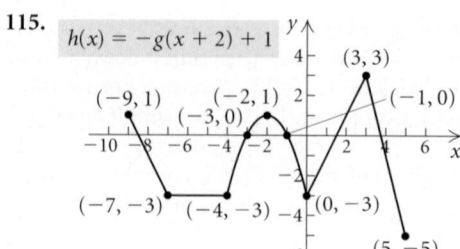

$h(x) = -g(x + 2) + 1$

117.

$h(x) = g(2x)$

119. (f)   **121.** (f)   **123.** (d)   **125.** (c)
127. $f(-x) = 2(-x)^4 - 35(-x)^3 + 3(-x) - 5 =$
$2x^4 + 35x^3 - 3x - 5 = g(x)$
129. $g(x) = x^3 - 3x^2 + 2$
131. $k(x) = (x + 1)^3 - 3(x + 1)^2$
133. Discussion and Writing   **135.** [1.2] **(a)** 38; **(b)** 38;
(c) $5a^2 - 7$; **(d)** $5a^2 - 7$ **136.** [1.2] **(a)** 22; **(b)** -22;
(c) $4a^3 - 5a$; **(d)** $-4a^3 + 5a$ **137.** [1.3] $y = -\frac{1}{8}x + \frac{7}{8}$
138. [1.3] Slope is $\frac{2}{9}$; y-intercept is $\left(0, \frac{1}{9}\right)$.
139.   **141.**

$|f(x)|$ $g(|x|)$

143. Odd   **145.** x-axis, yes; y-axis, no; origin, no
147. x-axis, yes; y-axis, no; origin, no   **149.** 5   **151.** True
153. $E(-x) = \dfrac{f(-x) + f(-(-x))}{2} = \dfrac{f(-x) + f(x)}{2} = E(x)$

155. (a) $E(x) + O(x) = \dfrac{f(x) + f(-x)}{2} + \dfrac{f(x) - f(-x)}{2} =$
$\dfrac{2f(x)}{2} = f(x)$; **(b)** $f(x) = \dfrac{-22x^2 + \sqrt{x} + \sqrt{-x} - 20}{2} +$
$\dfrac{8x^3 + \sqrt{x} - \sqrt{-x}}{2}$

Review Exercises: Chapter 1

1. False   **2.** True   **3.** True   **4.** False   **5.** True
6. False   **7.** Yes; no   **8.** Yes; no
9.   **10.**

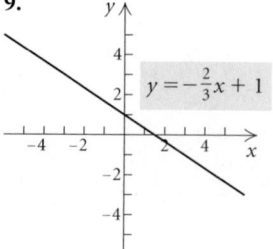

$y = -\frac{2}{3}x + 1$

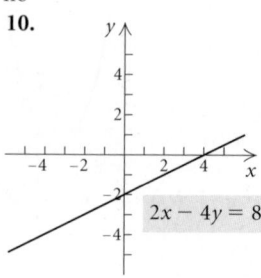

$2x - 4y = 8$

11.

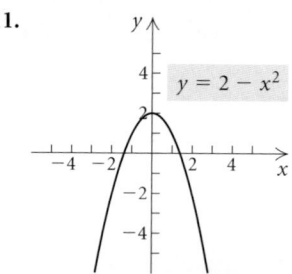

$y = 2 - x^2$

12. $\sqrt{34} \approx 5.831$ **13.** $\left(\frac{1}{2}, \frac{11}{2}\right)$
14. $(x + 2)^2 + (y - 6)^2 = 13$
15. Center: $(-1, 3)$; radius: 4
16. Center: $(3, -5)$; radius: 1
17. $(x - 2)^2 + (y - 4)^2 = 26$
18. Not a function; domain: $\{3, 5, 7\}$; range: $\{1, 3, 5, 7\}$
19. Function; domain: $\{-2, 0, 1, 2, 7\}$;
range: $\{-7, -4, -2, 2, 7\}$ **20.** No   **21.** Yes   **22.** No
23. Yes   **24.** $f(2) = -1; f(-4) = -3; f(0) = -1$
25. All real numbers   **26.** $\{x \mid x \neq 0\}$
27. $\{x \mid x \neq 5 \text{ and } x \neq 1\}$ **28.** $\{x \mid x \neq -4 \text{ and } x \neq 4\}$
29. Domain: $[-4, 4]$; range: $[0, 4]$
30. Domain: $(-\infty, \infty)$; range: $[0, \infty)$
31. Domain: $(-\infty, \infty)$; range: $(-\infty, \infty)$
32. Domain: $(-\infty, \infty)$; range: $[0, \infty)$
33. (a) -3; **(b)** 9; **(c)** $a^2 - 3a - 1$; **(d)** $2x + h - 1$
34. (a) Yes; **(b)** no; **(c)** no, strictly speaking, but data might
be modeled by a linear regression function.
35. (a) Yes; **(b)** yes; **(c)** yes   **36.** $\frac{5}{3}$ **37.** 0
38. Not defined   **39.** $m = -2$; y-intercept: $(0, -7)$
40. The average rate of change over the 10-yr period was
37,500 travelers per year.
41.

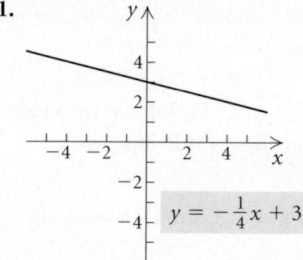

$y = -\frac{1}{4}x + 3$

42. $y = -\frac{2}{3}x - 4$ **43.** $y = 3x + 5$
44. $y = \frac{1}{3}x - \frac{1}{3}$ **45.** Parallel
46. Neither   **47.** Perpendicular
48. $y = -\frac{2}{3}x - \frac{1}{3}$ **49.** $y = \frac{3}{2}x - \frac{5}{2}$
50. $C(t) = 25 + 20t$; \$145
51. (a) 70°C, 220°C, 10,020°C; (b) $[0, 5600]$
52. Using $(3, 524)$ and $(6, 440)$: $y = -28x + 608$; 2009: 216

53.

54.

55.

56.

$f(x) = [\![x]\!]$

57.
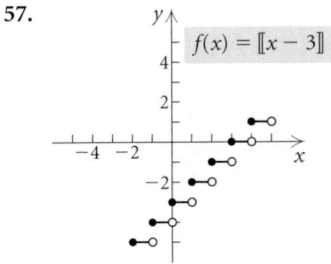

$f(x) = [\![x - 3]\!]$

58. $f(-1) = 1$; $f(5) = 2$; $f(-2) = 2$; $f(-3) = -27$
59. $A(x) = 2x\sqrt{4 - x^2}$
60. (a) $A(x) = x^2 + \dfrac{432}{x}$; (b) $(0, \infty)$;
(c) $x = 6$ in.; height $= 3$ in.
61. -33 **62.** 0   **63.** Does not exist
64. (a) Domain of f, $\{x \mid x \neq 0\}$; domain of g, all real numbers;
domain of $f + g$, $f - g$, and fg, $\{x \mid x \neq 0\}$;

domain of f/g, $\left\{ x \mid x \neq 0 \text{ and } x \neq \dfrac{3}{2} \right\}$;

(b) $(f + g)(x) = \dfrac{4}{x^2} + 3 - 2x$; $(f - g)(x) = \dfrac{4}{x^2} - 3 + 2x$;

$(fg)(x) = \dfrac{12}{x^2} - \dfrac{8}{x}$; $(f/g)(x) = \dfrac{4}{x^2(3 - 2x)}$

65. (a) Domain of f, g, $f + g$, $f - g$, and fg, all real

numbers; domain of f/g, $\left\{ x \mid x \neq \dfrac{1}{2} \right\}$;

(b) $(f + g)(x) = 3x^2 + 6x - 1$; $(f - g)(x) = 3x^2 + 2x + 1$;

$(fg)(x) = 6x^3 + 5x^2 - 4x$; $(f/g)(x) = \dfrac{3x^2 + 4x}{2x - 1}$

66. $P(x) = -0.5x^2 + 105x - 6$ **67.** $-2x - h$
68. (a) Domain of $f \circ g$, $\{x \mid x \neq \frac{3}{2}\}$; domain of $g \circ f$,

$\{x \mid x \neq 0\}$; (b) $(f \circ g)(x) = \dfrac{4}{(3 - 2x)^2}$; $(g \circ f)(x) = 3 - \dfrac{8}{x^2}$

69. (a) Domain of $f \circ g$ and $g \circ f$, all real numbers;
(b) $(f \circ g)(x) = 12x^2 - 4x - 1$; $(g \circ f)(x) = 6x^2 + 8x - 1$
70. $f(x) = \sqrt{x}$, $g(x) = 5x + 2$. Answers may vary.
71. $f(x) = 4x^2 + 9$, $g(x) = 5x - 1$. Answers may vary.
72. x-axis, yes; y-axis, yes; origin, yes
73. x-axis, yes; y-axis, yes; origin, yes
74. x-axis, no; y-axis, no; origin, no
75. x-axis, no; y-axis, yes; origin, no
76. x-axis, no; y-axis, no; origin, yes
77. x-axis, no; y-axis, yes; origin, no
78. Even   **79.** Even   **80.** Odd   **81.** Even   **82.** Even
83. Neither   **84.** Odd   **85.** Even   **86.** Even   **87.** Odd
88. $f(x) = (x + 3)^2$ **89.** $f(x) = -\sqrt{x - 3} + 4$
90. $f(x) = 2|x - 3|$
91.
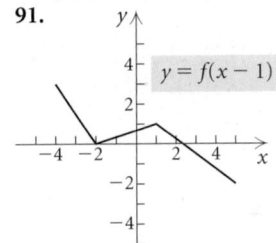

$y = f(x - 1)$

92.

$y = f(2x)$

93.

$y = -2f(x)$

94.
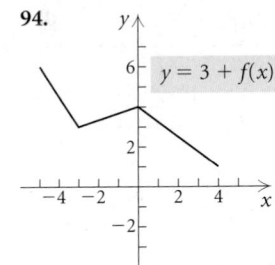

$y = 3 + f(x)$

95. B   **96.** B
97. (a) $y = -21.9x + 588.3$, about 282; (b) $r \approx -0.9903$; the
line fits the data well.
98. Discussion and Writing: (a) $4x^3 - 2x + 9$;
(b) $4x^3 + 24x^2 + 46x + 35$; (c) $4x^3 - 2x + 42$. (a) Adds 2
to each function value; (b) adds 2 to each input before finding
a function value; (c) adds the output for 2 to the output for x
99. Discussion and Writing: In the graph of $y = f(cx)$, the
constant c stretches or shrinks the graph of $y = f(x)$
horizontally. The constant c in $y = cf(x)$ stretches or shrinks
the graph of $y = f(x)$ vertically. For $y = f(cx)$, the
x-coordinates of $y = f(x)$ are divided by c; for $y = cf(x)$, the
y-coordinates of $y = f(x)$ are multiplied by c.

100. Discussion and Writing: **(a)** To draw the graph of y_2 from the graph of y_1, reflect across the x-axis the portions of the graph for which the y-coordinates are negative. **(b)** To draw the graph of y_2 from the graph of y_1, draw the portion of the graph of y_1 to the right of the y-axis; then draw its reflection across the y-axis.
101. $\{x \mid x < 0\}$
102. $\{x \mid x \neq -3 \text{ and } x \neq 0 \text{ and } x \neq 3\}$
103. Let $f(x)$ and $g(x)$ be odd functions. Then by definition, $f(-x) = -f(x)$, or $f(x) = -f(-x)$, and $g(-x) = -g(x)$, or $g(x) = -g(-x)$. Thus, $(f + g)(x) = f(x) + g(x) = -f(-x) + [-g(-x)] = -[f(-x) + g(-x)] = -(f + g)(-x)$ and $f + g$ is odd.
104. Reflect the graph of $y = f(x)$ across the x-axis and then across the y-axis.

Test: Chapter 1

1. [1.1]

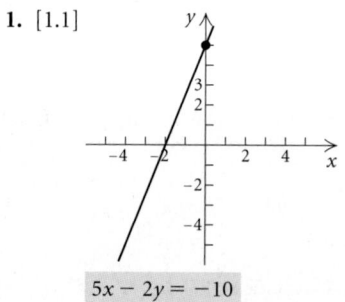

$$5x - 2y = -10$$

2. [1.1] $\sqrt{45} \approx 6.708$

3. [1.1] $\left(-3, \frac{9}{2}\right)$ **4.** [1.1] $(x + 1)^2 + (y - 2)^2 = 5$
5. [1.1] Center: $(-4, 5)$; radius: 6
6. [1.2] **(a)** Yes; **(b)** $\{-4, 3, 1, 0\}$; **(c)** $\{7, 0, 5\}$
7. [1.2] **(a)** 8; **(b)** $2a^2 + 7a + 11$
8. [1.2] **(a)**

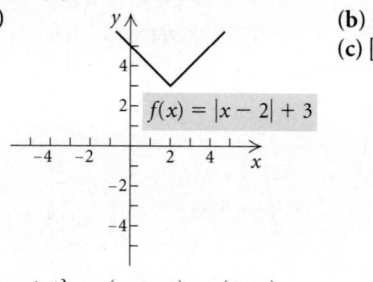

$$f(x) = |x - 2| + 3$$

(b) $(-\infty, \infty)$;
(c) $[3, \infty)$

9. [1.2] $\{x \mid x \neq 4\}$, or $(-\infty, 4) \cup (4, \infty)$
10. [1.2] $(-\infty, \infty)$
11. [1.2] $\{x \mid -5 \leq x \leq 5\}$, or $[-5, 5]$
12. [1.2] **(a)** No; **(b)** yes   **13.** [1.3] Not defined
14. [1.3] $-\frac{11}{6}$ **15.** [1.3] 0
16. [1.3] The average rate of change in weekly attendance from 1995 to 2004 was about 0.167 million, or 167,000, per year.
17. [1.4] Slope: $\frac{3}{2}$; y-intercept: $\left(0, \frac{5}{2}\right)$
18. [1.4] $y = -\frac{5}{8}x - 5$ **19.** [1.4] $y - 4 = -\frac{3}{4}(x - (-5))$, or $y - (-2) = -\frac{3}{4}(x - 3)$, or $y = -\frac{3}{4}x + \frac{1}{4}$
20. [1.4] $y - 3 = -\frac{1}{2}(x + 1)$, or $y = -\frac{1}{2}x + \frac{5}{2}$

21. [1.4] Perpendicular   **22.** [1.4] Using $(4, 5.06)$ and $(24, 12.03)$: $y = 0.3485x + 3.666$; 2010: $16.91
23. [1.5]

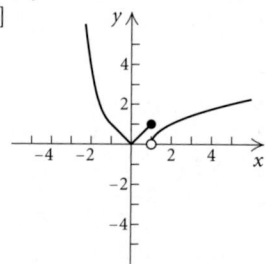

24. [1.5] $f\left(-\frac{7}{8}\right) = \frac{7}{8}$; $f(5) = 2$; $f(-4) = 16$
25. [1.5] $(f - g)(-1) = 6$
26. [1.6] **(a)** $(-\infty, \infty)$; **(b)** $[3, \infty)$; **(c)** $(f - g)(x) = x^2 - \sqrt{x - 3}$; **(d)** $(fg)(x) = x^2\sqrt{x - 3}$; **(e)** $(3, \infty)$
27. [1.6] $f(x) = x^4; g(x) = 2x - 7$ **28.** [1.6] $2x + h$
29. [1.6] $(f \circ g)(x) = \sqrt{x^2 - 4}$; $(g \circ f)(x) = x - 4$
30. [1.6] Domain of $(f \circ g)(x)$: $(-\infty, -2] \cup [2, \infty)$; domain of $(g \circ f)(x) = [5, \infty)$
31. [1.7] x-axis: no; y-axis: yes; origin: no   **32.** [1.7] Odd
33. [1.7] $f(x) = (x - 2)^2 - 1$
34. [1.7] $f(x) = (x + 2)^2 - 3$
35. [1.7]

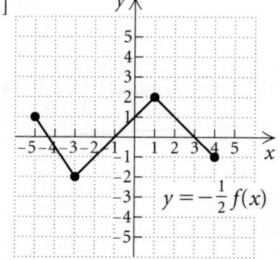

$$y = -\frac{1}{2}f(x)$$

36. [1.7] $(-1, 1)$

CHAPTER 2

Exercise Set 2.1

1. 4   **3.** $-\frac{3}{4}$ **5.** -9 **7.** $\frac{11}{5}$ **9.** 8   **11.** -4 **13.** 6
15. -1 **17.** $\frac{4}{5}$ **19.** $-\frac{3}{2}$ **21.** $-\frac{2}{3}$ **23.** $\frac{1}{2}$
25. About $6.9 billion   **27.** $2966   **29.** 406 GB
31. 2080 calories   **33.** CBS: 11.4 million viewers; ABC: 9.7 million viewers; NBC: 8.0 million viewers
35. $1300   **37.** $9800   **39.** 12 mi   **41.** 26°, 130°, 24°
43. Length: 93 m; width: 68 m   **45.** Length: 100 yd; width: 65 yd   **47.** 67.5 lb   **49.** 3 hr   **51.** 4.5 hr
53. 2.5 hr   **55.** $2400 at 3%; $2600 at 4%
57. Yogurt: 452 mg; cheese: 224 mg   **59.** $420 billion
61. 0.6336 in.   **63.** -5 **65.** 18   **67.** 16   **69.** -12
71. 6   **73.** 20   **75.** 6   **77.** 15   **79.** **(a)** $(4, 0)$; **(b)** 4
81. **(a)** $(-2, 0)$; **(b)** -2 **83.** **(a)** $(-4, 0)$; **(b)** -4
85. $b = \dfrac{2A}{h}$ **87.** $w = \dfrac{P - 2l}{2}$ **89.** $h = \dfrac{2A}{b_1 + b_2}$

91. $\pi = \dfrac{3V}{4r^3}$ **93.** $C = \dfrac{5}{9}(F - 32)$ **95.** $A = \dfrac{C - By}{x}$

97. $h = \dfrac{p - l - 2w}{2}$ **99.** $y = \dfrac{2x - 6}{3}$ **101.** $b = \dfrac{a}{1 + cd}$

103. $x = \dfrac{z}{y - y^2}$ **105.** Left to the student

107. Discussion and Writing   **109.** $[1.4]\ y = -\frac{3}{4}x + \frac{13}{4}$

110. $[1.4]\ y = -\frac{3}{4}x + \frac{1}{4}$

111. $[1.6]$ All real numbers, or $(-\infty, \infty)$

112. $[1.6]\ (-\infty, -2) \cup (-2, \infty)$ **113.** $[1.6]\ -x - 7$

114. $[1.6]\ -9$ **115.** Yes   **117.** No   **119.** $-\frac{2}{3}$

121. No; the 6-oz cup costs about 6.4% more per ounce.

123. 11.25 mi

Exercise Set 2.2

1. $\sqrt{3}i$ **3.** $5i$ **5.** $-\sqrt{33}i$ **7.** $-9i$ **9.** $7\sqrt{2}i$

11. $2 + 11i$ **13.** $5 - 12i$ **15.** $4 + 8i$ **17.** $-4 - 2i$

19. $5 + 9i$ **21.** $5 + 4i$ **23.** $5 + 7i$ **25.** $11 - 5i$

27. $-1 + 5i$ **29.** $2 - 12i$ **31.** $35 + 14i$

33. $6 + 16i$ **35.** $13 - i$ **37.** $-11 + 16i$

39. $-10 + 11i$ **41.** $-31 - 34i$ **43.** $-14 + 23i$

45. 41 **47.** 13 **49.** 74 **51.** $12 + 16i$

53. $-45 - 28i$ **55.** $-8 - 6i$ **57.** $2i$ **59.** $-7 + 24i$

61. $\frac{15}{146} + \frac{33}{146}i$ **63.** $\frac{10}{13} - \frac{15}{13}i$ **65.** $-\frac{14}{13} + \frac{5}{13}i$

67. $\frac{11}{25} - \frac{27}{25}i$ **69.** $\dfrac{-4\sqrt{3} + 10}{41} + \dfrac{5\sqrt{3} + 8}{41}i$

71. $-\frac{1}{2} + \frac{1}{2}i$ **73.** $-\frac{1}{2} - \frac{13}{2}i$ **75.** $-i$ **77.** $-i$

79. 1 **81.** i **83.** 625 **85.** Left to the student

87. Discussion and Writing   **89.** $[1.4]\ y = -2x + 1$

90. $[1.6]$ All real numbers, or $(-\infty, \infty)$

91. $[1.6]\ \left(-\infty, -\frac{5}{3}\right) \cup \left(-\frac{5}{3}, \infty\right)$

92. $[1.6]\ x^2 - 3x - 1$ **93.** $[1.6]\ \frac{8}{11}$

94. $[1.6]\ 2x + h - 3$ **95.** True   **97.** True   **99.** $a^2 + b^2$

Exercise Set 2.3

1. $\frac{2}{3}, \frac{3}{2}$ **3.** $-2, 10$ **5.** $-1, \frac{2}{3}$ **7.** $-\sqrt{3}, \sqrt{3}$

9. $-\sqrt{7}, \sqrt{7}$ **11.** $-\sqrt{2}i, \sqrt{2}i$ **13.** $-\sqrt{17}, \sqrt{17}$

15. $0, 3$ **17.** $-\frac{1}{3}, 0, 2$ **19.** $-1, -\frac{1}{7}, 1$

21. (a) $(-4, 0), (2, 0)$; (b) $-4, 2$

23. (a) $(-1, 0), (3, 0)$; (b) $-1, 3$

25. (a) $(-2, 0), (2, 0)$; (b) $-2, 2$ **27.** $-7, 1$

29. $4 \pm \sqrt{7}$ **31.** $-4 \pm 3i$ **33.** $-2, \frac{1}{3}$ **35.** $-3, 5$

37. $-1, \frac{2}{5}$ **39.** $\dfrac{5 \pm \sqrt{7}}{3}$ **41.** $-\dfrac{1}{2} \pm \dfrac{\sqrt{7}}{2}i$

43. $\dfrac{4 \pm \sqrt{31}}{5}$ **45.** $\dfrac{5}{6} \pm \dfrac{\sqrt{23}}{6}i$ **47.** $4 \pm \sqrt{11}$

49. $\dfrac{-1 \pm \sqrt{61}}{6}$ **51.** $\dfrac{5 \pm \sqrt{17}}{4}$ **53.** $-\dfrac{1}{5} \pm \dfrac{3}{5}i$

55. 144; two real   **57.** -7; two imaginary

59. 49; two real   **61.** $-5, -1$ **63.** $\dfrac{3 \pm \sqrt{21}}{2}$

65. $\dfrac{5 \pm \sqrt{21}}{2}$ **67.** $-1 \pm \sqrt{6}$ **69.** $\dfrac{1}{4} \pm \dfrac{\sqrt{31}}{4}i$

71. $\dfrac{1 \pm \sqrt{13}}{6}$ **73.** $\dfrac{1 \pm \sqrt{6}}{5}$ **75.** $\dfrac{-3 \pm \sqrt{57}}{8}$

77. $\pm 1, \pm\sqrt{2}$ **79.** $\pm\sqrt{2}, \pm\sqrt{5}i$ **81.** $\pm 1, \pm\sqrt{5}i$

83. 16   **85.** $-8, 64$ **87.** 1, 16   **89.** $\frac{5}{2}, 3$

91. $-\frac{3}{2}, -1, \frac{1}{2}, 1$ **93.** About 11.5 sec   **95.** 1985, 2002

97. Length: 4 ft; width: 3 ft   **99.** 4 and 9; -9 and -4

101. 2 cm   **103.** Length: 8 ft; width: 6 ft   **105.** Linear

107. Quadratic   **109.** Linear   **111.** 2, 6   **113.** 0.143, 6

115. $-0.151, 1.651$ **117.** $-0.637, 3.137$

119. $-1.535, 0.869$ **121.** $-0.347, 1.181$

123. Discussion and Writing

125. $[1.2]$ 551,453 associate's degrees

126. $[1.2]$ 660,605 associate's degrees

127. $[1.7]$ x-axis: yes; y-axis: yes; origin: yes

128. $[1.7]$ x-axis: no; y-axis: yes; origin: no

129. $[1.7]$ Odd   **130.** $[1.7]$ Neither   **131.** (a) 2; (b) $\frac{11}{2}$

133. (a) 2; (b) $1 - i$ **135.** 1   **137.** $-\sqrt{7}, -\frac{3}{2}, 0, \frac{1}{3}, \sqrt{7}$

139. $\dfrac{-1 \pm \sqrt{1 + 4\sqrt{2}}}{2}$ **141.** $3 \pm \sqrt{5}$ **143.** 19

145. $-2 \pm \sqrt{2}, \dfrac{1}{2} \pm \dfrac{\sqrt{7}}{2}i$ **147.** $t = \dfrac{-v_0 \pm \sqrt{v_0^2 - 2ax_0}}{a}$

Visualizing the Graph

1. C   **2.** B   **3.** A   **4.** J   **5.** F   **6.** D   **7.** I

8. G   **9.** H   **10.** E

Exercise Set 2.4

1. (a) $\left(-\frac{1}{2}, -\frac{9}{4}\right)$; (b) $x = -\frac{1}{2}$; (c) minimum: $-\frac{9}{4}$

3. (a) $(4, -4)$; (b) $x = 4$; (c) minimum: -4;

(d)

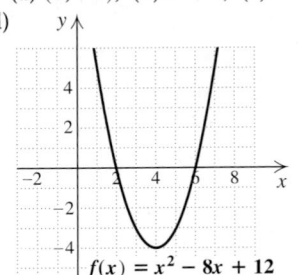

$f(x) = x^2 - 8x + 12$

5. (a) $\left(\frac{7}{2}, -\frac{1}{4}\right)$; (b) $x = \frac{7}{2}$; (c) minimum: $-\frac{1}{4}$;

(d)

$f(x) = x^2 - 7x + 12$

7. (a) $(-2, 1)$; **(b)** $x = -2$; **(c)** minimum: 1;
(d)

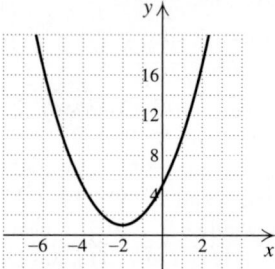

$f(x) = x^2 + 4x + 5$

9. (a) $(-4, -2)$; **(b)** $x = -4$; **(c)** minimum: -2;
(d)

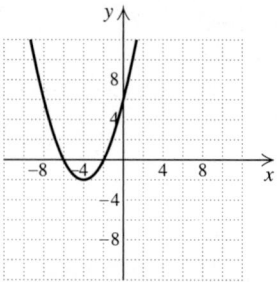

$g(x) = \dfrac{x^2}{2} + 4x + 6$

11. (a) $\left(-\frac{3}{2}, \frac{7}{2}\right)$; **(b)** $x = -\frac{3}{2}$; **(c)** minimum: $\frac{7}{2}$;
(d)

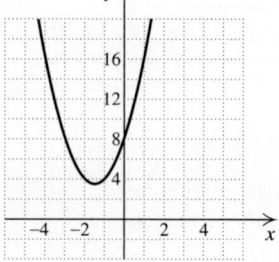

$g(x) = 2x^2 + 6x + 8$

13. (a) $(-3, 12)$; **(b)** $x = -3$; **(c)** maximum: 12;
(d)

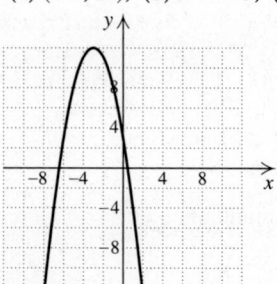

$f(x) = -x^2 - 6x + 3$

15. (a) $\left(\frac{1}{2}, \frac{3}{2}\right)$; **(b)** $x = \frac{1}{2}$; **(c)** maximum: $\frac{3}{2}$;
(d)

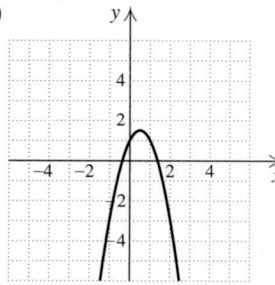

$g(x) = -2x^2 + 2x + 1$

17. (f)   **19. (b)**   **21. (h)**   **23. (c)**
25. (a) $(3, -4)$; **(b)** minimum: -4; **(c)** $[-4, \infty)$;
(d) increasing: $(3, \infty)$; decreasing: $(-\infty, 3)$
27. (a) $(-1, -18)$; **(b)** minimum: -18; **(c)** $[-18, \infty)$;
(d) increasing: $(-1, \infty)$; decreasing: $(-\infty, -1)$
29. (a) $\left(5, \frac{9}{2}\right)$; **(b)** maximum: $\frac{9}{2}$; **(c)** $\left(-\infty, \frac{9}{2}\right]$;
(d) increasing: $(-\infty, 5)$; decreasing: $(5, \infty)$
31. (a) $(-1, 2)$; **(b)** minimum: 2; **(c)** $[2, \infty)$;
(d) increasing: $(-1, \infty)$; decreasing: $(-\infty, -1)$
33. (a) $\left(-\frac{3}{2}, 18\right)$; **(b)** maximum: 18; **(c)** $\left(-\infty, 18\right]$;
(d) increasing: $\left(-\infty, -\frac{3}{2}\right)$; decreasing: $\left(-\frac{3}{2}, \infty\right)$
35. 0.625 sec; 12.25 ft   **37.** 3.75 sec; 305 ft   **39.** 4.5 in.
41. Base: 10 cm; height: 10 cm   **43.** 350 bicycles
45. $797; 40   **47.** 350.6 ft   **49.** 4800 yd^2
51. Left to the student   **53.** Left to the student
55. Discussion and Writing   **57.** Discussion and Writing
58. [1.6] 3   **59.** [1.6] $4x + 2h - 1$
60. [1.7]

61. [1.7]   **63.** -236.25

$g(x) = -2f(x)$

65.

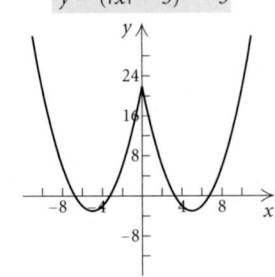

Exercise Set 2.5

1. $\frac{20}{9}$ **3.** 286   **5.** 6   **7.** 6   **9.** 2, 3   **11.** $-1, 6$
13. $\frac{1}{2}, 5$ **15.** 7   **17.** No solution   **19.** $-\frac{69}{14}$ **21.** $-\frac{37}{18}$
23. 2   **25.** No solution
27. $\{x \mid x \text{ is a real number } and \ x \neq 0 \ and \ x \neq 6\}$
29. $\frac{5}{3}$ **31.** $\frac{9}{2}$ **33.** 3   **35.** -4 **37.** -5
39. $\pm\sqrt{2}$ **41.** No solution   **43.** 6   **45.** -1 **47.** $\frac{35}{2}$
49. -98 **51.** -6 **53.** 5   **55.** 7   **57.** 2   **59.** $-1, 2$
61. 7   **63.** 7   **65.** No solution   **67.** 1   **69.** 3, 7
71. 5   **73.** -1 **75.** -8 **77.** 81   **79.** $-7, 7$
81. No solution   **83.** $-3, 5$ **85.** $-\frac{1}{3}, \frac{1}{3}$ **87.** 0
89. $-1, -\frac{1}{3}$ **91.** $-24, 44$ **93.** $-2, 4$ **95.** $-13, 7$
97. $-\frac{4}{3}, \frac{2}{3}$ **99.** $-\frac{3}{4}, \frac{9}{4}$ **101.** $-13, 1$
103. $T_1 = \dfrac{P_1 V_1 T_2}{P_2 V_2}$ **105.** $R_2 = \dfrac{RR_1}{R_1 - R}$ **107.** $p = \dfrac{Fm}{m - F}$
109. Left to the student   **111.** Discussion and Writing
112. [2.1] 3   **113.** [2.1] 7.5
114. [2.1] Mall of America: 96 acres; Disneyland: 85 acres
115. [2.1] 26.25 million prescriptions
117. $3 \pm 2\sqrt{2}$ **119.** -1

Exercise Set 2.6

1. $\{x \mid x > 3\}$, or $(3, \infty)$;

3. $\{x \mid x \geq -\frac{5}{12}\}$, or $\left[-\frac{5}{12}, \infty\right)$;

5. $\{y \mid y \geq \frac{22}{13}\}$, or $\left[\frac{22}{13}, \infty\right)$;

7. $\{x \mid x \leq \frac{15}{34}\}$, or $\left(-\infty, \frac{15}{34}\right]$;

9. $\{x \mid x < 1\}$, or $(-\infty, 1)$;

11. $[-3, 3)$;

13. $[8, 10]$;

15. $[-7, -1]$;

17. $\left(-\frac{3}{2}, 2\right)$;

19. $(1, 5]$;

21. $\left(-\frac{11}{3}, \frac{13}{3}\right)$;

23. $(-\infty, -2] \cup (1, \infty)$;

25. $\left(-\infty, -\frac{7}{2}\right] \cup \left[\frac{1}{2}, \infty\right)$;

27. $(-\infty, 9.6) \cup (10.4, \infty)$;

29. $\left(-\infty, -\frac{57}{4}\right] \cup \left[-\frac{55}{4}, \infty\right)$;

31. $(-7, 7)$;

33. $(-\infty, -4.5] \cup [4.5, \infty)$;

35. $(-17, 1)$;

37. $(-\infty, -17] \cup [1, \infty)$;

39. $\left(-\frac{1}{4}, \frac{3}{4}\right)$;

41. $\left(-\frac{1}{3}, \frac{1}{3}\right)$;

43. $[-6, 3]$;

45. $(-\infty, 4.9) \cup (5.1, \infty)$;

47. $\left[-\frac{1}{2}, \frac{7}{2}\right]$;

49. $\left[-\frac{7}{3}, 1\right]$;

51. $(-\infty, -8) \cup (7, \infty)$;

53. No solution   **55.** More than 4 yr after 2002
57. Less than 4 hr   **59.** $5000   **61.** More than 20 checks
63. Sales greater than $18,000   **65.** Left to the student
67. Discussion and Writing   **69.** [1.1] y-intercept
70. [1.1] Distance formula   **71.** [1.2] Relation
72. [1.2] Function   **73.** [1.3] Horizontal lines
74. [1.4] Parallel   **75.** [1.5] Decreasing
76. [1.7] Symmetric with respect to the y-axis
77. $\left(-\frac{1}{4}, \frac{5}{9}\right]$ **79.** $\left(-\infty, \frac{1}{2}\right)$ **81.** No solution
83. $\left(-\infty, -\frac{8}{3}\right) \cup (-2, \infty)$

Review Exercises: Chapter 2

1. False   **2.** True   **3.** True   **4.** True   **5.** False
6. False   **7.** $\frac{3}{2}$ **8.** -6 **9.** -1 **10.** -21
11. $-\frac{5}{2}, \frac{1}{3}$ **12.** $-5, 1$ **13.** $-2, \frac{4}{3}$ **14.** $-\sqrt{3}, \sqrt{3}$
15. $-\sqrt{10}, \sqrt{10}$ **16.** 3   **17.** 4   **18.** 0.2, or $\frac{1}{5}$

19. 4   **20.** 1   **21.** −5, 3   **22.** $\dfrac{1 \pm \sqrt{41}}{4}$

23. $\dfrac{-1 \pm \sqrt{10}}{3}$ **24.** $\dfrac{27}{7}$ **25.** $-\dfrac{1}{2}, \dfrac{9}{4}$ **26.** 0, 3

27. 5   **28.** 1, 7   **29.** −8, 1

30. $\left[-\dfrac{4}{3}, \dfrac{4}{3}\right]$;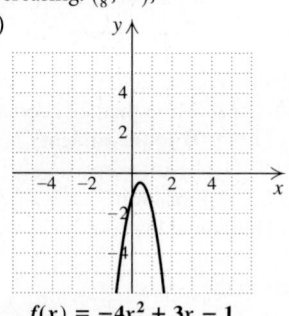

31. $\left(\dfrac{2}{5}, 2\right]$;

32. $(-\infty, \infty)$;

33. $\left(-\infty, -\dfrac{5}{3}\right] \cup [1, \infty)$;

34. $\left(-\dfrac{2}{3}, 1\right)$;

35. $(-\infty, -6] \cup [-2, \infty)$;

36. $h = \dfrac{V}{lw}$ **37.** $s = \dfrac{M - n}{0.3}$ **38.** $h = \dfrac{v^2}{2g}$

39. $t = \dfrac{ab}{a + b}$ **40.** $-2\sqrt{10}i$ **41.** $-4\sqrt{15}$ **42.** $-\dfrac{7}{8}$

43. $-18 - 26i$ **44.** $\dfrac{11}{10} + \dfrac{3}{10}i$ **45.** $1 - 4i$ **46.** $2 - i$

47. $-i$ **48.** 3^{28}

49. $x^2 - 3x + \dfrac{9}{4} = 18 + \dfrac{9}{4}; \left(x - \dfrac{3}{2}\right)^2 = \dfrac{81}{4}; x = \dfrac{3}{2} \pm \dfrac{9}{2}; -3, 6$

50. $x^2 - 4x = 2; x^2 - 4x + 4 = 2 + 4; (x - 2)^2 = 6$;
$x = 2 \pm \sqrt{6}; 2 - \sqrt{6}, 2 + \sqrt{6}$

51. $-4, \dfrac{2}{3}$ **52.** $1 - 3i, 1 + 3i$ **53.** $-2, 5$ **54.** 1

55. $\pm\sqrt{\dfrac{3 \pm \sqrt{5}}{2}}$ **56.** $-\sqrt{3}, 0, \sqrt{3}$ **57.** $-2, -\dfrac{2}{3}, 3$

58. $-5, -2, 2$ **59.** (a) $\left(\dfrac{3}{8}, -\dfrac{7}{16}\right)$; (b) $x = \dfrac{3}{8}$;
(c) maximum: $-\dfrac{7}{16}$; (d) $\left(-\infty, -\dfrac{7}{16}\right]$; (e) increasing: $\left(-\infty, \dfrac{3}{8}\right)$;
decreasing: $\left(\dfrac{3}{8}, \infty\right)$;
(f)

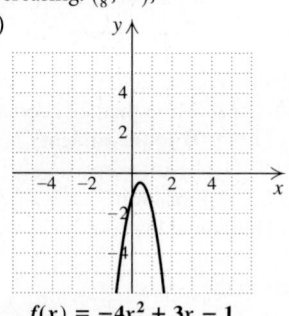

$f(x) = -4x^2 + 3x - 1$

60. (a) $(1, -2)$; (b) $x = 1$; (c) minimum: -2;
(d) $[-2, \infty)$; (e) increasing: $(1, \infty)$; decreasing: $(-\infty, 1)$;

(f)

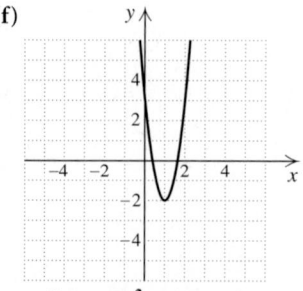

$f(x) = 5x^2 - 10x + 3$

61. (d)   **62.** (c)   **63.** (b)   **64.** (a)   **65.** 30 ft, 40 ft
66. 6 mph   **67.** 80 km/h
68. $35 - 5\sqrt{33}$ ft, or about 6.3 ft   **69.** 6 ft by 6 ft
70. $\dfrac{15 - \sqrt{115}}{2}$ cm, or about 2.1 cm   **71.** Years after 2004
72. Fahrenheit temperatures less than 113°
73. B   **74.** B
75. Left to the student   **76.** Left to the student
77. Left to the student   **78.** Left to the student
79. Discussion and Writing: If an equation contains no
fractions, using the addition principle before using the
multiplication principle eliminates the need to add or
subtract fractions.
80. Discussion and Writing: You can conclude that $|a_1| = |a_2|$
since these constants determine how wide the parabolas are.
Nothing can be concluded about the h's and the k's.
81. 256   **82.** $-7, 9$ **83.** $4 \pm \sqrt[4]{243}$, or 0.052, 7.948
84. -1 **85.** $-\dfrac{1}{4}, 2$ **86.** ± 6 **87.** 9%

Test: Chapter 2

1. [2.1] -1 **2.** [2.1] -5 **3.** [2.1] $\dfrac{21}{11}$ **4.** [2.3] $\dfrac{1}{2}, -5$
5. [2.3] $-\sqrt{6}, \sqrt{6}$ **6.** [2.3] $-2i, 2i$ **7.** [2.3] $-1, 3$
8. [2.3] $\dfrac{5 \pm \sqrt{13}}{2}$ **9.** [2.3] $\dfrac{3}{4} \pm \dfrac{\sqrt{23}}{4}i$
10. [2.5] 16   **11.** [2.5] $-1, \dfrac{13}{6}$ **12.** [2.5] 5
13. [2.5] 5   **14.** [2.5] $-\dfrac{1}{2}, 2$
15. [2.6] $(-5, 3)$;
16. [2.6] $(-\infty, 2] \cup [4, \infty)$;
17. [2.6] $[-7, 1]$;
18. [2.6] $(-\infty, -7) \cup (-3, \infty)$;
19. [2.1] $h = \dfrac{3V}{2\pi r^2}$ **20.** [2.5] $n = \dfrac{R^2}{3p}$
21. [2.3] $x^2 + 4x = 1; x^2 + 4x + 4 = 1 + 4; (x + 2)^2 = 5$;
$x = -2 \pm \sqrt{5}; -2 - \sqrt{5}, -2 + \sqrt{5}$
22. [2.1] Length: 60 m; width: 45 m
23. [2.1], [2.3], [2.5] 3 km/h   **24.** [2.1] $1.80
25. [2.2] $\sqrt{43}i$ **26.** [2.2] $-5i$ **27.** [2.2] $3 - 5i$
28. [2.2] $10 + 5i$ **29.** [2.2] $\dfrac{1}{10} - \dfrac{1}{5}i$ **30.** [2.2] i

31. [2.1] −3   **32.** [2.3] −$\frac{1}{4}$, 3   **33.** [2.3] $\frac{1 \pm \sqrt{57}}{4}$

34. [2.4] **(a)** (1, 9); **(b)** x = 1; **(c)** maximum: 9; **(d)** (−∞, 9];
(e) increasing: (−∞, 1); decreasing: (1, ∞);
(f)

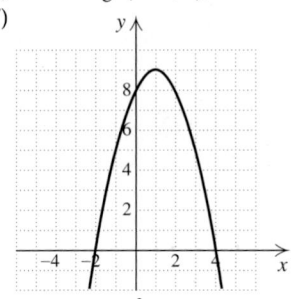

$f(x) = -x^2 + 2x + 8$

35. [2.4] 20 ft by 40 ft   **36.** [2.6] More than 6 hr
37. [2.4], [2.5] −$\frac{4}{9}$

CHAPTER 3

Exercise Set 3.1

1. $\frac{1}{2}x^3$; $\frac{1}{2}$; 3; cubic   **3.** 0.9x; 0.9; 1; linear
5. $305x^4$; 305; 4; quartic   **7.** x^4; 1; 4; quartic
9. $4x^3$; 4; 3; cubic   **11.** (d)   **13.** (b)   **15.** (c)   **17.** (a)
19. (c)   **21.** (d)   **23.** Yes; no; no   **25.** No; yes; yes
27. −3, multiplicity 2; 1, multiplicity 1
29. 4, multiplicity 3; −6, multiplicity 1
31. ±3i, each has multiplicity 3
33. 0, multiplicity 3; 1, multiplicity 2; −4, multiplicity 1
35. 3, multiplicity 2; −4, multiplicity 3; 0, multiplicity 4
37. ±$\sqrt{3}$, ±1, each has multiplicity 1
39. −3, −1, 1, each has multiplicity 1
41. ±2, $\frac{1}{2}$, each has multiplicity 1   **43.** False   **45.** True
47. 19,368,000 cows; 11,337,000 cows
49. About 23.2 million trees; about 27.4 million trees
51. $3240   **53.** $699; $686; $859   **55.** **(a)** $4\frac{1}{2}$%; **(b)** 10%
57. −1.532, −0.347, 1.879   **59.** −1.414, 0, 1.414
61. −1, 0, 1   **63.** −10.153, −1.871, −0.821, −0.303, 0.098,
0.535, 1.219, 3.297   **65.** Relative maximum: 1.506 at
x = −0.632, relative minimum: 0.494 at x = 0.632; (−∞, ∞)
67. Relative minimum: −3.8 at x = 0, no relative maxima;
[−3.8, ∞)   **69.** Relative maximum: 11.012 at x = 1.258,
relative minimum: −8.183 at x = −1.116; (−∞, ∞)
71. (b)   **73.** (c)   **75.** (a)
77. **(a)** Cubic: y = 0.000053215724x³ − 0.0059922487x² +
0.0288132843x + 14.25265259;
quartic: y = −0.0000007674506x⁴ + 0.0002128619x³ −
0.0163703506x² + 0.2450880151x + 13.59031965;
(b) quartic: 13.4%; answers may vary
79. **(a)** Cubic: y = −1.590909091x³ + 27.21678322x² −
113.3951049x + 421.3426573;
quartic: y = −0.2966200466x⁴ + 4.341491841x³ −
9.860722611x² − 39.24009324x + 399.986014;

(b) cubic: 231,000
81. Discussion and Writing   **83.** [1.1] 5   **84.** [1.1] $6\sqrt{2}$
85. [1.1] Center: (3, −5); radius 7
86. [1.1] Center: (−4, 3); radius $2\sqrt{2}$
87. [2.6] {y|y ≥ 3}, or [3, ∞)   **88.** [2.6] {x|x > $\frac{5}{3}$}, or ($\frac{5}{3}$, ∞)
89. [2.6] {x|x ≤ −13 or x ≥ 1}, or (−∞, −13] ∪ [1, ∞)
90. [2.6] {x|−$\frac{11}{12}$ ≤ x ≤ $\frac{5}{12}$}, or [−$\frac{11}{12}$, $\frac{5}{12}$]   **91.** 7%

Visualizing the Graph

1. H   **2.** D   **3.** J   **4.** B   **5.** A   **6.** C   **7.** I
8. E   **9.** G   **10.** F

Exercise Set 3.2

1. **(a)** 5; **(b)** 5; **(c)** 4   **3.** **(a)** 10; **(b)** 10; **(c)** 9
5. **(a)** 3; **(b)** 3; **(c)** 2   **7.** (d)   **9.** (f)   **11.** (b)
13.

15.

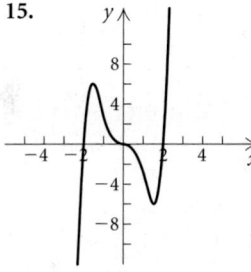

$h(x) = x^5 - 4x^3$

17.

$h(x) = x(x - 4)(x + 1)(x - 2)$

19.

$g(x) = -x^4 - 2x^3$

21.

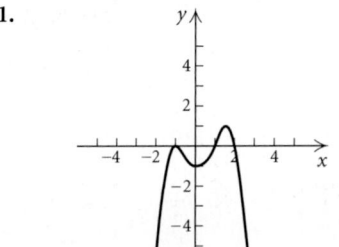

$f(x) = -\frac{1}{2}(x - 2)(x + 1)^2(x - 1)$

23.

$g(x) = -x(x - 1)^2(x + 4)^2$

25.

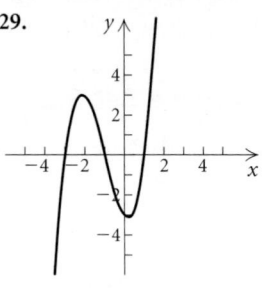

$f(x) = (x - 2)^2(x + 1)^4$

27.

$g(x) = -(x - 1)^4$

29.

$h(x) = x^3 + 3x^2 - x - 3$

31.

$f(x) = 6x^3 - 8x^2 - 54x + 72$

7. $P(x) = (x + 9)(x^2 - 3x + 2) + 0$
9. $P(x) = (x + 2)(x^3 - 2x^2 + 2x - 4) + 11$
11. $Q(x) = 2x^3 + x^2 - 3x + 10, R(x) = -42$
13. $Q(x) = x^2 - 4x + 8, R(x) = -24$
15. $Q(x) = 3x^2 - 4x + 8, R(x) = -18$
17. $Q(x) = x^4 + 3x^3 + 10x^2 + 30x + 89, R(x) = 267$
19. $Q(x) = x^3 + x^2 + x + 1, R(x) = 0$
21. $Q(x) = 2x^3 + x^2 + \frac{7}{2}x + \frac{7}{4}, R(x) = -\frac{1}{8}$
23. $0; -60; 0$ **25.** $10; 80; 998$ **27.** $5,935,988; -772$
29. $0; 0; 65; 1 - 12\sqrt{2}$ **31.** Yes; no   **33.** Yes; yes
35. No; yes   **37.** No; no
39. $f(x) = (x - 1)(x + 2)(x + 3); 1, -2, -3$
41. $f(x) = (x - 2)(x - 5)(x + 1); 2, 5, -1$
43. $f(x) = (x - 2)(x - 3)(x + 4); 2, 3, -4$
45. $f(x) = (x - 3)^3(x + 2); 3, -2$
47. $f(x) = (x - 1)(x - 2)(x - 3)(x + 5); 1, 2, 3, -5$

49.

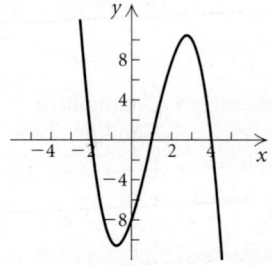

$f(x) = x^4 - x^3 - 7x^2 + x + 6$

51.

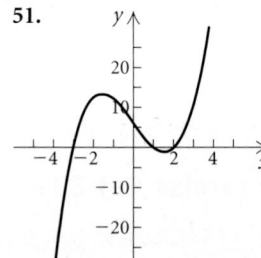

$f(x) = x^3 - 7x + 6$

53.

$f(x) = -x^3 + 3x^2 + 6x - 8$

55. Left to the student

33. $f(-5) = -18$ and $f(-4) = 7$. By the intermediate value theorem, since $f(-5)$ and $f(-4)$ have opposite signs, then $f(x)$ has a zero between -5 and -4.   **35.** $f(-3) = 22$ and $f(-2) = 5$. Both $f(-3)$ and $f(-2)$ are positive. We cannot use the intermediate value theorem to determine if there is a zero between -3 and -2.   **37.** $f(2) = 2$ and $f(3) = 57$. Both $f(2)$ and $f(3)$ are positive. We cannot use the intermediate value theorem to determine if there is a zero between 2 and 3.   **39.** $f(4) = -12$ and $f(5) = 4$. By the intermediate value theorem, since $f(4)$ and $f(5)$ have opposite signs, then $f(x)$ has a zero between 4 and 5.
41. Discussion and Writing   **43.** [1.1] (d)   **44.** [1.3] (f)
45. [1.1] (e)   **46.** [1.1] (a)   **47.** [1.1] (b)   **48.** [1.3] (c)
49. [2.1] $\frac{9}{10}$ **50.** [3.1] $-3, 0, 4$ **51.** [2.3] $-\frac{5}{3}, \frac{11}{2}$
52. [2.1] $\frac{196}{25}$

57. Discussion and Writing   **58.** [2.1] -5
59. [2.3] $\frac{5}{4} \pm \frac{\sqrt{71}}{4}i$ **60.** [2.3] $-1, \frac{3}{7}$ **61.** [2.3] $-5, 0$
62. [1.2] 10   **63.** [2.3] $-3, -2$
64. [1.4] $f(x) = \frac{56}{15}x + 27.2$; \$68.3 billion, \$86.9 billion, \$105.6 billion   **65.** [2.4] $b = 15$ in., $h = 15$ in.
67. (a) $x + 4, x + 3, x - 2, x - 5$;
(b) $P(x) = (x + 4)(x + 3)(x - 2)(x - 5)$; (c) yes; two examples are $f(x) = c \cdot P(x)$ for any nonzero constant c; and $g(x) = (x - a)P(x)$; (d) no   **69.** $\frac{14}{3}$ **71.** $-1 \pm \sqrt{7}$
73. Answers can vary. One possibility is $P(x) = x^{15} - x^{14}$.
75. $x - 3 + i, R\, 6 - 3i$

Exercise Set 3.3

1. (a) No; (b) yes; (c) no   **3.** (a) Yes; (b) no; (c) yes
5. $P(x) = (x + 2)(x^2 - 2x + 4) - 16$

Exercise Set 3.4

1. $f(x) = x^3 - 6x^2 - x + 30$
3. $f(x) = x^3 + 3x^2 + 4x + 12$
5. $f(x) = x^3 - 3x^2 - 2x + 6$ **7.** $f(x) = x^3 - 6x - 4$
9. $f(x) = x^3 + 2x^2 + 29x + 148$
11. $f(x) = x^3 - \frac{5}{3}x^2 - \frac{2}{3}x$
13. $f(x) = x^5 + 2x^4 - 2x^2 - x$
15. $f(x) = x^4 + 3x^3 + 3x^2 + x$ **17.** $-\sqrt{3}$
19. $i, 2 + \sqrt{5}$ **21.** $-3i$ **23.** $-4 + 3i, 2 + \sqrt{3}$
25. $-\sqrt{5}, 4i$ **27.** $2 + i$ **29.** $-3 - 4i, 4 + \sqrt{5}$
31. $4 + i$ **33.** $f(x) = (x - 1 - i)(x - 1 + i)(x - 2)$, or
$x^3 - 4x^2 + 6x - 4$ **35.** $f(x) = (x - 4i)(x + 4i)$, or
$x^2 + 16$ **37.** $f(x) = (x + 4i)(x - 4i)(x - 5)$, or
$x^3 - 5x^2 + 16x - 80$
39. $f(x) = (x - 1 + i)(x - 1 - i)(x + \sqrt{5})(x - \sqrt{5})$, or
$x^4 - 2x^3 - 3x^2 + 10x - 10$
41. $f(x) = (x - \sqrt{5})(x + \sqrt{5})(x + 3i)(x - 3i)$, or
$x^4 + 4x^2 - 45$ **43.** $-\sqrt{2}, \sqrt{2}$ **45.** $i, 2, 3$
47. $1 + 2i, 1 - 2i$ **49.** ± 1 **51.** $\pm 1, \pm\frac{1}{2}, \pm 2, \pm 4, \pm 8$
53. $\pm 1, \pm 2, \pm\frac{1}{3}, \pm\frac{1}{5}, \pm\frac{2}{3}, \pm\frac{2}{5}, \pm\frac{1}{15}, \pm\frac{2}{15}$
55. (a) Rational: -3; other: $\pm\sqrt{2}$;
(b) $f(x) = (x + 3)(x + \sqrt{2})(x - \sqrt{2})$
57. (a) Rational: $-2, 1$; other: none;
(b) $f(x) = (x + 2)(x - 1)^2$
59. (a) Rational: -1; other: $3 \pm 2\sqrt{2}i$;
(b) $f(x) = (x + 1)(x - 3 - 2\sqrt{2}i)(x - 3 + 2\sqrt{2}i)$
61. (a) Rational: $-\frac{1}{5}, 1$; other: $\pm 2i$;
(b) $f(x) = (5x + 1)(x - 1)(x + 2i)(x - 2i)$
63. (a) Rational: $-2, -1$; other: $3 \pm \sqrt{13}$;
(b) $f(x) = (x + 2)(x + 1)(x - 3 - \sqrt{13})(x - 3 + \sqrt{13})$
65. (a) Rational: 2; other: $1 \pm \sqrt{3}$;
(b) $f(x) = (x - 2)(x - 1 - \sqrt{3})(x - 1 + \sqrt{3})$
67. (a) Rational: -2; other: $1 \pm \sqrt{3}i$;
(b) $f(x) = (x + 2)(x - 1 - \sqrt{3}i)(x - 1 + \sqrt{3}i)$
69. (a) Rational: $\dfrac{1}{2}$; other: $\dfrac{1 \pm \sqrt{5}}{2}$;
(b) $f(x) = \dfrac{1}{3}\left(x - \dfrac{1}{2}\right)\left(x - \dfrac{1 + \sqrt{5}}{2}\right)\left(x - \dfrac{1 - \sqrt{5}}{2}\right)$
71. $1, -3$ **73.** No rational zeros   **75.** No rational zeros
77. $-2, 1, 2$ **79.** 3 or 1; 0   **81.** 0; 3 or 1
83. 2 or 0; 2 or 0   **85.** 1; 1   **87.** 1; 0   **89.** 2 or 0; 2 or 0
91. 3 or 1; 1   **93.** 1; 1
95.

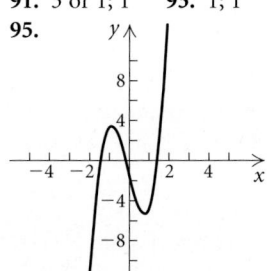

$f(x) = 4x^3 + x^2 - 8x - 2$

97.

$f(x) = 2x^4 - 3x^3 - 2x^2 + 3x$

99. Left to the student   **101.** Discussion and Writing
102. [2.4] (a) $(1, -4)$; (b) $x = 1$; (c) minimum: -4 at $x = 1$
103. [2.4] (a) $(4, -6)$; (b) $x = 4$; (c) minimum: -6 at $x = 4$
104. [2.3] $-3, 11$ **105.** [2.1] 10
106. [2.4] Quadratic; $-x^2$; -1; 2; as $x \to \infty$, $f(x) \to -\infty$, and
as $x \to -\infty$, $f(x) \to -\infty$
107. [3.1] Cubic; $-x^3$; -1; 3; as $x \to \infty$, $g(x) \to -\infty$, and as
$x \to -\infty$, $g(x) \to \infty$
108. [1.3] Linear; x; 1; 1; as $x \to \infty$, $h(x) \to \infty$, and as
$x \to -\infty$, $h(x) \to -\infty$
109. [1.3] Constant; $-\frac{4}{9}$; $-\frac{4}{9}$; zero degree; for all x, $f(x) = -\frac{4}{9}$
110. [3.1] Cubic; x^3; 1; 3; as $x \to \infty$, $h(x) \to \infty$, and as
$x \to -\infty$, $h(x) \to -\infty$
111. [3.1] Quartic; x^4; 1; 4; as $x \to \infty$, $g(x) \to \infty$, and as
$x \to -\infty$, $g(x) \to \infty$
113. $Q(x) = x^3 + x^2y + xy^2 + y^3$, $R(x) = 0$
115. (a) $-1, \frac{1}{2}, 3$; (b) $0, \frac{3}{2}, 4$; (c) $-3, -\frac{3}{2}, 1$; (d) $-\frac{1}{2}, \frac{1}{4}, \frac{3}{2}$
117. $-8, -\frac{3}{2}, 4, 7, 15$

Visualizing the Graph

1. A   **2.** C   **3.** D   **4.** H   **5.** G   **6.** F   **7.** B
8. I   **9.** J   **10.** E

Exercise Set 3.5

1. (d); $x = 2$, $x = -2$, $y = 0$ **3.** (e); $x = 2$, $x = -2$, $y = 0$
5. (c); $x = 2$, $x = -2$, $y = 8x$ **7.** $x = 0$ **9.** $x = 2$
11. $x = 4$, $x = -6$ **13.** $x = \frac{3}{2}$, $x = -1$ **15.** $y = \frac{3}{4}$
17. $y = 0$ **19.** No horizontal asymptote   **21.** $y = x + 1$
23. $y = x$ **25.** $y = x - 3$
27. Domain: $(-\infty, 0) \cup (0, \infty)$; no x-intercepts,
no y-intercepts;

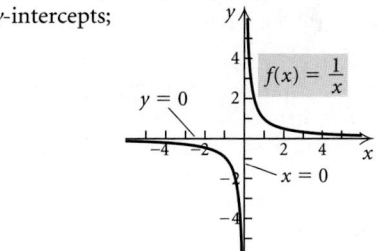

29. Domain: $(-\infty, 0) \cup (0, \infty)$; no x-intercepts,
no y-intercepts;

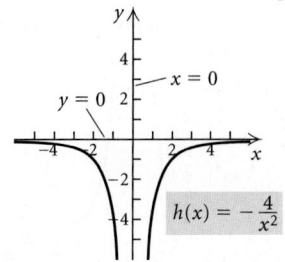

31. Domain: $(-\infty, -1) \cup (-1, \infty)$; x-intercepts: $(1, 0)$ and $(3, 0)$, y-intercept: $(0, 3)$;

$$g(x) = \frac{x^2 - 4x + 3}{x + 1}$$

33. Domain: $(-\infty, -3) \cup (-3, \infty)$; no x-intercepts, y-intercept: $\left(0, \frac{1}{3}\right)$;

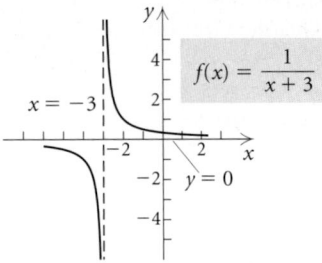

$$f(x) = \frac{1}{x + 3}$$

35. Domain: $(-\infty, 5) \cup (5, \infty)$; no x-intercepts, y-intercept: $\left(0, \frac{2}{5}\right)$;

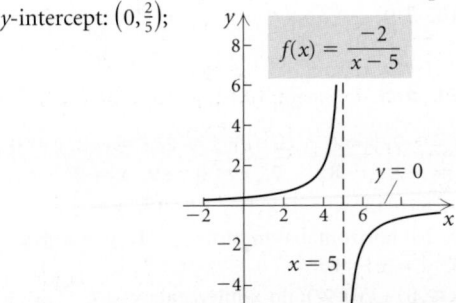

$$f(x) = \frac{-2}{x - 5}$$

37. Domain: $(-\infty, 0) \cup (0, \infty)$; x-intercept: $\left(-\frac{1}{2}, 0\right)$, no y-intercept;

$$f(x) = \frac{2x + 1}{x}$$

39. Domain: $(-\infty, 2) \cup (2, \infty)$; no x-intercepts, y-intercept: $\left(0, \frac{1}{4}\right)$;

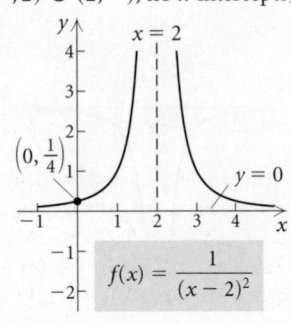

$$f(x) = \frac{1}{(x - 2)^2}$$

41. Domain: $(-\infty, 0) \cup (0, \infty)$; no x-intercepts, no y-intercept;

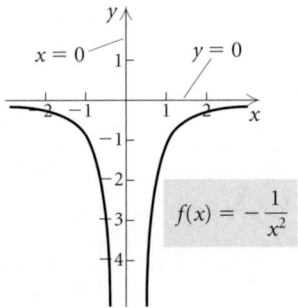

$$f(x) = -\frac{1}{x^2}$$

43. Domain: $(-\infty, \infty)$; no x-intercepts, y-intercept: $\left(0, \frac{1}{3}\right)$;

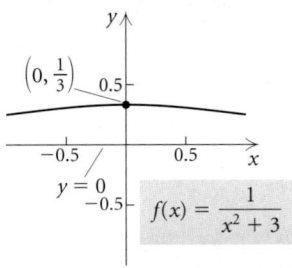

$$f(x) = \frac{1}{x^2 + 3}$$

45. Domain: $(-\infty, 2) \cup (2, \infty)$; x-intercept: $(-2, 0)$, y-intercept: $(0, 2)$;

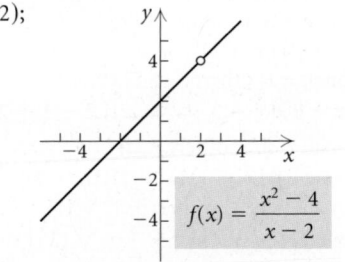

$$f(x) = \frac{x^2 - 4}{x - 2}$$

47. Domain: $(-\infty, -2) \cup (-2, \infty)$; x-intercept: $(1, 0)$, y-intercept: $\left(0, -\frac{1}{2}\right)$;

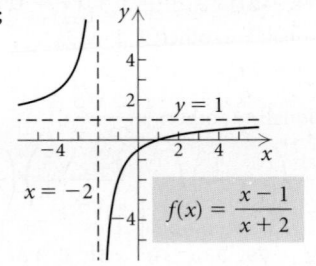

$$f(x) = \frac{x - 1}{x + 2}$$

49. Domain: $\left(-\infty, -\frac{1}{2}\right) \cup \left(-\frac{1}{2}, 3\right) \cup (3, \infty)$; x-intercept: $(-3, 0)$, y-intercept: $(0, -1)$;

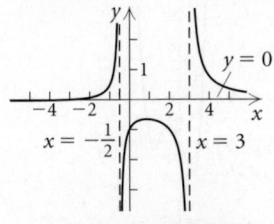

$$f(x) = \frac{x + 3}{2x^2 - 5x - 3}$$

51. Domain: $(-\infty, -1) \cup (-1, \infty)$; x-intercepts: $(-3, 0)$ and $(3, 0)$, y-intercept: $(0, -9)$;

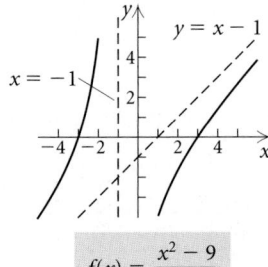

$$f(x) = \frac{x^2 - 9}{x + 1}$$

53. Domain: $(-\infty, \infty)$; x-intercepts: $(-2, 0)$ and $(1, 0)$, y-intercept: $(0, -2)$;

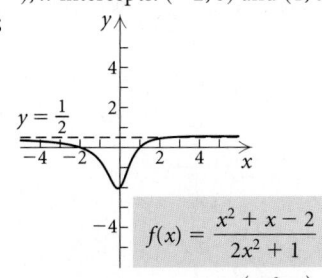

$$f(x) = \frac{x^2 + x - 2}{2x^2 + 1}$$

55. Domain: $(-\infty, 1) \cup (1, \infty)$; x-intercept: $\left(-\frac{2}{3}, 0\right)$, y-intercept: $(0, 2)$;

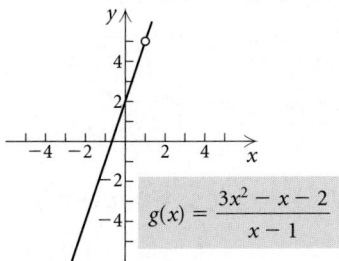

$$g(x) = \frac{3x^2 - x - 2}{x - 1}$$

57. Domain: $(-\infty, -1) \cup (-1, 3) \cup (3, \infty)$; x-intercept: $(1, 0)$, y-intercept: $\left(0, \frac{1}{3}\right)$;

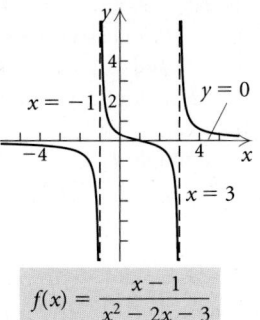

$$f(x) = \frac{x - 1}{x^2 - 2x - 3}$$

59. Domain: $(-\infty, -1) \cup (-1, \infty)$; x-intercept: $(3, 0)$, y-intercept: $(0, -3)$;

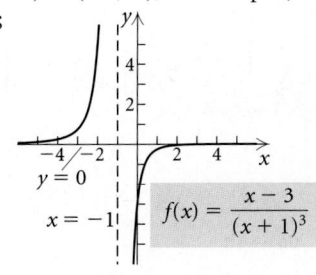

$$f(x) = \frac{x - 3}{(x + 1)^3}$$

61. Domain: $(-\infty, 0) \cup (0, \infty)$; x-intercept: $(-1, 0)$, no y-intercept;

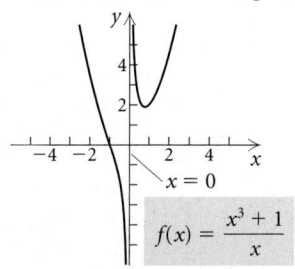

$$f(x) = \frac{x^3 + 1}{x}$$

63. Domain: $(-\infty, -2) \cup (-2, 7) \cup (7, \infty)$; x-intercepts: $(-5, 0)$, $(0, 0)$, and $(3, 0)$, y-intercept: $(0, 0)$;

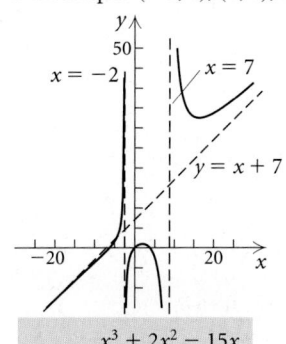

$$f(x) = \frac{x^3 + 2x^2 - 15x}{x^2 - 5x - 14}$$

65. Domain: $(-\infty, \infty)$; x-intercept: $(0, 0)$, y-intercept: $(0, 0)$;

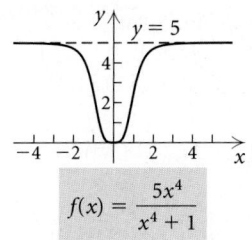

$$f(x) = \frac{5x^4}{x^4 + 1}$$

67. Domain: $(-\infty, -1) \cup (-1, 2) \cup (2, \infty)$; x-intercept: $(0, 0)$, y-intercept: $(0, 0)$;

$$f(x) = \frac{x^2}{x^2 - x - 2}$$

69. $f(x) = \dfrac{1}{x^2 - x - 20}$ **71.** $f(x) = \dfrac{3x^2 + 12x + 12}{2x^2 - 2x - 40}$

73. (a) $N(t) \to 0.16$ as $t \to \infty$; (b) The medication never completely disappears from the body; a trace amount remains.
75. (a) $P(0) = 0$; $P(1) = 45,455$; $P(3) = 55,556$; $P(8) = 29,197$; (b) $P(t) \to 0$ as $t \to \infty$; (c) In time, no one lives in Lordsburg.   **77.** 58,926 at $t \approx 2.12$ months

79. Discussion and Writing   **81.** [1.3] Slope
82. [1.4] Slope–intercept equation
83. [1.4] Point–slope equation
84. [1.2] Domain; range; domain; range
85. [1.7] $f(-x) = -f(x)$ **86.** [1.1] x-intercept
87. [1.1] Midpoint formula   **88.** [1.3] Vertical lines
89. $y = x^3 + 4$ **91.** $x = -3$

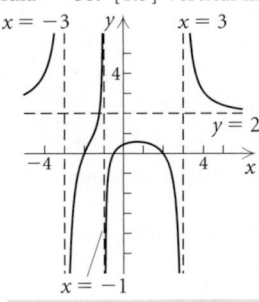

$$f(x) = \frac{2x^3 + x^2 - 8x - 4}{x^3 + x^2 - 9x - 9}$$

93. $(-\infty, -3) \cup (7, \infty)$

Exercise Set 3.6

1. $\{-5, 3\}$ **3.** $[-5, 3]$ **5.** $(-\infty, -5] \cup [3, \infty)$
7. $(-\infty, -3) \cup (0, 3)$ **9.** $(-3, 0) \cup (3, \infty)$
11. $(-\infty, -5) \cup (-3, 2)$ **13.** $(-2, 0] \cup (2, \infty)$
15. $(-4, 1)$ **17.** $(-\infty, -2] \cup [4, \infty)$
19. $(-\infty, -2) \cup (1, \infty)$ **21.** $(-\infty, -5) \cup (5, \infty)$
23. $(-\infty, -2] \cup [2, \infty)$ **25.** $(-\infty, 3) \cup (3, \infty)$
27. $\varnothing$ **29.** $\left(-\infty, -\frac{3}{2}\right] \cup [0, 3]$ **31.** $[-3, -1] \cup [1, \infty)$
33. $(-\infty, -2) \cup (1, 3)$ **35.** $\left[-\sqrt{2}, -1\right] \cup \left[\sqrt{2}, \infty\right)$
37. $(-\infty, -1] \cup \left[\frac{3}{2}, 2\right]$ **39.** $(-\infty, 5]$ **41.** $(-4, \infty)$
43. $\left(-\frac{5}{2}, \infty\right)$ **45.** $\left(-3, -\frac{1}{5}\right] \cup (1, \infty)$
47. $(-\infty, -3) \cup \left[\dfrac{5 - \sqrt{105}}{10}, -\dfrac{1}{3}\right) \cup \left[\dfrac{5 + \sqrt{105}}{10}, \infty\right)$
49. $\left(2, \frac{7}{2}\right]$ **51.** $\left(1 - \sqrt{2}, 0\right) \cup \left(1 + \sqrt{2}, \infty\right)$
53. $(-\infty, -3) \cup (1, 3) \cup \left[\frac{11}{3}, \infty\right)$ **55.** $(-\infty, \infty)$
57. $\left(-3, \dfrac{1 - \sqrt{61}}{6}\right) \cup \left(-\dfrac{1}{2}, 0\right) \cup \left(\dfrac{1 + \sqrt{61}}{6}, \infty\right)$
59. $(-1, 0) \cup \left(\frac{2}{7}, \frac{7}{2}\right)$
61. $\left[-6 - \sqrt{33}, -5\right) \cup \left[-6 + \sqrt{33}, 1\right) \cup (5, \infty)$
63. $(0.408, 2.449)$ **65.** (a) $(10, 200)$; (b) $(0, 10) \cup (200, \infty)$
67. $\{n \mid 9 \leq n \leq 23\}$ **69.** Left to the student
71. Discussion and Writing   **72.** [1.1] $x^2 + (y + 3)^2 = \frac{49}{16}$
73. [1.1] $(x + 2)^2 + (y - 4)^2 = 9$
74. [2.4] (a) $(5, -23)$; (b) minimum: -23 when $x = 5$;
(c) $[-23, \infty)$ **75.** [2.4] (a) $\left(\frac{3}{4}, -\frac{55}{8}\right)$; (b) maximum: $-\frac{55}{8}$
when $x = \frac{3}{4}$; (c) $\left(-\infty, -\frac{55}{8}\right]$ **77.** $(-\infty, \infty)$
79. $\left[-\sqrt{5}, \sqrt{5}\right]$ **81.** $\left[-\frac{3}{2}, \frac{3}{2}\right]$ **83.** $\left(-\infty, -\frac{1}{4}\right) \cup \left(\frac{1}{2}, \infty\right)$
85. $(-4, -2) \cup (-1, 1)$
87. $x^2 + x - 12 < 0$; answers may vary

Exercise Set 3.7

1. 4.5; $y = 4.5x$ **3.** 36; $y = \dfrac{36}{x}$ **5.** 4; $y = 4x$
7. 4; $y = \dfrac{4}{x}$ **9.** $\dfrac{3}{8}$; $y = \dfrac{3}{8}x$ **11.** 0.54; $y = \dfrac{0.54}{x}$
13. 3.5 hr   **15.** 90 g   **17.** About 686 kg   **19.** 40 lb
21. $66\frac{2}{3}$ cm   **23.** 1.92 ft   **25.** $y = \dfrac{0.0015}{x^2}$
27. $y = 15x^2$ **29.** $y = xz$ **31.** $y = \frac{3}{10}xz^2$
33. $y = \dfrac{xz}{5wp}$ **35.** 2.5 m   **37.** 36 mph
39. About 126 earned runs   **41.** Discussion and Writing
43. [1.5]

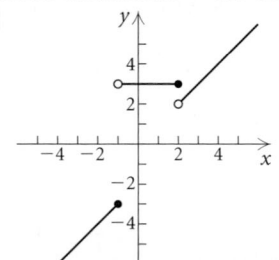

44. [1.7] x-axis, no; y-axis, yes; origin, no
45. [1.7] x-axis, yes; y-axis, no; origin, no
46. [1.7] x-axis, no; y-axis, no; origin, yes
47. $\$2.32$; $\$2.80$ **49.** $\dfrac{\pi}{4}$

Review Exercises: Chapter 3

1. True   **2.** True   **3.** False   **4.** False   **5.** False
6. $0.45x^4$, 0.45, 4, quartic   **7.** -25, -25, 0, constant
8. $-0.5x$, -0.5, 1, linear   **9.** $\frac{1}{3}x^3$, $\frac{1}{3}$, 3, cubic
10. As $x \to \infty$, $f(x) \to -\infty$, and as $x \to -\infty$, $f(x) \to -\infty$.
11. As $x \to \infty$, $f(x) \to \infty$, and as $x \to -\infty$, $f(x) \to -\infty$.
12. $\frac{2}{3}$, multiplicity 1; -2, multiplicity 3; 5, multiplicity 2
13. ± 1, ± 5, each has multiplicity 1
14. ± 3, -4, each has multiplicity 1   **15.** (a) 4%; (b) 5%
16.

$f(x) = -x^4 + 2x^3$

17.

$g(x) = (x - 1)^3(x + 2)^2$

18.

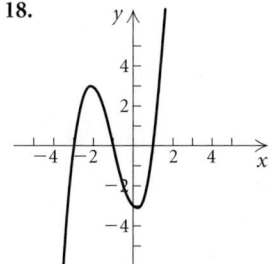

$h(x) = x^3 + 3x^2 - x - 3$

19.

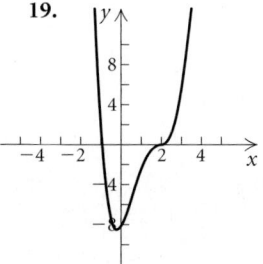

$f(x) = x^4 - 5x^3 + 6x^2 + 4x - 8$

20.

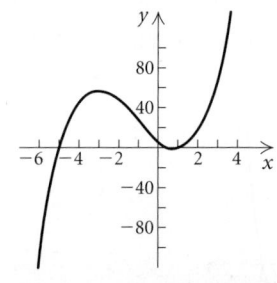

$g(x) = 2x^3 + 7x^2 - 14x + 5$

21. $f(1) = -4$ and $f(2) = 3$. Since $f(1)$ and $f(2)$ have opposite signs, $f(x)$ has a zero between 1 and 2.

22. $f(-1) = -3.5$ and $f(1) = -0.5$. Since $f(-1)$ and $f(1)$ have the same sign, the intermediate value theorem does not allow us to determine whether there is a zero between -1 and 1.

23. $Q(x) = 6x^2 + 16x + 52$, $R(x) = 155$; $P(x) = (x - 3)(6x^2 + 16x + 52) + 155$

24. $Q(x) = x^3 - 3x^2 + 3x - 2$, $R(x) = 7$; $P(x) = (x + 1)(x^3 - 3x^2 + 3x - 2) + 7$

25. $x^2 + 7x + 22$, R 120   **26.** $x^3 + x^2 + x + 1$, R 0

27. $x^4 - x^3 + x^2 - x - 1$, R 1   **28.** 36   **29.** 0

30. $-141{,}220$ **31.** Yes, no   **32.** No, yes   **33.** Yes, no

34. No, yes   **35.** $f(x) = (x - 1)^2(x + 4)$; $-4, 1$

36. $f(x) = (x - 2)(x + 3)^2$; $-3, 2$

37. $f(x) = (x - 2)^2(x - 5)(x + 5)$; $-5, 2, 5$

38. $f(x) = (x - 1)(x + 1)(x - \sqrt{2})(x + \sqrt{2})$; $-\sqrt{2}, -1, 1, \sqrt{2}$ **39.** $f(x) = x^3 + 3x^2 - 6x - 8$

40. $f(x) = x^3 + x^2 - 4x + 6$

41. $f(x) = x^3 - \frac{5}{2}x^2 + \frac{1}{2}$, or $2x^3 - 5x^2 + 1$

42. $f(x) = x^4 + \frac{29}{2}x^3 + \frac{135}{2}x^2 + \frac{175}{2}x - \frac{125}{2}$, or $2x^4 + 29x^3 + 135x^2 + 175x - 125$

43. $f(x) = x^5 + 4x^4 - 3x^3 - 18x^2$ **44.** $-\sqrt{5}, -i$

45. $1 - \sqrt{3}, \sqrt{3}$ **46.** $\sqrt{2}$ **47.** $f(x) = x^2 - 11$

48. $f(x) = x^3 - 6x^2 + x - 6$

49. $f(x) = x^4 - 5x^3 + 4x^2 + 2x - 8$

50. $f(x) = x^4 - x^2 - 20$ **51.** $f(x) = x^3 + \frac{8}{3}x^2 - x$

52. $\pm\frac{1}{4}, \pm\frac{1}{2}, \pm\frac{3}{4}, \pm 1, \pm\frac{3}{2}, \pm 2, \pm 3, \pm 4, \pm 6, \pm 12$

53. $\pm\frac{1}{3}, \pm 1$ **54.** $\pm 1, \pm 2, \pm 3, \pm 4, \pm 6, \pm 8, \pm 12, \pm 24$

55. (a) Rational: $0, -2, \frac{1}{3}, 3$; other: none;
(b) $f(x) = x(3x - 1)(x + 2)^2(x - 3)$

56. (a) Rational: 2; other: $\pm\sqrt{3}$;
(b) $f(x) = (x - 2)(x + \sqrt{3})(x - \sqrt{3})$

57. (a) Rational: $-1, 1$; other: $3 \pm i$;
(b) $f(x) = (x + 1)(x - 1)(x - 3 - i)(x - 3 + i)$

58. (a) Rational: -5; other: $1 \pm \sqrt{2}$;
(b) $f(x) = (x + 5)(x - 1 - \sqrt{2})(x - 1 + \sqrt{2})$

59. (a) Rational: $\frac{2}{3}, 1$; other: none;
(b) $f(x) = (3x - 2)(x - 1)^2$

60. (a) Rational: 2; other: $1 \pm \sqrt{5}$;
(b) $f(x) = (x - 2)^3(x - 1 + \sqrt{5})(x - 1 - \sqrt{5})$

61. (a) Rational: $-4, 0, 3, 4$; other: none;
(b) $f(x) = x^2(x + 4)^2(x - 3)(x - 4)$

62. (a) Rational: $\frac{5}{2}, 1$; other: none;
(b) $f(x) = (2x - 5)(x - 1)^4$

63. 3 or 1; 0   **64.** 4 or 2 or 0; 2 or 0

65. 3 or 1; 0

66. Domain: $(-\infty, -2) \cup (-2, \infty)$;
x-intercepts: $(-\sqrt{5}, 0)$ and $(\sqrt{5}, 0)$, y-intercept: $(0, -\frac{5}{2})$

67. Domain: $(-\infty, 2) \cup (2, \infty)$; x-intercepts: none, y-intercept: $(0, \frac{5}{4})$

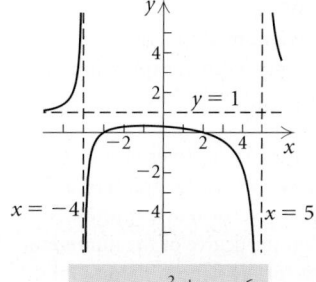

68. Domain: $(-\infty, -4) \cup (-4, 5) \cup (5, \infty)$;
x-intercepts: $(-3, 0)$ and $(2, 0)$, y-intercept: $(0, \frac{3}{10})$

69. Domain: $(-\infty, -3) \cup (-3, 5) \cup (5, \infty)$;
x-intercept: $(2, 0)$, y-intercept: $\left(0, \frac{2}{15}\right)$

$$f(x) = \frac{x - 2}{x^2 - 2x - 15}$$

70. $f(x) = \dfrac{1}{x^2 - x - 6}$ **71.** $f(x) = \dfrac{4x^2 + 12x}{x^2 - x - 6}$

72. (a) $N(t) \to 0.0875$ as $t \to \infty$; (b) The medication never completely disappears from the body; a trace amount remains.
73. $(-3, 3)$ **74.** $\left(-\infty, -\frac{1}{2}\right) \cup (2, \infty)$
75. $[-4, 1] \cup [2, \infty)$ **76.** $\left(-\infty, -\frac{14}{3}\right) \cup (-3, \infty)$
77. (a) $t = 7$; (b) $(2, 3)$ **78.** $\left[\dfrac{5 - \sqrt{15}}{2}, \dfrac{5 + \sqrt{15}}{2}\right]$
79. $y = 4x$ **80.** $y = \dfrac{2500}{x}$ **81.** 20 min   **82.** 500 watts
83. About 78   **84.** $y = \dfrac{48}{x^2}$ **85.** $y = \dfrac{xz^2}{10w}$ **86.** C
87. A   **88.** (a) $-2.637, 1.137$; (b) relative maximum: 7.125 at $x = -0.75$; (c) none; (d) domain: all real numbers; range: $(-\infty, 7.125]$
89. (a) $-3, -1.414, 1.414$; (b) relative maximum: 2.303 at $x = -2.291$; (c) relative minimum: -6.303 at $x = 0.291$; (d) domain: all real numbers; range: all real numbers
90. (a) $0, 1, 2$; (b) relative maximum: 0.202 at $x = 0.610$; (c) relative minima: 0 at $x = 0$, -0.620 at $x = 1.640$; (d) domain: all real numbers; range: $[-0.620, \infty)$
91. (a) Linear: $f(x) = 0.5408695652x - 30.30434783$; quadratic: $f(x) = 0.0030322581x^2 - 0.5764516129x + 57.53225806$; cubic: $f(x) = 0.0000247619x^3 - 0.0112857143x^2 + 2.002380952x - 82.14285714$; (b) the cubic function; (c) 298, 498
92. Discussion and Writing: A polynomial function is a function that can be defined by a polynomial expression. A rational function is a function that can be defined as a quotient of two polynomials.
93. Discussion and Writing: Vertical asymptotes occur at any x-values that make the denominator zero. The graph of a rational function does not cross any vertical asymptotes. Horizontal asymptotes occur when the degree of the numerator is less than or equal to the degree of the denominator. Oblique asymptotes occur when the degree of the numerator is 1 greater than the degree of the denominator. Graphs of rational functions may cross horizontal or oblique asymptotes.

94. $\left(-\infty, -1 - \sqrt{6}\right] \cup \left[-1 + \sqrt{6}, \infty\right)$
95. $\left(-\infty, -\frac{1}{2}\right) \cup \left(\frac{1}{2}, \infty\right)$
96. $\{1 + i, 1 - i, i, -i\}$ **97.** $(-\infty, 2)$
98. $(x - 1)\left(x + \dfrac{1}{2} - \dfrac{\sqrt{3}}{2}i\right)\left(x + \dfrac{1}{2} + \dfrac{\sqrt{3}}{2}i\right)$ **99.** 7
100. -4 **101.** $(-\infty, -5] \cup [2, \infty)$
102. $(-\infty, 1.1] \cup [2, \infty)$ **103.** $\left(-1, \frac{3}{7}\right)$

Test: Chapter 3

1. [3.1] $-x^4, -1, 4$; quartic   **2.** [3.1] $-4.7x, -4.7, 1$; linear
3. [3.1] $0, \frac{5}{3}$, each has multiplicity 1; 3, multiplicity 2; -1, multiplicity 3
4. [3.1] 3388; 5379; 3514
5. [3.2]

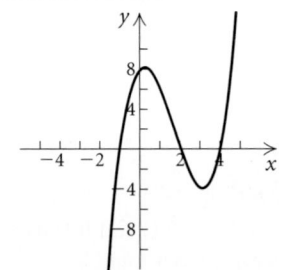

$$f(x) = x^3 - 5x^2 + 2x + 8$$

6. [3.2]

$$f(x) = -2x^4 + x^3 + 11x^2 - 4x - 12$$

7. [3.2] $f(0) = 3$ and $f(2) = -17$. Since $f(0)$ and $f(2)$ have opposite signs, $f(x)$ has a zero between 0 and 2.
8. [3.2] $g(-2) = 5$ and $g(-1) = 1$. Both $g(-2)$ and $g(-1)$ are positive. We cannot use the intermediate value theorem to determine if there is a zero between -2 and -1.
9. [3.3] $Q(x) = x^3 + 4x^2 + 4x + 6$, $R(x) = 1$; $P(x) = (x - 1)(x^3 + 4x^2 + 4x + 6) + 1$
10. [3.3] $3x^2 + 15x + 63$, R 322   **11.** [3.3] -115
12. [3.3] Yes   **13.** [3.3] $f(x) = x^4 - 27x^2 - 54x$
14. [3.4] $-\sqrt{3}, 2 + i$
15. [3.4] $f(x) = x^3 + 10x^2 + 9x + 90$
16. [3.4] $f(x) = x^5 - 2x^4 - x^3 + 6x^2 - 6x$
17. [3.4] $\pm 1, \pm 2, \pm 3, \pm 4, \pm 6, \pm 12, \pm\frac{1}{2}, \pm\frac{3}{2}$
18. [3.4] $\pm\frac{1}{10}, \pm\frac{1}{5}, \pm\frac{1}{2}, \pm 1, \pm\frac{5}{2}, \pm 5$
19. [3.4] (a) Rational: -1; other: $\pm\sqrt{5}$; (b) $f(x) = (x + 1)(x - \sqrt{5})(x + \sqrt{5})$

20. [3.4] (a) Rational: $-\frac{1}{2}$, 1, 2, 3; other: none;
(b) $f(x) = (2x + 1)(x - 1)(x - 2)(x - 3)$
21. [3.4] (a) Rational: -4; other: $\pm 2i$;
(b) $f(x) = (x - 2i)(x + 2i)(x + 4)$
22. [3.4] (a) Rational: $\frac{2}{3}$, 1; other: none;
(b) $f(x) = (x - 1)^3(3x - 2)$
23. [3.4] 2 or 0; 2 or 0
24. [3.5] Domain: $(-\infty, 3) \cup (3, \infty)$; x-intercepts: none,
y-intercept: $\left(0, \frac{2}{9}\right)$;

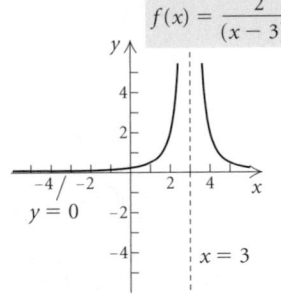

$$f(x) = \frac{2}{(x - 3)^2}$$

25. [3.5] Domain: $(-\infty, -1) \cup (-1, 4) \cup (4, \infty)$;
x-intercept: $(-3, 0)$, y-intercept: $\left(0, -\frac{3}{4}\right)$;

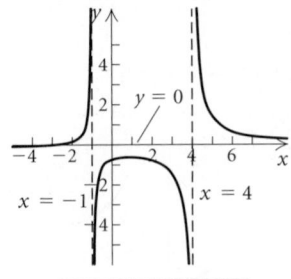

$$f(x) = \frac{x + 3}{x^2 - 3x - 4}$$

26. [3.5] Answers may vary; $f(x) = \dfrac{x + 4}{x^2 - x - 2}$
27. [3.6] $\left(-\infty, -\frac{1}{2}\right) \cup (3, \infty)$ **28.** [3.6] $(-\infty, 4) \cup \left[\frac{13}{2}, \infty\right)$
29. [3.5] (a) 6 sec; (b) $(1, 3)$ **30.** [3.7] $y = \dfrac{30}{x}$
31. [3.7] 50 ft   **32.** [3.7] $y = \dfrac{50xz^2}{w}$
33. [3.1] $(-\infty, -4] \cup [3, \infty)$

CHAPTER 4

Exercise Set 4.1

1. $\{(8, 7), (8, -2), (-4, 3), (-8, 8)\}$ **3.** $\{(-1, -1), (4, -3)\}$
5. $x = 4y - 5$ **7.** $y^3x = -5$ **9.** $y = x^2 - 2x$

11.

13.

15.

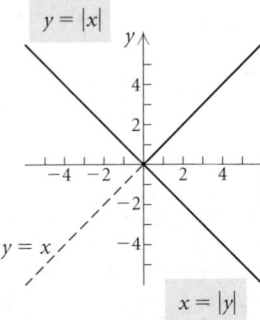

17. Assume $f(a) = f(b)$ for any numbers a and b in the domain of f. Since $f(a) = \frac{1}{3}a - 6$ and $f(b) = \frac{1}{3}b - 6$, we have

$$\frac{1}{3}a - 6 = \frac{1}{3}b - 6$$
$$\frac{1}{3}a = \frac{1}{3}b \qquad \text{Adding 6}$$
$$a = b. \qquad \text{Multiplying by 3}$$

Thus, if $f(a) = f(b)$, then $a = b$ and f is one-to-one.
19. Assume $f(a) = f(b)$ for any numbers a and b in the domain of f. Since $f(a) = a^3 + \frac{1}{2}$ and $f(b) = b^3 + \frac{1}{2}$, we have

$$a^3 + \frac{1}{2} = b^3 + \frac{1}{2}$$
$$a^3 = b^3 \qquad \text{Subtracting } \frac{1}{2}$$
$$a = b. \qquad \text{Taking the cube root}$$

Thus, if $f(a) = f(b)$, then $a = b$ and f is one-to-one.
21. Find two numbers a and b for which $a \neq b$ and $g(a) = g(b)$. Two such numbers are -2 and 2, because $g(-2) = g(2) = -3$. Thus, g is not one-to-one.
23. Find two numbers a and b for which $a \neq b$ and $g(a) = g(b)$. Two such numbers are -1 and 1, because $g(-1) = g(1) = 0$. Thus, g is not one-to-one.
25. Yes   **27.** No   **29.** No   **31.** Yes   **33.** Yes
35. No   **37.** No   **39.** Yes   **41.** No   **43.** No
45. (a) One-to-one; (b) $f^{-1}(x) = x - 4$
47. (a) One-to-one; (b) $f^{-1}(x) = \dfrac{x + 1}{2}$
49. (a) One-to-one; (b) $f^{-1}(x) = \dfrac{4}{x} - 7$
51. (a) One-to-one; (b) $f^{-1}(x) = \dfrac{3x + 4}{x - 1}$
53. (a) One-to-one; (b) $f^{-1}(x) = \sqrt[3]{x + 1}$
55. (a) Not one-to-one; (b) does not have an inverse that is a function

57. (a) One-to-one; **(b)** $f^{-1}(x) = \sqrt{\dfrac{x+2}{5}}$

59. (a) One-to-one; **(b)** $f^{-1}(x) = x^2 - 1, x \geq 0$

61. $\frac{1}{3}x$ **63.** $-x$ **65.** $x^3 + 5$

67.

69.

71.

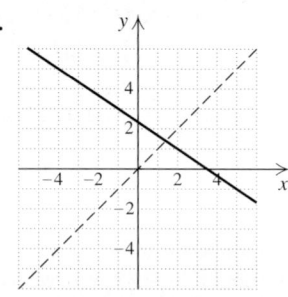

73. $f^{-1}(f(x)) = f^{-1}\left(\frac{7}{8}x\right) = \frac{8}{7} \cdot \frac{7}{8}x = x$;

$f(f^{-1}(x)) = f\left(\frac{8}{7}x\right) = \frac{7}{8} \cdot \frac{8}{7}x = x$

75. $f^{-1}(f(x)) = f^{-1}\left(\dfrac{1-x}{x}\right) = \dfrac{1}{\dfrac{1-x}{x}+1} =$

$\dfrac{1}{1-x+x} = \dfrac{1}{\dfrac{1}{x}} = 1 \cdot \dfrac{x}{1} = x; f(f^{-1}(x)) = f\left(\dfrac{1}{x+1}\right) =$

$\dfrac{1 - \dfrac{1}{x+1}}{\dfrac{1}{x+1}} = \dfrac{\dfrac{x+1-1}{x+1}}{\dfrac{1}{x+1}} = \dfrac{x}{x+1} \cdot \dfrac{x+1}{1} = x$

77. $f^{-1}(f(x)) = f^{-1}\left(\dfrac{2}{5}x + 1\right) = \dfrac{5\left(\dfrac{2}{5}x+1\right) - 5}{2} =$

$\dfrac{2x + 5 - 5}{2} = \dfrac{2x}{2} = x; f(f^{-1}(x)) = f\left(\dfrac{5x-5}{2}\right) =$

$\dfrac{2}{5}\left(\dfrac{5x-5}{2}\right) + 1 = x - 1 + 1 = x$

79. $f^{-1}(x) = \frac{1}{5}x + \frac{3}{5}$; domain of f and f^{-1}: $(-\infty, \infty)$;
range of f and f^{-1}: $(-\infty, \infty)$;

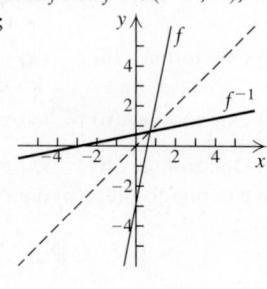

81. $f^{-1}(x) = \dfrac{2}{x}$; domain of f and f^{-1}: $(-\infty, 0) \cup (0, \infty)$;
range of f and f^{-1}: $(-\infty, 0) \cup (0, \infty)$;

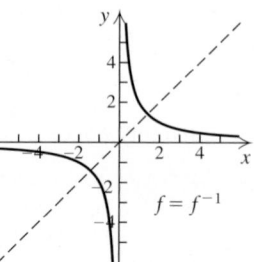

83. $f^{-1}(x) = \sqrt[3]{3x + 6}$; domain of f and f^{-1}: $(-\infty, \infty)$;
range of f and f^{-1}: $(-\infty, \infty)$

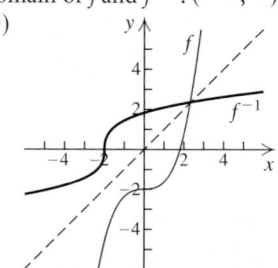

85. $f^{-1}(x) = \dfrac{3x + 1}{x - 1}$; domain of f: $(-\infty, 3) \cup (3, \infty)$;
range of f: $(-\infty, 1) \cup (1, \infty)$;
domain of f^{-1}: $(-\infty, 1) \cup (1, \infty)$;
range of f^{-1}: $(-\infty, 3) \cup (3, \infty)$;

87. $5; a$ **89. (a)** $3\frac{1}{2}, 6, 6\frac{1}{2}$; **(b)** $s^{-1}(x) = \dfrac{2x + 3}{2}$;

(c) $4\frac{1}{2}, 7, 8\frac{1}{2}$

91. $y_1 = 0.8x + 1.7$,   Domain and range of both f
$y_2 = \dfrac{x - 1.7}{0.8}$ and f^{-1}: all real numbers

93.
$y_1 = \frac{1}{2}x - 4,$
$y_2 = 2x + 8$

Domain and range of both f and f^{-1}: all real numbers

95.
$y_1 = \sqrt{x - 3},$
$y_2 = x^2 + 3, x \geqslant 0$

Domain of f: $[3, \infty)$, range of f: $[0, \infty)$; domain of f^{-1}: $[0, \infty)$, range of f^{-1}: $[3, \infty)$

97.
$y_1 = x^2 - 4, x \geqslant 0;$ $y_2 = \sqrt{4 + x}$

Domain of f: $[0, \infty)$, range of f: $[-4, \infty)$; domain of f^{-1}: $[-4, \infty)$, range of f^{-1}: $[0, \infty)$

99.
$y_1 = (3x - 9)^3,$ $y_2 = \dfrac{\sqrt[3]{x} + 9}{3}$

Domain and range of both f and f^{-1}: all real numbers

101. (a) 0.5, 11.5, 22.5, 55.5, 72; **(b)** $D^{-1}(r) = \dfrac{10r - 5}{11}$; the speed, in miles per hour, that the car is traveling when the reaction distance is r feet; **(c)**
$$y_1 = \frac{11x + 5}{10}, \quad y_2 = \frac{10x - 5}{11}$$

103. Discussion and Writing   **105.** [2.4] (b), (d), (f), (h)
106. [2.4] (a), (c), (e), (g)   **107.** [2.4] (a)   **108.** [2.4] (d)
109. [2.4] (f)   **110.** [2.4] (a), (b), (c), (d)
111. $f(x) = x^2 - 3$, for inputs $x \geqslant 0$; $f^{-1}(x) = \sqrt{x + 3}$, for inputs $x \geqslant -3$ **113.** Answers may vary. $f(x) = 3/x$, $f(x) = 1 - x, f(x) = x$ **115.** If the graph of $y = f^{-1}(x)$ is symmetric with respect to $y = x$, then $f^{-1}(x) = f(x)$.

Exercise Set 4.2

1. 54.5982   **3.** 0.0856   **5.** (f)   **7.** (e)   **9.** (a)

11.

13.

15.

17.

19.

21.

23.

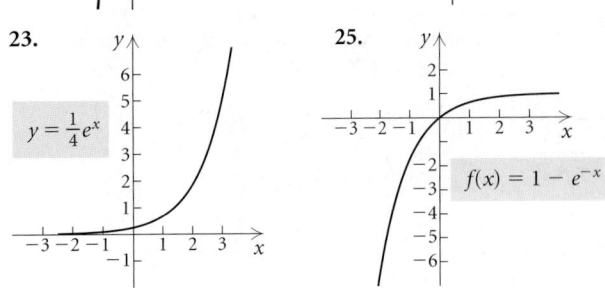

25.

27. Shift the graph of $y = 2^x$ left 1 unit.

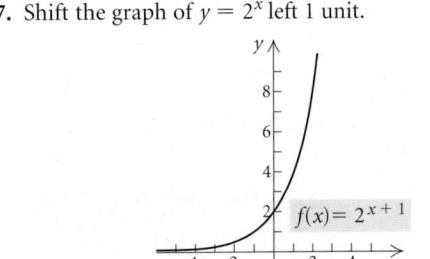

29. Shift the graph of $y = 2^x$ down 3 units.

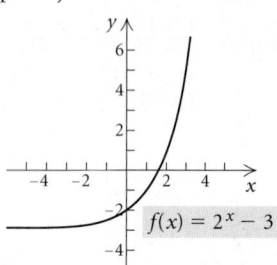

$f(x) = 2^x - 3$

31. Reflect the graph of $y = 3^x$ across the y-axis, then across the x-axis, and then shift it up 4 units.

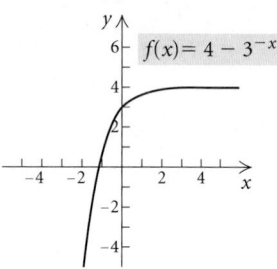

$f(x) = 4 - 3^{-x}$

33. Shift the graph of $y = \left(\frac{3}{2}\right)^x$ right 1 unit.

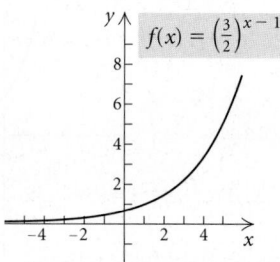

$f(x) = \left(\frac{3}{2}\right)^{x-1}$

35. Shift the graph of $y = 2^x$ left 3 units, and then down 5 units.

$f(x) = 2^{x+3} - 5$

37. Shrink the graph of $y = e^x$ horizontally.

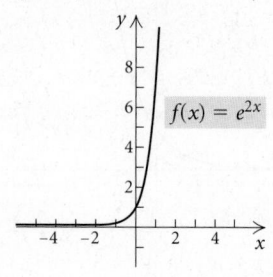

$f(x) = e^{2x}$

39. Shift the graph of $y = e^x$ left 1 unit and reflect it across the y-axis.

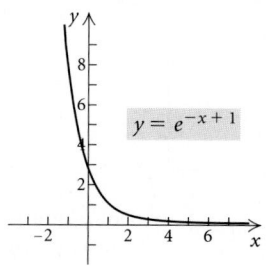

$y = e^{-x+1}$

41. Reflect the graph of $y = e^x$ across the y-axis, then across the x-axis, then shift it up 1 unit, and then stretch it vertically.

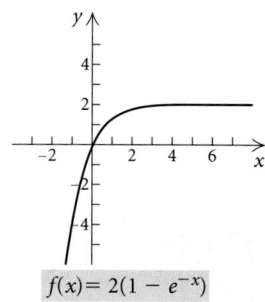

$f(x) = 2(1 - e^{-x})$

43. (a) $A(t) = 82{,}000(1.01125)^{4t}$; **(b)** \$82,000, \$89,677.22, \$102,561.54, \$128,278.90   **45.** \$4930.86   **47.** \$3247.30
49. \$153,610.15   **51.** \$76,305.59   **53.** \$26,086.69
55. 5.4 billion gal; 7.1 billion gal   **57.** 3293 GB; 25,004 GB
59. Exports: 2007, \$982.7 billion; 2012, \$2384.8 billion; 2020, \$9851.1 billion; imports: 2007, \$861.3 billion; 2012, \$2029.5 billion; 2020, \$7998.2 billion
61. \$1800; \$1440; \$1152; \$589.82; \$193.27
63. \$39.1 billion; \$171.1 billion; \$309.0 billion
65. About 63%   **67.** (c)   **69.** (a)   **71.** (1)   **73.** (g)
75. (i)   **77.** (k)   **79.** (m)   **81.** Discussion and Writing
83. Discussion and Writing   **85.** [2.2] $31 - 22i$
86. [2.2] $\frac{1}{2} - \frac{1}{2}i$ **87.** [2.3] $\left(-\frac{1}{2}, 0\right)$, $(7, 0)$; $-\frac{1}{2}, 7$
88. [3.4] $(1, 0)$; 1   **89.** [3.1] $(-1, 0)$, $(0, 0)$, $(1, 0)$; $-1, 0, 1$
90. [3.1] $(-4, 0)$, $(0, 0)$, $(3, 0)$; $-4, 0, 3$ **91.** [3.1] $-8, 0, 2$
92. [3.1] $\dfrac{5 \pm \sqrt{97}}{6}$ **93.** π^7; 70^{80}

Visualizing the Graph

1. J   **2.** F   **3.** H   **4.** B   **5.** E   **6.** A   **7.** C
8. I   **9.** D   **10.** G

Exercise Set 4.3

1.

3.

5.

7.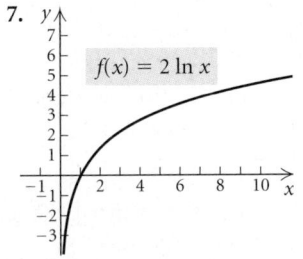

9. 4   **11.** 3   **13.** −3   **15.** −2   **17.** 0   **19.** 1
21. 4   **23.** $\frac{1}{4}$ **25.** −7   **27.** $\frac{1}{2}$ **29.** $\frac{3}{4}$ **31.** 0   **33.** $\frac{1}{2}$
35. $\log_{10} 1000 = 3$ **37.** $\log_8 2 = \frac{1}{3}$ **39.** $\log_e t = 3$, or
$\ln t = 3$ **41.** $\log_e 7.3891 = 2$, or $\ln 7.3891 = 2$
43. $\log_p 3 = k$ **45.** $5^1 = 5$ **47.** $10^{-2} = 0.01$
49. $e^{3.4012} = 30$ **51.** $a^{-x} = M$ **53.** $a^x = T^3$
55. 0.4771   **57.** 2.7259   **59.** −0.2441
61. Does not exist   **63.** 0.6931   **65.** 6.6962
67. Does not exist   **69.** 3.3219   **71.** −0.2614
73. 0.7384   **75.** 2.2619   **77.** 0.5880
79.   **81.**

83. Shift the graph of $y = \log_2 x$ left 3 units. Domain:
$(-3, \infty)$; vertical asymptote: $x = -3$;

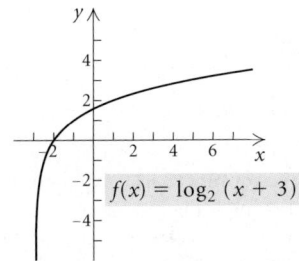

85. Shift the graph of $y = \log_3 x$ down 1 unit. Domain:
$(0, \infty)$; vertical asymptote: $x = 0$;

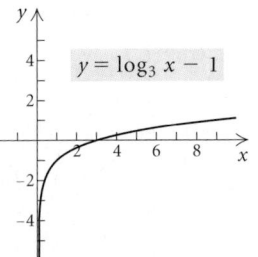

87. Stretch the graph of $y = \ln x$ vertically. Domain: $(0, \infty)$;
vertical asymptote: $x = 0$;

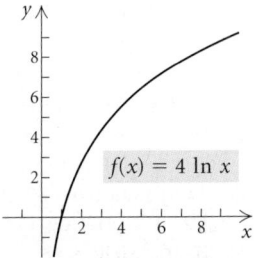

89. Reflect the graph of $y = \ln x$ across the x-axis and shift it
up 2 units. Domain: $(0, \infty)$; vertical asymptote: $x = 0$;

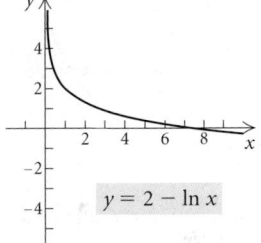

91. (a) 2.5 ft/sec; **(b)** 2.3 ft/sec; **(c)** 2.1 ft/sec; **(d)** 3.0 ft/sec;
(e) 2.4 ft/sec; **(f)** 2.2 ft/sec; **(g)** 3.4 ft/sec; **(h)** 1.8 ft/sec
93. (a) 7.85; **(b)** 8.25; **(c)** 9.6; **(d)** 7.9; **(e)** 6.9
95. (a) 10^{-7}; **(b)** 4.0×10^{-6}; **(c)** 6.3×10^{-4}; **(d)** 1.6×10^{-5}
97. (a) 34 decibels; **(b)** 64 decibels; **(c)** 60 decibels;
(d) 90 decibels   **99.** Discussion and Writing
101. [1.4] $m = 0$; y-intercept: $(0, 6)$
102. [1.4] $m = \frac{3}{10}$; y-intercept: $\left(0, -\frac{7}{5}\right)$
103. [1.4] $m = 2$; y-intercept: $\left(0, -\frac{3}{13}\right)$
104. [1.4] Slope is not defined; no y-intercept
105. [3.3] −280   **106.** [3.3] −4
107. [3.4] $f(x) = x^3 - 7x$
108. [3.4] $f(x) = x^3 - x^2 + 16x - 16$ **109.** 3
111. $(0, \infty)$ **113.** $(-\infty, 0) \cup (0, \infty)$ **115.** $\left(-\frac{5}{2}, -2\right)$
117. (d)   **119.** (b)

Exercise Set 4.4

1. $\log_3 81 + \log_3 27 = 4 + 3 = 7$
3. $\log_5 5 + \log_5 125 = 1 + 3 = 4$

5. $\log_t 8 + \log_t Y$ **7.** $\ln x + \ln y$ **9.** $3\log_b t$
11. $8\log y$ **13.** $-6\log_c K$ **15.** $\frac{1}{3}\ln 4$
17. $\log_t M - \log_t 8$ **19.** $\log x - \log y$ **21.** $\ln r - \ln s$
23. $\log_a 6 + \log_a x + 5\log_a y + 4\log_a z$
25. $2\log_b p + 5\log_b q - 4\log_b m - 9$
27. $\ln 2 - \ln 3 - 3\ln x - \ln y$
29. $\frac{3}{2}\log r + \frac{1}{2}\log t$ **31.** $3\log_a x - \frac{5}{2}\log_a p - 4\log_a q$
33. $2\log_a m + 3\log_a n - \frac{3}{4} - \frac{5}{4}\log_a b$ **35.** $\log_a 150$
37. $\log 100 = 2$ **39.** $\log m^3\sqrt{n}$

41. $\log_a x^{-5/2}y^4$, or $\log_a \dfrac{y^4}{x^{5/2}}$ **43.** $\ln x$ **45.** $\ln(x-2)$

47. $\log\dfrac{x-7}{x-2}$ **49.** $\ln\dfrac{x}{(x^2-25)^3}$ **51.** $\ln\dfrac{2^{11/5}x^9}{y^8}$

53. -0.74 **55.** 1.991 **57.** 0.356 **59.** 4.827
61. -1.792 **63.** 0.099 **65.** 3 **67.** $|x-4|$ **69.** $4x$
71. w **73.** $8t$ **75.** $\frac{1}{2}$ **77.** Discussion and Writing
79. [3.1] Quartic   **80.** [4.2] Exponential
81. [1.4] Linear (constant)   **82.** [4.2] Exponential
83. [3.5] Rational   **84.** [4.3] Logarithmic
85. [3.1] Cubic   **86.** [3.5] Rational   **87.** [1.4] Linear
88. [2.4] Quadratic   **89.** 4 **91.** $\log_a(x^3 - y^3)$
93. $\frac{1}{2}\log_a(x-y) - \frac{1}{2}\log_a(x+y)$ **95.** 7 **97.** True
99. True   **101.** True   **103.** -2 **105.** 3

107. $e^{-xy} = \dfrac{a}{b}$, or $e^{xy} = \dfrac{b}{a}$

109. $\log_a\left(\dfrac{x + \sqrt{x^2-5}}{5} \cdot \dfrac{x - \sqrt{x^2-5}}{x - \sqrt{x^2-5}}\right)$

$$= \log_a\dfrac{5}{5(x - \sqrt{x^2-5})}$$

$$= -\log_a(x - \sqrt{x^2-5})$$

Exercise Set 4.5

1. 4 **3.** $\frac{3}{2}$ **5.** 5.044 **7.** $\frac{5}{2}$ **9.** $-3, \frac{1}{2}$ **11.** 0.959
13. 0 **15.** 6.908 **17.** 84.191 **19.** -1.710 **21.** 2.844
23. $-1.567, 1.567$ **25.** 0.347 **27.** 625 **29.** 0.0001
31. $-\frac{1}{3}$ **33.** e **35.** $\frac{22}{3}$ **37.** 10 **39.** 4 **41.** $\frac{2}{5}$
43. $\frac{1}{63}$ **45.** 2 **47.** 5 **49.** $\frac{21}{8}$ **51.** $\frac{8}{7}$ **53.** 6
55. 6.192 **57.** 0 **59.** 0.367 **61.** 0.621 **63.** -1.532
65. 7.062 **67.** 2.444 **69.** $(4.093, 0.786)$
71. $(7.586, 6.684)$ **73.** Discussion and Writing
74. [2.4] (a) $(3,1)$; (b) $x = 3$; (c) maximum: 1 when $x = 3$
75. [2.4] (a) $(0, -6)$; (b) $x = 0$; (c) minimum: -6 when
$x = 0$ **76.** [2.4] (a) $(2, 4)$; (b) $x = 2$; (c) minimum: 4
when $x = 2$ **77.** [2.4] (a) $(-1, -5)$; (b) $x = -1$;
(c) maximum: -5 when $x = -1$ **79.** 10
81. $1, e^4$ or $1, 54.598$ **83.** $\frac{1}{3}, 27$ **85.** $1, e^2$ or $1, 7.389$
87. $0, 0.431$ **89.** $-9, 9$ **91.** e^{-2}, e^2 or $0.135, 7.389$
93. $\frac{7}{4}$ **95.** 5 **97.** $a = \frac{2}{3}b$ **99.** 88

Exercise Set 4.6

1. (a) $P(t) = 6.4e^{0.012t}$;   (b) 6.6 billion, 6.8 billion;
(c) about 18.6 yr after 2005;   (d) 57.8 yr
3. (a) 28.9 yr;   (b) 1.1% per year;   (c) 49.5 yr;   (d) 346.6 yr;
(e) 1.8% per year;   (f) 1.9% per year;   (g) 77.0 yr;
(h) 1.0% per year;   (i) 57.8 yr;   (j) 26.7 yr
5. About 637 yr   **7.** (a) $P(t) = 10,000e^{0.054t}$;
(b) \$10,555; \$11,140; \$13,100; \$17,160;   (c) 12.8 yr
9. About 5135 yr   **11.** (a) 23.1% per minute;   (b) 3.15% per
year;   (c) 7.2 days;   (d) 11 yr;   (e) 2.8% per year;   (f) 0.015%
per year;   (g) 0.003% per year
13. (a) $k \approx 0.1630$; $N(t) = 125e^{-0.1630t}$;   (b) 17.7 students;
2.5 students;   (c) in 2013
15. (a) 167;   (b) 500; 1758; 3007; 3449; 3495;   (c) as $t \to \infty$,
$N(t) \to 3500$; the number approaches 3500 but never actually
reaches it.   **17.** 46.7°F   **19.** 59.6°F
21. (a) $y = 0.1367470864(1.024068023)^x$, where x is the
number of years after 1900; since $r^2 = 0.968816816$, the
function is a good fit.
(b)   (c) 1.7%; 2.1%; 2.4%

23. (a)

(b) linear: $y = 0.3920710572x + 0.695407279$, $r^2 \approx 0.9465$;
quadratic: $y = 0.0072218083x^2 + 0.1172668587x + 1.973805022$, $r^2 \approx 0.9851$;
exponential: $y = 2.062091236(1.059437743)^x$, $r^2 \approx 0.9775$;
the quadratic has the best fit;
(c)

(d) linear: 16.8%; quadratic: 18.9%; exponential: 22.0%; the
percentage from the quadratic model seems most realistic.
Answers may vary.
25. (a) $y = 255.0890581(1.277632801)^x$, where x is the
number of years since 1995;   (b) 2956 surgeries;
7877 surgeries;   (c) in 2011

27. Discussion and Writing   **29.** [2.6] Multiplication principle for inequalities   **30.** [4.4] Product rule
31. [2.3] Principle of zero products   **32.** [2.3] Principle of square roots   **33.** [4.4] Power rule
34. [2.1] Multiplication principle for equations
35. $166.16   **37.** $14,182.70

39. $t = -\dfrac{L}{R}\left[\ln\left(1 - \dfrac{iR}{V}\right)\right]$ **41.** Linear

Review Exercises: Chapter 4

1. True   **2.** False   **3.** False   **4.** True   **5.** False
6. True   **7.** $\{(-2.7, 1.3), (-3, 8), (3, -5), (-3, 6), (-5, 7)\}$
8. (a) $x = -2y + 3$; (b) $x = 3y^2 + 2y - 1$;
(c) $0.8y^3 - 5.4x^2 = 3y$ **9.** No   **10.** No   **11.** Yes

12. Yes   **13.** (a) Yes; (b) $f^{-1}(x) = \dfrac{-x + 2}{3}$

14. (a) Yes; (b) $f^{-1}(x) = \dfrac{x + 2}{x - 1}$

15. (a) Yes; (b) $f^{-1}(x) = x^2 + 6, x \geq 0$
16. (a) Yes; (b) $f^{-1}(x) = \sqrt[3]{x + 8}$ **17.** (a) No
18. (a) Yes; (b) $f^{-1}(x) = \ln x$

19. $f^{-1}(f(x)) = f^{-1}(6x - 5) = \dfrac{6x - 5 + 5}{6} = \dfrac{6x}{6} = x$;

$f(f^{-1}(x)) = f\left(\dfrac{x + 5}{6}\right) = 6\left(\dfrac{x + 5}{6}\right) - 5 = x + 5 - 5 = x$

20. $f^{-1}(f(x)) = f^{-1}\left(\dfrac{x + 1}{x}\right) = \dfrac{1}{\dfrac{x + 1}{x} - 1} =$

$\dfrac{1}{\dfrac{x + 1 - x}{x}} = \dfrac{1}{\dfrac{1}{x}} = x; f(f^{-1}(x)) = f\left(\dfrac{1}{x - 1}\right) =$

$\dfrac{\dfrac{1}{x - 1} + 1}{\dfrac{1}{x - 1}} = \dfrac{\dfrac{1 + x - 1}{x - 1}}{\dfrac{1}{x - 1}} = \dfrac{x}{x - 1} \cdot \dfrac{x - 1}{1} = x$

21. $f^{-1}(x) = \dfrac{2 - x}{5}$; domain of f and f^{-1}: $(-\infty, \infty)$;
range of f and f^{-1}: $(-\infty, \infty)$;

22. $f^{-1}(x) = \dfrac{-2x - 3}{x - 1}$;
domain of f: $(-\infty, -2) \cup (-2, \infty)$;
range of f: $(-\infty, 1) \cup (1, \infty)$;
domain of f^{-1}: $(-\infty, 1) \cup (1, \infty)$;
range of f^{-1}: $(-\infty, -2) \cup (-2, \infty)$

23. 657   **24.** a

25.   **26.**

27.   **28.**

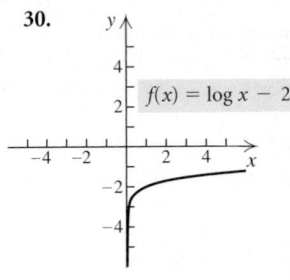

29.   **30.**

31. (c)   **32.** (a)   **33.** (b)   **34.** (f)   **35.** (e)
36. (d)   **37.** 3   **38.** 5   **39.** 1   **40.** 0   **41.** $\frac{1}{4}$
42. $\frac{1}{2}$ **43.** 0   **44.** 1   **45.** $\frac{1}{3}$ **46.** -2 **47.** $4^2 = x$
48. $a^k = Q$ **49.** $\log_4 \frac{1}{64} = -3$ **50.** $\ln 80 = x$
51. 1.0414   **52.** -0.6308 **53.** 1.0986   **54.** -3.6119
55. Does not exist   **56.** Does not exist   **57.** 1.9746
58. 0.5283   **59.** $\log_b \dfrac{x^3\sqrt{z}}{y^4}$ **60.** $\ln(x^2 - 4)$
61. $\frac{1}{4}\ln w + \frac{1}{2}\ln r$ **62.** $\frac{2}{3}\log M - \frac{1}{3}\log N$ **63.** 0.477
64. 1.699   **65.** -0.699 **66.** 0.233   **67.** $-5k$

68. $-6t$ **69.** 16 **70.** $\frac{1}{5}$ **71.** 4.382 **72.** 2
73. $\frac{1}{2}$ **74.** 5 **75.** 4 **76.** 9 **77.** 1 **78.** 3.912
79. (a) $A(t) = 16{,}000(1.0105)^{4t}$; (b) $16,000, $20,588.51,
$26,415.77, $33,941.80
80. 3837 cases, 8836 cases; 15,844 cases **81.** 8.1 yr
82. 2.3% **83.** About 2623 yr **84.** 5.6 **85.** 6.3
86. 30 decibels **87.** (a) 2.2 ft/sec; (b) 8,553,143
88. (a) $k \approx 0.1492$; (b) $S(t) = 0.035e^{0.1492t}$;
(c) about $1.459 billion; about $128.2 billion; about
$2534 billion, or $2.534 trillion; (d) in 2009
89. (a) $P(t) = 3.039e^{0.013t}$, where t is the number of years
since 2005; (b) 3.201 million, 3.461 million; (c) in 92 yr;
(d) 53.3 yr **90.** D **91.** A
92. (a) $y = 2.518123986(1.301660678)^x$;
(b) $y = 2.518123986(1.301660678)^x$

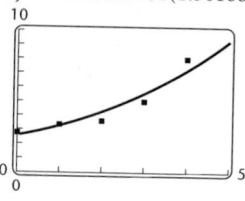

(c) about $27 million
93. No **94.** (a) $y = 5e^{-x}\ln x$

(b) relative maximum: 0.486 at $x = 1.763$; no relative
minimum **95.** Discussion and Writing: By the product rule,
$\log_2 x + \log_2 5 = \log_2 5x$, not $\log_2 (x + 5)$. Also, substituting
various numbers for x shows that both sides of the inequality
are indeed unequal. You could also graph each side and show
that the graphs do not coincide.
96. Discussion and Writing: The inverse of a function $f(x)$ is
written $f^{-1}(x)$, whereas $[f(x)]^{-1}$ means $\dfrac{1}{f(x)}$.
97. $\frac{1}{64}$, 64 **98.** 1 **99.** 16 **100.** $(1, \infty)$

Test: Chapter 4

1. [4.1] $\{(5, -2), (3, 4), (-1, 0), (-3, -6)\}$
2. [4.1] No **3.** [4.1] Yes
4. [4.1] (a) Yes; (b) $f^{-1}(x) = \sqrt[3]{x - 1}$
5. [4.1] (a) Yes; (b) $f^{-1}(x) = 1 - x$
6. [4.1] (a) Yes; (b) $f^{-1}(x) = \dfrac{2x}{1 + x}$ **7.** [4.1] (a) No
8. [4.1] $f^{-1}(f(x)) = f^{-1}(-4x + 3) = \dfrac{3 - (-4x + 3)}{4} =$
$\dfrac{4x}{4} = x; f(f^{-1}(x)) = f\left(\dfrac{3 - x}{4}\right) = -4\left(\dfrac{3 - x}{4}\right) + 3 =$
$-3 + x + 3 = x$

9. [4.1] $f^{-1}(x) = \dfrac{4x + 1}{x}$; domain of f: $(-\infty, 4) \cup (4, \infty)$;
range of f: $(-\infty, 0) \cup (0, \infty)$;
domain of f^{-1}: $(-\infty, 0) \cup (0, \infty)$;
range of f^{-1}: $(-\infty, 4) \cup (4, \infty)$;

10. [4.2]

11. [4.3]

12. [4.2]

13. [4.3]

14. [4.3] -5 **15.** [4.3] 1 **16.** [4.3] 0 **17.** [4.3] $\frac{1}{5}$
18. [4.3] $x = e^4$ **19.** [4.3] $x = \log_3 5.4$ **20.** [4.3] 2.7726
21. [4.3] -0.5331 **22.** [4.3] 1.2851 **23.** [4.4] $\log_a \dfrac{x^2\sqrt{z}}{y}$
24. [4.4] $\frac{2}{5}\ln x + \frac{1}{5}\ln y$ **25.** [4.4] 0.656 **26.** [4.4] $-4t$
27. [4.5] $\frac{1}{2}$ **28.** [4.5] 1 **29.** [4.5] 1 **30.** [4.5] 4.174
31. [4.3] 6.6 **32.** [4.6] 0.0154 **33.** [4.6] (a) 4.5%;
(b) $P(t) = 1000e^{0.045t}$; (c) $1433.33; (d) 15.4 yr
34. [4.5] $\frac{27}{8}$

CHAPTER 5

Exercise Set 5.1

1. $\sin \phi = \frac{15}{17}, \cos \phi = \frac{8}{17}, \tan \phi = \frac{15}{8}, \csc \phi = \frac{17}{15}, \sec \phi = \frac{17}{8}$,
$\cot \phi = \frac{8}{15}$
3. $\sin \alpha = \dfrac{\sqrt{3}}{2}, \cos \alpha = \dfrac{1}{2}, \tan \alpha = \sqrt{3}, \csc \alpha = \dfrac{2\sqrt{3}}{3}$,
$\sec \alpha = 2, \cot \alpha = \dfrac{\sqrt{3}}{3}$

5. $\sin \phi = \dfrac{7\sqrt{65}}{65}$, $\cos \phi = \dfrac{4\sqrt{65}}{65}$, $\tan \phi = \dfrac{7}{4}$,

$\csc \phi = \dfrac{\sqrt{65}}{7}$, $\sec \phi = \dfrac{\sqrt{65}}{4}$, $\cot \phi = \dfrac{4}{7}$

7. $\csc \alpha = \dfrac{3}{\sqrt{5}}$, or $\dfrac{3\sqrt{5}}{5}$; $\sec \alpha = \dfrac{3}{2}$; $\cot \alpha = \dfrac{2}{\sqrt{5}}$, or $\dfrac{2\sqrt{5}}{5}$

9. $\cos \theta = \dfrac{7}{25}$, $\tan \theta = \dfrac{24}{7}$, $\csc \theta = \dfrac{25}{24}$, $\sec \theta = \dfrac{25}{7}$, $\cot \theta = \dfrac{7}{24}$

11. $\sin \phi = \dfrac{2\sqrt{5}}{5}$, $\cos \phi = \dfrac{\sqrt{5}}{5}$, $\csc \phi = \dfrac{\sqrt{5}}{2}$, $\sec \phi = \sqrt{5}$,

$\cot \phi = \dfrac{1}{2}$

13. $\sin \theta = \dfrac{2}{3}$, $\cos \theta = \dfrac{\sqrt{5}}{3}$, $\tan \theta = \dfrac{2\sqrt{5}}{5}$, $\sec \theta = \dfrac{3\sqrt{5}}{5}$,

$\cot \theta = \dfrac{\sqrt{5}}{2}$

15. $\sin \beta = \dfrac{2\sqrt{5}}{5}$, $\tan \beta = 2$, $\csc \beta = \dfrac{\sqrt{5}}{2}$, $\sec \beta = \sqrt{5}$,

$\cot \beta = \dfrac{1}{2}$

17. $\dfrac{\sqrt{2}}{2}$ **19.** 2 **21.** $\dfrac{\sqrt{3}}{3}$ **23.** $\dfrac{1}{2}$ **25.** 1 **27.** 2

29. 62.4 m **31.** 9.72° **33.** 35.01° **35.** 3.03°
37. 49.65° **39.** 0.25° **41.** 5.01° **43.** 17°36′
45. 83°1′30″ **47.** 11°45′ **49.** 47°49′36″ **51.** 0°54′
53. 39°27′ **55.** 0.6293 **57.** 0.0737 **59.** 1.2765
61. 0.7621 **63.** 0.9336 **65.** 12.4288 **67.** 1.0000
69. 1.7032 **71.** 30.8° **73.** 12.5° **75.** 64.4°
77. 46.5° **79.** 25.2° **81.** 38.6° **83.** 45° **85.** 60°
87. 45° **89.** 60° **91.** 30°

93. $\cos 20° = \sin 70° = \dfrac{1}{\sec 20°}$

95. $\tan 52° = \cot 38° = \dfrac{1}{\cot 52°}$

97. $\sin 25° \approx 0.4226$, $\cos 25° \approx 0.9063$, $\tan 25° \approx 0.4663$, $\csc 25° \approx 2.3662$, $\sec 25° \approx 1.1034$, $\cot 25° \approx 2.1445$
99. $\sin 18°49′55″ \approx 0.3228$, $\cos 18°49′55″ \approx 0.9465$, $\tan 18°49′55″ \approx 0.3411$, $\csc 18°49′55″ \approx 3.0979$, $\sec 18°49′55″ \approx 1.0565$, $\cot 18°49′55″ \approx 2.9317$

101. $\sin 8° = q$, $\cos 8° = p$, $\tan 8° = \dfrac{1}{r}$, $\csc 8° = \dfrac{1}{q}$,

$\sec 8° = \dfrac{1}{p}$, $\cot 8° = r$ **103.** Discussion and Writing
105. [4.2]

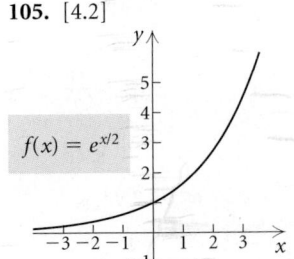

$f(x) = e^{x/2}$

106. [4.2]

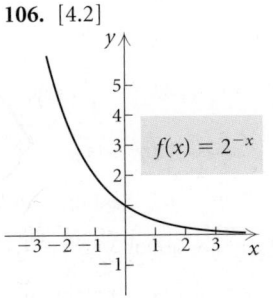

$f(x) = 2^{-x}$

107. [4.3]

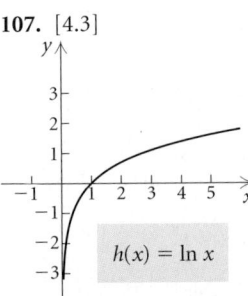

$h(x) = \ln x$

108. [4.3]

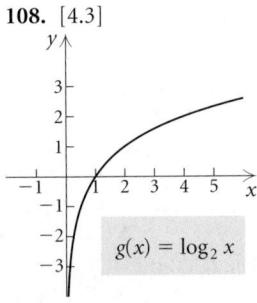

$g(x) = \log_2 x$

109. [4.5] 4 **110.** [4.5] 9.21 **111.** [4.5] 343
112. [4.5] $\dfrac{101}{97}$ **113.** 0.6534
115. Area $= \dfrac{1}{2}ab$. But $a = c \sin A$, so Area $= \dfrac{1}{2}bc \sin A$.

Exercise Set 5.2

1. $F = 60°$, $d = 3$, $f \approx 5.2$
3. $A = 22.7°$, $a \approx 52.7$, $c \approx 136.6$
5. $P = 47°38′$, $n \approx 34.4$, $p \approx 25.4$
7. $B = 2°17′$, $b \approx 0.39$, $c \approx 9.74$
9. $A \approx 77.2°$, $B \approx 12.8°$, $a \approx 439$
11. $B = 42.42°$, $a \approx 35.7$, $b \approx 32.6$
13. $B = 55°$, $a \approx 28.0$, $c \approx 48.8$
15. $A \approx 62.4°$, $B \approx 27.6°$, $a \approx 3.56$ **17.** Approximately 34°
19. About 62.2 ft **21.** 110 ft **23.** 750 ft
25. About 92.9 cm **27.** About 599 ft
29. Radius: 9.15 in.; length: 73.20 in.; width: 54.90 in.
31. 17.9 ft **33.** About 8 km **35.** About 19.5 mi
37. About 24 km **39.** Discussion and Writing
40. [1.1] $3\sqrt{10}$, or about 9.487
41. [1.1] $10\sqrt{2}$, or about 14.142
42. [4.3] $\ln t = 4$ **43.** [4.3] $10^{-3} = 0.001$ **45.** 3.3
47. Cut so that $\theta = 79.38°$ **49.** $\theta \approx 27°$

Exercise Set 5.3

1. III **3.** III **5.** I **7.** III **9.** II **11.** II
13. 434°, 794°, −286°, −646°
15. 475.3°, 835.3°, −244.7°, −604.7°
17. 180°, 540°, −540°, −900° **19.** 72.89°, 162.89°
21. 77°56′46″, 167°56′46″ **23.** 44.8°, 134.8°
25. $\sin \beta = \dfrac{5}{13}$, $\cos \beta = -\dfrac{12}{13}$, $\tan \beta = -\dfrac{5}{12}$, $\csc \beta = \dfrac{13}{5}$, $\sec \beta = -\dfrac{13}{12}$, $\cot \beta = -\dfrac{12}{5}$
27. $\sin \phi = -\dfrac{2\sqrt{7}}{7}$, $\cos \phi = -\dfrac{\sqrt{21}}{7}$, $\tan \phi = \dfrac{2\sqrt{3}}{3}$,

$\csc \phi = -\dfrac{\sqrt{7}}{2}$, $\sec \phi = -\dfrac{\sqrt{21}}{3}$, $\cot \phi = \dfrac{\sqrt{3}}{2}$

29. $\sin \theta = -\dfrac{2\sqrt{13}}{13}$, $\cos \theta = \dfrac{3\sqrt{13}}{13}$, $\tan \theta = -\dfrac{2}{3}$

31. $\sin \theta = \dfrac{5\sqrt{41}}{41}$, $\cos \theta = \dfrac{4\sqrt{41}}{41}$, $\tan \theta = \dfrac{5}{4}$

33. $\cos \theta = -\dfrac{2\sqrt{2}}{3}$, $\tan \theta = \dfrac{\sqrt{2}}{4}$, $\csc \theta = -3$,
$\sec \theta = -\dfrac{3\sqrt{2}}{4}$, $\cot \theta = 2\sqrt{2}$

35. $\sin \theta = -\dfrac{\sqrt{5}}{5}$, $\cos \theta = \dfrac{2\sqrt{5}}{5}$, $\tan \theta = -\dfrac{1}{2}$,
$\csc \theta = -\sqrt{5}$, $\sec \theta = \dfrac{\sqrt{5}}{2}$

37. $\sin \phi = -\frac{4}{5}$, $\tan \phi = -\frac{4}{3}$, $\csc \phi = -\frac{5}{4}$, $\sec \phi = \frac{5}{3}$,
$\cot \phi = -\frac{3}{4}$

39. $30°$; $-\dfrac{\sqrt{3}}{2}$ **41.** $45°$; 1 **43.** 0 **45.** $45°$; $-\dfrac{\sqrt{2}}{2}$

47. $30°$; 2 **49.** $30°$; $\sqrt{3}$ **51.** $30°$; $-\dfrac{\sqrt{3}}{3}$

53. Not defined   **55.** -1 **57.** $60°$; $\sqrt{3}$

59. $45°$; $\dfrac{\sqrt{2}}{2}$ **61.** $45°$; $-\sqrt{2}$ **63.** 1 **65.** 0 **67.** 0

69. 0 **71.** Positive: cos, sec; negative: sin, csc, tan, cot
73. Positive: tan, cot; negative: sin, csc, cos, sec
75. Positive: sin, csc; negative: cos, sec, tan, cot
77. Positive: all   **79.** $\sin 319° = -0.6561$,
$\cos 319° = 0.7547$, $\tan 319° = -0.8693$, $\csc 319° \approx -1.5242$,
$\sec 319° \approx 1.3250$, $\cot 319° \approx -1.1504$
81. $\sin 115° = 0.9063$, $\cos 115° = -0.4226$,
$\tan 115° = -2.1445$, $\csc 115° \approx 1.1034$, $\sec 115° \approx -2.3663$,
$\cot 115° \approx -0.4663$ **83.** East: about 130 km; south: 75 km
85. About 223 km   **87.** -1.1585 **89.** -1.4910
91. 0.8771 **93.** 0.4352 **95.** 0.9563 **97.** 2.9238
99. $275.4°$ **101.** $200.1°$ **103.** $288.1°$ **105.** $72.6°$
107. Discussion and Writing
109. [3.5]

$x = -5$ $\qquad$ $x = 5$

$f(x) = \dfrac{1}{x^2 - 25}$

110. [3.2]

$g(x) = x^3 - 2x + 1$

111. [1.2], [3.5] Domain: $\{x \mid x \neq -2\}$; range: $\{x \mid x \neq 1\}$
112. [1.2], [3.1] Domain: $\{x \mid x \neq -\frac{3}{2} \text{ and } x \neq 5\}$;
range: all real numbers
113. [2.1] 12 **114.** [2.3] $-2, 3$ **115.** [2.1] $(12, 0)$
116. [2.3] $(-2, 0), (3, 0)$ **117.** 19.625 in.

Exercise Set 5.4

1.

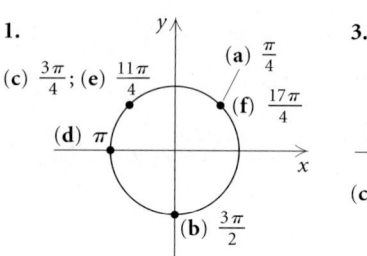

(c) $\dfrac{3\pi}{4}$; (e) $\dfrac{11\pi}{4}$
(a) $\dfrac{\pi}{4}$
(f) $\dfrac{17\pi}{4}$
(d) π
(b) $\dfrac{3\pi}{2}$

3.

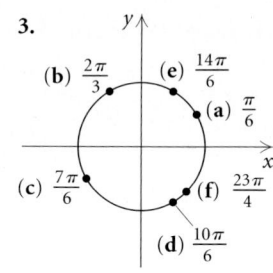

(b) $\dfrac{2\pi}{3}$ (e) $\dfrac{14\pi}{6}$
(a) $\dfrac{\pi}{6}$
(c) $\dfrac{7\pi}{6}$ (f) $\dfrac{23\pi}{4}$
(d) $\dfrac{10\pi}{6}$

5. $M: \dfrac{2\pi}{3}, -\dfrac{4\pi}{3}$; $N: \dfrac{3\pi}{2}, -\dfrac{\pi}{2}$; $P: \dfrac{5\pi}{4}, -\dfrac{3\pi}{4}$; $Q: \dfrac{11\pi}{6}, -\dfrac{\pi}{6}$

7.

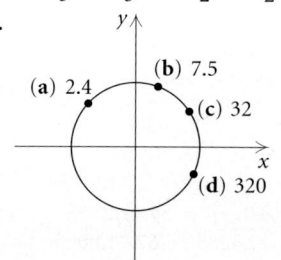

(b) 7.5
(a) 2.4
(c) 32
(d) 320

9. $\dfrac{9\pi}{4}, -\dfrac{7\pi}{4}$ **11.** $\dfrac{19\pi}{6}, -\dfrac{5\pi}{6}$ **13.** $\dfrac{4\pi}{3}, -\dfrac{8\pi}{3}$

15. Complement: $\dfrac{\pi}{6}$; supplement: $\dfrac{2\pi}{3}$

17. Complement: $\dfrac{\pi}{8}$; supplement: $\dfrac{5\pi}{8}$

19. Complement: $\dfrac{5\pi}{12}$; supplement: $\dfrac{11\pi}{12}$

21. $\dfrac{5\pi}{12}$ **23.** $\dfrac{10\pi}{9}$ **25.** $-\dfrac{214.6\pi}{180}$, or $-\dfrac{1073\pi}{900}$ **27.** $-\pi$

29. $\dfrac{12.5\pi}{180}$, or $\dfrac{5\pi}{72}$ **31.** $-\dfrac{17\pi}{9}$ **33.** 4.19 **35.** -1.05

37. 2.06 **39.** 0.02 **41.** 6.02 **43.** 1.66 **45.** $-135°$
47. $1440°$ **49.** $57.30°$ **51.** $134.47°$ **53.** $225°$
55. $-5156.62°$ **57.** $51.43°$

59. $0° = 0$ radians, $30° = \dfrac{\pi}{6}$, $45° = \dfrac{\pi}{4}$, $60° = \dfrac{\pi}{3}$,
$90° = \dfrac{\pi}{2}$, $135° = \dfrac{3\pi}{4}$, $180° = \pi$, $225° = \dfrac{5\pi}{4}$, $270° = \dfrac{3\pi}{2}$,
$315° = \dfrac{7\pi}{4}$, $360° = 2\pi$

61. 2.29 **63.** 5.50 in.   **65.** 1.1; $63°$ **67.** 3.2 yd

69. $\dfrac{5\pi}{3}$, or about 5.24 **71.** $3150 \dfrac{\text{cm}}{\text{min}}$

73. About $12{,}003$ revolutions per hour   **75.** 1047 mph

77. 19,205 revolutions/hr   **79.** About 202
81. Left to the student   **83.** Discussion and Writing
85. [4.1] One-to-one   **86.** [5.1] Cosine of θ
87. [4.2] Exponential function   **88.** [3.5] Horizontal
asymptote   **89.** [1.7] Odd function   **90.** [4.3] Natural
91. [4.1] Horizontal line; inverse   **92.** [4.3] Logarithm
93. 111.7 km; 69.8 mi   **95.** (a) $5°37'30''$; (b) $19°41'15''$
97. 1.676 radians/sec   **99.** 1.46 nautical miles

Exercise Set 5.5

1. (a) $\left(-\dfrac{3}{4}, -\dfrac{\sqrt{7}}{4}\right)$; (b) $\left(\dfrac{3}{4}, \dfrac{\sqrt{7}}{4}\right)$; (c) $\left(\dfrac{3}{4}, -\dfrac{\sqrt{7}}{4}\right)$

3. (a) $\left(\dfrac{2}{5}, \dfrac{\sqrt{21}}{5}\right)$; (b) $\left(-\dfrac{2}{5}, -\dfrac{\sqrt{21}}{5}\right)$; (c) $\left(-\dfrac{2}{5}, \dfrac{\sqrt{21}}{5}\right)$

5. $\left(\dfrac{\sqrt{2}}{2}, -\dfrac{\sqrt{2}}{2}\right)$ **7.** 0   **9.** $\sqrt{3}$ **11.** 0   **13.** $-\dfrac{\sqrt{3}}{2}$

15. Not defined   **17.** $\dfrac{\sqrt{3}}{2}$ **19.** $-\dfrac{\sqrt{2}}{2}$ **21.** 0   **23.** 0

25. 0.4816   **27.** 1.3065   **29.** -2.1599 **31.** 1
33. -1.1747 **35.** -1 **37.** -0.7071 **39.** 0
41. 0.8391
43. (a)

(b)

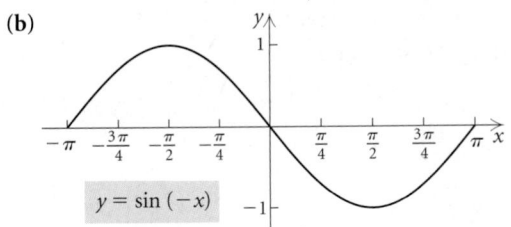

(c) same as (b); (d) the same
45. (a) See Exercise 43(a);
(b)

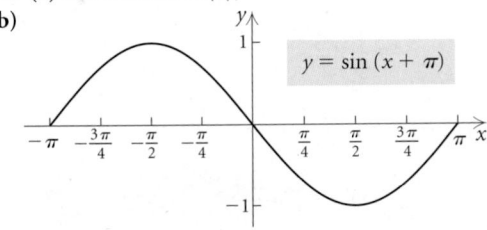

(c) same as (b); (d) the same

47. (a)

(b)

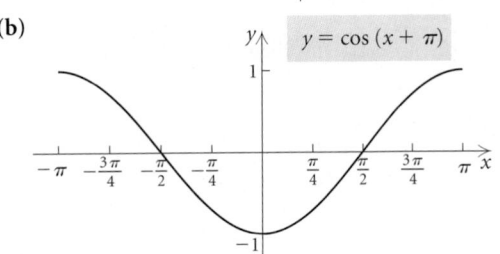

(c) same as (b); (d) the same
49. (a)

(b)

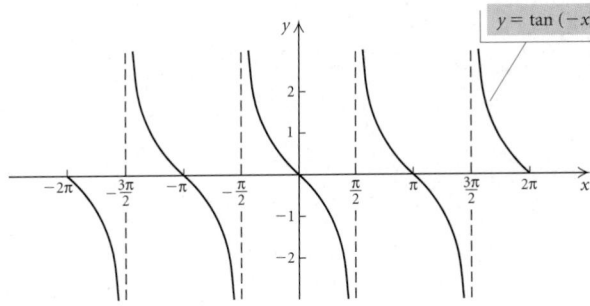

(c) same as (b); (d) the same
51. Even: cosine, secant; odd: sine, tangent, cosecant,
cotangent   **53.** Positive: I, III; negative: II, IV
55. Positive: I, IV; negative: II, III
57. Domain: $(-\infty, \infty)$; range: $[0, 1]$; period: π;
amplitude: $\frac{1}{2}$ **59.** 1   **61.** Discussion and Writing

63. [1.7]

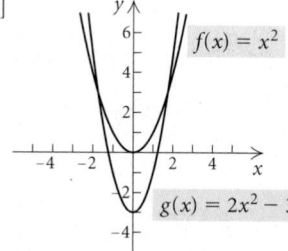

Stretch the graph of f vertically, then shift it down 3 units.

64. [1.7]

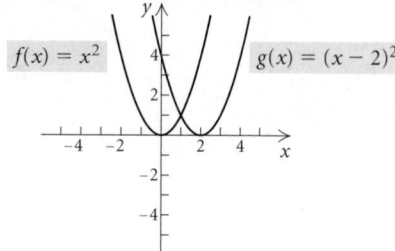

Shift the graph of f right 2 units.

65. [1.7]

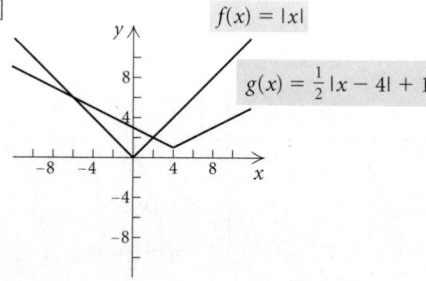

Shift the graph of f to the right 4 units, shrink it vertically, then shift it up 1 unit.

66. [1.7]

Reflect the graph of f across the x-axis.

67. [1.7] $y = -(x - 2)^3 - 1$ **68.** [1.7] $y = \dfrac{1}{4x} + 3$

69. $\cos x$ **71.** $\sin x$ **73.** $\sin x$ **75.** $-\cos x$

77. $-\sin x$ **79. (a)** $\dfrac{\pi}{2} + 2k\pi, k \in \mathbb{Z}$; **(b)** $\pi + 2k\pi$, $k \in \mathbb{Z}$; **(c)** $k\pi, k \in \mathbb{Z}$

81. $\left[-\dfrac{\pi}{2} + 2k\pi, \dfrac{\pi}{2} + 2k\pi \right], k \in \mathbb{Z}$

83. $\left\{ x \,\middle|\, x \neq \dfrac{\pi}{2} + k\pi, k \in \mathbb{Z} \right\}$

85.

87.

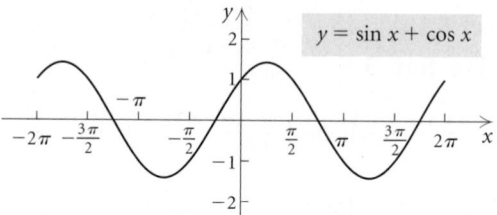

89. (a) $\triangle OPA \sim \triangle ODB$;
Thus, $\dfrac{AP}{OA} = \dfrac{BD}{OB}$
$\dfrac{\sin \theta}{\cos \theta} = \dfrac{BD}{1}$
$\tan \theta = BD$

(b) $\triangle OPA \sim \triangle ODB$;
$\dfrac{OD}{OP} = \dfrac{OB}{OA}$
$\dfrac{OD}{1} = \dfrac{1}{\cos \theta}$
$OD = \sec \theta$

(c) $\triangle OAP \sim \triangle ECO$;
$\dfrac{OE}{PO} = \dfrac{CO}{AP}$
$\dfrac{OE}{1} = \dfrac{1}{\sin \theta}$
$OE = \csc \theta$

(d) $\triangle OAP \sim \triangle ECO$
$\dfrac{CE}{AO} = \dfrac{CO}{AP}$
$\dfrac{CE}{\cos \theta} = \dfrac{1}{\sin \theta}$
$CE = \dfrac{\cos \theta}{\sin \theta}$
$CE = \cot \theta$

Visualizing the Graph

1. J   **2.** H   **3.** E   **4.** F   **5.** B   **6.** D   **7.** G
8. A   **9.** C   **10.** I

Exercise Set 5.6

1. Amplitude: 1; period: 2π; phase shift: 0

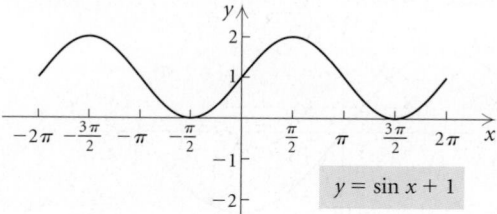

3. Amplitude: 3; period: 2π; phase shift: 0

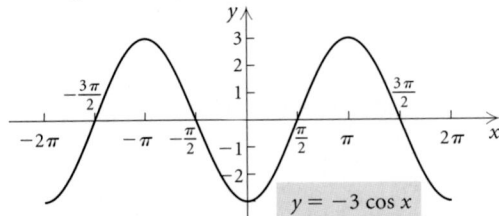

$y = -3 \cos x$

5. Amplitude: $\frac{1}{2}$; period: 2π; phase shift: 0

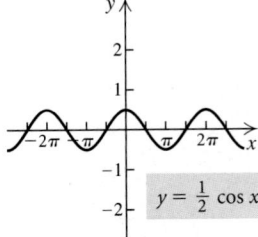

$y = \frac{1}{2} \cos x$

7. Amplitude: 1; period: π; phase shift: 0

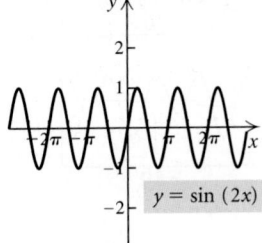

$y = \sin (2x)$

9. Amplitude: 2; period: 4π; phase shift: 0

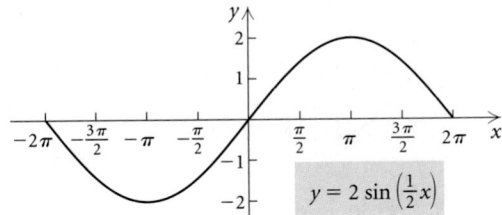

$y = 2 \sin \left(\frac{1}{2}x\right)$

11. Amplitude: $\frac{1}{2}$; period: 2π; phase shift: $-\frac{\pi}{2}$

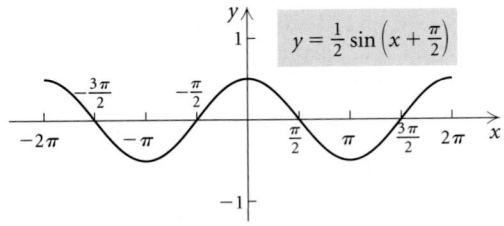

$y = \frac{1}{2} \sin \left(x + \frac{\pi}{2}\right)$

13. Amplitude: 3; period: 2π; phase shift: π

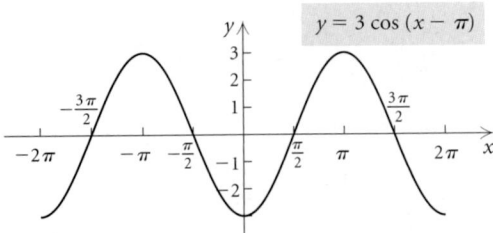

$y = 3 \cos (x - \pi)$

15. Amplitude: $\frac{1}{3}$; period: 2π; phase shift: 0

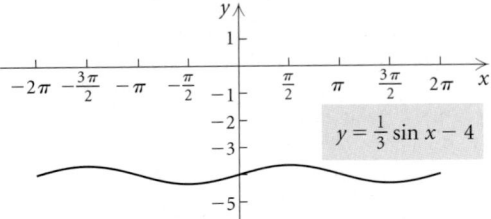

$y = \frac{1}{3} \sin x - 4$

17. Amplitude: 1; period: 2π; phase shift: 0

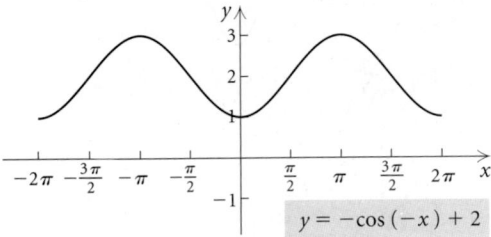

$y = -\cos (-x) + 2$

19. Amplitude: 2; period: 4π; phase shift: π

21. Amplitude: $\frac{1}{2}$; period: π; phase shift: $-\frac{\pi}{4}$

23. Amplitude: 3; period: 2; phase shift: $\frac{3}{\pi}$

25. Amplitude: $\frac{1}{2}$; period: 1; phase shift: 0

27. Amplitude: 1; period: 4π; phase shift: π

29. Amplitude: 1; period: 1; phase shift: 0

31. Amplitude: $\frac{1}{4}$; period: 2; phase shift: $\frac{4}{\pi}$

33. (b)   **35.** (h)   **37.** (a)   **39.** (f)

41. $y = \frac{1}{2} \cos x + 1$ **43.** $y = \cos \left(x + \frac{\pi}{2}\right) - 2$

45.

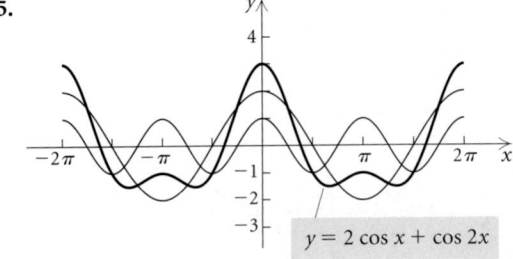

$y = 2 \cos x + \cos 2x$

47.

$y = \sin x + \cos 2x$

49.

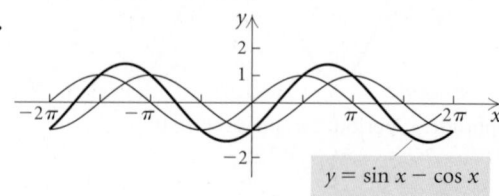

$y = \sin x - \cos x$

51.

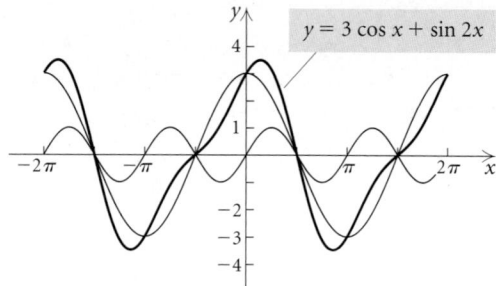

$y = 3 \cos x + \sin 2x$

53.

$f(x) = e^{-x/2} \cos x$

$y = e^{-x/2}$

$y = -e^{-x/2}$

55.

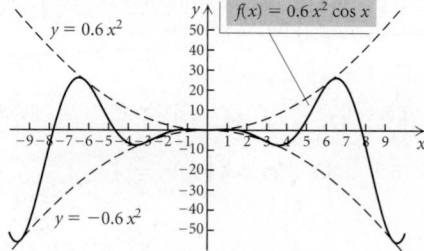

$f(x) = 0.6 x^2 \cos x$

$y = 0.6 x^2$

$y = -0.6 x^2$

57.

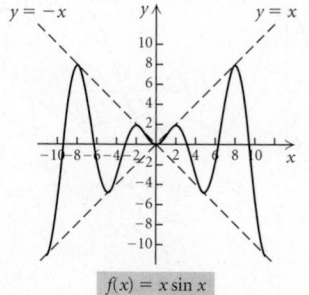

$y = -x$ $y = x$

$f(x) = x \sin x$

59.

$y = 2^{-x}$

$y = -2^{-x}$

$f(x) = 2^{-x} \sin x$

61.

$y = x + \sin x$

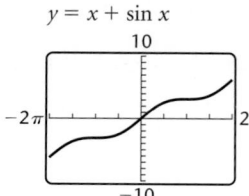

63.

$y = \cos x - x$

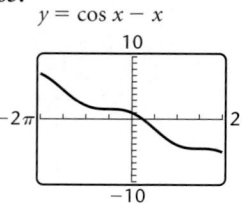

65.

$y = \cos 2x + 2x$

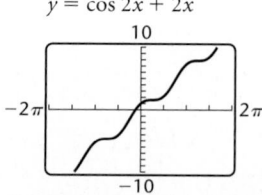

67.

$y = 4 \cos 2x - 2 \sin x$

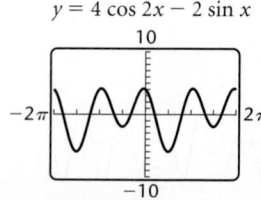

69. $-9.42, -6.28, -3.14, 3.14, 6.28, 9.42$

71. $-3.14, 0, 3.14$

73. **(a)** $y = 101.6 + 3 \sin \left(\frac{\pi}{8}x\right)$ **(b)** $104.6°, 98.6°$

75. Discussion and Writing

77. [3.5] Rational   **78.** [4.3] Logarithmic

79. [3.1] Quartic   **80.** [1.3] Linear

81. [5.6] Trigonometric   **82.** [4.2] Exponential

83. [1.3] Linear   **84.** [5.6] Trigonometric

85. [3.1] Cubic   **86.** [4.2] Exponential

87. Maximum: 8; minimum: 4

89.

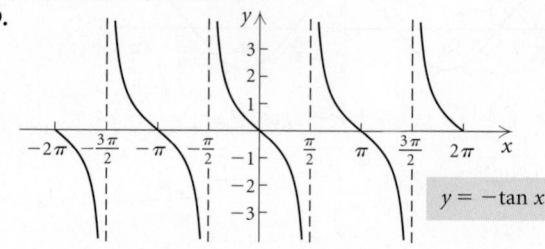

$y = -\tan x$

91.

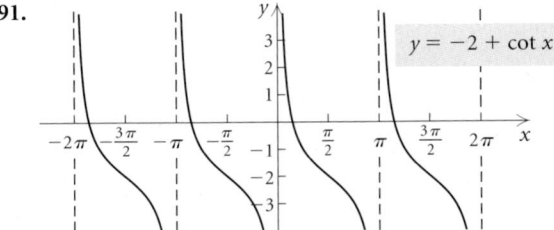

$y = -2 + \cot x$

93.

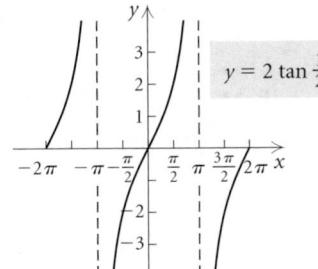

$y = 2 \tan \frac{1}{2}x$

95.

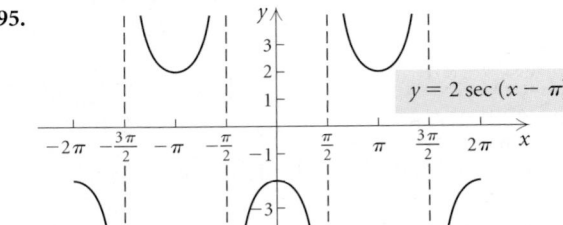

$y = 2 \sec(x - \pi)$

97.

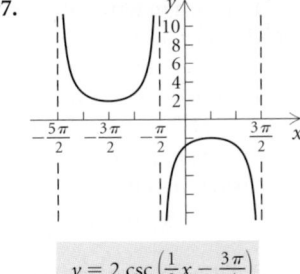

$y = 2 \csc\left(\frac{1}{2}x - \frac{3\pi}{4}\right)$

99. Amplitude: 3000; period: 90; phase shift: 10   **101.** 4 in.

Review Exercises: Chapter 5

1. False   **2.** True   **3.** True   **4.** True   **5.** False
6. False   **7.** $\sin\theta = \dfrac{3\sqrt{73}}{73}$, $\cos\theta = \dfrac{8\sqrt{73}}{73}$, $\tan\theta = \dfrac{3}{8}$,
$\csc\theta = \dfrac{\sqrt{73}}{3}$, $\sec\theta = \dfrac{\sqrt{73}}{8}$, $\cot\theta = \dfrac{8}{3}$

8. $\cos\beta = \dfrac{3}{10}$, $\tan\beta = \dfrac{\sqrt{91}}{3}$, $\csc\beta = \dfrac{10\sqrt{91}}{91}$,
$\sec\beta = \dfrac{10}{3}$, $\cot\beta = \dfrac{3\sqrt{91}}{91}$ **9.** $\dfrac{\sqrt{2}}{2}$ **10.** $\dfrac{\sqrt{3}}{3}$
11. $-\dfrac{\sqrt{2}}{2}$ **12.** $\dfrac{1}{2}$ **13.** Not defined   **14.** $-\sqrt{3}$
15. $\dfrac{2\sqrt{3}}{3}$ **16.** -1 **17.** $22°16'12''$ **18.** $47.56°$

19. 0.4452   **20.** 1.1315   **21.** 0.9498   **22.** -0.9092
23. -1.5282 **24.** -0.2778 **25.** $205.3°$
26. $47.2°$ **27.** $60°$ **28.** $60°$ **29.** $45°$ **30.** $30°$
31. $\sin 30.9° \approx 0.5135$, $\cos 30.9° \approx 0.8581$,
$\tan 30.9° \approx 0.5985$, $\csc 30.9° \approx 1.9474$, $\sec 30.9° \approx 1.1654$,
$\cot 30.9° \approx 1.6709$ **32.** $b \approx 4.5$, $A \approx 58.1°$, $B \approx 31.9°$
33. $A = 38.83°$, $b \approx 37.9$, $c \approx 48.6$ **34.** 1748 m
35. 14 ft   **36.** II   **37.** I   **38.** IV   **39.** $425°, -295°$
40. $\dfrac{\pi}{3}, -\dfrac{5\pi}{3}$ **41.** Complement: $76.6°$; supplement: $166.6°$
42. Complement: $\dfrac{\pi}{3}$; supplement: $\dfrac{5\pi}{6}$
43. $\sin\theta = \dfrac{3\sqrt{13}}{13}$, $\cos\theta = \dfrac{-2\sqrt{13}}{13}$, $\tan\theta = -\dfrac{3}{2}$,
$\csc\theta = \dfrac{\sqrt{13}}{3}$, $\sec\theta = -\dfrac{\sqrt{13}}{2}$, $\cot\theta = -\dfrac{2}{3}$
44. $\sin\theta = -\dfrac{2}{3}$, $\cos\theta = -\dfrac{\sqrt{5}}{3}$, $\cot\theta = \dfrac{\sqrt{5}}{2}$,
$\sec\theta = -\dfrac{3\sqrt{5}}{5}$, $\csc\theta = -\dfrac{3}{2}$ **45.** About 1743 mi

46.

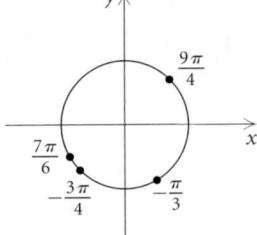

47. $\dfrac{121}{150}\pi$, 2.53   **48.** $-\dfrac{\pi}{6}$, -0.52 **49.** $270°$ **50.** $171.89°$
51. $-257.83°$ **52.** $1980°$ **53.** $\dfrac{7\pi}{4}$, or 5.5 cm
54. 2.25, $129°$ **55.** About 37.7 ft/min
56. 497,829 radians/hr   **57.** $\left(\frac{3}{5}, \frac{4}{5}\right), \left(-\frac{3}{5}, -\frac{4}{5}\right), \left(-\frac{3}{5}, \frac{4}{5}\right)$
58. -1 **59.** 1   **60.** $-\dfrac{\sqrt{3}}{2}$ **61.** $\dfrac{1}{2}$ **62.** $\dfrac{\sqrt{3}}{3}$ **63.** -1
64. -0.9056 **65.** 0.9218   **66.** Not defined   **67.** 4.3813
68. -6.1685 **69.** 0.8090
70.

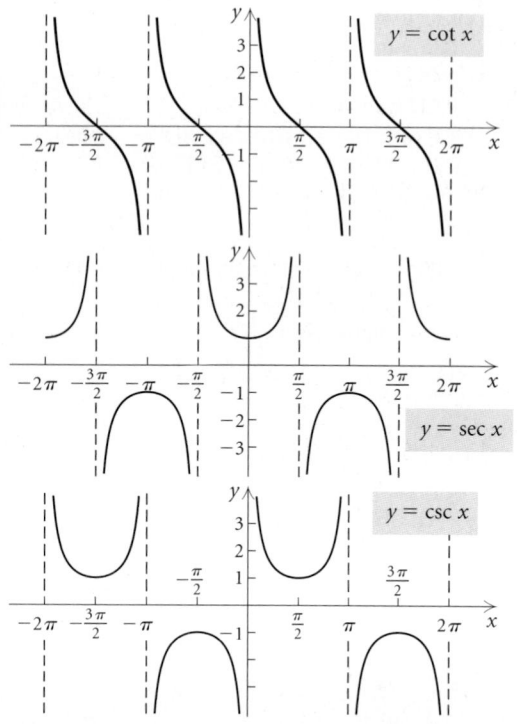

71. Period of sin, cos, sec, csc: 2π; period of tan, cot: π

72.

FUNCTION	DOMAIN	RANGE
Sine	$(-\infty, \infty)$	$[-1, 1]$
Cosine	$(-\infty, \infty)$	$[-1, 1]$
Tangent	$\left\{x \mid x \neq \dfrac{\pi}{2} + k\pi, k \in \mathbb{Z}\right\}$	$(-\infty, \infty)$

73.

FUNCTION	I	II	III	IV
Sine	+	+	−	−
Cosine	+	−	−	+
Tangent	+	−	+	−

74. Amplitude: 1; period: 2π; phase shift: $-\dfrac{\pi}{2}$

75. Amplitude: $\dfrac{1}{2}$; period: π; phase shift: $\dfrac{\pi}{4}$

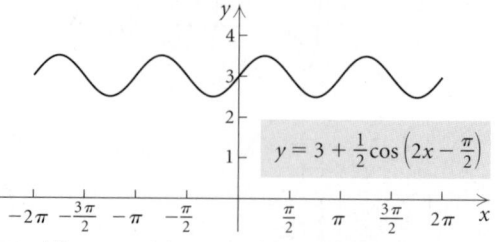

76. (d)   **77.** (a)   **78.** (c)   **79.** (b)

80.

81.

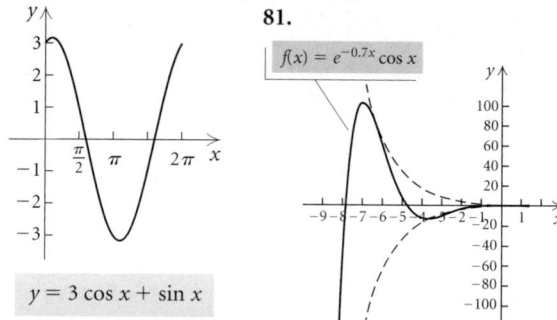

82. C   **83.** B

84. Discussion and Writing: Both degrees and radians are units of angle measure. A degree is defined to be $\frac{1}{360}$ of one complete positive revolution. Degree notation has been in use since Babylonian times. Radians are defined in terms of intercepted arc length on a circle, with one radian being the measure of the angle for which the arc length equals the radius. There are 2π radians in one complete revolution.

85. Discussion and Writing: The graph of the cosine function is shaped like a continuous wave, with "high" points at $y = 1$ and "low" points at $y = -1$. The maximum value of the cosine function is 1, and it occurs at all points where $x = 2k\pi$, $k \in \mathbb{Z}$.

86. Discussion and Writing: No; sin x is never greater than 1.

87. Domain: $(-\infty, \infty)$; range: $[-3, 3]$; period 4π

88. $y_2 = 2 \sin\left(x + \dfrac{\pi}{2}\right) - 2$

89. The domain consists of the intervals
$$\left(-\dfrac{\pi}{2} + 2k\pi, \dfrac{\pi}{2} + 2k\pi\right), k \in \mathbb{Z}.$$

90. cos $x = -0.7890$, tan $x = -0.7787$, cot $x = -1.2842$, sec $x = -1.2674$, csc $x = 1.6276$

Test: Chapter 5

1. [5.1] $\sin \theta = \dfrac{4}{\sqrt{65}}$, or $\dfrac{4\sqrt{65}}{65}$; $\cos \theta = \dfrac{7}{\sqrt{65}}$, or $\dfrac{7\sqrt{65}}{65}$;

$\tan \theta = \dfrac{4}{7}$; $\csc \theta = \dfrac{\sqrt{65}}{4}$; $\sec \theta = \dfrac{\sqrt{65}}{7}$; $\cot \theta = \dfrac{7}{4}$

2. [5.3] $\dfrac{\sqrt{3}}{2}$ **3.** [5.3] -1 **4.** [5.4] -1 **5.** [5.4] $-\sqrt{2}$

6. [5.1] $38.47°$ **7.** [5.3] -0.2419 **8.** [5.3] -0.2079
9. [5.4] -5.7588 **10.** [5.4] 0.7827 **11.** [5.1] $30°$
12. [5.1] $\sin 61.6° \approx 0.8796$; $\cos 61.6° \approx 0.4756$;
$\tan 61.6° \approx 1.8495$; $\csc 61.6° \approx 1.1369$; $\sec 61.6° \approx 2.1026$;
$\cot 61.6° \approx 0.5407$ **13.** [5.2] $B = 54.1°$, $a \approx 32.6$, $c \approx 55.7$

14. [5.3] Answers may vary; $472°$, $-248°$ **15.** [5.4] $\dfrac{\pi}{6}$

16. [5.3] $\cos \theta = \dfrac{5}{\sqrt{41}}$; $\tan \theta = -\dfrac{4}{5}$; $\csc \theta = -\dfrac{\sqrt{41}}{4}$;

$\sec \theta = \dfrac{\sqrt{41}}{5}$; $\cot \theta = -\dfrac{5}{4}$ **17.** [5.4] $\dfrac{7\pi}{6}$ **18.** [5.4] $135°$

19. [5.4] $\dfrac{16\pi}{3} \approx 16.755$ cm   **20.** [5.5] 1 **21.** [5.5] 2π

22. [5.5] $\dfrac{\pi}{2}$ **23.** [5.6] (c)   **24.** [5.2] About 444 ft

25. [5.2] About 272 mi   **26.** [5.4] $18\pi \approx 56.55$ m/min
27. [5.6]

28. [5.5] $\left\{x \left| -\dfrac{\pi}{2} + 2k\pi < x < \dfrac{\pi}{2} + 2k\pi, k \text{ an integer} \right.\right\}$

CHAPTER 6

Exercise Set 6.1

1. $\sin^2 x - \cos^2 x$ **3.** $\sin y + \cos y$ **5.** $1 - 2\sin \phi \cos \phi$
7. $\sin^3 x + \csc^3 x$ **9.** $\cos x (\sin x + \cos x)$
11. $(\sin x + \cos x)(\sin x - \cos x)$
13. $(2\cos x + 3)(\cos x - 1)$
15. $(\sin x + 3)(\sin^2 x - 3\sin x + 9)$ **17.** $\tan x$
19. $\sin x + 1$ **21.** $\dfrac{2\tan t + 1}{3\tan t + 1}$ **23.** 1

25. $\dfrac{5\cot \phi}{\sin \phi + \cos \phi}$ **27.** $\dfrac{1 + 2\sin s + 2\cos s}{\sin^2 s - \cos^2 s}$

29. $\dfrac{5(\sin \theta - 3)}{3}$ **31.** $\sin x \cos x$

33. $\sqrt{\cos \alpha}\,(\sin \alpha - \cos \alpha)$ **35.** $1 - \sin y$
37. $\dfrac{\sqrt{\sin x \cos x}}{\cos x}$ **39.** $\dfrac{\sqrt{2}\cot y}{2}$ **41.** $\dfrac{\cos x}{\sqrt{\sin x \cos x}}$

43. $\dfrac{1 + \sin y}{\cos y}$ **45.** $\cos \theta = \dfrac{\sqrt{a^2 - x^2}}{a}$, $\tan \theta = \dfrac{x}{\sqrt{a^2 - x^2}}$

47. $\sin \theta = \dfrac{\sqrt{x^2 - 9}}{x}$, $\cos \theta = \dfrac{3}{x}$ **49.** $\sin \theta \tan \theta$

51. $\dfrac{\sqrt{6} - \sqrt{2}}{4}$ **53.** $\dfrac{\sqrt{3} + 1}{1 - \sqrt{3}}$, or $-2 - \sqrt{3}$

55. $\dfrac{\sqrt{6} + \sqrt{2}}{4}$ **57.** $\sin 59° \approx 0.8572$

59. $\cos 24° \approx 0.9135$ **61.** $\tan 52° \approx 1.2799$

63. $\tan(\mu + \nu) = \dfrac{\sin(\mu + \nu)}{\cos(\mu + \nu)}$

$= \dfrac{\sin \mu \cos \nu + \cos \mu \sin \nu}{\cos \mu \cos \nu - \sin \mu \sin \nu}$

$= \dfrac{\sin \mu \cos \nu + \cos \mu \sin \nu}{\cos \mu \cos \nu - \sin \mu \sin \nu} \cdot \dfrac{\dfrac{1}{\cos \mu \cos \nu}}{\dfrac{1}{\cos \mu \cos \nu}}$

$= \dfrac{\dfrac{\sin \mu}{\cos \mu} + \dfrac{\sin \nu}{\cos \nu}}{1 - \dfrac{\sin \mu \sin \nu}{\cos \mu \cos \nu}}$

$= \dfrac{\tan \mu + \tan \nu}{1 - \tan \mu \tan \nu}$

65. 0 **67.** $-\dfrac{7}{25}$ **69.** -1.5789 **71.** 0.7071

73. $2\sin \alpha \cos \beta$ **75.** $\cos u$ **77.** Left to the student
79. Discussion and Writing   **81.** [2.1] All real numbers
82. [2.1] No solution   **83.** [5.1] 1.9417 **84.** [5.1] 1.6645

85. $0°$; the lines are parallel   **87.** $\dfrac{3\pi}{4}$, or $135°$ **89.** $4.57°$

91. $\dfrac{\cos(x + h) - \cos x}{h}$

$= \dfrac{\cos x \cos h - \sin x \sin h - \cos x}{h}$

$= \dfrac{\cos x \cos h - \cos x}{h} - \dfrac{\sin x \sin h}{h}$

$= \cos x \left(\dfrac{\cos h - 1}{h}\right) - \sin x \left(\dfrac{\sin h}{h}\right)$

93. Let $x = \dfrac{\pi}{5}$. Then $\dfrac{\sin 5x}{x} = \dfrac{\sin \pi}{\pi/5} = 0 \neq \sin 5$.

Answers may vary.

95. Let $\alpha = \dfrac{\pi}{4}$. Then $\cos(2\alpha) = \cos \dfrac{\pi}{2} = 0$, but

$2\cos \alpha = 2\cos \dfrac{\pi}{4} = \sqrt{2}$. Answers may vary.

97. Let $x = \dfrac{\pi}{6}$. Then $\dfrac{\cos 6x}{\cos x} = \dfrac{\cos \pi}{\cos \dfrac{\pi}{6}} = \dfrac{-1}{\sqrt{3}/2} \neq 6.$

Answers may vary.   **99.** $\dfrac{6 - 3\sqrt{3}}{9 + 2\sqrt{3}} \approx 0.0645$

101. $168.7°$ **103.** $\cos 2\theta = \cos^2\theta - \sin^2\theta$, or $1 - 2\sin^2\theta$, or $2\cos^2\theta - 1$

105. $\tan\left(x + \dfrac{\pi}{4}\right) = \dfrac{\tan x + \tan\dfrac{\pi}{4}}{1 - \tan x\tan\dfrac{\pi}{4}} = \dfrac{1 + \tan x}{1 - \tan x}$

107. $\sin(\alpha + \beta) + \sin(\alpha - \beta) = \sin\alpha\cos\beta + \cos\alpha\sin\beta + \sin\alpha\cos\beta - \cos\alpha\sin\beta = 2\sin\alpha\cos\beta$

Exercise Set 6.2

1. (a) $\tan\dfrac{3\pi}{10} \approx 1.3763$, $\csc\dfrac{3\pi}{10} \approx 1.2361$, $\sec\dfrac{3\pi}{10} \approx 1.7013$, $\cot\dfrac{3\pi}{10} \approx 0.7266$; **(b)** $\sin\dfrac{\pi}{5} \approx 0.5878$, $\cos\dfrac{\pi}{5} \approx 0.8090$, $\tan\dfrac{\pi}{5} \approx 0.7266$, $\csc\dfrac{\pi}{5} \approx 1.7013$, $\sec\dfrac{\pi}{5} \approx 1.2361$, $\cot\dfrac{\pi}{5} \approx 1.3763$

3. (a) $\cos\theta = -\dfrac{2\sqrt{2}}{3}$, $\tan\theta = -\dfrac{\sqrt{2}}{4}$, $\csc\theta = 3$, $\sec\theta = -\dfrac{3\sqrt{2}}{4}$, $\cot\theta = -2\sqrt{2}$;

(b) $\sin\left(\dfrac{\pi}{2} - \theta\right) = -\dfrac{2\sqrt{2}}{3}$, $\cos\left(\dfrac{\pi}{2} - \theta\right) = \dfrac{1}{3}$, $\tan\left(\dfrac{\pi}{2} - \theta\right) = -2\sqrt{2}$, $\csc\left(\dfrac{\pi}{2} - \theta\right) = -\dfrac{3\sqrt{2}}{4}$, $\sec\left(\dfrac{\pi}{2} - \theta\right) = 3$, $\cot\left(\dfrac{\pi}{2} - \theta\right) = -\dfrac{\sqrt{2}}{4}$;

(c) $\sin\left(\theta - \dfrac{\pi}{2}\right) = \dfrac{2\sqrt{2}}{3}$, $\cos\left(\theta - \dfrac{\pi}{2}\right) = \dfrac{1}{3}$, $\tan\left(\theta - \dfrac{\pi}{2}\right) = 2\sqrt{2}$, $\csc\left(\theta - \dfrac{\pi}{2}\right) = \dfrac{3\sqrt{2}}{4}$, $\sec\left(\theta - \dfrac{\pi}{2}\right) = 3$, $\cot\left(\theta - \dfrac{\pi}{2}\right) = \dfrac{\sqrt{2}}{4}$;

5. $\sec\left(x + \dfrac{\pi}{2}\right) = -\csc x$ **7.** $\tan\left(x - \dfrac{\pi}{2}\right) = -\cot x$

9. $\sin 2\theta = \dfrac{24}{25}$, $\cos 2\theta = -\dfrac{7}{25}$, $\tan 2\theta = -\dfrac{24}{7}$; II

11. $\sin 2\theta = \dfrac{24}{25}$, $\cos 2\theta = -\dfrac{7}{25}$, $\tan 2\theta = -\dfrac{24}{7}$; II

13. $\sin 2\theta = -\dfrac{120}{169}$, $\cos 2\theta = \dfrac{119}{169}$, $\tan 2\theta = -\dfrac{120}{119}$; IV

15. $\cos 4x = 1 - 8\sin^2 x\cos^2 x$, or $\cos^4 x - 6\sin^2 x\cos^2 x + \sin^4 x$, or $8\cos^4 x - 8\cos^2 x + 1$

17. $\dfrac{\sqrt{2 + \sqrt{3}}}{2}$ **19.** $\dfrac{\sqrt{2 + \sqrt{2}}}{2}$ **21.** $2 + \sqrt{3}$
23. 0.6421 **25.** 0.1735 **27.** $\cos x$ **29.** 1
31. $\cos 2x$ **33.** 8

35. (d); $\dfrac{\cos 2x}{\cos x - \sin x} = \dfrac{\cos^2 x - \sin^2 x}{\cos x - \sin x}$
$= \dfrac{(\cos x + \sin x)(\cos x - \sin x)}{\cos x - \sin x}$
$= \cos x + \sin x$
$= \dfrac{\sin x}{\sin x}(\cos x + \sin x)$
$= \sin x\left(\dfrac{\cos x}{\sin x} + \dfrac{\sin x}{\sin x}\right)$
$= \sin x(\cot x + 1)$

37. (d); $\dfrac{\sin 2x}{2\cos x} = \dfrac{2\sin x\cos x}{2\cos x} = \sin x$

39. Discussion and Writing   **41.** [6.1] $\sin^2 x$ **42.** [6.1] 1
43. [6.1] $-\cos^2 x$ **44.** [6.1] $\csc^2 x$ **45.** [6.1] 1
46. [6.1] $\sec^2 x$ **47.** [6.1] $\cos^2 x$ **48.** [6.1] $\tan^2 x$
49. [5.5] (a), (e)   **50.** [5.5] (b), (c), (f)   **51.** [5.5] (d)
52. [5.5] (e)   **53.** $\sin 141° \approx 0.6293$, $\cos 141° \approx -0.7772$, $\tan 141° \approx -0.8097$, $\csc 141° \approx 1.5891$, $\sec 141° \approx -1.2867$, $\cot 141° \approx -1.2350$
55. $-\cos x(1 + \cot x)$ **57.** $\cot^2 y$
59. $\sin\theta = -\dfrac{15}{17}$, $\cos\theta = -\dfrac{8}{17}$, $\tan\theta = \dfrac{15}{8}$
61. (a) 9.80359 m/sec^2; **(b)** 9.80180 m/sec^2;
(c) $g = 9.78049(1 + 0.005264\sin^2\phi + 0.000024\sin^4\phi)$

Exercise Set 6.3

1.

$\sec x - \sin x\tan x$	$\cos x$
$\dfrac{1}{\cos x} - \sin x \cdot \dfrac{\sin x}{\cos x}$	
$\dfrac{1 - \sin^2 x}{\cos x}$	
$\dfrac{\cos^2 x}{\cos x}$	
$\cos x$	

3.

$\dfrac{1 - \cos x}{\sin x}$	$\dfrac{\sin x}{1 + \cos x}$
	$\dfrac{\sin x}{1 + \cos x} \cdot \dfrac{1 - \cos x}{1 - \cos x}$
	$\dfrac{\sin x(1 - \cos x)}{1 - \cos^2 x}$
	$\dfrac{\sin x(1 - \cos x)}{\sin^2 x}$
	$\dfrac{1 - \cos x}{\sin x}$

5.

$$\dfrac{1+\tan\theta}{1-\tan\theta}+\dfrac{1+\cot\theta}{1-\cot\theta} \;\Big|\; 0$$

$$\dfrac{1+\dfrac{\sin\theta}{\cos\theta}}{1-\dfrac{\sin\theta}{\cos\theta}}+\dfrac{1+\dfrac{\cos\theta}{\sin\theta}}{1-\dfrac{\cos\theta}{\sin\theta}}$$

$$\dfrac{\dfrac{\cos\theta+\sin\theta}{\cos\theta}}{\dfrac{\cos\theta-\sin\theta}{\cos\theta}}+\dfrac{\dfrac{\sin\theta+\cos\theta}{\sin\theta}}{\dfrac{\sin\theta-\cos\theta}{\sin\theta}}$$

$$\dfrac{\cos\theta+\sin\theta}{\cos\theta}\cdot\dfrac{\cos\theta}{\cos\theta-\sin\theta}+$$

$$\dfrac{\sin\theta+\cos\theta}{\sin\theta}\cdot\dfrac{\sin\theta}{\sin\theta-\cos\theta}$$

$$\dfrac{\cos\theta+\sin\theta}{\cos\theta-\sin\theta}+\dfrac{\sin\theta+\cos\theta}{\sin\theta-\cos\theta}$$

$$\dfrac{\cos\theta+\sin\theta}{\cos\theta-\sin\theta}-\dfrac{\cos\theta+\sin\theta}{\cos\theta-\sin\theta}$$

$$0$$

7.

$$\dfrac{\cos^2\alpha+\cot\alpha}{\cos^2\alpha-\cot\alpha} \;\Big|\; \dfrac{\cos^2\alpha\tan\alpha+1}{\cos^2\alpha\tan\alpha-1}$$

$$\dfrac{\cos^2\alpha+\dfrac{\cos\alpha}{\sin\alpha}}{\cos^2\alpha-\dfrac{\cos\alpha}{\sin\alpha}} \;\Big|\; \dfrac{\cos^2\alpha\,\dfrac{\sin\alpha}{\cos\alpha}+1}{\cos^2\alpha\,\dfrac{\sin\alpha}{\cos\alpha}-1}$$

$$\dfrac{\cos\alpha\left(\cos\alpha+\dfrac{1}{\sin\alpha}\right)}{\cos\alpha\left(\cos\alpha-\dfrac{1}{\sin\alpha}\right)} \;\Big|\; \dfrac{\sin\alpha\cos\alpha+1}{\sin\alpha\cos\alpha-1}$$

$$\dfrac{\cos\alpha+\dfrac{1}{\sin\alpha}}{\cos\alpha-\dfrac{1}{\sin\alpha}}$$

$$\dfrac{\dfrac{\sin\alpha\cos\alpha+1}{\sin\alpha}}{\dfrac{\sin\alpha\cos\alpha-1}{\sin\alpha}}$$

$$\dfrac{\sin\alpha\cos\alpha+1}{\sin\alpha\cos\alpha-1}$$

9.

$$\dfrac{2\tan\theta}{1+\tan^2\theta} \;\Big|\; \sin 2\theta$$

$$\dfrac{2\tan\theta}{\sec^2\theta} \;\Big|\; 2\sin\theta\cos\theta$$

$$\dfrac{2\sin\theta}{\cos\theta}\cdot\dfrac{\cos^2\theta}{1}$$

$$2\sin\theta\cos\theta$$

11.

$$1-\cos 5\theta\cos 3\theta-\sin 5\theta\sin 3\theta \;\Big|\; 2\sin^2\theta$$

$$1-[\cos 5\theta\cos 3\theta+\sin 5\theta\sin 3\theta] \;\Big|\; 1-\cos 2\theta$$

$$1-\cos(5\theta-3\theta)$$

$$1-\cos 2\theta$$

13.

$$2\sin\theta\cos^3\theta+2\sin^3\theta\cos\theta \;\Big|\; \sin 2\theta$$

$$2\sin\theta\cos\theta\,(\cos^2\theta+\sin^2\theta) \;\Big|\; 2\sin\theta\cos\theta$$

$$2\sin\theta\cos\theta$$

15.

$$\dfrac{\tan x-\sin x}{2\tan x} \;\Big|\; \sin^2\dfrac{x}{2}$$

$$\dfrac{1}{2}\left[\dfrac{\dfrac{\sin x}{\cos x}-\sin x}{\dfrac{\sin x}{\cos x}}\right] \;\Big|\; \dfrac{1-\cos x}{2}$$

$$\dfrac{1}{2}\,\dfrac{\sin x-\sin x\cos x}{\cos x}\cdot\dfrac{\cos x}{\sin x}$$

$$\dfrac{1-\cos x}{2}$$

17.

$$\sin(\alpha+\beta)\sin(\alpha-\beta) \;\Big|\; \sin^2\alpha-\sin^2\beta$$

$$\left(\begin{array}{c}\sin\alpha\cos\beta+\\ \cos\alpha\sin\beta\end{array}\right)\left(\begin{array}{c}\sin\alpha\cos\beta-\\ \cos\alpha\sin\beta\end{array}\right) \;\Big|\; \begin{array}{l}1-\cos^2\alpha-\\ (1-\cos^2\beta)\end{array}$$

$$\sin^2\alpha\cos^2\beta-\cos^2\alpha\sin^2\beta \;\Big|\; \cos^2\beta-\cos^2\alpha$$

$$\cos^2\beta(1-\cos^2\alpha)-$$

$$\cos^2\alpha(1-\cos^2\beta)$$

$$\cos^2\beta-\cos^2\alpha\cos^2\beta-$$

$$\cos^2\alpha+\cos^2\alpha\cos^2\beta$$

$$\cos^2\beta-\cos^2\alpha$$

19.

$$\tan\theta\,(\tan\theta+\cot\theta) \;\Big|\; \sec^2\theta$$

$$\tan^2\theta+\tan\theta\cot\theta$$

$$\tan^2\theta+1$$

$$\sec^2\theta$$

21.

$$\dfrac{1+\cos^2 x}{\sin^2 x} \;\Big|\; 2\csc^2 x-1$$

$$\dfrac{1}{\sin^2 x}+\dfrac{\cos^2 x}{\sin^2 x}$$

$$\csc^2 x+\cot^2 x$$

$$\csc^2 x+\csc^2 x-1$$

$$2\csc^2 x-1$$

23.

$$\dfrac{1+\sin x}{1-\sin x}+\dfrac{\sin x-1}{1+\sin x} \;\Big|\; 4\sec x\tan x$$

$$\dfrac{(1+\sin x)^2-(1-\sin x)^2}{1-\sin^2 x} \;\Big|\; 4\cdot\dfrac{1}{\cos x}\cdot\dfrac{\sin x}{\cos x}$$

$$\dfrac{(1+2\sin x+\sin^2 x)-(1-2\sin x+\sin^2 x)}{\cos^2 x} \;\Big|\; \dfrac{4\sin x}{\cos^2 x}$$

$$\dfrac{4\sin x}{\cos^2 x}$$

25.

$\cos^2\alpha \cot^2\alpha$	$\cot^2\alpha - \cos^2\alpha$
$(1 - \sin^2\alpha)\cot^2\alpha$	
$\cot^2\alpha - \sin^2\alpha \cdot \dfrac{\cos^2\alpha}{\sin^2\alpha}$	
$\cot^2\alpha - \cos^2\alpha$	

27.

$2\sin^2\theta\cos^2\theta + \cos^4\theta$	$1 - \sin^4\theta$
$\cos^2\theta\,(2\sin^2\theta + \cos^2\theta)$	$(1 + \sin^2\theta)(1 - \sin^2\theta)$
$\cos^2\theta\,(\sin^2\theta + \sin^2\theta + \cos^2\theta)$	$(1 + \sin^2\theta)(\cos^2\theta)$
$\cos^2\theta\,(\sin^2\theta + 1)$	

29.

$\dfrac{1 + \sin x}{1 - \sin x}$	$(\sec x + \tan x)^2$
$\dfrac{1 + \sin x}{1 - \sin x} \cdot \dfrac{1 + \sin x}{1 + \sin x}$	$\left(\dfrac{1}{\cos x} + \dfrac{\sin x}{\cos x}\right)^2$
$\dfrac{(1 + \sin x)^2}{1 - \sin^2 x}$	$\dfrac{(1 + \sin x)^2}{\cos^2 x}$
$\dfrac{(1 + \sin x)^2}{\cos^2 x}$	

31. Sine sum and difference identities:
$$\sin(x + y) = \sin x\cos y + \cos x\sin y,$$
$$\sin(x - y) = \sin x\cos y - \cos x\sin y.$$

Add the sum and difference identities:
$$\sin(x + y) + \sin(x - y) = 2\sin x\cos y$$
$$\tfrac{1}{2}[\sin(x + y) + \sin(x - y)] = \sin x\cos y. \quad (3)$$

Subtract the difference identity from the sum identity:
$$\sin(x + y) - \sin(x - y) = 2\cos x\sin y$$
$$\tfrac{1}{2}[\sin(x + y) - \sin(x - y)] = \cos x\sin y. \quad (4)$$

33. $\sin 3\theta - \sin 5\theta = 2\cos\dfrac{8\theta}{2}\sin\dfrac{-2\theta}{2} = -2\cos 4\theta\sin\theta$

35. $\sin 8\theta + \sin 5\theta = 2\sin\dfrac{13\theta}{2}\cos\dfrac{3\theta}{2}$

37. $\sin 7u\sin 5u = \tfrac{1}{2}(\cos 2u - \cos 12u)$

39. $7\cos\theta\sin 7\theta = \tfrac{7}{2}[\sin 8\theta - \sin(-6\theta)]$
$$= \tfrac{7}{2}(\sin 8\theta + \sin 6\theta)$$

41. $\cos 55°\sin 25° = \tfrac{1}{2}(\sin 80° - \sin 30°) = \tfrac{1}{2}\sin 80° - \tfrac{1}{4}$

43.

$\sin 4\theta + \sin 6\theta$	$\cot\theta\,(\cos 4\theta - \cos 6\theta)$
$2\sin\dfrac{10\theta}{2}\cos\dfrac{-2\theta}{2}$	$\dfrac{\cos\theta}{\sin\theta}\left(2\sin\dfrac{10\theta}{2}\sin\dfrac{2\theta}{2}\right)$
$2\sin 5\theta\cos(-\theta)$	$\dfrac{\cos\theta}{\sin\theta}(2\sin 5\theta\sin\theta)$
$2\sin 5\theta\cos\theta$	$2\sin 5\theta\cos\theta$

45.

$\cot 4x\,(\sin x + \sin 4x + \sin 7x)$	$\cos x + \cos 4x + \cos 7x$
$\dfrac{\cos 4x}{\sin 4x}\left(\sin 4x + 2\sin\dfrac{8x}{2}\cos\dfrac{-6x}{2}\right)$	$\cos 4x + 2\cos\dfrac{8x}{2}\cdot\cos\dfrac{6x}{2}$
$\dfrac{\cos 4x}{\sin 4x}(\sin 4x + 2\sin 4x\cos 3x)$	$\cos 4x + 2\cos 4x\cdot\cos 3x$
$\cos 4x\,(1 + 2\cos 3x)$	$\cos 4x\,(1 + 2\cos 3x)$

47.

$\cot\dfrac{x + y}{2}$	$\dfrac{\sin y - \sin x}{\cos x - \cos y}$
$\dfrac{\cos\dfrac{x + y}{2}}{\sin\dfrac{x + y}{2}}$	$\dfrac{2\cos\dfrac{x + y}{2}\sin\dfrac{y - x}{2}}{2\sin\dfrac{x + y}{2}\sin\dfrac{y - x}{2}}$
	$\dfrac{\cos\dfrac{x + y}{2}}{\sin\dfrac{x + y}{2}}$

49.

$\tan\dfrac{\theta + \phi}{2}(\sin\theta - \sin\phi)$	$\tan\dfrac{\theta - \phi}{2}(\sin\theta + \sin\phi)$
$\dfrac{\sin\dfrac{\theta + \phi}{2}}{\cos\dfrac{\theta + \phi}{2}}\left(2\cos\dfrac{\theta + \phi}{2}\sin\dfrac{\theta - \phi}{2}\right)$	$\dfrac{\sin\dfrac{\theta - \phi}{2}}{\cos\dfrac{\theta - \phi}{2}}\left(2\sin\dfrac{\theta + \phi}{2}\cos\dfrac{\theta - \phi}{2}\right)$
$2\sin\dfrac{\theta + \phi}{2}\cdot\sin\dfrac{\theta - \phi}{2}$	$2\sin\dfrac{\theta + \phi}{2}\cdot\sin\dfrac{\theta - \phi}{2}$

51. B;

$\dfrac{\cos x + \cot x}{1 + \csc x}$	$\cos x$
$\dfrac{\cos x + \dfrac{\cos x}{\sin x}}{1 + \dfrac{1}{\sin x}}$	
$\dfrac{\sin x\cos x + \cos x}{\sin x}\cdot\dfrac{\sin x}{\sin x + 1}$	
$\dfrac{\cos x\,(\sin x + 1)}{\sin x + 1}$	
$\cos x$	

53. A;

$\sin x\cos x + 1$	$\dfrac{\sin^3 x - \cos^3 x}{\sin x - \cos x}$
	$\dfrac{(\sin x - \cos x)(\sin^2 x + \sin x\cos x + \cos^2 x)}{\sin x - \cos x}$
	$\sin^2 x + \sin x\cos x + \cos^2 x$
	$\sin x\cos x + 1$

55. C;

$\dfrac{1}{\cot x\sin^2 x}$	$\tan x + \cot x$
$\dfrac{1}{\dfrac{\cos x}{\sin x}\cdot\sin^2 x}$	$\dfrac{\sin x}{\cos x} + \dfrac{\cos x}{\sin x}$
$\dfrac{1}{\cos x\sin x}$	$\dfrac{\sin^2 x + \cos^2 x}{\cos x\sin x}$
	$\dfrac{1}{\cos x\sin x}$

57. Discussion and Writing

59. [4.1] **(a)**, **(d)**

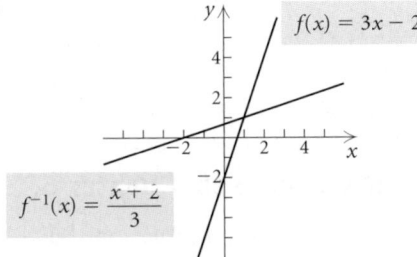

$f(x) = 3x - 2$

$f^{-1}(x) = \dfrac{x + 2}{3}$

(b) yes; **(c)** $f^{-1}(x) = \dfrac{x + 2}{3}$

60. [4.1] **(a)**, **(d)**

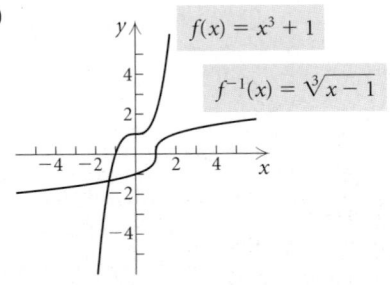

$f(x) = x^3 + 1$

$f^{-1}(x) = \sqrt[3]{x - 1}$

(b) yes; **(c)** $f^{-1}(x) = \sqrt[3]{x - 1}$

61. [4.1] **(a)**, **(d)**

$f(x) = x^2 - 4,\ x \geqslant 0$

$f^{-1}(x) = \sqrt{x + 4}$

(b) yes; **(c)** $f^{-1}(x) = \sqrt{x + 4}$

62. [4.1] **(a)**, **(d)**

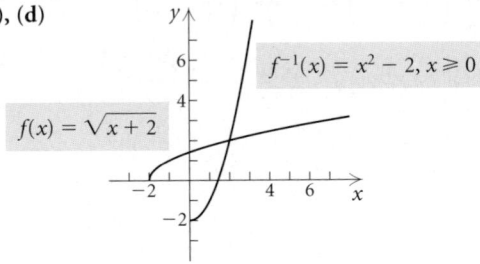

$f^{-1}(x) = x^2 - 2,\ x \geqslant 0$

$f(x) = \sqrt{x + 2}$

(b) yes; **(c)** $f^{-1}(x) = x^2 - 2,\ x \geqslant 0$

63. [2.3] $0, \frac{5}{2}$ **64.** [2.3] $-4, \frac{7}{3}$ **65.** [2.3] $\pm 2, \pm 3i$

66. [2.3] $5 \pm 2\sqrt{6}$ **67.** [2.5] 27   **68.** [2.5] 9

69.

$\ln |\tan x|$	$-\ln |\cot x|$
$\ln \left| \dfrac{1}{\cot x} \right|$	
$\ln |1| - \ln |\cot x|$	
$0 - \ln |\cot x|$	
$-\ln |\cot x|$	

71. $\log (\cos x - \sin x) + \log (\cos x + \sin x)$
$$= \log [(\cos x - \sin x)(\cos x + \sin x)]$$
$$= \log (\cos^2 x - \sin^2 x) = \log \cos 2x$$

73. $\dfrac{1}{\omega C(\tan \theta + \tan \phi)} = \dfrac{1}{\omega C \left(\dfrac{\sin \theta}{\cos \theta} + \dfrac{\sin \phi}{\cos \phi} \right)}$

$$= \dfrac{1}{\omega C \left(\dfrac{\sin \theta \cos \phi + \sin \phi \cos \theta}{\cos \theta \cos \phi} \right)}$$

$$= \dfrac{\cos \theta \cos \phi}{\omega C \sin (\theta + \phi)}$$

Exercise Set 6.4

1. $-\dfrac{\pi}{3}, -60°$ **3.** $\dfrac{\pi}{4}, 45°$ **5.** $\dfrac{\pi}{4}, 45°$ **7.** $0, 0°$

9. $\dfrac{\pi}{6}, 30°$ **11.** $\dfrac{\pi}{6}, 30°$ **13.** $-\dfrac{\pi}{6}, -30°$

15. $-\dfrac{\pi}{6}, -30°$ **17.** $\dfrac{\pi}{2}, 90°$ **19.** $\dfrac{\pi}{3}, 60°$

21. $0.3520, 20.2°$ **23.** $1.2917, 74.0°$ **25.** $2.9463, 168.8°$
27. $-0.1600, -9.2°$ **29.** $0.8289, 47.5°$
31. $-0.9600, -55.0°$
33. $\sin^{-1}: [-1, 1]; \cos^{-1}: [-1, 1]; \tan^{-1}: (-\infty, \infty)$

35. $\theta = \sin^{-1} \left(\dfrac{2000}{d} \right)$ **37.** 0.3 **39.** $\dfrac{\pi}{4}$ **41.** $\dfrac{\pi}{5}$

43. $-\dfrac{\pi}{3}$ **45.** $\frac{1}{2}$ **47.** 1 **49.** $\dfrac{\pi}{3}$ **51.** $\dfrac{\sqrt{11}}{33}$

53. $-\dfrac{\pi}{6}$ **55.** $\dfrac{a}{\sqrt{a^2 + 9}}$ **57.** $\dfrac{\sqrt{q^2 - p^2}}{p}$ **59.** $\dfrac{p}{3}$

61. $\dfrac{\sqrt{3}}{2}$ **63.** $-\dfrac{\sqrt{2}}{10}$ **65.** $xy + \sqrt{(1 - x^2)(1 - y^2)}$

67. 0.9861 **69.** Discussion and Writing
71. Discussion and Writing   **72.** [5.5] Periodic
73. [5.4] Radian measure   **74.** [5.1] Similar
75. [5.2] Angle of depression   **76.** [5.4] Angular speed
77. [5.3] Supplementary   **78.** [5.5] Amplitude
79. [5.1] Acute   **80.** [5.5] Circular
81.

$\sin^{-1} x + \cos^{-1} x$	$\dfrac{\pi}{2}$
$\sin (\sin^{-1} x + \cos^{-1} x)$	$\sin \dfrac{\pi}{2}$
$[\sin (\sin^{-1} x)][\cos (\cos^{-1} x)] +$ $[\cos (\sin^{-1} x)][\sin (\cos^{-1} x)]$ $x \cdot x + \sqrt{1 - x^2} \cdot \sqrt{1 - x^2}$ $x^2 + 1 - x^2$ 1	1

83.

$\sin^{-1} x$	$\tan^{-1} \dfrac{x}{\sqrt{1-x^2}}$
$\sin\left(\sin^{-1} x\right)$	$\sin\left(\tan^{-1} \dfrac{x}{\sqrt{1-x^2}}\right)$
x	x

85.

$\sin^{-1} x$	$\cos^{-1} \sqrt{1-x^2}$
$\sin\left(\sin^{-1} x\right)$	$\sin\left(\cos^{-1} \sqrt{1-x^2}\right)$
x	x

87. $\theta = \tan^{-1} \dfrac{y+h}{x} - \tan^{-1} \dfrac{y}{x}$; 38.7°

Visualizing the Graph

1. D   **2.** G   **3.** C   **4.** H   **5.** I   **6.** A   **7.** E
8. J   **9.** F   **10.** B

Exercise Set 6.5

1. $\dfrac{\pi}{6} + 2k\pi, \dfrac{11\pi}{6} + 2k\pi$, or $30° + k \cdot 360°, 330° + k \cdot 360°$

3. $\dfrac{2\pi}{3} + k\pi$, or $120° + k \cdot 180°$

5. $\dfrac{\pi}{6} + 2k\pi, \dfrac{5\pi}{6} + 2k\pi$, or $30° + k \cdot 360°, 150° + k \cdot 360°$

7. $\dfrac{3\pi}{4} + 2k\pi, \dfrac{5\pi}{4} + 2k\pi$, or $135° + k \cdot 360°, 225° + k \cdot 360°$

9. 98.09°, 261.91°   **11.** $\dfrac{4\pi}{3}, \dfrac{5\pi}{3}$ **13.** $\dfrac{\pi}{4}, \dfrac{3\pi}{4}, \dfrac{5\pi}{4}, \dfrac{7\pi}{4}$

15. $\dfrac{\pi}{6}, \dfrac{5\pi}{6}, \dfrac{3\pi}{2}$ **17.** $\dfrac{\pi}{6}, \dfrac{\pi}{2}, \dfrac{3\pi}{2}, \dfrac{11\pi}{6}$

19. 109.47°, 120°, 240°, 250.53°

21. $0, \dfrac{\pi}{4}, \dfrac{3\pi}{4}, \pi, \dfrac{5\pi}{4}, \dfrac{7\pi}{4}$ **23.** 139.81°, 220.19°

25. 37.22°, 169.35°, 217.22°, 349.35°   **27.** $0, \pi, \dfrac{7\pi}{6}, \dfrac{11\pi}{6}$

29. $0, \dfrac{\pi}{2}, \pi, \dfrac{3\pi}{2}$ **31.** $0, \pi$ **33.** $\dfrac{3\pi}{4}, \dfrac{7\pi}{4}$

35. $\dfrac{2\pi}{3}, \dfrac{4\pi}{3}, \dfrac{3\pi}{2}$ **37.** $\dfrac{\pi}{4}, \dfrac{3\pi}{4}, \dfrac{5\pi}{4}, \dfrac{7\pi}{4}$ **39.** $\dfrac{\pi}{12}, \dfrac{5\pi}{12}$

41. 0.967, 1.853, 4.109, 4.994   **43.** $\dfrac{2\pi}{3}, \dfrac{4\pi}{3}$

45. Left to the student   **47.** 1.114, 2.773

49. 0.515   **51.** 0.422, 1.756

53. (a) $y = 7 \sin(-2.6180x + 0.5236) + 7$;
(b) $10,500$, $13,062

55. Discussion and Writing

57. [5.2] $B = 35°, b \approx 140.7, c \approx 245.4$

58. [5.2] $R \approx 15.5°, T \approx 74.5°, t \approx 13.7$ **59.** [2.1] 36

60. [2.1] 14   **61.** $\dfrac{\pi}{3}, \dfrac{2\pi}{3}, \dfrac{4\pi}{3}, \dfrac{5\pi}{3}$ **63.** $\dfrac{\pi}{3}, \dfrac{4\pi}{3}$

65. 0   **67.** $e^{3\pi/2 + 2k\pi}$, where k (an integer) ≤ -1

69. 1.24 days, 6.76 days   **71.** 16.5°N   **73.** 1   **75.** 0.1923

Review Exercises: Chapter 6

1. True   **2.** True   **3.** True   **4.** False   **5.** False

6. $\csc^2 x$ **7.** 1   **8.** $\tan^2 y - \cot^2 y$ **9.** $\dfrac{(\cos^2 x + 1)^2}{\cos^2 x}$

10. $\csc x(\sec x - \csc x)$ **11.** $(3 \sin y + 5)(\sin y - 4)$
12. $(10 - \cos u)(100 + 10 \cos u + \cos^2 u)$ **13.** 1

14. $\frac{1}{2} \sec x$ **15.** $\dfrac{3 \tan x}{\sin x - \cos x}$ **16.** $\dfrac{3 \cos y + 3 \sin y + 2}{\cos^2 y - \sin^2 y}$

17. 1   **18.** $\frac{1}{4} \cot x$ **19.** $\sin x + \cos x$ **20.** $\dfrac{\cos x}{1 - \sin x}$

21. $\dfrac{\cos x}{\sqrt{\sin x}}$ **22.** $3 \sec \theta$ **23.** $\cos x \cos \dfrac{3\pi}{2} - \sin x \sin \dfrac{3\pi}{2}$

24. $\dfrac{\tan 45° - \tan 30°}{1 + \tan 45° \tan 30°}$ **25.** $\cos(27° - 16°)$, or $\cos 11°$

26. $\dfrac{-\sqrt{6} - \sqrt{2}}{4}$ **27.** $2 - \sqrt{3}$ **28.** -0.3745

29. $-\sin x$ **30.** $\sin x$ **31.** $-\cos x$

32. (a) $\sin \alpha = -\dfrac{4}{5}, \tan \alpha = \dfrac{4}{3}, \cot \alpha = \dfrac{3}{4},$

$\sec \alpha = -\dfrac{5}{3}, \csc \alpha = -\dfrac{5}{4};$ (b) $\sin\left(\dfrac{\pi}{2} - \alpha\right) = -\dfrac{3}{5},$

$\cos\left(\dfrac{\pi}{2} - \alpha\right) = -\dfrac{4}{5}, \tan\left(\dfrac{\pi}{2} - \alpha\right) = \dfrac{3}{4},$

$\cot\left(\dfrac{\pi}{2} - \alpha\right) = \dfrac{4}{3}, \sec\left(\dfrac{\pi}{2} - \alpha\right) = -\dfrac{5}{4},$

$\csc\left(\dfrac{\pi}{2} - \alpha\right) = -\dfrac{5}{3};$ (c) $\sin\left(\alpha + \dfrac{\pi}{2}\right) = -\dfrac{3}{5},$

$\cos\left(\alpha + \dfrac{\pi}{2}\right) = \dfrac{4}{5}, \tan\left(\alpha + \dfrac{\pi}{2}\right) = -\dfrac{3}{4},$

$\cot\left(\alpha + \dfrac{\pi}{2}\right) = -\dfrac{4}{3}, \sec\left(\alpha + \dfrac{\pi}{2}\right) = \dfrac{5}{4},$

$\csc\left(\alpha + \dfrac{\pi}{2}\right) = -\dfrac{5}{3}$ **33.** $-\sec x$

34. $\tan 2\theta = \frac{24}{7}, \cos 2\theta = \frac{7}{25}, \sin 2\theta = \frac{24}{25}$; I

35. $\dfrac{\sqrt{2 - \sqrt{2}}}{2}$

36. $\sin 2\beta = 0.4261, \cos \dfrac{\beta}{2} = 0.9940, \cos 4\beta = 0.6369$

37. $\cos x$ **38.** 1   **39.** $\sin 2x$ **40.** $\tan 2x$

41.

$\dfrac{1-\sin x}{\cos x}$ | $\dfrac{\cos x}{1+\sin x}$
$\dfrac{1-\sin x}{\cos x}\cdot\dfrac{\cos x}{\cos x}$ | $\dfrac{\cos x}{1+\sin x}\cdot\dfrac{1-\sin x}{1-\sin x}$
$\dfrac{\cos x-\sin x\cos x}{\cos^2 x}$ | $\dfrac{\cos x-\sin x\cos x}{1-\sin^2 x}$
| $\dfrac{\cos x-\sin x\cos x}{\cos^2 x}$

42.

$\dfrac{1+\cos 2\theta}{\sin 2\theta}$ | $\cot\theta$
$\dfrac{1+2\cos^2\theta-1}{2\sin\theta\cos\theta}$ | $\dfrac{\cos\theta}{\sin\theta}$
$\dfrac{\cos\theta}{\sin\theta}$ |

43.

$\dfrac{\tan y+\sin y}{2\tan y}$ | $\cos^2\dfrac{y}{2}$
$\dfrac{1}{2}\left[\dfrac{\dfrac{\sin y+\sin y\cos y}{\cos y}}{\dfrac{\sin y}{\cos y}}\right]$ | $\dfrac{1+\cos y}{2}$
$\dfrac{1}{2}\left[\dfrac{\sin y(1+\cos y)}{\cos y}\cdot\dfrac{\cos y}{\sin y}\right]$ |
$\dfrac{1+\cos y}{2}$ |

44.

$\dfrac{\sin x-\cos x}{\cos^2 x}$ | $\dfrac{\tan^2 x-1}{\sin x+\cos x}$
| $\dfrac{\dfrac{\sin^2 x}{\cos^2 x}-1}{\sin x+\cos x}$
| $\dfrac{\sin^2 x-\cos^2 x}{\cos^2 x}\cdot\dfrac{1}{\sin x+\cos x}$
| $\dfrac{\sin x-\cos x}{\cos^2 x}$

45. $3\cos 2\theta\sin\theta=\frac{3}{2}(\sin 3\theta-\sin\theta)$

46. $\sin\theta-\sin 4\theta=-2\cos\dfrac{5\theta}{2}\sin\dfrac{3\theta}{2}$

47. $-\dfrac{\pi}{6},-30°$ **48.** $\dfrac{\pi}{6},30°$ **49.** $\dfrac{\pi}{4},45°$ **50.** $0,0°$

51. $1.7920,102.7°$ **52.** $0.3976,22.8°$ **53.** $\frac{1}{2}$ **54.** $\dfrac{\sqrt{3}}{3}$

55. $\dfrac{\pi}{7}$ **56.** $\dfrac{\sqrt{2}}{2}$ **57.** $\dfrac{3}{\sqrt{b^2+9}}$ **58.** $-\frac{7}{25}$

59. $\dfrac{3\pi}{4}+2k\pi,\dfrac{5\pi}{4}+2k\pi,$ or $135°+k\cdot360°,225°+k\cdot360°$

60. $\dfrac{\pi}{3}+k\pi,$ or $60°+k\cdot180°$ **61.** $\dfrac{\pi}{6},\dfrac{5\pi}{6},\dfrac{7\pi}{6},\dfrac{11\pi}{6}$

62. $\dfrac{\pi}{4},\dfrac{\pi}{2},\dfrac{3\pi}{4},\dfrac{5\pi}{4},\dfrac{3\pi}{2},\dfrac{7\pi}{4}$ **63.** $\dfrac{2\pi}{3},\pi,\dfrac{4\pi}{3}$ **64.** $0,\pi$

65. $\dfrac{\pi}{4},\dfrac{3\pi}{4},\dfrac{5\pi}{4},\dfrac{7\pi}{4}$ **66.** $0,\dfrac{\pi}{2},\pi,\dfrac{3\pi}{2}$ **67.** $\dfrac{7\pi}{12},\dfrac{23\pi}{12}$

68. $0.864,2.972,4.006,6.114$ **69.** B **70.** A

71. B;

$\csc x-\cos x\cot x$ | $\sin x$
$\dfrac{1}{\sin x}-\cos x\dfrac{\cos x}{\sin x}$ |
$\dfrac{1-\cos^2 x}{\sin x}$ |
$\dfrac{\sin^2 x}{\sin x}$ |
$\sin x$ |

72. D;

$\dfrac{1}{\sin x\cos x}-\dfrac{\cos x}{\sin x}$ | $\dfrac{\sin x\cos x}{1-\sin^2 x}$
$\dfrac{1}{\sin x\cos x}-\dfrac{\cos^2 x}{\sin x\cos x}$ | $\dfrac{\sin x\cos x}{\cos^2 x}$
$\dfrac{1-\cos^2 x}{\sin x\cos x}$ | $\dfrac{\sin x}{\cos x}$
$\dfrac{\sin^2 x}{\sin x\cos x}$ |
$\dfrac{\sin x}{\cos x}$ |

73. A;

$\dfrac{\cot x-1}{1-\tan x}$ | $\dfrac{\csc x}{\sec x}$
$\dfrac{\dfrac{\cos x}{\sin x}-\dfrac{\sin x}{\sin x}}{\dfrac{\sin x}{\cos x}}$ | $\dfrac{\dfrac{1}{\sin x}}{\dfrac{1}{\cos x}}$
$\dfrac{\dfrac{\cos x}{\cos x}-\dfrac{\sin x}{\cos x}}{}$ |
$\dfrac{\cos x-\sin x}{\sin x}\cdot\dfrac{\cos x}{\cos x-\sin x}$ | $\dfrac{1}{\sin x}\cdot\dfrac{\cos x}{1}$
$\dfrac{\cos x}{\sin x}$ | $\dfrac{\cos x}{\sin x}$

74. C;

$\dfrac{\cos x+1}{\sin x}+\dfrac{\sin x}{\cos x+1}$ | $\dfrac{2}{\sin x}$
$\dfrac{(\cos x+1)^2+\sin^2 x}{\sin x(\cos x+1)}$ |
$\dfrac{\cos^2 x+2\cos x+1+\sin^2 x}{\sin x(\cos x+1)}$ |
$\dfrac{2\cos x+2}{\sin x(\cos x+1)}$ |
$\dfrac{2(\cos x+1)}{\sin x(\cos x+1)}$ |
$\dfrac{2}{\sin x}$ |

75. 4.917 **76.** No solution in $[0,2\pi)$

77. Discussion and Writing
(a) $2\cos^2 x - 1 = \cos 2x = \cos^2 x - \sin^2 x$
$$= 1 \cdot (\cos^2 x - \sin^2 x)$$
$$= (\cos^2 x + \sin^2 x)(\cos^2 x - \sin^2 x)$$
$$= \cos^4 x \cdot\cdot \sin^4 x;$$
(b) $\cos^4 x - \sin^4 x = (\cos^2 x + \sin^2 x)(\cos^2 x - \sin^2 x)$
$$= 1 \cdot (\cos^2 x - \sin^2 x)$$
$$= \cos^2 x - \sin^2 x = \cos 2x$$
$$= 2\cos^2 x - 1;$$
(c)

$2\cos^2 x - 1$	$\cos^4 x - \sin^4 x$
$\cos 2x$	$(\cos^2 x + \sin^2 x)(\cos^2 x - \sin^2 x)$
	$1 \cdot (\cos^2 x - \sin^2 x)$
	$\cos^2 x - \sin^2 x$
	$\cos 2x$

Answers may vary. Method 2 may be the more efficient because it involves straightforward factorization and simplification. Method 1(a) requires a "trick" such as multiplying by a particular expression equivalent to 1.
78. Discussion and Writing: The ranges of the inverse trigonometric functions are restricted in order that they might be functions.
79. $108.4°$
80.
$$\cos(u + v) = \cos u \cos v - \sin u \sin v$$
$$= \cos u \cos v - \cos\left(\frac{\pi}{2} - u\right)\cos\left(\frac{\pi}{2} - v\right)$$
81. $\cos^2 x$
82. $\sin\theta = \sqrt{\dfrac{1}{2} + \dfrac{\sqrt 6}{5}};\ \cos\theta = \sqrt{\dfrac{1}{2} - \dfrac{\sqrt 6}{5}};$
$\tan\theta = \sqrt{\dfrac{5 + 2\sqrt 6}{5 - 2\sqrt 6}}$ **83.** $\ln e^{\sin t} = \log_e e^{\sin t} = \sin t$
84.

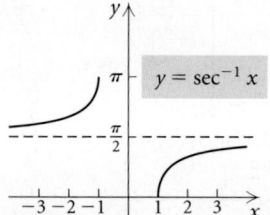

85. Let $x = \dfrac{\sqrt 2}{2}$. Then $\tan^{-1}\dfrac{\sqrt 2}{2} \approx 0.6155$ and
$\dfrac{\sin^{-1}\dfrac{\sqrt 2}{2}}{\cos^{-1}\dfrac{\sqrt 2}{2}} = \dfrac{\dfrac{\pi}{4}}{\dfrac{\pi}{4}} = 1.$ **86.** $\dfrac{\pi}{2}, \dfrac{3\pi}{2}$

Test: Chapter 6

1. [6.1] $2\cos x + 1$ **2.** [6.1] 1 **3.** [6.1] $\dfrac{\cos\theta}{1 + \sin\theta}$
4. [6.1] $2\cos\theta$ **5.** [6.1] $\dfrac{\sqrt 2 + \sqrt 6}{4}$ **6.** [6.1] $\dfrac{3 - \sqrt 3}{3 + \sqrt 3}$

7. [6.1] $\dfrac{120}{169}$ **8.** [6.2] $\dfrac{\sqrt 5}{3}$ **9.** [6.2] $\dfrac{24}{25}$, II
10. [6.2] $\dfrac{\sqrt{2 + \sqrt 3}}{2}$ **11.** [6.2] 0.9304
12. [6.2] $3\sin 2x$
13. [6.3]

$\csc x - \cos x \cot x$	$\sin x$
$\dfrac{1}{\sin x} - \cos x \cdot \dfrac{\cos x}{\sin x}$	
$\dfrac{1 - \cos^2 x}{\sin x}$	
$\dfrac{\sin^2 x}{\sin x}$	
$\sin x$	

14. [6.3]

$(\sin x + \cos x)^2$	$1 + \sin 2x$
$\sin^2 x + 2\sin x\cos x + \cos^2 x$	
$1 + 2\sin x\cos x$	
$1 + \sin 2x$	

15. [6.3]

$(\csc\beta + \cot\beta)^2$	$\dfrac{1 + \cos\beta}{1 - \cos\beta}$
$\left(\dfrac{1}{\sin\beta} + \dfrac{\cos\beta}{\sin\beta}\right)^2$	$\dfrac{1 + \cos\beta}{1 - \cos\beta} \cdot \dfrac{1 + \cos\beta}{1 + \cos\beta}$
$\left(\dfrac{1 + \cos\beta}{\sin\beta}\right)^2$	$\dfrac{(1 + \cos\beta)^2}{1 - \cos^2\beta}$
$\dfrac{(1 + \cos\beta)^2}{\sin^2\beta}$	$\dfrac{(1 + \cos\beta)^2}{\sin^2\beta}$

16. [6.3]

$\dfrac{1 + \sin\alpha}{1 + \csc\alpha}$	$\tan\alpha$
	$\sec\alpha$
$\dfrac{1 + \sin\alpha}{1 + \dfrac{1}{\sin\alpha}}$	$\dfrac{\sin\alpha}{\cos\alpha}$
	$\dfrac{1}{\cos\alpha}$
$\dfrac{1 + \sin\alpha}{\dfrac{\sin\alpha + 1}{\sin\alpha}}$	$\sin\alpha$
$\dfrac{\sin\alpha}{\sin\alpha}$	

17. [6.4] $\cos 8\alpha - \cos\alpha = -2\sin\dfrac{9\alpha}{2}\sin\dfrac{7\alpha}{2}$
18. [6.4] $4\sin\beta\cos 3\beta = 2(\sin 4\beta - \sin 2\beta)$
19. [6.4] $-45°$ **20.** [6.4] $\dfrac{\pi}{3}$ **21.** [6.4] 2.3072
22. [6.4] $\dfrac{\sqrt 3}{2}$ **23.** [6.4] $\dfrac{5}{\sqrt{x^2 - 25}}$ **24.** [6.4] 0
25. [6.5] $\dfrac{\pi}{6}, \dfrac{5\pi}{6}, \dfrac{7\pi}{6}, \dfrac{11\pi}{6}$ **26.** [6.5] $0, \dfrac{\pi}{4}, \dfrac{3\pi}{4}, \pi$
27. [6.5] $\dfrac{\pi}{2}, \dfrac{11\pi}{6}$ **28.** [6.2] $\sqrt{\dfrac{11}{12}}$

CHAPTER 7

Exercise Set 7.1

1. $A = 121°$, $a \approx 33$, $c \approx 14$ **3.** $B \approx 57.4°$, $C \approx 86.1°$, $c \approx 40$, or $B \approx 122.6°$, $C \approx 20.9°$, $c \approx 14$ **5.** $B \approx 44°24'$, $A \approx 74°26'$, $a \approx 33.3$ **7.** $A = 110.36°$, $a \approx 5$ mi, $b \approx 3$ mi   **9.** $B \approx 83.78°$, $A \approx 12.44°$, $a \approx 12.30$ yd   **11.** $B \approx 14.7°$, $C \approx 135.0°$, $c \approx 28.04$ cm   **13.** No solution   **15.** $B = 125.27°$, $b \approx 302$ m, $c \approx 138$ m   **17.** 8.2 ft^2 **19.** 12 yd^2 **21.** 596.98 ft^2 **23.** 76.3 m   **25.** 787 ft^2 **27.** About 51 ft   **29.** From A: about 35 mi; from B: about 66 mi   **31.** About 22 mi   **33.** Discussion and Writing   **35.** [5.1] 1.348, 77.2°   **36.** [5.1] No angle   **37.** [5.1] 18.24°   **38.** [5.1] 125.06°   **39.** [R.1] 5   **40.** [5.3] $\dfrac{\sqrt{3}}{2}$ **41.** [5.3] $\dfrac{\sqrt{2}}{2}$ **42.** [5.3] $-\dfrac{\sqrt{3}}{2}$ **43.** [5.3] $-\dfrac{1}{2}$ **44.** [2.2] 2   **45.** Use the formula for the area of a triangle and the law of sines.

$$K = \frac{1}{2} bc \sin A \quad \text{and} \quad b = \frac{c \sin B}{\sin C},$$

$$\text{so} \quad K = \frac{c^2 \sin A \sin B}{2 \sin C}.$$

$$K = \frac{1}{2} ab \sin C \quad \text{and} \quad b = \frac{a \sin B}{\sin A},$$

$$\text{so} \quad K = \frac{a^2 \sin B \sin C}{2 \sin A}.$$

$$K = \frac{1}{2} bc \sin A \quad \text{and} \quad c = \frac{b \sin C}{\sin B},$$

$$\text{so} \quad K = \frac{b^2 \sin A \sin C}{2 \sin B}.$$

47.

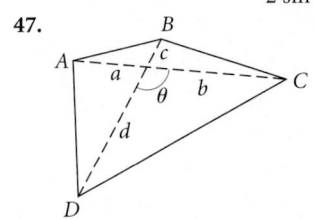

For the quadrilateral $ABCD$, we have

$$\text{Area} = \frac{1}{2} bd \sin \theta + \frac{1}{2} ac \sin \theta$$
$$+ \frac{1}{2} ad(\sin 180° - \theta) + \frac{1}{2} bc \sin (180° - \theta)$$

Note: $\sin \theta = \sin(180° - \theta)$.

$$= \frac{1}{2} (bd + ac + ad + bc) \sin \theta$$
$$= \frac{1}{2} (a + b)(c + d) \sin \theta$$
$$= \frac{1}{2} d_1 d_2 \sin \theta,$$

where $d_1 = a + b$ and $d_2 = c + d$.
49. 44.1 ″ from wall 1 and 104.3 ″ from wall 4

Exercise Set 7.2

1. $a \approx 15$, $B \approx 24°$, $C \approx 126°$ **3.** $A \approx 36.18°$, $B \approx 43.53°$, $C \approx 100.29°$ **5.** $b \approx 75$ m, $A \approx 94°51'$, $C \approx 12°29'$ **7.** $A \approx 24.15°$, $B \approx 30.75°$, $C \approx 125.10°$ **9.** No solution   **11.** $A \approx 79.93°$, $B \approx 53.55°$, $C \approx 46.52°$ **13.** $c \approx 45.17$ mi, $A \approx 89.3°$, $B \approx 42.0°$ **15.** $a \approx 13.9$ in., $B \approx 36.127°$, $C \approx 90.417°$ **17.** Law of sines; $C = 98°$, $a \approx 96.7$, $c \approx 101.9$ **19.** Law of cosines; $A \approx 73.71°$, $B \approx 51.75°$, $C \approx 54.54°$ **21.** Cannot be solved   **23.** Law of cosines; $A \approx 33.71°$, $B \approx 107.08°$, $C \approx 39.21°$ **25.** About 367 ft   **27.** About 1.5 mi   **29.** $S \approx 112.5°$, $T \approx 27.2°$, $U \approx 40.3°$ **31.** About 912 km   **33. (a)** About 16 ft; **(b)** about 122 ft^2 **35.** About 4.7 cm   **37.** Discussion and Writing   **39.** [3.1] Quartic   **40.** [1.3] Linear   **41.** [5.5] Trigonometric   **42.** [4.2] Exponential   **43.** [3.5] Rational   **44.** [3.1] Cubic   **45.** [4.2] Exponential   **46.** [4.3] Logarithmic   **47.** [5.5] Trigonometric   **48.** [2.3] Quadratic   **49.** About 9386 ft   **51.** $A = \dfrac{1}{2} a^2 \sin \theta$; when $\theta = 90°$

Exercise Set 7.3

1. 5;

Imaginary axis with point $4 + 3i$ plotted, Real axis labeled.

3. 1;

Imaginary axis with point i plotted, Real axis labeled.

5. $\sqrt{17}$;

Imaginary axis with point $4 - i$ plotted, Real axis labeled.

7. 3;

Imaginary axis with point 3 plotted, Real axis labeled.

9. $3 - 3i$; $3\sqrt{2}\left(\cos\dfrac{7\pi}{4} + i\sin\dfrac{7\pi}{4}\right)$, or $3\sqrt{2}(\cos 315° + i\sin 315°)$

11. $4i$; $4\left(\cos\dfrac{\pi}{2} + i\sin\dfrac{\pi}{2}\right)$, or $4(\cos 90° + i\sin 90°)$

13. $\sqrt{2}\left(\cos\dfrac{7\pi}{4} + i\sin\dfrac{7\pi}{4}\right)$, or $\sqrt{2}(\cos 315° + i\sin 315°)$

15. $3\left(\cos\dfrac{3\pi}{2} + i\sin\dfrac{3\pi}{2}\right)$, or $3(\cos 270° + i\sin 270°)$

17. $2\left(\cos\dfrac{\pi}{6} + i\sin\dfrac{\pi}{6}\right)$, or $2(\cos 30° + i\sin 30°)$

19. $\dfrac{2}{5}(\cos 0 + i\sin 0)$, or $\dfrac{2}{5}(\cos 0° + i\sin 0°)$

21. $6\left(\cos\dfrac{5\pi}{4} + i\sin\dfrac{5\pi}{4}\right)$, or $6(\cos 225° + i\sin 225°)$

23. $\dfrac{3\sqrt{3}}{2} + \dfrac{3}{2}i$ **25.** $-10i$ **27.** $2 + 2i$ **29.** $2i$

31. $\dfrac{\sqrt{2}}{2} - \dfrac{\sqrt{6}}{2}i$ **33.** $4(\cos 42° + i\sin 42°)$

35. $11.25(\cos 56° + i\sin 56°)$ **37.** 4

39. $-i$ **41.** $6 + 6\sqrt{3}i$ **43.** $-2i$

45. $8(\cos\pi + i\sin\pi)$ **47.** $8\left(\cos\dfrac{3\pi}{2} + i\sin\dfrac{3\pi}{2}\right)$

49. $\dfrac{27}{2} + \dfrac{27\sqrt{3}}{2}i$ **51.** $-4 + 4i$ **53.** -1

55. $-\dfrac{\sqrt{2}}{2} + \dfrac{\sqrt{2}}{2}i,\ \dfrac{\sqrt{2}}{2} - \dfrac{\sqrt{2}}{2}i$

57. $2(\cos 157.5° + i\sin 157.5°),\ 2(\cos 337.5° + i\sin 337.5°)$

59. $\dfrac{\sqrt{3}}{2} + \dfrac{1}{2}i,\ -\dfrac{\sqrt{3}}{2} + \dfrac{1}{2}i,\ -i$

61. $\sqrt[3]{4}(\cos 110° + i\sin 110°),\ \sqrt[3]{4}(\cos 230° + i\sin 230°),$
$\sqrt[3]{4}(\cos 350° + i\sin 350°)$

63. $2, 2i, -2, -2i;$

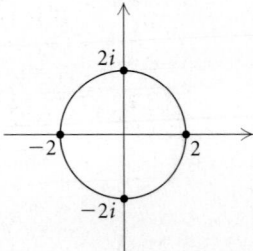

65. $\cos 36° + i\sin 36°,$
$\cos 108° + i\sin 108°, -1,$
$\cos 252° + i\sin 252°,$
$\cos 324° + i\sin 324°;$

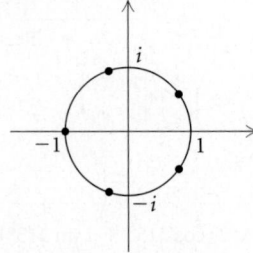

67. $\sqrt[10]{8},\ \sqrt[10]{8}(\cos 36° + i\sin 36°),\ \sqrt[10]{8}(\cos 72° + i\sin 72°),$
$\sqrt[10]{8}(\cos 108° + i\sin 108°),\ \sqrt[10]{8}(\cos 144° + i\sin 144°),\ -\sqrt[10]{8},$
$\sqrt[10]{8}(\cos 216° + i\sin 216°),\ \sqrt[10]{8}(\cos 252° + i\sin 252°),$
$\sqrt[10]{8}(\cos 288° + i\sin 288°),\ \sqrt[10]{8}(\cos 324° + i\sin 324°)$

69. $\dfrac{\sqrt{3}}{2} + \dfrac{1}{2}i,\ i,\ -\dfrac{\sqrt{3}}{2} + \dfrac{1}{2}i,\ -\dfrac{\sqrt{3}}{2} - \dfrac{1}{2}i,\ -i,\ \dfrac{\sqrt{3}}{2} - \dfrac{1}{2}i$

71. $1,\ -\dfrac{1}{2} + \dfrac{\sqrt{3}}{2}i,\ -\dfrac{1}{2} - \dfrac{\sqrt{3}}{2}i$

73. $\cos 67.5° + i\sin 67.5°,\ \cos 157.5° + i\sin 157.5°,$
$\cos 247.5° + i\sin 247.5°,\ \cos 337.5° + i\sin 337.5°$

75. $\sqrt{3} + i,\ 2i,\ -\sqrt{3} + i,\ -\sqrt{3} - i,\ -2i,\ \sqrt{3} - i$

77. Left to the student   **79.** Discussion and Writing

81. [5.4] $15°$ **82.** [5.4] $540°$ **83.** [5.4] $\dfrac{11\pi}{6}$

84. [5.4] $-\dfrac{5\pi}{4}$ **85.** [R.6] $3\sqrt{5}$

86. [1.1]

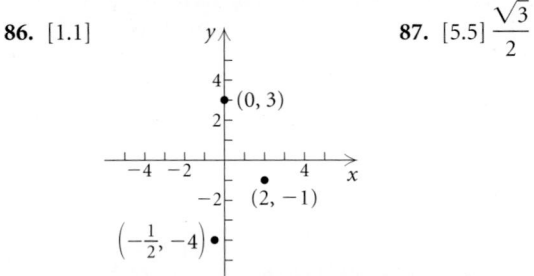

87. [5.5] $\dfrac{\sqrt{3}}{2}$

88. [5.5] $\dfrac{\sqrt{3}}{2}$ **89.** [5.5] $\dfrac{\sqrt{2}}{2}$ **90.** [5.5] $\dfrac{1}{2}$

91. $-\dfrac{1 + \sqrt{3}}{2} + \dfrac{1 + \sqrt{3}}{2}i,\ -\dfrac{1 - \sqrt{3}}{2} + \dfrac{1 - \sqrt{3}}{2}i$

93. $\cos\theta - i\sin\theta$

95. $z = a + bi, |z| = \sqrt{a^2 + b^2};\ \bar{z} = a - bi,$
$|\bar{z}| = \sqrt{a^2 + (-b)^2} = \sqrt{a^2 + b^2},\ \therefore |z| = |\bar{z}|$

97. $|(a + bi)^2| = |a^2 - b^2 + 2abi| = \sqrt{(a^2 - b^2)^2 + 4a^2b^2}$
$= \sqrt{a^4 + 2a^2b^2 + b^4} = a^2 + b^2,$
$|a + bi|^2 = \left(\sqrt{a^2 + b^2}\right)^2 = a^2 + b^2$

99. $\dfrac{z}{w} = \dfrac{r_1(\cos\theta_1 + i\sin\theta_1)}{r_2(\cos\theta_2 + i\sin\theta_2)}$

$= \dfrac{r_1}{r_2}(\cos(\theta_1 - \theta_2) + i\sin(\theta_1 - \theta_2)),$

$\left|\dfrac{z}{w}\right| = \sqrt{\left[\dfrac{r_1}{r_2}\cos(\theta_1 - \theta_2)\right]^2 + \left[\dfrac{r_1}{r_2}\sin(\theta_1 - \theta_2)\right]^2}$

$= \sqrt{\dfrac{r_1^2}{r_2^2}} = \dfrac{|r_1|}{|r_2|};$

$|z| = \sqrt{(r_1\cos\theta_1)^2 + (r_1\sin\theta_1)^2} = \sqrt{r_1^2} = |r_1|;$
$|w| = \sqrt{(r_2\cos\theta_2)^2 + (r_2\sin\theta_2)^2} = \sqrt{r_2^2} = |r_2|;$

Then $\left|\dfrac{z}{w}\right| = \dfrac{|r_1|}{|r_2|} = \dfrac{|z|}{|w|}.$

101.

Visualizing the Graph

1. J   **2.** C   **3.** E   **4.** H   **5.** I   **6.** A   **7.** D
8. G   **9.** B   **10.** F

Exercise Set 7.4

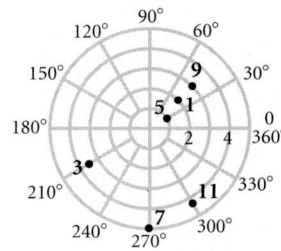

13. *A*: $(4, 30°), (4, 390°), (-4, 210°)$; *B*: $(5, 300°), (5, -60°)$, $(-5, 120°)$; *C*: $(2, 150°), (2, 510°), (-2, 330°)$; *D*: $(3, 225°)$, $(3, -135°), (-3, 45°)$; answers may vary

15. $(3, 270°), \left(3, \dfrac{3\pi}{2}\right)$ **17.** $(6, 300°), \left(6, \dfrac{5\pi}{3}\right)$

19. $(8, 330°), \left(8, \dfrac{11\pi}{6}\right)$ **21.** $(2, 225°), \left(2, \dfrac{5\pi}{4}\right)$

23. $(2, 60°), \left(2, \dfrac{\pi}{3}\right)$ **25.** $(5, 315°), \left(5, \dfrac{7\pi}{4}\right)$

27. $\left(\dfrac{5}{2}, \dfrac{5\sqrt{3}}{2}\right)$ **29.** $\left(-\dfrac{3\sqrt{2}}{2}, -\dfrac{3\sqrt{2}}{2}\right)$

31. $\left(-\dfrac{3}{2}, -\dfrac{3\sqrt{3}}{2}\right)$ **33.** $(-1, \sqrt{3})$ **35.** $(-\sqrt{3}, -1)$

37. $(3\sqrt{3}, -3)$ **39.** $r(3\cos\theta + 4\sin\theta) = 5$
41. $r\cos\theta = 5$ **43.** $r = 6$ **45.** $r^2\cos^2\theta = 25r\sin\theta$
47. $r^2\sin^2\theta - 5r\cos\theta - 25 = 0$ **49.** $r^2 = 2r\cos\theta$
51. $x^2 + y^2 = 25$ **53.** $y = 2$ **55.** $y^2 = -6x + 9$
57. $x^2 - 9x + y^2 - 7y = 0$ **59.** $x = 5$ **61.** $y = -\sqrt{3}x$
63.   **65.**

$r = \sin\theta$

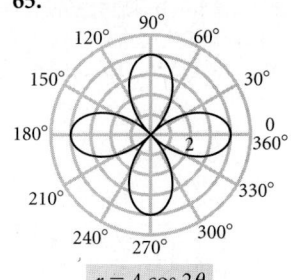
$r = 4\cos 2\theta$

67.   **69.**

$r = \cos\theta$

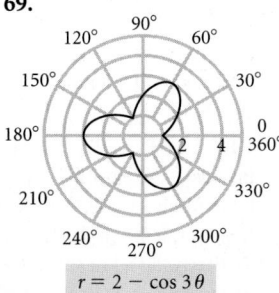
$r = 2 - \cos 3\theta$

71. $(7.616, 66.8°), (7.616, 1.166)$
73. $(4.643, 132.9°), (4.643, 2.320)$ **75.** $(2.19, -2.05)$
77. $(1.30, -3.99)$ **79.** (d)   **81.** (g)   **83.** (j)   **85.** (b)
87. (e)   **89.** (k)
91.   **93.**

$r = \sin\theta\tan\theta$

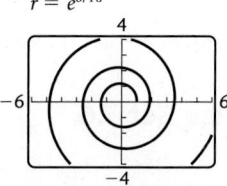
$r = e^{\theta/10}$

95.   **97.**

$r = \cos 2\theta\sec\theta$

$r = \frac{1}{4}\tan^2\theta\sec\theta$

99. Discussion and Writing   **101.** [2.1] 12   **102.** [2.1] $\frac{1}{5}$
103. [1.3]   **104.** [1.3]

$y = 2x - 5$

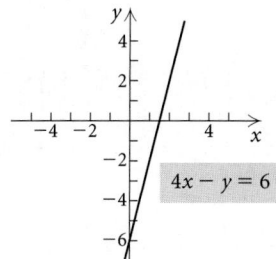
$4x - y = 6$

105. [1.3]   **106.** [1.3]

$x = -3$

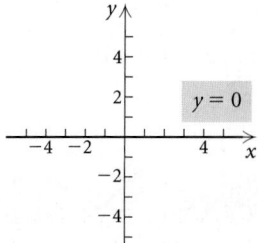
$y = 0$

107. $y^2 = -4x + 4$

Exercise Set 7.5

1. Yes   **3.** No   **5.** Yes   **7.** No   **9.** No   **11.** Yes
13. 55 N, 55°   **15.** 929 N, 19°   **17.** 57.0, 38°
19. 18.4, 37°   **21.** 20.9, 58°   **23.** 68.3, 18°
25. 11 ft/sec, 63°   **27.** 726 lb, 47°   **29.** 60°
31. 70.7 east; 70.7 south
33. Horizontal: 215.17 mph forward; vertical: 65.78 mph up
35. Horizontal: 390 lb forward; vertical: 675.5 lb up
37. Northerly: 115 km/h; westerly: 164 km/h
39. Perpendicular: 90.6 lb; parallel: 42.3 lb   **41.** 48.1 lb
43. Discussion and Writing   **45.** [4.3] Natural
46. [6.2] Half-angle   **47.** [5.4] Linear speed
48. [5.1] Cosine   **49.** [6.1] Identity
50. [5.1] Cotangent of θ **51.** [5.3] Coterminal
52. [7.1] Sines   **53.** [4.1] Horizontal line; inverse
54. [5.3] Reference angle; acute
55. (a) (4.950, 4.950); (b) (0.950, -1.978)

Exercise Set 7.6

1. $\langle -9, 5 \rangle$; $\sqrt{106}$ **3.** $\langle -3, 6 \rangle$; $3\sqrt{5}$ **5.** $\langle 4, 0 \rangle$; 4
7. $\sqrt{37}$ **9.** $\langle 4, -5 \rangle$ **11.** $\sqrt{257}$ **13.** $\langle -9, 9 \rangle$
15. $\langle 41, -38 \rangle$ **17.** $\sqrt{261} - \sqrt{65}$ **19.** $\langle -1, -1 \rangle$
21. $\langle -8, 14 \rangle$ **23.** 1   **25.** -34
27.

29.

31. (a) $\mathbf{w} = \mathbf{u} + \mathbf{v}$; (b) $\mathbf{v} = \mathbf{w} - \mathbf{u}$
33. $\langle -\frac{5}{13}, \frac{12}{13} \rangle$ **35.** $\langle \frac{1}{\sqrt{101}}, -\frac{10}{\sqrt{101}} \rangle$
37. $\langle -\frac{1}{\sqrt{17}}, -\frac{4}{\sqrt{17}} \rangle$ **39.** $\mathbf{w} = -4\mathbf{i} + 6\mathbf{j}$
41. $\mathbf{s} = 2\mathbf{i} + 5\mathbf{j}$ **43.** $-7\mathbf{i} + 5\mathbf{j}$
45. (a) $3\mathbf{i} + 29\mathbf{j}$; (b) $\langle 3, 29 \rangle$ **47.** (a) $4\mathbf{i} + 16\mathbf{j}$; (b) $\langle 4, 16 \rangle$
49. $\mathbf{j}$, or $\langle 0, 1 \rangle$ **51.** $-\frac{1}{2}\mathbf{i} - \frac{\sqrt{3}}{2}\mathbf{j}$, or $\langle -\frac{1}{2}, -\frac{\sqrt{3}}{2} \rangle$
53. 248°   **55.** 63°   **57.** 50°   **59.** $|\mathbf{u}| = 3$; $\theta = 45°$
61. 1; 120°   **63.** 144.2°   **65.** 14.0°   **67.** 101.3°
69.

$$\theta = \frac{3\pi}{4}$$
$$\mathbf{u} = \frac{\sqrt{3}}{2}\mathbf{i} + \frac{1}{2}\mathbf{j}$$
$$\theta = \frac{\pi}{6}$$
$$\mathbf{u} = -\frac{\sqrt{2}}{2}\mathbf{i} + \frac{\sqrt{2}}{2}\mathbf{j}$$

71. $\mathbf{u} = -\dfrac{\sqrt{2}}{2}\mathbf{i} - \dfrac{\sqrt{2}}{2}\mathbf{j}$ **73.** $\mathbf{u} = -\dfrac{\sqrt{10}}{10}\mathbf{i} + \dfrac{3\sqrt{10}}{10}\mathbf{j}$

75. $\sqrt{13}\left(\dfrac{2\sqrt{13}}{13}\mathbf{i} - \dfrac{3\sqrt{13}}{13}\mathbf{j} \right)$

77.

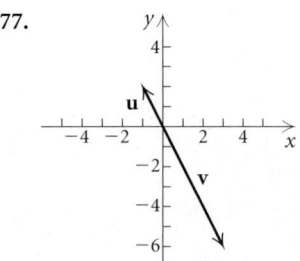

79. 174 nautical mi, S17°E   **81.** 60°
83. 500 lb on left, 866 lb on right
85. Cable: 224-lb tension; boom: 167-lb compression
87. $\mathbf{u} + \mathbf{v} = \langle u_1, u_2 \rangle + \langle v_1, v_2 \rangle$
$= \langle u_1 + v_1, u_2 + v_2 \rangle$
$= \langle v_1 + u_1, v_2 + u_2 \rangle$
$= \langle v_1, v_2 \rangle + \langle u_1, u_2 \rangle$
$= \mathbf{v} + \mathbf{u}$
89. Discussion and Writing
91. [1.4] $-\frac{1}{5}$; (0, -15)   **92.** [1.4] 0; (0, 7)
93. [3.1] 0, 4   **94.** [2.3] $-\frac{11}{3}, \frac{5}{2}$
95. (a) $\cos \theta = \dfrac{\mathbf{u} \cdot \mathbf{v}}{|\mathbf{u}||\mathbf{v}|} = \dfrac{0}{|\mathbf{u}||\mathbf{v}|}$, $\therefore \cos \theta = 0$ and $\theta = 90°$.
(b) Answers may vary. $\mathbf{u} = \langle 2, -3 \rangle$ and $\mathbf{v} = \langle -3, -2 \rangle$;
$\mathbf{u} \cdot \mathbf{v} = 2(-3) + (-3)(-2) = 0$
97. $\frac{3}{5}\mathbf{i} - \frac{4}{5}\mathbf{j}, -\frac{3}{5}\mathbf{i} + \frac{4}{5}\mathbf{j}$ **99.** (5, 8)

Review Exercises: Chapter 7

1. True   **2.** False   **3.** False   **4.** False   **5.** False   **6.** True
7. $A \approx 153°$, $B \approx 18°$, $C \approx 9°$
8. $A = 118°$, $a \approx 37$ in., $c \approx 24$ in.
9. $B = 14°50'$, $a \approx 2523$ m, $c \approx 1827$ m
10. No solution   **11.** 33 m²   **12.** 13.72 ft²   **13.** 63 ft²
14. 92°, 33°, 55°   **15.** 419 ft   **16.** About 650 km
17. $\sqrt{29}$;   **18.** 4;

19. 2;

Imaginary

20. $\sqrt{10}$;

Imaginary

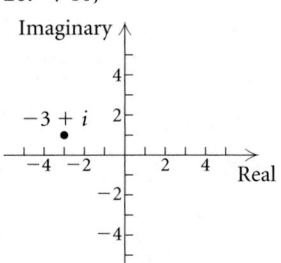

21. $\sqrt{2}\left(\cos\dfrac{\pi}{4}+i\sin\dfrac{\pi}{4}\right)$, or $\sqrt{2}(\cos 45°+i\sin 45°)$

22. $4\left(\cos\dfrac{3\pi}{2}+i\sin\dfrac{3\pi}{2}\right)$, or $4(\cos 270°+i\sin 270°)$

23. $10\left(\cos\dfrac{5\pi}{6}+i\sin\dfrac{5\pi}{6}\right)$, or $10(\cos 150°+i\sin 150°)$

24. $\frac{3}{4}(\cos 0+i\sin 0)$, or $\frac{3}{4}(\cos 0°+i\sin 0°)$

25. $2+2\sqrt{3}i$ **26.** 7   **27.** $-\dfrac{5}{2}+\dfrac{5\sqrt{3}}{2}i$

28. $1-\sqrt{3}i$ **29.** $1+\sqrt{3}+\left(-1+\sqrt{3}\right)i$

30. $-i$ **31.** $2i$ **32.** $3\sqrt{3}+3i$

33. $8(\cos 180°+i\sin 180°)$

34. $4(\cos 7\pi+i\sin 7\pi)$ **35.** $-8i$

36. $-\dfrac{1}{2}-\dfrac{\sqrt{3}}{2}i$

37. $\sqrt[4]{2}\left(\cos\dfrac{3\pi}{8}+i\sin\dfrac{3\pi}{8}\right)$,

$\sqrt[4]{2}\left(\cos\dfrac{11\pi}{8}+i\sin\dfrac{11\pi}{8}\right)$

38. $\sqrt[3]{6}(\cos 110°+i\sin 110°)$,

$\sqrt[3]{6}(\cos 230°+i\sin 230°)$, $\sqrt[3]{6}(\cos 350°+i\sin 350°)$

39. $3, 3i, -3, -3i$

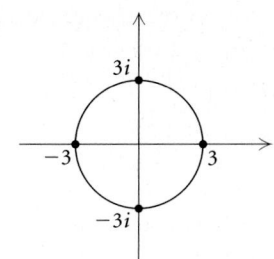

40. $1, \cos 72°+i\sin 72°, \cos 144°+i\sin 144°,$
$\cos 216°+i\sin 216°, \cos 288°+i\sin 288°$

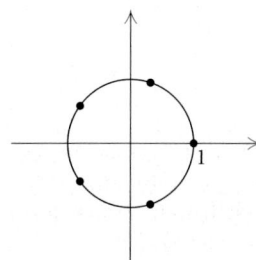

41. $\cos 22.5°+i\sin 22.5°, \cos 112.5°+i\sin 112.5°,$
$\cos 202.5°+i\sin 202.5°, \cos 292.5°+i\sin 292.5°$

42. $\dfrac{1}{2}+\dfrac{\sqrt{3}}{2}i, -1, \dfrac{1}{2}-\dfrac{\sqrt{3}}{2}i$

43. A: $(5, 120°), (5, 480°), (-5, 300°)$; B: $(3, 210°),$
$(-3, 30°), (-3, 390°)$; C: $(4, 60°), (4, 420°), (-4, 240°)$;
D: $(1, 300°), (1, -60°), (-1, 120°)$; answers may vary

44. $(8, 135°), \left(8, \dfrac{3\pi}{4}\right)$ **45.** $(5, 270°), \left(5, \dfrac{3\pi}{2}\right)$

46. $\left(\dfrac{3\sqrt{2}}{2}, \dfrac{3\sqrt{2}}{2}\right)$ **47.** $\left(3, 3\sqrt{3}\right)$

48. $r(5\cos\theta-2\sin\theta)=6$ **49.** $r\sin\theta=3$

50. $r=3$ **51.** $r^2\sin^2\theta-4r\cos\theta-16=0$

52. $x^2+y^2=36$ **53.** $x^2+2y=1$

54. $y^2-6x=9$ **55.** $x^2-2x+y^2-3y=0$

56. (b)   **57.** (d)   **58.** (a)   **59.** (c)

60. $13.7, 71°$ **61.** $98.7, 15°$

62.

63.

64. 666.7 N, 36°   **65.** 29 km/h, 149°

66. 102.4 nautical mi, S43°E   **67.** $\langle -4, 3\rangle$

68. $\langle 2, -6\rangle$ **69.** $\sqrt{61}$ **70.** $\langle 10, -21\rangle$

71. $\langle 14, -64\rangle$ **72.** $5+\sqrt{116}$ **73.** 14

74. $\left\langle -\dfrac{3}{\sqrt{10}}, -\dfrac{1}{\sqrt{10}}\right\rangle$ **75.** $-9\mathbf{i}+4\mathbf{j}$

76. $194.0°$ **77.** $\sqrt{34}; \theta=211.0°$

78. $111.8°$ **79.** $85.1°$ **80.** $34\mathbf{i}-55\mathbf{j}$

81. $\mathbf{i}-12\mathbf{j}$ **82.** $5\sqrt{2}$

83. $3\sqrt{65}+\sqrt{109}$ **84.** $-5\mathbf{i}+5\mathbf{j}$

85.   **86.**

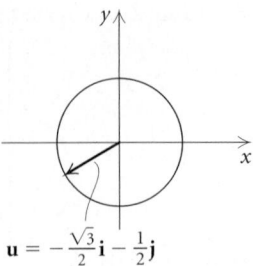

87. $\sqrt{10}\left(\dfrac{3\sqrt{10}}{10}\,\mathbf{i} - \dfrac{\sqrt{10}}{10}\,\mathbf{j}\right)$

88. D   **89.** A

90. $(5.385, 111.8°), (5.385, 1.951)$

91. $(4.964, 147.8°), (4.964, 2.579)$ **92.** $(1.93, -0.52)$

93. $(-1.86, -1.35)$

94. Discussion and Writing: A nonzero complex number has n different complex nth roots. Thus, 1 has three different complex cube roots, one of which is the real number 1. The other two are complex conjugates. Since the set of reals is a subset of the set of complex numbers, the real cube root of 1 is also a complex root of 1.

95. Discussion and Writing: A triangle has no solution when a sine or cosine value found is less than -1 or greater than 1. A triangle also has no solution if the sum of the angle measures calculated is greater than 180°. A triangle has only one solution if only one possible answer is found, or if one of the possible answers has an angle sum greater than 180°. A triangle has two solutions when two possible answers are found and neither results in an angle sum greater than 180°.

96. Discussion and Writing: For 150-yd shot, about 13.1 yd; for 300-yd shot, about 26.2 yd

97. $\frac{36}{13}\mathbf{i} + \frac{15}{13}\mathbf{j}$ **98.** $50.52°, 129.48°$

Test: Chapter 7

1. $[7.1]\ A = 83°,\ b \approx 14.7\ \text{ft},\ c \approx 12.4\ \text{ft}$

2. $[7.1]\ A \approx 73.9°,\ B \approx 70.1°,\ a \approx 8.2\ \text{m, or}\ A \approx 34.1°,$
$B \approx 109.9°,\ a \approx 4.8\ \text{m}$

3. $[7.2]\ A \approx 99.9°,\ B \approx 36.8°,\ C \approx 43.3°$

4. $[7.1]$ About $43.6\ \text{cm}^2$ **5.** $[7.1]$ About 77 m

6. $[7.5]$ About 930 km

7. $[7.3]$

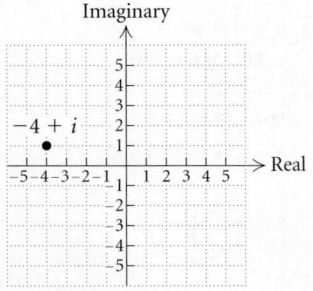

8. $[7.3]\ \sqrt{13}$ **9.** $[7.3]\ 3\sqrt{2}(\cos 315° + i \sin 315°)$

10. $[7.3]\ \frac{1}{4}i$ **11.** $[7.3]\ 16$

12. $[7.4]\ 2(\cos 120° + i \sin 120°)$

13. $[7.4]\ \left(\dfrac{1}{2}, -\dfrac{\sqrt{3}}{2}\right)$ **14.** $[7.4]\ r = \sqrt{10}$

15. $[7.4]$

$r = 1 - \cos\theta$

16. $[7.4]$ (a)   **17.** $[7.5]$ Magnitude: 11.2; direction: 23.4°

18. $[7.6]\ -11\mathbf{i} - 17\mathbf{j}$ **19.** $[7.6]\ -\frac{4}{5}\mathbf{i} + \frac{3}{5}\mathbf{j}$

20. $[7.1]\ 28.9°, 151.1°$

CHAPTER 8

Visualizing the Graph

1. C   **2.** G   **3.** D   **4.** J   **5.** A   **6.** F   **7.** I

8. B   **9.** H   **10.** E

Exercise Set 8.1

1. (c)   **3.** (f)   **5.** (b)   **7.** $(-1, 3)$ **9.** $(-1, 1)$

11. No solution   **13.** $(-2, 4)$ **15.** Infinitely many

solutions; $\left(x, \dfrac{x - 1}{2}\right)$, or $(2y + 1, y)$ **17.** $(5, 4)$

19. $(1, -3)$ **21.** $(2, -2)$ **23.** $\left(\frac{39}{11}, -\frac{1}{11}\right)$ **25.** $(1, -1)$

27. $\left(\frac{1}{2}, \frac{3}{4}\right)$ **29.** $(1, 3)$; consistent, independent

31. $(-4, -2)$; consistent, independent

33. $(4y + 2, y)$ or $\left(x, \frac{1}{4}x - \frac{1}{2}\right)$; consistent, dependent

35. $(1, 1)$; consistent, independent   **37.** $(-3, 0)$; consistent, independent   **39.** $(10, 8)$; consistent, independent

41. Skiing: 144,400 injuries; snowboarding: 144,000 injuries

43. Second Street: 7972; Main Street: 7712

45. Museums: 24 million visitors; website: 118 million visitors

47. Free rentals: 10; popcorn: 38   **49.** $(15, \$100)$ **51.** 140

53. 6000   **55.** 1.5 servings of spaghetti, 2 servings of lettuce

57. Boat: 20 km/h; stream: 3 km/h   **59.** $6000 at 7%, $9000 at 9%   **61.** 6 lb of French roast, 4 lb of Kenyan

63. Plane: 550 mph; wind: 50 mph   **65.** Left to the student

67. (a) $b(x) = -0.0657894737x + 63.95394737$;
$c(x) = 1.186842105x + 48.24078947$;
(b) about 12.5 yr after 1995   **69.** Discussion and Writing

71. $[2.1]$ Hardback: 35 million books; paperback: 75 million books   **72.** $[2.1]$ About $2.8 billion   **73.** $[2.3]\ -2, 6$

74. [2.3] $-1, 5$ **75.** [1.2] 15   **76.** [2.3] 1, 3   **77.** 4 km
79. First train: 36 km/h; second train: 54 km/h
81. $A = \frac{1}{10}, B = -\frac{7}{10}$ **83.** City: 294 mi; highway: 153 mi

Exercise Set 8.2

1. $(3, -2, 1)$ **3.** $(-3, 2, 1)$ **5.** $\left(2, \frac{1}{2}, -2\right)$

7. No solution   **9.** $\left(\dfrac{11y + 19}{5}, y, \dfrac{9y + 11}{5}\right)$

11. $\left(\frac{1}{2}, \frac{2}{3}, -\frac{5}{6}\right)$ **13.** $(-1, 4, 3)$ **15.** $(1, -2, 4, -1)$
17. Cross-training: \$1.4 billion; running: \$1.8 billion; walking:
\$3.5 billion   **19.** Brewed coffee: 80 mg; Red Bull: 80 mg;
Mountain Dew: 37 mg   **21.** Lettuce: 1 g; asparagus: 3 g;
tomato: 8 g   **23.** Under 10 lb: 60; 10 lb up to 15 lb: 70;
15 lb or more: 20   **25.** $1\frac{1}{4}$ servings of beef, 1 baked potato,
$\frac{3}{4}$ serving of strawberries   **27.** 3%: \$1300; 4%: \$900; 6%:
\$2800   **29.** Orange juice: \$1.20; bagel: \$2; coffee: \$0.90
31. Par-3: 4; par-4: 10; par-5: 4

33. (a) $f(x) = -\dfrac{10{,}013}{3}x^2 + \dfrac{34{,}219}{3}x + 279$; **(b)** about

8348 fines   **35. (a)** $f(x) = -0.15x^2 + 2.1x + 36$;
(b) about 25 thousand marriages
37. (a) $f(x) = 0.1822373078x^2 - 11.23256978x +$
468.7226133; **(b)** about 892 morning newspapers
39. Discussion and Writing   **41.** [1.4] Perpendicular
42. [3.1] The leading-term test   **43.** [1.2] A vertical line
44. [4.1] A one-to-one function
45. [3.5] A rational function   **46.** [3.7] Inverse variation
47. [3.5] A vertical asymptote
48. [3.5] A horizontal asymptote
49. $\left(-1, \frac{1}{5}, -\frac{1}{2}\right)$ **51.** $180°$ **53.** $3x + 4y + 2z = 12$
55. $y = -4x^3 + 5x^2 - 3x + 1$
57. Adults: 5; students: 1; children: 94

Exercise Set 8.3

1. 3×2 **3.** 1×4 **5.** 3×3 **7.** $\begin{bmatrix} 2 & -1 & | & 7 \\ 1 & 4 & | & -5 \end{bmatrix}$

9. $\begin{bmatrix} 1 & -2 & 3 & | & 12 \\ 2 & 0 & -4 & | & 8 \\ 0 & 3 & 1 & | & 7 \end{bmatrix}$

11. $3x - 5y = 1,$
$\quad x + 4y = -2$
13. $2x + y - 4z = 12,$
$\quad 3x \quad + 5z = -1,$
$\quad x - y + z = 2$
15. $\left(\frac{3}{2}, \frac{5}{2}\right)$ **17.** $\left(-\frac{63}{29}, -\frac{114}{29}\right)$ **19.** $\left(-1, \frac{5}{2}\right)$
21. $(0, 3)$ **23.** No solution   **25.** $(3y - 2, y)$
27. $(-1, 2, -2)$ **29.** $\left(\frac{3}{2}, -4, 3\right)$ **31.** $(-1, 6, 3)$
33. $\left(\frac{1}{2}z + \frac{1}{2}, -\frac{1}{2}z - \frac{1}{2}, z\right)$ **35.** $(r - 2, -2r + 3, r)$
37. No solution   **39.** $(1, -3, -2, -1)$ **41.** 1:00 A.M.
43. \$8000 at 8%; \$12,000 at 10%; \$10,000 at 12%

45. Discussion and Writing   **47.** [4.2] Exponential
48. [1.3] Linear   **49.** [3.5] Rational   **50.** [3.1] Quartic
51. [4.3] Logarithmic   **52.** [3.1] Cubic   **53.** [1.3] Linear
54. [2.3] Quadratic   **55.** $y = 3x^2 + \frac{5}{2}x - \frac{15}{2}$

57. $\begin{bmatrix} 1 & 5 \\ 0 & 1 \end{bmatrix}, \begin{bmatrix} 1 & 0 \\ 0 & 1 \end{bmatrix}$ **59.** $\left(-\frac{4}{3}, -\frac{1}{3}, 1\right)$

61. $\left(-\frac{14}{13}z - 1, \frac{3}{13}z - 2, z\right)$ **63.** $(-3, 3)$

Exercise Set 8.4

1. $x = -3, y = 5$ **3.** $x = -1, y = 1$

5. $\begin{bmatrix} -2 & 7 \\ 6 & 2 \end{bmatrix}$ **7.** $\begin{bmatrix} 1 & 3 \\ 2 & 6 \end{bmatrix}$ **9.** $\begin{bmatrix} 9 & 9 \\ -3 & -3 \end{bmatrix}$

11. $\begin{bmatrix} 11 & 13 \\ 5 & 3 \end{bmatrix}$ **13.** $\begin{bmatrix} -4 & 3 \\ -2 & -4 \end{bmatrix}$ **15.** $\begin{bmatrix} 17 & 9 \\ -2 & 1 \end{bmatrix}$

17. $\begin{bmatrix} 0 & 0 \\ 0 & 0 \end{bmatrix}$ **19.** $\begin{bmatrix} 1 & 2 \\ 4 & 3 \end{bmatrix}$ **21.** $\begin{bmatrix} 1 \\ 40 \end{bmatrix}$

23. $\begin{bmatrix} -10 & 28 \\ 14 & -26 \\ 0 & -6 \end{bmatrix}$ **25.** Not defined   **27.** $\begin{bmatrix} 3 & 16 & 3 \\ 0 & -32 & 0 \\ -6 & 4 & 5 \end{bmatrix}$

29. (a) $[150 \quad 80 \quad 40]$; **(b)** $[157.5 \quad 84 \quad 42]$;
(c) $[307.5 \quad 164 \quad 82]$, the total budget for each area in June
and July   **31. (a)** $\mathbf{C} = [140 \quad 27 \quad 3 \quad 13 \quad 64]$,
$\mathbf{P} = [180 \quad 4 \quad 11 \quad 24 \quad 662], \mathbf{B} = [50 \quad 5 \quad 1 \quad 82 \quad 20]$;
(b) $[650 \quad 50 \quad 28 \quad 307 \quad 1448]$, the total nutritional values
of a meal of 1 serving of chicken, 1 cup of potato salad, and
3 broccoli spears

33. (a) $\begin{bmatrix} 45.29 & 6.63 & 10.94 & 7.42 & 8.01 \\ 53.78 & 4.95 & 9.83 & 6.16 & 12.56 \\ 47.13 & 8.47 & 12.66 & 8.29 & 9.43 \\ 51.64 & 7.12 & 11.57 & 9.35 & 10.72 \end{bmatrix}$;

(b) $[65 \quad 48 \quad 93 \quad 57]$;
(c) $[12{,}851.86 \quad 1862.1 \quad 3019.81 \quad 2081.9 \quad 2611.56]$;
(d) the total cost, in cents, for each item for the day's meals

35. (a) $\begin{bmatrix} 8 & 15 \\ 6 & 10 \\ 4 & 3 \end{bmatrix}$; **(b)** $[3 \quad 1.50 \quad 2]$; **(c)** $[41 \quad 66]$;

(d) the total cost, in dollars, of ingredients for each coffee shop
37. (a) $[6 \quad 4.50 \quad 5.20]$; **(b)** $\mathbf{PS} = [95.80 \quad 150.60]$

39. $\begin{bmatrix} 2 & -3 \\ 1 & 5 \end{bmatrix} \begin{bmatrix} x \\ y \end{bmatrix} = \begin{bmatrix} 7 \\ -6 \end{bmatrix}$

41. $\begin{bmatrix} 1 & 1 & -2 \\ 3 & -1 & 1 \\ 2 & 5 & -3 \end{bmatrix} \begin{bmatrix} x \\ y \\ z \end{bmatrix} = \begin{bmatrix} 6 \\ 7 \\ 8 \end{bmatrix}$

43. $\begin{bmatrix} 3 & -2 & 4 \\ 2 & 1 & -5 \end{bmatrix} \begin{bmatrix} x \\ y \\ z \end{bmatrix} = \begin{bmatrix} 17 \\ 13 \end{bmatrix}$

45. $\begin{bmatrix} -4 & 1 & -1 & 2 \\ 1 & 2 & -1 & -1 \\ -1 & 1 & 4 & -3 \\ 2 & 3 & 5 & -7 \end{bmatrix} \begin{bmatrix} w \\ x \\ y \\ z \end{bmatrix} = \begin{bmatrix} 12 \\ 0 \\ 1 \\ 9 \end{bmatrix}$

47. Left to the student   **49.** Discussion and Writing

51. [2.4] (a) $\left(\frac{1}{2}, -\frac{25}{4}\right)$; (b) $x = \frac{1}{2}$; (c) minimum: $-\frac{25}{4}$;
(d)

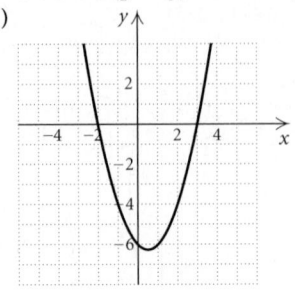

$f(x) = x^2 - x - 6$

52. [2.4] (a) $\left(\frac{5}{4}, -\frac{49}{8}\right)$; (b) $x = \frac{5}{4}$; (c) minimum: $-\frac{49}{8}$;
(d)

$f(x) = 2x^2 - 5x - 3$

53. [2.4] (a) $\left(-\frac{3}{2}, \frac{17}{4}\right)$; (b) $x = -\frac{3}{2}$; (c) maximum: $\frac{17}{4}$;
(d)

$f(x) = -x^2 - 3x + 2$

54. [2.4] (a) $\left(\frac{2}{3}, \frac{16}{3}\right)$; (b) $x = \frac{2}{3}$; (c) maximum: $\frac{16}{3}$;
(d)

$f(x) = -3x^2 + 4x + 4$

55. $(\mathbf{A} + \mathbf{B})(\mathbf{A} - \mathbf{B}) = \begin{bmatrix} -2 & 1 \\ 2 & -1 \end{bmatrix}$; $\mathbf{A}^2 - \mathbf{B}^2 = \begin{bmatrix} 0 & 3 \\ 0 & -3 \end{bmatrix}$

57. $(\mathbf{A} + \mathbf{B})(\mathbf{A} - \mathbf{B}) = \begin{bmatrix} -2 & 1 \\ 2 & -1 \end{bmatrix}$

$= \mathbf{A}^2 + \mathbf{BA} - \mathbf{AB} - \mathbf{B}^2$

59. $\mathbf{A} + \mathbf{B} =$
$\begin{bmatrix} a_{11} + b_{11} & a_{12} + b_{12} & a_{13} + b_{13} & \cdots & a_{1n} + b_{1n} \\ a_{21} + b_{21} & a_{22} + b_{22} & a_{23} + b_{23} & \cdots & a_{2n} + b_{2n} \\ a_{31} + b_{31} & a_{32} + b_{32} & a_{33} + b_{33} & \cdots & a_{3n} + b_{3n} \\ \vdots & \vdots & \vdots & & \vdots \\ a_{m1} + b_{m1} & a_{m2} + b_{m2} & a_{m3} + b_{m3} & \cdots & a_{mn} + b_{mn} \end{bmatrix}$
$=$
$\begin{bmatrix} b_{11} + a_{11} & b_{12} + a_{12} & b_{13} + a_{13} & \cdots & b_{1n} + a_{1n} \\ b_{21} + a_{21} & b_{22} + a_{22} & b_{23} + a_{23} & \cdots & b_{2n} + a_{2n} \\ b_{31} + a_{31} & b_{32} + a_{32} & b_{33} + a_{33} & \cdots & b_{3n} + a_{3n} \\ \vdots & \vdots & \vdots & & \vdots \\ b_{m1} + a_{m1} & b_{m2} + a_{m2} & b_{m3} + a_{m3} & \cdots & b_{mn} + a_{mn} \end{bmatrix}$
$= \mathbf{B} + \mathbf{A}$

61. $(kl)\mathbf{A} = \begin{bmatrix} (kl)a_{11} & (kl)a_{12} & (kl)a_{13} & \cdots & (kl)a_{1n} \\ (kl)a_{21} & (kl)a_{22} & (kl)a_{23} & \cdots & (kl)a_{2n} \\ (kl)a_{31} & (kl)a_{32} & (kl)a_{33} & \cdots & (kl)a_{3n} \\ \vdots & \vdots & \vdots & & \vdots \\ (kl)a_{m1} & (kl)a_{m2} & (kl)a_{m3} & \cdots & (kl)a_{mn} \end{bmatrix}$
$= \begin{bmatrix} k(la_{11}) & k(la_{12}) & k(la_{13}) & \cdots & k(la_{1n}) \\ k(la_{21}) & k(la_{22}) & k(la_{23}) & \cdots & k(la_{2n}) \\ k(la_{31}) & k(la_{32}) & k(la_{33}) & \cdots & k(la_{3n}) \\ \vdots & \vdots & \vdots & & \vdots \\ k(la_{m1}) & k(la_{m2}) & k(la_{m3}) & \cdots & k(la_{mn}) \end{bmatrix}$
$= k \begin{bmatrix} la_{11} & la_{12} & la_{13} & \cdots & la_{1n} \\ la_{21} & la_{22} & la_{23} & \cdots & la_{2n} \\ la_{31} & la_{32} & la_{33} & \cdots & la_{3n} \\ \vdots & \vdots & \vdots & & \vdots \\ la_{m1} & la_{m2} & la_{m3} & \cdots & la_{mn} \end{bmatrix} = k(l\mathbf{A})$

63. $(k + l)\mathbf{A} =$
$\begin{bmatrix} (k+l)a_{11} & (k+l)a_{12} & (k+l)a_{13} & \cdots & (k+l)a_{1n} \\ (k+l)a_{21} & (k+l)a_{22} & (k+l)a_{23} & \cdots & (k+l)a_{2n} \\ (k+l)a_{31} & (k+l)a_{32} & (k+l)a_{33} & \cdots & (k+l)a_{3n} \\ \vdots & \vdots & \vdots & & \vdots \\ (k+l)a_{m1} & (k+l)a_{m2} & (k+l)a_{m3} & \cdots & (k+l)a_{mn} \end{bmatrix}$
$=$
$\begin{bmatrix} ka_{11} + la_{11} & ka_{12} + la_{12} & ka_{13} + la_{13} & \cdots & ka_{1n} + la_{1n} \\ ka_{21} + la_{21} & ka_{22} + la_{22} & ka_{23} + la_{23} & \cdots & ka_{2n} + la_{2n} \\ ka_{31} + la_{31} & ka_{32} + la_{32} & ka_{33} + la_{33} & \cdots & ka_{3n} + la_{3n} \\ \vdots & \vdots & \vdots & & \vdots \\ ka_{m1} + la_{m1} & ka_{m2} + la_{m2} & ka_{m3} + la_{m3} & \cdots & ka_{mn} + la_{mn} \end{bmatrix}$
$= k\mathbf{A} + l\mathbf{A}$

Exercise Set 8.5

1. Yes   **3.** No   **5.** $\begin{bmatrix} -3 & 2 \\ 5 & -3 \end{bmatrix}$ **7.** Does not exist

9. $\begin{bmatrix} \frac{2}{5} & -\frac{3}{5} \\ \frac{1}{5} & -\frac{4}{5} \end{bmatrix}$ **11.** $\begin{bmatrix} \frac{3}{8} & -\frac{1}{4} & \frac{1}{8} \\ -\frac{1}{8} & \frac{3}{4} & -\frac{3}{8} \\ -\frac{1}{4} & \frac{1}{2} & \frac{1}{4} \end{bmatrix}$ **13.** Does not exist

15. $\begin{bmatrix} -1 & -1 & -6 \\ 1 & 0 & 2 \\ 0 & 1 & 3 \end{bmatrix}$ **17.** $\begin{bmatrix} 1 & 1 & 2 \\ 1 & 1 & 1 \\ 2 & 3 & 4 \end{bmatrix}$

19. Does not exist   **21.** $\begin{bmatrix} 1 & -2 & 3 & 8 \\ 0 & 1 & -3 & 1 \\ 0 & 0 & 1 & -2 \\ 0 & 0 & 0 & -1 \end{bmatrix}$

23. $\begin{bmatrix} 0.25 & 0.25 & 1.25 & -0.25 \\ 0.5 & 1.25 & 1.75 & -1 \\ -0.25 & -0.25 & -0.75 & 0.75 \\ 0.25 & 0.5 & 0.75 & -0.5 \end{bmatrix}$

25. $(-23, 83)$ **27.** $(-1, 5, 1)$ **29.** $(2, -2)$ **31.** $(0, 2)$
33. $(3, -3, -2)$ **35.** $(-1, 0, 1)$ **37.** $(1, -1, 0, 1)$
39. 50 sausages, 95 hot dogs   **41.** Topsoil: \$239; mulch: \$179; pea gravel: \$222   **43.** Left to the student
45. Left to the student   **47.** Discussion and Writing
49. [3.3] -48 **50.** [3.3] 194 **51.** [2.3] $\dfrac{-1 \pm \sqrt{57}}{4}$
52. [2.5] $-3, -2$ **53.** [2.5] 4
54. [2.5] 9 **55.** [3.3] $(x + 2)(x - 1)(x - 4)$
56. [3.3] $(x + 5)(x + 1)(x - 1)(x - 3)$
57. $\mathbf{A}^{-1}$ exists if and only if $x \neq 0$. $\mathbf{A}^{-1} = \begin{bmatrix} \frac{1}{x} \end{bmatrix}$
59. $\mathbf{A}^{-1}$ exists if and only if $xyz \neq 0$. $\mathbf{A}^{-1} = \begin{bmatrix} 0 & 0 & \frac{1}{z} \\ 0 & \frac{1}{y} & 0 \\ \frac{1}{x} & 0 & 0 \end{bmatrix}$

Exercise Set 8.6

1. -14 **3.** -2 **5.** -11 **7.** $x^3 - 4x$
9. $M_{11} = 6, M_{32} = -9, M_{22} = -29$
11. $A_{11} = 6, A_{32} = 9, A_{22} = -29$
13. -10 **15.** -10 **17.** $M_{41} = -14, M_{33} = 20$
19. $A_{24} = 15, A_{43} = 30$ **21.** 110 **23.** -109
25. $-x^4 + x^2 - 5x$ **27.** $\left(-\frac{25}{2}, -\frac{11}{2}\right)$ **29.** $(3, 1)$

31. $\left(\frac{1}{2}, -\frac{1}{3}\right)$ **33.** $(1, 1)$ **35.** $\left(\frac{3}{2}, \frac{13}{14}, \frac{33}{14}\right)$
37. $(3, -2, 1)$ **39.** $(1, 3, -2)$ **41.** $\left(\frac{1}{2}, \frac{2}{3}, -\frac{5}{6}\right)$
43. Left to the student   **45.** 110   **47.** Left to the student
49. Discussion and Writing   **51.** [4.1] $f^{-1}(x) = \dfrac{x - 2}{3}$
52. [4.1] Not one-to-one   **53.** [4.1] Not one-to-one
54. [4.1] $f^{-1}(x) = (x - 1)^3$ **55.** [2.2] $5 - 3i$
56. [2.2] $6 - 2i$ **57.** [2.2] $10 - 10i$ **58.** [2.2] $\frac{9}{25} + \frac{13}{25}i$
59. ± 2 **61.** $\left(-\infty, -\sqrt{3}\right] \cup \left[\sqrt{3}, \infty\right)$ **63.** -34
65. 4   **67.** Answers may vary.   **69.** Answers may vary.
$\begin{vmatrix} L & -W \\ 2 & 2 \end{vmatrix}$ $\begin{vmatrix} a & b \\ -b & a \end{vmatrix}$
71. Answers may vary.
$\begin{vmatrix} 2\pi r & 2\pi r \\ -h & r \end{vmatrix}$

Exercise Set 8.7

1. (f)   **3.** (h)   **5.** (g)   **7.** (b)
9.   **11.**

$y > 2x$

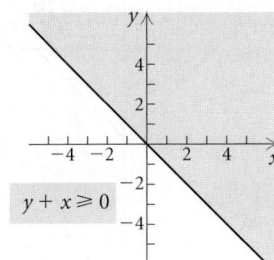
$y + x \geqslant 0$

13.   **15.**

$y > x - 3$

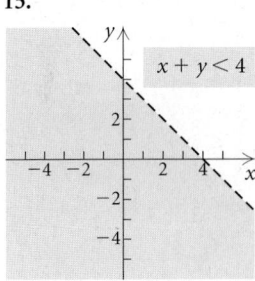
$x + y < 4$

17.   **19.**

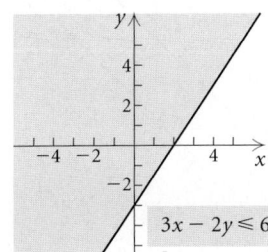
$3x - 2y \leqslant 6$

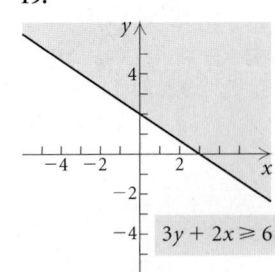
$3y + 2x \geqslant 6$

21.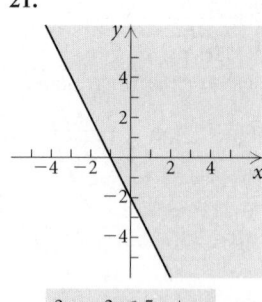

$3x - 2 \leq 5x + y$

23.

$x < -4$

25.

$y > -3$

27.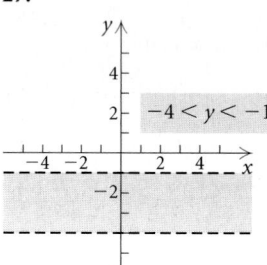

$-4 < y < -1$

29.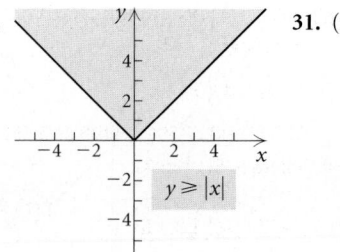

$y \geq |x|$

31. (f)   **33.** (a)   **35.** (b)

37. $y \leq -x + 4$,
$y \leq 3x$

39. $x < 2$,
$y > -1$

41. $y \leq -x + 3$,
$y \leq x + 1$,
$x \geq 0$,
$y \geq 0$

43.

45.

47.

49.

51.

53.

55.

57.

59.

61. Maximum: 179 when $x = 7$ and $y = 0$; minimum: 48 when $x = 0$ and $y = 4$

63. Maximum: 216 when $x = 0$ and $y = 6$; minimum: 0 when $x = 0$ and $y = 0$

65. Maximum income of $18 is achieved when 100 of each type of biscuit is made.

67. Maximum profit of $11,000 is achieved by producing 100 units of lumber and 300 units of plywood.

69. Minimum cost of $\$36\frac{12}{13}$ is achieved by using $1\frac{11}{13}$ sacks of soybean meal and $1\frac{11}{13}$ sacks of oats.

71. Maximum income of $3110 is achieved when $22,000 is invested in corporate bonds and $18,000 is invested in municipal bonds.

73. Minimum cost of $460 thousand is achieved using 30 P_1's and 10 P_2's.
75. Maximum profit per day of $192 is achieved when 2 knit suits and 4 worsted suits are made.
77. Minimum weekly cost of $19.05 is achieved when 1.5 lb of meat and 3 lb of cheese are used.
79. Maximum total number of 800 is achieved when there are 550 of A and 250 of B.
81. Left to the student   **83.** Discussion and Writing
85. [2.6] $\{x \mid -7 \le x < 2\}$, or $[-7, 2)$
86. [2.6] $\{x \mid x \le 1 \text{ or } x \ge 5\}$, or $(-\infty, 1] \cup [5, \infty)$
87. [3.6] $\{x \mid -1 \le x \le 3\}$, or $[-1, 3]$
88. [3.6] $\{x \mid -3 < x < -2\}$, or $(-3, -2)$
89.

91.

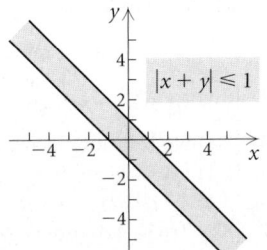

$|x + y| \le 1$

93.

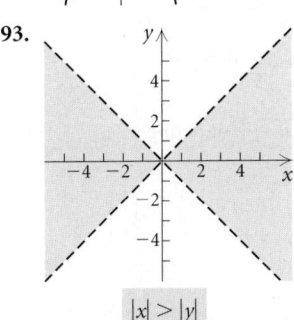

$|x| > |y|$

95. Maximum income of $28,500 is achieved by making 30 less expensive assemblies and 30 more expensive assemblies.

Exercise Set 8.8

1. $\dfrac{2}{x-3} - \dfrac{1}{x+2}$ **3.** $-\dfrac{4}{3x-1} + \dfrac{5}{2x-1}$

5. $-\dfrac{3}{x-2} + \dfrac{2}{x+2} + \dfrac{4}{x+1}$

7. $-\dfrac{3}{(x+2)^2} - \dfrac{1}{x+2} + \dfrac{1}{x-1}$ **9.** $\dfrac{3}{x-1} - \dfrac{4}{2x-1}$

11. $x - 2 - \dfrac{\frac{11}{4}}{(x+1)^2} + \dfrac{\frac{17}{16}}{x+1} - \dfrac{\frac{17}{16}}{x-3}$

13. $\dfrac{3x+5}{x^2+2} - \dfrac{4}{x-1}$ **15.** $-\dfrac{2}{x+2} + \dfrac{10}{(x+2)^2} + \dfrac{3}{2x-1}$

17. $3x + 1 + \dfrac{2}{2x-1} + \dfrac{3}{x+1}$

19. $-\dfrac{1}{x-3} + \dfrac{3x}{x^2+2x-5}$

21. $\dfrac{5}{3x+5} - \dfrac{3}{x+1} + \dfrac{4}{(x+1)^2}$ **23.** $\dfrac{8}{4x-5} + \dfrac{3}{3x+2}$

25. $\dfrac{2x-5}{3x^2+1} - \dfrac{2}{x-2}$ **27.** Discussion and Writing

29. Discussion and Writing   **30.** [3.4] $3, \pm i$

31. [3.4] $-2, \dfrac{1 \pm \sqrt{5}}{2}$ **32.** [3.4] $-2, 3, \pm i$

33. [3.4] $-3, -1 \pm \sqrt{2}$

35. $-\dfrac{\frac{1}{2a^2}x}{x^2+a^2} + \dfrac{\frac{1}{4a^2}}{x-a} + \dfrac{\frac{1}{4a^2}}{x+a}$

37. $-\dfrac{3}{25(\ln x + 2)} + \dfrac{3}{25(\ln x - 3)} + \dfrac{7}{5(\ln x - 3)^2}$

Review Exercises: Chapter 8

1. True   **2.** False   **3.** True   **4.** False   **5.** (a)   **6.** (e)
7. (h)   **8.** (d)   **9.** (b)   **10.** (g)   **11.** (c)   **12.** (f)
13. $(-2, -2)$ **14.** $(-5, 4)$ **15.** No solution
16. $(-y-2, y)$, or $(x, -x-2)$ **17.** No solution
18. $(0, 0, 0)$ **19.** $(-5, 13, 8, 2)$ **20.** Consistent: 13, 14, 16, 18, 19; the others are inconsistent.   **21.** Dependent: 16; the others are independent.   **22.** $(1, 2)$ **23.** $(-3, 4, -2)$

24. $\left(\dfrac{z}{2}, -\dfrac{z}{2}, z\right)$ **25.** $(-4, 1, -2, 3)$

26. 31 nickels, 44 dimes   **27.** $1600 at 3%, $3400 at 3.5%
28. 1 bagel, $\frac{1}{2}$ serving cream cheese, 2 bananas
29. 75, 69, 82
30. (a) $f(x) = 0.2x^2 - 0.8x + 7.3$; (b) 8.3 lb

31. $\begin{bmatrix} 0 & -1 & 6 \\ 3 & 1 & -2 \\ -2 & 1 & -2 \end{bmatrix}$ **32.** $\begin{bmatrix} -3 & 3 & 0 \\ -6 & -9 & 6 \\ 6 & 0 & -3 \end{bmatrix}$

33. $\begin{bmatrix} -1 & 1 & 0 \\ -2 & -3 & 2 \\ 2 & 0 & -1 \end{bmatrix}$ **34.** $\begin{bmatrix} -2 & 2 & 6 \\ 1 & -8 & 18 \\ 2 & 1 & -15 \end{bmatrix}$

35. Not possible   **36.** $\begin{bmatrix} 2 & -1 & -6 \\ 1 & 5 & -2 \\ -2 & -1 & 4 \end{bmatrix}$

37. $\begin{bmatrix} -13 & 1 & 6 \\ -3 & -7 & 4 \\ 8 & 3 & -5 \end{bmatrix}$ **38.** $\begin{bmatrix} -2 & -1 & 18 \\ 5 & -3 & -2 \\ -2 & 3 & -8 \end{bmatrix}$

39. (a) $\begin{bmatrix} 46.1 & 5.9 & 10.1 & 8.5 & 11.4 \\ 54.6 & 4.6 & 9.6 & 7.6 & 10.6 \\ 48.9 & 5.5 & 12.7 & 9.4 & 9.3 \\ 51.3 & 4.8 & 11.3 & 6.9 & 12.7 \end{bmatrix}$

(b) $[32 \quad 19 \quad 43 \quad 38]$;
(c) $[6564.7 \quad 695.1 \quad 1481.1 \quad 1082.8 \quad 1448.7]$;
(d) the total cost, in cents, for each item for the day's meals

40. $\begin{bmatrix} -\frac{1}{2} & 0 \\ \frac{1}{6} & \frac{1}{3} \end{bmatrix}$ **41.** $\begin{bmatrix} 0 & 0 & \frac{1}{4} \\ 0 & -\frac{1}{2} & 0 \\ \frac{1}{3} & 0 & 0 \end{bmatrix}$

42. $\begin{bmatrix} 1 & 0 & 0 & 0 \\ 0 & \frac{1}{9} & \frac{5}{18} & 0 \\ 0 & -\frac{1}{9} & \frac{2}{9} & 0 \\ 0 & 0 & 0 & 1 \end{bmatrix}$

43. $\begin{bmatrix} 3 & -2 & 4 \\ 1 & 5 & -3 \\ 2 & -3 & 7 \end{bmatrix}\begin{bmatrix} x \\ y \\ z \end{bmatrix} = \begin{bmatrix} 13 \\ 7 \\ -8 \end{bmatrix}$ **44.** $(-8, 7)$

45. $(1, -2, 5)$ **46.** $(2, -1, 1, -3)$ **47.** 10   **48.** -18
49. -6 **50.** -1 **51.** $(3, -2)$ **52.** $(-1, 5)$
53. $\left(\frac{3}{2}, \frac{13}{14}, \frac{33}{14}\right)$ **54.** $(2, -1, 3)$

55.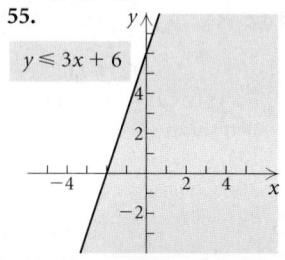
$y \leq 3x + 6$

56.
$4x - 3y \geq 12$

57.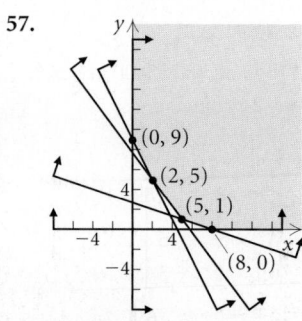
$(0, 9)$
$(2, 5)$
$(5, 1)$
$(8, 0)$

58. Minimum $= 52$ at $(2, 4)$; maximum $= 92$ at $(2, 8)$
59. Maximum score of 96 when 0 group A questions and 8 group B questions are answered
60. $\dfrac{5}{x + 1} - \dfrac{5}{x + 2} - \dfrac{5}{(x + 2)^2}$ **61.** $\dfrac{2}{2x - 3} - \dfrac{5}{x + 4}$
62. C   **63.** A
64. Discussion and Writing: During a holiday season, a caterer sold a total of 55 food trays. She sold 15 more seafood trays than cheese trays. How many of each were sold?
65. Discussion and Writing: In general, $(\mathbf{AB})^2 \neq \mathbf{A}^2\mathbf{B}^2$. $(\mathbf{AB})^2 = \mathbf{ABAB}$ and $\mathbf{A}^2\mathbf{B}^2 = \mathbf{AABB}$. Since matrix multiplication is not commutative, $\mathbf{BA} \neq \mathbf{AB}$, so $(\mathbf{AB})^2 \neq \mathbf{A}^2\mathbf{B}^2$.
66. 4%: $10,000; 5%: $12,000; $5\frac{1}{2}$%: $18,000
67. $\left(\frac{5}{18}, \frac{1}{7}\right)$ **68.** $\left(1, \frac{1}{2}, \frac{1}{3}\right)$

69.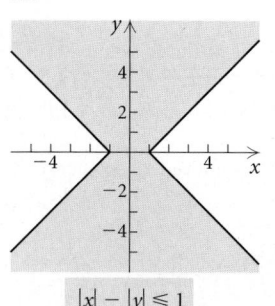
$|x| - |y| \leq 1$

70.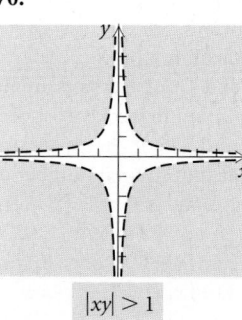
$|xy| > 1$

Test: Chapter 8

1. [8.1] $(-3, 5)$; consistent, independent
2. [8.1] $(x, 2x - 3)$ or $\left(\dfrac{y + 3}{2}, y\right)$; consistent, dependent
3. [8.1] No solution; inconsistent, independent
4. [8.1] $(1, -2)$; consistent, independent
5. [8.2] $(-1, 3, 2)$ **6.** [8.1] Student: 342; nonstudent: 408
7. [8.2] Tricia: 120 orders; Maria: 104 orders; Antonio: 128 orders
8. [8.4] $\begin{bmatrix} -2 & -3 \\ -3 & 4 \end{bmatrix}$ **9.** [8.4] Not defined
10. [8.4] $\begin{bmatrix} -7 & -13 \\ 5 & -1 \end{bmatrix}$ **11.** [8.4] Not defined
12. [8.4] $\begin{bmatrix} 2 & -2 & 6 \\ -4 & 10 & 4 \end{bmatrix}$ **13.** [8.5] $\begin{bmatrix} 0 & -1 \\ -\frac{1}{4} & -\frac{3}{4} \end{bmatrix}$
14. [8.4] **(a)** $\begin{bmatrix} 49 & 10 & 13 \\ 43 & 12 & 11 \\ 51 & 8 & 12 \end{bmatrix}$; **(b)** $\begin{bmatrix} 26 & 18 & 23 \end{bmatrix}$;
(c) $\begin{bmatrix} 3221 & 660 & 812 \end{bmatrix}$; **(d)** the total cost, in cents, for each type of menu item served on the given day
15. [8.4] $\begin{bmatrix} 3 & -4 & 2 \\ 2 & 3 & 1 \\ 1 & -5 & -3 \end{bmatrix}\begin{bmatrix} x \\ y \\ z \end{bmatrix} = \begin{bmatrix} -8 \\ 7 \\ 3 \end{bmatrix}$ **16.** [8.5] $(-2, 1, 1)$
17. [8.6] 61   **18.** [8.6] -33 **19.** [8.6] $\left(-\frac{1}{2}, \frac{3}{4}\right)$
20. [8.7]

$3x + 4y \leq -12$

21. [8.7] Maximum: 15 at $(3, 3)$; minimum: 2 at $(1, 0)$
22. [8.7] Pound cakes: 25; carrot cakes: 75
23. [8.8] $-\dfrac{2}{x - 1} + \dfrac{5}{x + 3}$
24. [8.2] $A = 1$, $B = -3$, $C = 2$

CHAPTER 9

Exercise Set 9.1

1. (f)   **3.** (b)   **5.** (d)

7. $V: (0,0)$; $F: (0,5)$; $D: y = -5$

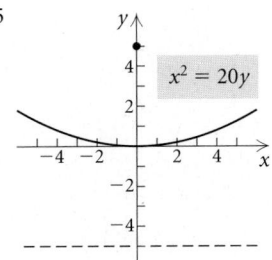

$x^2 = 20y$

9. $V: (0,0)$; $F: \left(-\frac{3}{2}, 0\right)$; $D: x = \frac{3}{2}$

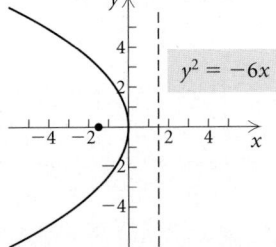

$y^2 = -6x$

11. $V: (0,0)$; $F: (0,1)$; $D: y = -1$

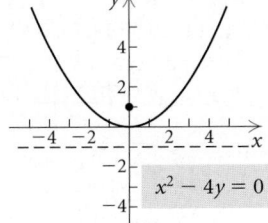

$x^2 - 4y = 0$

13. $V: (0,0)$; $F: \left(\frac{1}{8}, 0\right)$; $D: x = -\frac{1}{8}$

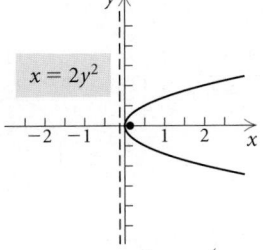

$x = 2y^2$

15. $y^2 = 16x$ **17.** $x^2 = -4\pi y$ **19.** $(y-2)^2 = 14\left(x + \frac{1}{2}\right)$

21. $V: (-2,1)$; $F: \left(-2, -\frac{1}{2}\right)$; $D: y = \frac{5}{2}$

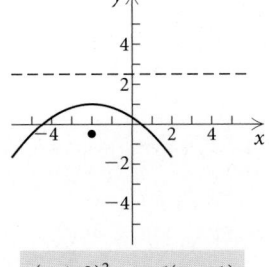

$(x+2)^2 = -6(y-1)$

23. $V: (-1,-3)$; $F: \left(-1, -\frac{7}{2}\right)$; $D: y = -\frac{5}{2}$

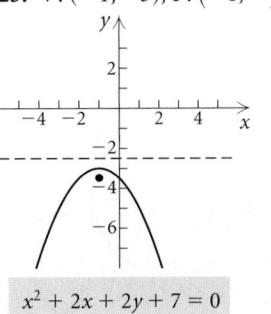

$x^2 + 2x + 2y + 7 = 0$

25. $V: (0,-2)$; $F: \left(0, -1\frac{3}{4}\right)$; $D: y = -2\frac{1}{4}$

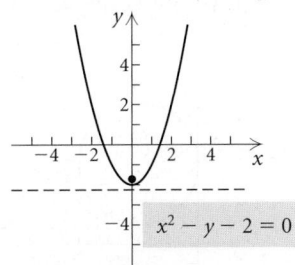

$x^2 - y - 2 = 0$

27. $V: (-2,-1)$; $F: \left(-2, -\frac{3}{4}\right)$; $D: y = -1\frac{1}{4}$

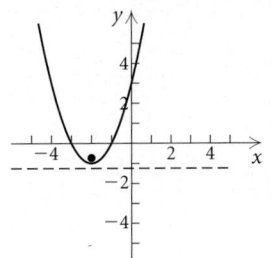

$y = x^2 + 4x + 3$

29. $V: \left(5\frac{3}{4}, \frac{1}{2}\right)$; $F: \left(6, \frac{1}{2}\right)$; $D: x = 5\frac{1}{2}$

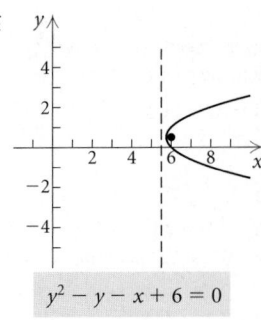

$y^2 - y - x + 6 = 0$

31. (a) $y^2 = 16x$; (b) $3\frac{33}{64}$ ft   **33.** $\frac{2}{3}$ ft, or 8 in.
35. $V: (0.867, 0.348)$; $F: (0.867, -0.190)$; $D: y = 0.887$
37. Discussion and Writing   **39.** [1.1] (h)
40. [1.1], [1.4] (d)   **41.** [1.3] (a), (b), (f), (g)
42. [1.3] (b)   **43.** [1.4] (b)   **44.** [1.1] (f)
45. [1.4] (a) and (g)   **46.** [1.4] (a) and (h); (g) and (h); (b) and (c)   **47.** $(x+1)^2 = -4(y-2)$
49. 10 ft, 11.6 ft, 16.4 ft, 24.4 ft, 35.6 ft, 50 ft

Exercise Set 9.2

1. (b)   **3.** (d)   **5.** (a)

7. $(7, -2)$; 8

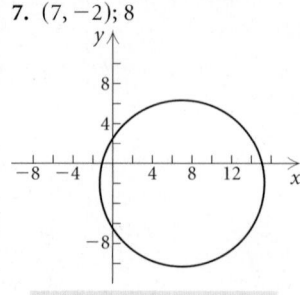

$$x^2 + y^2 - 14x + 4y = 11$$

9. $(-3, 1)$; 4

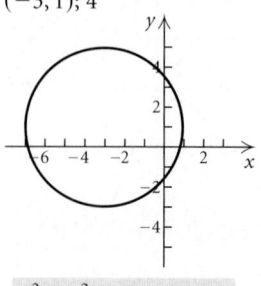

$$x^2 + y^2 + 6x - 2y = 6$$

11. $(-2, 3)$; 5

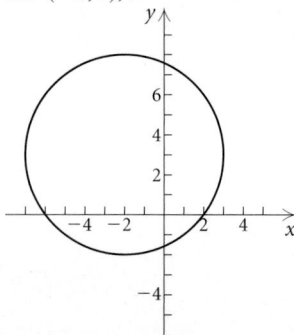

$$x^2 + y^2 + 4x - 6y - 12 = 0$$

13. $(3, 4)$; 3

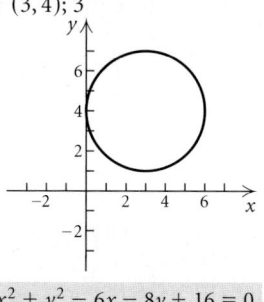

$$x^2 + y^2 - 6x - 8y + 16 = 0$$

15. $(-3, 5)$; $\sqrt{34}$

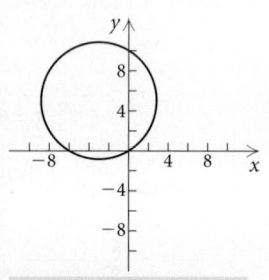

$$x^2 + y^2 + 6x - 10y = 0$$

17. $\left(\dfrac{9}{2}, -2\right)$; $\dfrac{5\sqrt{5}}{2}$

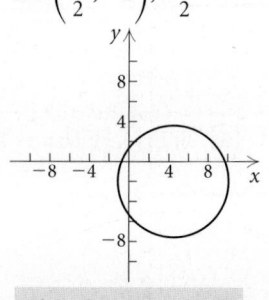

$$x^2 + y^2 - 9x = 7 - 4y$$

19. (c)   **21.** (d)

23. $V: (2, 0), (-2, 0)$;
$F: \left(\sqrt{3}, 0\right), \left(-\sqrt{3}, 0\right)$

$$\dfrac{x^2}{4} + \dfrac{y^2}{1} = 1$$

25. $V: (0, 4), (0, -4)$;
$F: \left(0, \sqrt{7}\right), \left(0, -\sqrt{7}\right)$

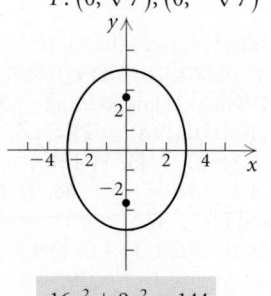

$$16x^2 + 9y^2 = 144$$

27. $V: \left(-\sqrt{3}, 0\right), \left(\sqrt{3}, 0\right)$;
$F: (-1, 0), (1, 0)$

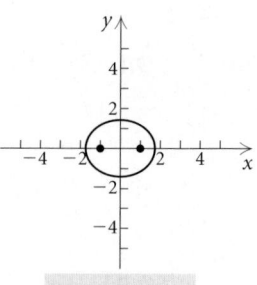

$$2x^2 + 3y^2 = 6$$

29. $V: \left(-\dfrac{1}{2}, 0\right), \left(\dfrac{1}{2}, 0\right)$;
$F: \left(-\dfrac{\sqrt{5}}{6}, 0\right), \left(\dfrac{\sqrt{5}}{6}, 0\right)$

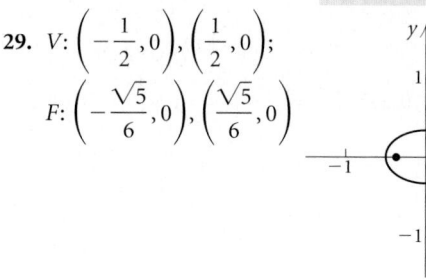

$$4x^2 + 9y^2 = 1$$

31. $\dfrac{x^2}{49} + \dfrac{y^2}{40} = 1$ **33.** $\dfrac{x^2}{25} + \dfrac{y^2}{64} = 1$ **35.** $\dfrac{x^2}{9} + \dfrac{y^2}{5} = 1$

37. $C: (1, 2)$; $V: (4, 2), (-2, 2)$; $F: \left(1 + \sqrt{5}, 2\right), \left(1 - \sqrt{5}, 2\right)$

$$\dfrac{(x - 1)^2}{9} + \dfrac{(y - 2)^2}{4} = 1$$

39. $C: (-3, 5)$; $V: (-3, 11), (-3, -1)$; $F: \left(-3, 5 + \sqrt{11}\right),$
$\left(-3, 5 - \sqrt{11}\right)$

$$\dfrac{(x + 3)^2}{25} + \dfrac{(y - 5)^2}{36} = 1$$

41. $C: (-2, 1); V: (-10, 1), (6, 1); F: (-6, 1), (2, 1)$

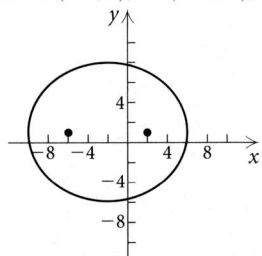

$$3(x + 2)^2 + 4(y - 1)^2 = 192$$

43. $C: (2, -1); V: (-1, -1), (5, -1); F: (2 + \sqrt{5}, -1),$
$(2 - \sqrt{5}, -1)$

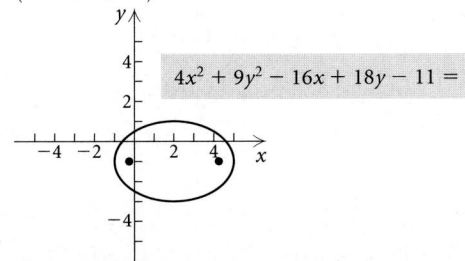

$$4x^2 + 9y^2 - 16x + 18y - 11 = 0$$

45. $C: (1, 1); V: (1, 3), (1, -1); F: (1, 1 + \sqrt{3}), (1, 1 - \sqrt{3})$

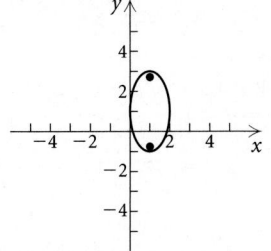

$$4x^2 + y^2 - 8x - 2y + 1 = 0$$

47. Example 2; $\dfrac{3}{5} < \dfrac{\sqrt{12}}{4}$ **49.** $\dfrac{x^2}{15} + \dfrac{y^2}{16} = 1$

51. $\dfrac{x^2}{2500} + \dfrac{y^2}{144} = 1$ **53.** 2×10^6 mi

55. $C: (2.003, -1.005); V: (-1.017, -1.005), (5.023, -1.005)$
57. Discussion and Writing   **59.** [1.1] Midpoint
60. [2.1] Zero   **61.** [1.1] y-intercept
62. [2.3] Two different real-number solutions
63. [3.3] Remainder   **64.** [6.2] Ellipse   **65.** [6.1] Parabola
66. [6.2] Circle   **67.** $\dfrac{(x - 3)^2}{4} + \dfrac{(y - 1)^2}{25} = 1$

69. $\dfrac{x^2}{9} + \dfrac{y^2}{484/5} = 1$ **71.** About 9.1 ft

Exercise Set 9.3

1. (b)   **3.** (c)   **5.** (a)   **7.** $\dfrac{y^2}{9} - \dfrac{x^2}{16} = 1$ **9.** $\dfrac{x^2}{4} - \dfrac{y^2}{9} = 1$

11. $C: (0, 0); V: (2, 0), (-2, 0); F: (2\sqrt{2}, 0), (-2\sqrt{2}, 0);$
$A: y = x, y = -x$

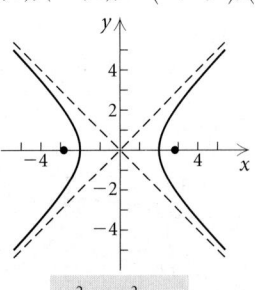

$$\dfrac{x^2}{4} - \dfrac{y^2}{4} = 1$$

13. $C: (2, -5); V: (-1, -5), (5, -5); F: (2 - \sqrt{10}, -5),$
$(2 + \sqrt{10}, -5); A: y = -\dfrac{x}{3} - \dfrac{13}{3}, y = \dfrac{x}{3} - \dfrac{17}{3}$

$$\dfrac{(x - 2)^2}{9} - \dfrac{(y + 5)^2}{1} = 1$$

15. $C: (-1, -3); V: (-1, -1), (-1, -5);$
$F: (-1, -3 + 2\sqrt{5}), (-1, -3 - 2\sqrt{5});$
$A: y = \frac{1}{2}x - \frac{5}{2}, y = -\frac{1}{2}x - \frac{7}{2}$

$$\dfrac{(y + 3)^2}{4} - \dfrac{(x + 1)^2}{16} = 1$$

17. $C: (0, 0); V: (-2, 0), (2, 0); F: (-\sqrt{5}, 0), (\sqrt{5}, 0);$
$A: y = -\frac{1}{2}x, y = \frac{1}{2}x$

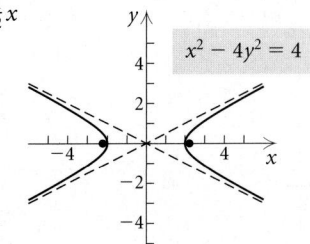

$$x^2 - 4y^2 = 4$$

19. C: $(0,0)$; V: $(0,-3)$, $(0,3)$; F: $(0,-3\sqrt{10})$, $(0,3\sqrt{10})$; A: $y = \frac{1}{3}x$, $y = -\frac{1}{3}x$

$$9y^2 - x^2 = 81$$

21. C: $(0,0)$; V: $(-\sqrt{2},0)$, $(\sqrt{2},0)$; F: $(-2,0)$, $(2,0)$; A: $y = x$, $y = -x$

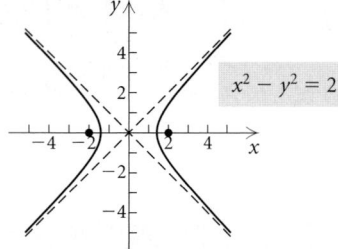

$$x^2 - y^2 = 2$$

23. C: $(0,0)$; V: $\left(0,-\frac{1}{2}\right)$, $\left(0,\frac{1}{2}\right)$; F: $\left(0,-\frac{\sqrt{2}}{2}\right)$, $\left(0,\frac{\sqrt{2}}{2}\right)$; A: $y = x$, $y = -x$

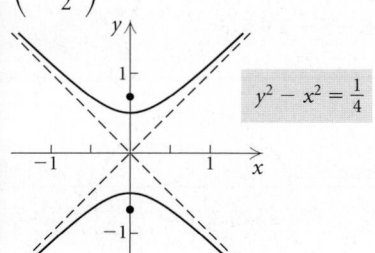

$$y^2 - x^2 = \frac{1}{4}$$

25. C: $(1,-2)$; V: $(0,-2)$, $(2,-2)$; F: $(1-\sqrt{2},-2)$, $(1+\sqrt{2},-2)$; A: $y = -x-1$, $y = x-3$

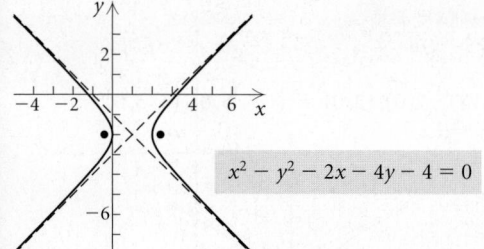

$$x^2 - y^2 - 2x - 4y - 4 = 0$$

27. C: $\left(\frac{1}{3},3\right)$; V: $\left(-\frac{2}{3},3\right)$, $\left(\frac{4}{3},3\right)$; F: $\left(\frac{1}{3}-\sqrt{37},3\right)$, $\left(\frac{1}{3}+\sqrt{37},3\right)$; A: $y = 6x+1$, $y = -6x+5$

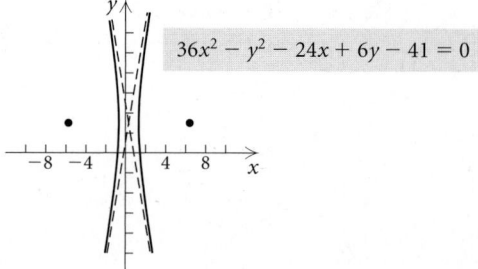

$$36x^2 - y^2 - 24x + 6y - 41 = 0$$

29. C: $(3,1)$; V: $(3,3)$, $(3,-1)$; F: $(3,1+\sqrt{13})$, $(3,1-\sqrt{13})$; A: $y = \frac{2}{3}x-1$, $y = -\frac{2}{3}x+3$

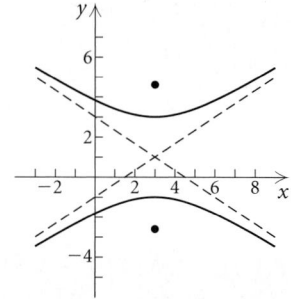

$$9y^2 - 4x^2 - 18y + 24x - 63 = 0$$

31. C: $(1,-2)$; V: $(2,-2)$, $(0,-2)$; F: $(1+\sqrt{2},-2)$, $(1-\sqrt{2},-2)$; A: $y = x-3$, $y = -x-1$

$$x^2 - y^2 - 2x - 4y = 4$$

33. C: $(-3,4)$; V: $(-3,10)$, $(-3,-2)$; F: $(-3,4+6\sqrt{2})$, $(-3,4-6\sqrt{2})$; A: $y = x+7$, $y = -x+1$

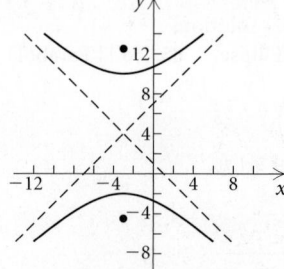

$$y^2 - x^2 - 6x - 8y - 29 = 0$$

35. Example 3; $\dfrac{\sqrt{5}}{1} > \dfrac{5}{4}$ **37.** $\dfrac{x^2}{9} - \dfrac{(y-7)^2}{16} = 1$

39. $\dfrac{y^2}{25} - \dfrac{x^2}{11} = 1$ **41.** $C\colon (-1.460, -0.957)$;

$V\colon (-2.360, -0.957), (-0.560, -0.957)$;

$A\colon y = -1.429x - 3.043, \ y = 1.429x + 1.129$

43. Discussion and Writing

45. [4.1] **(a)** Yes; **(b)** $f^{-1}(x) = \dfrac{x+3}{2}$

46. [4.1] **(a)** Yes; **(b)** $f^{-1}(x) = \sqrt[3]{x-2}$

47. [4.1] **(a)** Yes; **(b)** $f^{-1}(x) = \dfrac{5}{x} + 1$, or $\dfrac{5+x}{x}$

48. [4.1] **(a)** Yes; **(b)** $f^{-1}(x) = x^2 - 4, \ x \geq 0$

49. [5.1], [5.3], [5.5], [5.6] $(6, -1)$

50. [5.1], [5.3], [5.5], [5.6] $(1, -1)$

51. [5.1], [5.3], [5.5], [5.6] $(2, -1)$

52. [5.1], [5.3], [5.5], [5.6] $(-3, 4)$

53. $\dfrac{(y+5)^2}{9} - (x-3)^2 = 1$

55. $\dfrac{x^2}{345.96} - \dfrac{y^2}{22{,}154.04} = 1$

Visualizing the Graph

1. B   **2.** J   **3.** F   **4.** I   **5.** H   **6.** G   **7.** E
8. D   **9.** C   **10.** A

Exercise Set 9.4

1. (e)   **3.** (c)   **5.** (b)   **7.** $(-4, -3), (3, 4)$

9. $(0, 2), (3, 0)$ **11.** $(-5, 0), (4, 3), (4, -3)$

13. $(3, 0), (-3, 0)$ **15.** $(0, -3), (4, 5)$ **17.** $(-2, 1)$

19. $(3, 4), (-3, -4), (4, 3), (-4, -3)$

21. $\left(\dfrac{6\sqrt{21}}{7}, \dfrac{4i\sqrt{35}}{7}\right), \left(\dfrac{6\sqrt{21}}{7}, -\dfrac{4i\sqrt{35}}{7}\right),$

$\left(-\dfrac{6\sqrt{21}}{7}, \dfrac{4i\sqrt{35}}{7}\right), \left(-\dfrac{6\sqrt{21}}{7}, -\dfrac{4i\sqrt{35}}{7}\right)$

23. $(3, 2), \left(4, \dfrac{3}{2}\right)$

25. $\left(\dfrac{5+\sqrt{70}}{3}, \dfrac{-1+\sqrt{70}}{3}\right), \left(\dfrac{5-\sqrt{70}}{3}, \dfrac{-1-\sqrt{70}}{3}\right)$

27. $\left(\sqrt{2}, \sqrt{14}\right), \left(-\sqrt{2}, \sqrt{14}\right), \left(\sqrt{2}, -\sqrt{14}\right), \left(-\sqrt{2}, -\sqrt{14}\right)$

29. $(1, 2), (-1, -2), (2, 1), (-2, -1)$

31. $\left(\dfrac{15+\sqrt{561}}{8}, \dfrac{11-3\sqrt{561}}{8}\right),$

$\left(\dfrac{15-\sqrt{561}}{8}, \dfrac{11+3\sqrt{561}}{8}\right)$

33. $\left(\dfrac{7-\sqrt{33}}{2}, \dfrac{7+\sqrt{33}}{2}\right), \left(\dfrac{7+\sqrt{33}}{2}, \dfrac{7-\sqrt{33}}{2}\right)$

35. $(3, 2), (-3, -2), (2, 3), (-2, -3)$

37. $\left(\dfrac{5-9\sqrt{15}}{20}, \dfrac{-45+3\sqrt{15}}{20}\right),$

$\left(\dfrac{5+9\sqrt{15}}{20}, \dfrac{-45-3\sqrt{15}}{20}\right)$

39. $(3, -5), (-1, 3)$ **41.** $(8, 5), (-5, -8)$ **43.** $(3, 2),$
$(-3, -2)$ **45.** $(2, 1), (-2, -1), (1, 2), (-1, -2)$

47. $\left(4 + \dfrac{3i\sqrt{6}}{2}, -4 + \dfrac{3i\sqrt{6}}{2}\right), \left(4 - \dfrac{3i\sqrt{6}}{2}, -4 - \dfrac{3i\sqrt{6}}{2}\right)$

49. $\left(3, \sqrt{5}\right), \left(-3, -\sqrt{5}\right), \left(\sqrt{5}, 3\right), \left(-\sqrt{5}, -3\right)$

51. $\left(\dfrac{8\sqrt{5}}{5}i, \dfrac{3\sqrt{105}}{5}\right), \left(\dfrac{8\sqrt{5}}{5}i, -\dfrac{3\sqrt{105}}{5}\right),$

$\left(-\dfrac{8\sqrt{5}}{5}i, \dfrac{3\sqrt{105}}{5}\right), \left(-\dfrac{8\sqrt{5}}{5}i, -\dfrac{3\sqrt{105}}{5}\right)$

53. $(2, 1), (-2, -1), \left(-i\sqrt{5}, \dfrac{2i\sqrt{5}}{5}\right), \left(i\sqrt{5}, -\dfrac{2i\sqrt{5}}{5}\right)$

55. 6 cm by 8 cm   **57.** 4 in. by 5 in.
59. Length: $\sqrt{3}$ m; width: 1 m   **61.** 30 yd by 75 yd
63. 16 ft, 24 ft   **65.** (b)   **67.** (d)   **69.** (a)
71.

73.   **75.**

77.   **79.**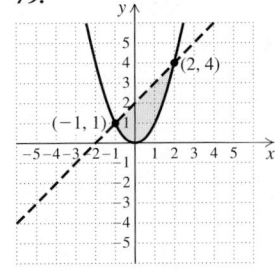

81. $(1.564, 2.448), (0.138, 0.019)$ **83.** $(0.871, 1.388)$
85. $(1.146, 3.146), (-1.841, 0.159)$
87. $(0.965, 4402.33), (-0.965, -4402.33)$
89. $(2.112, -0.109), (-13.041, -13.337)$
91. $(400, 1.431), (-400, 1.431), (400, -1.431), (-400, -1.431)$

93. Discussion and Writing   **95.** [4.5] 2   **96.** [4.5] 2.048
97. [4.5] 81   **98.** [4.5] 5   **99.** $(x-2)^2 + (y-3)^2 = 1$

101. $\dfrac{x^2}{4} + y^2 = 1$ **103.** $\left(x + \dfrac{5}{13}\right)^2 + \left(y - \dfrac{32}{13}\right)^2 = \dfrac{5365}{169}$

105. There is no number x such that $\dfrac{x^2}{a^2} - \dfrac{\left(\dfrac{b}{a}x\right)^2}{b^2} = 1$,

because the left side simplifies to $\dfrac{x^2}{a^2} - \dfrac{x^2}{a^2}$, which is 0.

107. $\left(\tfrac{1}{2}, \tfrac{1}{4}\right), \left(\tfrac{1}{2}, -\tfrac{1}{4}\right), \left(-\tfrac{1}{2}, \tfrac{1}{4}\right), \left(-\tfrac{1}{2}, -\tfrac{1}{4}\right)$

109. Factor: $x^3 + y^3 = (x+y)(x^2 - xy + y^2)$. We know that $x + y = 1$, so $(x+y)^2 = x^2 + 2xy + y^2 = 1$, or $x^2 + y^2 = 1 - 2xy$. We also know that $xy = 1$, so $x^2 + y^2 = 1 - 2 \cdot 1 = -1$. Then $x^3 + y^3 = 1 \cdot (-1 - 1) = -2$.

111. $(2,4), (4,2)$ **113.** $(3,-2), (-3,2), (2,-3), (-2,3)$

115. $\left(\dfrac{2\log 3 + 3\log 5}{3(\log 3 \cdot \log 5)}, \dfrac{4\log 3 - 3\log 5}{3(\log 3 \cdot \log 5)}\right)$

Exercise Set 9.5

1. $(0,-2)$ **3.** $\left(1, \sqrt{3}\right)$ **5.** $\left(\sqrt{2}, 0\right)$ **7.** $\left(\sqrt{3}, 1\right)$
9. Ellipse or circle   **11.** Hyperbola   **13.** Parabola
15. Hyperbola   **17.** Ellipse or circle
19.

$\dfrac{(x')^2}{4} + \dfrac{(y')^2}{8} = 1$

21.

$\dfrac{(x')^2}{9} - \dfrac{(y')^2}{6} = 1$

23.

$(y')^2 = 6x'$

25.

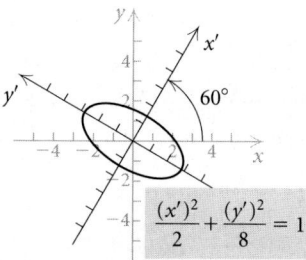

$\dfrac{(x')^2}{2} + \dfrac{(y')^2}{8} = 1$

27.

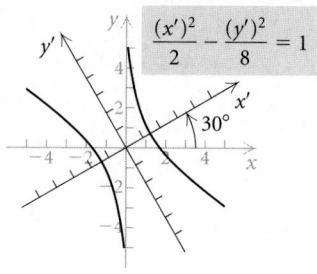

$\dfrac{(x')^2}{2} - \dfrac{(y')^2}{8} = 1$

29.

$y' = -\dfrac{1}{4}(x')^2$

31.

$\dfrac{(x')^2}{10} - \dfrac{(y' + 1)^2}{5} = 1$

33.

$\dfrac{(x')^2}{16} + \dfrac{(y')^2}{48} = 1$

35.

$(y')^2 = 8x'$

37.

$$\frac{(x')^2}{54} - \frac{(y')^2}{46} = 1$$

39. Discussion and Writing   **41.** [5.4] $\dfrac{2\pi}{3}$

42. [5.4] $-\dfrac{7\pi}{4}$ **43.** [5.4] $60°$ **44.** [5.4] $135°$

45. $x = x' \cos \theta - y' \sin \theta, y = x' \sin \theta + y' \cos \theta$

47. $A' + C' = A \cos^2 \theta + B \sin \theta \cos \theta + C \sin^2 \theta$
$\qquad\qquad + A \sin^2 \theta - B \sin \theta \cos \theta + C \cos^2 \theta$
$\qquad = A(\sin^2 \theta + \cos^2 \theta) + C(\sin^2 \theta + \cos^2 \theta)$
$\qquad = A + C$

Exercise Set 9.6

1. (b)   **3.** (a)   **5.** (d)   **7.** (a) Parabola; (b) vertical,
1 unit to the right of the pole; (c) $\left(\frac{1}{2}, 0\right)$;
(d)

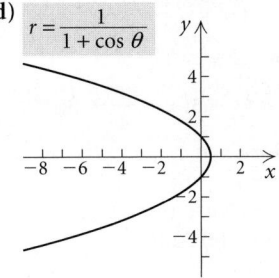

$r = \dfrac{1}{1 + \cos \theta}$

9. (a) Hyperbola; (b) horizontal, $\frac{3}{2}$ units below the pole;
(c) $\left(-3, \dfrac{\pi}{2}\right), \left(1, \dfrac{3\pi}{2}\right)$;
(d)

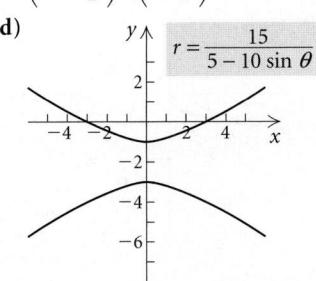

$r = \dfrac{15}{5 - 10 \sin \theta}$

11. (a) Ellipse; (b) vertical, $\frac{8}{3}$ units to the left of the pole;
(c) $\left(\frac{8}{3}, 0\right), \left(\frac{8}{9}, \pi\right)$;
(d)

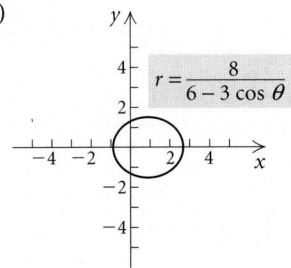

$r = \dfrac{8}{6 - 3 \cos \theta}$

13. (a) Hyperbola; (b) horizontal, $\frac{4}{3}$ units above the pole;
(c) $\left(\dfrac{4}{5}, \dfrac{\pi}{2}\right), \left(-4, \dfrac{3\pi}{2}\right)$;
(d)

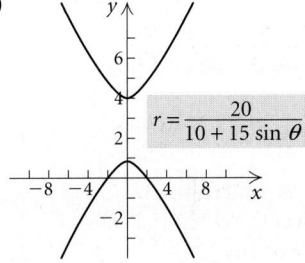

$r = \dfrac{20}{10 + 15 \sin \theta}$

15. (a) Ellipse; (b) vertical, 3 units to the right of the pole;
(c) $(1, 0), (3, \pi)$;
(d)

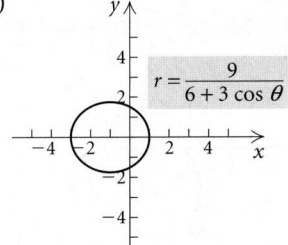

$r = \dfrac{9}{6 + 3 \cos \theta}$

17. (a) Parabola; (b) horizontal, $\frac{3}{2}$ units below the pole;
(c) $\left(\dfrac{3}{4}, \dfrac{3\pi}{2}\right)$;
(d)

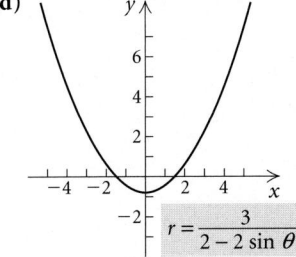

$r = \dfrac{3}{2 - 2 \sin \theta}$

19. (a) Ellipse; **(b)** vertical, 4 units to the left of the pole;
(c) $(4, 0), \left(\frac{4}{3}, \pi\right)$;
(d)

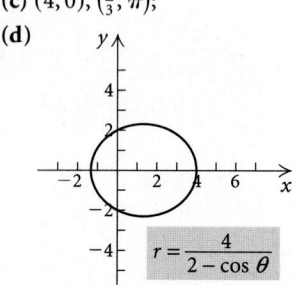

$$r = \frac{4}{2 - \cos \theta}$$

21. (a) Hyperbola; **(b)** horizontal, $\frac{7}{10}$ units above the pole;
(c) $\left(\frac{7}{12}, \frac{\pi}{2}\right), \left(-\frac{7}{8}, \frac{3\pi}{2}\right)$;
(d)

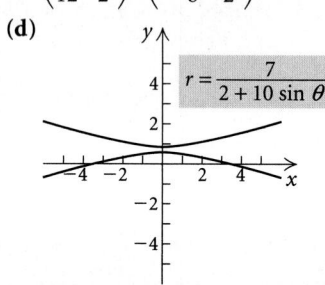

$$r = \frac{7}{2 + 10 \sin \theta}$$

23. $y^2 + 2x - 1 = 0$ **25.** $x^2 - 3y^2 - 12y - 9 = 0$
27. $27x^2 + 36y^2 - 48x - 64 = 0$
29. $4x^2 - 5y^2 + 24y - 16 = 0$
31. $3x^2 + 4y^2 + 6x - 9 = 0$ **33.** $4x^2 - 12y - 9 = 0$
35. $3x^2 + 4y^2 - 8x - 16 = 0$
37. $4x^2 - 96y^2 + 140y - 49 = 0$ **39.** $r = \dfrac{6}{1 + 2 \sin \theta}$
41. $r = \dfrac{4}{1 + \cos \theta}$ **43.** $r = \dfrac{2}{2 - \cos \theta}$
45. $r = \dfrac{15}{4 + 3 \sin \theta}$ **47.** $r = \dfrac{8}{1 - 4 \sin \theta}$
49. Discussion and Writing
51. [1.1] $f(t) = (t - 3)^2 + 4$, or $t^2 - 6t + 13$
52. [1.1] $f(2t) = (2t - 3)^2 + 4$, or $4t^2 - 12t + 13$
53. [1.1] $f(t - 1) = (t - 4)^2 + 4$, or $t^2 - 8t + 20$
54. [1.1] $f(t + 2) = (t - 1)^2 + 4$, or $t^2 - 2t + 5$
55. $r = \dfrac{1.5 \times 10^8}{1 + \sin \theta}$

Exercise Set 9.7

1.

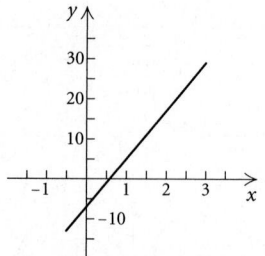

$$x = \tfrac{1}{2}t, \, y = 6t - 7; \, -1 \le t \le 6$$

$$y = 12x - 7, \, -\tfrac{1}{2} \le x \le 3$$

3.

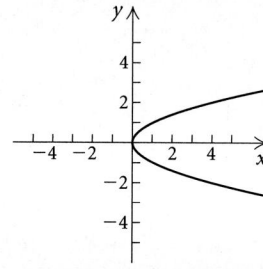

$$x = 4t^2, \, y = 2t; \, -1 \le t \le 1$$

$$x = y^2, \, 0 \le x \le 4$$

5. $x = y^4, \, 0 \le x \le 16$ **7.** $y = \dfrac{1}{x}, \, 1 \le x \le 5$

9. $y = \tfrac{1}{4}(x + 1)^2, \, -7 \le x \le 5$ **11.** $y = \dfrac{1}{x}, \, x > 0$

13. $x^2 + y^2 = 9, \, -3 \le x \le 3$

15. $x^2 + \dfrac{y^2}{4} = 1, \, -1 \le x \le 1$ **17.** $y = \dfrac{1}{x}, \, x \ge 1$

19. $(x - 1)^2 + (y - 2)^2 = 4, \, -1 \le x \le 3$

21. Answers may vary. $x = t, \, y = 4t - 3; \, x = \dfrac{t}{4} + 3,$

$y = t + 9$ **23.** Answers may vary. $x = t,$
$y = (t - 2)^2 - 6t; \, x = t + 2, \, y = t^2 - 6t - 12$
25. (a) $x = 40\sqrt{3}t, \, y = 7 + 40t - 16t^2$; **(b)** 31 ft, 23 ft;
(c) about 2.7 sec; **(d)** about 187.1 ft; **(e)** 32 ft
27. Discussion and Writing
29. [1.1]   **30.** [1.1]

$$y = x^3$$

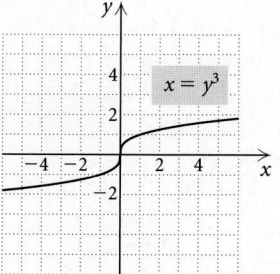

$$x = y^3$$

31. [1.2]

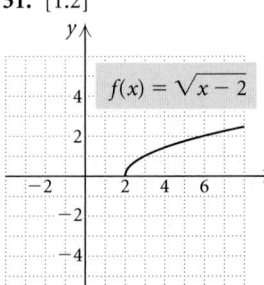
$f(x) = \sqrt{x - 2}$

32. [3.6]

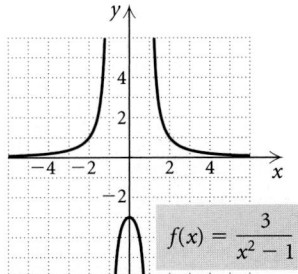
$f(x) = \dfrac{3}{x^2 - 1}$

33. $x^{2/3} + y^{2/3} = 1$

Review Exercises: Chapter 9

1. True   **2.** False   **3.** True   **4.** False   **5.** False
6. (d)   **7.** (a)   **8.** (e)   **9.** (g)   **10.** (b)   **11.** (f)
12. (h)   **13.** (c)   **14.** $x^2 = -6y$ **15.** $F: (-3, 0)$;
$V: (0, 0)$; $D: x = 3$ **16.** $V: (-5, 8)$; $F: \left(-5, \frac{15}{2}\right)$; $D: y = \frac{17}{2}$
17. $C: (2, -1)$; $V: (-3, -1), (7, -1)$; $F: (-1, -1), (5, -1)$;

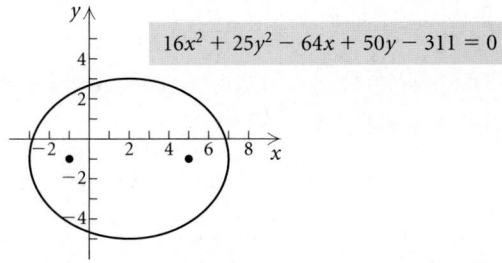
$16x^2 + 25y^2 - 64x + 50y - 311 = 0$

18. $\dfrac{x^2}{9} + \dfrac{y^2}{16} = 1$

19. $C: \left(-2, \dfrac{1}{4}\right)$; $V: \left(0, \dfrac{1}{4}\right), \left(-4, \dfrac{1}{4}\right)$;

$F: \left(-2 + \sqrt{6}, \dfrac{1}{4}\right), \left(-2 - \sqrt{6}, \dfrac{1}{4}\right)$;

$A: y - \dfrac{1}{4} = \dfrac{\sqrt{2}}{2}(x + 2), y - \dfrac{1}{4} = -\dfrac{\sqrt{2}}{2}(x + 2)$
20. 0.167 ft   **21.** $\left(-8\sqrt{2}, 8\right), \left(8\sqrt{2}, 8\right)$
22. $\left(3, \dfrac{\sqrt{29}}{2}\right), \left(-3, \dfrac{\sqrt{29}}{2}\right), \left(3, -\dfrac{\sqrt{29}}{2}\right), \left(-3, -\dfrac{\sqrt{29}}{2}\right)$
23. $(7, 4)$ **24.** $(2, 2), \left(\frac{32}{9}, -\frac{10}{9}\right)$ **25.** $(0, -3), (2, 1)$

26. $(4, 3), (4, -3), (-4, 3), (-4, -3)$
27. $\left(-\sqrt{3}, 0\right), \left(\sqrt{3}, 0\right), (-2, 1), (2, 1)$ **28.** $\left(-\frac{3}{5}, \frac{21}{5}\right), (3, -3)$
29. $(6, 8), (6, -8), (-6, 8), (-6, -8)$
30. $(2, 2), (-2, -2), \left(2\sqrt{2}, \sqrt{2}\right), \left(-2\sqrt{2}, -\sqrt{2}\right)$ **31.** 7, 4
32. 7 m by 12 m   **33.** 4, 8   **34.** 32 cm, 20 cm
35. 11 ft, 3 ft

36.

37.

38.

39.

40.

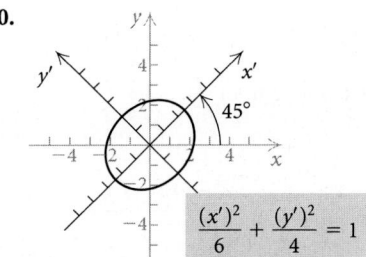
$\dfrac{(x')^2}{6} + \dfrac{(y')^2}{4} = 1$

41.

$\dfrac{(x')^2}{3} - \dfrac{(y')^2}{2} = 1$

42.

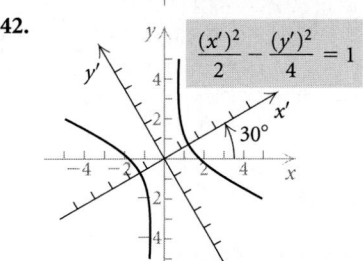
$\dfrac{(x')^2}{2} - \dfrac{(y')^2}{4} = 1$

43.

$(x')^2 = -y'$

44.

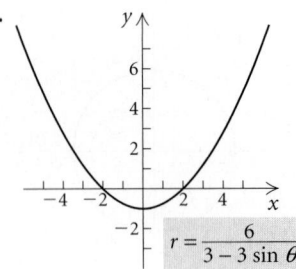

$$r = \frac{6}{3 - 3\sin\theta}$$

Horizontal directrix 2 units below the pole; vertex: $\left(1, \frac{3\pi}{2}\right)$

45.

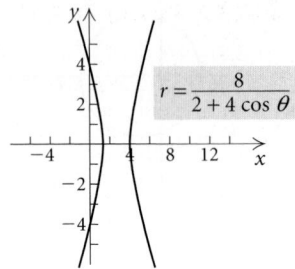

$$r = \frac{8}{2 + 4\cos\theta}$$

Vertical directrix 2 units to the right of the pole; vertices: $\left(\frac{4}{3}, 0\right), (-4, \pi)$

46.

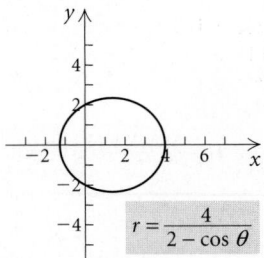

$$r = \frac{4}{2 - \cos\theta}$$

Vertical directrix 4 units to the left of the pole; vertices: $(4, 0), \left(\frac{4}{3}, \pi\right)$

47.

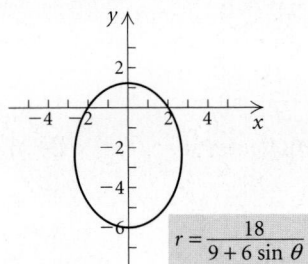

$$r = \frac{18}{9 + 6\sin\theta}$$

Horizontal directrix 3 units above the pole; vertices: $\left(\frac{6}{5}, \frac{\pi}{2}\right), \left(6, \frac{3\pi}{2}\right)$

48. $x^2 - 4y - 4 = 0$ **49.** $3x^2 - y^2 - 16x + 16 = 0$
50. $3x^2 + 4y^2 - 8x - 16 = 0$
51. $9x^2 + 5y^2 + 24y - 36 = 0$
52. $r = \dfrac{1}{1 + \frac{1}{2}\cos\theta}$, or $r = \dfrac{2}{2 + \cos\theta}$ **53.** $r = \dfrac{18}{1 - 3\sin\theta}$
54. $r = \dfrac{4}{1 - \cos\theta}$ **55.** $r = \dfrac{6}{1 + 2\sin\theta}$

56.

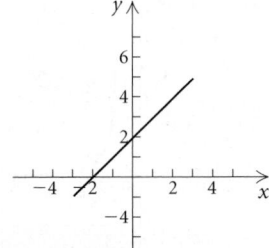

$x = t, \ y = 2 + t; \ -3 \leqslant t \leqslant 3$

$y = 2 + x, \ -3 \leqslant x \leqslant 3$

57.

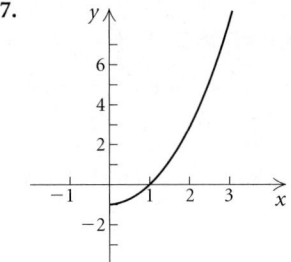

$x = \sqrt{t}, \ y = t - 1; \ 0 \leqslant t \leqslant 9$

$y = x^2 - 1, \ 0 \leqslant x \leqslant 3$

58.

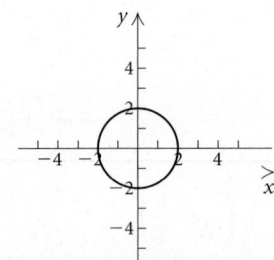

$x = 2\cos t, \ y = 2\sin t; \ 0 \leqslant t \leqslant 2\pi$

$x^2 + y^2 = 4$

59.

$x = 3\sin t, \ y = \cos t; \ 0 \leqslant t \leqslant 2\pi$

$$\frac{x^2}{9} + y^2 = 1$$

60. Answers may vary. $x = t, y = 2t - 3; x = t + 1,$ $y = 2t - 1$
61. Answers may vary. $x = t, y = t^2 + 4; x = t - 2,$ $y = t^2 - 4t + 8$

62. (a) $x = 75\sqrt{2}t$, $y = 75\sqrt{2}t - 16t^2$; (b) 174.2 ft, 60.4 ft;
(c) about 6.6 sec; (d) about 700.0 ft; (e) about 175.8 ft
63. B   **64.** D
65. Discussion and Writing: Although we can always visualize
the real-number solutions, we cannot visualize the imaginary-
number solutions.
66. Discussion and Writing: The equation of a circle can be
written as

$$\frac{(x - h)^2}{a^2} + \frac{(y - k)^2}{b^2} = 1,$$

where $a = b = r$, the radius of the circle. In an ellipse, $a > b$,
so a circle is not a special type of ellipse.
67. $x^2 + \dfrac{y^2}{9} = 1$ **68.** $\dfrac{8}{7}, \dfrac{7}{2}$
69. $(x - 2)^2 + (y - 1)^2 = 100$
70. $\dfrac{x^2}{778.41} - \dfrac{y^2}{39,221.59} = 1$

Test: Chapter 9

1. [9.3] (c)   **2.** [9.1] (b)   **3.** [9.2] (a)   **4.** [9.2] (d)
5. [9.1] $V: (0, 0)$; $F: (0, 3)$; $D: y = -3$

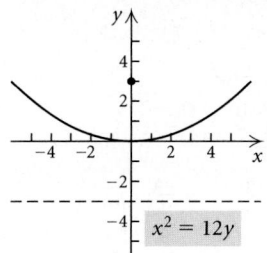

$x^2 = 12y$

6. [9.1] $V: (-1, -1)$; $F: (1, -1)$; $D: x = -3$

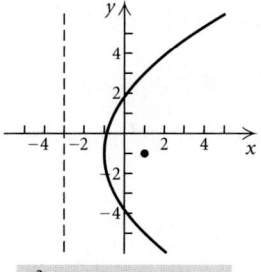

$y^2 + 2y - 8x - 7 = 0$

7. [9.1] $x^2 = 8y$

8. [9.2] Center: $(-1, 3)$; radius: 5

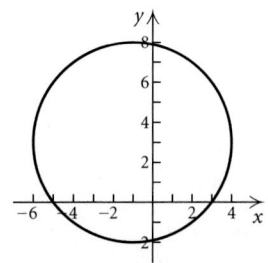

$x^2 + y^2 + 2x - 6y - 15 = 0$

9. [9.2] $C: (0, 0)$; $V: (-4, 0), (4, 0)$; $F: \left(-\sqrt{7}, 0\right), \left(\sqrt{7}, 0\right)$

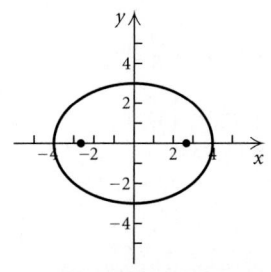

$9x^2 + 16y^2 = 144$

10. [9.2] $C: (-1, 2)$; $V: (-1, -1), (-1, 5)$;
$F: \left(-1, 2 - \sqrt{5}\right), \left(-1, 2 + \sqrt{5}\right)$

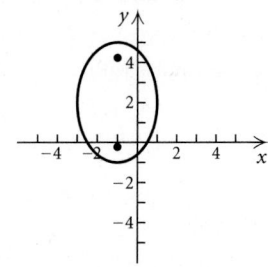

$\dfrac{(x + 1)^2}{4} + \dfrac{(y - 2)^2}{9} = 1$

11. [9.2] $\dfrac{x^2}{4} + \dfrac{y^2}{25} = 1$
12. [9.3] $C: (0, 0)$; $V: (-1, 0), (1, 0)$; $F: \left(-\sqrt{5}, 0\right), \left(\sqrt{5}, 0\right)$;
$A: y = -2x, y = 2x$

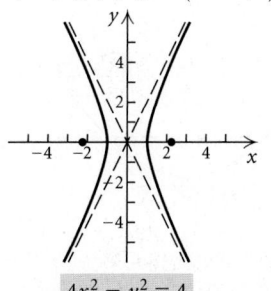

$4x^2 - y^2 = 4$

13. [9.3] $C: (-1, 2); V: (-1, 0), (-1, 4); F: \left(-1, 2 - \sqrt{13}\right),$
$\left(-1, 2 + \sqrt{13}\right); A: y = -\frac{2}{3}x + \frac{4}{3}, y = \frac{2}{3}x + \frac{8}{3}$

$$\frac{(y - 2)^2}{4} - \frac{(x + 1)^2}{9} = 1$$

14. [9.3] $y = \dfrac{\sqrt{2}}{2}x, y = -\dfrac{\sqrt{2}}{2}x$ **15.** [9.1] $\dfrac{27}{8}$ in.

16. [9.4] $(1, 2), (1, -2), (-1, 2), (-1, -2)$
17. [9.4] $(3, -2), (-2, 3)$ **18.** [9.4] $(2, 3), (3, 2)$
19. [9.4] 5 ft by 4 ft   **20.** [9.4] 60 ft by 45 ft
21. [9.4]

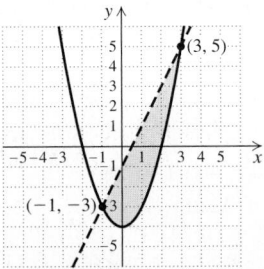

22. [9.5] After using the rotation of axes formulas with $\theta = 45°$, we have $\dfrac{(x')^2}{9} + (y')^2 = 1$.

23. [9.6]

Horizontal directrix 2 units below the pole; vertex: $\left(1, \dfrac{3\pi}{2}\right)$

24. [9.6] $r = \dfrac{6}{1 + 2 \cos \theta}$

25. [9.7]

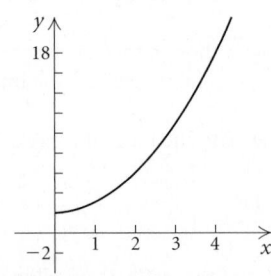

$x = \sqrt{t}, y = t + 2; 0 \leqslant t \leqslant 16$

26. [9.7] $x^2 + y^2 = 9, -3 \leqslant x \leqslant 3$
27. [9.7] Answers may vary. $x = t, y = t - 5; x = t + 5,$
$y = t$
28. [9.7] **(a)** $x = 125\sqrt{3}t, y = 10 + 125t - 16t^2$;
(b) 119 ft, 241 ft; **(c)** about 7.9 sec; **(d)** about 1710.4 ft;
(e) about 254.1 ft   **29.** [9.2] $(x - 3)^2 + (y + 1)^2 = 8$

CHAPTER 10

Exercise Set 10.1

1. 3, 7, 11, 15; 39; 59   **3.** $2, \frac{3}{2}, \frac{4}{3}, \frac{5}{4}; \frac{10}{9}; \frac{15}{14}$
5. $0, \frac{3}{5}, \frac{4}{5}, \frac{15}{17}; \frac{99}{101}; \frac{112}{113}$ **7.** $-1, 4, -9, 16; 100; -225$
9. 7, 3, 7, 3; 3; 7   **11.** 34   **13.** 225   **15.** $-33,880$
17. 67   **19.** $2n$ **21.** $(-1)^n \cdot 2 \cdot 3^{n-1}$ **23.** $\dfrac{n + 1}{n + 2}$
25. $n(n + 1)$ **27.** $\log 10^{n-1}$, or $n - 1$ **29.** 6; 28
31. 20; 30   **33.** $\frac{1}{2} + \frac{1}{4} + \frac{1}{6} + \frac{1}{8} + \frac{1}{10} = \frac{137}{120}$
35. $1 + 2 + 4 + 8 + 16 + 32 + 64 = 127$
37. $\ln 7 + \ln 8 + \ln 9 + \ln 10 = \ln(7 \cdot 8 \cdot 9 \cdot 10) =$
$\ln 5040 \approx 8.5252$
39. $\frac{1}{2} + \frac{2}{3} + \frac{3}{4} + \frac{4}{5} + \frac{5}{6} + \frac{6}{7} + \frac{7}{8} + \frac{8}{9} = \frac{15,551}{2520}$
41. $-1 + 1 - 1 + 1 - 1 = -1$
43. $3 - 6 + 9 - 12 + 15 - 18 + 21 - 24 = -12$
45. $2 + 1 + \frac{2}{5} + \frac{1}{5} + \frac{2}{17} + \frac{1}{13} + \frac{2}{37} = \frac{157,351}{40,885}$
47. $3 + 2 + 3 + 6 + 11 + 18 = 43$
49. $\frac{1}{2} + \frac{2}{3} + \frac{4}{5} + \frac{8}{9} + \frac{16}{17} + \frac{32}{33} + \frac{64}{65} + \frac{128}{129} + \frac{256}{257} + \frac{512}{513} + \frac{1024}{1025}$
≈ 9.736
51. $\displaystyle\sum_{k=1}^{\infty} 5k$ **53.** $\displaystyle\sum_{k=1}^{6} (-1)^{k+1}2^k$ **55.** $\displaystyle\sum_{k=1}^{6} (-1)^k \dfrac{k}{k + 1}$
57. $\displaystyle\sum_{k=2}^{n} (-1)^k k^2$ **59.** $\displaystyle\sum_{k=1}^{\infty} \dfrac{1}{k(k + 1)}$ **61.** $4, 1\frac{1}{4}, 1\frac{4}{5}, 1\frac{5}{9}$
63. $6561, -81, 9i, -3\sqrt{i}$ **65.** 2, 3, 5, 8
67. **(a)** 1062, 1127.84, 1197.77, 1272.03, 1350.90, 1434.65,
1523.60, 1618.07, 1718.39, 1824.93; **(b)** \$3330.35

69. 1, 2, 4, 8, 16, 32, 64, 128, 256, 512, 1024, 2048, 4096, 8192, 16,384, 32,768, 65,536   **71.** 1, 1, 2, 3, 5, 8, 13

73.

n	U_n
1	2
2	2.25
3	2.3704
4	2.4414
5	2.4883
6	2.5216
7	2.5465
8	2.5658
9	2.5812
10	2.5937

75.

n	U_n
1	2
2	1.5538
3	1.4988
4	1.4914
5	1.4904
6	1.4902
7	1.4902
8	1.4902
9	1.4902
10	1.4902

77. (a) $a_n = -13.21231156n^2 + 52,871.41834n - 52,893,240.07$;
(b) 253 thousand, 350 thousand, 342 thousand, 131 thousand
79. Discussion and Writing
80. [8.1], [8.3], [8.5], [8.6] $(-1, -3)$
81. [8.1], [8.3], [8.5], [8.6] Yahoo: 122.9 million; Google: 105.2 million
82. [9.2] $(3, -2)$; 4   **83.** [9.2] $\left(-\dfrac{5}{2}, 4\right)$; $\dfrac{\sqrt{97}}{2}$
85. $i, -1, -i, 1, i; i$ **87.** $\ln(1 \cdot 2 \cdot 3 \cdot \cdots \cdot n)$

Exercise Set 10.2

1. $a_1 = 3, d = 5$ **3.** $a_1 = 9, d = -4$ **5.** $a_1 = \frac{3}{2}, d = \frac{3}{4}$
7. $a_1 = \$316, d = -\$3$ **9.** $a_{12} = 46$ **11.** $a_{14} = -\frac{17}{3}$
13. $a_{10} = \$7941.62$ **15.** 33rd   **17.** 46th   **19.** $a_1 = 5$
21. $n = 39$ **23.** $a_1 = \frac{1}{3}; d = \frac{1}{2}; \frac{1}{3}, \frac{5}{6}, \frac{4}{3}, \frac{11}{6}, \frac{7}{3}$ **25.** 670
27. 160,400   **29.** 735   **31.** 990   **33.** 1760   **35.** $\frac{65}{2}$
37. $-\frac{6026}{13}$ **39.** 1260 poles   **41.** 3 plants; 171 plants
43. 4960¢, or $49.60   **45.** 1320 seats   **47.** Yes; 3
49. Discussion and Writing
50. [8.1], [8.3], [8.5], [8.6] $(2, 5)$
51. [8.2], [8.3], [8.5], [8.6] $(2, -1, 3)$
52. [9.2] $(-4, 0), (4, 0); \left(-\sqrt{7}, 0\right), \left(\sqrt{7}, 0\right)$
53. [9.2] $\dfrac{x^2}{4} + \dfrac{y^2}{25} = 1$ **55.** n^2
57. $a_1 = 60 - 5p - 5q; d = 5p + 2q - 20$ **59.** 6, 8, 10
61. $5\frac{4}{5}, 7\frac{3}{5}, 9\frac{2}{5}, 11\frac{1}{5}$ **63.** Insert 16 arithmetic means between 1 and 50 with $d = \frac{49}{17}$.
65.
$$\begin{aligned} m &= p + d \\ m &= q - d \\ \hline 2m &= p + q \quad \textbf{Adding} \\ m &= \frac{p+q}{2} \end{aligned}$$

Visualizing the Graph

1. J   **2.** A   **3.** C   **4.** G   **5.** F   **6.** H   **7.** E
8. D   **9.** B   **10.** I

Exercise Set 10.3

1. 2   **3.** -1 **5.** -2 **7.** 0.1   **9.** $\dfrac{a}{2}$ **11.** 128
13. 162   **15.** $7(5)^{40}$ **17.** 3^{n-1} **19.** $(-1)^{n-1}$
21. $\dfrac{1}{x^n}$ **23.** 762   **25.** $\frac{4921}{18}$ **27.** 8   **29.** 125
31. Does not exist   **33.** $\frac{2}{3}$ **35.** $29\frac{38,569}{59,049}$ **37.** 2
39. Does not exist   **41.** $\$4545.\overline{45}$ **43.** $\frac{160}{9}$ **45.** $\frac{13}{99}$
47. 9   **49.** $\frac{34,091}{9990}$ **51.** $\$2,684,354.55$
53. (a) About 297 ft; **(b)** 300 ft   **55.** $23,841.50
57. $523,619.17   **59.** $86,666,666,667
61. Left to the student   **63.** Discussion and Writing
65. [1.6] $(f \circ g)(x) = 16x^2 + 40x + 25$;
$(g \circ f)(x) = 4x^2 + 5$ **66.** [1.6] $(f \circ g)(x) = x^2 + x + 2$;
$(g \circ f)(x) = x^2 - x + 3$ **67.** [4.5] 2.209   **68.** [4.5] $\frac{1}{16}$
69. $\left(4 - \sqrt{6}\right)/\left(\sqrt{3} - \sqrt{2}\right) = 2\sqrt{3} + \sqrt{2}$,
$\left(6\sqrt{3} - 2\sqrt{2}\right)/\left(4 - \sqrt{6}\right) = 2\sqrt{3} + \sqrt{2}$; there exists a common ratio, $2\sqrt{3} + \sqrt{2}$; thus the sequence is geometric.
71. (a) $\frac{13}{3}; \frac{22}{3}, \frac{34}{3}, \frac{46}{3}, \frac{58}{3}$; **(b)** $-\frac{11}{3}; -\frac{2}{3}, \frac{10}{3}, -\frac{50}{3}, \frac{250}{3}$ or 5; 8, 12, 18, 27   **73.** $S_n = \dfrac{x^2(1 - (-x)^n)}{x + 1}$

75. $\dfrac{a_{n+1}}{a_n} = r$, so $\ln \dfrac{a_{n+1}}{a_n} = \ln r$. But $\ln \dfrac{a_{n+1}}{a_n} = \ln a_{n+1} - \ln a_n = \ln r$. Thus, $\ln a_1, \ln a_2, \dots$, is an arithmetic sequence with common difference $\ln r$.   **77.** 512 cm^2

Exercise Set 10.4

1. $1^2 < 1^3$, false; $2^2 < 2^3$, true; $3^2 < 3^3$, true; $4^2 < 4^3$, true; $5^2 < 5^3$, true

3. A polygon of 3 sides has $\dfrac{3(3 - 3)}{2}$ diagonals. True; A polygon of 4 sides has $\dfrac{4(4 - 3)}{2}$ diagonals. True; A polygon of 5 sides has $\dfrac{5(5 - 3)}{2}$ diagonals. True; A polygon of 6 sides has $\dfrac{6(6 - 3)}{2}$ diagonals. True; A polygon of 7 sides has $\dfrac{7(7 - 3)}{2}$ diagonals. True.

5. S_n: $2 + 4 + 6 + \cdots + 2n = n(n + 1)$
   S_1: $2 = 1(1 + 1)$
   S_k: $2 + 4 + 6 + \cdots + 2k = k(k + 1)$
   S_{k+1}: $2 + 4 + 6 + \cdots + 2k + 2(k + 1)$
      $= (k + 1)(k + 2)$
(1) *Basis step*: S_1 true by substitution.

(2) *Induction step*: Assume S_k. Deduce S_{k+1}.
Starting with the left side of S_{k+1}, we have
$$2 + 4 + 6 + \cdots + 2k + 2(k + 1)$$
$$= k(k + 1) + 2(k + 1) \quad \textbf{By } S_k$$
$$= (k + 1)(k + 2). \quad \textbf{Distributive law}$$

7. S_n: $1 + 5 + 9 + \cdots + (4n - 3) = n(2n - 1)$
S_1: $1 = 1(2 \cdot 1 - 1)$
S_k: $1 + 5 + 9 + \cdots + (4k - 3) = k(2k - 1)$
S_{k+1}: $1 + 5 + 9 + \cdots + (4k - 3) + [4(k + 1) - 3]$
$$= (k + 1)[2(k + 1) - 1]$$
$$= (k + 1)(2k + 1)$$
(1) *Basis step*: S_1 true by substitution.
(2) *Induction step*: Assume S_k. Deduce S_{k+1}.
Starting with the left side of S_{k+1}, we have
$$1 + 5 + 9 + \cdots + (4k - 3) + [4(k + 1) - 3]$$
$$= k(2k - 1) + [4(k + 1) - 3] \quad \textbf{By } S_k$$
$$= 2k^2 - k + 4k + 4 - 3$$
$$= (k + 1)(2k + 1).$$

9. S_n: $2 + 4 + 8 + \cdots + 2^n = 2(2^n - 1)$
S_1: $2 = 2(2 - 1)$
S_k: $2 + 4 + 8 + \cdots + 2^k = 2(2^k - 1)$
S_{k+1}: $2 + 4 + 8 + \cdots + 2^k + 2^{k+1} = 2(2^{k+1} - 1)$
(1) *Basis step*: S_1 is true by substitution.
(2) *Induction step*: Assume S_k. Deduce S_{k+1}.
Starting with the left side of S_{k+1}, we have
$$\underbrace{2 + 4 + 8 + \cdots + 2^k} + 2^{k+1}$$
$$= \quad 2(2^k - 1) \quad + 2^{k+1} \quad \textbf{By } S_k$$
$$= 2^{k+1} - 2 + 2^{k+1}$$
$$= 2 \cdot 2^{k+1} - 2$$
$$= 2(2^{k+1} - 1).$$

11. S_n: $n < n + 1$
S_1: $1 < 1 + 1$
S_k: $k < k + 1$
S_{k+1}: $k + 1 < (k + 1) + 1$
(1) *Basis step*: Since $1 < 1 + 1$, S_1 is true.
(2) *Induction step*: Assume S_k. Deduce S_{k+1}. Now
$$k < k + 1 \quad \textbf{By } S_k$$
$$k + 1 < k + 1 + 1. \quad \textbf{Adding 1}$$

13. S_n: $2n \le 2^n$
S_1: $2 \cdot 1 \le 2^1$
S_k: $2k \le 2^k$
S_{k+1}: $2(k + 1) \le 2^{k+1}$
(1) *Basis step*: Since $2 = 2$, S_1 is true.
(2) *Induction step*: Let k be any natural number. Assume S_k. Deduce S_{k+1}.
$$2k \le 2^k \quad \textbf{By } S_k$$
$$2 \cdot 2k \le 2 \cdot 2^k \quad \textbf{Multiplying by 2}$$
$$4k \le 2^{k+1}$$
Since $1 \le k$, $k + 1 \le k + k$, or $k + 1 \le 2k$.
Then $2(k + 1) \le 4k$.
Thus, $2(k + 1) \le 4k \le 2^{k+1}$, so $2(k + 1) \le 2^{k+1}$.

15.
S_n: $\dfrac{1}{1 \cdot 2 \cdot 3} + \dfrac{1}{2 \cdot 3 \cdot 4} + \dfrac{1}{3 \cdot 4 \cdot 5} + \cdots$
$$+ \dfrac{1}{n(n + 1)(n + 2)} = \dfrac{n(n + 3)}{4(n + 1)(n + 2)}$$
S_1: $\dfrac{1}{1 \cdot 2 \cdot 3} = \dfrac{1(1 + 3)}{4(1 + 1)(1 + 2)}$
S_k: $\dfrac{1}{1 \cdot 2 \cdot 3} + \dfrac{1}{2 \cdot 3 \cdot 4} + \cdots + \dfrac{1}{k(k + 1)(k + 2)}$
$$= \dfrac{k(k + 3)}{4(k + 1)(k + 2)}$$
S_{k+1}: $\dfrac{1}{1 \cdot 2 \cdot 3} + \dfrac{1}{2 \cdot 3 \cdot 4} + \cdots + \dfrac{1}{k(k + 1)(k + 2)}$
$$+ \dfrac{1}{(k + 1)(k + 2)(k + 3)}$$
$$= \dfrac{(k + 1)(k + 1 + 3)}{4(k + 1 + 1)(k + 1 + 2)} = \dfrac{(k + 1)(k + 4)}{4(k + 2)(k + 3)}$$
(1) *Basis step*: Since $\dfrac{1}{1 \cdot 2 \cdot 3} = \dfrac{1}{6}$ and $\dfrac{1(1 + 3)}{4(1 + 1)(1 + 2)} =$
$\dfrac{1 \cdot 4}{4 \cdot 2 \cdot 3} = \dfrac{1}{6}$, S_1 is true.
(2) *Induction step*: Assume S_k. Deduce S_{k+1}.
Add $\dfrac{1}{(k + 1)(k + 2)(k + 3)}$ on both sides of S_k and
simplify the right side. Only the right side is shown here.
$$\dfrac{k(k + 3)}{4(k + 1)(k + 2)} + \dfrac{1}{(k + 1)(k + 2)(k + 3)}$$
$$= \dfrac{k(k + 3)(k + 3) + 4}{4(k + 1)(k + 2)(k + 3)}$$
$$= \dfrac{k^3 + 6k^2 + 9k + 4}{4(k + 1)(k + 2)(k + 3)}$$
$$= \dfrac{(k + 1)^2(k + 4)}{4(k + 1)(k + 2)(k + 3)}$$
$$= \dfrac{(k + 1)(k + 4)}{4(k + 2)(k + 3)}$$

17. S_n: $1 + 2 + 3 + \cdots + n = \dfrac{n(n + 1)}{2}$
S_1: $1 = \dfrac{1(1 + 1)}{2}$
S_k: $1 + 2 + 3 + \cdots + k = \dfrac{k(k + 1)}{2}$
S_{k+1}: $1 + 2 + 3 + \cdots + k + (k + 1) = \dfrac{(k + 1)(k + 2)}{2}$
(1) *Basis step*: S_1 true by substitution.

(2) *Induction step:* Assume S_k. Deduce S_{k+1}.
Starting with the left side of S_{k+1}, we have

$$\underbrace{1 + 2 + 3 + \cdots + k} + (k + 1)$$

$$= \frac{k(k + 1)}{2} + (k + 1) \qquad \textbf{By } S_k$$

$$= \frac{k(k + 1) + 2(k + 1)}{2} \qquad \textbf{Adding}$$

$$= \frac{(k + 1)(k + 2)}{2}. \qquad \textbf{Distributive law}$$

19. S_n: $1^3 + 2^3 + 3^3 + \cdots + n^3 = \dfrac{n^2(n + 1)^2}{4}$

S_1: $1^3 = \dfrac{1^2(1 + 1)^2}{4}$

S_k: $1^3 + 2^3 + 3^3 + \cdots + k^3 = \dfrac{k^2(k + 1)^2}{4}$

S_{k+1}: $1^3 + 2^3 + 3^3 + \cdots + k^3 + (k + 1)^3$
$$= \frac{(k + 1)^2[(k + 1) + 1]^2}{4}$$

(1) *Basis step.* S_1: $1^3 = \dfrac{1^2(1 + 1)^2}{4} = 1$. True.

(2) *Induction step:* Assume S_k. Deduce S_{k+1}.

$$1^3 + 2^3 + \cdots + k^3 = \frac{k^2(k + 1)^2}{4} \qquad S_k$$

$$1^3 + 2^3 + \cdots + k^3 + (k + 1)^3 = \frac{k^2(k + 1)^2}{4} + (k + 1)^3$$

$$\textbf{Adding } (k + 1)^3$$

$$= \frac{k^2(k + 1)^2 + 4(k + 1)^3}{4}$$

$$= \frac{(k + 1)^2}{4}[k^2 + 4(k + 1)]$$

$$= \frac{(k + 1)^2}{4}(k^2 + 4k + 4)$$

$$= \frac{(k + 1)^2(k + 2)^2}{4}$$

21. S_n: $1^5 + 2^5 + 3^5 + \cdots + n^5$
$$= \frac{n^2(n + 1)^2(2n^2 + 2n - 1)}{12}$$

S_1: $1^5 = \dfrac{1^2(1 + 1)^2(2 \cdot 1^2 + 2 \cdot 1 - 1)}{12}$

S_k: $1^5 + 2^5 + 3^5 + \cdots + k^5$
$$= \frac{k^2(k + 1)^2(2k^2 + 2k - 1)}{12}$$

S_{k+1}: $1^5 + 2^5 + 3^5 + \cdots + k^5 + (k + 1)^5$
$$= \frac{(k + 1)^2[(k + 1) + 1]^2[2(k + 1)^2 + 2(k + 1) - 1]}{12}$$

(1) *Basis step:* S_1: $1^5 = \dfrac{1^2(1 + 1)^2(2 \cdot 1^2 + 2 \cdot 1 - 1)}{12}$. True.

(2) *Induction step.* Assume S_k:
$$1^5 + 2^5 + \cdots + k^5 = \frac{k^2(k + 1)^2(2k^2 + 2k - 1)}{12}.$$

Then $1^5 + 2^5 + \cdots + k^5 + (k + 1)^5$
$$= \frac{k^2(k + 1)^2(2k^2 + 2k - 1)}{12} + (k + 1)^5$$

$$= \frac{k^2(k + 1)^2(2k^2 + 2k - 1) + 12(k + 1)^5}{12}$$

$$= \frac{(k + 1)^2(2k^4 + 14k^3 + 35k^2 + 36k + 12)}{12}$$

$$= \frac{(k + 1)^2(k + 2)^2(2k^2 + 6k + 3)}{12}$$

$$= \frac{(k + 1)^2(k + 1 + 1)^2(2(k + 1)^2 + 2(k + 1) - 1)}{12}.$$

23. S_n: $2 + 6 + 12 + \cdots + n(n + 1) = \dfrac{n(n + 1)(n + 2)}{3}$

S_1: $1(1 + 1) = \dfrac{1(1 + 1)(1 + 2)}{3}$

S_k: $2 + 6 + 12 + \cdots + k(k + 1) = \dfrac{k(k + 1)(k + 2)}{3}$

S_{k+1}:
$$2 + 6 + 12 + \cdots + k(k + 1) + (k + 1)[(k + 1) + 1]$$
$$= \frac{(k + 1)[(k + 1) + 1][(k + 1) + 2]}{3}$$

(1) *Basis step:* S_1: $1(1 + 1) = \dfrac{1(1 + 1)(1 + 2)}{3}$. True.

(2) *Induction step:* Assume S_k:
$$2 + 6 + 12 + \cdots + k(k + 1)$$
$$= \frac{k(k + 1)(k + 2)}{3}.$$

Then $2 + 6 + 12 + \cdots + k(k + 1) + (k + 1)(k + 1 + 1)$
$$= \frac{k(k + 1)(k + 2)}{3} + (k + 1)(k + 2)$$

$$= \frac{k(k + 1)(k + 2) + 3(k + 1)(k + 2)}{3}$$

$$= \frac{(k + 1)(k + 2)(k + 3)}{3}$$

$$= \frac{(k + 1)(k + 1 + 1)(k + 1 + 2)}{3}.$$

25. S_n: $a_1 + (a_1 + d) + (a_1 + 2d) + \cdots +$
$$[a_1 + (n - 1)d] = \frac{n}{2}[2a_1 + (n - 1)d]$$

S_1: $a_1 = \dfrac{1}{2}[2a_1 + (1 - 1)d]$

S_k: $a_1 + (a_1 + d) + (a_1 + 2d) + \cdots +$
$$[a_1 + (k - 1)d] = \frac{k}{2}[2a_1 + (k - 1)d]$$

S_{k+1}: $a_1 + (a_1 + d) + (a_1 + 2d) + \cdots +$
$$[a_1 + (k - 1)d] + [a_1 + ((k + 1) - 1)d]$$
$$= \frac{k + 1}{2}[2a_1 + ((k + 1) - 1)d]$$

(1) *Basis step:* Since $\frac{1}{2}[2a_1 + (1 - 1)d] = \frac{1}{2} \cdot 2a_1 = a_1$, is true.

(2) *Induction step*: Assume S_k. Deduce S_{k+1}. Starting with the left side of S_{k+1}, we have

$$\underbrace{a_1 + (a_1 + d) + \cdots + [a_1 + (k-1)d]} + [a_1 + kd]$$

$$= \frac{k}{2}[2a_1 + (k-1)d] \qquad\qquad + [a_1 + kd] \qquad \text{By } S_k$$

$$= \frac{k[2a_1 + (k-1)d]}{2} + \frac{2[a_1 + kd]}{2}$$

$$= \frac{2ka_1 + k(k-1)d + 2a_1 + 2kd}{2}$$

$$= \frac{2a_1(k+1) + k(k-1)d + 2kd}{2}$$

$$= \frac{2a_1(k+1) + (k-1+2)kd}{2}$$

$$= \frac{2a_1(k+1) + (k+1)kd}{2}$$

$$= \frac{k+1}{2}[2a_1 + kd].$$

27. Discussion and Writing
28. [8.1], [8.3], [8.5], [8.6] (5, 3)
29. [8.2], [8.3], [8.5], [8.6] $(2, -3, 4)$
30. [8.1], [8.3], [8.5], [8.6] Hardback: 50; paperback: 30
31. [8.2], [8.3], [8.5], [8.6] $800 at 1.5%, $1600 at 2%, $2000 at 3%

33. S_n: $x + y$ is a factor of $x^{2n} - y^{2n}$.
    S_1: $x + y$ is a factor of $x^2 - y^2$.
    S_k: $x + y$ is a factor of $x^{2k} - y^{2k}$.
    S_{k+1}: $x + y$ is a factor of $x^{2(k+1)} - y^{2(k+1)}$.
(1) *Basis step*: S_1: $x + y$ is a factor of $x^2 - y^2$. True.
             S_2: $x + y$ is a factor of $x^4 - y^4$. True.
(2) *Induction step*: Assume S_{k-1}: $x + y$ is a factor of $x^{2(k-1)} - y^{2(k-1)}$. Then $x^{2(k-1)} - y^{2(k-1)} = (x + y)Q(x)$ for some polynomial Q.
Assume S_k: $x + y$ is a factor of $x^{2k} - y^{2k}$. Then $x^{2k} - y^{2k} = (x + y)P(x)$ for some polynomial P.

$x^{2(k+1)} - y^{2(k+1)}$
$= (x^{2k} - y^{2k})(x^2 + y^2) - (x^{2(k-1)} - y^{2(k-1)})(x^2y^2)$
$= (x + y)P(x)(x^2 + y^2) - (x + y)Q(x)(x^2y^2)$
$= (x + y)[P(x)(x^2 + y^2) - Q(x)(x^2y^2)]$
so $x + y$ is a factor of $x^{2(k+1)} - y^{2(k+1)}$.

35. S_2: $\log_a(b_1b_2) = \log_a b_1 + \log_a b_2$
     S_k: $\log_a(b_1b_2\cdots b_k) = \log_a b_1 + \log_a b_2 + \cdots + \log_a b_k$
     S_{k+1}: $\log_a(b_1b_2\cdots b_{k+1}) = \log_a b_1 + \log_a b_2 + \cdots + \log_a b_{k+1}$
(1) *Basis step*: S_2 is true by the properties of logarithms.
(2) *Induction step*: Let k be a natural number $k \geq 2$. Assume S_k. Deduce S_{k+1}.

$\log_a(b_1b_2\cdots b_{k+1})$ **Left side of S_{k+1}**
   $= \log_a(b_1b_2\cdots b_k) + \log_a b_{k+1}$ **By S_2**
   $= \log_a b_1 + \log_a b_2 + \cdots + \log_a b_k + \log_a b_{k+1}$

37. S_2: $\overline{z_1 + z_2} = \bar{z}_1 + \bar{z}_2$:
     $\overline{(a + bi) + (c + di)} = \overline{(a + c) + (b + d)i}$
                   $= (a + c) - (b + d)i$
     $\overline{(a + bi)} + \overline{(c + di)} = a - bi + c - di$
                   $= (a + c) - (b + d)i.$
    S_k: $\overline{z_1 + z_2 + \cdots + z_k} = \bar{z}_1 + \bar{z}_2 + \cdots + \bar{z}_k.$
     $\overline{(z_1 + z_2 + \cdots + z_k) + z_{k+1}}$
       $= \overline{(z_1 + z_2 + \cdots + z_k)} + \overline{z_{k+1}}$ **By S_2**
       $= \bar{z}_1 + \bar{z}_2 + \cdots + \bar{z}_k + \bar{z}_{k+1}$ **By S_k**

39. S_1: i is either i or -1 or $-i$ or 1.
    S_k: i^k is either i or -1 or $-i$ or 1.
    $i^{k+1} = i^k \cdot i$ is then $i \cdot i = -1$ or $-1 \cdot i = -i$ or $-i \cdot i = 1$ or $1 \cdot i = i.$

41. S_1:   3 is a factor of $1^3 + 2 \cdot 1$.
    S_k: 3 is a factor of $k^3 + 2k$, i.e., $k^3 + 2k = 3 \cdot m.$
    S_{k+1}:   3 is a factor of $(k+1)^3 + 2(k+1)$.
    Consider
$$(k+1)^3 + 2(k+1) = k^3 + 3k^2 + 5k + 3$$
$$= (k^3 + 2k) + 3k^2 + 3k + 3$$
$$= 3m + 3(k^2 + k + 1).$$

A multiple of 3

Exercise Set 10.5

1. 720   **3.** 604,800   **5.** 120   **7.** 1   **9.** 3024   **11.** 120
13. 120   **15.** 1   **17.** 6,497,400   **19.** $n(n-1)(n-2)$
21. n **23.** $6! = 720$ **25.** $9! = 362,880$
27. $_9P_4 = 3024$ **29.** $_5P_5 = 120; 5^5 = 3125$
31. $_5P_5 \cdot {_4P_4} = 2880$ **33.** $8 \cdot 10^6 = 8,000,000$; 8 million
35. $\dfrac{9!}{2!\,3!\,4!} = 1260$ **37.** (a) $_6P_5 = 720$; (b) $6^5 = 7776$;
(c) $1 \cdot {_5P_4} = 120$; (d) $1 \cdot 1 \cdot {_4P_3} = 24$ **39.** (a) 10^5, or
100,000; (b) 100,000   **41.** (a) $10^9 = 1,000,000,000$; (b) yes
43. Discussion and Writing   **44.** [2.1] $\frac{9}{4}$, or 2.25
45. [2.3] $-3, 2$ **46.** [2.3] $\dfrac{3 \pm \sqrt{17}}{4}$ **47.** [3.4] $-2, 1, 5$
49. 8   **51.** 11   **53.** $n - 1$

Exercise Set 10.6

1. 78   **3.** 78   **5.** 7   **7.** 10   **9.** 1   **11.** 15   **13.** 128
15. 270,725   **17.** 13,037,895   **19.** n **21.** 1
23. $_{23}C_4 = 8855$ **25.** $_{13}C_{10} = 286$
27. $\begin{pmatrix} 10 \\ 7 \end{pmatrix} \cdot \begin{pmatrix} 5 \\ 3 \end{pmatrix} = 1200$ **29.** $\begin{pmatrix} 52 \\ 5 \end{pmatrix} = 2,598,960$
31. (a) $_{31}P_2 = 930$; (b) $31^2 = 961$; (c) $_{31}C_2 = 465$
33. Discussion and Writing   **34.** [2.1] $-\frac{17}{2}$
35. [2.3] $-1, \frac{3}{2}$ **36.** [2.3] $\dfrac{-5 \pm \sqrt{21}}{2}$
37. [3.4] $-4, -2, 3$ **39.** $\begin{pmatrix} 13 \\ 5 \end{pmatrix} = 1287$ **41.** $\begin{pmatrix} n \\ 2 \end{pmatrix}; 2\begin{pmatrix} n \\ 2 \end{pmatrix}$
43. 4   **45.** 7

47. $\dbinom{n}{k-1} + \dbinom{n}{k}$

$$= \frac{n!}{(k-1)!\,(n-k+1)!} \cdot \frac{k}{k}$$

$$+ \frac{n!}{k!\,(n-k)!} \cdot \frac{(n-k+1)}{(n-k+1)}$$

$$= \frac{n!\,(k+(n-k+1))}{k!\,(n-k+1)!}$$

$$= \frac{(n+1)!}{k!\,(n-k+1)!} = \dbinom{n+1}{k}$$

Exercise Set 10.7

1. $x^4 + 20x^3 + 150x^2 + 500x + 625$
3. $x^5 - 15x^4 + 90x^3 - 270x^2 + 405x - 243$
5. $x^5 - 5x^4y + 10x^3y^2 - 10x^2y^3 + 5xy^4 - y^5$
7. $15{,}625x^6 + 75{,}000x^5y + 150{,}000x^4y^2 +$
$160{,}000x^3y^3 + 96{,}000x^2y^4 + 30{,}720xy^5 + 4096y^6$
9. $128t^7 + 448t^5 + 672t^3 + 560t + 280t^{-1} + 84t^{-3} +$
$14t^{-5} + t^{-7}$ **11.** $x^{10} - 5x^8 + 10x^6 - 10x^4 + 5x^2 - 1$
13. $125 + 150\sqrt{5}\,t + 375t^2 + 100\sqrt{5}\,t^3 + 75t^4 +$
$6\sqrt{5}\,t^5 + t^6$
15. $a^9 - 18a^7 + 144a^5 - 672a^3 + 2016a - 4032a^{-1} +$
$5376a^{-3} - 4608a^{-5} + 2304a^{-7} - 512a^{-9}$
17. $140\sqrt{2}$ **19.** $x^{-8} + 4x^{-4} + 6 + 4x^4 + x^8$
21. $21a^5b^2$ **23.** $-252x^5y^5$ **25.** $-745{,}472a^3$
27. $1120x^{12}y^2$ **29.** $-1{,}959{,}552u^5v^{10}$ **31.** 2^7, or 128
33. 2^{24}, or $16{,}777{,}216$ **35.** 20 **37.** $-12 + 316i$
39. $-7 - 4\sqrt{2}i$ **41.** $\displaystyle\sum_{k=0}^{n} \dbinom{n}{k}(-1)^k a^{n-k}b^k$

43. $\displaystyle\sum_{k=1}^{n} \dbinom{n}{k} x^{n-k}h^{k-1}$ **45.** Discussion and Writing

46. [1.6] $x^2 + 2x - 2$ **47.** [1.6] $2x^3 - 3x^2 + 2x - 3$
48. [1.6] $4x^2 - 12x + 10$ **49.** [1.6] $2x^2 - 1$
51. $3, 9, 6 \pm 3i$ **53.** $-4320x^6y^{9/2}$
55. $-\dfrac{35}{x^{1/6}}$ **57.** 2^{100} **59.** $[\log_a (xt)]^{23}$

61. **(1)** *Basis step*: Since $a + b = (a + b)^1$, S_1 is true.
(2) *Induction step*: Let S_k be the statement of the
binomial theorem with n replaced by k. Multiply both
sides of S_k by $(a + b)$ to obtain
$(a + b)^{k+1}$
$$= \left[a^k + \cdots + \dbinom{k}{r-1}a^{k-(r-1)}b^{r-1} \right.$$
$$\left. + \dbinom{k}{r}a^{k-r}b^r + \cdots + b^k \right](a + b)$$
$$= a^{k+1} + \cdots + \left[\dbinom{k}{r-1} + \dbinom{k}{r} \right]a^{(k+1)-r}b^r$$
$$+ \cdots + b^{k+1}$$
$$= a^{k+1} + \cdots + \dbinom{k+1}{r}a^{(k+1)-r}b^r + \cdots + b^{k+1}.$$
This proves S_{k+1}, assuming S_k. Hence S_n is true for $n = 1, 2,$
$3, \ldots$.

Exercise Set 10.8

1. **(a)** $0.18, 0.24, 0.23, 0.23, 0.12$; **(b)** Opinions may vary, but
it seems that people tend not to pick the first or last numbers.
3. $11{,}700$ pieces   **5.** **(a)** T, S, R, N, L; **(b)** E; **(c)** yes
7. **(a)** $\frac{2}{7}$; **(b)** $\frac{5}{7}$; **(c)** 0; **(d)** 1 **9.** $\frac{350}{31{,}977}$ **11.** $\frac{1}{108{,}290}$
13. $\frac{33}{66{,}640}$ **15.** **(a)** HHH, HHT, HTH, HTT, THH, THT,
TTH, TTT; **(b)** $\frac{3}{8}$; **(c)** $\frac{7}{8}$; **(d)** $\frac{7}{8}$; **(e)** $\frac{3}{8}$ **17.** $\frac{9}{19}$ **19.** $\frac{1}{38}$
21. $\frac{18}{19}$ **23.** $\frac{9}{19}$ **25.** Answers will vary.
27. Discussion and Writing   **28.** [2.1] Zero
29. [4.1] One-to-one   **30.** [1.2] Function; domain; range;
domain; range   **31.** [2.1] Zero   **32.** [10.6] Combination
33. [3.7] Inverse variation   **34.** [3.3] Factor
35. [10.3] Geometric sequence

37. **(a)** 36; **(b)** $\dfrac{36}{_{52}C_5} \approx 1.39 \times 10^{-5}$

39. **(a)** $(13 \cdot {}_4C_3) \cdot (12 \cdot {}_4C_2) = 3744$; **(b)** 0.00144

41. **(a)** $4 \cdot \dbinom{13}{5} - 4 - 36 = 5108$; **(b)** 0.00197

43. **(a)** $\dbinom{10}{1}\dbinom{4}{1}\dbinom{4}{1}\dbinom{4}{1}\dbinom{4}{1}\dbinom{4}{1} - 4 - 36 = 10{,}200$;
(b) 0.00392

Review Exercises: Chapter 10

1. True   **2.** False   **3.** True   **4.** False   **5.** $-\frac{1}{2}, \frac{4}{17}, -\frac{9}{82},$
$\frac{16}{257}; -\frac{121}{14{,}642}; -\frac{529}{279{,}842}$ **6.** $(-1)^{n+1}(n^2 + 1)$
7. $\frac{3}{2} - \frac{9}{8} + \frac{27}{26} - \frac{81}{80} = \frac{417}{1040}$ **8.** $\displaystyle\sum_{k=1}^{7} (k^2 - 1)$ **9.** $\frac{15}{4}$
10. $a + 4b$ **11.** 531 **12.** $20{,}100$ **13.** 11 **14.** -4
15. $n = 6, S_n = -126$ **16.** $a_1 = 8, a_5 = \frac{1}{2}$
17. Does not exist   **18.** $\frac{3}{11}$ **19.** $\frac{3}{8}$ **20.** $\frac{241}{99}$
21. $5\frac{4}{5}, 6\frac{3}{5}, 7\frac{2}{5}, 8\frac{1}{5}$ **22.** 167.3 ft   **23.** $\$45{,}993.04$
24. **(a)** $\$7.38$; **(b)** $\$1365.10$ **25.** $\$88{,}888{,}888{,}889$

26. S_n: $1 + 4 + 7 + \cdots + (3n - 2) = \dfrac{n(3n - 1)}{2}$

S_1: $1 = \dfrac{1(3 - 1)}{2}$

S_k: $1 + 4 + 7 + \cdots + (3k - 2) = \dfrac{k(3k - 1)}{2}$

S_{k+1}: $1 + 4 + 7 + \cdots + (3k - 2) + [3(k + 1) - 2]$
$\qquad = 1 + 4 + 7 + \cdots + (3k - 2) + (3k + 1)$
$\qquad = \dfrac{(k + 1)(3k + 2)}{2}$

(1) *Basis step*: $\dfrac{1(3 - 1)}{2} = \dfrac{2}{2} = 1$ is true.

(2) *Induction step*: Assume S_k. Add $(3k + 1)$ on both sides.

$1 + 4 + 7 + \cdots + (3k - 2) + (3k + 1)$

$$= \frac{k(3k - 1)}{2} + (3k + 1)$$

$$= \frac{k(3k - 1)}{2} + \frac{2(3k + 1)}{2}$$

$$= \frac{3k^2 - k + 6k + 2}{2}$$

$$= \frac{3k^2 + 5k + 2}{2}$$

$$= \frac{(k + 1)(3k + 2)}{2}$$

27. S_n: $1 + 3 + 3^2 + \cdots + 3^{n-1} = \dfrac{3^n - 1}{2}$

S_1: $1 = \dfrac{3^1 - 1}{2}$

S_k: $1 + 3 + 3^2 + \cdots + 3^{k-1} = \dfrac{3^k - 1}{2}$

S_{k+1}: $1 + 3 + 3^2 + \cdots + 3^{(k+1)-1} = \dfrac{3^{k+1} - 1}{2}$

(1) *Basis step*: $\dfrac{3^1 - 1}{2} = \dfrac{2}{2} = 1$ is true.

(2) *Induction step*: Assume S_k. Add 3^k on both sides.

$1 + 3 + \cdots + 3^{k-1} + 3^k$

$$= \frac{3^k - 1}{2} + 3^k = \frac{3^k - 1}{2} + 3^k \cdot \frac{2}{2}$$

$$= \frac{3 \cdot 3^k - 1}{2} = \frac{3^{k+1} - 1}{2}$$

28.

S_n: $\left(1 - \dfrac{1}{2}\right)\left(1 - \dfrac{1}{3}\right) \cdots \left(1 - \dfrac{1}{n}\right) = \dfrac{1}{n}$

S_2: $\left(1 - \dfrac{1}{2}\right) = \dfrac{1}{2}$

S_k: $\left(1 - \dfrac{1}{2}\right)\left(1 - \dfrac{1}{3}\right) \cdots \left(1 - \dfrac{1}{k}\right) = \dfrac{1}{k}$

S_{k+1}: $\left(1 - \dfrac{1}{2}\right)\left(1 - \dfrac{1}{3}\right) \cdots \left(1 - \dfrac{1}{k}\right)\left(1 - \dfrac{1}{k + 1}\right)$

$$= \frac{1}{k + 1}$$

(1) *Basis step*: S_2 is true by substitution.

(2) *Induction step*: Assume S_k. Deduce S_{k+1}. Starting with the left side of S_{k+1}, we have

$$\underbrace{\left(1 - \frac{1}{2}\right)\left(1 - \frac{1}{3}\right) \cdots \left(1 - \frac{1}{k}\right)}\left(1 - \frac{1}{k + 1}\right)$$

$$= \frac{1}{k} \cdot \left(1 - \frac{1}{k + 1}\right) \qquad \text{By } S_k$$

$$= \frac{1}{k} \cdot \left(\frac{k + 1 - 1}{k + 1}\right)$$

$$= \frac{1}{k} \cdot \frac{k}{k + 1} = \frac{1}{k + 1}. \qquad \text{Simplifying}$$

29. $6! = 720$ 30. $9 \cdot 8 \cdot 7 \cdot 6 = 3024$

31. $\dbinom{15}{8} = 6435$ 32. $24 \cdot 23 \cdot 22 = 12{,}144$

33. $\dfrac{9!}{1!\,4!\,2!\,2!} = 3780$ 34. $3 \cdot 4 \cdot 3 = 36$

35. (a) $_6P_5 = 720$; (b) $6^5 = 7776$; (c) $_5P_4 = 120$; (d) $_3P_2 = 6$ 36. 2^8, or 256

37. $m^7 + 7m^6n + 21m^5n^2 + 35m^4n^3 + 35m^3n^4 + 21m^2n^5 + 7mn^6 + n^7$

38. $x^5 - 5\sqrt{2}\,x^4 + 20x^3 - 20\sqrt{2}\,x^2 + 20x - 4\sqrt{2}$

39. $x^8 - 12x^6y + 54x^4y^2 - 108x^2y^3 + 81y^4$

40. $a^8 + 8a^6 + 28a^4 + 56a^2 + 70 + 56a^{-2} + 28a^{-4} + 8a^{-6} + a^{-8}$ 41. $-6624 + 16{,}280i$

42. $220a^9x^3$ 43. $-\dbinom{18}{11}128a^7b^{11}$ 44. $\frac{1}{12}; 0$ 45. $\frac{1}{4}$

46. $\frac{6}{5525}$ 47. $\frac{86}{206} \approx 0.42, \frac{97}{206} \approx 0.47, \frac{23}{206} \approx 0.11$

48. B   49. A

50.

n	U_n
1	0.3
2	2.5
3	13.5
4	68.5
5	343.5
6	1718.5
7	8593.5
8	42968.5
9	214843.5
10	1074218.5

51. (a) $a_n = 0.9694927954n + 46.17184726$; (b) 75.257 million

52. Discussion and Writing: A list of 9 candidates for an office is to be narrowed down to 4 candidates. In how many ways can this be done?

53. Discussion and Writing: Someone who has managed several sequences of hiring has a considerable income from the sales of the people in the lower levels. However, with a finite population, it will not be long before the salespersons in the lowest level have no one to hire and no one to sell to.

54. S_1 fails for both (a) and (b).

55. $\dfrac{a_{k+1}}{a_k} = r_1, \dfrac{b_{k+1}}{b_k} = r_2$, so $\dfrac{a_{k+1}b_{k+1}}{a_k b_k} = r_1 r_2$, a constant

56. **(a)** No (unless a_n is all positive or all negative);
(b) yes; **(c)** yes; **(d)** no (unless a_n is constant); **(e)** no (unless a_n is constant); **(f)** no (unless a_n is constant)

57. $-2, 0, 2, 4$ **58.** $\frac{1}{2}, -\frac{1}{6}, \frac{1}{18}$ **59.** $\left(\log \dfrac{x}{y}\right)^{10}$ **60.** 18

61. 36 **62.** -9

Test: Chapter 10

1. [10.1] -43 **2.** [10.1] $\frac{2}{3}, \frac{3}{4}, \frac{4}{5}, \frac{5}{6}, \frac{6}{7}$

3. [10.1] $2 + 5 + 10 + 17 = 34$ **4.** [10.1] $\displaystyle\sum_{k=1}^{6} 4k$

5. [10.1] $\displaystyle\sum_{k=1}^{\infty} 2^k$ **6.** [10.1] $3, 2\frac{1}{3}, 2\frac{3}{7}, 2\frac{7}{17}$ **7.** [10.2] 44

8. [10.2] 38 **9.** [10.2] -420 **10.** [10.2] 675

11. [10.3] $\frac{5}{512}$ **12.** [10.3] 1000 **13.** [10.3] 510

14. [10.3] 27 **15.** [10.3] $\frac{56}{99}$

16. [10.1] \$10,000, \$8000, \$6400, \$5120, \$4096, \$3276.80

17. [10.2] \$12.50 **18.** [10.3] \$74,399.77

19. [10.4]

S_n: $\quad 2 + 5 + 8 + \cdots + (3n - 1) = \dfrac{n(3n + 1)}{2}$

S_1: $\quad 2 = \dfrac{1(3 \cdot 1 + 1)}{2}$

S_k: $\quad 2 + 5 + 8 + \cdots + (3k - 1) = \dfrac{k(3k + 1)}{2}$

S_{k+1}: $\quad 2 + 5 + 8 + \cdots + (3k - 1) + [3(k + 1) - 1]$
$\qquad\qquad = \dfrac{(k + 1)[3(k + 1) + 1]}{2}$

(1) *Basis step:* $\dfrac{1(3 \cdot 1 + 1)}{2} = \dfrac{1 \cdot 4}{2} = 2$, so S_1 is true.

(2) *Induction step:*

$2 + 5 + 8 + \cdots + (3k - 1) + [3(k + 1) - 1]$
$\qquad = \dfrac{k(3k + 1)}{2} + [3k + 3 - 1]$

$\qquad\qquad\qquad\qquad\qquad\qquad$ **By** S_k

$\qquad = \dfrac{3k^2}{2} + \dfrac{k}{2} + 3k + 2$

$\qquad = \dfrac{3k^2}{2} + \dfrac{7k}{2} + 2$

$\qquad = \dfrac{3k^2 + 7k + 4}{2}$

$\qquad = \dfrac{(k + 1)(3k + 4)}{2}$

$\qquad = \dfrac{(k + 1)[3(k + 1) + 1]}{2}$

20. [10.5] 3,603,600 **21.** [10.6] 352,716

22. [10.6] $\dfrac{n(n - 1)(n - 2)(n - 3)}{24}$ **23.** [10.5] $_6P_4 = 360$

24. [10.5] **(a)** $6^4 = 1296$; **(b)** $_5P_3 = 60$

25. [10.6] $_{28}C_4 = 20,475$ **26.** [10.6] $_{12}C_8 \cdot {}_8C_4 = 34,650$

27. [10.7] $x^5 + 5x^4 + 10x^3 + 10x^2 + 5x + 1$

28. [10.7] $35x^3y^4$ **29.** [10.7] $2^9 = 512$ **30.** [10.8] $\frac{4}{7}$

31. [10.8] $\frac{48}{1001}$ **32.** [10.5] 15

APPENDIX

1. Acute **2.** Acute **3.** Straight **4.** Right

5. Obtuse **6.** Obtuse **7.** $79°$ **8.** $7°$ **9.** $23°$

10. $85°$ **11.** $32°$ **12.** $58°$ **13.** $61°$ **14.** $36°$

15. $177°$ **16.** $126°$ **17.** $41°$ **18.** $167°$ **19.** $95°$

20. $51°$ **21.** $78°$ **22.** $135°$

23. $\angle R \leftrightarrow \angle A, \angle S \leftrightarrow \angle B, \angle T \leftrightarrow \angle C$;
$\overline{RS} \leftrightarrow \overline{AB}, \overline{RT} \leftrightarrow \overline{AC}, \overline{ST} \leftrightarrow \overline{BC}$

24. $\angle D \leftrightarrow \angle C, \angle E \leftrightarrow \angle N, \angle F \leftrightarrow \angle B$;
$\overline{DE} \leftrightarrow \overline{CN}, \overline{EF} \leftrightarrow \overline{NB}, \overline{FD} \leftrightarrow \overline{BC}$

25. $\angle C \leftrightarrow \angle W, \angle B \leftrightarrow \angle J, \angle S \leftrightarrow \angle Z$;
$\overline{CB} \leftrightarrow \overline{WJ}, \overline{CS} \leftrightarrow \overline{WZ}, \overline{BS} \leftrightarrow \overline{JZ}$

26. $\angle B \leftrightarrow \angle S, \angle V \leftrightarrow \angle T, \angle W \leftrightarrow \angle A$;
$\overline{BV} \leftrightarrow \overline{ST}, \overline{VW} \leftrightarrow \overline{TA}, \overline{WB} \leftrightarrow \overline{AS}$

27. $\angle A \leftrightarrow \angle R, \angle B \leftrightarrow \angle S, \angle C \leftrightarrow \angle T; \dfrac{AB}{RS} = \dfrac{AC}{RT} = \dfrac{BC}{ST}$

28. $\angle P \leftrightarrow \angle S, \angle Q \leftrightarrow \angle T, \angle R \leftrightarrow \angle V; \dfrac{PQ}{ST} = \dfrac{PR}{SV} = \dfrac{QR}{TV}$

29. $\angle M \leftrightarrow \angle C, \angle E \leftrightarrow \angle L, \angle S \leftrightarrow \angle F; \dfrac{ME}{CL} = \dfrac{MS}{CF} = \dfrac{ES}{LF}$

30. $\angle S \leftrightarrow \angle W, \angle M \leftrightarrow \angle L, \angle H \leftrightarrow \angle K; \dfrac{SM}{WL} = \dfrac{SH}{WK} = \dfrac{MH}{LK}$

31. $\dfrac{PS}{ND} = \dfrac{SQ}{DM} = \dfrac{PQ}{NM}$ **32.** $\dfrac{GH}{UT} = \dfrac{GK}{UV} = \dfrac{HK}{TV}$

33. $\dfrac{TA}{GF} = \dfrac{TW}{GC} = \dfrac{AW}{FC}$ **34.** $\dfrac{JK}{ON} = \dfrac{JL}{OM} = \dfrac{KL}{NM}$

35. $QR = 10, PR = 8$ **36.** $AM = 24, GT = 25$

37. 36 ft **38.** 33 ft **39.** 100 ft **40.** 72 ft **41.** 17

42. $\sqrt{34} \approx 5.831$ **43.** $\sqrt{32} \approx 5.657$ **44.** $\sqrt{98} \approx 9.899$

45. 12 **46.** 5 **47.** 4 **48.** $\sqrt{31} \approx 5.568$ **49.** 26

50. 13 **51.** 12 **52.** 24 **53.** 2 **54.** 1

55. $\sqrt{2} \approx 1.414$ **56.** $\sqrt{8} \approx 2.828$ **57.** 5

58. $\sqrt{50} \approx 7.071$ **59.** 3 **60.** $\sqrt{5} \approx 2.236$

61. $\sqrt{211,200,000}$ ft $\approx 14,533$ ft

62. $\sqrt{1850}$ yd ≈ 43.012 yd **63.** 240 ft **64.** 25 ft

65. $\sqrt{18}$ cm ≈ 4.243 cm **66.** $\sqrt{75}$ m ≈ 8.660 m

67. $\sqrt{208}$ ft ≈ 14.422 ft **68.** $\sqrt{26,900}$ yd ≈ 164.012 yd

Photo Credits

Index

Index of Applications

$2w$

$P = 4s$

gle
a: $A = \frac{1}{2}bh$

Sum of Angle Measures
$A + B + C = 180°$

Right Triangle
Pythagorean theorem
(equation):
$a^2 + b^2 = c^2$

Parallelogram
Area: $A = bh$

Trapezoid
Area: $A = \frac{1}{2}h(a + b)$

Circle
Area: $A = \pi r^2$
Circumference:
$C = \pi d = 2\pi r$

Solid Geometry

Rectangular Solid
Volume: $V = lwh$

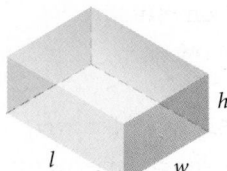

Cube
Volume: $V = s^3$

Right Circular Cylinder
Volume: $V = \pi r^2 h$
Lateral surface area:
$\quad L = 2\pi rh$
Total surface area:
$\quad S = 2\pi rh + 2\pi r^2$

Right Circular Cone
Volume: $V = \frac{1}{3}\pi r^2 h$
Lateral surface area:
$\quad L = \pi rs$
Total surface area:
$\quad S = \pi r^2 + \pi rs$
Slant height:
$\quad s = \sqrt{r^2 + h^2}$

Sphere
Volume: $V = \frac{4}{3}\pi r^3$
Surface area: $S = 4\pi r^2$

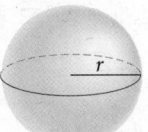

...gebra

...rties of Real Numbers

...mutative: $\quad a + b = b + a; \quad ab = ba$

...ociative: $\quad a + (b + c) = (a + b) + c;$
$\quad\quad a(bc) = (ab)c$

...ditive Identity: $\quad a + 0 = 0 + a = a$

...dditive Inverse: $\quad -a + a = a + (-a) = 0$

...ultiplicative Identity: $\quad a \cdot 1 = 1 \cdot a = a$

Multiplicative Inverse: $\quad a \cdot \dfrac{1}{a} = 1, \ a \neq 0$

Distributive: $\quad a(b + c) = ab + ac$

Exponents and Radicals

$a^m \cdot a^n = a^{m+n}$ $\qquad \dfrac{a^m}{a^n} = a^{m-n}$

$(a^m)^n = a^{mn}$ $\qquad (ab)^m = a^m b^m$

$\left(\dfrac{a}{b}\right)^m = \dfrac{a^m}{b^m}$ $\qquad a^{-n} = \dfrac{1}{a^n}$

If n is even, $\sqrt[n]{a^n} = |a|$.

If n is odd, $\sqrt[n]{a^n} = a$.

$\sqrt[n]{a} \cdot \sqrt[n]{b} = \sqrt[n]{ab}, \ a, b \geq 0$

$\sqrt[n]{\dfrac{a}{b}} = \dfrac{\sqrt[n]{a}}{\sqrt[n]{b}}$

$\sqrt[n]{a^m} = \left(\sqrt[n]{a}\right)^m = a^{m/n}$

Special-Product Formulas

$(a + b)(a - b) = a^2 - b^2$

$(a + b)^2 = a^2 + 2ab + b^2$

$(a - b)^2 = a^2 - 2ab + b^2$

$(a + b)^3 = a^3 + 3a^2 b + 3ab^2 + b^3$

$(a - b)^3 = a^3 - 3a^2 b + 3ab^2 - b^3$

$(a + b)^n = \displaystyle\sum_{k=0}^{n} \binom{n}{k} a^{n-k} b^k, \quad$ where

$\binom{n}{k} = \dfrac{n!}{k!\,(n - k)!}$

$\quad = \dfrac{n(n - 1)(n - 2) \cdots [n - (k - 1)]}{k!}$

Factoring Formulas

$a^2 - b^2 = (a + b)(a - b)$

$a^2 + 2ab + b^2 = (a + b)^2$

$a^2 - 2ab + b^2 = (a - b)^2$

$a^3 + b^3 = (a + b)(a^2 - ab + b^2)$

$a^3 - b^3 = (a - b)(a^2 + ab + b^2)$

Interval Notation

$(a, b) = \{x \mid a < x < b\}$

$[a, b] = \{x \mid a \leq x \leq b\}$

$(a, b] = \{x \mid a < x \leq b\}$

$[a, b) = \{x \mid a \leq x < b\}$

$(-\infty, a) = \{x \mid x < a\}$

$(a, \infty) = \{x \mid x > a\}$

$(-\infty, a] = \{x \mid x \leq a\}$

$[a, \infty) = \{x \mid x \geq a\}$

Absolute Value

$|a| \geq 0$

For $a > 0$,

$\quad\quad |X| = a \rightarrow X = -a \quad$ or $\quad X = a,$

$\quad\quad |X| < a \rightarrow -a < X < a,$

$\quad\quad |X| > a \rightarrow X < -a \quad$ or $\quad X > a.$

Equation-Solving Principles

$a = b \rightarrow a + c = b + c$

$a = b \rightarrow ac = bc$

$a = b \rightarrow a^n = b^n$

$ab = 0 \leftrightarrow a = 0 \quad$ or $\quad b = 0$

$x^2 = k \rightarrow x = \sqrt{k} \quad$ or $\quad x = -\sqrt{k}$

Inequality-Solving Principles

$a < b \rightarrow a + c < b + c$

$a < b$ and $c > 0 \rightarrow ac < bc$

$a < b$ and $c < 0 \rightarrow ac > bc$

(Algebra continued)

Algebra *(continued)*

The Distance Formula

The distance from (x_1, y_1) to (x_2, y_2) is given by

$$d = \sqrt{(x_2 - x_1)^2 + (y_2 - y_1)^2}.$$

The Midpoint Formula

The midpoint of the line segment from (x_1, y_1) to (x_2, y_2) is given by

$$\left(\frac{x_1 + x_2}{2}, \frac{y_1 + y_2}{2} \right).$$

Formulas Involving Lines

The slope of the line containing points (x_1, y_1) and (x_2, y_2) is given by

$$m = \frac{y_2 - y_1}{x_2 - x_1}.$$

Slope–intercept equation: $\quad y = f(x) = mx + b$

Horizontal line: $\quad y = b \quad \text{or} \quad f(x) = b$

Vertical line: $\quad x = a$

Point–slope equation: $\quad y - y_1 = m(x - x_1)$

The Quadratic Formula

The solutions of $ax^2 + bx + c = 0$, $a \neq 0$, are given by

$$x = \frac{-b \pm \sqrt{b^2 - 4ac}}{2a}.$$

Compound Interest Formulas

Compounded n times per year: $\quad A = P\left(1 + \frac{i}{n}\right)^{nt}$

Compounded continuously: $\quad P(t) = P_0 e^{kt}$

Properties of Exponential and Logarithmic Functions

$$\log_a x = y \leftrightarrow x = a^y \qquad a^x = a^y \leftrightarrow x =$$
$$\log_a MN = \log_a M + \log_a N \qquad \log_a M^p = p \log_a$$
$$\log_a \frac{M}{N} = \log_a M - \log_a N$$
$$\log_b M = \frac{\log_a M}{\log_a b}$$
$$\log_a a = 1 \qquad\qquad \log_a 1 = 0$$
$$\log_a a^x = x \qquad\qquad a^{\log_a x} = x$$

Conic Sections

Circle: $\qquad (x - h)^2 + (y - k)^2 = r^2$

Ellipse: $\qquad \dfrac{(x - h)^2}{a^2} + \dfrac{(y - k)^2}{b^2} = 1,$

$\qquad\qquad \dfrac{(x - h)^2}{b^2} + \dfrac{(y - k)^2}{a^2} = 1$

Parabola: $\qquad (x - h)^2 = 4p(y - k),$

$\qquad\qquad (y - k)^2 = 4p(x - h)$

Hyperbola: $\qquad \dfrac{(x - h)^2}{a^2} - \dfrac{(y - k)^2}{b^2} = 1,$

$\qquad\qquad \dfrac{(y - k)^2}{a^2} - \dfrac{(x - h)^2}{b^2} = 1$

Arithmetic Sequences and Series

$$a_1, a_1 + d, a_1 + 2d, a_1 + 3d, \ldots$$
$$a_{n+1} = a_n + d \qquad a_n = a_1 + (n - 1)d$$
$$S_n = \frac{n}{2}(a_1 + a_n)$$

Geometric Sequences and Series

$$a_1, a_1 r, a_1 r^2, a_1 r^3, \ldots$$
$$a_{n+1} = a_n r \qquad a_n = a_1 r^{n-1}$$
$$S_n = \frac{a_1(1 - r^n)}{1 - r} \qquad S_\infty = \frac{a_1}{1 - r}, \ |r| < 1$$